THE BEST LAWYERS IN AMERICA

THE BEST LAWYERS IN AMERICA

II

NEVADA - WYOMING

2009

W O O D W A R D / W H I T E

Published and distributed by Woodward/White, Inc.
129 First Avenue, SW, Aiken, SC 29801

PLEASE NOTE

Woodward/White has used its best efforts in assembling material for inclusion in The Best Lawyers in America® 2009 but does not warrant that the information contained in the book is complete or accurate, and does not assume, and hereby disclaims, any liability to any person for any loss or damage caused by errors or omissions in The Best Lawyers in America® 2009 whether such errors or omissions result from negligence, accident, or any other cause.

Woodward/White makes every reasonable effort to check all of its lists against publicly-available records on lawyers who have been sanctioned by their state bar associations. Lawyers are removed from the lists if they have had a significant, fully-adjudicated sanction within the past ten to fifteen years depending on their state bar's standards for imposing sanctions and on the manner in which information about sanctions is made available to the public, both of which vary widely from state to state.

Library of Congress Cataloging in Publication Data

Naifeh, Steven W., 1952-
The best lawyers in America.

1. Lawyers--United States--Directories. 2. Lawyers--United States--Rating of. 3.Lawyers--Specialties and specialists--United States--Directories. I. Smith, Gregory White. II. Title.

ISBN 978-0980025330 (v. 1)
ISBN 978-0980025347 (v. 2)
ISBN 978-0980025354 (2 vol. set)

PRINTED IN THE UNITED STATES OF AMERICA

CONTENTS – Volume I

Volume II

⑩ *Lawyers who have been listed in* Best Lawyers *for at least ten years.*

⑳ *Lawyers who have been listed in* Best Lawyers *for at least twenty years.*

㉕ *Lawyers who have been listed in* Best Lawyers *for at least twenty-five years.*

NEVADA

ADMINISTRATIVE LAW

Las Vegas

Jeffrey A. Silver · Gordon & Silver · 3960 Howard Hughes Parkway, Ninth Floor · Las Vegas, NV 89169 · 702-796-5555

Reno

C. Robert Cox · a · Maupin, Cox & LeGoy · 4785 Caughlin Parkway · P.O. Box 30000 · Reno, NV 89520 775-827-2000

Shawn M. Elicegui · Lionel Sawyer & Collins · http://www.lionelsawyer.com · 1100 Bank of America Plaza · 50 West Liberty Street · Reno, NV 89501 · 775-788-8666

Thomas R. C. Wilson II · a · McDonald Carano Wilson · http://www.mcdonaldcarano.com · 100 West Liberty Street, 10th Floor · P.O. Box 2670 · Reno, NV 89505 · 775-788-2000

ALTERNATIVE DISPUTE RESOLUTION

Las Vegas

John D. O'Brien · 2) · John D. O'Brien · 700 South Seventh Street · Las Vegas, NV 89101 · 702-382-5222

Reno

John A. Aberasturi · Erickson, Thorpe & Swainston · 99 West Arroyo Street · P.O. Box 3559 · Reno, NV 89505 · 775-786-3930

Frank Cassas · Parsons Behle & Latimer · http://www.parsonsbehlelaw.com · 50 West Liberty Street, Suite 750 · Reno, NV 89501 · 775-323-1601

William G. Cobb · Erickson, Thorpe & Swainston · 99 West Arroyo Street · P.O. Box 3559 · Reno, NV 89505 · 775-786-3930

Robert F. Enzenberger · Law Offices of Robert F. Enzenberger · 1885 South Arlington Avenue, Suite 205 · Reno, NV 89509-3370 · 775-786-7000

Albert F. Pagni · Jones Vargas · 100 West Liberty Street, 12th Floor · P.O. Box 281 · Reno, NV 89504 · 775-786-5000

Harold B. Thompson · Georgeson Angaran · 5450 Longley Lane · Reno, NV 89511 · 775-827-6440

ANTITRUST LAW

Las Vegas

James G. Armstrong · Thorndal, Armstrong, Delk, Balkenbush & Eisinger · 1100 East Bridger Avenue · P.O. Drawer 2070 · Las Vegas, NV 89125-2070 · 702-366-0622

APPELLATE LAW

Las Vegas

David N. Frederick · Lionel Sawyer & Collins · http://www.lionelsawyer.com · 1700 Bank of America Plaza · 300 South Fourth Street · Las Vegas, NV 89101 · 702-383-8888

Daniel F. Polsenberg · Lewis and Roca · http://www.lrlaw.com · 3993 Howard Hughes Parkway, Suite 600 · Las Vegas, NV 89169 · 702-949-8200

Reno

Robert L. Eisenberg · Lemons, Grundy & Eisenberg · 6005 Plumas Street, Suite 300 · Reno, NV 89509 · 775-786-6868

BANKRUPTCY AND CREDITOR-DEBTOR RIGHTS LAW

Las Vegas

Candace C. Carlyon · a · Shea & Carlyon · 701 Bridger Avenue, Suite 850 · Las Vegas, NV 89101 · 702-471-7432

Laurel E. Davis · Fennemore Craig · http://www.fclaw.com · 300 South Fourth Street, Suite 1400 · Las Vegas, NV 89101 · 702-692-8000

Thomas H. Fell · Gordon & Silver · 3960 Howard Hughes Parkway, Ninth Floor · Las Vegas, NV 89169 · 702-796-5555

Gregory E. Garman · Gordon & Silver · 3960 Howard Hughes Parkway, Ninth Floor · Las Vegas, NV 89169 · 702-796-5555

Gerald M. Gordon · 2) · Gordon & Silver · 3960 Howard Hughes Parkway, Ninth Floor · Las Vegas, NV 89169 · 702-796-5555

James D. Greene · Brownstein Hyatt Farber Schreck · http://www.bhfs.com · 100 City Parkway, Suite 1600 · Las Vegas, NV 89106-4614 · 702-382-2101

Richard F. Holley · a · Santoro, Driggs, Walch, Kearney, Johnson & Thompson · 400 South Fourth Street, Third Floor · Las Vegas, NV 89101 · 702-791-0308

Robert Richard Kinas · Snell & Wilmer · 3883 Howard Hughes Parkway, 11th Floor · Las Vegas, NV 89169 · 702-784-5200

Jeanette E. McPherson · Schwartzer & McPherson Law Firm · 2850 South Jones Boulevard, Suite One · Las Vegas, NV 89146 · 702-228-7590

William M. Noall · Gordon & Silver · 3960 Howard Hughes Parkway, Ninth Floor · Las Vegas, NV 89169 702-796-5555

Lenard E. Schwartzer · a · Schwartzer & McPherson Law Firm · 2850 South Jones Boulevard, Suite One · Las Vegas, NV 89146 · 702-228-7590

James Patrick Shea · Shea & Carlyon · 701 Bridger Avenue, Suite 850 · Las Vegas, NV 89101 · 702-471-7432

Reno

Sallie Bernard Armstrong · 2) · Downey Brand · 427 West Plumb Lane · Reno, NV 89509 · 775-329-5900

Bruce T. Beesley · a · Lewis and Roca · http://www.lrlaw.com · 50 West Libery Street, Suite 410 · Reno, NV 89501 · 775-823-2900

Janet L. Chubb · 2) · Jones Vargas · 100 West Liberty Street, 12th Floor · P.O. Box 281 · Reno, NV 89504 775-786-5000

Rew R. Goodenow · Parsons Behle & Latimer · http://www.parsonsbehlelaw.com · 50 West Liberty Street, Suite 750 · Reno, NV 89501 · 775-323-1601

Stephen R. Harris · a · Belding, Harris & Petroni · 417 West Plumb Lane · Reno, NV 89509 · 775-786-7600

Jeffrey L. Hartman · a · Hartman & Hartman · 510 West Plumb Lane, Suite B · Reno, NV 89509 · 775-324-2800

Timothy A. Lukas · Holland & Hart · 5441 Kietzke Lane, Second Floor · Reno, NV 89511 · 775-327-3000

John F. Murtha · a · Woodburn and Wedge · Sierra Plaza, Suite 500 · 6100 Neil Road · P.O. Box 2311 · Reno, NV 89505 · 775-688-3000

Bridget Robb Peck · Lewis and Roca · http://www.lrlaw.com · 50 West Libery Street, Suite 410 · Reno, NV 89501 · 775-823-2900

Jennifer A. Smith · Lionel Sawyer & Collins · http://www.lionelsawyer.com · 1100 Bank of America Plaza 50 West Liberty Street · Reno, NV 89501 · 775-788-8666

Las Vegas

Donald J. Campbell · a · Campbell & Williams · 700 South Seventh Street · Las Vegas, NV 89101-6908 702-382-5222

Cam Ferenbach · Lionel Sawyer & Collins · http://www.lionelsawyer.com · 1700 Bank of America Plaza · 300 South Fourth Street · Las Vegas, NV 89101 · 702-383-8888

David N. Frederick · Lionel Sawyer & Collins · http://www.lionelsawyer.com · 1700 Bank of America Plaza · 300 South Fourth Street · Las Vegas, NV 89101 · 702-383-8888

Gary R. Goodheart · Jones Vargas · 3773 Howard Hughes Parkway, Third Floor South · Las Vegas, NV 89109 · 702-862-3300

Andrew P. Gordon · McDonald Carano Wilson · http://www.mcdonaldcarano.com · 2300 West Sahara Avenue, Suite 1000 · Las Vegas, NV 89102 · 702-873-4100

Kirk R. Harrison · Harrison, Kemp, Jones & Coulthard · 3800 Howard Hughes Parkway, Suite 1700 · Las Vegas, NV 89169 · 702-385-6000

Paul Hejmanowski · 2) · Lionel Sawyer & Collins · http://www.lionelsawyer.com · 1700 Bank of America Plaza · 300 South Fourth Street · Las Vegas, NV 89101 · 702-383-8888

C. Stanley Hunterton · Hunterton & Associates · 333 South Sixth Street · Las Vegas, NV 89101 · 702-388-0098

R. Gardner Jolley · a · Jolley Urga Wirth Woodbury & Standish · 3800 Howard Hughes Parkway, Suite 1600 · Las Vegas, NV 89169 · 702-699-7500

J. Randall Jones · a · Harrison, Kemp, Jones & Coulthard · 3800 Howard Hughes Parkway, Suite 1700 · Las Vegas, NV 89169 · 702-385-6000

William S. Kemp · Harrison, Kemp, Jones & Coulthard · 3800 Howard Hughes Parkway, Suite 1700 · Las Vegas, NV 89169 · 702-385-6000

Dennis L. Kennedy · a · Bailey Kennedy · 8984 Spanish Ridge Avenue · Las Vegas, NV 89148 · 702-562-8820

Todd E. Kennedy · Lionel Sawyer & Collins · http://www.lionelsawyer.com · 1700 Bank of America Plaza 300 South Fourth Street · Las Vegas, NV 89101 · 702-383-8888

Thomas F. Kummer · Kummer Kaempfer Bonner Renshaw & Ferrario · 3800 Howard Hughes Parkway, Seventh Floor · Las Vegas, NV 89169 · 702-792-7000

Kirk B. Lenhard · a · Jones Vargas · 3773 Howard Hughes Parkway, Third Floor South · Las Vegas, NV 89109 · 702-862-3300

Samuel S. Lionel · 2% · Lionel Sawyer & Collins · http://www.lionelsawyer.com · 1700 Bank of America Plaza · 300 South Fourth Street · Las Vegas, NV 89101 · 702-383-8888

Steve Morris · 2) · Morris Pickering · 900 Bank of America Plaza · 300 South Fourth Street · Las Vegas, NV 89101 · 702-474-9400

J. Stephen Peek · Holland & Hart · 3930 Howard Hughes Parkway, Fourth Floor · Las Vegas, NV 89169 775-327-3000

Mary Kristina Pickering · Morris Pickering · 900 Bank of America Plaza · 300 South Fourth Street · Las Vegas, NV 89101 · 702-474-9400

James J. Pisanelli · Brownstein Hyatt Farber Schreck · http://www.bhfs.com · 100 City Parkway, Suite 1600 · Las Vegas, NV 89106-4614 · 702-382-2101

Thomas G. Ryan · Lewis and Roca · http://www.lrlaw.com · 3993 Howard Hughes Parkway, Suite 600 · Las Vegas, NV 89169 · 702-949-8200

Nicholas J. Santoro · Santoro, Driggs, Walch, Kearney, Johnson & Thompson · 400 South Fourth Street, Third Floor · Las Vegas, NV 89101 · 702-791-0308

Abran E. Vigil · Lewis and Roca · http://www.lrlaw.com · 3993 Howard Hughes Parkway, Suite 600 · Las Vegas, NV 89169 · 702-949-8200

J. Colby Williams · Campbell & Williams · 700 South Seventh Street · Las Vegas, NV 89101-6908 · 702-382-5222

Reno

Matthew C. Addison · McDonald Carano Wilson · http://www.mcdonaldcarano.com · 100 West Liberty Street, 10th Floor · P.O. Box 2670 · Reno, NV 89505 · 775-788-2000

Dan C. Bowen · a · Bowen Hall Ohlson & Osborne · http://bowenhall.com · 555 South Center Street · Reno, NV 89501 · 775-323-8678

C. Robert Cox · a · Maupin, Cox & LeGoy · 4785 Caughlin Parkway · P.O. Box 30000 · Reno, NV 89520 775-827-2000

Richard L. Elmore · Holland & Hart · 5441 Kietzke Lane, Second Floor · Reno, NV 89511 · 775-327-3000

Suellen Fulstone · Morris Pickering · 6100 Neil Road, Suite 555 · Reno, NV 89511 · 775-829-6000

Bruce Laxalt · a · Laxalt & Nomura · http://www.laxalt-nomura.com · 9600 Gateway Drive · Reno, NV 89521 · 775-322-1170

Keegan G. Low · Robison, Belaustegui, Sharp & Low · 71 Washington Street · Reno, NV 89503 · 775-329-3151

Pat Lundvall · McDonald Carano Wilson · http://www.mcdonaldcarano.com · 100 West Liberty Street, 10th Floor · P.O. Box 2670 · Reno, NV 89505 · 775-788-2000

William A. S. Magrath II · McDonald Carano Wilson · http://www.mcdonaldcarano.com · 100 West Liberty Street, 10th Floor · P.O. Box 2670 · Reno, NV 89505 · 775-788-2000

Kent R. Robison · a · Robison, Belaustegui, Sharp & Low · 71 Washington Street · Reno, NV 89503 · 775-329-3151

Thomas R. C. Wilson II · a · McDonald Carano Wilson · http://www.mcdonaldcarano.com · 100 West Liberty Street, 10th Floor · P.O. Box 2670 · Reno, NV 89505 · 775-788-2000

Allen Jay Wilt · Lionel Sawyer & Collins · http://www.lionelsawyer.com · 1100 Bank of America Plaza · 50 West Liberty Street · Reno, NV 89501 · 775-788-8666

CONSTRUCTION LAW

Henderson

Richard L. Peel · Peel Brimley · 3333 East Serene Avenue, Suite 200 · Henderson, NV 89074-6571 · 702-990-7272

Las Vegas

Andrew P. Gordon · McDonald Carano Wilson · http://www.mcdonaldcarano.com · 2300 West Sahara Avenue, Suite 1000 · Las Vegas, NV 89102 · 702-873-4100

Dennis R. Haney · Santoro, Driggs, Walch, Kearney, Johnson & Thompson · 400 South Fourth Street, Third Floor · Las Vegas, NV 89101 · 702-791-0308

Leon F. Mead II · Snell & Wilmer · 3883 Howard Hughes Parkway, 11th Floor · Las Vegas, NV 89169 · 702-784-5200

George Ogilvie · McDonald Carano Wilson · http://www.mcdonaldcarano.com · 2300 West Sahara Avenue, Suite 1000 · Las Vegas, NV 89102 · 702-873-4100

James J. Pisanelli · Brownstein Hyatt Farber Schreck · http://www.bhfs.com · 100 City Parkway, Suite 1600 · Las Vegas, NV 89106-4614 · 702-382-2101

Todd M. Touton · Lionel Sawyer & Collins · http://www.lionelsawyer.com · 1700 Bank of America Plaza · 300 South Fourth Street · Las Vegas, NV 89101 · 702-383-8888

Reno

Frank Cassas · Parsons Behle & Latimer · http://www.parsonsbehlelaw.com · 50 West Liberty Street, Suite 750 · Reno, NV 89501 · 775-323-1601

William A. S. Magrath II · McDonald Carano Wilson · http://www.mcdonaldcarano.com · 100 West Liberty Street, 10th Floor · P.O. Box 2670 · Reno, NV 89505 · 775-788-2000

CORPORATE LAW

Las Vegas

Robert C. Anderson · 2) · Holland & Hart · 3930 Howard Hughes Parkway, Fourth Floor · Las Vegas, NV 89169 · 775-327-3000

Michael J. Bonner · Kummer Kaempfer Bonner Renshaw & Ferrario · 3800 Howard Hughes Parkway, Seventh Floor · Las Vegas, NV 89169 · 702-792-7000

John N. Brewer · Kummer Kaempfer Bonner Renshaw & Ferrario · 3800 Howard Hughes Parkway, Seventh Floor · Las Vegas, NV 89169 · 702-792-7000

Sherwood N. Cook · Bolick & Boyer · 10785 West Twain Avenue, Suite 200 · Las Vegas, NV 89135-3028 · 702-870-6060

Charles W. Deaner · 2% · Deaner, Deaner, Scann, Malan & Larsen · 720 South Fourth Street, Suite 300 · Las Vegas, NV 89101 · 702-382-6911

Mary J. Drury · Marquis & Aurbach · 10001 Park Run Drive · Las Vegas, NV 89145 · 702-382-0711

Marc C. Gordon · Jennings, Strouss & Salmon · http://www.jsslaw.com · 8330 West Sahara Avenue, Suite 290 · Las Vegas, NV 89117 · 702-227-0700

Norman Ty Hilbrecht · a · Hilbrecht & Associates · 723 South Casino Center Boulevard · Las Vegas, NV 89101-6716 · 702-384-1036

R. Gardner Jolley · a · Jolley Urga Wirth Woodbury & Standish · 3800 Howard Hughes Parkway, Suite 1600 · Las Vegas, NV 89169 · 702-699-7500

Robert C. Kim · Ballard Spahr Andrews & Ingersoll · 100 City Parkway, Suite 1750 · Las Vegas, NV 89106 · 702-471-7000

Neal A. Klegerman · Kummer Kaempfer Bonner Renshaw & Ferrario · 3800 Howard Hughes Parkway, Seventh Floor · Las Vegas, NV 89169 · 702-792-7000

Samuel S. Lionel · 2% · Lionel Sawyer & Collins · http://www.lionelsawyer.com · 1700 Bank of America Plaza · 300 South Fourth Street · Las Vegas, NV 89101 · 702-383-8888

Scott Y. MacTaggart · Lewis and Roca · http://www.lrlaw.com · 3993 Howard Hughes Parkway, Suite 600 Las Vegas, NV 89169 · 702-949-8200

John D. O'Brien · 2) · John D. O'Brien · 700 South Seventh Street · Las Vegas, NV 89101 · 702-382-5222

Ellen Schulhofer · Brownstein Hyatt Farber Schreck · http://www.bhfs.com · 100 City Parkway, Suite 1600 · Las Vegas, NV 89106-4614 · 702-382-2101

William Silbey · Rice Silbey Reuther & Sullivan · http://www.rsrslaw.com · 3960 Howard Hughes Parkway, Suite 700 · Las Vegas, NV 89169 · 702-732-9099

Sonia Church Vermeys · Brownstein Hyatt Farber Schreck · http://www.bhfs.com · 100 City Parkway, Suite 1600 · Las Vegas, NV 89106-4614 · 702-382-2101

Kenneth A. Woloson · a · Santoro, Driggs, Walch, Kearney, Johnson & Thompson · 400 South Fourth Street, Third Floor · Las Vegas, NV 89101 · 702-791-0308

Reno

Robert E. Armstrong · a · McDonald Carano Wilson · http://www.mcdonaldcarano.com · 100 West Liberty Street, 10th Floor · P.O. Box 2670 · Reno, NV 89505 · 775-788-2000

Richard Bennett · a · Holland & Hart · 5441 Kietzke Lane, Second Floor · Reno, NV 89511 · 775-327-3000

C. Thomas Burton, Jr. · Burton, Bartlett & Glogovac · 50 West Liberty Street, Suite 700 · Reno, NV 89501 · 775-333-0400

C. Robert Cox · a · Maupin, Cox & LeGoy · 4785 Caughlin Parkway · P.O. Box 30000 · Reno, NV 89520 775-827-2000

John P. Fowler · a · Woodburn and Wedge · Sierra Plaza, Suite 500 · 6100 Neil Road · P.O. Box 2311 · Reno, NV 89505 · 775-688-3000

David A. Garcia · Holland & Hart · 5441 Kietzke Lane, Second Floor · Reno, NV 89511 · 775-327-3000

Prince A. Hawkins · Hawkins, Folsom & Muir · U.S. Bank Building, Suite 416 · One East Liberty Street P.O. Box 750 · Reno, NV 89504 · 775-786-4646

Mark W. Knobel · a · Avansino, Melarky, Knobel & Mulligan · http://www.amklaw.com · 4795 Caughlin Parkway, Suite 100 · Reno, NV 89519 · 775-333-0300

F. Dearmond Sharp · 2) · Robison, Belaustegui, Sharp & Low · 71 Washington Street · Reno, NV 89503 775-329-3151

EDUCATION LAW

Reno

C. Robert Cox · a · Maupin, Cox & LeGoy · 4785 Caughlin Parkway · P.O. Box 30000 · Reno, NV 89520 775-827-2000

EMINENT DOMAIN AND CONDEMNATION LAW

Las Vegas

Kermitt Waters · Law Office of Kermitt L. Waters · 704 South Ninth Street · Las Vegas, NV 89101 · 702-733-8877

EMPLOYEE BENEFITS LAW

Las Vegas

Andrew S. Brignone · a · Brownstein Hyatt Farber Schreck · http://www.bhfs.com · 100 City Parkway, Suite 1600 · Las Vegas, NV 89106-4614 · 702-382-2101

A. Kent Greene · 2) · Clark, Greene & Associates · 3770 Howard Hughes Parkway, Suite 195 · Las Vegas, NV 89109-0940 · 702-369-2900

Adam P. Segal · Brownstein Hyatt Farber Schreck · http://www.bhfs.com · 100 City Parkway, Suite 1600 · Las Vegas, NV 89106-4614 · 702-382-2101

Reno

L. Robert LeGoy, Jr. · 2) · Maupin, Cox & LeGoy · 4785 Caughlin Parkway · P.O. Box 30000 · Reno, NV 89520 · 775-827-2000

ENERGY LAW

Carson City

Robert L. Crowell · a · Kummer Kaempfer Bonner Renshaw & Ferrario · 510 West Fourth Street · Carson City, NV 89703 · 775-882-1311

Patrick V. Fagan · Allison, MacKenzie, Russell, Pavlakis, Wright & Fagan · 402 North Division Street · P.O. Box 646 · Carson City, NV 89702 · 775-687-0202

Robert Graeme Johnston · Kilpatrick, Johnston & Adler · 412 North Division Street · Carson City, NV 89703-4168 · 775-882-6112

Frederick J. Schmidt · Holland & Hart · 777 East William Street, Suite 200 · Carson City, NV 89701 · 775-684-6000

Steven E. Tackes · Kummer Kaempfer Bonner Renshaw & Ferrario · 510 West Fourth Street · Carson City, NV 89703 · 775-882-1311

Reno

Kathleen M. Drakulich · Kummer Kaempfer Bonner Renshaw & Ferrario · 5585 Kietzke Lane · Reno, NV 89511 · 775-852-3900

Shawn M. Elicegui · Lionel Sawyer & Collins · http://www.lionelsawyer.com · 1100 Bank of America Plaza · 50 West Liberty Street · Reno, NV 89501 · 775-788-8666

Earl M. Hill · 2) · Parsons Behle & Latimer · http://www.parsonsbehlelaw.com · 50 West Liberty Street, Suite 750 · Reno, NV 89501 · 775-323-1601

Dan R. Reaser · Lionel Sawyer & Collins · http://www.lionelsawyer.com · 1100 Bank of America Plaza · 50 West Liberty Street · Reno, NV 89501 · 775-788-8666

Harvey Whittemore · Lionel Sawyer & Collins · http://www.lionelsawyer.com · 1100 Bank of America Plaza · 50 West Liberty Street · Reno, NV 89501 · 775-788-8666

ENVIRONMENTAL LAW

Reno

Ross E. de Lipkau · a · Parsons Behle & Latimer · http://www.parsonsbehlelaw.com · 50 West Liberty Street, Suite 750 · Reno, NV 89501 · 775-323-1601

Earl M. Hill · 2) · Parsons Behle & Latimer · http://www.parsonsbehlelaw.com · 50 West Liberty Street, Suite 750 · Reno, NV 89501 · 775-323-1601

Roger W. Jeppson · a · Holland & Hart · 5441 Kietzke Lane, Second Floor · Reno, NV 89511 · 775-327-3000

FAMILY LAW

Las Vegas

Howard Ecker · a · Ecker & Kainen · 300 South Fourth Street, Suite 901 · Las Vegas, NV 89101 · 702-384-1700

Edward Kainen · Ecker & Kainen · 300 South Fourth Street, Suite 901 · Las Vegas, NV 89101 · 702-384-1700

Paul A. Lemcke · Jones Vargas · 3773 Howard Hughes Parkway, Third Floor South · Las Vegas, NV 89109 · 702-862-3300

Daniel Marks · 2) · Daniel Marks · 302 East Carson Avenue, Suite 702 · Las Vegas, NV 89101 · 702-386-0536

Reno

Mary Anne Decaria · Silverman, Decaria & Kattelman · 290 South Arlington Avenue, Suite 100 · Reno, NV 89501 · 775-322-3223

Ronald J. Logar · 2) · Logar & Pulver · 225 South Arlington Avenue, Suite A · Reno, NV 89501 · 775-786-5040

Raymond E. Oster · Fahrendorf, Viloria, Oliphant & Oster · 327 California Avenue · Reno, NV 89519 · 775-348-9999

Kathleen T. Price · Kathleen T. Price · 462 Court Street · Reno, NV 89501 · 775-786-5055

Gary R. Silverman · a · Silverman, Decaria & Kattelman · 290 South Arlington Avenue, Suite 100 · Reno, NV 89501 · 775-322-3223

Richard W. Young · a · Law Offices of Richard W. Young · 327 Marsh Avenue · Reno, NV 89509-1611 · 775-322-9477

FIRST AMENDMENT LAW

Las Vegas

Todd L. Bice · Brownstein Hyatt Farber Schreck · http://www.bhfs.com · 100 City Parkway, Suite 1600 · Las Vegas, NV 89106-4614 · 702-382-2101

Allen Lichtenstein · Allen Lichtenstein · 3315 Russell Road, Suite 222 · Las Vegas, NV 89120 · 702-433-2666

J. Colby Williams · Campbell & Williams · 700 South Seventh Street · Las Vegas, NV 89101-6908 · 702-382-5222

FRANCHISE LAW

Las Vegas

Paul E. Larsen · Lionel Sawyer & Collins · http://www.lionelsawyer.com · 1700 Bank of America Plaza · 300 South Fourth Street · Las Vegas, NV 89101 · 702-383-8888

GAMING LAW

Las Vegas

David R. Arrajj · Brownstein Hyatt Farber Schreck · http://www.bhfs.com · 100 City Parkway, Suite 1600 Las Vegas, NV 89106-4614 · 702-382-2101

Peter Bernhard · Bullivant Houser Bailey · 3883 Howard Hughes Parkway, Suite 550 · Las Vegas, NV 89169 · 702-669-3600

Michael J. Bonner · Kummer Kaempfer Bonner Renshaw & Ferrario · 3800 Howard Hughes Parkway, Seventh Floor · Las Vegas, NV 89169 · 702-792-7000

Anthony N. Cabot · Lewis and Roca · http://www.lrlaw.com · 3993 Howard Hughes Parkway, Suite 600 · Las Vegas, NV 89169 · 702-949-8200

William P. Curran · Ballard Spahr Andrews & Ingersoll · 100 City Parkway, Suite 1750 · Las Vegas, NV 89106 · 702-471-7000

Robert D. Faiss · Lionel Sawyer & Collins · http://www.lionelsawyer.com · 1700 Bank of America Plaza · 300 South Fourth Street · Las Vegas, NV 89101 · 702-383-8888

P. Gregory Giordano · Snell & Wilmer · 3883 Howard Hughes Parkway, 11th Floor · Las Vegas, NV 89169 · 702-784-5200

Frank A. Schreck · Brownstein Hyatt Farber Schreck · http://www.bhfs.com · 100 City Parkway, Suite 1600 · Las Vegas, NV 89106-4614 · 702-382-2101

Jeffrey A. Silver · Gordon & Silver · 3960 Howard Hughes Parkway, Ninth Floor · Las Vegas, NV 89169 · 702-796-5555

William R. Urga · Jolley Urga Wirth Woodbury & Standish · 3800 Howard Hughes Parkway, Suite 1600 · Las Vegas, NV 89169 · 702-699-7500

Ellen Whittemore · Lionel Sawyer & Collins · http://www.lionelsawyer.com · 1700 Bank of America Plaza 300 South Fourth Street · Las Vegas, NV 89101 · 702-383-8888

Reno

Michael G. Alonso · Jones Vargas · 100 West Liberty Street, 12th Floor · P.O. Box 281 · Reno, NV 89504 775-786-5000

Paul A. Bible · Bible Mousel · http://www.nvgaminglaw.com · 6140 Plumas Street, Suite 300 · Reno, NV 89519-6061 · 775-824-0123

Alvin J. Hicks · McDonald Carano Wilson · http://www.mcdonaldcarano.com · 100 West Liberty Street, 10th Floor · P.O. Box 2670 · Reno, NV 89505 · 775-788-2000

Sean M. McGuinness · Lewis and Roca · http://www.lrlaw.com · 50 West Libery Street, Suite 410 · Reno, NV 89501 · 775-823-2900

David L. Mousel · Bible Mousel · http://www.nvgaminglaw.com · 6140 Plumas Street, Suite 300 · Reno, NV 89519-6061 · 775-824-0123

Dan R. Reaser · Lionel Sawyer & Collins · http://www.lionelsawyer.com · 1100 Bank of America Plaza · 50 West Liberty Street · Reno, NV 89501 · 775-788-8666

GOVERNMENT RELATIONS LAW

Carson City

Robert L. Crowell · a · Kummer Kaempfer Bonner Renshaw & Ferrario · 510 West Fourth Street · Carson City, NV 89703 · 775-882-1311

Las Vegas

Joseph W. Brown · Jones Vargas · 3773 Howard Hughes Parkway, Third Floor South · Las Vegas, NV 89109 · 702-862-3300

Richard H. Bryan · Lionel Sawyer & Collins · http://www.lionelsawyer.com · 1700 Bank of America Plaza 300 South Fourth Street · Las Vegas, NV 89101 · 702-383-8888

William P. Curran · Ballard Spahr Andrews & Ingersoll · 100 City Parkway, Suite 1750 · Las Vegas, NV 89106 · 702-471-7000

Mark H. Fiorentino · Kummer Kaempfer Bonner Renshaw & Ferrario · 3800 Howard Hughes Parkway, Seventh Floor · Las Vegas, NV 89169 · 702-792-7000

Edward M. Garcia · Jones Vargas · 3773 Howard Hughes Parkway, Third Floor South · Las Vegas, NV 89109 · 702-862-3300

Christopher L. Kaempfer · Kummer Kaempfer Bonner Renshaw & Ferrario · 3800 Howard Hughes Parkway, Seventh Floor · Las Vegas, NV 89169 · 702-792-7000

Jennifer Lazovich · Kummer Kaempfer Bonner Renshaw & Ferrario · 3800 Howard Hughes Parkway, Seventh Floor · Las Vegas, NV 89169 · 702-792-7000

Russell M. Rowe · Kummer Kaempfer Bonner Renshaw & Ferrario · 3800 Howard Hughes Parkway, Seventh Floor · Las Vegas, NV 89169 · 702-792-7000

James L. Wadhams · Jones Vargas · 3773 Howard Hughes Parkway, Third Floor South · Las Vegas, NV 89109 · 702-862-3300

Reno

Michael G. Alonso · Jones Vargas · 100 West Liberty Street, 12th Floor · P.O. Box 281 · Reno, NV 89504 775-786-5000

John Griffin · Kummer Kaempfer Bonner Renshaw & Ferrario · 5585 Kietzke Lane · Reno, NV 89511 · 775-852-3900

John P. Sande III · Jones Vargas · 100 West Liberty Street, 12th Floor · P.O. Box 281 · Reno, NV 89504 · 775-786-5000

Harvey Whittemore · Lionel Sawyer & Collins · http://www.lionelsawyer.com · 1100 Bank of America Plaza · 50 West Liberty Street · Reno, NV 89501 · 775-788-8666

HEALTH CARE LAW

Henderson

Maria Nutile · Nutile Law & Associates · 1070 West Horizon Ridge Parkway, Suite 210 · Henderson, NV 89012 · 702-307-4880

Las Vegas

Lynn S. Fulstone · Lionel Sawyer & Collins · http://www.lionelsawyer.com · 1700 Bank of America Plaza 300 South Fourth Street · Las Vegas, NV 89101 · 702-383-8888

Dennis L. Kennedy · a · Bailey Kennedy · 8984 Spanish Ridge Avenue · Las Vegas, NV 89148 · 702-562-8820

Sherman B. Mayor · a · Mayor Law Firm · 701 South Ninth Street, Suite 210 · Las Vegas, NV 89101 · 702-387-9604

Reno

Keith L. Lee · a · Law Offices of Keith L. Lee · 3400 Kauai Court, Suite 204 · Reno, NV 89509 · 775-829-1400

Kim G. Rowe · a · Maupin, Cox & LeGoy · 4785 Caughlin Parkway · P.O. Box 30000 · Reno, NV 89520 · 775-827-2000

IMMIGRATION LAW

Las Vegas

M. Edwin Prudhomme · Prudhomme Law Firm · 6565 Spencer Street, Suite 208 · Las Vegas, NV 89119 702-258-0032

Jeremiah Wolf-Stuchiner · Prudhomme Law Firm · 6565 Spencer Street, Suite 208 · Las Vegas, NV 89119 · 702-258-0032

INFORMATION TECHNOLOGY LAW

Las Vegas

Anthony N. Cabot · Lewis and Roca · http://www.lrlaw.com · 3993 Howard Hughes Parkway, Suite 600 · Las Vegas, NV 89169 · 702-949-8200

Robert Ryan Morishita · Morishita Law Firm · 3800 Howard Hughes Parkway, Suite 850 · Las Vegas, NV 89109 · 702-222-2113

Ellen Whittemore · Lionel Sawyer & Collins · http://www.lionelsawyer.com · 1700 Bank of America Plaza 300 South Fourth Street · Las Vegas, NV 89101 · 702-383-8888

INTELLECTUAL PROPERTY LAW

Las Vegas

Edward J. Quirk · a · Greenberg Traurig · http://www.gtlaw.com · 3773 Howard Hughes Parkway, Suite 400 North · Las Vegas, NV 89169 · 702-792-3773

Mark G. Tratos · Greenberg Traurig · http://www.gtlaw.com · 3773 Howard Hughes Parkway, Suite 400 North · Las Vegas, NV 89169 · 702-792-3773

LABOR AND EMPLOYMENT LAW

Las Vegas

Scott M. Abbott · Kamer Zucker Abbott · 3000 West Charleston Boulevard, Suite Three · Las Vegas, NV 89102 · 702-259-8640

Frederic I. Berkley · 2) · Jennings, Strouss & Salmon · http://www.jsslaw.com · 8330 West Sahara Avenue, Suite 290 · Las Vegas, NV 89117 · 702-227-0700

Howard E. Cole · Lewis and Roca · http://www.lrlaw.com · 3993 Howard Hughes Parkway, Suite 600 · Las Vegas, NV 89169 · 702-949-8200

Kathleen J. England · a · Kathleen Jane England · 630 South Third Street · Las Vegas, NV 89101 · 702-385-3300

Von S. Heinz · Lewis and Roca · http://www.lrlaw.com · 3993 Howard Hughes Parkway, Suite 600 · Las Vegas, NV 89169 · 702-949-8200

Gregory J. Kamer · 2) · Kamer Zucker Abbott · 3000 West Charleston Boulevard, Suite Three · Las Vegas, NV 89102 · 702-259-8640

Edwin A. Keller, Jr. · Kamer Zucker Abbott · 3000 West Charleston Boulevard, Suite Three · Las Vegas, NV 89102 · 702-259-8640

Joanne S. Kishner · DLA Piper · 3960 Howard Hughes Parkway, Suite 400 · Las Vegas, NV 89109 · 702-737-3433

Malani L. Kotchka · Lionel Sawyer & Collins · http://www.lionelsawyer.com · 1700 Bank of America Plaza · 300 South Fourth Street · Las Vegas, NV 89101 · 702-383-8888

Keith M. Lyons · Lyons Law Firm · 512 South Eighth Street · Las Vegas, NV 89101 · 702-432-8655

Daniel Marks · 2) · Daniel Marks · 302 East Carson Avenue, Suite 702 · Las Vegas, NV 89101 · 702-386-0536

Gary C. Moss · Jackson Lewis · http://www.jacksonlewis.com · 3960 Howard Hughes Parkway, Suite 500 · Las Vegas, NV 89169 · 702-921-2460

Mark J. Ricciardi · a · Fisher & Phillips · http://www.laborlawyers.com · 3993 Howard Hughes Parkway, Suite 650 · Las Vegas, NV 89169 · 702-252-3131

Richard S. Segerblom · 2) · Richard S. Segerblom · 704 South Ninth Street · Las Vegas, NV 89101 · 702-388-9600

Gregory E. Smith · Lionel Sawyer & Collins · http://www.lionelsawyer.com · 1700 Bank of America Plaza 300 South Fourth Street · Las Vegas, NV 89101 · 702-383-8888

Elayna J. Youchah · Brownstein Hyatt Farber Schreck · http://www.bhfs.com · 100 City Parkway, Suite 1600 · Las Vegas, NV 89106-4614 · 702-382-2101

Carol Davis Zucker · a · Kamer Zucker Abbott · 3000 West Charleston Boulevard, Suite Three · Las Vegas, NV 89102 · 702-259-8640

Reno

Michael E. Langton · a · Michael E. Langton · 801 Riverside Drive · Reno, NV 89503 · 775-329-7557

Michael E. Malloy · Maupin, Cox & LeGoy · 4785 Caughlin Parkway · P.O. Box 30000 · Reno, NV 89520 775-827-2000

Ann Morgan · Jones Vargas · 100 West Liberty Street, 12th Floor · P.O. Box 281 · Reno, NV 89504 · 775-786-5000

LAND USE & ZONING LAW

Las Vegas

Thomas D. Amick · Kummer Kaempfer Bonner Renshaw & Ferrario · 3800 Howard Hughes Parkway, Seventh Floor · Las Vegas, NV 89169 · 702-792-7000

William P. Curran · Ballard Spahr Andrews & Ingersoll · 100 City Parkway, Suite 1750 · Las Vegas, NV 89106 · 702-471-7000

Mark H. Fiorentino · Kummer Kaempfer Bonner Renshaw & Ferrario · 3800 Howard Hughes Parkway, Seventh Floor · Las Vegas, NV 89169 · 702-792-7000

Edward M. Garcia · Jones Vargas · 3773 Howard Hughes Parkway, Third Floor South · Las Vegas, NV 89109 · 702-862-3300

Robert J. Gronauer · Kummer Kaempfer Bonner Renshaw & Ferrario · 3800 Howard Hughes Parkway, Seventh Floor · Las Vegas, NV 89169 · 702-792-7000

Christopher L. Kaempfer · Kummer Kaempfer Bonner Renshaw & Ferrario · 3800 Howard Hughes Parkway, Seventh Floor · Las Vegas, NV 89169 · 702-792-7000

Stanley W. Parry · Ballard Spahr Andrews & Ingersoll · 100 City Parkway, Suite 1750 · Las Vegas, NV 89106 · 702-471-7000

Jeffrey A. Silver · Gordon & Silver · 3960 Howard Hughes Parkway, Ninth Floor · Las Vegas, NV 89169 · 702-796-5555

Reno

Jim B. Butler · Parsons Behle & Latimer · http://www.parsonsbehlelaw.com · 50 West Liberty Street, Suite 750 · Reno, NV 89501 · 775-323-1601

Pierre A. Hascheff · Pierre A. Hascheff · 1029 Riverside Drive · P.O. Box 40667 · Reno, NV 89502 · 775-786-4121

Stephen C. Mollath · Prezant & Mollath · 6560 Southwest McCarran Boulevard, Suite A · Reno, NV 89509 · 775-786-3011

MEDICAL MALPRACTICE LAW

Las Vegas

Neil G. Galatz · 2% · Galatz, Gillock & Associates · 428 South Fourth Street · Las Vegas, NV 89101 · 702-386-0000

Gerald I. Gillock · a · Galatz, Gillock & Associates · 428 South Fourth Street · Las Vegas, NV 89101 · 702-386-0000

Lynn M. Hansen · Jimmerson Hansen · 415 South Sixth Street, Suite 100 · Las Vegas, NV 89101 · 702-388-7171

MERGERS & ACQUISITIONS LAW

Las Vegas

Michael J. Bonner · Kummer Kaempfer Bonner Renshaw & Ferrario · 3800 Howard Hughes Parkway, Seventh Floor · Las Vegas, NV 89169 · 702-792-7000

MINING LAW

Reno

Jim B. Butler · Parsons Behle & Latimer · http://www.parsonsbehlelaw.com · 50 West Liberty Street, Suite 750 · Reno, NV 89501 · 775-323-1601

Ross E. de Lipkau · a · Parsons Behle & Latimer · http://www.parsonsbehlelaw.com · 50 West Liberty Street, Suite 750 · Reno, NV 89501 · 775-323-1601

Earl M. Hill · 2) · Parsons Behle & Latimer · http://www.parsonsbehlelaw.com · 50 West Liberty Street, Suite 750 · Reno, NV 89501 · 775-323-1601

Roger W. Jeppson · a · Holland & Hart · 5441 Kietzke Lane, Second Floor · Reno, NV 89511 · 775-327-3000

NATURAL RESOURCES LAW

Reno

Jim B. Butler · Parsons Behle & Latimer · http://www.parsonsbehlelaw.com · 50 West Liberty Street, Suite 750 · Reno, NV 89501 · 775-323-1601

Ross E. de Lipkau · a · Parsons Behle & Latimer · http://www.parsonsbehlelaw.com · 50 West Liberty Street, Suite 750 · Reno, NV 89501 · 775-323-1601

Gordon H. DePaoli · Woodburn and Wedge · Sierra Plaza, Suite 500 · 6100 Neil Road · P.O. Box 2311 · Reno, NV 89505 · 775-688-3000

Earl M. Hill · 2) · Parsons Behle & Latimer · http://www.parsonsbehlelaw.com · 50 West Liberty Street, Suite 750 · Reno, NV 89501 · 775-323-1601

Roger W. Jeppson · a · Holland & Hart · 5441 Kietzke Lane, Second Floor · Reno, NV 89511 · 775-327-3000

NON-PROFIT/CHARITIES LAW

Reno

G. Barton Mowry · 2) · Maupin, Cox & LeGoy · 4785 Caughlin Parkway · P.O. Box 30000 · Reno, NV 89520 · 775-827-2000

NON-WHITE-COLLAR CRIMINAL DEFENSE

Las Vegas

Frank J. Cremen · Frank J. Cremen · 715 South Fourth Street · Las Vegas, NV 89101 · 702-385-7475

Dominic P. Gentile · 2% · Gordon & Silver · 3960 Howard Hughes Parkway, Ninth Floor · Las Vegas, NV 89169 · 702-796-5555

Thomas F. Pitaro · a · Thomas F. Pitaro · 815 South Third Street · Las Vegas, NV 89101 · 702-382-9221

William B. Terry · a · William B. Terry · 530 South Seventh Street · Las Vegas, NV 89101 · 702-385-0799

Richard A. Wright · 2) · Wright Stanish & Winckler · http://www.wjwprofcorp.com · 300 South Fourth Street, Suite 701 · Las Vegas, NV 89101 · 702-382-4004

Reno

C. Frederick Pinkerton · 2) · C. Frederick Pinkerton · 1265 Tarleton Way · Reno, NV 89523 · 775-322-7553

PERSONAL INJURY LITIGATION

Las Vegas

J. Mitchell Cobeaga · a · Cobeaga Tomlinson · 228 South Fourth Street · Las Vegas, NV 89101 · 702-240-2499

Douglas M. Cohen · Jones Vargas · 3773 Howard Hughes Parkway, Third Floor South · Las Vegas, NV 89109 · 702-862-3300

Kerry L. Earley · a · Kerry L. Earley · 801 South Fourth Street · Las Vegas, NV 89101 · 702-388-0113

Neil G. Galatz · 2% · Galatz, Gillock & Associates · 428 South Fourth Street · Las Vegas, NV 89101 · 702-386-0000

Gerald I. Gillock · a · Galatz, Gillock & Associates · 428 South Fourth Street · Las Vegas, NV 89101 · 702-386-0000

Steven J. Parsons · a · Steven J. Parsons · City Center West, Suite 108 · 7201 West Lake Mead Boulevard · Las Vegas, NV 89128-8354 · 702-384-9900

James F. Pico · 2) · Pico Escobar Rosenberger · 2000 South Eastern Avenue · Las Vegas, NV 89104 · 702-457-9099

Reno

Thomas P. Beko · Erickson, Thorpe & Swainston · 99 West Arroyo Street · P.O. Box 3559 · Reno, NV 89505 · 775-786-3930

Bill O. Bradley, Jr. · Bradley, Drendel & Jeanney · 401 Flint Street · Reno, NV 89505-1987 · 775-335-9999

Thomas R. Brennan · Durney & Brennan · 150 West Huffaker Lane, Suite 101 · Reno, NV 89511 · 775-322-2923

William G. Cobb · Erickson, Thorpe & Swainston · 99 West Arroyo Street · P.O. Box 3559 · Reno, NV 89505 · 775-786-3930

Thomas E. Drendel · Bradley, Drendel & Jeanney · 401 Flint Street · Reno, NV 89505-1987 · 775-335-9999

Peter D. Durney · Durney & Brennan · 150 West Huffaker Lane, Suite 101 · Reno, NV 89511 · 775-322-2923

John Echeverria · John Echeverria · 9432 Double R Boulevard · Reno, NV 89521 · 775-786-4800

Robert L. Eisenberg · Lemons, Grundy & Eisenberg · 6005 Plumas Street, Suite 300 · Reno, NV 89509 · 775-786-6868

Robert F. Enzenberger · Law Offices of Robert F. Enzenberger · 1885 South Arlington Avenue, Suite 205 · Reno, NV 89509-3370 · 775-786-7000

C. James Georgeson · 2) · Georgeson Angaran · 5450 Longley Lane · Reno, NV 89511 · 775-827-6440

William C. Jeanney · Bradley, Drendel & Jeanney · 401 Flint Street · Reno, NV 89505-1987 · 775-335-9999

Michael R. Kealy · Parsons Behle & Latimer · http://www.parsonsbehlelaw.com · 50 West Liberty Street, Suite 750 · Reno, NV 89501 · 775-323-1601

Bruce Laxalt · a · Laxalt & Nomura · http://www.laxalt-nomura.com · 9600 Gateway Drive · Reno, NV 89521 · 775-322-1170

Peter Chase Neumann · 2) · Peter Chase Neumann · 136 Ridge Street · Reno, NV 89501 · 775-786-3750

Don G. Nomura · Laxalt & Nomura · http://www.laxalt-nomura.com · 9600 Gateway Drive · Reno, NV 89521 · 775-322-1170

Kent R. Robison · a · Robison, Belaustegui, Sharp & Low · 71 Washington Street · Reno, NV 89503 · 775-329-3151

Wayne A. Shaffer · Laxalt & Nomura · http://www.laxalt-nomura.com · 9600 Gateway Drive · Reno, NV 89521 · 775-322-1170

Eugene J. Wait, Jr. · 2) · Wait Law Firm · 305 West Moana Lane, Second Floor · Reno, NV 89509 · 775-827-5500

PRODUCT LIABILITY LITIGATION

Las Vegas

Neil G. Galatz · 2% · Galatz, Gillock & Associates · 428 South Fourth Street · Las Vegas, NV 89101 · 702-386-0000

Reno

Peter Chase Neumann · 2) · Peter Chase Neumann · 136 Ridge Street · Reno, NV 89501 · 775-786-3750

Wayne A. Shaffer · Laxalt & Nomura · http://www.laxalt-nomura.com · 9600 Gateway Drive · Reno, NV 89521 · 775-322-1170

PUBLIC FINANCE LAW

Reno

Jennifer Stern · Sherman & Howard · 50 West Liberty Street, Suite 1000 · Reno, NV 89501 · 775-323-1980

John O. Swendseid · Sherman & Howard · 50 West Liberty Street, Suite 1000 · Reno, NV 89501 · 775-323-1980

REAL ESTATE LAW

Las Vegas

Peter Bernhard · Bullivant Houser Bailey · 3883 Howard Hughes Parkway, Suite 550 · Las Vegas, NV 89169 · 702-669-3600

Christine A. Bricker · Gordon & Silver · 3960 Howard Hughes Parkway, Ninth Floor · Las Vegas, NV 89169 · 702-796-5555

Michael E. Buckley · 2) · Jones Vargas · 3773 Howard Hughes Parkway, Third Floor South · Las Vegas, NV 89109 · 702-862-3300

Layne J. Butt · Layne J. Butt · 1496 East Lawman Court · Las Vegas, NV 89119 · 702-361-1391

William P. Curran · Ballard Spahr Andrews & Ingersoll · 100 City Parkway, Suite 1750 · Las Vegas, NV 89106 · 702-471-7000

Patricia J. Curtis · Snell & Wilmer · 3883 Howard Hughes Parkway, 11th Floor · Las Vegas, NV 89169 · 702-784-5200

Charles W. Deaner · 2% · Deaner, Deaner, Scann, Malan & Larsen · 720 South Fourth Street, Suite 300 · Las Vegas, NV 89101 · 702-382-6911

Andrew S. Gabriel · McDonald Carano Wilson · http://www.mcdonaldcarano.com · 2300 West Sahara Avenue, Suite 1000 · Las Vegas, NV 89102 · 702-873-4100

Mark H. Goldstein · a · Lionel Sawyer & Collins · http://www.lionelsawyer.com · 1700 Bank of America Plaza · 300 South Fourth Street · Las Vegas, NV 89101 · 702-383-8888

Jodi R. Goodheart · Jones Vargas · 3773 Howard Hughes Parkway, Third Floor South · Las Vegas, NV 89109 · 702-862-3300

Barry Stephen Goold · 2) · Goold Patterson Ales & Day · http://www.gooldpatterson.com · 4496 South Pecos Road · Las Vegas, NV 89121 · 702-436-2600

Andrew P. Gordon · McDonald Carano Wilson · http://www.mcdonaldcarano.com · 2300 West Sahara Avenue, Suite 1000 · Las Vegas, NV 89102 · 702-873-4100

Leslie Terry Jones · Brownstein Hyatt Farber Schreck · http://www.bhfs.com · 100 City Parkway, Suite 1600 · Las Vegas, NV 89106-4614 · 702-382-2101

Christopher L. Kaempfer · Kummer Kaempfer Bonner Renshaw & Ferrario · 3800 Howard Hughes Parkway, Seventh Floor · Las Vegas, NV 89169 · 702-792-7000

James Mace · Christensen, Glaser, Fink, Jacobs, Weil & Shapiro · 3763 Howard Hughes Parkway, Suite 300 · Las Vegas, NV 89169 · 702-242-4200

Jeffrey D. Patterson · Goold Patterson Ales & Day · http://www.gooldpatterson.com · 4496 South Pecos Road · Las Vegas, NV 89121 · 702-436-2600

Renee R. Reuther · Rice Silbey Reuther & Sullivan · http://www.rsrslaw.com · 3960 Howard Hughes Parkway, Suite 700 · Las Vegas, NV 89169 · 702-732-9099

Stephen Rice · Rice Silbey Reuther & Sullivan · http://www.rsrslaw.com · 3960 Howard Hughes Parkway, Suite 700 · Las Vegas, NV 89169 · 702-732-9099

Mandy S. Shavinsky · Christensen, Glaser, Fink, Jacobs, Weil & Shapiro · 3763 Howard Hughes Parkway, Suite 300 · Las Vegas, NV 89169 · 702-242-4200

Stephen B. Yoken · Snell & Wilmer · 3883 Howard Hughes Parkway, 11th Floor · Las Vegas, NV 89169 · 702-784-5200

Jeffrey P. Zucker · 2% · Lionel Sawyer & Collins · http://www.lionelsawyer.com · 1700 Bank of America Plaza · 300 South Fourth Street · Las Vegas, NV 89101 · 702-383-8888

Reno

Leo P. Bergin III · McDonald Carano Wilson · http://www.mcdonaldcarano.com · 100 West Liberty Street, 10th Floor · P.O. Box 2670 · Reno, NV 89505 · 775-788-2000

William C. Davis, Jr. · Jones Vargas · 100 West Liberty Street, 12th Floor · P.O. Box 281 · Reno, NV 89504 · 775-786-5000

Karen D. Dennison · a · Holland & Hart · 5441 Kietzke Lane, Second Floor · Reno, NV 89511 · 775-327-3000

Colleen A. Dolan · a · Lionel Sawyer & Collins · http://www.lionelsawyer.com · 1100 Bank of America Plaza · 50 West Liberty Street · Reno, NV 89501 · 775-788-8666

Craig E. Etem · Lionel Sawyer & Collins · http://www.lionelsawyer.com · 1100 Bank of America Plaza · 50 West Liberty Street · Reno, NV 89501 · 775-788-8666

Elizabeth M. Fielder · Jones Vargas · 100 West Liberty Street, 12th Floor · P.O. Box 281 · Reno, NV 89504 · 775-786-5000

Douglas Flowers · Holland & Hart · 5441 Kietzke Lane, Second Floor · Reno, NV 89511 · 775-327-3000

John Frankovich · McDonald Carano Wilson · http://www.mcdonaldcarano.com · 100 West Liberty Street, 10th Floor · P.O. Box 2670 · Reno, NV 89505 · 775-788-2000

Pierre A. Hascheff · Pierre A. Hascheff · 1029 Riverside Drive · P.O. Box 40667 · Reno, NV 89502 · 775-786-4121

Timothy J. Henderson · a · Henderson & Morgan · 4600 Kietzke Lane, Suite K-228 · Reno, NV 89502 · 775-825-7000

R. Craig Howard · Holland & Hart · 5441 Kietzke Lane, Second Floor · Reno, NV 89511 · 775-327-3000

David R. Hoy · 2) · Hoy & Hoy · 1495 Ridgeview Drive, Suite 90 · Reno, NV 89501-1808 · 775-786-8000

Procter J. Hug · Maupin, Cox & LeGoy · 4785 Caughlin Parkway · P.O. Box 30000 · Reno, NV 89520 · 775-827-2000

W. Douglas Maupin · a · Maupin, Cox & LeGoy · 4785 Caughlin Parkway · P.O. Box 30000 · Reno, NV 89520 · 775-827-2000

James L. Morgan · Henderson & Morgan · 4600 Kietzke Lane, Suite K-228 · Reno, NV 89502 · 775-825-7000

Stephen V. Novacek · a · Holland & Hart · 5441 Kietzke Lane, Second Floor · Reno, NV 89511 · 775-327-3000

Robert M. Sader · Robert M. Sader · 8600 Technology Way, Suite 101 · Reno, NV 89521 · 775-329-8310

F. Dearmond Sharp · 2) · Robison, Belaustegui, Sharp & Low · 71 Washington Street · Reno, NV 89503 775-329-3151

TAX LAW

Henderson

Jeffrey L. Burr · 2) · Jeffrey L. Burr & Associates · 2600 Paseo Verde Parkway · Henderson, NV 89074 · 702-433-4455

Las Vegas

Robert C. Anderson · 2) · Holland & Hart · 3930 Howard Hughes Parkway, Fourth Floor · Las Vegas, NV 89169 · 775-327-3000

Richard A. Oshins · 2% · Oshins & Associates · 1645 Village Center Circle, Suite 170 · Las Vegas, NV 89134 · 702-341-6000

Steven J. Oshins · Oshins & Associates · 1645 Village Center Circle, Suite 170 · Las Vegas, NV 89134 · 702-341-6000

Reno

Robert E. Armstrong · a · McDonald Carano Wilson · http://www.mcdonaldcarano.com · 100 West Liberty Street, 10th Floor · P.O. Box 2670 · Reno, NV 89505 · 775-788-2000

Kurt O. Hunsberger · Maupin, Cox & LeGoy · 4785 Caughlin Parkway · P.O. Box 30000 · Reno, NV 89520 · 775-827-2000

Mark W. Knobel · a · Avansino, Melarky, Knobel & Mulligan · http://www.amklaw.com · 4795 Caughlin Parkway, Suite 100 · Reno, NV 89519 · 775-333-0300

Ernest J. Maupin · 2) · Maupin, Cox & LeGoy · 4785 Caughlin Parkway · P.O. Box 30000 · Reno, NV 89520 · 775-827-2000

Michael J. Melarkey · a · Avansino, Melarky, Knobel & Mulligan · http://www.amklaw.com · 4795 Caughlin Parkway, Suite 100 · Reno, NV 89519 · 775-333-0300

G. Barton Mowry · 2) · Maupin, Cox & LeGoy · 4785 Caughlin Parkway · P.O. Box 30000 · Reno, NV 89520 · 775-827-2000

TRUSTS AND ESTATES

Henderson

Jeffrey L. Burr · 2) · Jeffrey L. Burr & Associates · 2600 Paseo Verde Parkway · Henderson, NV 89074 · 702-433-4455

Las Vegas

Richard A. Oshins · 2% · Oshins & Associates · 1645 Village Center Circle, Suite 170 · Las Vegas, NV 89134 · 702-341-6000

Steven J. Oshins · Oshins & Associates · 1645 Village Center Circle, Suite 170 · Las Vegas, NV 89134 · 702-341-6000

Layne T. Rushforth · 2) · The Rushforth Firm · http://www.rushforthfirm.com · 9505 Hillwood Drive, Suite 100 · Las Vegas, NV 89134 · 702-255-4552

Scott A. Swain · McDonald Carano Wilson · http://www.mcdonaldcarano.com · 2300 West Sahara Avenue, Suite 1000 · Las Vegas, NV 89102 · 702-873-4100

Reno

Robert E. Armstrong · a · McDonald Carano Wilson · http://www.mcdonaldcarano.com · 100 West Liberty Street, 10th Floor · P.O. Box 2670 · Reno, NV 89505 · 775-788-2000

Kurt O. Hunsberger · Maupin, Cox & LeGoy · 4785 Caughlin Parkway · P.O. Box 30000 · Reno, NV 89520 · 775-827-2000

Mark W. Knobel · a · Avansino, Melarky, Knobel & Mulligan · http://www.amklaw.com · 4795 Caughlin Parkway, Suite 100 · Reno, NV 89519 · 775-333-0300

Ernest J. Maupin · 2) · Maupin, Cox & LeGoy · 4785 Caughlin Parkway · P.O. Box 30000 · Reno, NV 89520 · 775-827-2000

Michael J. Melarkey · a · Avansino, Melarky, Knobel & Mulligan · http://www.amklaw.com · 4795 Caughlin Parkway, Suite 100 · Reno, NV 89519 · 775-333-0300

G. Barton Mowry · 2) · Maupin, Cox & LeGoy · 4785 Caughlin Parkway · P.O. Box 30000 · Reno, NV 89520 · 775-827-2000

Matthew E. Woodhead · Holland & Hart · 5441 Kietzke Lane, Second Floor · Reno, NV 89511 · 775-327-3000

WATER LAW

Reno

Ross E. de Lipkau · a · Parsons Behle & Latimer · http://www.parsonsbehlelaw.com · 50 West Liberty Street, Suite 750 · Reno, NV 89501 · 775-323-1601

Gordon H. DePaoli · Woodburn and Wedge · Sierra Plaza, Suite 500 · 6100 Neil Road · P.O. Box 2311 · Reno, NV 89505 · 775-688-3000

Roger W. Jeppson · a · Holland & Hart · 5441 Kietzke Lane, Second Floor · Reno, NV 89511 · 775-327-3000

WHITE-COLLAR CRIMINAL DEFENSE

Las Vegas

Donald J. Campbell · a · Campbell & Williams · 700 South Seventh Street · Las Vegas, NV 89101-6908 702-382-5222

Frank J. Cremen · Frank J. Cremen · 715 South Fourth Street · Las Vegas, NV 89101 · 702-385-7475

Dominic P. Gentile · 2% · Gordon & Silver · 3960 Howard Hughes Parkway, Ninth Floor · Las Vegas, NV 89169 · 702-796-5555

C. Stanley Hunterton · Hunterton & Associates · 333 South Sixth Street · Las Vegas, NV 89101 · 702-388-0098

Thomas F. Pitaro · a · Thomas F. Pitaro · 815 South Third Street · Las Vegas, NV 89101 · 702-382-9221

William B. Terry · a · William B. Terry · 530 South Seventh Street · Las Vegas, NV 89101 · 702-385-0799

Richard A. Wright · 2) · Wright Stanish & Winckler · http://www.wjwprofcorp.com · 300 South Fourth Street, Suite 701 · Las Vegas, NV 89101 · 702-382-4004

Reno

C. Frederick Pinkerton · 2) · C. Frederick Pinkerton · 1265 Tarleton Way · Reno, NV 89523 · 775-322-7553

WORKERS' COMPENSATION LAW

Carson City

Raymond L. Badger, Jr. · a · Badger & Baker · 312 West Third Street · Carson City, NV 89703 · 775-882-5515

R. Scott Baker · a · Badger & Baker · 312 West Third Street · Carson City, NV 89703 · 775-882-5515

Las Vegas

Aubrey Goldberg · a · Greenman, Goldberg, Raby & Martinez · 601 South Ninth Street · Las Vegas, NV 89101-7012 · 702-384-1616

Marvin S. Gross · a · King, Gross & Sutcliffe · 3017 West Charleston Boulevard, Suite 50 · Las Vegas, NV 89102 · 702-870-3555

Dean A. Hardy · a · Hardy, Hardy & McNicholas · 610 South Ninth Street · Las Vegas, NV 89101 · 702-366-1366

Reno

Barbara J. Gruenewald · Law Office of Barbara Gruenewald · 439 Marsh Avenue · Reno, NV 89509-1522 · 775-322-3366

Timothy E. Rowe · a · McDonald Carano Wilson · http://www.mcdonaldcarano.com · 100 West Liberty Street, 10th Floor · P.O. Box 2670 · Reno, NV 89505 · 775-788-2000

NEW HAMPSHIRE

ADMINISTRATIVE LAW

Concord

Gregory H. Smith · ⑩ · McLane, Graf, Raulerson & Middleton · http://www.mclane.com · 11 South Main Street, Suite 500 · Concord, NH 03301 · 603-226-0400

Manchester

Kimon S. Zachos · Sheehan Phinney Bass Green · 1000 Elm Street, 17th Floor · P.O. Box 3701 · Manchester, NH 03105-3701 · 603-668-0300

ALTERNATIVE DISPUTE RESOLUTION

Bow

Melinda S. Gehris · Hess & Fraas · 501 Hall Street · Bow, NH 03304 · 603-225-0477

Concord

Charles P. Bauer · Gallagher, Callahan & Gartrell · http://www.gcglaw.com · 214 North Main Street · P.O. Box 1415 · Concord, NH 03302-1415 · 603-228-1181

David A. Garfunkel · ⑩ · Gallagher, Callahan & Gartrell · http://www.gcglaw.com · 214 North Main Street · P.O. Box 1415 · Concord, NH 03302-1415 · 603-228-1181

Michael M. Lonergan · Sulloway & Hollis · Nine Capitol Street & Twenty Nine School Street · P.O. Box 1256 · Concord, NH 03301-1256 · 603-224-2341

Manchester

W. Michael Dunn · Sheehan Phinney Bass Green · 1000 Elm Street, 17th Floor · P.O. Box 3701 · Manchester, NH 03105-3701 · 603-668-0300

Portsmouth

Russell F. Hilliard · ⑩ · Upton & Hatfield · 159 Middle Street · Portsmouth, NH 03801 · 603-436-7046

William A. Mulvey, Jr. · Mulvey Professional Association · 378 Islington Street · Portsmouth, NH 03801-7202 · 603-431-1333

APPELLATE LAW

Concord

William L. Chapman · ⑩ · Orr and Reno · http://www.orr-reno.com · One Eagle Square · P.O. Box 3550 · Concord, NH 03302-3550 · 603-224-2381

Manchester

Bruce W. Felmly · ⑩ · McLane, Graf, Raulerson & Middleton · http://www.mclane.com · 900 Elm Street P.O. Box 326 · Manchester, NH 03105 · 603-625-6464

Wilbur A. Glahn III · McLane, Graf, Raulerson & Middleton · http://www.mclane.com · 900 Elm Street · P.O. Box 326 · Manchester, NH 03105 · 603-625-6464

Edward A. Haffer · Sheehan Phinney Bass Green · 1000 Elm Street, 17th Floor · P.O. Box 3701 · Manchester, NH 03105-3701 · 603-668-0300

Jon Meyer · ⑩ · Backus, Meyer & Branch · 116 Lowell Street · P.O. Box 516 · Manchester, NH 03105 · 603-668-7272

BANKING LAW

Concord

W. John Funk · ⑩ · Gallagher, Callahan & Gartrell · http://www.gcglaw.com · 214 North Main Street · P.O. Box 1415 · Concord, NH 03302-1415 · 603-228-1181

Christopher C. Gallagher · ⑩ · Gallagher, Callahan & Gartrell · http://www.gcglaw.com · 214 North Main Street · P.O. Box 1415 · Concord, NH 03302-1415 · 603-228-1181

Donald J. Pfundstein · Gallagher, Callahan & Gartrell · http://www.gcglaw.com · 214 North Main Street · P.O. Box 1415 · Concord, NH 03302-1415 · 603-228-1181

Manchester

Peter B. Rotch · ⑩ · McLane, Graf, Raulerson & Middleton · http://www.mclane.com · 900 Elm Street · P.O. Box 326 · Manchester, NH 03105 · 603-625-6464

Richard A. Samuels · ⑩ · McLane, Graf, Raulerson & Middleton · http://www.mclane.com · 900 Elm Street · P.O. Box 326 · Manchester, NH 03105 · 603-625-6464

Henry B. Stebbins · ⑩ · Stebbins, Lazos & Van Der Beken · 66 Hanover Street, Suite 301 · Manchester, NH 03101 · 603-627-3700

BANKRUPTCY AND CREDITOR-DEBTOR RIGHTS LAW

Concord

John M. Sullivan · ⑩ · Preti, Flaherty, Beliveau & Pachios · http://www.preti.com · 57 North Main Street P.O. Box 1318 · Concord, NH 03302-1318 · 603-410-1500

Manchester

Daniel J. Callaghan · ⑳ · Devine, Millimet & Branch · 111 Amherst Street · Manchester, NH 03101 · 603-669-1000

Joseph A. Foster · McLane, Graf, Raulerson & Middleton · http://www.mclane.com · 900 Elm Street · P.O. Box 326 · Manchester, NH 03105 · 603-625-6464

William S. Gannon · Gannon Law Firm · 889 Elm Street, Fourth Floor · Manchester, NH 03101 · 603-621-0833

Bruce A. Harwood · ⑩ · Sheehan Phinney Bass Green · 1000 Elm Street, 17th Floor · P.O. Box 3701 · Manchester, NH 03105-3701 · 603-668-0300

Daniel W. Sklar · ⑳ · Nixon Peabody · 900 Elm Street · Manchester, NH 03101 · 603-628-4000

Nashua

Steven Notinger · Donchess & Notinger · 547 Amherst Street · Nashua, NH 03063 · 603-886-7266

BET-THE-COMPANY LITIGATION

Manchester

Wilbur A. Glahn III · McLane, Graf, Raulerson & Middleton · http://www.mclane.com · 900 Elm Street · P.O. Box 326 · Manchester, NH 03105 · 603-625-6464

Jack B. Middleton · ⑳ · McLane, Graf, Raulerson & Middleton · http://www.mclane.com · 900 Elm Street · P.O. Box 326 · Manchester, NH 03105 · 603-625-6464

COMMERCIAL LITIGATION

Concord

David A. Garfunkel · ⑩ · Gallagher, Callahan & Gartrell · http://www.gcglaw.com · 214 North Main Street · P.O. Box 1415 · Concord, NH 03302-1415 · 603-228-1181

Irvin D. Gordon · Sulloway & Hollis · Nine Capitol Street & Twenty Nine School Street · P.O. Box 1256 Concord, NH 03301-1256 · 603-224-2341

Manchester

Peter S. Cowan · Sheehan Phinney Bass Green · 1000 Elm Street, 17th Floor · P.O. Box 3701 · Manchester, NH 03105-3701 · 603-668-0300

W. Wright Danenbarger · 20 · Wiggin & Nourie · 670 North Commercial Street, Suite 305 · P.O. Box 808 Manchester, NH 03105-0808 · 603-669-2211

Thomas J. Donovan · McLane, Graf, Raulerson & Middleton · http://www.mclane.com · 900 Elm Street · P.O. Box 326 · Manchester, NH 03105 · 603-625-6464

Bruce W. Felmly · 10 · McLane, Graf, Raulerson & Middleton · http://www.mclane.com · 900 Elm Street P.O. Box 326 · Manchester, NH 03105 · 603-625-6464

Wilbur A. Glahn III · McLane, Graf, Raulerson & Middleton · http://www.mclane.com · 900 Elm Street · P.O. Box 326 · Manchester, NH 03105 · 603-625-6464

Edward A. Haffer · Sheehan Phinney Bass Green · 1000 Elm Street, 17th Floor · P.O. Box 3701 · Manchester, NH 03105-3701 · 603-668-0300

Michael C. Harvell · 10 · Sheehan Phinney Bass Green · 1000 Elm Street, 17th Floor · P.O. Box 3701 · Manchester, NH 03105-3701 · 603-668-0300

Ovide M. Lamontagnes · Devine, Millimet & Branch · 111 Amherst Street · Manchester, NH 03101 · 603-669-1000

Richard B. McNamara · 10 · Wiggin & Nourie · 670 North Commercial Street, Suite 305 · P.O. Box 808 · Manchester, NH 03105-0808 · 603-669-2211

Jack B. Middleton · 20 · McLane, Graf, Raulerson & Middleton · http://www.mclane.com · 900 Elm Street · P.O. Box 326 · Manchester, NH 03105 · 603-625-6464

Thomas J. Pappas · Wiggin & Nourie · 670 North Commercial Street, Suite 305 · P.O. Box 808 · Manchester, NH 03105-0808 · 603-669-2211

Arnold Rosenblatt · Cook Little Rosenblatt & Manson · http://www.clrm.com · 650 Elm Street, Fourth Floor · Manchester, NH 03101 · 603-621-7100

James Q. Shirley · Sheehan Phinney Bass Green · 1000 Elm Street, 17th Floor · P.O. Box 3701 · Manchester, NH 03105-3701 · 603-668-0300

Eugene M. Van Loan III · 20 · Wadleigh, Starr & Peters · http://www.wadleighlaw.com · 95 Market Street Manchester, NH 03101 · 603-669-4140

David Vicinanzo · Nixon Peabody · 900 Elm Street · Manchester, NH 03101 · 603-628-4000

Andru H. Volinsky · 10 · Bernstein Shur · Jefferson Mill Building, Suite 108 · 670 North Commercial Street · P.O. Box 1120 · Manchester, NH 03105-1120 · 603-623-8700

James C. Wheat · Wadleigh, Starr & Peters · http://www.wadleighlaw.com · 95 Market Street · Manchester, NH 03101 · 603-669-4140

CORPORATE LAW

Concord

Peter F. Burger · Orr and Reno · http://www.orr-reno.com · One Eagle Square · P.O. Box 3550 · Concord, NH 03302-3550 · 603-224-2381

Neil F. Castaldo · 10 · Hinckley, Allen & Snyder · http://www.haslaw.com · 11 South Main Street, Suite 400 · Concord, NH 03301-4846 · 603-225-4334

Mary Susan Leahy · ⑩ · McLane, Graf, Raulerson & Middleton · http://www.mclane.com · 11 South Main Street, Suite 500 · Concord, NH 03301 · 603-226-0400

Peter W. Leberman · Sheehan Phinney Bass Green · Two Eagle Square, Third Floor · Concord, NH 03301 · 603-223-2020

Mark S. McCue · Hinckley, Allen & Snyder · http://www.haslaw.com · 11 South Main Street, Suite 400 · Concord, NH 03301-4846 · 603-225-4334

Fred L. Potter · ⑩ · Sulloway & Hollis · Nine Capitol Street & Twenty Nine School Street · P.O. Box 1256 · Concord, NH 03301-1256 · 603-224-2341

Charles F. Sheridan, Jr. · ⑩ · Sulloway & Hollis · Nine Capitol Street & Twenty Nine School Street · P.O. Box 1256 · Concord, NH 03301-1256 · 603-224-2341

John M. Sullivan · ⑩ · Preti, Flaherty, Beliveau & Pachios · http://www.preti.com · 57 North Main Street P.O. Box 1318 · Concord, NH 03302-1318 · 603-410-1500

Manchester

Steven M. Burke · McLane, Graf, Raulerson & Middleton · http://www.mclane.com · 900 Elm Street · P.O. Box 326 · Manchester, NH 03105 · 603-625-6464

Steven Cohen · ⑩ · Devine, Millimet & Branch · 111 Amherst Street · Manchester, NH 03101 · 603-669-1000

James G. Cook · ⑩ · Cook Little Rosenblatt & Manson · http://www.clrm.com · 650 Elm Street, Fourth Floor · Manchester, NH 03101 · 603-621-7100

Robert E. Dastin · ⑳ · Sheehan Phinney Bass Green · 1000 Elm Street, 17th Floor · P.O. Box 3701 · Manchester, NH 03105-3701 · 603-668-0300

Joseph A. DiBrigida · Sheehan Phinney Bass Green · 1000 Elm Street, 17th Floor · P.O. Box 3701 · Manchester, NH 03105-3701 · 603-668-0300

Scott W. Ellison · Cook Little Rosenblatt & Manson · http://www.clrm.com · 650 Elm Street, Fourth Floor · Manchester, NH 03101 · 603-621-7100

Benjamin F. Gayman · Wiggin & Nourie · 670 North Commercial Street, Suite 305 · P.O. Box 808 · Manchester, NH 03105-0808 · 603-669-2211

James C. Hood · Nixon Peabody · 900 Elm Street · Manchester, NH 03101 · 603-628-4000

Curtis W. Little · Cook Little Rosenblatt & Manson · http://www.clrm.com · 650 Elm Street, Fourth Floor · Manchester, NH 03101 · 603-621-7100

Thomas P. Manson · Cook Little Rosenblatt & Manson · http://www.clrm.com · 650 Elm Street, Fourth Floor · Manchester, NH 03101 · 603-621-7100

John R. Monson · ⑳ · Wiggin & Nourie · 670 North Commercial Street, Suite 305 · P.O. Box 808 · Manchester, NH 03105-0808 · 603-669-2211

Alan L. Reische · ⑳ · Sheehan Phinney Bass Green · 1000 Elm Street, 17th Floor · P.O. Box 3701 · Manchester, NH 03105-3701 · 603-668-0300

Richard A. Samuels · ⑩ · McLane, Graf, Raulerson & Middleton · http://www.mclane.com · 900 Elm Street · P.O. Box 326 · Manchester, NH 03105 · 603-625-6464

Jon B. Sparkman · Devine, Millimet & Branch · 111 Amherst Street · Manchester, NH 03101 · 603-669-1000

Henry B. Stebbins · ⑩ · Stebbins, Lazos & Van Der Beken · 66 Hanover Street, Suite 301 · Manchester, NH 03101 · 603-627-3700

Nashua

Chester H. Lopez, Jr. · ⑳ · Hamblett & Kerrigan · 146 Main Street · Nashua, NH 03060 · 603-883-5501

DUI/DWI DEFENSE

Concord

George T. Campbell III · Robert Stein & Associates · http://www.robertsteinandassociates.com · One Barberry Lane · P.O. Box 2159 · Concord, NH 03302-2159 · 603-228-1109

EDUCATION LAW

Concord

John F. Teague · Upton & Hatfield · 10 Centre Street · P.O. Box 1090 · Concord, NH 03302-1090 · 603-224-7791

Manchester

Linda S. Johnson · McLane, Graf, Raulerson & Middleton · http://www.mclane.com · 900 Elm Street · P.O. Box 326 · Manchester, NH 03105 · 603-625-6464

Andru H. Volinsky · ⑩ · Bernstein Shur · Jefferson Mill Building, Suite 108 · 670 North Commercial Street · P.O. Box 1120 · Manchester, NH 03105-1120 · 603-623-8700

Portsmouth

Jeanne M. Kincaid · Drummond Woodsum & MacMahon · http://www.dwmlaw.com · 40 Pleasant Street Portsmouth, NH 03801 · 603-433-3317

David Wolowitz · ⑩ · McLane, Graf, Raulerson & Middleton · http://www.mclane.com · 100 Market Street, Suite 301 · P.O. Box 459 · Portsmouth, NH 03802-0459 · 603-436-2818

Gerald M. Zelin · Drummond Woodsum & MacMahon · http://www.dwmlaw.com · 40 Pleasant Street · Portsmouth, NH 03801 · 603-433-3317

ELDER LAW

Bedford

Christine S. Anderson · Ansell & Anderson · Bedford Place, Unit 32 · 40 South River Road · Bedford, NH 03110 · 603-644-8211

Concord

Michelle M. Arruda · Cleveland, Waters & Bass · Two Capital Plaza · P.O. Box 1137 · Concord, NH 03302-1137 · 603-224-7761

Virginia Symmes Sheehan · Flood, Sheehan & Tobin · Two Delta Drive, Suite 303 · Concord, NH 03301 · 603-415-4200

Manchester

Ann N. Butenhof · Butenhof & Bomster · 132 Middle Street · Manchester, NH 03101 · 603-296-0428

Portsmouth

Andrea Sennott · Robinson, Boesch & Sennott · 20 International Drive, Suite 300 · Portsmouth, NH 03801-3271 · 603-427-5380

EMPLOYEE BENEFITS LAW

Concord

Douglas R. Chamberlain · ⑳ · Sulloway & Hollis · Nine Capitol Street & Twenty Nine School Street · P.O. Box 1256 · Concord, NH 03301-1256 · 603-224-2341

Manchester

Alan P. Cleveland · ⑳ · Sheehan Phinney Bass Green · 1000 Elm Street, 17th Floor · P.O. Box 3701 · Manchester, NH 03105-3701 · 603-668-0300

Newton H. Kershaw, Jr. · ⑩ · Devine, Millimet & Branch · 111 Amherst Street · Manchester, NH 03101 603-669-1000

Patricia M. McGrath · Devine, Millimet & Branch · 111 Amherst Street · Manchester, NH 03101 · 603-669-1000

John E. Rich, Jr. · McLane, Graf, Raulerson & Middleton · http://www.mclane.com · 900 Elm Street · P.O. Box 326 · Manchester, NH 03105 · 603-625-6464

ENERGY LAW

Concord

Peter W. Brown · Brown, Olson & Gould · Two Delta Drive, Suite 301 · Concord, NH 03301 · 603-225-9716

Steven V. Camerino · ⑩ · McLane, Graf, Raulerson & Middleton · http://www.mclane.com · 11 South Main Street, Suite 500 · Concord, NH 03301 · 603-226-0400

Robert P. Cheney · ⑩ · Sheehan Phinney Bass Green · Two Eagle Square, Third Floor · Concord, NH 03301 · 603-223-2020

Frederick J. Coolbroth · ⑩ · Devine, Millimet & Branch · 43 North Main Street · Concord, NH 03301 · 603-226-1000

Susan S. Geiger · Orr and Reno · http://www.orr-reno.com · One Eagle Square · P.O. Box 3550 · Concord, NH 03302-3550 · 603-224-2381

Margaret H. Nelson · ⑩ · Sulloway & Hollis · Nine Capitol Street & Twenty Nine School Street · P.O. Box 1256 · Concord, NH 03301-1256 · 603-224-2341

Robert A. Olson · Brown, Olson & Gould · Two Delta Drive, Suite 301 · Concord, NH 03301 · 603-225-9716

Douglas L. Patch · Orr and Reno · http://www.orr-reno.com · One Eagle Square · P.O. Box 3550 · Concord, NH 03302-3550 · 603-224-2381

Mack Curtis Whittaker · Rath, Young and Pignatelli · One Capital Plaza · P.O. Box 1500 · Concord, NH 03302-1500 · 603-226-2600

Hopkinton

Mark W. Dean · Mark Dean · 344 Moran Road · Hopkinton, NH 03229 · 603-746-6300

Manchester

Sarah B. Knowlton · McLane, Graf, Raulerson & Middleton · http://www.mclane.com · 900 Elm Street · P.O. Box 326 · Manchester, NH 03105 · 603-625-6464

Richard A. Samuels · ⑩ · McLane, Graf, Raulerson & Middleton · http://www.mclane.com · 900 Elm Street · P.O. Box 326 · Manchester, NH 03105 · 603-625-6464

ENVIRONMENTAL LAW

Concord

Robert P. Cheney · ⑩ · Sheehan Phinney Bass Green · Two Eagle Square, Third Floor · Concord, NH 03301 · 603-223-2020

Barry Needleman · McLane, Graf, Raulerson & Middleton · http://www.mclane.com · 11 South Main Street, Suite 500 · Concord, NH 03301 · 603-226-0400

Gregory H. Smith · ⑩ · McLane, Graf, Raulerson & Middleton · http://www.mclane.com · 11 South Main Street, Suite 500 · Concord, NH 03301 · 603-226-0400

Sherilyn Burnett Young · ⑩ · Rath, Young and Pignatelli · One Capital Plaza · P.O. Box 1500 · Concord, NH 03302-1500 · 603-226-2600

Manchester

Peter G. Beeson · Devine, Millimet & Branch · 111 Amherst Street · Manchester, NH 03101 · 603-669-1000

E. Tupper Kinder, Jr. · ⑩ · Nelson, Kinder, Mosseau & Saturley · http://www.nkms.com · 99 Middle Street · Manchester, NH 03101 · 603-647-1800

Jeff Meyers · Nelson, Kinder, Mosseau & Saturley · http://www.nkms.com · 99 Middle Street · Manchester, NH 03101 · 603-647-1800

John E. Peltonen · ⑩ · Sheehan Phinney Bass Green · 1000 Elm Street, 17th Floor · P.O. Box 3701 · Manchester, NH 03105-3701 · 603-668-0300

Nashua

John V. Dwyer, Jr. · ⑩ · Winer & Bennett · 111 Concord Street · P.O. Box 488 · Nashua, NH 03061-0488 · 603-882-5157

Portsmouth

Mark E. Beliveau · Pierce Atwood · One New Hampshire Avenue, Suite 350 · Portsmouth, NH 03801 · 603-433-6300

George Dana Bisbee · Pierce Atwood · One New Hampshire Avenue, Suite 350 · Portsmouth, NH 03801 603-433-6300

Michael J. Quinn · McLane, Graf, Raulerson & Middleton · http://www.mclane.com · 100 Market Street, Suite 301 · P.O. Box 459 · Portsmouth, NH 03802-0459 · 603-436-2818

Stephen H. Roberts · ⑩ · Hoefle, Phoenix & Gormley · 402 State Street · P.O. Box 4480 · Portsmouth, NH 03802-4480 · 603-436-0666

FAMILY LAW

Concord

Michael R. Callahan · ⑩ · Gallagher, Callahan & Gartrell · http://www.gcglaw.com · 214 North Main Street · P.O. Box 1415 · Concord, NH 03302-1415 · 603-228-1181

Judith A. Fairclough · Orr and Reno · http://www.orr-reno.com · One Eagle Square · P.O. Box 3550 · Concord, NH 03302-3550 · 603-224-2381

Robert A. Stein · ⑳ · Robert Stein & Associates · http://www.robertsteinandassociates.com · One Barberry Lane · P.O. Box 2159 · Concord, NH 03302-2159 · 603-228-1109

Ronna F. Wise · ⑩ · Sulloway & Hollis · Nine Capitol Street & Twenty Nine School Street · P.O. Box 1256 · Concord, NH 03301-1256 · 603-224-2341

Manchester

William E. Brennan · ⑩ · Brennan, Caron, Lenehan & Lacopino · 85 Brook Street · Manchester, NH 03104 · 603-668-8300

R. David Depuy · McLane, Graf, Raulerson & Middleton · http://www.mclane.com · 900 Elm Street · P.O. Box 326 · Manchester, NH 03105 · 603-625-6464

James V. Ferro, Jr. · Wiggin & Nourie · 670 North Commercial Street, Suite 305 · P.O. Box 808 · Manchester, NH 03105-0808 · 603-669-2211

Ellen M. Joseph · Wiggin & Nourie · 670 North Commercial Street, Suite 305 · P.O. Box 808 · Manchester, NH 03105-0808 · 603-669-2211

James F. Ogorchock · Sheehan Phinney Bass Green · 1000 Elm Street, 17th Floor · P.O. Box 3701 · Manchester, NH 03105-3701 · 603-668-0300

Jeanmarie Papelian · McLane, Graf, Raulerson & Middleton · http://www.mclane.com · 900 Elm Street · P.O. Box 326 · Manchester, NH 03105 · 603-625-6464

David S. Phillips · Devine, Millimet & Branch · 111 Amherst Street · Manchester, NH 03101 · 603-669-1000

L. Jonathan Ross · ㉕ · Wiggin & Nourie · 670 North Commercial Street, Suite 305 · P.O. Box 808 · Manchester, NH 03105-0808 · 603-669-2211

Portsmouth

Stephen L. Tober · Tober Law Offices · 381 Middle Street · P.O. Box 1377 · Portsmouth, NH 03801-5075 · 603-431-1003

FAMILY LAW MEDIATION

Manchester

James V. Ferro, Jr. · Wiggin & Nourie · 670 North Commercial Street, Suite 305 · P.O. Box 808 · Manchester, NH 03105-0808 · 603-669-2211

FIRST AMENDMENT LAW

Concord

William L. Chapman · ⑩ · Orr and Reno · http://www.orr-reno.com · One Eagle Square · P.O. Box 3550 · Concord, NH 03302-3550 · 603-224-2381

Steven M. Gordon · ⑳ · Shaheen & Gordon · http://www.shaheengordon.com · 107 Storrs Street · P.O. Box 2703 · Concord, NH 03302-2703 · 603-225-7262

Manchester

Jon Meyer · ⑩ · Backus, Meyer & Branch · 116 Lowell Street · P.O. Box 516 · Manchester, NH 03105 · 603-668-7272

Merrimack

Richard C. Gagliuso · ⑩ · Gagliuso & Gagliuso · Harris Pond Office Park, Suite 14 · 32 Daniel Webster Highway · Merrimack, NH 03054 · 603-595-4500

Portsmouth

David Wolowitz · ⑩ · McLane, Graf, Raulerson & Middleton · http://www.mclane.com · 100 Market Street, Suite 301 · P.O. Box 459 · Portsmouth, NH 03802-0459 · 603-436-2818

GOVERNMENT RELATIONS LAW

Concord

Thomas D. Rath · ⑩ · Rath, Young and Pignatelli · One Capital Plaza · P.O. Box 1500 · Concord, NH 03302-1500 · 603-226-2600

George W. Roussos · Orr and Reno · http://www.orr-reno.com · One Eagle Square · P.O. Box 3550 · Concord, NH 03302-3550 · 603-224-2381

Manchester

James V. Hatem · Nixon Peabody · 900 Elm Street · Manchester, NH 03101 · 603-628-4000

Kimon S. Zachos · Sheehan Phinney Bass Green · 1000 Elm Street, 17th Floor · P.O. Box 3701 · Manchester, NH 03105-3701 · 603-668-0300

HEALTH CARE LAW

Concord

Neil F. Castaldo · (10) · Hinckley, Allen & Snyder · http://www.haslaw.com · 11 South Main Street, Suite 400 · Concord, NH 03301-4846 · 603-225-4334

Lucy C. Hodder · Rath, Young and Pignatelli · One Capital Plaza · P.O. Box 1500 · Concord, NH 03302-1500 · 603-226-2600

Michel A. LaFond · Sulloway & Hollis · Nine Capitol Street & Twenty Nine School Street · P.O. Box 1256 · Concord, NH 03301-1256 · 603-224-2341

Eleanor Holmes MacLellan · (10) · Sulloway & Hollis · Nine Capitol Street & Twenty Nine School Street P.O. Box 1256 · Concord, NH 03301-1256 · 603-224-2341

Howard Moffett · Orr and Reno · http://www.orr-reno.com · One Eagle Square · P.O. Box 3550 · Concord, NH 03302-3550 · 603-224-2381

Arpiar G. Saunders, Jr. · Shaheen & Gordon · http://www.shaheengordon.com · 107 Storrs Street · P.O. Box 2703 · Concord, NH 03302-2703 · 603-225-7262

Manchester

David H. Barnes · (10) · Devine, Millimet & Branch · 111 Amherst Street · Manchester, NH 03101 · 603-669-1000

William J. Donovan · (10) · Sheehan Phinney Bass Green · 1000 Elm Street, 17th Floor · P.O. Box 3701 · Manchester, NH 03105-3701 · 603-668-0300

Katherine M. Hanna · (10) · Sheehan Phinney Bass Green · 1000 Elm Street, 17th Floor · P.O. Box 3701 · Manchester, NH 03105-3701 · 603-668-0300

Priscilla Kimball · Sheehan Phinney Bass Green · 1000 Elm Street, 17th Floor · P.O. Box 3701 · Manchester, NH 03105-3701 · 603-668-0300

Eugene M. Van Loan III · (20) · Wadleigh, Starr & Peters · http://www.wadleighlaw.com · 95 Market Street Manchester, NH 03101 · 603-669-4140

IMMIGRATION LAW

Concord

Susan T. Goff · GoffWilson · http://www.goffwilson.com · Two Capital Plaza, Suite 403 · P.O. Box 347 · Concord, NH 03302-0347 · 603-228-1277

John R. Wilson · GoffWilson · http://www.goffwilson.com · Two Capital Plaza, Suite 403 · P.O. Box 347 · Concord, NH 03302-0347 · 603-228-1277

Manchester

Thomas W. Hildreth · McLane, Graf, Raulerson & Middleton · http://www.mclane.com · 900 Elm Street P.O. Box 326 · Manchester, NH 03105 · 603-625-6464

Merrimack

Mona T. Movafaghi · Law Offices of Mona T. Movafaghi · 419 Daniel Webster Highway · Merrimack, NH 03054 · 603-424-2000

INSURANCE LAW

Concord

Margaret H. Nelson · ⑩ · Sulloway & Hollis · Nine Capitol Street & Twenty Nine School Street · P.O. Box 1256 · Concord, NH 03301-1256 · 603-224-2341

Donald J. Pfundstein · Gallagher, Callahan & Gartrell · http://www.gcglaw.com · 214 North Main Street · P.O. Box 1415 · Concord, NH 03302-1415 · 603-228-1181

George W. Roussos · Orr and Reno · http://www.orr-reno.com · One Eagle Square · P.O. Box 3550 · Concord, NH 03302-3550 · 603-224-2381

Manchester

James V. Hatem · Nixon Peabody · 900 Elm Street · Manchester, NH 03101 · 603-628-4000

Eugene M. Van Loan III · ⑳ · Wadleigh, Starr & Peters · http://www.wadleighlaw.com · 95 Market Street Manchester, NH 03101 · 603-669-4140

INTELLECTUAL PROPERTY LAW

Manchester

Daniel J. Bourque · Bourque & Associates · 835 Hanover Street, Suite 301 · Manchester, NH 03104 · 603-623-5111

James G. Cook · ⑩ · Cook Little Rosenblatt & Manson · http://www.clrm.com · 650 Elm Street, Fourth Floor · Manchester, NH 03101 · 603-621-7100

Paul C. Remus · ⑩ · Devine, Millimet & Branch · 111 Amherst Street · Manchester, NH 03101 · 603-669-1000

Mark A. Wright · McLane, Graf, Raulerson & Middleton · http://www.mclane.com · 900 Elm Street · P.O. Box 326 · Manchester, NH 03105 · 603-625-6464

LABOR AND EMPLOYMENT LAW

Concord

Heather M. Burns · Upton & Hatfield · 10 Centre Street · P.O. Box 1090 · Concord, NH 03302-1090 · 603-224-7791

Edward M. Kaplan · ⑳ · Sulloway & Hollis · Nine Capitol Street & Twenty Nine School Street · P.O. Box 1256 · Concord, NH 03301-1256 · 603-224-2341

Eleanor Holmes MacLellan · ⑩ · Sulloway & Hollis · Nine Capitol Street & Twenty Nine School Street P.O. Box 1256 · Concord, NH 03301-1256 · 603-224-2341

Richard E. Molan · ⑩ · Cook & Molan · 100 Hall Street · P.O. Box 1465 · Concord, NH 03302 · 603-225-3323

Exeter

Thomas J. Flygare · Flygare Schwarz & Closson · 11 Court Street · Exeter, NH 03833 · 603-778-7300

Manchester

Mark T. Broth · ⑩ · Devine, Millimet & Branch · 111 Amherst Street · Manchester, NH 03101 · 603-669-1000

Linda S. Johnson · McLane, Graf, Raulerson & Middleton · http://www.mclane.com · 900 Elm Street · P.O. Box 326 · Manchester, NH 03105 · 603-625-6464

Andrea K. Johnstone · ⑩ · Bernstein Shur · Jefferson Mill Building, Suite 108 · 670 North Commercial Street · P.O. Box 1120 · Manchester, NH 03105-1120 · 603-623-8700

David McGrath · Sheehan Phinney Bass Green · 1000 Elm Street, 17th Floor · P.O. Box 3701 · Manchester, NH 03105-3701 · 603-668-0300

Jon Meyer · ⑩ · Backus, Meyer & Branch · 116 Lowell Street · P.O. Box 516 · Manchester, NH 03105 · 603-668-7272

James P. Reidy · Sheehan Phinney Bass Green · 1000 Elm Street, 17th Floor · P.O. Box 3701 · Manchester, NH 03105-3701 · 603-668-0300

Andru H. Volinsky · ⑩ · Bernstein Shur · Jefferson Mill Building, Suite 108 · 670 North Commercial Street · P.O. Box 1120 · Manchester, NH 03105-1120 · 603-623-8700

North Hampton

Debra Ford · Jackson Lewis · http://www.jacksonlewis.com · 216 Lafayette Road, Suite 103 · North Hampton, NH 03862 · 603-294-4125

Portsmouth

David Wolowitz · ⑩ · McLane, Graf, Raulerson & Middleton · http://www.mclane.com · 100 Market Street, Suite 301 · P.O. Box 459 · Portsmouth, NH 03802-0459 · 603-436-2818

LAND USE & ZONING LAW

Concord

Raymond P. D'Amante · D'Amante Couser Steiner Pellerin · http://www.damantelaw.com · Nine Triangle Park Drive · P.O. Box 2650 · Concord, NH 03302-2650 · 603-224-6777

Manchester

Linda C. Connell · McLane, Graf, Raulerson & Middleton · http://www.mclane.com · 900 Elm Street · P.O. Box 326 · Manchester, NH 03105 · 603-625-6464

Susan V. Duprey · Devine, Millimet & Branch · 111 Amherst Street · Manchester, NH 03101 · 603-669-1000

Nicholas J. Lazos · Stebbins, Lazos & Van Der Beken · 66 Hanover Street, Suite 301 · Manchester, NH 03101 · 603-627-3700

Karen S. McGinley · Devine, Millimet & Branch · 111 Amherst Street · Manchester, NH 03101 · 603-669-1000

Gregory E. Michael · Wiggin & Nourie · 670 North Commercial Street, Suite 305 · P.O. Box 808 · Manchester, NH 03105-0808 · 603-669-2211

Henry B. Stebbins · (10) · Stebbins, Lazos & Van Der Beken · 66 Hanover Street, Suite 301 · Manchester, NH 03101 · 603-627-3700

Kathleen Sullivan · Wadleigh, Starr & Peters · http://www.wadleighlaw.com · 95 Market Street · Manchester, NH 03101 · 603-669-4140

William C. Tucker · (25) · Wadleigh, Starr & Peters · http://www.wadleighlaw.com · 95 Market Street · Manchester, NH 03101 · 603-669-4140

Nashua

Morgan A. Hollis · Gottesman & Hollis · http://www.nh-lawyers.com · 39 East Pearl Street · Nashua, NH 03060 · 603-889-5959

LEGAL MALPRACTICE LAW

Concord

Emily Gray Rice · Orr and Reno · http://www.orr-reno.com · One Eagle Square · P.O. Box 3550 · Concord, NH 03302-3550 · 603-224-2381

Martha Van Oot · (10) · Orr and Reno · http://www.orr-reno.com · One Eagle Square · P.O. Box 3550 · Concord, NH 03302-3550 · 603-224-2381

Manchester

Peter G. Beeson · Devine, Millimet & Branch · 111 Amherst Street · Manchester, NH 03101 · 603-669-1000

Richard C. Nelson · (10) · Nelson, Kinder, Mosseau & Saturley · http://www.nkms.com · 99 Middle Street · Manchester, NH 03101 · 603-647-1800

William Saturley · Nelson, Kinder, Mosseau & Saturley · http://www.nkms.com · 99 Middle Street · Manchester, NH 03101 · 603-647-1800

MEDICAL MALPRACTICE LAW

Concord

Michael P. Lehman · (10) · Sulloway & Hollis · Nine Capitol Street & Twenty Nine School Street · P.O. Box 1256 · Concord, NH 03301-1256 · 603-224-2341

Michael A. Pignatelli · Rath, Young and Pignatelli · One Capital Plaza · P.O. Box 1500 · Concord, NH 03302-1500 · 603-226-2600

Gary B. Richardson · (10) · Upton & Hatfield · 10 Centre Street · P.O. Box 1090 · Concord, NH 03302-1090 · 603-224-7791

Manchester

Mark A. Abramson · ⑩ · Abramson, Brown & Dugan · http://www.arbd.com · 1819 Elm Street · Manchester, NH 03104-2910 · 603-647-0300

Kevin F. Dugan · Abramson, Brown & Dugan · http://www.arbd.com · 1819 Elm Street · Manchester, NH 03104-2910 · 603-647-0300

John E. Friberg, Sr. · ㉕ · Wadleigh, Starr & Peters · http://www.wadleighlaw.com · 95 Market Street · Manchester, NH 03101 · 603-669-4140

Peter W. Mosseau · ⑩ · Nelson, Kinder, Mosseau & Saturley · http://www.nkms.com · 99 Middle Street · Manchester, NH 03101 · 603-647-1800

Gregory G. Peters · Wadleigh, Starr & Peters · http://www.wadleighlaw.com · 95 Market Street · Manchester, NH 03101 · 603-669-4140

MERGERS & ACQUISITIONS LAW

Manchester

Peter T. Beach · Sheehan Phinney Bass Green · 1000 Elm Street, 17th Floor · P.O. Box 3701 · Manchester, NH 03105-3701 · 603-668-0300

James C. Hood · Nixon Peabody · 900 Elm Street · Manchester, NH 03101 · 603-628-4000

David P. Van Der Beken · Stebbins, Lazos & Van Der Beken · 66 Hanover Street, Suite 301 · Manchester, NH 03101 · 603-627-3700

MUNICIPAL LAW

Concord

Barton L. Mayer · Upton & Hatfield · 10 Centre Street · P.O. Box 1090 · Concord, NH 03302-1090 · 603-224-7791

North Conway

Robert W. Upton II · Upton & Hatfield · 23 Seavey Street · P.O. Box 2242 · North Conway, NH 03860 · 603-356-3332

NON-PROFIT/CHARITIES LAW

Manchester

Bradford E. Cook · Sheehan Phinney Bass Green · 1000 Elm Street, 17th Floor · P.O. Box 3701 · Manchester, NH 03105-3701 · 603-668-0300

Rolf Goodwin · McLane, Graf, Raulerson & Middleton · http://www.mclane.com · 900 Elm Street · P.O. Box 326 · Manchester, NH 03105 · 603-625-6464

Newton H. Kershaw, Jr. · ⑩ · Devine, Millimet & Branch · 111 Amherst Street · Manchester, NH 03101 603-669-1000

Jon B. Sparkman · Devine, Millimet & Branch · 111 Amherst Street · Manchester, NH 03101 · 603-669-1000

Robert A. Wells · ⑩ · McLane, Graf, Raulerson & Middleton · http://www.mclane.com · 900 Elm Street · P.O. Box 326 · Manchester, NH 03105 · 603-625-6464

NON-WHITE-COLLAR CRIMINAL DEFENSE

Chichester

Mark Sisti · Sisti Law Offices · 387 Dover Road · Chichester, NH 03258 · 603-224-4220

Concord

Robert A. Stein · ⑳ · Robert Stein & Associates · http://www.robertsteinandassociates.com · One Barberry Lane · P.O. Box 2159 · Concord, NH 03302-2159 · 603-228-1109

Manchester

William E. Brennan · ⑩ · Brennan, Caron, Lenehan & Lacopino · 85 Brook Street · Manchester, NH 03104 · 603-668-8300

Cathy J. Green · ⑳ · Green & Utter · 764 Chestnut Street · Manchester, NH 03104-2910 · 603-669-8446

Gary S. Lenehan · ⑩ · Brennan, Caron, Lenehan & Lacopino · 85 Brook Street · Manchester, NH 03104 603-668-8300

Portsmouth

Alan J. Cronheim · Sisti Law Offices · 78 Fleet Street · Portsmouth, NH 03801 · 603-433-7117

PERSONAL INJURY LITIGATION

Colebrook

Philip R. Waystack, Jr. · ⑩ · Waystack & King · 251 Main Street · P.O. Box 137 · Colebrook, NH 03576 · 603-237-8322

Concord

Michael R. Callahan · ⑩ · Gallagher, Callahan & Gartrell · http://www.gcglaw.com · 214 North Main Street · P.O. Box 1415 · Concord, NH 03302-1415 · 603-228-1181

Edward M. Kaplan · ⑳ · Sulloway & Hollis · Nine Capitol Street & Twenty Nine School Street · P.O. Box 1256 · Concord, NH 03301-1256 · 603-224-2341

Robert J. Lanney · Sulloway & Hollis · Nine Capitol Street & Twenty Nine School Street · P.O. Box 1256 · Concord, NH 03301-1256 · 603-224-2341

Michael P. Lehman · ⑩ · Sulloway & Hollis · Nine Capitol Street & Twenty Nine School Street · P.O. Box 1256 · Concord, NH 03301-1256 · 603-224-2341

Michael M. Lonergan · Sulloway & Hollis · Nine Capitol Street & Twenty Nine School Street · P.O. Box 1256 · Concord, NH 03301-1256 · 603-224-2341

Michael A. Pignatelli · Rath, Young and Pignatelli · One Capital Plaza · P.O. Box 1500 · Concord, NH 03302-1500 · 603-226-2600

Gary B. Richardson · ⑩ · Upton & Hatfield · 10 Centre Street · P.O. Box 1090 · Concord, NH 03302-1090 · 603-224-7791

Lawrence S. Smith · Ransmeier & Spellman · One Capitol Street · P.O. Box 600 · Concord, NH 03302 · 603-228-0477

Dover

Matthew B. Cox · Burns, Bryant, Cox, Rockefeller & Dirkin · Burns Building · 255 Washington Street · P.O. Box 608 · Dover, NH 03821-0608 · 603-742-2332

D. Michael Noonan · Shaheen & Gordon · http://www.shaheengordon.com · 140 Washington Street, Second Floor · P.O. Box 977 · Dover, NH 03821-0977 · 603-749-5000

Hampton

Ken Bouchard · Bouchard, Kleinman & Wright · One Merrill Drive, Suite Six · Hampton, NH 03842 · 603-926-9333

Manchester

Mark A. Abramson · ⑩ · Abramson, Brown & Dugan · http://www.arbd.com · 1819 Elm Street · Manchester, NH 03104-2910 · 603-647-0300

R. David Depuy · McLane, Graf, Raulerson & Middleton · http://www.mclane.com · 900 Elm Street · P.O. Box 326 · Manchester, NH 03105 · 603-625-6464

Dennis T. Ducharme · Wiggin & Nourie · 670 North Commercial Street, Suite 305 · P.O. Box 808 · Manchester, NH 03105-0808 · 603-669-2211

Kevin F. Dugan · Abramson, Brown & Dugan · http://www.arbd.com · 1819 Elm Street · Manchester, NH 03104-2910 · 603-647-0300

Andrew D. Dunn · ⑩ · Devine, Millimet & Branch · 111 Amherst Street · Manchester, NH 03101 · 603-669-1000

Bruce W. Felmly · ⑩ · McLane, Graf, Raulerson & Middleton · http://www.mclane.com · 900 Elm Street P.O. Box 326 · Manchester, NH 03105 · 603-625-6464

John E. Friberg, Sr. · ㉕ · Wadleigh, Starr & Peters · http://www.wadleighlaw.com · 95 Market Street · Manchester, NH 03101 · 603-669-4140

Ralph F. Holmes · McLane, Graf, Raulerson & Middleton · http://www.mclane.com · 900 Elm Street · P.O. Box 326 · Manchester, NH 03105 · 603-625-6464

Joseph F. McDowell III · ⑩ · McDowell & Osburn · 282 River Road · P.O. Box 3360 · Manchester, NH 03105-3360 · 603-623-9300

Jack B. Middleton · ⑳ · McLane, Graf, Raulerson & Middleton · http://www.mclane.com · 900 Elm Street · P.O. Box 326 · Manchester, NH 03105 · 603-625-6464

Richard C. Moquin · Moquin & Daley · 226 Coolidge Avenue · Manchester, NH 03102 · 603-669-9400

Peter W. Mosseau · ⑩ · Nelson, Kinder, Mosseau & Saturley · http://www.nkms.com · 99 Middle Street · Manchester, NH 03101 · 603-647-1800

David L. Nixon · ⑳ · Nixon, Raiche, Vogelman, Barry & Slawsky · 77 Central Street · Manchester, NH 03101 · 603-669-7070

Jeffrey B. Osburn · ⑩ · McDowell & Osburn · 282 River Road · P.O. Box 3360 · Manchester, NH 03105-3360 · 603-623-9300

Gordon A. Rehnborg, Jr. · Wiggin & Nourie · 670 North Commercial Street, Suite 305 · P.O. Box 808 · Manchester, NH 03105-0808 · 603-669-2211

Nashua

David Gottesman · Gottesman & Hollis · http://www.nh-lawyers.com · 39 East Pearl Street · Nashua, NH 03060 · 603-889-5959

Portsmouth

Russell F. Hilliard · ⑩ · Upton & Hatfield · 159 Middle Street · Portsmouth, NH 03801 · 603-436-7046

REAL ESTATE LAW

Concord

R. Carl Anderson · Sulloway & Hollis · Nine Capitol Street & Twenty Nine School Street · P.O. Box 1256 · Concord, NH 03301-1256 · 603-224-2341

Alexandra T. Breed · McLane, Graf, Raulerson & Middleton · http://www.mclane.com · 11 South Main Street, Suite 500 · Concord, NH 03301 · 603-226-0400

Timothy E. Britain · Cleveland, Waters & Bass · Two Capital Plaza · P.O. Box 1137 · Concord, NH 03302-1137 · 603-224-7761

Peter F. Burger · Orr and Reno · http://www.orr-reno.com · One Eagle Square · P.O. Box 3550 · Concord, NH 03302-3550 · 603-224-2381

Raymond P. D'Amante · D'Amante Couser Steiner Pellerin · http://www.damantelaw.com · Nine Triangle Park Drive · P.O. Box 2650 · Concord, NH 03302-2650 · 603-224-6777

Donald E. Gartrell · ⑳ · Gallagher, Callahan & Gartrell · http://www.gcglaw.com · 214 North Main Street P.O. Box 1415 · Concord, NH 03302-1415 · 603-228-1181

Peter F. Imse · ⑩ · Sulloway & Hollis · Nine Capitol Street & Twenty Nine School Street · P.O. Box 1256 · Concord, NH 03301-1256 · 603-224-2341

Simon Leeming · Preti, Flaherty, Beliveau & Pachios · http://www.preti.com · 57 North Main Street · P.O. Box 1318 · Concord, NH 03302-1318 · 603-410-1500

James Morris · Orr and Reno · http://www.orr-reno.com · One Eagle Square · P.O. Box 3550 · Concord, NH 03302-3550 · 603-224-2381

Ari B. Pollack · Gallagher, Callahan & Gartrell · http://www.gcglaw.com · 214 North Main Street · P.O. Box 1415 · Concord, NH 03302-1415 · 603-228-1181

John H. Sokul, Jr. · Hinckley, Allen & Snyder · http://www.haslaw.com · 11 South Main Street, Suite 400 · Concord, NH 03301-4846 · 603-225-4334

Laconia

Edmund S. Hibbard · Wescott, Millham & Dyer · The Bowman Street School · 28 Bowman Street · P.O. Box 1700 · Laconia, NH 03247-1700 · 603-524-2166

Manchester

Linda C. Connell · McLane, Graf, Raulerson & Middleton · http://www.mclane.com · 900 Elm Street · P.O. Box 326 · Manchester, NH 03105 · 603-625-6464

Susan V. Duprey · Devine, Millimet & Branch · 111 Amherst Street · Manchester, NH 03101 · 603-669-1000

Nicholas J. Lazos · Stebbins, Lazos & Van Der Beken · 66 Hanover Street, Suite 301 · Manchester, NH 03101 · 603-627-3700

Susan A. Manchester · Sheehan Phinney Bass Green · 1000 Elm Street, 17th Floor · P.O. Box 3701 · Manchester, NH 03105-3701 · 603-668-0300

Karen S. McGinley · Devine, Millimet & Branch · 111 Amherst Street · Manchester, NH 03101 · 603-669-1000

Gregory E. Michael · Wiggin & Nourie · 670 North Commercial Street, Suite 305 · P.O. Box 808 · Manchester, NH 03105-0808 · 603-669-2211

Stephen J. Patterson · Wiggin & Nourie · 670 North Commercial Street, Suite 305 · P.O. Box 808 · Manchester, NH 03105-0808 · 603-669-2211

Peter B. Rotch · ⑩ · McLane, Graf, Raulerson & Middleton · http://www.mclane.com · 900 Elm Street · P.O. Box 326 · Manchester, NH 03105 · 603-625-6464

Henry B. Stebbins · ⑩ · Stebbins, Lazos & Van Der Beken · 66 Hanover Street, Suite 301 · Manchester, NH 03101 · 603-627-3700

Kathleen Sullivan · Wadleigh, Starr & Peters · http://www.wadleighlaw.com · 95 Market Street · Manchester, NH 03101 · 603-669-4140

William C. Tucker · ㉕ · Wadleigh, Starr & Peters · http://www.wadleighlaw.com · 95 Market Street · Manchester, NH 03101 · 603-669-4140

Kenneth A. Viscarello · Sheehan Phinney Bass Green · 1000 Elm Street, 17th Floor · P.O. Box 3701 · Manchester, NH 03105-3701 · 603-668-0300

Meredith

Douglas P. Hill · Nungesser & Hill · 56 New Hampshire, Route 25 · P.O. Box 665 · Meredith, NH 03253 603-279-8182

Lee W. Mattson · Lee W. Mattson · Eight New Hampshire Route 25 · P.O. Box 1596 · Meredith, NH 03253-1596 · 603-279-9940

Nashua

J. Jefferson Davis · ⑩ · Davis & Boghigian · 221 Main Street, Suite 301 · P.O. Box 525 · Nashua, NH 03061-0525 · 603-595-0210

Morgan A. Hollis · Gottesman & Hollis · http://www.nh-lawyers.com · 39 East Pearl Street · Nashua, NH 03060 · 603-889-5959

J. Bradford Westgate · Winer & Bennett · 111 Concord Street · P.O. Box 488 · Nashua, NH 03061-0488 · 603-882-5157

North Conway

Robert W. Upton II · Upton & Hatfield · 23 Seavey Street · P.O. Box 2242 · North Conway, NH 03860 · 603-356-3332

SECURITIES LAW

Manchester

Wilbur A. Glahn III · McLane, Graf, Raulerson & Middleton · http://www.mclane.com · 900 Elm Street · P.O. Box 326 · Manchester, NH 03105 · 603-625-6464

Richard A. Samuels · ⑩ · McLane, Graf, Raulerson & Middleton · http://www.mclane.com · 900 Elm Street · P.O. Box 326 · Manchester, NH 03105 · 603-625-6464

TAX LAW

Concord

William F. J. Ardinger · Rath, Young and Pignatelli · One Capital Plaza · P.O. Box 1500 · Concord, NH 03302-1500 · 603-226-2600

Amy K. Kanyuk · McDonald & Kanyuk · http://www.mckan.com · Seven Hills Avenue · Concord, NH 03301 · 603-228-9900

David M. Law · Cleveland, Waters & Bass · Two Capital Plaza · P.O. Box 1137 · Concord, NH 03302-1137 · 603-224-7761

Donald Saxon · Gallagher, Callahan & Gartrell · http://www.gcglaw.com · 214 North Main Street · P.O. Box 1415 · Concord, NH 03302-1415 · 603-228-1181

Manchester

Peter T. Beach · Sheehan Phinney Bass Green · 1000 Elm Street, 17th Floor · P.O. Box 3701 · Manchester, NH 03105-3701 · 603-668-0300

Steven M. Burke · McLane, Graf, Raulerson & Middleton · http://www.mclane.com · 900 Elm Street · P.O. Box 326 · Manchester, NH 03105 · 603-625-6464

William V. A. Zorn · ⑳ · McLane, Graf, Raulerson & Middleton · http://www.mclane.com · 900 Elm Street · P.O. Box 326 · Manchester, NH 03105 · 603-625-6464

TRUSTS AND ESTATES

Bedford

Christine S. Anderson · Ansell & Anderson · Bedford Place, Unit 32 · 40 South River Road · Bedford, NH 03110 · 603-644-8211

Ruth T. Ansell · ⑩ · Ansell & Anderson · Bedford Place, Unit 32 · 40 South River Road · Bedford, NH 03110 · 603-644-8211

Maureen Dwyer · Barradale, O'Connell, Newkirk & Dwyer · Three Executive Park Drive, Suite 12 · Bedford, NH 03110 · 603-644-0275

Colleen D. O'Connell · Barradale, O'Connell, Newkirk & Dwyer · Three Executive Park Drive, Suite 12 Bedford, NH 03110 · 603-644-0275

Concord

Michelle M. Arruda · Cleveland, Waters & Bass · Two Capital Plaza · P.O. Box 1137 · Concord, NH 03302-1137 · 603-224-7761

Alexandra T. Breed · McLane, Graf, Raulerson & Middleton · http://www.mclane.com · 11 South Main Street, Suite 500 · Concord, NH 03301 · 603-226-0400

Ann Meissner Flood · Flood, Sheehan & Tobin · Two Delta Drive, Suite 303 · Concord, NH 03301 · 603-415-4200

Amy K. Kanyuk · McDonald & Kanyuk · http://www.mckan.com · Seven Hills Avenue · Concord, NH 03301 · 603-228-9900

Charles F. Leahy · ⑳ · McLane, Graf, Raulerson & Middleton · http://www.mclane.com · 11 South Main Street, Suite 500 · Concord, NH 03301 · 603-226-0400

Mary Susan Leahy · ⑩ · McLane, Graf, Raulerson & Middleton · http://www.mclane.com · 11 South Main Street, Suite 500 · Concord, NH 03301 · 603-226-0400

Joseph F. McDonald III · ⑩ · McDonald & Kanyuk · http://www.mckan.com · Seven Hills Avenue · Concord, NH 03301 · 603-228-9900

John C. Ransmeier · ⑩ · Ransmeier & Spellman · One Capitol Street · P.O. Box 600 · Concord, NH 03302 · 603-228-0477

Virginia Symmes Sheehan · Flood, Sheehan & Tobin · Two Delta Drive, Suite 303 · Concord, NH 03301 · 603-415-4200

Charles F. Sheridan, Jr. · ⑩ · Sulloway & Hollis · Nine Capitol Street & Twenty Nine School Street · P.O. Box 1256 · Concord, NH 03301-1256 · 603-224-2341

Hanover

Nicholas D. N. Harvey, Jr. · ⑩ · Stebbins Bradley Harvey Miller & Brooks · 41 South Park Street · P.O. Box 382 · Hanover, NH 03755 · 603-643-3737

Willemien Dingemans Miller · Stebbins Bradley Harvey Miller & Brooks · 41 South Park Street · P.O. Box 382 · Hanover, NH 03755 · 603-643-3737

Lebanon

Timothy W. Caldwell · Caldwell Law · Hanover Road Professional Center · 367 Route 120, Unit B-6 · Lebanon, NH 03766 · 603-643-7577

Manchester

James T. Cain · ⑩ · Sheehan Phinney Bass Green · 1000 Elm Street, 17th Floor · P.O. Box 3701 · Manchester, NH 03105-3701 · 603-668-0300

Steven Cohen · ⑩ · Devine, Millimet & Branch · 111 Amherst Street · Manchester, NH 03101 · 603-669-1000

Bradford E. Cook · Sheehan Phinney Bass Green · 1000 Elm Street, 17th Floor · P.O. Box 3701 · Manchester, NH 03105-3701 · 603-668-0300

Ralph F. Holmes · McLane, Graf, Raulerson & Middleton · http://www.mclane.com · 900 Elm Street · P.O. Box 326 · Manchester, NH 03105 · 603-625-6464

John E. Hughes · McLane, Graf, Raulerson & Middleton · http://www.mclane.com · 900 Elm Street · P.O. Box 326 · Manchester, NH 03105 · 603-625-6464

Anu R. Mullikin · Devine, Millimet & Branch · 111 Amherst Street · Manchester, NH 03101 · 603-669-1000

Robert A. Wells · ⑩ · McLane, Graf, Raulerson & Middleton · http://www.mclane.com · 900 Elm Street · P.O. Box 326 · Manchester, NH 03105 · 603-625-6464

Kimon S. Zachos · Sheehan Phinney Bass Green · 1000 Elm Street, 17th Floor · P.O. Box 3701 · Manchester, NH 03105-3701 · 603-668-0300

William V. A. Zorn · ⑳ · McLane, Graf, Raulerson & Middleton · http://www.mclane.com · 900 Elm Street · P.O. Box 326 · Manchester, NH 03105 · 603-625-6464

Portsmouth

William S. Boesch · Robinson, Boesch & Sennott · 20 International Drive, Suite 300 · Portsmouth, NH 03801-3271 · 603-427-5380

Charles A. DeGrandpre · ⑳ · McLane, Graf, Raulerson & Middleton · http://www.mclane.com · 100 Market Street, Suite 301 · P.O. Box 459 · Portsmouth, NH 03802-0459 · 603-436-2818

Denis P. Dillon · McLane, Graf, Raulerson & Middleton · http://www.mclane.com · 100 Market Street, Suite 301 · P.O. Box 459 · Portsmouth, NH 03802-0459 · 603-436-2818

Sally H. Mulhern · Mulhern & Scott · 155 Fleet Street · Portsmouth, NH 03801 · 603-436-1211

Kathleen M. Robinson · ⑩ · Robinson, Boesch & Sennott · 20 International Drive, Suite 300 · Portsmouth, NH 03801-3271 · 603-427-5380

David Wolowitz · ⑩ · McLane, Graf, Raulerson & Middleton · http://www.mclane.com · 100 Market Street, Suite 301 · P.O. Box 459 · Portsmouth, NH 03802-0459 · 603-436-2818

WHITE-COLLAR CRIMINAL DEFENSE

Chichester

Mark Sisti · Sisti Law Offices · 387 Dover Road · Chichester, NH 03258 · 603-224-4220

Colebrook

Philip R. Waystack, Jr. · ⑩ · Waystack & King · 251 Main Street · P.O. Box 137 · Colebrook, NH 03576 · 603-237-8322

Concord

Michael J. Connolly · Hinckley, Allen & Snyder · http://www.haslaw.com · 11 South Main Street, Suite 400 · Concord, NH 03301-4846 · 603-225-4334

Steven M. Gordon · ⑳ · Shaheen & Gordon · http://www.shaheengordon.com · 107 Storrs Street · P.O. Box 2703 · Concord, NH 03302-2703 · 603-225-7262

Robert A. Stein · ⑳ · Robert Stein & Associates · http://www.robertsteinandassociates.com · One Barberry Lane · P.O. Box 2159 · Concord, NH 03302-2159 · 603-228-1109

Manchester

Peter D. Anderson · McLane, Graf, Raulerson & Middleton · http://www.mclane.com · 900 Elm Street · P.O. Box 326 · Manchester, NH 03105 · 603-625-6464

William E. Brennan · ⑩ · Brennan, Caron, Lenehan & Lacopino · 85 Brook Street · Manchester, NH 03104 · 603-668-8300

Cathy J. Green · ⑳ · Green & Utter · 764 Chestnut Street · Manchester, NH 03104-2910 · 603-669-8446

Gary S. Lenehan · ⑩ · Brennan, Caron, Lenehan & Lacopino · 85 Brook Street · Manchester, NH 03104 603-668-8300

Andru H. Volinsky · ⑩ · Bernstein Shur · Jefferson Mill Building, Suite 108 · 670 North Commercial Street · P.O. Box 1120 · Manchester, NH 03105-1120 · 603-623-8700

Portsmouth

Alan J. Cronheim · Sisti Law Offices · 78 Fleet Street · Portsmouth, NH 03801 · 603-433-7117

WORKERS' COMPENSATION LAW

Concord

James E. Owers · ⑩ · Sulloway & Hollis · Nine Capitol Street & Twenty Nine School Street · P.O. Box 1256 · Concord, NH 03301-1256 · 603-224-2341

Laconia

Jerry O'Neil · Normandin, Cheney & O'Neil · 213 Union Avenue · P.O. Box 575 · Laconia, NH 03247 · 603-524-4380

Manchester

Terrence J. Daley · ⑩ · Moquin & Daley · 226 Coolidge Avenue · Manchester, NH 03102 · 603-669-9400

Charles T. Giacopelli · Devine, Millimet & Branch · 111 Amherst Street · Manchester, NH 03101 · 603-669-1000

Andrew A. Merrill · ⑩ · Bernard & Merrill · 814 Elm Street, Suite 407 · Manchester, NH 03101 · 603-622-8454

Paul L. Salafia · Devine, Millimet & Branch · 111 Amherst Street · Manchester, NH 03101 · 603-669-1000

Edward W. Stewart, Jr. · ⑩ · Stewart & Murphy · 80 Merrimack Street · Manchester, NH 03101 · 603-669-8080

NEW JERSEY

ADMINISTRATIVE LAW

Newark

Brian S. Montag · K&L Gates · One Newark Center, 10th Floor · Newark, NJ 07102-5285 · 973-848-4000

West Orange

David Samson · Wolff & Samson · The Offices at Crystal Lake · One Boland Drive · West Orange, NJ 07052 · 973-325-1500

Woodbridge

Anne S. Babineau · a · Wilentz, Goldman & Spitzer · http://www.wilentz.com · 90 Woodbridge Center Drive, Suite 900 · P.O. Box 10 · Woodbridge, NJ 07095-0958 · 732-636-8000

John A. Hoffman · a · Wilentz, Goldman & Spitzer · http://www.wilentz.com · 90 Woodbridge Center Drive, Suite 900 · P.O. Box 10 · Woodbridge, NJ 07095-0958 · 732-636-8000

ALTERNATIVE DISPUTE RESOLUTION

Florham Park

Robert G. Rose · Day Pitney · 200 Campus Drive · P.O. Box 1945 · Florham Park, NJ 07962-1945 · 973-966-6300

David S. Sager · Day Pitney · 200 Campus Drive · P.O. Box 1945 · Florham Park, NJ 07962-1945 · 973-966-6300

Hackensack

Charles C. Abut · a · Charles C. Abut · Court Plaza South, West Wing · 21 Main Street · Hackensack, NJ 07601 · 201-342-0404

Jersey City

Harold I. Braff · Margulies Wind · Harborside Financial Center Plaza 10, Suite 1201 · Three Second Street · Jersey City, NJ 07311-3988 · 201-333-0400

Robert E. Margulies · Margulies Wind · Harborside Financial Center Plaza 10, Suite 1201 · Three Second Street · Jersey City, NJ 07311-3988 · 201-333-0400

Linwood

L. Anthony Gibson · Youngblood, Corcoran, Lafferty & Hyberg · Cornerstone Commerce Center, Suite 230 · 1201 New Road · Linwood, NJ 08221 · 609-601-6600

Marlton

Leonard N. Arnold · Stark & Stark · 40 Lake Center Executive Park, Suite 130 · 401 Route 73 North · Marlton, NJ 08053 · 856-874-4443

Morristown

Herbert S. Glickman · Cutler, Simeone, Townsend, Tomaio & Newmark · 1776 On The Green, Seventh Floor · 67 East Park Place · P.O. Box 1119 · Morristown, NJ 07962-1119 · 973-539-0075

Stewart G. Pollock · Riker, Danzig, Scherer, Hyland & Perretti · Headquarters Plaza · One Speedwell Avenue · Morristown, NJ 07962-1981 · 973-538-0800

Alvin Weiss · Porzio, Bromberg & Newman · 100 Southgate Parkway · P.O. Box 1997 · Morristown, NJ 07962-1997 · 973-538-4006

Newark

John J. Gibbons · a · Gibbons · http://www.gibbonslaw.com · One Gateway Center · Newark, NJ 07102-5310 · 973-596-4500

Herman D. Michels · Gibbons · http://www.gibbonslaw.com · One Gateway Center · Newark, NJ 07102-5310 · 973-596-4500

Princeton

Hanan M. Isaacs · Hanan M. Isaacs · http://www.hananisaacs.com · 601 Ewing Street, Suite C-12 · Princeton, NJ 08540 · 609-683-7400

Richard H. Steen · Richard H. Steen · P.O. Box 2178 · Princeton, NJ 08543-2178 · 609-895-0071

Roseland

Melvin S. Whitken · Weinstein Snyder Lindemann Sarno · http://www.familylawnj.com · 101 Eisenhower Parkway · Roseland, NJ 07068 · 973-403-6000

Somerville

William A. Dreier · Norris, McLaughlin & Marcus · http://www.nmmlaw.com · 721 Route 202-206 · P.O. Box 1018 · Somerville, NJ 08876-1018 · 908-722-0700

John J. Trombadore · a · John J. Trombadore · 31 East High Street · Somerville, NJ 08876 · 908-927-0200

Warren

Amy Zylman Shimalla · Copeland, Shimalla & Wechsler · 101 Town Center, Suite 117 · P.O. Box 4643 · Warren, NJ 07059-0643 · 908-753-3833

Westfield

John M. Boyle · Lindabury, McCormick, Estabrook & Cooper · 53 Cardinal Drive · P.O. Box 2369 · Westfield, NJ 07091 · 908-233-6800

Woodbridge

Douglas K. Wolfson · Greenbaum, Rowe, Smith & Davis · http://www.greenbaumlaw.com · Metro Corporate Campus One · 99 Wood Avenue South · P.O. Box 5600 · Woodbridge, NJ 08830-2712 · 732-549-5600

ANTITRUST LAW

Florham Park

Murray J. Laulicht · Day Pitney · 200 Campus Drive · P.O. Box 1945 · Florham Park, NJ 07962-1945 · 973-966-6300

Newark

Michael R. Griffinger · a · Gibbons · http://www.gibbonslaw.com · One Gateway Center · Newark, NJ 07102-5310 · 973-596-4500

Brian J. McMahon · Gibbons · http://www.gibbonslaw.com · One Gateway Center · Newark, NJ 07102-5310 · 973-596-4500

APPELLATE LAW

Chatham

David W. Fassett · Arseneault, Whipple, Farmer, Fassett & Azzarello · http://www.awffa.com · 560 Main Street · Chatham, NJ 07928 · 973-635-3366

Kevin H. Marino · Marino Tortorella · 437 Southern Boulevard · Chatham, NJ 07928-1488 · 973-824-9300

Alan L. Zegas · a · Law Offices of Alan L. Zegas · http://www.zegaslaw.com · 552 Main Street · Chatham, NJ 07928 · 973-701-7080

Cherry Hill

Carl D. Poplar · 2% · Carl D. Poplar · Building Two · 1010 Kings Highway South · Cherry Hill, NJ 08034 · 856-216-9979

Florham Park

Thomas F. Campion · 2% · Drinker Biddle & Reath · 500 Campus Drive · Florham Park, NJ 07932-1047 · 973-360-1100

Hackensack

Morrill J. Cole · 2% · Cole, Schotz, Meisel, Forman & Leonard · http://www.coleschotz.com · Court Plaza North, Fourth Floor · 25 Main Street · Hackensack, NJ 07601 · 201-489-3000

Michael S. Meisel · a · Cole, Schotz, Meisel, Forman & Leonard · http://www.coleschotz.com · Court Plaza North, Fourth Floor · 25 Main Street · Hackensack, NJ 07601 · 201-489-3000

Kingston

Dale Console · Dale Console, Esquire · 4478 Route 27, Suite 102 · P.O. Box 363 · Kingston, NJ 08528-0363 · 609-683-0003

Murray Hill

Cynthia M. Jacob · a · Fisher & Phillips · http://www.laborlawyers.com · 430 Mountain Avenue · Murray Hill, NJ 07974 · 908-516-1050

Newark

Andrew T. Berry · a · McCarter & English · Four Gateway Center · 100 Mulberry Street · Newark, NJ 07102 · 973-622-4444

Clive S. Cummis · 2% · Sills Cummis & Gross · http://www.sillscummis.com · The Legal Center · One Riverfront Plaza · Newark, NJ 07102-5400 · 973-643-7000

Edward J. Dauber · a · Greenberg, Dauber, Epstein & Tucker · http://www.greenbergdauber.com · One Gateway Center, Suite 600 · Newark, NJ 07102-5311 · 973-643-3700

Paul J. Fishman · Friedman Kaplan Seiler & Adelman · http://www.fklaw.com · One Gateway Center, 25th Floor · Newark, NJ 07102-5311 · 973-877-6400

Bruce I. Goldstein · a · Sills Cummis & Gross · http://www.sillscummis.com · The Legal Center · One Riverfront Plaza · Newark, NJ 07102-5400 · 973-643-7000

Michael R. Griffinger · a · Gibbons · http://www.gibbonslaw.com · One Gateway Center · Newark, NJ 07102-5310 · 973-596-4500

Lawrence S. Lustberg · a · Gibbons · http://www.gibbonslaw.com · One Gateway Center · Newark, NJ 07102-5310 · 973-596-4500

Kevin McNulty · Gibbons · http://www.gibbonslaw.com · One Gateway Center · Newark, NJ 07102-5310 973-596-4500

William J. O'Shaughnessy · a · McCarter & English · Four Gateway Center · 100 Mulberry Street · Newark, NJ 07102 · 973-622-4444

Ronald J. Riccio · McElroy, Deutsch, Mulvaney & Carpenter · http://www.mdmc-law.com · Three Gateway Center, 17th Floor · 100 Mulberry Street · Newark, NJ 07102-4079 · 973-622-7711

Donald A. Robinson · 2% · Robinson & Livelli · Two Penn Plaza East, 11th Floor · Newark, NJ 07105-2237 · 973-690-5400

Peter G. Verniero · Sills Cummis & Gross · http://www.sillscummis.com · The Legal Center · One Riverfront Plaza · Newark, NJ 07102-5400 · 973-643-7000

Roseland

Richard D. Catenacci · Connell Foley · 85 Livingston Avenue · Roseland, NJ 07068 · 973-535-0500

Secaucus

Joel A. Leyner · a · Chasan, Leyner & Lamparello · 300 Harmon Meadow Boulevard · Secaucus, NJ 07094 · 201-348-6000

Voorhees

Joseph H. Kenney · 2% · Ballard Spahr Andrews & Ingersoll · Plaza 1000, Suite 500 · Main Street · Voorhees, NJ 08043-4636 · 856-761-3400

Woodbridge

Frederic K. Becker · 2% · Wilentz, Goldman & Spitzer · http://www.wilentz.com · 90 Woodbridge Center Drive, Suite 900 · P.O. Box 10 · Woodbridge, NJ 07095-0958 · 732-636-8000

Brian J. Molloy · Wilentz, Goldman & Spitzer · http://www.wilentz.com · 90 Woodbridge Center Drive, Suite 900 · P.O. Box 10 · Woodbridge, NJ 07095-0958 · 732-636-8000

Paul A. Rowe · a · Greenbaum, Rowe, Smith & Davis · http://www.greenbaumlaw.com · Metro Corporate Campus One · 99 Wood Avenue South · P.O. Box 5600 · Woodbridge, NJ 08830-2712 · 732-549-5600

BANKING LAW

Florham Park

Jeffrey M. Rosenthal · Greenberg Traurig · http://www.gtlaw.com · 200 Park Avenue · P.O. Box 677 · Florham Park, NJ 07932-0677 · 973-360-7900

Joy Harmon Sperling · Day Pitney · 200 Campus Drive · P.O. Box 1945 · Florham Park, NJ 07962-1945 · 973-966-6300

Michael P. Turner · Day Pitney · 200 Campus Drive · P.O. Box 1945 · Florham Park, NJ 07962-1945 · 973-966-6300

Middletown

Bernard J. Berry · Giordano, Halleran & Ciesla · http://www.ghclaw.com · 125 Half Mile Road, Suite 300 P.O. Box 190 · Middletown, NJ 07748 · 732-741-3900

Morristown

Gerald A. Liloia · Riker, Danzig, Scherer, Hyland & Perretti · Headquarters Plaza · One Speedwell Avenue · Morristown, NJ 07962-1981 · 973-538-0800

Mark S. Rattner · Riker, Danzig, Scherer, Hyland & Perretti · Headquarters Plaza · One Speedwell Avenue · Morristown, NJ 07962-1981 · 973-538-0800

Anthony J. Sylvester · Riker, Danzig, Scherer, Hyland & Perretti · Headquarters Plaza · One Speedwell Avenue · Morristown, NJ 07962-1981 · 973-538-0800

Kenneth M. Van Deventer · Riker, Danzig, Scherer, Hyland & Perretti · Headquarters Plaza · One Speedwell Avenue · Morristown, NJ 07962-1981 · 973-538-0800

New Brunswick

Kevin T. McNamara · Windels, Marx, Lane & Mittendorf · 120 Albany Street Plaza · New Brunswick, NJ 08901 · 732-846-7600

Newark

Steven D. Fleissig · Herrick Feinstein · One Gateway Centre, 22nd Floor · Newark, NJ 07102 · 973-274-2000

Michael M. Horn · a · McCarter & English · Four Gateway Center · 100 Mulberry Street · Newark, NJ 07102 · 973-622-4444

Michael J. Lubben · Gibbons · http://www.gibbonslaw.com · One Gateway Center · Newark, NJ 07102-5310 · 973-596-4500

Princeton

Leonard A. Bernstein · a · Reed Smith · Princeton Forrestal Village, Suite 250 · 136 Main Street · P.O. Box 7839 · Princeton, NJ 08543-7839 · 609-987-0050

J. Ferd Convery III · a · Reed Smith · Princeton Forrestal Village, Suite 250 · 136 Main Street · P.O. Box 7839 · Princeton, NJ 08543-7839 · 609-987-0050

Somerville

Joel N. Jacobson · Norris, McLaughlin & Marcus · http://www.nmmlaw.com · 721 Route 202-206 · P.O. Box 1018 · Somerville, NJ 08876-1018 · 908-722-0700

Kevin T. O'Brien · Norris, McLaughlin & Marcus · http://www.nmmlaw.com · 721 Route 202-206 · P.O. Box 1018 · Somerville, NJ 08876-1018 · 908-722-0700

West Orange

Laurence M. Smith · Wolff & Samson · The Offices at Crystal Lake · One Boland Drive · West Orange, NJ 07052 · 973-325-1500

Woodbridge

Peter R. Herman · Wilentz, Goldman & Spitzer · http://www.wilentz.com · 90 Woodbridge Center Drive, Suite 900 · P.O. Box 10 · Woodbridge, NJ 07095-0958 · 732-636-8000

Stuart A. Hoberman · a · Wilentz, Goldman & Spitzer · http://www.wilentz.com · 90 Woodbridge Center Drive, Suite 900 · P.O. Box 10 · Woodbridge, NJ 07095-0958 · 732-636-8000

BANKRUPTCY AND CREDITOR-DEBTOR RIGHTS LAW

Cherry Hill

Arthur J. Abramowitz · 2) · Cozen O'Connor · Liberty View Building, Suite 300 · 457 Haddonfield Road P.O. Box 5459 · Cherry Hill, NJ 08002-2220 · 856-910-5000

Hackensack

Gerald Gline · Cole, Schotz, Meisel, Forman & Leonard · http://www.coleschotz.com · Court Plaza North, Fourth Floor · 25 Main Street · Hackensack, NJ 07601 · 201-489-3000

Robert P. Shapiro · a · Shapiro & Croland · Continental Plaza II, Sixth Floor · 411 Hackensack Avenue · Hackensack, NJ 07601 · 201-488-3900

Michael D. Sirota · a · Cole, Schotz, Meisel, Forman & Leonard · http://www.coleschotz.com · Court Plaza North, Fourth Floor · 25 Main Street · Hackensack, NJ 07601 · 201-489-3000

Lawrenceville

Timothy P. Duggan · Stark & Stark · 993 Lenox Drive, Building Two · P.O. Box 5315 · Lawrenceville, NJ 08543 · 609-896-9060

Livingston

Ben H. Becker · Becker Meisel · Eisenhower Plaza II, Suite 2800 · 354 Eisenhower Parkway · Livingston, NJ 07039 · 973-422-1100

Jay L. Lubetkin · Rabinowitz, Lubetkin & Tully · 293 Eisenhower Parkway, Suite 100 · Livingston, NJ 07039 · 973-597-9100

Jonathan I. Rabinowitz · Rabinowitz, Lubetkin & Tully · 293 Eisenhower Parkway, Suite 100 · Livingston, NJ 07039 · 973-597-9100

Millburn

Steven Z. Jurista · a · Wasserman, Jurista & Stolz · 225 Millburn Avenue, Suite 207 · P.O. Box 1029 · Millburn, NJ 07041 · 973-467-2700

Daniel M. Stolz · Wasserman, Jurista & Stolz · 225 Millburn Avenue, Suite 207 · P.O. Box 1029 · Millburn, NJ 07041 · 973-467-2700

Robert B. Wasserman · a · Wasserman, Jurista & Stolz · 225 Millburn Avenue, Suite 207 · P.O. Box 1029 Millburn, NJ 07041 · 973-467-2700

Morristown

Dennis J. O'Grady · Riker, Danzig, Scherer, Hyland & Perretti · Headquarters Plaza · One Speedwell Avenue · Morristown, NJ 07962-1981 · 973-538-0800

Newark

Todd M. Galante · LeClair Ryan · Two Penn Plaza East · Newark, NJ 07105 · 973-491-3600

Karen A. Giannelli · Gibbons · http://www.gibbonslaw.com · One Gateway Center · Newark, NJ 07102-5310 · 973-596-4500

Michael R. Griffinger · a · Gibbons · http://www.gibbonslaw.com · One Gateway Center · Newark, NJ 07102-5310 · 973-596-4500

Richard B. Honig · Hellring Lindeman Goldstein & Siegal · One Gateway Center, Eighth Floor · Newark, NJ 07102 · 973-621-9020

William S. Katchen · a · Duane Morris · 744 Broad Street, Suite 1200 · Newark, NJ 07102-3889 · 973-424-2000

Vincent F. Papalia · Saiber · One Gateway Center, 13th Floor · Newark, NJ 07102 · 973-622-3333

Andrew H. Sherman · Sills Cummis & Gross · http://www.sillscummis.com · The Legal Center · One Riverfront Plaza · Newark, NJ 07102-5400 · 973-643-7000

Frank J. Vecchione · a · Gibbons · http://www.gibbonslaw.com · One Gateway Center · Newark, NJ 07102-5310 · 973-596-4500

Jack M. Zackin · Sills Cummis & Gross · http://www.sillscummis.com · The Legal Center · One Riverfront Plaza · Newark, NJ 07102-5400 · 973-643-7000

Paramus

Charles M. Forman · Forman Holt & Eliades · 80 Route Four East · Paramus, NJ 07652 · 201-845-1000

Princeton

Simon Kimmelman · Sills Cummis & Gross · http://www.sillscummis.com · 650 College Road East, Fourth Floor · Princeton, NJ 08540 · 609-227-4600

Roseland

Michael S. Etkin · Lowenstein Sandler · http://www.lowenstein.com · 65 Livingston Avenue · Roseland, NJ 07068-1791 · 973-597-2500

Howard S. Greenberg · a · Ravin Greenberg · 101 Eisenhower Parkway · Roseland, NJ 07068 · 973-226-1500

Kenneth A. Rosen · Lowenstein Sandler · http://www.lowenstein.com · 65 Livingston Avenue · Roseland, NJ 07068-1791 · 973-597-2500

Somerville

Gary Marks · Norris, McLaughlin & Marcus · http://www.nmmlaw.com · 721 Route 202-206 · P.O. Box 1018 · Somerville, NJ 08876-1018 · 908-722-0700

Bruce J. Wisotsky · Norris, McLaughlin & Marcus · http://www.nmmlaw.com · 721 Route 202-206 · P.O. Box 1018 · Somerville, NJ 08876-1018 · 908-722-0700

West Orange

Karen Gilman · Wolff & Samson · The Offices at Crystal Lake · One Boland Drive · West Orange, NJ 07052 · 973-325-1500

Robert E. Neis · Wolff & Samson · The Offices at Crystal Lake · One Boland Drive · West Orange, NJ 07052 · 973-325-1500

David N. Ravin · a · Wolff & Samson · The Offices at Crystal Lake · One Boland Drive · West Orange, NJ 07052 · 973-325-1500

Richard D. Trenk · Trenk, DiPasquale, Webster, Della Fera & Sodono · 347 Mount Pleasant Avenue, Suite 300 · West Orange, NJ 07052 · 973-243-8600

Woodbridge

David L. Bruck · Greenbaum, Rowe, Smith & Davis · http://www.greenbaumlaw.com · Metro Corporate Campus One · 99 Wood Avenue South · P.O. Box 5600 · Woodbridge, NJ 08830-2712 · 732-549-5600

Lawrence P. Maher · Greenbaum, Rowe, Smith & Davis · http://www.greenbaumlaw.com · Metro Corporate Campus One · 99 Wood Avenue South · P.O. Box 5600 · Woodbridge, NJ 08830-2712 · 732-549-5600

BET-THE-COMPANY LITIGATION

Florham Park

Thomas F. Campion · 2% · Drinker Biddle & Reath · 500 Campus Drive · Florham Park, NJ 07932-1047 · 973-360-1100

Hackensack

Morrill J. Cole · 2% · Cole, Schotz, Meisel, Forman & Leonard · http://www.coleschotz.com · Court Plaza North, Fourth Floor · 25 Main Street · Hackensack, NJ 07601 · 201-489-3000

Michael S. Meisel · a · Cole, Schotz, Meisel, Forman & Leonard · http://www.coleschotz.com · Court Plaza North, Fourth Floor · 25 Main Street · Hackensack, NJ 07601 · 201-489-3000

Newark

Andrew T. Berry · a · McCarter & English · Four Gateway Center · 100 Mulberry Street · Newark, NJ 07102 · 973-622-4444

Edward J. Dauber · a · Greenberg, Dauber, Epstein & Tucker · http://www.greenbergdauber.com · One Gateway Center, Suite 600 · Newark, NJ 07102-5311 · 973-643-3700

Bruce I. Goldstein · a · Sills Cummis & Gross · http://www.sillscummis.com · The Legal Center · One Riverfront Plaza · Newark, NJ 07102-5400 · 973-643-7000

Michael R. Griffinger · a · Gibbons · http://www.gibbonslaw.com · One Gateway Center · Newark, NJ 07102-5310 · 973-596-4500

Donald A. Robinson · 2% · Robinson & Livelli · Two Penn Plaza East, 11th Floor · Newark, NJ 07105-2237 · 973-690-5400

Roseland

Douglas S. Eakeley · Lowenstein Sandler · http://www.lowenstein.com · 65 Livingston Avenue · Roseland, NJ 07068-1791 · 973-597-2500

Michael B. Himmel · a · Lowenstein Sandler · http://www.lowenstein.com · 65 Livingston Avenue · Roseland, NJ 07068-1791 · 973-597-2500

Laurence B. Orloff · 2) · Orloff, Lowenbach, Stifelman & Siegel · 101 Eisenhower Parkway · Roseland, NJ 07068-1082 · 973-622-6200

Secaucus

Joel A. Leyner · a · Chasan, Leyner & Lamparello · 300 Harmon Meadow Boulevard · Secaucus, NJ 07094 · 201-348-6000

Voorhees

Joseph H. Kenney · 2% · Ballard Spahr Andrews & Ingersoll · Plaza 1000, Suite 500 · Main Street · Voorhees, NJ 08043-4636 · 856-761-3400

Woodbridge

Frederic K. Becker · 2% · Wilentz, Goldman & Spitzer · http://www.wilentz.com · 90 Woodbridge Center Drive, Suite 900 · P.O. Box 10 · Woodbridge, NJ 07095-0958 · 732-636-8000

Paul A. Rowe · a · Greenbaum, Rowe, Smith & Davis · http://www.greenbaumlaw.com · Metro Corporate Campus One · 99 Wood Avenue South · P.O. Box 5600 · Woodbridge, NJ 08830-2712 · 732-549-5600

COMMERCIAL LITIGATION

Florham Park

Thomas F. Campion · 2% · Drinker Biddle & Reath · 500 Campus Drive · Florham Park, NJ 07932-1047 · 973-360-1100

Paul J. Halasz · Day Pitney · 200 Campus Drive · P.O. Box 1945 · Florham Park, NJ 07962-1945 · 973-966-6300

Roger B. Kaplan · Greenberg Traurig · http://www.gtlaw.com · 200 Park Avenue · P.O. Box 677 · Florham Park, NJ 07932-0677 · 973-360-7900

Dennis T. Kearney · Day Pitney · 200 Campus Drive · P.O. Box 1945 · Florham Park, NJ 07962-1945 · 973-966-6300

Anthony J. Marchetta · Day Pitney · 200 Campus Drive · P.O. Box 1945 · Florham Park, NJ 07962-1945 973-966-6300

Richard L. Plotkin · Day Pitney · 200 Campus Drive · P.O. Box 1945 · Florham Park, NJ 07962-1945 · 973-966-6300

Robert G. Rose · Day Pitney · 200 Campus Drive · P.O. Box 1945 · Florham Park, NJ 07962-1945 · 973-966-6300

Philip R. Sellinger · Greenberg Traurig · http://www.gtlaw.com · 200 Park Avenue · P.O. Box 677 · Florham Park, NJ 07932-0677 · 973-360-7900

Elizabeth J. Sher · Day Pitney · 200 Campus Drive · P.O. Box 1945 · Florham Park, NJ 07962-1945 · 973-966-6300

Richard C. Szuch · Bressler, Amery & Ross · http://www.bressler.com · 325 Columbia Turnpike · Florham Park, NJ 07932 · 973-514-1200

Hackensack

Frank Careri, Jr. · Pisarri, McEnroe & Careri · 126 State Street · Hackensack, NJ 07601 · 201-342-3038

Morrill J. Cole · 2% · Cole, Schotz, Meisel, Forman & Leonard · http://www.coleschotz.com · Court Plaza North, Fourth Floor · 25 Main Street · Hackensack, NJ 07601 · 201-489-3000

Steven R. Klein · Cole, Schotz, Meisel, Forman & Leonard · http://www.coleschotz.com · Court Plaza North, Fourth Floor · 25 Main Street · Hackensack, NJ 07601 · 201-489-3000

Kenneth Lehn · Winne, Banta, Hetherington, Basralian & Kahn · Court Plaza South, East Wing, Suite 101 · 21 Main Street · P.O. Box 647 · Hackensack, NJ 07601-0647 · 201-487-3800

Michael S. Meisel · a · Cole, Schotz, Meisel, Forman & Leonard · http://www.coleschotz.com · Court Plaza North, Fourth Floor · 25 Main Street · Hackensack, NJ 07601 · 201-489-3000

Stuart Reiser · Shapiro & Croland · Continental Plaza II, Sixth Floor · 411 Hackensack Avenue · Hackensack, NJ 07601 · 201-488-3900

Robert L. Ritter · Schiffman, Abraham, Kaufman & Ritter · http://www.sakr-law.com · Three University Plaza, Suite 410, Fourth Floor · Hackensack, NJ 07601 · 201-488-2600

Warren A. Usatine · Cole, Schotz, Meisel, Forman & Leonard · http://www.coleschotz.com · Court Plaza North, Fourth Floor · 25 Main Street · Hackensack, NJ 07601 · 201-489-3000

Lawrenceville

Howard D. Cohen · Parker McCay · Building Four East, Suite 102-A · 1009 Lenox Drive · Lawrenceville, NJ 08648-2321 · 609-896-4222

Kevin M. Hart · Stark & Stark · 993 Lenox Drive, Building Two · P.O. Box 5315 · Lawrenceville, NJ 08543 · 609-896-9060

Lewis J. Pepperman · Stark & Stark · 993 Lenox Drive, Building Two · P.O. Box 5315 · Lawrenceville, NJ 08543 · 609-896-9060

Thomas J. Pryor · Stark & Stark · 993 Lenox Drive, Building Two · P.O. Box 5315 · Lawrenceville, NJ 08543 · 609-896-9060

Livingston

Judson M. Stein · Stein, McGuire, Pantages & Gigl · Eisenhower Plaza II, Second Floor · 354 Eisenhower Parkway · P.O. Box 460 · Livingston, NJ 07039 · 973-992-1100

Madison

Robert Novack · Edwards Angell Palmer & Dodge · One Giralda Farms · Madison, NJ 07940 · 973-520-2300

Morristown

Jan L. Bernstein · Riker, Danzig, Scherer, Hyland & Perretti · Headquarters Plaza · One Speedwell Avenue · Morristown, NJ 07962-1981 · 973-538-0800

Thomas J. Bitar · 2% · Dillon, Bitar & Luther · 53 Maple Avenue · P.O. Box 398 · Morristown, NJ 07963 · 973-539-3100

Glenn A. Clark · Riker, Danzig, Scherer, Hyland & Perretti · Headquarters Plaza · One Speedwell Avenue · Morristown, NJ 07962-1981 · 973-538-0800

Glenn D. Curving · Riker, Danzig, Scherer, Hyland & Perretti · Headquarters Plaza · One Speedwell Avenue · Morristown, NJ 07962-1981 · 973-538-0800

Edward B. Deutsch · McElroy, Deutsch, Mulvaney & Carpenter · http://www.mdmc-law.com · 1300 Mount Kemble Avenue · P.O. Box 2075 · Morristown, NJ 07962-2075 · 973-993-8100

Stephen J. Edelstein · Schwartz Simon Edelstein Celso & Kessler · 44 Whippany Road, Suite 210 · P.O. Box 2355 · Morristown, NJ 07962 · 973-301-0001

Sigrid S. Franzblau · Riker, Danzig, Scherer, Hyland & Perretti · Headquarters Plaza · One Speedwell Avenue · Morristown, NJ 07962-1981 · 973-538-0800

Lance J. Kalik · Riker, Danzig, Scherer, Hyland & Perretti · Headquarters Plaza · One Speedwell Avenue Morristown, NJ 07962-1981 · 973-538-0800

Shawn L. Kelly · Riker, Danzig, Scherer, Hyland & Perretti · Headquarters Plaza · One Speedwell Avenue · Morristown, NJ 07962-1981 · 973-538-0800

Stuart M. Lederman · Riker, Danzig, Scherer, Hyland & Perretti · Headquarters Plaza · One Speedwell Avenue · Morristown, NJ 07962-1981 · 973-538-0800

Michael R. O'Donnell · Riker, Danzig, Scherer, Hyland & Perretti · Headquarters Plaza · One Speedwell Avenue · Morristown, NJ 07962-1981 · 973-538-0800

Anne M. Patterson · Riker, Danzig, Scherer, Hyland & Perretti · Headquarters Plaza · One Speedwell Avenue · Morristown, NJ 07962-1981 · 973-538-0800

Robert J. Schoenberg · Riker, Danzig, Scherer, Hyland & Perretti · Headquarters Plaza · One Speedwell Avenue · Morristown, NJ 07962-1981 · 973-538-0800

Kenneth M. Van Deventer · Riker, Danzig, Scherer, Hyland & Perretti · Headquarters Plaza · One Speedwell Avenue · Morristown, NJ 07962-1981 · 973-538-0800

Julian W. Wells · Riker, Danzig, Scherer, Hyland & Perretti · Headquarters Plaza · One Speedwell Avenue · Morristown, NJ 07962-1981 · 973-538-0800

Andrew T. Berry · a · McCarter & English · Four Gateway Center · 100 Mulberry Street · Newark, NJ 07102 · 973-622-4444

Joseph L. Buckley · Sills Cummis & Gross · http://www.sillscummis.com · The Legal Center · One Riverfront Plaza · Newark, NJ 07102-5400 · 973-643-7000

Clive S. Cummis · 2% · Sills Cummis & Gross · http://www.sillscummis.com · The Legal Center · One Riverfront Plaza · Newark, NJ 07102-5400 · 973-643-7000

Edward J. Dauber · a · Greenberg, Dauber, Epstein & Tucker · http://www.greenbergdauber.com · One Gateway Center, Suite 600 · Newark, NJ 07102-5311 · 973-643-3700

Thomas J. Demski · Sills Cummis & Gross · http://www.sillscummis.com · The Legal Center · One Riverfront Plaza · Newark, NJ 07102-5400 · 973-643-7000

Patrick C. Dunican, Jr. · Gibbons · http://www.gibbonslaw.com · One Gateway Center · Newark, NJ 07102-5310 · 973-596-4500

Angelo J. Genova · 2) · Genova, Burns & Vernoia · 494 Broad Street · Newark, NJ 07102 · 973-533-0777

Bruce I. Goldstein · a · Sills Cummis & Gross · http://www.sillscummis.com · The Legal Center · One Riverfront Plaza · Newark, NJ 07102-5400 · 973-643-7000

Jonathan L. Goldstein · a · Hellring Lindeman Goldstein & Siegal · One Gateway Center, Eighth Floor Newark, NJ 07102 · 973-621-9020

Jeffrey J. Greenbaum · Sills Cummis & Gross · http://www.sillscummis.com · The Legal Center · One Riverfront Plaza · Newark, NJ 07102-5400 · 973-643-7000

Melvin Greenberg · a · Greenberg, Dauber, Epstein & Tucker · http://www.greenbergdauber.com · One Gateway Center, Suite 600 · Newark, NJ 07102-5311 · 973-643-3700

Michael R. Griffinger · a · Gibbons · http://www.gibbonslaw.com · One Gateway Center · Newark, NJ 07102-5310 · 973-596-4500

Alan E. Kraus · Latham & Watkins · One Newark Center, 16th Floor · Newark, NJ 07101-3174 · 973-639-1234

Michael R. McDonald · Gibbons · http://www.gibbonslaw.com · One Gateway Center · Newark, NJ 07102-5310 · 973-596-4500

William B. McGuire · 2% · Tompkins, McGuire, Wachenfeld & Barry · Four Gateway Center, Fifth Floor 100 Mulberry Street · Newark, NJ 07102-4070 · 973-622-3000

Kevin J. McKenna · Gibbons · http://www.gibbonslaw.com · One Gateway Center · Newark, NJ 07102-5310 · 973-596-4500

Brian J. McMahon · Gibbons · http://www.gibbonslaw.com · One Gateway Center · Newark, NJ 07102-5310 · 973-596-4500

William J. O'Shaughnessy · a · McCarter & English · Four Gateway Center · 100 Mulberry Street · Newark, NJ 07102 · 973-622-4444

Mark S. Olinsky · Sills Cummis & Gross · http://www.sillscummis.com · The Legal Center · One Riverfront Plaza · Newark, NJ 07102-5400 · 973-643-7000

Robert L. Podvey · a · Podvey Meanor Catenacci Hildner Cocoziello & Chattman · The Legal Center, Eighth Floor · One Riverfront Plaza · Newark, NJ 07102-5497 · 973-623-1000

William W. Robertson · Robertson, Freilich, Bruno & Cohen · The Legal Center, Ninth Floor · One Riverfront Plaza · Newark, NJ 07102 · 973-848-2100

Donald A. Robinson · 2% · Robinson & Livelli · Two Penn Plaza East, 11th Floor · Newark, NJ 07105-2237 · 973-690-5400

Beth S. Rose · Sills Cummis & Gross · http://www.sillscummis.com · The Legal Center · One Riverfront Plaza · Newark, NJ 07102-5400 · 973-643-7000

Gita F. Rothschild · McCarter & English · Four Gateway Center · 100 Mulberry Street · Newark, NJ 07102 · 973-622-4444

James A. Scarpone · Robertson, Freilich, Bruno & Cohen · The Legal Center, Ninth Floor · One Riverfront Plaza · Newark, NJ 07102 · 973-848-2100

Peter J. Torcicollo · Gibbons · http://www.gibbonslaw.com · One Gateway Center · Newark, NJ 07102-5310 · 973-596-4500

James E. Tyrrell, Jr. · Patton Boggs · One Riverfront Palaza, Sixth Floor · Newark, NJ 07102 · 973-848-5600

Princeton

Diane P. Sullivan · Dechert · 902 Carnegie Center, Suite 500 · Princeton, NJ 08540-6531 · 609-620-3200

Roseland

Richard D. Catenacci · Connell Foley · 85 Livingston Avenue · Roseland, NJ 07068 · 973-535-0500

Dennis J. Drasco · Lum, Drasco & Positan · http://www.lumlaw.com · 103 Eisenhower Parkway · Roseland, NJ 07068-1049 · 973-403-9000

Douglas S. Eakeley · Lowenstein Sandler · http://www.lowenstein.com · 65 Livingston Avenue · Roseland, NJ 07068-1791 · 973-597-2500

Adrian M. Foley, Jr. · 2% · Connell Foley · 85 Livingston Avenue · Roseland, NJ 07068 · 973-535-0500

Kevin R. Gardner · Connell Foley · 85 Livingston Avenue · Roseland, NJ 07068 · 973-535-0500

David L. Harris · Lowenstein Sandler · http://www.lowenstein.com · 65 Livingston Avenue · Roseland, NJ 07068-1791 · 973-597-2500

Michael B. Himmel · a · Lowenstein Sandler · http://www.lowenstein.com · 65 Livingston Avenue · Roseland, NJ 07068-1791 · 973-597-2500

Kenneth F. Kunzman · a · Connell Foley · 85 Livingston Avenue · Roseland, NJ 07068 · 973-535-0500

Edward R. McMahon · Lum, Drasco & Positan · http://www.lumlaw.com · 103 Eisenhower Parkway · Roseland, NJ 07068-1049 · 973-403-9000

Laurence B. Orloff · 2) · Orloff, Lowenbach, Stifelman & Siegel · 101 Eisenhower Parkway · Roseland, NJ 07068-1082 · 973-622-6200

Gregory B. Reilly · Lowenstein Sandler · http://www.lowenstein.com · 65 Livingston Avenue · Roseland, NJ 07068-1791 · 973-597-2500

Jay J. Rice · Nagel Rice · 103 Eisenhower Parkway · Roseland, NJ 07068 · 973-618-0400

Lawrence M. Rolnick · Lowenstein Sandler · http://www.lowenstein.com · 65 Livingston Avenue · Roseland, NJ 07068-1791 · 973-597-2500

Herbert J. Stern · a · Stern & Kilcullen · 75 Livingston Avenue, Second Floor · P.O. Box 430 · Roseland, NJ 07068 · 973-535-1900

Liza M. Walsh · Connell Foley · 85 Livingston Avenue · Roseland, NJ 07068 · 973-535-0500

Secaucus

Joel A. Leyner · a · Chasan, Leyner & Lamparello · 300 Harmon Meadow Boulevard · Secaucus, NJ 07094 · 201-348-6000

Short Hills

Peter John Frazza · Budd Larner · http://www.buddlarner.com · 150 John F. Kennedy Parkway, Third Floor · Short Hills, NJ 07078-2703 · 973-379-4800

Michael M. Rosenbaum · Budd Larner · http://www.buddlarner.com · 150 John F. Kennedy Parkway, Third Floor · Short Hills, NJ 07078-2703 · 973-379-4800

Norman G. Sade · Budd Larner · http://www.buddlarner.com · 150 John F. Kennedy Parkway, Third Floor · Short Hills, NJ 07078-2703 · 973-379-4800

Joseph J. Schiavone · Budd Larner · http://www.buddlarner.com · 150 John F. Kennedy Parkway, Third Floor · Short Hills, NJ 07078-2703 · 973-379-4800

Somerville

Joseph J. Fleischman · Norris, McLaughlin & Marcus · http://www.nmmlaw.com · 721 Route 202-206 · P.O. Box 1018 · Somerville, NJ 08876-1018 · 908-722-0700

James J. Shrager · Norris, McLaughlin & Marcus · http://www.nmmlaw.com · 721 Route 202-206 · P.O. Box 1018 · Somerville, NJ 08876-1018 · 908-722-0700

Edward G. Sponzilli · Norris, McLaughlin & Marcus · http://www.nmmlaw.com · 721 Route 202-206 · P.O. Box 1018 · Somerville, NJ 08876-1018 · 908-722-0700

Vineland

Joseph D. O'Neill · O'Neill & Coant · 30 West Chestnut Avenue · Vineland, NJ 08360-5401 · 856-692-2400

Voorhees

Joseph H. Kenney · 2% · Ballard Spahr Andrews & Ingersoll · Plaza 1000, Suite 500 · Main Street · Voorhees, NJ 08043-4636 · 856-761-3400

Warren

Andrew F. McBride III · Kalison, McBride, Jackson & Murphy · 25 Independence Boulevard, Suite 401 · P.O. Box 4990 · Warren, NJ 07059 · 908-647-4600

West Orange

Gage Andretta · Wolff & Samson · The Offices at Crystal Lake · One Boland Drive · West Orange, NJ 07052 · 973-325-1500

Adam K. Derman · Wolff & Samson · The Offices at Crystal Lake · One Boland Drive · West Orange, NJ 07052 · 973-325-1500

Arthur S. Goldstein · Wolff & Samson · The Offices at Crystal Lake · One Boland Drive · West Orange, NJ 07052 · 973-325-1500

Kenneth N. Laptook · Wolff & Samson · The Offices at Crystal Lake · One Boland Drive · West Orange, NJ 07052 · 973-325-1500

Michael A. Saffer · Mandelbaum, Salsburg, Gold, Lazris & Discenza · 155 Prospect Avenue · West Orange, NJ 07052 · 973-736-4600

David Samson · Wolff & Samson · The Offices at Crystal Lake · One Boland Drive · West Orange, NJ 07052 · 973-325-1500

Armen Shahinian · Wolff & Samson · The Offices at Crystal Lake · One Boland Drive · West Orange, NJ 07052 · 973-325-1500

Joseph Tripodi · Wolff & Samson · The Offices at Crystal Lake · One Boland Drive · West Orange, NJ 07052 · 973-325-1500

Woodbridge

Frederic K. Becker · 2% · Wilentz, Goldman & Spitzer · http://www.wilentz.com · 90 Woodbridge Center Drive, Suite 900 · P.O. Box 10 · Woodbridge, NJ 07095-0958 · 732-636-8000

Marvin J. Brauth · Wilentz, Goldman & Spitzer · http://www.wilentz.com · 90 Woodbridge Center Drive, Suite 900 · P.O. Box 10 · Woodbridge, NJ 07095-0958 · 732-636-8000

Dennis A. Estis · Greenbaum, Rowe, Smith & Davis · http://www.greenbaumlaw.com · Metro Corporate Campus One · 99 Wood Avenue South · P.O. Box 5600 · Woodbridge, NJ 08830-2712 · 732-549-5600

Edward T. Kole · Wilentz, Goldman & Spitzer · http://www.wilentz.com · 90 Woodbridge Center Drive, Suite 900 · P.O. Box 10 · Woodbridge, NJ 07095-0958 · 732-636-8000

Brian J. Molloy · Wilentz, Goldman & Spitzer · http://www.wilentz.com · 90 Woodbridge Center Drive, Suite 900 · P.O. Box 10 · Woodbridge, NJ 07095-0958 · 732-636-8000

Alan S. Naar · Greenbaum, Rowe, Smith & Davis · http://www.greenbaumlaw.com · Metro Corporate Campus One · 99 Wood Avenue South · P.O. Box 5600 · Woodbridge, NJ 08830-2712 · 732-549-5600

Paul A. Rowe · a · Greenbaum, Rowe, Smith & Davis · http://www.greenbaumlaw.com · Metro Corporate Campus One · 99 Wood Avenue South · P.O. Box 5600 · Woodbridge, NJ 08830-2712 · 732-549-5600

Franklin M. Sachs · a · Greenbaum, Rowe, Smith & Davis · http://www.greenbaumlaw.com · Metro Corporate Campus One · 99 Wood Avenue South · P.O. Box 5600 · Woodbridge, NJ 08830-2712 · 732-549-5600

Alan Wasserman · Wilentz, Goldman & Spitzer · http://www.wilentz.com · 90 Woodbridge Center Drive, Suite 900 · P.O. Box 10 · Woodbridge, NJ 07095-0958 · 732-636-8000

COMMUNICATIONS LAW

Newark

Francis Ray Perkins · a · Meyner and Landis · One Gateway Center, Suite 2500 · Newark, NJ 07102 · 973-624-2800

Somerville

James H. Laskey · a · Norris, McLaughlin & Marcus · http://www.nmmlaw.com · 721 Route 202-206 · P.O. Box 1018 · Somerville, NJ 08876-1018 · 908-722-0700

Woodbridge

Anne S. Babineau · a · Wilentz, Goldman & Spitzer · http://www.wilentz.com · 90 Woodbridge Center Drive, Suite 900 · P.O. Box 10 · Woodbridge, NJ 07095-0958 · 732-636-8000

Hesser G. McBride, Jr. · Wilentz, Goldman & Spitzer · http://www.wilentz.com · 90 Woodbridge Center Drive, Suite 900 · P.O. Box 10 · Woodbridge, NJ 07095-0958 · 732-636-8000

CONSTRUCTION LAW

Bridgewater

Kenneth R. Rothschild · Golden, Rothschild, Spagnola, Lundell, Levitt & Boylan · 1011 Route 22 West, Third Floor · P.O. Box 6881 · Bridgewater, NJ 08807-0881 · 908-722-6300

Hackensack

Michael B. Oropollo · Harwood Lloyd · 130 Main Street · Hackensack, NJ 07601 · 201-487-1080

Montville

E. Richard Kennedy, Sr. · Kennedy, Wronko, Kennedy · 150 River Road, Suite 4-K · Montville, NJ 07045 · 973-334-1355

Morristown

Thomas M. Moore · McElroy, Deutsch, Mulvaney & Carpenter · http://www.mdmc-law.com · 1300 Mount Kemble Avenue · P.O. Box 2075 · Morristown, NJ 07962-2075 · 973-993-8100

Mount Laurel

James H. Landgraf · Cureton Caplan · 3000 Midlantic Drive, Suite 200 · Mount Laurel, NJ 08054 · 856-824-1001

New Brunswick

Andrew J. Carlowicz, Jr. · Hoagland, Longo, Moran, Dunst & Doukas · 40 Paterson Street · P.O. Box 480 · New Brunswick, NJ 08903 · 732-545-4717

Robert G. Kenny · Hoagland, Longo, Moran, Dunst & Doukas · 40 Paterson Street · P.O. Box 480 · New Brunswick, NJ 08903 · 732-545-4717

Lawrence P. Powers · Hoagland, Longo, Moran, Dunst & Doukas · 40 Paterson Street · P.O. Box 480 · New Brunswick, NJ 08903 · 732-545-4717

Newark

Philip R. White · Sills Cummis & Gross · http://www.sillscummis.com · The Legal Center · One Riverfront Plaza · Newark, NJ 07102-5400 · 973-643-7000

Princeton

Richard H. Steen · Richard H. Steen · P.O. Box 2178 · Princeton, NJ 08543-2178 · 609-895-0071

River Edge

Patrick Greene, Jr. · Peckar & Abramson · http://www.pecklaw.com · 70 Grand Avenue · River Edge, NJ 07661 · 201-343-3434

Charles F. Kenny · Peckar & Abramson · http://www.pecklaw.com · 70 Grand Avenue · River Edge, NJ 07661 · 201-343-3434

Bruce D. Meller · Peckar & Abramson · http://www.pecklaw.com · 70 Grand Avenue · River Edge, NJ 07661 · 201-343-3434

Roseland

Steven E. Brawer · Lowenstein Sandler · http://www.lowenstein.com · 65 Livingston Avenue · Roseland, NJ 07068-1791 · 973-597-2500

Dennis J. Drasco · Lum, Drasco & Positan · http://www.lumlaw.com · 103 Eisenhower Parkway · Roseland, NJ 07068-1049 · 973-403-9000

Paul A. Sandars III · Lum, Drasco & Positan · http://www.lumlaw.com · 103 Eisenhower Parkway · Roseland, NJ 07068-1049 · 973-403-9000

Peter J. Smith · Connell Foley · 85 Livingston Avenue · Roseland, NJ 07068 · 973-535-0500

West Orange

Armen Shahinian · Wolff & Samson · The Offices at Crystal Lake · One Boland Drive · West Orange, NJ 07052 · 973-325-1500

Woodbridge

Dennis A. Estis · Greenbaum, Rowe, Smith & Davis · http://www.greenbaumlaw.com · Metro Corporate Campus One · 99 Wood Avenue South · P.O. Box 5600 · Woodbridge, NJ 08830-2712 · 732-549-5600

CORPORATE GOVERNANCE AND COMPLIANCE LAW

Florham Park

Warren J. Casey · Day Pitney · 200 Campus Drive · P.O. Box 1945 · Florham Park, NJ 07962-1945 · 973-966-6300

Michael T. Rave · Day Pitney · 200 Campus Drive · P.O. Box 1945 · Florham Park, NJ 07962-1945 · 973-966-6300

Newark

Alyce C. Halchak · Gibbons · http://www.gibbonslaw.com · One Gateway Center · Newark, NJ 07102-5310 · 973-596-4500

Peter G. Verniero · Sills Cummis & Gross · http://www.sillscummis.com · The Legal Center · One Riverfront Plaza · Newark, NJ 07102-5400 · 973-643-7000

Woodbridge

Raymond M. Brown · 2) · Greenbaum, Rowe, Smith & Davis · http://www.greenbaumlaw.com · Metro Corporate Campus One · 99 Wood Avenue South · P.O. Box 5600 · Woodbridge, NJ 08830-2712 · 732-549-5600

CORPORATE LAW

Florham Park

Lori J. Braender · Day Pitney · 200 Campus Drive · P.O. Box 1945 · Florham Park, NJ 07962-1945 · 973-966-6300

Warren J. Casey · Day Pitney · 200 Campus Drive · P.O. Box 1945 · Florham Park, NJ 07962-1945 · 973-966-6300

Romney L. Grippo · Drinker Biddle & Reath · 500 Campus Drive · Florham Park, NJ 07932-1047 · 973-360-1100

John Kandravy · a · Drinker Biddle & Reath · 500 Campus Drive · Florham Park, NJ 07932-1047 · 973-360-1100

Stewart E. Lavey · Drinker Biddle & Reath · 500 Campus Drive · Florham Park, NJ 07932-1047 · 973-360-1100

Henry Nelson Massey · Day Pitney · 200 Campus Drive · P.O. Box 1945 · Florham Park, NJ 07962-1945 · 973-966-6300

Jeffrey M. Rosenthal · Greenberg Traurig · http://www.gtlaw.com · 200 Park Avenue · P.O. Box 677 · Florham Park, NJ 07932-0677 · 973-360-7900

Michael P. Turner · Day Pitney · 200 Campus Drive · P.O. Box 1945 · Florham Park, NJ 07962-1945 · 973-966-6300

Hackensack

Henry M. Matri · Cole, Schotz, Meisel, Forman & Leonard · http://www.coleschotz.com · Court Plaza North, Fourth Floor · 25 Main Street · Hackensack, NJ 07601 · 201-489-3000

Gianfranco A. Pietrafesa · Herten, Burstein, Sheridan, Cevasco, Bottinelli, Litt & Harz · Court Plaza South, Third Floor · 21 Main Street · Hackensack, NJ 07601-7032 · 201-342-6000

Alan Rubin · Cole, Schotz, Meisel, Forman & Leonard · http://www.coleschotz.com · Court Plaza North, Fourth Floor · 25 Main Street · Hackensack, NJ 07601 · 201-489-3000

Lawrenceville

Allen M. Silk · Stark & Stark · 993 Lenox Drive, Building Two · P.O. Box 5315 · Lawrenceville, NJ 08543 · 609-896-9060

Middletown

John A. Aiello · 2) · Giordano, Halleran & Ciesla · http://www.ghclaw.com · 125 Half Mile Road, Suite 300 · P.O. Box 190 · Middletown, NJ 07748 · 732-741-3900

Bernard J. Berry · Giordano, Halleran & Ciesla · http://www.ghclaw.com · 125 Half Mile Road, Suite 300 P.O. Box 190 · Middletown, NJ 07748 · 732-741-3900

Paul T. Colella · Giordano, Halleran & Ciesla · http://www.ghclaw.com · 125 Half Mile Road, Suite 300 · P.O. Box 190 · Middletown, NJ 07748 · 732-741-3900

Philip D. Forlenza · Giordano, Halleran & Ciesla · http://www.ghclaw.com · 125 Half Mile Road, Suite 300 · P.O. Box 190 · Middletown, NJ 07748 · 732-741-3900

Morristown

Harold S. Atlas · Riker, Danzig, Scherer, Hyland & Perretti · Headquarters Plaza · One Speedwell Avenue · Morristown, NJ 07962-1981 · 973-538-0800

Thomas J. Bitar · 2% · Dillon, Bitar & Luther · 53 Maple Avenue · P.O. Box 398 · Morristown, NJ 07963 · 973-539-3100

William G. Connolly · Riker, Danzig, Scherer, Hyland & Perretti · Headquarters Plaza · One Speedwell Avenue · Morristown, NJ 07962-1981 · 973-538-0800

Charles S. Detrizio · Riker, Danzig, Scherer, Hyland & Perretti · Headquarters Plaza · One Speedwell Avenue · Morristown, NJ 07962-1981 · 973-538-0800

Mark S. Rattner · Riker, Danzig, Scherer, Hyland & Perretti · Headquarters Plaza · One Speedwell Avenue · Morristown, NJ 07962-1981 · 973-538-0800

Andrew J. Stamelman · Riker, Danzig, Scherer, Hyland & Perretti · Headquarters Plaza · One Speedwell Avenue · Morristown, NJ 07962-1981 · 973-538-0800

Newark

David F. Broderick · McCarter & English · Four Gateway Center · 100 Mulberry Street · Newark, NJ 07102 · 973-622-4444

Frank T. Cannone · Gibbons · http://www.gibbonslaw.com · One Gateway Center · Newark, NJ 07102-5310 · 973-596-4500

Steven E. Gross · a · Sills Cummis & Gross · http://www.sillscummis.com · The Legal Center · One Riverfront Plaza · Newark, NJ 07102-5400 · 973-643-7000

Alyce C. Halchak · Gibbons · http://www.gibbonslaw.com · One Gateway Center · Newark, NJ 07102-5310 · 973-596-4500

Michael M. Horn · a · McCarter & English · Four Gateway Center · 100 Mulberry Street · Newark, NJ 07102 · 973-622-4444

Arlene E. Mirsky · Sills Cummis & Gross · http://www.sillscummis.com · The Legal Center · One Riverfront Plaza · Newark, NJ 07102-5400 · 973-643-7000

Laurence Reich · a · McElroy, Deutsch, Mulvaney & Carpenter · http://www.mdmc-law.com · Three Gateway Center, 17th Floor · 100 Mulberry Street · Newark, NJ 07102-4079 · 973-622-7711

Ira A. Rosenberg · a · Sills Cummis & Gross · http://www.sillscummis.com · The Legal Center · One Riverfront Plaza · Newark, NJ 07102-5400 · 973-643-7000

H. Glenn Tucker · Greenberg, Dauber, Epstein & Tucker · http://www.greenbergdauber.com · One Gateway Center, Suite 600 · Newark, NJ 07102-5311 · 973-643-3700

Princeton

Steven M. Cohen · Morgan Lewis & Bockius · 502 Carnegie Center · Princeton, NJ 08540-6289 · 609-919-6600

J. Ferd Convery III · a · Reed Smith · Princeton Forrestal Village, Suite 250 · 136 Main Street · P.O. Box 7839 · Princeton, NJ 08543-7839 · 609-987-0050

Andrew P. Gilbert · Morgan Lewis & Bockius · 502 Carnegie Center · Princeton, NJ 08540-6289 · 609-919-6600

John E. Stoddard III · Drinker Biddle & Reath · 105 College Road East, Suite 300 · P.O. Box 627 · Princeton, NJ 08542-0627 · 609-716-6500

Diane P. Sullivan · Dechert · 902 Carnegie Center, Suite 500 · Princeton, NJ 08540-6531 · 609-620-3200

Roseland

Philip L. Chapman · 2) · Lum, Drasco & Positan · http://www.lumlaw.com · 103 Eisenhower Parkway · Roseland, NJ 07068-1049 · 973-403-9000

Peter H. Ehrenberg · 2) · Lowenstein Sandler · http://www.lowenstein.com · 65 Livingston Avenue · Roseland, NJ 07068-1791 · 973-597-2500

John D. Hogoboom · Lowenstein Sandler · http://www.lowenstein.com · 65 Livingston Avenue · Roseland, NJ 07068-1791 · 973-597-2500

Stephen H. Knee · 2) · Greenbaum, Rowe, Smith & Davis · http://www.greenbaumlaw.com · 75 Livingston Avenue · Roseland, NJ 07068-3701 · 973-535-1600

Allen B. Levithan · a · Lowenstein Sandler · http://www.lowenstein.com · 65 Livingston Avenue · Roseland, NJ 07068-1791 · 973-597-2500

Ralph M. Lowenbach · 2% · Orloff, Lowenbach, Stifelman & Siegel · 101 Eisenhower Parkway · Roseland, NJ 07068-1082 · 973-622-6200

Edward R. McMahon · Lum, Drasco & Positan · http://www.lumlaw.com · 103 Eisenhower Parkway · Roseland, NJ 07068-1049 · 973-403-9000

Robert G. Minion · Lowenstein Sandler · http://www.lowenstein.com · 65 Livingston Avenue · Roseland, NJ 07068-1791 · 973-597-2500

Stuart L. Pachman · a · WolfBlock · http://wolfblock.com · 101 Eisenhower Parkway, Suite 200 · Roseland, NJ 07068 · 973-228-5700

Anthony O. Pergola · Lowenstein Sandler · http://www.lowenstein.com · 65 Livingston Avenue · Roseland, NJ 07068-1791 · 973-597-2500

David J. Ritter · WolfBlock · http://wolfblock.com · 101 Eisenhower Parkway, Suite 200 · Roseland, NJ 07068 · 973-228-5700

John D. Schupper · 2) · Lowenstein Sandler · http://www.lowenstein.com · 65 Livingston Avenue · Roseland, NJ 07068-1791 · 973-597-2500

Alan Wovsaniker · Lowenstein Sandler · http://www.lowenstein.com · 65 Livingston Avenue · Roseland, NJ 07068-1791 · 973-597-2500

Edward M. Zimmerman · Lowenstein Sandler · http://www.lowenstein.com · 65 Livingston Avenue · Roseland, NJ 07068-1791 · 973-597-2500

Short Hills

Victor H. Boyajian · Sonnenschein Nath & Rosenthal · 101 JFK Parkway, Fourth Floor · Short Hills, NJ 07078-2708 · 973-912-7100

Mark D. Larner · Budd Larner · http://www.buddlarner.com · 150 John F. Kennedy Parkway, Third Floor Short Hills, NJ 07078-2703 · 973-379-4800

Somerville

Peter D. Hutcheon · 2) · Norris, McLaughlin & Marcus · http://www.nmmlaw.com · 721 Route 202-206 · P.O. Box 1018 · Somerville, NJ 08876-1018 · 908-722-0700

G. Robert Marcus · Norris, McLaughlin & Marcus · http://www.nmmlaw.com · 721 Route 202-206 · P.O. Box 1018 · Somerville, NJ 08876-1018 · 908-722-0700

Warren

Paul R. Murphy · Kalison, McBride, Jackson & Murphy · 25 Independence Boulevard, Suite 401 · P.O. Box 4990 · Warren, NJ 07059 · 908-647-4600

West Orange

Morris Bienenfeld · Wolff & Samson · The Offices at Crystal Lake · One Boland Drive · West Orange, NJ 07052 · 973-325-1500

Roger J. Breene · Wolff & Samson · The Offices at Crystal Lake · One Boland Drive · West Orange, NJ 07052 · 973-325-1500

David M. Hyman · Wolff & Samson · The Offices at Crystal Lake · One Boland Drive · West Orange, NJ 07052 · 973-325-1500

Daniel A. Schwartz · Wolff & Samson · The Offices at Crystal Lake · One Boland Drive · West Orange, NJ 07052 · 973-325-1500

Michael R. Spar · Goldberg, Mufson & Spar · 200 Executive Drive · West Orange, NJ 07052 · 973-736-0100

Woodbridge

Frederic K. Becker · 2% · Wilentz, Goldman & Spitzer · http://www.wilentz.com · 90 Woodbridge Center Drive, Suite 900 · P.O. Box 10 · Woodbridge, NJ 07095-0958 · 732-636-8000

Alan E. Davis · 2) · Greenbaum, Rowe, Smith & Davis · http://www.greenbaumlaw.com · Metro Corporate Campus One · 99 Wood Avenue South · P.O. Box 5600 · Woodbridge, NJ 08830-2712 · 732-549-5600

W. Raymond Felton · a · Greenbaum, Rowe, Smith & Davis · http://www.greenbaumlaw.com · Metro Corporate Campus One · 99 Wood Avenue South · P.O. Box 5600 · Woodbridge, NJ 08830-2712 · 732-549-5600

Brett R. Harris · Wilentz, Goldman & Spitzer · http://www.wilentz.com · 90 Woodbridge Center Drive, Suite 900 · P.O. Box 10 · Woodbridge, NJ 07095-0958 · 732-636-8000

Stuart A. Hoberman · a · Wilentz, Goldman & Spitzer · http://www.wilentz.com · 90 Woodbridge Center Drive, Suite 900 · P.O. Box 10 · Woodbridge, NJ 07095-0958 · 732-636-8000

Cherry Hill

Evan M. Levow · Levow & Costello · Cherry Hill Plaza, Suite 200 · 1415 Route 70 East · Cherry Hill, NJ 08034 · 856-428-5055

Carl D. Poplar · 2% · Carl D. Poplar · Building Two · 1010 Kings Highway South · Cherry Hill, NJ 08034 · 856-216-9979

Freehold

Peter Lederman · Lomurro, Davison, Eastman and Muñoz · http://www.lomurrolaw.com · Monmouth Executive Center, Building One · 100 Willowbrook Road · Freehold, NJ 07728 · 732-462-7170

Hackensack

Joseph P. Rem, Jr. · Rem Zeller Law Group · 25 East Salem Street, Suite 400 · Hackensack, NJ 07601-7412 · 201-488-1234

Haddon Heights

Yaron Helmer · Helmer, Paul, Conley & Kasselman · http://www.helmerlegal.com · 111 White Horse Pike · Haddon Heights, NJ 08035 · 856-547-7888

Hoboken

Brian J. Neary · a · Law Offices of Brian J. Neary · http://www.nearylaw.com · Hoboken Land Building · One Newark Street · Hoboken, NJ 07030 · 201-420-8101

Point Pleasant

John Menzel · Law Offices of John Menzel · 2911 Route 88, Suite Six · Point Pleasant, NJ 08742 · 732-899-1899

Vineland

Charles I. Coant · O'Neill & Coant · 30 West Chestnut Avenue · Vineland, NJ 08360-5401 · 856-692-2400

Joseph D. O'Neill · O'Neill & Coant · 30 West Chestnut Avenue · Vineland, NJ 08360-5401 · 856-692-2400

West Orange

Timothy Donohue · Arleo & Donohue · 622 Eagle Rock Avenue · West Orange, NJ 07052 · 973-736-8660

Woodbridge

James E. Trabilsy · Wilentz, Goldman & Spitzer · http://www.wilentz.com · 90 Woodbridge Center Drive, Suite 900 · P.O. Box 10 · Woodbridge, NJ 07095-0958 · 732-636-8000

EMINENT DOMAIN AND CONDEMNATION LAW

Lakewood

Peter H. Wegener · Bathgate, Wegener & Wolf · One Airport Road · P.O. Box 2043 · Lakewood, NJ 08701 · 732-363-0666

Morristown

Jack H. Buonocore, Jr. · McKirdy and Riskin · 136 South Street · Morristown, NJ 07960 · 973-539-8900

Stuart M. Lederman · Riker, Danzig, Scherer, Hyland & Perretti · Headquarters Plaza · One Speedwell Avenue · Morristown, NJ 07962-1981 · 973-538-0800

Edward D. McKirdy · McKirdy and Riskin · 136 South Street · Morristown, NJ 07960 · 973-539-8900

Roseland

Kevin J. Coakley · a · Connell Foley · 85 Livingston Avenue · Roseland, NJ 07068 · 973-535-0500

Westfield

John J. Reilly · Farer Fersko · http://www.farerlaw.com · 600 South Avenue · P.O. Box 580 · Westfield, NJ 07091-0580 · 908-789-8550

Woodbridge

Marvin J. Brauth · Wilentz, Goldman & Spitzer · http://www.wilentz.com · 90 Woodbridge Center Drive, Suite 900 · P.O. Box 10 · Woodbridge, NJ 07095-0958 · 732-636-8000

William D. Grand · Greenbaum, Rowe, Smith & Davis · http://www.greenbaumlaw.com · Metro Corporate Campus One · 99 Wood Avenue South · P.O. Box 5600 · Woodbridge, NJ 08830-2712 · 732-549-5600

EMPLOYEE BENEFITS LAW

Florham Park

David P. Doyle · Day Pitney · 200 Campus Drive · P.O. Box 1945 · Florham Park, NJ 07962-1945 · 973-966-6300

Kathy A. Lawler · a · Day Pitney · 200 Campus Drive · P.O. Box 1945 · Florham Park, NJ 07962-1945 · 973-966-6300

Joy M. Mercer · a · Joy M. Mercer · 30 Columbia Turnpike · Florham Park, NJ 07932 · 973-377-0500

Gary D. Stadtmauer · Witman Stadtmauer · 26 Columbia Turnpike · Florham Park, NJ 07932-2246 · 973-822-0220

Leonard J. Witman · 2) · Witman Stadtmauer · 26 Columbia Turnpike · Florham Park, NJ 07932-2246 · 973-822-0220

Newark

John B. Brescher, Jr. · a · McCarter & English · Four Gateway Center · 100 Mulberry Street · Newark, NJ 07102 · 973-622-4444

Mark A. Daniele · McCarter & English · Four Gateway Center · 100 Mulberry Street · Newark, NJ 07102 973-622-4444

Stanley A. Epstein · a · Greenberg, Dauber, Epstein & Tucker · http://www.greenbergdauber.com · One Gateway Center, Suite 600 · Newark, NJ 07102-5311 · 973-643-3700

Princeton

Francis W. Palmieri · a · Palmieri & Eisenberg · 715 Executive Drive · Princeton, NJ 08540 · 609-497-0400

Roseland

Andrew E. Graw · Lowenstein Sandler · http://www.lowenstein.com · 65 Livingston Avenue · Roseland, NJ 07068-1791 · 973-597-2500

West Orange

Stephen L. Ferszt · Wolff & Samson · The Offices at Crystal Lake · One Boland Drive · West Orange, NJ 07052 · 973-325-1500

Woodbridge

Thomas C. Senter · Greenbaum, Rowe, Smith & Davis · http://www.greenbaumlaw.com · Metro Corporate Campus One · 99 Wood Avenue South · P.O. Box 5600 · Woodbridge, NJ 08830-2712 · 732-549-5600

ENERGY LAW

Cherry Hill

Ira G. Megdal · Cozen O'Connor · Liberty View Building, Suite 300 · 457 Haddonfield Road · P.O. Box 5459 · Cherry Hill, NJ 08002-2220 · 856-910-5000

Florham Park

Marc B. Lasky · Thelen Reid Brown Raysman & Steiner · 200 Campus Drive, Suite 210 · Florham Park, NJ 07932 · 973-660-4400

Morristown

Edward K. DeHope · a · Riker, Danzig, Scherer, Hyland & Perretti · Headquarters Plaza · One Speedwell Avenue · Morristown, NJ 07962-1981 · 973-538-0800

James C. Meyer · Riker, Danzig, Scherer, Hyland & Perretti · Headquarters Plaza · One Speedwell Avenue · Morristown, NJ 07962-1981 · 973-538-0800

Stewart G. Pollock · Riker, Danzig, Scherer, Hyland & Perretti · Headquarters Plaza · One Speedwell Avenue · Morristown, NJ 07962-1981 · 973-538-0800

Newark

Colleen A. Foley · Saul Ewing · One River Front Plaza · Newark, NJ 07102 · 973-286-6700

Stephen B. Genzer · a · Saul Ewing · One River Front Plaza · Newark, NJ 07102 · 973-286-6700

Mark L. Mucci · Saul Ewing · One River Front Plaza · Newark, NJ 07102 · 973-286-6700

Princeton

Steven S. Goldenberg · Fox Rothschild · Princeton Pike Corporate Center, Building Three · 997 Lenox Drive · Princeton, NJ 08648-2311 · 609-896-3600

Somerville

Edward A. Hogan · a · Norris, McLaughlin & Marcus · http://www.nmmlaw.com · 721 Route 202-206 · P.O. Box 1018 · Somerville, NJ 08876-1018 · 908-722-0700

James H. Laskey · a · Norris, McLaughlin & Marcus · http://www.nmmlaw.com · 721 Route 202-206 · P.O. Box 1018 · Somerville, NJ 08876-1018 · 908-722-0700

Walter G. Reinhard · a · Norris, McLaughlin & Marcus · http://www.nmmlaw.com · 721 Route 202-206 · P.O. Box 1018 · Somerville, NJ 08876-1018 · 908-722-0700

Woodbridge

Anne S. Babineau · a · Wilentz, Goldman & Spitzer · http://www.wilentz.com · 90 Woodbridge Center Drive, Suite 900 · P.O. Box 10 · Woodbridge, NJ 07095-0958 · 732-636-8000

John A. Hoffman · a · Wilentz, Goldman & Spitzer · http://www.wilentz.com · 90 Woodbridge Center Drive, Suite 900 · P.O. Box 10 · Woodbridge, NJ 07095-0958 · 732-636-8000

Hesser G. McBride, Jr. · Wilentz, Goldman & Spitzer · http://www.wilentz.com · 90 Woodbridge Center Drive, Suite 900 · P.O. Box 10 · Woodbridge, NJ 07095-0958 · 732-636-8000

ENVIRONMENTAL LAW

Cherry Hill

Bruce S. Katcher · a · Manko, Gold, Katcher & Fox · http://www.mgkflaw.com · Cherry Hill Corporate Center, Suite 145-A · 535 Route 38 · Cherry Hill, NJ 08002 · 856-317-1299

Florham Park

Colleen R. Donovan · Day Pitney · 200 Campus Drive · P.O. Box 1945 · Florham Park, NJ 07962-1945 · 973-966-6300

William S. Hatfield · Day Pitney · 200 Campus Drive · P.O. Box 1945 · Florham Park, NJ 07962-1945 · 973-966-6300

Haddonfield

Christopher R. Gibson · Archer & Greiner · http://www.archerlaw.com · One Centennial Square · 56 Haddon Avenue · P.O. Box 3000 · Haddonfield, NJ 08033-0968 · 856-795-2121

Lloyd H. Tubman · Archer & Greiner · http://www.archerlaw.com · One Centennial Square · 56 Haddon Avenue · P.O. Box 3000 · Haddonfield, NJ 08033-0968 · 856-795-2121

Middletown

Michael J. Gross · Giordano, Halleran & Ciesla · http://www.ghclaw.com · 125 Half Mile Road, Suite 300 P.O. Box 190 · Middletown, NJ 07748 · 732-741-3900

Paul Schneider · Giordano, Halleran & Ciesla · http://www.ghclaw.com · 125 Half Mile Road, Suite 300 · P.O. Box 190 · Middletown, NJ 07748 · 732-741-3900

Morristown

Dennis J. Krumholz · a · Riker, Danzig, Scherer, Hyland & Perretti · Headquarters Plaza · One Speedwell Avenue · Morristown, NJ 07962-1981 · 973-538-0800

Samuel P. Moulthrop · a · Riker, Danzig, Scherer, Hyland & Perretti · Headquarters Plaza · One Speedwell Avenue · Morristown, NJ 07962-1981 · 973-538-0800

Jeffrey B. Wagenbach · Riker, Danzig, Scherer, Hyland & Perretti · Headquarters Plaza · One Speedwell Avenue · Morristown, NJ 07962-1981 · 973-538-0800

Newark

Kevin J. Bruno · Robertson, Freilich, Bruno & Cohen · The Legal Center, Ninth Floor · One Riverfront Plaza · Newark, NJ 07102 · 973-848-2100

Lawrence W. Diamond · Duane Morris · 744 Broad Street, Suite 1200 · Newark, NJ 07102-3889 · 973-424-2000

Irvin M. Freilich · a · Robertson, Freilich, Bruno & Cohen · The Legal Center, Ninth Floor · One Riverfront Plaza · Newark, NJ 07102 · 973-848-2100

William H. Hyatt, Jr. · 2) · K&L Gates · One Newark Center, 10th Floor · Newark, NJ 07102-5285 · 973-848-4000

John H. Klock · Gibbons · http://www.gibbonslaw.com · One Gateway Center · Newark, NJ 07102-5310 · 973-596-4500

Edward F. McTiernan · Gibbons · http://www.gibbonslaw.com · One Gateway Center · Newark, NJ 07102-5310 · 973-596-4500

Brian S. Montag · K&L Gates · One Newark Center, 10th Floor · Newark, NJ 07102-5285 · 973-848-4000

Princeton

Kenneth H. Mack · Fox Rothschild · Princeton Pike Corporate Center, Building Three · 997 Lenox Drive · Princeton, NJ 08648-2311 · 609-896-3600

Steven J. Picco · 2) · Saul Ewing · 750 College Road East, Suite 100 · Princeton, NJ 08540-6617 · 609-452-3100

Jeffrey M. Pollock · Fox Rothschild · Princeton Pike Corporate Center, Building Three · 997 Lenox Drive · Princeton, NJ 08648-2311 · 609-896-3600

William L. Warren · a · Drinker Biddle & Reath · 105 College Road East, Suite 300 · P.O. Box 627 · Princeton, NJ 08542-0627 · 609-716-6500

Robbinsville

George J. Tyler · a · Tyler & Carmeli · 520 Horizon Center Boulevard · Robbinsville, NJ 08691 · 609-631-0600

Roseland

Michael Dore · Lowenstein Sandler · http://www.lowenstein.com · 65 Livingston Avenue · Roseland, NJ 07068-1791 · 973-597-2500

Richard F. Ricci · Lowenstein Sandler · http://www.lowenstein.com · 65 Livingston Avenue · Roseland, NJ 07068-1791 · 973-597-2500

Michael L. Rodburg · 2) · Lowenstein Sandler · http://www.lowenstein.com · 65 Livingston Avenue · Roseland, NJ 07068-1791 · 973-597-2500

James Stewart · Lowenstein Sandler · http://www.lowenstein.com · 65 Livingston Avenue · Roseland, NJ 07068-1791 · 973-597-2500

Somerville

Edward A. Hogan · a · Norris, McLaughlin & Marcus · http://www.nmmlaw.com · 721 Route 202-206 · P.O. Box 1018 · Somerville, NJ 08876-1018 · 908-722-0700

Voorhees

Richard M. Hluchan · Ballard Spahr Andrews & Ingersoll · Plaza 1000, Suite 500 · Main Street · Voorhees, NJ 08043-4636 · 856-761-3400

West Orange

John A. McKinney, Jr. · a · Wolff & Samson · The Offices at Crystal Lake · One Boland Drive · West Orange, NJ 07052 · 973-325-1500

Dennis M. Toft · Wolff & Samson · The Offices at Crystal Lake · One Boland Drive · West Orange, NJ 07052 · 973-325-1500

Westfield

David B. Farer · Farer Fersko · http://www.farerlaw.com · 600 South Avenue · P.O. Box 580 · Westfield, NJ 07091-0580 · 908-789-8550

Ann M. Waeger · Farer Fersko · http://www.farerlaw.com · 600 South Avenue · P.O. Box 580 · Westfield, NJ 07091-0580 · 908-789-8550

ETHICS AND PROFESSIONAL RESPONSIBILITY LAW

Cherry Hill

Carl D. Poplar · 2% · Carl D. Poplar · Building Two · 1010 Kings Highway South · Cherry Hill, NJ 08034 · 856-216-9979

Flemington

Kevin H. Michels · Michels & Hockenjos · 151 Main Street · Flemington, NJ 08822 · 908-806-4100

Hackensack

Kim D. Ringler · Kim D. Ringler · Continental Plaza III, Second Floor · 433 Hackensack Avenue · Hackensack, NJ 07601-6319 · 201-342-7100

Medford

David H. Dugan III · David H. Dugan, III · One North Main Street · Medford, NJ 08055-2445 · 609-953-1666

Metuchen

David B. Rubin · David B. Rubin · 44 Bridge Street · P.O. Box 4579 · Metuchen, NJ 08840 · 732-767-0440

Woodbridge

Frederick J. Dennehy · Wilentz, Goldman & Spitzer · http://www.wilentz.com · 90 Woodbridge Center Drive, Suite 900 · P.O. Box 10 · Woodbridge, NJ 07095-0958 · 732-636-8000

FAMILY LAW

Atlantic City

Mark Biel · Mairone, Biel, Zlotnick & Feinberg · 3201 Atlantic Avenue · Atlantic City, NJ 08401 · 609-344-1173

Denville

Patricia M. Barbarito · Einhorn Harris Ascher Barbarito Frost & Ironson · 165 East Main Street · P.O. Box 3010 · Denville, NJ 07834 · 973-627-7300

Fair Lawn

John E. Finnerty · Finnerty, Canda & Drisgula · 1717 Route 208 North · Fair Lawn, NJ 07410 · 201-845-4000

Florham Park

Hope S. Cone · Day Pitney · 200 Campus Drive · P.O. Box 1945 · Florham Park, NJ 07962-1945 · 973-966-6300

Hackensack

Charles C. Abut · a · Charles C. Abut · Court Plaza South, West Wing · 21 Main Street · Hackensack, NJ 07601 · 201-342-0404

Robert T. Corcoran · Robert T. Corcoran · http://www.robertcorcoran.com · Continental Plaza, Fifth Floor · 401 Hackensack Avenue · Hackensack, NJ 07601 · 201-342-5151

Charles M. De Fuccio · a · Rose & De Fuccio · 35 Essex Street · Hackensack, NJ 07601 · 201-488-7800

Haddonfield

Lee M. Hymerling · 2% · Archer & Greiner · http://www.archerlaw.com · One Centennial Square · 56 Haddon Avenue · P.O. Box 3000 · Haddonfield, NJ 08033-0968 · 856-795-2121

William J. Thompson · Archer & Greiner · http://www.archerlaw.com · One Centennial Square · 56 Haddon Avenue · P.O. Box 3000 · Haddonfield, NJ 08033-0968 · 856-795-2121

Lawrenceville

Robert J. Durst II · a · Stark & Stark · 993 Lenox Drive, Building Two · P.O. Box 5315 · Lawrenceville, NJ 08543 · 609-896-9060

Livingston

Gary N. Skoloff · 2% · Skoloff & Wolfe · 293 Eisenhower Parkway, Suite 390 · Livingston, NJ 07039 · 973-992-0900

Morris Plains

Sheldon M. Simon · 2% · Simon & Enright · 555 Speedwell Avenue · Morris Plains, NJ 07950 · 973-538-2266

Morristown

Laurence J. Cutler · a · Cutler, Simeone, Townsend, Tomaio & Newmark · 1776 On The Green, Seventh Floor · 67 East Park Place · P.O. Box 1119 · Morristown, NJ 07962-1119 · 973-539-0075

Francis W. Donahue · Donahue, Hagan, Klein, Newsome & O'Donnell · http://www.dhkno.com · 360 Mount Kemble Avenue · Morristown, NJ 07960 · 973-467-5556

Ocean City

Richard A. Russell · Richard A. Russell · 117 Atlantic Avenue · P.O. Box 30 · Ocean City, NJ 08226 · 609-398-1900

Pennington

Barbara Ulrichsen · Ulrichsen, Rosen & Freed · http://www.urf-law.com · Two Tree Farm Road, Suite B-100 · Pennington, NJ 08534 · 609-730-3850

Princeton

Mark Z. Segal · Fox Rothschild · Princeton Pike Corporate Center, Building Three · 997 Lenox Drive · Princeton, NJ 08648-2311 · 609-896-3600

Roseland

Edward S. Snyder · a · Weinstein Snyder Lindemann Sarno · http://www.familylawnj.com · 101 Eisenhower Parkway · Roseland, NJ 07068 · 973-403-6000

Mark H. Sobel · Greenbaum, Rowe, Smith & Davis · http://www.greenbaumlaw.com · 75 Livingston Avenue · Roseland, NJ 07068-3701 · 973-535-1600

Jeffrey P. Weinstein · a · Weinstein Snyder Lindemann Sarno · http://www.familylawnj.com · 101 Eisenhower Parkway · Roseland, NJ 07068 · 973-403-6000

Somerville

Richard A. Norris · a · Norris, McLaughlin & Marcus · http://www.nmmlaw.com · 721 Route 202-206 · P.O. Box 1018 · Somerville, NJ 08876-1018 · 908-722-0700

Michael J. Stanton · Norris, McLaughlin & Marcus · http://www.nmmlaw.com · 721 Route 202-206 · P.O. Box 1018 · Somerville, NJ 08876-1018 · 908-722-0700

John J. Trombadore · a · John J. Trombadore · 31 East High Street · Somerville, NJ 08876 · 908-927-0200

Summit

Lizanne Ceconi · Ceconi & Cheifetz · 480 Morris Avenue · Summit, NJ 07901 · 908-273-6300

Cary B. Cheifetz · Ceconi & Cheifetz · 480 Morris Avenue · Summit, NJ 07901 · 908-273-6300

Toms River

Frank A. Louis · a · Frank A. Louis · Toms River Corporate Center, Suite 212 · 1144 Hooper Avenue · P.O. Box 461 · Toms River, NJ 08754-0461 · 732-349-0600

Warren

Frederick J. Sikora · Frederick J. Sikora · 51 Mount Bethel Road · P.O. Box 4623 · Warren, NJ 07059-0623 · 908-755-8700

Woodbridge

John P. Paone, Jr. · Paone & Zaleski · http://www.paone-zaleski.com · 146 Green Street · P.O. Box 249 · Woodbridge, NJ 07095-0249 · 732-750-9797

Paul A. Rowe · a · Greenbaum, Rowe, Smith & Davis · http://www.greenbaumlaw.com · Metro Corporate Campus One · 99 Wood Avenue South · P.O. Box 5600 · Woodbridge, NJ 08830-2712 · 732-549-5600

Noel S. Tonneman · Wilentz, Goldman & Spitzer · http://www.wilentz.com · 90 Woodbridge Center Drive, Suite 900 · P.O. Box 10 · Woodbridge, NJ 07095-0958 · 732-636-8000

Charles F. Vuotto, Jr. · Wilentz, Goldman & Spitzer · http://www.wilentz.com · 90 Woodbridge Center Drive, Suite 900 · P.O. Box 10 · Woodbridge, NJ 07095-0958 · 732-636-8000

David M. Wildstein · 2% · Wilentz, Goldman & Spitzer · http://www.wilentz.com · 90 Woodbridge Center Drive, Suite 900 · P.O. Box 10 · Woodbridge, NJ 07095-0958 · 732-636-8000

FAMILY LAW MEDIATION

Hackensack

Charles C. Abut · a · Charles C. Abut · Court Plaza South, West Wing · 21 Main Street · Hackensack, NJ 07601 · 201-342-0404

Morristown

Herbert S. Glickman · Cutler, Simeone, Townsend, Tomaio & Newmark · 1776 On The Green, Seventh Floor · 67 East Park Place · P.O. Box 1119 · Morristown, NJ 07962-1119 · 973-539-0075

Roseland

Melvin S. Whitken · Weinstein Snyder Lindemann Sarno · http://www.familylawnj.com · 101 Eisenhower Parkway · Roseland, NJ 07068 · 973-403-6000

Skillman

Donna P. Legband · Altman, Legband & Mayrides · 37 Tamarack Circle · Skillman, NJ 08558 · 609-921-8070

Somerville

Richard A. Norris · a · Norris, McLaughlin & Marcus · http://www.nmmlaw.com · 721 Route 202-206 · P.O. Box 1018 · Somerville, NJ 08876-1018 · 908-722-0700

John J. Trombadore · a · John J. Trombadore · 31 East High Street · Somerville, NJ 08876 · 908-927-0200

Warren

Amy Zylman Shimalla · Copeland, Shimalla & Wechsler · 101 Town Center, Suite 117 · P.O. Box 4643 · Warren, NJ 07059-0643 · 908-753-3833

FIRST AMENDMENT LAW

Florham Park

Bruce S. Rosen · McCusker, Anselmi, Rosen, Carvelli & Walsh · http://www.marcw.com · 210 Park Avenue, Suite 301 · Florham Park, NJ 07932 · 973-635-6300

Hackensack

Peter G. Banta · a · Winne, Banta, Hetherington, Basralian & Kahn · Court Plaza South, East Wing, Suite 101 · 21 Main Street · P.O. Box 647 · Hackensack, NJ 07601-0647 · 201-487-3800

Haddonfield

John C. Connell · a · Archer & Greiner · http://www.archerlaw.com · One Centennial Square · 56 Haddon Avenue · P.O. Box 3000 · Haddonfield, NJ 08033-0968 · 856-795-2121

Lyndhurst

Thomas J. Cafferty · a · Scarinci & Hollenbeck · 1100 Valley Brook Avenue · P.O. Box 790 · Lyndhurst, NJ 07071-0790 · 201-896-4100

Newark

Frank Askin · Frank Askin · Rutgers Law School · 123 Washington Street · Newark, NJ 07102-3192 · 973-353-5687

Richard M. Eittreim · a · McCarter & English · Four Gateway Center · 100 Mulberry Street · Newark, NJ 07102 · 973-622-4444

John J. Gibbons · a · Gibbons · http://www.gibbonslaw.com · One Gateway Center · Newark, NJ 07102-5310 · 973-596-4500

Donald A. Robinson · 2% · Robinson & Livelli · Two Penn Plaza East, 11th Floor · Newark, NJ 07105-2237 · 973-690-5400

Princeton

Richard A. Ragsdale · a · Carchman, Sochor, Ragsdale & Cohen · Montgomery Knoll · 37 Tamarack Circle · Princeton, NJ 08558 · 609-924-7179

Roseland

Peter L. Skolnik · Lowenstein Sandler · http://www.lowenstein.com · 65 Livingston Avenue · Roseland, NJ 07068-1791 · 973-597-2500

Westmont

Warren W. Faulk · a · Brown & Connery · 360 Haddon Avenue · P.O. Box 539 · Westmont, NJ 08108 · 856-854-8900

Wildwood

Frank L. Corrado · Barry, Corrado, Grassi & Gibson · 2700 Pacific Avenue · Wildwood, NJ 08260 · 609-729-1333

FRANCHISE LAW

Florham Park

Richard H. Brown III · Day Pitney · 200 Campus Drive · P.O. Box 1945 · Florham Park, NJ 07962-1945 · 973-966-6300

Dennis R. LaFiura · Day Pitney · 200 Campus Drive · P.O. Box 1945 · Florham Park, NJ 07962-1945 · 973-966-6300

David S. Sager · Day Pitney · 200 Campus Drive · P.O. Box 1945 · Florham Park, NJ 07962-1945 · 973-966-6300

Newark

H. John Schank II · Gibbons · http://www.gibbonslaw.com · One Gateway Center · Newark, NJ 07102-5310 · 973-596-4500

Voorhees

Benjamin A. Levin · Ballard Spahr Andrews & Ingersoll · Plaza 1000, Suite 500 · Main Street · Voorhees, NJ 08043-4636 · 856-761-3400

GAMING LAW

Atlantic City

Nicholas Casiello, Jr. · Fox Rothschild · Midtown Building, Suite 400 · 1301 Atlantic Avenue · Atlantic City, NJ 08401-7212 · 609-348-4515

Lloyd D. Levenson · Cooper Levenson · 1125 Atlantic Avenue · Atlantic City, NJ 08401 · 609-344-3161

Guy S. Michael · Michael & Carroll · 1125 Atlantic Avenue, Suite 619 · Atlantic City, NJ 08401 · 609-441-9292

Cherry Hill

Hersh Kozlov · WolfBlock · http://wolfblock.com · 1940 Route 70 East, Suite 200 · Cherry Hill, NJ 08003 856-424-8200

Linwood

Scott N. Silver · Scott N. Silver · 524 Maple Avenue · Linwood, NJ 08221 · 609-927-0800

Newark

Clive S. Cummis · 2% · Sills Cummis & Gross · http://www.sillscummis.com · The Legal Center · One Riverfront Plaza · Newark, NJ 07102-5400 · 973-643-7000

North Haledon

Frank Catania · Catania Consulting Group · 909 Belmont Avenue · North Haledon, NJ 07508 · 973-427-7990

Joseph M. Kelly · Catania Consulting Group · 909 Belmont Avenue · North Haledon, NJ 07508 · 973-427-7990

Trenton

Paul O'Gara · Sterns & Weinroth · One State Street Square Office Building, Suite 1400 · 50 West State Street · P.O. Box 1298 · Trenton, NJ 08607-1298 · 609-392-2100

GOVERNMENT RELATIONS LAW

Morristown

John M. Pellecchia · Riker, Danzig, Scherer, Hyland & Perretti · Headquarters Plaza · One Speedwell Avenue · Morristown, NJ 07962-1981 · 973-538-0800

Princeton

William F. Megna · Megna Law Firm · 601 Ewing Street, Suite C-8 · Princeton, NJ 08540 · 609-430-1414

Trenton

David J. Pascrell · Gibbons · http://www.gibbonslaw.com · The Lutine House · 224 West State Street · Trenton, NJ 08608-1002 · 609-394-5300

Mary Kathryn Roberts · Riker, Danzig, Scherer, Hyland & Perretti · 50 West State Street, Suite 1010 · Trenton, NJ 08608-1220 · 609-396-2121

Rich Van Wagener · Sterns & Weinroth · One State Street Square Office Building, Suite 1400 · 50 West State Street · P.O. Box 1298 · Trenton, NJ 08607-1298 · 609-392-2100

HEALTH CARE LAW

Florham Park

Daniel F. O'Connell · a · Drinker Biddle & Reath · 500 Campus Drive · Florham Park, NJ 07932-1047 · 973-360-1100

Middletown

Frank R. Ciesla · a · Giordano, Halleran & Ciesla · http://www.ghclaw.com · 125 Half Mile Road, Suite 300 · P.O. Box 190 · Middletown, NJ 07748 · 732-741-3900

Sharlene Hunt · Giordano, Halleran & Ciesla · http://www.ghclaw.com · 125 Half Mile Road, Suite 300 · P.O. Box 190 · Middletown, NJ 07748 · 732-741-3900

New Brunswick

Michael J. Baker · Hoagland, Longo, Moran, Dunst & Doukas · 40 Paterson Street · P.O. Box 480 · New Brunswick, NJ 08903 · 732-545-4717

Princeton

Phillip E. Griffin · Fox Rothschild · Princeton Pike Corporate Center, Building Three · 997 Lenox Drive Princeton, NJ 08648-2311 · 609-896-3600

Murray J. Klein · a · Reed Smith · Princeton Forrestal Village, Suite 250 · 136 Main Street · P.O. Box 7839 · Princeton, NJ 08543-7839 · 609-987-0050

Jonathan D. Weiner · a · Fox Rothschild · Princeton Pike Corporate Center, Building Three · 997 Lenox Drive · Princeton, NJ 08648-2311 · 609-896-3600

Roseland

Burton L. Eichler · a · WolfBlock · http://wolfblock.com · 101 Eisenhower Parkway, Suite 200 · Roseland, NJ 07068 · 973-228-5700

John D. Fanburg · a · WolfBlock · http://wolfblock.com · 101 Eisenhower Parkway, Suite 200 · Roseland, NJ 07068 · 973-228-5700

Joseph M. Gorrell · a · WolfBlock · http://wolfblock.com · 101 Eisenhower Parkway, Suite 200 · Roseland, NJ 07068 · 973-228-5700

Lisa Deitsch Taylor · Stern & Kilcullen · 75 Livingston Avenue, Second Floor · P.O. Box 430 · Roseland, NJ 07068 · 973-535-1900

Somerville

J. Anthony Manger · a · Norris, McLaughlin & Marcus · http://www.nmmlaw.com · 721 Route 202-206 · P.O. Box 1018 · Somerville, NJ 08876-1018 · 908-722-0700

Ira S. Novak · a · Norris, McLaughlin & Marcus · http://www.nmmlaw.com · 721 Route 202-206 · P.O. Box 1018 · Somerville, NJ 08876-1018 · 908-722-0700

Warren

James V. Hetzel · Kalison, McBride, Jackson & Murphy · 25 Independence Boulevard, Suite 401 · P.O. Box 4990 · Warren, NJ 07059 · 908-647-4600

John Zen Jackson · Kalison, McBride, Jackson & Murphy · 25 Independence Boulevard, Suite 401 · P.O. Box 4990 · Warren, NJ 07059 · 908-647-4600

Michael J. Kalison · a · Kalison, McBride, Jackson & Murphy · 25 Independence Boulevard, Suite 401 · P.O. Box 4990 · Warren, NJ 07059 · 908-647-4600

Andrew F. McBride III · Kalison, McBride, Jackson & Murphy · 25 Independence Boulevard, Suite 401 · P.O. Box 4990 · Warren, NJ 07059 · 908-647-4600

James A. Robertson · Kalison, McBride, Jackson & Murphy · 25 Independence Boulevard, Suite 401 · P.O. Box 4990 · Warren, NJ 07059 · 908-647-4600

Woodbridge

Francis V. Bonello · Wilentz, Goldman & Spitzer · http://www.wilentz.com · 90 Woodbridge Center Drive, Suite 900 · P.O. Box 10 · Woodbridge, NJ 07095-0958 · 732-636-8000

Michael F. Schaff · Wilentz, Goldman & Spitzer · http://www.wilentz.com · 90 Woodbridge Center Drive, Suite 900 · P.O. Box 10 · Woodbridge, NJ 07095-0958 · 732-636-8000

IMMIGRATION LAW

Clifton

William E. McAlvanah · a · Hilberth & McAlvanah · 790 Bloomfield Avenue, Suite A-9 · Clifton, NJ 07012 · 973-773-4748

Matawan

Jonathan C. Adams · Fragomen, Del Rey, Bernsen & Loewy · http://www.fragomen.com · 90 Matawan Road · P.O. Box 2001 · Matawan, NJ 07747 · 732-862-5000

Lance Kaplan · Fragomen, Del Rey, Bernsen & Loewy · http://www.fragomen.com · 90 Matawan Road · P.O. Box 2001 · Matawan, NJ 07747 · 732-862-5000

Gwendolyn M. Robosson · Fragomen, Del Rey, Bernsen & Loewy · http://www.fragomen.com · 90 Matawan Road · P.O. Box 2001 · Matawan, NJ 07747 · 732-862-5000

Susan B. Storch · Fragomen, Del Rey, Bernsen & Loewy · http://www.fragomen.com · 90 Matawan Road P.O. Box 2001 · Matawan, NJ 07747 · 732-862-5000

Newark

Neil S. Dornbaum · a · Dornbaum & Peregoy · http://www.immigrationlawyersnj.com · 744 Broad Street, Suite 1700 · Newark, NJ 07102 · 973-623-7777

Regis Fernandez · Law Office of Regis Fernandez · 18 Green Street, Third Floor · Newark, NJ 07102 · 973-297-0002

Robert Frank · a · Frank & York · http://immigrationlawnj.com · 60 Park Place, Suite 1304 · Newark, NJ 07102 · 973-642-1111

David M. Grunblatt · a · Proskauer Rose · http://www.proskauer.com · One Newark Center · Newark, NJ 07102-5211 · 973-274-3200

Thomas E. Moseley · a · Thomas E. Moseley · One Gateway Center, Suite 2600 · Newark, NJ 07102-5397 · 973-622-8176

Joseph J. Parlapiano · Joseph J. Parlapiano · 54 Barbara Street · Newark, NJ 07105 · 973-589-6611

Kathleen M. Peregoy · Dornbaum & Peregoy · http://www.immigrationlawyersnj.com · 744 Broad Street, Suite 1700 · Newark, NJ 07102 · 973-623-7777

Edwin R. Rubin · a · Law Office of Edwin Rubin · 744 Broad Street, 16th Floor · Newark, NJ 07102 · 973-735-2730

Harlan G. York · Frank & York · http://immigrationlawnj.com · 60 Park Place, Suite 1304 · Newark, NJ 07102 · 973-642-1111

Paterson

Edward Shulman · The Shulman Law Group · 152 Market Street, Suite 300 · Paterson, NJ 07505-1710 · 973-345-1151

Voorhees

Shereen C. Chen · Ballard Spahr Andrews & Ingersoll · Plaza 1000, Suite 500 · Main Street · Voorhees, NJ 08043-4636 · 856-761-3400

INFORMATION TECHNOLOGY LAW

Cliffside Park

Richard L. Field · Richard L. Field · 755 Anderson Avenue, Suite 4-A · Cliffside Park, NJ 07010 · 201-941-8015

Florham Park

Michael J. Dunne · Day Pitney · 200 Campus Drive · P.O. Box 1945 · Florham Park, NJ 07962-1945 · 973-966-6300

Newark

Scott S. Christie · McCarter & English · Four Gateway Center · 100 Mulberry Street · Newark, NJ 07102 973-622-4444

William J. Heller · McCarter & English · Four Gateway Center · 100 Mulberry Street · Newark, NJ 07102 · 973-622-4444

Charles R. Merrill · McCarter & English · Four Gateway Center · 100 Mulberry Street · Newark, NJ 07102 · 973-622-4444

INSURANCE LAW

Basking Ridge

Gary S. Kull · Carroll, McNulty & Kull · 120 Mountainview Boulevard · Basking Ridge, NJ 07920 · 908-848-6300

Bedminster

Michael F. O'Neill · Purcell, Ries, Shannon, Mulcahy & O'Neill · Crossroads Buisness Center · One Pluckemin Way · P.O. Box 754 · Bedminster, NJ 07921 · 908-658-3800

Clark

Eugene Killian, Jr. · Killian & Salisbury · 77 Brant Avenue, Suite 115 · Clark, NJ 07066 · 732-827-8600

Carl A. Salisbury · Killian & Salisbury · 77 Brant Avenue, Suite 115 · Clark, NJ 07066 · 732-827-8600

Cranberry

Edward M. Napierkowski · Colliau, Elenius, Murphy, Carluccio, Keener And Morrow · 1249 South River Road, Suite 300-A · Cranberry, NJ 08812 · 609-395-5500

Florham Park

James M. Altieri · Drinker Biddle & Reath · 500 Campus Drive · Florham Park, NJ 07932-1047 · 973-360-1100

Philip R. Sellinger · Greenberg Traurig · http://www.gtlaw.com · 200 Park Avenue · P.O. Box 677 · Florham Park, NJ 07932-0677 · 973-360-7900

Mark M. Tallmadge · Bressler, Amery & Ross · http://www.bressler.com · 325 Columbia Turnpike · Florham Park, NJ 07932 · 973-514-1200

Hackensack

Brian R. Ade · Rivkin Radler · Court Plaza South, First Floor, West Wing, Suite 158 · 21 Main Street · Hackensack, NJ 07601 · 201-287-2460

Haddonfield

Ellis I. Medoway · Archer & Greiner · http://www.archerlaw.com · One Centennial Square · 56 Haddon Avenue · P.O. Box 3000 · Haddonfield, NJ 08033-0968 · 856-795-2121

Livingston

Henry G. Morgan · Morgan Melhuish Abrutyn · 651 West Mount Pleasant Avenue, Suite 200 · Livingston, NJ 07039 · 973-994-2500

Montclair

Antonio D. Favetta · Garrity, Graham, Murphy, Garofalo & Flinn · One Lackawanna Plaza · Montclair, NJ 07042 · 973-509-7500

Francis X. Garrity · Garrity, Graham, Murphy, Garofalo & Flinn · One Lackawanna Plaza · Montclair, NJ 07042 · 973-509-7500

Morristown

John M. Bowens · Schenck, Price, Smith & King · 10 Washington Street · P.O. Box 905 · Morristown, NJ 07963-0905 · 973-539-1000

Michael H. Cohen · Schwartz Simon Edelstein Celso & Kessler · 44 Whippany Road, Suite 210 · P.O. Box 2355 · Morristown, NJ 07962 · 973-301-0001

Kevin T. Coughlin · Coughlin Duffy · 350 Mount Kemble Avenue · P.O. Box 1917 · Morristown, NJ 07962-1917 · 973-267-0058

John T. Coyne · McElroy, Deutsch, Mulvaney & Carpenter · http://www.mdmc-law.com · 1300 Mount Kemble Avenue · P.O. Box 2075 · Morristown, NJ 07962-2075 · 973-993-8100

James R. Greene · Schenck, Price, Smith & King · 10 Washington Street · P.O. Box 905 · Morristown, NJ 07963-0905 · 973-539-1000

Lance J. Kalik · Riker, Danzig, Scherer, Hyland & Perretti · Headquarters Plaza · One Speedwell Avenue Morristown, NJ 07962-1981 · 973-538-0800

Shawn L. Kelly · Riker, Danzig, Scherer, Hyland & Perretti · Headquarters Plaza · One Speedwell Avenue · Morristown, NJ 07962-1981 · 973-538-0800

Robert W. Mauriello, Jr. · Graham, Curtin & Sheridan · Four Headquarters Plaza North Tower, Sixth Floor · P.O. Box 1991 · Morristown, NJ 07962-1991 · 973-292-1700

Brian E. O'Donnell · Riker, Danzig, Scherer, Hyland & Perretti · Headquarters Plaza · One Speedwell Avenue · Morristown, NJ 07962-1981 · 973-538-0800

Loren L. Pierce · McElroy, Deutsch, Mulvaney & Carpenter · http://www.mdmc-law.com · 1300 Mount Kemble Avenue · P.O. Box 2075 · Morristown, NJ 07962-2075 · 973-993-8100

Robert J. Re · Coughlin Duffy · 350 Mount Kemble Avenue · P.O. Box 1917 · Morristown, NJ 07962-1917 · 973-267-0058

J. Michael Riordan · McElroy, Deutsch, Mulvaney & Carpenter · http://www.mdmc-law.com · 1300 Mount Kemble Avenue · P.O. Box 2075 · Morristown, NJ 07962-2075 · 973-993-8100

Kevin E. Wolff · Coughlin Duffy · 350 Mount Kemble Avenue · P.O. Box 1917 · Morristown, NJ 07962-1917 · 973-267-0058

Mount Laurel

Jerrald J. Hochman · Siegel & Park · 533 Fellowship Road, Suite 120 · Mount Laurel, NJ 08054 · 856-380-8900

Newark

Lynda A. Bennett · Robertson, Freilich, Bruno & Cohen · The Legal Center, Ninth Floor · One Riverfront Plaza · Newark, NJ 07102 · 973-848-2100

Kevin J. Bruno · Robertson, Freilich, Bruno & Cohen · The Legal Center, Ninth Floor · One Riverfront Plaza · Newark, NJ 07102 · 973-848-2100

Jeffrey A. Cohen · Robertson, Freilich, Bruno & Cohen · The Legal Center, Ninth Floor · One Riverfront Plaza · Newark, NJ 07102 · 973-848-2100

Brian J. Coyle · Cozen O'Connor · One Newark Center, Suite 2600 · Newark, NJ 07102 · 973-353-8400

David R. Gross · 2% · Saiber · One Gateway Center, 13th Floor · Newark, NJ 07102 · 973-622-3333

Steven E. Gross · a · Sills Cummis & Gross · http://www.sillscummis.com · The Legal Center · One Riverfront Plaza · Newark, NJ 07102-5400 · 973-643-7000

Gregory H. Horowitz · McCarter & English · Four Gateway Center · 100 Mulberry Street · Newark, NJ 07102 · 973-622-4444

Donald W. Kiel · K&L Gates · One Newark Center, 10th Floor · Newark, NJ 07102-5285 · 973-848-4000

Anthony P. La Rocco · K&L Gates · One Newark Center, 10th Floor · Newark, NJ 07102-5285 · 973-848-4000

William B. McGuire · 2% · Tompkins, McGuire, Wachenfeld & Barry · Four Gateway Center, Fifth Floor 100 Mulberry Street · Newark, NJ 07102-4070 · 973-622-3000

Arnold L. Natali · McCarter & English · Four Gateway Center · 100 Mulberry Street · Newark, NJ 07102 973-622-4444

Robert F. Priestly · Mendes & Mount · One Newark Center, 19th Floor · Newark, NJ 07102 · 973-639-7300

Thomas F. Quinn · Wilson Elser Moskowitz Edelman & Dicker · 33 Washington Street · Newark, NJ 07102-3017 · 973-624-0800

Gita F. Rothschild · McCarter & English · Four Gateway Center · 100 Mulberry Street · Newark, NJ 07102 · 973-622-4444

Karol Corbin Walker · LeClair Ryan · Two Penn Plaza East · Newark, NJ 07105 · 973-491-3600

Brian J. Whiteman · Wilson Elser Moskowitz Edelman & Dicker · 33 Washington Street · Newark, NJ 07102-3017 · 973-624-0800

Parsippany

Stefano V. Calogero · Cuyler Burk · Parsippany Corporate Center, Third Floor · Four Century Drive · Parsippany, NJ 07054 · 973-734-3200

Stephen D. Cuyler · Cuyler Burk · Parsippany Corporate Center, Third Floor · Four Century Drive · Parsippany, NJ 07054 · 973-734-3200

Princeton

Thomas E. Hastings · Smith, Stratton, Wise, Heher & Brennan · Two Research Way · Princeton, NJ 08540 · 609-924-6000

Wendy L. Mager · Smith, Stratton, Wise, Heher & Brennan · Two Research Way · Princeton, NJ 08540 · 609-924-6000

Thomas E. Schorr · Smith, Stratton, Wise, Heher & Brennan · Two Research Way · Princeton, NJ 08540 609-924-6000

Virginia G. White · Blank Rome · 301 Carnegie Center, Third Floor · Princeton, NJ 08540 · 609-750-7700

Roseland

Robert D. Chesler · a · Lowenstein Sandler · http://www.lowenstein.com · 65 Livingston Avenue · Roseland, NJ 07068-1791 · 973-597-2500

Daren S. McNally · Connell Foley · 85 Livingston Avenue · Roseland, NJ 07068 · 973-535-0500

Short Hills

Robert F. Cossolini · Budd Larner · http://www.buddlarner.com · 150 John F. Kennedy Parkway, Third Floor · Short Hills, NJ 07078-2703 · 973-379-4800

Joseph J. Schiavone · Budd Larner · http://www.buddlarner.com · 150 John F. Kennedy Parkway, Third Floor · Short Hills, NJ 07078-2703 · 973-379-4800

Warren

Sheryl Mintz Goski · Herold and Haines · http://www.heroldhaines.com · 25 Independence Boulevard · Warren, NJ 07059-6747 · 908-647-1022

INTELLECTUAL PROPERTY LAW

Morristown

Robert J. Schoenberg · Riker, Danzig, Scherer, Hyland & Perretti · Headquarters Plaza · One Speedwell Avenue · Morristown, NJ 07962-1981 · 973-538-0800

Newark

David E. DeLorenzi · Gibbons · http://www.gibbonslaw.com · One Gateway Center · Newark, NJ 07102-5310 · 973-596-4500

William J. Heller · McCarter & English · Four Gateway Center · 100 Mulberry Street · Newark, NJ 07102 · 973-622-4444

Short Hills

Andrew J. Miller · Budd Larner · http://www.buddlarner.com · 150 John F. Kennedy Parkway, Third Floor · Short Hills, NJ 07078-2703 · 973-379-4800

Somerville

William R. Robinson · Norris, McLaughlin & Marcus · http://www.nmmlaw.com · 721 Route 202-206 · P.O. Box 1018 · Somerville, NJ 08876-1018 · 908-722-0700

Westfield

Sidney David · a · Lerner, David, Littenberg, Krumholz & Mentlik · 600 South Avenue West · Westfield, NJ 07090-1497 · 908-654-5000

Charles P. Kennedy · Lerner, David, Littenberg, Krumholz & Mentlik · 600 South Avenue West · Westfield, NJ 07090-1497 · 908-654-5000

Arnold H. Krumholz · a · Lerner, David, Littenberg, Krumholz & Mentlik · 600 South Avenue West · Westfield, NJ 07090-1497 · 908-654-5000

Joseph S. Littenberg · a · Lerner, David, Littenberg, Krumholz & Mentlik · 600 South Avenue West · Westfield, NJ 07090-1497 · 908-654-5000

William L. Mentlik · a · Lerner, David, Littenberg, Krumholz & Mentlik · 600 South Avenue West · Westfield, NJ 07090-1497 · 908-654-5000

Woodbridge

Brett R. Harris · Wilentz, Goldman & Spitzer · http://www.wilentz.com · 90 Woodbridge Center Drive, Suite 900 · P.O. Box 10 · Woodbridge, NJ 07095-0958 · 732-636-8000

INTERNATIONAL TRADE AND FINANCE LAW

Hamilton

Steven M. Richman · Duane Morris · 100 American Metro Boulevard, Suite 150 · P.O. Box 5203 · Hamilton, NJ 08543-5203 · 609-631-2400

Newark

Steven E. Gross · a · Sills Cummis & Gross · http://www.sillscummis.com · The Legal Center · One Riverfront Plaza · Newark, NJ 07102-5400 · 973-643-7000

Woodbridge

Stuart A. Hoberman · a · Wilentz, Goldman & Spitzer · http://www.wilentz.com · 90 Woodbridge Center Drive, Suite 900 · P.O. Box 10 · Woodbridge, NJ 07095-0958 · 732-636-8000

Cherry Hill

James Katz · a · Spear Wilderman · 1040 North Kings Highway, Suite 202 · Cherry Hill, NJ 08034 · 856-482-8799

Robert F. O'Brien · 2) · O'Brien, Belland & Bushinsky · 1526 Berlin Road · Cherry Hill, NJ 08003 · 856-795-2181

Florham Park

Michael T. Bissinger · Day Pitney · 200 Campus Drive · P.O. Box 1945 · Florham Park, NJ 07962-1945 · 973-966-6300

Patrick J. McCarthy · Day Pitney · 200 Campus Drive · P.O. Box 1945 · Florham Park, NJ 07962-1945 · 973-966-6300

Gregory C. Parliman · Day Pitney · 200 Campus Drive · P.O. Box 1945 · Florham Park, NJ 07962-1945 · 973-966-6300

John A. Ridley · Drinker Biddle & Reath · 500 Campus Drive · Florham Park, NJ 07932-1047 · 973-360-1100

Mary B. Rogers · Day Pitney · 200 Campus Drive · P.O. Box 1945 · Florham Park, NJ 07962-1945 · 973-966-6300

Fort Lee

Stephen H. Kahn · Kahn Opton · One Parker Plaza · Fort Lee, NJ 07024 · 201-947-9200

Hackensack

Steven I. Adler · Cole, Schotz, Meisel, Forman & Leonard · http://www.coleschotz.com · Court Plaza North, Fourth Floor · 25 Main Street · Hackensack, NJ 07601 · 201-489-3000

Kenilworth

David Grossman · Cohen, Leder, Montalbano & Grossman · 1700 Galloping Hill Road, Third Floor · Kenilworth, NJ 07033 · 908-298-8800

Bruce D. Leder · a · Cohen, Leder, Montalbano & Grossman · 1700 Galloping Hill Road, Third Floor · Kenilworth, NJ 07033 · 908-298-8800

Paul A. Montalbano · 2) · Cohen, Leder, Montalbano & Grossman · 1700 Galloping Hill Road, Third Floor · Kenilworth, NJ 07033 · 908-298-8800

Lawrenceville

Sidney H. Lehmann · Szaferman, Lakind, Blumstein, Blader & Lehmann · Quakerbridge Executive Center, Suite 200 · 101 Grovers Mill Road · Lawrenceville, NJ 08648 · 609-275-0400

Liberty Corner

Mark J. Blunda · Apruzzese, McDermott, Mastro & Murphy · Somerset Hills Corporate Center · 25 Independence Boulevard · P.O. Box 112 · Liberty Corner, NJ 07938 · 908-580-1776

Robert T. Clarke · Apruzzese, McDermott, Mastro & Murphy · Somerset Hills Corporate Center · 25 Independence Boulevard · P.O. Box 112 · Liberty Corner, NJ 07938 · 908-580-1776

Maurice J. Nelligan, Jr. · a · Apruzzese, McDermott, Mastro & Murphy · Somerset Hills Corporate Center · 25 Independence Boulevard · P.O. Box 112 · Liberty Corner, NJ 07938 · 908-580-1776

Manasquan

Douglas S. Bramley · McMoran, O'Connor & Bramley · Ramshorn Executive Centre, Building D, Suite D-1 · 2399 Highway 34 · Manasquan, NJ 08736 · 732-223-7711

Bruce P. McMoran · McMoran, O'Connor & Bramley · Ramshorn Executive Centre, Building D, Suite D-1 · 2399 Highway 34 · Manasquan, NJ 08736 · 732-223-7711

Michael F. O'Connor · McMoran, O'Connor & Bramley · Ramshorn Executive Centre, Building D, Suite D-1 · 2399 Highway 34 · Manasquan, NJ 08736 · 732-223-7711

Montclair

Neil Mullin · a · Smith Mullin · http://www.smithmullin-law.com · 240 Claremont Avenue · Montclair, NJ 07042 · 973-783-7607

Nancy Erika Smith · 2) · Smith Mullin · http://www.smithmullin-law.com · 240 Claremont Avenue · Montclair, NJ 07042 · 973-783-7607

Moorestown

Richard M. Schall · Schall & Barasch · 110 Marter Avenue, Suite 302 · Moorestown, NJ 08057 · 856-914-9200

Morristown

Domenick Carmagnola · a · Carmagnola & Ritardi · 60 Washington Street · Morristown, NJ 07960 · 973-267-4445

Mark Diana · Ogletree Deakins · http://www.ogletreedeakins.com · 10 Madison Avenue, Suite 402 · Morristown, NJ 07960 · 973-656-1600

Carmen J. DiMaria · Ogletree Deakins · http://www.ogletreedeakins.com · 10 Madison Avenue, Suite 402 · Morristown, NJ 07960 · 973-656-1600

Stephen J. Edelstein · Schwartz Simon Edelstein Celso & Kessler · 44 Whippany Road, Suite 210 · P.O. Box 2355 · Morristown, NJ 07962 · 973-301-0001

Michael K. Furey · Riker, Danzig, Scherer, Hyland & Perretti · Headquarters Plaza · One Speedwell Avenue · Morristown, NJ 07962-1981 · 973-538-0800

Peter O. Hughes · Ogletree Deakins · http://www.ogletreedeakins.com · 10 Madison Avenue, Suite 402 · Morristown, NJ 07960 · 973-656-1600

Leslie Ann Lajewski · Coughlin Duffy · 350 Mount Kemble Avenue · P.O. Box 1917 · Morristown, NJ 07962-1917 · 973-267-0058

Christopher P. Lenzo · Green, Savits & Lenzo · http://www.greensavits.com · 35 Airport Road · Morristown, NJ 07960 · 973-695-7777

Sharon Margello · Ogletree Deakins · http://www.ogletreedeakins.com · 10 Madison Avenue, Suite 402 · Morristown, NJ 07960 · 973-656-1600

Richard C. Mariani · a · Ogletree Deakins · http://www.ogletreedeakins.com · 10 Madison Avenue, Suite 402 · Morristown, NJ 07960 · 973-656-1600

Scott A. Ohnegian · Riker, Danzig, Scherer, Hyland & Perretti · Headquarters Plaza · One Speedwell Avenue · Morristown, NJ 07962-1981 · 973-538-0800

John J. Peirano · a · McElroy, Deutsch, Mulvaney & Carpenter · http://www.mdmc-law.com · 1300 Mount Kemble Avenue · P.O. Box 2075 · Morristown, NJ 07962-2075 · 973-993-8100

J. Michael Riordan · McElroy, Deutsch, Mulvaney & Carpenter · http://www.mdmc-law.com · 1300 Mount Kemble Avenue · P.O. Box 2075 · Morristown, NJ 07962-2075 · 973-993-8100

Lawrence S. Schwartz · Schwartz Simon Edelstein Celso & Kessler · 44 Whippany Road, Suite 210 · P.O. Box 2355 · Morristown, NJ 07962 · 973-301-0001

Patrick M. Stanton · a · Ogletree Deakins · http://www.ogletreedeakins.com · 10 Madison Avenue, Suite 402 · Morristown, NJ 07960 · 973-656-1600

Mount Laurel

Steven R. Cohen · a · Selikoff & Cohen · 307 Fellowship Road, Suite 314 · Mount Laurel, NJ 08054 · 856-778-6055

Joel S. Selikoff · a · Selikoff & Cohen · 307 Fellowship Road, Suite 314 · Mount Laurel, NJ 08054 · 856-778-6055

Murray Hill

Rosemary S. Gousman · Fisher & Phillips · http://www.laborlawyers.com · 430 Mountain Avenue · Murray Hill, NJ 07974 · 908-516-1050

Cynthia M. Jacob · a · Fisher & Phillips · http://www.laborlawyers.com · 430 Mountain Avenue · Murray Hill, NJ 07974 · 908-516-1050

Alan G. Lesnewich · Fisher & Phillips · http://www.laborlawyers.com · 430 Mountain Avenue · Murray Hill, NJ 07974 · 908-516-1050

Christopher Mills · Fisher & Phillips · http://www.laborlawyers.com · 430 Mountain Avenue · Murray Hill, NJ 07974 · 908-516-1050

Newark

Rosemary Alito · a · K&L Gates · One Newark Center, 10th Floor · Newark, NJ 07102-5285 · 973-848-4000

Christine A. Amalfe · Gibbons · http://www.gibbonslaw.com · One Gateway Center · Newark, NJ 07102-5310 · 973-596-4500

Lynne Anne Anderson · Sills Cummis & Gross · http://www.sillscummis.com · The Legal Center · One Riverfront Plaza · Newark, NJ 07102-5400 · 973-643-7000

John P. Barry · Proskauer Rose · http://www.proskauer.com · One Newark Center · Newark, NJ 07102-5211 · 973-274-3200

Patrick G. Brady · Gibbons · http://www.gibbonslaw.com · One Gateway Center · Newark, NJ 07102-5310 · 973-596-4500

Arnold Shep Cohen · a · Oxfeld Cohen · 60 Park Place, Sixth Floor · Newark, NJ 07102-4003 · 973-642-0161

Francis X. Dee · 2) · McElroy, Deutsch, Mulvaney & Carpenter · http://www.mdmc-law.com · Three Gateway Center, 17th Floor · 100 Mulberry Street · Newark, NJ 07102-4079 · 973-622-7711

H. Reed Ellis · a · Littler Mendelson · One Gateway Center, Third Floor · Newark, NJ 07102-5311 · 973-848-4700

David W. Garland · Sills Cummis & Gross · http://www.sillscummis.com · The Legal Center · One Riverfront Plaza · Newark, NJ 07102-5400 · 973-643-7000

Angelo J. Genova · 2) · Genova, Burns & Vernoia · 494 Broad Street · Newark, NJ 07102 · 973-533-0777

Marvin M. Goldstein · 2% · Proskauer Rose · http://www.proskauer.com · One Newark Center · Newark, NJ 07102-5211 · 973-274-3200

Brian Kronick · Genova, Burns & Vernoia · 494 Broad Street · Newark, NJ 07102 · 973-533-0777

James J. McGovern III · Genova, Burns & Vernoia · 494 Broad Street · Newark, NJ 07102 · 973-533-0777

John C. Petrella · Genova, Burns & Vernoia · 494 Broad Street · Newark, NJ 07102 · 973-533-0777

Donald A. Romano · 2) · McElroy, Deutsch, Mulvaney & Carpenter · http://www.mdmc-law.com · Three Gateway Center, 17th Floor · 100 Mulberry Street · Newark, NJ 07102-4079 · 973-622-7711

Francis J. Vernoia · Genova, Burns & Vernoia · 494 Broad Street · Newark, NJ 07102 · 973-533-0777

Bennet D. Zurofsky · a · Reitman Parsonnet · 744 Broad Street, Suite 1807 · Newark, NJ 07102-3867 · 973-642-0885

Princeton

Richard G. Rosenblatt · Morgan Lewis & Bockius · 502 Carnegie Center · Princeton, NJ 08540-6289 · 609-919-6600

Roseland

Michael Barabander · Fox Rothschild · 75 Eisenhower Parkway, Suite 201 · Roseland, NJ 07068 · 973-992-4800

John K. Bennett · Connell Foley · 85 Livingston Avenue · Roseland, NJ 07068 · 973-535-0500

Theodore M. Eisenberg · a · Fox Rothschild · 75 Eisenhower Parkway, Suite 201 · Roseland, NJ 07068 · 973-992-4800

Jerold E. Glassman · 2% · Fox Rothschild · 75 Eisenhower Parkway, Suite 201 · Roseland, NJ 07068 · 973-992-4800

Stanley L. Goodman · a · Fox Rothschild · 75 Eisenhower Parkway, Suite 201 · Roseland, NJ 07068 · 973-992-4800

Harold L. Hoffman · 2% · Fox Rothschild · 75 Eisenhower Parkway, Suite 201 · Roseland, NJ 07068 · 973-992-4800

Desmond Massey · Fox Rothschild · 75 Eisenhower Parkway, Suite 201 · Roseland, NJ 07068 · 973-992-4800

Jedd E. Mendelson · Fox Rothschild · 75 Eisenhower Parkway, Suite 201 · Roseland, NJ 07068 · 973-992-4800

Stephen A. Ploscowe · 2% · Fox Rothschild · 75 Eisenhower Parkway, Suite 201 · Roseland, NJ 07068 · 973-992-4800

Wayne J. Positan · a · Lum, Drasco & Positan · http://www.lumlaw.com · 103 Eisenhower Parkway · Roseland, NJ 07068-1049 · 973-403-9000

Scotch Plains

Patricia Breuninger · Breuninger & Fellman · 1829 Front Street · Scotch Plains, NJ 07076 · 908-490-9900

Secaucus

Ralph J. Lamparello · Chasan, Leyner & Lamparello · 300 Harmon Meadow Boulevard · Secaucus, NJ 07094 · 201-348-6000

Somerset

Steven P. Weissman · a · Weissman & Mintz · One Executive Drive, Suite 200 · Somerset, NJ 08873 · 732-563-4565

Somerville

Stephen B. Hunter · a · Detzky & Hunter · 33 North Bridge Street · Somerville, NJ 08876 · 908-707-4560

M. Karen Thompson · Norris, McLaughlin & Marcus · http://www.nmmlaw.com · 721 Route 202-206 · P.O. Box 1018 · Somerville, NJ 08876-1018 · 908-722-0700

Voorhees

Denise M. Keyser · Ballard Spahr Andrews & Ingersoll · Plaza 1000, Suite 500 · Main Street · Voorhees, NJ 08043-4636 · 856-761-3400

Steven W. Suflas · 2) · Ballard Spahr Andrews & Ingersoll · Plaza 1000, Suite 500 · Main Street · Voorhees, NJ 08043-4636 · 856-761-3400

Westmont

William M. Tambussi · Brown & Connery · 360 Haddon Avenue · P.O. Box 539 · Westmont, NJ 08108 · 856-854-8900

Woodbridge

Maureen S. Binetti · Wilentz, Goldman & Spitzer · http://www.wilentz.com · 90 Woodbridge Center Drive, Suite 900 · P.O. Box 10 · Woodbridge, NJ 07095-0958 · 732-636-8000

James M. Mets · Mets Schiro & McGovern · 655 Florida Grove Road · P.O. Box 668 · Woodbridge, NJ 07095 · 732-636-0040

Leonard Schiro · Mets Schiro & McGovern · 655 Florida Grove Road · P.O. Box 668 · Woodbridge, NJ 07095 · 732-636-0040

LAND USE & ZONING LAW

Hackensack

Wendy M. Berger · Cole, Schotz, Meisel, Forman & Leonard · http://www.coleschotz.com · Court Plaza North, Fourth Floor · 25 Main Street · Hackensack, NJ 07601 · 201-489-3000

Haddonfield

Lloyd H. Tubman · Archer & Greiner · http://www.archerlaw.com · One Centennial Square · 56 Haddon Avenue · P.O. Box 3000 · Haddonfield, NJ 08033-0968 · 856-795-2121

Lawrenceville

Howard D. Cohen · Parker McCay · Building Four East, Suite 102-A · 1009 Lenox Drive · Lawrenceville, NJ 08648-2321 · 609-896-4222

Arnold Lakind · Szaferman, Lakind, Blumstein, Blader & Lehmann · Quakerbridge Executive Center, Suite 200 · 101 Grovers Mill Road · Lawrenceville, NJ 08648 · 609-275-0400

Parsippany

Glenn C. Kienz · Weiner Lesniak · 629 Parsippany Road · P.O. Box 438 · Parsippany, NJ 07054 · 973-403-1100

West Orange

Daniel Murphy · Wolff & Samson · The Offices at Crystal Lake · One Boland Drive · West Orange, NJ 07052 · 973-325-1500

Woodbridge

Dean A. Gaver · a · Greenbaum, Rowe, Smith & Davis · http://www.greenbaumlaw.com · Metro Corporate Campus One · 99 Wood Avenue South · P.O. Box 5600 · Woodbridge, NJ 08830-2712 · 732-549-5600

Meryl A.G. Gonchar · Greenbaum, Rowe, Smith & Davis · http://www.greenbaumlaw.com · Metro Corporate Campus One · 99 Wood Avenue South · P.O. Box 5600 · Woodbridge, NJ 08830-2712 · 732-549-5600

Wendell A. Smith · 2% · Greenbaum, Rowe, Smith & Davis · http://www.greenbaumlaw.com · Metro Corporate Campus One · 99 Wood Avenue South · P.O. Box 5600 · Woodbridge, NJ 08830-2712 · 732-549-5600

Douglas K. Wolfson · Greenbaum, Rowe, Smith & Davis · http://www.greenbaumlaw.com · Metro Corporate Campus One · 99 Wood Avenue South · P.O. Box 5600 · Woodbridge, NJ 08830-2712 · 732-549-5600

LEGAL MALPRACTICE LAW

Absecon

Timothy P. O'Brien · Crammer & Bishop · 508 New Jersey Avenue, Suite B-3 · Absecon, NJ 08201 · 609-677-6996

Florham Park

Murray J. Laulicht · Day Pitney · 200 Campus Drive · P.O. Box 1945 · Florham Park, NJ 07962-1945 · 973-966-6300

Marlton

Yves Veenstra · a · Parker McCay · Three Greentree Centre · 7001 Lincoln Drive West · P.O. Box 974 · Marlton, NJ 08053-0974 · 856-596-8900

Morristown

William W. Voorhees · William W. Voorhees Counsellor of Law · Courthouse Plaza, Suite 105 · 60 Washington Street · Morristown, NJ 07960 · 973-267-6677

Roseland

David A. Mazie · Mazie Slater Katz & Freeman · 103 Eisenhower Parkway, Second Floor · Roseland, NJ 07068 · 973-228-9898

LEVERAGED BUYOUTS AND PRIVATE EQUITY LAW

Princeton

Andrew P. Gilbert · Morgan Lewis & Bockius · 502 Carnegie Center · Princeton, NJ 08540-6289 · 609-919-6600

Roseland

Allen B. Levithan · a · Lowenstein Sandler · http://www.lowenstein.com · 65 Livingston Avenue · Roseland, NJ 07068-1791 · 973-597-2500

Robert G. Minion · Lowenstein Sandler · http://www.lowenstein.com · 65 Livingston Avenue · Roseland, NJ 07068-1791 · 973-597-2500

Anthony O. Pergola · Lowenstein Sandler · http://www.lowenstein.com · 65 Livingston Avenue · Roseland, NJ 07068-1791 · 973-597-2500

Edward M. Zimmerman · Lowenstein Sandler · http://www.lowenstein.com · 65 Livingston Avenue · Roseland, NJ 07068-1791 · 973-597-2500

Short Hills

Victor H. Boyajian · Sonnenschein Nath & Rosenthal · 101 JFK Parkway, Fourth Floor · Short Hills, NJ 07078-2708 · 973-912-7100

John L. Cleary II · Sonnenschein Nath & Rosenthal · 101 JFK Parkway, Fourth Floor · Short Hills, NJ 07078-2708 · 973-912-7100

MARITIME LAW

Hoboken

Jorden N. Pedersen, Jr. · Baker, Garber, Duffy & Pedersen · One Newark Street · P.O. Box 1278 · Hoboken, NJ 07030 · 201-659-2635

Florham Park

Thomas F. Campion · 2% · Drinker Biddle & Reath · 500 Campus Drive · Florham Park, NJ 07932-1047 · 973-360-1100

Benjamin E. Haglund · Day Pitney · 200 Campus Drive · P.O. Box 1945 · Florham Park, NJ 07962-1945 · 973-966-6300

Robert L. Hollingshead · Day Pitney · 200 Campus Drive · P.O. Box 1945 · Florham Park, NJ 07962-1945 · 973-966-6300

Susan M. Sharko · Drinker Biddle & Reath · 500 Campus Drive · Florham Park, NJ 07932-1047 · 973-360-1100

Morristown

Lauren E. Handler · Porzio, Bromberg & Newman · 100 Southgate Parkway · P.O. Box 1997 · Morristown, NJ 07962-1997 · 973-538-4006

Newark

Jeffrey J. Greenbaum · Sills Cummis & Gross · http://www.sillscummis.com · The Legal Center · One Riverfront Plaza · Newark, NJ 07102-5400 · 973-643-7000

David R. Gross · 2% · Saiber · One Gateway Center, 13th Floor · Newark, NJ 07102 · 973-622-3333

Beth S. Rose · Sills Cummis & Gross · http://www.sillscummis.com · The Legal Center · One Riverfront Plaza · Newark, NJ 07102-5400 · 973-643-7000

Michael A. Tanenbaum · Sedgwick, Detert, Moran & Arnold · Three Gateway Center, 12th Floor · Newark, NJ 07102 · 973-242-0002

Princeton

Ezra D. Rosenberg · Dechert · 902 Carnegie Center, Suite 500 · Princeton, NJ 08540-6531 · 609-620-3200

Diane P. Sullivan · Dechert · 902 Carnegie Center, Suite 500 · Princeton, NJ 08540-6531 · 609-620-3200

Red Bank

Christopher M. Placitella · Cohen, Placitella & Roth · 115 Maple Avenue · Red Bank, NJ 07701 · 732-747-9003

Short Hills

Terence W. Camp · Budd Larner · http://www.buddlarner.com · 150 John F. Kennedy Parkway, Third Floor · Short Hills, NJ 07078-2703 · 973-379-4800

Woodbridge

Angelo J. Cifaldi · Wilentz, Goldman & Spitzer · http://www.wilentz.com · 90 Woodbridge Center Drive, Suite 900 · P.O. Box 10 · Woodbridge, NJ 07095-0958 · 732-636-8000

Barry M. Epstein · a · Wilentz, Goldman & Spitzer · http://www.wilentz.com · 90 Woodbridge Center Drive, Suite 900 · P.O. Box 10 · Woodbridge, NJ 07095-0958 · 732-636-8000

Lynne M. Kizis · Wilentz, Goldman & Spitzer · http://www.wilentz.com · 90 Woodbridge Center Drive, Suite 900 · P.O. Box 10 · Woodbridge, NJ 07095-0958 · 732-636-8000

Barry R. Sugarman · Wilentz, Goldman & Spitzer · http://www.wilentz.com · 90 Woodbridge Center Drive, Suite 900 · P.O. Box 10 · Woodbridge, NJ 07095-0958 · 732-636-8000

MEDICAL MALPRACTICE LAW

Atlantic City

Donald G. Targan · Targan & Pender · One South New York Avenue, Suite 212 · Atlantic City, NJ 08401 · 609-348-1106

Bedminster

Alfred D. Dimiero · Mella and Dimiero · 364 Main Street · Bedminster, NJ 07921 · 908-781-2004

Brick

Richard A. Grossman · a · Grossman & Heavey · 1608 Highway 88 West, Suite 200 · Brick, NJ 08724 · 732-206-0200

Bridgeton

Roseann Sellani · Roseann Sellani · P.O. Box 259 · Bridgeton, NJ 08302 · 856-451-5134

Chatham

Kenneth A. Berkowitz · a · Blume, Goldfaden, Berkowitz, Donnelly, Fried & Forte · http://www.njatty.com · One Main Street · Chatham, NJ 07928 · 973-635-5400

John M. Blume · 2% · Blume, Goldfaden, Berkowitz, Donnelly, Fried & Forte · http://www.njatty.com · One Main Street · Chatham, NJ 07928 · 973-635-5400

Dennis M. Donnelly · a · Blume, Goldfaden, Berkowitz, Donnelly, Fried & Forte · http://www.njatty.com · One Main Street · Chatham, NJ 07928 · 973-635-5400

Carol L. Forte · Blume, Goldfaden, Berkowitz, Donnelly, Fried & Forte · http://www.njatty.com · One Main Street · Chatham, NJ 07928 · 973-635-5400

Ronald Goldfaden · Blume, Goldfaden, Berkowitz, Donnelly, Fried & Forte · http://www.njatty.com · One Main Street · Chatham, NJ 07928 · 973-635-5400

Scott A. Parsons · O'Connor, Parsons & Lane · 383 Main Street · Chatham, NJ 07928-2105 · 973-635-2210

Michael B. Zerres · Blume, Goldfaden, Berkowitz, Donnelly, Fried & Forte · http://www.njatty.com · One Main Street · Chatham, NJ 07928 · 973-635-5400

Eatontown

George N. Arvanitis · a · Martin J. McGreevy · West Ridge, Building A · One Industrial Way West · P.O. Box 820 · Eatontown, NJ 07755 · 732-542-0084

Martin J. McGreevy · Martin J. McGreevy · West Ridge, Building A · One Industrial Way West · P.O. Box 820 · Eatontown, NJ 07755 · 732-542-0084

Haddonfield

Michael S. Berger · Andres & Berger · 264 Kings Highway East · Haddonfield, NJ 08033 · 856-795-1444

Hoboken

Gerald H. Baker · Baker, Garber, Duffy & Pedersen · One Newark Street · P.O. Box 1278 · Hoboken, NJ 07030 · 201-659-2635

Jorden N. Pedersen, Jr. · Baker, Garber, Duffy & Pedersen · One Newark Street · P.O. Box 1278 · Hoboken, NJ 07030 · 201-659-2635

Marlton

Yves Veenstra · a · Parker McCay · Three Greentree Centre · 7001 Lincoln Drive West · P.O. Box 974 · Marlton, NJ 08053-0974 · 856-596-8900

Millburn

David P. Weeks · Ruprecht, Hart & Weeks · 306 Main Street · Millburn, NJ 07041 · 973-379-2400

Morristown

Lauren E. Handler · Porzio, Bromberg & Newman · 100 Southgate Parkway · P.O. Box 1997 · Morristown, NJ 07962-1997 · 973-538-4006

New Brunswick

Thomas B. Leyhane · Hoagland, Longo, Moran, Dunst & Doukas · 40 Paterson Street · P.O. Box 480 · New Brunswick, NJ 08903 · 732-545-4717

Roseland

Bruce H. Nagel · Nagel Rice · 103 Eisenhower Parkway · Roseland, NJ 07068 · 973-618-0400

Vineland

Joseph D. O'Neill · O'Neill & Coant · 30 West Chestnut Avenue · Vineland, NJ 08360-5401 · 856-692-2400

MERGERS & ACQUISITIONS LAW

Florham Park

Warren J. Casey · Day Pitney · 200 Campus Drive · P.O. Box 1945 · Florham Park, NJ 07962-1945 · 973-966-6300

Stewart E. Lavey · Drinker Biddle & Reath · 500 Campus Drive · Florham Park, NJ 07932-1047 · 973-360-1100

Henry Nelson Massey · Day Pitney · 200 Campus Drive · P.O. Box 1945 · Florham Park, NJ 07962-1945 · 973-966-6300

Middletown

John A. Aiello · 2) · Giordano, Halleran & Ciesla · http://www.ghclaw.com · 125 Half Mile Road, Suite 300 · P.O. Box 190 · Middletown, NJ 07748 · 732-741-3900

Paul T. Colella · Giordano, Halleran & Ciesla · http://www.ghclaw.com · 125 Half Mile Road, Suite 300 · P.O. Box 190 · Middletown, NJ 07748 · 732-741-3900

Philip D. Forlenza · Giordano, Halleran & Ciesla · http://www.ghclaw.com · 125 Half Mile Road, Suite 300 · P.O. Box 190 · Middletown, NJ 07748 · 732-741-3900

Morristown

Andrew J. Stamelman · Riker, Danzig, Scherer, Hyland & Perretti · Headquarters Plaza · One Speedwell Avenue · Morristown, NJ 07962-1981 · 973-538-0800

Newark

Alyce C. Halchak · Gibbons · http://www.gibbonslaw.com · One Gateway Center · Newark, NJ 07102-5310 · 973-596-4500

Princeton

Steven M. Cohen · Morgan Lewis & Bockius · 502 Carnegie Center · Princeton, NJ 08540-6289 · 609-919-6600

Roseland

Peter H. Ehrenberg · 2) · Lowenstein Sandler · http://www.lowenstein.com · 65 Livingston Avenue · Roseland, NJ 07068-1791 · 973-597-2500

Stephen H. Knee · 2) · Greenbaum, Rowe, Smith & Davis · http://www.greenbaumlaw.com · 75 Livingston Avenue · Roseland, NJ 07068-3701 · 973-535-1600

Allen B. Levithan · a · Lowenstein Sandler · http://www.lowenstein.com · 65 Livingston Avenue · Roseland, NJ 07068-1791 · 973-597-2500

John D. Schupper · 2) · Lowenstein Sandler · http://www.lowenstein.com · 65 Livingston Avenue · Roseland, NJ 07068-1791 · 973-597-2500

Alan Wovsaniker · Lowenstein Sandler · http://www.lowenstein.com · 65 Livingston Avenue · Roseland, NJ 07068-1791 · 973-597-2500

Edward M. Zimmerman · Lowenstein Sandler · http://www.lowenstein.com · 65 Livingston Avenue · Roseland, NJ 07068-1791 · 973-597-2500

Somerville

Peter D. Hutcheon · 2) · Norris, McLaughlin & Marcus · http://www.nmmlaw.com · 721 Route 202-206 · P.O. Box 1018 · Somerville, NJ 08876-1018 · 908-722-0700

West Orange

Daniel A. Schwartz · Wolff & Samson · The Offices at Crystal Lake · One Boland Drive · West Orange, NJ 07052 · 973-325-1500

Woodbridge

Alan E. Davis · 2) · Greenbaum, Rowe, Smith & Davis · http://www.greenbaumlaw.com · Metro Corporate Campus One · 99 Wood Avenue South · P.O. Box 5600 · Woodbridge, NJ 08830-2712 · 732-549-5600

W. Raymond Felton · a · Greenbaum, Rowe, Smith & Davis · http://www.greenbaumlaw.com · Metro Corporate Campus One · 99 Wood Avenue South · P.O. Box 5600 · Woodbridge, NJ 08830-2712 · 732-549-5600

MUNICIPAL LAW

West Orange

Richard D. Trenk · Trenk, DiPasquale, Webster, Della Fera & Sodono · 347 Mount Pleasant Avenue, Suite 300 · West Orange, NJ 07052 · 973-243-8600

Woodbridge

Dennis A. Estis · Greenbaum, Rowe, Smith & Davis · http://www.greenbaumlaw.com · Metro Corporate Campus One · 99 Wood Avenue South · P.O. Box 5600 · Woodbridge, NJ 08830-2712 · 732-549-5600

NATURAL RESOURCES LAW

Newark

Edward F. McTiernan · Gibbons · http://www.gibbonslaw.com · One Gateway Center · Newark, NJ 07102-5310 · 973-596-4500

Somerville

Edward A. Hogan · a · Norris, McLaughlin & Marcus · http://www.nmmlaw.com · 721 Route 202-206 · P.O. Box 1018 · Somerville, NJ 08876-1018 · 908-722-0700

Voorhees

Richard M. Hluchan · Ballard Spahr Andrews & Ingersoll · Plaza 1000, Suite 500 · Main Street · Voorhees, NJ 08043-4636 · 856-761-3400

NON-PROFIT/CHARITIES LAW

Haddonfield

Glenn A. Henkel · Kulzer & Di Padova · 76 East Euclid Avenue, Suite 300 · Haddonfield, NJ 08033-2342 · 856-795-7744

NON-WHITE-COLLAR CRIMINAL DEFENSE

Atlantic City

Edwin J. Jacobs, Jr. · a · Jacobs & Barbone · 1125 Pacific Avenue · Atlantic City, NJ 08401 · 609-348-1125

Chatham

John D. Arseneault · a · Arseneault, Whipple, Farmer, Fassett & Azzarello · http://www.awffa.com · 560 Main Street · Chatham, NJ 07928 · 973-635-3366

Kevin H. Marino · Marino Tortorella · 437 Southern Boulevard · Chatham, NJ 07928-1488 · 973-824-9300

John C. Whipple · Arseneault, Whipple, Farmer, Fassett & Azzarello · http://www.awffa.com · 560 Main Street · Chatham, NJ 07928 · 973-635-3366

Alan L. Zegas · a · Law Offices of Alan L. Zegas · http://www.zegaslaw.com · 552 Main Street · Chatham, NJ 07928 · 973-701-7080

Cherry Hill

Carl D. Poplar · 2% · Carl D. Poplar · Building Two · 1010 Kings Highway South · Cherry Hill, NJ 08034 · 856-216-9979

Hackensack

Raymond F. Flood · a · Flood & Basile · 39 Hudson Street · Hackensack, NJ 07601 · 201-487-0700

Hoboken

Brian J. Neary · a · Law Offices of Brian J. Neary · http://www.nearylaw.com · Hoboken Land Building · One Newark Street · Hoboken, NJ 07030 · 201-420-8101

Manasquan

Cathy Waldor · a · Waldor & Carlesimo · Building L, Suite 101 · 2517 Highway 35 · Manasquan, NJ 08736 · 732-528-5040

Montclair

David A. Ruhnke · a · Ruhnke & Barrett · 47 Park Street · Montclair, NJ 07042 · 973-744-1000

Moorestown

Francis J. Hartman · 2% · Attorneys Hartman · 505 South Lenola Road, Suite 121 · Moorestown, NJ 08057-1590 · 856-235-0220

Morristown

Stephen S. Weinstein · a · Stephen S. Weinstein · http://www.sswpa.com · 20 Park Place, Suite 301 · Morristown, NJ 07960-7102 · 973-267-5200

New Brunwick

Steven D. Altman · Benedict & Altman · 247 Livingston Avenue · New Brunwick, NJ 08901 · 732-745-9000

Joseph J. Benedict · a · Benedict & Altman · 247 Livingston Avenue · New Brunwick, NJ 08901 · 732-745-9000

Newark

Thomas R. Ashley · 2) · Thomas R. Ashley · 50 Park Place, Suite 1400 · Newark, NJ 07102 · 973-623-0501

Raymond A. Brown · 2% · Brown & Brown · One Gateway Center, Suite 105 · Newark, NJ 07102 · 973-622-1846

Red Bank

Edward J. Plaza · Weir & Plaza · 321 Broad Street · Red Bank, NJ 07701 · 732-741-8181

Roseland

Michael Critchley · 2) · Critchley & Kinum · 75 Livingston Avenue · Roseland, NJ 07068 · 973-422-9200

Michael D'Alessio, Jr. · 2% · Walder, Hayden & Brogan · Five Becker Farm Road · Roseland, NJ 07068 · 973-992-5300

Robert L. Penza · Walder, Hayden & Brogan · Five Becker Farm Road · Roseland, NJ 07068 · 973-992-5300

Alan Silber · Walder, Hayden & Brogan · Five Becker Farm Road · Roseland, NJ 07068 · 973-992-5300

Somerville

John P. McDonald · a · McDonald & Rogers · 181 West High Street · Somerville, NJ 08876 · 908-722-4100

Vineland

Jay H. Greenblatt · Greenblatt & Laube · 200 North Eighth Street · P.O. Box 883 · Vineland, NJ 08362-0883 · 856-691-0424

Joseph D. O'Neill · O'Neill & Coant · 30 West Chestnut Avenue · Vineland, NJ 08360-5401 · 856-692-2400

West Orange

Timothy Donohue · Arleo & Donohue · 622 Eagle Rock Avenue · West Orange, NJ 07052 · 973-736-8660

Woodbridge

Raymond M. Brown · 2) · Greenbaum, Rowe, Smith & Davis · http://www.greenbaumlaw.com · Metro Corporate Campus One · 99 Wood Avenue South · P.O. Box 5600 · Woodbridge, NJ 08830-2712 · 732-549-5600

James E. Trabilsy · Wilentz, Goldman & Spitzer · http://www.wilentz.com · 90 Woodbridge Center Drive, Suite 900 · P.O. Box 10 · Woodbridge, NJ 07095-0958 · 732-636-8000

Warren W. Wilentz · Wilentz, Goldman & Spitzer · http://www.wilentz.com · 90 Woodbridge Center Drive, Suite 900 · P.O. Box 10 · Woodbridge, NJ 07095-0958 · 732-636-8000

PERSONAL INJURY LITIGATION

Bedminster

Michel F. Baumeister · Baumeister & Samuels · 445 Main Street · P.O. Box 1116 · Bedminster, NJ 07921 973-267-6666

Brick

Richard A. Grossman · a · Grossman & Heavey · 1608 Highway 88 West, Suite 200 · Brick, NJ 08724 · 732-206-0200

Bridgeton

Roseann Sellani · Roseann Sellani · P.O. Box 259 · Bridgeton, NJ 08302 · 856-451-5134

Chatham

Kenneth A. Berkowitz · a · Blume, Goldfaden, Berkowitz, Donnelly, Fried & Forte · http://www.njatty.com · One Main Street · Chatham, NJ 07928 · 973-635-5400

John M. Blume · 2% · Blume, Goldfaden, Berkowitz, Donnelly, Fried & Forte · http://www.njatty.com · One Main Street · Chatham, NJ 07928 · 973-635-5400

Cynthia M. Craig · Blume, Goldfaden, Berkowitz, Donnelly, Fried & Forte · http://www.njatty.com · One Main Street · Chatham, NJ 07928 · 973-635-5400

Dennis M. Donnelly · a · Blume, Goldfaden, Berkowitz, Donnelly, Fried & Forte · http://www.njatty.com · One Main Street · Chatham, NJ 07928 · 973-635-5400

Carol L. Forte · Blume, Goldfaden, Berkowitz, Donnelly, Fried & Forte · http://www.njatty.com · One Main Street · Chatham, NJ 07928 · 973-635-5400

David M. Fried · Blume, Goldfaden, Berkowitz, Donnelly, Fried & Forte · http://www.njatty.com · One Main Street · Chatham, NJ 07928 · 973-635-5400

Ronald Goldfaden · Blume, Goldfaden, Berkowitz, Donnelly, Fried & Forte · http://www.njatty.com · One Main Street · Chatham, NJ 07928 · 973-635-5400

Gerald B. O'Connor · 2% · O'Connor, Parsons & Lane · 383 Main Street · Chatham, NJ 07928-2105 · 973-635-2210

Michael B. Zerres · Blume, Goldfaden, Berkowitz, Donnelly, Fried & Forte · http://www.njatty.com · One Main Street · Chatham, NJ 07928 · 973-635-5400

Cherry Hill

Louis J. DeVoto · Rossetti & DeVoto · 20 Brace Road, Suite 115 · Cherry Hill, NJ 08034 · 856-354-0900

Michael A. Ferrara, Jr. · The Ferrara Law Firm · 601 Longwood Avenue, State Highway 38 · Cherry Hill, NJ 08002 · 856-779-9500

Carl D. Poplar · 2% · Carl D. Poplar · Building Two · 1010 Kings Highway South · Cherry Hill, NJ 08034 · 856-216-9979

Andrew J. Rossetti · Rossetti & DeVoto · 20 Brace Road, Suite 115 · Cherry Hill, NJ 08034 · 856-354-0900

Cranford

Vivian Demas · Vivian Demas · 190 North Avenue East, Second Floor · P.O. Box Eight · Cranford, NJ 07016 · 908-272-2700

Eatontown

George N. Arvanitis · a · Martin J. McGreevy · West Ridge, Building A · One Industrial Way West · P.O. Box 820 · Eatontown, NJ 07755 · 732-542-0084

Martin J. McGreevy · Martin J. McGreevy · West Ridge, Building A · One Industrial Way West · P.O. Box 820 · Eatontown, NJ 07755 · 732-542-0084

Florham Park

Richard E. Brennan · Drinker Biddle & Reath · 500 Campus Drive · Florham Park, NJ 07932-1047 · 973-360-1100

Thomas F. Campion · 2% · Drinker Biddle & Reath · 500 Campus Drive · Florham Park, NJ 07932-1047 · 973-360-1100

Robert L. Hollingshead · Day Pitney · 200 Campus Drive · P.O. Box 1945 · Florham Park, NJ 07962-1945 · 973-966-6300

Jeffrey A. Peck · Drinker Biddle & Reath · 500 Campus Drive · Florham Park, NJ 07932-1047 · 973-360-1100

Susan M. Sharko · Drinker Biddle & Reath · 500 Campus Drive · Florham Park, NJ 07932-1047 · 973-360-1100

Fort Lee

Michael J. Maggiano · Maggiano, DiGirolamo, Lizzi & Roberts · 201 Columbia Avenue · Fort Lee, NJ 07024-4134 · 201-585-9111

Haddonfield

Kenneth Andres · Andres & Berger · 264 Kings Highway East · Haddonfield, NJ 08033 · 856-795-1444

Timothy Annin · Kelley, Wardell, Craig, Annin & Baxter · 41 Grove Street · Haddonfield, NJ 08033 · 856-795-2220

Michael S. Berger · Andres & Berger · 264 Kings Highway East · Haddonfield, NJ 08033 · 856-795-1444

Hoboken

Gerald H. Baker · Baker, Garber, Duffy & Pedersen · One Newark Street · P.O. Box 1278 · Hoboken, NJ 07030 · 201-659-2635

Jorden N. Pedersen, Jr. · Baker, Garber, Duffy & Pedersen · One Newark Street · P.O. Box 1278 · Hoboken, NJ 07030 · 201-659-2635

Lawrenceville

John A. Sakson · Stark & Stark · 993 Lenox Drive, Building Two · P.O. Box 5315 · Lawrenceville, NJ 08543 · 609-896-9060

Albert M. Stark · Stark & Stark · 993 Lenox Drive, Building Two · P.O. Box 5315 · Lawrenceville, NJ 08543 · 609-896-9060

Bruce H. Stern · Stark & Stark · 993 Lenox Drive, Building Two · P.O. Box 5315 · Lawrenceville, NJ 08543 · 609-896-9060

Linwood

Paul R. D'Amato · a · D'Amato & D'Amato · 401 New Road, Suite 103 · Linwood, NJ 08221 · 609-926-3300

Livingston

Jeffrey M. Kadish · Morgan Melhuish Abrutyn · 651 West Mount Pleasant Avenue, Suite 200 · Livingston, NJ 07039 · 973-994-2500

Leonard C. Leicht · Morgan Melhuish Abrutyn · 651 West Mount Pleasant Avenue, Suite 200 · Livingston, NJ 07039 · 973-994-2500

Marlton

Yves Veenstra · a · Parker McCay · Three Greentree Centre · 7001 Lincoln Drive West · P.O. Box 974 · Marlton, NJ 08053-0974 · 856-596-8900

Thomas M. Walsh · Parker McCay · Three Greentree Centre · 7001 Lincoln Drive West · P.O. Box 974 · Marlton, NJ 08053-0974 · 856-596-8900

Millburn

Louis A. Ruprecht · a · Ruprecht, Hart & Weeks · 306 Main Street · Millburn, NJ 07041 · 973-379-2400

David P. Weeks · Ruprecht, Hart & Weeks · 306 Main Street · Millburn, NJ 07041 · 973-379-2400

Moorestown

Francis J. Hartman · 2% · Attorneys Hartman · 505 South Lenola Road, Suite 121 · Moorestown, NJ 08057-1590 · 856-235-0220

Morristown

Jefferson T. Barnes · Porzio, Bromberg & Newman · 100 Southgate Parkway · P.O. Box 1997 · Morristown, NJ 07962-1997 · 973-538-4006

Timothy L. Barnes · a · Porzio, Bromberg & Newman · 100 Southgate Parkway · P.O. Box 1997 · Morristown, NJ 07962-1997 · 973-538-4006

Lauren E. Handler · Porzio, Bromberg & Newman · 100 Southgate Parkway · P.O. Box 1997 · Morristown, NJ 07962-1997 · 973-538-4006

Stephen S. Weinstein · a · Stephen S. Weinstein · http://www.sswpa.com · 20 Park Place, Suite 301 · Morristown, NJ 07960-7102 · 973-267-5200

Mount Laurel

Robert E. Paarz · Weiss & Paarz · 3000 Atrium Way, Suite 200 · Mount Laurel, NJ 08054 · 856-778-0444

Newark

David R. Gross · 2% · Saiber · One Gateway Center, 13th Floor · Newark, NJ 07102 · 973-622-3333

William B. McGuire · 2% · Tompkins, McGuire, Wachenfeld & Barry · Four Gateway Center, Fifth Floor 100 Mulberry Street · Newark, NJ 07102-4070 · 973-622-3000

Alan Y. Medvin · a · Medvin & Elberg · One Gateway Center, Sixth Floor · Newark, NJ 07102 · 973-642-1300

Beth S. Rose · Sills Cummis & Gross · http://www.sillscummis.com · The Legal Center · One Riverfront Plaza · Newark, NJ 07102-5400 · 973-643-7000

Gita F. Rothschild · McCarter & English · Four Gateway Center · 100 Mulberry Street · Newark, NJ 07102 · 973-622-4444

Princeton

Diane P. Sullivan · Dechert · 902 Carnegie Center, Suite 500 · Princeton, NJ 08540-6531 · 609-620-3200

Red Bank

Christopher M. Placitella · Cohen, Placitella & Roth · 115 Maple Avenue · Red Bank, NJ 07701 · 732-747-9003

Ridgewood

Arthur J. Messineo, Jr. · Messineo & Messineo · 34 Cottage Place · Ridgewood, NJ 07450 · 201-444-4124

Roseland

David W. Field · Lowenstein Sandler · http://www.lowenstein.com · 65 Livingston Avenue · Roseland, NJ 07068-1791 · 973-597-2500

Cynthia A. Matheke · Lum, Drasco & Positan · http://www.lumlaw.com · 103 Eisenhower Parkway · Roseland, NJ 07068-1049 · 973-403-9000

David A. Mazie · Mazie Slater Katz & Freeman · 103 Eisenhower Parkway, Second Floor · Roseland, NJ 07068 · 973-228-9898

Kathleen S. Murphy · Connell Foley · 85 Livingston Avenue · Roseland, NJ 07068 · 973-535-0500

Adam M. Slater · Mazie Slater Katz & Freeman · 103 Eisenhower Parkway, Second Floor · Roseland, NJ 07068 · 973-228-9898

Saddle Brook

Albert L. Cohn · Cohn Lifland Pearlman Herrmann & Knopf · http://www.njlawfirm.com · Park 80 Plaza West-One · Saddle Brook, NJ 07663 · 201-845-9600

Secaucus

Joel A. Leyner · a · Chasan, Leyner & Lamparello · 300 Harmon Meadow Boulevard · Secaucus, NJ 07094 · 201-348-6000

Short Hills

Carl Greenberg · 2% · Budd Larner · http://www.buddlarner.com · 150 John F. Kennedy Parkway, Third Floor · Short Hills, NJ 07078-2703 · 973-379-4800

David J. Novack · Budd Larner · http://www.buddlarner.com · 150 John F. Kennedy Parkway, Third Floor · Short Hills, NJ 07078-2703 · 973-379-4800

Cynthia A. Walters · Budd Larner · http://www.buddlarner.com · 150 John F. Kennedy Parkway, Third Floor · Short Hills, NJ 07078-2703 · 973-379-4800

Springfield

Kenneth S. Javerbaum · Javerbaum Wurgaft Hicks Kahn Wikstrom & Sinins · Park Place Legal Center · 959 South Springfield Avenue · Springfield, NJ 07081-3555 · 973-379-4200

Stephen O. Mortenson · Mortenson and Pomeroy · 150 Morris Avenue · Springfield, NJ 07081-1224 · 973-467-9600

Jack Wurgaft · Javerbaum Wurgaft Hicks Kahn Wikstrom & Sinins · Park Place Legal Center · 959 South Springfield Avenue · Springfield, NJ 07081-3555 · 973-379-4200

Trenton

James J. McLaughlin · McLaughlin & Cooper · 949 West State Street · P.O. Box 1718 · Trenton, NJ 08607-1718 · 609-989-8050

Vineland

Jay H. Greenblatt · Greenblatt & Laube · 200 North Eighth Street · P.O. Box 883 · Vineland, NJ 08362-0883 · 856-691-0424

Joseph D. O'Neill · O'Neill & Coant · 30 West Chestnut Avenue · Vineland, NJ 08360-5401 · 856-692-2400

Voorhees

Joseph H. Kenney · 2% · Ballard Spahr Andrews & Ingersoll · Plaza 1000, Suite 500 · Main Street · Voorhees, NJ 08043-4636 · 856-761-3400

West Atlantic City

Thomas J. Vesper · a · Westmoreland, Vesper & Quattrone · 8025 Black Horse Pike, Suite 500 · West Atlantic City, NJ 08232 · 609-645-1111

West Orange

Alan W. Roth · Bendit Weinstock · 80 Main Street · West Orange, NJ 07052 · 973-736-9800

Westmont

Burchard V. Martin · 2% · Martin, Gunn & Martin · Sentry Office Plaza, Suite 420 · 216 Haddon Avenue · P.O. Box 358 · Westmont, NJ 08108 · 856-858-0900

Woodbridge

Michael J. Barrett · Wilentz, Goldman & Spitzer · http://www.wilentz.com · 90 Woodbridge Center Drive, Suite 900 · P.O. Box 10 · Woodbridge, NJ 07095-0958 · 732-636-8000

Morris Brown · 2) · Wilentz, Goldman & Spitzer · http://www.wilentz.com · 90 Woodbridge Center Drive, Suite 900 · P.O. Box 10 · Woodbridge, NJ 07095-0958 · 732-636-8000

Barry M. Epstein · a · Wilentz, Goldman & Spitzer · http://www.wilentz.com · 90 Woodbridge Center Drive, Suite 900 · P.O. Box 10 · Woodbridge, NJ 07095-0958 · 732-636-8000

Raymond A. Gill, Jr. · Gill and Chamas · 655 Florida Grove Road · P.O. Box 760 · Woodbridge, NJ 07095 · 732-324-7600

Brian J. Molloy · Wilentz, Goldman & Spitzer · http://www.wilentz.com · 90 Woodbridge Center Drive, Suite 900 · P.O. Box 10 · Woodbridge, NJ 07095-0958 · 732-636-8000

Randall J. Richards · Wilentz, Goldman & Spitzer · http://www.wilentz.com · 90 Woodbridge Center Drive, Suite 900 · P.O. Box 10 · Woodbridge, NJ 07095-0958 · 732-636-8000

PRIVATE FUNDS LAW

Roseland

Allen B. Levithan · a · Lowenstein Sandler · http://www.lowenstein.com · 65 Livingston Avenue · Roseland, NJ 07068-1791 · 973-597-2500

PRODUCT LIABILITY LITIGATION

Bedminster

Alfred D. Dimiero · Mella and Dimiero · 364 Main Street · Bedminster, NJ 07921 · 908-781-2004

Chatham

Kenneth A. Berkowitz · a · Blume, Goldfaden, Berkowitz, Donnelly, Fried & Forte · http://www.njatty.com · One Main Street · Chatham, NJ 07928 · 973-635-5400

John M. Blume · 2% · Blume, Goldfaden, Berkowitz, Donnelly, Fried & Forte · http://www.njatty.com · One Main Street · Chatham, NJ 07928 · 973-635-5400

Dennis M. Donnelly · a · Blume, Goldfaden, Berkowitz, Donnelly, Fried & Forte · http://www.njatty.com · One Main Street · Chatham, NJ 07928 · 973-635-5400

David M. Fried · Blume, Goldfaden, Berkowitz, Donnelly, Fried & Forte · http://www.njatty.com · One Main Street · Chatham, NJ 07928 · 973-635-5400

Michael B. Zerres · Blume, Goldfaden, Berkowitz, Donnelly, Fried & Forte · http://www.njatty.com · One Main Street · Chatham, NJ 07928 · 973-635-5400

Cherry Hill

Louis J. DeVoto · Rossetti & DeVoto · 20 Brace Road, Suite 115 · Cherry Hill, NJ 08034 · 856-354-0900

Michael A. Ferrara, Jr. · The Ferrara Law Firm · 601 Longwood Avenue, State Highway 38 · Cherry Hill, NJ 08002 · 856-779-9500

Andrew J. Rossetti · Rossetti & DeVoto · 20 Brace Road, Suite 115 · Cherry Hill, NJ 08034 · 856-354-0900

Hoboken

Gerald H. Baker · Baker, Garber, Duffy & Pedersen · One Newark Street · P.O. Box 1278 · Hoboken, NJ 07030 · 201-659-2635

Jorden N. Pedersen, Jr. · Baker, Garber, Duffy & Pedersen · One Newark Street · P.O. Box 1278 · Hoboken, NJ 07030 · 201-659-2635

Jersey City

Harold I. Braff · Margulies Wind · Harborside Financial Center Plaza 10, Suite 1201 · Three Second Street · Jersey City, NJ 07311-3988 · 201-333-0400

New Brunswick

James Moran · Hoagland, Longo, Moran, Dunst & Doukas · 40 Paterson Street · P.O. Box 480 · New Brunswick, NJ 08903 · 732-545-4717

Newark

Andrew T. Berry · a · McCarter & English · Four Gateway Center · 100 Mulberry Street · Newark, NJ 07102 · 973-622-4444

David R. Kott · McCarter & English · Four Gateway Center · 100 Mulberry Street · Newark, NJ 07102 · 973-622-4444

Beth S. Rose · Sills Cummis & Gross · http://www.sillscummis.com · The Legal Center · One Riverfront Plaza · Newark, NJ 07102-5400 · 973-643-7000

Princeton

Ezra D. Rosenberg · Dechert · 902 Carnegie Center, Suite 500 · Princeton, NJ 08540-6531 · 609-620-3200

Roseland

Robert M. Goodman · Greenbaum, Rowe, Smith & Davis · http://www.greenbaumlaw.com · 75 Livingston Avenue · Roseland, NJ 07068-3701 · 973-535-1600

Vineland

Joseph D. O'Neill · O'Neill & Coant · 30 West Chestnut Avenue · Vineland, NJ 08360-5401 · 856-692-2400

Woodbridge

Michael J. Barrett · Wilentz, Goldman & Spitzer · http://www.wilentz.com · 90 Woodbridge Center Drive, Suite 900 · P.O. Box 10 · Woodbridge, NJ 07095-0958 · 732-636-8000

Barry M. Epstein · a · Wilentz, Goldman & Spitzer · http://www.wilentz.com · 90 Woodbridge Center Drive, Suite 900 · P.O. Box 10 · Woodbridge, NJ 07095-0958 · 732-636-8000

Randall J. Richards · Wilentz, Goldman & Spitzer · http://www.wilentz.com · 90 Woodbridge Center Drive, Suite 900 · P.O. Box 10 · Woodbridge, NJ 07095-0958 · 732-636-8000

PROFESSIONAL MALPRACTICE LAW

Chatham

John M. Blume · 2% · Blume, Goldfaden, Berkowitz, Donnelly, Fried & Forte · http://www.njatty.com · One Main Street · Chatham, NJ 07928 · 973-635-5400

New Brunswick

Alan I. Dunst · Hoagland, Longo, Moran, Dunst & Doukas · 40 Paterson Street · P.O. Box 480 · New Brunswick, NJ 08903 · 732-545-4717

PUBLIC FINANCE LAW

Newark

Joseph P. Baumann · McManimon & Scotland · One Riverfront Plaza, Fourth Floor · Newark, NJ 07102-5311 · 973-622-1800

Jeannette M. Bond · McCarter & English · Four Gateway Center · 100 Mulberry Street · Newark, NJ 07102 · 973-622-4444

John D. Draikiwicz · Gibbons · http://www.gibbonslaw.com · One Gateway Center · Newark, NJ 07102-5310 · 973-596-4500

Trenton

Howard Eichenbaum · Gluck Walrath · 428 River View Plaza, Second Floor · Trenton, NJ 08611 · 609-278-1900

REAL ESTATE LAW

Chatham

H. Harding Brown · 2) · Epstein, Brown, Gioia, Jacobs & Sprouls · 245 Green Village Road · P.O. Box 901 · Chatham, NJ 07928-0901 · 973-593-4900

Barnet H. Epstein · Epstein, Brown, Gioia, Jacobs & Sprouls · 245 Green Village Road · P.O. Box 901 · Chatham, NJ 07928-0901 · 973-593-4900

Cherry Hill

Carl S. Bisgaier · Flaster/Greenberg · 1810 Chapel Avenue West · Cherry Hill, NJ 08002-4609 · 856-661-1900

Florham Park

Robert C. Epstein · Greenberg Traurig · http://www.gtlaw.com · 200 Park Avenue · P.O. Box 677 · Florham Park, NJ 07932-0677 · 973-360-7900

Deirdre E. Moore · Day Pitney · 200 Campus Drive · P.O. Box 1945 · Florham Park, NJ 07962-1945 · 973-966-6300

Glenn S. Pantel · Drinker Biddle & Reath · 500 Campus Drive · Florham Park, NJ 07932-1047 · 973-360-1100

Lawrence F. Reilly · Day Pitney · 200 Campus Drive · P.O. Box 1945 · Florham Park, NJ 07962-1945 · 973-966-6300

Michael E. Rothpletz, Jr. · Drinker Biddle & Reath · 500 Campus Drive · Florham Park, NJ 07932-1047 973-360-1100

Hackensack

Mitchell W. Abrahams · Cole, Schotz, Meisel, Forman & Leonard · http://www.coleschotz.com · Court Plaza North, Fourth Floor · 25 Main Street · Hackensack, NJ 07601 · 201-489-3000

Richard W. Abramson · Cole, Schotz, Meisel, Forman & Leonard · http://www.coleschotz.com · Court Plaza North, Fourth Floor · 25 Main Street · Hackensack, NJ 07601 · 201-489-3000

Wendy M. Berger · Cole, Schotz, Meisel, Forman & Leonard · http://www.coleschotz.com · Court Plaza North, Fourth Floor · 25 Main Street · Hackensack, NJ 07601 · 201-489-3000

Michael E. Jones · Cole, Schotz, Meisel, Forman & Leonard · http://www.coleschotz.com · Court Plaza North, Fourth Floor · 25 Main Street · Hackensack, NJ 07601 · 201-489-3000

Richard R. Kahn · Winne, Banta, Hetherington, Basralian & Kahn · Court Plaza South, East Wing, Suite 101 · 21 Main Street · P.O. Box 647 · Hackensack, NJ 07601-0647 · 201-487-3800

Michael R. Leighton · Cole, Schotz, Meisel, Forman & Leonard · http://www.coleschotz.com · Court Plaza North, Fourth Floor · 25 Main Street · Hackensack, NJ 07601 · 201-489-3000

W. John Park · Cole, Schotz, Meisel, Forman & Leonard · http://www.coleschotz.com · Court Plaza North, Fourth Floor · 25 Main Street · Hackensack, NJ 07601 · 201-489-3000

Edward M. Schotz · 2% · Cole, Schotz, Meisel, Forman & Leonard · http://www.coleschotz.com · Court Plaza North, Fourth Floor · 25 Main Street · Hackensack, NJ 07601 · 201-489-3000

Stanley Stern · Cole, Schotz, Meisel, Forman & Leonard · http://www.coleschotz.com · Court Plaza North, Fourth Floor · 25 Main Street · Hackensack, NJ 07601 · 201-489-3000

Michael Sternlieb · Cole, Schotz, Meisel, Forman & Leonard · http://www.coleschotz.com · Court Plaza North, Fourth Floor · 25 Main Street · Hackensack, NJ 07601 · 201-489-3000

Harold N. Tolchinsky · Cole, Schotz, Meisel, Forman & Leonard · http://www.coleschotz.com · Court Plaza North, Fourth Floor · 25 Main Street · Hackensack, NJ 07601 · 201-489-3000

Lawrenceville

Daniel L. Haggerty · Stark & Stark · 993 Lenox Drive, Building Two · P.O. Box 5315 · Lawrenceville, NJ 08543 · 609-896-9060

Middletown

John A. Giunco, Jr. · Giordano, Halleran & Ciesla · http://www.ghclaw.com · 125 Half Mile Road, Suite 300 · P.O. Box 190 · Middletown, NJ 07748 · 732-741-3900

Michael J. Gross · Giordano, Halleran & Ciesla · http://www.ghclaw.com · 125 Half Mile Road, Suite 300 P.O. Box 190 · Middletown, NJ 07748 · 732-741-3900

Edward S. Radzely · 2% · Giordano, Halleran & Ciesla · http://www.ghclaw.com · 125 Half Mile Road, Suite 300 · P.O. Box 190 · Middletown, NJ 07748 · 732-741-3900

Morristown

Peter L. Berkley · a · Riker, Danzig, Scherer, Hyland & Perretti · Headquarters Plaza · One Speedwell Avenue · Morristown, NJ 07962-1981 · 973-538-0800

Nicholas Racioppi, Jr. · Riker, Danzig, Scherer, Hyland & Perretti · Headquarters Plaza · One Speedwell Avenue · Morristown, NJ 07962-1981 · 973-538-0800

Newark

Russell B. Bershad · Gibbons · http://www.gibbonslaw.com · One Gateway Center · Newark, NJ 07102-5310 · 973-596-4500

Peter J. Carton · Gibbons · http://www.gibbonslaw.com · One Gateway Center · Newark, NJ 07102-5310 973-596-4500

Robert R. DiVita · Sills Cummis & Gross · http://www.sillscummis.com · The Legal Center · One Riverfront Plaza · Newark, NJ 07102-5400 · 973-643-7000

Martin F. Dowd · McCarter & English · Four Gateway Center · 100 Mulberry Street · Newark, NJ 07102 973-622-4444

Thomas J. Hall · Sills Cummis & Gross · http://www.sillscummis.com · The Legal Center · One Riverfront Plaza · Newark, NJ 07102-5400 · 973-643-7000

Robert R. Hempstead · Sills Cummis & Gross · http://www.sillscummis.com · The Legal Center · One Riverfront Plaza · Newark, NJ 07102-5400 · 973-643-7000

Mark S. Levenson · Sills Cummis & Gross · http://www.sillscummis.com · The Legal Center · One Riverfront Plaza · Newark, NJ 07102-5400 · 973-643-7000

Jeffrey H. Newman · Sills Cummis & Gross · http://www.sillscummis.com · The Legal Center · One Riverfront Plaza · Newark, NJ 07102-5400 · 973-643-7000

Robert A. Wayne · LeClair Ryan · Two Penn Plaza East · Newark, NJ 07105 · 973-491-3600

Ted Zangari · Sills Cummis & Gross · http://www.sillscummis.com · The Legal Center · One Riverfront Plaza · Newark, NJ 07102-5400 · 973-643-7000

Princeton

Stephen M. Eisdorfer · Hill Wallack · 202 Carnegie Center · Princeton, NJ 08543-5226 · 609-924-0808

Jonathan I. Epstein · Drinker Biddle & Reath · 105 College Road East, Suite 300 · P.O. Box 627 · Princeton, NJ 08542-0627 · 609-716-6500

Kenneth E. Meiser · Hill Wallack · 202 Carnegie Center · Princeton, NJ 08543-5226 · 609-924-0808

Kevin J. Moore · Sills Cummis & Gross · http://www.sillscummis.com · 650 College Road East, Fourth Floor · Princeton, NJ 08540 · 609-227-4600

Roseland

Philip L. Chapman · 2) · Lum, Drasco & Positan · http://www.lumlaw.com · 103 Eisenhower Parkway · Roseland, NJ 07068-1049 · 973-403-9000

Kevin J. Coakley · a · Connell Foley · 85 Livingston Avenue · Roseland, NJ 07068 · 973-535-0500

Thomas E. Cohn · WolfBlock · http://wolfblock.com · 101 Eisenhower Parkway, Suite 200 · Roseland, NJ 07068 · 973-228-5700

Alan R. Hammer · WolfBlock · http://wolfblock.com · 101 Eisenhower Parkway, Suite 200 · Roseland, NJ 07068 · 973-228-5700

Stanley Schwartz · Orloff, Lowenbach, Stifelman & Siegel · 101 Eisenhower Parkway · Roseland, NJ 07068-1082 · 973-622-6200

Ira M. Starr · Starr, Gern, Davison & Rubin · 105 Eisenhower Parkway · Roseland, NJ 07068-1050 · 973-403-9200

Joseph LeVow Steinberg · 2% · Lowenstein Sandler · http://www.lowenstein.com · 65 Livingston Avenue Roseland, NJ 07068-1791 · 973-597-2500

Short Hills

Henry A. Larner · Budd Larner · http://www.buddlarner.com · 150 John F. Kennedy Parkway, Third Floor · Short Hills, NJ 07078-2703 · 973-379-4800

Voorhees

Richard M. Hluchan · Ballard Spahr Andrews & Ingersoll · Plaza 1000, Suite 500 · Main Street · Voorhees, NJ 08043-4636 · 856-761-3400

West Orange

Jeffrey L. Kantowitz · Goldberg, Mufson & Spar · 200 Executive Drive · West Orange, NJ 07052 · 973-736-0100

Fredric P. Lavinthal · Wolff & Samson · The Offices at Crystal Lake · One Boland Drive · West Orange, NJ 07052 · 973-325-1500

Barry R. Mandelbaum · Mandelbaum, Salsburg, Gold, Lazris & Discenza · 155 Prospect Avenue · West Orange, NJ 07052 · 973-736-4600

Westfield

Jack Fersko · Farer Fersko · http://www.farerlaw.com · 600 South Avenue · P.O. Box 580 · Westfield, NJ 07091-0580 · 908-789-8550

Ann M. Waeger · Farer Fersko · http://www.farerlaw.com · 600 South Avenue · P.O. Box 580 · Westfield, NJ 07091-0580 · 908-789-8550

Woodbridge

Anne S. Babineau · a · Wilentz, Goldman & Spitzer · http://www.wilentz.com · 90 Woodbridge Center Drive, Suite 900 · P.O. Box 10 · Woodbridge, NJ 07095-0958 · 732-636-8000

Kenneth T. Bills · Greenbaum, Rowe, Smith & Davis · http://www.greenbaumlaw.com · Metro Corporate Campus One · 99 Wood Avenue South · P.O. Box 5600 · Woodbridge, NJ 08830-2712 · 732-549-5600

Thomas J. Denitzio, Jr. · Greenbaum, Rowe, Smith & Davis · http://www.greenbaumlaw.com · Metro Corporate Campus One · 99 Wood Avenue South · P.O. Box 5600 · Woodbridge, NJ 08830-2712 · 732-549-5600

Martin E. Dollinger · 2) · Greenbaum, Rowe, Smith & Davis · http://www.greenbaumlaw.com · Metro Corporate Campus One · 99 Wood Avenue South · P.O. Box 5600 · Woodbridge, NJ 08830-2712 · 732-549-5600

Dean A. Gaver · a · Greenbaum, Rowe, Smith & Davis · http://www.greenbaumlaw.com · Metro Corporate Campus One · 99 Wood Avenue South · P.O. Box 5600 · Woodbridge, NJ 08830-2712 · 732-549-5600

Robert S. Goldsmith · Greenbaum, Rowe, Smith & Davis · http://www.greenbaumlaw.com · Metro Corporate Campus One · 99 Wood Avenue South · P.O. Box 5600 · Woodbridge, NJ 08830-2712 · 732-549-5600

Meryl A.G. Gonchar · Greenbaum, Rowe, Smith & Davis · http://www.greenbaumlaw.com · Metro Corporate Campus One · 99 Wood Avenue South · P.O. Box 5600 · Woodbridge, NJ 08830-2712 · 732-549-5600

David S. Gordon · Wilentz, Goldman & Spitzer · http://www.wilentz.com · 90 Woodbridge Center Drive, Suite 900 · P.O. Box 10 · Woodbridge, NJ 07095-0958 · 732-636-8000

Arthur M. Greenbaum · a · Greenbaum, Rowe, Smith & Davis · http://www.greenbaumlaw.com · Metro Corporate Campus One · 99 Wood Avenue South · P.O. Box 5600 · Woodbridge, NJ 08830-2712 · 732-549-5600

Robert S. Greenbaum · 2% · Greenbaum, Rowe, Smith & Davis · http://www.greenbaumlaw.com · Metro Corporate Campus One · 99 Wood Avenue South · P.O. Box 5600 · Woodbridge, NJ 08830-2712 · 732-549-5600

Stewart M. Hutt · Hutt & Shimanowitz · 459 Amboy Avenue · P.O. Box 648 · Woodbridge, NJ 07095 · 732-634-6400

Nicholas L. Santowasso · Wilentz, Goldman & Spitzer · http://www.wilentz.com · 90 Woodbridge Center Drive, Suite 900 · P.O. Box 10 · Woodbridge, NJ 07095-0958 · 732-636-8000

Robert C. Schachter · Greenbaum, Rowe, Smith & Davis · http://www.greenbaumlaw.com · Metro Corporate Campus One · 99 Wood Avenue South · P.O. Box 5600 · Woodbridge, NJ 08830-2712 · 732-549-5600

Wendell A. Smith · 2% · Greenbaum, Rowe, Smith & Davis · http://www.greenbaumlaw.com · Metro Corporate Campus One · 99 Wood Avenue South · P.O. Box 5600 · Woodbridge, NJ 08830-2712 · 732-549-5600

Douglas K. Wolfson · Greenbaum, Rowe, Smith & Davis · http://www.greenbaumlaw.com · Metro Corporate Campus One · 99 Wood Avenue South · P.O. Box 5600 · Woodbridge, NJ 08830-2712 · 732-549-5600

SECURITIES LAW

Florham Park

Warren J. Casey · Day Pitney · 200 Campus Drive · P.O. Box 1945 · Florham Park, NJ 07962-1945 · 973-966-6300

Middletown

Philip D. Forlenza · Giordano, Halleran & Ciesla · http://www.ghclaw.com · 125 Half Mile Road, Suite 300 · P.O. Box 190 · Middletown, NJ 07748 · 732-741-3900

Roseland

Peter H. Ehrenberg · 2) · Lowenstein Sandler · http://www.lowenstein.com · 65 Livingston Avenue · Roseland, NJ 07068-1791 · 973-597-2500

John D. Hogoboom · Lowenstein Sandler · http://www.lowenstein.com · 65 Livingston Avenue · Roseland, NJ 07068-1791 · 973-597-2500

John D. Schupper · 2) · Lowenstein Sandler · http://www.lowenstein.com · 65 Livingston Avenue · Roseland, NJ 07068-1791 · 973-597-2500

Alan Wovsaniker · Lowenstein Sandler · http://www.lowenstein.com · 65 Livingston Avenue · Roseland, NJ 07068-1791 · 973-597-2500

Somerville

Peter D. Hutcheon · 2) · Norris, McLaughlin & Marcus · http://www.nmmlaw.com · 721 Route 202-206 · P.O. Box 1018 · Somerville, NJ 08876-1018 · 908-722-0700

Woodbridge

W. Raymond Felton · a · Greenbaum, Rowe, Smith & Davis · http://www.greenbaumlaw.com · Metro Corporate Campus One · 99 Wood Avenue South · P.O. Box 5600 · Woodbridge, NJ 08830-2712 · 732-549-5600

STRUCTURED FINANCE LAW

Roseland

Gary M. Wingens · Lowenstein Sandler · http://www.lowenstein.com · 65 Livingston Avenue · Roseland, NJ 07068-1791 · 973-597-2500

TAX LAW

Cherry Hill

Richard J. Flaster · Flaster/Greenberg · 1810 Chapel Avenue West · Cherry Hill, NJ 08002-4609 · 856-661-1900

Florham Park

Michael J. Guerriero · Day Pitney · 200 Campus Drive · P.O. Box 1945 · Florham Park, NJ 07962-1945 · 973-966-6300

Frederick M. Lappin · a · Greenberg Traurig · http://www.gtlaw.com · 200 Park Avenue · P.O. Box 677 · Florham Park, NJ 07932-0677 · 973-360-7900

Kenneth J. Norcross · a · Drinker Biddle & Reath · 500 Campus Drive · Florham Park, NJ 07932-1047 · 973-360-1100

Paul I. Rosenberg · 2% · Bressler, Amery & Ross · http://www.bressler.com · 325 Columbia Turnpike · Florham Park, NJ 07932 · 973-514-1200

Hackensack

Michael H. Forman · a · Cole, Schotz, Meisel, Forman & Leonard · http://www.coleschotz.com · Court Plaza North, Fourth Floor · 25 Main Street · Hackensack, NJ 07601 · 201-489-3000

Haddonfield

James B. Evans, Jr. · Kulzer & Di Padova · 76 East Euclid Avenue, Suite 300 · Haddonfield, NJ 08033-2342 · 856-795-7744

Michael A. Kulzer · Kulzer & Di Padova · 76 East Euclid Avenue, Suite 300 · Haddonfield, NJ 08033-2342 · 856-795-7744

Morristown

Sandra Brown Sherman · Riker, Danzig, Scherer, Hyland & Perretti · Headquarters Plaza · One Speedwell Avenue · Morristown, NJ 07962-1981 · 973-538-0800

Charles Edward Falk · Porzio, Bromberg & Newman · 100 Southgate Parkway · P.O. Box 1997 · Morristown, NJ 07962-1997 · 973-538-4006

Andrew J. Stamelman · Riker, Danzig, Scherer, Hyland & Perretti · Headquarters Plaza · One Speedwell Avenue · Morristown, NJ 07962-1981 · 973-538-0800

Murray Hill

Bruce E. Mantell · a · Mantell & Prince · Mountain Heights Center at Berkeley Heights · 430 Mountain Avenue · Murray Hill, NJ 07974 · 908-464-5900

Newark

Robert J. Alter · Sills Cummis & Gross · http://www.sillscummis.com · The Legal Center · One Riverfront Plaza · Newark, NJ 07102-5400 · 973-643-7000

Jeannette M. Bond · McCarter & English · Four Gateway Center · 100 Mulberry Street · Newark, NJ 07102 · 973-622-4444

Mark A. Daniele · McCarter & English · Four Gateway Center · 100 Mulberry Street · Newark, NJ 07102 973-622-4444

Stanley A. Epstein · a · Greenberg, Dauber, Epstein & Tucker · http://www.greenbergdauber.com · One Gateway Center, Suite 600 · Newark, NJ 07102-5311 · 973-643-3700

Susan A. Feeney · McCarter & English · Four Gateway Center · 100 Mulberry Street · Newark, NJ 07102 · 973-622-4444

Michael A. Guariglia · McCarter & English · Four Gateway Center · 100 Mulberry Street · Newark, NJ 07102 · 973-622-4444

Alyce C. Halchak · Gibbons · http://www.gibbonslaw.com · One Gateway Center · Newark, NJ 07102-5310 · 973-596-4500

Simon Levin · Sills Cummis & Gross · http://www.sillscummis.com · The Legal Center · One Riverfront Plaza · Newark, NJ 07102-5400 · 973-643-7000

Laurence Reich · a · McElroy, Deutsch, Mulvaney & Carpenter · http://www.mdmc-law.com · Three Gateway Center, 17th Floor · 100 Mulberry Street · Newark, NJ 07102-4079 · 973-622-7711

Peter J. Ulrich · Gibbons · http://www.gibbonslaw.com · One Gateway Center · Newark, NJ 07102-5310 · 973-596-4500

Stephen M. Vajtay, Jr. · McCarter & English · Four Gateway Center · 100 Mulberry Street · Newark, NJ 07102 · 973-622-4444

Roseland

Stuart M. Gladstone · WolfBlock · http://wolfblock.com · 101 Eisenhower Parkway, Suite 200 · Roseland, NJ 07068 · 973-228-5700

Susan M. Holzman · Orloff, Lowenbach, Stifelman & Siegel · 101 Eisenhower Parkway · Roseland, NJ 07068-1082 · 973-622-6200

Benedict M. Kohl · 2% · Lowenstein Sandler · http://www.lowenstein.com · 65 Livingston Avenue · Roseland, NJ 07068-1791 · 973-597-2500

Alan F. Kornstein · Orloff, Lowenbach, Stifelman & Siegel · 101 Eisenhower Parkway · Roseland, NJ 07068-1082 · 973-622-6200

Kenneth J. Slutsky · a · Lowenstein Sandler · http://www.lowenstein.com · 65 Livingston Avenue · Roseland, NJ 07068-1791 · 973-597-2500

Ashley Steinhart · a · Lowenstein Sandler · http://www.lowenstein.com · 65 Livingston Avenue · Roseland, NJ 07068-1791 · 973-597-2500

Frank L. Stifelman · Orloff, Lowenbach, Stifelman & Siegel · 101 Eisenhower Parkway · Roseland, NJ 07068-1082 · 973-622-6200

Eugenia Yudanin · Orloff, Lowenbach, Stifelman & Siegel · 101 Eisenhower Parkway · Roseland, NJ 07068-1082 · 973-622-6200

Warren

Robert B. Haines · a · Herold and Haines · http://www.heroldhaines.com · 25 Independence Boulevard · Warren, NJ 07059-6747 · 908-647-1022

West Orange

Leonard M. Goldberg · a · Goldberg, Mufson & Spar · 200 Executive Drive · West Orange, NJ 07052 · 973-736-0100

David L. Schlossberg · Wolff & Samson · The Offices at Crystal Lake · One Boland Drive · West Orange, NJ 07052 · 973-325-1500

Woodbridge

Richard H. Greenberg · Greenberg & Schulman · 90 Woodbridge Center Drive, Suite 610 · Woodbridge, NJ 07095-1142 · 732-636-8800

Robert C. Kautz · Wilentz, Goldman & Spitzer · http://www.wilentz.com · 90 Woodbridge Center Drive, Suite 900 · P.O. Box 10 · Woodbridge, NJ 07095-0958 · 732-636-8000

Martin L. Lepelstat · Greenbaum, Rowe, Smith & Davis · http://www.greenbaumlaw.com · Metro Corporate Campus One · 99 Wood Avenue South · P.O. Box 5600 · Woodbridge, NJ 08830-2712 · 732-549-5600

TRANSPORTATION LAW

Livingston

Leonard C. Leicht · Morgan Melhuish Abrutyn · 651 West Mount Pleasant Avenue, Suite 200 · Livingston, NJ 07039 · 973-994-2500

TRUSTS AND ESTATES

Florham Park

John M. Elias · Greenberg Traurig · http://www.gtlaw.com · 200 Park Avenue · P.O. Box 677 · Florham Park, NJ 07932-0677 · 973-360-7900

Edward A. Gramigna, Jr. · Drinker Biddle & Reath · 500 Campus Drive · Florham Park, NJ 07932-1047 973-360-1100

Richard Kahn · 2% · Day Pitney · 200 Campus Drive · P.O. Box 1945 · Florham Park, NJ 07962-1945 · 973-966-6300

Frederick M. Lappin · a · Greenberg Traurig · http://www.gtlaw.com · 200 Park Avenue · P.O. Box 677 · Florham Park, NJ 07932-0677 · 973-360-7900

Alvin C. Martin · Drinker Biddle & Reath · 500 Campus Drive · Florham Park, NJ 07932-1047 · 973-360-1100

Mary Lou Parker · a · Day Pitney · 200 Campus Drive · P.O. Box 1945 · Florham Park, NJ 07962-1945 · 973-966-6300

Paul I. Rosenberg · 2% · Bressler, Amery & Ross · http://www.bressler.com · 325 Columbia Turnpike · Florham Park, NJ 07932 · 973-514-1200

Hackensack

Jerome A. Deener · a · Deener, Hirsch & Shramenko · Two University Plaza, Suite 111 · Hackensack, NJ 07601 · 201-343-8788

Michael H. Forman · a · Cole, Schotz, Meisel, Forman & Leonard · http://www.coleschotz.com · Court Plaza North, Fourth Floor · 25 Main Street · Hackensack, NJ 07601 · 201-489-3000

Steven D. Leipzig · Cole, Schotz, Meisel, Forman & Leonard · http://www.coleschotz.com · Court Plaza North, Fourth Floor · 25 Main Street · Hackensack, NJ 07601 · 201-489-3000

Samuel Weiner · Cole, Schotz, Meisel, Forman & Leonard · http://www.coleschotz.com · Court Plaza North, Fourth Floor · 25 Main Street · Hackensack, NJ 07601 · 201-489-3000

Haddonfield

Frank R. Demmerly, Jr. · a · Archer & Greiner · http://www.archerlaw.com · One Centennial Square · 56 Haddon Avenue · P.O. Box 3000 · Haddonfield, NJ 08033-0968 · 856-795-2121

Arthur Di Padova · Kulzer & Di Padova · 76 East Euclid Avenue, Suite 300 · Haddonfield, NJ 08033-2342 · 856-795-7744

Peter E. Driscoll · 2) · Archer & Greiner · http://www.archerlaw.com · One Centennial Square · 56 Haddon Avenue · P.O. Box 3000 · Haddonfield, NJ 08033-0968 · 856-795-2121

Glenn A. Henkel · Kulzer & Di Padova · 76 East Euclid Avenue, Suite 300 · Haddonfield, NJ 08033-2342 · 856-795-7744

Steven K. Mignogna · Archer & Greiner · http://www.archerlaw.com · One Centennial Square · 56 Haddon Avenue · P.O. Box 3000 · Haddonfield, NJ 08033-0968 · 856-795-2121

Livingston

Robert D. Borteck · a · Borteck & Sanders · 70 South Orange Avenue · Livingston, NJ 07039 · 973-994-2050

Judson M. Stein · Stein, McGuire, Pantages & Gigl · Eisenhower Plaza II, Second Floor · 354 Eisenhower Parkway · P.O. Box 460 · Livingston, NJ 07039 · 973-992-1100

Morristown

Sandra Brown Sherman · Riker, Danzig, Scherer, Hyland & Perretti · Headquarters Plaza · One Speedwell Avenue · Morristown, NJ 07962-1981 · 973-538-0800

Charles Edward Falk · Porzio, Bromberg & Newman · 100 Southgate Parkway · P.O. Box 1997 · Morristown, NJ 07962-1997 · 973-538-4006

Gary Mazart · Schenck, Price, Smith & King · 10 Washington Street · P.O. Box 905 · Morristown, NJ 07963-0905 · 973-539-1000

Anita J. Siegel · a · Siegel & Bergman · 365 South Street · Morristown, NJ 07960 · 973-285-5007

Murray Hill

Bruce E. Mantell · a · Mantell & Prince · Mountain Heights Center at Berkeley Heights · 430 Mountain Avenue · Murray Hill, NJ 07974 · 908-464-5900

Newark

Allan C. Bell · Sills Cummis & Gross · http://www.sillscummis.com · The Legal Center · One Riverfront Plaza · Newark, NJ 07102-5400 · 973-643-7000

Gerard G. Brew · McCarter & English · Four Gateway Center · 100 Mulberry Street · Newark, NJ 07102 973-622-4444

David A. Ludgin · a · McCarter & English · Four Gateway Center · 100 Mulberry Street · Newark, NJ 07102 · 973-622-4444

Francis X. O'Brien · McElroy, Deutsch, Mulvaney & Carpenter · http://www.mdmc-law.com · Three Gateway Center, 17th Floor · 100 Mulberry Street · Newark, NJ 07102-4079 · 973-622-7711

Howard G. Wachenfeld · 2% · Tompkins, McGuire, Wachenfeld & Barry · Four Gateway Center, Fifth Floor · 100 Mulberry Street · Newark, NJ 07102-4070 · 973-622-3000

Paramus

Joel L. Shoobe · a · Shoobe and Bakarich · 17 Arcadian Avenue · Paramus, NJ 07652 · 201-587-9004

Red Bank

George A. Aguilar · Neff Aguilar · 125 Half Mile Road, Suite 101 · Red Bank, NJ 07701 · 732-224-1200

Stuart T. Cox, Jr. · Neff Aguilar · 125 Half Mile Road, Suite 101 · Red Bank, NJ 07701 · 732-224-1200

Andrew J. DeMaio · Neff Aguilar · 125 Half Mile Road, Suite 101 · Red Bank, NJ 07701 · 732-224-1200

Mary Patricia MaGee · Neff Aguilar · 125 Half Mile Road, Suite 101 · Red Bank, NJ 07701 · 732-224-1200

Robert C. Neff · a · Neff Aguilar · 125 Half Mile Road, Suite 101 · Red Bank, NJ 07701 · 732-224-1200

Stephen J. Oppenheim · Neff Aguilar · 125 Half Mile Road, Suite 101 · Red Bank, NJ 07701 · 732-224-1200

Roseland

Stuart M. Gladstone · WolfBlock · http://wolfblock.com · 101 Eisenhower Parkway, Suite 200 · Roseland, NJ 07068 · 973-228-5700

Michael N. Gooen · Lowenstein Sandler · http://www.lowenstein.com · 65 Livingston Avenue · Roseland, NJ 07068-1791 · 973-597-2500

Susan M. Holzman · Orloff, Lowenbach, Stifelman & Siegel · 101 Eisenhower Parkway · Roseland, NJ 07068-1082 · 973-622-6200

Benedict M. Kohl · 2% · Lowenstein Sandler · http://www.lowenstein.com · 65 Livingston Avenue · Roseland, NJ 07068-1791 · 973-597-2500

David J. Ritter · WolfBlock · http://wolfblock.com · 101 Eisenhower Parkway, Suite 200 · Roseland, NJ 07068 · 973-228-5700

Joel D. Siegel · Orloff, Lowenbach, Stifelman & Siegel · 101 Eisenhower Parkway · Roseland, NJ 07068-1082 · 973-622-6200

Ashley Steinhart · a · Lowenstein Sandler · http://www.lowenstein.com · 65 Livingston Avenue · Roseland, NJ 07068-1791 · 973-597-2500

Frank L. Stifelman · Orloff, Lowenbach, Stifelman & Siegel · 101 Eisenhower Parkway · Roseland, NJ 07068-1082 · 973-622-6200

Short Hills

Robert W. Cockren · Sonnenschein Nath & Rosenthal · 101 JFK Parkway, Fourth Floor · Short Hills, NJ 07078-2708 · 973-912-7100

Somerville

Victor S. Elgort · Norris, McLaughlin & Marcus · http://www.nmmlaw.com · 721 Route 202-206 · P.O. Box 1018 · Somerville, NJ 08876-1018 · 908-722-0700

Kenneth D. Meskin · Norris, McLaughlin & Marcus · http://www.nmmlaw.com · 721 Route 202-206 · P.O. Box 1018 · Somerville, NJ 08876-1018 · 908-722-0700

Summit

David G. Hardin · Lindabury, McCormick, Estabrook & Cooper · 480 Morris Avenue · Summit, NJ 07901 · 908-273-1212

Joseph E. Imbriaco · 2) · Lindabury, McCormick, Estabrook & Cooper · 480 Morris Avenue · Summit, NJ 07901 · 908-273-1212

Warren

Robert B. Haines · a · Herold and Haines · http://www.heroldhaines.com · 25 Independence Boulevard · Warren, NJ 07059-6747 · 908-647-1022

Richard H. Herold, Sr. · a · Herold and Haines · http://www.heroldhaines.com · 25 Independence Boulevard · Warren, NJ 07059-6747 · 908-647-1022

Gordon A. Millspaugh, Jr. · 2% · Herold and Haines · http://www.heroldhaines.com · 25 Independence Boulevard · Warren, NJ 07059-6747 · 908-647-1022

Kevin J. O'Donnell · Herold and Haines · http://www.heroldhaines.com · 25 Independence Boulevard · Warren, NJ 07059-6747 · 908-647-1022

West Orange

Stephen L. Ferszt · Wolff & Samson · The Offices at Crystal Lake · One Boland Drive · West Orange, NJ 07052 · 973-325-1500

Leonard M. Goldberg · a · Goldberg, Mufson & Spar · 200 Executive Drive · West Orange, NJ 07052 · 973-736-0100

David L. Schlossberg · Wolff & Samson · The Offices at Crystal Lake · One Boland Drive · West Orange, NJ 07052 · 973-325-1500

Woodbridge

Michael A. Backer · a · Greenbaum, Rowe, Smith & Davis · http://www.greenbaumlaw.com · Metro Corporate Campus One · 99 Wood Avenue South · P.O. Box 5600 · Woodbridge, NJ 08830-2712 · 732-549-5600

Michael K. Feinberg · Greenbaum, Rowe, Smith & Davis · http://www.greenbaumlaw.com · Metro Corporate Campus One · 99 Wood Avenue South · P.O. Box 5600 · Woodbridge, NJ 08830-2712 · 732-549-5600

Richard H. Greenberg · Greenberg & Schulman · 90 Woodbridge Center Drive, Suite 610 · Woodbridge, NJ 07095-1142 · 732-636-8800

Martin L. Lepelstat · Greenbaum, Rowe, Smith & Davis · http://www.greenbaumlaw.com · Metro Corporate Campus One · 99 Wood Avenue South · P.O. Box 5600 · Woodbridge, NJ 08830-2712 · 732-549-5600

Richard F. Lert · 2% · Wilentz, Goldman & Spitzer · http://www.wilentz.com · 90 Woodbridge Center Drive, Suite 900 · P.O. Box 10 · Woodbridge, NJ 07095-0958 · 732-636-8000

VENTURE CAPITAL LAW

Roseland

Edward M. Zimmerman · Lowenstein Sandler · http://www.lowenstein.com · 65 Livingston Avenue · Roseland, NJ 07068-1791 · 973-597-2500

WATER LAW

Newark

Stephen B. Genzer · a · Saul Ewing · One River Front Plaza · Newark, NJ 07102 · 973-286-6700

WHITE-COLLAR CRIMINAL DEFENSE

Atlantic City

Edwin J. Jacobs, Jr. · a · Jacobs & Barbone · 1125 Pacific Avenue · Atlantic City, NJ 08401 · 609-348-1125

Chatham

John D. Arseneault · a · Arseneault, Whipple, Farmer, Fassett & Azzarello · http://www.awffa.com · 560 Main Street · Chatham, NJ 07928 · 973-635-3366

John A. Azzarello · Arseneault, Whipple, Farmer, Fassett & Azzarello · http://www.awffa.com · 560 Main Street · Chatham, NJ 07928 · 973-635-3366

John J. Farmer · Arseneault, Whipple, Farmer, Fassett & Azzarello · http://www.awffa.com · 560 Main Street · Chatham, NJ 07928 · 973-635-3366

David W. Fassett · Arseneault, Whipple, Farmer, Fassett & Azzarello · http://www.awffa.com · 560 Main Street · Chatham, NJ 07928 · 973-635-3366

Kevin H. Marino · Marino Tortorella · 437 Southern Boulevard · Chatham, NJ 07928-1488 · 973-824-9300

John C. Whipple · Arseneault, Whipple, Farmer, Fassett & Azzarello · http://www.awffa.com · 560 Main Street · Chatham, NJ 07928 · 973-635-3366

Alan L. Zegas · a · Law Offices of Alan L. Zegas · http://www.zegaslaw.com · 552 Main Street · Chatham, NJ 07928 · 973-701-7080

Cherry Hill

Carl D. Poplar · 2% · Carl D. Poplar · Building Two · 1010 Kings Highway South · Cherry Hill, NJ 08034 · 856-216-9979

Florham Park

Dennis T. Kearney · Day Pitney · 200 Campus Drive · P.O. Box 1945 · Florham Park, NJ 07962-1945 · 973-966-6300

Paul G. Nittoly · Drinker Biddle & Reath · 500 Campus Drive · Florham Park, NJ 07932-1047 · 973-360-1100

John J. O'Reilly · Day Pitney · 200 Campus Drive · P.O. Box 1945 · Florham Park, NJ 07962-1945 · 973-966-6300

Freehold

Robert S. Bonney, Jr. · Lomurro, Davison, Eastman and Muñoz · http://www.lomurrolaw.com · Monmouth Executive Center, Building One · 100 Willowbrook Road · Freehold, NJ 07728 · 732-462-7170

Hackensack

Raymond F. Flood · a · Flood & Basile · 39 Hudson Street · Hackensack, NJ 07601 · 201-487-0700

Hoboken

Brian J. Neary · a · Law Offices of Brian J. Neary · http://www.nearylaw.com · Hoboken Land Building · One Newark Street · Hoboken, NJ 07030 · 201-420-8101

Manasquan

Cathy Waldor · a · Waldor & Carlesimo · Building L, Suite 101 · 2517 Highway 35 · Manasquan, NJ 08736 · 732-528-5040

Montclair

David A. Ruhnke · a · Ruhnke & Barrett · 47 Park Street · Montclair, NJ 07042 · 973-744-1000

Moorestown

Francis J. Hartman · 2% · Attorneys Hartman · 505 South Lenola Road, Suite 121 · Moorestown, NJ 08057-1590 · 856-235-0220

Morristown

Stephen S. Weinstein · a · Stephen S. Weinstein · http://www.sswpa.com · 20 Park Place, Suite 301 · Morristown, NJ 07960-7102 · 973-267-5200

New Brunwick

Steven D. Altman · Benedict & Altman · 247 Livingston Avenue · New Brunwick, NJ 08901 · 732-745-9000

Joseph J. Benedict · a · Benedict & Altman · 247 Livingston Avenue · New Brunwick, NJ 08901 · 732-745-9000

Newark

Thomas R. Ashley · 2) · Thomas R. Ashley · 50 Park Place, Suite 1400 · Newark, NJ 07102 · 973-623-0501

Raymond A. Brown · 2% · Brown & Brown · One Gateway Center, Suite 105 · Newark, NJ 07102 · 973-622-1846

Lawrence S. Horn · Sills Cummis & Gross · http://www.sillscummis.com · The Legal Center · One Riverfront Plaza · Newark, NJ 07102-5400 · 973-643-7000

Gerald Krovatin · a · Krovatin & Associates · 744 Broad Street, Suite 1903 · Newark, NJ 07102 · 973-424-9777

Lawrence S. Lustberg · a · Gibbons · http://www.gibbonslaw.com · One Gateway Center · Newark, NJ 07102-5310 · 973-596-4500

Princeton

Alain Leibman · Fox Rothschild · Princeton Pike Corporate Center, Building Three · 997 Lenox Drive · Princeton, NJ 08648-2311 · 609-896-3600

Red Bank

Edward J. Plaza · Weir & Plaza · 321 Broad Street · Red Bank, NJ 07701 · 732-741-8181

Roseland

Michael Critchley · 2) · Critchley & Kinum · 75 Livingston Avenue · Roseland, NJ 07068 · 973-422-9200

Michael D'Alessio, Jr. · 2% · Walder, Hayden & Brogan · Five Becker Farm Road · Roseland, NJ 07068 · 973-992-5300

Joseph A. Hayden, Jr. · 2) · Walder, Hayden & Brogan · Five Becker Farm Road · Roseland, NJ 07068 · 973-992-5300

Michael B. Himmel · a · Lowenstein Sandler · http://www.lowenstein.com · 65 Livingston Avenue · Roseland, NJ 07068-1791 · 973-597-2500

Robert L. Penza · Walder, Hayden & Brogan · Five Becker Farm Road · Roseland, NJ 07068 · 973-992-5300

Alan Silber · Walder, Hayden & Brogan · Five Becker Farm Road · Roseland, NJ 07068 · 973-992-5300

Justin P. Walder · 2% · Walder, Hayden & Brogan · Five Becker Farm Road · Roseland, NJ 07068 · 973-992-5300

Somerville

John P. McDonald · a · McDonald & Rogers · 181 West High Street · Somerville, NJ 08876 · 908-722-4100

Vineland

Joseph D. O'Neill · O'Neill & Coant · 30 West Chestnut Avenue · Vineland, NJ 08360-5401 · 856-692-2400

West Orange

Timothy Donohue · Arleo & Donohue · 622 Eagle Rock Avenue · West Orange, NJ 07052 · 973-736-8660

Woodbridge

Raymond M. Brown · 2) · Greenbaum, Rowe, Smith & Davis · http://www.greenbaumlaw.com · Metro Corporate Campus One · 99 Wood Avenue South · P.O. Box 5600 · Woodbridge, NJ 08830-2712 · 732-549-5600

James E. Trabilsy · Wilentz, Goldman & Spitzer · http://www.wilentz.com · 90 Woodbridge Center Drive, Suite 900 · P.O. Box 10 · Woodbridge, NJ 07095-0958 · 732-636-8000

Warren W. Wilentz · Wilentz, Goldman & Spitzer · http://www.wilentz.com · 90 Woodbridge Center Drive, Suite 900 · P.O. Box 10 · Woodbridge, NJ 07095-0958 · 732-636-8000

WORKERS' COMPENSATION LAW

Atlantic City

Kenneth Mackler · Goldenberg, Mackler, Sayegh, Mintz, Pfeffer, Bonchi & Gill · http://www.gmslaw.com · 1030 Atlantic Avenue · Atlantic City, NJ 08401 · 609-344-7131

Lawrence A. Mintz · Goldenberg, Mackler, Sayegh, Mintz, Pfeffer, Bonchi & Gill · http://www.gmslaw.com · 1030 Atlantic Avenue · Atlantic City, NJ 08401 · 609-344-7131

Cherry Hill

J. David Nemeth · J. David Nemeth · 20 Brace Road · Cherry Hill, NJ 08034 · 856-795-2070

Edison

John R. Tort, Jr. · Leitner, Tort & DeFazio · 244 Fernwood Avenue · P.O. Box 6270 · Edison, NJ 08818 732-417-9700

Florham Park

Richard V. Jones · Bressler, Amery & Ross · http://www.bressler.com · 325 Columbia Turnpike · Florham Park, NJ 07932 · 973-514-1200

Hackensack

Joyce A. Parisi · Parisi and Gerlanc · 190 Moore Street, Suite 460 · Hackensack, NJ 07601 · 201-343-9000

Lawrenceville

Vicki W. Beyer · Stark & Stark · 993 Lenox Drive, Building Two · P.O. Box 5315 · Lawrenceville, NJ 08543 · 609-896-9060

Robert M. Capuano · a · Stark & Stark · 993 Lenox Drive, Building Two · P.O. Box 5315 · Lawrenceville, NJ 08543 · 609-896-9060

Newark

Samuel E. Bass · a · Freeman & Bass · 24 Commerce Street, Suite 726 · Newark, NJ 07102 · 973-623-7932

North Field

Frank A. Petro · a · Petro Cohen Petro Matarazzo Warrington · The Executive Plaza, Suite 202 · 2111 New Road · North Field, NJ 08225 · 609-677-1700

Ocean Township

Raymond P. Shebell · Shebell & Shebell · 1398 Highway 35 South · Ocean Township, NJ 07712-3522 · 732-663-1122

Princeton

Bruce P. Miller · a · Pellettieri, Rabstein and Altman · http://www.pralaw.com · 100 Nassau Park Boulevard, Suite 111 · Princeton, NJ 08540 · 609-520-0900

Toms River

Frank S. Salzer · Frank S. Salzer · 611 Main Street · P.O. Box 4806 · Toms River, NJ 08753 · 732-240-4215

Wayne

Jon L. Gelman · a · Jon L. Gelman · http://www.gelmans.com · 1450 Valley Road, First Floor · P.O. Box 934 · Wayne, NJ 07474-0934 · 973-696-7900

NEW MEXICO

ADMINISTRATIVE LAW

Albuquerque

Jeffrey H. Albright · Lewis and Roca · http://www.lrlaw.com · 201 Third Street, NW, Suite 1950 · Albuquerque, NM 87102 · 505-764-5400

John J. Kelly · Modrall, Sperling, Roehl, Harris & Sisk · Bank of America Centre, Suite 1000 · 500 Fourth Street, NW · P.O. Box 2168 · Albuquerque, NM 87103-2168 · 505-848-1800

Arthur Melendres · Modrall, Sperling, Roehl, Harris & Sisk · Bank of America Centre, Suite 1000 · 500 Fourth Street, NW · P.O. Box 2168 · Albuquerque, NM 87103-2168 · 505-848-1800

Richard C. Minzner · Rodey, Dickason, Sloan, Akin, & Robb · Albuquerque Plaza, Suite 2200 · 201 Third Street, NW · P.O. Box 1888 · Albuquerque, NM 87102 · 505-765-5900

Patrick J. Rogers · Modrall, Sperling, Roehl, Harris & Sisk · Bank of America Centre, Suite 1000 · 500 Fourth Street, NW · P.O. Box 2168 · Albuquerque, NM 87103-2168 · 505-848-1800

Santa Fe

Louis W. Rose · Montgomery & Andrews · 325 Paseo De Peralta · P.O. Box 2307 · Santa Fe, NM 87504-2307 · 505-982-3873

William P. Templeman · Comeau, Maldegen, Templeman & Indall · Coronado Building · 141 East Palace Avenue · P.O. Box 669 · Santa Fe, NM 87504-0669 · 505-982-4611

ALTERNATIVE DISPUTE RESOLUTION

Albuquerque

Paul G. Bardacke · ⑩ · Sutin, Thayer & Browne · http://www.sutinfirm.com · Two Park Square, Suite 1000 · 6565 Americas Parkway, NE · P.O. Box 1945 · Albuquerque, NM 87103 · 505-883-2500

Briggs F. Cheney · ⑩ · Sheehan, Sheehan & Stelzner · http://www.ssslawfirm.com · 40 First Plaza, NW, Suite 740 · Albuquerque, NM 87102 · 505-247-0411

Bruce Hall · ⑩ · Rodey, Dickason, Sloan, Akin, & Robb · Albuquerque Plaza, Suite 2200 · 201 Third Street, NW · P.O. Box 1888 · Albuquerque, NM 87102 · 505-765-5900

William C. Madison · Madison, Harbour, Mroz & Brennan · Albuquerque Plaza, Suite 1600 · 201 Third Street, NW · P.O. Box 25467 · Albuquerque, NM 87125-0467 · 505-242-2177

Charles A. Pharris · ⑩ · Keleher & McLeod · http://www.keleher-law.com · Albuquerque Plaza, 12th Floor · 201 Third Street, NW · P.O. Drawer AA · Albuquerque, NM 87103 · 505-346-4646

W. C. Smith · Professional Settlement Services · 1519 Eastridge Court, NE · Albuquerque, NM 87112 · 505-271-8194

Luis G. Stelzner · ⑩ · Sheehan, Sheehan & Stelzner · http://www.ssslawfirm.com · 40 First Plaza, NW, Suite 740 · Albuquerque, NM 87102 · 505-247-0411

Farmington

Richard L. Gerding · ⑩ · Gerding & O'Loughlin · 304 North Behrend Avenue · P.O. Box 1020 · Farmington, NM 87499-1020 · 505-325-1804

Las Cruces

Denise M. Torres · Saenz & Torres · 333 South Campo Street · Las Cruces, NM 88001 · 505-526-3333

Roswell

Robert E. Sabin · ⑩ · Atwood, Malone, Turner & Sabin · 400 North Pennsylvania Avenue, Suite 1100 · P.O. Drawer 700 · Roswell, NM 88202-0700 · 575-622-6221

Santa Fe

W. Mark Mowery · Rodey, Dickason, Sloan, Akin, & Robb · 315 Paseo de Peralta · P.O. Box 1357 · Santa Fe, NM 87501-2034 · 505-954-3900

Kimball R. Udall · Sommer, Udall, Hardwick, Ahern & Hyatt · 200 West Marcy Street, Suite 129 · P.O. Box 1984 · Santa Fe, NM 87504-1984 · 505-982-4676

Mel Yost · Scheuer, Yost & Patterson · 125 Lincoln Avenue, Suite 223 · P.O. Drawer 9570 · Santa Fe, NM 87504-9570 · 505-982-9911

ANTITRUST LAW

Albuquerque

Thomas C. Bird · Keleher & McLeod · http://www.keleher-law.com · Albuquerque Plaza, 12th Floor · 201 Third Street, NW · P.O. Drawer AA · Albuquerque, NM 87103 · 505-346-4646

John W. Boyd · ⑩ · Freedman Boyd Hollander Goldberg & Ives · http://www.fbdlaw.com · 20 First Plaza, Suite 700 · Albuquerque, NM 87102 · 505-842-9960

David A. Freedman · ⑩ · Freedman Boyd Hollander Goldberg & Ives · http://www.fbdlaw.com · 20 First Plaza, Suite 700 · Albuquerque, NM 87102 · 505-842-9960

Joseph Goldberg · ⑩ · Freedman Boyd Hollander Goldberg & Ives · http://www.fbdlaw.com · 20 First Plaza, Suite 700 · Albuquerque, NM 87102 · 505-842-9960

Norman S. Thayer, Jr. · ⑩ · Sutin, Thayer & Browne · http://www.sutinfirm.com · Two Park Square, Suite 1000 · 6565 Americas Parkway, NE · P.O. Box 1945 · Albuquerque, NM 87103 · 505-883-2500

Santa Fe

Michael B. Campbell · Holland & Hart · Jefferson Place, Suite One · 110 North Guadalupe · P.O. Box 2208 · Santa Fe, NM 87504-2208 · 505-988-4421

Mark F. Sheridan · Holland & Hart · Jefferson Place, Suite One · 110 North Guadalupe · P.O. Box 2208 · Santa Fe, NM 87504-2208 · 505-988-4421

Mel Yost · Scheuer, Yost & Patterson · 125 Lincoln Avenue, Suite 223 · P.O. Drawer 9570 · Santa Fe, NM 87504-9570 · 505-982-9911

APPELLATE LAW

Albuquerque

Thomas C. Bird · Keleher & McLeod · http://www.keleher-law.com · Albuquerque Plaza, 12th Floor · 201 Third Street, NW · P.O. Drawer AA · Albuquerque, NM 87103 · 505-346-4646

Bruce Hall · ⑩ · Rodey, Dickason, Sloan, Akin, & Robb · Albuquerque Plaza, Suite 2200 · 201 Third Street, NW · P.O. Box 1888 · Albuquerque, NM 87102 · 505-765-5900

Tova Indritz · ⑩ · Tova Indritz · 2040 Fourth Street, NW · Albuquerque, NM 87102 · 505-242-4003

Kerry Kiernan · Sutin, Thayer & Browne · http://www.sutinfirm.com · Two Park Square, Suite 1000 · 6565 Americas Parkway, NE · P.O. Box 1945 · Albuquerque, NM 87103 · 505-883-2500

Alice Tomlinson Lorenz · Lorenz & Goble · 6301 Indian School Road, NE, Suite 900 · Albuquerque, NM 87110-8199 · 505-889-4050

Charles K. Purcell · Rodey, Dickason, Sloan, Akin, & Robb · Albuquerque Plaza, Suite 2200 · 201 Third Street, NW · P.O. Box 1888 · Albuquerque, NM 87102 · 505-765-5900

Edward Ricco · ⑩ · Rodey, Dickason, Sloan, Akin, & Robb · Albuquerque Plaza, Suite 2200 · 201 Third Street, NW · P.O. Box 1888 · Albuquerque, NM 87102 · 505-765-5900

Santa Fe

Sarah M. Singleton · Montgomery & Andrews · 325 Paseo De Peralta · P.O. Box 2307 · Santa Fe, NM 87504-2307 · 505-982-3873

Steven L. Tucker · Tucker Law Firm · http://www.stevetucker.net · 520 Agua Fria Street · Santa Fe, NM 87501-2508 · 505-982-3467

BANKING LAW

Albuquerque

John W. Anderson · ⑩ · John W. Anderson · 7770 Jefferson Street, NE, Suite 430 · Albuquerque, NM 87109 · 505-822-7900

Perry E. Bendicksen · ⑩ · Brownstein Hyatt Farber Schreck · http://www.bhfs.com · 201 Third Street NW, Suite 1700 · Albuquerque, NM 87102-4386 · 505-244-0770

David P. Buchholtz · ⑩ · Brownstein Hyatt Farber Schreck · http://www.bhfs.com · 201 Third Street NW, Suite 1700 · Albuquerque, NM 87102-4386 · 505-244-0770

Dale Wallace Ek · ⑩ · Modrall, Sperling, Roehl, Harris & Sisk · Bank of America Centre, Suite 1000 · 500 Fourth Street, NW · P.O. Box 2168 · Albuquerque, NM 87103-2168 · 505-848-1800

Dennis J. Falk · ⑩ · Modrall, Sperling, Roehl, Harris & Sisk · Bank of America Centre, Suite 1000 · 500 Fourth Street, NW · P.O. Box 2168 · Albuquerque, NM 87103-2168 · 505-848-1800

Catherine T. Goldberg · ⑩ · Rodey, Dickason, Sloan, Akin, & Robb · Albuquerque Plaza, Suite 2200 · 201 Third Street, NW · P.O. Box 1888 · Albuquerque, NM 87102 · 505-765-5900

Jay D. Hertz · Sutin, Thayer & Browne · http://www.sutinfirm.com · Two Park Square, Suite 1000 · 6565 Americas Parkway, NE · P.O. Box 1945 · Albuquerque, NM 87103 · 505-883-2500

Gordon S. Little · Little & Turner · 500 Marquette Avenue, NW, Suite 1410 · Albuquerque, NM 87102-5313 · 505-242-6888

W. Spencer Reid · Keleher & McLeod · http://www.keleher-law.com · Albuquerque Plaza, 12th Floor · 201 Third Street, NW · P.O. Drawer AA · Albuquerque, NM 87103 · 505-346-4646

Ruth M. Schifani · Modrall, Sperling, Roehl, Harris & Sisk · Bank of America Centre, Suite 1000 · 500 Fourth Street, NW · P.O. Box 2168 · Albuquerque, NM 87103-2168 · 505-848-1800

Robert M. St. John · ⑩ · Rodey, Dickason, Sloan, Akin, & Robb · Albuquerque Plaza, Suite 2200 · 201 Third Street, NW · P.O. Box 1888 · Albuquerque, NM 87102 · 505-765-5900

James Widland · Miller Stratvert · 500 Marquette Avenue, NW, Suite 1100 · P.O. Box 25687 · Albuquerque, NM 87125-0687 · 505-842-1950

Santa Fe

John P. Burton · ⑳ · Rodey, Dickason, Sloan, Akin, & Robb · 315 Paseo de Peralta · P.O. Box 1357 · Santa Fe, NM 87501-2034 · 505-954-3900

Robert G. Heyman · ⑩ · Sutin, Thayer & Browne · http://www.sutinfirm.com · 317 Paseo de Peralta · P.O. Box 2187 · Santa Fe, NM 87504 · 505-988-5521

BANKRUPTCY AND CREDITOR-DEBTOR RIGHTS LAW

Albuquerque

James A. Askew · Rodey, Dickason, Sloan, Akin, & Robb · Albuquerque Plaza, Suite 2200 · 201 Third Street, NW · P.O. Box 1888 · Albuquerque, NM 87102 · 505-765-5900

Paul M. Fish · ㉕ · Modrall, Sperling, Roehl, Harris & Sisk · Bank of America Centre, Suite 1000 · 500 Fourth Street, NW · P.O. Box 2168 · Albuquerque, NM 87103-2168 · 505-848-1800

Gail A. Gottlieb · Sutin, Thayer & Browne · http://www.sutinfirm.com · Two Park Square, Suite 1000 · 6565 Americas Parkway, NE · P.O. Box 1945 · Albuquerque, NM 87103 · 505-883-2500

Robert H. Jacobvitz · ⑩ · Jacobvitz, Thuma & Walker · http://www.jtwlawfirm.com · 500 Marquette Avenue, NW, Suite 650 · Albuquerque, NM 87102 · 505-766-9272

Robert A. Johnson · ⑩ · Johnson & Nelson · 3800 Osuna, NE, Suite One · P.O. Box 25547 · Albuquerque, NM 87125-5547 · 505-764-9900

William Reeves Keleher · Modrall, Sperling, Roehl, Harris & Sisk · Bank of America Centre, Suite 1000 · 500 Fourth Street, NW · P.O. Box 2168 · Albuquerque, NM 87103-2168 · 505-848-1800

George M. Moore · Moore, Berkson & Gandarilla · P.O. Box 216 · Albuquerque, NM 87103-0216 · 505-242-1218

David T. Thuma · Jacobvitz, Thuma & Walker · http://www.jtwlawfirm.com · 500 Marquette Avenue, NW, Suite 650 · Albuquerque, NM 87102 · 505-766-9272

Douglas R. Vadnais · Modrall, Sperling, Roehl, Harris & Sisk · Bank of America Centre, Suite 1000 · 500 Fourth Street, NW · P.O. Box 2168 · Albuquerque, NM 87103-2168 · 505-848-1800

Thomas Walker · Jacobvitz, Thuma & Walker · http://www.jtwlawfirm.com · 500 Marquette Avenue, NW, Suite 650 · Albuquerque, NM 87102 · 505-766-9272

Santa Fe

William J. Arland III · Rodey, Dickason, Sloan, Akin, & Robb · 315 Paseo de Peralta · P.O. Box 1357 · Santa Fe, NM 87501-2034 · 505-954-3900

BET-THE-COMPANY LITIGATION

Albuquerque

Paul G. Bardacke · ⑩ · Sutin, Thayer & Browne · http://www.sutinfirm.com · Two Park Square, Suite 1000 · 6565 Americas Parkway, NE · P.O. Box 1945 · Albuquerque, NM 87103 · 505-883-2500

Joseph Goldberg · ⑩ · Freedman Boyd Hollander Goldberg & Ives · http://www.fbdlaw.com · 20 First Plaza, Suite 700 · Albuquerque, NM 87102 · 505-842-9960

Bruce Hall · ⑩ · Rodey, Dickason, Sloan, Akin, & Robb · Albuquerque Plaza, Suite 2200 · 201 Third Street, NW · P.O. Box 1888 · Albuquerque, NM 87102 · 505-765-5900

Kenneth L. Harrigan · ⑩ · Modrall, Sperling, Roehl, Harris & Sisk · Bank of America Centre, Suite 1000 · 500 Fourth Street, NW · P.O. Box 2168 · Albuquerque, NM 87103-2168 · 505-848-1800

Charles R. Peifer · Peifer, Hanson & Mullins · 20 First Plaza, Suite 725 · P.O. Box 25245 · Albuquerque, NM 87125-5245 · 505-247-4800

CIVIL RIGHTS LAW

Santa Fe

Michael Schwarz · Michael Schwarz · P.O. Box 1656 · Santa Fe, NM 87504-1656 · 505-988-2053

COMMERCIAL LITIGATION

Albuquerque

Leslie McCarthy Apodaca · Rodey, Dickason, Sloan, Akin, & Robb · Albuquerque Plaza, Suite 2200 · 201 Third Street, NW · P.O. Box 1888 · Albuquerque, NM 87102 · 505-765-5900

Douglas A. Baker · ⑩ · Modrall, Sperling, Roehl, Harris & Sisk · Bank of America Centre, Suite 1000 · 500 Fourth Street, NW · P.O. Box 2168 · Albuquerque, NM 87103-2168 · 505-848-1800

John A. Bannerman · ⑩ · Bannerman & Williams · Building Two, Suite 207 · 2201 San Pedro, NE · Albuquerque, NM 87110 · 505-837-1900

Paul G. Bardacke · ⑩ · Sutin, Thayer & Browne · http://www.sutinfirm.com · Two Park Square, Suite 1000 · 6565 Americas Parkway, NE · P.O. Box 1945 · Albuquerque, NM 87103 · 505-883-2500

Henry M. Bohnhoff · Rodey, Dickason, Sloan, Akin, & Robb · Albuquerque Plaza, Suite 2200 · 201 Third Street, NW · P.O. Box 1888 · Albuquerque, NM 87102 · 505-765-5900

David W. Bunting · Rodey, Dickason, Sloan, Akin, & Robb · Albuquerque Plaza, Suite 2200 · 201 Third Street, NW · P.O. Box 1888 · Albuquerque, NM 87102 · 505-765-5900

William H. Carpenter · ㉕ · Carpenter & Stout · 1600 University Boulevard, NE, Suite A · Albuquerque, NM 87102-1724 · 505-243-1336

Robert C. Conklin · Conklin, Jenke, Woodcock & Ziegler · 320 Gold Avenue, SW, Suite 1111 · Albuquerque, NM 87102-3246 · 505-224-9160

John R. Cooney · ⑩ · Modrall, Sperling, Roehl, Harris & Sisk · Bank of America Centre, Suite 1000 · 500 Fourth Street, NW · P.O. Box 2168 · Albuquerque, NM 87103-2168 · 505-848-1800

John M. Eaves · Eaves & Mendenhall · http://www.eavesandmendenhall.com · 6565 Americas Parkway, Suite 950 · Albuquerque, NM 87110 · 505-888-4300

Nelson Franse · Rodey, Dickason, Sloan, Akin, & Robb · Albuquerque Plaza, Suite 2200 · 201 Third Street, NW · P.O. Box 1888 · Albuquerque, NM 87102 · 505-765-5900

David A. Freedman · ⑩ · Freedman Boyd Hollander Goldberg & Ives · http://www.fbdlaw.com · 20 First Plaza, Suite 700 · Albuquerque, NM 87102 · 505-842-9960

Joseph Goldberg · ⑩ · Freedman Boyd Hollander Goldberg & Ives · http://www.fbdlaw.com · 20 First Plaza, Suite 700 · Albuquerque, NM 87102 · 505-842-9960

Scott D. Gordon · Rodey, Dickason, Sloan, Akin, & Robb · Albuquerque Plaza, Suite 2200 · 201 Third Street, NW · P.O. Box 1888 · Albuquerque, NM 87102 · 505-765-5900

Bruce Hall · ⑩ · Rodey, Dickason, Sloan, Akin, & Robb · Albuquerque Plaza, Suite 2200 · 201 Third Street, NW · P.O. Box 1888 · Albuquerque, NM 87102 · 505-765-5900

Kenneth L. Harrigan · ⑩ · Modrall, Sperling, Roehl, Harris & Sisk · Bank of America Centre, Suite 1000 · 500 Fourth Street, NW · P.O. Box 2168 · Albuquerque, NM 87103-2168 · 505-848-1800

Phil Krehbiel · Phil Krehbiel · 5901 Tierra Viva, NW · Albuquerque, NM 87107-5275 · 505-401-3860

Ronald C. Morgan · ⑩ · Ron Morgan · 500 Tijeras Avenue, NW · Albuquerque, NM 87102 · 505-842-1905

Thomas A. Outler · Rodey, Dickason, Sloan, Akin, & Robb · Albuquerque Plaza, Suite 2200 · 201 Third Street, NW · P.O. Box 1888 · Albuquerque, NM 87102 · 505-765-5900

Charles R. Peifer · Peifer, Hanson & Mullins · 20 First Plaza, Suite 725 · P.O. Box 25245 · Albuquerque, NM 87125-5245 · 505-247-4800

Charles A. Pharris · ⑩ · Keleher & McLeod · http://www.keleher-law.com · Albuquerque Plaza, 12th Floor · 201 Third Street, NW · P.O. Drawer AA · Albuquerque, NM 87103 · 505-346-4646

Charles K. Purcell · Rodey, Dickason, Sloan, Akin, & Robb · Albuquerque Plaza, Suite 2200 · 201 Third Street, NW · P.O. Box 1888 · Albuquerque, NM 87102 · 505-765-5900

W. Spencer Reid · Keleher & McLeod · http://www.keleher-law.com · Albuquerque Plaza, 12th Floor · 201 Third Street, NW · P.O. Drawer AA · Albuquerque, NM 87103 · 505-346-4646

Edward Ricco · ⑩ · Rodey, Dickason, Sloan, Akin, & Robb · Albuquerque Plaza, Suite 2200 · 201 Third Street, NW · P.O. Box 1888 · Albuquerque, NM 87102 · 505-765-5900

Douglas G. Schneebeck · Modrall, Sperling, Roehl, Harris & Sisk · Bank of America Centre, Suite 1000 · 500 Fourth Street, NW · P.O. Box 2168 · Albuquerque, NM 87103-2168 · 505-848-1800

Andrew G. Schultz · Rodey, Dickason, Sloan, Akin, & Robb · Albuquerque Plaza, Suite 2200 · 201 Third Street, NW · P.O. Box 1888 · Albuquerque, NM 87102 · 505-765-5900

Norman S. Thayer, Jr. · ⑩ · Sutin, Thayer & Browne · http://www.sutinfirm.com · Two Park Square, Suite 1000 · 6565 Americas Parkway, NE · P.O. Box 1945 · Albuquerque, NM 87103 · 505-883-2500

Charles J. Vigil · Rodey, Dickason, Sloan, Akin, & Robb · Albuquerque Plaza, Suite 2200 · 201 Third Street, NW · P.O. Box 1888 · Albuquerque, NM 87102 · 505-765-5900

Roswell

Richard E. Olson · ⑩ · Hinkle, Hensley, Shanor & Martin · 400 Penn Plaza, Suite 700 · P.O. Box 10 · Roswell, NM 88202 · 505-622-6510

Robert E. Sabin · ⑩ · Atwood, Malone, Turner & Sabin · 400 North Pennsylvania Avenue, Suite 1100 · P.O. Drawer 700 · Roswell, NM 88202-0700 · 575-622-6221

Stuart D. Shanor · ⑳ · Hinkle, Hensley, Shanor & Martin · 400 Penn Plaza, Suite 700 · P.O. Box 10 · Roswell, NM 88202 · 505-622-6510

Santa Fe

J. E. Gallegos · ⑳ · Gallegos Law Firm · 460 St. Michaels Drive, Suite 300 · Santa Fe, NM 87505-7687 · 505-983-6686

John B. Pound · ⑩ · Long, Pound & Komer · 2200 Brothers Road · P.O. Box 5098 · Santa Fe, NM 87502 505-982-8405

COMMUNICATIONS LAW

Albuquerque

Jeffrey H. Albright · Lewis and Roca · http://www.lrlaw.com · 201 Third Street, NW, Suite 1950 · Albuquerque, NM 87102 · 505-764-5400

CONSTRUCTION LAW

Albuquerque

David W. Bunting · Rodey, Dickason, Sloan, Akin, & Robb · Albuquerque Plaza, Suite 2200 · 201 Third Street, NW · P.O. Box 1888 · Albuquerque, NM 87102 · 505-765-5900

Clayton Crowley · Crowley & Gribble · 4811 Hardware, NE, Building A, Suites Three & Four · Albuquerque, NM 87109 · 505-314-1450

James P. Houghton · Modrall, Sperling, Roehl, Harris & Sisk · Bank of America Centre, Suite 1000 · 500 Fourth Street, NW · P.O. Box 2168 · Albuquerque, NM 87103-2168 · 505-848-1800

CORPORATE LAW

Albuquerque

Richard K. Barlow · ⑳ · Barlow & Wilcox · Albuquerque Plaza, Suite 1130 · 201 Third Street, NW · Albuquerque, NM 87102 · 505-248-1300

Perry E. Bendicksen · ⑩ · Brownstein Hyatt Farber Schreck · http://www.bhfs.com · 201 Third Street NW, Suite 1700 · Albuquerque, NM 87102-4386 · 505-244-0770

Thomas Blueher · Vogel Campbell & Blueher · 6100 Uptown Boulevard, NE, Suite 500 · Albuquerque, NM 87110-4187 · 505-884-8444

Duane E. Brown · Modrall, Sperling, Roehl, Harris & Sisk · Bank of America Centre, Suite 1000 · 500 Fourth Street, NW · P.O. Box 2168 · Albuquerque, NM 87103-2168 · 505-848-1800

David P. Buchholtz · 10 · Brownstein Hyatt Farber Schreck · http://www.bhfs.com · 201 Third Street NW, Suite 1700 · Albuquerque, NM 87102-4386 · 505-244-0770

Dennis J. Falk · 10 · Modrall, Sperling, Roehl, Harris & Sisk · Bank of America Centre, Suite 1000 · 500 Fourth Street, NW · P.O. Box 2168 · Albuquerque, NM 87103-2168 · 505-848-1800

Alan Hall · Rodey, Dickason, Sloan, Akin, & Robb · Albuquerque Plaza, Suite 2200 · 201 Third Street, NW · P.O. Box 1888 · Albuquerque, NM 87102 · 505-765-5900

Dennis Jontz · Lewis and Roca · http://www.lrlaw.com · 201 Third Street, NW, Suite 1950 · Albuquerque, NM 87102 · 505-764-5400

William B. Keleher · 20 · Keleher & McLeod · http://www.keleher-law.com · Albuquerque Plaza, 12th Floor · 201 Third Street, NW · P.O. Drawer AA · Albuquerque, NM 87103 · 505-346-4646

Henry A. Kelly · 20 · Sutin, Thayer & Browne · http://www.sutinfirm.com · Two Park Square, Suite 1000 · 6565 Americas Parkway, NE · P.O. Box 1945 · Albuquerque, NM 87103 · 505-883-2500

Randall J. McDonald · Miller Stratvert · 500 Marquette Avenue, NW, Suite 1100 · P.O. Box 25687 · Albuquerque, NM 87125-0687 · 505-842-1950

Margaret Lewis Meister · Modrall, Sperling, Roehl, Harris & Sisk · Bank of America Centre, Suite 1000 · 500 Fourth Street, NW · P.O. Box 2168 · Albuquerque, NM 87103-2168 · 505-848-1800

Donald B. Monnheimer · Rodey, Dickason, Sloan, Akin, & Robb · Albuquerque Plaza, Suite 2200 · 201 Third Street, NW · P.O. Box 1888 · Albuquerque, NM 87102 · 505-765-5900

Bonnie J. Paisley · Brownstein Hyatt Farber Schreck · http://www.bhfs.com · 201 Third Street NW, Suite 1700 · Albuquerque, NM 87102-4386 · 505-244-0770

James M. Parker · 10 · Modrall, Sperling, Roehl, Harris & Sisk · Bank of America Centre, Suite 1000 · 500 Fourth Street, NW · P.O. Box 2168 · Albuquerque, NM 87103-2168 · 505-848-1800

Jay D. Rosenblum · 10 · Sutin, Thayer & Browne · http://www.sutinfirm.com · Two Park Square, Suite 1000 · 6565 Americas Parkway, NE · P.O. Box 1945 · Albuquerque, NM 87103 · 505-883-2500

Alison K. Schuler · Schuler Daly · 2155 Louisiana Boulevard, NE, Suite 8500 · Albuquerque, NM 87110-5843 · 505-872-0800

Robert M. St. John · 10 · Rodey, Dickason, Sloan, Akin, & Robb · Albuquerque Plaza, Suite 2200 · 201 Third Street, NW · P.O. Box 1888 · Albuquerque, NM 87102 · 505-765-5900

Thomas Toevs · Hurley, Toevs, Styles, Hamblin & Panter · 4155 Montgomery Boulevard, NE · Albuquerque, NM 87109 · 505-888-1188

James Widland · Miller Stratvert · 500 Marquette Avenue, NW, Suite 1100 · P.O. Box 25687 · Albuquerque, NM 87125-0687 · 505-842-1950

Santa Fe

Mark K. Adams · 20 · Rodey, Dickason, Sloan, Akin, & Robb · 315 Paseo de Peralta · P.O. Box 1357 · Santa Fe, NM 87501-2034 · 505-954-3900

Robert G. Heyman · 10 · Sutin, Thayer & Browne · http://www.sutinfirm.com · 317 Paseo de Peralta · P.O. Box 2187 · Santa Fe, NM 87504 · 505-988-5521

DUI/DWI DEFENSE

Albuquerque

Ousama M. Rasheed · Ousama Rasheed · 1024 Second Street NW · Albuquerque, NM 87102 · 505-246-8474

EDUCATION LAW

Albuquerque

Arthur Melendres · Modrall, Sperling, Roehl, Harris & Sisk · Bank of America Centre, Suite 1000 · 500 Fourth Street, NW · P.O. Box 2168 · Albuquerque, NM 87103-2168 · 505-848-1800

ELDER LAW

Albuquerque

Mary Ann Green · Mary Ann Green · 1825 San Mateo Boulevard, NE · Albuquerque, NM 87110-5145 · 505-254-0600

Randolph L. Hamblin · Hurley, Toevs, Styles, Hamblin & Panter · 4155 Montgomery Boulevard, NE · Albuquerque, NM 87109 · 505-888-1188

Nell Graham Sale · Pregenzer, Baysinger, Wideman & Sale · 2424 Louisiana Boulevard, NE, Suite 200 · P.O. Box 3694 · Albuquerque, NM 87190-3694 · 505-872-0505

EMINENT DOMAIN AND CONDEMNATION LAW

Albuquerque

Bernard P. Metzgar · Crowley & Gribble · 4811 Hardware, NE, Building A, Suites Three & Four · Albuquerque, NM 87109 · 505-314-1450

John A. Myers · ⑳ · Myers, Oliver & Price · 1401 Central Avenue, NW · Albuquerque, NM 87104-1138 · 505-247-9080

John P. Salazar · ⑳ · Rodey, Dickason, Sloan, Akin, & Robb · Albuquerque Plaza, Suite 2200 · 201 Third Street, NW · P.O. Box 1888 · Albuquerque, NM 87102 · 505-765-5900

Santa Fe

Stephen S. Hamilton · Montgomery & Andrews · 325 Paseo De Peralta · P.O. Box 2307 · Santa Fe, NM 87504-2307 · 505-982-3873

EMPLOYEE BENEFITS LAW

Albuquerque

Tracy J. Ahr · Ahr, Foster & Quezada · 6751 Academy Road, NE, Suite C · Albuquerque, NM 87109 · 505-821-5122

John E. Heer III · ⑳ · Laflin, Pick & Heer · 8500 Menaul Boulevard, NE, Suite B-450 · P.O. Box 3260 · Albuquerque, NM 87190-3260 · 505-883-0679

Karen L. Kahn · Modrall, Sperling, Roehl, Harris & Sisk · Bank of America Centre, Suite 1000 · 500 Fourth Street, NW · P.O. Box 2168 · Albuquerque, NM 87103-2168 · 505-848-1800

John N. Lieuwen · ⑳ · Lieuwen, La Fata & Tucker · 4101 Indian School Road, NE, Suite 310-N · Albuquerque, NM 87110 · 505-262-6000

Julie P. Neerken · ⑩ · Rodey, Dickason, Sloan, Akin, & Robb · Albuquerque Plaza, Suite 2200 · 201 Third Street, NW · P.O. Box 1888 · Albuquerque, NM 87102 · 505-765-5900

Danielle R. Panter · Hurley, Toevs, Styles, Hamblin & Panter · 4155 Montgomery Boulevard, NE · Albuquerque, NM 87109 · 505-888-1188

James M. Parker · ⑩ · Modrall, Sperling, Roehl, Harris & Sisk · Bank of America Centre, Suite 1000 · 500 Fourth Street, NW · P.O. Box 2168 · Albuquerque, NM 87103-2168 · 505-848-1800

Marjorie A. Rogers · Modrall, Sperling, Roehl, Harris & Sisk · Bank of America Centre, Suite 1000 · 500 Fourth Street, NW · P.O. Box 2168 · Albuquerque, NM 87103-2168 · 505-848-1800

ENERGY LAW

Albuquerque

Larry P. Ausherman · ⑳ · Modrall, Sperling, Roehl, Harris & Sisk · Bank of America Centre, Suite 1000 · 500 Fourth Street, NW · P.O. Box 2168 · Albuquerque, NM 87103-2168 · 505-848-1800

Richard B. Cole · ⑩ · Keleher & McLeod · http://www.keleher-law.com · Albuquerque Plaza, 12th Floor 201 Third Street, NW · P.O. Drawer AA · Albuquerque, NM 87103 · 505-346-4646

John R. Cooney · ⑩ · Modrall, Sperling, Roehl, Harris & Sisk · Bank of America Centre, Suite 1000 · 500 Fourth Street, NW · P.O. Box 2168 · Albuquerque, NM 87103-2168 · 505-848-1800

Lynn H. Slade · ⑳ · Modrall, Sperling, Roehl, Harris & Sisk · Bank of America Centre, Suite 1000 · 500 Fourth Street, NW · P.O. Box 2168 · Albuquerque, NM 87103-2168 · 505-848-1800

Walter E. Stern III · ⑩ · Modrall, Sperling, Roehl, Harris & Sisk · Bank of America Centre, Suite 1000 · 500 Fourth Street, NW · P.O. Box 2168 · Albuquerque, NM 87103-2168 · 505-848-1800

Clyde F. Worthen · ⑩ · Keleher & McLeod · http://www.keleher-law.com · Albuquerque Plaza, 12th Floor · 201 Third Street, NW · P.O. Drawer AA · Albuquerque, NM 87103 · 505-346-4646

Farmington

Richard T. C. Tully · ⑩ · Tully Law Firm · 500 West Broadway, Suite 301 · P.O. Box 268 · Farmington, NM 87499-0268 · 505-327-3388

Hobbs

Scotty A. Holloman · Maddox, Holloman & Kirksey · http://www.hobbsnmlaw.com · 205 East Bender, Suite 150 · P.O. Box 2508 · Hobbs, NM 88241-2508 · 575-393-0505

Roswell

Douglas L. Lunsford · ⑩ · Hinkle, Hensley, Shanor & Martin · 400 Penn Plaza, Suite 700 · P.O. Box 10 · Roswell, NM 88202 · 505-622-6510

John S. Nelson · ⑩ · Atwood, Malone, Turner & Sabin · 400 North Pennsylvania Avenue, Suite 1100 · P.O. Drawer 700 · Roswell, NM 88202-0700 · 575-622-6221

Gregory J. Nibert · ⑩ · Hinkle, Hensley, Shanor & Martin · 400 Penn Plaza, Suite 700 · P.O. Box 10 · Roswell, NM 88202 · 505-622-6510

Santa Fe

Mark K. Adams · ⑳ · Rodey, Dickason, Sloan, Akin, & Robb · 315 Paseo de Peralta · P.O. Box 1357 · Santa Fe, NM 87501-2034 · 505-954-3900

Wayne H. Bladh · Nordhaus Law Firm · 1239 Paseo de Peralta · Santa Fe, NM 87501 · 505-982-3622

William F. Carr · ⑩ · Holland & Hart · Jefferson Place, Suite One · 110 North Guadalupe · P.O. Box 2208 Santa Fe, NM 87504-2208 · 505-988-4421

Carol A. Clifford · Jones, Snead, Wertheim, Wentworth & Jaramillo · 1800 Old Pecos Trail · P.O. Box 2228 · Santa Fe, NM 87504-2228 · 505-982-0011

David S. Cohen · ⑩ · Cohen & Cohen · P.O. Box 789 · Santa Fe, NM 87504-0789 · 505-983-9277

Jeffrey L. Fornaciari · Hinkle, Hensley, Shanor & Martin · 218 Montezuma · P.O. Box 2068 · Santa Fe, NM 87504 · 505-982-4554

Peter J. Gould · Peter J. Gould · 900 Gildersleeve Street · P.O. Box 34127 · Santa Fe, NM 87594-4127 · 505-988-4804

Daniel A. Najjar · ⑩ · Virtue Najjar & Brown · 2200 Brothers Road · P.O. Box 22249 · Santa Fe, NM 87502-2249 · 505-983-6101

Sunny Jeane Nixon · ⑩ · Rodey, Dickason, Sloan, Akin, & Robb · 315 Paseo de Peralta · P.O. Box 1357 · Santa Fe, NM 87501-2034 · 505-954-3900

Thomas W. Olson · ⑩ · Montgomery & Andrews · 325 Paseo De Peralta · P.O. Box 2307 · Santa Fe, NM 87504-2307 · 505-982-3873

ENVIRONMENTAL LAW

Albuquerque

Jeffrey H. Albright · Lewis and Roca · http://www.lrlaw.com · 201 Third Street, NW, Suite 1950 · Albuquerque, NM 87102 · 505-764-5400

Richard L. Alvidrez · Miller Stratvert · 500 Marquette Avenue, NW, Suite 1100 · P.O. Box 25687 · Albuquerque, NM 87125-0687 · 505-842-1950

Clifford K. Atkinson · ⑳ · Atkinson & Thal · Albuquerque Plaza, Suite 1850 · 201 Third Street, NW · Albuquerque, NM 87102 · 505-764-8111

Stuart R. Butzier · Modrall, Sperling, Roehl, Harris & Sisk · Bank of America Centre, Suite 1000 · 500 Fourth Street, NW · P.O. Box 2168 · Albuquerque, NM 87103-2168 · 505-848-1800

Daniel R. Dolan II · ⑩ · Dolan & Associates, Inc. · 5801 Osuna Road, NE, Suite 106 · Albuquerque, NM 87109 · 505-883-1266

Peter V. Domenici, Jr. · ⑩ · Domenici Law Firm · 320 Gold Street, SW, Suite 1000 · Albuquerque, NM 87102 · 505-883-6250

Charles T. DuMars · ⑩ · Law & Resource Planning Associates · Albuquerque Plaza, Suite 1750 · 201 Third Street, NW · Albuquerque, NM 87102 · 505-346-0998

William C. Scott · Modrall, Sperling, Roehl, Harris & Sisk · Bank of America Centre, Suite 1000 · 500 Fourth Street, NW · P.O. Box 2168 · Albuquerque, NM 87103-2168 · 505-848-1800

John W. Utton · Sheehan, Sheehan & Stelzner · http://www.ssslawfirm.com · 40 First Plaza, NW, Suite 740 · Albuquerque, NM 87102 · 505-247-0411

Santa Fe

Mark K. Adams · ⑳ · Rodey, Dickason, Sloan, Akin, & Robb · 315 Paseo de Peralta · P.O. Box 1357 · Santa Fe, NM 87501-2034 · 505-954-3900

Bradford C. Berge · Holland & Hart · Jefferson Place, Suite One · 110 North Guadalupe · P.O. Box 2208 · Santa Fe, NM 87504-2208 · 505-988-4421

John B. Draper · ⑳ · Montgomery & Andrews · 325 Paseo De Peralta · P.O. Box 2307 · Santa Fe, NM 87504-2307 · 505-982-3873

Bruce S. Garber · Garber & Hallmark · 200 West Marcy, Suite 203 · P.O. Box 850 · Santa Fe, NM 87504-0850 · 505-983-3233

Thomas M. Hnasko · Hinkle, Hensley, Shanor & Martin · 218 Montezuma · P.O. Box 2068 · Santa Fe, NM 87504 · 505-982-4554

Edmund H. Kendrick · Montgomery & Andrews · 325 Paseo De Peralta · P.O. Box 2307 · Santa Fe, NM 87504-2307 · 505-982-3873

Louis W. Rose · Montgomery & Andrews · 325 Paseo De Peralta · P.O. Box 2307 · Santa Fe, NM 87504-2307 · 505-982-3873

Richard L. C. Virtue · ⑩ · Virtue Najjar & Brown · 2200 Brothers Road · P.O. Box 22249 · Santa Fe, NM 87502-2249 · 505-983-6101

FAMILY LAW

Albuquerque

Roberta S. Batley · Little & Gilman-Tepper · 500 Marquette Avenue, NW, Suite 770 · P.O. Box 26717 · Albuquerque, NM 87125 · 505-246-0500

Jan B. Gilman-Tepper · ⑳ · Little & Gilman-Tepper · 500 Marquette Avenue, NW, Suite 770 · P.O. Box 26717 · Albuquerque, NM 87125 · 505-246-0500

David H. Kelsey · ㉕ · Atkinson & Kelsey · 2155 Louisiana Boulevard, NE · P.O. Box 3070 · Albuquerque, NM 87190 · 505-883-3070

Twila B. Larkin · Sutin, Thayer & Browne · http://www.sutinfirm.com · Two Park Square, Suite 1000 · 6565 Americas Parkway, NE · P.O. Box 1945 · Albuquerque, NM 87103 · 505-883-2500

Gerard J. Lavelle · Gerard J. Lavelle · 4010 Carlisle Boulevard, NE, Suite D · Albuquerque, NM 87107-4532 · 505-884-2556

Sandra Morgan Little · ⓴ · Little & Gilman-Tepper · 500 Marquette Avenue, NW, Suite 770 · P.O. Box 26717 · Albuquerque, NM 87125 · 505-246-0500

Gretchen Walther · Walther Family Law · http://www.waltherfamilylaw.com · One Park Square, Suite 620 · 6501 Americas Parkway, NE · Albuquerque, NM 87110 · 505-889-8240

Las Cruces

Carolyn Baca-Waters · Carolyn Baca-Waters · 741 North Alameada Boulevard, Suite Eight · Las Cruces, NM 88005-2172 · 505-524-2992

Sandia Park

Muriel McClelland · Muriel McClelland · Two Vista De Santa Fe · P. O. Box 259 · Sandia Park, NM 87008-0259 · 505-286-8865

Santa Fe

Sarah E. Bennett · Rothstein, Donatelli, Hughes, Dahlstrom, Schoenburg & Bienvenu · 1215 Paseo De Peralta · P.O. Box 8180 · Santa Fe, NM 87504-8180 · 505-988-8004

Janet E. Clow · Thompson, Hickey, Cunningham, Clow & April · Building 1100, Suite 1103 · 460 Saint Michaels Drive · Santa Fe, NM 87505-7619 · 505-988-2900

Michael J. Golden · Sutin, Thayer & Browne · http://www.sutinfirm.com · 317 Paseo de Peralta · P.O. Box 2187 · Santa Fe, NM 87504 · 505-988-5521

David L. Walther · ⓴ · Walther Family Law · http://www.waltherfamilylaw.com · 150 Washington Avenue, Suite 204 · Santa Fe, NM 87501 · 505-984-0097

Julie Wittenberger · White, Koch, Kelly & McCarthy · 433 Paseo de Peralta · P.O. Box 787 · Santa Fe, NM 87504-0787 · 505-982-4374

Taos

Catherine E. Oliver · Catherine E. Oliver · 705 B Paseo del Pueblo Sur · Taos, NM 87571-5997 · 505-737-5250

FIRST AMENDMENT LAW

Albuquerque

John W. Boyd · ❿ · Freedman Boyd Hollander Goldberg & Ives · http://www.fbdlaw.com · 20 First Plaza, Suite 700 · Albuquerque, NM 87102 · 505-842-9960

Philip B. Davis · ❿ · Philip B. Davis · 814 Marquette Avenue, NW · Albuquerque, NM 87102 · 505-242-1904

Martin Esquivel · Narvaez Law Firm · 601 Rio Grande Boulevard, NW · P.O. Box 25967 · Albuquerque, NM 87125-0967 · 505-248-0500

Charles R. Peifer · Peifer, Hanson & Mullins · 20 First Plaza, Suite 725 · P.O. Box 25245 · Albuquerque, NM 87125-5245 · 505-247-4800

Charles K. Purcell · Rodey, Dickason, Sloan, Akin, & Robb · Albuquerque Plaza, Suite 2200 · 201 Third Street, NW · P.O. Box 1888 · Albuquerque, NM 87102 · 505-765-5900

Andrew G. Schultz · Rodey, Dickason, Sloan, Akin, & Robb · Albuquerque Plaza, Suite 2200 · 201 Third Street, NW · P.O. Box 1888 · Albuquerque, NM 87102 · 505-765-5900

Santa Fe

Daniel Yohalem · Daniel Yohalem · 1121 Paseo de Peralta · Santa Fe, NM 87501-2888 · 505-983-9433

GAMING LAW

Santa Fe

Richard W. Hughes · Rothstein, Donatelli, Hughes, Dahlstrom, Schoenburg & Bienvenu · 1215 Paseo De Peralta · P.O. Box 8180 · Santa Fe, NM 87504-8180 · 505-988-8004

GOVERNMENT RELATIONS LAW

Albuquerque

Thomas J. Horan · Presbyterian Healthcare Services · P.O. Box 26666 · Albuquerque, NM 87125 · 505-923-6350

Robert H. McBride · Robert H. McBride · 5854 Osuna Road, NE · Albuquerque, NM 87109 · 505-837-8500

Richard C. Minzner · Rodey, Dickason, Sloan, Akin, & Robb · Albuquerque Plaza, Suite 2200 · 201 Third Street, NW · P.O. Box 1888 · Albuquerque, NM 87102 · 505-765-5900

R. E. Thompson · Modrall, Sperling, Roehl, Harris & Sisk · Bank of America Centre, Suite 1000 · 500 Fourth Street, NW · P.O. Box 2168 · Albuquerque, NM 87103-2168 · 505-848-1800

Ruidoso

H. John Underwood · H. John Underwood · 1221 Mechem Drive, Suite Five · Ruidoso, NM 88345-7224 505-258-9090

Santa Fe

Gary Kilpatric · Montgomery & Andrews · 325 Paseo De Peralta · P.O. Box 2307 · Santa Fe, NM 87504-2307 · 505-982-3873

Nancy M. King · Montgomery & Andrews · 325 Paseo De Peralta · P.O. Box 2307 · Santa Fe, NM 87504-2307 · 505-982-3873

Daniel A. Najjar · ⑩ · Virtue Najjar & Brown · 2200 Brothers Road · P.O. Box 22249 · Santa Fe, NM 87502-2249 · 505-983-6101

HEALTH CARE LAW

Albuquerque

John A. Bannerman · ⑩ · Bannerman & Williams · Building Two, Suite 207 · 2201 San Pedro, NE · Albuquerque, NM 87110 · 505-837-1900

Bruce Hall · ⑩ · Rodey, Dickason, Sloan, Akin, & Robb · Albuquerque Plaza, Suite 2200 · 201 Third Street, NW · P.O. Box 1888 · Albuquerque, NM 87102 · 505-765-5900

David H. Johnson · Bannerman & Williams · Building Two, Suite 207 · 2201 San Pedro, NE · Albuquerque, NM 87110 · 505-837-1900

George F. Koinis · George F. Koinis · 620 Roma Avenue, NW · Albuquerque, NM 87102-2037 · 505-244-4110

James M. Parker · ⑩ · Modrall, Sperling, Roehl, Harris & Sisk · Bank of America Centre, Suite 1000 · 500 Fourth Street, NW · P.O. Box 2168 · Albuquerque, NM 87103-2168 · 505-848-1800

Edward Ricco · ⑩ · Rodey, Dickason, Sloan, Akin, & Robb · Albuquerque Plaza, Suite 2200 · 201 Third Street, NW · P.O. Box 1888 · Albuquerque, NM 87102 · 505-765-5900

Robert L. Schwartz · ⑩ · University of New Mexico School of Law · 1117 Stanford Drive, NE · Albuquerque, NM 87131-1431 · 505-277-3119

Santa Fe

Daniel A. Najjar · ⑩ · Virtue Najjar & Brown · 2200 Brothers Road · P.O. Box 22249 · Santa Fe, NM 87502-2249 · 505-983-6101

Thomas W. Olson · ⑩ · Montgomery & Andrews · 325 Paseo De Peralta · P.O. Box 2307 · Santa Fe, NM 87504-2307 · 505-982-3873

John B. Pound · ⑩ · Long, Pound & Komer · 2200 Brothers Road · P.O. Box 5098 · Santa Fe, NM 87502 505-982-8405

IMMIGRATION LAW

Albuquerque

John W. Lawit · ⑩ · John W. Lawit · http://www.jlawit.com · 2305 Renard Place, SE, Suite 210 · Albuquerque, NM 87106 · 505-243-0733

INSURANCE LAW

Albuquerque

William P. Gralow · Civerolo, Gralow, Hill & Curtis · 20 First Plaza Galleria, NW, Suite 500 · Albuquerque, NM 87102 · 505-842-8255

Lawrence H. Hill · Civerolo, Gralow, Hill & Curtis · 20 First Plaza Galleria, NW, Suite 500 · Albuquerque, NM 87102 · 505-842-8255

Rudolph Lucero · Miller Stratvert · 500 Marquette Avenue, NW, Suite 1100 · P.O. Box 25687 · Albuquerque, NM 87125-0687 · 505-842-1950

Lisa Mann · Modrall, Sperling, Roehl, Harris & Sisk · Bank of America Centre, Suite 1000 · 500 Fourth Street, NW · P.O. Box 2168 · Albuquerque, NM 87103-2168 · 505-848-1800

Jennifer A. Noya · Modrall, Sperling, Roehl, Harris & Sisk · Bank of America Centre, Suite 1000 · 500 Fourth Street, NW · P.O. Box 2168 · Albuquerque, NM 87103-2168 · 505-848-1800

David J. Stout · Carpenter & Stout · 1600 University Boulevard, NE, Suite A · Albuquerque, NM 87102-1724 · 505-243-1336

INTELLECTUAL PROPERTY LAW

Albuquerque

Dennis F. Armijo · Dennis F. Armijo · 6300 Montano Road, NW, Suite D · Albuquerque, NM 87120-2151 · 505-899-0269

Robert W. Harris · ⑩ · Robert W. Harris · 5906 Painted Pony Drive, NW · Albuquerque, NM 87120 · 505-897-1066

Dewitt Michael Morgan · ⑩ · Rodey, Dickason, Sloan, Akin, & Robb · Albuquerque Plaza, Suite 2200 · 201 Third Street, NW · P.O. Box 1888 · Albuquerque, NM 87102 · 505-765-5900

Jeffrey D. Myers · ⑩ · Peacock Myers · http://www.peacocklaw.com · Albuquerque Plaza, Suite 1340 · 201 Third Street, NW · P.O. Box 26927 · Albuquerque, NM 87125 · 505-998-1500

Deborah A. Peacock · ⑩ · Peacock Myers · http://www.peacocklaw.com · Albuquerque Plaza, Suite 1340 201 Third Street, NW · P.O. Box 26927 · Albuquerque, NM 87125 · 505-998-1500

Corrales

Ray R. Regan · Ray R. Regan · http://www.rayregan.com · P.O. Box 1442 · Corrales, NM 87048 · 505-897-7200

Santa Fe

Timothy L. Butler · Timothy L. Butler · 125 Lincoln Avenue, Suite 400 · Santa Fe, NM 87501 · 505-820-3375

Saul Cohen · ⑩ · Sutin, Thayer & Browne · http://www.sutinfirm.com · 317 Paseo de Peralta · P.O. Box 2187 · Santa Fe, NM 87504 · 505-988-5521

Tijeras

Rod D. Baker · The Law Office of Rod D. Baker · 707 State Highway 333, Suite B · Tijeras, NM 87059 · 505-286-9700

LABOR AND EMPLOYMENT LAW

Albuquerque

John W. Boyd · ⑩ · Freedman Boyd Hollander Goldberg & Ives · http://www.fbdlaw.com · 20 First Plaza, Suite 700 · Albuquerque, NM 87102 · 505-842-9960

Robert C. Conklin · Conklin, Jenke, Woodcock & Ziegler · 320 Gold Avenue, SW, Suite 1111 · Albuquerque, NM 87102-3246 · 505-224-9160

Philip B. Davis · ⑩ · Philip B. Davis · 814 Marquette Avenue, NW · Albuquerque, NM 87102 · 505-242-1904

Stephen Guy French · French & Associates · 500 Marquette Avenue, NW, Suite 500 · Albuquerque, NM 87102-5312 · 505-843-7075

Duane C. Gilkey · ⑩ · Gilkey & Stephenson · 500 Marquette Avenue, NW, Suite 505 · P.O. Drawer 25566 · Albuquerque, NM 87102 · 505-242-4466

Theresa W. Parrish · Rodey, Dickason, Sloan, Akin, & Robb · Albuquerque Plaza, Suite 2200 · 201 Third Street, NW · P.O. Box 1888 · Albuquerque, NM 87102 · 505-765-5900

Barbara G. Stephenson · ⑩ · Gilkey & Stephenson · 500 Marquette Avenue, NW, Suite 505 · P.O. Drawer 25566 · Albuquerque, NM 87102 · 505-242-4466

Robert P. Tinnin, Jr. · ㉕ · Tinnin Law Firm · http://www.tinninlawfirm.com · 500 Marquette Avenue, NW, Suite 1300 · Albuquerque, NM 87102 · 505-768-1500

Santa Fe

John C. Bienvenu · Rothstein, Donatelli, Hughes, Dahlstrom, Schoenburg & Bienvenu · 1215 Paseo De Peralta · P.O. Box 8180 · Santa Fe, NM 87504-8180 · 505-988-8004

Richard H. Rosenstock · ⑩ · Richard H. Rosenstock · 1121 Paseo de Peralta · P.O. Box 10230 · Santa Fe, NM 87504-6230 · 505-988-5324

Robert R. Rothstein · ⑳ · Rothstein, Donatelli, Hughes, Dahlstrom, Schoenburg & Bienvenu · 1215 Paseo De Peralta · P.O. Box 8180 · Santa Fe, NM 87504-8180 · 505-988-8004

Daniel Yohalem · Daniel Yohalem · 1121 Paseo de Peralta · Santa Fe, NM 87501-2888 · 505-983-9433

LAND USE & ZONING LAW

Albuquerque

David S. Campbell · ⑩ · Vogel Campbell & Blueher · 6100 Uptown Boulevard, NE, Suite 500 · Albuquerque, NM 87110-4187 · 505-884-8444

John J. Kelly · Modrall, Sperling, Roehl, Harris & Sisk · Bank of America Centre, Suite 1000 · 500 Fourth Street, NW · P.O. Box 2168 · Albuquerque, NM 87103-2168 · 505-848-1800

Paul M. Kienzle · Scott & Kienzle · 201 Third Street, NW, Suite 1570 · P.O. Box 587 · Albuquerque, NM 87103 · 505-246-8600

Anita Miller · Anita P. Miller · 223 Spring Creek Lane, NE · Albuquerque, NM 87122-2013 · 505-878-9598

John A. Myers · ⑳ · Myers, Oliver & Price · 1401 Central Avenue, NW · Albuquerque, NM 87104-1138 · 505-247-9080

John P. Salazar · ⑳ · Rodey, Dickason, Sloan, Akin, & Robb · Albuquerque Plaza, Suite 2200 · 201 Third Street, NW · P.O. Box 1888 · Albuquerque, NM 87102 · 505-765-5900

Hessel E. Yntema · Oman & Yntema · 215 Gold Avenue, SW, Suite 201 · P.O. Box 1748 · Albuquerque, NM 87103 · 505-843-9565

Santa Fe

Frank T. Herdman · Rubin Katz Law Firm · Marcy Plaza, Suite 200 · 123 East Marcy Street · P.O. Drawer 250 · Santa Fe, NM 87504 · 505-982-3610

James S. Rubin · Rubin Katz Law Firm · Marcy Plaza, Suite 200 · 123 East Marcy Street · P.O. Drawer 250 · Santa Fe, NM 87504 · 505-982-3610

LEGAL MALPRACTICE LAW

Albuquerque

Jeffrey L. Baker · Baker Law Firm · 20 First Plaza Center, NW, Suite 402 · Albuquerque, NM 87102-3351 · 505-247-1855

Jack M. Brant · ⑩ · Law Office of Jack Brant · 202 Tulane Drive, SE · Albuquerque, NM 87106-1414 · 505-232-5300

Briggs F. Cheney · ⑩ · Sheehan, Sheehan & Stelzner · http://www.ssslawfirm.com · 40 First Plaza, NW, Suite 740 · Albuquerque, NM 87102 · 505-247-0411

Ronald C. Morgan · ⑩ · Ron Morgan · 500 Tijeras Avenue, NW · Albuquerque, NM 87102 · 505-842-1905

Charles R. Peifer · Peifer, Hanson & Mullins · 20 First Plaza, Suite 725 · P.O. Box 25245 · Albuquerque, NM 87125-5245 · 505-247-4800

Charles K. Purcell · Rodey, Dickason, Sloan, Akin, & Robb · Albuquerque Plaza, Suite 2200 · 201 Third Street, NW · P.O. Box 1888 · Albuquerque, NM 87102 · 505-765-5900

Rebecca Sitterly · Rebecca Sitterly · 500 Marquette Avenue, NW, Suite 280 · P.O. Box 7790 · Albuquerque, NM 87194-7790 · 505-238-5151

LEVERAGED BUYOUTS AND PRIVATE EQUITY LAW

Albuquerque

Richard K. Barlow · ⑳ · Barlow & Wilcox · Albuquerque Plaza, Suite 1130 · 201 Third Street, NW · Albuquerque, NM 87102 · 505-248-1300

Perry E. Bendicksen · ⑩ · Brownstein Hyatt Farber Schreck · http://www.bhfs.com · 201 Third Street NW, Suite 1700 · Albuquerque, NM 87102-4386 · 505-244-0770

Henry A. Kelly · ⑳ · Sutin, Thayer & Browne · http://www.sutinfirm.com · Two Park Square, Suite 1000 · 6565 Americas Parkway, NE · P.O. Box 1945 · Albuquerque, NM 87103 · 505-883-2500

MASS TORT LITIGATION

Albuquerque

William H. Carpenter · ㉕ · Carpenter & Stout · 1600 University Boulevard, NE, Suite A · Albuquerque, NM 87102-1724 · 505-243-1336

Philip C. Gaddy · The Gaddy Law Firm · 2025 San Pedro Drive, NE · Albuquerque, NM 87110 · 505-254-9090

Bruce Hall · ⑩ · Rodey, Dickason, Sloan, Akin, & Robb · Albuquerque Plaza, Suite 2200 · 201 Third Street, NW · P.O. Box 1888 · Albuquerque, NM 87102 · 505-765-5900

Robert E. Hanson · Peifer, Hanson & Mullins · 20 First Plaza, Suite 725 · P.O. Box 25245 · Albuquerque, NM 87125-5245 · 505-247-4800

Thomas A. Outler · Rodey, Dickason, Sloan, Akin, & Robb · Albuquerque Plaza, Suite 2200 · 201 Third Street, NW · P.O. Box 1888 · Albuquerque, NM 87102 · 505-765-5900

Douglas G. Schneebeck · Modrall, Sperling, Roehl, Harris & Sisk · Bank of America Centre, Suite 1000 · 500 Fourth Street, NW · P.O. Box 2168 · Albuquerque, NM 87103-2168 · 505-848-1800

Santa Fe

John C. Bienvenu · Rothstein, Donatelli, Hughes, Dahlstrom, Schoenburg & Bienvenu · 1215 Paseo De Peralta · P.O. Box 8180 · Santa Fe, NM 87504-8180 · 505-988-8004

MEDICAL MALPRACTICE LAW

Albuquerque

Ben M. Allen · Hatch, Allen & Shepherd · 4801 Lang Avenue, Suite 200 · P.O. Box 94750 · Albuquerque, NM 87199-4750 · 505-341-0110

Rick Beitler · Rodey, Dickason, Sloan, Akin, & Robb · Albuquerque Plaza, Suite 2200 · 201 Third Street, NW · P.O. Box 1888 · Albuquerque, NM 87102 · 505-765-5900

Carl J. Bettinger · Shapiro Bettinger Chase · 7411 Jefferson Street, NE · Albuquerque, NM 87109 · 505-888-6463

Robert J. Curtis · Civerolo, Gralow, Hill & Curtis · 20 First Plaza Galleria, NW, Suite 500 · Albuquerque, NM 87102 · 505-842-8255

Gary L. Gordon · Miller Stratvert · 500 Marquette Avenue, NW, Suite 1100 · P.O. Box 25687 · Albuquerque, NM 87125-0687 · 505-842-1950

Bruce Hall · 10 · Rodey, Dickason, Sloan, Akin, & Robb · Albuquerque Plaza, Suite 2200 · 201 Third Street, NW · P.O. Box 1888 · Albuquerque, NM 87102 · 505-765-5900

W. Robert Lasater, Jr. · 20 · Rodey, Dickason, Sloan, Akin, & Robb · Albuquerque Plaza, Suite 2200 · 201 Third Street, NW · P.O. Box 1888 · Albuquerque, NM 87102 · 505-765-5900

Charles K. Purcell · Rodey, Dickason, Sloan, Akin, & Robb · Albuquerque Plaza, Suite 2200 · 201 Third Street, NW · P.O. Box 1888 · Albuquerque, NM 87102 · 505-765-5900

Ellen T. Skrak · Rodey, Dickason, Sloan, Akin, & Robb · Albuquerque Plaza, Suite 2200 · 201 Third Street, NW · P.O. Box 1888 · Albuquerque, NM 87102 · 505-765-5900

Terry M. Word · 10 · Terry M. Word · http://www.terrymwordpc.com · 500 Tijeras Avenue, NW · Albuquerque, NM 87102 · 505-842-1905

Roswell

Rodney M. Schumacher · Atwood, Malone, Turner & Sabin · 400 North Pennsylvania Avenue, Suite 1100 · P.O. Drawer 700 · Roswell, NM 88202-0700 · 575-622-6221

MERGERS & ACQUISITIONS LAW

Albuquerque

Richard K. Barlow · 20 · Barlow & Wilcox · Albuquerque Plaza, Suite 1130 · 201 Third Street, NW · Albuquerque, NM 87102 · 505-248-1300

Perry E. Bendicksen · ⑩ · Brownstein Hyatt Farber Schreck · http://www.bhfs.com · 201 Third Street NW, Suite 1700 · Albuquerque, NM 87102-4386 · 505-244-0770

David P. Buchholtz · ⑩ · Brownstein Hyatt Farber Schreck · http://www.bhfs.com · 201 Third Street NW, Suite 1700 · Albuquerque, NM 87102-4386 · 505-244-0770

Alan Hall · Rodey, Dickason, Sloan, Akin, & Robb · Albuquerque Plaza, Suite 2200 · 201 Third Street, NW · P.O. Box 1888 · Albuquerque, NM 87102 · 505-765-5900

Randall J. McDonald · Miller Stratvert · 500 Marquette Avenue, NW, Suite 1100 · P.O. Box 25687 · Albuquerque, NM 87125-0687 · 505-842-1950

Donald B. Monnheimer · Rodey, Dickason, Sloan, Akin, & Robb · Albuquerque Plaza, Suite 2200 · 201 Third Street, NW · P.O. Box 1888 · Albuquerque, NM 87102 · 505-765-5900

Bonnie J. Paisley · Brownstein Hyatt Farber Schreck · http://www.bhfs.com · 201 Third Street NW, Suite 1700 · Albuquerque, NM 87102-4386 · 505-244-0770

Jay D. Rosenblum · ⑩ · Sutin, Thayer & Browne · http://www.sutinfirm.com · Two Park Square, Suite 1000 · 6565 Americas Parkway, NE · P.O. Box 1945 · Albuquerque, NM 87103 · 505-883-2500

Alison K. Schuler · Schuler Daly · 2155 Louisiana Boulevard, NE, Suite 8500 · Albuquerque, NM 87110-5843 · 505-872-0800

R. Tracy Sprouls · Rodey, Dickason, Sloan, Akin, & Robb · Albuquerque Plaza, Suite 2200 · 201 Third Street, NW · P.O. Box 1888 · Albuquerque, NM 87102 · 505-765-5900

MINING LAW

Albuquerque

Larry P. Ausherman · ⑳ · Modrall, Sperling, Roehl, Harris & Sisk · Bank of America Centre, Suite 1000 · 500 Fourth Street, NW · P.O. Box 2168 · Albuquerque, NM 87103-2168 · 505-848-1800

Stuart R. Butzier · Modrall, Sperling, Roehl, Harris & Sisk · Bank of America Centre, Suite 1000 · 500 Fourth Street, NW · P.O. Box 2168 · Albuquerque, NM 87103-2168 · 505-848-1800

John R. Cooney · ⑩ · Modrall, Sperling, Roehl, Harris & Sisk · Bank of America Centre, Suite 1000 · 500 Fourth Street, NW · P.O. Box 2168 · Albuquerque, NM 87103-2168 · 505-848-1800

Walter E. Stern III · ⑩ · Modrall, Sperling, Roehl, Harris & Sisk · Bank of America Centre, Suite 1000 · 500 Fourth Street, NW · P.O. Box 2168 · Albuquerque, NM 87103-2168 · 505-848-1800

Santa Fe

Mark K. Adams · ⑳ · Rodey, Dickason, Sloan, Akin, & Robb · 315 Paseo de Peralta · P.O. Box 1357 · Santa Fe, NM 87501-2034 · 505-954-3900

Sunny Jeane Nixon · ⑩ · Rodey, Dickason, Sloan, Akin, & Robb · 315 Paseo de Peralta · P.O. Box 1357 · Santa Fe, NM 87501-2034 · 505-954-3900

Sarah M. Singleton · Montgomery & Andrews · 325 Paseo De Peralta · P.O. Box 2307 · Santa Fe, NM 87504-2307 · 505-982-3873

MUNICIPAL LAW

Albuquerque

Duane E. Brown · Modrall, Sperling, Roehl, Harris & Sisk · Bank of America Centre, Suite 1000 · 500 Fourth Street, NW · P.O. Box 2168 · Albuquerque, NM 87103-2168 · 505-848-1800

David P. Buchholtz · ⑩ · Brownstein Hyatt Farber Schreck · http://www.bhfs.com · 201 Third Street NW, Suite 1700 · Albuquerque, NM 87102-4386 · 505-244-0770

Arthur Melendres · Modrall, Sperling, Roehl, Harris & Sisk · Bank of America Centre, Suite 1000 · 500 Fourth Street, NW · P.O. Box 2168 · Albuquerque, NM 87103-2168 · 505-848-1800

NATIVE AMERICAN LAW

Albuquerque

Thomas C. Bird · Keleher & McLeod · http://www.keleher-law.com · Albuquerque Plaza, 12th Floor · 201 Third Street, NW · P.O. Drawer AA · Albuquerque, NM 87103 · 505-346-4646

William C. Scott · Modrall, Sperling, Roehl, Harris & Sisk · Bank of America Centre, Suite 1000 · 500 Fourth Street, NW · P.O. Box 2168 · Albuquerque, NM 87103-2168 · 505-848-1800

Lynn H. Slade · ⑳ · Modrall, Sperling, Roehl, Harris & Sisk · Bank of America Centre, Suite 1000 · 500 Fourth Street, NW · P.O. Box 2168 · Albuquerque, NM 87103-2168 · 505-848-1800

Walter E. Stern III · ⑩ · Modrall, Sperling, Roehl, Harris & Sisk · Bank of America Centre, Suite 1000 · 500 Fourth Street, NW · P.O. Box 2168 · Albuquerque, NM 87103-2168 · 505-848-1800

Corrales

Susan Williams · Williams & Works · 565 West Ella · P.O. Box 1483 · Corrales, NM 87048-1483 · 505-899-7994

Santa Fe

Mark K. Adams · ⑳ · Rodey, Dickason, Sloan, Akin, & Robb · 315 Paseo de Peralta · P.O. Box 1357 · Santa Fe, NM 87501-2034 · 505-954-3900

Wayne H. Bladh · Nordhaus Law Firm · 1239 Paseo de Peralta · Santa Fe, NM 87501 · 505-982-3622

John P. Burton · ⑳ · Rodey, Dickason, Sloan, Akin, & Robb · 315 Paseo de Peralta · P.O. Box 1357 · Santa Fe, NM 87501-2034 · 505-954-3900

Richard W. Hughes · Rothstein, Donatelli, Hughes, Dahlstrom, Schoenburg & Bienvenu · 1215 Paseo De Peralta · P.O. Box 8180 · Santa Fe, NM 87504-8180 · 505-988-8004

NATURAL RESOURCES LAW

Albuquerque

Clifford K. Atkinson · ⑳ · Atkinson & Thal · Albuquerque Plaza, Suite 1850 · 201 Third Street, NW · Albuquerque, NM 87102 · 505-764-8111

Larry P. Ausherman · ⑳ · Modrall, Sperling, Roehl, Harris & Sisk · Bank of America Centre, Suite 1000 · 500 Fourth Street, NW · P.O. Box 2168 · Albuquerque, NM 87103-2168 · 505-848-1800

Thomas C. Bird · Keleher & McLeod · http://www.keleher-law.com · Albuquerque Plaza, 12th Floor · 201 Third Street, NW · P.O. Drawer AA · Albuquerque, NM 87103 · 505-346-4646

Stuart R. Butzier · Modrall, Sperling, Roehl, Harris & Sisk · Bank of America Centre, Suite 1000 · 500 Fourth Street, NW · P.O. Box 2168 · Albuquerque, NM 87103-2168 · 505-848-1800

John R. Cooney · ⑩ · Modrall, Sperling, Roehl, Harris & Sisk · Bank of America Centre, Suite 1000 · 500 Fourth Street, NW · P.O. Box 2168 · Albuquerque, NM 87103-2168 · 505-848-1800

Charles T. DuMars · ⑩ · Law & Resource Planning Associates · Albuquerque Plaza, Suite 1750 · 201 Third Street, NW · Albuquerque, NM 87102 · 505-346-0998

Lynn H. Slade · ⑳ · Modrall, Sperling, Roehl, Harris & Sisk · Bank of America Centre, Suite 1000 · 500 Fourth Street, NW · P.O. Box 2168 · Albuquerque, NM 87103-2168 · 505-848-1800

Walter E. Stern III · ⑩ · Modrall, Sperling, Roehl, Harris & Sisk · Bank of America Centre, Suite 1000 · 500 Fourth Street, NW · P.O. Box 2168 · Albuquerque, NM 87103-2168 · 505-848-1800

John W. Utton · Sheehan, Sheehan & Stelzner · http://www.ssslawfirm.com · 40 First Plaza, NW, Suite 740 · Albuquerque, NM 87102 · 505-247-0411

Farmington

Richard T. C. Tully · ⑩ · Tully Law Firm · 500 West Broadway, Suite 301 · P.O. Box 268 · Farmington, NM 87499-0268 · 505-327-3388

Hobbs

Scotty A. Holloman · Maddox, Holloman & Kirksey · http://www.hobbsnmlaw.com · 205 East Bender, Suite 150 · P.O. Box 2508 · Hobbs, NM 88241-2508 · 575-393-0505

Roswell

Douglas L. Lunsford · ⑩ · Hinkle, Hensley, Shanor & Martin · 400 Penn Plaza, Suite 700 · P.O. Box 10 · Roswell, NM 88202 · 505-622-6510

John S. Nelson · ⑩ · Atwood, Malone, Turner & Sabin · 400 North Pennsylvania Avenue, Suite 1100 · P.O. Drawer 700 · Roswell, NM 88202-0700 · 575-622-6221

Gregory J. Nibert · ⑩ · Hinkle, Hensley, Shanor & Martin · 400 Penn Plaza, Suite 700 · P.O. Box 10 · Roswell, NM 88202 · 505-622-6510

Santa Fe

Mark K. Adams · ⑳ · Rodey, Dickason, Sloan, Akin, & Robb · 315 Paseo de Peralta · P.O. Box 1357 · Santa Fe, NM 87501-2034 · 505-954-3900

Bradford C. Berge · Holland & Hart · Jefferson Place, Suite One · 110 North Guadalupe · P.O. Box 2208 · Santa Fe, NM 87504-2208 · 505-988-4421

Michael B. Campbell · Holland & Hart · Jefferson Place, Suite One · 110 North Guadalupe · P.O. Box 2208 · Santa Fe, NM 87504-2208 · 505-988-4421

William F. Carr · ⑩ · Holland & Hart · Jefferson Place, Suite One · 110 North Guadalupe · P.O. Box 2208 Santa Fe, NM 87504-2208 · 505-988-4421

John B. Draper · ⑳ · Montgomery & Andrews · 325 Paseo De Peralta · P.O. Box 2307 · Santa Fe, NM 87504-2307 · 505-982-3873

J. E. Gallegos · ⑳ · Gallegos Law Firm · 460 St. Michaels Drive, Suite 300 · Santa Fe, NM 87505-7687 · 505-983-6686

Richard W. Hughes · Rothstein, Donatelli, Hughes, Dahlstrom, Schoenburg & Bienvenu · 1215 Paseo De Peralta · P.O. Box 8180 · Santa Fe, NM 87504-8180 · 505-988-8004

Sunny Jeane Nixon · ⑩ · Rodey, Dickason, Sloan, Akin, & Robb · 315 Paseo de Peralta · P.O. Box 1357 · Santa Fe, NM 87501-2034 · 505-954-3900

Richard A. Simms · ⑳ · Richard A. Simms · 217 Camino Encantado · Santa Fe, NM 87501 · 505-699-8599

Sarah M. Singleton · Montgomery & Andrews · 325 Paseo De Peralta · P.O. Box 2307 · Santa Fe, NM 87504-2307 · 505-982-3873

NON-PROFIT/CHARITIES LAW

Albuquerque

Richard K. Barlow · ⑳ · Barlow & Wilcox · Albuquerque Plaza, Suite 1130 · 201 Third Street, NW · Albuquerque, NM 87102 · 505-248-1300

NON-WHITE-COLLAR CRIMINAL DEFENSE

Albuquerque

David A. Freedman · ⑩ · Freedman Boyd Hollander Goldberg & Ives · http://www.fbdlaw.com · 20 First Plaza, Suite 700 · Albuquerque, NM 87102 · 505-842-9960

Robert J. Gorence · Robert J. Gorence · 201 Twelfth Street, NW · Albuquerque, NM 87102-1815 · 505-244-0214

Mary Y. C. Han · Kennedy & Han · 201 Twelfth Street, NW · Albuquerque, NM 87102 · 505-842-8662

Nancy Hollander · ⑳ · Freedman Boyd Hollander Goldberg & Ives · http://www.fbdlaw.com · 20 First Plaza, Suite 700 · Albuquerque, NM 87102 · 505-842-9960

Tova Indritz · ⑩ · Tova Indritz · 2040 Fourth Street, NW · Albuquerque, NM 87102 · 505-242-4003

Paul J. Kennedy · ⑩ · Kennedy & Han · 201 Twelfth Street, NW · Albuquerque, NM 87102 · 505-842-8662

Randi McGinn · ⑩ · McGinn, Carpenter, Montoya & Love · 201 Broadway Boulevard, SE · Albuquerque, NM 87102 · 505-843-6161

Jacquelyn Robins · Jacquelyn Robins · 812 Marquette Avenue, NW · Albuquerque, NM 87102-1959 · 505-242-5359

Peter Schoenburg · ⑩ · Rothstein, Donatelli, Hughes, Dahlstrom, Schoenburg & Bienvenu · Bank of America Centre, Suite 400 · 500 Fourth Street, NW · Albuquerque, NM 87102 · 505-243-1443

Luis G. Stelzner · ⑩ · Sheehan, Sheehan & Stelzner · http://www.ssslawfirm.com · 40 First Plaza, NW, Suite 740 · Albuquerque, NM 87102 · 505-247-0411

Ray R. Twohig · ⑳ · Ray Twohig · 8998 Rio Grande Boulevard, NW · Albuquerque, NM 87114 · 505-898-0400

Las Cruces

Michael W. Lilley · ⑩ · Lilley Law Offices · 1014 South Main Street · Las Cruces, NM 88005 · 505-524-7809

Mark Pickett · Pickett Law Firm · 500 North Church Street · P.O. Box 1239 · Las Cruces, NM 88004 · 505-526-3338

Michael L. Stout · ⑩ · Law Offices of Michael L. Stout · 910 Lake Tahoe Street · Las Cruces, NM 88007-4103 · 505-524-1471

Ruidoso

Gary C. Mitchell · ⑩ · Gary C. Mitchell · 443 Mechem Drive · P.O. Box 2460 · Ruidoso, NM 88355 · 505-257-3070

Santa Fe

Dan Cron · ⑩ · Dan Cron Law Firm · 125 Lincoln Avenue, Suite 400 · P.O. Box 40 · Santa Fe, NM 87504-0040 · 505-986-1334

Mark H. Donatelli · ⑳ · Rothstein, Donatelli, Hughes, Dahlstrom, Schoenburg & Bienvenu · 1215 Paseo De Peralta · P.O. Box 8180 · Santa Fe, NM 87504-8180 · 505-988-8004

Robert R. Rothstein · ⑳ · Rothstein, Donatelli, Hughes, Dahlstrom, Schoenburg & Bienvenu · 1215 Paseo De Peralta · P.O. Box 8180 · Santa Fe, NM 87504-8180 · 505-988-8004

OIL & GAS LAW

Albuquerque

John R. Cooney · ⑩ · Modrall, Sperling, Roehl, Harris & Sisk · Bank of America Centre, Suite 1000 · 500 Fourth Street, NW · P.O. Box 2168 · Albuquerque, NM 87103-2168 · 505-848-1800

Earl E. DeBrine · Modrall, Sperling, Roehl, Harris & Sisk · Bank of America Centre, Suite 1000 · 500 Fourth Street, NW · P.O. Box 2168 · Albuquerque, NM 87103-2168 · 505-848-1800

Marte D. Lightstone · Modrall, Sperling, Roehl, Harris & Sisk · Bank of America Centre, Suite 1000 · 500 Fourth Street, NW · P.O. Box 2168 · Albuquerque, NM 87103-2168 · 505-848-1800

Lynn H. Slade · ⑳ · Modrall, Sperling, Roehl, Harris & Sisk · Bank of America Centre, Suite 1000 · 500 Fourth Street, NW · P.O. Box 2168 · Albuquerque, NM 87103-2168 · 505-848-1800

Walter E. Stern III · ⑩ · Modrall, Sperling, Roehl, Harris & Sisk · Bank of America Centre, Suite 1000 · 500 Fourth Street, NW · P.O. Box 2168 · Albuquerque, NM 87103-2168 · 505-848-1800

Artesia

Jeffrey L. Bowman · Vandiver & Bowman · 611 West Mahone Drive, Suite E · Artesia, NM 88210-2075 · 505-746-9841

David R. Vandiver · Vandiver & Bowman · 611 West Mahone Drive, Suite E · Artesia, NM 88210-2075 · 505-746-9841

Farmington

Richard T. C. Tully · ⑩ · Tully Law Firm · 500 West Broadway, Suite 301 · P.O. Box 268 · Farmington, NM 87499-0268 · 505-327-3388

Roswell

Phillip T. Brewer · Phillip T. Brewer Attorney · 125 West Fourth Street · P.O. Box 298 · Roswell, NM 88202-0298 · 505-625-0298

T. Calder Ezzell · Hinkle, Hensley, Shanor & Martin · 400 Penn Plaza, Suite 700 · P.O. Box 10 · Roswell, NM 88202 · 505-622-6510

Don M. Fedric · ⑳ · Don M. Fedric · 215 West Third Street · P.O. Box 1837 · Roswell, NM 88202-1837 · 505-622-2700

Douglas L. Lunsford · ⑩ · Hinkle, Hensley, Shanor & Martin · 400 Penn Plaza, Suite 700 · P.O. Box 10 · Roswell, NM 88202 · 505-622-6510

John S. Nelson · ⑩ · Atwood, Malone, Turner & Sabin · 400 North Pennsylvania Avenue, Suite 1100 · P.O. Drawer 700 · Roswell, NM 88202-0700 · 575-622-6221

Gregory J. Nibert · ⑩ · Hinkle, Hensley, Shanor & Martin · 400 Penn Plaza, Suite 700 · P.O. Box 10 · Roswell, NM 88202 · 505-622-6510

Santa Fe

Mark K. Adams · ⑳ · Rodey, Dickason, Sloan, Akin, & Robb · 315 Paseo de Peralta · P.O. Box 1357 · Santa Fe, NM 87501-2034 · 505-954-3900

Michael B. Campbell · Holland & Hart · Jefferson Place, Suite One · 110 North Guadalupe · P.O. Box 2208 · Santa Fe, NM 87504-2208 · 505-988-4421

William F. Carr · ⑩ · Holland & Hart · Jefferson Place, Suite One · 110 North Guadalupe · P.O. Box 2208 Santa Fe, NM 87504-2208 · 505-988-4421

J. E. Gallegos · ⑳ · Gallegos Law Firm · 460 St. Michaels Drive, Suite 300 · Santa Fe, NM 87505-7687 · 505-983-6686

PERSONAL INJURY LITIGATION

Albuquerque

Douglas A. Baker · ⑩ · Modrall, Sperling, Roehl, Harris & Sisk · Bank of America Centre, Suite 1000 · 500 Fourth Street, NW · P.O. Box 2168 · Albuquerque, NM 87103-2168 · 505-848-1800

Arthur Beach · Keleher & McLeod · http://www.keleher-law.com · Albuquerque Plaza, 12th Floor · 201 Third Street, NW · P.O. Drawer AA · Albuquerque, NM 87103 · 505-346-4646

Allegra Carroll Carpenter · McGinn, Carpenter, Montoya & Love · 201 Broadway Boulevard, SE · Albuquerque, NM 87102 · 505-843-6161

William H. Carpenter · ㉕ · Carpenter & Stout · 1600 University Boulevard, NE, Suite A · Albuquerque, NM 87102-1724 · 505-243-1336

Gregory W. Chase · ⑩ · Shapiro Bettinger Chase · 7411 Jefferson Street, NE · Albuquerque, NM 87109 · 505-888-6463

Stephen Durkovich · ⑳ · Law Office of Stephen Durkovich · 534 Old Santa Fe Trail · Albuquerque, NM 87505-0372 · 505-986-1800

Philip C. Gaddy · The Gaddy Law Firm · 2025 San Pedro Drive, NE · Albuquerque, NM 87110 · 505-254-9090

Gary L. Gordon · Miller Stratvert · 500 Marquette Avenue, NW, Suite 1100 · P.O. Box 25687 · Albuquerque, NM 87125-0687 · 505-842-1950

Bruce Hall · ⑩ · Rodey, Dickason, Sloan, Akin, & Robb · Albuquerque Plaza, Suite 2200 · 201 Third Street, NW · P.O. Box 1888 · Albuquerque, NM 87102 · 505-765-5900

Kenneth L. Harrigan · ⑩ · Modrall, Sperling, Roehl, Harris & Sisk · Bank of America Centre, Suite 1000 · 500 Fourth Street, NW · P.O. Box 2168 · Albuquerque, NM 87103-2168 · 505-848-1800

F. Michael Hart · Martinez & Hart · 1801 Rio Grande Boulevard, NW · Albuquerque, NM 87104 · 505-343-1776

Paul R. Koller · Rodey, Dickason, Sloan, Akin, & Robb · Albuquerque Plaza, Suite 2200 · 201 Third Street, NW · P.O. Box 1888 · Albuquerque, NM 87102 · 505-765-5900

W. Robert Lasater, Jr. · ⑳ · Rodey, Dickason, Sloan, Akin, & Robb · Albuquerque Plaza, Suite 2200 · 201 Third Street, NW · P.O. Box 1888 · Albuquerque, NM 87102 · 505-765-5900

William C. Madison · Madison, Harbour, Mroz & Brennan · Albuquerque Plaza, Suite 1600 · 201 Third Street, NW · P.O. Box 25467 · Albuquerque, NM 87125-0467 · 505-242-2177

Robert G. McCorkle · ⑳ · Rodey, Dickason, Sloan, Akin, & Robb · Albuquerque Plaza, Suite 2200 · 201 Third Street, NW · P.O. Box 1888 · Albuquerque, NM 87102 · 505-765-5900

Randi McGinn · ⑩ · McGinn, Carpenter, Montoya & Love · 201 Broadway Boulevard, SE · Albuquerque, NM 87102 · 505-843-6161

Mark C. Meiering · Rodey, Dickason, Sloan, Akin, & Robb · Albuquerque Plaza, Suite 2200 · 201 Third Street, NW · P.O. Box 1888 · Albuquerque, NM 87102 · 505-765-5900

Ranne B. Miller · ⑳ · Miller Stratvert · 500 Marquette Avenue, NW, Suite 1100 · P.O. Box 25687 · Albuquerque, NM 87125-0687 · 505-842-1950

Ronald C. Morgan · ⑩ · Ron Morgan · 500 Tijeras Avenue, NW · Albuquerque, NM 87102 · 505-842-1905

Charles A. Pharris · ⑩ · Keleher & McLeod · http://www.keleher-law.com · Albuquerque Plaza, 12th Floor · 201 Third Street, NW · P.O. Drawer AA · Albuquerque, NM 87103 · 505-346-4646

Andrew G. Schultz · Rodey, Dickason, Sloan, Akin, & Robb · Albuquerque Plaza, Suite 2200 · 201 Third Street, NW · P.O. Box 1888 · Albuquerque, NM 87102 · 505-765-5900

Ronald J. Segel · Sutin, Thayer & Browne · http://www.sutinfirm.com · Two Park Square, Suite 1000 · 6565 Americas Parkway, NE · P.O. Box 1945 · Albuquerque, NM 87103 · 505-883-2500

Richard J. Shane · ⑩ · Riley, Shane & Hale · 4101 Indian School Road, NE, Suite 420 · Albuquerque, NM 87110 · 505-883-5030

Patrick M. Shay · Rodey, Dickason, Sloan, Akin, & Robb · Albuquerque Plaza, Suite 2200 · 201 Third Street, NW · P.O. Box 1888 · Albuquerque, NM 87102 · 505-765-5900

Rebecca Sitterly · Rebecca Sitterly · 500 Marquette Avenue, NW, Suite 280 · P.O. Box 7790 · Albuquerque, NM 87194-7790 · 505-238-5151

William E. Snead · ㉕ · William E. Snead · 201 Twelfth Street, NW · Albuquerque, NM 87106-1439 · 505-842-8177

David J. Stout · Carpenter & Stout · 1600 University Boulevard, NE, Suite A · Albuquerque, NM 87102-1724 · 505-243-1336

Terry M. Word · ⑩ · Terry M. Word · http://www.terrymwordpc.com · 500 Tijeras Avenue, NW · Albuquerque, NM 87102 · 505-842-1905

Farmington

Richard L. Gerding · ⑩ · Gerding & O'Loughlin · 304 North Behrend Avenue · P.O. Box 1020 · Farmington, NM 87499-1020 · 505-325-1804

Las Cruces

Lawrence Pickett · Pickett Law Firm · 500 North Church Street · P.O. Box 1239 · Las Cruces, NM 88004 · 505-526-3338

Angel Saenz · Saenz & Torres · 333 South Campo Street · Las Cruces, NM 88001 · 505-526-3333

Denise M. Torres · Saenz & Torres · 333 South Campo Street · Las Cruces, NM 88001 · 505-526-3333

Roswell

Robert E. Sabin · ⑩ · Atwood, Malone, Turner & Sabin · 400 North Pennsylvania Avenue, Suite 1100 · P.O. Drawer 700 · Roswell, NM 88202-0700 · 575-622-6221

Rodney M. Schumacher · Atwood, Malone, Turner & Sabin · 400 North Pennsylvania Avenue, Suite 1100 · P.O. Drawer 700 · Roswell, NM 88202-0700 · 575-622-6221

Santa Fe

Bradford C. Berge · Holland & Hart · Jefferson Place, Suite One · 110 North Guadalupe · P.O. Box 2208 · Santa Fe, NM 87504-2208 · 505-988-4421

Jeffrey R. Brannen · ⑩ · Jeffrey R. Brannen · 644 Don Gaspar Avenue · P.O. Box 10166 · Santa Fe, NM 87504-0166 · 505-983-4429

Walter Melendres · Montgomery & Andrews · 325 Paseo De Peralta · P.O. Box 2307 · Santa Fe, NM 87504-2307 · 505-982-3873

W. Mark Mowery · Rodey, Dickason, Sloan, Akin, & Robb · 315 Paseo de Peralta · P.O. Box 1357 · Santa Fe, NM 87501-2034 · 505-954-3900

Robert R. Rothstein · ⑳ · Rothstein, Donatelli, Hughes, Dahlstrom, Schoenburg & Bienvenu · 1215 Paseo De Peralta · P.O. Box 8180 · Santa Fe, NM 87504-8180 · 505-988-8004

Thomas A. Simons IV · Simons & Slattery · 1660 Old Pecos Trail, Suite A · P.O. Box 5333 · Santa Fe, NM 87502-5333 · 505-988-5600

William P. Slattery · Simons & Slattery · 1660 Old Pecos Trail, Suite A · P.O. Box 5333 · Santa Fe, NM 87502-5333 · 505-988-5600

PRODUCT LIABILITY LITIGATION

Albuquerque

Douglas A. Baker · ⑩ · Modrall, Sperling, Roehl, Harris & Sisk · Bank of America Centre, Suite 1000 · 500 Fourth Street, NW · P.O. Box 2168 · Albuquerque, NM 87103-2168 · 505-848-1800

Arthur Beach · Keleher & McLeod · http://www.keleher-law.com · Albuquerque Plaza, 12th Floor · 201 Third Street, NW · P.O. Drawer AA · Albuquerque, NM 87103 · 505-346-4646

William H. Carpenter · ㉕ · Carpenter & Stout · 1600 University Boulevard, NE, Suite A · Albuquerque, NM 87102-1724 · 505-243-1336

Robert J. Curtis · Civerolo, Gralow, Hill & Curtis · 20 First Plaza Galleria, NW, Suite 500 · Albuquerque, NM 87102 · 505-842-8255

Nelson Franse · Rodey, Dickason, Sloan, Akin, & Robb · Albuquerque Plaza, Suite 2200 · 201 Third Street, NW · P.O. Box 1888 · Albuquerque, NM 87102 · 505-765-5900

Philip C. Gaddy · The Gaddy Law Firm · 2025 San Pedro Drive, NE · Albuquerque, NM 87110 · 505-254-9090

Bruce Hall · ⑩ · Rodey, Dickason, Sloan, Akin, & Robb · Albuquerque Plaza, Suite 2200 · 201 Third Street, NW · P.O. Box 1888 · Albuquerque, NM 87102 · 505-765-5900

Kenneth L. Harrigan · ⑩ · Modrall, Sperling, Roehl, Harris & Sisk · Bank of America Centre, Suite 1000 · 500 Fourth Street, NW · P.O. Box 2168 · Albuquerque, NM 87103-2168 · 505-848-1800

Randi McGinn · ⑩ · McGinn, Carpenter, Montoya & Love · 201 Broadway Boulevard, SE · Albuquerque, NM 87102 · 505-843-6161

Thomas A. Outler · Rodey, Dickason, Sloan, Akin, & Robb · Albuquerque Plaza, Suite 2200 · 201 Third Street, NW · P.O. Box 1888 · Albuquerque, NM 87102 · 505-765-5900

Douglas G. Schneebeck · Modrall, Sperling, Roehl, Harris & Sisk · Bank of America Centre, Suite 1000 · 500 Fourth Street, NW · P.O. Box 2168 · Albuquerque, NM 87103-2168 · 505-848-1800

David J. Stout · Carpenter & Stout · 1600 University Boulevard, NE, Suite A · Albuquerque, NM 87102-1724 · 505-243-1336

Santa Fe

Bradford C. Berge · Holland & Hart · Jefferson Place, Suite One · 110 North Guadalupe · P.O. Box 2208 · Santa Fe, NM 87504-2208 · 505-988-4421

PROFESSIONAL MALPRACTICE LAW

Albuquerque

Jack M. Brant · ⑩ · Law Office of Jack Brant · 202 Tulane Drive, SE · Albuquerque, NM 87106-1414 · 505-232-5300

Gerald George Dixon · Dixon, Scholl & Bailey · 707 Broadway, NE, Suite 505 · P.O. Box 26746 · Albuquerque, NM 87125-6746 · 505-244-3890

Steven C. Ewing · Steven C. Ewing · Third Central Plaza, Suite 1000 West · 300 Central Avenue, SW · Albuquerque, NM 87102 · 505-247-4051

Nelson Franse · Rodey, Dickason, Sloan, Akin, & Robb · Albuquerque Plaza, Suite 2200 · 201 Third Street, NW · P.O. Box 1888 · Albuquerque, NM 87102 · 505-765-5900

Charles J. Vigil · Rodey, Dickason, Sloan, Akin, & Robb · Albuquerque Plaza, Suite 2200 · 201 Third Street, NW · P.O. Box 1888 · Albuquerque, NM 87102 · 505-765-5900

PUBLIC FINANCE LAW

Albuquerque

Perry E. Bendicksen · ⑩ · Brownstein Hyatt Farber Schreck · http://www.bhfs.com · 201 Third Street NW, Suite 1700 · Albuquerque, NM 87102-4386 · 505-244-0770

Duane E. Brown · Modrall, Sperling, Roehl, Harris & Sisk · Bank of America Centre, Suite 1000 · 500 Fourth Street, NW · P.O. Box 2168 · Albuquerque, NM 87103-2168 · 505-848-1800

David P. Buchholtz · ⑩ · Brownstein Hyatt Farber Schreck · http://www.bhfs.com · 201 Third Street NW, Suite 1700 · Albuquerque, NM 87102-4386 · 505-244-0770

Dennis J. Falk · ⑩ · Modrall, Sperling, Roehl, Harris & Sisk · Bank of America Centre, Suite 1000 · 500 Fourth Street, NW · P.O. Box 2168 · Albuquerque, NM 87103-2168 · 505-848-1800

Donald B. Monnheimer · Rodey, Dickason, Sloan, Akin, & Robb · Albuquerque Plaza, Suite 2200 · 201 Third Street, NW · P.O. Box 1888 · Albuquerque, NM 87102 · 505-765-5900

Christopher P. Muirhead · Modrall, Sperling, Roehl, Harris & Sisk · Bank of America Centre, Suite 1000 500 Fourth Street, NW · P.O. Box 2168 · Albuquerque, NM 87103-2168 · 505-848-1800

Jill K. Sweeney · Brownstein Hyatt Farber Schreck · http://www.bhfs.com · 201 Third Street NW, Suite 1700 · Albuquerque, NM 87102-4386 · 505-244-0770

Santa Fe

Peter Franklin · Modrall, Sperling, Roehl, Harris & Sisk · 123 East Marcy Street, Suite 201 · P.O. Box 9318 · Santa Fe, NM 87504-9318 · 505-983-2020

Robert G. Heyman · ⑩ · Sutin, Thayer & Browne · http://www.sutinfirm.com · 317 Paseo de Peralta · P.O. Box 2187 · Santa Fe, NM 87504 · 505-988-5521

RAILROAD LAW

Albuquerque

Clifford K. Atkinson · ⑳ · Atkinson & Thal · Albuquerque Plaza, Suite 1850 · 201 Third Street, NW · Albuquerque, NM 87102 · 505-764-8111

Earl E. DeBrine · Modrall, Sperling, Roehl, Harris & Sisk · Bank of America Centre, Suite 1000 · 500 Fourth Street, NW · P.O. Box 2168 · Albuquerque, NM 87103-2168 · 505-848-1800

Timothy L. Fields · Modrall, Sperling, Roehl, Harris & Sisk · Bank of America Centre, Suite 1000 · 500 Fourth Street, NW · P.O. Box 2168 · Albuquerque, NM 87103-2168 · 505-848-1800

Timothy C. Holm · Modrall, Sperling, Roehl, Harris & Sisk · Bank of America Centre, Suite 1000 · 500 Fourth Street, NW · P.O. Box 2168 · Albuquerque, NM 87103-2168 · 505-848-1800

Michael Kaemper · Atkinson & Thal · Albuquerque Plaza, Suite 1850 · 201 Third Street, NW · Albuquerque, NM 87102 · 505-764-8111

John S. Thal · Atkinson & Thal · Albuquerque Plaza, Suite 1850 · 201 Third Street, NW · Albuquerque, NM 87102 · 505-764-8111

REAL ESTATE LAW

Albuquerque

Thomas C. Bird · Keleher & McLeod · http://www.keleher-law.com · Albuquerque Plaza, 12th Floor · 201 Third Street, NW · P.O. Drawer AA · Albuquerque, NM 87103 · 505-346-4646

Thomas Blueher · Vogel Campbell & Blueher · 6100 Uptown Boulevard, NE, Suite 500 · Albuquerque, NM 87110-4187 · 505-884-8444

Anne P. Browne · Sutin, Thayer & Browne · http://www.sutinfirm.com · Two Park Square, Suite 1000 · 6565 Americas Parkway, NE · P.O. Box 1945 · Albuquerque, NM 87103 · 505-883-2500

David S. Campbell · ⑩ · Vogel Campbell & Blueher · 6100 Uptown Boulevard, NE, Suite 500 · Albuquerque, NM 87110-4187 · 505-884-8444

Bill Chappell, Jr. · ⑩ · Chappell Law Firm · Albuquerque Centre, Suite 150 · 6001 Indian School Road, NE · Albuquerque, NM 87110-4167 · 505-878-9600

Dale Wallace Ek · ⑩ · Modrall, Sperling, Roehl, Harris & Sisk · Bank of America Centre, Suite 1000 · 500 Fourth Street, NW · P.O. Box 2168 · Albuquerque, NM 87103-2168 · 505-848-1800

Catherine T. Goldberg · ⑩ · Rodey, Dickason, Sloan, Akin, & Robb · Albuquerque Plaza, Suite 2200 · 201 Third Street, NW · P.O. Box 1888 · Albuquerque, NM 87102 · 505-765-5900

Jay D. Hill · Vogel Campbell & Blueher · 6100 Uptown Boulevard, NE, Suite 500 · Albuquerque, NM 87110-4187 · 505-884-8444

James P. Houghton · Modrall, Sperling, Roehl, Harris & Sisk · Bank of America Centre, Suite 1000 · 500 Fourth Street, NW · P.O. Box 2168 · Albuquerque, NM 87103-2168 · 505-848-1800

Kenneth A. Hunt · Hunt & Davis · 2632 Mesilla, NE · P.O. Box 30088 · Albuquerque, NM 87190-0088 · 505-881-3191

Patrick W. Hurley · ⑳ · Hurley, Toevs, Styles, Hamblin & Panter · 4155 Montgomery Boulevard, NE · Albuquerque, NM 87109 · 505-888-1188

Dennis Jontz · Lewis and Roca · http://www.lrlaw.com · 201 Third Street, NW, Suite 1950 · Albuquerque, NM 87102 · 505-764-5400

William B. Keleher · ⑳ · Keleher & McLeod · http://www.keleher-law.com · Albuquerque Plaza, 12th Floor · 201 Third Street, NW · P.O. Drawer AA · Albuquerque, NM 87103 · 505-346-4646

Henry A. Kelly · ⑳ · Sutin, Thayer & Browne · http://www.sutinfirm.com · Two Park Square, Suite 1000 · 6565 Americas Parkway, NE · P.O. Box 1945 · Albuquerque, NM 87103 · 505-883-2500

Margaret Lewis Meister · Modrall, Sperling, Roehl, Harris & Sisk · Bank of America Centre, Suite 1000 · 500 Fourth Street, NW · P.O. Box 2168 · Albuquerque, NM 87103-2168 · 505-848-1800

John A. Myers · ⑳ · Myers, Oliver & Price · 1401 Central Avenue, NW · Albuquerque, NM 87104-1138 · 505-247-9080

Scott N. Oliver · Myers, Oliver & Price · 1401 Central Avenue, NW · Albuquerque, NM 87104-1138 · 505-247-9080

Charles P. Price III · ⑳ · Myers, Oliver & Price · 1401 Central Avenue, NW · Albuquerque, NM 87104-1138 · 505-247-9080

John P. Salazar · ⑳ · Rodey, Dickason, Sloan, Akin, & Robb · Albuquerque Plaza, Suite 2200 · 201 Third Street, NW · P.O. Box 1888 · Albuquerque, NM 87102 · 505-765-5900

Ruth M. Schifani · Modrall, Sperling, Roehl, Harris & Sisk · Bank of America Centre, Suite 1000 · 500 Fourth Street, NW · P.O. Box 2168 · Albuquerque, NM 87103-2168 · 505-848-1800

Charles A. Seibert III · Rodey, Dickason, Sloan, Akin, & Robb · Albuquerque Plaza, Suite 2200 · 201 Third Street, NW · P.O. Box 1888 · Albuquerque, NM 87102 · 505-765-5900

Robert M. St. John · ⑩ · Rodey, Dickason, Sloan, Akin, & Robb · Albuquerque Plaza, Suite 2200 · 201 Third Street, NW · P.O. Box 1888 · Albuquerque, NM 87102 · 505-765-5900

Mark Styles · Hurley, Toevs, Styles, Hamblin & Panter · 4155 Montgomery Boulevard, NE · Albuquerque, NM 87109 · 505-888-1188

Bradley D. Tepper · Miller Stratvert · 500 Marquette Avenue, NW, Suite 1100 · P.O. Box 25687 · Albuquerque, NM 87125-0687 · 505-842-1950

Albert T. Ussery · Ussery & Parrish · 121Tijeras, NE, Suite 3400 · P.O. Box 487 · Albuquerque, NM 87103 · 505-247-0145

Lawrence M. Wells · Campbell & Wells · 2155 Louisiana Boulevard, NE, Suite 10300 · Albuquerque, NM 87110 · 505-766-9926

Raton

Paul Kastler · ⑩ · Kastler Law Offices · 188 Hospital Drive · Raton, NM 87740 · 575-445-1065

Rio Rancho

Christopher M. Pacheco · Lastrapes, Spangler & Pacheco · 333 Rio Rancho Drive, Suite 401 · P.O. Box 15698 · Rio Rancho, NM 87174 · 505-892-3607

Santa Fe

Janice M. Ahern · Sommer, Udall, Hardwick, Ahern & Hyatt · 200 West Marcy Street, Suite 129 · P.O. Box 1984 · Santa Fe, NM 87504-1984 · 505-982-4676

John P. Burton · ⑳ · Rodey, Dickason, Sloan, Akin, & Robb · 315 Paseo de Peralta · P.O. Box 1357 · Santa Fe, NM 87501-2034 · 505-954-3900

Leonard S. Katz · ⑩ · Rubin Katz Law Firm · Marcy Plaza, Suite 200 · 123 East Marcy Street · P.O. Drawer 250 · Santa Fe, NM 87504 · 505-982-3610

John N. Patterson · ⑩ · Scheuer, Yost & Patterson · 125 Lincoln Avenue, Suite 223 · P.O. Drawer 9570 · Santa Fe, NM 87504-9570 · 505-982-9911

James S. Rubin · Rubin Katz Law Firm · Marcy Plaza, Suite 200 · 123 East Marcy Street · P.O. Drawer 250 · Santa Fe, NM 87504 · 505-982-3610

Thomas A. Simons IV · Simons & Slattery · 1660 Old Pecos Trail, Suite A · P.O. Box 5333 · Santa Fe, NM 87502-5333 · 505-988-5600

Michael G. Sutin · ⑩ · Sutin, Thayer & Browne · http://www.sutinfirm.com · 324 Paseo De Peralta, Suite B · Santa Fe, NM 87501 · 505-986-5554

SECURITIES LAW

Albuquerque

Richard K. Barlow · ⑳ · Barlow & Wilcox · Albuquerque Plaza, Suite 1130 · 201 Third Street, NW · Albuquerque, NM 87102 · 505-248-1300

Alan Hall · Rodey, Dickason, Sloan, Akin, & Robb · Albuquerque Plaza, Suite 2200 · 201 Third Street, NW · P.O. Box 1888 · Albuquerque, NM 87102 · 505-765-5900

Donald B. Monnheimer · Rodey, Dickason, Sloan, Akin, & Robb · Albuquerque Plaza, Suite 2200 · 201 Third Street, NW · P.O. Box 1888 · Albuquerque, NM 87102 · 505-765-5900

Bonnie J. Paisley · Brownstein Hyatt Farber Schreck · http://www.bhfs.com · 201 Third Street NW, Suite 1700 · Albuquerque, NM 87102-4386 · 505-244-0770

Santa Fe

Robert G. Heyman · ⑩ · Sutin, Thayer & Browne · http://www.sutinfirm.com · 317 Paseo de Peralta · P.O. Box 2187 · Santa Fe, NM 87504 · 505-988-5521

TAX LAW

Albuquerque

Richard K. Barlow · ⑳ · Barlow & Wilcox · Albuquerque Plaza, Suite 1130 · 201 Third Street, NW · Albuquerque, NM 87102 · 505-248-1300

James F. Beckley · Beckley Law Firm · One Executive Center, Suite A-400 · 8500 Menaul Boulevard, NE · P.O. Box 30868 · Albuquerque, NM 87112 · 505-275-1222

Gary D. Eisenberg · Betzer, Roybal & Eisenberg · 4900 Lang Avenue, NE, Suite 202 · Albuquerque, NM 87109-4304 · 505-797-0105

John E. Heer III · ⑳ · Laflin, Pick & Heer · 8500 Menaul Boulevard, NE, Suite B-450 · P.O. Box 3260 · Albuquerque, NM 87190-3260 · 505-883-0679

John N. Lieuwen · ⑳ · Lieuwen, La Fata & Tucker · 4101 Indian School Road, NE, Suite 310-N · Albuquerque, NM 87110 · 505-262-6000

James M. Parker · ⑩ · Modrall, Sperling, Roehl, Harris & Sisk · Bank of America Centre, Suite 1000 · 500 Fourth Street, NW · P.O. Box 2168 · Albuquerque, NM 87103-2168 · 505-848-1800

Daniel E. Pick · ⑩ · Laflin, Pick & Heer · 8500 Menaul Boulevard, NE, Suite B-450 · P.O. Box 3260 · Albuquerque, NM 87190-3260 · 505-883-0679

Benjamin C. Roybal · ⑩ · Betzer, Roybal & Eisenberg · 4900 Lang Avenue, NE, Suite 202 · Albuquerque, NM 87109-4304 · 505-797-0105

Kendall O. Schlenker · ㉕ · Schlenker & Urrea · 7850 Jefferson, NE, Suite 140 · P.O. Box 90637 · Albuquerque, NM 87199-0637 · 505-244-0090

Thomas Smidt II · ㉕ · Tax, Estate & Business Law · 4811 Hardware Drive, NE, Suite A-4 · Albuquerque, NM 87109 · 505-830-2200

Donald E. Swaim · ⑩ · Swaim, Schrandt & Millet · 4830 Juan Tabo Boulevard, NE, Suite F · Albuquerque, NM 87111 · 505-237-0064

Patricia Belle Tucker · ⑳ · Lieuwen, La Fata & Tucker · 4101 Indian School Road, NE, Suite 310-N · Albuquerque, NM 87110 · 505-262-6000

Timothy R. Van Valen · Brownstein Hyatt Farber Schreck · http://www.bhfs.com · 201 Third Street NW, Suite 1700 · Albuquerque, NM 87102-4386 · 505-244-0770

Vickie R. Wilcox · Barlow & Wilcox · Albuquerque Plaza, Suite 1130 · 201 Third Street, NW · Albuquerque, NM 87102 · 505-248-1300

Santa Fe

Curtis W. Schwartz · ⑩ · Modrall, Sperling, Roehl, Harris & Sisk · 123 East Marcy Street, Suite 201 · P.O. Box 9318 · Santa Fe, NM 87504-9318 · 505-983-2020

TRANSPORTATION LAW

Albuquerque

Jeffrey M. Croasdell · Rodey, Dickason, Sloan, Akin, & Robb · Albuquerque Plaza, Suite 2200 · 201 Third Street, NW · P.O. Box 1888 · Albuquerque, NM 87102 · 505-765-5900

William P. Gralow · Civerolo, Gralow, Hill & Curtis · 20 First Plaza Galleria, NW, Suite 500 · Albuquerque, NM 87102 · 505-842-8255

J. Duke Thornton · Butt, Thornton & Baehr · 4101 Indian School Road, NE, Suite 300 South · P.O. Box 3170 · Albuquerque, NM 87190 · 505-884-0777

Paul T. Yarbrough · Butt, Thornton & Baehr · 4101 Indian School Road, NE, Suite 300 South · P.O. Box 3170 · Albuquerque, NM 87190 · 505-884-0777

Albuquerque

Richard K. Barlow · 20 · Barlow & Wilcox · Albuquerque Plaza, Suite 1130 · 201 Third Street, NW · Albuquerque, NM 87102 · 505-248-1300

James F. Beckley · Beckley Law Firm · One Executive Center, Suite A-400 · 8500 Menaul Boulevard, NE · P.O. Box 30868 · Albuquerque, NM 87112 · 505-275-1222

Gary D. Eisenberg · Betzer, Roybal & Eisenberg · 4900 Lang Avenue, NE, Suite 202 · Albuquerque, NM 87109-4304 · 505-797-0105

Margaret A. Foster · Ahr, Foster & Quezada · 6751 Academy Road, NE, Suite C · Albuquerque, NM 87109 · 505-821-5122

Mary Ann Green · Mary Ann Green · 1825 San Mateo Boulevard, NE · Albuquerque, NM 87110-5145 · 505-254-0600

Sharon P. Gross · Miller Stratvert · 500 Marquette Avenue, NW, Suite 1100 · P.O. Box 25687 · Albuquerque, NM 87125-0687 · 505-842-1950

Randolph L. Hamblin · Hurley, Toevs, Styles, Hamblin & Panter · 4155 Montgomery Boulevard, NE · Albuquerque, NM 87109 · 505-888-1188

Lawrence W. Kay · Lawrence W. Kay · 1825 San Mateo Boulevard, NE · Albuquerque, NM 87110 · 505-254-0600

Kenneth C. Leach · 10 · Leach & Finlayson · Sun Valley Center, Unit G4, Box 15 · 320 Osuna Road, NE · Albuquerque, NM 87107 · 505-883-2702

John N. Lieuwen · 20 · Lieuwen, La Fata & Tucker · 4101 Indian School Road, NE, Suite 310-N · Albuquerque, NM 87110 · 505-262-6000

Gaelle D. McConnell · Barlow & Wilcox · Albuquerque Plaza, Suite 1130 · 201 Third Street, NW · Albuquerque, NM 87102 · 505-248-1300

James M. Parker · 10 · Modrall, Sperling, Roehl, Harris & Sisk · Bank of America Centre, Suite 1000 · 500 Fourth Street, NW · P.O. Box 2168 · Albuquerque, NM 87103-2168 · 505-848-1800

Daniel E. Pick · 10 · Laflin, Pick & Heer · 8500 Menaul Boulevard, NE, Suite B-450 · P.O. Box 3260 · Albuquerque, NM 87190-3260 · 505-883-0679

Marjorie A. Rogers · Modrall, Sperling, Roehl, Harris & Sisk · Bank of America Centre, Suite 1000 · 500 Fourth Street, NW · P.O. Box 2168 · Albuquerque, NM 87103-2168 · 505-848-1800

Kendall O. Schlenker · 25 · Schlenker & Urrea · 7850 Jefferson, NE, Suite 140 · P.O. Box 90637 · Albuquerque, NM 87199-0637 · 505-244-0090

Judith D. Schrandt · Swaim, Schrandt & Millet · 4830 Juan Tabo Boulevard, NE, Suite F · Albuquerque, NM 87111 · 505-237-0064

Thomas Smidt II · 25 · Tax, Estate & Business Law · 4811 Hardware Drive, NE, Suite A-4 · Albuquerque, NM 87109 · 505-830-2200

R. Tracy Sprouls · Rodey, Dickason, Sloan, Akin, & Robb · Albuquerque Plaza, Suite 2200 · 201 Third Street, NW · P.O. Box 1888 · Albuquerque, NM 87102 · 505-765-5900

Donald E. Swaim · ⑩ · Swaim, Schrandt & Millet · 4830 Juan Tabo Boulevard, NE, Suite F · Albuquerque, NM 87111 · 505-237-0064

Susan K. Tomita · Susan K. Tomita Law Office · 4263 Montgomery Boulevard, NE, Suite 210 · Albuquerque, NM 87109 · 505-883-4993

Vickie R. Wilcox · Barlow & Wilcox · Albuquerque Plaza, Suite 1130 · 201 Third Street, NW · Albuquerque, NM 87102 · 505-248-1300

Hobbs

James M. Maddox · Maddox, Holloman & Kirksey · http://www.hobbsnmlaw.com · 205 East Bender, Suite 150 · P.O. Box 2508 · Hobbs, NM 88241-2508 · 575-393-0505

Roswell

Brian W. Copple · Bassett & Copple · 400 North Pennsylvania, Suite 250 · P.O. Box 2448 · Roswell, NM 88202-2448 · 505-622-3100

Santa Fe

John M. Hickey · Thompson, Hickey, Cunningham, Clow & April · Building 1100, Suite 1103 · 460 Saint Michaels Drive · Santa Fe, NM 87505-7619 · 505-988-2900

Ralph H. Scheuer · Scheuer, Yost & Patterson · 125 Lincoln Avenue, Suite 223 · P.O. Drawer 9570 · Santa Fe, NM 87504-9570 · 505-982-9911

Curtis W. Schwartz · ⑩ · Modrall, Sperling, Roehl, Harris & Sisk · 123 East Marcy Street, Suite 201 · P.O. Box 9318 · Santa Fe, NM 87504-9318 · 505-983-2020

Kurt A. Sommer · Sommer, Udall, Hardwick, Ahern & Hyatt · 200 West Marcy Street, Suite 129 · P.O. Box 1984 · Santa Fe, NM 87504-1984 · 505-982-4676

Michael G. Sutin · ⑩ · Sutin, Thayer & Browne · http://www.sutinfirm.com · 324 Paseo De Peralta, Suite B · Santa Fe, NM 87501 · 505-986-5554

Timothy Vidal · Canepa & Vidal · 200 West DeVargas, Suite Seven · P.O. Box 8980 · Santa Fe, NM 87504-8980 · 505-982-9229

Robert P. Worcester · ⑩ · Worcester & McKay · 324 Paseo de Peralta · P.O. Box 1717 · Santa Fe, NM 87504-1717 · 505-820-2244

WATER LAW

Albuquerque

Timothy J. De Young · Modrall, Sperling, Roehl, Harris & Sisk · Bank of America Centre, Suite 1000 · 500 Fourth Street, NW · P.O. Box 2168 · Albuquerque, NM 87103-2168 · 505-848-1800

Charles T. DuMars · ⑩ · Law & Resource Planning Associates · Albuquerque Plaza, Suite 1750 · 201 Third Street, NW · Albuquerque, NM 87102 · 505-346-0998

Sarita Nair · Sutin, Thayer & Browne · http://www.sutinfirm.com · Two Park Square, Suite 1000 · 6565 Americas Parkway, NE · P.O. Box 1945 · Albuquerque, NM 87103 · 505-883-2500

Maria O'Brien · Modrall, Sperling, Roehl, Harris & Sisk · Bank of America Centre, Suite 1000 · 500 Fourth Street, NW · P.O. Box 2168 · Albuquerque, NM 87103-2168 · 505-848-1800

John W. Utton · Sheehan, Sheehan & Stelzner · http://www.ssslawfirm.com · 40 First Plaza, NW, Suite 740 · Albuquerque, NM 87102 · 505-247-0411

Las Cruces

Steven L. Hernandez · Hubert & Hernandez · 2100 North Main Street · P.O. Box 2857 · Las Cruces, NM 88004-2857 · 505-526-2101

Roswell

Fred H. Hennighausen · Hennighausen and Olsen · 604 North Richardson Avenue · P. O. Box 1415 · Roswell, NM 88202-1415 · 505-624-2463

Stuart D. Shanor · ⓴ · Hinkle, Hensley, Shanor & Martin · 400 Penn Plaza, Suite 700 · P.O. Box 10 · Roswell, NM 88202 · 505-622-6510

Santa Fe

Mark K. Adams · ⓴ · Rodey, Dickason, Sloan, Akin, & Robb · 315 Paseo de Peralta · P.O. Box 1357 · Santa Fe, NM 87501-2034 · 505-954-3900

John B. Draper · ⓴ · Montgomery & Andrews · 325 Paseo De Peralta · P.O. Box 2307 · Santa Fe, NM 87504-2307 · 505-982-3873

Richard A. Simms · ⓴ · Richard A. Simms · 217 Camino Encantado · Santa Fe, NM 87501 · 505-699-8599

Jay F. Stein · Stein & Brockmann · 460 St. Michaels Drive, Suite 603 · Santa Fe, NM 87505 · 505-983-3880

WHITE-COLLAR CRIMINAL DEFENSE

Albuquerque

Gregg Vance Fallick · Gregg Vance Fallick · Gold Avenue Lofts, Suite 205 · 100 Gold Avenue, SW · Albuquerque, NM 87102 · 505-842-6000

David A. Freedman · ❿ · Freedman Boyd Hollander Goldberg & Ives · http://www.fbdlaw.com · 20 First Plaza, Suite 700 · Albuquerque, NM 87102 · 505-842-9960

Robert J. Gorence · Robert J. Gorence · 201 Twelfth Street, NW · Albuquerque, NM 87102-1815 · 505-244-0214

Mary Y. C. Han · Kennedy & Han · 201 Twelfth Street, NW · Albuquerque, NM 87102 · 505-842-8662

Nancy Hollander · ⓴ · Freedman Boyd Hollander Goldberg & Ives · http://www.fbdlaw.com · 20 First Plaza, Suite 700 · Albuquerque, NM 87102 · 505-842-9960

Tova Indritz · ❿ · Tova Indritz · 2040 Fourth Street, NW · Albuquerque, NM 87102 · 505-242-4003

Zachary A. Ives · Freedman Boyd Hollander Goldberg & Ives · http://www.fbdlaw.com · 20 First Plaza, Suite 700 · Albuquerque, NM 87102 · 505-842-9960

Paul J. Kennedy · ❿ · Kennedy & Han · 201 Twelfth Street, NW · Albuquerque, NM 87102 · 505-842-8662

Randi McGinn · ⑩ · McGinn, Carpenter, Montoya & Love · 201 Broadway Boulevard, SE · Albuquerque, NM 87102 · 505-843-6161

Peter Schoenburg · ⑩ · Rothstein, Donatelli, Hughes, Dahlstrom, Schoenburg & Bienvenu · Bank of America Centre, Suite 400 · 500 Fourth Street, NW · Albuquerque, NM 87102 · 505-243-1443

Luis G. Stelzner · ⑩ · Sheehan, Sheehan & Stelzner · http://www.ssslawfirm.com · 40 First Plaza, NW, Suite 740 · Albuquerque, NM 87102 · 505-247-0411

Ray R. Twohig · ⑳ · Ray Twohig · 8998 Rio Grande Boulevard, NW · Albuquerque, NM 87114 · 505-898-0400

Las Cruces

Michael W. Lilley · ⑩ · Lilley Law Offices · 1014 South Main Street · Las Cruces, NM 88005 · 505-524-7809

William L. Lutz · Martin, Lutz, Roggow, Hosford & Eubanks · 2100 North Main Street, Suite Two · P.O. Box 1837 · Las Cruces, NM 88004-1837 · 505-526-2449

Michael L. Stout · ⑩ · Law Offices of Michael L. Stout · 910 Lake Tahoe Street · Las Cruces, NM 88007-4103 · 505-524-1471

Santa Fe

Dan Cron · ⑩ · Dan Cron Law Firm · 125 Lincoln Avenue, Suite 400 · P.O. Box 40 · Santa Fe, NM 87504-0040 · 505-986-1334

Mark H. Donatelli · ⑳ · Rothstein, Donatelli, Hughes, Dahlstrom, Schoenburg & Bienvenu · 1215 Paseo De Peralta · P.O. Box 8180 · Santa Fe, NM 87504-8180 · 505-988-8004

Robert R. Rothstein · ⑳ · Rothstein, Donatelli, Hughes, Dahlstrom, Schoenburg & Bienvenu · 1215 Paseo De Peralta · P.O. Box 8180 · Santa Fe, NM 87504-8180 · 505-988-8004

WORKERS' COMPENSATION LAW

Albuquerque

Timothy R. Briggs · ⑩ · Miller Stratvert · 500 Marquette Avenue, NW, Suite 1100 · P.O. Box 25687 · Albuquerque, NM 87125-0687 · 505-842-1950

Jeffrey C. Brown · Law Offices of Jeffrey C. Brown · 1604 San Pedro Drive, NE · Albuquerque, NM 87110-6734 · 505-275-6600

Gerald A. Hanrahan · ⑩ · Gerald A. Hanrahan · 203 Hermosa Drive, NE · Albuquerque, NM 87108 · 505-255-2229

Paul Maestas · ⑩ · Maestas & Suggett · Albuquerque Plaza, Suite 1880 · 201 Third Street, NW · P.O. Box 1578 · Albuquerque, NM 87102-1578 · 505-247-8100

Carlos G. Martinez · ⑩ · Butt, Thornton & Baehr · 4101 Indian School Road, NE, Suite 300 South · P.O. Box 3170 · Albuquerque, NM 87190 · 505-884-0777

Richard J. Shane · ⑩ · Riley, Shane & Hale · 4101 Indian School Road, NE, Suite 420 · Albuquerque, NM 87110 · 505-883-5030

David L. Skinner · David L. Skinner · 2403 San Mateo Boulevard, NE, Suite W-9 · Albuquerque, NM 87110-4070 · 505-244-0700

Katherine E. Tourek · ⑩ · French & Associates · 500 Marquette Avenue, NW, Suite 500 · Albuquerque, NM 87102-5312 · 505-843-7075

Donald D. Vigil · Law Office of Donald D. Vigil · 100 Fourteenth Street, SW · Albuquerque, NM 87102 · 505-247-2020

George W. Weeth · Weeth Law Office · P.O. Box 91478 · Albuquerque, NM 87199-1478 · 505-828-1122

David M. Whitham · ⑩ · Butt, Thornton & Baehr · 4101 Indian School Road, NE, Suite 300 South · P.O. Box 3170 · Albuquerque, NM 87190 · 505-884-0777

Farmington

Victor A. Titus · ⑩ · Titus & Murphy · 2021 East 20th Street · Farmington, NM 87401 · 505-326-6503

Los Lunas

Mark Jarner · Law Offices of Mark Jarner · 235 Main Street · Los Lunas, NM 87031 · 505-865-1200

Rio Rancho

Rod Dunn · ⑩ · Dunn Law Offices · P.O. Box 15490 · Rio Rancho, NM 87174-0490 · 505-896-3650

NEW YORK

ADMINISTRATIVE LAW

Buffalo

Frederick A. Wolf · Damon & Morey · http://www.damonmorey.com · 1000 Cathedral Place · 298 Main Street · Buffalo, NY 14202-4096 · 716-856-5500

New York

Dana G. Fleischman · Cleary Gottlieb Steen & Hamilton · One Liberty Plaza · New York, NY 10006 · 212-225-2000

Julian W. Friedman · Stillman, Friedman & Shechtman · http://www.stillmanfriedman.com · 425 Park Avenue · New York, NY 10022 · 212-223-0200

Ben A. Indek · Morgan Lewis & Bockius · 101 Park Avenue · New York, NY 10178-0060 · 212-309-6000

Carmen J. Lawrence · Fried, Frank, Harris, Shriver & Jacobson · One New York Plaza · New York, NY 10004-1980 · 212-859-8000

Steven D. Lofchie · Cadwalader, Wickersham & Taft · http://www.cadwalader.com · One World Financial Center · New York, NY 10281 · 212-504-6000

Robert C. Mendelson · Morgan Lewis & Bockius · 101 Park Avenue · New York, NY 10178-0060 · 212-309-6000

Bruce H. Newman · WilmerHale · http://www.wilmerhale.com · 399 Park Avenue · New York, NY 10022 212-230-8800

Marjorie J. Peerce · Stillman, Friedman & Shechtman · http://www.stillmanfriedman.com · 425 Park Avenue · New York, NY 10022 · 212-223-0200

Robert M. Romano · Morgan Lewis & Bockius · 101 Park Avenue · New York, NY 10178-0060 · 212-309-6000

Lanny A. Schwartz · Davis Polk & Wardwell · 450 Lexington Avenue · New York, NY 10017 · 212-450-4000

Andrew W. Sidman · Bressler, Amery & Ross · http://www.bressler.com · 17 State Street · New York, NY 10014 · 212-425-9300

Audrey Strauss · a · Fried, Frank, Harris, Shriver & Jacobson · One New York Plaza · New York, NY 10004-1980 · 212-859-8000

ADVERTISING LAW

New York

Lewis R. Clayton · Paul, Weiss, Rifkind, Wharton & Garrison · 1285 Avenue of the Americas · New York, NY 10019-6064 · 212-373-3000

Jeffrey S. Edelstein · Manatt, Phelps & Phillips · Seven Times Square · New York, NY 10036 · 212-790-4500

Linda A. Goldstein · Manatt, Phelps & Phillips · Seven Times Square · New York, NY 10036 · 212-790-4500

Bruce P. Keller · a · Debevoise & Plimpton · 919 Third Avenue · New York, NY 10022 · 212-909-6000

Rick Kurnit · Frankfurt Kurnit Klein & Selz · http://www.fkks.com · 488 Madison Avenue, Tenth Floor · New York, NY 10022 · 212-980-0120

Thomas C. Morrison · Patterson Belknap Webb & Tyler · http://www.pbwt.com · 1133 Avenue of the Americas · New York, NY 10036-6710 · 212-336-2000

Brendan J. O'Rourke · Proskauer Rose · http://www.proskauer.com · 1585 Broadway · New York, NY 10036-8299 · 212-969-3000

Kenneth A. Plevan · Skadden, Arps, Slate, Meagher & Flom · Four Times Square · New York, NY 10036 212-735-3000

Harold P. Weinberger · Kramer Levin Naftalis & Frankel · http://www.kramerlevin.com · 1177 Avenue of the Americas · New York, NY 10036 · 212-715-9100

Lawrence I. Weinstein · Proskauer Rose · http://www.proskauer.com · 1585 Broadway · New York, NY 10036-8299 · 212-969-3000

Douglas Wood · Reed Smith · 599 Lexington Avenue, 29th Floor · New York, NY 10022 · 212-521-5400

Steven A. Zalesin · Patterson Belknap Webb & Tyler · http://www.pbwt.com · 1133 Avenue of the Americas · New York, NY 10036-6710 · 212-336-2000

ALTERNATIVE DISPUTE RESOLUTION

Binghamton

Richard B. Long · a · Coughlin & Gerhart · 20 Hawley Street · P.O. Box 2039 · Binghamton, NY 13902-2039 · 607-723-9511

Buffalo

Krista Gottlieb · Mattar, D'Agostino & Gottlieb · 17 Court Street, Suite 600 · Buffalo, NY 14202-3294 · 716-856-4022

Richard F. Griffin · 2% · Kavinoky & Cook · 726 Exchange Street, Suite 800 · Buffalo, NY 14210 · 716-845-6000

Paul D. Pearson · a · Paul Pearson · 1100 Main Place Tower · Buffalo, NY 14202 · 716-854-6424

Great Neck

Elayne E. Greenberg · Elayne E. Greenberg · 25 Potters Lane · Great Neck, NY 11024 · 516-829-5521

Kenmore

Steven R. Sugarman · Pusatier, Sherman, Abbott & Sugarman · 2464 Elmwood Avenue · Kenmore, NY 14217 · 716-873-6765

Manhasset

Louis A. Craco · 2% · Craco & Ellsworth · 36 Maple Place, Second Floor · Manhasset, NY 11030 · 516-365-9100

New York

Mark H. Alcott · a · Paul, Weiss, Rifkind, Wharton & Garrison · 1285 Avenue of the Americas · New York, NY 10019-6064 · 212-373-3000

Simeon H. Baum · Resolve Mediation Services · 575 Lexington Avenue, 10th Floor · New York, NY 10022 · 212-355-6527

Paul J. Bschorr · Gregory P. Joseph · 485 Lexington Avenue, 30th Floor · New York, NY 10017 · 212-407-1200

James H. Carter · Sullivan & Cromwell · 125 Broad Street · New York, NY 10004-2498 · 212-558-4000

Jay Cohen · Paul, Weiss, Rifkind, Wharton & Garrison · 1285 Avenue of the Americas · New York, NY 10019-6064 · 212-373-3000

Michael A. Cooper · 2) · Sullivan & Cromwell · 125 Broad Street · New York, NY 10004-2498 · 212-558-4000

George A. Davidson · a · Hughes Hubbard & Reed · http://www.hugheshubbard.com · One Battery Park Plaza · New York, NY 10004-1482 · 212-837-6000

Evan A. Davis · Cleary Gottlieb Steen & Hamilton · One Liberty Plaza · New York, NY 10006 · 212-225-2000

Bruce E. Fader · Proskauer Rose · http://www.proskauer.com · 1585 Broadway · New York, NY 10036-8299 · 212-969-3000

Robert B. Fiske, Jr. · 2% · Davis Polk & Wardwell · 450 Lexington Avenue · New York, NY 10017 · 212-450-4000

Barry H. Garfinkel · Skadden, Arps, Slate, Meagher & Flom · Four Times Square · New York, NY 10036 212-735-3000

David Geronemus · JAMS · 620 Eighth Avenue, 34th Floor · New York, NY 10018 · 212-751-2700

Gregory P. Joseph · a · Gregory P. Joseph · 485 Lexington Avenue, 30th Floor · New York, NY 10017 · 212-407-1200

John S. Kiernan · Debevoise & Plimpton · 919 Third Avenue · New York, NY 10022 · 212-909-6000

Carroll E. Neesemann · Morrison & Foerster · http://www.mofo.com · 1290 Avenue of the Americas · New York, NY 10104-0050 · 212-468-8000

Abigail J. Pessen · Abigail Pessen Mediation Services · http://www.pessenadr.com · 80 Broad Street, 30th Floor · New York, NY 10004 · 212-961-0668

Roy L. Reardon · 2% · Simpson Thacher · 425 Lexington Avenue · New York, NY 10017-3954 · 212-455-2000

Theodore O. Rogers, Jr. · Sullivan & Cromwell · 125 Broad Street · New York, NY 10004-2498 · 212-558-4000

Paul C. Saunders · Cravath, Swaine & Moore · Worldwide Plaza · 825 Eighth Avenue · New York, NY 10019-7475 · 212-474-1000

Margaret L. Shaw · JAMS · 620 Eighth Avenue, 34th Floor · New York, NY 10018 · 212-751-2700

Richard Silberberg · Dorsey & Whitney · 250 Park Avenue · New York, NY 10177-1500 · 212-415-9200

Edna Sussman · Hoguet Newman Regal & Kenney · 10 East 40th Street · New York, NY 10016-0301 · 212-689-8808

John H. Wilkinson · Fulton, Rowe & Hart · One Rockefeller Plaza, Suite 301 · New York, NY 10020 · 212-586-0700

Michael D. Young · JAMS · 620 Eighth Avenue, 34th Floor · New York, NY 10018 · 212-751-2700

Rochester

Harold A. Kurland · Ward, Norris, Heller & Reidy · http://www.wnhr.com · 300 State Street · Rochester, NY 14614 · 585-454-0700

James C. Moore · 2) · Harter Secrest & Emery · http://www.hselaw.com · 1600 Bausch & Lomb Place · Rochester, NY 14604-2711 · 585-232-6500

James E. Morris · Morris & Morris · 120 Corporate Woods, Suite 240 · Rochester, NY 14623 · 585-292-5750

Richard D. Rosenbloom · Boylan, Brown, Code, Vigdor & Wilson · http://www.boylanbrown.com · 2400 Chase Square · Rochester, NY 14604 · 585-232-5300

White Plains

Eugene I. Farber · Farber, Pappalardo & Carbonari · 200 East Post Road, Suite 202 · White Plains, NY 10601-4959 · 914-761-9400

ANTITRUST LAW

Armonk

David Boies · 2) · Boies, Schiller & Flexner · 333 Main Street · Armonk, NY 10504 · 914-749-8200

Buffalo

Robert B. Fleming, Jr. · a · Hodgson Russ · One Guaranty Building, Suite 100 · 140 Pearl Street · Buffalo, NY 14202 · 716-856-4000

New York

Joseph Angland · Heller Ehrman · Times Square Tower, 40th Floor · Seven Times Square · New York, NY 10036-6524 · 212-832-8300

Clifford H. Aronson · Skadden, Arps, Slate, Meagher & Flom · Four Times Square · New York, NY 10036 · 212-735-3000

Kevin J. Arquit · Simpson Thacher · 425 Lexington Avenue · New York, NY 10017-3954 · 212-455-2000

Stephen M. Axinn · 2) · Axinn, Veltrop & Harkrider · 114 West 47th Street · New York, NY 10036 · 212-728-2200

Paul W. Bartel II · Davis Polk & Wardwell · 450 Lexington Avenue · New York, NY 10017 · 212-450-4000

Michael D. Blechman · Kaye Scholer · 425 Park Avenue · New York, NY 10022-3598 · 212-836-8000

Molly S. Boast · Debevoise & Plimpton · 919 Third Avenue · New York, NY 10022 · 212-909-6000

Barry J. Brett · Troutman Sanders · The Chrysler Building · 405 Lexington Avenue · New York, NY 10174 · 212-704-6000

Michael H. Byowitz · Wachtell, Lipton, Rosen & Katz · 51 West 52nd Street · New York, NY 10019 · 212-403-1000

William F. Cavanaugh · Patterson Belknap Webb & Tyler · http://www.pbwt.com · 1133 Avenue of the Americas · New York, NY 10036-6710 · 212-336-2000

Evan R. Chesler · Cravath, Swaine & Moore · Worldwide Plaza · 825 Eighth Avenue · New York, NY 10019-7475 · 212-474-1000

Joel M. Cohen · Davis Polk & Wardwell · 450 Lexington Avenue · New York, NY 10017 · 212-450-4000

John F. Collins · Dewey & LeBoeuf · 1301 Avenue of the Americas · New York, NY 10019-6092 · 212-259-8000

Wayne Dale Collins · Shearman & Sterling · 599 Lexington Avenue · New York, NY 10022-6069 · 212-848-4000

Wayne A. Cross · White & Case · http://www.whitecase.com · 1155 Avenue of the Americas · New York, NY 10036-2787 · 212-819-8200

Steven M. Edwards · Hogan & Hartson · 875 Third Avenue, 25th Floor · New York, NY 10022 · 212-918-3000

Jay N. Fastow · Dickstein Shapiro · http://www.dicksteinshapiro.com · 1177 Avenue of the Americas · New York, NY 10036-2714 · 212-277-6500

Donald L. Flexner · 2) · Boies, Schiller & Flexner · 575 Lexington Avenue, Seventh Floor · New York, NY 10022 · 212-446-2300

Lawrence I. Fox · McDermott Will & Emery · 340 Madison Avenue · New York, NY 10173-1922 · 212-547-5400

Arthur F. Golden · Davis Polk & Wardwell · 450 Lexington Avenue · New York, NY 10017 · 212-450-4000

Shepard Goldfein · Skadden, Arps, Slate, Meagher & Flom · Four Times Square · New York, NY 10036 · 212-735-3000

Ilene Knable Gotts · Wachtell, Lipton, Rosen & Katz · 51 West 52nd Street · New York, NY 10019 · 212-403-1000

Ronan P. Harty · Davis Polk & Wardwell · 450 Lexington Avenue · New York, NY 10017 · 212-450-4000

Barry E. Hawk · Skadden, Arps, Slate, Meagher & Flom · Four Times Square · New York, NY 10036 · 212-735-3000

John A. Herfort · Gibson, Dunn & Crutcher · 200 Park Avenue, 47th Floor · New York, NY 10166-0193 · 212-351-4000

Helene D. Jaffe · Weil Gotshal & Manges · 767 Fifth Avenue · New York, NY 10153 · 212-310-8000

Robert D. Joffe · Cravath, Swaine & Moore · Worldwide Plaza · 825 Eighth Avenue · New York, NY 10019-7475 · 212-474-1000

Jeffrey L. Kessler · Dewey & LeBoeuf · 1301 Avenue of the Americas · New York, NY 10019-6092 · 212-259-8000

David Klingsberg · a · Kaye Scholer · 425 Park Avenue · New York, NY 10022-3598 · 212-836-8000

Daniel F. Kolb · a · Davis Polk & Wardwell · 450 Lexington Avenue · New York, NY 10017 · 212-450-4000

Charles E. Koob · Simpson Thacher · 425 Lexington Avenue · New York, NY 10017-3954 · 212-455-2000

Kenneth R. Logan · Simpson Thacher · 425 Lexington Avenue · New York, NY 10017-3954 · 212-455-2000

Ira M. Millstein · 2) · Weil Gotshal & Manges · 767 Fifth Avenue · New York, NY 10153 · 212-310-8000

Robert A. Milne · White & Case · http://www.whitecase.com · 1155 Avenue of the Americas · New York, NY 10036-2787 · 212-819-8200

Saul P. Morgenstern · Kaye Scholer · 425 Park Avenue · New York, NY 10022-3598 · 212-836-8000

Thomas M. Mueller · Morrison & Foerster · http://www.mofo.com · 1290 Avenue of the Americas · New York, NY 10104-0050 · 212-468-8000

Debra J. Pearlstein · Weil Gotshal & Manges · 767 Fifth Avenue · New York, NY 10153 · 212-310-8000

Bernard Persky · Labaton Sucharow · 140 Broadway · New York, NY 10005 · 212-907-0700

Yvonne S. Quinn · Sullivan & Cromwell · 125 Broad Street · New York, NY 10004-2498 · 212-558-4000

Ronald S. Rolfe · Cravath, Swaine & Moore · Worldwide Plaza · 825 Eighth Avenue · New York, NY 10019-7475 · 212-474-1000

Irving Scher · Weil Gotshal & Manges · 767 Fifth Avenue · New York, NY 10153 · 212-310-8000

Randolph S. Sherman · Kaye Scholer · 425 Park Avenue · New York, NY 10022-3598 · 212-836-8000

Richard M. Steuer · Mayer Brown · 1675 Broadway · New York, NY 10019-5820 · 212-506-2500

Neal R. Stoll · Skadden, Arps, Slate, Meagher & Flom · Four Times Square · New York, NY 10036 · 212-735-3000

Peter Sullivan · Gibson, Dunn & Crutcher · 200 Park Avenue, 47th Floor · New York, NY 10166-0193 · 212-351-4000

Joseph F. Tringali · Simpson Thacher · 425 Lexington Avenue · New York, NY 10017-3954 · 212-455-2000

Richard J. Urowsky · Sullivan & Cromwell · 125 Broad Street · New York, NY 10004-2498 · 212-558-4000

A. Paul Victor · Dewey & LeBoeuf · 1301 Avenue of the Americas · New York, NY 10019-6092 · 212-259-8000

John L. Warden · Sullivan & Cromwell · 125 Broad Street · New York, NY 10004-2498 · 212-558-4000

Michael L. Weiner · Skadden, Arps, Slate, Meagher & Flom · Four Times Square · New York, NY 10036 212-735-3000

Alan J. Weinschel · Weil Gotshal & Manges · 767 Fifth Avenue · New York, NY 10153 · 212-310-8000

Fredric Yerman · Kaye Scholer · 425 Park Avenue · New York, NY 10022-3598 · 212-836-8000

Rochester

Kenneth A. Payment · a · Harter Secrest & Emery · http://www.hselaw.com · 1600 Bausch & Lomb Place · Rochester, NY 14604-2711 · 585-232-6500

APPELLATE LAW

Albany

Michelle M. Monserrate · O'Connor, O'Connor, Bresee & First · http://www.1stlaw.com · 20 Corporate Woods Boulevard · Albany, NY 12211-0400 · 518-465-0400

James A. Resila · Carter, Conboy, Case, Blackmore, Maloney & Laird · 20 Corporate Woods Boulevard · Albany, NY 12211-2362 · 518-465-3484

Armonk

David Boies · 2) · Boies, Schiller & Flexner · 333 Main Street · Armonk, NY 10504 · 914-749-8200

Buffalo

Lawrence J. Vilardo · Connors & Vilardo · 1000 Liberty Building · 424 Main Street · Buffalo, NY 14202 · 716-852-5533

Lake Success

Steven J. Ahmuty, Jr. · Shaub, Ahmuty, Citrin & Spratt · 1983 Marcus Avenue · Lake Success, NY 11042-1056 · 516-488-3300

New York

Floyd Abrams · 2% · Cahill Gordon & Reindel · 80 Pine Street · New York, NY 10005-1702 · 212-701-3000

Seymour Boyers · Gair, Gair, Conason, Steigman & Mackauf · http://www.gairgair.com · 80 Pine Street, 34th Floor · New York, NY 10005 · 212-943-1090

Herald Price Fahringer · 2% · Herald Price Fahringer · 120 East 56TH Street, Suite 1150 · New York, NY 10022-3607 · 212-319-5351

Robert B. Fiske, Jr. · 2% · Davis Polk & Wardwell · 450 Lexington Avenue · New York, NY 10017 · 212-450-4000

Andrew L. Frey · a · Mayer Brown · 1675 Broadway · New York, NY 10019-5820 · 212-506-2500

Steven C. Krane · Proskauer Rose · http://www.proskauer.com · 1585 Broadway · New York, NY 10036-8299 · 212-969-3000

Frederick B. Lacey · 2) · Dewey & LeBoeuf · 125 West 55th Street · New York, NY 10019-5389 · 212-424-8000

Philip Allen Lacovara · Mayer Brown · 1675 Broadway · New York, NY 10019-5820 · 212-506-2500

Leo Milonas · Pillsbury Winthrop Shaw Pittman · http://www.pillsburylaw.com · 1540 Broadway · New York, NY 10036-4039 · 212-858-1000

Steven F. Molo · a · Shearman & Sterling · 599 Lexington Avenue · New York, NY 10022-6069 · 212-848-4000

Thomas R. Newman · Duane Morris · 1540 Broadway · New York, NY 10036-4086 · 212-692-1000

Gloria C. Phares · Patterson Belknap Webb & Tyler · http://www.pbwt.com · 1133 Avenue of the Americas · New York, NY 10036-6710 · 212-336-2000

Bettina B. Plevan · a · Proskauer Rose · http://www.proskauer.com · 1585 Broadway · New York, NY 10036-8299 · 212-969-3000

Roy L. Reardon · 2% · Simpson Thacher · 425 Lexington Avenue · New York, NY 10017-3954 · 212-455-2000

Alexandra A. E. Shapiro · Latham & Watkins · 885 Third Avenue · New York, NY 10022-4834 · 212-906-1200

Paul Shechtman · Stillman, Friedman & Shechtman · http://www.stillmanfriedman.com · 425 Park Avenue · New York, NY 10022 · 212-223-0200

Rochester

A. Vincent Buzard · Harris Beach · The Granite Building · 130 East Main Street · Rochester, NY 14604 · 585-419-8800

David M. Lascell · a · Harter Secrest & Emery · http://www.hselaw.com · 1600 Bausch & Lomb Place · Rochester, NY 14604-2711 · 585-232-6500

Syracuse

Alan J. Pierce · Hancock & Estabrook · 1500 Axa Tower I · 100 Madison Street · Syracuse, NY 13202 · 315-471-3151

Nancy L. Pontius · Mackenzie Hughes · 101 South Salina Street, Suite 600 · P.O. Box 4967 · Syracuse, NY 13221-4967 · 315-474-7571

BANKING LAW

Albany

Marc J. Lifset · McGlinchey Stafford · http://www.mcglinchey.com · 194 Washington Avenue, Suite 600 · Albany, NY 12210 · 518-432-1200

Buffalo

John P. Amershadian · a · Hodgson Russ · One Guaranty Building, Suite 100 · 140 Pearl Street · Buffalo, NY 14202 · 716-856-4000

George F. Bellows · Jaeckle Fleischmann & Mugel · 12 Fountain Plaza · Buffalo, NY 14202-2292 · 716-856-0600

Christian G. Koelbl III · a · Hodgson Russ · One Guaranty Building, Suite 100 · 140 Pearl Street · Buffalo, NY 14202 · 716-856-4000

Victoria J. Saxon · Hodgson Russ · One Guaranty Building, Suite 100 · 140 Pearl Street · Buffalo, NY 14202 · 716-856-4000

Raymond H. Seitz · a · Phillips Lytle · 3400 HSBC Center · Buffalo, NY 14203-2887 · 716-847-8400

New York

Jay G. Baris · Kramer Levin Naftalis & Frankel · http://www.kramerlevin.com · 1177 Avenue of the Americas · New York, NY 10036 · 212-715-9100

Kevin F. Barnard · Arnold & Porter · 399 Park Avenue, 34th Floor · New York, NY 10022-4690 · 212-715-1000

Ronald M. Bayer · a · Shearman & Sterling · 599 Lexington Avenue · New York, NY 10022-6069 · 212-848-4000

Eric L. Berg · White & Case · http://www.whitecase.com · 1155 Avenue of the Americas · New York, NY 10036-2787 · 212-819-8200

Warren T. Buhle · Weil Gotshal & Manges · 767 Fifth Avenue · New York, NY 10153 · 212-310-8000

James C. Buresh · Simpson Thacher · 425 Lexington Avenue · New York, NY 10017-3954 · 212-455-2000

H. Rodgin Cohen · 2% · Sullivan & Cromwell · 125 Broad Street · New York, NY 10004-2498 · 212-558-4000

James D. Cooper · a · Cravath, Swaine & Moore · Worldwide Plaza · 825 Eighth Avenue · New York, NY 10019-7475 · 212-474-1000

Elizabeth T. Davy · Sullivan & Cromwell · 125 Broad Street · New York, NY 10004-2498 · 212-558-4000

Hendrik de Jong · ⑩ · Latham & Watkins · 885 Third Avenue · New York, NY 10022-4834 · 212-906-1200

Luc A. Despins · Paul Hastings · Park Avenue Tower, First Floor · 75 East 55th Street · New York, NY 10022 · 212-318-6000

Daniel S. Dokos · Weil Gotshal & Manges · 767 Fifth Avenue · New York, NY 10153 · 212-310-8000

James M. Douglas · Skadden, Arps, Slate, Meagher & Flom · Four Times Square · New York, NY 10036 212-735-3000

Peter R. Douglas · ⑳ · Davis Polk & Wardwell · 450 Lexington Avenue · New York, NY 10017 · 212-450-4000

Dennis F. Dunne · Milbank, Tweed, Hadley & McCloy · http://www.milbank.com · One Chase Manhattan Plaza · New York, NY 10005-1413 · 212-530-5000

Mitchell S. Eitel · Sullivan & Cromwell · 125 Broad Street · New York, NY 10004-2498 · 212-558-4000

Robert S. Finley · King & Spalding · 1185 Avenue of the Americas · New York, NY 10036-4003 · 212-556-2100

James A. Florack · Davis Polk & Wardwell · 450 Lexington Avenue · New York, NY 10017 · 212-450-4000

Lawrence D. Frishman · Skadden, Arps, Slate, Meagher & Flom · Four Times Square · New York, NY 10036 · 212-735-3000

Elliot Gewirtz · Milbank, Tweed, Hadley & McCloy · http://www.milbank.com · One Chase Manhattan Plaza · New York, NY 10005-1413 · 212-530-5000

Paul E. Glotzer · Cleary Gottlieb Steen & Hamilton · One Liberty Plaza · New York, NY 10006 · 212-225-2000

Michael S. Goldman · Cravath, Swaine & Moore · Worldwide Plaza · 825 Eighth Avenue · New York, NY 10019-7475 · 212-474-1000

Gilson B. Gray III · ⑩ · Duane Morris · 1540 Broadway · New York, NY 10036-4086 · 212-692-1000

Randall D. Guynn · Davis Polk & Wardwell · 450 Lexington Avenue · New York, NY 10017 · 212-450-4000

Joseph W. Halliday · ㉕ · Skadden, Arps, Slate, Meagher & Flom · Four Times Square · New York, NY 10036 · 212-735-3000

Marc P. Hanrahan · Latham & Watkins · 885 Third Avenue · New York, NY 10022-4834 · 212-906-1200

Edward D. Herlihy · ⑩ · Wachtell, Lipton, Rosen & Katz · 51 West 52nd Street · New York, NY 10019 · 212-403-1000

William E. Hirschberg · Shearman & Sterling · 599 Lexington Avenue · New York, NY 10022-6069 · 212-848-4000

L. Francis Huck · Simpson Thacher · 425 Lexington Avenue · New York, NY 10017-3954 · 212-455-2000

Kenneth C. Kettering · ⑩ · New York Law School · 57 Worth Street · New York, NY 10013 · 212-431-2100

B. Robbins Kiessling · a · Cravath, Swaine & Moore · Worldwide Plaza · 825 Eighth Avenue · New York, NY 10019-7475 · 212-474-1000

James T. Knight · Simpson Thacher · 425 Lexington Avenue · New York, NY 10017-3954 · 212-455-2000

Alan W. Kornberg · Paul, Weiss, Rifkind, Wharton & Garrison · 1285 Avenue of the Americas · New York, NY 10019-6064 · 212-373-3000

Paul L. Lee · Debevoise & Plimpton · 919 Third Avenue · New York, NY 10022 · 212-909-6000

Peter S. W. Levin · Davis Polk & Wardwell · 450 Lexington Avenue · New York, NY 10017 · 212-450-4000

Erik D. Lindauer · Sullivan & Cromwell · 125 Broad Street · New York, NY 10004-2498 · 212-558-4000

Kevin T. McNamara · Windels, Marx, Lane & Mittendorf · 156 West 56th Street, 22nd Floor · New York, NY 10019 · 212-237-1000

Barbara R. Mendelson · Morrison & Foerster · http://www.mofo.com · 1290 Avenue of the Americas · New York, NY 10104-0050 · 212-468-8000

Mark J. Menting · Sullivan & Cromwell · 125 Broad Street · New York, NY 10004-2498 · 212-558-4000

Lee A. Meyerson · Simpson Thacher · 425 Lexington Avenue · New York, NY 10017-3954 · 212-455-2000

Michael E. Michetti · Cahill Gordon & Reindel · 80 Pine Street · New York, NY 10005-1702 · 212-701-3000

Robin J. Miles · Bracewell & Giuliani · http://www.bgllp.com · 1177 Avenue of the Americas, 19th Floor · New York, NY 10036-2714 · 212-508-6100

Jiro Murase · a · Bingham McCutchen · http://www.bingham.com · 399 Park Avenue · New York, NY 10022-4689 · 212-705-7000

Brian D. Murphy · a · Fried, Frank, Harris, Shriver & Jacobson · One New York Plaza · New York, NY 10004-1980 · 212-859-8000

Toby S. Myerson · a · Paul, Weiss, Rifkind, Wharton & Garrison · 1285 Avenue of the Americas · New York, NY 10019-6064 · 212-373-3000

Peter J. Neckles · Skadden, Arps, Slate, Meagher & Flom · Four Times Square · New York, NY 10036 · 212-735-3000

Maura E. O'Sullivan · Shearman & Sterling · 599 Lexington Avenue · New York, NY 10022-6069 · 212-848-4000

C. Allen Parker · a · Cravath, Swaine & Moore · Worldwide Plaza · 825 Eighth Avenue · New York, NY 10019-7475 · 212-474-1000

Patrick J. Ryan · Simpson Thacher · 425 Lexington Avenue · New York, NY 10017-3954 · 212-455-2000

Bradley K. Sabel · Shearman & Sterling · 599 Lexington Avenue · New York, NY 10022-6069 · 212-848-4000

Ivan Serchuk · Todtman, Nachamie, Spizz & Johns · 425 Park Avenue · New York, NY 10022 · 212-754-9400

Paul H. Shur · Sills Cummis & Gross · http://www.sillscummis.com · One Rockefeller Plaza · New York, NY 10020 · 212-643-7000

Marsha E. Simms · a · Weil Gotshal & Manges · 767 Fifth Avenue · New York, NY 10153 · 212-310-8000

Bradley Y. Smith · a · Davis Polk & Wardwell · 450 Lexington Avenue · New York, NY 10017 · 212-450-4000

William E. Stern · Goodwin Procter · The New York Times Building · 620 Eighth Avenue · New York, NY 10018 · 212-813-8800

Robert L. Tortoriello · a · Cleary Gottlieb Steen & Hamilton · One Liberty Plaza · New York, NY 10006 · 212-225-2000

Donald J. Toumey · Sullivan & Cromwell · 125 Broad Street · New York, NY 10004-2498 · 212-558-4000

Marc R. Trevino · Sullivan & Cromwell · 125 Broad Street · New York, NY 10004-2498 · 212-558-4000

James C. Vardell III · Cravath, Swaine & Moore · Worldwide Plaza · 825 Eighth Avenue · New York, NY 10019-7475 · 212-474-1000

Charles H. Vejvoda · a · Pillsbury Winthrop Shaw Pittman · http://www.pillsburylaw.com · 1540 Broadway · New York, NY 10036-4039 · 212-858-1000

John L. Walker · Simpson Thacher · 425 Lexington Avenue · New York, NY 10017-3954 · 212-455-2000

Duane D. Wall · a · White & Case · http://www.whitecase.com · 1155 Avenue of the Americas · New York, NY 10036-2787 · 212-819-8200

Craig M. Wasserman · Wachtell, Lipton, Rosen & Katz · 51 West 52nd Street · New York, NY 10019 · 212-403-1000

Marissa C. Wesely · Simpson Thacher · 425 Lexington Avenue · New York, NY 10017-3954 · 212-455-2000

Lawrence E. Wieman · Davis Polk & Wardwell · 450 Lexington Avenue · New York, NY 10017 · 212-450-4000

Michael M. Wiseman · Sullivan & Cromwell · 125 Broad Street · New York, NY 10004-2498 · 212-558-4000

Rochester

Michael C. Dwyer · a · Harter Secrest & Emery · http://www.hselaw.com · 1600 Bausch & Lomb Place · Rochester, NY 14604-2711 · 585-232-6500

Patrick M. Malgieri · Woods Oviatt Gilman · http://www.woodsoviatt.com · 700 Crossroads Building · Two State Street · Rochester, NY 14614 · 585-987-2800

Raymond L. Ruff · Phillips Lytle · 1400 First Federal Plaza · Rochester, NY 14614 · 585-238-2000

Beth Ela Wilkens · a · Harris Beach · The Granite Building · 130 East Main Street · Rochester, NY 14604 · 585-419-8800

Syracuse

Richard W. Cook · Hancock & Estabrook · 1500 Axa Tower I · 100 Madison Street · Syracuse, NY 13202 315-471-3151

George S. Deptula · a · Hiscock & Barclay · One Park Place · 300 South State Street · Syracuse, NY 13202-2078 · 315-422-2131

Albany

William M. McCarthy · 2) · Law Offices of William M. McCarthy · 60 South Swan Street · Albany, NY 12210 · 518-434-6141

Michael J. O'Connor · a · O'Connor, O'Connor, Bresee & First · http://www.1stlaw.com · 20 Corporate Woods Boulevard · Albany, NY 12211-0400 · 518-465-0400

Richard H. Weiner · a · Nolan & Heller · 39 North Pearl Street · Albany, NY 12207-2797 · 518-449-3300

Buffalo

Jospeh W. Allen · Jaeckle Fleischmann & Mugel · 12 Fountain Plaza · Buffalo, NY 14202-2292 · 716-856-0600

William J. Brown · a · Phillips Lytle · 3400 HSBC Center · Buffalo, NY 14203-2887 · 716-847-8400

Harold P. Bulan · 2) · Bulan, Chiari, Horwitz & Ilecki · 1321 Millersport Highway, Suite 101 · Buffalo, NY 14221-2900 · 716-838-4300

Robert J. Feldman · Gross, Shuman, Brizdle & Gilfillan · Fayette Court Building, Suite 600 · 465 Main Street · Buffalo, NY 14203 · 716-854-4300

Raymond L. Fink · Harter Secrest & Emery · http://www.hselaw.com · 12 Fountain Plaza, Suite 400 · Buffalo, NY 14202-2293 · 716-853-1616

Garry M. Graber · a · Hodgson Russ · One Guaranty Building, Suite 100 · 140 Pearl Street · Buffalo, NY 14202 · 716-856-4000

Franklin W. Heller · Damon & Morey · http://www.damonmorey.com · 1000 Cathedral Place · 298 Main Street · Buffalo, NY 14202-4096 · 716-856-5500

William E. Lawson · 2) · Aaron, Dautch, Sternberg & Lawson · 730 Convention Tower · 43 Court Street · Buffalo, NY 14202-3101 · 716-854-3015

William F. Savino · Damon & Morey · http://www.damonmorey.com · 1000 Cathedral Place · 298 Main Street · Buffalo, NY 14202-4096 · 716-856-5500

Francis P. Weimer · Aaron, Dautch, Sternberg & Lawson · 730 Convention Tower · 43 Court Street · Buffalo, NY 14202-3101 · 716-854-3015

New York

Marc R. Abrams · a · Willkie Farr & Gallagher · 787 Seventh Avenue · New York, NY 10019-6099 · 212-728-8000

Joshua J. Angel · Herrick Feinstein · Two Park Avenue, 20th Floor · New York, NY 10016 · 212-592-1400

Philip Anker · WilmerHale · http://www.wilmerhale.com · 399 Park Avenue · New York, NY 10022 · 212-230-8800

D. J. Baker · 2) · Skadden, Arps, Slate, Meagher & Flom · Four Times Square · New York, NY 10036 · 212-735-3000

Corinne Ball · a · Jones Day · 222 East 41st Street · New York, NY 10017-6702 · 212-326-3939

Mark I. Bane · Ropes & Gray · http://www.ropesgray.com · 1211 Avenue of the Americas · New York, NY 10036-8704 · 212-596-9000

Douglas P. Bartner · Shearman & Sterling · 599 Lexington Avenue · New York, NY 10022-6069 · 212-848-4000

Paul M. Basta · Kirkland & Ellis · Citigroup Center · 153 East 53rd Street · New York, NY 10022-4611 · 212-446-4800

Howard S. Beltzer · Morgan Lewis & Bockius · 101 Park Avenue · New York, NY 10178-0060 · 212-309-6000

Donald S. Bernstein · a · Davis Polk & Wardwell · 450 Lexington Avenue · New York, NY 10017 · 212-450-4000

Martin J. Bienenstock · a · Dewey & LeBoeuf · 1301 Avenue of the Americas · New York, NY 10019-6092 · 212-259-8000

Cornelius Blackshear · Dewey & LeBoeuf · 125 West 55th Street · New York, NY 10019-5389 · 212-424-8000

Peter L. Borowitz · Debevoise & Plimpton · 919 Third Avenue · New York, NY 10022 · 212-909-6000

Allan S. Brilliant · Goodwin Procter · The New York Times Building · 620 Eighth Avenue · New York, NY 10018 · 212-813-8800

Andrew P. Brozman · Clifford Chance · 31 West 52nd Street · New York, NY 10019-6131 · 212-878-8000

Martin G. Bunin · Alston + Bird · http://www.alston.com · 90 Park Avenue · New York, NY 10016-1387 · 212-210-9400

Thomas R. Califano · DLA Piper · 1251 Avenue of the Americas · New York, NY 10020-1104 · 212-335-4500

Richard F. Casher · 2) · Kasowitz, Benson, Torres & Friedman · 1633 Broadway · New York, NY 10019 · 212-506-1700

Scott K. Charles · Wachtell, Lipton, Rosen & Katz · 51 West 52nd Street · New York, NY 10019 · 212-403-1000

Richard M. Cieri · a · Kirkland & Ellis · Citigroup Center · 153 East 53rd Street · New York, NY 10022-4611 · 212-446-4800

Kathryn A. Coleman · a · Gibson, Dunn & Crutcher · 200 Park Avenue, 47th Floor · New York, NY 10166-0193 · 212-351-4000

Michael L. Cook · 2) · Schulte Roth & Zabel · 919 Third Avenue · New York, NY 10022 · 212-756-2000

Michael J. Crames · 2% · Kaye Scholer · 425 Park Avenue · New York, NY 10022-3598 · 212-836-8000

Denis F. Cronin · 2) · Vinson & Elkins · http://www.velaw.com · 666 Fifth Avenue, 26th Floor · New York, NY 10103-0040 · 212-237-0000

H. Slayton Dabney, Jr. · a · King & Spalding · 1185 Avenue of the Americas · New York, NY 10036-4003 · 212-556-2100

George A. Davis · Cadwalader, Wickersham & Taft · http://www.cadwalader.com · One World Financial Center · New York, NY 10281 · 212-504-6000

Paul R. DeFilippo · Wollmuth, Maher & Deutsh · 500 Fifth Avenue · New York, NY 10110 · 212-382-3300

Andrew P. DeNatale · White & Case · http://www.whitecase.com · 1155 Avenue of the Americas · New York, NY 10036-2787 · 212-819-8200

Luc A. Despins · Paul Hastings · Park Avenue Tower, First Floor · 75 East 55th Street · New York, NY 10022 · 212-318-6000

John H. Drucker · Cole, Schotz, Meisel, Forman & Leonard · http://www.coleschotz.com · 900 Third Avenue, 16th Floor · New York, NY 10022 · 212-752-8000

Dennis F. Dunne · Milbank, Tweed, Hadley & McCloy · http://www.milbank.com · One Chase Manhattan Plaza · New York, NY 10005-1413 · 212-530-5000

David W. Dykhouse · Patterson Belknap Webb & Tyler · http://www.pbwt.com · 1133 Avenue of the Americas · New York, NY 10036-6710 · 212-336-2000

Kenneth H. Eckstein · Kramer Levin Naftalis & Frankel · http://www.kramerlevin.com · 1177 Avenue of the Americas · New York, NY 10036 · 212-715-9100

Judith Elkin · Haynes and Boone · 153 East 53rd Street, 49th Floor · New York, NY 10022 · 212-659-7300

Richard L. Epling · Pillsbury Winthrop Shaw Pittman · http://www.pillsburylaw.com · 1540 Broadway · New York, NY 10036-4039 · 212-858-1000

Matthew A. Feldman · Willkie Farr & Gallagher · 787 Seventh Avenue · New York, NY 10019-6099 · 212-728-8000

David M. Friedman · Kasowitz, Benson, Torres & Friedman · 1633 Broadway · New York, NY 10019 · 212-506-1700

James L. Garrity, Jr. · Shearman & Sterling · 599 Lexington Avenue · New York, NY 10022-6069 · 212-848-4000

Jay M. Goffman · Skadden, Arps, Slate, Meagher & Flom · Four Times Square · New York, NY 10036 · 212-735-3000

Daniel H. Golden · Akin Gump Strauss Hauer & Feld · 590 Madison Avenue, 22nd Floor · New York, NY 10022-2524 · 212-872-1000

Marcia L. Goldstein · ⑳ · Weil Gotshal & Manges · 767 Fifth Avenue · New York, NY 10153 · 212-310-8000

Andrew D. Gottfried · Morgan Lewis & Bockius · 101 Park Avenue · New York, NY 10178-0060 · 212-309-6000

Lawrence C. Gottlieb · Cooley Godward Kronish · The Grace Building, 46th Floor · 1114 Avenue of the Americas · New York, NY 10036-7798 · 212-479-6000

Alan S. Gover · ⑩ · White & Case · http://www.whitecase.com · 1155 Avenue of the Americas · New York, NY 10036-2787 · 212-819-8200

Steven R. Gross · ⑩ · Debevoise & Plimpton · 919 Third Avenue · New York, NY 10022 · 212-909-6000

Lawrence M. Handelsman · Stroock & Stroock & Lavan · 180 Maiden Lane · New York, NY 10038-4982 212-806-5400

Adam C. Harris · Schulte Roth & Zabel · 919 Third Avenue · New York, NY 10022 · 212-756-2000

Scott L. Hazan · Otterbourg, Steindler, Houston & Rosen · 230 Park Avenue · New York, NY 10169-0075 · 212-661-9100

Sally McDonald Henry · Skadden, Arps, Slate, Meagher & Flom · Four Times Square · New York, NY 10036 · 212-735-3000

Stuart Hirshfield · Mintz, Levin, Cohn, Ferris, Glovsky and Popeo · Chrysler Center · 666 Third Avenue New York, NY 10017 · 212-935-3000

Benjamin Hoch · Covington & Burling · The New York Times Building · 620 Eighth Avenue · New York, NY 10018 · 212-841-1000

Marshall S. Huebner · Davis Polk & Wardwell · 450 Lexington Avenue · New York, NY 10017 · 212-450-4000

Elihu Inselbuch · Caplin & Drysdale · http://www.capdale.com · 375 Park Avenue, 35th Floor · New York, NY 10152 · 212-319-7125

Marvin E. Jacob · 2) · Weil Gotshal & Manges · 767 Fifth Avenue · New York, NY 10153 · 212-310-8000

Stephen Karotkin · Weil Gotshal & Manges · 767 Fifth Avenue · New York, NY 10153 · 212-310-8000

Susheel Kirpalani · Quinn Emanuel Urquhart Oliver & Hedges · 51 Madison Avenue, 22nd Floor · New York, NY 10010 · 212-849-7000

Alan W. Kornberg · Paul, Weiss, Rifkind, Wharton & Garrison · 1285 Avenue of the Americas · New York, NY 10019-6064 · 212-373-3000

Richard P. Krasnow · a · Weil Gotshal & Manges · 767 Fifth Avenue · New York, NY 10153 · 212-310-8000

Lewis Kruger · a · Stroock & Stroock & Lavan · 180 Maiden Lane · New York, NY 10038-4982 · 212-806-5400

Jonathan M. Landers · a · Gibson, Dunn & Crutcher · 200 Park Avenue, 47th Floor · New York, NY 10166-0193 · 212-351-4000

David M. LeMay · Chadbourne & Parke · http://www.chadbourne.com · 30 Rockefeller Plaza · New York, NY 10112-0127 · 212-408-5100

Richard B. Levin · a · Cravath, Swaine & Moore · Worldwide Plaza · 825 Eighth Avenue · New York, NY 10019-7475 · 212-474-1000

Joel H. Levitin · Cahill Gordon & Reindel · 80 Pine Street · New York, NY 10005-1702 · 212-701-3000

Mark F. Liscio · Kaye Scholer · 425 Park Avenue · New York, NY 10022-3598 · 212-836-8000

Kayalyn A. Marafioti · Skadden, Arps, Slate, Meagher & Flom · Four Times Square · New York, NY 10036 · 212-735-3000

Richard G. Mason · Wachtell, Lipton, Rosen & Katz · 51 West 52nd Street · New York, NY 10019 · 212-403-1000

Laurence May · Cole, Schotz, Meisel, Forman & Leonard · http://www.coleschotz.com · 900 Third Avenue, 16th Floor · New York, NY 10022 · 212-752-8000

Thomas Moers Mayer · Kramer Levin Naftalis & Frankel · http://www.kramerlevin.com · 1177 Avenue of the Americas · New York, NY 10036 · 212-715-9100

Alan B. Miller · 2% · Weil Gotshal & Manges · 767 Fifth Avenue · New York, NY 10153 · 212-310-8000

Richard S. Miller · K&L Gates · 599 Lexington Avenue · New York, NY 10022-6030 · 212-536-3900

J. Gregory Milmoe · Skadden, Arps, Slate, Meagher & Flom · Four Times Square · New York, NY 10036 212-735-3000

Phillip Mindlin · Wachtell, Lipton, Rosen & Katz · 51 West 52nd Street · New York, NY 10019 · 212-403-1000

Christopher R. Mirick · Cadwalader, Wickersham & Taft · http://www.cadwalader.com · One World Financial Center · New York, NY 10281 · 212-504-6000

Nancy A. Mitchell · Greenberg Traurig · http://www.gtlaw.com · MetLife Building · 200 Park Avenue · New York, NY 10166 · 212-801-9200

Satoru Murase · Bingham McCutchen · http://www.bingham.com · 399 Park Avenue · New York, NY 10022-4689 · 212-705-7000

Harold S. Novikoff · 2) · Wachtell, Lipton, Rosen & Katz · 51 West 52nd Street · New York, NY 10019 · 212-403-1000

Peter V. Pantaleo · Simpson Thacher · 425 Lexington Avenue · New York, NY 10017-3954 · 212-455-2000

Lenard M. Parkins · Haynes and Boone · 153 East 53rd Street, 49th Floor · New York, NY 10022 · 212-659-7300

Peter S. Partee · Hunton & Williams · 200 Park Avenue, Fifty-Second Floor · New York, NY 10166-0091 212-309-1000

Mitchel H. Perkiel · Troutman Sanders · The Chrysler Building · 405 Lexington Avenue · New York, NY 10174 · 212-704-6000

Alesia Ranney-Marinelli · a · Skadden, Arps, Slate, Meagher & Flom · Four Times Square · New York, NY 10036 · 212-735-3000

John J. Rapisardi · Cadwalader, Wickersham & Taft · http://www.cadwalader.com · One World Financial Center · New York, NY 10281 · 212-504-6000

Jeffrey N. Rich · K&L Gates · 599 Lexington Avenue · New York, NY 10022-6030 · 212-536-3900

Brian S. Rosen · Weil Gotshal & Manges · 767 Fifth Avenue · New York, NY 10153 · 212-310-8000

Robert J. Rosenberg · Latham & Watkins · 885 Third Avenue · New York, NY 10022-4834 · 212-906-1200

Robert H. Scheibe · Morgan Lewis & Bockius · 101 Park Avenue · New York, NY 10178-0060 · 212-309-6000

Brad Eric Scheler · a · Fried, Frank, Harris, Shriver & Jacobson · One New York Plaza · New York, NY 10004-1980 · 212-859-8000

Margot B. Schonholtz · Kaye Scholer · 425 Park Avenue · New York, NY 10022-3598 · 212-836-8000

H. Jeffrey Schwartz · Dechert · 30 Rockefeller Plaza · 1095 Avenue of the Americas · New York, NY 10036-6797 · 212-698-3500

Howard Seife · Chadbourne & Parke · http://www.chadbourne.com · 30 Rockefeller Plaza · New York, NY 10112-0127 · 212-408-5100

Stephen J. Shimshak · Paul, Weiss, Rifkind, Wharton & Garrison · 1285 Avenue of the Americas · New York, NY 10019-6064 · 212-373-3000

Ronald J. Silverman · Bingham McCutchen · http://www.bingham.com · 399 Park Avenue · New York, NY 10022-4689 · 212-705-7000

Arthur Steinberg · Kaye Scholer · 425 Park Avenue · New York, NY 10022-3598 · 212-836-8000

Jeffrey L. Tanenbaum · Weil Gotshal & Manges · 767 Fifth Avenue · New York, NY 10153 · 212-310-8000

Richard S. Toder · Morgan Lewis & Bockius · 101 Park Avenue · New York, NY 10178-0060 · 212-309-6000

Myron E. Trepper · 2% · Willkie Farr & Gallagher · 787 Seventh Avenue · New York, NY 10019-6099 · 212-728-8000

Andrew M. Troop · Cadwalader, Wickersham & Taft · http://www.cadwalader.com · One World Financial Center · New York, NY 10281 · 212-504-6000

J. Ronald Trost · a · Vinson & Elkins · http://www.velaw.com · 666 Fifth Avenue, 26th Floor · New York, NY 10103-0040 · 212-237-0000

Thomas J. Weber · Greenberg Traurig · http://www.gtlaw.com · MetLife Building · 200 Park Avenue · New York, NY 10166 · 212-801-9200

William P. Weintraub · a · Friedman Kaplan Seiler & Adelman · http://www.fklaw.com · 1633 Broadway, 46th Floor · New York, NY 10019-6708 · 212-833-1100

Edward S. Weisfelner · Brown Rudnick · http://www.brbilaw.com · Seven Times Square, 47th Floor · New York, NY 10036 · 212-209-4800

M. Stephanie Wickouski · Drinker Biddle & Reath · 140 Broadway, 39th Floor · New York, NY 10005 · 212-248-3140

Peter D. Wolfson · Sonnenschein Nath & Rosenthal · 1221 Avenue of the Americas, 25th Floor · New York, NY 10020-1089 · 212-768-6700

Kenneth S. Ziman · Simpson Thacher · 425 Lexington Avenue · New York, NY 10017-3954 · 212-455-2000

Bruce R. Zirinsky · a · Cadwalader, Wickersham & Taft · http://www.cadwalader.com · One World Financial Center · New York, NY 10281 · 212-504-6000

Rochester

Paul S. Groschadl · a · Woods Oviatt Gilman · http://www.woodsoviatt.com · 700 Crossroads Building · Two State Street · Rochester, NY 14614 · 585-987-2800

C. Bruce Lawrence · 2) · Boylan, Brown, Code, Vigdor & Wilson · http://www.boylanbrown.com · 2400 Chase Square · Rochester, NY 14604 · 585-232-5300

David D. MacKnight · a · Lacy Katzen · http://www.lacykatzen.com · The Granite Building, Second Floor · 130 East Main Street · Rochester, NY 14604 · 585-454-5650

William S. Thomas, Jr. · 2) · Nixon Peabody · 1100 Clinton Square · P.O. Box 31051 · Rochester, NY 14604 · 585-263-1000

John R. Weider · 2) · Harter Secrest & Emery · http://www.hselaw.com · 1600 Bausch & Lomb Place · Rochester, NY 14604-2711 · 585-232-6500

Syracuse

Michael J. Balanoff · 2) · Green & Seifter · One Lincoln Center, Suite 900 · 110 West Fayette Street · Syracuse, NY 13202 · 315-422-1391

Stephen A. Donato · a · Bond, Schoeneck & King · One Lincoln Center · Syracuse, NY 13202-1355 · 315-218-8000

Jeffrey A. Dove · Menter, Rudin & Trivelpiece · 308 Maltbie Street, Suite 200 · Syracuse, NY 13204-1498 · 315-474-7541

Peter L. Hubbard · 2) · Menter, Rudin & Trivelpiece · 308 Maltbie Street, Suite 200 · Syracuse, NY 13204-1498 · 315-474-7541

Wendy A. Kinsella · Harris Beach · One Park Place, Fourth Floor · 300 South State Street · Syracuse, NY 13202 · 315-423-7100

Lee E. Woodard · Harris Beach · One Park Place, Fourth Floor · 300 South State Street · Syracuse, NY 13202 · 315-423-7100

Joseph Zagraniczny · Bond, Schoeneck & King · One Lincoln Center · Syracuse, NY 13202-1355 · 315-218-8000

White Plains

Lawrence R. Reich · Reich Reich & Reich · http://www.reichpc.com · 235 Main Street, Suite 450 · White Plains, NY 10601-3257 · 914-949-2126

Williamsville

Donald P. Sheldon · 2) · Donald P. Sheldon · 300 International Drive, Suite 100 · Williamsville, NY 14221 · 716-626-3534

BET-THE-COMPANY LITIGATION

Armonk

David Boies · 2) · Boies, Schiller & Flexner · 333 Main Street · Armonk, NY 10504 · 914-749-8200

Buffalo

Robert B. Conklin · a · Hodgson Russ · One Guaranty Building, Suite 100 · 140 Pearl Street · Buffalo, NY 14202 · 716-856-4000

Terrence M. Connors · a · Connors & Vilardo · 1000 Liberty Building · 424 Main Street · Buffalo, NY 14202 · 716-852-5533

Paul B. Zuydhoek · a · Phillips Lytle · 3400 HSBC Center · Buffalo, NY 14203-2887 · 716-847-8400

New York

Mark H. Alcott · a · Paul, Weiss, Rifkind, Wharton & Garrison · 1285 Avenue of the Americas · New York, NY 10019-6064 · 212-373-3000

Joseph S. Allerhand · Weil Gotshal & Manges · 767 Fifth Avenue · New York, NY 10153 · 212-310-8000

Bruce D. Angiolillo · Simpson Thacher · 425 Lexington Avenue · New York, NY 10017-3954 · 212-455-2000

David M. Brodsky · Latham & Watkins · 885 Third Avenue · New York, NY 10022-4834 · 212-906-1200

Michael J. Chepiga · Simpson Thacher · 425 Lexington Avenue · New York, NY 10017-3954 · 212-455-2000

Evan R. Chesler · Cravath, Swaine & Moore · Worldwide Plaza · 825 Eighth Avenue · New York, NY 10019-7475 · 212-474-1000

Richard W. Clary · Cravath, Swaine & Moore · Worldwide Plaza · 825 Eighth Avenue · New York, NY 10019-7475 · 212-474-1000

Paul C. Curnin · Simpson Thacher · 425 Lexington Avenue · New York, NY 10017-3954 · 212-455-2000

Evan A. Davis · Cleary Gottlieb Steen & Hamilton · One Liberty Plaza · New York, NY 10006 · 212-225-2000

Gandolfo V. DiBlasi · a · Sullivan & Cromwell · 125 Broad Street · New York, NY 10004-2498 · 212-558-4000

Scott A. Edelman · Milbank, Tweed, Hadley & McCloy · http://www.milbank.com · One Chase Manhattan Plaza · New York, NY 10005-1413 · 212-530-5000

Jeremy G. Epstein · a · Shearman & Sterling · 599 Lexington Avenue · New York, NY 10022-6069 · 212-848-4000

Leslie Gordon Fagen · Paul, Weiss, Rifkind, Wharton & Garrison · 1285 Avenue of the Americas · New York, NY 10019-6064 · 212-373-3000

Robert B. Fiske, Jr. · 2% · Davis Polk & Wardwell · 450 Lexington Avenue · New York, NY 10017 · 212-450-4000

Martin Flumenbaum · a · Paul, Weiss, Rifkind, Wharton & Garrison · 1285 Avenue of the Americas · New York, NY 10019-6064 · 212-373-3000

Philip R. Forlenza · Patterson Belknap Webb & Tyler · http://www.pbwt.com · 1133 Avenue of the Americas · New York, NY 10036-6710 · 212-336-2000

William P. Frank · a · Skadden, Arps, Slate, Meagher & Flom · Four Times Square · New York, NY 10036 · 212-735-3000

Andrew L. Frey · a · Mayer Brown · 1675 Broadway · New York, NY 10019-5820 · 212-506-2500

Max Gitter · a · Cleary Gottlieb Steen & Hamilton · One Liberty Plaza · New York, NY 10006 · 212-225-2000

Patricia M. Hynes · a · Allen & Overy · 1221 Avenue of the Americas · New York, NY 10020 · 212-610-6300

Gregory P. Joseph · a · Gregory P. Joseph · 485 Lexington Avenue, 30th Floor · New York, NY 10017 · 212-407-1200

Brad S. Karp · Paul, Weiss, Rifkind, Wharton & Garrison · 1285 Avenue of the Americas · New York, NY 10019-6064 · 212-373-3000

Jay B. Kasner · Skadden, Arps, Slate, Meagher & Flom · Four Times Square · New York, NY 10036 · 212-735-3000

Daniel J. Kramer · Paul, Weiss, Rifkind, Wharton & Garrison · 1285 Avenue of the Americas · New York, NY 10019-6064 · 212-373-3000

Frederick B. Lacey · 2) · Dewey & LeBoeuf · 125 West 55th Street · New York, NY 10019-5389 · 212-424-8000

Jonathan J. Lerner · Skadden, Arps, Slate, Meagher & Flom · Four Times Square · New York, NY 10036 · 212-735-3000

Andrew J. Levander · Dechert · 30 Rockefeller Plaza · 1095 Avenue of the Americas · New York, NY 10036-6797 · 212-698-3500

Martin London · 2) · Paul, Weiss, Rifkind, Wharton & Garrison · 1285 Avenue of the Americas · New York, NY 10019-6064 · 212-373-3000

Robert B. McCaw · WilmerHale · http://www.wilmerhale.com · 399 Park Avenue · New York, NY 10022 · 212-230-8800

Theodore N. Mirvis · Wachtell, Lipton, Rosen & Katz · 51 West 52nd Street · New York, NY 10019 · 212-403-1000

Gary P. Naftalis · a · Kramer Levin Naftalis & Frankel · http://www.kramerlevin.com · 1177 Avenue of the Americas · New York, NY 10036 · 212-715-9100

Bernard W. Nussbaum · 2% · Wachtell, Lipton, Rosen & Katz · 51 West 52nd Street · New York, NY 10019 · 212-403-1000

Barry R. Ostrager · Simpson Thacher · 425 Lexington Avenue · New York, NY 10017-3954 · 212-455-2000

Lawrence B. Pedowitz · a · Wachtell, Lipton, Rosen & Katz · 51 West 52nd Street · New York, NY 10019 · 212-403-1000

Mark F. Pomerantz · Paul, Weiss, Rifkind, Wharton & Garrison · 1285 Avenue of the Americas · New York, NY 10019-6064 · 212-373-3000

James W. Quinn · Weil Gotshal & Manges · 767 Fifth Avenue · New York, NY 10153 · 212-310-8000

Anthony M. Radice · Morrison & Foerster · http://www.mofo.com · 1290 Avenue of the Americas · New York, NY 10104-0050 · 212-468-8000

Roy L. Reardon · 2% · Simpson Thacher · 425 Lexington Avenue · New York, NY 10017-3954 · 212-455-2000

Paul C. Saunders · Cravath, Swaine & Moore · Worldwide Plaza · 825 Eighth Avenue · New York, NY 10019-7475 · 212-474-1000

Herbert M. Wachtell · 2) · Wachtell, Lipton, Rosen & Katz · 51 West 52nd Street · New York, NY 10019 212-403-1000

Theodore V. Wells, Jr. · a · Paul, Weiss, Rifkind, Wharton & Garrison · 1285 Avenue of the Americas · New York, NY 10019-6064 · 212-373-3000

Mary Jo White · Debevoise & Plimpton · 919 Third Avenue · New York, NY 10022 · 212-909-6000

Peter L. Zimroth · Arnold & Porter · 399 Park Avenue, 34th Floor · New York, NY 10022-4690 · 212-715-1000

Rochester

Michael R. Wolford · ⑩ · The Wolford Law Firm · http://www.wolfordfirm.com · 600 Reynolds Arcade Building · 16 East Main Street · Rochester, NY 14614 · 585-325-8000

Paul J. Yesawich III · ⑩ · Harris Beach · The Granite Building · 130 East Main Street · Rochester, NY 14604 · 585-419-8800

Syracuse

Carter H. Strickland · ⑳ · Mackenzie Hughes · 101 South Salina Street, Suite 600 · P.O. Box 4967 · Syracuse, NY 13221-4967 · 315-474-7571

BIOTECHNOLOGY LAW

New York

Samuel B. Abrams · Dechert · 30 Rockefeller Plaza · 1095 Avenue of the Americas · New York, NY 10036-6797 · 212-698-3500

Laura A. Coruzzi · Jones Day · 222 East 41st Street · New York, NY 10017-6702 · 212-326-3939

Stephen M. Davis · Goodwin Procter · The New York Times Building · 620 Eighth Avenue · New York, NY 10018 · 212-813-8800

Dan DiNapoli · Kaye Scholer · 425 Park Avenue · New York, NY 10022-3598 · 212-836-8000

Jennifer Gordon · Sidley Austin · 787 Seventh Avenue · New York, NY 10019 · 212-839-5300

James F. Haley, Jr. · ⑩ · Ropes & Gray · http://www.ropesgray.com · 1211 Avenue of the Americas · New York, NY 10036-8704 · 212-596-9000

Stephen S. Rabinowitz · Fried, Frank, Harris, Shriver & Jacobson · One New York Plaza · New York, NY 10004-1980 · 212-859-8000

Gerald Sobel · ⑩ · Kaye Scholer · 425 Park Avenue · New York, NY 10022-3598 · 212-836-8000

Blaine E. Templeman · Sheppard, Mullin, Richter & Hampton · http://www.sheppardmullin.com · 30 Rockefeller Plaza, 24th Floor · New York, NY 10112 · 212-332-3800

CIVIL RIGHTS LAW

Buffalo

Michael A. Brady · Hagerty & Brady · 69 Delaware Avenue, Suite 1010 · Buffalo, NY 14202-3875 · 716-856-9443

Daniel T. Lukasik · Cantor, Lukasik, Dolce & Panepinto · http://cldplaw.com · 1600 Main Place Tower · 350 Main Street · Buffalo, NY 14202 · 716-852-1888

Harry F. Mooney · Hurwitz & Fine · http://www.hurwitzfine.com · 1300 Liberty Building · Buffalo, NY 14202 · 716-849-8900

Susan C. Roney · Nixon Peabody · Key Towers at Fountain Plaza, Suite 500 · 40 Fountain Plaza · Buffalo, NY 14202 · 716-853-8100

New York

Jonathan S. Abady · Emery Celli Brinckerhoff & Abady · 75 Rockefeller Plaza, 20th Floor · New York, NY 10019 · 212-763-5000

COLLABORATIVE LAW: FAMILY LAW

Buffalo

Patrick C. O'Reilly · a · Lipsitz Green Scime Cambria · http://www.lipsitzgreen.com · 42 Delaware Avenue, Suite 120 · Buffalo, NY 14202 · 716-849-1333

Rochester

Suzanne Brunsting · a · Suzanne L. Brunsting · 202 Clovercrest Drive · Rochester, NY 14618 · 585-244-4239

Richard G. Curtis · Kaman, Berlove, Marafioti, Jacobstein & Goldman · http://www.kamanesq.com · 135 Corporate Woods, Suite 300 · Rochester, NY 14623 · 585-325-7440

Diana Deyo Ryan · Kaman, Berlove, Marafioti, Jacobstein & Goldman · http://www.kamanesq.com · 135 Corporate Woods, Suite 300 · Rochester, NY 14623 · 585-325-7440

Webster

David R. Murch · Murch & Wise · 674 Ridge Road · Webster, NY 14580-2394 · 716-671-4473

COMMERCIAL LITIGATION

Albany

Robert J. Alessi · Dewey & LeBoeuf · One Commerce Plaza, Suite 2020 · 99 Washington Avenue · Albany, NY 12210-2820 · 518-626-9000

John T. DeGraff, Jr. · 2) · DeGraff, Foy & Kunz · 90 State Street · Albany, NY 12207 · 518-462-5300

Armonk

David Boies · 2) · Boies, Schiller & Flexner · 333 Main Street · Armonk, NY 10504 · 914-749-8200

Binghamton

James S. Gleason · Hinman, Howard & Kattell · 700 Security Mutual Building · 80 Exchange Street · P.O. Box 5250 · Binghamton, NY 13902-5250 · 607-723-5341

David M. Gouldin · a · Levene, Gouldin & Thompson · http://www.binghamtonlaw.com · 71 State Street · P.O. Box F-1706 · Binghamton, NY 13902 · 607-763-9200

Buffalo

Peter D. Braun · Phillips Lytle · 3400 HSBC Center · Buffalo, NY 14203-2887 · 716-847-8400

Robert B. Conklin · a · Hodgson Russ · One Guaranty Building, Suite 100 · 140 Pearl Street · Buffalo, NY 14202 · 716-856-4000

Terrence M. Connors · a · Connors & Vilardo · 1000 Liberty Building · 424 Main Street · Buffalo, NY 14202 · 716-852-5533

Kevin J. English · Phillips Lytle · 3400 HSBC Center · Buffalo, NY 14203-2887 · 716-847-8400

Morgan G. Graham · Phillips Lytle · 3400 HSBC Center · Buffalo, NY 14203-2887 · 716-847-8400

Richard F. Griffin · 2% · Kavinoky & Cook · 726 Exchange Street, Suite 800 · Buffalo, NY 14210 · 716-845-6000

Tamar P. Halpern · Phillips Lytle · 3400 HSBC Center · Buffalo, NY 14203-2887 · 716-847-8400

Kevin M. Hogan · Phillips Lytle · 3400 HSBC Center · Buffalo, NY 14203-2887 · 716-847-8400

Paul F. Jones · Phillips Lytle · 3400 HSBC Center · Buffalo, NY 14203-2887 · 716-847-8400

Kevin M. Kearney · Hodgson Russ · One Guaranty Building, Suite 100 · 140 Pearl Street · Buffalo, NY 14202 · 716-856-4000

Dan D. Kohane · Hurwitz & Fine · http://www.hurwitzfine.com · 1300 Liberty Building · Buffalo, NY 14202 · 716-849-8900

Robert J. Lane, Jr. · Hodgson Russ · One Guaranty Building, Suite 100 · 140 Pearl Street · Buffalo, NY 14202 · 716-856-4000

Kenneth A. Manning · Phillips Lytle · 3400 HSBC Center · Buffalo, NY 14203-2887 · 716-847-8400

Harry F. Mooney · Hurwitz & Fine · http://www.hurwitzfine.com · 1300 Liberty Building · Buffalo, NY 14202 · 716-849-8900

Daniel T. Roach · 2% · Roach, Brown, McCarthy & Gruber · 1620 Liberty Building · 420 Main Street · Buffalo, NY 14202 · 716-852-0400

William F. Savino · Damon & Morey · http://www.damonmorey.com · 1000 Cathedral Place · 298 Main Street · Buffalo, NY 14202-4096 · 716-856-5500

Joseph V. Sedita · 2% · Hodgson Russ · One Guaranty Building, Suite 100 · 140 Pearl Street · Buffalo, NY 14202 · 716-856-4000

Paul K. Stecker · Phillips Lytle · 3400 HSBC Center · Buffalo, NY 14203-2887 · 716-847-8400

Richard T. Sullivan · Harris Beach · Larkin at Exchange, Suite 1000 · 726 Exchange Street · Buffalo, NY 14210 · 716-200-5050

Thomas S. Wiswall · Phillips Lytle · 3400 HSBC Center · Buffalo, NY 14203-2887 · 716-847-8400

Benjamin M. Zuffranieri · Hodgson Russ · One Guaranty Building, Suite 100 · 140 Pearl Street · Buffalo, NY 14202 · 716-856-4000

Paul B. Zuydhoek · a · Phillips Lytle · 3400 HSBC Center · Buffalo, NY 14203-2887 · 716-847-8400

New York

Mark H. Alcott · a · Paul, Weiss, Rifkind, Wharton & Garrison · 1285 Avenue of the Americas · New York, NY 10019-6064 · 212-373-3000

Joseph S. Allerhand · Weil Gotshal & Manges · 767 Fifth Avenue · New York, NY 10153 · 212-310-8000

Bruce D. Angiolillo · Simpson Thacher · 425 Lexington Avenue · New York, NY 10017-3954 · 212-455-2000

Michael F. Armstrong · 2% · Howrey · Citigroup Center, 54th Floor · 153 East 53rd Street · New York, NY 10022 · 212-896-6500

Jack C. Auspitz · 2) · Morrison & Foerster · http://www.mofo.com · 1290 Avenue of the Americas · New York, NY 10104-0050 · 212-468-8000

Celia Goldwag Barenholtz · Cooley Godward Kronish · The Grace Building, 46th Floor · 1114 Avenue of the Americas · New York, NY 10036-7798 · 212-479-6000

Robert H. Baron · Cravath, Swaine & Moore · Worldwide Plaza · 825 Eighth Avenue · New York, NY 10019-7475 · 212-474-1000

Francis Patrick Barron · Cravath, Swaine & Moore · Worldwide Plaza · 825 Eighth Avenue · New York, NY 10019-7475 · 212-474-1000

Stuart J. Baskin · Shearman & Sterling · 599 Lexington Avenue · New York, NY 10022-6069 · 212-848-4000

James N. Benedict · Milbank, Tweed, Hadley & McCloy · http://www.milbank.com · One Chase Manhattan Plaza · New York, NY 10005-1413 · 212-530-5000

Max W. Berger · Bernstein Litowitz Berger & Grossmann · http://www.blbglaw.com · 1285 Avenue of the Americas · New York, NY 10019 · 212-554-1400

David H. Braff · Sullivan & Cromwell · 125 Broad Street · New York, NY 10004-2498 · 212-558-4000

William A. Brewer III · Bickel & Brewer · 767 Fifth Avenue, 50th Floor · New York, NY 10153 · 212-489-1400

David M. Brodsky · Latham & Watkins · 885 Third Avenue · New York, NY 10022-4834 · 212-906-1200

Steven G. Brody · McKee Nelson · One Battery Park Plaza, 34th Floor · New York, NY 10004 · 917-777-4200

Paul J. Bschorr · Gregory P. Joseph · 485 Lexington Avenue, 30th Floor · New York, NY 10017 · 212-407-1200

John F. Cambria · Alston + Bird · http://www.alston.com · 90 Park Avenue · New York, NY 10016-1387 · 212-210-9400

William F. Cavanaugh · Patterson Belknap Webb & Tyler · http://www.pbwt.com · 1133 Avenue of the Americas · New York, NY 10036-6710 · 212-336-2000

Michael J. Chepiga · Simpson Thacher · 425 Lexington Avenue · New York, NY 10017-3954 · 212-455-2000

Evan R. Chesler · Cravath, Swaine & Moore · Worldwide Plaza · 825 Eighth Avenue · New York, NY 10019-7475 · 212-474-1000

Richard W. Clary · Cravath, Swaine & Moore · Worldwide Plaza · 825 Eighth Avenue · New York, NY 10019-7475 · 212-474-1000

John P. Coffey · Bernstein Litowitz Berger & Grossmann · http://www.blbglaw.com · 1285 Avenue of the Americas · New York, NY 10019 · 212-554-1400

Warren H. Colodner · K&L Gates · 599 Lexington Avenue · New York, NY 10022-6030 · 212-536-3900

John P. Cooney, Jr. · a · Davis Polk & Wardwell · 450 Lexington Avenue · New York, NY 10017 · 212-450-4000

Leslie D. Corwin · Greenberg Traurig · http://www.gtlaw.com · MetLife Building · 200 Park Avenue · New York, NY 10166 · 212-801-9200

Paul C. Curnin · Simpson Thacher · 425 Lexington Avenue · New York, NY 10017-3954 · 212-455-2000

Evan A. Davis · Cleary Gottlieb Steen & Hamilton · One Liberty Plaza · New York, NY 10006 · 212-225-2000

Frederick T. Davis · a · Debevoise & Plimpton · 919 Third Avenue · New York, NY 10022 · 212-909-6000

Robert J. Del Tufo · a · Skadden, Arps, Slate, Meagher & Flom · Four Times Square · New York, NY 10036 · 212-735-3000

Gandolfo V. DiBlasi · a · Sullivan & Cromwell · 125 Broad Street · New York, NY 10004-2498 · 212-558-4000

Gregory L. Diskant · Patterson Belknap Webb & Tyler · http://www.pbwt.com · 1133 Avenue of the Americas · New York, NY 10036-6710 · 212-336-2000

Carey R. Dunne · Davis Polk & Wardwell · 450 Lexington Avenue · New York, NY 10017 · 212-450-4000

Scott A. Edelman · Milbank, Tweed, Hadley & McCloy · http://www.milbank.com · One Chase Manhattan Plaza · New York, NY 10005-1413 · 212-530-5000

Steven M. Edwards · Hogan & Hartson · 875 Third Avenue, 25th Floor · New York, NY 10022 · 212-918-3000

Sheldon H. Elsen · a · Orans, Elsen, Lupert & Brown · http://www.oellaw.com · 875 Third Avenue, 28th Floor · New York, NY 10022 · 212-586-2211

Jeremy G. Epstein · a · Shearman & Sterling · 599 Lexington Avenue · New York, NY 10022-6069 · 212-848-4000

Leslie Gordon Fagen · Paul, Weiss, Rifkind, Wharton & Garrison · 1285 Avenue of the Americas · New York, NY 10019-6064 · 212-373-3000

Marshall H. Fishman · Kramer Levin Naftalis & Frankel · http://www.kramerlevin.com · 1177 Avenue of the Americas · New York, NY 10036 · 212-715-9100

Robert B. Fiske, Jr. · 2% · Davis Polk & Wardwell · 450 Lexington Avenue · New York, NY 10017 · 212-450-4000

Donald L. Flexner · 2) · Boies, Schiller & Flexner · 575 Lexington Avenue, Seventh Floor · New York, NY 10022 · 212-446-2300

Martin Flumenbaum · a · Paul, Weiss, Rifkind, Wharton & Garrison · 1285 Avenue of the Americas · New York, NY 10019-6064 · 212-373-3000

Philip R. Forlenza · Patterson Belknap Webb & Tyler · http://www.pbwt.com · 1133 Avenue of the Americas · New York, NY 10036-6710 · 212-336-2000

William P. Frank · a · Skadden, Arps, Slate, Meagher & Flom · Four Times Square · New York, NY 10036 · 212-735-3000

Charles A. Gilman · Cahill Gordon & Reindel · 80 Pine Street · New York, NY 10005-1702 · 212-701-3000

Max Gitter · a · Cleary Gottlieb Steen & Hamilton · One Liberty Plaza · New York, NY 10006 · 212-225-2000

Robert J. Giuffra, Jr. · Sullivan & Cromwell · 125 Broad Street · New York, NY 10004-2498 · 212-558-4000

Dennis E. Glazer · Davis Polk & Wardwell · 450 Lexington Avenue · New York, NY 10017 · 212-450-4000

Linda A. Goldstein · Manatt, Phelps & Phillips · Seven Times Square · New York, NY 10036 · 212-790-4500

Henry B. Gutman · Simpson Thacher · 425 Lexington Avenue · New York, NY 10017-3954 · 212-455-2000

Patricia M. Hynes · a · Allen & Overy · 1221 Avenue of the Americas · New York, NY 10020 · 212-610-6300

David W. Ichel · Simpson Thacher · 425 Lexington Avenue · New York, NY 10017-3954 · 212-455-2000

Elihu Inselbuch · Caplin & Drysdale · http://www.capdale.com · 375 Park Avenue, 35th Floor · New York, NY 10152 · 212-319-7125

Gregory P. Joseph · a · Gregory P. Joseph · 485 Lexington Avenue, 30th Floor · New York, NY 10017 · 212-407-1200

Robert J. Jossen · a · Dechert · 30 Rockefeller Plaza · 1095 Avenue of the Americas · New York, NY 10036-6797 · 212-698-3500

Samuel Kadet · Skadden, Arps, Slate, Meagher & Flom · Four Times Square · New York, NY 10036 · 212-735-3000

Brad S. Karp · Paul, Weiss, Rifkind, Wharton & Garrison · 1285 Avenue of the Americas · New York, NY 10019-6064 · 212-373-3000

Jay B. Kasner · Skadden, Arps, Slate, Meagher & Flom · Four Times Square · New York, NY 10036 · 212-735-3000

Jerome C. Katz · Ropes & Gray · http://www.ropesgray.com · 1211 Avenue of the Americas · New York, NY 10036-8704 · 212-596-9000

Thomas J. Kavaler · Cahill Gordon & Reindel · 80 Pine Street · New York, NY 10005-1702 · 212-701-3000

David N. Kelley · Cahill Gordon & Reindel · 80 Pine Street · New York, NY 10005-1702 · 212-701-3000

David G. Keyko · Pillsbury Winthrop Shaw Pittman · http://www.pillsburylaw.com · 1540 Broadway · New York, NY 10036-4039 · 212-858-1000

Allen Kezsbom · 2) · Fried, Frank, Harris, Shriver & Jacobson · One New York Plaza · New York, NY 10004-1980 · 212-859-8000

John S. Kiernan · Debevoise & Plimpton · 919 Third Avenue · New York, NY 10022 · 212-909-6000

T. Barry Kingham · 2% · Curtis, Mallet-Prevost, Colt & Mosle · 101 Park Avenue · New York, NY 10178 · 212-696-6000

David Klingsberg · a · Kaye Scholer · 425 Park Avenue · New York, NY 10022-3598 · 212-836-8000

Charles E. Koob · Simpson Thacher · 425 Lexington Avenue · New York, NY 10017-3954 · 212-455-2000

Daniel J. Kornstein · 2) · Kornstein Veisz Wexler & Pollard · 757 Third Avenue, 18th Floor · New York, NY 10017 · 212-418-8600

Daniel J. Kramer · Paul, Weiss, Rifkind, Wharton & Garrison · 1285 Avenue of the Americas · New York, NY 10019-6064 · 212-373-3000

Steven C. Krane · Proskauer Rose · http://www.proskauer.com · 1585 Broadway · New York, NY 10036-8299 · 212-969-3000

Douglas M. Kraus · Skadden, Arps, Slate, Meagher & Flom · Four Times Square · New York, NY 10036 212-735-3000

Harvey Kurzweil · Dewey & LeBoeuf · 1301 Avenue of the Americas · New York, NY 10019-6092 · 212-259-8000

Frederick B. Lacey · 2) · Dewey & LeBoeuf · 125 West 55th Street · New York, NY 10019-5389 · 212-424-8000

Martin N. Leaf · 2% · Martin N. Leaf & Associates · 165 West End Avenue, Suite 19-G · New York, NY 10023 · 212-721-7900

Jonathan J. Lerner · Skadden, Arps, Slate, Meagher & Flom · Four Times Square · New York, NY 10036 · 212-735-3000

Andrew J. Levander · Dechert · 30 Rockefeller Plaza · 1095 Avenue of the Americas · New York, NY 10036-6797 · 212-698-3500

Lewis J. Liman · Cleary Gottlieb Steen & Hamilton · One Liberty Plaza · New York, NY 10006 · 212-225-2000

Carl H. Loewenson, Jr. · Morrison & Foerster · http://www.mofo.com · 1290 Avenue of the Americas · New York, NY 10104-0050 · 212-468-8000

Martin London · 2) · Paul, Weiss, Rifkind, Wharton & Garrison · 1285 Avenue of the Americas · New York, NY 10019-6064 · 212-373-3000

Mitchell A. Lowenthal · Cleary Gottlieb Steen & Hamilton · One Liberty Plaza · New York, NY 10006 · 212-225-2000

Michael J. Malone · King & Spalding · 1185 Avenue of the Americas · New York, NY 10036-4003 · 212-556-2100

Alan E. Mansfield · Greenberg Traurig · http://www.gtlaw.com · MetLife Building · 200 Park Avenue · New York, NY 10166 · 212-801-9200

Aaron R. Marcu · Covington & Burling · The New York Times Building · 620 Eighth Avenue · New York, NY 10018 · 212-841-1000

Gregory A. Markel · Cadwalader, Wickersham & Taft · http://www.cadwalader.com · One World Financial Center · New York, NY 10281 · 212-504-6000

Randy M. Mastro · Gibson, Dunn & Crutcher · 200 Park Avenue, 47th Floor · New York, NY 10166-0193 212-351-4000

Robert B. McCaw · WilmerHale · http://www.wilmerhale.com · 399 Park Avenue · New York, NY 10022 · 212-230-8800

John S. McGeeney · 2) · Paul Hastings · Park Avenue Tower, First Floor · 75 East 55th Street · New York, NY 10022 · 212-318-6000

Ronald W. Meister · Cowan, Liebowitz & Latman · 1133 Avenue of the Americas, 35th Floor · New York, NY 10036-6799 · 212-790-9200

Francis Menton, Jr. · Willkie Farr & Gallagher · 787 Seventh Avenue · New York, NY 10019-6099 · 212-728-8000

Leo Milonas · Pillsbury Winthrop Shaw Pittman · http://www.pillsburylaw.com · 1540 Broadway · New York, NY 10036-4039 · 212-858-1000

Theodore N. Mirvis · Wachtell, Lipton, Rosen & Katz · 51 West 52nd Street · New York, NY 10019 · 212-403-1000

Michael W. Mitchell · 2) · Skadden, Arps, Slate, Meagher & Flom · Four Times Square · New York, NY 10036 · 212-735-3000

Steven F. Molo · a · Shearman & Sterling · 599 Lexington Avenue · New York, NY 10022-6069 · 212-848-4000

Scott D. Musoff · Skadden, Arps, Slate, Meagher & Flom · Four Times Square · New York, NY 10036 · 212-735-3000

Gary P. Naftalis · a · Kramer Levin Naftalis & Frankel · http://www.kramerlevin.com · 1177 Avenue of the Americas · New York, NY 10036 · 212-715-9100

John M. Nonna · Dewey & LeBoeuf · 125 West 55th Street · New York, NY 10019-5389 · 212-424-8000

Bernard W. Nussbaum · 2% · Wachtell, Lipton, Rosen & Katz · 51 West 52nd Street · New York, NY 10019 · 212-403-1000

Dennis P. Orr · Morrison & Foerster · http://www.mofo.com · 1290 Avenue of the Americas · New York, NY 10104-0050 · 212-468-8000

Barry R. Ostrager · Simpson Thacher · 425 Lexington Avenue · New York, NY 10017-3954 · 212-455-2000

Robert D. Owen · Fulbright & Jaworski · http://www.fulbright.com · 666 Fifth Avenue · New York, NY 10103-3198 · 212-318-3000

Marcia B. Paul · Davis Wright Tremaine · 1633 Broadway, 27th Floor · New York, NY 10019-6708 · 212-489-8230

Lawrence B. Pedowitz · a · Wachtell, Lipton, Rosen & Katz · 51 West 52nd Street · New York, NY 10019 · 212-403-1000

Steven R. Peikin · Sullivan & Cromwell · 125 Broad Street · New York, NY 10004-2498 · 212-558-4000

Owen C. Pell · White & Case · http://www.whitecase.com · 1155 Avenue of the Americas · New York, NY 10036-2787 · 212-819-8200

Martin L. Perschetz · Schulte Roth & Zabel · 919 Third Avenue · New York, NY 10022 · 212-756-2000

A. Robert Pietrzak · Sidley Austin · 787 Seventh Avenue · New York, NY 10019 · 212-839-5300

Jonathan D. Polkes · Weil Gotshal & Manges · 767 Fifth Avenue · New York, NY 10153 · 212-310-8000

Daniel A. Pollack · 2% · Pollack & Kaminsky · 114 West 47th Street, Suite 1900 · New York, NY 10036 · 212-575-4700

Mark F. Pomerantz · Paul, Weiss, Rifkind, Wharton & Garrison · 1285 Avenue of the Americas · New York, NY 10019-6064 · 212-373-3000

William Pratt · Kirkland & Ellis · Citigroup Center · 153 East 53rd Street · New York, NY 10022-4611 · 212-446-4800

John Pritchard · Pillsbury Winthrop Shaw Pittman · http://www.pillsburylaw.com · 1540 Broadway · New York, NY 10036-4039 · 212-858-1000

Thomas J. Quigley · Winston & Strawn · 200 Park Avenue · New York, NY 10166-4193 · 212-294-6700

James W. Quinn · Weil Gotshal & Manges · 767 Fifth Avenue · New York, NY 10153 · 212-310-8000

Anthony M. Radice · Morrison & Foerster · http://www.mofo.com · 1290 Avenue of the Americas · New York, NY 10104-0050 · 212-468-8000

James W. Rayhill · 2% · Carter Ledyard & Milburn · Two Wall Street, 18th Floor · New York, NY 10005 · 212-732-3200

Roy L. Reardon · 2% · Simpson Thacher · 425 Lexington Avenue · New York, NY 10017-3954 · 212-455-2000

Steven A. Reiss · Weil Gotshal & Manges · 767 Fifth Avenue · New York, NY 10153 · 212-310-8000

Richard A. Rosen · Paul, Weiss, Rifkind, Wharton & Garrison · 1285 Avenue of the Americas · New York, NY 10019-6064 · 212-373-3000

Eric M. Roth · Wachtell, Lipton, Rosen & Katz · 51 West 52nd Street · New York, NY 10019 · 212-403-1000

Richard A. Rothman · Weil Gotshal & Manges · 767 Fifth Avenue · New York, NY 10153 · 212-310-8000

Aaron Rubinstein · Kaye Scholer · 425 Park Avenue · New York, NY 10022-3598 · 212-836-8000

Betty Santangelo · Schulte Roth & Zabel · 919 Third Avenue · New York, NY 10022 · 212-756-2000

Paul C. Saunders · Cravath, Swaine & Moore · Worldwide Plaza · 825 Eighth Avenue · New York, NY 10019-7475 · 212-474-1000

Howard Schiffman · Schulte Roth & Zabel · 919 Third Avenue · New York, NY 10022 · 212-756-2000

Lorna G. Schofield · Debevoise & Plimpton · 919 Third Avenue · New York, NY 10022 · 212-909-6000

Amy W. Schulman · DLA Piper · 1251 Avenue of the Americas · New York, NY 10020-1104 · 212-335-4500

Karen P. Seymour · Sullivan & Cromwell · 125 Broad Street · New York, NY 10004-2498 · 212-558-4000

Samuel W. Seymour · Sullivan & Cromwell · 125 Broad Street · New York, NY 10004-2498 · 212-558-4000

Stuart L. Shapiro · Shapiro Forman Allen & Sava · 380 Madison Avenue · New York, NY 10017 · 212-972-4900

David J. Sheehan · Baker Hostetler · http://www.bakerlaw.com · 45 Rockefeller Plaza, 11th Floor · New York, NY 10111 · 212-589-4200

Max R. Shulman · Cravath, Swaine & Moore · Worldwide Plaza · 825 Eighth Avenue · New York, NY 10019-7475 · 212-474-1000

Jeffrey Q. Smith · McKee Nelson · One Battery Park Plaza, 34th Floor · New York, NY 10004 · 917-777-4200

Robert E. Smith · Katten Muchin Rosenman · 575 Madison Avenue · New York, NY 10022-2585 · 212-940-8800

Louis M. Solomon · Proskauer Rose · http://www.proskauer.com · 1585 Broadway · New York, NY 10036-8299 · 212-969-3000

Ira Lee Sorkin · Dickstein Shapiro · http://www.dicksteinshapiro.com · 1177 Avenue of the Americas · New York, NY 10036-2714 · 212-277-6500

Alan J. Stone · Milbank, Tweed, Hadley & McCloy · http://www.milbank.com · One Chase Manhattan Plaza · New York, NY 10005-1413 · 212-530-5000

Guy M. Struve · a · Davis Polk & Wardwell · 450 Lexington Avenue · New York, NY 10017 · 212-450-4000

Clifford Thau · Vinson & Elkins · http://www.velaw.com · 666 Fifth Avenue, 26th Floor · New York, NY 10103-0040 · 212-237-0000

David B. Tulchin · a · Sullivan & Cromwell · 125 Broad Street · New York, NY 10004-2498 · 212-558-4000

H. Barry Vasios · Holland & Knight · http://www.hklaw.com · 195 Broadway, 24th Floor · New York, NY 10007-3189 · 212-513-3200

Peter K. Vigeland · WilmerHale · http://www.wilmerhale.com · 399 Park Avenue · New York, NY 10022 · 212-230-8800

Alan Vinegrad · Covington & Burling · The New York Times Building · 620 Eighth Avenue · New York, NY 10018 · 212-841-1000

Paul Vizcarrondo, Jr. · Wachtell, Lipton, Rosen & Katz · 51 West 52nd Street · New York, NY 10019 · 212-403-1000

Herbert M. Wachtell · 2) · Wachtell, Lipton, Rosen & Katz · 51 West 52nd Street · New York, NY 10019 212-403-1000

George Wailand · Cahill Gordon & Reindel · 80 Pine Street · New York, NY 10005-1702 · 212-701-3000

Gerald Walpin · 2% · Katten Muchin Rosenman · 575 Madison Avenue · New York, NY 10022-2585 · 212-940-8800

Peter N. Wang · Foley & Lardner · 90 Park Avenue · New York, NY 10016 · 212-682-7474

John L. Warden · Sullivan & Cromwell · 125 Broad Street · New York, NY 10004-2498 · 212-558-4000

James B. Weidner · a · Clifford Chance · 31 West 52nd Street · New York, NY 10019-6131 · 212-878-8000

Harold P. Weinberger · Kramer Levin Naftalis & Frankel · http://www.kramerlevin.com · 1177 Avenue of the Americas · New York, NY 10036 · 212-715-9100

Stephen A. Weiner · 2% · Pillsbury Winthrop Shaw Pittman · http://www.pillsburylaw.com · 1540 Broadway · New York, NY 10036-4039 · 212-858-1000

Theodore V. Wells, Jr. · a · Paul, Weiss, Rifkind, Wharton & Garrison · 1285 Avenue of the Americas · New York, NY 10019-6064 · 212-373-3000

Mary Jo White · Debevoise & Plimpton · 919 Third Avenue · New York, NY 10022 · 212-909-6000

Robert F. Wise, Jr. · Davis Polk & Wardwell · 450 Lexington Avenue · New York, NY 10017 · 212-450-4000

Roger Witten · WilmerHale · http://www.wilmerhale.com · 399 Park Avenue · New York, NY 10022 · 212-230-8800

Frank H. Wohl · Lankler Siffert & Wohl · 500 Fifth Avenue, 33rd Floor · New York, NY 10110-3398 · 212-921-8399

Fredric Yerman · Kaye Scholer · 425 Park Avenue · New York, NY 10022-3598 · 212-836-8000

Edward J. Yodowitz · Skadden, Arps, Slate, Meagher & Flom · Four Times Square · New York, NY 10036 · 212-735-3000

Michael R. Young · Willkie Farr & Gallagher · 787 Seventh Avenue · New York, NY 10019-6099 · 212-728-8000

Joseph P. Zammit · Fulbright & Jaworski · http://www.fulbright.com · 666 Fifth Avenue · New York, NY 10103-3198 · 212-318-3000

Peter L. Zimroth · Arnold & Porter · 399 Park Avenue, 34th Floor · New York, NY 10022-4690 · 212-715-1000

James D. Zirin · a · Sidley Austin · 787 Seventh Avenue · New York, NY 10019 · 212-839-5300

Plattsburgh

Dennis D. Curtin · Stafford, Owens, Curtin & Trombley · One Cumberland Avenue · P.O. Box 2947 · Plattsburgh, NY 12901 · 518-561-4400

Rochester

Peter H. Abdella · Harter Secrest & Emery · http://www.hselaw.com · 1600 Bausch & Lomb Place · Rochester, NY 14604-2711 · 585-232-6500

William G. Bauer · Woods Oviatt Gilman · http://www.woodsoviatt.com · 700 Crossroads Building · Two State Street · Rochester, NY 14614 · 585-987-2800

Jerauld E. Brydges · Harter Secrest & Emery · http://www.hselaw.com · 1600 Bausch & Lomb Place · Rochester, NY 14604-2711 · 585-232-6500

Thomas C. Burke · a · Osborn, Reed & Burke · 45 Exchange Boulevard · Rochester, NY 14614-1403 · 585-454-6480

Alexander Geiger · a · Geiger and Rothenberg · Times Square Building, Suite 800 · 45 Exchange Street Rochester, NY 14614 · 585-232-1946

Mary Jo S. Korona · Leclair Korona Giordano Cole · 150 State Street, Suite 300 · Rochester, NY 14614 · 585-327-4100

David M. Lascell · a · Harter Secrest & Emery · http://www.hselaw.com · 1600 Bausch & Lomb Place · Rochester, NY 14604-2711 · 585-232-6500

Paul L. Leclair · Leclair Korona Giordano Cole · 150 State Street, Suite 300 · Rochester, NY 14614 · 585-327-4100

Michael J. Masino · Harris Beach · The Granite Building · 130 East Main Street · Rochester, NY 14604 · 585-419-8800

Mark J. Moretti · Phillips Lytle · 1400 First Federal Plaza · Rochester, NY 14614 · 585-238-2000

Carolyn G. Nussbaum · Nixon Peabody · 1100 Clinton Square · P.O. Box 31051 · Rochester, NY 14604 · 585-263-1000

Anthony R. Palermo · 2) · Woods Oviatt Gilman · http://www.woodsoviatt.com · 700 Crossroads Building Two State Street · Rochester, NY 14614 · 585-987-2800

Kenneth A. Payment · a · Harter Secrest & Emery · http://www.hselaw.com · 1600 Bausch & Lomb Place · Rochester, NY 14604-2711 · 585-232-6500

Warren B. Rosenbaum · Woods Oviatt Gilman · http://www.woodsoviatt.com · 700 Crossroads Building · Two State Street · Rochester, NY 14614 · 585-987-2800

David Rothenberg · a · Geiger and Rothenberg · Times Square Building, Suite 800 · 45 Exchange Street Rochester, NY 14614 · 585-232-1946

David M. Schraver · Nixon Peabody · 1100 Clinton Square · P.O. Box 31051 · Rochester, NY 14604 · 585-263-1000

Philip G. Spellane · Harris Beach · The Granite Building · 130 East Main Street · Rochester, NY 14604 · 585-419-8800

Michael R. Wolford · a · The Wolford Law Firm · http://www.wolfordfirm.com · 600 Reynolds Arcade Building · 16 East Main Street · Rochester, NY 14614 · 585-325-8000

Paul J. Yesawich III · a · Harris Beach · The Granite Building · 130 East Main Street · Rochester, NY 14604 · 585-419-8800

Syracuse

Paul M. Hanrahan · a · Hancock & Estabrook · 1500 Axa Tower I · 100 Madison Street · Syracuse, NY 13202 · 315-471-3151

Stephen T. Helmer · Mackenzie Hughes · 101 South Salina Street, Suite 600 · P.O. Box 4967 · Syracuse, NY 13221-4967 · 315-474-7571

Mitchell J. Katz · Menter, Rudin & Trivelpiece · 308 Maltbie Street, Suite 200 · Syracuse, NY 13204-1498 · 315-474-7541

James H. McGowan · Menter, Rudin & Trivelpiece · 308 Maltbie Street, Suite 200 · Syracuse, NY 13204-1498 · 315-474-7541

John G. McGowan · Bond, Schoeneck & King · One Lincoln Center · Syracuse, NY 13202-1355 · 315-218-8000

Thomas E. Myers · Bond, Schoeneck & King · One Lincoln Center · Syracuse, NY 13202-1355 · 315-218-8000

Carter H. Strickland · 2) · Mackenzie Hughes · 101 South Salina Street, Suite 600 · P.O. Box 4967 · Syracuse, NY 13221-4967 · 315-474-7571

White Plains

Henry G. Miller · 2% · Clark, Gagliardi & Miller · http://www.cgmlaw.com · Inns of Court Building · 99 Court Street · White Plains, NY 10601 · 914-946-8900

COMMUNICATIONS LAW

New York

Floyd Abrams · 2% · Cahill Gordon & Reindel · 80 Pine Street · New York, NY 10005-1702 · 212-701-3000

Kevin W. Goering · Sheppard, Mullin, Richter & Hampton · http://www.sheppardmullin.com · 30 Rockefeller Plaza, 24th Floor · New York, NY 10112 · 212-332-3800

Judith D. O'Neill · Greenberg Traurig · http://www.gtlaw.com · MetLife Building · 200 Park Avenue · New York, NY 10166 · 212-801-9200

CONSTRUCTION LAW

New York

Richard L. Abramson · Peckar & Abramson · http://www.pecklaw.com · 41 Madison Avenue, 20th Floor · New York, NY 10010 · 212-382-0909

Steven M. Charney · Peckar & Abramson · http://www.pecklaw.com · 41 Madison Avenue, 20th Floor · New York, NY 10010 · 212-382-0909

Frederick Cohen · Thelen Reid Brown Raysman & Steiner · 900 Third Avenue · New York, NY 10022 · 212-895-2000

Michael K. De Chiara · Zetlin & De Chiara · http://www.zetlindechiarallp.com · 801 Second Avenue · New York, NY 10017 · 212-682-6800

Richard P. Dyer · Thelen Reid Brown Raysman & Steiner · 900 Third Avenue · New York, NY 10022 · 212-895-2000

Peter Goetz · Goetz Fitzpatrick · One Penn Plaza · New York, NY 10119 · 212-695-8100

John F. Grubin · Wasserman, Grubin & Rogers · 1700 Broadway · New York, NY 10019-5905 · 212-581-3320

Barry B. LePatner · LePatner & Associates · 600 Lexington Avenue, 21st Floor · New York, NY 10022 · 212-935-4400

Alan Levy · Levy, Tolman & Costello · 630 Third Avenue · New York, NY 10017 · 212-949-8770

Brian Lustbader · Mazur Carp & Rubin · 1250 Broadway, Suite 3800 · New York, NY 10001 · 212-686-7700

Robert J. MacPherson · Thelen Reid Brown Raysman & Steiner · 900 Third Avenue · New York, NY 10022 · 212-895-2000

Sayward Mazur · Mazur Carp & Rubin · 1250 Broadway, Suite 3800 · New York, NY 10001 · 212-686-7700

David E. Montgomery · Sacks Montgomery · 800 Third Avenue · New York, NY 10022 · 212-355-4660

Robert S. Peckar · Peckar & Abramson · http://www.pecklaw.com · 41 Madison Avenue, 20th Floor · New York, NY 10010 · 212-382-0909

Frederick R. Rohn · Sacks Montgomery · 800 Third Avenue · New York, NY 10022 · 212-355-4660

Howard M. Rosen · Peckar & Abramson · http://www.pecklaw.com · 41 Madison Avenue, 20th Floor · New York, NY 10010 · 212-382-0909

Allen J. Ross · Thelen Reid Brown Raysman & Steiner · 900 Third Avenue · New York, NY 10022 · 212-895-2000

Gary Rubin · Mazur Carp & Rubin · 1250 Broadway, Suite 3800 · New York, NY 10001 · 212-686-7700

Robert A. Rubin · McCarter & English · 245 Park Avenue, 27th Floor · New York, NY 10167 · 212-609-6800

Ira Schulman · Mazur Carp & Rubin · 1250 Broadway, Suite 3800 · New York, NY 10001 · 212-686-7700

Arthur C. Silverman · Thelen Reid Brown Raysman & Steiner · 900 Third Avenue · New York, NY 10022 · 212-895-2000

Scott D. St. Marie · Schnader Harrison Segal & Lewis · http://www.schnader.com · 140 Broadway, Suite 3100 · New York, NY 10005-1101 · 212-973-8000

Michael S. Zetlin · Zetlin & De Chiara · http://www.zetlindechiarallp.com · 801 Second Avenue · New York, NY 10017 · 212-682-6800

Rochester

Anthony J. Adams, Jr. · Gates & Adams · 28 East Main Street, Suite 600 · Rochester, NY 14614 · 585-232-6900

Joseph A. Turri · Harris Beach · The Granite Building · 130 East Main Street · Rochester, NY 14604 · 585-419-8800

Syracuse

Henry H. Melchor · Bond, Schoeneck & King · One Lincoln Center · Syracuse, NY 13202-1355 · 315-218-8000

White Plains

Thomas H. Welby · Welby, Brady & Greenblatt · Westchester Financial Center, 15th Floor · 11 Martine Avenue · White Plains, NY 10606 · 914-428-2100

CORPORATE GOVERNANCE AND COMPLIANCE LAW

New York

Roger S. Aaron, Sr. · 2% · Skadden, Arps, Slate, Meagher & Flom · Four Times Square · New York, NY 10036 · 212-735-3000

Francis Patrick Barron · Cravath, Swaine & Moore · Worldwide Plaza · 825 Eighth Avenue · New York, NY 10019-7475 · 212-474-1000

Richard I. Beattie · 2) · Simpson Thacher · 425 Lexington Avenue · New York, NY 10017-3954 · 212-455-2000

Candace Krugman Beinecke · Hughes Hubbard & Reed · http://www.hugheshubbard.com · One Battery Park Plaza · New York, NY 10004-1482 · 212-837-6000

John T. Bostelman · Sullivan & Cromwell · 125 Broad Street · New York, NY 10004-2498 · 212-558-4000

David M. Brodsky · Latham & Watkins · 885 Third Avenue · New York, NY 10022-4834 · 212-906-1200

Charles I. Cogut · Simpson Thacher · 425 Lexington Avenue · New York, NY 10017-3954 · 212-455-2000

H. Rodgin Cohen · 2% · Sullivan & Cromwell · 125 Broad Street · New York, NY 10004-2498 · 212-558-4000

Kenneth Conboy · a · Latham & Watkins · 885 Third Avenue · New York, NY 10022-4834 · 212-906-1200

Greg A. Danilow · Weil Gotshal & Manges · 767 Fifth Avenue · New York, NY 10153 · 212-310-8000

Richard J. Davis · Weil Gotshal & Manges · 767 Fifth Avenue · New York, NY 10153 · 212-310-8000

Gandolfo V. DiBlasi · a · Sullivan & Cromwell · 125 Broad Street · New York, NY 10004-2498 · 212-558-4000

Carey R. Dunne · Davis Polk & Wardwell · 450 Lexington Avenue · New York, NY 10017 · 212-450-4000

Scott A. Edelman · Milbank, Tweed, Hadley & McCloy · http://www.milbank.com · One Chase Manhattan Plaza · New York, NY 10005-1413 · 212-530-5000

John G. Finley · Simpson Thacher · 425 Lexington Avenue · New York, NY 10017-3954 · 212-455-2000

Robert B. Fiske, Jr. · 2% · Davis Polk & Wardwell · 450 Lexington Avenue · New York, NY 10017 · 212-450-4000

Joseph H. Flom · 2% · Skadden, Arps, Slate, Meagher & Flom · Four Times Square · New York, NY 10036 · 212-735-3000

Faith Elizabeth Gay · Quinn Emanuel Urquhart Oliver & Hedges · 51 Madison Avenue, 22nd Floor · New York, NY 10010 · 212-849-7000

Harvey J. Goldschmid · Weil Gotshal & Manges · 767 Fifth Avenue · New York, NY 10153 · 212-310-8000

Philip K. Howard · Covington & Burling · The New York Times Building · 620 Eighth Avenue · New York, NY 10018 · 212-841-1000

Lawrence Iason · Morvillo, Abramowitz, Grand, Iason, Anello & Bohrer · 565 Fifth Avenue, Ninth Floor · New York, NY 10017 · 212-856-9600

David A. Katz · Wachtell, Lipton, Rosen & Katz · 51 West 52nd Street · New York, NY 10019 · 212-403-1000

John J. Kenney · Hoguet Newman Regal & Kenney · 10 East 40th Street · New York, NY 10016-0301 · 212-689-8808

Frederick B. Lacey · 2) · Dewey & LeBoeuf · 125 West 55th Street · New York, NY 10019-5389 · 212-424-8000

Martin Lipton · 2% · Wachtell, Lipton, Rosen & Katz · 51 West 52nd Street · New York, NY 10019 · 212-403-1000

Carl H. Loewenson, Jr. · Morrison & Foerster · http://www.mofo.com · 1290 Avenue of the Americas · New York, NY 10104-0050 · 212-468-8000

Aaron R. Marcu · Covington & Burling · The New York Times Building · 620 Eighth Avenue · New York, NY 10018 · 212-841-1000

Robert B. McCaw · WilmerHale · http://www.wilmerhale.com · 399 Park Avenue · New York, NY 10022 · 212-230-8800

Ira M. Millstein · 2) · Weil Gotshal & Manges · 767 Fifth Avenue · New York, NY 10153 · 212-310-8000

James C. Morphy · a · Sullivan & Cromwell · 125 Broad Street · New York, NY 10004-2498 · 212-558-4000

Martin Nussbaum · Dechert · 30 Rockefeller Plaza · 1095 Avenue of the Americas · New York, NY 10036-6797 · 212-698-3500

Lawrence B. Pedowitz · a · Wachtell, Lipton, Rosen & Katz · 51 West 52nd Street · New York, NY 10019 · 212-403-1000

Guy Petrillo · Dechert · 30 Rockefeller Plaza · 1095 Avenue of the Americas · New York, NY 10036-6797 212-698-3500

Mark F. Pomerantz · Paul, Weiss, Rifkind, Wharton & Garrison · 1285 Avenue of the Americas · New York, NY 10019-6064 · 212-373-3000

Lee S. Richards III · Richards Kibbe & Orbe · One World Financial Center, 29th Floor · New York, NY 10281-1003 · 212-530-1800

Thomas A. Roberts · Weil Gotshal & Manges · 767 Fifth Avenue · New York, NY 10153 · 212-310-8000

John F. Savarese · Wachtell, Lipton, Rosen & Katz · 51 West 52nd Street · New York, NY 10019 · 212-403-1000

Paul T. Schnell · Skadden, Arps, Slate, Meagher & Flom · Four Times Square · New York, NY 10036 · 212-735-3000

Benjamin F. Stapleton · 2) · Sullivan & Cromwell · 125 Broad Street · New York, NY 10004-2498 · 212-558-4000

Audrey Strauss · a · Fried, Frank, Harris, Shriver & Jacobson · One New York Plaza · New York, NY 10004-1980 · 212-859-8000

John L. Warden · Sullivan & Cromwell · 125 Broad Street · New York, NY 10004-2498 · 212-558-4000

Mary Jo White · Debevoise & Plimpton · 919 Third Avenue · New York, NY 10022 · 212-909-6000

John R. Wing · 2) · Lankler Siffert & Wohl · 500 Fifth Avenue, 33rd Floor · New York, NY 10110-3398 · 212-921-8399

Albany

Gregory J. Champion · Bond, Schoeneck & King · 111 Washington Avenue · Albany, NY 12210-2211 · 518-533-3000

A. Joseph Scott · Hodgson Russ · 677 Broadway, Suite 301 · Albany, NY 12207 · 518-465-2333

Amherst

Thomas A. Palmer · a · Jaeckle Fleischmann & Mugel · Centerpointe Corporate Park, Suite 320 · 400 Essjay Road · Amherst, NY 14221 · 716-250-1800

Buffalo

David H. Alexander · Gross, Shuman, Brizdle & Gilfillan · Fayette Court Building, Suite 600 · 465 Main Street · Buffalo, NY 14203 · 716-854-4300

Frederick G. Attea · 2) · Phillips Lytle · 3400 HSBC Center · Buffalo, NY 14203-2887 · 716-847-8400

Thomas C. Bailey · Phillips Lytle · 3400 HSBC Center · Buffalo, NY 14203-2887 · 716-847-8400

Richard F. Campbell · Hodgson Russ · One Guaranty Building, Suite 100 · 140 Pearl Street · Buffalo, NY 14202 · 716-856-4000

John B. Drenning · a · Hodgson Russ · One Guaranty Building, Suite 100 · 140 Pearl Street · Buffalo, NY 14202 · 716-856-4000

Anthony L. Eugeni · Damon & Morey · http://www.damonmorey.com · 1000 Cathedral Place · 298 Main Street · Buffalo, NY 14202-4096 · 716-856-5500

Ann E. Evanko · Hurwitz & Fine · http://www.hurwitzfine.com · 1300 Liberty Building · Buffalo, NY 14202 · 716-849-8900

Robert P. Fine · Hurwitz & Fine · http://www.hurwitzfine.com · 1300 Liberty Building · Buffalo, NY 14202 · 716-849-8900

Robert B. Fleming, Jr. · a · Hodgson Russ · One Guaranty Building, Suite 100 · 140 Pearl Street · Buffalo, NY 14202 · 716-856-4000

Lawrence C. Franco · Hurwitz & Fine · http://www.hurwitzfine.com · 1300 Liberty Building · Buffalo, NY 14202 · 716-849-8900

Kenneth P. Friedman · Hodgson Russ · One Guaranty Building, Suite 100 · 140 Pearl Street · Buffalo, NY 14202 · 716-856-4000

Arnold B. Gardner · 2) · Kavinoky & Cook · 726 Exchange Street, Suite 800 · Buffalo, NY 14210 · 716-845-6000

Jonathan H. Gardner · a · Kavinoky & Cook · 726 Exchange Street, Suite 800 · Buffalo, NY 14210 · 716-845-6000

James W. Gormley · Damon & Morey · http://www.damonmorey.com · 1000 Cathedral Place · 298 Main Street · Buffalo, NY 14202-4096 · 716-856-5500

Christopher T. Greene · Damon & Morey · http://www.damonmorey.com · 1000 Cathedral Place · 298 Main Street · Buffalo, NY 14202-4096 · 716-856-5500

Pamela Davis Heilman · Hodgson Russ · One Guaranty Building, Suite 100 · 140 Pearl Street · Buffalo, NY 14202 · 716-856-4000

Jeffrey A. Human · Gross, Shuman, Brizdle & Gilfillan · Fayette Court Building, Suite 600 · 465 Main Street · Buffalo, NY 14203 · 716-854-4300

Tim C. Loftis · Jaeckle Fleischmann & Mugel · 12 Fountain Plaza · Buffalo, NY 14202-2292 · 716-856-0600

David Murray · Phillips Lytle · 3400 HSBC Center · Buffalo, NY 14203-2887 · 716-847-8400

Robert J. Portin · Damon & Morey · http://www.damonmorey.com · 1000 Cathedral Place · 298 Main Street · Buffalo, NY 14202-4096 · 716-856-5500

Arthur A. Russ, Jr. · Phillips Lytle · 3400 HSBC Center · Buffalo, NY 14203-2887 · 716-847-8400

William I. Schapiro · 2% · Jaeckle Fleischmann & Mugel · 12 Fountain Plaza · Buffalo, NY 14202-2292 · 716-856-0600

Michael Schiavone · Lipsitz Green Scime Cambria · http://www.lipsitzgreen.com · 42 Delaware Avenue, Suite 120 · Buffalo, NY 14202 · 716-849-1333

Gary M. Schober · a · Hodgson Russ · One Guaranty Building, Suite 100 · 140 Pearl Street · Buffalo, NY 14202 · 716-856-4000

Raymond H. Seitz · a · Phillips Lytle · 3400 HSBC Center · Buffalo, NY 14203-2887 · 716-847-8400

Samuel L. Shapiro · Kavinoky & Cook · 726 Exchange Street, Suite 800 · Buffalo, NY 14210 · 716-845-6000

James W. Smyton · Phillips Lytle · 3400 HSBC Center · Buffalo, NY 14203-2887 · 716-847-8400

Gregory C. Yungbluth · Damon & Morey · http://www.damonmorey.com · 1000 Cathedral Place · 298 Main Street · Buffalo, NY 14202-4096 · 716-856-5500

John J. Zak · Hodgson Russ · One Guaranty Building, Suite 100 · 140 Pearl Street · Buffalo, NY 14202 · 716-856-4000

Johnstown

Mario J. Papa · Hodgson Russ · 55 East Main Street, Suite 100 · Johnstown, NY 12095 · 518-736-2900

New York

Michael J. Aiello · Weil Gotshal & Manges · 767 Fifth Avenue · New York, NY 10153 · 212-310-8000

Julie M. Allen · Proskauer Rose · http://www.proskauer.com · 1585 Broadway · New York, NY 10036-8299 · 212-969-3000

Theodore Altman · DLA Piper · 1251 Avenue of the Americas · New York, NY 10020-1104 · 212-335-4500

Ralph Arditi · a · Skadden, Arps, Slate, Meagher & Flom · Four Times Square · New York, NY 10036 · 212-735-3000

Joseph W. Armbrust · Sidley Austin · 787 Seventh Avenue · New York, NY 10019 · 212-839-5300

Peter Allan Atkins · 2% · Skadden, Arps, Slate, Meagher & Flom · Four Times Square · New York, NY 10036 · 212-735-3000

Alan P. Baden · Vinson & Elkins · http://www.velaw.com · 666 Fifth Avenue, 26th Floor · New York, NY 10103-0040 · 212-237-0000

William Barnett · a · Herrick Feinstein · Two Park Avenue, 20th Floor · New York, NY 10016 · 212-592-1400

Scott A. Barshay · Cravath, Swaine & Moore · Worldwide Plaza · 825 Eighth Avenue · New York, NY 10019-7475 · 212-474-1000

E. William Bates II · King & Spalding · 1185 Avenue of the Americas · New York, NY 10036-4003 · 212-556-2100

Gregg J. Berman · Fulbright & Jaworski · http://www.fulbright.com · 666 Fifth Avenue · New York, NY 10103-3198 · 212-318-3000

David W. Bernstein · 2% · Clifford Chance · 31 West 52nd Street · New York, NY 10019-6131 · 212-878-8000

Louis J. Bevilacqua · Cadwalader, Wickersham & Taft · http://www.cadwalader.com · One World Financial Center · New York, NY 10281 · 212-504-6000

Kenneth J. Bialkin · 2% · Skadden, Arps, Slate, Meagher & Flom · Four Times Square · New York, NY 10036 · 212-735-3000

Michael W. Blair · Debevoise & Plimpton · 919 Third Avenue · New York, NY 10022 · 212-909-6000

James H. Bluck · Hughes Hubbard & Reed · http://www.hugheshubbard.com · One Battery Park Plaza · New York, NY 10004-1482 · 212-837-6000

Richard D. Bohm · a · Debevoise & Plimpton · 919 Third Avenue · New York, NY 10022 · 212-909-6000

Richard S. Borisoff · a · Paul, Weiss, Rifkind, Wharton & Garrison · 1285 Avenue of the Americas · New York, NY 10019-6064 · 212-373-3000

John T. Bostelman · Sullivan & Cromwell · 125 Broad Street · New York, NY 10004-2498 · 212-558-4000

Robert E. Buckholz · Sullivan & Cromwell · 125 Broad Street · New York, NY 10004-2498 · 212-558-4000

Robert A. Cantone · Proskauer Rose · http://www.proskauer.com · 1585 Broadway · New York, NY 10036-8299 · 212-969-3000

Michael A. Chapnick · 2% · Morgan Lewis & Bockius · 101 Park Avenue · New York, NY 10178-0060 · 212-309-6000

Howard Chatzinoff · Weil Gotshal & Manges · 767 Fifth Avenue · New York, NY 10153 · 212-310-8000

Richard Chirls · Orrick, Herrington & Sutcliffe · 666 Fifth Avenue · New York, NY 10103-0001 · 212-506-5000

Jerome Alan Cohen · a · Paul, Weiss, Rifkind, Wharton & Garrison · 1285 Avenue of the Americas · New York, NY 10019-6064 · 212-373-3000

Thomas E. Constance · Kramer Levin Naftalis & Frankel · http://www.kramerlevin.com · 1177 Avenue of the Americas · New York, NY 10036 · 212-715-9100

Stephen J. Dannhauser · a · Weil Gotshal & Manges · 767 Fifth Avenue · New York, NY 10153 · 212-310-8000

Edward S. Davis · 2% · Hughes Hubbard & Reed · http://www.hugheshubbard.com · One Battery Park Plaza · New York, NY 10004-1482 · 212-837-6000

Robert P. Davis · Cleary Gottlieb Steen & Hamilton · One Liberty Plaza · New York, NY 10006 · 212-225-2000

Randolph A. DelFranco · Holland & Knight · http://www.hklaw.com · 195 Broadway, 24th Floor · New York, NY 10007-3189 · 212-513-3200

J. Kevin Dougherty · McGuireWoods · http://www.mcguirewoods.com · 1345 Avenue of the Americas, Seventh Floor · New York, NY 10105-0106 · 212-548-2100

Wolcott B. Dunham, Jr. · a · Debevoise & Plimpton · 919 Third Avenue · New York, NY 10022 · 212-909-6000

Daniel Dunson · a · Sullivan & Cromwell · 125 Broad Street · New York, NY 10004-2498 · 212-558-4000

Todd W. Eckland · Pillsbury Winthrop Shaw Pittman · http://www.pillsburylaw.com · 1540 Broadway · New York, NY 10036-4039 · 212-858-1000

Richard A. Edlin · Greenberg Traurig · http://www.gtlaw.com · MetLife Building · 200 Park Avenue · New York, NY 10166 · 212-801-9200

Klaus Eppler · 2% · Proskauer Rose · http://www.proskauer.com · 1585 Broadway · New York, NY 10036-8299 · 212-969-3000

Ronald A. Fleming · Pillsbury Winthrop Shaw Pittman · http://www.pillsburylaw.com · 1540 Broadway · New York, NY 10036-4039 · 212-858-1000

Joseph H. Flom · 2% · Skadden, Arps, Slate, Meagher & Flom · Four Times Square · New York, NY 10036 · 212-735-3000

Richard E. Floor · 2) · Goodwin Procter · The New York Times Building · 620 Eighth Avenue · New York, NY 10018 · 212-813-8800

Blaine V. Fogg · 2% · Skadden, Arps, Slate, Meagher & Flom · Four Times Square · New York, NY 10036 212-735-3000

E. Michael Greaney · a · Gibson, Dunn & Crutcher · 200 Park Avenue, 47th Floor · New York, NY 10166-0193 · 212-351-4000

Frederick S. Green · Weil Gotshal & Manges · 767 Fifth Avenue · New York, NY 10153 · 212-310-8000

Yaacov Gross · Morrison & Foerster · http://www.mofo.com · 1290 Avenue of the Americas · New York, NY 10104-0050 · 212-468-8000

Joseph W. Halliday · 2% · Skadden, Arps, Slate, Meagher & Flom · Four Times Square · New York, NY 10036 · 212-735-3000

Bruce C. Herzog · Willkie Farr & Gallagher · 787 Seventh Avenue · New York, NY 10019-6099 · 212-728-8000

Jeffrey A. Horwitz · Proskauer Rose · http://www.proskauer.com · 1585 Broadway · New York, NY 10036-8299 · 212-969-3000

Philip K. Howard · Covington & Burling · The New York Times Building · 620 Eighth Avenue · New York, NY 10018 · 212-841-1000

Arnold S. Jacobs · 2% · Proskauer Rose · http://www.proskauer.com · 1585 Broadway · New York, NY 10036-8299 · 212-969-3000

Paul Jacobs · Fulbright & Jaworski · http://www.fulbright.com · 666 Fifth Avenue · New York, NY 10103-3198 · 212-318-3000

Ronald H. Janis · a · Day Pitney · Times Square Tower · Seven Times Square · New York, NY 10036-7311 · 212-297-5800

Howard S. Kelberg · 2% · Milbank, Tweed, Hadley & McCloy · http://www.milbank.com · One Chase Manhattan Plaza · New York, NY 10005-1413 · 212-530-5000

Thomas N. Keltner, Jr. · Wien & Malkin · Lincoln Building · 60 East 42nd Street · New York, NY 10165-0015 · 212-687-8700

B. Robbins Kiessling · a · Cravath, Swaine & Moore · Worldwide Plaza · 825 Eighth Avenue · New York, NY 10019-7475 · 212-474-1000

Donald G. Kilpatrick · Pillsbury Winthrop Shaw Pittman · http://www.pillsburylaw.com · 1540 Broadway New York, NY 10036-4039 · 212-858-1000

Steven L. Kirshenbaum · Proskauer Rose · http://www.proskauer.com · 1585 Broadway · New York, NY 10036-8299 · 212-969-3000

Morris J. Kramer · 2% · Skadden, Arps, Slate, Meagher & Flom · Four Times Square · New York, NY 10036 · 212-735-3000

William C. F. Kurz · 2) · Pillsbury Winthrop Shaw Pittman · http://www.pillsburylaw.com · 1540 Broadway · New York, NY 10036-4039 · 212-858-1000

Robert Todd Lang · 2) · Weil Gotshal & Manges · 767 Fifth Avenue · New York, NY 10153 · 212-310-8000

Joseph M. Leccese · Proskauer Rose · http://www.proskauer.com · 1585 Broadway · New York, NY 10036-8299 · 212-969-3000

Ezra G. Levin · 2% · Kramer Levin Naftalis & Frankel · http://www.kramerlevin.com · 1177 Avenue of the Americas · New York, NY 10036 · 212-715-9100

Bruce L. Lieb · Proskauer Rose · http://www.proskauer.com · 1585 Broadway · New York, NY 10036-8299 212-969-3000

George P. Lindsay · Sullivan & Worcester · 1290 Avenue of the Americas · New York, NY 10104 · 212-660-3000

Peter J. Loughran · Debevoise & Plimpton · 919 Third Avenue · New York, NY 10022 · 212-909-6000

James M. Lurie · Osler, Hoskin & Harcourt · http://www.osler.com · 620 Eigth Avenue, 36th Floor · New York, NY 10018 · 212-867-5800

Matthew J. Mallow · 2) · Skadden, Arps, Slate, Meagher & Flom · Four Times Square · New York, NY 10036 · 212-735-3000

Ivan E. Mattei · Debevoise & Plimpton · 919 Third Avenue · New York, NY 10022 · 212-909-6000

Mark F. McElreath · Alston + Bird · http://www.alston.com · 90 Park Avenue · New York, NY 10016-1387 · 212-210-9400

Michael V. McKay · Vinson & Elkins · http://www.velaw.com · 666 Fifth Avenue, 26th Floor · New York, NY 10103-0040 · 212-237-0000

Barbara Meili · Greenberg Traurig · http://www.gtlaw.com · MetLife Building · 200 Park Avenue · New York, NY 10166 · 212-801-9200

Carlos E. Mendez-Penate · Thompson & Knight · http://www.tklaw.com · 919 Third Avenue, 39th Floor New York, NY 10022-3915 · 212-751-3001

Barry Metzger · Baker & McKenzie · 1114 Avenue of the Americas · New York, NY 10036 · 212-626-4100

James Modlin · Hughes Hubbard & Reed · http://www.hugheshubbard.com · One Battery Park Plaza · New York, NY 10004-1482 · 212-837-6000

Satoru Murase · Bingham McCutchen · http://www.bingham.com · 399 Park Avenue · New York, NY 10022-4689 · 212-705-7000

Lance D. Myers · Holland & Knight · http://www.hklaw.com · 195 Broadway, 24th Floor · New York, NY 10007-3189 · 212-513-3200

Toby S. Myerson · a · Paul, Weiss, Rifkind, Wharton & Garrison · 1285 Avenue of the Americas · New York, NY 10019-6064 · 212-373-3000

Jack H. Nusbaum · 2% · Willkie Farr & Gallagher · 787 Seventh Avenue · New York, NY 10019-6099 · 212-728-8000

Martin Nussbaum · Dechert · 30 Rockefeller Plaza · 1095 Avenue of the Americas · New York, NY 10036-6797 · 212-698-3500

Michael J. O'Brien · WilmerHale · http://www.wilmerhale.com · 399 Park Avenue · New York, NY 10022 212-230-8800

Ellen J. Odoner · Weil Gotshal & Manges · 767 Fifth Avenue · New York, NY 10153 · 212-310-8000

Peter F. Olberg · Manatt, Phelps & Phillips · Seven Times Square · New York, NY 10036 · 212-790-4500

Ronald R. Papa · Proskauer Rose · http://www.proskauer.com · 1585 Broadway · New York, NY 10036-8299 · 212-969-3000

Joel I. Papernik · a · Mintz, Levin, Cohn, Ferris, Glovsky and Popeo · Chrysler Center · 666 Third Avenue · New York, NY 10017 · 212-935-3000

Clyde E. Rankin III · Baker & McKenzie · 1114 Avenue of the Americas · New York, NY 10036 · 212-626-4100

Robert J. Rawn · Bryan Cave · 1290 Avenue of the Americas · New York, NY 10104-3300 · 212-541-2000

Thomas A. Roberts · Weil Gotshal & Manges · 767 Fifth Avenue · New York, NY 10153 · 212-310-8000

Kathy H. Rocklen · Proskauer Rose · http://www.proskauer.com · 1585 Broadway · New York, NY 10036-8299 · 212-969-3000

Richard A. Rosenbaum · Greenberg Traurig · http://www.gtlaw.com · MetLife Building · 200 Park Avenue · New York, NY 10166 · 212-801-9200

Mike Rosenwasser · Vinson & Elkins · http://www.velaw.com · 666 Fifth Avenue, 26th Floor · New York, NY 10103-0040 · 212-237-0000

Jeffrey W. Rubin · Hogan & Hartson · 875 Third Avenue, 25th Floor · New York, NY 10022 · 212-918-3000

Frederic A. Rubinstein · 2) · Kelley Drye & Warren · 101 Park Avenue · New York, NY 10178-0002 · 212-808-7800

Paul S. Schreiber · a · Shearman & Sterling · 599 Lexington Avenue · New York, NY 10022-6069 · 212-848-4000

Isaac Shapiro · 2% · Skadden, Arps, Slate, Meagher & Flom · Four Times Square · New York, NY 10036 · 212-735-3000

Howard L. Shecter · Morgan Lewis & Bockius · 101 Park Avenue · New York, NY 10178-0060 · 212-309-6000

Paul H. Shur · Sills Cummis & Gross · http://www.sillscummis.com · One Rockefeller Plaza · New York, NY 10020 · 212-643-7000

Rebecca F. Silberstein · Debevoise & Plimpton · 919 Third Avenue · New York, NY 10022 · 212-909-6000

Bradley Y. Smith · a · Davis Polk & Wardwell · 450 Lexington Avenue · New York, NY 10017 · 212-450-4000

Scott F. Smith · Covington & Burling · The New York Times Building · 620 Eighth Avenue · New York, NY 10018 · 212-841-1000

Marilyn Sobel · Paul, Weiss, Rifkind, Wharton & Garrison · 1285 Avenue of the Americas · New York, NY 10019-6064 · 212-373-3000

Robin L. Spear · Pillsbury Winthrop Shaw Pittman · http://www.pillsburylaw.com · 1540 Broadway · New York, NY 10036-4039 · 212-858-1000

William S. Sterns III · Alston + Bird · http://www.alston.com · 90 Park Avenue · New York, NY 10016-1387 · 212-210-9400

Alan J. Stone · Milbank, Tweed, Hadley & McCloy · http://www.milbank.com · One Chase Manhattan Plaza · New York, NY 10005-1413 · 212-530-5000

Michael J. Swidler · Vinson & Elkins · http://www.velaw.com · 666 Fifth Avenue, 26th Floor · New York, NY 10103-0040 · 212-237-0000

Jeffrey E. Tabak · Weil Gotshal & Manges · 767 Fifth Avenue · New York, NY 10153 · 212-310-8000

Jeremiah L. Thomas III · a · Simpson Thacher · 425 Lexington Avenue · New York, NY 10017-3954 · 212-455-2000

Robert M. Thomas, Jr. · a · Sullivan & Cromwell · 125 Broad Street · New York, NY 10004-2498 · 212-558-4000

Judith R. Thoyer · 2) · Paul, Weiss, Rifkind, Wharton & Garrison · 1285 Avenue of the Americas · New York, NY 10019-6064 · 212-373-3000

Robert L. Tortoriello · a · Cleary Gottlieb Steen & Hamilton · One Liberty Plaza · New York, NY 10006 · 212-225-2000

Mark A. Walker · a · Cleary Gottlieb Steen & Hamilton · One Liberty Plaza · New York, NY 10006 · 212-225-2000

Edward C. Wallace · Greenberg Traurig · http://www.gtlaw.com · MetLife Building · 200 Park Avenue · New York, NY 10166 · 212-801-9200

Irwin H. Warren · Weil Gotshal & Manges · 767 Fifth Avenue · New York, NY 10153 · 212-310-8000

Jeffrey J. Weinberg · Weil Gotshal & Manges · 767 Fifth Avenue · New York, NY 10153 · 212-310-8000

Jonathan M. Weld · Shearman & Sterling · 599 Lexington Avenue · New York, NY 10022-6069 · 212-848-4000

Christopher M. Wells · Proskauer Rose · http://www.proskauer.com · 1585 Broadway · New York, NY 10036-8299 · 212-969-3000

Paul H. Wilson, Jr. · 2) · Debevoise & Plimpton · 919 Third Avenue · New York, NY 10022 · 212-909-6000

William F. Wynne, Jr. · 2) · White & Case · http://www.whitecase.com · 1155 Avenue of the Americas · New York, NY 10036-2787 · 212-819-8200

Howard Zucker · Hawkins Delafield & Wood · http://www.hawkins.com · One Chase Manhattan Plaza, 42nd Floor · New York, NY 10005-1401 · 212-820-9300

Rochester

Jeffrey H. Bowen · Harter Secrest & Emery · http://www.hselaw.com · 1600 Bausch & Lomb Place · Rochester, NY 14604-2711 · 585-232-6500

Gunther K. Buerman · a · Harris Beach · The Granite Building · 130 East Main Street · Rochester, NY 14604 · 585-419-8800

Thomas R. Burns · Phillips Lytle · 1400 First Federal Plaza · Rochester, NY 14614 · 585-238-2000

Patrick J. Dalton · Harris Beach · The Granite Building · 130 East Main Street · Rochester, NY 14604 · 585-419-8800

Justin P. Doyle · Nixon Peabody · 1100 Clinton Square · P.O. Box 31051 · Rochester, NY 14604 · 585-263-1000

Gordon E. Forth · Woods Oviatt Gilman · http://www.woodsoviatt.com · 700 Crossroads Building · Two State Street · Rochester, NY 14614 · 585-987-2800

Christopher D. Jagel · Harris Beach · The Granite Building · 130 East Main Street · Rochester, NY 14604 · 585-419-8800

James M. Jenkins · Harter Secrest & Emery · http://www.hselaw.com · 1600 Bausch & Lomb Place · Rochester, NY 14604-2711 · 585-232-6500

James A. Locke III · a · Nixon Peabody · 1100 Clinton Square · P.O. Box 31051 · Rochester, NY 14604 · 585-263-1000

B. G. Staffan Lundback · a · Nixon Peabody · 1100 Clinton Square · P.O. Box 31051 · Rochester, NY 14604 · 585-263-1000

Albert M. Mercury · Phillips Lytle · 1400 First Federal Plaza · Rochester, NY 14614 · 585-238-2000

Ralph K. Merzbach · Merzbach Law Office · 73 State Street · Rochester, NY 14614 · 585-454-3030

Harry P. Messina, Jr. · a · Woods Oviatt Gilman · http://www.woodsoviatt.com · 700 Crossroads Building · Two State Street · Rochester, NY 14614 · 585-987-2800

J. William Reeves · a · Boylan, Brown, Code, Vigdor & Wilson · http://www.boylanbrown.com · 2400 Chase Square · Rochester, NY 14604 · 585-232-5300

Justin L. Vigdor · 2% · Boylan, Brown, Code, Vigdor & Wilson · http://www.boylanbrown.com · 2400 Chase Square · Rochester, NY 14604 · 585-232-5300

Beth Ela Wilkens · a · Harris Beach · The Granite Building · 130 East Main Street · Rochester, NY 14604 · 585-419-8800

Thomas E. Willett · a · Harris Beach · The Granite Building · 130 East Main Street · Rochester, NY 14604 · 585-419-8800

Craig S. Wittlin · Harter Secrest & Emery · http://www.hselaw.com · 1600 Bausch & Lomb Place · Rochester, NY 14604-2711 · 585-232-6500

Robert F. Zogas · Phillips Lytle · 1400 First Federal Plaza · Rochester, NY 14614 · 585-238-2000

Syracuse

Ronald C. Berger · Bond, Schoeneck & King · One Lincoln Center · Syracuse, NY 13202-1355 · 315-218-8000

George S. Deptula · a · Hiscock & Barclay · One Park Place · 300 South State Street · Syracuse, NY 13202-2078 · 315-422-2131

Thomas S. Evans · Bond, Schoeneck & King · One Lincoln Center · Syracuse, NY 13202-1355 · 315-218-8000

Richard D. Hole · 2) · Bond, Schoeneck & King · One Lincoln Center · Syracuse, NY 13202-1355 · 315-218-8000

Edward J. Moses · Mackenzie Hughes · 101 South Salina Street, Suite 600 · P.O. Box 4967 · Syracuse, NY 13221-4967 · 315-474-7571

Richard S. Scolaro · a · Scolaro, Shulman, Cohen, Fetter & Burstein · 507 Plum Street, Suite 300 · Syracuse, NY 13204 · 315-471-8111

White Plains

Harris Markhoff · 2) · Danziger & Markhoff · Centroplex, Suite 900 · 123 Main Street · White Plains, NY 10601 · 914-948-1556

DERIVATIVES LAW

New York

John M. Brandow · Davis Polk & Wardwell · 450 Lexington Avenue · New York, NY 10017 · 212-450-4000

Daniel N. Budofsky · Davis Polk & Wardwell · 450 Lexington Avenue · New York, NY 10017 · 212-450-4000

Raymond B. Check · Cleary Gottlieb Steen & Hamilton · One Liberty Plaza · New York, NY 10006 · 212-225-2000

Daniel P. Cunningham · a · Allen & Overy · 1221 Avenue of the Americas · New York, NY 10020 · 212-610-6300

Thomas V. D'Ambrosio · Morgan Lewis & Bockius · 101 Park Avenue · New York, NY 10178-0060 · 212-309-6000

Michael D. Dayan · Cleary Gottlieb Steen & Hamilton · One Liberty Plaza · New York, NY 10006 · 212-225-2000

David J. Gilberg · Sullivan & Cromwell · 125 Broad Street · New York, NY 10004-2498 · 212-558-4000

Marvin J. Goldstein · Stroock & Stroock & Lavan · 180 Maiden Lane · New York, NY 10038-4982 · 212-806-5400

Seth Grosshandler · Cleary Gottlieb Steen & Hamilton · One Liberty Plaza · New York, NY 10006 · 212-225-2000

David H. Kaufman · Morrison & Foerster · http://www.mofo.com · 1290 Avenue of the Americas · New York, NY 10104-0050 · 212-468-8000

Steven D. Lofchie · Cadwalader, Wickersham & Taft · http://www.cadwalader.com · One World Financial Center · New York, NY 10281 · 212-504-6000

David S. Mitchell · Fried, Frank, Harris, Shriver & Jacobson · One New York Plaza · New York, NY 10004-1980 · 212-859-8000

John W. Osborn · Skadden, Arps, Slate, Meagher & Flom · Four Times Square · New York, NY 10036 · 212-735-3000

Kenneth M. Raisler · Sullivan & Cromwell · 125 Broad Street · New York, NY 10004-2498 · 212-558-4000

Robert W. Reeder III · Sullivan & Cromwell · 125 Broad Street · New York, NY 10004-2498 · 212-558-4000

Edward J. Rosen · Cleary Gottlieb Steen & Hamilton · One Liberty Plaza · New York, NY 10006 · 212-225-2000

James T. Rothwell · Davis Polk & Wardwell · 450 Lexington Avenue · New York, NY 10017 · 212-450-4000

Richard M. Schetman · Cadwalader, Wickersham & Taft · http://www.cadwalader.com · One World Financial Center · New York, NY 10281 · 212-504-6000

Ray I. Shirazi · Cadwalader, Wickersham & Taft · http://www.cadwalader.com · One World Financial Center · New York, NY 10281 · 212-504-6000

Linda A. Simpson · Davis Polk & Wardwell · 450 Lexington Avenue · New York, NY 10017 · 212-450-4000

Robert L. Tortoriello · a · Cleary Gottlieb Steen & Hamilton · One Liberty Plaza · New York, NY 10006 · 212-225-2000

David Yeres · Clifford Chance · 31 West 52nd Street · New York, NY 10019-6131 · 212-878-8000

DUI/DWI DEFENSE

Albany

Stephen R. Coffey · a · O'Connell & Aronowitz · 54 State Street, Ninth Floor · Albany, NY 12207-2501 · 518-462-5601

Peter Gerstenzang · Gerstenzang, O'Hern, Hickey & Gerstenzang · 210 Great Oaks Boulevard · Albany, NY 12203 · 518-456-6456

Thomas O'Hern · Gerstenzang, O'Hern, Hickey & Gerstenzang · 210 Great Oaks Boulevard · Albany, NY 12203 · 518-456-6456

Eric H. Sills · Gerstenzang, O'Hern, Hickey & Gerstenzang · 210 Great Oaks Boulevard · Albany, NY 12203 · 518-456-6456

Buffalo

Joel L. Daniels · 2% · Joel L. Daniels · 1366 Statler Building · Buffalo, NY 14202 · 716-856-5140

Joseph M. LaTona · 2) · Law Office of Joseph M. LaTona · 716 Brisbane Building · 403 Main Street · Buffalo, NY 14203 · 716-842-0416

Glenn E. Murray · Law Office of Glenn Edward Murray · 484 Delaware Avenue · Buffalo, NY 14202-1304 · 716-884-0139

Michael S. Taheri · Taheri & Todoro · 388 Evans Street, Suite 2-D · Buffalo, NY 14221-5626 · 716-633-0374

Peter J. Todoro · Taheri & Todoro · 388 Evans Street, Suite 2-D · Buffalo, NY 14221-5626 · 716-633-0374

Rochester

Michael Thomas DiPrima · 2) · Law Offices of Michael Thomas DiPrima · 40 Humboltt Street · Rochester, NY 14609 · 585-797-7926

Edward L. Fiandach · Fiandach & Fiandach · 100 Allens Creek Road, Building 100, First Floor · Rochester, NY 14618-3303 · 585-244-8910

David A. Murante · 2) · David A. Murante · Wilder Building, Suite 711 · Eight Exchange Street · Rochester, NY 14614 · 585-546-1770

Timothy C. Rath · Fiandach & Fiandach · 100 Allens Creek Road, Building 100, First Floor · Rochester, NY 14618-3303 · 585-244-8910

Karl F. Salzer · 2% · Trevett, Criste, Salzer & Andolina · Two State Street · 1000 Crossroads Building · Rochester, NY 14614 · 585-454-2181

Troy

E. Stewart Jones, Jr. · 2% · E. Stewart Jones · http://www.esjlaw.com · The Jones Building · 28 Second Street · Troy, NY 12180 · 518-274-5820

EDUCATION LAW

Albany

John A. Miller · Bond, Schoeneck & King · 111 Washington Avenue · Albany, NY 12210-2211 · 518-533-3000

Buffalo

David A. Farmelo · Hodgson Russ · One Guaranty Building, Suite 100 · 140 Pearl Street · Buffalo, NY 14202 · 716-856-4000

East Syracuse

Dennis T. Barrett · Ferrara, Fiorenza, Larrison, Barrett & Reitz · 5010 Campuswood Drive · East Syracuse, NY 13057 · 315-437-7600

Benjamin J. Ferrara · a · Ferrara, Fiorenza, Larrison, Barrett & Reitz · 5010 Campuswood Drive · East Syracuse, NY 13057 · 315-437-7600

Norman H. Gross · Ferrara, Fiorenza, Larrison, Barrett & Reitz · 5010 Campuswood Drive · East Syracuse, NY 13057 · 315-437-7600

Glen Falls

Monica A. Duffy · Judge & Duffy · One Broad Street Plaza, Suite Two · P. O. Box 2850 · Glen Falls, NY 12801 · 518-745-5030

Rochester

Thomas D'Antonio · a · Ward, Norris, Heller & Reidy · http://www.wnhr.com · 300 State Street · Rochester, NY 14614 · 585-454-0700

Ronald J. Mendrick · Harter Secrest & Emery · http://www.hselaw.com · 1600 Bausch & Lomb Place · Rochester, NY 14604-2711 · 585-232-6500

Laura M. Purcell · Harris Beach · The Granite Building · 130 East Main Street · Rochester, NY 14604 · 585-419-8800

Syracuse

Thomas S. Evans · Bond, Schoeneck & King · One Lincoln Center · Syracuse, NY 13202-1355 · 315-218-8000

Williamson

Wayne A. Vander Byl · Wayne A. Vander Byl · 3800 Railroad Avenue · P.O. Box 937 · Williamson, NY 14589-9340 · 315-589-4500

ELDER LAW

Albany

Louis W. Pierro · Pierro and Associates · 20 Corporate Woods Boulevard, Third Floor · Albany, NY 12211 · 518-459-2100

Binghamton

Kathryn Grant Madigan · Levene, Gouldin & Thompson · http://www.binghamtonlaw.com · 71 State Street · P.O. Box F-1706 · Binghamton, NY 13902 · 607-763-9200

Beth E. Westfall · Coughlin & Gerhart · 20 Hawley Street · P.O. Box 2039 · Binghamton, NY 13902-2039 607-723-9511

Brooklyn

Judith D. Grimaldi · Grimaldi & Yeung · 9201 Fourth Avenue, Fifth Floor · Brooklyn, NY 11209 · 718-238-6960

Buffalo

Gayle L. Eagan · Jaeckle Fleischmann & Mugel · 12 Fountain Plaza · Buffalo, NY 14202-2292 · 716-856-0600

Bruce R. Reinoso · Magavern, Magavern & Grimm · 1100 Rand Building · 14 Lafayette Square · Buffalo, NY 14203 · 716-856-3500

George E. Riedel, Jr. · Lipsitz Green Scime Cambria · http://www.lipsitzgreen.com · 42 Delaware Avenue, Suite 120 · Buffalo, NY 14202 · 716-849-1333

Camillus

Denise P. Cambs · a · The Cambs Law Firm · 5701 West Genesee Street · Camillus, NY 13031 · 315-484-1200

Great Neck

Ronald Fatoullah · Ronald Fatoullah & Associates · http://www.elderlaw-newyork.com · 425 Northern Boulevard, Suite 20 · Great Neck, NY 11021 · 516-466-4422

Islandia

Lawrence Eric Davidow · Davidow, Davidow, Siegel & Stern · One Suffolk Square, Suite 330 · 1601 Veterans Memorial Highway · Islandia, NY 11749 · 631-234-3030

Vincent J. Russo · Vincent J. Russo and Associates · 3740 Expressway Drive South · Islandia, NY 11749 · 631-582-1919

Steven H. Stern · Davidow, Davidow, Siegel & Stern · One Suffolk Square, Suite 330 · 1601 Veterans Memorial Highway · Islandia, NY 11749 · 631-234-3030

Lockport

Patricia A. George · Patricia A. George · 37 East Avenue · P.O. Box 456 · Lockport, NY 14095 · 716-434-6641

New York

Russel N. Adler · Epstein, Becker & Green · 250 Park Avenue, 14th Floor · New York, NY 10177-1211 · 212-351-4500

Daniel G. Fish · Daniel G. Fish · 260 Madison Avenue · New York, NY 10016 · 212-448-6224

Robert M. Freedman · Mazur, Carp & Rubin · 1250 Broadway · New York, NY 10001 · 212-686-7700

Bernard A. Krooks · Littman Krooks · 655 Third Avenue · New York, NY 10017-5617 · 212-490-2020

Peter J. Strauss · Epstein, Becker & Green · 250 Park Avenue, 14th Floor · New York, NY 10177-1211 · 212-351-4500

Rochester

Rene H. Reixach · Woods Oviatt Gilman · http://www.woodsoviatt.com · 700 Crossroads Building · Two State Street · Rochester, NY 14614 · 585-987-2800

Syracuse

Cora A. Alsante · Hancock & Estabrook · 1500 Axa Tower I · 100 Madison Street · Syracuse, NY 13202 · 315-471-3151

Ami Longstreet · Mackenzie Hughes · 101 South Salina Street, Suite 600 · P.O. Box 4967 · Syracuse, NY 13221-4967 · 315-474-7571

EMINENT DOMAIN AND CONDEMNATION LAW

New York

M. Robert Goldstein · Goldstein, Goldstein, Rikon & Gottlieb · 80 Pine Street · New York, NY 10005-1702 · 212-422-4000

Michael Rikon · Goldstein, Goldstein, Rikon & Gottlieb · 80 Pine Street · New York, NY 10005-1702 · 212-422-4000

Rochester

James S. Grossman · Hiscock & Barclay · 2000 HSBC Plaza · 100 Chestnut Street · Rochester, NY 14604-2404 · 585-325-7570

Syracuse

Sidney Devorsetz · Sidney Devorsetz · 307 South Townsend Street · Syracuse, NY 13202-2128 · 315-442-6600

EMPLOYEE BENEFITS LAW

Albany

Brian P. Goldstein · a · The Goldstein Law Firm · 16 Corporate Woods Boulevard · Albany, NY 12211-2350 · 518-427-7595

Amelia M. Klein · Bond, Schoeneck & King · 111 Washington Avenue · Albany, NY 12210-2211 · 518-533-3000

Richard A. Langer · a · McNamee, Lochner, Titus & Williams · 677 Broadway, Fifth Floor · P.O. Box 459 · Albany, NY 12201-0459 · 518-447-3200

Buffalo

Raymond H. Barr · Phillips Lytle · 3400 HSBC Center · Buffalo, NY 14203-2887 · 716-847-8400

Peter K. Bradley · Hodgson Russ · One Guaranty Building, Suite 100 · 140 Pearl Street · Buffalo, NY 14202 · 716-856-4000

Michele O. Heffernan · Jaeckle Fleischmann & Mugel · 12 Fountain Plaza · Buffalo, NY 14202-2292 · 716-856-0600

Thomas J. Hurley · Harter Secrest & Emery · http://www.hselaw.com · 12 Fountain Plaza, Suite 400 · Buffalo, NY 14202-2293 · 716-853-1616

David H. Kernan · Phillips Lytle · 3400 HSBC Center · Buffalo, NY 14203-2887 · 716-847-8400

Arthur A. Marrapese III · Hodgson Russ · One Guaranty Building, Suite 100 · 140 Pearl Street · Buffalo, NY 14202 · 716-856-4000

Samuel J. Palisano · a · Harter Secrest & Emery · http://www.hselaw.com · 12 Fountain Plaza, Suite 400 Buffalo, NY 14202-2293 · 716-853-1616

Robert W. Patterson · Jaeckle Fleischmann & Mugel · 12 Fountain Plaza · Buffalo, NY 14202-2292 · 716-856-0600

Daniel R. Sharpe · 2) · Hodgson Russ · One Guaranty Building, Suite 100 · 140 Pearl Street · Buffalo, NY 14202 · 716-856-4000

Mark L. Stulmaker · Lipsitz Green Scime Cambria · http://www.lipsitzgreen.com · 42 Delaware Avenue, Suite 120 · Buffalo, NY 14202 · 716-849-1333

Loudonville

Robert E. Helm · a · Robert E. Helm · 57 Loudonwood East · Loudonville, NY 12211-1469 · 518-433-0530

New York

Howard B. Adler · Fried, Frank, Harris, Shriver & Jacobson · One New York Plaza · New York, NY 10004-1980 · 212-859-8000

Rory Judd Albert · Proskauer Rose · http://www.proskauer.com · 1585 Broadway · New York, NY 10036-8299 · 212-969-3000

Michael J. Album · Proskauer Rose · http://www.proskauer.com · 1585 Broadway · New York, NY 10036-8299 · 212-969-3000

Mary E. Alcock · Cleary Gottlieb Steen & Hamilton · One Liberty Plaza · New York, NY 10006 · 212-225-2000

Stuart N. Alperin · a · Skadden, Arps, Slate, Meagher & Flom · Four Times Square · New York, NY 10036 · 212-735-3000

Alan L. Aronson · Fulbright & Jaworski · http://www.fulbright.com · 666 Fifth Avenue · New York, NY 10103-3198 · 212-318-3000

Alvin H. Brown · Simpson Thacher · 425 Lexington Avenue · New York, NY 10017-3954 · 212-455-2000

Lawrence K. Cagney · Debevoise & Plimpton · 919 Third Avenue · New York, NY 10022 · 212-909-6000

Donald P. Carleen · Fried, Frank, Harris, Shriver & Jacobson · One New York Plaza · New York, NY 10004-1980 · 212-859-8000

David M. Cohen · Schulte Roth & Zabel · 919 Third Avenue · New York, NY 10022 · 212-756-2000

John R. Cornell · Jones Day · 222 East 41st Street · New York, NY 10017-6702 · 212-326-3939

Frank A. Daniele · Willkie Farr & Gallagher · 787 Seventh Avenue · New York, NY 10019-6099 · 212-728-8000

Kathleen M. Emberger · Cleary Gottlieb Steen & Hamilton · One Liberty Plaza · New York, NY 10006 · 212-225-2000

Edmond T. Fitzgerald · Davis Polk & Wardwell · 450 Lexington Avenue · New York, NY 10017 · 212-450-4000

Robert C. Fleder · 2) · Paul, Weiss, Rifkind, Wharton & Garrison · 1285 Avenue of the Americas · New York, NY 10019-6064 · 212-373-3000

Andrew L. Gaines · Weil Gotshal & Manges · 767 Fifth Avenue · New York, NY 10153 · 212-310-8000

Richard A. Gilbert · Orrick, Herrington & Sutcliffe · 666 Fifth Avenue · New York, NY 10103-0001 · 212-506-5000

Bronislaw E. Grala · a · Cadwalader, Wickersham & Taft · http://www.cadwalader.com · One World Financial Center · New York, NY 10281 · 212-504-6000

Lawrence J. Hass · a · Paul Hastings · Park Avenue Tower, First Floor · 75 East 55th Street · New York, NY 10022 · 212-318-6000

James S. Hutchinson · Alston + Bird · http://www.alston.com · 90 Park Avenue · New York, NY 10016-1387 · 212-210-9400

George R. Ince, Jr. · Davis Polk & Wardwell · 450 Lexington Avenue · New York, NY 10017 · 212-450-4000

Barbara D. Klippert · McKee Nelson · One Battery Park Plaza, 34th Floor · New York, NY 10004 · 917-777-4200

Frederick C. Kneip · a · Milbank, Tweed, Hadley & McCloy · http://www.milbank.com · One Chase Manhattan Plaza · New York, NY 10005-1413 · 212-530-5000

Arthur H. Kohn · Cleary Gottlieb Steen & Hamilton · One Liberty Plaza · New York, NY 10006 · 212-225-2000

Joel I. Krasnow · Milbank, Tweed, Hadley & McCloy · http://www.milbank.com · One Chase Manhattan Plaza · New York, NY 10005-1413 · 212-530-5000

Neil M. Leff · Skadden, Arps, Slate, Meagher & Flom · Four Times Square · New York, NY 10036 · 212-735-3000

Stephen T. Lindo · Willkie Farr & Gallagher · 787 Seventh Avenue · New York, NY 10019-6099 · 212-728-8000

Richard Loebl · Epstein, Becker & Green · 250 Park Avenue, 14th Floor · New York, NY 10177-1211 · 212-351-4500

Michael Macris · Cahill Gordon & Reindel · 80 Pine Street · New York, NY 10005-1702 · 212-701-3000

Jeffrey D. Mamorsky · Greenberg Traurig · http://www.gtlaw.com · MetLife Building · 200 Park Avenue New York, NY 10166 · 212-801-9200

Henry Morgenbesser · Allen & Overy · 1221 Avenue of the Americas · New York, NY 10020 · 212-610-6300

Michael J. Nassau · 2) · Kramer Levin Naftalis & Frankel · http://www.kramerlevin.com · 1177 Avenue of the Americas · New York, NY 10036 · 212-715-9100

Barbara Nims · Davis Polk & Wardwell · 450 Lexington Avenue · New York, NY 10017 · 212-450-4000

Jeannemarie O'Brien · Wachtell, Lipton, Rosen & Katz · 51 West 52nd Street · New York, NY 10019 · 212-403-1000

Regina Olshan · Skadden, Arps, Slate, Meagher & Flom · Four Times Square · New York, NY 10036 · 212-735-3000

Andrew Oringer · White & Case · http://www.whitecase.com · 1155 Avenue of the Americas · New York, NY 10036-2787 · 212-819-8200

Howard Pianko · 2) · Epstein, Becker & Green · 250 Park Avenue, 14th Floor · New York, NY 10177-1211 · 212-351-4500

Linda E. Rappaport · a · Shearman & Sterling · 599 Lexington Avenue · New York, NY 10022-6069 · 212-848-4000

Kenneth A. Raskin · White & Case · http://www.whitecase.com · 1155 Avenue of the Americas · New York, NY 10036-2787 · 212-819-8200

Robert J. Raymond · Cleary Gottlieb Steen & Hamilton · One Liberty Plaza · New York, NY 10006 · 212-225-2000

Edward J. Rayner · Katten Muchin Rosenman · 575 Madison Avenue · New York, NY 10022-2585 · 212-940-8800

Paul M. Ritter · Kramer Levin Naftalis & Frankel · http://www.kramerlevin.com · 1177 Avenue of the Americas · New York, NY 10036 · 212-715-9100

Brian D. Robbins · Simpson Thacher · 425 Lexington Avenue · New York, NY 10017-3954 · 212-455-2000

Gary S. Rothstein · Morgan Lewis & Bockius · 101 Park Avenue · New York, NY 10178-0060 · 212-309-6000

S. John Ryan · Seward & Kissel · One Battery Park Plaza · New York, NY 10004 · 212-574-1200

Max J. Schwartz · a · Sullivan & Cromwell · 125 Broad Street · New York, NY 10004-2498 · 212-558-4000

Robert M. Sedgwick · Morrison Cohen · 909 Third Avenue · New York, NY 10022-4731 · 212-735-8600

Michael J. Segal · Wachtell, Lipton, Rosen & Katz · 51 West 52nd Street · New York, NY 10019 · 212-403-1000

Susan P. Serota · 2) · Pillsbury Winthrop Shaw Pittman · http://www.pillsburylaw.com · 1540 Broadway · New York, NY 10036-4039 · 212-858-1000

Michael S. Sirkin · Proskauer Rose · http://www.proskauer.com · 1585 Broadway · New York, NY 10036-8299 · 212-969-3000

Martha N. Steinman · Dewey & LeBoeuf · 125 West 55th Street · New York, NY 10019-5389 · 212-424-8000

A. Richard Susko · 2) · Cleary Gottlieb Steen & Hamilton · One Liberty Plaza · New York, NY 10006 · 212-225-2000

Paul J. Wessel · Milbank, Tweed, Hadley & McCloy · http://www.milbank.com · One Chase Manhattan Plaza · New York, NY 10005-1413 · 212-530-5000

Arthur F. Woodard · a · Kaye Scholer · 425 Park Avenue · New York, NY 10022-3598 · 212-836-8000

Rochester

Paul W. Holloway · Harter Secrest & Emery · http://www.hselaw.com · 1600 Bausch & Lomb Place · Rochester, NY 14604-2711 · 585-232-6500

Syracuse

Stephen H. Cohen · a · Scolaro, Shulman, Cohen, Fetter & Burstein · 507 Plum Street, Suite 300 · Syracuse, NY 13204 · 315-471-8111

Brian K. Haynes · Bond, Schoeneck & King · One Lincoln Center · Syracuse, NY 13202-1355 · 315-218-8000

Richard D. Hole · 2) · Bond, Schoeneck & King · One Lincoln Center · Syracuse, NY 13202-1355 · 315-218-8000

Thaddeus J. Lewkowicz · Bond, Schoeneck & King · One Lincoln Center · Syracuse, NY 13202-1355 · 315-218-8000

White Plains

Donald L. Sapir · Sapir & Frumkin · 399 Knollwood Road, Suite 300 · White Plains, NY 10603 · 914-328-0366

ENERGY LAW

Albany

Jeffrey C. Cohen · a · Cohen & Dax · 90 State Street, Suite 1030 · Albany, NY 12207 · 518-432-1002

N. Jonathan Peress · Dewey & LeBoeuf · One Commerce Plaza, Suite 2020 · 99 Washington Avenue · Albany, NY 12210-2820 · 518-626-9000

Michael Whiteman · a · Whiteman Osterman & Hanna · One Commerce Plaza · Albany, NY 12260 · 518-487-7600

Brooklyn

Joseph P. Stevens · a · Cullen and Dykman · 177 Montague Street · Brooklyn, NY 11201-3611 · 718-855-9000

New York

Sheldon S. Adler · Skadden, Arps, Slate, Meagher & Flom · Four Times Square · New York, NY 10036 · 212-735-3000

William T. Baker, Jr. · a · Thelen Reid Brown Raysman & Steiner · 875 Third Avenue, 10th Floor · New York, NY 10022-6225 · 212-603-2000

Michael F. Cusick · a · Jones Day · 222 East 41st Street · New York, NY 10017-6702 · 212-326-3939

Steven H. Davis · Dewey & LeBoeuf · 125 West 55th Street · New York, NY 10019-5389 · 212-424-8000

M. Douglas Dunn · a · Milbank, Tweed, Hadley & McCloy · http://www.milbank.com · One Chase Manhattan Plaza · New York, NY 10005-1413 · 212-530-5000

Richard M. Farmer · a · Thelen Reid Brown Raysman & Steiner · 875 Third Avenue, 10th Floor · New York, NY 10022-6225 · 212-603-2000

Joseph B. Frumkin · Sullivan & Cromwell · 125 Broad Street · New York, NY 10004-2498 · 212-558-4000

Richard S. Green · Thelen Reid Brown Raysman & Steiner · 875 Third Avenue, 10th Floor · New York, NY 10022-6225 · 212-603-2000

William F. Henze II · Jones Day · 222 East 41st Street · New York, NY 10017-6702 · 212-326-3939

John T. Hood · Thelen Reid Brown Raysman & Steiner · 875 Third Avenue, 10th Floor · New York, NY 10022-6225 · 212-603-2000

Thomas J. Igoe, Jr. · a · Thelen Reid Brown Raysman & Steiner · 875 Third Avenue, 10th Floor · New York, NY 10022-6225 · 212-603-2000

William S. Lamb · Dewey & LeBoeuf · 125 West 55th Street · New York, NY 10019-5389 · 212-424-8000

Robert J. Reger, Jr. · Thelen Reid Brown Raysman & Steiner · 875 Third Avenue, 10th Floor · New York, NY 10022-6225 · 212-603-2000

J. Anthony Terrell · a · Dewey & LeBoeuf · 1301 Avenue of the Americas · New York, NY 10019-6092 · 212-259-8000

Rochester

Stanley W. Widger, Jr. · a · Nixon Peabody · 1100 Clinton Square · P.O. Box 31051 · Rochester, NY 14604 · 585-263-1000

Syracuse

Kevin M. Bernstein · Bond, Schoeneck & King · One Lincoln Center · Syracuse, NY 13202-1355 · 315-218-8000

ENTERTAINMENT LAW

New York

Roger Arar · Loeb & Loeb · 345 Park Avenue, 18th Floor · New York, NY 10154-0037 · 212-407-4000

R. Andrew Boose · Davis Wright Tremaine · 1633 Broadway, 27th Floor · New York, NY 10019-6708 · 212-489-8230

John F. Breglio · 2) · Paul, Weiss, Rifkind, Wharton & Garrison · 1285 Avenue of the Americas · New York, NY 10019-6064 · 212-373-3000

Elliot H. Brown · Franklin, Weinrib, Rudell & Vassallo · 488 Madison Avenue, 18th Floor · New York, NY 10022 · 212-935-5500

Aydin S. Caginalp · Manatt, Phelps & Phillips · Seven Times Square · New York, NY 10036 · 212-790-4500

Marc Chamlin · Loeb & Loeb · 345 Park Avenue, 18th Floor · New York, NY 10154-0037 · 212-407-4000

Alvin Deutsch · 2) · McLaughlin & Stern · 260 Madison Avenue, Suite 1800 · New York, NY 10016 · 212-448-1100

John L. Eastman · a · Eastman & Eastman · 39 West 54th Street, Suite Two · New York, NY 10019 · 212-246-5757

Peter L. Felcher · a · Paul, Weiss, Rifkind, Wharton & Garrison · 1285 Avenue of the Americas · New York, NY 10019-6064 · 212-373-3000

Michael P. Frankfurt · 2) · Frankfurt Kurnit Klein & Selz · http://www.fkks.com · 488 Madison Avenue, Tenth Floor · New York, NY 10022 · 212-980-0120

Martin Garbus · 2) · Davis & Gilbert · 1740 Broadway · New York, NY 10019 · 212-468-4800

Seth D. Gelblum · Loeb & Loeb · 345 Park Avenue, 18th Floor · New York, NY 10154-0037 · 212-407-4000

Allen J. Grubman · Grubman Indursky & Shire · Carnegie Hall Tower · 152 West 57th Street · New York, NY 10019 · 212-554-0400

Steven M. Hayes · Hanly Conroy Bierstein & Sheridan · 112 Madison Avenue, Seventh Floor · New York, NY 10016 · 212-784-6400

Richard B. Heller · Frankfurt Kurnit Klein & Selz · http://www.fkks.com · 488 Madison Avenue, Tenth Floor · New York, NY 10022 · 212-980-0120

Richard Hofstetter · Frankfurt Kurnit Klein & Selz · http://www.fkks.com · 488 Madison Avenue, Tenth Floor · New York, NY 10022 · 212-980-0120

Arthur I. Indursky · Grubman Indursky & Shire · Carnegie Hall Tower · 152 West 57th Street · New York, NY 10019 · 212-554-0400

Rick Kurnit · Frankfurt Kurnit Klein & Selz · http://www.fkks.com · 488 Madison Avenue, Tenth Floor · New York, NY 10022 · 212-980-0120

Scott R. Lazarus · Lazarus & Harris · 561 Seventh Avenue · New York, NY 10036 · 212-302-5252

Elizabeth A. McNamara · Davis Wright Tremaine · 1633 Broadway, 27th Floor · New York, NY 10019-6708 · 212-489-8230

Charles B. Ortner · Proskauer Rose · http://www.proskauer.com · 1585 Broadway · New York, NY 10036-8299 · 212-969-3000

L. Peter Parcher · Manatt, Phelps & Phillips · Seven Times Square · New York, NY 10036 · 212-790-4500

Edward H. Rosenthal · Frankfurt Kurnit Klein & Selz · http://www.fkks.com · 488 Madison Avenue, Tenth Floor · New York, NY 10022 · 212-980-0120

Michael I. Rudell · 2) · Franklin, Weinrib, Rudell & Vassallo · 488 Madison Avenue, 18th Floor · New York, NY 10022 · 212-935-5500

Paul D. Schindler · Greenberg Traurig · http://www.gtlaw.com · MetLife Building · 200 Park Avenue · New York, NY 10166 · 212-801-9200

Ira Schreck · Schreck, Rose Dapello & Adams · 1790 Broadway, 20th Floor · New York, NY 10019-1412 · 212-832-1958

Thomas D. Selz · a · Frankfurt Kurnit Klein & Selz · http://www.fkks.com · 488 Madison Avenue, Tenth Floor · New York, NY 10022 · 212-980-0120

George L. Sheanshang · George Sheanshang · 130 West 57th Street, Apartment 5-B · New York, NY 10019-3314 · 212-956-9200

Laurence A. Silverman · Covington & Burling · The New York Times Building · 620 Eighth Avenue · New York, NY 10018 · 212-841-1000

Orin Snyder · Gibson, Dunn & Crutcher · 200 Park Avenue, 47th Floor · New York, NY 10166-0193 · 212-351-4000

Kenneth M. Weinrib · Franklin, Weinrib, Rudell & Vassallo · 488 Madison Avenue, 18th Floor · New York, NY 10022 · 212-935-5500

ENVIRONMENTAL LAW

Albany

Robert J. Alessi · Dewey & LeBoeuf · One Commerce Plaza, Suite 2020 · 99 Washington Avenue · Albany, NY 12210-2820 · 518-626-9000

Richard M. Cogen · Nixon Peabody · 677 Broadway, 10th Floor · Albany, NY 12207 · 518-427-2650

Robert H. Feller · Bond, Schoeneck & King · 111 Washington Avenue · Albany, NY 12210-2211 · 518-533-3000

John L. Greenthal · Nixon Peabody · 677 Broadway, 10th Floor · Albany, NY 12207 · 518-427-2650

John Hanna, Jr. · Whiteman Osterman & Hanna · One Commerce Plaza · Albany, NY 12260 · 518-487-7600

Daniel A. Ruzow · Whiteman Osterman & Hanna · One Commerce Plaza · Albany, NY 12260 · 518-487-7600

Dean S. Sommer · Young, Sommer, Ward, Ritzenberg, Baker & Moore · http://www.youngsommer.com · Executive Woods · Five Palisades Drive · Albany, NY 12205-6433 · 518-438-9907

Thomas S. West · The West Firm · 677 Broadway, Eighth Floor · Albany, NY 12207-2990 · 518-641-0500

Buffalo

Robert E. Glanville · Phillips Lytle · 3400 HSBC Center · Buffalo, NY 14203-2887 · 716-847-8400

Morgan G. Graham · Phillips Lytle · 3400 HSBC Center · Buffalo, NY 14203-2887 · 716-847-8400

Dennis P. Harkawik · Jaeckle Fleischmann & Mugel · 12 Fountain Plaza · Buffalo, NY 14202-2292 · 716-856-0600

Craig A. Slater · Harter Secrest & Emery · http://www.hselaw.com · 12 Fountain Plaza, Suite 400 · Buffalo, NY 14202-2293 · 716-853-1616

New York

Gregory J. Battista · Cravath, Swaine & Moore · Worldwide Plaza · 825 Eighth Avenue · New York, NY 10019-7475 · 212-474-1000

Matthew J. Brennan · Sullivan & Cromwell · 125 Broad Street · New York, NY 10004-2498 · 212-558-4000

Mark A. Chertok · Sive Paget & Riesel · 460 Park Avenue, 10th Floor · New York, NY 10022 · 212-421-2150

Robert S. Davis · Bryan Cave · 1290 Avenue of the Americas · New York, NY 10104-3300 · 212-541-2000

Adeeb R. Fadil · Simpson Thacher · 425 Lexington Avenue · New York, NY 10017-3954 · 212-455-2000

Gail A. Flesher · Davis Polk & Wardwell · 450 Lexington Avenue · New York, NY 10017 · 212-450-4000

Michael B. Gerrard · Arnold & Porter · 399 Park Avenue, 34th Floor · New York, NY 10022-4690 · 212-715-1000

Jeffrey B. Gracer · Sive Paget & Riesel · 460 Park Avenue, 10th Floor · New York, NY 10022 · 212-421-2150

Robert M. Hallman · Cahill Gordon & Reindel · 80 Pine Street · New York, NY 10005-1702 · 212-701-3000

Richard A. Horsch · White & Case · http://www.whitecase.com · 1155 Avenue of the Americas · New York, NY 10036-2787 · 212-819-8200

Robert J. Kafin · Proskauer Rose · http://www.proskauer.com · 1585 Broadway · New York, NY 10036-8299 · 212-969-3000

Stephen L. Kass · Carter Ledyard & Milburn · Two Wall Street, 18th Floor · New York, NY 10005 · 212-732-3200

Paul K. Milmed · White & Case · http://www.whitecase.com · 1155 Avenue of the Americas · New York, NY 10036-2787 · 212-819-8200

David Paget · Sive Paget & Riesel · 460 Park Avenue, 10th Floor · New York, NY 10022 · 212-421-2150

Gail S. Port · Proskauer Rose · http://www.proskauer.com · 1585 Broadway · New York, NY 10036-8299 · 212-969-3000

Daniel Riesel · Sive Paget & Riesel · 460 Park Avenue, 10th Floor · New York, NY 10022 · 212-421-2150

Eric B. Rothenberg · O'Melveny & Myers · Times Square Tower · Seven Times Square · New York, NY 10036 · 212-326-2000

Jeffrey A. Smith · Cravath, Swaine & Moore · Worldwide Plaza · 825 Eighth Avenue · New York, NY 10019-7475 · 212-474-1000

Donald W. Stever · 2) · K&L Gates · 599 Lexington Avenue · New York, NY 10022-6030 · 212-536-3900

Charles S. Warren · Kramer Levin Naftalis & Frankel · http://www.kramerlevin.com · 1177 Avenue of the Americas · New York, NY 10036 · 212-715-9100

Rochester

Alan J. Knauf · Knauf Shaw · 1125 Crossroads Building · Two State Street · Rochester, NY 14614 · 585-546-8430

Neal D. Madden · a · Harter Secrest & Emery · http://www.hselaw.com · 1600 Bausch & Lomb Place · Rochester, NY 14604-2711 · 585-232-6500

Jean H. McCreary · Nixon Peabody · 1100 Clinton Square · P.O. Box 31051 · Rochester, NY 14604 · 585-263-1000

Edward F. Premo II · Harter Secrest & Emery · http://www.hselaw.com · 1600 Bausch & Lomb Place · Rochester, NY 14604-2711 · 585-232-6500

Paul D. Sylvestri · Harter Secrest & Emery · http://www.hselaw.com · 1600 Bausch & Lomb Place · Rochester, NY 14604-2711 · 585-232-6500

Scott M. Turner · Nixon Peabody · 1100 Clinton Square · P.O. Box 31051 · Rochester, NY 14604 · 585-263-1000

Syracuse

S. Paul Battaglia · 2) · Bond, Schoeneck & King · One Lincoln Center · Syracuse, NY 13202-1355 · 315-218-8000

Kevin M. Bernstein · Bond, Schoeneck & King · One Lincoln Center · Syracuse, NY 13202-1355 · 315-218-8000

Thomas J. Fucillo · Menter, Rudin & Trivelpiece · 308 Maltbie Street, Suite 200 · Syracuse, NY 13204-1498 · 315-474-7541

Barry R. Kogut · Bond, Schoeneck & King · One Lincoln Center · Syracuse, NY 13202-1355 · 315-218-8000

Virginia C. Robbins · Bond, Schoeneck & King · One Lincoln Center · Syracuse, NY 13202-1355 · 315-218-8000

Thomas R. Smith · Bond, Schoeneck & King · One Lincoln Center · Syracuse, NY 13202-1355 · 315-218-8000

White Plains

Joel H. Sachs · Keane & Beane · 445 Hamilton Avenue, 15th Floor · White Plains, NY 10601 · 914-946-4777

EQUIPMENT FINANCE LAW

Buffalo

Raymond H. Seitz · a · Phillips Lytle · 3400 HSBC Center · Buffalo, NY 14203-2887 · 716-847-8400

New York

Richard A. Aborn · Cadwalader, Wickersham & Taft · http://www.cadwalader.com · One World Financial Center · New York, NY 10281 · 212-504-6000

Fredric K. Bass · Dewey & LeBoeuf · 1301 Avenue of the Americas · New York, NY 10019-6092 · 212-259-8000

Alan Christenfeld · Clifford Chance · 31 West 52nd Street · New York, NY 10019-6131 · 212-878-8000

Elliot Gewirtz · Milbank, Tweed, Hadley & McCloy · http://www.milbank.com · One Chase Manhattan Plaza · New York, NY 10005-1413 · 212-530-5000

Robert J. Gillespie · Sullivan & Worcester · 1290 Avenue of the Americas · New York, NY 10104 · 212-660-3000

John P. Howitt · Clifford Chance · 31 West 52nd Street · New York, NY 10019-6131 · 212-878-8000

John K. Hoyns · Hughes Hubbard & Reed · http://www.hugheshubbard.com · One Battery Park Plaza · New York, NY 10004-1482 · 212-837-6000

Martin D. Jacobson · Simpson Thacher · 425 Lexington Avenue · New York, NY 10017-3954 · 212-455-2000

Shephard Wayne Melzer · Fulbright & Jaworski · http://www.fulbright.com · 666 Fifth Avenue · New York, NY 10103-3198 · 212-318-3000

John F. Pritchard · Holland & Knight · http://www.hklaw.com · 195 Broadway, 24th Floor · New York, NY 10007-3189 · 212-513-3200

Elihu F. Robertson · Milbank, Tweed, Hadley & McCloy · http://www.milbank.com · One Chase Manhattan Plaza · New York, NY 10005-1413 · 212-530-5000

Sandra M. Rocks · Cleary Gottlieb Steen & Hamilton · One Liberty Plaza · New York, NY 10006 · 212-225-2000

Ronald Scheinberg · Vedder Price · 1633 Broadway, 47th Floor · New York, NY 10019 · 212-407-7700

Michael P. Schumaecker · Pillsbury Winthrop Shaw Pittman · http://www.pillsburylaw.com · 1540 Broadway · New York, NY 10036-4039 · 212-858-1000

Ian Shrank · Allen & Overy · 1221 Avenue of the Americas · New York, NY 10020 · 212-610-6300

Marsha E. Simms · a · Weil Gotshal & Manges · 767 Fifth Avenue · New York, NY 10153 · 212-310-8000

James D. Tussing · Fulbright & Jaworski · http://www.fulbright.com · 666 Fifth Avenue · New York, NY 10103-3198 · 212-318-3000

ETHICS AND PROFESSIONAL RESPONSIBILITY LAW

Buffalo

Stephen E. Barnes · Cellino & Barnes · 17 Court Street, Seventh Floor · Buffalo, NY 14202 · 716-854-2020

Cheryl Smith Fisher · Magavern, Magavern & Grimm · 1100 Rand Building · 14 Lafayette Square · Buffalo, NY 14203 · 716-856-3500

Brian A. Goldstein · Cellino & Barnes · 17 Court Street, Seventh Floor · Buffalo, NY 14202 · 716-854-2020

Gerald W. Schaffer · Cellino & Barnes · 17 Court Street, Seventh Floor · Buffalo, NY 14202 · 716-854-2020

Barbara L. Schifeling · Damon & Morey · http://www.damonmorey.com · 1000 Cathedral Place · 298 Main Street · Buffalo, NY 14202-4096 · 716-856-5500

Robert J. Schreck · Cellino & Barnes · 17 Court Street, Seventh Floor · Buffalo, NY 14202 · 716-854-2020

FAMILY LAW

Albany

David M. Siegal · Siegal Law Offices · 16 Corporate Woods Boulevard · Albany, NY 12211-2350 · 518-431-1000

Bruce J. Wagner · a · McNamee, Lochner, Titus & Williams · 677 Broadway, Fifth Floor · P.O. Box 459 Albany, NY 12201-0459 · 518-447-3200

Binghamton

Bruno Colapietro · 2% · Levene, Gouldin & Thompson · http://www.binghamtonlaw.com · 71 State Street P.O. Box F-1706 · Binghamton, NY 13902 · 607-763-9200

Sharon L. Dyer · a · Levene, Gouldin & Thompson · http://www.binghamtonlaw.com · 71 State Street · P.O. Box F-1706 · Binghamton, NY 13902 · 607-763-9200

Carman Michael Garufi · Carman M. Garufi · 45 Chenango Street, Suite Two · Binghamton, NY 13901 · 607-722-5000

Donald M. Sukloff · 2% · Sukloff & Schanz · The Press Building, Ninth Floor · 19 Chenango Street · Binghamton, NY 13901-2905 · 607-723-7913

Buffalo

Joan Casilio Adams · Offermann, Cassano, Greco, Slisz & Adams · 1776 Statler Towers · Buffalo, NY 14202 · 716-856-4800

Grace Marie Ange · 2% · Ange & Ange · 110 Pearl Street, Suite 500 · Buffalo, NY 14202 · 716-332-3680

Thomas R. Cassano · a · Offermann, Cassano, Greco, Slisz & Adams · 1776 Statler Towers · Buffalo, NY 14202 · 716-856-4800

Peter J. Fiorella, Jr. · 2% · Fiorella & Zakia · 155 Summer Street · Buffalo, NY 14222 · 716-882-3333

Barbara Ellen Handschu · a · Barbara Ellen Handschu · 155 Summer Street · Buffalo, NY 14222 · 716-885-8005

Mark G. Hirschorn · 2% · Siegel, Kelleher & Kahn · 426 Franklin Street · Buffalo, NY 14202 · 716-881-5800

Christopher S. Mattingly · Lipsitz Green Scime Cambria · http://www.lipsitzgreen.com · 42 Delaware Avenue, Suite 120 · Buffalo, NY 14202 · 716-849-1333

Patrick C. O'Reilly · a · Lipsitz Green Scime Cambria · http://www.lipsitzgreen.com · 42 Delaware Avenue, Suite 120 · Buffalo, NY 14202 · 716-849-1333

Paul D. Pearson · a · Paul Pearson · 1100 Main Place Tower · Buffalo, NY 14202 · 716-854-6424

James P. Renda · Renda, Pares & Pfalzgraf · 455 Cayuga Road, Suite 600 · Buffalo, NY 14225-1306 · 716-885-4395

John E. Spadafora · a · Matusick, Spadafora & Verrastro · 101 Niagara Street · Buffalo, NY 14202 · 716-854-1111

David G. Stiller · 2) · Stiller & Vance · 300 Pearl Street, Suite 1000 · Buffalo, NY 14202 · 716-854-4474

Paul A. Vance · a · Stiller & Vance · 300 Pearl Street, Suite 1000 · Buffalo, NY 14202 · 716-854-4474

Nelson F. Zakia · a · Fiorella & Zakia · 155 Summer Street · Buffalo, NY 14222 · 716-882-3333

Forest Hills

John A. Gemelli · John A. Gemelli · 10515 Metropolitan Avenue · Forest Hills, NY 11375-6737 · 718-261-2323

Garden City

Robert H. Brodrick · a · Moran, Brodrick & Elliot · 300 Garden City Plaza, Suite 414 · Garden City, NY 11530 · 516-741-3060

Willard H. DaSilva · 2% · DaSilva, Hilowitz & McEvily · 585 Stewart Avenue, Suite L-16 · Garden City, NY 11530 · 516-222-0700

Stephen Gassman · 2% · Gassman, Baiamonte, Betts & Tannenbaum · 666 Old Country Road, Suite 801 · Garden City, NY 11530 · 516-228-9181

Richard L. Hause · Samuelson, Hause & Samuelson · 300 Garden City Plaza, Suite 444 · Garden City, NY 11530 · 516-294-6666

Kenneth Koopersmith · 2% · The Law Offices of Kenneth Koopersmith · 200 Garden City Plaza, Suite 301 · Garden City, NY 11530-3338 · 516-354-0800

Charles J. McEvily · DaSilva, Hilowitz & McEvily · 585 Stewart Avenue, Suite L-16 · Garden City, NY 11530 · 516-222-0700

Michael J. Ostrow · 2% · Schlissel Ostrow Karabatos · http://www.soklaw.com · 200 Garden City Plaza, Suite 301 · Garden City, NY 11530 · 516-877-8000

Elliot D. Samuelson · a · Samuelson, Hause & Samuelson · 300 Garden City Plaza, Suite 444 · Garden City, NY 11530 · 516-294-6666

Stephen W. Schlissel · 2% · Schlissel Ostrow Karabatos · http://www.soklaw.com · 200 Garden City Plaza, Suite 301 · Garden City, NY 11530 · 516-877-8000

Vincent F. Stempel · Vincent F. Stempel · 1205 Franklin Avenue, Suite 280 · Garden City, NY 11530-1629 · 516-742-8620

Glenville

Eric A. Tepper · Gordon, Tepper & DeCoursey · http://www.gtdlaw.com · Socha Plaza South · 113 Saratoga Road, Route 50 · Glenville, NY 12302 · 518-399-5400

Lake Success

Michael Dikman · 2% · Dikman & Dikman · Five Dakota Drive, Suite 208 · Lake Success, NY 11042 · 516-354-2526

New York

Alton L. Abramowitz · Mayerson Stutman Abramowitz Royer · http://www.msarllp.com · 292 Madison Avenue, 18th Floor · New York, NY 10017 · 212-685-7474

Eleanor Breitel Alter · 2% · Kasowitz, Benson, Torres & Friedman · 1633 Broadway · New York, NY 10019 · 212-506-1700

David Aronson · Sheresky, Aronson, Mayefsky & Sloan · 485 Lexington Avenue · New York, NY 10017 · 212-521-3500

Susan L. Bender · Bender Burrows & Rosenthal · 451 Park Avenue South, Eighth Floor · New York, NY 10016-7390 · 212-725-7111

Peter Bienstock · Cohen Hennessey Bienstock & Rabin · 11 West 42nd Street, 19th Floor · New York, NY 10036-8002 · 212-575-0007

Sharon Blau · Edmonds & Company · 112 Madison Avenue, Third Floor · New York, NY 10016 · 212-703-5400

Peter E. Bronstein · Dreier · 499 Park Avenue · New York, NY 10022 · 212-328-6100

Kenneth David Burrows · Bender Burrows & Rosenthal · 451 Park Avenue South, Eighth Floor · New York, NY 10016-7390 · 212-725-7111

Bernard E. Clair · Clair, Greifer · 555 Madison Avenue, Ninth Floor · New York, NY 10022 · 212-300-1100

Robert Stephan Cohen · 2% · Cohen Lans · 885 Third Avenue, 32nd Floor · New York, NY 10022 · 212-980-4500

Robert Z. Dobrish · 2) · Dobrish Zeif Gross & Wrubel · http://www.dobrishlaw.com · 757 Third Avenue, 15th Floor · New York, NY 10017 · 212-532-4000

Saul Edelstein · 2% · The Edelsteins, Faegenburg & Brown · 61 Broadway, Suite 2210 · New York, NY 10006-2839 · 212-425-1999

Myrna Felder · 2) · The Law Office of Myrna Felder · 437 Madison Avenue, 30th Floor · New York, NY 10022 · 212-752-3668

Donald Frank · Blank Rome · The Chrysler Building · 405 Lexington Avenue · New York, NY 10174 · 212-885-5000

Ira E. Garr · Ira E. Garr · 777 Third Avenue, 32nd Floor · New York, NY 10017 · 212-750-1333

Norman Heller · Blank Rome · The Chrysler Building · 405 Lexington Avenue · New York, NY 10174 · 212-885-5000

William C. Herman · 2) · Herman, Sloan, Robarge & Sullivan · 60 East 42nd Street, Suite 3210 · New York, NY 10165 · 212-370-4900

Michele A. Katz · Cohen Lans · 885 Third Avenue, 32nd Floor · New York, NY 10022 · 212-980-4500

Deborah E. Lans · Cohen Lans · 885 Third Avenue, 32nd Floor · New York, NY 10022 · 212-980-4500

Allan D. Mantel · Stein, Riso, Mantel · The Chrysler Building, 42nd Floor · 405 Lexington Avenue · New York, NY 10174 · 212-599-1515

Allan E. Mayefsky · Sheresky, Aronson, Mayefsky & Sloan · 485 Lexington Avenue · New York, NY 10017 · 212-521-3500

Hal A. Mayerson · Mayerson Stutman Abramowitz Royer · http://www.msarllp.com · 292 Madison Avenue, 18th Floor · New York, NY 10017 · 212-685-7474

Stanley Plesent · 2) · Hogan & Hartson · 875 Third Avenue, 25th Floor · New York, NY 10022 · 212-918-3000

Sheila Ginsberg Riesel · Blank Rome · The Chrysler Building · 405 Lexington Avenue · New York, NY 10174 · 212-885-5000

Donald L. Schuck · Dreier · 499 Park Avenue · New York, NY 10022 · 212-328-6100

Norman M. Sheresky · 2% · Sheresky, Aronson, Mayefsky & Sloan · 485 Lexington Avenue · New York, NY 10017 · 212-521-3500

Judith E. Siegel-Baum · a · WolfBlock · http://wolfblock.com · 250 Park Avenue · New York, NY 10177 212-986-1116

Pamela M. Sloan · Sheresky, Aronson, Mayefsky & Sloan · 485 Lexington Avenue · New York, NY 10017 · 212-521-3500

Michael Stutman · Mayerson Stutman Abramowitz Royer · http://www.msarllp.com · 292 Madison Avenue, 18th Floor · New York, NY 10017 · 212-685-7474

Michele D. Tortorelli · Michelle Tortorelli · 444 Madison Avenue, 17th Floor · New York, NY 10022 · 212-207-4006

Marcy L. Wachtel · Katsky Korins · 605 Third Avenue, 16th Floor · New York, NY 10158-0038 · 212-953-6000

Robert S. Zeif · Dobrish Zeif Gross & Wrubel · http://www.dobrishlaw.com · 757 Third Avenue, 15th Floor · New York, NY 10017 · 212-532-4000

John F. Zulack · Flemming Zulack Williamson Zauderer · One Liberty Plaza · New York, NY 10006-1404 · 212-412-9500

Nyack

Ronald A. Phillips · McCormack & Phillips · 51 North Broadway, Suite Two · Nyack, NY 10960 · 845-353-0100

Pearl River

Martin T. Johnson · a · Johnson & Cohen · One Blue Hill Plaza, 11th Floor · P.O. Box 1629 · Pearl River, NY 10965-8629 · 845-735-7000

Rochester

Brian J. Barney · 2% · Barney and Affronti · 130 Linden Oaks, Suite D · Rochester, NY 14625 · 585-248-0140

David C. Boysen · Harris Beach · The Granite Building · 130 East Main Street · Rochester, NY 14604 · 585-419-8800

Suzanne Brunsting · a · Suzanne L. Brunsting · 202 Clovercrest Drive · Rochester, NY 14618 · 585-244-4239

S. Gerald Davidson · 2% · Davidson, Fink, Cook, Kelly & Galbraith · 28 Main Street East, Suite 1700 · Rochester, NY 14614 · 585-546-6448

Lewis J. Gould · 2% · Gould, Peck, Metzler & Cognata · 45 Exchange Boulevard, Suite 200 · Rochester, NY 14614 · 585-546-3065

Charles P. Inclima · Biernbaum, Inclima & Meyer · Union Trust Building, Suite 900 · 19 West Main Street · Rochester, NY 14614-1581 · 585-546-2350

Stephen M. Jacobstein · Kaman, Berlove, Marafioti, Jacobstein & Goldman · http://www.kamanesq.com · 135 Corporate Woods, Suite 300 · Rochester, NY 14623 · 585-325-7440

Gregory J. Mott · 2) · Davidson, Fink, Cook, Kelly & Galbraith · 28 Main Street East, Suite 1700 · Rochester, NY 14614 · 585-546-6448

Joan de R. O'Byrne · 2% · Joan de R. O'Byrne · 19 West Main Street, Suite 250 · Rochester, NY 14614-1581 · 585-546-3340

Sharon Kelly Sayers · Sharon Kelly Sayers · 30 West Broad Sreet, Suite 506 · Rochester, NY 14614-2120 · 716-454-2320

Schenectady

Vincent Capasso, Jr. · Capasso & Massaroni · 215 State Street · P.O. Box 1088 · Schenectady, NY 12301-1088 · 518-374-1800

Syracuse

Edward B. Alderman · 2% · Alderman and Alderman · Empire Building, Suite 555 · 472 South Salina Street · Syracuse, NY 13202 · 315-422-8131

Richard B. Alderman · a · Alderman and Alderman · Empire Building, Suite 555 · 472 South Salina Street · Syracuse, NY 13202 · 315-422-8131

Jon W. Brenizer · Macht, Brenizer & Gingold · State Tower Building · 109 South Warren Street · Syracuse, NY 13202 · 315-422-2255

C. Gay Custer · Field & Custer · 472 South Salina Street, Suite 422 · Syracuse, NY 13202 · 315-422-0420

Deborah K. Field · Field & Custer · 472 South Salina Street, Suite 422 · Syracuse, NY 13202 · 315-422-0420

Richard E. Gordon · a · Richard E. Gordon · One Lincoln Center, Suite 275 · Syracuse, NY 13202-1326 315-701-9998

Gary L. Orenstein · 2) · Gary L. Orenstein · State Tower Building, Suite 818 · 109 South Warren Street · Syracuse, NY 13202 · 315-422-8185

Howard J. Woronov · Melvin & Melvin · 217 South Salina Street, Seventh Floor · Syracuse, NY 13202-1390 · 315-422-1311

White Plains

Joel C. Bender · a · Bender Jenson Brennan & Silverstein · 120 Bloomingdale Road, Suite 104 · White Plains, NY 10605-1518 · 914-997-1100

Henry S. Berman · 2) · Berman Bavero Frucco & Gouz · 123 Main Street, Suite 1700 · White Plains, NY 10601 · 914-997-7100

Peter O. Bodnar · a · Bodnar & Milone · Courthouse Square, Suite 401 · 140 Grand Street · White Plains, NY 10601 · 914-997-2500

Donna M. Genovese · Goldschmidt & Genovese · One North Lexington Avenue · White Plains, NY 10601 · 914-681-6006

Sylvia Goldschmidt · a · Goldschmidt & Genovese · One North Lexington Avenue · White Plains, NY 10601 · 914-681-6006

Lydia A. Milone · Bodnar & Milone · Courthouse Square, Suite 401 · 140 Grand Street · White Plains, NY 10601 · 914-997-2500

Terri L. Weiss · Marino & Weiss · 162 Grand Street · White Plains, NY 10601 · 914-761-0640

FAMILY LAW MEDIATION

Rochester

Suzanne Brunsting · a · Suzanne L. Brunsting · 202 Clovercrest Drive · Rochester, NY 14618 · 585-244-4239

FIRST AMENDMENT LAW

Albany

Peter Danziger · a · O'Connell & Aronowitz · 54 State Street, Ninth Floor · Albany, NY 12207-2501 · 518-462-5601

Buffalo

Paul J. Cambria, Jr. · 2% · Lipsitz Green Scime Cambria · http://www.lipsitzgreen.com · 42 Delaware Avenue, Suite 120 · Buffalo, NY 14202 · 716-849-1333

Barry N. Covert · Lipsitz Green Scime Cambria · http://www.lipsitzgreen.com · 42 Delaware Avenue, Suite 120 · Buffalo, NY 14202 · 716-849-1333

New York

Floyd Abrams · 2% · Cahill Gordon & Reindel · 80 Pine Street · New York, NY 10005-1702 · 212-701-3000

Susan Buckley · Cahill Gordon & Reindel · 80 Pine Street · New York, NY 10005-1702 · 212-701-3000

Edward J. Davis · Davis Wright Tremaine · 1633 Broadway, 27th Floor · New York, NY 10019-6708 · 212-489-8230

Leon Friedman · a · Leon Friedman · 148 East 78th Street · New York, NY 10075 · 212-737-0400

Kevin W. Goering · Sheppard, Mullin, Richter & Hampton · http://www.sheppardmullin.com · 30 Rockefeller Plaza, 24th Floor · New York, NY 10112 · 212-332-3800

Laura R. Handman · a · Davis Wright Tremaine · 1633 Broadway, 27th Floor · New York, NY 10019-6708 · 212-489-8230

Victor A. Kovner · a · Davis Wright Tremaine · 1633 Broadway, 27th Floor · New York, NY 10019-6708 212-489-8230

Elizabeth A. McNamara · Davis Wright Tremaine · 1633 Broadway, 27th Floor · New York, NY 10019-6708 · 212-489-8230

Slade R. Metcalf · a · Hogan & Hartson · 875 Third Avenue, 25th Floor · New York, NY 10022 · 212-918-3000

Ronald S. Rauchberg · a · Proskauer Rose · http://www.proskauer.com · 1585 Broadway · New York, NY 10036-8299 · 212-969-3000

R. Bruce Rich · a · Weil Gotshal & Manges · 767 Fifth Avenue · New York, NY 10153 · 212-310-8000

Dean Ringel · a · Cahill Gordon & Reindel · 80 Pine Street · New York, NY 10005-1702 · 212-701-3000

David A. Schulz · a · Levine Sullivan Koch & Schulz · 321 West 44th Street, Suite 510 · New York, NY 10036 · 212-850-6100

Charles S. Sims · Proskauer Rose · http://www.proskauer.com · 1585 Broadway · New York, NY 10036-8299 · 212-969-3000

Robert G. Sugarman · a · Weil Gotshal & Manges · 767 Fifth Avenue · New York, NY 10153 · 212-310-8000

Jack M. Weiss · a · Gibson, Dunn & Crutcher · 200 Park Avenue, 47th Floor · New York, NY 10166-0193 · 212-351-4000

Syracuse

S. Paul Battaglia · 2) · Bond, Schoeneck & King · One Lincoln Center · Syracuse, NY 13202-1355 · 315-218-8000

FRANCHISE LAW

Buffalo

Thomas C. Bailey · Phillips Lytle · 3400 HSBC Center · Buffalo, NY 14203-2887 · 716-847-8400

New York

Daniel Gildin · Kaufmann, Feiner, Yamin, Gildin & Robbins · 777 Third Avenue, 24th Floor · New York, NY 10017 · 212-755-3100

David J. Kaufmann · Kaufmann, Feiner, Yamin, Gildin & Robbins · 777 Third Avenue, 24th Floor · New York, NY 10017 · 212-755-3100

David Oppenehim · Kaufmann, Feiner, Yamin, Gildin & Robbins · 777 Third Avenue, 24th Floor · New York, NY 10017 · 212-755-3100

Richard L. Rosen · The Richard L. Rosen Law Firm · 110 East 59th Street, 23rd Floor · New York, NY 10022-1330 · 212-644-6644

Craig R. Tractenberg · Nixon Peabody · 437 Madison Avenue, 23rd Floor · New York, NY 10022 · 212-940-3000

Rochester

Robert B. Calihan · a · Nixon Peabody · 1100 Clinton Square · P.O. Box 31051 · Rochester, NY 14604 · 585-263-1000

Uniondale

Harold L. Kestenbaum · a · Ruskin Moscau Faltischeck · East Tower, 15th Floor · 1425 Rexcorp Plaza · Uniondale, NY 11556-1425 · 516-663-6600

GAMING LAW

New York

Daniel Schiffman · Daniel Schiffman · http://www.schiffman.us · 903 Park Avenue · New York, NY 10075 · 212-628-6433

GOVERNMENT RELATIONS LAW

Albany

Kevin P. Quinn · Whiteman Osterman & Hanna · One Commerce Plaza · Albany, NY 12260 · 518-487-7600

HEALTH CARE LAW

Albany

Harold N. Iselin · Greenberg Traurig · http://www.gtlaw.com · 54 State Street, Sixth Floor · Albany, NY 12207 · 518-689-1400

Robert H. Iseman · a · Iseman, Cunningham, Riester & Hyde · http://www.icrh.com · Nine Thurlow Terrace · Albany, NY 12203 · 518-462-3000

Peter J. Millock · Nixon Peabody · 677 Broadway, 10th Floor · Albany, NY 12207 · 518-427-2650

Cornelius D. Murray · a · O'Connell & Aronowitz · 54 State Street, Ninth Floor · Albany, NY 12207-2501 · 518-462-5601

Jeffrey J. Sherrin · a · O'Connell & Aronowitz · 54 State Street, Ninth Floor · Albany, NY 12207-2501 · 518-462-5601

Buffalo

Susan A. Benz · Damon & Morey · http://www.damonmorey.com · 1000 Cathedral Place · 298 Main Street · Buffalo, NY 14202-4096 · 716-856-5500

Christopher T. Greene · Damon & Morey · http://www.damonmorey.com · 1000 Cathedral Place · 298 Main Street · Buffalo, NY 14202-4096 · 716-856-5500

Robert M. Greene · Phillips Lytle · 3400 HSBC Center · Buffalo, NY 14203-2887 · 716-847-8400

Robert J. Portin · Damon & Morey · http://www.damonmorey.com · 1000 Cathedral Place · 298 Main Street · Buffalo, NY 14202-4096 · 716-856-5500

Great Neck

Frederick I. Miller · Garfunkel, Wild & Travis · http://www.gwtlaw.com · 111 Great Neck Road, Suite 503 · Great Neck, NY 11021 · 516-393-2200

Norton L. Travis · a · Garfunkel, Wild & Travis · http://www.gwtlaw.com · 111 Great Neck Road, Suite 503 · Great Neck, NY 11021 · 516-393-2200

Robert A. Wild · a · Garfunkel, Wild & Travis · http://www.gwtlaw.com · 111 Great Neck Road, Suite 503 · Great Neck, NY 11021 · 516-393-2200

Jericho

David DeCerbo · a · Nixon Peabody · 50 Jericho Quadrangle, Suite 300 · Jericho, NY 11753-2728 · 516-832-7500

Richard F. Minicucci · a · Nixon Peabody · 50 Jericho Quadrangle, Suite 300 · Jericho, NY 11753-2728 · 516-832-7500

New York

Mark Barnes · a · Ropes & Gray · http://www.ropesgray.com · 1211 Avenue of the Americas · New York, NY 10036-8704 · 212-596-9000

Jeffrey H. Becker · a · Epstein, Becker & Green · 250 Park Avenue, 14th Floor · New York, NY 10177-1211 · 212-351-4500

Robert D. Belfort · Manatt, Phelps & Phillips · Seven Times Square · New York, NY 10036 · 212-790-4500

Peter G. Bergmann · a · Cadwalader, Wickersham & Taft · http://www.cadwalader.com · One World Financial Center · New York, NY 10281 · 212-504-6000

William S. Bernstein · a · Manatt, Phelps & Phillips · Seven Times Square · New York, NY 10036 · 212-790-4500

Herschel Goldfield · Proskauer Rose · http://www.proskauer.com · 1585 Broadway · New York, NY 10036-8299 · 212-969-3000

George Kalkines · a · Manatt, Phelps & Phillips · Seven Times Square · New York, NY 10036 · 212-790-4500

Robert M. Kaufman · a · Proskauer Rose · http://www.proskauer.com · 1585 Broadway · New York, NY 10036-8299 · 212-969-3000

Edward S. Kornreich · a · Proskauer Rose · http://www.proskauer.com · 1585 Broadway · New York, NY 10036-8299 · 212-969-3000

Jerome T. Levy · a · Duane Morris · 1540 Broadway · New York, NY 10036-4086 · 212-692-1000

Ellen H. Moskowitz · a · Proskauer Rose · http://www.proskauer.com · 1585 Broadway · New York, NY 10036-8299 · 212-969-3000

Peter F. Nadel · a · Katten Muchin Rosenman · 575 Madison Avenue · New York, NY 10022-2585 · 212-940-8800

Susan S. Robfogel · 2) · Nixon Peabody · 437 Madison Avenue, 23rd Floor · New York, NY 10022 · 212-940-3000

Stephen A. Warnke · Ropes & Gray · http://www.ropesgray.com · 1211 Avenue of the Americas · New York, NY 10036-8704 · 212-596-9000

Ellen V. Weissman · a · Hodgson Russ · 1540 Broadway, 24th Floor · New York, NY 10036 · 212-751-4300

Richard J. Zall · a · Proskauer Rose · http://www.proskauer.com · 1585 Broadway · New York, NY 10036-8299 · 212-969-3000

Rochester

Thomas D'Antonio · a · Ward, Norris, Heller & Reidy · http://www.wnhr.com · 300 State Street · Rochester, NY 14614 · 585-454-0700

Philip Fileri · Harter Secrest & Emery · http://www.hselaw.com · 1600 Bausch & Lomb Place · Rochester, NY 14604-2711 · 585-232-6500

Joyce R. Parker · a · Harris Beach · The Granite Building · 130 East Main Street · Rochester, NY 14604 585-419-8800

Rene H. Reixach · Woods Oviatt Gilman · http://www.woodsoviatt.com · 700 Crossroads Building · Two State Street · Rochester, NY 14614 · 585-987-2800

Mary E. Ross · a · Harter Secrest & Emery · http://www.hselaw.com · 1600 Bausch & Lomb Place · Rochester, NY 14604-2711 · 585-232-6500

Thomas G. Smith · Harter Secrest & Emery · http://www.hselaw.com · 1600 Bausch & Lomb Place · Rochester, NY 14604-2711 · 585-232-6500

Eric Stonehill · a · Harris Beach · The Granite Building · 130 East Main Street · Rochester, NY 14604 · 585-419-8800

Syracuse

Stephen H. Cohen · a · Scolaro, Shulman, Cohen, Fetter & Burstein · 507 Plum Street, Suite 300 · Syracuse, NY 13204 · 315-471-8111

Raymond R. D'Agostino · a · Hancock & Estabrook · 1500 Axa Tower I · 100 Madison Street · Syracuse, NY 13202 · 315-471-3151

White Plains

James G. Eberz · Meiselman, Denlea, Packman, Carton & Eberz · 1311 Mamaroneck Avenue, Suite 220 · White Plains, NY 10605 · 914-517-5000

IMMIGRATION LAW

Buffalo

Michael B. Berger · a · Berger & Berger · 555 International Drive, Suite 800 · Buffalo, NY 14221 · 716-634-6500

Daniel P. Joyce · Jaeckle Fleischmann & Mugel · 12 Fountain Plaza · Buffalo, NY 14202-2292 · 716-856-0600

Mark T. Kenmore · a · Mark Tolbert Kenmore · Statler Towers, Suite 1620 · 107 Delaware Avenue · Buffalo, NY 14202 · 716-853-2700

Lance J. Madden · Hodgson Russ · One Guaranty Building, Suite 100 · 140 Pearl Street · Buffalo, NY 14202 · 716-856-4000

William Z. Reich · a · Serotte Reich Wilson · 300 Delaware Avenue · Buffalo, NY 14202 · 716-854-7525

Andrew Wilson · Serotte Reich Wilson · 300 Delaware Avenue · Buffalo, NY 14202 · 716-854-7525

Melville

Michael P. DiRaimondo · a · DiRaimondo & Masi · 401 Broadhollow Road, Suite 302 · Melville, NY 11747-4721 · 631-777-5557

New York

Jonathan E. Avirom · a · Avirom & Associates · 42 Broadway, Suite 1220 · New York, NY 10004 · 212-747-8787

Frances C. Berger · a · Law Offices of Frances C. Berger · 335 Broadway, Suite 1103 · New York, NY 10013 · 212-925-6688

Suzan C. Brauwerman · Suzan C. Brauwerman & Associates · 160 West End Avenue, Suite 9-U · New York, NY 10023-5607 · 212-799-0337

Alison J. Brown · Alison J. Brown · 924 West End Avenue, Apartment 92 · New York, NY 10025

Ted J. Chiappari · a · Satterlee Stephens Burke & Burke · 230 Park Avenue, Eleventh Floor · New York, NY 10169-0079 · 212-818-9200

Jules E. Coven · a · Bretz & Coven · 305 Broadway, Suite 100 · New York, NY 10007 · 212-267-2555

Matthew S. Dunn · Kramer Levin Naftalis & Frankel · http://www.kramerlevin.com · 1177 Avenue of the Americas · New York, NY 10036 · 212-715-9100

Austin T. Fragomen, Jr. · a · Fragomen, Del Rey, Bernsen & Loewy · http://www.fragomen.com · Seven Hanover Square · New York, NY 10004-2756 · 212-688-8555

Robert N. Gottfried · a · Hodgson Russ · The Lincoln Building, 37th Floor · 60 East 42nd Street · New York, NY 10165 · 212-661-3535

Ethan E. Kaufman · Fragomen, Del Rey, Bernsen & Loewy · http://www.fragomen.com · Seven Hanover Square · New York, NY 10004-2756 · 212-688-8555

Allen E. Kaye · a · Law Offices of Allen E. Kaye · Trinity Building, 13th Floor · 111 Broadway · New York, NY 10006 · 212-964-5858

Mark D. Koestler · Kramer Levin Naftalis & Frankel · http://www.kramerlevin.com · 1177 Avenue of the Americas · New York, NY 10036 · 212-715-9100

Andrew Roy Lerner · Wormser, Kiely, Galef & Jacobs · 825 Third Avenue · New York, NY 10022-7519 · 212-687-4900

Stanley Mailman · a · Satterlee Stephens Burke & Burke · 230 Park Avenue, Eleventh Floor · New York, NY 10169-0079 · 212-818-9200

Elihu S. Massel · a · Elihu S. Massel · 122 East 42nd Street · New York, NY 10168-2194 · 212-867-3810

Cyrus D. Mehta · Cyrus D. Mehta & Associates · http://www.cyrusmehta.com · 67 Wall Street, Suite 1801 New York, NY 10005 · 212-425-0555

Marcia N. Needleman · a · Levitt & Needleman · 1780 Broadway, 10th Floor · New York, NY 10019-1414 · 212-757-8438

Deborah J. Notkin · a · Barst & Mukamal · Two Park Avenue, 19th Floor · New York, NY 10016 · 212-686-3838

Michael D. Patrick · a · Fragomen, Del Rey, Bernsen & Loewy · http://www.fragomen.com · Seven Hanover Square · New York, NY 10004-2756 · 212-688-8555

Patrick J. Quane · Fragomen, Del Rey, Bernsen & Loewy · http://www.fragomen.com · Seven Hanover Square · New York, NY 10004-2756 · 212-688-8555

Jan Allen Reiner · a · Jan Allen Reiner · 350 Broadway, Suite 200 · New York, NY 10013 · 212-925-1919

Martin L. Rothstein · a · Barst & Mukamal · Two Park Avenue, 19th Floor · New York, NY 10016 · 212-686-3838

Theodore Ruthizer · a · Kramer Levin Naftalis & Frankel · http://www.kramerlevin.com · 1177 Avenue of the Americas · New York, NY 10036 · 212-715-9100

Naomi Schorr · Kramer Levin Naftalis & Frankel · http://www.kramerlevin.com · 1177 Avenue of the Americas · New York, NY 10036 · 212-715-9100

Kenneth A. Schultz · a · Satterlee Stephens Burke & Burke · 230 Park Avenue, Eleventh Floor · New York, NY 10169-0079 · 212-818-9200

Suzanne B. Seltzer · Klasko, Rulon, Stock & Seltzer · 317 Madison Avenue, Suite 1518 · New York, NY 10017 · 212-796-8846

Annie Jen Wang · a · Wormser, Kiely, Galef & Jacobs · 825 Third Avenue · New York, NY 10022-7519 · 212-687-4900

Freddi M. Weintraub · Fragomen, Del Rey, Bernsen & Loewy · http://www.fragomen.com · Seven Hanover Square · New York, NY 10004-2756 · 212-688-8555

Allan H. Wernick · a · Allan H. Wernick · 325 Broadway, Suite 405 · New York, NY 10007 · 212-964-1210

Leon Wildes · a · Wildes & Weinberg · http://www.wildesweinberg.com · 515 Madison Avenue, Eighth Floor · New York, NY 10022 · 212-753-3468

Donald Jay Wolfson · a · Wormser, Kiely, Galef & Jacobs · 825 Third Avenue · New York, NY 10022-7519 · 212-687-4900

Rochester

Margaret A. Catillaz · a · Harter Secrest & Emery · http://www.hselaw.com · 1600 Bausch & Lomb Place · Rochester, NY 14604-2711 · 585-232-6500

INFORMATION TECHNOLOGY LAW

Armonk

Henry Beck · Law Office of Henry Beck · Nine Frog Rock Road · Armonk, NY 10504-1013 · 914-273-1435

New York

Ronald Abramson · Hughes Hubbard & Reed · http://www.hugheshubbard.com · One Battery Park Plaza · New York, NY 10004-1482 · 212-837-6000

Carole Aciman · Greenberg Traurig · http://www.gtlaw.com · MetLife Building · 200 Park Avenue · New York, NY 10166 · 212-801-9200

Peter Brown · Baker Hostetler · http://www.bakerlaw.com · 45 Rockefeller Plaza, 11th Floor · New York, NY 10111 · 212-589-4200

John F. Delaney · Morrison & Foerster · http://www.mofo.com · 1290 Avenue of the Americas · New York, NY 10104-0050 · 212-468-8000

Morton David Goldberg · a · Cowan, Liebowitz & Latman · 1133 Avenue of the Americas, 35th Floor · New York, NY 10036-6799 · 212-790-9200

Henry B. Gutman · Simpson Thacher · 425 Lexington Avenue · New York, NY 10017-3954 · 212-455-2000

Vivian L. Hanson · Morrison & Foerster · http://www.mofo.com · 1290 Avenue of the Americas · New York, NY 10104-0050 · 212-468-8000

Nigel L. Howard · Covington & Burling · The New York Times Building · 620 Eighth Avenue · New York, NY 10018 · 212-841-1000

John B. Kennedy · Dewey & LeBoeuf · 125 West 55th Street · New York, NY 10019-5389 · 212-424-8000

Lori E. Lesser · Simpson Thacher · 425 Lexington Avenue · New York, NY 10017-3954 · 212-455-2000

Stuart D. Levi · Skadden, Arps, Slate, Meagher & Flom · Four Times Square · New York, NY 10036 · 212-735-3000

Julian S. Millstein · Thelen Reid Brown Raysman & Steiner · 875 Third Avenue, 10th Floor · New York, NY 10022-6225 · 212-603-2000

Jeffrey D. Neuburger · Proskauer Rose · http://www.proskauer.com · 1585 Broadway · New York, NY 10036-8299 · 212-969-3000

Stephen D. Nordahl · Milbank, Tweed, Hadley & McCloy · http://www.milbank.com · One Chase Manhattan Plaza · New York, NY 10005-1413 · 212-530-5000

Richard Raysman · Thelen Reid Brown Raysman & Steiner · 875 Third Avenue, 10th Floor · New York, NY 10022-6225 · 212-603-2000

Rita A. Rodin · Skadden, Arps, Slate, Meagher & Flom · Four Times Square · New York, NY 10036 · 212-735-3000

Harry Rubin · Ropes & Gray · http://www.ropesgray.com · 1211 Avenue of the Americas · New York, NY 10036-8704 · 212-596-9000

Alan N. Sutin · Greenberg Traurig · http://www.gtlaw.com · MetLife Building · 200 Park Avenue · New York, NY 10166 · 212-801-9200

William A. Tanenbaum · Kaye Scholer · 425 Park Avenue · New York, NY 10022-3598 · 212-836-8000

Albert L. Wells · Covington & Burling · The New York Times Building · 620 Eighth Avenue · New York, NY 10018 · 212-841-1000

Joseph P. Zammit · Fulbright & Jaworski · http://www.fulbright.com · 666 Fifth Avenue · New York, NY 10103-3198 · 212-318-3000

Albany

Fredric Bodner · Hinman Straub · 121 State Street · Albany, NY 12207-1622 · 518-436-0751

Binghamton

John P. Rittinger · Levene, Gouldin & Thompson · http://www.binghamtonlaw.com · 71 State Street · P.O. Box F-1706 · Binghamton, NY 13902 · 607-763-9200

Buffalo

Dan D. Kohane · Hurwitz & Fine · http://www.hurwitzfine.com · 1300 Liberty Building · Buffalo, NY 14202 · 716-849-8900

New York

Marcia D. Alazraki · Manatt, Phelps & Phillips · Seven Times Square · New York, NY 10036 · 212-790-4500

Andrew S. Amer · Simpson Thacher · 425 Lexington Avenue · New York, NY 10017-3954 · 212-455-2000

Eugene R. Anderson · Anderson Kill & Olick · http://www.andersonkill.com · 1251 Avenue of the Americas · New York, NY 10020-1182 · 212-278-1000

Jane Boisseau · Dewey & LeBoeuf · 125 West 55th Street · New York, NY 10019-5389 · 212-424-8000

Lawrence I. Brandes · DLA Piper · 1251 Avenue of the Americas · New York, NY 10020-1104 · 212-335-4500

Paul Evan Breene · Reed Smith · 599 Lexington Avenue, 29th Floor · New York, NY 10022 · 212-521-5400

Wolcott B. Dunham, Jr. · a · Debevoise & Plimpton · 919 Third Avenue · New York, NY 10022 · 212-909-6000

Alexander M. Dye · Dewey & LeBoeuf · 125 West 55th Street · New York, NY 10019-5389 · 212-424-8000

James A. FitzPatrick, Jr. · Dewey & LeBoeuf · 1301 Avenue of the Americas · New York, NY 10019-6092 · 212-259-8000

Mary Beth Forshaw · Simpson Thacher · 425 Lexington Avenue · New York, NY 10017-3954 · 212-455-2000

Jonathan L. Freedman · Sidley Austin · 787 Seventh Avenue · New York, NY 10019 · 212-839-5300

Donald D. Gabay · Stroock & Stroock & Lavan · 180 Maiden Lane · New York, NY 10038-4982 · 212-806-5400

Lawrence S. Greengrass · Mound Cotton Wollan & Greengrass · One Battery Park Plaza · 24 Whitehall Street · New York, NY 10004 · 212-804-4200

Michael Groll · Dewey & LeBoeuf · 125 West 55th Street · New York, NY 10019-5389 · 212-424-8000

John H. Gross · Proskauer Rose · http://www.proskauer.com · 1585 Broadway · New York, NY 10036-8299 · 212-969-3000

Donald B. Henderson, Jr. · Dewey & LeBoeuf · 125 West 55th Street · New York, NY 10019-5389 · 212-424-8000

Robert Horkovich · Anderson Kill & Olick · http://www.andersonkill.com · 1251 Avenue of the Americas New York, NY 10020-1182 · 212-278-1000

Thomas M. Kelly · Debevoise & Plimpton · 919 Third Avenue · New York, NY 10022 · 212-909-6000

Daniel F. Kolb · a · Davis Polk & Wardwell · 450 Lexington Avenue · New York, NY 10017 · 212-450-4000

Jeff S. Liebmann · Sidley Austin · 787 Seventh Avenue · New York, NY 10019 · 212-839-5300

Paul Meyer · Clifford Chance · 31 West 52nd Street · New York, NY 10019-6131 · 212-878-8000

Thomas R. Newman · Duane Morris · 1540 Broadway · New York, NY 10036-4086 · 212-692-1000

John M. Nonna · Dewey & LeBoeuf · 125 West 55th Street · New York, NY 10019-5389 · 212-424-8000

Barry R. Ostrager · Simpson Thacher · 425 Lexington Avenue · New York, NY 10017-3954 · 212-455-2000

Randy Paar · Dickstein Shapiro · http://www.dicksteinshapiro.com · 1177 Avenue of the Americas · New York, NY 10036-2714 · 212-277-6500

Neil R. Pearson · Edwards Angell Palmer & Dodge · 750 Lexington Avenue · New York, NY 10022 · 212-308-4411

Charles C. Platt · WilmerHale · http://www.wilmerhale.com · 399 Park Avenue · New York, NY 10022 · 212-230-8800

Lawrence W. Pollack · a · Dewey & LeBoeuf · 125 West 55th Street · New York, NY 10019-5389 · 212-424-8000

Nicholas F. Potter · Debevoise & Plimpton · 919 Third Avenue · New York, NY 10022 · 212-909-6000

Seth L. Rosen · Debevoise & Plimpton · 919 Third Avenue · New York, NY 10022 · 212-909-6000

William W. Rosenblatt · Stroock & Stroock & Lavan · 180 Maiden Lane · New York, NY 10038-4982 · 212-806-5400

Andrew S. Rowen · Sullivan & Cromwell · 125 Broad Street · New York, NY 10004-2498 · 212-558-4000

John J. Sarchio · Chadbourne & Parke · http://www.chadbourne.com · 30 Rockefeller Plaza · New York, NY 10112-0127 · 212-408-5100

Clifford H. Schoenberg · Cadwalader, Wickersham & Taft · http://www.cadwalader.com · One World Financial Center · New York, NY 10281 · 212-504-6000

John M. Schwolsky · Dewey & LeBoeuf · 125 West 55th Street · New York, NY 10019-5389 · 212-424-8000

Cynthia R. Shoss · Dewey & LeBoeuf · 125 West 55th Street · New York, NY 10019-5389 · 212-424-8000

Robert J. Sullivan · Skadden, Arps, Slate, Meagher & Flom · Four Times Square · New York, NY 10036 212-735-3000

Susan J. Sutherland · Skadden, Arps, Slate, Meagher & Flom · Four Times Square · New York, NY 10036 · 212-735-3000

Joseph T. Verdesca · Weil Gotshal & Manges · 767 Fifth Avenue · New York, NY 10153 · 212-310-8000

Vincent J. Vitkowsky · Edwards Angell Palmer & Dodge · 750 Lexington Avenue · New York, NY 10022 · 212-308-4411

Mary Kay Vyskocil · Simpson Thacher · 425 Lexington Avenue · New York, NY 10017-3954 · 212-455-2000

Rochester

Laurie A. Giordano · Leclair Korona Giordano Cole · 150 State Street, Suite 300 · Rochester, NY 14614 · 585-327-4100

INTELLECTUAL PROPERTY LAW

Buffalo

Ranjana Kadle · Hodgson Russ · One Guaranty Building, Suite 100 · 140 Pearl Street · Buffalo, NY 14202 716-856-4000

Gust P. Pullman · Damon & Morey · http://www.damonmorey.com · 1000 Cathedral Place · 298 Main Street · Buffalo, NY 14202-4096 · 716-856-5500

Peter K. Sommer · Phillips Lytle · 3400 HSBC Center · Buffalo, NY 14203-2887 · 716-847-8400

New York

Mark J. Abate · Goodwin Procter · The New York Times Building · 620 Eighth Avenue · New York, NY 10018 · 212-813-8800

Gregory S. Arovas · Kirkland & Ellis · Citigroup Center · 153 East 53rd Street · New York, NY 10022-4611 · 212-446-4800

Bruce W. Baber · a · King & Spalding · 1185 Avenue of the Americas · New York, NY 10036-4003 · 212-556-2100

Robert L. Baechtold · a · Fitzpatrick, Cella, Harper & Scinto · http://www.fitzpatrickcella.com · 30 Rockefeller Plaza · New York, NY 10112-3801 · 212-218-2100

W. Edward Bailey · a · Heller Ehrman · Times Square Tower, 40th Floor · Seven Times Square · New York, NY 10036-6524 · 212-832-8300

Thomas H. Beck · a · Sidley Austin · 787 Seventh Avenue · New York, NY 10019 · 212-839-5300

Alan Behr · Alston + Bird · http://www.alston.com · 90 Park Avenue · New York, NY 10016-1387 · 212-210-9400

Leora Ben-Ami · Kaye Scholer · 425 Park Avenue · New York, NY 10022-3598 · 212-836-8000

David H. Bernstein · Debevoise & Plimpton · 919 Third Avenue · New York, NY 10022 · 212-909-6000

Robert J. Bernstein · a · The Law Office of Robert J. Bernstein · 488 Madison Avenue, Ninth Floor · New York, NY 10022 · 212-705-4811

William M. Borchard · Cowan, Liebowitz & Latman · 1133 Avenue of the Americas, 35th Floor · New York, NY 10036-6799 · 212-790-9200

Joseph A. Calvaruso · Orrick, Herrington & Sutcliffe · 666 Fifth Avenue · New York, NY 10103-0001 · 212-506-5000

Nicholas M. Cannella · a · Fitzpatrick, Cella, Harper & Scinto · http://www.fitzpatrickcella.com · 30 Rockefeller Plaza · New York, NY 10112-3801 · 212-218-2100

Baila H. Celedonia · Cowan, Liebowitz & Latman · 1133 Avenue of the Americas, 35th Floor · New York, NY 10036-6799 · 212-790-9200

Dale Cendali · O'Melveny & Myers · Times Square Tower · Seven Times Square · New York, NY 10036 212-326-2000

Steven C. Cherny · Latham & Watkins · 885 Third Avenue · New York, NY 10022-4834 · 212-906-1200

Robert W. Clarida · Cowan, Liebowitz & Latman · 1133 Avenue of the Americas, 35th Floor · New York, NY 10036-6799 · 212-790-9200

Nicholas L. Coch · Kramer Levin Naftalis & Frankel · http://www.kramerlevin.com · 1177 Avenue of the Americas · New York, NY 10036 · 212-715-9100

Laura A. Coruzzi · Jones Day · 222 East 41st Street · New York, NY 10017-6702 · 212-326-3939

Thomas L. Creel · Offices of Thomas Creel · 25 Beekman Place, Suite Five · New York, NY 10022 · 212-421-4213

Kevin J. Culligan · Heller Ehrman · Times Square Tower, 40th Floor · Seven Times Square · New York, NY 10036-6524 · 212-832-8300

Janet Cullum · Cooley Godward Kronish · The Grace Building, 46th Floor · 1114 Avenue of the Americas New York, NY 10036-7798 · 212-479-6000

Victoria A. Cundiff · Paul Hastings · Park Avenue Tower, First Floor · 75 East 55th Street · New York, NY 10022 · 212-318-6000

Richard Dannay · a · Cowan, Liebowitz & Latman · 1133 Avenue of the Americas, 35th Floor · New York, NY 10036-6799 · 212-790-9200

Richard L. DeLucia · Kenyon & Kenyon · One Broadway · New York, NY 10004-1050 · 212-425-7200

John M. Desmarais · Kirkland & Ellis · Citigroup Center · 153 East 53rd Street · New York, NY 10022-4611 · 212-446-4800

Andrew L. Deutsch · DLA Piper · 1251 Avenue of the Americas · New York, NY 10020-1104 · 212-335-4500

Dickerson M. Downing · Crowell & Moring · 153 East 53rd Street, 31st Floor · New York, NY 10022 · 212-223-4000

Marie V. Driscoll · a · Fross, Zelnick, Lehrman & Zissu · 866 United Nations Plaza · New York, NY 10017 · 212-813-5900

Dimitrios T. Drivas · White & Case · http://www.whitecase.com · 1155 Avenue of the Americas · New York, NY 10036-2787 · 212-819-8200

Sandra Edelman · Dorsey & Whitney · 250 Park Avenue · New York, NY 10177-1500 · 212-415-9200

Bruce R. Ewing · Dorsey & Whitney · 250 Park Avenue · New York, NY 10177-1500 · 212-415-9200

Edward V. Filardi · Skadden, Arps, Slate, Meagher & Flom · Four Times Square · New York, NY 10036 212-735-3000

Joseph M. Fitzpatrick · 2) · Fitzpatrick, Cella, Harper & Scinto · http://www.fitzpatrickcella.com · 30 Rockefeller Plaza · New York, NY 10112-3801 · 212-218-2100

Anthony L. Fletcher · a · Fish & Richardson · Citigroup Center, 52nd Floor · 153 East 53rd Street · New York, NY 10022-4611 · 212-765-5070

David R. Francescani · Fish & Richardson · Citigroup Center, 52nd Floor · 153 East 53rd Street · New York, NY 10022-4611 · 212-765-5070

Marc S. Friedman · Sills Cummis & Gross · http://www.sillscummis.com · One Rockefeller Plaza · New York, NY 10020 · 212-643-7000

Theresa M. Gillis · Howrey · Citigroup Center, 54th Floor · 153 East 53rd Street · New York, NY 10022 · 212-896-6500

Steven D. Glazer · Weil Gotshal & Manges · 767 Fifth Avenue · New York, NY 10153 · 212-310-8000

Morton David Goldberg · a · Cowan, Liebowitz & Latman · 1133 Avenue of the Americas, 35th Floor · New York, NY 10036-6799 · 212-790-9200

Arthur J. Greenbaum · a · Cowan, Liebowitz & Latman · 1133 Avenue of the Americas, 35th Floor · New York, NY 10036-6799 · 212-790-9200

James F. Haley, Jr. · a · Ropes & Gray · http://www.ropesgray.com · 1211 Avenue of the Americas · New York, NY 10036-8704 · 212-596-9000

Christopher J. Harnett · Ropes & Gray · http://www.ropesgray.com · 1211 Avenue of the Americas · New York, NY 10036-8704 · 212-596-9000

William M. Hart · a · Proskauer Rose · http://www.proskauer.com · 1585 Broadway · New York, NY 10036-8299 · 212-969-3000

Alan J. Hartnick · Abelman Frayne & Schwab · 666 Third Avenue · New York, NY 10017-5612 · 212-949-9022

Kenneth B. Herman · Ropes & Gray · http://www.ropesgray.com · 1211 Avenue of the Americas · New York, NY 10036-8704 · 212-596-9000

Ethan Horwitz · King & Spalding · 1185 Avenue of the Americas · New York, NY 10036-4003 · 212-556-2100

Christopher A. Hughes · Cadwalader, Wickersham & Taft · http://www.cadwalader.com · One World Financial Center · New York, NY 10281 · 212-504-6000

Jesse J. Jenner · a · Ropes & Gray · http://www.ropesgray.com · 1211 Avenue of the Americas · New York, NY 10036-8704 · 212-596-9000

J. Christopher Jensen · Cowan, Liebowitz & Latman · 1133 Avenue of the Americas, 35th Floor · New York, NY 10036-6799 · 212-790-9200

Stephen B. Judlowe · a · Morgan Lewis & Bockius · 101 Park Avenue · New York, NY 10178-0060 · 212-309-6000

Siegrun D. Kane · a · Morgan & Finnegan · http://www.morganfinnegan.com · Three World Financial Center, 20th Floor · New York, NY 10281-2101 · 212-415-8700

Salem M. Katsh · Katsh & Shapiro · 44 West 62nd Street, Suite 16B · New York, NY 10023-7011 · 212-678-9214

Bruce P. Keller · a · Debevoise & Plimpton · 919 Third Avenue · New York, NY 10022 · 212-909-6000

Mary L. Kevlin · Cowan, Liebowitz & Latman · 1133 Avenue of the Americas, 35th Floor · New York, NY 10036-6799 · 212-790-9200

I. Fred Koenigsberg · White & Case · http://www.whitecase.com · 1155 Avenue of the Americas · New York, NY 10036-2787 · 212-819-8200

Josh A. Krevitt · Gibson, Dunn & Crutcher · 200 Park Avenue, 47th Floor · New York, NY 10166-0193 · 212-351-4000

Clark W. Lackert · King & Spalding · 1185 Avenue of the Americas · New York, NY 10036-4003 · 212-556-2100

Steven J. Lee · Kenyon & Kenyon · One Broadway · New York, NY 10004-1050 · 212-425-7200

Richard Z. Lehv · Fross, Zelnick, Lehrman & Zissu · 866 United Nations Plaza · New York, NY 10017 · 212-813-5900

Harry C. Marcus · Morgan & Finnegan · http://www.morganfinnegan.com · Three World Financial Center, 20th Floor · New York, NY 10281-2101 · 212-415-8700

Patricia A. Martone · Ropes & Gray · http://www.ropesgray.com · 1211 Avenue of the Americas · New York, NY 10036-8704 · 212-596-9000

Roger M. Milgrim · 2% · Paul Hastings · Park Avenue Tower, First Floor · 75 East 55th Street · New York, NY 10022 · 212-318-6000

Robert C. Morgan · a · Ropes & Gray · http://www.ropesgray.com · 1211 Avenue of the Americas · New York, NY 10036-8704 · 212-596-9000

John E. Nathan · a · Paul, Weiss, Rifkind, Wharton & Garrison · 1285 Avenue of the Americas · New York, NY 10019-6064 · 212-373-3000

Robert Neuner · Baker Botts · http://www.bakerbotts.com · 30 Rockefeller Plaza · New York, NY 10112 · 212-408-2500

Brendan J. O'Rourke · Proskauer Rose · http://www.proskauer.com · 1585 Broadway · New York, NY 10036-8299 · 212-969-3000

Marcia B. Paul · Davis Wright Tremaine · 1633 Broadway, 27th Floor · New York, NY 10019-6708 · 212-489-8230

John B. Pegram · a · Fish & Richardson · Citigroup Center, 52nd Floor · 153 East 53rd Street · New York, NY 10022-4611 · 212-765-5070

Robert F. Perry · King & Spalding · 1185 Avenue of the Americas · New York, NY 10036-4003 · 212-556-2100

Kenneth A. Plevan · Skadden, Arps, Slate, Meagher & Flom · Four Times Square · New York, NY 10036 212-735-3000

Rory J. Radding · Morrison & Foerster · http://www.mofo.com · 1290 Avenue of the Americas · New York, NY 10104-0050 · 212-468-8000

Pasquale A. Razzano · a · Fitzpatrick, Cella, Harper & Scinto · http://www.fitzpatrickcella.com · 30 Rockefeller Plaza · New York, NY 10112-3801 · 212-218-2100

Henry J. Renk · Fitzpatrick, Cella, Harper & Scinto · http://www.fitzpatrickcella.com · 30 Rockefeller Plaza · New York, NY 10112-3801 · 212-218-2100

R. Bruce Rich · a · Weil Gotshal & Manges · 767 Fifth Avenue · New York, NY 10153 · 212-310-8000

Virginia R. Richard · Winston & Strawn · 200 Park Avenue · New York, NY 10166-4193 · 212-294-6700

Albert Robin · a · Cowan, Liebowitz & Latman · 1133 Avenue of the Americas, 35th Floor · New York, NY 10036-6799 · 212-790-9200

Kenneth Rubenstein · Proskauer Rose · http://www.proskauer.com · 1585 Broadway · New York, NY 10036-8299 · 212-969-3000

Robert C. Scheinfeld · Baker Botts · http://www.bakerbotts.com · 30 Rockefeller Plaza · New York, NY 10112 · 212-408-2500

Lawrence F. Scinto · a · Fitzpatrick, Cella, Harper & Scinto · http://www.fitzpatrickcella.com · 30 Rockefeller Plaza · New York, NY 10112-3801 · 212-218-2100

Howard J. Shire · Kenyon & Kenyon · One Broadway · New York, NY 10004-1050 · 212-425-7200

Charles S. Sims · Proskauer Rose · http://www.proskauer.com · 1585 Broadway · New York, NY 10036-8299 · 212-969-3000

Thomas A. Smart · Kaye Scholer · 425 Park Avenue · New York, NY 10022-3598 · 212-836-8000

Gerald Sobel · a · Kaye Scholer · 425 Park Avenue · New York, NY 10022-3598 · 212-836-8000

John F. Sweeney · a · Morgan & Finnegan · http://www.morganfinnegan.com · Three World Financial Center, 20th Floor · New York, NY 10281-2101 · 212-415-8700

James B. Swire · a · Arnold & Porter · 399 Park Avenue, 34th Floor · New York, NY 10022-4690 · 212-715-1000

Edward E. Vassallo · Fitzpatrick, Cella, Harper & Scinto · http://www.fitzpatrickcella.com · 30 Rockefeller Plaza · New York, NY 10112-3801 · 212-218-2100

John C. Vassil · a · Morgan & Finnegan · http://www.morganfinnegan.com · Three World Financial Center, 20th Floor · New York, NY 10281-2101 · 212-415-8700

Roger L. Zissu · a · Fross, Zelnick, Lehrman & Zissu · 866 United Nations Plaza · New York, NY 10017 212-813-5900

INTERNATIONAL ARBITRATION

Manhasset

Louis A. Craco · 2% · Craco & Ellsworth · 36 Maple Place, Second Floor · Manhasset, NY 11030 · 516-365-9100

New York

Gerald Aksen · Gerald Aksen, Arbitrator - Mediator · 875 Third Avenue, 10th Floor · New York, NY 10022-6225 · 212-603-2174

James H. Carter · Sullivan & Cromwell · 125 Broad Street · New York, NY 10004-2498 · 212-558-4000

Kenneth Conboy · a · Latham & Watkins · 885 Third Avenue · New York, NY 10022-4834 · 212-906-1200

Michael A. Cooper · 2) · Sullivan & Cromwell · 125 Broad Street · New York, NY 10004-2498 · 212-558-4000

Donald F. Donovan · Debevoise & Plimpton · 919 Third Avenue · New York, NY 10022 · 212-909-6000

John Fellas · Hughes Hubbard & Reed · http://www.hugheshubbard.com · One Battery Park Plaza · New York, NY 10004-1482 · 212-837-6000

Dana H. Freyer · Skadden, Arps, Slate, Meagher & Flom · Four Times Square · New York, NY 10036 · 212-735-3000

Paul D. Friedland · White & Case · http://www.whitecase.com · 1155 Avenue of the Americas · New York, NY 10036-2787 · 212-819-8200

John L. Gardiner · Skadden, Arps, Slate, Meagher & Flom · Four Times Square · New York, NY 10036 · 212-735-3000

Barry H. Garfinkel · Skadden, Arps, Slate, Meagher & Flom · Four Times Square · New York, NY 10036 212-735-3000

Marc J. Goldstein · Marc J. Goldstein Law Offices and Arbitration Chambers · 1230 Avenue of the Americas, Seventh Floor · New York, NY 10020 · 212-799-8605

Steven A. Hammond · Hughes Hubbard & Reed · http://www.hugheshubbard.com · One Battery Park Plaza · New York, NY 10004-1482 · 212-837-6000

John J. Kerr, Jr. · Simpson Thacher · 425 Lexington Avenue · New York, NY 10017-3954 · 212-455-2000

David M. Lindsey · Clifford Chance · 31 West 52nd Street · New York, NY 10019-6131 · 212-878-8000

Joseph E. Neuhaus · Sullivan & Cromwell · 125 Broad Street · New York, NY 10004-2498 · 212-558-4000

Lawrence W. Newman · Baker & McKenzie · 1114 Avenue of the Americas · New York, NY 10036 · 212-626-4100

James W. Quinn · Weil Gotshal & Manges · 767 Fifth Avenue · New York, NY 10153 · 212-310-8000

Roy L. Reardon · 2% · Simpson Thacher · 425 Lexington Avenue · New York, NY 10017-3954 · 212-455-2000

Lucy Reed · Freshfields Bruckhaus Deringer · 520 Madison Avenue, 34th Floor · New York, NY 10022 · 212-277-4000

Robert S. Rifkind · 2% · Cravath, Swaine & Moore · Worldwide Plaza · 825 Eighth Avenue · New York, NY 10019-7475 · 212-474-1000

David W. Rivkin · Debevoise & Plimpton · 919 Third Avenue · New York, NY 10022 · 212-909-6000

Arthur W. Rovine · Baker & McKenzie · 1114 Avenue of the Americas · New York, NY 10036 · 212-626-4100

Robert H. Smit · Simpson Thacher · 425 Lexington Avenue · New York, NY 10017-3954 · 212-455-2000

Robert B. von Mehren · Debevoise & Plimpton · 919 Third Avenue · New York, NY 10022 · 212-909-6000

Daniel H. Weiner · Hughes Hubbard & Reed · http://www.hugheshubbard.com · One Battery Park Plaza New York, NY 10004-1482 · 212-837-6000

John H. Wilkinson · Fulton, Rowe & Hart · One Rockefeller Plaza, Suite 301 · New York, NY 10020 · 212-586-0700

INTERNATIONAL TRADE AND FINANCE LAW

New York

Jerome Alan Cohen · a · Paul, Weiss, Rifkind, Wharton & Garrison · 1285 Avenue of the Americas · New York, NY 10019-6064 · 212-373-3000

Carmen Amalia Corrales · Cleary Gottlieb Steen & Hamilton · One Liberty Plaza · New York, NY 10006 · 212-225-2000

Robert P. Davis · Cleary Gottlieb Steen & Hamilton · One Liberty Plaza · New York, NY 10006 · 212-225-2000

Nancy L. Hengen · Holland & Knight · http://www.hklaw.com · 195 Broadway, 24th Floor · New York, NY 10007-3189 · 212-513-3200

Allen I. Isaacson · a · Fried, Frank, Harris, Shriver & Jacobson · One New York Plaza · New York, NY 10004-1980 · 212-859-8000

Carlos E. Mendez-Penate · Thompson & Knight · http://www.tklaw.com · 919 Third Avenue, 39th Floor New York, NY 10022-3915 · 212-751-3001

Jiro Murase · a · Bingham McCutchen · http://www.bingham.com · 399 Park Avenue · New York, NY 10022-4689 · 212-705-7000

Satoru Murase · Bingham McCutchen · http://www.bingham.com · 399 Park Avenue · New York, NY 10022-4689 · 212-705-7000

Paul S. Schreiber · a · Shearman & Sterling · 599 Lexington Avenue · New York, NY 10022-6069 · 212-848-4000

Isaac Shapiro · 2% · Skadden, Arps, Slate, Meagher & Flom · Four Times Square · New York, NY 10036 · 212-735-3000

Arbie R. Thalacker · 2% · Shearman & Sterling · 599 Lexington Avenue · New York, NY 10022-6069 · 212-848-4000

LABOR AND EMPLOYMENT LAW

Albany

John M. Bagyi · Bond, Schoeneck & King · 111 Washington Avenue · Albany, NY 12210-2211 · 518-533-3000

Bruce C. Bramley · 2) · Pozefsky, Bramley & Murphy · 90 State Street, Suite 1405 · Albany, NY 12207 · 518-434-2622

Nicholas J. D'Ambrosio, Jr. · a · Bond, Schoeneck & King · 111 Washington Avenue · Albany, NY 12210-2211 · 518-533-3000

Ronald G. Dunn · Gleason, Dunn, Walsh & O'Shea · 40 Beaver Street · Albany, NY 12207 · 518-432-7511

Franklin H. Goldberger · ⑳ · Jackson Lewis · 18 Corporate Woods Boulevard, Third Floor · Albany, NY 12211 · 518-434-1300

Richard C. Heffern · ⑳ · Bond, Schoeneck & King · 111 Washington Avenue · Albany, NY 12210-2211 · 518-533-3000

John E. Higgins · Nixon Peabody · 677 Broadway, 10th Floor · Albany, NY 12207 · 518-427-2650

Richard A. Kohn · ⑩ · Law Office of Richard A. Kohn · 74 Chapel Street · Albany, NY 12207 · 518-458-8080

Norma G. Meacham · Whiteman Osterman & Hanna · One Commerce Plaza · Albany, NY 12260 · 518-487-7600

William Pozefsky · ⑳ · Pozefsky, Bramley & Murphy · 90 State Street, Suite 1405 · Albany, NY 12207 · 518-434-2622

Richard R. Rowley · ⑳ · Cooper Erving & Savage · 39 North Pearl Street · Albany, NY 12207-2797 · 518-449-3900

Binghamton

Frank A. Nemia · ⑳ · Coughlin & Gerhart · 20 Hawley Street · P.O. Box 2039 · Binghamton, NY 13902-2039 · 607-723-9511

Joseph J. Steflik, Jr. · ⑩ · Coughlin & Gerhart · 20 Hawley Street · P.O. Box 2039 · Binghamton, NY 13902-2039 · 607-723-9511

Buffalo

Sean P. Beiter · Jaeckle Fleischmann & Mugel · 12 Fountain Plaza · Buffalo, NY 14202-2292 · 716-856-0600

Robert L. Boreanaz · Lipsitz Green Scime Cambria · http://www.lipsitzgreen.com · 42 Delaware Avenue, Suite 120 · Buffalo, NY 14202 · 716-849-1333

Thomas E. Brydges · Jaeckle Fleischmann & Mugel · 12 Fountain Plaza · Buffalo, NY 14202-2292 · 716-856-0600

Hugh C. Carlin · Gross, Shuman, Brizdle & Gilfillan · Fayette Court Building, Suite 600 · 465 Main Street · Buffalo, NY 14203 · 716-854-4300

Melinda G. Disare · Damon & Morey · http://www.damonmorey.com · 1000 Cathedral Place · 298 Main Street · Buffalo, NY 14202-4096 · 716-856-5500

James D. Donathen · Phillips Lytle · 3400 HSBC Center · Buffalo, NY 14203-2887 · 716-847-8400

Robert A. Doren · ⑳ · Bond, Schoeneck & King · Key Center, Suite 600 · 40 Fountain Plaza · Buffalo, NY 14202-2200 · 716-566-2800

David A. Farmelo · Hodgson Russ · One Guaranty Building, Suite 100 · 140 Pearl Street · Buffalo, NY 14202 · 716-856-4000

Daniel P. Forsyth · ⑩ · Bond, Schoeneck & King · Key Center, Suite 600 · 40 Fountain Plaza · Buffalo, NY 14202-2200 · 716-566-2800

E. Joseph Giroux, Jr. · 2% · Creighton, Pearce, Johnsen & Giroux · Ellicott Square Building, Suite 560 · 295 Main Street · Buffalo, NY 14203 · 716-854-0007

James R. Grasso · Phillips Lytle · 3400 HSBC Center · Buffalo, NY 14203-2887 · 716-847-8400

Karl W. Kristoff · Hodgson Russ · One Guaranty Building, Suite 100 · 140 Pearl Street · Buffalo, NY 14202 · 716-856-4000

Richard Lipsitz · 2% · Lipsitz Green Scime Cambria · http://www.lipsitzgreen.com · 42 Delaware Avenue, Suite 120 · Buffalo, NY 14202 · 716-849-1333

Michael R. Moravec · Phillips Lytle · 3400 HSBC Center · Buffalo, NY 14203-2887 · 716-847-8400

Randall M. Odza · 2% · Jaeckle Fleischmann & Mugel · 12 Fountain Plaza · Buffalo, NY 14202-2292 · 716-856-0600

Randolph C. Oppenheimer · Damon & Morey · http://www.damonmorey.com · 1000 Cathedral Place · 298 Main Street · Buffalo, NY 14202-4096 · 716-856-5500

Edward G. Piwowarczyk · 2) · Jaeckle Fleischmann & Mugel · 12 Fountain Plaza · Buffalo, NY 14202-2292 · 716-856-0600

Eugene W. Salisbury · 2% · Lipsitz Green Scime Cambria · http://www.lipsitzgreen.com · 42 Delaware Avenue, Suite 120 · Buffalo, NY 14202 · 716-849-1333

James N. Schmit · 2) · Damon & Morey · http://www.damonmorey.com · 1000 Cathedral Place · 298 Main Street · Buffalo, NY 14202-4096 · 716-856-5500

Anne S. Simet · Hodgson Russ · One Guaranty Building, Suite 100 · 140 Pearl Street · Buffalo, NY 14202 716-856-4000

East Syracuse

Benjamin J. Ferrara · a · Ferrara, Fiorenza, Larrison, Barrett & Reitz · 5010 Campuswood Drive · East Syracuse, NY 13057 · 315-437-7600

Garden City

Terry O'Neil · Bond, Schoeneck & King · 1399 Franklin Avenue, Suite 200 · Garden City, NY 11530-1679 · 516-267-6300

Jamestown

Martin F. Idzik · 2) · Phillips Lytle · Eight East Third Street, Suite 307 · P.O. Box 1279 · Jamestown, NY 14702-1279 · 716-664-3906

Jericho

Daniel A. Rizzi · a · Nixon Peabody · 50 Jericho Quadrangle, Suite 300 · Jericho, NY 11753-2728 · 516-832-7500

New York

Neil H. Abramson · Proskauer Rose · http://www.proskauer.com · 1585 Broadway · New York, NY 10036-8299 · 212-969-3000

Marshall B. Babson · a · Hughes Hubbard & Reed · http://www.hugheshubbard.com · One Battery Park Plaza · New York, NY 10004-1482 · 212-837-6000

Ned H. Bassen · Hughes Hubbard & Reed · http://www.hugheshubbard.com · One Battery Park Plaza · New York, NY 10004-1482 · 212-837-6000

L. Robert Batterman · 2) · Proskauer Rose · http://www.proskauer.com · 1585 Broadway · New York, NY 10036-8299 · 212-969-3000

Joseph Baumgarten · Proskauer Rose · http://www.proskauer.com · 1585 Broadway · New York, NY 10036-8299 · 212-969-3000

Jonathan Ben-Asher · Beranbaum Menken Ben-Asher & Bierman · 80 Pine Street, 32nd Floor · New York, NY 10005 · 212-509-1616

John A. Beranbaum · Beranbaum Menken Ben-Asher & Bierman · 80 Pine Street, 32nd Floor · New York, NY 10005 · 212-509-1616

Laurie Berke-Weiss · Berke-Weiss & Pechman · 488 Madison Avenue, 11th Floor · New York, NY 10022 212-583-9500

Philip M. Berkowitz · Nixon Peabody · 437 Madison Avenue, 23rd Floor · New York, NY 10022 · 212-940-3000

Michael I. Bernstein · 2) · Bond, Schoeneck & King · 330 Madison Avenue, 39th Floor · New York, NY 10017-5001 · 646-253-2300

Richard H. Block · Dreier · 499 Park Avenue · New York, NY 10022 · 212-328-6100

Elise M. Bloom · Proskauer Rose · http://www.proskauer.com · 1585 Broadway · New York, NY 10036-8299 · 212-969-3000

Frederick D. Braid · Holland & Knight · http://www.hklaw.com · 195 Broadway, 24th Floor · New York, NY 10007-3189 · 212-513-3200

Mark E. Brossman · Schulte Roth & Zabel · 919 Third Avenue · New York, NY 10022 · 212-756-2000

John D. Canoni · 2) · Nixon Peabody · 437 Madison Avenue, 23rd Floor · New York, NY 10022 · 212-940-3000

William A. Carmell · a · Ford & Harrison · http://www.fordharrison.com · 100 Park Avenue, Suite 2500 · New York, NY 10017-5536 · 212-453-5900

Douglas P. Catalano · Fulbright & Jaworski · http://www.fulbright.com · 666 Fifth Avenue · New York, NY 10103-3198 · 212-318-3000

Anne L. Clark · Vladeck, Waldman, Elias & Engelhard · 1501 Broadway, Suite 800 · New York, NY 10036-5560 · 212-403-7300

Miriam F. Clark · Ritz & Clark · http://www.ritzandclark.com · 40 Exchange Place, Suite 2010 · New York, NY 10005-2701 · 212-321-7075

Michael A. Curley · Morgan Lewis & Bockius · 101 Park Avenue · New York, NY 10178-0060 · 212-309-6000

Michael Delikat · Orrick, Herrington & Sutcliffe · 666 Fifth Avenue · New York, NY 10103-0001 · 212-506-5000

Louis P. DiLorenzo · a · Bond, Schoeneck & King · 330 Madison Avenue, 39th Floor · New York, NY 10017-5001 · 646-253-2300

Herbert Eisenberg · a · Eisenberg & Schnell · 233 Broadway, Suite 2704 · New York, NY 10279 · 212-966-8900

Eugene G. Eisner · 2) · Eisner & Associates · 113 University Place, Eighth Floor · New York, NY 10003-4588 · 212-473-8700

Samuel Estreicher · Jones Day · 222 East 41st Street · New York, NY 10017-6702 · 212-326-3939

Allen I. Fagin · 2) · Proskauer Rose · http://www.proskauer.com · 1585 Broadway · New York, NY 10036-8299 · 212-969-3000

Zachary D. Fasman · a · Paul Hastings · Park Avenue Tower, First Floor · 75 East 55th Street · New York, NY 10022 · 212-318-6000

Joel L. Finger · Littler Mendelson · 885 Third Avenue, 16th Floor · New York, NY 10022-4834 · 212-583-9600

Eugene S. Friedman · 2) · Friedman & Wolf · 1500 Broadway, Suite 2300 · New York, NY 10036 · 212-354-4500

John F. Fullerton III · Sullivan & Cromwell · 125 Broad Street · New York, NY 10004-2498 · 212-558-4000

Howard L. Ganz · 2) · Proskauer Rose · http://www.proskauer.com · 1585 Broadway · New York, NY 10036-8299 · 212-969-3000

Amy Gladstein · a · Gladstein, Reif & Meginniss · 817 Broadway, Sixth Floor · New York, NY 10003 · 212-228-7727

Anne Golden · Outten & Golden · Three Park Avenue, 29th Floor · New York, NY 10016 · 212-245-1000

Willis J. Goldsmith · a · Jones Day · 222 East 41st Street · New York, NY 10017-6702 · 212-326-3939

Janice Goodman · 2) · Law Office of Janice Goodman · 275 Seventh Avenue, Suite 2300 · New York, NY 10001 · 212-869-1940

Kenneth E. Gordon · 2) · Gordon, Gordon & Schnapp · 437 Madison Avenue, 39th Floor · New York, NY 10022 · 212-355-3200

Ronald M. Green · 2) · Epstein, Becker & Green · 250 Park Avenue, 14th Floor · New York, NY 10177-1211 · 212-351-4500

Edward Hernstadt · Frankfurt Kurnit Klein & Selz · http://www.fkks.com · 488 Madison Avenue, Tenth Floor · New York, NY 10022 · 212-980-0120

Mark A. Jacoby · 2) · Weil Gotshal & Manges · 767 Fifth Avenue · New York, NY 10153 · 212-310-8000

Alan S. Jaffe · 2) · Proskauer Rose · http://www.proskauer.com · 1585 Broadway · New York, NY 10036-8299 · 212-969-3000

Jerome B. Kauff · 2) · Kauff, McClain & McGuire · 950 Third Avenue, 14th Floor · New York, NY 10022 212-644-1010

Adam T. Klein · Outten & Golden · Three Park Avenue, 29th Floor · New York, NY 10016 · 212-245-1000

Jeffrey S. Klein · Weil Gotshal & Manges · 767 Fifth Avenue · New York, NY 10153 · 212-310-8000

Kevin B. LeBlang · Kramer Levin Naftalis & Frankel · http://www.kramerlevin.com · 1177 Avenue of the Americas · New York, NY 10036 · 212-715-9100

Leonard Leibowitz · 2) · Law Offices of Leonard Leibowitz · 322 West 48th Street · New York, NY 10036 · 212-765-4300

Richard A. Levy · 2) · Levy Ratner · 80 Eighth Avenue, Eighth Floor · New York, NY 10011-5126 · 212-627-8100

Ellen M. Martin · Patterson Belknap Webb & Tyler · http://www.pbwt.com · 1133 Avenue of the Americas · New York, NY 10036-6710 · 212-336-2000

Kathleen M. McKenna · Proskauer Rose · http://www.proskauer.com · 1585 Broadway · New York, NY 10036-8299 · 212-969-3000

Walter M. Meginniss, Jr. · a · Gladstein, Reif & Meginniss · 817 Broadway, Sixth Floor · New York, NY 10003 · 212-228-7727

Matthew T. Miklave · Epstein, Becker & Green · 250 Park Avenue, 14th Floor · New York, NY 10177-1211 · 212-351-4500

William J. Milani · Epstein, Becker & Green · 250 Park Avenue, 14th Floor · New York, NY 10177-1211 212-351-4500

Laurence S. Moy · Outten & Golden · Three Park Avenue, 29th Floor · New York, NY 10016 · 212-245-1000

Daniel F. Murphy, Jr. · Putney, Twombly, Hall & Hirson · 521 Fifth Avenue, 10th Floor · New York, NY 10175 · 212-682-0020

Martin J. Oppenheimer · 2) · Proskauer Rose · http://www.proskauer.com · 1585 Broadway · New York, NY 10036-8299 · 212-969-3000

Wayne Norris Outten · 2) · Outten & Golden · Three Park Avenue, 29th Floor · New York, NY 10016 · 212-245-1000

Peter M. Panken · 2) · Epstein, Becker & Green · 250 Park Avenue, 14th Floor · New York, NY 10177-1211 · 212-351-4500

Louis Pechman · Berke-Weiss & Pechman · 488 Madison Avenue, 11th Floor · New York, NY 10022 · 212-583-9500

Bettina B. Plevan · a · Proskauer Rose · http://www.proskauer.com · 1585 Broadway · New York, NY 10036-8299 · 212-969-3000

Bernard M. Plum · Proskauer Rose · http://www.proskauer.com · 1585 Broadway · New York, NY 10036-8299 · 212-969-3000

Bertrand B. Pogrebin · 2) · Littler Mendelson · 885 Third Avenue, 16th Floor · New York, NY 10022-4834 · 212-583-9600

Gregory I. Rasin · 2) · Proskauer Rose · http://www.proskauer.com · 1585 Broadway · New York, NY 10036-8299 · 212-969-3000

Debra L. Raskin · a · Vladeck, Waldman, Elias & Engelhard · 1501 Broadway, Suite 800 · New York, NY 10036-5560 · 212-403-7300

Daniel J. Ratner · a · Levy Ratner · 80 Eighth Avenue, Eighth Floor · New York, NY 10011-5126 · 212-627-8100

Susan R. Ritz · a · Ritz & Clark · http://www.ritzandclark.com · 40 Exchange Place, Suite 2010 · New York, NY 10005-2701 · 212-321-7075

Allen B. Roberts · Epstein, Becker & Green · 250 Park Avenue, 14th Floor · New York, NY 10177-1211 · 212-351-4500

Susan S. Robfogel · 2) · Nixon Peabody · 437 Madison Avenue, 23rd Floor · New York, NY 10022 · 212-940-3000

Theodore O. Rogers, Jr. · Sullivan & Cromwell · 125 Broad Street · New York, NY 10004-2498 · 212-558-4000

Jill L. Rosenberg · Orrick, Herrington & Sutcliffe · 666 Fifth Avenue · New York, NY 10103-0001 · 212-506-5000

Paul Salvatore · Proskauer Rose · http://www.proskauer.com · 1585 Broadway · New York, NY 10036-8299 · 212-969-3000

Paul Schachter · 2) · Levy Ratner · 80 Eighth Avenue, Eighth Floor · New York, NY 10011-5126 · 212-627-8100

Andrew J. Schaffran · Morgan Lewis & Bockius · 101 Park Avenue · New York, NY 10178-0060 · 212-309-6000

Stanley Schair · 2) · Bond, Schoeneck & King · 330 Madison Avenue, 39th Floor · New York, NY 10017-5001 · 646-253-2300

Laura S. Schnell · Eisenberg & Schnell · 233 Broadway, Suite 2704 · New York, NY 10279 · 212-966-8900

Samuel S. Shaulson · Morgan Lewis & Bockius · 101 Park Avenue · New York, NY 10178-0060 · 212-309-6000

Patrick W. Shea · Paul Hastings · Park Avenue Tower, First Floor · 75 East 55th Street · New York, NY 10022 · 212-318-6000

Bruce H. Simon · 2% · Cohen, Weiss and Simon · 330 West 42nd Street · New York, NY 10036 · 212-563-4100

Stephen P. Sonnenberg · Paul Hastings · Park Avenue Tower, First Floor · 75 East 55th Street · New York, NY 10022 · 212-318-6000

Evan J. Spelfogel · a · Epstein, Becker & Green · 250 Park Avenue, 14th Floor · New York, NY 10177-1211 · 212-351-4500

Michael Starr · Hogan & Hartson · 875 Third Avenue, 25th Floor · New York, NY 10022 · 212-918-3000

Lewis M. Steel · 2) · Outten & Golden · Three Park Avenue, 29th Floor · New York, NY 10016 · 212-245-1000

Kenneth D. Stein · Ford & Harrison · http://www.fordharrison.com · 100 Park Avenue, Suite 2500 · New York, NY 10017-5536 · 212-453-5900

Darnley D. Stewart · Giskan, Solotaroff, Anderson & Stewart · 11 Broadway, Suite 2150 · New York, NY 10004 · 212-847-8315

Steven M. Swirsky · Epstein, Becker & Green · 250 Park Avenue, 14th Floor · New York, NY 10177-1211 · 212-351-4500

Anne C. Vladeck · a · Vladeck, Waldman, Elias & Engelhard · 1501 Broadway, Suite 800 · New York, NY 10036-5560 · 212-403-7300

Jay W. Waks · 2) · Kaye Scholer · 425 Park Avenue · New York, NY 10022-3598 · 212-836-8000

Seymour M. Waldman · 2% · Vladeck, Waldman, Elias & Engelhard · 1501 Broadway, Suite 800 · New York, NY 10036-5560 · 212-403-7300

Douglas H. Wigdor · Thompson Wigdor & Gilly · http://www.twglawyers.com · 350 Fifth Avenue, Suite 5720 · New York, NY 10118 · 212-239-9292

Gwynne A. Wilcox · Levy Ratner · 80 Eighth Avenue, Eighth Floor · New York, NY 10011-5126 · 212-627-8100

Miriam Hauser Wugmeister · Morrison & Foerster · http://www.mofo.com · 1290 Avenue of the Americas · New York, NY 10104-0050 · 212-468-8000

Pearl Zuchlewski · Kraus & Zuchlewski · 500 Fifth Avenue, Suite 5100 · New York, NY 10110-5199 · 212-869-4646

Rochester

Stephanie M. Caffera · Nixon Peabody · 1100 Clinton Square · P.O. Box 31051 · Rochester, NY 14604 · 585-263-1000

Richard N. Chapman · a · Harris Beach · The Granite Building · 130 East Main Street · Rochester, NY 14604 · 585-419-8800

Margaret A. Clemens · Nixon Peabody · 1100 Clinton Square · P.O. Box 31051 · Rochester, NY 14604 · 585-263-1000

Jack D. Eisenberg · a · Harter Secrest & Emery · http://www.hselaw.com · 1600 Bausch & Lomb Place · Rochester, NY 14604-2711 · 585-232-6500

Matthew J. Fusco · a · Chamberlain D'Amanda Oppenheimer & Greenfield · 1600 Crossroads Building · Two State Street · Rochester, NY 14614 · 585-232-3730

Michael T. Harren · 2) · Chamberlain D'Amanda Oppenheimer & Greenfield · 1600 Crossroads Building Two State Street · Rochester, NY 14614 · 585-232-3730

Michael A. Hausknecht · a · Nixon Peabody · 1100 Clinton Square · P.O. Box 31051 · Rochester, NY 14604 · 585-263-1000

James C. Holahan · Ward, Norris, Heller & Reidy · http://www.wnhr.com · 300 State Street · Rochester, NY 14614 · 585-454-0700

Todd R. Shinaman · Nixon Peabody · 1100 Clinton Square · P.O. Box 31051 · Rochester, NY 14604 · 585-263-1000

Jules L. Smith · 2) · Blitman & King · The Powers Building, Suite 207 · 16 West Main Street · Rochester, NY 14614 · 585-232-5600

Peter Joseph Spinelli · a · Harris Beach · The Granite Building · 130 East Main Street · Rochester, NY 14604 · 585-419-8800

James A. Spitz, Jr. · Harris Beach · The Granite Building · 130 East Main Street · Rochester, NY 14604 · 585-419-8800

Edward A. Trevvett · Harris Beach · The Granite Building · 130 East Main Street · Rochester, NY 14604 585-419-8800

Smithtown

Jerry I. Lefkowitz · a · Jerry I. Lefkowitz · Five Stanley Place · Smithtown, NY 11788 · 631-979-8585

Syracuse

R. Daniel Bordoni · Bond, Schoeneck & King · One Lincoln Center · Syracuse, NY 13202-1355 · 315-218-8000

Thomas G. Eron · Bond, Schoeneck & King · One Lincoln Center · Syracuse, NY 13202-1355 · 315-218-8000

John Gaal · Bond, Schoeneck & King · One Lincoln Center · Syracuse, NY 13202-1355 · 315-218-8000

Thomas J. Grooms · a · Bond, Schoeneck & King · One Lincoln Center · Syracuse, NY 13202-1355 · 315-218-8000

Peter A. Jones · Bond, Schoeneck & King · One Lincoln Center · Syracuse, NY 13202-1355 · 315-218-8000

Bernard T. King · 2) · Blitman & King · Franklin Center, Suite 300 · 443 North Franklin Street · Syracuse, NY 13204-1415 · 315-422-7111

Robert A. LaBerge · Bond, Schoeneck & King · One Lincoln Center · Syracuse, NY 13202-1355 · 315-218-8000

James R. LaVaute · 2) · Blitman & King · Franklin Center, Suite 300 · 443 North Franklin Street · Syracuse, NY 13204-1415 · 315-422-7111

Larry P. Malfitano · Bond, Schoeneck & King · One Lincoln Center · Syracuse, NY 13202-1355 · 315-218-8000

Donald D. Oliver · Blitman & King · Franklin Center, Suite 300 · 443 North Franklin Street · Syracuse, NY 13204-1415 · 315-422-7111

Mimi Satter · Satter & Andrews · McCarthy Building, Sixth Floor · 217 South Salina Street · Syracuse, NY 13202 · 315-471-0405

Stephen J. Vollmer · Bond, Schoeneck & King · One Lincoln Center · Syracuse, NY 13202-1355 · 315-218-8000

White Plains

William D. Frumkin · Sapir & Frumkin · 399 Knollwood Road, Suite 300 · White Plains, NY 10603 · 914-328-0366

Donald L. Sapir · Sapir & Frumkin · 399 Knollwood Road, Suite 300 · White Plains, NY 10603 · 914-328-0366

Patrick L. Vaccaro · 2) · Jackson Lewis · http://www.jacksonlewis.com · One North Broadway, 15th Floor White Plains, NY 10601-2305 · 914-328-0404

Albany

Victor A. Caponera, Jr. · Victor A. Caponera · Three Atrium Drive, Suite 220 · Albany, NY 12205-1417 · 518-453-8381

Mary Elizabeth Slevin · Stockli Greene & Slevin · 90 State Street · Albany, NY 12207 · 518-449-3125

John W. Tabner · a · Tabner, Ryan & Keniry · 18 Corporate Woods Boulevard · Albany, NY 12211 · 800-713-7583

Donald Zee · Donald Zee · One Winners Circle, Suite 140 · Albany, NY 12205-5974 · 518-489-9423

Amherst

Michael A. Piette · Jaeckle Fleischmann & Mugel · Centerpointe Corporate Park, Suite 320 · 400 Essjay Road · Amherst, NY 14221 · 716-250-1800

Buffalo

Barry N. Covert · Lipsitz Green Scime Cambria · http://www.lipsitzgreen.com · 42 Delaware Avenue, Suite 120 · Buffalo, NY 14202 · 716-849-1333

Frederick A. Wolf · Damon & Morey · http://www.damonmorey.com · 1000 Cathedral Place · 298 Main Street · Buffalo, NY 14202-4096 · 716-856-5500

Fairport

Jerry A. Goldman · Fix Spindelman Brovitz & Goldman · http://www.fixspin.com · 295 Woodcliff Drive, Suite 200 · Fairport, NY 14450 · 585-641-8000

Glens Falls

Jonathan C. Lapper · Bartlett, Pontiff, Stewart & Rhodes · One Washington Street · P.O. Box 2168 · Glens Falls, NY 12801-2168 · 518-792-2117

Marietta

Scott F. Chatfield · Scott F. Chatfield · 3100 Brewer Road, Suite 70 · Marietta, NY 13110-3305 · 315-636-7911

New York

Michael D. Bailkin · Akerman Senterfitt · http://www.akerman.com · 335 Madison Avenue, Suite 2600 · New York, NY 10017-4636 · 212-880-3800

Mark A. Chertok · Sive Paget & Riesel · 460 Park Avenue, 10th Floor · New York, NY 10022 · 212-421-2150

Robert S. Davis · Bryan Cave · 1290 Avenue of the Americas · New York, NY 10104-3300 · 212-541-2000

Howard G. Goldman · Law Offices of Howard J. Goldman · 475 Park Avenue South, 28th Floor · New York, NY 10016 · 212-935-1622

Stephen Lefkowitz · a · Fried, Frank, Harris, Shriver & Jacobson · One New York Plaza · New York, NY 10004-1980 · 212-859-8000

Samuel H. Lindenbaum · 2% · Kramer Levin Naftalis & Frankel · http://www.kramerlevin.com · 1177 Avenue of the Americas · New York, NY 10036 · 212-715-9100

Melanie Meyers · Fried, Frank, Harris, Shriver & Jacobson · One New York Plaza · New York, NY 10004-1980 · 212-859-8000

Jay A. Segal · Greenberg Traurig · http://www.gtlaw.com · MetLife Building · 200 Park Avenue · New York, NY 10166 · 212-801-9200

Paul D. Selver · Kramer Levin Naftalis & Frankel · http://www.kramerlevin.com · 1177 Avenue of the Americas · New York, NY 10036 · 212-715-9100

Michael T. Sillerman · Kramer Levin Naftalis & Frankel · http://www.kramerlevin.com · 1177 Avenue of the Americas · New York, NY 10036 · 212-715-9100

Gary R. Tarnoff · Kramer Levin Naftalis & Frankel · http://www.kramerlevin.com · 1177 Avenue of the Americas · New York, NY 10036 · 212-715-9100

Rochester

Thomas C. Greiner, Jr. · Nixon Peabody · 1100 Clinton Square · P.O. Box 31051 · Rochester, NY 14604 585-263-1000

Alan J. Knauf · Knauf Shaw · 1125 Crossroads Building · Two State Street · Rochester, NY 14614 · 585-546-8430

Robert Koegel · Remington, Gifford, Williams & Colicchio · 1400 Alliance Building · 183 East Main Street · Rochester, NY 14604-1617 · 585-232-5225

Edward F. Premo II · Harter Secrest & Emery · http://www.hselaw.com · 1600 Bausch & Lomb Place · Rochester, NY 14604-2711 · 585-232-6500

Paul D. Sylvestri · Harter Secrest & Emery · http://www.hselaw.com · 1600 Bausch & Lomb Place · Rochester, NY 14604-2711 · 585-232-6500

Williamsville

Sean W. Hopkins · Hopkins, Garas & Sorgi · 5500 Main Street, Suite 215 · Williamsville, NY 14221-6755 716-614-8801

LEGAL MALPRACTICE LAW

Albany

Stephen R. Coffey · a · O'Connell & Aronowitz · 54 State Street, Ninth Floor · Albany, NY 12207-2501 · 518-462-5601

Eugene E. Napierski, Sr. · a · Napierski, VanDenburgh & Napierski · 296 Washington Avenue Extension · Albany, NY 12203 · 518-862-9292

Buffalo

Terrence M. Connors · a · Connors & Vilardo · 1000 Liberty Building · 424 Main Street · Buffalo, NY 14202 · 716-852-5533

Brian P. Crosby · a · Gibson, McAskill & Crosby · 69 Delaware Avenue, Suite 900 · Buffalo, NY 14202 · 716-856-4200

Carl A. Green · a · Lipsitz Green Scime Cambria · http://www.lipsitzgreen.com · 42 Delaware Avenue, Suite 120 · Buffalo, NY 14202 · 716-849-1333

Joseph V. McCarthy · a · Roach, Brown, McCarthy & Gruber · 1620 Liberty Building · 420 Main Street · Buffalo, NY 14202 · 716-852-0400

Daniel T. Roach · 2% · Roach, Brown, McCarthy & Gruber · 1620 Liberty Building · 420 Main Street · Buffalo, NY 14202 · 716-852-0400

Terry D. Smith · 2% · Smith, Keller, Miner & O'Shea · 69 Delaware Avenue, Suite 1212 · Buffalo, NY 14202-3801 · 716-855-3611

Menands

Mae A. D'Agostino · a · D'Agostino, Krackeler, Baynes & Maguire · The Sage Mansion · 16 Sage Estate · Menands, NY 12204 · 518-434-9807

New York

Jeffrey B. Bloom · Gair, Gair, Conason, Steigman & Mackauf · http://www.gairgair.com · 80 Pine Street, 34th Floor · New York, NY 10005 · 212-943-1090

Peter T. Crean · Martin Clearwater & Bell · http://www.mcblaw.com · 220 East 42nd Street, Suite 1300 · New York, NY 10017 · 212-697-3122

Philip R. Forlenza · Patterson Belknap Webb & Tyler · http://www.pbwt.com · 1133 Avenue of the Americas · New York, NY 10036-6710 · 212-336-2000

Bruce G. Habian · a · Martin Clearwater & Bell · http://www.mcblaw.com · 220 East 42nd Street, Suite 1300 · New York, NY 10017 · 212-697-3122

Rochester

David E. Brown · a · Brown & Tarantino · Times Square Building, Suite 300 · 45 Exchange Boulevard · Rochester, NY 14614 · 585-454-3377

Thomas C. Burke · a · Osborn, Reed & Burke · 45 Exchange Boulevard · Rochester, NY 14614-1403 · 585-454-6480

Angelo G. Faraci · 2% · Faraci Lange · http://www.faraci.com · 28 East Main Street, Suite 1100 · Rochester, NY 14614 · 585-325-5150

Syracuse

Paul M. Hanrahan · a · Hancock & Estabrook · 1500 Axa Tower I · 100 Madison Street · Syracuse, NY 13202 · 315-471-3151

James D. Lantier · Smith, Sovik, Kendrick & Sugnet · 250 South Clinton Street, Suite 600 · Syracuse, NY 13202 · 315-474-2911

Michael P. Ringwood · Smith, Sovik, Kendrick & Sugnet · 250 South Clinton Street, Suite 600 · Syracuse, NY 13202 · 315-474-2911

Laurence F. Sovik · a · Smith, Sovik, Kendrick & Sugnet · 250 South Clinton Street, Suite 600 · Syracuse, NY 13202 · 315-474-2911

E. Stewart Jones, Jr. · 2% · E. Stewart Jones · http://www.esjlaw.com · The Jones Building · 28 Second Street · Troy, NY 12180 · 518-274-5820

LEVERAGED BUYOUTS AND PRIVATE EQUITY LAW

New York

Christopher K. Aidun · Weil Gotshal & Manges · 767 Fifth Avenue · New York, NY 10153 · 212-310-8000

Peter Allan Atkins · 2% · Skadden, Arps, Slate, Meagher & Flom · Four Times Square · New York, NY 10036 · 212-735-3000

Richard I. Beattie · 2) · Simpson Thacher · 425 Lexington Avenue · New York, NY 10017-3954 · 212-455-2000

John A. Bick · Davis Polk & Wardwell · 450 Lexington Avenue · New York, NY 10017 · 212-450-4000

Franci J. Blassberg · Debevoise & Plimpton · 919 Third Avenue · New York, NY 10022 · 212-909-6000

Charles I. Cogut · Simpson Thacher · 425 Lexington Avenue · New York, NY 10017-3954 · 212-455-2000

William E. Curbow · Simpson Thacher · 425 Lexington Avenue · New York, NY 10017-3954 · 212-455-2000

Margaret A. Davenport · Debevoise & Plimpton · 919 Third Avenue · New York, NY 10022 · 212-909-6000

Daniel J. Eisner · Proskauer Rose · http://www.proskauer.com · 1585 Broadway · New York, NY 10036-8299 · 212-969-3000

John R. Ettinger · Davis Polk & Wardwell · 450 Lexington Avenue · New York, NY 10017 · 212-450-4000

John Evangelakos · Sullivan & Cromwell · 125 Broad Street · New York, NY 10004-2498 · 212-558-4000

Joseph B. Frumkin · Sullivan & Cromwell · 125 Broad Street · New York, NY 10004-2498 · 212-558-4000

Steven J. Gartner · Willkie Farr & Gallagher · 787 Seventh Avenue · New York, NY 10019-6099 · 212-728-8000

Louis L. Goldberg · Davis Polk & Wardwell · 450 Lexington Avenue · New York, NY 10017 · 212-450-4000

Bruce C. Herzog · Willkie Farr & Gallagher · 787 Seventh Avenue · New York, NY 10019-6099 · 212-728-8000

R. Ronald Hopkinson · Cadwalader, Wickersham & Taft · http://www.cadwalader.com · One World Financial Center · New York, NY 10281 · 212-504-6000

Robert F. Kennedy · Jones Day · 222 East 41st Street · New York, NY 10017-6702 · 212-326-3939

Stephen M. Kotran · Sullivan & Cromwell · 125 Broad Street · New York, NY 10004-2498 · 212-558-4000

James C. Morphy · a · Sullivan & Cromwell · 125 Broad Street · New York, NY 10004-2498 · 212-558-4000

Wilson S. Neely · Simpson Thacher · 425 Lexington Avenue · New York, NY 10017-3954 · 212-455-2000

Eileen T. Nugent · Skadden, Arps, Slate, Meagher & Flom · Four Times Square · New York, NY 10036 · 212-735-3000

Richard A. Pollack · Sullivan & Cromwell · 125 Broad Street · New York, NY 10004-2498 · 212-558-4000

Othon A. Prounis · Ropes & Gray · http://www.ropesgray.com · 1211 Avenue of the Americas · New York, NY 10036-8704 · 212-596-9000

Kirk A. Radke · Kirkland & Ellis · Citigroup Center · 153 East 53rd Street · New York, NY 10022-4611 · 212-446-4800

Eric S. Robinson · Wachtell, Lipton, Rosen & Katz · 51 West 52nd Street · New York, NY 10019 · 212-403-1000

Philip T. Ruegger III · Simpson Thacher · 425 Lexington Avenue · New York, NY 10017-3954 · 212-455-2000

Paul T. Schnell · Skadden, Arps, Slate, Meagher & Flom · Four Times Square · New York, NY 10036 · 212-735-3000

Benjamin F. Stapleton · 2) · Sullivan & Cromwell · 125 Broad Street · New York, NY 10004-2498 · 212-558-4000

Frederick Tanne · Kirkland & Ellis · Citigroup Center · 153 East 53rd Street · New York, NY 10022-4611 212-446-4800

Douglas P. Warner · Weil Gotshal & Manges · 767 Fifth Avenue · New York, NY 10153 · 212-310-8000

Marc Weingarten · Schulte Roth & Zabel · 919 Third Avenue · New York, NY 10022 · 212-756-2000

MARITIME LAW

Brooklyn

Geoffrey J. Ginos · Geoffrey J. Ginos · 1323 Ditmas Avenue · Brooklyn, NY 11226 · 718-284-9774

Hicksville

Harold M. Kingsley · Kingsley, Kingsley & Calkins · 91 West Cherry Street · Hicksville, NY 11801-3856 516-931-0064

New York

Juan A. Anduiza · Squire Sanders · http://www.ssd.com · 350 Park Avenue · New York, NY 10022-6022 · 212-872-9800

Patrick J. Bonner · Freehill Hogan & Mahar · 80 Pine Street · New York, NY 10005-1759 · 212-425-1900

Lawrence J. Bowles · a · Nourse & Bowles · One Exchange Plaza at 55 Broadway · New York, NY 10006-3030 · 212-952-6200

John E. Bradley · Vedder Price · 1633 Broadway, 47th Floor · New York, NY 10019 · 212-407-7700

Raymond J. Burke, Jr. · 2) · Burke & Parsons · 100 Park Avenue, 30th Floor · New York, NY 10017-5533 · 212-354-3800

Douglas R. Burnett · Squire Sanders · http://www.ssd.com · 350 Park Avenue · New York, NY 10022-6022 · 212-872-9800

Lizabeth L. Burrell · Curtis, Mallet-Prevost, Colt & Mosle · 101 Park Avenue · New York, NY 10178 · 212-696-6000

Leo Chang · Watson, Farley & Williams · 100 Park Avenue, 31st Floor · New York, NY 10017 · 212-922-2200

Robert G. Clyne · Hill Rivkins & Hayden · 45 Broadway, Suite 1500 · New York, NY 10006 · 212-669-0600

Michael Marks Cohen · 2) · Nicoletti Hornig & Sweeney · Wall Street Plaza, Seventh Floor · 88 Pine Street · New York, NY 10005-1801 · 212-220-3830

Raymond A. Connell · a · Raymond A. Connell · 132 Nassau Street, Suite 900 · New York, NY 10038-2400 · 212-233-0440

Martin F. Conniff · Morgan Lewis & Bockius · 101 Park Avenue · New York, NY 10178-0060 · 212-309-6000

Vincent M. DeOrchis · DeOrchis & Partners · 61 Broadway, Suite 2600 · New York, NY 10006 · 212-344-4700

Christopher H. Dillon · Burke & Parsons · 100 Park Avenue, 30th Floor · New York, NY 10017-5533 · 212-354-3800

Craig S. English · Kennedy Lillis Schmidt & English · 75 Maiden Lane, Suite 402 · New York, NY 10038-4816 · 212-430-0800

Jack A. Greenbaum · a · Blank Rome · The Chrysler Building · 405 Lexington Avenue · New York, NY 10174 · 212-885-5000

Robert J. Gruendel · a · DLA Piper · 1251 Avenue of the Americas · New York, NY 10020-1104 · 212-335-4500

Peter J. Gutowski · Freehill Hogan & Mahar · 80 Pine Street · New York, NY 10005-1759 · 212-425-1900

Raymond P. Hayden · a · Hill Rivkins & Hayden · 45 Broadway, Suite 1500 · New York, NY 10006 · 212-669-0600

Keith W. Heard · Burke & Parsons · 100 Park Avenue, 30th Floor · New York, NY 10017-5533 · 212-354-3800

Nancy L. Hengen · Holland & Knight · http://www.hklaw.com · 195 Broadway, 24th Floor · New York, NY 10007-3189 · 212-513-3200

James H. Hohenstein · Holland & Knight · http://www.hklaw.com · 195 Broadway, 24th Floor · New York, NY 10007-3189 · 212-513-3200

William J. Honan · a · Holland & Knight · http://www.hklaw.com · 195 Broadway, 24th Floor · New York, NY 10007-3189 · 212-513-3200

Chester D. Hooper · a · Holland & Knight · http://www.hklaw.com · 195 Broadway, 24th Floor · New York, NY 10007-3189 · 212-513-3200

Mark M. Jaffe · Hill, Betts & Nash · One World Financial, 26th Floor · 200 Liberty Street · New York, NY 10048 · 212-839-7000

Edward A. Keane · Mahiney & Keane · 111 Broadway, 10th Floor · New York, NY 10006 · 212-385-1422

Paul Keane · Cichanowicz, Callan, Keane, Vengrow & Textor · 61 Broadway, Suite 3000 · New York, NY 10006 · 212-344-7042

Donald J. Kennedy · Carter Ledyard & Milburn · Two Wall Street, 18th Floor · New York, NY 10005 · 212-732-3200

John D. Kimball · 2) · Blank Rome · The Chrysler Building · 405 Lexington Avenue · New York, NY 10174 · 212-885-5000

Stephen P. Kyne · Burke & Parsons · 100 Park Avenue, 30th Floor · New York, NY 10017-5533 · 212-354-3800

LeRoy Lambert · Blank Rome · The Chrysler Building · 405 Lexington Avenue · New York, NY 10174 · 212-885-5000

John T. Lillis, Jr. · Kennedy Lillis Schmidt & English · 75 Maiden Lane, Suite 402 · New York, NY 10038-4816 · 212-430-0800

Christopher H. Mansuy · Mahoney & Keane · 11 Hanover Square, 10th Floor · New York, NY 10005 · 212-385-1422

David L. Mazaroli · David L. Mazaroli Law Office · 11 Park Place, Suite 1214 · New York, NY 10007 · 212-267-8480

Howard M. McCormack · a · Burke & Parsons · 100 Park Avenue, 30th Floor · New York, NY 10017-5533 · 212-354-3800

Daniel G. McDermott · McDermott & Radzik · Wall Street Plaza, 21st Floor · 88 Pine Street · New York, NY 10005-1801 · 212-376-6400

Wayne D. Meehan · Freehill Hogan & Mahar · 80 Pine Street · New York, NY 10005-1759 · 212-425-1900

Don P. Murnane · Freehill Hogan & Mahar · 80 Pine Street · New York, NY 10005-1759 · 212-425-1900

John A.V. Nicoletti · Nicoletti Hornig & Sweeney · Wall Street Plaza, Seventh Floor · 88 Pine Street · New York, NY 10005-1801 · 212-220-3830

David A. Nourse · 2) · Nourse & Bowles · One Exchange Plaza at 55 Broadway · New York, NY 10006-3030 · 212-952-6200

John Eric Olson · Hill Rivkins & Hayden · 45 Broadway, Suite 1500 · New York, NY 10006 · 212-669-0600

Armand M. Paré, Jr. · Nourse & Bowles · One Exchange Plaza at 55 Broadway · New York, NY 10006-3030 · 212-952-6200

Robert L. Poster · a · Gilmartin, Poster & Shafto · 845 Third Avenue, 18th Floor · New York, NY 10022 212-425-3220

Anthony J. Pruzinsky · Hill Rivkins & Hayden · 45 Broadway, Suite 1500 · New York, NY 10006 · 212-669-0600

Edward Radzik · McDermott & Radzik · Wall Street Plaza, 21st Floor · 88 Pine Street · New York, NY 10005-1801 · 212-376-6400

Christopher Raleigh · Cozen O'Connor · 45 Broadway Atrium, 16th Floor · New York, NY 10006 · 212-509-9400

Lawrence Rutkowski · Seward & Kissel · One Battery Park Plaza · New York, NY 10004 · 212-574-1200

James T. Shirley · Holland & Knight · http://www.hklaw.com · 195 Broadway, 24th Floor · New York, NY 10007-3189 · 212-513-3200

Brian D. Starer · Squire Sanders · http://www.ssd.com · 350 Park Avenue · New York, NY 10022-6022 · 212-872-9800

Terry L. Stoltz · Nicoletti Hornig & Sweeney · Wall Street Plaza, Seventh Floor · 88 Pine Street · New York, NY 10005-1801 · 212-220-3830

Richard W. Stone II · Waesche, Sheinbaum & O'Regan · 111 Broadway, Fourth Floor · New York, NY 10006-1901 · 212-227-3550

John P. Vayda · Nourse & Bowles · One Exchange Plaza at 55 Broadway · New York, NY 10006-3030 · 212-952-6200

Richard H. Webber · 2) · Hill Rivkins & Hayden · 45 Broadway, Suite 1500 · New York, NY 10006 · 212-669-0600

Thomas E. Willoughby, Jr. · Hill Rivkins & Hayden · 45 Broadway, Suite 1500 · New York, NY 10006 · 212-669-0600

John M. Woods · Thacher Proffitt & Wood · Two World Financial Center · New York, NY 10281 · 212-912-7400

Alfred E. Yudes, Jr. · Watson, Farley & Williams · 100 Park Avenue, 31st Floor · New York, NY 10017 · 212-922-2200

MASS TORT LITIGATION

Buffalo

James T. Scime · Lipsitz Green Scime Cambria · http://www.lipsitzgreen.com · 42 Delaware Avenue, Suite 120 · Buffalo, NY 14202 · 716-849-1333

New York

Brian J. Alexander · Kreindler & Kreindler · 100 Park Avenue · New York, NY 10017-5590 · 212-687-8181

Joseph W. Belluck · Belluck & Fox · 295 Madison Avenue, 37th Floor · New York, NY 10017 · 212-681-1575

Kevin M. Berry · Wilentz, Goldman & Spitzer · http://www.wilentz.com · 110 William Street, 26th Floor · New York, NY 10038-3091 · 212-267-3091

Sheila L. Birnbaum · 2) · Skadden, Arps, Slate, Meagher & Flom · Four Times Square · New York, NY 10036 · 212-735-3000

Jerome H. Block · Levy Phillips & Konigsberg · 800 Third Avenue, 13th Floor · New York, NY 10022 · 212-605-6200

David R. Buchanan · Seeger Weiss · One William Street · New York, NY 10004 · 212-584-0700

David C. Cook · Kreindler & Kreindler · 100 Park Avenue · New York, NY 10017-5590 · 212-687-8181

David M. Covey · Sedgwick, Detert, Moran & Arnold · 125 Broad Street, 39th Floor · New York, NY 10004-2400 · 212-422-0202

Randal R. Craft, Jr. · Holland & Knight · http://www.hklaw.com · 195 Broadway, 24th Floor · New York, NY 10007-3189 · 212-513-3200

Julie Evans · Wilson Elser Moskowitz Edelman & Dicker · 150 East 42nd Street · New York, NY 10017-5639 · 212-490-3000

Stephen J. Fearon, Jr. · Squitieri & Fearon · 32 East 57th Street, 12th Floor · New York, NY 10022 · 212-421-6492

Steven E. Fineman · Lieff Cabraser Heimann & Bernstein · 780 Third Avenue, 48th Floor · New York, NY 10017-2024 · 212-355-9500

Jordan C. Fox · Belluck & Fox · 295 Madison Avenue, 37th Floor · New York, NY 10017 · 212-681-1575

Anthony H. Gair · Gair, Gair, Conason, Steigman & Mackauf · http://www.gairgair.com · 80 Pine Street, 34th Floor · New York, NY 10005 · 212-943-1090

Steven Glickstein · Kaye Scholer · 425 Park Avenue · New York, NY 10022-3598 · 212-836-8000

Philip Goldstein · McGuireWoods · http://www.mcguirewoods.com · 1345 Avenue of the Americas, Seventh Floor · New York, NY 10105-0106 · 212-548-2100

Robert J. Gordon · Weitz & Luxenberg · http://www.weitzlux.com · 180 Maiden Lane, 17th Floor · New York, NY 10038 · 212-558-5500

Robert I. Komitor · Levy Phillips & Konigsberg · 800 Third Avenue, 13th Floor · New York, NY 10022 · 212-605-6200

Eric M. Kraus · Sedgwick, Detert, Moran & Arnold · 125 Broad Street, 39th Floor · New York, NY 10004-2400 · 212-422-0202

James P. Kreindler · Kreindler & Kreindler · 100 Park Avenue · New York, NY 10017-5590 · 212-687-8181

Jerry Kristal · Weitz & Luxenberg · http://www.weitzlux.com · 180 Maiden Lane, 17th Floor · New York, NY 10038 · 212-558-5500

Lori B. Leskin · Kaye Scholer · 425 Park Avenue · New York, NY 10022-3598 · 212-836-8000

Jeffrey S. Lichtman · Skadden, Arps, Slate, Meagher & Flom · Four Times Square · New York, NY 10036 · 212-735-3000

James C. Long · Weitz & Luxenberg · http://www.weitzlux.com · 180 Maiden Lane, 17th Floor · New York, NY 10038 · 212-558-5500

Arthur Luxenberg · Weitz & Luxenberg · http://www.weitzlux.com · 180 Maiden Lane, 17th Floor · New York, NY 10038 · 212-558-5500

James R. Lynch · Lynch Daskal Emery · 264 West 40th Street · New York, NY 10018 · 212-302-2400

Moshe Maimon · Levy Phillips & Konigsberg · 800 Third Avenue, 13th Floor · New York, NY 10022 · 212-605-6200

Jay P. Mayesh · Kaye Scholer · 425 Park Avenue · New York, NY 10022-3598 · 212-836-8000

Marc S. Moller · Kreindler & Kreindler · 100 Park Avenue · New York, NY 10017-5590 · 212-687-8181

Paul J. Pennock · Weitz & Luxenberg · http://www.weitzlux.com · 180 Maiden Lane, 17th Floor · New York, NY 10038 · 212-558-5500

Glenn J. Pogust · Kaye Scholer · 425 Park Avenue · New York, NY 10022-3598 · 212-836-8000

Steven R. Pounian · Kreindler & Kreindler · 100 Park Avenue · New York, NY 10017-5590 · 212-687-8181

Michael P. Roberts · Weitz & Luxenberg · http://www.weitzlux.com · 180 Maiden Lane, 17th Floor · New York, NY 10038 · 212-558-5500

Michael K. Rozen · The Feinberg Group · 780 Third Avenue, 26th Floor · New York, NY 10017-2024 · 212-527-9600

Paul A. Scrudato · Schiff Hardin · 900 Third Avenue · New York, NY 10022 · 212-753-5000

Christopher A. Seeger · Seeger Weiss · One William Street · New York, NY 10004 · 212-584-0700

Perry Weitz · Weitz & Luxenberg · http://www.weitzlux.com · 180 Maiden Lane, 17th Floor · New York, NY 10038 · 212-558-5500

Barbara Wrubel · Skadden, Arps, Slate, Meagher & Flom · Four Times Square · New York, NY 10036 · 212-735-3000

Judith A. Yavitz · Reed Smith · 599 Lexington Avenue, 29th Floor · New York, NY 10022 · 212-521-5400

MEDIA LAW

Albany

Michael J. Grygiel · Hiscock & Barclay · 50 Beaver Street · Albany, NY 12207-2830 · 518-434-2163

New York

Richard A. Bernstein · Sabin, Bermant & Gould · Four Times Square, Twenty-Third Floor · New York, NY 10036 · 212-381-7000

Kevin W. Goering · Sheppard, Mullin, Richter & Hampton · http://www.sheppardmullin.com · 30 Rockefeller Plaza, 24th Floor · New York, NY 10112 · 212-332-3800

Laura R. Handman · a · Davis Wright Tremaine · 1633 Broadway, 27th Floor · New York, NY 10019-6708 · 212-489-8230

Rick Kurnit · Frankfurt Kurnit Klein & Selz · http://www.fkks.com · 488 Madison Avenue, Tenth Floor · New York, NY 10022 · 212-980-0120

Elizabeth A. McNamara · Davis Wright Tremaine · 1633 Broadway, 27th Floor · New York, NY 10019-6708 · 212-489-8230

Marcia B. Paul · Davis Wright Tremaine · 1633 Broadway, 27th Floor · New York, NY 10019-6708 · 212-489-8230

Albany

John T. Maloney · Carter, Conboy, Case, Blackmore, Maloney & Laird · 20 Corporate Woods Boulevard · Albany, NY 12211-2362 · 518-465-3484

Eugene E. Napierski, Sr. · a · Napierski, VanDenburgh & Napierski · 296 Washington Avenue Extension · Albany, NY 12203 · 518-862-9292

Thomas J. O'Connor · Napierski, VanDenburgh & Napierski · 296 Washington Avenue Extension · Albany, NY 12203 · 518-862-9292

John K. Powers · 2) · Powers & Santola · http://www.powers-santola.com · 39 North Pearl Street, Sixth Floor · Albany, NY 12207-2785 · 518-478-6616

Daniel R. Santola · a · Powers & Santola · http://www.powers-santola.com · 39 North Pearl Street, Sixth Floor · Albany, NY 12207-2785 · 518-478-6616

Binghamton

John J. Carlin · Levene, Gouldin & Thompson · http://www.binghamtonlaw.com · 71 State Street · P.O. Box F-1706 · Binghamton, NY 13902 · 607-763-9200

James S. Gleason · Hinman, Howard & Kattell · 700 Security Mutual Building · 80 Exchange Street · P.O. Box 5250 · Binghamton, NY 13902-5250 · 607-723-5341

Charles O. Ingraham · a · Aswad & Ingraham · 46 Front Street · Binghamton, NY 13905 · 607-722-3495

James F. Moran · Aswad & Ingraham · 46 Front Street · Binghamton, NY 13905 · 607-722-3495

Thomas A. Saitta · Aswad & Ingraham · 46 Front Street · Binghamton, NY 13905 · 607-722-3495

Buffalo

Terrence M. Connors · a · Connors & Vilardo · 1000 Liberty Building · 424 Main Street · Buffalo, NY 14202 · 716-852-5533

Laraine Kelley · Lipsitz Green Scime Cambria · http://www.lipsitzgreen.com · 42 Delaware Avenue, Suite 120 · Buffalo, NY 14202 · 716-849-1333

Victor Alan Oliveri · Gibson, McAskill & Crosby · 69 Delaware Avenue, Suite 900 · Buffalo, NY 14202 · 716-856-4200

James T. Scime · Lipsitz Green Scime Cambria · http://www.lipsitzgreen.com · 42 Delaware Avenue, Suite 120 · Buffalo, NY 14202 · 716-849-1333

Terry D. Smith · 2% · Smith, Keller, Miner & O'Shea · 69 Delaware Avenue, Suite 1212 · Buffalo, NY 14202-3801 · 716-855-3611

Kathleen M. Sweet · Gibson, McAskill & Crosby · 69 Delaware Avenue, Suite 900 · Buffalo, NY 14202 · 716-856-4200

DeWitt

Paul A. Brown · a · Martin, Ganotis, Brown, Mould & Currie · 5790 Widewaters Parkway · DeWitt, NY 13214 · 315-449-2616

George F. Mould · a · Martin, Ganotis, Brown, Mould & Currie · 5790 Widewaters Parkway · DeWitt, NY 13214 · 315-449-2616

Fishkill

Jeffrey M. Feldman · Feldman, Kleidman and Coffey · 995 Main Street · Fishkill, NY 12524 · 845-897-5199

Garden City

Joseph P. Awad · Silberstein, Awad & Miklos · 600 Old Country Road · Garden City, NY 11530 · 516-832-7777

Anthony M. Heller · Heidell, Pittoni, Murphy & Bach · 1050 Franklin Avenue · Garden City, NY 11530 · 516-408-1600

Lake Success

Annamarie Bondi-Stoddard · Pegalis & Erickson · http://www.pegalisanderickson.com · One Hollow Lane, Suite 107 · Lake Success, NY 11042 · 516-684-2900

Stephen E. Erickson · Pegalis & Erickson · http://www.pegalisanderickson.com · One Hollow Lane, Suite 107 · Lake Success, NY 11042 · 516-684-2900

Steven E. Pegalis · Pegalis & Erickson · http://www.pegalisanderickson.com · One Hollow Lane, Suite 107 · Lake Success, NY 11042 · 516-684-2900

Melville

Frederick C. Johs · Lewis Johs Avallone Aviles · 425 Broad Hollow Road, Suite 400 · Melville, NY 11747-4712 · 631-755-0101

Menands

Mae A. D'Agostino · a · D'Agostino, Krackeler, Baynes & Maguire · The Sage Mansion · 16 Sage Estate · Menands, NY 12204 · 518-434-9807

Mineola

Clifford A. Bartlett, Jr. · Bartlett, McDonough, Bastone & Monaghan · 300 Old Country Road, Suite 301 Mineola, NY 11501 · 516-877-2900

New York

Mark J. Aaronson · Aaronson Rappaport Feinstein & Deutsch · 757 Third Avenue · New York, NY 10017 · 212-593-6700

Walter G. Alton, Jr. · Walter G. Alton, Jr. & Associates · 548 West 28th Street, Suite 670 · New York, NY 10001 · 212-629-6151

Charles L. Bach, Jr. · Heidell, Pittoni, Murphy & Bach · 99 Park Avenue, Seventh Floor · New York, NY 10016 · 212-286-8585

Jeffrey B. Bloom · Gair, Gair, Conason, Steigman & Mackauf · http://www.gairgair.com · 80 Pine Street, 34th Floor · New York, NY 10005 · 212-943-1090

Joseph R. Cammarosano · Kopff, Nardelli & Dopf · 440 Ninth Avenue, 15th Floor · New York, NY 10001-1620 · 212-244-2999

Richard V. Caplan · Aaronson Rappaport Feinstein & Deutsch · 757 Third Avenue · New York, NY 10017 · 212-593-6700

Marc J. Citrin · Shaub, Ahmuty, Citrin & Spratt · 655 Third Avenue, 28th Floor · New York, NY 10017-5617 · 212-599-8200

Eleni Coffinas · Sullivan, Papain, Block, McGrath & Cannavo · 120 Broadway, 18th Floor · New York, NY 10271 · 212-732-9000

Robert L. Conason · 2% · Gair, Gair, Conason, Steigman & Mackauf · http://www.gairgair.com · 80 Pine Street, 34th Floor · New York, NY 10005 · 212-943-1090

Elizabeth Cornacchio · Heidell, Pittoni, Murphy & Bach · 99 Park Avenue, Seventh Floor · New York, NY 10016 · 212-286-8585

Peter T. Crean · Martin Clearwater & Bell · http://www.mcblaw.com · 220 East 42nd Street, Suite 1300 · New York, NY 10017 · 212-697-3122

Robert S. Deutsch · Aaronson Rappaport Feinstein & Deutsch · 757 Third Avenue · New York, NY 10017 · 212-593-6700

Robin R. Dolsky · Heidell, Pittoni, Murphy & Bach · 99 Park Avenue, Seventh Floor · New York, NY 10016 · 212-286-8585

Glenn W. Dopf · Kopff, Nardelli & Dopf · 440 Ninth Avenue, 15th Floor · New York, NY 10001-1620 · 212-244-2999

Anthony H. Gair · Gair, Gair, Conason, Steigman & Mackauf · http://www.gairgair.com · 80 Pine Street, 34th Floor · New York, NY 10005 · 212-943-1090

Andrew S. Garson · Garson DeCorato & Cohen · http://www.nygdc.com · 110 Wall Street, 10th Floor · New York, NY 10005 · 212-742-8700

Anthony P. Gentile · Godosky & Gentile · http://www.godoskygentile.com · 61 Broadway, Suite 2010 · New York, NY 10006 · 212-742-9700

Richard Godosky · 2% · Godosky & Gentile · http://www.godoskygentile.com · 61 Broadway, Suite 2010 · New York, NY 10006 · 212-742-9700

Adam Goldsmith · McAloon & Friedman · 123 William Street, 25th Floor · New York, NY 10038-3804 · 212-732-8700

Gary Greenfield · McAloon & Friedman · 123 William Street, 25th Floor · New York, NY 10038-3804 · 212-732-8700

Bruce G. Habian · a · Martin Clearwater & Bell · http://www.mcblaw.com · 220 East 42nd Street, Suite 1300 · New York, NY 10017 · 212-697-3122

Howard S. Hershenhorn · Gair, Gair, Conason, Steigman & Mackauf · http://www.gairgair.com · 80 Pine Street, 34th Floor · New York, NY 10005 · 212-943-1090

Peter C. Kopff · Kopff, Nardelli & Dopf · 440 Ninth Avenue, 15th Floor · New York, NY 10001-1620 · 212-244-2999

Brendan J. Lantier · McAloon & Friedman · 123 William Street, 25th Floor · New York, NY 10038-3804 212-732-8700

Judy A. Livingston · a · Kramer, Dillof, Livingston & Moore · 217 Broadway · New York, NY 10007 · 212-267-4177

John L. A. Lyddane · a · Martin Clearwater & Bell · http://www.mcblaw.com · 220 East 42nd Street, Suite 1300 · New York, NY 10017 · 212-697-3122

Stephen H. Mackauf · a · Gair, Gair, Conason, Steigman & Mackauf · http://www.gairgair.com · 80 Pine Street, 34th Floor · New York, NY 10005 · 212-943-1090

Nicholas J. Marotta · Aaronson Rappaport Feinstein & Deutsch · 757 Third Avenue · New York, NY 10017 · 212-593-6700

Roger P. McTiernan, Sr. · 2) · Barry, McTiernan & Moore · Two Rector Street, 14th Floor · New York, NY 10006 · 212-313-3600

Robert Steven Melnick · Aaronson Rappaport Feinstein & Deutsch · 757 Third Avenue · New York, NY 10017 · 212-593-6700

Thomas A. Moore · 2) · Kramer, Dillof, Livingston & Moore · 217 Broadway · New York, NY 10007 · 212-267-4177

Rosary A. Morelli · Heidell, Pittoni, Murphy & Bach · 99 Park Avenue, Seventh Floor · New York, NY 10016 · 212-286-8585

Steven E. North · a · Steven E. North · http://www.north-law.com · 148 East 74th Street · New York, NY 10021 · 212-861-5000

Luke M. Pittoni · 2) · Heidell, Pittoni, Murphy & Bach · 99 Park Avenue, Seventh Floor · New York, NY 10016 · 212-286-8585

Jay A. Rappaport · Aaronson Rappaport Feinstein & Deutsch · 757 Third Avenue · New York, NY 10017 · 212-593-6700

Theodore B. Rosenzweig · a · McAloon & Friedman · 123 William Street, 25th Floor · New York, NY 10038-3804 · 212-732-8700

Wayne M. Roth · McAloon & Friedman · 123 William Street, 25th Floor · New York, NY 10038-3804 · 212-732-8700

Ben B. Rubinowitz · Gair, Gair, Conason, Steigman & Mackauf · http://www.gairgair.com · 80 Pine Street, 34th Floor · New York, NY 10005 · 212-943-1090

Laura R. Shapiro · McAloon & Friedman · 123 William Street, 25th Floor · New York, NY 10038-3804 · 212-732-8700

Paul Simonson · Simonson Hess & Leibowitz · 15 Maiden Lane · New York, NY 10038 · 212-233-5000

Anthony M. Sola · a · Martin Clearwater & Bell · http://www.mcblaw.com · 220 East 42nd Street, Suite 1300 · New York, NY 10017 · 212-697-3122

Palmyra

James F. Foley · Foley & Foley · 235 East Main Street · P.O. Box 211 · Palmyra, NY 14522-0211 · 315-597-6611

Pittsford

Christopher A. DiPasquale · Harris Beach · 99 Garnsey Road · Pittsford, NY 14534 · 585-419-8800

Sue S. Tebor · Harris Beach · 99 Garnsey Road · Pittsford, NY 14534 · 585-419-8800

Port Washington

David S. Pollack · David S. Pollack · 151 Haven Avenue · Port Washington, NY 11050 · 516-767-8888

Rochester

Thomas C. Burke · a · Osborn, Reed & Burke · 45 Exchange Boulevard · Rochester, NY 14614-1403 · 585-454-6480

Angelo G. Faraci · 2% · Faraci Lange · http://www.faraci.com · 28 East Main Street, Suite 1100 · Rochester, NY 14614 · 585-325-5150

Dennis Gruttadaro · Brown & Tarantino · Times Square Building, Suite 300 · 45 Exchange Boulevard · Rochester, NY 14614 · 585-454-3377

Cheryl A. Heller · a · Ward, Norris, Heller & Reidy · http://www.wnhr.com · 300 State Street · Rochester, NY 14614 · 585-454-0700

Harold A. Kurland · Ward, Norris, Heller & Reidy · http://www.wnhr.com · 300 State Street · Rochester, NY 14614 · 585-454-0700

Paul K. Lange · Faraci Lange · http://www.faraci.com · 28 East Main Street, Suite 1100 · Rochester, NY 14614 · 585-325-5150

Joseph A. Regan · Faraci Lange · http://www.faraci.com · 28 East Main Street, Suite 1100 · Rochester, NY 14614 · 585-325-5150

Peter T. Rodgers · Lacy Katzen · http://www.lacykatzen.com · The Granite Building, Second Floor · 130 East Main Street · Rochester, NY 14604 · 585-454-5650

Stephen G. Schwarz · a · Faraci Lange · http://www.faraci.com · 28 East Main Street, Suite 1100 · Rochester, NY 14614 · 585-325-5150

Margaret E. Somerset · The Somerset Firm · The Powers Building, Suite 231 · 16 West Main Street · Rochester, NY 14614 · 585-919-0009

Eric J. Ward · Ward, Norris, Heller & Reidy · http://www.wnhr.com · 300 State Street · Rochester, NY 14614 · 585-454-0700

Jeffrey M. Wilkens · 2) · Osborn, Reed & Burke · 45 Exchange Boulevard · Rochester, NY 14614-1403 · 585-454-6480

Brian M. Zorn · a · Faraci Lange · http://www.faraci.com · 28 East Main Street, Suite 1100 · Rochester, NY 14614 · 585-325-5150

Staten Island

Jeffrey J. Cohen · Amabile & Erman · 1000 South Avenue · Staten Island, NY 10314-3407 · 718-370-7030

Carl M. Erman · Amabile & Erman · 1000 South Avenue · Staten Island, NY 10314-3407 · 718-370-7030

Syracuse

Paul M. Hanrahan · a · Hancock & Estabrook · 1500 Axa Tower I · 100 Madison Street · Syracuse, NY 13202 · 315-471-3151

Robert E. Lahm · a · Robert E. Lahm · 711 East Genesee Street · Syracuse, NY 13210 · 315-472-3434

James D. Lantier · Smith, Sovik, Kendrick & Sugnet · 250 South Clinton Street, Suite 600 · Syracuse, NY 13202 · 315-474-2911

Laurence F. Sovik · a · Smith, Sovik, Kendrick & Sugnet · 250 South Clinton Street, Suite 600 · Syracuse, NY 13202 · 315-474-2911

Uniondale

James R. Duffy · a · Duffy Duffy & Burdo · West Tower, 13th Floor · 1370 Reckson Plaza · Uniondale, NY 11556-0188 · 516-394-4200

James Wilkens · Duffy Duffy & Burdo · West Tower, 13th Floor · 1370 Reckson Plaza · Uniondale, NY 11556-0188 · 516-394-4200

White Plains

Frank Bastone · Bartlett, McDonough, Bastone & Monaghan · 81 Main Street · White Plains, NY 10601 · 914-448-0200

Duane M. Fiedler · Duane M. Fiedler · 81 Main Street, Suite 304 · White Plains, NY 10601 · 914-993-0393

Garrett P. Lewis · Wilson Elser Moskowitz Edelman & Dicker · Three Gannett Drive · White Plains, NY 10604-3407 · 914-323-7000

Michael D. Shalhoub · Goldberg Segalla · 170 Hamilton Avenue, Suite 203 · White Plains, NY 10601-1717 · 914-798-5400

MERGERS & ACQUISITIONS LAW

New York

Roger S. Aaron, Sr. · 2% · Skadden, Arps, Slate, Meagher & Flom · Four Times Square · New York, NY 10036 · 212-735-3000

Neil T. Anderson · 2) · Sullivan & Cromwell · 125 Broad Street · New York, NY 10004-2498 · 212-558-4000

Francis J. Aquila · Sullivan & Cromwell · 125 Broad Street · New York, NY 10004-2498 · 212-558-4000

Peter Allan Atkins · 2% · Skadden, Arps, Slate, Meagher & Flom · Four Times Square · New York, NY 10036 · 212-735-3000

Christopher E. Austin · Cleary Gottlieb Steen & Hamilton · One Liberty Plaza · New York, NY 10006 · 212-225-2000

Scott A. Barshay · Cravath, Swaine & Moore · Worldwide Plaza · 825 Eighth Avenue · New York, NY 10019-7475 · 212-474-1000

George R. Bason, Jr. · Davis Polk & Wardwell · 450 Lexington Avenue · New York, NY 10017 · 212-450-4000

Richard I. Beattie · 2) · Simpson Thacher · 425 Lexington Avenue · New York, NY 10017-3954 · 212-455-2000

Kenneth J. Bialkin · 2% · Skadden, Arps, Slate, Meagher & Flom · Four Times Square · New York, NY 10036 · 212-735-3000

Paul S. Bird · Debevoise & Plimpton · 919 Third Avenue · New York, NY 10022 · 212-909-6000

Dennis J. Block · Cadwalader, Wickersham & Taft · http://www.cadwalader.com · One World Financial Center · New York, NY 10281 · 212-504-6000

Meredith M. Brown · 2% · Debevoise & Plimpton · 919 Third Avenue · New York, NY 10022 · 212-909-6000

Andrew R. Brownstein · a · Wachtell, Lipton, Rosen & Katz · 51 West 52nd Street · New York, NY 10019 · 212-403-1000

Thomas M. Cerabino · Willkie Farr & Gallagher · 787 Seventh Avenue · New York, NY 10019-6099 · 212-728-8000

Howard Chatzinoff · Weil Gotshal & Manges · 767 Fifth Avenue · New York, NY 10153 · 212-310-8000

Leonard Chazen · Covington & Burling · The New York Times Building · 620 Eighth Avenue · New York, NY 10018 · 212-841-1000

Charles I. Cogut · Simpson Thacher · 425 Lexington Avenue · New York, NY 10017-3954 · 212-455-2000

H. Rodgin Cohen · 2% · Sullivan & Cromwell · 125 Broad Street · New York, NY 10004-2498 · 212-558-4000

Crieghton O'M. Condon · Shearman & Sterling · 599 Lexington Avenue · New York, NY 10022-6069 · 212-848-4000

Peter R. Douglas · 2) · Davis Polk & Wardwell · 450 Lexington Avenue · New York, NY 10017 · 212-450-4000

W. Leslie Duffy · 2% · Cahill Gordon & Reindel · 80 Pine Street · New York, NY 10005-1702 · 212-701-3000

Mitchell S. Eitel · Sullivan & Cromwell · 125 Broad Street · New York, NY 10004-2498 · 212-558-4000

Adam O. Emmerich · Wachtell, Lipton, Rosen & Katz · 51 West 52nd Street · New York, NY 10019 · 212-403-1000

Allen Finkelson · 2% · Cravath, Swaine & Moore · Worldwide Plaza · 825 Eighth Avenue · New York, NY 10019-7475 · 212-474-1000

John G. Finley · Simpson Thacher · 425 Lexington Avenue · New York, NY 10017-3954 · 212-455-2000

Arthur Fleischer, Jr. · 2% · Fried, Frank, Harris, Shriver & Jacobson · One New York Plaza · New York, NY 10004-1980 · 212-859-8000

Joseph H. Flom · 2% · Skadden, Arps, Slate, Meagher & Flom · Four Times Square · New York, NY 10036 · 212-735-3000

Blaine V. Fogg · 2% · Skadden, Arps, Slate, Meagher & Flom · Four Times Square · New York, NY 10036 212-735-3000

David Fox · Skadden, Arps, Slate, Meagher & Flom · Four Times Square · New York, NY 10036 · 212-735-3000

Stephen Fraidin · 2% · Kirkland & Ellis · Citigroup Center · 153 East 53rd Street · New York, NY 10022-4611 · 212-446-4800

Dennis J. Friedman · Gibson, Dunn & Crutcher · 200 Park Avenue, 47th Floor · New York, NY 10166-0193 · 212-351-4000

Joseph B. Frumkin · Sullivan & Cromwell · 125 Broad Street · New York, NY 10004-2498 · 212-558-4000

Philip A. Gelston · Cravath, Swaine & Moore · Worldwide Plaza · 825 Eighth Avenue · New York, NY 10019-7475 · 212-474-1000

Franklin M. Gittes · a · Skadden, Arps, Slate, Meagher & Flom · Four Times Square · New York, NY 10036 · 212-735-3000

Richard Hall · Cravath, Swaine & Moore · Worldwide Plaza · 825 Eighth Avenue · New York, NY 10019-7475 · 212-474-1000

Henry Henryson II · WolfBlock · http://wolfblock.com · 250 Park Avenue · New York, NY 10177 · 212-986-1116

Edward D. Herlihy · a · Wachtell, Lipton, Rosen & Katz · 51 West 52nd Street · New York, NY 10019 · 212-403-1000

Matthew G. Hurd · Sullivan & Cromwell · 125 Broad Street · New York, NY 10004-2498 · 212-558-4000

Allen I. Isaacson · a · Fried, Frank, Harris, Shriver & Jacobson · One New York Plaza · New York, NY 10004-1980 · 212-859-8000

Richard D. Katcher · 2% · Wachtell, Lipton, Rosen & Katz · 51 West 52nd Street · New York, NY 10019 · 212-403-1000

David A. Katz · Wachtell, Lipton, Rosen & Katz · 51 West 52nd Street · New York, NY 10019 · 212-403-1000

Stuart Z. Katz · 2% · Fried, Frank, Harris, Shriver & Jacobson · One New York Plaza · New York, NY 10004-1980 · 212-859-8000

Diane G. Kerr · Davis Polk & Wardwell · 450 Lexington Avenue · New York, NY 10017 · 212-450-4000

Lou R. Kling · Skadden, Arps, Slate, Meagher & Flom · Four Times Square · New York, NY 10036 · 212-735-3000

Alexandra D. Korry · Sullivan & Cromwell · 125 Broad Street · New York, NY 10004-2498 · 212-558-4000

Stephen M. Kotran · Sullivan & Cromwell · 125 Broad Street · New York, NY 10004-2498 · 212-558-4000

Morris J. Kramer · 2% · Skadden, Arps, Slate, Meagher & Flom · Four Times Square · New York, NY 10036 · 212-735-3000

Kenneth A. Lefkowitz · Hughes Hubbard & Reed · http://www.hugheshubbard.com · One Battery Park Plaza · New York, NY 10004-1482 · 212-837-6000

Victor I. Lewkow · 2) · Cleary Gottlieb Steen & Hamilton · One Liberty Plaza · New York, NY 10006 · 212-225-2000

Martin Lipton · 2% · Wachtell, Lipton, Rosen & Katz · 51 West 52nd Street · New York, NY 10019 · 212-403-1000

Peter D. Lyons · Shearman & Sterling · 599 Lexington Avenue · New York, NY 10022-6069 · 212-848-4000

John J. Madden · 2) · Shearman & Sterling · 599 Lexington Avenue · New York, NY 10022-6069 · 212-848-4000

Phillip R. Mills · Davis Polk & Wardwell · 450 Lexington Avenue · New York, NY 10017 · 212-450-4000

James C. Morphy · a · Sullivan & Cromwell · 125 Broad Street · New York, NY 10004-2498 · 212-558-4000

Daniel A. Neff · a · Wachtell, Lipton, Rosen & Katz · 51 West 52nd Street · New York, NY 10019 · 212-403-1000

Eileen T. Nugent · Skadden, Arps, Slate, Meagher & Flom · Four Times Square · New York, NY 10036 · 212-735-3000

Jack H. Nusbaum · 2% · Willkie Farr & Gallagher · 787 Seventh Avenue · New York, NY 10019-6099 · 212-728-8000

Martin Nussbaum · Dechert · 30 Rockefeller Plaza · 1095 Avenue of the Americas · New York, NY 10036-6797 · 212-698-3500

Clare O'Brien · Shearman & Sterling · 599 Lexington Avenue · New York, NY 10022-6069 · 212-848-4000

Ellen J. Odoner · Weil Gotshal & Manges · 767 Fifth Avenue · New York, NY 10153 · 212-310-8000

Morton A. Pierce · Dewey & LeBoeuf · 1301 Avenue of the Americas · New York, NY 10019-6092 · 212-259-8000

Robert A. Profusek · Jones Day · 222 East 41st Street · New York, NY 10017-6702 · 212-326-3939

Thomas A. Roberts · Weil Gotshal & Manges · 767 Fifth Avenue · New York, NY 10153 · 212-310-8000

Jeffrey J. Rosen · Debevoise & Plimpton · 919 Third Avenue · New York, NY 10022 · 212-909-6000

Steven A. Rosenblum · Wachtell, Lipton, Rosen & Katz · 51 West 52nd Street · New York, NY 10019 · 212-403-1000

Philip T. Ruegger III · Simpson Thacher · 425 Lexington Avenue · New York, NY 10017-3954 · 212-455-2000

Faiza J. Saeed · Cravath, Swaine & Moore · Worldwide Plaza · 825 Eighth Avenue · New York, NY 10019-7475 · 212-474-1000

James M. Schell · a · Skadden, Arps, Slate, Meagher & Flom · Four Times Square · New York, NY 10036 · 212-735-3000

Paul T. Schnell · Skadden, Arps, Slate, Meagher & Flom · Four Times Square · New York, NY 10036 · 212-735-3000

Robert B. Schumer · Paul, Weiss, Rifkind, Wharton & Garrison · 1285 Avenue of the Americas · New York, NY 10019-6064 · 212-373-3000

Howard L. Shecter · Morgan Lewis & Bockius · 101 Park Avenue · New York, NY 10178-0060 · 212-309-6000

Robert C. Sheehan · Skadden, Arps, Slate, Meagher & Flom · Four Times Square · New York, NY 10036 · 212-735-3000

Paul J. Shim · Cleary Gottlieb Steen & Hamilton · One Liberty Plaza · New York, NY 10006 · 212-225-2000

Robert E. Spatt · Simpson Thacher · 425 Lexington Avenue · New York, NY 10017-3954 · 212-455-2000

Benjamin F. Stapleton · 2) · Sullivan & Cromwell · 125 Broad Street · New York, NY 10004-2498 · 212-558-4000

Alan C. Stephenson · 2% · Cravath, Swaine & Moore · Worldwide Plaza · 825 Eighth Avenue · New York, NY 10019-7475 · 212-474-1000

Milton G. Strom · 2% · Skadden, Arps, Slate, Meagher & Flom · Four Times Square · New York, NY 10036 · 212-735-3000

Robert I. Townsend III · Cravath, Swaine & Moore · Worldwide Plaza · 825 Eighth Avenue · New York, NY 10019-7475 · 212-474-1000

Patricia Ann Vlahakis · a · Wachtell, Lipton, Rosen & Katz · 51 West 52nd Street · New York, NY 10019 · 212-403-1000

Craig M. Wasserman · Wachtell, Lipton, Rosen & Katz · 51 West 52nd Street · New York, NY 10019 · 212-403-1000

Margaret L. Wolff · Skadden, Arps, Slate, Meagher & Flom · Four Times Square · New York, NY 10036 212-735-3000

MUTUAL FUNDS LAW

New York

Jay G. Baris · Kramer Levin Naftalis & Frankel · http://www.kramerlevin.com · 1177 Avenue of the Americas · New York, NY 10036 · 212-715-9100

John E. Baumgardner, Jr. · a · Sullivan & Cromwell · 125 Broad Street · New York, NY 10004-2498 · 212-558-4000

Frank P. Bruno · Sidley Austin · 787 Seventh Avenue · New York, NY 10019 · 212-839-5300

Sarah E. Cogan · Simpson Thacher · 425 Lexington Avenue · New York, NY 10017-3954 · 212-455-2000

Stuart H. Coleman · Stroock & Stroock & Lavan · 180 Maiden Lane · New York, NY 10038-4982 · 212-806-5400

Donald R. Crawshaw · Sullivan & Cromwell · 125 Broad Street · New York, NY 10004-2498 · 212-558-4000

Carl Frischling · Kramer Levin Naftalis & Frankel · http://www.kramerlevin.com · 1177 Avenue of the Americas · New York, NY 10036 · 212-715-9100

Joel H. Goldberg · Willkie Farr & Gallagher · 787 Seventh Avenue · New York, NY 10019-6099 · 212-728-8000

Nora M. Jordan · Davis Polk & Wardwell · 450 Lexington Avenue · New York, NY 10017 · 212-450-4000

Brian M. Kaplowitz · Sidley Austin · 787 Seventh Avenue · New York, NY 10019 · 212-839-5300

Burton M. Leibert · Willkie Farr & Gallagher · 787 Seventh Avenue · New York, NY 10019-6099 · 212-728-8000

John A. MacKinnon · Sidley Austin · 787 Seventh Avenue · New York, NY 10019 · 212-839-5300

Margery K. Neale · Willkie Farr & Gallagher · 787 Seventh Avenue · New York, NY 10019-6099 · 212-728-8000

Richard T. Prins · Skadden, Arps, Slate, Meagher & Flom · Four Times Square · New York, NY 10036 · 212-735-3000

Jon S. Rand · Dechert · 30 Rockefeller Plaza · 1095 Avenue of the Americas · New York, NY 10036-6797 212-698-3500

Paul S. Schreiber · a · Shearman & Sterling · 599 Lexington Avenue · New York, NY 10022-6069 · 212-848-4000

Stuart Strauss · Clifford Chance · 31 West 52nd Street · New York, NY 10019-6131 · 212-878-8000

NATIVE AMERICAN LAW

New York

Steven Paul McSloy · Hughes Hubbard & Reed · http://www.hugheshubbard.com · One Battery Park Plaza · New York, NY 10004-1482 · 212-837-6000

NATURAL RESOURCES LAW

New York

Sheldon S. Adler · Skadden, Arps, Slate, Meagher & Flom · Four Times Square · New York, NY 10036 · 212-735-3000

Steven H. Davis · Dewey & LeBoeuf · 125 West 55th Street · New York, NY 10019-5389 · 212-424-8000

Joseph B. Frumkin · Sullivan & Cromwell · 125 Broad Street · New York, NY 10004-2498 · 212-558-4000

William S. Lamb · Dewey & LeBoeuf · 125 West 55th Street · New York, NY 10019-5389 · 212-424-8000

NON-PROFIT/CHARITIES LAW

Amherst

Paul A. Battaglia · Jaeckle Fleischmann & Mugel · Centerpointe Corporate Park, Suite 320 · 400 Essjay Road · Amherst, NY 14221 · 716-250-1800

Buffalo

Pamela Davis Heilman · Hodgson Russ · One Guaranty Building, Suite 100 · 140 Pearl Street · Buffalo, NY 14202 · 716-856-4000

Edward C. Northwood · Edward C. Northwood · 155 Summer Street · Buffalo, NY 14222 · 716-332-3456

New York

Victoria B. Bjorklund · Simpson Thacher · 425 Lexington Avenue · New York, NY 10017-3954 · 212-455-2000

Albert Kalter · a · Albert Kalter · 225 Broadway, Suite 1806 · New York, NY 10007 · 212-964-5485

Rochelle Korman · Patterson Belknap Webb & Tyler · http://www.pbwt.com · 1133 Avenue of the Americas · New York, NY 10036-6710 · 212-336-2000

Pamela A. Mann · Law Offices of Pamela A. Mann · http://www.pamelamann.com · 45 Broadway, 31st Floor · New York, NY 10006 · 212-566-3200

Christine D. Rogers · Arnold & Porter · 399 Park Avenue, 34th Floor · New York, NY 10022-4690 · 212-715-1000

David G. Samuels · Duval & Stachenfeld · 300 East 42nd Street, Third Floor · New York, NY 10017 · 212-883-1700

Sanford J. Schlesinger · 2) · Schlesinger Gannon & Lazetera · http://www.sglllp.com · 499 Park Avenue, 20th Floor · New York, NY 10022 · 212-652-3800

Rochester

Michael J. Cooney · Nixon Peabody · 1100 Clinton Square · P.O. Box 31051 · Rochester, NY 14604 · 585-263-1000

White Plains

Philip T. Temple · a · McCarthy, Fingar, Donovan, Drazen & Smith · 11 Martine Avenue, 12th Floor · White Plains, NY 10606-1934 · 914-946-3700

Williamsville

Michael A.O. De Freitas · William C. Moran & Associates · 6500 Main Street, Suite Five · Williamsville, NY 14421 · 716-633-6500

NON-WHITE-COLLAR CRIMINAL DEFENSE

Albany

Stephen R. Coffey · a · O'Connell & Aronowitz · 54 State Street, Ninth Floor · Albany, NY 12207-2501 · 518-462-5601

Buffalo

Paul J. Cambria, Jr. · 2% · Lipsitz Green Scime Cambria · http://www.lipsitzgreen.com · 42 Delaware Avenue, Suite 120 · Buffalo, NY 14202 · 716-849-1333

Terrence M. Connors · a · Connors & Vilardo · 1000 Liberty Building · 424 Main Street · Buffalo, NY 14202 · 716-852-5533

Joel L. Daniels · 2% · Joel L. Daniels · 1366 Statler Building · Buffalo, NY 14202 · 716-856-5140

Herbert L. Greenman · 2) · Lipsitz Green Scime Cambria · http://www.lipsitzgreen.com · 42 Delaware Avenue, Suite 120 · Buffalo, NY 14202 · 716-849-1333

James P. Harrington · Harrington & Mahoney · 70 Niagara Street, Third Floor · Buffalo, NY 14202 · 716-853-3700

Joseph M. LaTona · 2) · Law Office of Joseph M. LaTona · 716 Brisbane Building · 403 Main Street · Buffalo, NY 14203 · 716-842-0416

Mark J. Mahoney · 2) · Harrington & Mahoney · 70 Niagara Street, Third Floor · Buffalo, NY 14202 · 716-853-3700

New York

Charles D. Abercrombie · Seiff Kretz & Abercrombie · 444 Madison Avenue, 30th Floor · New York, NY 10022 · 212-371-4500

Martin B. Adelman · Martin B. Adelman · 225 Broadway, Suite 1804 · New York, NY 10007 · 212-732-4343

Paul B. Bergman · a · Paul B. Bergman · 950 Third Avenue, 32nd Floor · New York, NY 10022-2705 · 212-355-7711

Jerry D. Bernstein · Blank Rome · The Chrysler Building · 405 Lexington Avenue · New York, NY 10174 · 212-885-5000

Benjamin Brafman · a · Brafman & Associates · 767 Third Avenue, 26th Floor · New York, NY 10017-2023 · 212-750-7800

Austin V. Campriello · Bryan Cave · 1290 Avenue of the Americas · New York, NY 10104-3300 · 212-541-2000

Herald Price Fahringer · 2% · Herald Price Fahringer · 120 East 56TH Street, Suite 1150 · New York, NY 10022-3607 · 212-319-5351

Ronald P. Fischetti · a · Ronald P. Fischetti · 950 Third Avenue, 32nd Floor · New York, NY 10022 · 212-593-7100

Lawrence S. Goldman · a · Law Offices of Lawrence S. Goldman · 500 Fifth Avenue, 29th Floor · New York, NY 10110 · 212-997-7499

Franklyn Gould · a · Gould Fishbein Reimer · 61 Broadway, Suite 1601 · New York, NY 10006 · 212-267-2600

Mark R. Hellerer · Pillsbury Winthrop Shaw Pittman · http://www.pillsburylaw.com · 1540 Broadway · New York, NY 10036-4039 · 212-858-1000

Lawrence Hochheiser · Hochheiser & Hochheiser · 270 Madison Avenue, Suite 1203 · New York, NY 10016 · 212-689-4343

Jack S. Hoffinger · 2% · Hoffinger Stern & Ross · 150 East 58th Street, 19th Floor · New York, NY 10155 212-421-4000

Kenneth J. Kaplan · Kaplan & Katzberg · 767 Third Avenue · New York, NY 10017-2023 · 212-750-3100

James M. LaRossa · 2% · Law Offices of James LaRossa · 1790 Broadway, Suite 1501 · New York, NY 10019 · 212-696-9700

Gerald B. Lefcourt · 2% · Gerald B. Lefcourt · 148 East 78th Street · New York, NY 10021 · 212-737-0400

Jack T. Litman · 2% · Litman, Asche & Gioiella · 45 Broadway, 30th Floor · New York, NY 10006 · 212-809-4500

Peter J. Neufeld · a · Cochran Neufeld & Scheck · 99 Hudson Street, Eighth Floor · New York, NY 10013-2815 · 212-965-9081

Gustave H. Newman · 2% · Newman & Greenberg · 950 Third Avenue, 32nd Floor · New York, NY 10022 · 212-308-7900

Barry C. Scheck · a · Cardozo Law School · 100 Fifth Avenue, Third Floor · New York, NY 10011 · 212-364-5340

Eric A. Seiff · Seiff Kretz & Abercrombie · 444 Madison Avenue, 30th Floor · New York, NY 10022 · 212-371-4500

Gerald L. Shargel · a · Law Offices of Gerald L. Shargel · 570 Lexington Avenue, 45th Floor · New York, NY 10022 · 212-446-2323

Edward M. Shaw · 2% · Law Office of Edward M. Shaw · 420 Fifth Avenue, 25th Floor · New York, NY 10018-2729 · 212-703-5430

Rochester

Lawrence J. Andolina · 2% · Trevett, Criste, Salzer & Andolina · Two State Street · 1000 Crossroads Building · Rochester, NY 14614 · 585-454-2181

Thomas J. Cocuzzi · a · Thomas J. Cocuzzi · Time Square Building, Suite 900 · 45 Exchange Street · Rochester, NY 14614 · 585-546-1734

Michael Thomas DiPrima · 2) · Law Offices of Michael Thomas DiPrima · 40 Humbolt Street · Rochester, NY 14609 · 585-797-7926

Felix V. Lapine · 2) · Felix V. Lapine · One East Main Street, Suite 711 · Rochester, NY 14614 · 585-454-6690

David A. Murante · 2) · David A. Murante · Wilder Building, Suite 711 · Eight Exchange Street · Rochester, NY 14614 · 585-546-1770

Norman A. Palmiere · 2% · Norman A. Palmiere · Reynolds Arcade, Suite 210 · 16 East Main Street · Rochester, NY 14614 · 585-262-2729

John R. Parrinello · 2% · Redmond & Parrinello · Executive Office Building, Suite 400 · 36 West Main Street · Rochester, NY 14614 · 585-454-2321

David Rothenberg · a · Geiger and Rothenberg · Times Square Building, Suite 800 · 45 Exchange Street Rochester, NY 14614 · 585-232-1946

Karl F. Salzer · 2% · Trevett, Criste, Salzer & Andolina · Two State Street · 1000 Crossroads Building · Rochester, NY 14614 · 585-454-2181

John F. Speranza · 2) · John F. Speranza · First Federal Plaza, Suite 1800 · 28 East Main Street · Rochester, NY 14614 · 585-454-1500

Syracuse

Edward Z. Menkin · a · Edward Z. Menkin · http://www.edmenkin.com · State Tower Building, Suite 909 · 109 South Warren Street · Syracuse, NY 13202 · 315-425-1212

Emil M. Rossi · 2) · Emil M. Rossi Law Office · The Hamilton White House · 307 South Townsend Street · Syracuse, NY 13202 · 315-471-0126

Troy

E. Stewart Jones, Jr. · 2% · E. Stewart Jones · http://www.esjlaw.com · The Jones Building · 28 Second Street · Troy, NY 12180 · 518-274-5820

White Plains

William I. Aronwald · Aronwald & Pykett · 81 Main Street, Suite 450 · White Plains, NY 10601 · 914-946-6565

PERSONAL INJURY LITIGATION

Albany

Stephen R. Coffey · a · O'Connell & Aronowitz · 54 State Street, Ninth Floor · Albany, NY 12207-2501 · 518-462-5601

Michael W. Kessler · Rosenblum, Ronan, Kessler & Sarachan · 110 Great Oaks Boulevard · Albany, NY 12203 · 518-464-0444

James D. Linnan · Linnan & Fallon · 61 Columbia Street, Suite 300 · Albany, NY 12210 · 518-449-5400

Eugene E. Napierski, Sr. · a · Napierski, VanDenburgh & Napierski · 296 Washington Avenue Extension · Albany, NY 12203 · 518-862-9292

John K. Powers · 2) · Powers & Santola · http://www.powers-santola.com · 39 North Pearl Street, Sixth Floor · Albany, NY 12207-2785 · 518-478-6616

Daniel R. Santola · a · Powers & Santola · http://www.powers-santola.com · 39 North Pearl Street, Sixth Floor · Albany, NY 12207-2785 · 518-478-6616

Arthur H. Thorn · a · Thorn Gershon Tymann and Bonanni · Five Wembley Court · New Karner Road · P.O. Box 15054 · Albany, NY 12212-5054 · 518-464-6770

Dale M. Thuillez · a · Thuillez, Ford, Gold, Johnson & Butler · 20 Corporate Woods Boulevard, Sixth Floor · Albany, NY 12211 · 518-455-9952

Auburn

Lee S. Michaels · 2) · Michaels & Smolak · 71 South Street · Auburn, NY 13021 · 315-253-3293

Binghamton

Peter H. Bouman · Coughlin & Gerhart · 20 Hawley Street · P.O. Box 2039 · Binghamton, NY 13902-2039 · 607-723-9511

David M. Gouldin · a · Levene, Gouldin & Thompson · http://www.binghamtonlaw.com · 71 State Street · P.O. Box F-1706 · Binghamton, NY 13902 · 607-763-9200

Charles O. Ingraham · a · Aswad & Ingraham · 46 Front Street · Binghamton, NY 13905 · 607-722-3495

Philip C. Johnson · a · Levene, Gouldin & Thompson · http://www.binghamtonlaw.com · 71 State Street · P.O. Box F-1706 · Binghamton, NY 13902 · 607-763-9200

Richard B. Long · a · Coughlin & Gerhart · 20 Hawley Street · P.O. Box 2039 · Binghamton, NY 13902-2039 · 607-723-9511

Kevin F. McDonough · McDonough & Artz · The Perry Building · 89 Court Street · P.O. Box 1740 · Binghamton, NY 13902-1740 · 607-772-6070

Brooklyn

John A. Bonina III · Bonina & Bonina · 16 Court Street, Suite 1800 · Brooklyn, NY 11241 · 718-522-1786

Buffalo

Stephen E. Barnes · Cellino & Barnes · 17 Court Street, Seventh Floor · Buffalo, NY 14202 · 716-854-2020

Paul W. Beltz · 2% · Paul William Beltz · 36 Church Street · Buffalo, NY 14202-3905 · 716-852-1000

Peter D. Braun · Phillips Lytle · 3400 HSBC Center · Buffalo, NY 14203-2887 · 716-847-8400

David G. Brock · Jaeckle Fleischmann & Mugel · 12 Fountain Plaza · Buffalo, NY 14202-2292 · 716-856-0600

John F. Canale · 2) · Bouvier Partnership · 350 Main Street, Suite 1400 · Buffalo, NY 14202 · 716-856-1344

Terrence M. Connors · a · Connors & Vilardo · 1000 Liberty Building · 424 Main Street · Buffalo, NY 14202 · 716-852-5533

Brian P. Crosby · a · Gibson, McAskill & Crosby · 69 Delaware Avenue, Suite 900 · Buffalo, NY 14202 · 716-856-4200

Thomas J. Drury · Damon & Morey · http://www.damonmorey.com · 1000 Cathedral Place · 298 Main Street · Buffalo, NY 14202-4096 · 716-856-5500

Carl A. Green · a · Lipsitz Green Scime Cambria · http://www.lipsitzgreen.com · 42 Delaware Avenue, Suite 120 · Buffalo, NY 14202 · 716-849-1333

Richard F. Griffin · 2% · Kavinoky & Cook · 726 Exchange Street, Suite 800 · Buffalo, NY 14210 · 716-845-6000

J. Michael Hayes · J. Michael Hayes · 69 Delaware Avenue, Suite1111 · Buffalo, NY 14202 · 716-852-1111

Laraine Kelley · Lipsitz Green Scime Cambria · http://www.lipsitzgreen.com · 42 Delaware Avenue, Suite 120 · Buffalo, NY 14202 · 716-849-1333

Francis M. Letro · Francis M. Letro · The Dun Building, 10th Floor · 110 Pearl Street · Buffalo, NY 14202 · 718-852-1234

Kenneth A. Manning · Phillips Lytle · 3400 HSBC Center · Buffalo, NY 14203-2887 · 716-847-8400

Paul Morrison-Taylor · Phillips Lytle · 3400 HSBC Center · Buffalo, NY 14203-2887 · 716-847-8400

Victor Alan Oliveri · Gibson, McAskill & Crosby · 69 Delaware Avenue, Suite 900 · Buffalo, NY 14202 · 716-856-4200

Michael B. Powers · Phillips Lytle · 3400 HSBC Center · Buffalo, NY 14203-2887 · 716-847-8400

Daniel T. Roach · 2% · Roach, Brown, McCarthy & Gruber · 1620 Liberty Building · 420 Main Street · Buffalo, NY 14202 · 716-852-0400

James T. Scime · Lipsitz Green Scime Cambria · http://www.lipsitzgreen.com · 42 Delaware Avenue, Suite 120 · Buffalo, NY 14202 · 716-849-1333

Terry D. Smith · 2% · Smith, Keller, Miner & O'Shea · 69 Delaware Avenue, Suite 1212 · Buffalo, NY 14202-3801 · 716-855-3611

Richard T. Sullivan · Harris Beach · Larkin at Exchange, Suite 1000 · 726 Exchange Street · Buffalo, NY 14210 · 716-200-5050

Eugene C. Tenney · Law Offices of Eugene C. Tenney · Five Niagara Square · Buffalo, NY 14202 · 716-853-1887

Richard P. Weisbeck, Jr. · Lipsitz Green Scime Cambria · http://www.lipsitzgreen.com · 42 Delaware Avenue, Suite 120 · Buffalo, NY 14202 · 716-849-1333

James W. Whitcomb · Phillips Lytle · 3400 HSBC Center · Buffalo, NY 14203-2887 · 716-847-8400

DeWitt

Paul A. Brown · a · Martin, Ganotis, Brown, Mould & Currie · 5790 Widewaters Parkway · DeWitt, NY 13214 · 315-449-2616

George F. Mould · a · Martin, Ganotis, Brown, Mould & Currie · 5790 Widewaters Parkway · DeWitt, NY 13214 · 315-449-2616

Garden City

Joseph P. Awad · Silberstein, Awad & Miklos · 600 Old Country Road · Garden City, NY 11530 · 516-832-7777

Jericho

Emmet J. Agoglia · 2% · Agoglia, Holland & Agoglia · 500 North Broadway, Suite 237 · Jericho, NY 11753 516-396-0800

Lake Success

Annamarie Bondi-Stoddard · Pegalis & Erickson · http://www.pegalisanderickson.com · One Hollow Lane, Suite 107 · Lake Success, NY 11042 · 516-684-2900

Stephen E. Erickson · Pegalis & Erickson · http://www.pegalisanderickson.com · One Hollow Lane, Suite 107 · Lake Success, NY 11042 · 516-684-2900

Steven E. Pegalis · Pegalis & Erickson · http://www.pegalisanderickson.com · One Hollow Lane, Suite 107 · Lake Success, NY 11042 · 516-684-2900

Melville

Frederick C. Johs · Lewis Johs Avallone Aviles · 425 Broad Hollow Road, Suite 400 · Melville, NY 11747-4712 · 631-755-0101

Menands

Mae A. D'Agostino · a · D'Agostino, Krackeler, Baynes & Maguire · The Sage Mansion · 16 Sage Estate · Menands, NY 12204 · 518-434-9807

Mineola

Clifford A. Bartlett, Jr. · Bartlett, McDonough, Bastone & Monaghan · 300 Old Country Road, Suite 301 Mineola, NY 11501 · 516-877-2900

William F. Levine · a · Levine & Grossman · 114 Old Country Road, Suite 460 · Mineola, NY 11501-4410 · 516-248-7575

Robert G. Sullivan · 2) · Sullivan, Papain, Block, McGrath & Cannavo · 55 Mineola Boulevard · Mineola, NY 11501 · 516-742-0707

New York

Mark J. Aaronson · Aaronson Rappaport Feinstein & Deutsch · 757 Third Avenue · New York, NY 10017 · 212-593-6700

Brian J. Alexander · Kreindler & Kreindler · 100 Park Avenue · New York, NY 10017-5590 · 212-687-8181

Walter G. Alton, Jr. · Walter G. Alton, Jr. & Associates · 548 West 28th Street, Suite 670 · New York, NY 10001 · 212-629-6151

Charles L. Bach, Jr. · Heidell, Pittoni, Murphy & Bach · 99 Park Avenue, Seventh Floor · New York, NY 10016 · 212-286-8585

Sheila L. Birnbaum · 2) · Skadden, Arps, Slate, Meagher & Flom · Four Times Square · New York, NY 10036 · 212-735-3000

Jeffrey B. Bloom · Gair, Gair, Conason, Steigman & Mackauf · http://www.gairgair.com · 80 Pine Street, 34th Floor · New York, NY 10005 · 212-943-1090

Vito A. Cannavo · Sullivan, Papain, Block, McGrath & Cannavo · 120 Broadway, 18th Floor · New York, NY 10271 · 212-732-9000

Richard V. Caplan · Aaronson Rappaport Feinstein & Deutsch · 757 Third Avenue · New York, NY 10017 · 212-593-6700

Eleni Coffinas · Sullivan, Papain, Block, McGrath & Cannavo · 120 Broadway, 18th Floor · New York, NY 10271 · 212-732-9000

Robert L. Conason · 2% · Gair, Gair, Conason, Steigman & Mackauf · http://www.gairgair.com · 80 Pine Street, 34th Floor · New York, NY 10005 · 212-943-1090

David C. Cook · Kreindler & Kreindler · 100 Park Avenue · New York, NY 10017-5590 · 212-687-8181

Elizabeth Cornacchio · Heidell, Pittoni, Murphy & Bach · 99 Park Avenue, Seventh Floor · New York, NY 10016 · 212-286-8585

Randal R. Craft, Jr. · Holland & Knight · http://www.hklaw.com · 195 Broadway, 24th Floor · New York, NY 10007-3189 · 212-513-3200

Peter T. Crean · Martin Clearwater & Bell · http://www.mcblaw.com · 220 East 42nd Street, Suite 1300 · New York, NY 10017 · 212-697-3122

Robert S. Deutsch · Aaronson Rappaport Feinstein & Deutsch · 757 Third Avenue · New York, NY 10017 · 212-593-6700

Robin R. Dolsky · Heidell, Pittoni, Murphy & Bach · 99 Park Avenue, Seventh Floor · New York, NY 10016 · 212-286-8585

Richard Eniclerico · Lester Schwab Katz & Dwyer · 120 Broadway, 38th Floor · New York, NY 10271-0071 · 212-964-6611

Anthony P. Gentile · Godosky & Gentile · http://www.godoskygentile.com · 61 Broadway, Suite 2010 · New York, NY 10006 · 212-742-9700

Richard Godosky · 2% · Godosky & Gentile · http://www.godoskygentile.com · 61 Broadway, Suite 2010 · New York, NY 10006 · 212-742-9700

Bruce G. Habian · a · Martin Clearwater & Bell · http://www.mcblaw.com · 220 East 42nd Street, Suite 1300 · New York, NY 10017 · 212-697-3122

Howard S. Hershenhorn · Gair, Gair, Conason, Steigman & Mackauf · http://www.gairgair.com · 80 Pine Street, 34th Floor · New York, NY 10005 · 212-943-1090

Alan Kaminsky · Lewis, Brisbois, Bisgaard & Smith · 199 Water Street, 25th Floor · New York, NY 10038 212-232-1300

Leslie Debra Kelmachter · The Jacob D. Fuchsberg Law Firm · 500 Fifth Avenue · New York, NY 10110 · 212-869-3500

Peter C. Kopff · Kopff, Nardelli & Dopf · 440 Ninth Avenue, 15th Floor · New York, NY 10001-1620 · 212-244-2999

Jeff S. Korek · Gersowitz Libo & Korek · 111 Broadway, 12th Floor, Suite 1204 · New York, NY 10006 · 212-385-4410

James P. Kreindler · Kreindler & Kreindler · 100 Park Avenue · New York, NY 10017-5590 · 212-687-8181

Brendan J. Lantier · McAloon & Friedman · 123 William Street, 25th Floor · New York, NY 10038-3804 212-732-8700

Stanley J. Levy · a · Levy Phillips & Konigsberg · 800 Third Avenue, 13th Floor · New York, NY 10022 212-605-6200

William J. Lewis · Lewis Johs Avallone Aviles · 30 Vessey Street, Eighth Floor · New York, NY 10007 · 212-233-7195

Judy A. Livingston · a · Kramer, Dillof, Livingston & Moore · 217 Broadway · New York, NY 10007 · 212-267-4177

John L. A. Lyddane · a · Martin Clearwater & Bell · http://www.mcblaw.com · 220 East 42nd Street, Suite 1300 · New York, NY 10017 · 212-697-3122

Stephen H. Mackauf · a · Gair, Gair, Conason, Steigman & Mackauf · http://www.gairgair.com · 80 Pine Street, 34th Floor · New York, NY 10005 · 212-943-1090

Nicholas J. Marotta · Aaronson Rappaport Feinstein & Deutsch · 757 Third Avenue · New York, NY 10017 · 212-593-6700

Roger P. McTiernan, Sr. · 2) · Barry, McTiernan & Moore · Two Rector Street, 14th Floor · New York, NY 10006 · 212-313-3600

Robert Steven Melnick · Aaronson Rappaport Feinstein & Deutsch · 757 Third Avenue · New York, NY 10017 · 212-593-6700

Marc S. Moller · Kreindler & Kreindler · 100 Park Avenue · New York, NY 10017-5590 · 212-687-8181

Thomas A. Moore · 2) · Kramer, Dillof, Livingston & Moore · 217 Broadway · New York, NY 10007 · 212-267-4177

Benedict P. Morelli · a · Morelli Ratner · http://www.morellilaw.com · 950 Third Avenue, 10th Floor · New York, NY 10022 · 212-751-9800

Steven E. North · a · Steven E. North · http://www.north-law.com · 148 East 74th Street · New York, NY 10021 · 212-861-5000

David H. Perecman · Perecman & Fanning · http://www.perecman.com · 250 West 57th Street · New York, NY 10107 · 212-977-7033

Steven J. Phillips · Levy Phillips & Konigsberg · 800 Third Avenue, 13th Floor · New York, NY 10022 · 212-605-6200

Luke M. Pittoni · 2) · Heidell, Pittoni, Murphy & Bach · 99 Park Avenue, Seventh Floor · New York, NY 10016 · 212-286-8585

Steven R. Pounian · Kreindler & Kreindler · 100 Park Avenue · New York, NY 10017-5590 · 212-687-8181

Jay A. Rappaport · Aaronson Rappaport Feinstein & Deutsch · 757 Third Avenue · New York, NY 10017 · 212-593-6700

Roy L. Reardon · 2% · Simpson Thacher · 425 Lexington Avenue · New York, NY 10017-3954 · 212-455-2000

Theodore B. Rosenzweig · a · McAloon & Friedman · 123 William Street, 25th Floor · New York, NY 10038-3804 · 212-732-8700

Ben B. Rubinowitz · Gair, Gair, Conason, Steigman & Mackauf · http://www.gairgair.com · 80 Pine Street, 34th Floor · New York, NY 10005 · 212-943-1090

Marvin Salenger · Salenger, Sack, Schwartz & Kimmel · The Woolworth Building, Suite 950 · 233 Broadway · New York, NY 10279 · 212-267-1950

Roy F. Scaffidi · Scaffidi & Associates · 150 East 52nd Street, 20th Floor · New York, NY 10022 · 212-935-9500

Harold Lee Schwab · 2% · Lester Schwab Katz & Dwyer · 120 Broadway, 38th Floor · New York, NY 10271-0071 · 212-964-6611

Laura R. Shapiro · McAloon & Friedman · 123 William Street, 25th Floor · New York, NY 10038-3804 · 212-732-8700

Anthony M. Sola · a · Martin Clearwater & Bell · http://www.mcblaw.com · 220 East 42nd Street, Suite 1300 · New York, NY 10017 · 212-697-3122

William G. Spratt · Shaub, Ahmuty, Citrin & Spratt · 655 Third Avenue, 28th Floor · New York, NY 10017-5617 · 212-599-8200

Ernest R. Steigman · Gair, Gair, Conason, Steigman & Mackauf · http://www.gairgair.com · 80 Pine Street, 34th Floor · New York, NY 10005 · 212-943-1090

George N. Tompkins, Jr. · a · Wilson Elser Moskowitz Edelman & Dicker · 150 East 42nd Street · New York, NY 10017-5639 · 212-490-3000

Evan Torgan · Torgan & Cooper · 17 State Street, 39th Floor · New York, NY 10005 · 212-232-2500

Harvey Weitz · 2) · Weitz & Associates · The Woolworth Building, Fifth Floor · 233 Broadway · New York, NY 10279 · 212-553-9300

Paul Brian Weitz · Paul B. Weitz & Associates · The Woolworth Building · 233 Broadway · New York, NY 10279 · 212-346-0045

Saul Wilensky · Schnader Harrison Segal & Lewis · http://www.schnader.com · 140 Broadway, Suite 3100 New York, NY 10005-1101 · 212-973-8000

Barbara Wrubel · Skadden, Arps, Slate, Meagher & Flom · Four Times Square · New York, NY 10036 · 212-735-3000

Oneonta

John F. Scarzafava · a · Scarzafava & Basdekis · 48 Deitz Street, Suite C · Oneonta, NY 13820-5107 · 607-432-9341

Palmyra

James F. Foley · Foley & Foley · 235 East Main Street · P.O. Box 211 · Palmyra, NY 14522-0211 · 315-597-6611

Port Washington

David S. Pollack · David S. Pollack · 151 Haven Avenue · Port Washington, NY 11050 · 516-767-8888

Rochester

Matthew F. Belanger · Faraci Lange · http://www.faraci.com · 28 East Main Street, Suite 1100 · Rochester, NY 14614 · 585-325-5150

Sheldon W. Boyce · Brenna, Brenna & Boyce · http://www.brennalaw.com · 31 East Main Street, Suite 2000 · Rochester, NY 14614 · 585-454-2000

David E. Brown · a · Brown & Tarantino · Times Square Building, Suite 300 · 45 Exchange Boulevard · Rochester, NY 14614 · 585-454-3377

Thomas C. Burke · a · Osborn, Reed & Burke · 45 Exchange Boulevard · Rochester, NY 14614-1403 · 585-454-6480

John A. Falk · Faraci Lange · http://www.faraci.com · 28 East Main Street, Suite 1100 · Rochester, NY 14614 · 585-325-5150

Angelo G. Faraci · 2% · Faraci Lange · http://www.faraci.com · 28 East Main Street, Suite 1100 · Rochester, NY 14614 · 585-325-5150

Cheryl A. Heller · a · Ward, Norris, Heller & Reidy · http://www.wnhr.com · 300 State Street · Rochester, NY 14614 · 585-454-0700

John C. Herbert · Harter Secrest & Emery · http://www.hselaw.com · 1600 Bausch & Lomb Place · Rochester, NY 14604-2711 · 585-232-6500

Paul K. Lange · Faraci Lange · http://www.faraci.com · 28 East Main Street, Suite 1100 · Rochester, NY 14614 · 585-325-5150

Michael R. Law · a · Phillips Lytle · 1400 First Federal Plaza · Rochester, NY 14614 · 585-238-2000

James P. McElheny · Woods Oviatt Gilman · http://www.woodsoviatt.com · 700 Crossroads Building · Two State Street · Rochester, NY 14614 · 585-987-2800

James C. Moore · 2) · Harter Secrest & Emery · http://www.hselaw.com · 1600 Bausch & Lomb Place · Rochester, NY 14604-2711 · 585-232-6500

Paul V. Nunes · Underberg & Kessler · 300 Bausch & Lomb Place · Rochester, NY 14604 · 585-258-2800

Donald W. O'Brien, Jr. · Woods Oviatt Gilman · http://www.woodsoviatt.com · 700 Crossroads Building · Two State Street · Rochester, NY 14614 · 585-987-2800

Anthony R. Palermo · 2) · Woods Oviatt Gilman · http://www.woodsoviatt.com · 700 Crossroads Building Two State Street · Rochester, NY 14614 · 585-987-2800

Norman A. Palmiere · 2% · Norman A. Palmiere · Reynolds Arcade, Suite 210 · 16 East Main Street · Rochester, NY 14614 · 585-262-2729

Joseph A. Regan · Faraci Lange · http://www.faraci.com · 28 East Main Street, Suite 1100 · Rochester, NY 14614 · 585-325-5150

Thomas E. Reidy · Ward, Norris, Heller & Reidy · http://www.wnhr.com · 300 State Street · Rochester, NY 14614 · 585-454-0700

David Rothenberg · a · Geiger and Rothenberg · Times Square Building, Suite 800 · 45 Exchange Street Rochester, NY 14614 · 585-232-1946

Stephen G. Schwarz · a · Faraci Lange · http://www.faraci.com · 28 East Main Street, Suite 1100 · Rochester, NY 14614 · 585-325-5150

Eric J. Ward · Ward, Norris, Heller & Reidy · http://www.wnhr.com · 300 State Street · Rochester, NY 14614 · 585-454-0700

Jeffrey M. Wilkens · 2) · Osborn, Reed & Burke · 45 Exchange Boulevard · Rochester, NY 14614-1403 · 585-454-6480

Michael R. Wolford · a · The Wolford Law Firm · http://www.wolfordfirm.com · 600 Reynolds Arcade Building · 16 East Main Street · Rochester, NY 14614 · 585-325-8000

Brian M. Zorn · a · Faraci Lange · http://www.faraci.com · 28 East Main Street, Suite 1100 · Rochester, NY 14614 · 585-325-5150

Schenectady

James W. Bendall · a · Bendall & Mednick · 836 Plymouth Avenue · Schenectady, NY 12308 · 518-370-2211

Seaford

Raymond J. Furey · Furey, Kerley, Walsh, Matera & Cinquemani · http://www.fureykerley.com · 2174 Jackson Avenue · Seaford, NY 11783 · 516-409-6200

Syracuse

John D. Allen · Bond, Schoeneck & King · One Lincoln Center · Syracuse, NY 13202-1355 · 315-218-8000

S. Paul Battaglia · 2) · Bond, Schoeneck & King · One Lincoln Center · Syracuse, NY 13202-1355 · 315-218-8000

Anthony S. Bottar · Bottar & Leone · Axa Tower Two, Suite 1600 · 120 Madison Street · Syracuse, NY 13202 · 315-422-3466

John H. Callahan · Bond, Schoeneck & King · One Lincoln Center · Syracuse, NY 13202-1355 · 315-218-8000

Paul M. Hanrahan · a · Hancock & Estabrook · 1500 Axa Tower I · 100 Madison Street · Syracuse, NY 13202 · 315-471-3151

Herbert J. Hubert · Bond, Schoeneck & King · One Lincoln Center · Syracuse, NY 13202-1355 · 315-218-8000

Thomas D. Keleher · Bond, Schoeneck & King · One Lincoln Center · Syracuse, NY 13202-1355 · 315-218-8000

Robert E. Lahm · a · Robert E. Lahm · 711 East Genesee Street · Syracuse, NY 13210 · 315-472-3434

William F. Lynn · 2) · Lynn Law Firm · M&T Bank Building, Suite 802 · 101 South Salina Street · Syracuse, NY 13202 · 315-474-1267

Walter L. Meagher, Jr. · a · Hancock & Estabrook · 1500 Axa Tower I · 100 Madison Street · Syracuse, NY 13202 · 315-471-3151

Timothy P. Murphy · Hancock & Estabrook · 1500 Axa Tower I · 100 Madison Street · Syracuse, NY 13202 · 315-471-3151

Thomas E. Myers · Bond, Schoeneck & King · One Lincoln Center · Syracuse, NY 13202-1355 · 315-218-8000

James E. Reid · Greene & Reid · http://www.greenereid.com · 173 Intrepid Lane · Syracuse, NY 13205 · 315-492-9665

Laurence F. Sovik · a · Smith, Sovik, Kendrick & Sugnet · 250 South Clinton Street, Suite 600 · Syracuse, NY 13202 · 315-474-2911

Steve W. Williams · Smith, Sovik, Kendrick & Sugnet · 250 South Clinton Street, Suite 600 · Syracuse, NY 13202 · 315-474-2911

Troy

E. Stewart Jones, Jr. · 2% · E. Stewart Jones · http://www.esjlaw.com · The Jones Building · 28 Second Street · Troy, NY 12180 · 518-274-5820

Uniondale

James R. Duffy · a · Duffy Duffy & Burdo · West Tower, 13th Floor · 1370 Reckson Plaza · Uniondale, NY 11556-0188 · 516-394-4200

Vestal

Sanford P. Tanenhaus · a · Levene, Gouldin & Thompson · http://www.binghamtonlaw.com · 450 Plaza Drive · Vestal, NY 13850 · 607-584-5793

White Plains

Frank Bastone · Bartlett, McDonough, Bastone & Monaghan · 81 Main Street · White Plains, NY 10601 · 914-448-0200

Garrett P. Lewis · Wilson Elser Moskowitz Edelman & Dicker · Three Gannett Drive · White Plains, NY 10604-3407 · 914-323-7000

Henry G. Miller · 2% · Clark, Gagliardi & Miller · http://www.cgmlaw.com · Inns of Court Building · 99 Court Street · White Plains, NY 10601 · 914-946-8900

Joseph G. Rende · Rende, Ryan & Downes · 202 Mamaroneck Avenue, Sixth Floor · White Plains, NY 10601-5312 · 914-681-0444

PRIVATE FUNDS LAW

New York

Thomas H. Bell · Simpson Thacher · 425 Lexington Avenue · New York, NY 10017-3954 · 212-455-2000

Scott Bowie · Linklaters · 1345 Avenue of the Americas · New York, NY 10105 · 212-903-9000

Stephanie R. Breslow · Schulte Roth & Zabel · 919 Third Avenue · New York, NY 10022 · 212-756-2000

Jennifer J. Burleigh · Debevoise & Plimpton · 919 Third Avenue · New York, NY 10022 · 212-909-6000

Woodrow W. Campbell · a · Debevoise & Plimpton · 919 Third Avenue · New York, NY 10022 · 212-909-6000

Stephen Culhane · Linklaters · 1345 Avenue of the Americas · New York, NY 10105 · 212-903-9000

Laurel Fitzpatrick · Ropes & Gray · http://www.ropesgray.com · 1211 Avenue of the Americas · New York, NY 10036-8704 · 212-596-9000

Steven J. Fredman · Schulte Roth & Zabel · 919 Third Avenue · New York, NY 10022 · 212-756-2000

Michael A. Gerstenzang · Cleary Gottlieb Steen & Hamilton · One Liberty Plaza · New York, NY 10006 212-225-2000

Shukie Grossman · Weil Gotshal & Manges · 767 Fifth Avenue · New York, NY 10153 · 212-310-8000

Michael P. Harrell · Debevoise & Plimpton · 919 Third Avenue · New York, NY 10022 · 212-909-6000

Philip H. Harris · Skadden, Arps, Slate, Meagher & Flom · Four Times Square · New York, NY 10036 · 212-735-3000

William J. Hewitt · Ropes & Gray · http://www.ropesgray.com · 1211 Avenue of the Americas · New York, NY 10036-8704 · 212-596-9000

Robert M. Hirsh · Paul, Weiss, Rifkind, Wharton & Garrison · 1285 Avenue of the Americas · New York, NY 10019-6064 · 212-373-3000

Adele Karig · Debevoise & Plimpton · 919 Third Avenue · New York, NY 10022 · 212-909-6000

Yukako Kawata · Davis Polk & Wardwell · 450 Lexington Avenue · New York, NY 10017 · 212-450-4000

Bruce L. Lieb · Proskauer Rose · http://www.proskauer.com · 1585 Broadway · New York, NY 10036-8299 212-969-3000

John C. MacMurray · Ropes & Gray · http://www.ropesgray.com · 1211 Avenue of the Americas · New York, NY 10036-8704 · 212-596-9000

Marco V. Masotti · Paul, Weiss, Rifkind, Wharton & Garrison · 1285 Avenue of the Americas · New York, NY 10019-6064 · 212-373-3000

William Natbony · Katten Muchin Rosenman · 575 Madison Avenue · New York, NY 10022-2585 · 212-940-8800

Paul N. Roth · a · Schulte Roth & Zabel · 919 Third Avenue · New York, NY 10022 · 212-756-2000

Glenn Sarno · Simpson Thacher · 425 Lexington Avenue · New York, NY 10017-3954 · 212-455-2000

Phyllis A. Schwartz · Schulte Roth & Zabel · 919 Third Avenue · New York, NY 10022 · 212-756-2000

Rebecca F. Silberstein · Debevoise & Plimpton · 919 Third Avenue · New York, NY 10022 · 212-909-6000

Louis H. Singer · Morgan Lewis & Bockius · 101 Park Avenue · New York, NY 10178-0060 · 212-309-6000

Edward D. Sopher · Gibson, Dunn & Crutcher · 200 Park Avenue, 47th Floor · New York, NY 10166-0193 · 212-351-4000

Jeffrey E. Tabak · Weil Gotshal & Manges · 767 Fifth Avenue · New York, NY 10153 · 212-310-8000

Michael G. Tannenbaum · Tannenbaum Helpern Syracuse & Hirschtritt · 900 Third Avenue · New York, NY 10022 · 212-508-6700

Stephen M. Vine · Akin Gump Strauss Hauer & Feld · 590 Madison Avenue, 22nd Floor · New York, NY 10022-2524 · 212-872-1000

Barry M. Wolf · Weil Gotshal & Manges · 767 Fifth Avenue · New York, NY 10153 · 212-310-8000

Michael W. Wolitzer · Simpson Thacher · 425 Lexington Avenue · New York, NY 10017-3954 · 212-455-2000

PRODUCT LIABILITY LITIGATION

Albany

John T. Maloney · Carter, Conboy, Case, Blackmore, Maloney & Laird · 20 Corporate Woods Boulevard · Albany, NY 12211-2362 · 518-465-3484

Terence Peter O'Connor · O'Connor, O'Connor, Bresee & First · http://www.1stlaw.com · 20 Corporate Woods Boulevard · Albany, NY 12211-0400 · 518-465-0400

John K. Powers · 2) · Powers & Santola · http://www.powers-santola.com · 39 North Pearl Street, Sixth Floor · Albany, NY 12207-2785 · 518-478-6616

Daniel R. Santola · a · Powers & Santola · http://www.powers-santola.com · 39 North Pearl Street, Sixth Floor · Albany, NY 12207-2785 · 518-478-6616

Buffalo

Brian P. Crosby · a · Gibson, McAskill & Crosby · 69 Delaware Avenue, Suite 900 · Buffalo, NY 14202 · 716-856-4200

Richard F. Griffin · 2% · Kavinoky & Cook · 726 Exchange Street, Suite 800 · Buffalo, NY 14210 · 716-845-6000

Laraine Kelley · Lipsitz Green Scime Cambria · http://www.lipsitzgreen.com · 42 Delaware Avenue, Suite 120 · Buffalo, NY 14202 · 716-849-1333

Hugh M. Russ III · Hodgson Russ · One Guaranty Building, Suite 100 · 140 Pearl Street · Buffalo, NY 14202 · 716-856-4000

James T. Scime · Lipsitz Green Scime Cambria · http://www.lipsitzgreen.com · 42 Delaware Avenue, Suite 120 · Buffalo, NY 14202 · 716-849-1333

Terry D. Smith · 2% · Smith, Keller, Miner & O'Shea · 69 Delaware Avenue, Suite 1212 · Buffalo, NY 14202-3801 · 716-855-3611

New York

Jerome H. Block · Levy Phillips & Konigsberg · 800 Third Avenue, 13th Floor · New York, NY 10022 · 212-605-6200

Randal R. Craft, Jr. · Holland & Knight · http://www.hklaw.com · 195 Broadway, 24th Floor · New York, NY 10007-3189 · 212-513-3200

Jay W. Dankner · Dankner & Milstein · 41 East 57th Street, 36th Floor · New York, NY 10022 · 212-751-8000

Robert S. Deutsch · Aaronson Rappaport Feinstein & Deutsch · 757 Third Avenue · New York, NY 10017 · 212-593-6700

Richard Eniclerico · Lester Schwab Katz & Dwyer · 120 Broadway, 38th Floor · New York, NY 10271-0071 · 212-964-6611

Howard A. Fried · Segal McCambridge Singer & Mahoney · 830 Third Avenue, Suite 400 · New York, NY 10022 · 212-651-7500

Anthony H. Gair · Gair, Gair, Conason, Steigman & Mackauf · http://www.gairgair.com · 80 Pine Street, 34th Floor · New York, NY 10005 · 212-943-1090

Steven Glickstein · Kaye Scholer · 425 Park Avenue · New York, NY 10022-3598 · 212-836-8000

Beth L. Kaufman · Schoeman, Updike & Kaufman · 60 East 42nd Street, 39th Floor · New York, NY 10165 · 212-661-5030

David Klingsberg · a · Kaye Scholer · 425 Park Avenue · New York, NY 10022-3598 · 212-836-8000

Stanley J. Levy · a · Levy Phillips & Konigsberg · 800 Third Avenue, 13th Floor · New York, NY 10022 212-605-6200

Theodore V. H. Mayer · Hughes Hubbard & Reed · http://www.hugheshubbard.com · One Battery Park Plaza · New York, NY 10004-1482 · 212-837-6000

Jay P. Mayesh · Kaye Scholer · 425 Park Avenue · New York, NY 10022-3598 · 212-836-8000

Peter C. Neger · Bingham McCutchen · http://www.bingham.com · 399 Park Avenue · New York, NY 10022-4689 · 212-705-7000

Dennis P. Orr · Morrison & Foerster · http://www.mofo.com · 1290 Avenue of the Americas · New York, NY 10104-0050 · 212-468-8000

Robb Patryk · Hughes Hubbard & Reed · http://www.hugheshubbard.com · One Battery Park Plaza · New York, NY 10004-1482 · 212-837-6000

Glenn J. Pogust · Kaye Scholer · 425 Park Avenue · New York, NY 10022-3598 · 212-836-8000

Jay A. Rappaport · Aaronson Rappaport Feinstein & Deutsch · 757 Third Avenue · New York, NY 10017 · 212-593-6700

Harold Lee Schwab · 2% · Lester Schwab Katz & Dwyer · 120 Broadway, 38th Floor · New York, NY 10271-0071 · 212-964-6611

Robert W. Sparks · Dechert · 30 Rockefeller Plaza · 1095 Avenue of the Americas · New York, NY 10036-6797 · 212-698-3500

Saul Wilensky · Schnader Harrison Segal & Lewis · http://www.schnader.com · 140 Broadway, Suite 3100 New York, NY 10005-1101 · 212-973-8000

Oneonta

John F. Scarzafava · a · Scarzafava & Basdekis · 48 Deitz Street, Suite C · Oneonta, NY 13820-5107 · 607-432-9341

Rochester

Richard E. Alexander · Harter Secrest & Emery · http://www.hselaw.com · 1600 Bausch & Lomb Place · Rochester, NY 14604-2711 · 585-232-6500

Matthew F. Belanger · Faraci Lange · http://www.faraci.com · 28 East Main Street, Suite 1100 · Rochester, NY 14614 · 585-325-5150

Angelo G. Faraci · 2% · Faraci Lange · http://www.faraci.com · 28 East Main Street, Suite 1100 · Rochester, NY 14614 · 585-325-5150

John C. Herbert · Harter Secrest & Emery · http://www.hselaw.com · 1600 Bausch & Lomb Place · Rochester, NY 14604-2711 · 585-232-6500

Henry R. Ippolito · Chamberlain D'Amanda Oppenheimer & Greenfield · 1600 Crossroads Building · Two State Street · Rochester, NY 14614 · 585-232-3730

Paul K. Lange · Faraci Lange · http://www.faraci.com · 28 East Main Street, Suite 1100 · Rochester, NY 14614 · 585-325-5150

David M. Lascell · a · Harter Secrest & Emery · http://www.hselaw.com · 1600 Bausch & Lomb Place · Rochester, NY 14604-2711 · 585-232-6500

James C. Moore · 2) · Harter Secrest & Emery · http://www.hselaw.com · 1600 Bausch & Lomb Place · Rochester, NY 14604-2711 · 585-232-6500

Anthony R. Palermo · 2) · Woods Oviatt Gilman · http://www.woodsoviatt.com · 700 Crossroads Building Two State Street · Rochester, NY 14614 · 585-987-2800

Joseph A. Regan · Faraci Lange · http://www.faraci.com · 28 East Main Street, Suite 1100 · Rochester, NY 14614 · 585-325-5150

Stephen G. Schwarz · a · Faraci Lange · http://www.faraci.com · 28 East Main Street, Suite 1100 · Rochester, NY 14614 · 585-325-5150

Jeffrey M. Wilkens · 2) · Osborn, Reed & Burke · 45 Exchange Boulevard · Rochester, NY 14614-1403 · 585-454-6480

Brian M. Zorn · a · Faraci Lange · http://www.faraci.com · 28 East Main Street, Suite 1100 · Rochester, NY 14614 · 585-325-5150

Syracuse

Paul M. Hanrahan · a · Hancock & Estabrook · 1500 Axa Tower I · 100 Madison Street · Syracuse, NY 13202 · 315-471-3151

Stephen T. Helmer · Mackenzie Hughes · 101 South Salina Street, Suite 600 · P.O. Box 4967 · Syracuse, NY 13221-4967 · 315-474-7571

Thomas D. Keleher · Bond, Schoeneck & King · One Lincoln Center · Syracuse, NY 13202-1355 · 315-218-8000

Robert J. Smith · Costello, Cooney & Fearon · Salina Place, Fourth Floor · 205 South Salina Street · Syracuse, NY 13202 · 315-422-1152

Laurence F. Sovik · a · Smith, Sovik, Kendrick & Sugnet · 250 South Clinton Street, Suite 600 · Syracuse, NY 13202 · 315-474-2911

Steve W. Williams · Smith, Sovik, Kendrick & Sugnet · 250 South Clinton Street, Suite 600 · Syracuse, NY 13202 · 315-474-2911

White Plains

Michael D. Shalhoub · Goldberg Segalla · 170 Hamilton Avenue, Suite 203 · White Plains, NY 10601-1717 · 914-798-5400

PROFESSIONAL MALPRACTICE LAW

Buffalo

Frank J. Frascogna · Rosenthal, Siegel & Muenkel · 300 Main Street · Buffalo, NY 14202 · 716-854-1300

Mark Spitler · Gibson, McAskill & Crosby · 69 Delaware Avenue, Suite 900 · Buffalo, NY 14202 · 716-856-4200

New York

Max W. Berger · Bernstein Litowitz Berger & Grossmann · http://www.blbglaw.com · 1285 Avenue of the Americas · New York, NY 10019 · 212-554-1400

Jeffrey B. Bloom · Gair, Gair, Conason, Steigman & Mackauf · http://www.gairgair.com · 80 Pine Street, 34th Floor · New York, NY 10005 · 212-943-1090

Rochester

Peter H. Abdella · Harter Secrest & Emery · http://www.hselaw.com · 1600 Bausch & Lomb Place · Rochester, NY 14604-2711 · 585-232-6500

James C. Moore · 2) · Harter Secrest & Emery · http://www.hselaw.com · 1600 Bausch & Lomb Place · Rochester, NY 14604-2711 · 585-232-6500

Thomas G. Smith · Harter Secrest & Emery · http://www.hselaw.com · 1600 Bausch & Lomb Place · Rochester, NY 14604-2711 · 585-232-6500

Jeffrey M. Wilkens · 2) · Osborn, Reed & Burke · 45 Exchange Boulevard · Rochester, NY 14614-1403 · 585-454-6480

Syracuse

Thomas D. Keleher · Bond, Schoeneck & King · One Lincoln Center · Syracuse, NY 13202-1355 · 315-218-8000

Michael P. Ringwood · Smith, Sovik, Kendrick & Sugnet · 250 South Clinton Street, Suite 600 · Syracuse, NY 13202 · 315-474-2911

Robert J. Smith · Costello, Cooney & Fearon · Salina Place, Fourth Floor · 205 South Salina Street · Syracuse, NY 13202 · 315-422-1152

Laurence F. Sovik · a · Smith, Sovik, Kendrick & Sugnet · 250 South Clinton Street, Suite 600 · Syracuse, NY 13202 · 315-474-2911

James G. Stevens, Jr. · Sugarman Law Firm · HSBC Center, Fifth Floor · 360 South Warren Street · Syracuse, NY 13202-2680 · 315-474-2943

Samuel Vulcano · Sugarman Law Firm · HSBC Center, Fifth Floor · 360 South Warren Street · Syracuse, NY 13202-2680 · 315-474-2943

PROJECT FINANCE LAW

New York

Todd E. Alexander · Chadbourne & Parke · http://www.chadbourne.com · 30 Rockefeller Plaza · New York, NY 10112-0127 · 212-408-5100

Troy Alexander · White & Case · http://www.whitecase.com · 1155 Avenue of the Americas · New York, NY 10036-2787 · 212-819-8200

Richard S. Brach · Milbank, Tweed, Hadley & McCloy · http://www.milbank.com · One Chase Manhattan Plaza · New York, NY 10005-1413 · 212-530-5000

Richard J. Cooper · Cleary Gottlieb Steen & Hamilton · One Liberty Plaza · New York, NY 10006 · 212-225-2000

Sergio J. Galvis · Sullivan & Cromwell · 125 Broad Street · New York, NY 10004-2498 · 212-558-4000

William R. Giusti · Baker Botts · http://www.bakerbotts.com · 30 Rockefeller Plaza · New York, NY 10112 · 212-408-2500

Eugene W. Goodwillie, Jr. · White & Case · http://www.whitecase.com · 1155 Avenue of the Americas · New York, NY 10036-2787 · 212-819-8200

David A. Gordon · Latham & Watkins · 885 Third Avenue · New York, NY 10022-4834 · 212-906-1200

Jonathan J. Green · Milbank, Tweed, Hadley & McCloy · http://www.milbank.com · One Chase Manhattan Plaza · New York, NY 10005-1413 · 212-530-5000

Jeffrey B. Greenberg · Latham & Watkins · 885 Third Avenue · New York, NY 10022-4834 · 212-906-1200

Joseph P. Hadley · Davis Polk & Wardwell · 450 Lexington Avenue · New York, NY 10017 · 212-450-4000

L. Douglas Harris · Milbank, Tweed, Hadley & McCloy · http://www.milbank.com · One Chase Manhattan Plaza · New York, NY 10005-1413 · 212-530-5000

Martin D. Jacobson · Simpson Thacher · 425 Lexington Avenue · New York, NY 10017-3954 · 212-455-2000

David M. Lieberman · Simpson Thacher · 425 Lexington Avenue · New York, NY 10017-3954 · 212-455-2000

Christopher L. Mann · Sullivan & Cromwell · 125 Broad Street · New York, NY 10004-2498 · 212-558-4000

George K. Miller · Simpson Thacher · 425 Lexington Avenue · New York, NY 10017-3954 · 212-455-2000

Harold F. Moore · Skadden, Arps, Slate, Meagher & Flom · Four Times Square · New York, NY 10036 · 212-735-3000

Frederic C. Rich · Sullivan & Cromwell · 125 Broad Street · New York, NY 10004-2498 · 212-558-4000

Jonathan R. Rod · Latham & Watkins · 885 Third Avenue · New York, NY 10022-4834 · 212-906-1200

Arthur A. Scavone · White & Case · http://www.whitecase.com · 1155 Avenue of the Americas · New York, NY 10036-2787 · 212-819-8200

Richard Shutran · Dewey & LeBoeuf · 1301 Avenue of the Americas · New York, NY 10019-6092 · 212-259-8000

Eric F. Silverman · Milbank, Tweed, Hadley & McCloy · http://www.milbank.com · One Chase Manhattan Plaza · New York, NY 10005-1413 · 212-530-5000

William H. Voge · Latham & Watkins · 885 Third Avenue · New York, NY 10022-4834 · 212-906-1200

Chaim Wachsberger · Chadbourne & Parke · http://www.chadbourne.com · 30 Rockefeller Plaza · New York, NY 10112-0127 · 212-408-5100

E. Waide Warner, Jr. · Davis Polk & Wardwell · 450 Lexington Avenue · New York, NY 10017 · 212-450-4000

Kenneth S. Wyman · Simpson Thacher · 425 Lexington Avenue · New York, NY 10017-3954 · 212-455-2000

PUBLIC FINANCE LAW

Albany

Harrie C. Patrick · Harris Beach · 54 State Street, Eighth Floor · Albany, NY 12207 · 518-427-9700

New York

Jackson B. Browning, Jr. · Squire Sanders · http://www.ssd.com · 350 Park Avenue · New York, NY 10022-6022 · 212-872-9800

Richard Chirls · Orrick, Herrington & Sutcliffe · 666 Fifth Avenue · New York, NY 10103-0001 · 212-506-5000

Linda L. D'Onofrio · Blank Rome · The Chrysler Building · 405 Lexington Avenue · New York, NY 10174 · 212-885-5000

J. Kevin Dougherty · McGuireWoods · http://www.mcguirewoods.com · 1345 Avenue of the Americas, Seventh Floor · New York, NY 10105-0106 · 212-548-2100

Kevin P. Downes · McGuireWoods · http://www.mcguirewoods.com · 1345 Avenue of the Americas, Seventh Floor · New York, NY 10105-0106 · 212-548-2100

Eugene W. Harper · Squire Sanders · http://www.ssd.com · 350 Park Avenue · New York, NY 10022-6022 212-872-9800

Edward S. Sinick · Squire Sanders · http://www.ssd.com · 350 Park Avenue · New York, NY 10022-6022 · 212-872-9800

Jeremy A. Spector · Mintz, Levin, Cohn, Ferris, Glovsky and Popeo · Chrysler Center · 666 Third Avenue · New York, NY 10017 · 212-935-3000

Howard Zucker · Hawkins Delafield & Wood · http://www.hawkins.com · One Chase Manhattan Plaza, 42nd Floor · New York, NY 10005-1401 · 212-820-9300

Syracuse

Edwin J. Kelley, Jr. · Bond, Schoeneck & King · One Lincoln Center · Syracuse, NY 13202-1355 · 315-218-8000

RAILROAD LAW

New York

Lawrence R. Bailey, Jr. · Hodgson Russ · 1540 Broadway, 24th Floor · New York, NY 10036 · 212-751-4300

Mark S. Landman · Landman Corsi Ballaine & Ford · 120 Broadway, 27th Floor · New York, NY 10271-0079 · 212-238-4800

James M. Woolsey III · Landman Corsi Ballaine & Ford · 120 Broadway, 27th Floor · New York, NY 10271-0079 · 212-238-4800

REAL ESTATE LAW

Albany

James C. Blackmore · Carter, Conboy, Case, Blackmore, Maloney & Laird · 20 Corporate Woods Boulevard · Albany, NY 12211-2362 · 518-465-3484

John W. Tabner · a · Tabner, Ryan & Keniry · 18 Corporate Woods Boulevard · Albany, NY 12211 · 800-713-7583

Edward J. Trombly · 2) · Hiscock & Barclay · 50 Beaver Street · Albany, NY 12207-2830 · 518-434-2163

Amherst

Richard F. DiGiacomo · a · Nesper Ferber & DiGiacomo · One Towne Centre, Suite 300 · 501 John James Audubon Parkway · Amherst, NY 14228 · 716-688-3800

Michael A. Piette · Jaeckle Fleischmann & Mugel · Centerpointe Corporate Park, Suite 320 · 400 Essjay Road · Amherst, NY 14221 · 716-250-1800

Jean C. Powers · Jaeckle Fleischmann & Mugel · Centerpointe Corporate Park, Suite 320 · 400 Essjay Road · Amherst, NY 14221 · 716-250-1800

Buffalo

James J. Contino · Phillips Lytle · 3400 HSBC Center · Buffalo, NY 14203-2887 · 716-847-8400

Anne C. Evans · Damon & Morey · http://www.damonmorey.com · 1000 Cathedral Place · 298 Main Street · Buffalo, NY 14202-4096 · 716-856-5500

Terrence M. Gilbride · Hodgson Russ · One Guaranty Building, Suite 100 · 140 Pearl Street · Buffalo, NY 14202 · 716-856-4000

Peter S. Gilfillan · Gross, Shuman, Brizdle & Gilfillan · Fayette Court Building, Suite 600 · 465 Main Street · Buffalo, NY 14203 · 716-854-4300

F. William Gray III · a · Hodgson Russ · One Guaranty Building, Suite 100 · 140 Pearl Street · Buffalo, NY 14202 · 716-856-4000

Vincent O. Hanley · Jaeckle Fleischmann & Mugel · 12 Fountain Plaza · Buffalo, NY 14202-2292 · 716-856-0600

Harry G. Meyer · a · Hodgson Russ · One Guaranty Building, Suite 100 · 140 Pearl Street · Buffalo, NY 14202 · 716-856-4000

Vincent J. Moore · Damon & Morey · http://www.damonmorey.com · 1000 Cathedral Place · 298 Main Street · Buffalo, NY 14202-4096 · 716-856-5500

John A. Pappano · Phillips Lytle · 3400 HSBC Center · Buffalo, NY 14203-2887 · 716-847-8400

Roger L. Ross · Hurwitz & Fine · http://www.hurwitzfine.com · 1300 Liberty Building · Buffalo, NY 14202 · 716-849-8900

Alan S. Wexler · Lippes Mathias Wexler Friedman · 665 Main Street, Suite 300 · Buffalo, NY 14203 · 716-853-5100

Cheektowaga

Nancy W. Saia · Law Offices of Nancy W. Saia · 1925 Kensington Avenue · Cheektowaga, NY 14225 · 716-832-1118

Fairport

T. Mary McDonald · a · Fix Spindelman Brovitz & Goldman · http://www.fixspin.com · 295 Woodcliff Drive, Suite 200 · Fairport, NY 14450 · 585-641-8000

Garden City

Bruce J. Bergman · Berkman, Henoch, Peterson & Peddy · 100 Garden City Plaza · Garden City, NY 11530 · 516-222-6200

Kenmore

Michael M. Blinkoff · a · Michael M. Blinkoff · 2746 Delaware Avenue · Kenmore, NY 14217 · 716-875-8916

New York

Arthur S. Adler · Sullivan & Cromwell · 125 Broad Street · New York, NY 10004-2498 · 212-558-4000

Steven M. Alden · 2% · Debevoise & Plimpton · 919 Third Avenue · New York, NY 10022 · 212-909-6000

Fredric L. Altschuler · Cadwalader, Wickersham & Taft · http://www.cadwalader.com · One World Financial Center · New York, NY 10281 · 212-504-6000

Warren J. Bernstein · Kaye Scholer · 425 Park Avenue · New York, NY 10022-3598 · 212-836-8000

Lester M. Bliwise · Sutherland · http://www.sutherland.com · Grace Building, 40th Floor · 1114 Avenue of the Americas · New York, NY 10036-7703 · 212-389-5000

W. Michael Bond · Weil Gotshal & Manges · 767 Fifth Avenue · New York, NY 10153 · 212-310-8000

Leonard Boxer · 2) · Stroock & Stroock & Lavan · 180 Maiden Lane · New York, NY 10038-4982 · 212-806-5400

Peter S. Britell · Dewey & LeBoeuf · 125 West 55th Street · New York, NY 10019-5389 · 212-424-8000

Richard L. Chadakoff · Latham & Watkins · 885 Third Avenue · New York, NY 10022-4834 · 212-906-1200

Anthony J. Colletta · Sullivan & Cromwell · 125 Broad Street · New York, NY 10004-2498 · 212-558-4000

Bruce S. Cybul · Schulte Roth & Zabel · 919 Third Avenue · New York, NY 10022 · 212-756-2000

Martin L. Edelman · a · Paul Hastings · Park Avenue Tower, First Floor · 75 East 55th Street · New York, NY 10022 · 212-318-6000

Mark S. Edelstein · Morrison & Foerster · http://www.mofo.com · 1290 Avenue of the Americas · New York, NY 10104-0050 · 212-468-8000

Martha Feltenstein · Skadden, Arps, Slate, Meagher & Flom · Four Times Square · New York, NY 10036 · 212-735-3000

Eric M. Feuerstein · Gibson, Dunn & Crutcher · 200 Park Avenue, 47th Floor · New York, NY 10166-0193 · 212-351-4000

Susanna S. Fodor · a · Jones Day · 222 East 41st Street · New York, NY 10017-6702 · 212-326-3939

Joseph P. Forte · Alston + Bird · http://www.alston.com · 90 Park Avenue · New York, NY 10016-1387 · 212-210-9400

Richard S. Fries · DLA Piper · 1251 Avenue of the Americas · New York, NY 10020-1104 · 212-335-4500

Stephen Gliatta · Kaye Scholer · 425 Park Avenue · New York, NY 10022-3598 · 212-836-8000

Andrew L. Herz · Patterson Belknap Webb & Tyler · http://www.pbwt.com · 1133 Avenue of the Americas · New York, NY 10036-6710 · 212-336-2000

James I. Hisiger · Latham & Watkins · 885 Third Avenue · New York, NY 10022-4834 · 212-906-1200

Karl B. Holtzschue · Karl B. Holtzschue · 122 East 82nd Street, Apartment 3C · New York, NY 10028-0859 · 212-472-1421

Steven G. Horowitz · Cleary Gottlieb Steen & Hamilton · One Liberty Plaza · New York, NY 10006 · 212-225-2000

Gary Israel · Sullivan & Cromwell · 125 Broad Street · New York, NY 10004-2498 · 212-558-4000

Robert J. Ivanhoe · Greenberg Traurig · http://www.gtlaw.com · MetLife Building · 200 Park Avenue · New York, NY 10166 · 212-801-9200

Meredith J. Kane · Paul, Weiss, Rifkind, Wharton & Garrison · 1285 Avenue of the Americas · New York, NY 10019-6064 · 212-373-3000

Steven D. Klein · Willkie Farr & Gallagher · 787 Seventh Avenue · New York, NY 10019-6099 · 212-728-8000

Gary S. Kleinman · Greenberg Traurig · http://www.gtlaw.com · MetLife Building · 200 Park Avenue · New York, NY 10166 · 212-801-9200

Scott M. Kobak · Simpson Thacher · 425 Lexington Avenue · New York, NY 10017-3954 · 212-455-2000

Steven C. Koppel · Jones Day · 222 East 41st Street · New York, NY 10017-6702 · 212-326-3939

Michael Paul Korotkin · Kramer Levin Naftalis & Frankel · http://www.kramerlevin.com · 1177 Avenue of the Americas · New York, NY 10036 · 212-715-9100

Andrew Lance · Gibson, Dunn & Crutcher · 200 Park Avenue, 47th Floor · New York, NY 10166-0193 · 212-351-4000

Matthew J. Leeds · Ganfer & Shore · 360 Lexington Avenue, 14th Floor · New York, NY 10017 · 212-922-9250

Stephen Lefkowitz · (10) · Fried, Frank, Harris, Shriver & Jacobson · One New York Plaza · New York, NY 10004-1980 · 212-859-8000

Jeffrey A. Lenobel · Schulte Roth & Zabel · 919 Third Avenue · New York, NY 10022 · 212-756-2000

Andrew Levy · Gibson, Dunn & Crutcher · 200 Park Avenue, 47th Floor · New York, NY 10166-0193 · 212-351-4000

Samuel H. Lindenbaum · (25) · Kramer Levin Naftalis & Frankel · http://www.kramerlevin.com · 1177 Avenue of the Americas · New York, NY 10036 · 212-715-9100

Mark W. Lipschutz · Cooley Godward Kronish · The Grace Building, 46th Floor · 1114 Avenue of the Americas · New York, NY 10036-7798 · 212-479-6000

Lawrence J. Lipson · (10) · Proskauer Rose · http://www.proskauer.com · 1585 Broadway · New York, NY 10036-8299 · 212-969-3000

Larry M. Loeb · Kramer Levin Naftalis & Frankel · http://www.kramerlevin.com · 1177 Avenue of the Americas · New York, NY 10036 · 212-715-9100

Martin Luskin · Blank Rome · The Chrysler Building · 405 Lexington Avenue · New York, NY 10174 · 212-885-5000

John J. McCarthy, Jr. · Morrison & Foerster · http://www.mofo.com · 1290 Avenue of the Americas · New York, NY 10104-0050 · 212-468-8000

Jonathan Mechanic · Fried, Frank, Harris, Shriver & Jacobson · One New York Plaza · New York, NY 10004-1980 · 212-859-8000

Joshua Mermelstein · Fried, Frank, Harris, Shriver & Jacobson · One New York Plaza · New York, NY 10004-1980 · 212-859-8000

Martin P. Miner · Holland & Knight · http://www.hklaw.com · 195 Broadway, 24th Floor · New York, NY 10007-3189 · 212-513-3200

Sanford W. Morhouse · Dewey & LeBoeuf · 1301 Avenue of the Americas · New York, NY 10019-6092 · 212-259-8000

Benjamin F. Needell · 2% · Skadden, Arps, Slate, Meagher & Flom · Four Times Square · New York, NY 10036 · 212-735-3000

Jay A. Neveloff · Kramer Levin Naftalis & Frankel · http://www.kramerlevin.com · 1177 Avenue of the Americas · New York, NY 10036 · 212-715-9100

Robin Panovka · Wachtell, Lipton, Rosen & Katz · 51 West 52nd Street · New York, NY 10019 · 212-403-1000

Keith M. Pattiz · McDermott Will & Emery · 340 Madison Avenue · New York, NY 10173-1922 · 212-547-5400

Ruth S. Perfido · a · Reed Smith · 599 Lexington Avenue, 29th Floor · New York, NY 10022 · 212-521-5400

Eugene A. Pinover · a · Willkie Farr & Gallagher · 787 Seventh Avenue · New York, NY 10019-6099 · 212-728-8000

Martin D. Polevoy · DLA Piper · 1251 Avenue of the Americas · New York, NY 10020-1104 · 212-335-4500

David J. Rabinowitz · Sutherland · http://www.sutherland.com · Grace Building, 40th Floor · 1114 Avenue of the Americas · New York, NY 10036-7703 · 212-389-5000

Stephen L. Rabinowitz · Greenberg Traurig · http://www.gtlaw.com · MetLife Building · 200 Park Avenue · New York, NY 10166 · 212-801-9200

Gregory J. Ressa · Simpson Thacher · 425 Lexington Avenue · New York, NY 10017-3954 · 212-455-2000

Philip Rosen · Weil Gotshal & Manges · 767 Fifth Avenue · New York, NY 10153 · 212-310-8000

Barry C. Ross · Bryan Cave · 1290 Avenue of the Americas · New York, NY 10104-3300 · 212-541-2000

Robert M. Safron · Patterson Belknap Webb & Tyler · http://www.pbwt.com · 1133 Avenue of the Americas · New York, NY 10036-6710 · 212-336-2000

Raymond A. Sanseverino · Loeb & Loeb · 345 Park Avenue, 18th Floor · New York, NY 10154-0037 · 212-407-4000

Paul D. Selver · Kramer Levin Naftalis & Frankel · http://www.kramerlevin.com · 1177 Avenue of the Americas · New York, NY 10036 · 212-715-9100

Joseph C. Shenker · Sullivan & Cromwell · 125 Broad Street · New York, NY 10004-2498 · 212-558-4000

Steven Simkin · Paul, Weiss, Rifkind, Wharton & Garrison · 1285 Avenue of the Americas · New York, NY 10019-6064 · 212-373-3000

Donald H. Siskind · 2% · Katten Muchin Rosenman · 575 Madison Avenue · New York, NY 10022-2585 · 212-940-8800

Chris M. Smith · Shearman & Sterling · 599 Lexington Avenue · New York, NY 10022-6069 · 212-848-4000

Timothy A. Stafford · Dechert · 30 Rockefeller Plaza · 1095 Avenue of the Americas · New York, NY 10036-6797 · 212-698-3500

Joshua Stein · Latham & Watkins · 885 Third Avenue · New York, NY 10022-4834 · 212-906-1200

Mario J. Suarez · Thompson Hine · 335 Madison Avenue, 12th Floor · New York, NY 10017-4611 · 212-344-5680

Gary R. Tarnoff · Kramer Levin Naftalis & Frankel · http://www.kramerlevin.com · 1177 Avenue of the Americas · New York, NY 10036 · 212-715-9100

Neil R. Tucker · Kramer Levin Naftalis & Frankel · http://www.kramerlevin.com · 1177 Avenue of the Americas · New York, NY 10036 · 212-715-9100

Harvey R. Uris · Skadden, Arps, Slate, Meagher & Flom · Four Times Square · New York, NY 10036 · 212-735-3000

David J. Weinberger · Proskauer Rose · http://www.proskauer.com · 1585 Broadway · New York, NY 10036-8299 · 212-969-3000

Michael D. Weinberger · Cleary Gottlieb Steen & Hamilton · One Liberty Plaza · New York, NY 10006 · 212-225-2000

Andrew J. Weiner · Morrison & Foerster · http://www.mofo.com · 1290 Avenue of the Americas · New York, NY 10104-0050 · 212-468-8000

Robert J. Wertheimer · Paul Hastings · Park Avenue Tower, First Floor · 75 East 55th Street · New York, NY 10022 · 212-318-6000

W. Christopher White · Cadwalader, Wickersham & Taft · http://www.cadwalader.com · One World Financial Center · New York, NY 10281 · 212-504-6000

Lawrence J. Wolk · Holland & Knight · http://www.hklaw.com · 195 Broadway, 24th Floor · New York, NY 10007-3189 · 212-513-3200

Samuel M. Zylberberg · Weil Gotshal & Manges · 767 Fifth Avenue · New York, NY 10153 · 212-310-8000

Pittsford

John E. Blyth · 2) · John E. Blyth · 141 Sully's Trail, Suite 12 · Pittsford, NY 14534 · 585-586-0590

Rochester

Richard M. Beers, Jr. · Phillips Lytle · 1400 First Federal Plaza · Rochester, NY 14614 · 585-238-2000

John B. Hood · 2) · Nixon Peabody · 1100 Clinton Square · P.O. Box 31051 · Rochester, NY 14604 · 585-263-1000

Mitchell S. Nusbaum · Woods Oviatt Gilman · http://www.woodsoviatt.com · 700 Crossroads Building · Two State Street · Rochester, NY 14614 · 585-987-2800

Cathy Kaman Ryan · Harter Secrest & Emery · http://www.hselaw.com · 1600 Bausch & Lomb Place · Rochester, NY 14604-2711 · 585-232-6500

Leon T. Sawyko · a · Harris Beach · The Granite Building · 130 East Main Street · Rochester, NY 14604 585-419-8800

W. Stephen Tierney · a · Woods Oviatt Gilman · http://www.woodsoviatt.com · 700 Crossroads Building · Two State Street · Rochester, NY 14614 · 585-987-2800

Samuel O. Tilton · a · Woods Oviatt Gilman · http://www.woodsoviatt.com · 700 Crossroads Building · Two State Street · Rochester, NY 14614 · 585-987-2800

Saratoga Springs

Joseph M. Walsh · Walsh & Walsh · 42 Long Alley · Saratoga Springs, NY 12866 · 518-583-0171

Syracuse

Stephen L. Johnson · 2) · Bond, Schoeneck & King · One Lincoln Center · Syracuse, NY 13202-1355 · 315-218-8000

Alfred W. Popkess · a · Mackenzie Hughes · 101 South Salina Street, Suite 600 · P.O. Box 4967 · Syracuse, NY 13221-4967 · 315-474-7571

C. Daniel Shulman · 2) · Shulman Curtin Grundner & Regan · 250 South Clinton Street, Suite 502 · Syracuse, NY 13202-1262 · 315-424-8944

John P. Sindoni · a · Hiscock & Barclay · One Park Place · 300 South State Street · Syracuse, NY 13202-2078 · 315-422-2131

Francis D. Stinziano · Gilberti, Stinziano, Heintz & Smith · 555 East Genesee Street · Syracuse, NY 13202-2519 · 315-442-0100

Uniondale

Benjamin Weinstock · Ruskin Moscau Faltischeck · East Tower, 15th Floor · 1425 Rexcorp Plaza · Uniondale, NY 11556-1425 · 516-663-6600

White Plains

Robert Feder · a · Cuddy & Feder · 445 Hamilton Avenue, 14th Floor · White Plains, NY 10601 · 914-761-1300

SECURITIES LAW

Armonk

Robin A. Henry · Boies, Schiller & Flexner · 333 Main Street · Armonk, NY 10504 · 914-749-8200

New York

Roger S. Aaron, Sr. · 2% · Skadden, Arps, Slate, Meagher & Flom · Four Times Square · New York, NY 10036 · 212-735-3000

Peter Allan Atkins · 2% · Skadden, Arps, Slate, Meagher & Flom · Four Times Square · New York, NY 10036 · 212-735-3000

Sarah E. Beshar · Davis Polk & Wardwell · 450 Lexington Avenue · New York, NY 10017 · 212-450-4000

Kenneth J. Bialkin · 2% · Skadden, Arps, Slate, Meagher & Flom · Four Times Square · New York, NY 10036 · 212-735-3000

John T. Bostelman · Sullivan & Cromwell · 125 Broad Street · New York, NY 10004-2498 · 212-558-4000

John M. Brandow · Davis Polk & Wardwell · 450 Lexington Avenue · New York, NY 10017 · 212-450-4000

Andrew R. Brownstein · a · Wachtell, Lipton, Rosen & Katz · 51 West 52nd Street · New York, NY 10019 · 212-403-1000

Robert E. Buckholz · Sullivan & Cromwell · 125 Broad Street · New York, NY 10004-2498 · 212-558-4000

Stephen L. Burns · Cravath, Swaine & Moore · Worldwide Plaza · 825 Eighth Avenue · New York, NY 10019-7475 · 212-474-1000

Lee D. Charles · Baker Botts · http://www.bakerbotts.com · 30 Rockefeller Plaza · New York, NY 10112 · 212-408-2500

James J. Clark · Cahill Gordon & Reindel · 80 Pine Street · New York, NY 10005-1702 · 212-701-3000

Eric L. Cochran · Skadden, Arps, Slate, Meagher & Flom · Four Times Square · New York, NY 10036 · 212-735-3000

Winthrop B. Conrad, Jr. · Davis Polk & Wardwell · 450 Lexington Avenue · New York, NY 10017 · 212-450-4000

Kirk A. Davenport II · Latham & Watkins · 885 Third Avenue · New York, NY 10022-4834 · 212-906-1200

Robert W. Downes · Sullivan & Cromwell · 125 Broad Street · New York, NY 10004-2498 · 212-558-4000

Ida W. Draim · Schulte Roth & Zabel · 919 Third Avenue · New York, NY 10022 · 212-756-2000

Richard A. Drucker · Davis Polk & Wardwell · 450 Lexington Avenue · New York, NY 10017 · 212-450-4000

Robert Evans III · Shearman & Sterling · 599 Lexington Avenue · New York, NY 10022-6069 · 212-848-4000

Gregory A. Fernicola · Skadden, Arps, Slate, Meagher & Flom · Four Times Square · New York, NY 10036 · 212-735-3000

Joseph H. Flom · 2% · Skadden, Arps, Slate, Meagher & Flom · Four Times Square · New York, NY 10036 · 212-735-3000

William V. Fogg · Cravath, Swaine & Moore · Worldwide Plaza · 825 Eighth Avenue · New York, NY 10019-7475 · 212-474-1000

Andres V. Gil · Davis Polk & Wardwell · 450 Lexington Avenue · New York, NY 10017 · 212-450-4000

Nicolas Grabar · Cleary Gottlieb Steen & Hamilton · One Liberty Plaza · New York, NY 10006 · 212-225-2000

Joel I. Greenberg · Kaye Scholer · 425 Park Avenue · New York, NY 10022-3598 · 212-836-8000

David B. Harms · Sullivan & Cromwell · 125 Broad Street · New York, NY 10004-2498 · 212-558-4000

William M. Hartnett · a · Cahill Gordon & Reindel · 80 Pine Street · New York, NY 10005-1702 · 212-701-3000

Kris F. Heinzelman · a · Cravath, Swaine & Moore · Worldwide Plaza · 825 Eighth Avenue · New York, NY 10019-7475 · 212-474-1000

Valerie Ford Jacob · Fried, Frank, Harris, Shriver & Jacobson · One New York Plaza · New York, NY 10004-1980 · 212-859-8000

David A. Katz · Wachtell, Lipton, Rosen & Katz · 51 West 52nd Street · New York, NY 10019 · 212-403-1000

Lou R. Kling · Skadden, Arps, Slate, Meagher & Flom · Four Times Square · New York, NY 10036 · 212-735-3000

Phyllis G. Korff · Skadden, Arps, Slate, Meagher & Flom · Four Times Square · New York, NY 10036 · 212-735-3000

Morris J. Kramer · 2% · Skadden, Arps, Slate, Meagher & Flom · Four Times Square · New York, NY 10036 · 212-735-3000

Edward A. Kwalwasser · Proskauer Rose · http://www.proskauer.com · 1585 Broadway · New York, NY 10036-8299 · 212-969-3000

John D. Lobrano · Simpson Thacher · 425 Lexington Avenue · New York, NY 10017-3954 · 212-455-2000

Matthew J. Mallow · 2) · Skadden, Arps, Slate, Meagher & Flom · Four Times Square · New York, NY 10036 · 212-735-3000

Joseph McLaughlin · a · Sidley Austin · 787 Seventh Avenue · New York, NY 10019 · 212-839-5300

Joseph M. McLaughlin · Simpson Thacher · 425 Lexington Avenue · New York, NY 10017-3954 · 212-455-2000

Bruce S. Mendelsohn · Akin Gump Strauss Hauer & Feld · 590 Madison Avenue, 22nd Floor · New York, NY 10022-2524 · 212-872-1000

Christian Nagler · Kirkland & Ellis · Citigroup Center · 153 East 53rd Street · New York, NY 10022-4611 212-446-4800

Eileen T. Nugent · Skadden, Arps, Slate, Meagher & Flom · Four Times Square · New York, NY 10036 · 212-735-3000

John W. Osborn · Skadden, Arps, Slate, Meagher & Flom · Four Times Square · New York, NY 10036 · 212-735-3000

Alan H. Paley · 2) · Debevoise & Plimpton · 919 Third Avenue · New York, NY 10022 · 212-909-6000

Vincent J. Pisano · Paul Hastings · Park Avenue Tower, First Floor · 75 East 55th Street · New York, NY 10022 · 212-318-6000

Robert W. Reeder III · Sullivan & Cromwell · 125 Broad Street · New York, NY 10004-2498 · 212-558-4000

Glenn M. Reiter · Simpson Thacher · 425 Lexington Avenue · New York, NY 10017-3954 · 212-455-2000

Marc S. Rosenberg · Cravath, Swaine & Moore · Worldwide Plaza · 825 Eighth Avenue · New York, NY 10019-7475 · 212-474-1000

Robert Rosenman · 2% · Cravath, Swaine & Moore · Worldwide Plaza · 825 Eighth Avenue · New York, NY 10019-7475 · 212-474-1000

Richard J. Sandler · Davis Polk & Wardwell · 450 Lexington Avenue · New York, NY 10017 · 212-450-4000

Jonathan A. Schaffzin · Cahill Gordon & Reindel · 80 Pine Street · New York, NY 10005-1702 · 212-701-3000

Michael J. Schiavone · Shearman & Sterling · 599 Lexington Avenue · New York, NY 10022-6069 · 212-848-4000

Howard Schiffman · Schulte Roth & Zabel · 919 Third Avenue · New York, NY 10022 · 212-756-2000

Leslie N. Silverman · Cleary Gottlieb Steen & Hamilton · One Liberty Plaza · New York, NY 10006 · 212-225-2000

Norman D. Slonaker · a · Sidley Austin · 787 Seventh Avenue · New York, NY 10019 · 212-839-5300

Jeffrey Small · a · Davis Polk & Wardwell · 450 Lexington Avenue · New York, NY 10017 · 212-450-4000

Andrew D. Soussloff · Sullivan & Cromwell · 125 Broad Street · New York, NY 10004-2498 · 212-558-4000

Allan G. Sperling · 2) · Cleary Gottlieb Steen & Hamilton · One Liberty Plaza · New York, NY 10006 · 212-225-2000

John B. Tehan · Simpson Thacher · 425 Lexington Avenue · New York, NY 10017-3954 · 212-455-2000

Arbie R. Thalacker · 2% · Shearman & Sterling · 599 Lexington Avenue · New York, NY 10022-6069 · 212-848-4000

Edward P. Tolley III · Simpson Thacher · 425 Lexington Avenue · New York, NY 10017-3954 · 212-455-2000

Rohan S. Weerasinghe · a · Shearman & Sterling · 599 Lexington Avenue · New York, NY 10022-6069 · 212-848-4000

William J. Whelan III · Cravath, Swaine & Moore · Worldwide Plaza · 825 Eighth Avenue · New York, NY 10019-7475 · 212-474-1000

William J. Williams, Jr. · 2% · Sullivan & Cromwell · 125 Broad Street · New York, NY 10004-2498 · 212-558-4000

SPORTS LAW

New York

L. Robert Batterman · 2) · Proskauer Rose · http://www.proskauer.com · 1585 Broadway · New York, NY 10036-8299 · 212-969-3000

Howard L. Ganz · 2) · Proskauer Rose · http://www.proskauer.com · 1585 Broadway · New York, NY 10036-8299 · 212-969-3000

Shepard Goldfein · Skadden, Arps, Slate, Meagher & Flom · Four Times Square · New York, NY 10036 · 212-735-3000

Jeffrey L. Kessler · Dewey & LeBoeuf · 1301 Avenue of the Americas · New York, NY 10019-6092 · 212-259-8000

Steven C. Krane · Proskauer Rose · http://www.proskauer.com · 1585 Broadway · New York, NY 10036-8299 · 212-969-3000

Joseph M. Leccese · Proskauer Rose · http://www.proskauer.com · 1585 Broadway · New York, NY 10036-8299 · 212-969-3000

Bruce S. Meyer · Weil Gotshal & Manges · 767 Fifth Avenue · New York, NY 10153 · 212-310-8000

Jeffrey A. Mishkin · Skadden, Arps, Slate, Meagher & Flom · Four Times Square · New York, NY 10036 212-735-3000

James W. Quinn · Weil Gotshal & Manges · 767 Fifth Avenue · New York, NY 10153 · 212-310-8000

Bradley I. Ruskin · Proskauer Rose · http://www.proskauer.com · 1585 Broadway · New York, NY 10036-8299 · 212-969-3000

STRUCTURED FINANCE LAW

New York

Reed D. Auerbach · McKee Nelson · One Battery Park Plaza, 34th Floor · New York, NY 10004 · 917-777-4200

Cameron L. Cowan · Orrick, Herrington & Sutcliffe · 666 Fifth Avenue · New York, NY 10103-0001 · 212-506-5000

James J. Croke · Orrick, Herrington & Sutcliffe · 666 Fifth Avenue · New York, NY 10103-0001 · 212-506-5000

William J. Cullen · Thacher Proffitt & Wood · Two World Financial Center · New York, NY 10281 · 212-912-7400

Susan M. Curtis · Skadden, Arps, Slate, Meagher & Flom · Four Times Square · New York, NY 10036 · 212-735-3000

Edward M. De Sear · McKee Nelson · One Battery Park Plaza, 34th Floor · New York, NY 10004 · 917-777-4200

David M. Eisenberg · Simpson Thacher · 425 Lexington Avenue · New York, NY 10017-3954 · 212-455-2000

Andrew M. Faulkner · Skadden, Arps, Slate, Meagher & Flom · Four Times Square · New York, NY 10036 · 212-735-3000

Michael S. Gambro · Cadwalader, Wickersham & Taft · http://www.cadwalader.com · One World Financial Center · New York, NY 10281 · 212-504-6000

Anna H. Glick · Cadwalader, Wickersham & Taft · http://www.cadwalader.com · One World Financial Center · New York, NY 10281 · 212-504-6000

Richard M. Horowitz · Thacher Proffitt & Wood · Two World Financial Center · New York, NY 10281 · 212-912-7400

Laurence B. Isaacson · McKee Nelson · One Battery Park Plaza, 34th Floor · New York, NY 10004 · 917-777-4200

Paul A. Jorissen · Mayer Brown · 1675 Broadway · New York, NY 10019-5820 · 212-506-2500

Richard F. Kadlick · Skadden, Arps, Slate, Meagher & Flom · Four Times Square · New York, NY 10036 212-735-3000

Jason H. P. Kravitt · Mayer Brown · 1675 Broadway · New York, NY 10019-5820 · 212-506-2500

Stephen S. Kudenholdt · Thacher Proffitt & Wood · Two World Financial Center · New York, NY 10281 · 212-912-7400

Renwick D. Martin · Sidley Austin · 787 Seventh Avenue · New York, NY 10019 · 212-839-5300

Frank P. Nocco · Weil Gotshal & Manges · 767 Fifth Avenue · New York, NY 10153 · 212-310-8000

Laura Palma · Simpson Thacher · 425 Lexington Avenue · New York, NY 10017-3954 · 212-455-2000

Joshua E. Raff · Orrick, Herrington & Sutcliffe · 666 Fifth Avenue · New York, NY 10103-0001 · 212-506-5000

Carlos A. Rodriguez · Sidley Austin · 787 Seventh Avenue · New York, NY 10019 · 212-839-5300

Jordan M. Schwartz · Cadwalader, Wickersham & Taft · http://www.cadwalader.com · One World Financial Center · New York, NY 10281 · 212-504-6000

Max Von Hollweg · Sidley Austin · 787 Seventh Avenue · New York, NY 10019 · 212-839-5300

Paul N. Watterson, Jr. · Schulte Roth & Zabel · 919 Third Avenue · New York, NY 10022 · 212-756-2000

Mark J. Welshimer · Sullivan & Cromwell · 125 Broad Street · New York, NY 10004-2498 · 212-558-4000

Robert C. Wipperman · McKee Nelson · One Battery Park Plaza, 34th Floor · New York, NY 10004 · 917-777-4200

TAX LAW

Albany

Richard V. D'Alessandro · 2) · Richard V. D'Alessandro Professional Corporation · 69 Columbia Street · Albany, NY 12210-2708 · 518-449-1421

Buffalo

Richard F. Campbell · Hodgson Russ · One Guaranty Building, Suite 100 · 140 Pearl Street · Buffalo, NY 14202 · 716-856-4000

Paul R. Comeau · 2) · Hodgson Russ · One Guaranty Building, Suite 100 · 140 Pearl Street · Buffalo, NY 14202 · 716-856-4000

Edward M. Griffith, Jr. · a · Phillips Lytle · 3400 HSBC Center · Buffalo, NY 14203-2887 · 716-847-8400

James A. Locke · a · Phillips Lytle · 3400 HSBC Center · Buffalo, NY 14203-2887 · 716-847-8400

Raymond P. Reichert · Jaeckle Fleischmann & Mugel · 12 Fountain Plaza · Buffalo, NY 14202-2292 · 716-856-0600

Loudonville

Robert E. Helm · a · Robert E. Helm · 57 Loudonwood East · Loudonville, NY 12211-1469 · 518-433-0530

New York

Martin B. Amdur · a · Weil Gotshal & Manges · 767 Fifth Avenue · New York, NY 10153 · 212-310-8000

Andrew N. Berg · Debevoise & Plimpton · 919 Third Avenue · New York, NY 10022 · 212-909-6000

Kimberly S. Blanchard · Weil Gotshal & Manges · 767 Fifth Avenue · New York, NY 10153 · 212-310-8000

Peter H. Blessing · Shearman & Sterling · 599 Lexington Avenue · New York, NY 10022-6069 · 212-848-4000

John R. Bonn · 20 · Sheppard, Mullin, Richter & Hampton · http://www.sheppardmullin.com · 30 Rockefeller Plaza, 24th Floor · New York, NY 10112 · 212-332-3800

Carol Seabrook Boulanger · 10 · Pillsbury Winthrop Shaw Pittman · http://www.pillsburylaw.com · 1540 Broadway · New York, NY 10036-4039 · 212-858-1000

William H. Bradley · 10 · Sutherland · http://www.sutherland.com · Grace Building, 40th Floor · 1114 Avenue of the Americas · New York, NY 10036-7703 · 212-389-5000

Andrew H. Braiterman · Hughes Hubbard & Reed · http://www.hugheshubbard.com · One Battery Park Plaza · New York, NY 10004-1482 · 212-837-6000

Richard J. Bronstein · 10 · Paul, Weiss, Rifkind, Wharton & Garrison · 1285 Avenue of the Americas · New York, NY 10019-6064 · 212-373-3000

William L. Burke · 10 · Pillsbury Winthrop Shaw Pittman · http://www.pillsburylaw.com · 1540 Broadway New York, NY 10036-4039 · 212-858-1000

Peter C. Canellos · 20 · Wachtell, Lipton, Rosen & Katz · 51 West 52nd Street · New York, NY 10019 · 212-403-1000

Robert Cassanos · Fried, Frank, Harris, Shriver & Jacobson · One New York Plaza · New York, NY 10004-1980 · 212-859-8000

William G. Cavanagh · 10 · Chadbourne & Parke · http://www.chadbourne.com · 30 Rockefeller Plaza · New York, NY 10112-0127 · 212-408-5100

Benjamin J. Cohen · 10 · Cahill Gordon & Reindel · 80 Pine Street · New York, NY 10005-1702 · 212-701-3000

Edmund S. Cohen · Winston & Strawn · 200 Park Avenue · New York, NY 10166-4193 · 212-294-6700

Richard G. Cohen · 25 · Pillsbury Winthrop Shaw Pittman · http://www.pillsburylaw.com · 1540 Broadway · New York, NY 10036-4039 · 212-858-1000

Ronald E. Creamer, Jr. · Sullivan & Cromwell · 125 Broad Street · New York, NY 10004-2498 · 212-558-4000

J. William Dantzler, Jr. · White & Case · http://www.whitecase.com · 1155 Avenue of the Americas · New York, NY 10036-2787 · 212-819-8200

Samuel Dimon · Davis Polk & Wardwell · 450 Lexington Avenue · New York, NY 10017 · 212-450-4000

David M. Einhorn · Wachtell, Lipton, Rosen & Katz · 51 West 52nd Street · New York, NY 10019 · 212-403-1000

James S. Eustice · 25 · Cooley Godward Kronish · The Grace Building, 46th Floor · 1114 Avenue of the Americas · New York, NY 10036-7798 · 212-479-6000

Peter L. Faber · 20 · McDermott Will & Emery · 340 Madison Avenue · New York, NY 10173-1922 · 212-547-5400

Michael R. Faber · Wilson Sonsini Goodrich & Rosati · 1301 Avenue of the Americas, 40th Floor · New York, NY 10017-8203 · 212-999-5800

Michael Farber · Davis Polk & Wardwell · 450 Lexington Avenue · New York, NY 10017 · 212-450-4000

M. Carr Ferguson · 2) · Davis Polk & Wardwell · 450 Lexington Avenue · New York, NY 10017 · 212-450-4000

Kathleen L. Ferrell · Davis Polk & Wardwell · 450 Lexington Avenue · New York, NY 10017 · 212-450-4000

Robert S. Fink · a · Kostelanetz & Fink · Seven World Trade Center, 34th Floor · 250 Greenwich Street New York, NY 10007 · 212-808-8100

Paul H. Frankel · Morrison & Foerster · http://www.mofo.com · 1290 Avenue of the Americas · New York, NY 10104-0050 · 212-468-8000

Gary M. Friedman · Debevoise & Plimpton · 919 Third Avenue · New York, NY 10022 · 212-909-6000

Phillip Gall · Cooley Godward Kronish · The Grace Building, 46th Floor · 1114 Avenue of the Americas · New York, NY 10036-7798 · 212-479-6000

Patrick C. Gallagher · Kirkland & Ellis · Citigroup Center · 153 East 53rd Street · New York, NY 10022-4611 · 212-446-4800

Stephen D. Gardner · a · Cooley Godward Kronish · The Grace Building, 46th Floor · 1114 Avenue of the Americas · New York, NY 10036-7798 · 212-479-6000

Peter A. Glicklich · Davies Ward Phillips & Vineberg · 625 Madison Avenue, 12th Floor · New York, NY 10022 · 212-588-5500

Sanford H. Goldberg · 2) · Roberts & Holland · Worldwide Plaza, 37th Floor · 825 Eighth Avenue · New York, NY 10019-7416 · 212-903-8700

Stuart J. Goldring · Weil Gotshal & Manges · 767 Fifth Avenue · New York, NY 10153 · 212-310-8000

Stephen L. Gordon · Cravath, Swaine & Moore · Worldwide Plaza · 825 Eighth Avenue · New York, NY 10019-7475 · 212-474-1000

Bruce D. Haims · a · Debevoise & Plimpton · 919 Third Avenue · New York, NY 10022 · 212-909-6000

David P. Hariton · Sullivan & Cromwell · 125 Broad Street · New York, NY 10004-2498 · 212-558-4000

John C. Hart · Simpson Thacher · 425 Lexington Avenue · New York, NY 10017-3954 · 212-455-2000

Kenneth H. Heitner · a · Weil Gotshal & Manges · 767 Fifth Avenue · New York, NY 10153 · 212-310-8000

Michael Hirschfeld · Dechert · 30 Rockefeller Plaza · 1095 Avenue of the Americas · New York, NY 10036-6797 · 212-698-3500

Thomas A. Humphreys · Morrison & Foerster · http://www.mofo.com · 1290 Avenue of the Americas · New York, NY 10104-0050 · 212-468-8000

William F. Indoe · Sullivan & Cromwell · 125 Broad Street · New York, NY 10004-2498 · 212-558-4000

Eliyahu D. Jacobson · Sullivan & Cromwell · 125 Broad Street · New York, NY 10004-2498 · 212-558-4000

Maria T. Jones · Kramer Levin Naftalis & Frankel · http://www.kramerlevin.com · 1177 Avenue of the Americas · New York, NY 10036 · 212-715-9100

Barbara T. Kaplan · Greenberg Traurig · http://www.gtlaw.com · MetLife Building · 200 Park Avenue · New York, NY 10166 · 212-801-9200

Bruce E. Kayle · Milbank, Tweed, Hadley & McCloy · http://www.milbank.com · One Chase Manhattan Plaza · New York, NY 10005-1413 · 212-530-5000

Mark S. Klein · a · Hodgson Russ · 1540 Broadway, 24th Floor · New York, NY 10036 · 212-751-4300

Edward D. Kleinbard · 2) · Cleary Gottlieb Steen & Hamilton · One Liberty Plaza · New York, NY 10006 · 212-225-2000

Janet B. Korins · Proskauer Rose · http://www.proskauer.com · 1585 Broadway · New York, NY 10036-8299 · 212-969-3000

Richard M. Leder · a · Chadbourne & Parke · http://www.chadbourne.com · 30 Rockefeller Plaza · New York, NY 10112-0127 · 212-408-5100

Carolyn Joy Lee · a · Jones Day · 222 East 41st Street · New York, NY 10017-6702 · 212-326-3939

Marc M. Levey · Baker & McKenzie · 1114 Avenue of the Americas · New York, NY 10036 · 212-626-4100

Richard O. Loengard, Jr. · 2) · Fried, Frank, Harris, Shriver & Jacobson · One New York Plaza · New York, NY 10004-1980 · 212-859-8000

Diana M. Lopo · a · Skadden, Arps, Slate, Meagher & Flom · Four Times Square · New York, NY 10036 212-735-3000

Gary Mandel · Simpson Thacher · 425 Lexington Avenue · New York, NY 10017-3954 · 212-455-2000

Andrew S. Mason · Sullivan & Cromwell · 125 Broad Street · New York, NY 10004-2498 · 212-558-4000

David S. Miller · Cadwalader, Wickersham & Taft · http://www.cadwalader.com · One World Financial Center · New York, NY 10281 · 212-504-6000

Stephen G. Mills · Goodwin Procter · The New York Times Building · 620 Eighth Avenue · New York, NY 10018 · 212-813-8800

Charles Morgan · a · Skadden, Arps, Slate, Meagher & Flom · Four Times Square · New York, NY 10036 · 212-735-3000

Ronald A. Morris · a · Roberts & Holland · Worldwide Plaza, 37th Floor · 825 Eighth Avenue · New York, NY 10019-7416 · 212-903-8700

Erika W. Nijenhuis · Cleary Gottlieb Steen & Hamilton · One Liberty Plaza · New York, NY 10006 · 212-225-2000

Stuart I. Odell · 2) · Dewey & LeBoeuf · 1301 Avenue of the Americas · New York, NY 10019-6092 · 212-259-8000

Deborah L. Paul · Wachtell, Lipton, Rosen & Katz · 51 West 52nd Street · New York, NY 10019 · 212-403-1000

James M. Peaslee · 2) · Cleary Gottlieb Steen & Hamilton · One Liberty Plaza · New York, NY 10006 · 212-225-2000

Barnet Phillips IV · Skadden, Arps, Slate, Meagher & Flom · Four Times Square · New York, NY 10036 212-735-3000

Elliot Pisem · Roberts & Holland · Worldwide Plaza, 37th Floor · 825 Eighth Avenue · New York, NY 10019-7416 · 212-903-8700

Martin D. Pollack · a · Weil Gotshal & Manges · 767 Fifth Avenue · New York, NY 10153 · 212-310-8000

Yaron Z. Reich · Cleary Gottlieb Steen & Hamilton · One Liberty Plaza · New York, NY 10006 · 212-225-2000

Richard L. Reinhold · a · Willkie Farr & Gallagher · 787 Seventh Avenue · New York, NY 10019-6099 · 212-728-8000

Sabino Rodriguez III · a · Day Pitney · Times Square Tower · Seven Times Square · New York, NY 10036-7311 · 212-297-5800

Kurt F. Rosell · Schulte Roth & Zabel · 919 Third Avenue · New York, NY 10022 · 212-756-2000

Arthur R. Rosen · a · McDermott Will & Emery · 340 Madison Avenue · New York, NY 10173-1922 · 212-547-5400

Burt Rosen · Debevoise & Plimpton · 919 Third Avenue · New York, NY 10022 · 212-909-6000

Matthew A. Rosen · a · Skadden, Arps, Slate, Meagher & Flom · Four Times Square · New York, NY 10036 · 212-735-3000

Seth L. Rosen · Debevoise & Plimpton · 919 Third Avenue · New York, NY 10022 · 212-909-6000

Edward F. Rover · White & Case · http://www.whitecase.com · 1155 Avenue of the Americas · New York, NY 10036-2787 · 212-819-8200

Jeffrey B. Samuels · Paul, Weiss, Rifkind, Wharton & Garrison · 1285 Avenue of the Americas · New York, NY 10019-6064 · 212-373-3000

Leslie B. Samuels · a · Cleary Gottlieb Steen & Hamilton · One Liberty Plaza · New York, NY 10006 · 212-225-2000

Robert H. Scarborough · Freshfields Bruckhaus Deringer · 520 Madison Avenue, 34th Floor · New York, NY 10022 · 212-277-4000

Donald Schapiro · 2% · Chadbourne & Parke · http://www.chadbourne.com · 30 Rockefeller Plaza · New York, NY 10112-0127 · 212-408-5100

Joel Scharfstein · a · Fried, Frank, Harris, Shriver & Jacobson · One New York Plaza · New York, NY 10004-1980 · 212-859-8000

Michael L. Schler · 2) · Cravath, Swaine & Moore · Worldwide Plaza · 825 Eighth Avenue · New York, NY 10019-7475 · 212-474-1000

David H. Schnabel · Debevoise & Plimpton · 919 Third Avenue · New York, NY 10022 · 212-909-6000

Jodi J. Schwartz · Wachtell, Lipton, Rosen & Katz · 51 West 52nd Street · New York, NY 10019 · 212-403-1000

Avishai Shachar · Davis Polk & Wardwell · 450 Lexington Avenue · New York, NY 10017 · 212-450-4000

David R. Sicular · Paul, Weiss, Rifkind, Wharton & Garrison · 1285 Avenue of the Americas · New York, NY 10019-6064 · 212-373-3000

Marc L. Silberberg · Weil Gotshal & Manges · 767 Fifth Avenue · New York, NY 10153 · 212-310-8000

Norman Sinrich · a · Feingold & Alpert · 1330 Avenue of the Americas, 25th Floor · New York, NY 10019 · 212-582-8000

Po Sit · Davis Polk & Wardwell · 450 Lexington Avenue · New York, NY 10017 · 212-450-4000

Bryan C. Skarlatos · Kostelanetz & Fink · Seven World Trade Center, 34th Floor · 250 Greenwich Street New York, NY 10007 · 212-808-8100

Andrew P. Solomon · Sullivan & Cromwell · 125 Broad Street · New York, NY 10004-2498 · 212-558-4000

Robert J. Staffaroni · Debevoise & Plimpton · 919 Third Avenue · New York, NY 10022 · 212-909-6000

Linda Z. Swartz · Cadwalader, Wickersham & Taft · http://www.cadwalader.com · One World Financial Center · New York, NY 10281 · 212-504-6000

Edward Tanenbaum · Alston + Bird · http://www.alston.com · 90 Park Avenue · New York, NY 10016-1387 · 212-210-9400

Willard B. Taylor · 2% · Sullivan & Cromwell · 125 Broad Street · New York, NY 10004-2498 · 212-558-4000

Sally A. Thurston · Skadden, Arps, Slate, Meagher & Flom · Four Times Square · New York, NY 10036 · 212-735-3000

David R. Tillinghast · 2% · Baker & McKenzie · 1114 Avenue of the Americas · New York, NY 10036 · 212-626-4100

Steven C. Todrys · a · Simpson Thacher · 425 Lexington Avenue · New York, NY 10017-3954 · 212-455-2000

Dana L. Trier · a · Davis Polk & Wardwell · 450 Lexington Avenue · New York, NY 10017 · 212-450-4000

Mary F. Voce · Greenberg Traurig · http://www.gtlaw.com · MetLife Building · 200 Park Avenue · New York, NY 10166 · 212-801-9200

Gordon E. Warnke · Dewey & LeBoeuf · 1301 Avenue of the Americas · New York, NY 10019-6092 · 212-259-8000

W. Thomas Weir · 2) · Akin Gump Strauss Hauer & Feld · 590 Madison Avenue, 22nd Floor · New York, NY 10022-2524 · 212-872-1000

Diana L. Wollman · Sullivan & Cromwell · 125 Broad Street · New York, NY 10004-2498 · 212-558-4000

Alfred D. Youngwood · 2% · Paul, Weiss, Rifkind, Wharton & Garrison · 1285 Avenue of the Americas · New York, NY 10019-6064 · 212-373-3000

George E. Zeitlin · a · Chadbourne & Parke · http://www.chadbourne.com · 30 Rockefeller Plaza · New York, NY 10112-0127 · 212-408-5100

Rochester

Robert E. Brown · a · Boylan, Brown, Code, Vigdor & Wilson · http://www.boylanbrown.com · 2400 Chase Square · Rochester, NY 14604 · 585-232-5300

Scott F. Cristman · a · Nixon Peabody · 1100 Clinton Square · P.O. Box 31051 · Rochester, NY 14604 · 585-263-1000

Sherry S. Kraus · Sherry S. Kraus · Times Square Building, Suite 513 · 45 Exchange Boulevard · Rochester, NY 14614 · 716-262-3360

Sherman F. Levey · 2) · Boylan, Brown, Code, Vigdor & Wilson · http://www.boylanbrown.com · 2400 Chase Square · Rochester, NY 14604 · 585-232-5300

Michael R. McEvoy · a · Harter Secrest & Emery · http://www.hselaw.com · 1600 Bausch & Lomb Place Rochester, NY 14604-2711 · 585-232-6500

Syracuse

Clayton H. Hale, Jr. · 2) · Mackenzie Hughes · 101 South Salina Street, Suite 600 · P.O. Box 4967 · Syracuse, NY 13221-4967 · 315-474-7571

Brian K. Haynes · Bond, Schoeneck & King · One Lincoln Center · Syracuse, NY 13202-1355 · 315-218-8000

Richard S. Scolaro · a · Scolaro, Shulman, Cohen, Fetter & Burstein · 507 Plum Street, Suite 300 · Syracuse, NY 13204 · 315-471-8111

Gerald F. Stack · a · Hiscock & Barclay · One Park Place · 300 South State Street · Syracuse, NY 13202-2078 · 315-422-2131

White Plains

Stanley E. Bulua · Danziger & Markhoff · Centroplex, Suite 900 · 123 Main Street · White Plains, NY 10601 · 914-948-1556

TECHNOLOGY LAW

New York

Robert A. Cantone · Proskauer Rose · http://www.proskauer.com · 1585 Broadway · New York, NY 10036-8299 · 212-969-3000

Jennifer B. Coplan · Cooley Godward Kronish · The Grace Building, 46th Floor · 1114 Avenue of the Americas · New York, NY 10036-7798 · 212-479-6000

Janet Cullum · Cooley Godward Kronish · The Grace Building, 46th Floor · 1114 Avenue of the Americas New York, NY 10036-7798 · 212-479-6000

Daryn A. Grossman · Proskauer Rose · http://www.proskauer.com · 1585 Broadway · New York, NY 10036-8299 · 212-969-3000

Frank A. Pugliese · Thelen Reid Brown Raysman & Steiner · 875 Third Avenue, 10th Floor · New York, NY 10022-6225 · 212-603-2000

Alan N. Sutin · Greenberg Traurig · http://www.gtlaw.com · MetLife Building · 200 Park Avenue · New York, NY 10166 · 212-801-9200

TRANSPORTATION LAW

New York

Sean F. Corrigan · Fulbright & Jaworski · http://www.fulbright.com · 666 Fifth Avenue · New York, NY 10103-3198 · 212-318-3000

James D. Tussing · Fulbright & Jaworski · http://www.fulbright.com · 666 Fifth Avenue · New York, NY 10103-3198 · 212-318-3000

TRUSTS AND ESTATES

Albany

James B. Ayers · 2) · Whiteman Osterman & Hanna · One Commerce Plaza · Albany, NY 12260 · 518-487-7600

Philip T. Dunne · a · Hinman Straub · 121 State Street · Albany, NY 12207-1622 · 518-436-0751

William S. Haase · 2) · McNamee, Lochner, Titus & Williams · 677 Broadway, Fifth Floor · P.O. Box 459 Albany, NY 12201-0459 · 518-447-3200

Timothy B. Thornton · 2) · McNamee, Lochner, Titus & Williams · 677 Broadway, Fifth Floor · P.O. Box 459 · Albany, NY 12201-0459 · 518-447-3200

Amherst

Peter J. Brevorka · a · Peter J. Brevorka · http://www.brevorkalaw.com · 4476 Main Street, Suite 108 · Amherst, NY 14226 · 716-332-3739

Patrick L. Emmerling · Jaeckle Fleischmann & Mugel · Centerpointe Corporate Park, Suite 320 · 400 Essjay Road · Amherst, NY 14221 · 716-250-1800

Binghamton

John G. Grall · Levene, Gouldin & Thompson · http://www.binghamtonlaw.com · 71 State Street · P.O. Box F-1706 · Binghamton, NY 13902 · 607-763-9200

Kathryn Grant Madigan · Levene, Gouldin & Thompson · http://www.binghamtonlaw.com · 71 State Street · P.O. Box F-1706 · Binghamton, NY 13902 · 607-763-9200

John M. Thomas · Coughlin & Gerhart · 20 Hawley Street · P.O. Box 2039 · Binghamton, NY 13902-2039 · 607-723-9511

Michael H. Zuckerman · a · Levene, Gouldin & Thompson · http://www.binghamtonlaw.com · 71 State Street · P.O. Box F-1706 · Binghamton, NY 13902 · 607-763-9200

Brooklyn

Marilyn G. Ordover · Cullen and Dykman · 177 Montague Street · Brooklyn, NY 11201-3611 · 718-855-9000

Buffalo

Paul R. Comeau · 2) · Hodgson Russ · One Guaranty Building, Suite 100 · 140 Pearl Street · Buffalo, NY 14202 · 716-856-4000

Gayle L. Eagan · Jaeckle Fleischmann & Mugel · 12 Fountain Plaza · Buffalo, NY 14202-2292 · 716-856-0600

Robert P. Fine · Hurwitz & Fine · http://www.hurwitzfine.com · 1300 Liberty Building · Buffalo, NY 14202 · 716-849-8900

Thomas R. Hyde · Hodgson Russ · One Guaranty Building, Suite 100 · 140 Pearl Street · Buffalo, NY 14202 · 716-856-4000

Stephen M. Newman · 2) · Nixon Peabody · Key Towers at Fountain Plaza, Suite 500 · 40 Fountain Plaza Buffalo, NY 14202 · 716-853-8100

Edward C. Northwood · Edward C. Northwood · 155 Summer Street · Buffalo, NY 14222 · 716-332-3456

Robert J. Plache · a · Damon & Morey · http://www.damonmorey.com · 1000 Cathedral Place · 298 Main Street · Buffalo, NY 14202-4096 · 716-856-5500

George E. Riedel, Jr. · Lipsitz Green Scime Cambria · http://www.lipsitzgreen.com · 42 Delaware Avenue, Suite 120 · Buffalo, NY 14202 · 716-849-1333

Arthur A. Russ, Jr. · Phillips Lytle · 3400 HSBC Center · Buffalo, NY 14203-2887 · 716-847-8400

John C. Spitzmiller · a · Phillips Lytle · 3400 HSBC Center · Buffalo, NY 14203-2887 · 716-847-8400

Sharon L. Wick · Phillips Lytle · 3400 HSBC Center · Buffalo, NY 14203-2887 · 716-847-8400

Camillus

Denise P. Cambs · a · The Cambs Law Firm · 5701 West Genesee Street · Camillus, NY 13031 · 315-484-1200

Elmira

Clover M. Drinkwater · a · Sayles & Evans · One West Church Street · Elmira, NY 14901 · 607-734-2271

Garden City

Andrea Hyde · a · Putney, Twombly, Hall & Hirson · 1205 Franklin Avenue · Garden City, NY 11503 · 516-746-0070

Glens Falls

Carl T. Baker · a · FitzGerald Morris Baker Firth · One Broad Street Plaza · P.O. Box 2017 · Glens Falls, NY 12801 · 518-745-1400

Paul E. Pontiff · a · Bartlett, Pontiff, Stewart & Rhodes · One Washington Street · P.O. Box 2168 · Glens Falls, NY 12801-2168 · 518-792-2117

Great Neck

Ronald Fatoullah · Ronald Fatoullah & Associates · http://www.elderlaw-newyork.com · 425 Northern Boulevard, Suite 20 · Great Neck, NY 11021 · 516-466-4422

Loudonville

Robert E. Helm · a · Robert E. Helm · 57 Loudonwood East · Loudonville, NY 12211-1469 · 518-433-0530

New York

Roy M. Adams · a · Constantine Cannon · 450 Lexington Avenue, 17th Floor · New York, NY 10017 · 212-350-2700

Christopher C. Angell · Patterson Belknap Webb & Tyler · http://www.pbwt.com · 1133 Avenue of the Americas · New York, NY 10036-6710 · 212-336-2000

Mal L. Barasch · 2% · Katten Muchin Rosenman · 575 Madison Avenue · New York, NY 10022-2585 · 212-940-8800

Jonathan R. Bell · a · Stern, Tannenbaum & Bell · 380 Lexington Avenue, Suite 3600 · New York, NY 10168 · 212-792-8484

Carl D. Bellows · Weil Gotshal & Manges · 767 Fifth Avenue · New York, NY 10153 · 212-310-8000

Christine Beshar · 2% · Cravath, Swaine & Moore · Worldwide Plaza · 825 Eighth Avenue · New York, NY 10019-7475 · 212-474-1000

Martha Gray Billman · John Silberman Associates · 145 East 57th Street, Ninth Floor · New York, NY 10022 · 212-319-3737

Howard Bindelglass · a · Phillips Nizer · 666 Fifth Avenue, 28th Floor · New York, NY 10103-0084 · 212-977-9700

James I. Black III · Sullivan & Cromwell · 125 Broad Street · New York, NY 10004-2498 · 212-558-4000

Jonathan G. Blattmachr · 2% · Milbank, Tweed, Hadley & McCloy · http://www.milbank.com · One Chase Manhattan Plaza · New York, NY 10005-1413 · 212-530-5000

Susan F. Bloom · Patterson Belknap Webb & Tyler · http://www.pbwt.com · 1133 Avenue of the Americas · New York, NY 10036-6710 · 212-336-2000

David P. Callahan · Davis Wright Tremaine · 1633 Broadway, 27th Floor · New York, NY 10019-6708 · 212-489-8230

Colleen F. Carew · Schram & Carew · 350 Broadway, Suite 515 · New York, NY 10013-3911 · 212-896-3310

Gerald I. Carp · Mazur Carp & Rubin · 1250 Broadway, Suite 3800 · New York, NY 10001 · 212-686-7700

Henry Christensen III · 2) · McDermott Will & Emery · 340 Madison Avenue · New York, NY 10173-1922 · 212-547-5400

Ronni G. Davidowitz · Katten Muchin Rosenman · 575 Madison Avenue · New York, NY 10022-2585 · 212-940-8800

James F. Downey · a · Stroock & Stroock & Lavan · 180 Maiden Lane · New York, NY 10038-4982 · 212-806-5400

Ralph M. Engel · Sonnenschein Nath & Rosenthal · 1221 Avenue of the Americas, 25th Floor · New York, NY 10020-1089 · 212-768-6700

Michael I. Frankel · 2) · Carter Ledyard & Milburn · Two Wall Street, 18th Floor · New York, NY 10005 212-732-3200

Susan C. Frunzi · Schulte Roth & Zabel · 919 Third Avenue · New York, NY 10022 · 212-756-2000

Elizabeth H. W. Fry · Pillsbury Winthrop Shaw Pittman · http://www.pillsburylaw.com · 1540 Broadway · New York, NY 10036-4039 · 212-858-1000

Jeffrey A. Galant · Herrick Feinstein · Two Park Avenue, 20th Floor · New York, NY 10016 · 212-592-1400

Michael W. Galligan · Phillips Nizer · 666 Fifth Avenue, 28th Floor · New York, NY 10103-0084 · 212-977-9700

Thomas P. Gannon, Jr. · Schlesinger Gannon & Lazetera · http://www.sglllp.com · 499 Park Avenue, 20th Floor · New York, NY 10022 · 212-652-3800

Brit L. Geiger · Sonnenschein Nath & Rosenthal · 1221 Avenue of the Americas, 25th Floor · New York, NY 10020-1089 · 212-768-6700

Charles F. Gibbs · a · Holland & Knight · http://www.hklaw.com · 195 Broadway, 24th Floor · New York, NY 10007-3189 · 212-513-3200

Martin R. Goodman · Schlesinger Gannon & Lazetera · http://www.sglllp.com · 499 Park Avenue, 20th Floor · New York, NY 10022 · 212-652-3800

Charles J. Groppe · a · Putney, Twombly, Hall & Hirson · 521 Fifth Avenue, 10th Floor · New York, NY 10175 · 212-682-0020

Cheryl E. Hader · Ropes & Gray · http://www.ropesgray.com · 1211 Avenue of the Americas · New York, NY 10036-8704 · 212-596-9000

Alan S. Halperin · a · Paul, Weiss, Rifkind, Wharton & Garrison · 1285 Avenue of the Americas · New York, NY 10019-6064 · 212-373-3000

Susan D. Harrington · Sidley Austin · 787 Seventh Avenue · New York, NY 10019 · 212-839-5300

Arlene Harris · a · Kaye Scholer · 425 Park Avenue · New York, NY 10022-3598 · 212-836-8000

T. Randolph Harris · McLaughlin & Stern · 260 Madison Avenue, Suite 1800 · New York, NY 10016 · 212-448-1100

Dan T. Hastings · Skadden, Arps, Slate, Meagher & Flom · Four Times Square · New York, NY 10036 · 212-735-3000

Linda B. Hirschson · 2) · Greenberg Traurig · http://www.gtlaw.com · MetLife Building · 200 Park Avenue · New York, NY 10166 · 212-801-9200

Dana Hiscock · Patterson Belknap Webb & Tyler · http://www.pbwt.com · 1133 Avenue of the Americas · New York, NY 10036-6710 · 212-336-2000

Mildred E. Kalik · 2) · Simpson Thacher · 425 Lexington Avenue · New York, NY 10017-3954 · 212-455-2000

Albert Kalter · a · Albert Kalter · 225 Broadway, Suite 1806 · New York, NY 10007 · 212-964-5485

Paul Richard Karan · a · Todtman, Nachamie, Spizz & Johns · 425 Park Avenue · New York, NY 10022 212-754-9400

Judith Kassel · Cleary Gottlieb Steen & Hamilton · One Liberty Plaza · New York, NY 10006 · 212-225-2000

Jonathan L. Koslow · Skadden, Arps, Slate, Meagher & Flom · Four Times Square · New York, NY 10036 · 212-735-3000

Jayne M. Kurzman · Davidson, Dawson & Clark · 60 East 42nd Street, 38th Floor · New York, NY 10165-3897 · 212-557-7700

John H. Lahey · Ferrell Law · 598 Madison Avenue, Second Floor · New York, NY 10022 · 212-813-9500

Robert C. Lawrence III · Cadwalader, Wickersham & Taft · http://www.cadwalader.com · One World Financial Center · New York, NY 10281 · 212-504-6000

Ralph E. Lerner · Withers Bergman · 430 Park Avenue, 10th Floor · New York, NY 10022-3505 · 212-848-9800

Jerome L. Levine · a · Loeb & Loeb · 345 Park Avenue, 18th Floor · New York, NY 10154-0037 · 212-407-4000

Seymour Levine · Troutman Sanders · The Chrysler Building · 405 Lexington Avenue · New York, NY 10174 · 212-704-6000

Steven M. Loeb · a · Cleary Gottlieb Steen & Hamilton · One Liberty Plaza · New York, NY 10006 · 212-225-2000

Dana Mark · Kaye Scholer · 425 Park Avenue · New York, NY 10022-3598 · 212-836-8000

Gordon H. Marsh · Marsh & Valentine · 10 East 40th Street, 42nd Floor · New York, NY 10016 · 212-689-1600

Carlyn S. McCaffrey · 2% · Weil Gotshal & Manges · 767 Fifth Avenue · New York, NY 10153 · 212-310-8000

Philip J. Michaels · Fulbright & Jaworski · http://www.fulbright.com · 666 Fifth Avenue · New York, NY 10103-3198 · 212-318-3000

Gloria S. Neuwirth · Davidson, Dawson & Clark · 60 East 42nd Street, 38th Floor · New York, NY 10165-3897 · 212-557-7700

Lawrence Newman · 2) · Lawrence Newman · 1633 Broadway, 46th Floor · New York, NY 10019-6708 · 212-833-1185

John C. Novogrod · Kramer Levin Naftalis & Frankel · http://www.kramerlevin.com · 1177 Avenue of the Americas · New York, NY 10036 · 212-715-9100

John J. O'Neil · a · Paul, Weiss, Rifkind, Wharton & Garrison · 1285 Avenue of the Americas · New York, NY 10019-6064 · 212-373-3000

Donald P. Perry · Phillips Nizer · 666 Fifth Avenue, 28th Floor · New York, NY 10103-0084 · 212-977-9700

Constantine P. Ralli · Dewey & LeBoeuf · 125 West 55th Street · New York, NY 10019-5389 · 212-424-8000

Jonathan J. Rikoon · Debevoise & Plimpton · 919 Third Avenue · New York, NY 10022 · 212-909-6000

Barbara Paul Robinson · 2% · Debevoise & Plimpton · 919 Third Avenue · New York, NY 10022 · 212-909-6000

Anita S. Rosenbloom · Stroock & Stroock & Lavan · 180 Maiden Lane · New York, NY 10038-4982 · 212-806-5400

Richard S. Rothberg · a · Cooley Godward Kronish · The Grace Building, 46th Floor · 1114 Avenue of the Americas · New York, NY 10036-7798 · 212-479-6000

Gideon Rothschild · Moses & Singer · The Chrysler Building · 405 Lexington Avenue · New York, NY 10174-1299 · 212-554-7800

Joshua S. Rubenstein · a · Katten Muchin Rosenman · 575 Madison Avenue · New York, NY 10022-2585 · 212-940-8800

Winthrop Rutherfurd, Jr. · White & Case · http://www.whitecase.com · 1155 Avenue of the Americas · New York, NY 10036-2787 · 212-819-8200

Dina Kapur Sanna · Day Pitney · Times Square Tower · Seven Times Square · New York, NY 10036-7311 · 212-297-5800

John P. Sare · a · Patterson Belknap Webb & Tyler · http://www.pbwt.com · 1133 Avenue of the Americas · New York, NY 10036-6710 · 212-336-2000

Edward S. Schlesinger · 2% · Hofheimer Gartlir & Gross · 530 Fifth Avenue · New York, NY 10036 · 212-818-9000

Sanford J. Schlesinger · 2) · Schlesinger Gannon & Lazetera · http://www.sglllp.com · 499 Park Avenue, 20th Floor · New York, NY 10022 · 212-652-3800

Eileen Caulfield Schwab · a · Sidley Austin · 787 Seventh Avenue · New York, NY 10019 · 212-839-5300

Abbe G. Shapiro · Fox Rothschild · 100 Park Avenue, Suite 1500 · New York, NY 10017 · 212-878-7900

Howard F. Sharfstein · Schulte Roth & Zabel · 919 Third Avenue · New York, NY 10022 · 212-756-2000

Robert W. Sheehan · Curtis, Mallet-Prevost, Colt & Mosle · 101 Park Avenue · New York, NY 10178 · 212-696-6000

Judith E. Siegel-Baum · a · WolfBlock · http://wolfblock.com · 250 Park Avenue · New York, NY 10177 212-986-1116

Georgiana J. Slade · a · Milbank, Tweed, Hadley & McCloy · http://www.milbank.com · One Chase Manhattan Plaza · New York, NY 10005-1413 · 212-530-5000

James S. Sligar · a · Milbank, Tweed, Hadley & McCloy · http://www.milbank.com · One Chase Manhattan Plaza · New York, NY 10005-1413 · 212-530-5000

Barbara A. Sloan · McLaughlin & Stern · 260 Madison Avenue, Suite 1800 · New York, NY 10016 · 212-448-1100

C. Michael Spero · Loeb & Loeb · 345 Park Avenue, 18th Floor · New York, NY 10154-0037 · 212-407-4000

David J. Stoll · Kaye Scholer · 425 Park Avenue · New York, NY 10022-3598 · 212-836-8000

Robert D. Taisey · a · Holland & Knight · http://www.hklaw.com · 195 Broadway, 24th Floor · New York, NY 10007-3189 · 212-513-3200

M. Antoinette Thomas · Carter Ledyard & Milburn · Two Wall Street, 18th Floor · New York, NY 10005 212-732-3200

Peter C. Valente · Blank Rome · The Chrysler Building · 405 Lexington Avenue · New York, NY 10174 · 212-885-5000

Theodore R. Wagner · a · Carter Ledyard & Milburn · Two Wall Street, 18th Floor · New York, NY 10005 · 212-732-3200

William B. Warren · 2% · Morris & McVeigh · 767 Third Avenue · New York, NY 10017 · 212-418-0500

Jay D. Waxenberg · Proskauer Rose · http://www.proskauer.com · 1585 Broadway · New York, NY 10036-8299 · 212-969-3000

Michael J. Weinberger · Sonnenschein Nath & Rosenthal · 1221 Avenue of the Americas, 25th Floor · New York, NY 10020-1089 · 212-768-6700

Ronald J. Weiss · Skadden, Arps, Slate, Meagher & Flom · Four Times Square · New York, NY 10036 · 212-735-3000

Bruce J. Wexler · Loeb & Loeb · 345 Park Avenue, 18th Floor · New York, NY 10154-0037 · 212-407-4000

G. Warren Whitaker · Day Pitney · Times Square Tower · Seven Times Square · New York, NY 10036-7311 · 212-297-5800

E. Lisk Wyckoff, Jr. · 2% · E. Lisk Wyckoff, Jr. · 505 Park Avenue, 20th Floor · New York, NY 10022 · 212-888-5959

William D. Zabel · 2% · Schulte Roth & Zabel · 919 Third Avenue · New York, NY 10022 · 212-756-2000

Harvey F. Zimand · a · Kelley Drye & Warren · 101 Park Avenue · New York, NY 10178-0002 · 212-808-7800

Basil P. Zirinis III · Sullivan & Cromwell · 125 Broad Street · New York, NY 10004-2498 · 212-558-4000

Pittsford

David C. Pettig · a · David C. Pettig & Associates · 65 Monroe Avenue, Suite A · Pittsford, NY 14534-1318 · 585-586-1430

Rochester

Edward D. Bloom · 2) · Harris Beach · The Granite Building · 130 East Main Street · Rochester, NY 14604 · 585-419-8800

Michael F. Buckley · 2) · Harter Secrest & Emery · http://www.hselaw.com · 1600 Bausch & Lomb Place Rochester, NY 14604-2711 · 585-232-6500

Philip L. Burke · a · Woods Oviatt Gilman · http://www.woodsoviatt.com · 700 Crossroads Building · Two State Street · Rochester, NY 14614 · 585-987-2800

Jill M. Cicero · Jill M. Cicero & Associates · 290 Linden Oaks · Rochester, NY 14625-2815 · 585-385-3100

Stewart D. Davis · a · Harris Beach · The Granite Building · 130 East Main Street · Rochester, NY 14604 · 585-419-8800

Mary V. Fisher · Boylan, Brown, Code, Vigdor & Wilson · http://www.boylanbrown.com · 2400 Chase Square · Rochester, NY 14604 · 585-232-5300

John T. Fitzgerald, Jr. · 2) · Nixon Peabody · 1100 Clinton Square · P.O. Box 31051 · Rochester, NY 14604 · 585-263-1000

Raymond Thompson Gilman · Woods Oviatt Gilman · http://www.woodsoviatt.com · 700 Crossroads Building · Two State Street · Rochester, NY 14614 · 585-987-2800

Warren H. Heilbronner · a · Boylan, Brown, Code, Vigdor & Wilson · http://www.boylanbrown.com · 2400 Chase Square · Rochester, NY 14604 · 585-232-5300

Lawrence P. Keller · Underberg & Kessler · 300 Bausch & Lomb Place · Rochester, NY 14604 · 585-258-2800

Robert W. Kessler · a · Woods Oviatt Gilman · http://www.woodsoviatt.com · 700 Crossroads Building · Two State Street · Rochester, NY 14614 · 585-987-2800

Martin O'Toole · a · Harter Secrest & Emery · http://www.hselaw.com · 1600 Bausch & Lomb Place · Rochester, NY 14604-2711 · 585-232-6500

David C. Reid · Law Office of David C. Reid · 290 Linden Oaks · Rochester, NY 14625 · 585-248-9620

Don H. Twietmeyer · Hiscock & Barclay · 2000 HSBC Plaza · 100 Chestnut Street · Rochester, NY 14604-2404 · 585-325-7570

Paul A. Vick · Phillips Lytle · 1400 First Federal Plaza · Rochester, NY 14614 · 585-238-2000

John D. Witmeyer · a · Nixon Peabody · 1100 Clinton Square · P.O. Box 31051 · Rochester, NY 14604 · 585-263-1000

Scarsdale

Frank M. Headley, Jr. · a · Bertine Hufnagel Headley Zeltner Drummond & Dohn · 700 White Plains Road, Suite 237 · Scarsdale, NY 10583-5017 · 914-472-7700

Schenectady

Michael R. Suprunowicz · a · Higgins, Roberts, Beyerl & Coan · 1430 Balltown Road · Schenectady, NY 12309-4332 · 518-374-3399

Syracuse

Robert F. Baldwin, Jr. · 2) · Baldwin & Sutphen · 100 Clinton Square, Suite 320 · 126 North Salina Street · Syracuse, NY 13202-1336 · 315-477-0100

Joseph A. Greenman · Bond, Schoeneck & King · One Lincoln Center · Syracuse, NY 13202-1355 · 315-218-8000

Elizabeth A. Hartnett · a · Mackenzie Hughes · 101 South Salina Street, Suite 600 · P.O. Box 4967 · Syracuse, NY 13221-4967 · 315-474-7571

John S. King · Scolaro, Shulman, Cohen, Fetter & Burstein · 507 Plum Street, Suite 300 · Syracuse, NY 13204 · 315-471-8111

James E. Mackin · a · Bond, Schoeneck & King · One Lincoln Center · Syracuse, NY 13202-1355 · 315-218-8000

Frederick S. Marty · a · Hiscock & Barclay · One Park Place · 300 South State Street · Syracuse, NY 13202-2078 · 315-422-2131

Michael E. O'Connor · a · DeLaney & O'Connor · One Lincoln Center, Suite 275 · Syracuse, NY 13202 315-476-8450

Gay M. Pomeroy · a · Mackenzie Hughes · 101 South Salina Street, Suite 600 · P.O. Box 4967 · Syracuse, NY 13221-4967 · 315-474-7571

James N. Seeley · Bond, Schoeneck & King · One Lincoln Center · Syracuse, NY 13202-1355 · 315-218-8000

Troy

Robert Wm. Johnson III · a · Martin, Shudt, Wallace, DiLorenzo & Johnson · The Dauchy Building · 279 River Street · P.O. Box 1530 · Troy, NY 12181 · 518-272-6565

Richard P. Wallace · 2) · Martin, Shudt, Wallace, DiLorenzo & Johnson · The Dauchy Building · 279 River Street · P.O. Box 1530 · Troy, NY 12181 · 518-272-6565

Uniondale

John J. Barnosky · a · Farrell Fritz · 1320 RexCorp Plaza · Uniondale, NY 11556-1320 · 516-227-0700

Michael K. Feigenbaum · a · Ruskin Moscau Faltischeck · East Tower, 15th Floor · 1425 Rexcorp Plaza Uniondale, NY 11556-1425 · 516-663-6600

White Plains

Harris Markhoff · 2) · Danziger & Markhoff · Centroplex, Suite 900 · 123 Main Street · White Plains, NY 10601 · 914-948-1556

Michael Markhoff · Danziger & Markhoff · Centroplex, Suite 900 · 123 Main Street · White Plains, NY 10601 · 914-948-1556

Philip T. Temple · a · McCarthy, Fingar, Donovan, Drazen & Smith · 11 Martine Avenue, 12th Floor · White Plains, NY 10606-1934 · 914-946-3700

VENTURE CAPITAL LAW

New York

Bruce C. Herzog · Willkie Farr & Gallagher · 787 Seventh Avenue · New York, NY 10019-6099 · 212-728-8000

WATER LAW

Albany

Robert J. Alessi · Dewey & LeBoeuf · One Commerce Plaza, Suite 2020 · 99 Washington Avenue · Albany, NY 12210-2820 · 518-626-9000

WHITE-COLLAR CRIMINAL DEFENSE

Albany

Stephen R. Coffey · a · O'Connell & Aronowitz · 54 State Street, Ninth Floor · Albany, NY 12207-2501 · 518-462-5601

William J. Dreyer · 2% · Dreyer Boyajian · 75 Columbia Street · Albany, NY 12210 · 518-463-7784

Buffalo

Paul J. Cambria, Jr. · 2% · Lipsitz Green Scime Cambria · http://www.lipsitzgreen.com · 42 Delaware Avenue, Suite 120 · Buffalo, NY 14202 · 716-849-1333

Terrence M. Connors · a · Connors & Vilardo · 1000 Liberty Building · 424 Main Street · Buffalo, NY 14202 · 716-852-5533

Joel L. Daniels · 2% · Joel L. Daniels · 1366 Statler Building · Buffalo, NY 14202 · 716-856-5140

Herbert L. Greenman · 2) · Lipsitz Green Scime Cambria · http://www.lipsitzgreen.com · 42 Delaware Avenue, Suite 120 · Buffalo, NY 14202 · 716-849-1333

James P. Harrington · Harrington & Mahoney · 70 Niagara Street, Third Floor · Buffalo, NY 14202 · 716-853-3700

Joseph M. LaTona · 2) · Law Office of Joseph M. LaTona · 716 Brisbane Building · 403 Main Street · Buffalo, NY 14203 · 716-842-0416

Mark J. Mahoney · 2) · Harrington & Mahoney · 70 Niagara Street, Third Floor · Buffalo, NY 14202 · 716-853-3700

Joseph V. Sedita · 2% · Hodgson Russ · One Guaranty Building, Suite 100 · 140 Pearl Street · Buffalo, NY 14202 · 716-856-4000

New York

Elkan Abramowitz · 2) · Morvillo, Abramowitz, Grand, Iason, Anello & Bohrer · 565 Fifth Avenue, Ninth Floor · New York, NY 10017 · 212-856-9600

Stanley S. Arkin · 2% · Arkin Kaplan · 590 Madison Avenue, 35th Floor · New York, NY 10022 · 212-333-0200

Michael F. Armstrong · 2% · Howrey · Citigroup Center, 54th Floor · 153 East 53rd Street · New York, NY 10022 · 212-896-6500

Daniel J. Beller · Paul, Weiss, Rifkind, Wharton & Garrison · 1285 Avenue of the Americas · New York, NY 10019-6064 · 212-373-3000

Paul B. Bergman · a · Paul B. Bergman · 950 Third Avenue, 32nd Floor · New York, NY 10022-2705 · 212-355-7711

Barry H. Berke · Kramer Levin Naftalis & Frankel · http://www.kramerlevin.com · 1177 Avenue of the Americas · New York, NY 10036 · 212-715-9100

Jerry D. Bernstein · Blank Rome · The Chrysler Building · 405 Lexington Avenue · New York, NY 10174 · 212-885-5000

Barry A. Bohrer · Morvillo, Abramowitz, Grand, Iason, Anello & Bohrer · 565 Fifth Avenue, Ninth Floor · New York, NY 10017 · 212-856-9600

Benjamin Brafman · a · Brafman & Associates · 767 Third Avenue, 26th Floor · New York, NY 10017-2023 · 212-750-7800

David E. Brodsky · Cleary Gottlieb Steen & Hamilton · One Liberty Plaza · New York, NY 10006 · 212-225-2000

David M. Brodsky · Latham & Watkins · 885 Third Avenue · New York, NY 10022-4834 · 212-906-1200

Susan Brune · Brune & Richard · http://www.bruneandrichard.com · 80 Broad Street · New York, NY 10004 · 212-668-1900

Lawrence Byrne · Linklaters · 1345 Avenue of the Americas · New York, NY 10105 · 212-903-9000

Austin V. Campriello · Bryan Cave · 1290 Avenue of the Americas · New York, NY 10104-3300 · 212-541-2000

George S. Canellos · Milbank, Tweed, Hadley & McCloy · http://www.milbank.com · One Chase Manhattan Plaza · New York, NY 10005-1413 · 212-530-5000

Charles M. Carberry · Jones Day · 222 East 41st Street · New York, NY 10017-6702 · 212-326-3939

John Carroll · Clifford Chance · 31 West 52nd Street · New York, NY 10019-6131 · 212-878-8000

Peter A. Chavkin · Mintz, Levin, Cohn, Ferris, Glovsky and Popeo · Chrysler Center · 666 Third Avenue New York, NY 10017 · 212-935-3000

Robert J. Cleary · Proskauer Rose · http://www.proskauer.com · 1585 Broadway · New York, NY 10036-8299 · 212-969-3000

John P. Cooney, Jr. · a · Davis Polk & Wardwell · 450 Lexington Avenue · New York, NY 10017 · 212-450-4000

Gandolfo V. DiBlasi · a · Sullivan & Cromwell · 125 Broad Street · New York, NY 10004-2498 · 212-558-4000

Peter J. Driscoll · Driscoll & Redlich · 521 Fifth Avenue, Suite 3300 · New York, NY 10017-3399 · 212-986-4030

Carey R. Dunne · Davis Polk & Wardwell · 450 Lexington Avenue · New York, NY 10017 · 212-450-4000

Scott A. Edelman · Milbank, Tweed, Hadley & McCloy · http://www.milbank.com · One Chase Manhattan Plaza · New York, NY 10005-1413 · 212-530-5000

Paul A. Engelmayer · WilmerHale · http://www.wilmerhale.com · 399 Park Avenue · New York, NY 10022 · 212-230-8800

Ronald P. Fischetti · a · Ronald P. Fischetti · 950 Third Avenue, 32nd Floor · New York, NY 10022 · 212-593-7100

Robert B. Fiske, Jr. · 2% · Davis Polk & Wardwell · 450 Lexington Avenue · New York, NY 10017 · 212-450-4000

Thomas Fitzpatrick · a · Thomas Fitzpatrick · 500 Fifth Avenue, 33rd Floor · New York, NY 10110-3398 · 212-930-1290

Peter E. Fleming, Jr. · 2% · Curtis, Mallet-Prevost, Colt & Mosle · 101 Park Avenue · New York, NY 10178 · 212-696-6000

Martin Flumenbaum · a · Paul, Weiss, Rifkind, Wharton & Garrison · 1285 Avenue of the Americas · New York, NY 10019-6064 · 212-373-3000

Andrew L. Frey · a · Mayer Brown · 1675 Broadway · New York, NY 10019-5820 · 212-506-2500

Faith Elizabeth Gay · Quinn Emanuel Urquhart Oliver & Hedges · 51 Madison Avenue, 22nd Floor · New York, NY 10010 · 212-849-7000

Robert J. Giuffra, Jr. · Sullivan & Cromwell · 125 Broad Street · New York, NY 10004-2498 · 212-558-4000

Jay Goldberg · 2) · Jay Goldberg · 250 Park Avenue, Suite 2020 · New York, NY 10177-2099 · 212-983-6000

Howard W. Goldstein · a · Fried, Frank, Harris, Shriver & Jacobson · One New York Plaza · New York, NY 10004-1980 · 212-859-8000

Paul R. Grand · 2) · Morvillo, Abramowitz, Grand, Iason, Anello & Bohrer · 565 Fifth Avenue, Ninth Floor · New York, NY 10017 · 212-856-9600

Helen Gredd · Lankler Siffert & Wohl · 500 Fifth Avenue, 33rd Floor · New York, NY 10110-3398 · 212-921-8399

Douglas E. Grover · Thompson Hine · 335 Madison Avenue, 12th Floor · New York, NY 10017-4611 · 212-344-5680

Frederick P. Hafetz · 2) · Hafetz & Necheles · 500 Fifth Avenue, 29th Floor · New York, NY 10110 · 212-997-7595

Mark R. Hellerer · Pillsbury Winthrop Shaw Pittman · http://www.pillsburylaw.com · 1540 Broadway · New York, NY 10036-4039 · 212-858-1000

Jack S. Hoffinger · 2% · Hoffinger Stern & Ross · 150 East 58th Street, 19th Floor · New York, NY 10155 212-421-4000

Lawrence Iason · Morvillo, Abramowitz, Grand, Iason, Anello & Bohrer · 565 Fifth Avenue, Ninth Floor · New York, NY 10017 · 212-856-9600

Robert J. Jossen · a · Dechert · 30 Rockefeller Plaza · 1095 Avenue of the Americas · New York, NY 10036-6797 · 212-698-3500

Kenneth J. Kaplan · Kaplan & Katzberg · 767 Third Avenue · New York, NY 10017-2023 · 212-750-3100

Stephen E. Kaufman · 2% · Stephen E. Kaufman · 277 Park Avenue, 47th Floor · New York, NY 10172 · 212-826-0820

David N. Kelley · Cahill Gordon & Reindel · 80 Pine Street · New York, NY 10005-1702 · 212-701-3000

John J. Kenney · Hoguet Newman Regal & Kenney · 10 East 40th Street · New York, NY 10016-0301 · 212-689-8808

T. Barry Kingham · 2% · Curtis, Mallet-Prevost, Colt & Mosle · 101 Park Avenue · New York, NY 10178 · 212-696-6000

Keith D. Krakaur · Skadden, Arps, Slate, Meagher & Flom · Four Times Square · New York, NY 10036 · 212-735-3000

Eliot Lauer · a · Curtis, Mallet-Prevost, Colt & Mosle · 101 Park Avenue · New York, NY 10178 · 212-696-6000

Andrew M. Lawler · 2% · Andrew M. Lawler · 641 Lexington Avenue, 27th Floor · New York, NY 10022 · 212-832-3160

Gerald B. Lefcourt · 2% · Gerald B. Lefcourt · 148 East 78th Street · New York, NY 10021 · 212-737-0400

Andrew J. Levander · Dechert · 30 Rockefeller Plaza · 1095 Avenue of the Americas · New York, NY 10036-6797 · 212-698-3500

Alan Levine · a · Cooley Godward Kronish · The Grace Building, 46th Floor · 1114 Avenue of the Americas · New York, NY 10036-7798 · 212-479-6000

Lewis J. Liman · Cleary Gottlieb Steen & Hamilton · One Liberty Plaza · New York, NY 10006 · 212-225-2000

Edward J.M. Little · Hughes Hubbard & Reed · http://www.hugheshubbard.com · One Battery Park Plaza · New York, NY 10004-1482 · 212-837-6000

Carl H. Loewenson, Jr. · Morrison & Foerster · http://www.mofo.com · 1290 Avenue of the Americas · New York, NY 10104-0050 · 212-468-8000

Aaron R. Marcu · Covington & Burling · The New York Times Building · 620 Eighth Avenue · New York, NY 10018 · 212-841-1000

Edward A. McDonald · Dechert · 30 Rockefeller Plaza · 1095 Avenue of the Americas · New York, NY 10036-6797 · 212-698-3500

Steven F. Molo · a · Shearman & Sterling · 599 Lexington Avenue · New York, NY 10022-6069 · 212-848-4000

Robert G. Morvillo · 2% · Morvillo, Abramowitz, Grand, Iason, Anello & Bohrer · 565 Fifth Avenue, Ninth Floor · New York, NY 10017 · 212-856-9600

Gary P. Naftalis · a · Kramer Levin Naftalis & Frankel · http://www.kramerlevin.com · 1177 Avenue of the Americas · New York, NY 10036 · 212-715-9100

Gustave H. Newman · 2% · Newman & Greenberg · 950 Third Avenue, 32nd Floor · New York, NY 10022 · 212-308-7900

Otto G. Obermaier · a · Martin & Obermaier · 565 Fifth Avenue, Eighth Floor · New York, NY 10017 · 212-883-0000

Lawrence B. Pedowitz · a · Wachtell, Lipton, Rosen & Katz · 51 West 52nd Street · New York, NY 10019 · 212-403-1000

Steven R. Peikin · Sullivan & Cromwell · 125 Broad Street · New York, NY 10004-2498 · 212-558-4000

Martin L. Perschetz · Schulte Roth & Zabel · 919 Third Avenue · New York, NY 10022 · 212-756-2000

Guy Petrillo · Dechert · 30 Rockefeller Plaza · 1095 Avenue of the Americas · New York, NY 10036-6797 212-698-3500

Jonathan D. Polkes · Weil Gotshal & Manges · 767 Fifth Avenue · New York, NY 10153 · 212-310-8000

Mark F. Pomerantz · Paul, Weiss, Rifkind, Wharton & Garrison · 1285 Avenue of the Americas · New York, NY 10019-6064 · 212-373-3000

Steven A. Reiss · Weil Gotshal & Manges · 767 Fifth Avenue · New York, NY 10153 · 212-310-8000

Lee S. Richards III · Richards Kibbe & Orbe · One World Financial Center, 29th Floor · New York, NY 10281-1003 · 212-530-1800

Paul K. Rooney · 2) · Howrey · Citigroup Center, 54th Floor · 153 East 53rd Street · New York, NY 10022 · 212-896-6500

Betty Santangelo · Schulte Roth & Zabel · 919 Third Avenue · New York, NY 10022 · 212-756-2000

John F. Savarese · Wachtell, Lipton, Rosen & Katz · 51 West 52nd Street · New York, NY 10019 · 212-403-1000

William J. Schwartz · Cooley Godward Kronish · The Grace Building, 46th Floor · 1114 Avenue of the Americas · New York, NY 10036-7798 · 212-479-6000

Karen P. Seymour · Sullivan & Cromwell · 125 Broad Street · New York, NY 10004-2498 · 212-558-4000

Samuel W. Seymour · Sullivan & Cromwell · 125 Broad Street · New York, NY 10004-2498 · 212-558-4000

Edward M. Shaw · 2% · Law Office of Edward M. Shaw · 420 Fifth Avenue, 25th Floor · New York, NY 10018-2729 · 212-703-5430

Paul Shechtman · Stillman, Friedman & Shechtman · http://www.stillmanfriedman.com · 425 Park Avenue · New York, NY 10022 · 212-223-0200

John S. Siffert · Lankler Siffert & Wohl · 500 Fifth Avenue, 33rd Floor · New York, NY 10110-3398 · 212-921-8399

Patrick Smith · Thacher Proffitt & Wood · Two World Financial Center · New York, NY 10281 · 212-912-7400

Ira Lee Sorkin · Dickstein Shapiro · http://www.dicksteinshapiro.com · 1177 Avenue of the Americas · New York, NY 10036-2714 · 212-277-6500

Mark J. Stein · Simpson Thacher · 425 Lexington Avenue · New York, NY 10017-3954 · 212-455-2000

Charles A. Stillman · 2% · Stillman, Friedman & Shechtman · http://www.stillmanfriedman.com · 425 Park Avenue · New York, NY 10022 · 212-223-0200

Richard M. Strassberg · Goodwin Procter · The New York Times Building · 620 Eighth Avenue · New York, NY 10018 · 212-813-8800

Audrey Strauss · a · Fried, Frank, Harris, Shriver & Jacobson · One New York Plaza · New York, NY 10004-1980 · 212-859-8000

John J. Tigue, Jr. · a · Morvillo, Abramowitz, Grand, Iason, Anello & Bohrer · 565 Fifth Avenue, Ninth Floor · New York, NY 10017 · 212-856-9600

Cyrus R. Vance, Jr. · a · Morvillo, Abramowitz, Grand, Iason, Anello & Bohrer · 565 Fifth Avenue, Ninth Floor · New York, NY 10017 · 212-856-9600

Peter K. Vigeland · WilmerHale · http://www.wilmerhale.com · 399 Park Avenue · New York, NY 10022 · 212-230-8800

Alan Vinegrad · Covington & Burling · The New York Times Building · 620 Eighth Avenue · New York, NY 10018 · 212-841-1000

Paul Vizcarrondo, Jr. · Wachtell, Lipton, Rosen & Katz · 51 West 52nd Street · New York, NY 10019 · 212-403-1000

Theodore V. Wells, Jr. · a · Paul, Weiss, Rifkind, Wharton & Garrison · 1285 Avenue of the Americas · New York, NY 10019-6064 · 212-373-3000

Mary Jo White · Debevoise & Plimpton · 919 Third Avenue · New York, NY 10022 · 212-909-6000

John R. Wing · 2) · Lankler Siffert & Wohl · 500 Fifth Avenue, 33rd Floor · New York, NY 10110-3398 · 212-921-8399

Roger Witten · WilmerHale · http://www.wilmerhale.com · 399 Park Avenue · New York, NY 10022 · 212-230-8800

Frank H. Wohl · Lankler Siffert & Wohl · 500 Fifth Avenue, 33rd Floor · New York, NY 10110-3398 · 212-921-8399

David M. Zornow · Skadden, Arps, Slate, Meagher & Flom · Four Times Square · New York, NY 10036 · 212-735-3000

Rochester

Lawrence J. Andolina · 2% · Trevett, Criste, Salzer & Andolina · Two State Street · 1000 Crossroads Building · Rochester, NY 14614 · 585-454-2181

Thomas A. DeSimon · Harris Beach · The Granite Building · 130 East Main Street · Rochester, NY 14604 · 585-419-8800

Michael Thomas DiPrima · 2) · Law Offices of Michael Thomas DiPrima · 40 Humboltt Street · Rochester, NY 14609 · 585-797-7926

Felix V. Lapine · 2) · Felix V. Lapine · One East Main Street, Suite 711 · Rochester, NY 14614 · 585-454-6690

David A. Murante · 2) · David A. Murante · Wilder Building, Suite 711 · Eight Exchange Street · Rochester, NY 14614 · 585-546-1770

Norman A. Palmiere · 2% · Norman A. Palmiere · Reynolds Arcade, Suite 210 · 16 East Main Street · Rochester, NY 14614 · 585-262-2729

John R. Parrinello · 2% · Redmond & Parrinello · Executive Office Building, Suite 400 · 36 West Main Street · Rochester, NY 14614 · 585-454-2321

David Rothenberg · a · Geiger and Rothenberg · Times Square Building, Suite 800 · 45 Exchange Street Rochester, NY 14614 · 585-232-1946

Karl F. Salzer · 2% · Trevett, Criste, Salzer & Andolina · Two State Street · 1000 Crossroads Building · Rochester, NY 14614 · 585-454-2181

John F. Speranza · 2) · John F. Speranza · First Federal Plaza, Suite 1800 · 28 East Main Street · Rochester, NY 14614 · 585-454-1500

Syracuse

Edward Z. Menkin · a · Edward Z. Menkin · http://www.edmenkin.com · State Tower Building, Suite 909 · 109 South Warren Street · Syracuse, NY 13202 · 315-425-1212

Emil M. Rossi · 2) · Emil M. Rossi Law Office · The Hamilton White House · 307 South Townsend Street · Syracuse, NY 13202 · 315-471-0126

Troy

Jerome K. Frost · a · Frost & Kavanaugh · Rensselaer Technology Park, Suite Five · 105 Jordan Road · Troy, NY 12180-8343 · 518-283-3000

E. Stewart Jones, Jr. · 2% · E. Stewart Jones · http://www.esjlaw.com · The Jones Building · 28 Second Street · Troy, NY 12180 · 518-274-5820

White Plains

William I. Aronwald · Aronwald & Pykett · 81 Main Street, Suite 450 · White Plains, NY 10601 · 914-946-6565

Luis Andrew Penichet · Law Offices of Luis Andrew Penichet · 140 Grand Street, Suite 401 · White Plains, NY 10601 · 914-997-7600

Andrew A. Rubin · Mancuso, Rubin & Fufidio · One North Broadway, Suite 1502 · White Plains, NY 10601 · 914-761-9200

WORKERS' COMPENSATION LAW

Albany

James E. Buckley · Buckley, Mendleson, Criscione & Quinn · 29 Wards Lane · Albany, NY 12204-2013 · 518-449-3107

Auburn

Paul A. Carbonaro · Carbonaro Law Offices · 110 Genessee, Suite 310 · Auburn, NY 13021 · 315-252-2352

Buffalo

Susan R. Duffy · Hamberger & Weiss · 1725 Statler Towers · 107 Delaware Avenue · Buffalo, NY 14202 · 716-852-5200

Mark W. Hamberger · a · Hamberger & Weiss · 1725 Statler Towers · 107 Delaware Avenue · Buffalo, NY 14202 · 716-852-5200

Rochester

Lewis F. Montemaggi · a · Montemaggi & Ferguson · Times Square Building, Suite 803 · 45 Exchange Street · Rochester, NY 14614-2078 · 585-325-3400

Ronald E. Weiss · a · Hamberger & Weiss · One South Washington Street, Suite 500 · Rochester, NY 14614 · 585-262-6390

Syracuse

Michael J. O'Brien · a · Michael J. O'Brien · 506 East Washington Street, Suite C · Syracuse, NY 13202 · 315-471-0003

NORTH CAROLINA

ADMINISTRATIVE LAW

Asheville

W. Louis Bissette, Jr. · McGuire, Wood & Bissette · Drhumor Building · 48 Patton Avenue · P.O. Box 3180 · Asheville, NC 28802-3180 · 828-254-8800

Charlotte

G. Michael Barnhill · Womble Carlyle Sandridge & Rice · One Wachovia Center, Suite 3500 · 301 South College Street · Charlotte, NC 28202-6037 · 704-331-4900

Raleigh

Noel L. Allen · Allen & Pinnix · 333 Fayetteville Street, Suite 1200 · P.O. Drawer 1270 · Raleigh, NC 27602-1270 · 919-755-0505

Carson Carmichael III · Bailey & Dixon · 2500 Two Hannover Square · P.O. Box 1351 · Raleigh, NC 27602-1351 · 919-828-0731

Charles D. Case · ⑳ · Hunton & Williams · One Bank Of America Plaza, Suite 1400 · 421 Fayetteville Street · P.O. Box 109 · Raleigh, NC 27602 · 919-899-3000

Anna Baird Choi · Allen & Pinnix · 333 Fayetteville Street, Suite 1200 · P.O. Drawer 1270 · Raleigh, NC 27602-1270 · 919-755-0505

John N. Fountain · Young, Moore & Henderson · 3101 Glenwood Avenue · P.O. Box 31627 · Raleigh, NC 27622-1627 · 919-782-6860

George G. Hearn · Johnson, Hearn, Vinegar, Gee & Glass · Two Hannover Square, Suite 2200 · P.O. Box 1776 · Raleigh, NC 27602-1776 · 919-743-2200

Noah H. Huffstetler III · ⑩ · Nelson Mullins Riley & Scarborough · GlenLake One, Suite 200 · 4140 Parklake Avenue · P.O. Box 30519 · Raleigh, NC 27622-0519 · 919-877-3800

Charles C. Meeker · Parker Poe Adams & Bernstein · http://www.parkerpoe.com · Wachovia Capitol Center, Suite 1400 · 150 Fayetteville Street · Raleigh, NC 27601 · 919-828-0564

Renee J. Montgomery · Parker Poe Adams & Bernstein · http://www.parkerpoe.com · Wachovia Capitol Center, Suite 1400 · 150 Fayetteville Street · Raleigh, NC 27601 · 919-828-0564

M. Jackson Nichols · Allen & Pinnix · 333 Fayetteville Street, Suite 1200 · P.O. Drawer 1270 · Raleigh, NC 27602-1270 · 919-755-0505

Alan M. Schneider · Cheshire, Parker, Schneider, Bryan & Vitale · http://www.cheshirepark.com · 133 Fayetteville Street, Suite 500 · P.O. Box 1029 · Raleigh, NC 27602-1029 · 919-833-3114

Steven M. Shaber · Poyner & Spruill · http://www.poynerspruill.com · 3600 Glenwood Avenue · P.O. Box 10096 · Raleigh, NC 27605-0096 · 919-783-6400

M. Denise Stanford · Bailey & Dixon · 2500 Two Hannover Square · P.O. Box 1351 · Raleigh, NC 27602-1351 · 919-828-0731

Thomas R. West · Poyner & Spruill · http://www.poynerspruill.com · 3600 Glenwood Avenue · P.O. Box 10096 · Raleigh, NC 27605-0096 · 919-783-6400

Lee M. Whitman · Wyrick Robbins Yates & Ponton · http://www.wyrick.com · The Summit, Suite 300 · 4101 Lake Boone Trail · P.O. Drawer 17803 · Raleigh, NC 27607-7506 · 919-781-4000

ALTERNATIVE DISPUTE RESOLUTION

Asheville

Frederick S. Barbour · Barbour Law Firm · 21 Battery Park Avenue, Suite 201 · Asheville, NC 28801 · 828-232-9156

Michael L. Miller · ⑩ · Michael L. Miller · Ninety Southside Avenue, Suite 100 · P.O. Box 2953 · Asheville, NC 28802 · 828-281-2100

Chapel Hill

Lynn G. Gullick · Lynn G. Gullick · P.O. Box 16205 · Chapel Hill, NC 27402 · 919-636-5697

J. Anderson Little · J. Anderson Little · P.O. Box 16205 · Chapel Hill, NC 27516 · 919-967-6611

Scott M. Taylor · Scott M. Taylor · 501 Weaver Mine Trail · Chapel Hill, NC 27709 · 919-942-4626

Charlotte

Jeffrey J. Davis · Jeffrey J. Davis · 400 North Church Street, Suite 222 · Charlotte, NC 28202 · 704-331-1037

Wayne P. Huckel · K&L Gates · Hearst Tower, 47th Floor · 214 North Tryon Street · Charlotte, NC 28202 · 704-331-7400

A. Ward McKeithen · ㉕ · Robinson, Bradshaw & Hinson · http://www.rbh.com · 101 North Tryon Street, Suite 1900 · Charlotte, NC 28246-1900 · 704-377-2536

Chase B. Saunders · McNair Law Firm · http://www.mcnair.net · Two Wachovia Center, Suite 1615 · 301 South Tryon Street · Charlotte, NC 28282 · 704-347-1170

Charles V. Tompkins, Jr. · ⑩ · K&L Gates · Hearst Tower, 47th Floor · 214 North Tryon Street · Charlotte, NC 28202 · 704-331-7400

Stacy K. Wood · Parker Poe Adams & Bernstein · http://www.parkerpoe.com · Three Wachovia Center, Suite 3000 · 401 South Tryon Street · Charlotte, NC 28202-1935 · 704-372-9000

Durham

Robert A. Beason · Beason & Ellis Conflict Resolution · 2741 University Drive · P.O. Box 52270 · Durham, NC 27717-2270 · 919-419-9979

René S. Ellis · Beason & Ellis Conflict Resolution · 2741 University Drive · P.O. Box 52270 · Durham, NC 27717-2270 · 919-419-9979

Margaret J. McCreary · Margaret J. McCreary · 155 East Main Street · Durham, NC 27701 · 919-682-7267

Greensboro

Frank W. Bullock, Jr. · Womble Carlyle Sandridge & Rice · 300 North Greene Street, Suite 1900 · Greensboro, NC 27401 · 336-574-8030

Thomas C. Duncan · Thomas C. Duncan · 500-D State Street · Greensboro, NC 27405 · 336-274-7243

Jonathan Ross Harkavy · ㉕ · Patterson Harkavy · 101 South Elm Street · P.O. Box 29269 · Greensboro, NC 27429-9269 · 336-370-4200

Nahomi Harkavy · ⑩ · Patterson Harkavy · 101 South Elm Street · P.O. Box 29269 · Greensboro, NC 27429-9269 · 336-370-4200

James A. Medford · Smith Moore Leatherwood · http://www.smithmoorelaw.com · 300 North Greene Street, Suite 1400 · P.O. Box 21927 · Greensboro, NC 27420-1927 · 336-378-5200

Marion

C. Frank Goldsmith, Jr. · Goldsmith, Goldsmith & Dews · 57 South Main Street · P.O. Box 1107 · Marion, NC 28752 · 828-652-3000

Morganton

Samuel E. Aycock · Starnes, Aycock & Haire · 118 North Sterling Street · Morganton, NC 28655 · 828-437-3335

Morrisville

William O. King · ⑩ · Moore & Van Allen · 430 Davis Drive, Suite 500 · P.O. Box 13706 · Morrisville, NC 27709 · 919-286-8000

New Bern

John A. J. Ward · John A. J. Ward · 219 Pollock Street · New Bern, NC 28560 · 252-633-4378

Pilot Mountain

M. Ann Anderson · M. Ann Anderson · http://www.annandersonmediator.com · 214 East Marion Street · P.O. Box 93 · Pilot Mountain, NC 27041 · 336-368-9621

Raleigh

Catharine Biggs Arrowood · Parker Poe Adams & Bernstein · http://www.parkerpoe.com · Wachovia Capitol Center, Suite 1400 · 150 Fayetteville Street · Raleigh, NC 27601 · 919-828-0564

Richard T. Boyette · Cranfill, Sumner & Hartzog · http://www.cshlaw.com · 5420 Wade Park Boulevard · P.O. Box 27808 · Raleigh, NC 27611-7808 · 919-828-5100

Sidney S. Eagles, Jr. · Smith Moore Leatherwood · http://www.smithmoorelaw.com · Two Hannover Square, Suite 2800 · P.O. Box 27525 · Raleigh, NC 27611 · 919-755-8700

Patricia L. Holland · Cranfill, Sumner & Hartzog · http://www.cshlaw.com · 5420 Wade Park Boulevard · P.O. Box 27808 · Raleigh, NC 27611-7808 · 919-828-5100

Lacy M. Presnell III · Burns, Day & Presnell · 2626 Glenwood Avenue, Suite 560 · P.O. Box 10867 · Raleigh, NC 27605 · 919-782-1441

Rocky Mount

Marshall Aubrey Gallop, Jr. · Battle, Winslow, Scott & Wiley · 2343 Professional Drive · P.O. Box 7100 · Rocky Mount, NC 27804-0100 · 252-937-2200

Tryon

Harry Goodheart III · Mediation Resources · 431 North Trade Street · Tryon, NC 28782 · 800-881-7776

Winston-Salem

Kenneth P. Carlson, Jr. · Constangy, Brooks & Smith · http://www.constangy.com · 100 North Cherry Street, Suite 300 · Winston-Salem, NC 27101-4016 · 336-721-1001

ANTITRUST LAW

Cary

Richard W. Ellis · ⑩ · Ellis & Winters · http://www.elliswinters.com · 1100 Crescent Green, Suite 200 · Cary, NC 27518 · 919-865-7000

Matthew W. Sawchak · Ellis & Winters · http://www.elliswinters.com · 1100 Crescent Green, Suite 200 · Cary, NC 27518 · 919-865-7000

Charlotte

Everett J. Bowman · Robinson, Bradshaw & Hinson · http://www.rbh.com · 101 North Tryon Street, Suite 1900 · Charlotte, NC 28246-1900 · 704-377-2536

Mark J. Horoschak · Womble Carlyle Sandridge & Rice · One Wachovia Center, Suite 3500 · 301 South College Street · Charlotte, NC 28202-6037 · 704-331-4900

Keith J. Merritt · Hamilton Moon Stephens Steele & Martin · 201 South College Street, Suite 2020 · Charlotte, NC 28244-2020 · 704-344-1117

Mark W. Merritt · ⑩ · Robinson, Bradshaw & Hinson · http://www.rbh.com · 101 North Tryon Street, Suite 1900 · Charlotte, NC 28246-1900 · 704-377-2536

John M. Murchison, Jr. · K&L Gates · Hearst Tower, 47th Floor · 214 North Tryon Street · Charlotte, NC 28202 · 704-331-7400

William L. Rikard, Jr. · ⑩ · Parker Poe Adams & Bernstein · http://www.parkerpoe.com · Three Wachovia Center, Suite 3000 · 401 South Tryon Street · Charlotte, NC 28202-1935 · 704-372-9000

Larry B. Sitton · ⑩ · Smith Moore Leatherwood · http://www.smithmoorelaw.com · 525 North Tryon Street, Suite 1400 · Charlotte, NC 28202 · 704-384-2600

Greensboro

J. Donald Cowan, Jr. · ⑳ · Ellis & Winters · http://www.elliswinters.com · 100 North Greene Street, Suite 102 · Greensboro, NC 27401 · 336-217-4193

Lisa Frye Garrison · Smith Moore Leatherwood · http://www.smithmoorelaw.com · 300 North Greene Street, Suite 1400 · P.O. Box 21927 · Greensboro, NC 27420-1927 · 336-378-5200

Jeffrey E. Oleynik · Brooks, Pierce, McLendon, Humphrey & Leonard · http://www.brookspierce.com · 2000 Renaissance Plaza · 230 North Elm Street · Greensboro, NC 27401 · 336-373-8850

Jennifer K. Van Zant · Brooks, Pierce, McLendon, Humphrey & Leonard · http://www.brookspierce.com 2000 Renaissance Plaza · 230 North Elm Street · Greensboro, NC 27401 · 336-373-8850

James T. Williams, Jr. · ⑩ · Brooks, Pierce, McLendon, Humphrey & Leonard · http://www.brookspierce.com · 2000 Renaissance Plaza · 230 North Elm Street · Greensboro, NC 27401 · 336-373-8850

New Bern

David L. Ward, Jr. · ㉕ · Ward and Smith · http://www.wardandsmith.com · 1001 College Court · P.O. Box 867 · New Bern, NC 28563-0867 · 252-672-5400

Raleigh

Noel L. Allen · Allen & Pinnix · 333 Fayetteville Street, Suite 1200 · P.O. Drawer 1270 · Raleigh, NC 27602-1270 · 919-755-0505

Catharine Biggs Arrowood · Parker Poe Adams & Bernstein · http://www.parkerpoe.com · Wachovia Capitol Center, Suite 1400 · 150 Fayetteville Street · Raleigh, NC 27601 · 919-828-0564

John F. Graybeal · Parker Poe Adams & Bernstein · http://www.parkerpoe.com · Wachovia Capitol Center, Suite 1400 · 150 Fayetteville Street · Raleigh, NC 27601 · 919-828-0564

Douglas W. Kenyon · Hunton & Williams · One Bank Of America Plaza, Suite 1400 · 421 Fayetteville Street · P.O. Box 109 · Raleigh, NC 27602 · 919-899-3000

Pressly M. Millen · Womble Carlyle Sandridge & Rice · 150 Fayetteville Street, Suite 2100 · P.O. Box 831 · Raleigh, NC 27601-0831 · 919-755-2100

Robert W. Spearman · ⑩ · Parker Poe Adams & Bernstein · http://www.parkerpoe.com · Wachovia Capitol Center, Suite 1400 · 150 Fayetteville Street · Raleigh, NC 27601 · 919-828-0564

Winston-Salem

W. Andrew Copenhaver · ⑩ · Womble Carlyle Sandridge & Rice · One West Fourth Street · Winston-Salem, NC 27101 · 336-721-3600

Rodrick J. Enns · Enns & Archer · http://www.ennsandarcher.com · 939 Burke Street · Winston-Salem, NC 27101 · 336-723-5180

Denise M. Gunter · Nelson Mullins Riley & Scarborough · The Knollwood, Suite 530 · 380 Knollwood Street · Winston-Salem, NC 27103 · 336-774-3300

George L. Little, Jr. · ⑩ · Kilpatrick Stockton · 1001 West Fourth Street · Winston-Salem, NC 27101-2400 · 336-607-7300

APPELLATE LAW

Cary

Matthew W. Sawchak · Ellis & Winters · http://www.elliswinters.com · 1100 Crescent Green, Suite 200 · Cary, NC 27518 · 919-865-7000

Paul K. Sun, Jr. · Ellis & Winters · http://www.elliswinters.com · 1100 Crescent Green, Suite 200 · Cary, NC 27518 · 919-865-7000

Chapel Hill

M. Gordon Widenhouse, Jr. · Rudolf Widenhouse & Fialko · http://www.rwf-law.com · 312 West Franklin Street · Chapel Hill, NC 27516 · 919-967-4900

Charlotte

Jack A. Gardner III · ⑩ · Hedrick, Gardner, Kincheloe & Garofalo · 6000 Fairview Road, Suite 1000 · P.O. Box 30397 · Charlotte, NC 28230 · 704-366-1101

A. Ward McKeithen · ㉕ · Robinson, Bradshaw & Hinson · http://www.rbh.com · 101 North Tryon Street, Suite 1900 · Charlotte, NC 28246-1900 · 704-377-2536

John R. Wester · ⑩ · Robinson, Bradshaw & Hinson · http://www.rbh.com · 101 North Tryon Street, Suite 1900 · Charlotte, NC 28246-1900 · 704-377-2536

Greensboro

Frank W. Bullock, Jr. · Womble Carlyle Sandridge & Rice · 300 North Greene Street, Suite 1900 · Greensboro, NC 27401 · 336-574-8030

J. Donald Cowan, Jr. · ⑳ · Ellis & Winters · http://www.elliswinters.com · 100 North Greene Street, Suite 102 · Greensboro, NC 27401 · 336-217-4193

James G. Exum, Jr. · Smith Moore Leatherwood · http://www.smithmoorelaw.com · 300 North Greene Street, Suite 1400 · P.O. Box 21927 · Greensboro, NC 27420-1927 · 336-378-5200

Norman B. Smith · ㉕ · Smith, James, Rowlett & Cohen · 101 South Elm Street, Suite 310 · P.O. Box 990 Greensboro, NC 27402 · 336-274-2992

Allison O. Van Laningham · Smith Moore Leatherwood · http://www.smithmoorelaw.com · 300 North Greene Street, Suite 1400 · P.O. Box 21927 · Greensboro, NC 27420-1927 · 336-378-5200

Raleigh

Sidney S. Eagles, Jr. · Smith Moore Leatherwood · http://www.smithmoorelaw.com · Two Hannover Square, Suite 2800 · P.O. Box 27525 · Raleigh, NC 27611 · 919-755-8700

K. Edward Greene · Wyrick Robbins Yates & Ponton · http://www.wyrick.com · The Summit, Suite 300 · 4101 Lake Boone Trail · P.O. Drawer 17803 · Raleigh, NC 27607-7506 · 919-781-4000

Noah H. Huffstetler III · ⑩ · Nelson Mullins Riley & Scarborough · GlenLake One, Suite 200 · 4140 Parklake Avenue · P.O. Box 30519 · Raleigh, NC 27622-0519 · 919-877-3800

Burley B. Mitchell, Jr. · Womble Carlyle Sandridge & Rice · 150 Fayetteville Street, Suite 2100 · P.O. Box 831 · Raleigh, NC 27601-0831 · 919-755-2100

Roger W. Smith, Sr. · ㉕ · Tharrington Smith · http://www.tharringtonsmith.com · 209 Fayetteville Street P.O. Box 1151 · Raleigh, NC 27602-1151 · 919-821-4711

Robert W. Spearman · ⑩ · Parker Poe Adams & Bernstein · http://www.parkerpoe.com · Wachovia Capitol Center, Suite 1400 · 150 Fayetteville Street · Raleigh, NC 27601 · 919-828-0564

Winston-Salem

Adam H. Charnes · Kilpatrick Stockton · 1001 West Fourth Street · Winston-Salem, NC 27101-2400 · 336-607-7300

BANKING LAW

Charlotte

Benjamin W. Baldwin · Robinson, Bradshaw & Hinson · http://www.rbh.com · 101 North Tryon Street, Suite 1900 · Charlotte, NC 28246-1900 · 704-377-2536

W. Doak Barnhardt · Moore & Van Allen · Bank of America Corporate Center, Suite 4700 · 100 North Tryon Street · Charlotte, NC 28202-4003 · 704-331-1000

David Line Batty · Winston & Strawn · 100 North Tryon Street, 33rd Floor · Charlotte, NC 28202 · 704-350-7720

Peter C. Buck · Robinson, Bradshaw & Hinson · http://www.rbh.com · 101 North Tryon Street, Suite 1900 · Charlotte, NC 28246-1900 · 704-377-2536

Stokely G. Caldwell, Jr. · Robinson, Bradshaw & Hinson · http://www.rbh.com · 101 North Tryon Street, Suite 1900 · Charlotte, NC 28246-1900 · 704-377-2536

George C. Covington · King & Spalding · 227 West Trade Street, Suite 600 · Charlotte, NC 28202 · 704-503-2600

Robert W. Cramer · McGuireWoods · http://www.mcguirewoods.com · 201 North Tryon Street, Suite 3000 · P.O. Box 31247 · Charlotte, NC 28231 · 704-343-2000

Larry J. Dagenhart · ⑩ · McGuireWoods · http://www.mcguirewoods.com · 201 North Tryon Street, Suite 3000 · P.O. Box 31247 · Charlotte, NC 28231 · 704-343-2000

Paul S. Donohue · Alston + Bird · http://www.alston.com · Bank of America Plaza, Suite 4000 · 101 South Tryon Street · Charlotte, NC 28280-4000 · 704-444-1000

J. Thomas Dunn, Jr. · Moore & Van Allen · Bank of America Corporate Center, Suite 4700 · 100 North Tryon Street · Charlotte, NC 28202-4003 · 704-331-1000

John C. Fennebresque · McGuireWoods · http://www.mcguirewoods.com · Bank of America Corporate Center, Suite 2900 · 100 North Tryon Street · Charlotte, NC 28202-4011 · 704-373-8999

William H. Fuller III · Moore & Van Allen · Bank of America Corporate Center, Suite 4700 · 100 North Tryon Street · Charlotte, NC 28202-4003 · 704-331-1000

J. Richard Hazlett · Moore & Van Allen · Bank of America Corporate Center, Suite 4700 · 100 North Tryon Street · Charlotte, NC 28202-4003 · 704-331-1000

James T. Hedrick, Jr. · Winston & Strawn · 100 North Tryon Street, 33rd Floor · Charlotte, NC 28202 · 704-350-7720

James W. Hovis · ⑩ · Moore & Van Allen · Bank of America Corporate Center, Suite 4700 · 100 North Tryon Street · Charlotte, NC 28202-4003 · 704-331-1000

Christopher C. Kupec · Mayer Brown · 214 North Tryon Street, Suite 2200 · Charlotte, NC 28202 · 704-444-3561

Donald C. Lampe · Womble Carlyle Sandridge & Rice · One Wachovia Center, Suite 3500 · 301 South College Street · Charlotte, NC 28202-6037 · 704-331-4900

J. Donnell Lassiter · ⑩ · K&L Gates · Hearst Tower, 47th Floor · 214 North Tryon Street · Charlotte, NC 28202 · 704-331-7400

Haynes P. Lea · Robinson, Bradshaw & Hinson · http://www.rbh.com · 101 North Tryon Street, Suite 1900 · Charlotte, NC 28246-1900 · 704-377-2536

Kristin P. Manzano · Alston + Bird · http://www.alston.com · Bank of America Plaza, Suite 4000 · 101 South Tryon Street · Charlotte, NC 28280-4000 · 704-444-1000

R. Malloy McKeithen · ⑩ · McGuireWoods · http://www.mcguirewoods.com · 201 North Tryon Street, Suite 3000 · P.O. Box 31247 · Charlotte, NC 28231 · 704-343-2000

Henry H. Ralston · Robinson, Bradshaw & Hinson · http://www.rbh.com · 101 North Tryon Street, Suite 1900 · Charlotte, NC 28246-1900 · 704-377-2536

S. Graham Robinson · Robinson, Bradshaw & Hinson · http://www.rbh.com · 101 North Tryon Street, Suite 1900 · Charlotte, NC 28246-1900 · 704-377-2536

W. Kent Walker, Jr. · Winston & Strawn · 100 North Tryon Street, 33rd Floor · Charlotte, NC 28202 · 704-350-7720

Dean A. Warren · Winston & Strawn · 100 North Tryon Street, 33rd Floor · Charlotte, NC 28202 · 704-350-7720

Fayetteville

Alfred E. Cleveland · ⑩ · McCoy, Weaver, Wiggins, Cleveland, Rose, Ray · 202 Fairway Drive · P.O. Box 87009 · Fayetteville, NC 28304 · 910-483-8104

Greensboro

June L. Basden · Carruthers & Roth · http://www.crlaw.com · 235 North Edgeworth Street · P.O. Box 540 Greensboro, NC 27402 · 336-379-8651

Herbert O. Davis · ⑩ · Smith Moore Leatherwood · http://www.smithmoorelaw.com · 300 North Greene Street, Suite 1400 · P.O. Box 21927 · Greensboro, NC 27420-1927 · 336-378-5200

Kenneth M. Greene · ⑩ · Carruthers & Roth · http://www.crlaw.com · 235 North Edgeworth Street · P.O. Box 540 · Greensboro, NC 27402 · 336-379-8651

Robert A. Singer · Brooks, Pierce, McLendon, Humphrey & Leonard · http://www.brookspierce.com · 2000 Renaissance Plaza · 230 North Elm Street · Greensboro, NC 27401 · 336-373-8850

Randall A. Underwood · Brooks, Pierce, McLendon, Humphrey & Leonard · http://www.brookspierce.com · 2000 Renaissance Plaza · 230 North Elm Street · Greensboro, NC 27401 · 336-373-8850

Thomas C. Watkins · ⑩ · Schell Bray Aycock Abel & Livingston · http://www.sbaal.com · Renaissance Plaza, Suite 1500 · 230 North Elm Street · Greensboro, NC 27401 · 336-370-8800

Edward C. Winslow III · Brooks, Pierce, McLendon, Humphrey & Leonard · http://www.brookspierce.com · 2000 Renaissance Plaza · 230 North Elm Street · Greensboro, NC 27401 · 336-373-8850

New Bern

William R. Lathan, Jr. · Ward and Smith · http://www.wardandsmith.com · 1001 College Court · P.O. Box 867 · New Bern, NC 28563-0867 · 252-672-5400

David L. Ward, Jr. · ㉕ · Ward and Smith · http://www.wardandsmith.com · 1001 College Court · P.O. Box 867 · New Bern, NC 28563-0867 · 252-672-5400

Raleigh

Anthony Gaeta, Jr. · ⑩ · Gaeta & Eveson · 8305 Falls of Neuse Road, Suite 203 · Raleigh, NC 27615 · 919-845-2558

Frank A. Hirsch, Jr. · Nelson Mullins Riley & Scarborough · GlenLake One, Suite 200 · 4140 Parklake Avenue · P.O. Box 30519 · Raleigh, NC 27622-0519 · 919-877-3800

John L. Jernigan · ⑩ · Smith, Anderson, Blount, Dorsett, Mitchell & Jernigan · http://www.smithlaw.com 2500 Wachovia Capitol Center · P.O. Box 2611 · Raleigh, NC 27602-2611 · 919-821-1220

Winston-Salem

Christopher E. Leon · Womble Carlyle Sandridge & Rice · One West Fourth Street · Winston-Salem, NC 27101 · 336-721-3600

Kenneth A. Moser · ⑩ · Womble Carlyle Sandridge & Rice · One West Fourth Street · Winston-Salem, NC 27101 · 336-721-3600

BANKRUPTCY AND CREDITOR-DEBTOR RIGHTS LAW

Angier

Richard DeWitte Sparkman · Richard D. Sparkman & Associates · 32 West Williams Street · P.O. Box 1687 · Angier, NC 27501 · 919-639-6181

Asheville

David G. Gray · Westall Gray Connolly & Davis · 81 Central Avenue · Asheville, NC 28801 · 828-254-6315

David Hillier · Gum, Hillier and McCroskey · http://www.gumandhillier.com · 47 North Market Street · P.O. Box 3235 · Asheville, NC 28802 · 828-258-3368

Albert L. Sneed, Jr. · ⑩ · The Van Winkle Law Firm · 11 North Market Street · P.O. Box 7376 · Asheville, NC 28801-7376 · 828-258-2991

Chapel Hill

John A. Northen · Northen Blue Law Firm · 1414 Raleigh Road, Suite 435 · P.O. Box 2208 · Chapel Hill, NC 27515-2208 · 919-968-4441

J. Michael Booe · ⑳ · K&L Gates · Hearst Tower, 47th Floor · 214 North Tryon Street · Charlotte, NC 28202 · 704-331-7400

Garland S. Cassada · Robinson, Bradshaw & Hinson · http://www.rbh.com · 101 North Tryon Street, Suite 1900 · Charlotte, NC 28246-1900 · 704-377-2536

Robert A. Cox, Jr. · McGuireWoods · http://www.mcguirewoods.com · Bank of America Corporate Center, Suite 2900 · 100 North Tryon Street · Charlotte, NC 28202-4011 · 704-373-8999

John H. Culver III · K&L Gates · Hearst Tower, 47th Floor · 214 North Tryon Street · Charlotte, NC 28202 · 704-331-7400

Albert F. Durham · ⑩ · Rayburn, Cooper & Durham · 227 West Trade Street, Suite 1200 · Charlotte, NC 28202-1672 · 704-334-0891

David L. Eades · ⑩ · Moore & Van Allen · Bank of America Corporate Center, Suite 4700 · 100 North Tryon Street · Charlotte, NC 28202-4003 · 704-331-1000

Joseph W. Grier III · Grier, Furr & Crisp · http://www.grierlaw.com · 101 North Tryon Street, Suite 1240 Charlotte, NC 28246-1240 · 704-375-3720

Stephen E. Gruendel · Moore & Van Allen · Bank of America Corporate Center, Suite 4700 · 100 North Tryon Street · Charlotte, NC 28202-4003 · 704-331-1000

W. B. Hawfield, Jr. · ⑳ · Moore & Van Allen · Bank of America Corporate Center, Suite 4700 · 100 North Tryon Street · Charlotte, NC 28202-4003 · 704-331-1000

Joseph B. C. Kluttz · K&L Gates · Hearst Tower, 47th Floor · 214 North Tryon Street · Charlotte, NC 28202 · 704-331-7400

Travis W. Moon · Hamilton Moon Stephens Steele & Martin · 201 South College Street, Suite 2020 · Charlotte, NC 28244-2020 · 704-344-1117

Alan W. Pope · Moore & Van Allen · Bank of America Corporate Center, Suite 4700 · 100 North Tryon Street · Charlotte, NC 28202-4003 · 704-331-1000

J. William Porter · Parker Poe Adams & Bernstein · http://www.parkerpoe.com · Three Wachovia Center, Suite 3000 · 401 South Tryon Street · Charlotte, NC 28202-1935 · 704-372-9000

Robert H. Pryor · McGuireWoods · http://www.mcguirewoods.com · 201 North Tryon Street, Suite 3000 · P.O. Box 31247 · Charlotte, NC 28231 · 704-343-2000

C. Richard Rayburn, Jr. · ⑩ · Rayburn, Cooper & Durham · 227 West Trade Street, Suite 1200 · Charlotte, NC 28202-1672 · 704-334-0891

David M. Schilli · Robinson, Bradshaw & Hinson · http://www.rbh.com · 101 North Tryon Street, Suite 1900 · Charlotte, NC 28246-1900 · 704-377-2536

Scott P. Vaughn · McGuireWoods · http://www.mcguirewoods.com · 201 North Tryon Street, Suite 3000 · P.O. Box 31247 · Charlotte, NC 28231 · 704-343-2000

David S. Walls · Moore & Van Allen · Bank of America Corporate Center, Suite 4700 · 100 North Tryon Street · Charlotte, NC 28202-4003 · 704-331-1000

Durham

Richard M. Hutson II · ⑳ · Hutson, Hughes & Powell · Durham Centre, Suite 1500 · 300 West Morgan Street · P.O. Drawer 2252-A · Durham, NC 27702 · 919-683-1561

Greensboro

June L. Basden · Carruthers & Roth · http://www.crlaw.com · 235 North Edgeworth Street · P.O. Box 540 Greensboro, NC 27402 · 336-379-8651

Kenneth M. Greene · ⑩ · Carruthers & Roth · http://www.crlaw.com · 235 North Edgeworth Street · P.O. Box 540 · Greensboro, NC 27402 · 336-379-8651

Charles M. Ivey III · ⑩ · Ivey, McClellan, Gatton & Talcott · 100 South Elm Street, Suite 500 · P.O. Box 3324 · Greensboro, NC 27401 · 336-274-4658

David F. Meschan · ⑳ · Tuggle Duggins & Meschan · http://www.tuggleduggins.com · 100 North Greene Street, Suite 600 · P.O. Box 2888 · Greensboro, NC 27402-2888 · 336-378-1431

Jeffrey E. Oleynik · Brooks, Pierce, McLendon, Humphrey & Leonard · http://www.brookspierce.com · 2000 Renaissance Plaza · 230 North Elm Street · Greensboro, NC 27401 · 336-373-8850

John H. Small · Brooks, Pierce, McLendon, Humphrey & Leonard · http://www.brookspierce.com · 2000 Renaissance Plaza · 230 North Elm Street · Greensboro, NC 27401 · 336-373-8850

Greenville

Michael P. Flanagan · ⑩ · Ward and Smith · http://www.wardandsmith.com · 120 West Fire Tower Road P.O. Box 8088 · Greenville, NC 27835-8088 · 252-215-4000

High Point

William P. Miller · Roberson, Haworth & Reese · High Point Bank & Trust Building, Suite 300 · 300 North Main Street · P.O. Box 1550 · High Point, NC 27261 · 336-889-8733

New Bern

Trawick H. Stubbs, Jr. · ⑳ · Stubbs & Perdue · 310 Craven Street · P.O. Box 1654 · New Bern, NC 28563-1654 · 252-633-2700

Raleigh

Gregory B. Crampton · ㉕ · Nicholls & Crampton · 3700 Glenwood Avenue, Suite 500 · P.O. Box 18237 · Raleigh, NC 27619 · 919-781-1311

Holmes P. Harden · Williams Mullen · http://www.williamsmullen.com · Highwoods Tower One, Suite 500 · 3200 Beechleaf Court · P.O. Drawer 19764 · Raleigh, NC 27619-9764 · 919-981-4000

A. Lee Hogewood III · K&L Gates · 4350 Lassiter at North Hills Avenue, Suite 300 · Raleigh, NC 27609 919-743-7300

William P. Janvier · Everett, Gaskins, Hancock & Stevens · The Professional Building, Suite 600 · 127 West Hargett Street · P.O. Box 911 · Raleigh, NC 27602-0911 · 919-755-0025

Gerald A. Jeutter, Jr. · The Jeutter Law Office · 615 Oberlin Road, Suite 102 · P.O. Box 12585 · Raleigh, NC 27605 · 919-334-6631

Amos U. Priester IV · Smith, Anderson, Blount, Dorsett, Mitchell & Jernigan · http://www.smithlaw.com 2500 Wachovia Capitol Center · P.O. Box 2611 · Raleigh, NC 27602-2611 · 919-821-1220

Wilmington

James Oliver Carter · Carter & Carter · 408 Market Street · Wilmington, NC 28402-2154 · 910-763-3626

Wilson

Stephen L. Beaman · ㉕ · The Law Office of Stephen L. Beaman · 304 West Nash Street · P.O. Box 1907 Wilson, NC 27894-1907 · 252-237-9020

Winston-Salem

C. Edwin Allman III · ⑩ · Allman Spry Leggett & Crumpler · 380 Knollwood Street, Suite 700 · P.O. Drawer 5129 · Winston-Salem, NC 27103-4152 · 336-722-2300

R. Bradford Leggett · ⑳ · Allman Spry Leggett & Crumpler · 380 Knollwood Street, Suite 700 · P.O. Drawer 5129 · Winston-Salem, NC 27103-4152 · 336-722-2300

Walter W. Pitt, Jr. · ⑩ · Bell, Davis & Pitt · http://www.belldavispitt.com · Century Plaza, Suite 600 · 100 North Cherry Street · P.O. Box 21029 · Winston-Salem, NC 27120 · 336-722-3700

William B. Sullivan · ⑩ · Womble Carlyle Sandridge & Rice · One West Fourth Street · Winston-Salem, NC 27101 · 336-721-3600

Gene B. Tarr · Blanco Tackabery Combs & Matamoros · Stratford Point Building, Fifth Floor · 110 South Stratford Road · Winston-Salem, NC 27104-4299 · 336-293-9000

BET-THE-COMPANY LITIGATION

Cary

Richard W. Ellis · ⑩ · Ellis & Winters · http://www.elliswinters.com · 1100 Crescent Green, Suite 200 · Cary, NC 27518 · 919-865-7000

Charlotte

Martin L. Brackett, Jr. · ⑩ · Robinson, Bradshaw & Hinson · http://www.rbh.com · 101 North Tryon Street, Suite 1900 · Charlotte, NC 28246-1900 · 704-377-2536

Jim D. Cooley · Womble Carlyle Sandridge & Rice · One Wachovia Center, Suite 3500 · 301 South College Street · Charlotte, NC 28202-6037 · 704-331-4900

James P. Cooney III · ⑩ · Womble Carlyle Sandridge & Rice · One Wachovia Center, Suite 3500 · 301 South College Street · Charlotte, NC 28202-6037 · 704-331-4900

Peter J. Covington · ⑩ · McGuireWoods · http://www.mcguirewoods.com · 201 North Tryon Street, Suite 3000 · P.O. Box 31247 · Charlotte, NC 28231 · 704-343-2000

Douglas W. Ey, Jr. · McGuireWoods · http://www.mcguirewoods.com · 201 North Tryon Street, Suite 3000 · P.O. Box 31247 · Charlotte, NC 28231 · 704-343-2000

Robert W. Fuller · Robinson, Bradshaw & Hinson · http://www.rbh.com · 101 North Tryon Street, Suite 1900 · Charlotte, NC 28246-1900 · 704-377-2536

Gary S. Hemric · James, McElroy & Diehl · 600 South College Street, Suite 3000 · Charlotte, NC 28202 · 704-372-9870

Edward T. Hinson, Jr. · James, McElroy & Diehl · 600 South College Street, Suite 3000 · Charlotte, NC 28202 · 704-372-9870

A. Ward McKeithen · ㉕ · Robinson, Bradshaw & Hinson · http://www.rbh.com · 101 North Tryon Street, Suite 1900 · Charlotte, NC 28246-1900 · 704-377-2536

Kiran H. Mehta · K&L Gates · Hearst Tower, 47th Floor · 214 North Tryon Street · Charlotte, NC 28202 704-331-7400

Mark W. Merritt · ⑩ · Robinson, Bradshaw & Hinson · http://www.rbh.com · 101 North Tryon Street, Suite 1900 · Charlotte, NC 28246-1900 · 704-377-2536

Larry B. Sitton · ⑩ · Smith Moore Leatherwood · http://www.smithmoorelaw.com · 525 North Tryon Street, Suite 1400 · Charlotte, NC 28202 · 704-384-2600

John R. Wester · ⑩ · Robinson, Bradshaw & Hinson · http://www.rbh.com · 101 North Tryon Street, Suite 1900 · Charlotte, NC 28246-1900 · 704-377-2536

James F. Wyatt III · ⑩ · Wyatt & Blake · 435 East Morehead Street · Charlotte, NC 28202-2609 · 704-331-0767

Greensboro

J. Donald Cowan, Jr. · ⑳ · Ellis & Winters · http://www.elliswinters.com · 100 North Greene Street, Suite 102 · Greensboro, NC 27401 · 336-217-4193

Alan W. Duncan · ⑩ · Smith Moore Leatherwood · http://www.smithmoorelaw.com · 300 North Greene Street, Suite 1400 · P.O. Box 21927 · Greensboro, NC 27420-1927 · 336-378-5200

James G. Exum, Jr. · Smith Moore Leatherwood · http://www.smithmoorelaw.com · 300 North Greene Street, Suite 1400 · P.O. Box 21927 · Greensboro, NC 27420-1927 · 336-378-5200

James T. Williams, Jr. · ⑩ · Brooks, Pierce, McLendon, Humphrey & Leonard · http://www.brookspierce.com · 2000 Renaissance Plaza · 230 North Elm Street · Greensboro, NC 27401 · 336-373-8850

Lexington

Walter F. Brinkley, Jr. · ⑩ · Brinkley Walser · 10 LSB Plaza · P.O. Box 1657 · Lexington, NC 27293-1657 · 336-249-2101

Raleigh

Catharine Biggs Arrowood · Parker Poe Adams & Bernstein · http://www.parkerpoe.com · Wachovia Capitol Center, Suite 1400 · 150 Fayetteville Street · Raleigh, NC 27601 · 919-828-0564

Burley B. Mitchell, Jr. · Womble Carlyle Sandridge & Rice · 150 Fayetteville Street, Suite 2100 · P.O. Box 831 · Raleigh, NC 27601-0831 · 919-755-2100

Robert W. Spearman · ⑩ · Parker Poe Adams & Bernstein · http://www.parkerpoe.com · Wachovia Capitol Center, Suite 1400 · 150 Fayetteville Street · Raleigh, NC 27601 · 919-828-0564

Winston-Salem

H. Grady Barnhill, Jr. · ㉕ · Womble Carlyle Sandridge & Rice · One West Fourth Street · Winston-Salem, NC 27101 · 336-721-3600

William Kearns Davis · ⑩ · Bell, Davis & Pitt · http://www.belldavispitt.com · Century Plaza, Suite 600 · 100 North Cherry Street · P.O. Box 21029 · Winston-Salem, NC 27120 · 336-722-3700

Michael L. Robinson · Robinson & Lawing · http://www.robinson-lawing.com · 101 North Cherry Street, Suite 720 · Winston-Salem, NC 27101 · 336-631-8500

Keith W. Vaughan · ⑩ · Womble Carlyle Sandridge & Rice · One West Fourth Street · Winston-Salem, NC 27101 · 336-721-3600

G. Gray Wilson · ⑩ · Wilson & Coffey · 110 Oakwood Drive, Suite 400 · Winston-Salem, NC 27103 · 336-631-8866

BIOTECHNOLOGY LAW

Morrisville

Allen R. Baum · Brinks Hofer Gilson & Lione · 2801 Slater Road, Suite 120 · Morrisville, NC 27560 · 919-481-1111

Raleigh

Kenneth E. Eheman, Jr. · Wyrick Robbins Yates & Ponton · http://www.wyrick.com · The Summit, Suite 300 · 4101 Lake Boone Trail · P.O. Drawer 17803 · Raleigh, NC 27607-7506 · 919-781-4000

W. Murray Spruill, Jr. · Alston + Bird · http://www.alston.com · 3201 Beechleaf Court, Suite 600 · Raleigh, NC 27604-1062 · 919-862-2210

William N. Wofford · Hutchison Law Group · http://www.hutchlaw.com · 5410 Trinity Road, Suite 400 · Raleigh, NC 27607 · 919-829-9600

Jason S. Wood · Wyrick Robbins Yates & Ponton · http://www.wyrick.com · The Summit, Suite 300 · 4101 Lake Boone Trail · P.O. Drawer 17803 · Raleigh, NC 27607-7506 · 919-781-4000

COMMERCIAL LITIGATION

Asheville

Robert B. Long, Jr. · ⑩ · Long, Parker, Warren & Anderson · 14 South Pack Square, Suite 600 · P.O. Box 7216 · Asheville, NC 28802 · 828-258-2296

Larry S. McDevitt · The Van Winkle Law Firm · 11 North Market Street · P.O. Box 7376 · Asheville, NC 28801-7376 · 828-258-2991

Philip J. Smith · ⑩ · The Van Winkle Law Firm · 11 North Market Street · P.O. Box 7376 · Asheville, NC 28801-7376 · 828-258-2991

Albert L. Sneed, Jr. · ⑩ · The Van Winkle Law Firm · 11 North Market Street · P.O. Box 7376 · Asheville, NC 28801-7376 · 828-258-2991

Cary

Richard W. Ellis · 10 · Ellis & Winters · http://www.elliswinters.com · 1100 Crescent Green, Suite 200 · Cary, NC 27518 · 919-865-7000

Jonathan D. Sasser · Ellis & Winters · http://www.elliswinters.com · 1100 Crescent Green, Suite 200 · Cary, NC 27518 · 919-865-7000

Matthew W. Sawchak · Ellis & Winters · http://www.elliswinters.com · 1100 Crescent Green, Suite 200 · Cary, NC 27518 · 919-865-7000

Paul K. Sun, Jr. · Ellis & Winters · http://www.elliswinters.com · 1100 Crescent Green, Suite 200 · Cary, NC 27518 · 919-865-7000

Chapel Hill

M. Gordon Widenhouse, Jr. · Rudolf Widenhouse & Fialko · http://www.rwf-law.com · 312 West Franklin Street · Chapel Hill, NC 27516 · 919-967-4900

Charlotte

E. Osborne Ayscue, Jr. · 20 · McGuireWoods · http://www.mcguirewoods.com · 201 North Tryon Street, Suite 3000 · P.O. Box 31247 · Charlotte, NC 28231 · 704-343-2000

Timothy G. Barber · Womble Carlyle Sandridge & Rice · One Wachovia Center, Suite 3500 · 301 South College Street · Charlotte, NC 28202-6037 · 704-331-4900

G. Michael Barnhill · Womble Carlyle Sandridge & Rice · One Wachovia Center, Suite 3500 · 301 South College Street · Charlotte, NC 28202-6037 · 704-331-4900

Kenneth D. Bell · Hunton & Williams · Bank of America Plaza, Suite 3500 · 101 South Tryon Street · Charlotte, NC 28280 · 704-378-4700

Louis A. Bledsoe III · Robinson, Bradshaw & Hinson · http://www.rbh.com · 101 North Tryon Street, Suite 1900 · Charlotte, NC 28246-1900 · 704-377-2536

Everett J. Bowman · Robinson, Bradshaw & Hinson · http://www.rbh.com · 101 North Tryon Street, Suite 1900 · Charlotte, NC 28246-1900 · 704-377-2536

Martin L. Brackett, Jr. · 10 · Robinson, Bradshaw & Hinson · http://www.rbh.com · 101 North Tryon Street, Suite 1900 · Charlotte, NC 28246-1900 · 704-377-2536

John H. Cobb · McGuireWoods · http://www.mcguirewoods.com · 201 North Tryon Street, Suite 3000 · P.O. Box 31247 · Charlotte, NC 28231 · 704-343-2000

Jim D. Cooley · Womble Carlyle Sandridge & Rice · One Wachovia Center, Suite 3500 · 301 South College Street · Charlotte, NC 28202-6037 · 704-331-4900

James P. Cooney III · 10 · Womble Carlyle Sandridge & Rice · One Wachovia Center, Suite 3500 · 301 South College Street · Charlotte, NC 28202-6037 · 704-331-4900

Robert B. Cordle · 10 · Mayer Brown · 214 North Tryon Street, Suite 2200 · Charlotte, NC 28202 · 704-444-3561

T. Thomas Cottingham III · Hunton & Williams · Bank of America Plaza, Suite 3500 · 101 South Tryon Street · Charlotte, NC 28280 · 704-378-4700

George C. Covington · King & Spalding · 227 West Trade Street, Suite 600 · Charlotte, NC 28202 · 704-503-2600

Peter J. Covington · ⑩ · McGuireWoods · http://www.mcguirewoods.com · 201 North Tryon Street, Suite 3000 · P.O. Box 31247 · Charlotte, NC 28231 · 704-343-2000

John H. Culver III · K&L Gates · Hearst Tower, 47th Floor · 214 North Tryon Street · Charlotte, NC 28202 · 704-331-7400

Jeffrey J. Davis · Jeffrey J. Davis · 400 North Church Street, Suite 222 · Charlotte, NC 28202 · 704-331-1037

William K. Diehl, Jr. · ⑳ · James, McElroy & Diehl · 600 South College Street, Suite 3000 · Charlotte, NC 28202 · 704-372-9870

Frank E. Emory, Jr. · Hunton & Williams · Bank of America Plaza, Suite 3500 · 101 South Tryon Street · Charlotte, NC 28280 · 704-378-4700

Douglas W. Ey, Jr. · McGuireWoods · http://www.mcguirewoods.com · 201 North Tryon Street, Suite 3000 · P.O. Box 31247 · Charlotte, NC 28231 · 704-343-2000

Robert W. Fuller · Robinson, Bradshaw & Hinson · http://www.rbh.com · 101 North Tryon Street, Suite 1900 · Charlotte, NC 28246-1900 · 704-377-2536

Jack A. Gardner III · ⑩ · Hedrick, Gardner, Kincheloe & Garofalo · 6000 Fairview Road, Suite 1000 · P.O. Box 30397 · Charlotte, NC 28230 · 704-366-1101

David B. Hamilton · Hamilton Moon Stephens Steele & Martin · 201 South College Street, Suite 2020 · Charlotte, NC 28244-2020 · 704-344-1117

Irvin W. Hankins III · Parker Poe Adams & Bernstein · http://www.parkerpoe.com · Three Wachovia Center, Suite 3000 · 401 South Tryon Street · Charlotte, NC 28202-1935 · 704-372-9000

George V. Hanna III · Moore & Van Allen · Bank of America Corporate Center, Suite 4700 · 100 North Tryon Street · Charlotte, NC 28202-4003 · 704-331-1000

Debbie Weston Harden · Womble Carlyle Sandridge & Rice · One Wachovia Center, Suite 3500 · 301 South College Street · Charlotte, NC 28202-6037 · 704-331-4900

Gary S. Hemric · James, McElroy & Diehl · 600 South College Street, Suite 3000 · Charlotte, NC 28202 · 704-372-9870

Edward F. Hennessey IV · Robinson, Bradshaw & Hinson · http://www.rbh.com · 101 North Tryon Street, Suite 1900 · Charlotte, NC 28246-1900 · 704-377-2536

Edward T. Hinson, Jr. · James, McElroy & Diehl · 600 South College Street, Suite 3000 · Charlotte, NC 28202 · 704-372-9870

Cory Hohnbaum · King & Spalding · 227 West Trade Street, Suite 600 · Charlotte, NC 28202 · 704-503-2600

Thomas P. Holderness · Robinson, Bradshaw & Hinson · http://www.rbh.com · 101 North Tryon Street, Suite 1900 · Charlotte, NC 28246-1900 · 704-377-2536

Wayne P. Huckel · K&L Gates · Hearst Tower, 47th Floor · 214 North Tryon Street · Charlotte, NC 28202 · 704-331-7400

Douglas Jarrell · Robinson, Bradshaw & Hinson · http://www.rbh.com · 101 North Tryon Street, Suite 1900 · Charlotte, NC 28246-1900 · 704-377-2536

Charles E. Johnson · Robinson, Bradshaw & Hinson · http://www.rbh.com · 101 North Tryon Street, Suite 1900 · Charlotte, NC 28246-1900 · 704-377-2536

C. Ralph Kinsey, Jr. · McGuireWoods · http://www.mcguirewoods.com · Bank of America Corporate Center, Suite 2900 · 100 North Tryon Street · Charlotte, NC 28202-4011 · 704-373-8999

Bradley R. Kutrow · McGuireWoods · http://www.mcguirewoods.com · 201 North Tryon Street, Suite 3000 · P.O. Box 31247 · Charlotte, NC 28231 · 704-343-2000

Dickson M. Lupo · Moore & Van Allen · Bank of America Corporate Center, Suite 4700 · 100 North Tryon Street · Charlotte, NC 28202-4003 · 704-331-1000

Mary K. Mandeville · Mayer Brown · 214 North Tryon Street, Suite 2200 · Charlotte, NC 28202 · 704-444-3561

Robert R. Marcus · Smith Moore Leatherwood · http://www.smithmoorelaw.com · 525 North Tryon Street, Suite 1400 · Charlotte, NC 28202 · 704-384-2600

A. Ward McKeithen · (25) · Robinson, Bradshaw & Hinson · http://www.rbh.com · 101 North Tryon Street, Suite 1900 · Charlotte, NC 28246-1900 · 704-377-2536

James P. McLoughlin, Jr. · Moore & Van Allen · Bank of America Corporate Center, Suite 4700 · 100 North Tryon Street · Charlotte, NC 28202-4003 · 704-331-1000

Kiran H. Mehta · K&L Gates · Hearst Tower, 47th Floor · 214 North Tryon Street · Charlotte, NC 28202 704-331-7400

Keith J. Merritt · Hamilton Moon Stephens Steele & Martin · 201 South College Street, Suite 2020 · Charlotte, NC 28244-2020 · 704-344-1117

Mark W. Merritt · (10) · Robinson, Bradshaw & Hinson · http://www.rbh.com · 101 North Tryon Street, Suite 1900 · Charlotte, NC 28246-1900 · 704-377-2536

Roy H. Michaux, Jr. · K&L Gates · Hearst Tower, 47th Floor · 214 North Tryon Street · Charlotte, NC 28202 · 704-331-7400

Gregory J. Murphy · Moore & Van Allen · Bank of America Corporate Center, Suite 4700 · 100 North Tryon Street · Charlotte, NC 28202-4003 · 704-331-1000

Raymond E. Owens, Jr. · (10) · K&L Gates · Hearst Tower, 47th Floor · 214 North Tryon Street · Charlotte, NC 28202 · 704-331-7400

William C. Raper · (20) · Womble Carlyle Sandridge & Rice · One Wachovia Center, Suite 3500 · 301 South College Street · Charlotte, NC 28202-6037 · 704-331-4900

C. Richard Rayburn, Jr. · (10) · Rayburn, Cooper & Durham · 227 West Trade Street, Suite 1200 · Charlotte, NC 28202-1672 · 704-334-0891

William L. Rikard, Jr. · (10) · Parker Poe Adams & Bernstein · http://www.parkerpoe.com · Three Wachovia Center, Suite 3000 · 401 South Tryon Street · Charlotte, NC 28202-1935 · 704-372-9000

Allan W. Singer · McNair Law Firm · http://www.mcnair.net · Two Wachovia Center, Suite 1615 · 301 South Tryon Street · Charlotte, NC 28282 · 704-347-1170

Larry B. Sitton · (10) · Smith Moore Leatherwood · http://www.smithmoorelaw.com · 525 North Tryon Street, Suite 1400 · Charlotte, NC 28202 · 704-384-2600

James C. Smith · Bradley Arant Rose & White · http://www.bradleyarant.com · Bank of America Corporate Center, Suite 2690 · 100 North Tryon Street · Charlotte, NC 28202 · 704-338-6000

Jackson N. Steele · (10) · Hamilton Moon Stephens Steele & Martin · 201 South College Street, Suite 2020 Charlotte, NC 28244-2020 · 704-344-1117

Catherine E. Thompson · McGuireWoods · http://www.mcguirewoods.com · 201 North Tryon Street, Suite 3000 · P.O. Box 31247 · Charlotte, NC 28231 · 704-343-2000

Richard A. Vinroot · Robinson, Bradshaw & Hinson · http://www.rbh.com · 101 North Tryon Street, Suite 1900 · Charlotte, NC 28246-1900 · 704-377-2536

John R. Wester · ⑩ · Robinson, Bradshaw & Hinson · http://www.rbh.com · 101 North Tryon Street, Suite 1900 · Charlotte, NC 28246-1900 · 704-377-2536

David C. Wright III · Robinson, Bradshaw & Hinson · http://www.rbh.com · 101 North Tryon Street, Suite 1900 · Charlotte, NC 28246-1900 · 704-377-2536

James F. Wyatt III · ⑩ · Wyatt & Blake · 435 East Morehead Street · Charlotte, NC 28202-2609 · 704-331-0767

Durham

James B. Maxwell · ⑳ · Maxwell, Freeman & Bowman · 2741 University Drive · P.O. Box 52396 · Durham, NC 27717-2396 · 919-493-6464

Elizabeth City

L. P. Hornthal, Jr. · Hornthal, Riley, Ellis & Maland · 301 East Main Street · P.O. Box 220 · Elizabeth City, NC 27907 · 252-335-0871

Greensboro

James C. Adams II · Brooks, Pierce, McLendon, Humphrey & Leonard · http://www.brookspierce.com · 2000 Renaissance Plaza · 230 North Elm Street · Greensboro, NC 27401 · 336-373-8850

J. Donald Cowan, Jr. · ⑳ · Ellis & Winters · http://www.elliswinters.com · 100 North Greene Street, Suite 102 · Greensboro, NC 27401 · 336-217-4193

Alan W. Duncan · ⑩ · Smith Moore Leatherwood · http://www.smithmoorelaw.com · 300 North Greene Street, Suite 1400 · P.O. Box 21927 · Greensboro, NC 27420-1927 · 336-378-5200

Gregory G. Holland · Smith Moore Leatherwood · http://www.smithmoorelaw.com · 300 North Greene Street, Suite 1400 · P.O. Box 21927 · Greensboro, NC 27420-1927 · 336-378-5200

Robert J. King III · Brooks, Pierce, McLendon, Humphrey & Leonard · http://www.brookspierce.com · 2000 Renaissance Plaza · 230 North Elm Street · Greensboro, NC 27401 · 336-373-8850

James A. Medford · Smith Moore Leatherwood · http://www.smithmoorelaw.com · 300 North Greene Street, Suite 1400 · P.O. Box 21927 · Greensboro, NC 27420-1927 · 336-378-5200

Jim W. Phillips, Jr. · Brooks, Pierce, McLendon, Humphrey & Leonard · http://www.brookspierce.com · 2000 Renaissance Plaza · 230 North Elm Street · Greensboro, NC 27401 · 336-373-8850

Reid L. Phillips · ⑩ · Brooks, Pierce, McLendon, Humphrey & Leonard · http://www.brookspierce.com · 2000 Renaissance Plaza · 230 North Elm Street · Greensboro, NC 27401 · 336-373-8850

S. Leigh Rodenbough IV · Brooks, Pierce, McLendon, Humphrey & Leonard · http://www.brookspierce.com · 2000 Renaissance Plaza · 230 North Elm Street · Greensboro, NC 27401 · 336-373-8850

Frederick K. Sharpless · Sharpless & Stavola · 200 South Elm Street · P.O. Box 22106 · Greensboro, NC 27420 · 336-333-6400

Mack Sperling · Brooks, Pierce, McLendon, Humphrey & Leonard · http://www.brookspierce.com · 2000 Renaissance Plaza · 230 North Elm Street · Greensboro, NC 27401 · 336-373-8850

Jennifer K. Van Zant · Brooks, Pierce, McLendon, Humphrey & Leonard · http://www.brookspierce.com 2000 Renaissance Plaza · 230 North Elm Street · Greensboro, NC 27401 · 336-373-8850

Richard L. Vanore · Carruthers & Roth · http://www.crlaw.com · 235 North Edgeworth Street · P.O. Box 540 · Greensboro, NC 27402 · 336-379-8651

James T. Williams, Jr. · ⑩ · Brooks, Pierce, McLendon, Humphrey & Leonard · http://www.brookspierce.com · 2000 Renaissance Plaza · 230 North Elm Street · Greensboro, NC 27401 · 336-373-8850

Greenville

Donalt J. Eglinton · Ward and Smith · http://www.wardandsmith.com · 120 West Fire Tower Road · P.O. Box 8088 · Greenville, NC 27835-8088 · 252-215-4000

Lexington

Walter F. Brinkley, Jr. · ⑩ · Brinkley Walser · 10 LSB Plaza · P.O. Box 1657 · Lexington, NC 27293-1657 · 336-249-2101

Mocksville

Henry P. Van Hoy II · Martin & Van Hoy · 10 Court Square · Mocksville, NC 27028-2415 · 336-751-2171

Morrisville

David E. Fox · Moore & Van Allen · 430 Davis Drive, Suite 500 · P.O. Box 13706 · Morrisville, NC 27709 919-286-8000

Reich L. Welborn · Moore & Van Allen · 430 Davis Drive, Suite 500 · P.O. Box 13706 · Morrisville, NC 27709 · 919-286-8000

New Bern

Gary J. Rickner · ⑩ · Ward and Smith · http://www.wardandsmith.com · 1001 College Court · P.O. Box 867 · New Bern, NC 28563-0867 · 252-672-5400

J. Troy Smith, Jr. · ⑳ · Ward and Smith · http://www.wardandsmith.com · 1001 College Court · P.O. Box 867 · New Bern, NC 28563-0867 · 252-672-5400

John A. J. Ward · John A. J. Ward · 219 Pollock Street · New Bern, NC 28560 · 252-633-4378

Kenneth R. Wooten · Ward and Smith · http://www.wardandsmith.com · 1001 College Court · P.O. Box 867 · New Bern, NC 28563-0867 · 252-672-5400

Raleigh

Catharine Biggs Arrowood · Parker Poe Adams & Bernstein · http://www.parkerpoe.com · Wachovia Capitol Center, Suite 1400 · 150 Fayetteville Street · Raleigh, NC 27601 · 919-828-0564

Mark A. Ash · Smith, Anderson, Blount, Dorsett, Mitchell & Jernigan · http://www.smithlaw.com · 2500 Wachovia Capitol Center · P.O. Box 2611 · Raleigh, NC 27602-2611 · 919-821-1220

David H. Batten · Cranfill, Sumner & Hartzog · http://www.cshlaw.com · 5420 Wade Park Boulevard · P.O. Box 27808 · Raleigh, NC 27611-7808 · 919-828-5100

James K. Dorsett III · Smith, Anderson, Blount, Dorsett, Mitchell & Jernigan · http://www.smithlaw.com 2500 Wachovia Capitol Center · P.O. Box 2611 · Raleigh, NC 27602-2611 · 919-821-1220

L. Neal Ellis, Jr. · Hunton & Williams · One Bank Of America Plaza, Suite 1400 · 421 Fayetteville Street · P.O. Box 109 · Raleigh, NC 27602 · 919-899-3000

James L. Gale · Smith Moore Leatherwood · http://www.smithmoorelaw.com · Two Hannover Square, Suite 2800 · P.O. Box 27525 · Raleigh, NC 27611 · 919-755-8700

Eura Duval Gaskins, Jr. · ⑩ · Everett, Gaskins, Hancock & Stevens · The Professional Building, Suite 600 · 127 West Hargett Street · P.O. Box 911 · Raleigh, NC 27602-0911 · 919-755-0025

Christopher T. Graebe · Graebe, Hannah & Wellborn · 4350 Lassiter at North Hills Avenue, Suite 375 · Raleigh, NC 27609 · 919-863-9092

Cecil W. Harrison · ⑩ · Poyner & Spruill · http://www.poynerspruill.com · 3600 Glenwood Avenue · P.O. Box 10096 · Raleigh, NC 27605-0096 · 919-783-6400

Dan M. Hartzog · Cranfill, Sumner & Hartzog · http://www.cshlaw.com · 5420 Wade Park Boulevard · P.O. Box 27808 · Raleigh, NC 27611-7808 · 919-828-5100

A. Lee Hogewood III · K&L Gates · 4350 Lassiter at North Hills Avenue, Suite 300 · Raleigh, NC 27609 919-743-7300

Noah H. Huffstetler III · ⑩ · Nelson Mullins Riley & Scarborough · GlenLake One, Suite 200 · 4140 Parklake Avenue · P.O. Box 30519 · Raleigh, NC 27622-0519 · 919-877-3800

David W. Long · ⑳ · Poyner & Spruill · http://www.poynerspruill.com · 3600 Glenwood Avenue · P.O. Box 10096 · Raleigh, NC 27605-0096 · 919-783-6400

Johnny M. Loper · Womble Carlyle Sandridge & Rice · 150 Fayetteville Street, Suite 2100 · P.O. Box 831 · Raleigh, NC 27601-0831 · 919-755-2100

Gregg E. McDougal · Kilpatrick Stockton · 3737 Glenwood Avenue, Suite 400 · Raleigh, NC 27612-5515 919-420-1700

Matthew P. McGuire · Nelson Mullins Riley & Scarborough · GlenLake One, Suite 200 · 4140 Parklake Avenue · P.O. Box 30519 · Raleigh, NC 27622-0519 · 919-877-3800

Michael T. Medford · Manning, Fulton & Skinner · http://www.manningfulton.com · 3605 Glenwood Avenue, Suite 500 · P.O. Box 20389 · Raleigh, NC 27619-0389 · 919-787-8880

Pressly M. Millen · Womble Carlyle Sandridge & Rice · 150 Fayetteville Street, Suite 2100 · P.O. Box 831 · Raleigh, NC 27601-0831 · 919-755-2100

Burley B. Mitchell, Jr. · Womble Carlyle Sandridge & Rice · 150 Fayetteville Street, Suite 2100 · P.O. Box 831 · Raleigh, NC 27601-0831 · 919-755-2100

Joseph C. Moore III · Allen & Moore · 3700 Computer Drive, Suite 320 · Raleigh, NC 27609-6505 · 919-783-8023

Gary S. Parsons · Troutman Sanders · Two Hannover Square, Suite 1900 · 434 Fayetteville Street · P.O. Box 1389 · Raleigh, NC 27602-1389 · 919-835-4100

Carl N. Patterson, Jr. · Smith, Anderson, Blount, Dorsett, Mitchell & Jernigan · http://www.smithlaw.com · 2500 Wachovia Capitol Center · P.O. Box 2611 · Raleigh, NC 27602-2611 · 919-821-1220

James A. Roberts III · Lewis & Roberts · 3700 Glenwood Avenue, Suite 410 · P.O. Box 17529 · Raleigh, NC 27619-7529 · 919-981-0191

John L. Sarratt · Harris, Winfield, Sarratt & Hodges · 225 Hillsborough Street, Suite 260 · Raleigh, NC 27603 · 919-546-8788

Hayden J. Silver III · Kilpatrick Stockton · 3737 Glenwood Avenue, Suite 400 · Raleigh, NC 27612-5515 919-420-1700

Theodore B. Smyth · Smyth & Cioffi · 3221 Blue Ridge Road, Suite 101 · Raleigh, NC 27612 · 919-782-2000

Robert W. Spearman · ⑩ · Parker Poe Adams & Bernstein · http://www.parkerpoe.com · Wachovia Capitol Center, Suite 1400 · 150 Fayetteville Street · Raleigh, NC 27601 · 919-828-0564

Benjamin Thompson · Wyrick Robbins Yates & Ponton · http://www.wyrick.com · The Summit, Suite 300 · 4101 Lake Boone Trail · P.O. Drawer 17803 · Raleigh, NC 27607-7506 · 919-781-4000

Donald H. Tucker, Jr. · Smith, Anderson, Blount, Dorsett, Mitchell & Jernigan · http://www.smithlaw.com · 2500 Wachovia Capitol Center · P.O. Box 2611 · Raleigh, NC 27602-2611 · 919-821-1220

Kirk G. Warner · Smith, Anderson, Blount, Dorsett, Mitchell & Jernigan · http://www.smithlaw.com · 2500 Wachovia Capitol Center · P.O. Box 2611 · Raleigh, NC 27602-2611 · 919-821-1220

Cynthia L. Wittmer · Parker Poe Adams & Bernstein · http://www.parkerpoe.com · Wachovia Capitol Center, Suite 1400 · 150 Fayetteville Street · Raleigh, NC 27601 · 919-828-0564

Rocky Mount

J. Nicholas Ellis · Poyner & Spruill · http://www.poynerspruill.com · 130 South Franklin Street · P.O. Box 353 · Rocky Mount, NC 27802-0353 · 252-446-2341

Marshall Aubrey Gallop, Jr. · Battle, Winslow, Scott & Wiley · 2343 Professional Drive · P.O. Box 7100 · Rocky Mount, NC 27804-0100 · 252-937-2200

Wilmington

Daniel Lee Brawley · ⑩ · Williams Mullen · http://www.williamsmullen.com · 300 North Third Street, Suite 420 · Wilmington, NC 28401 · 910-256-5135

Henry L. Kitchin, Jr. · McGuireWoods · http://www.mcguirewoods.com · 300 North Third Street, Suite 400 · P.O. Box 599 · Wilmington, NC 28402 · 910-254-3800

George Rountree III · ⑩ · Rountree Losee & Baldwin · 2419 Market Street · P.O. Box 1409 · Wilmington, NC 28403 · 910-763-3404

Winston-Salem

H. Grady Barnhill, Jr. · ㉕ · Womble Carlyle Sandridge & Rice · One West Fourth Street · Winston-Salem, NC 27101 · 336-721-3600

Susan H. Boyles · Kilpatrick Stockton · 1001 West Fourth Street · Winston-Salem, NC 27101-2400 · 336-607-7300

Adam H. Charnes · Kilpatrick Stockton · 1001 West Fourth Street · Winston-Salem, NC 27101-2400 · 336-607-7300

Keith A. Clinard · Womble Carlyle Sandridge & Rice · One West Fourth Street · Winston-Salem, NC 27101 · 336-721-3600

W. Andrew Copenhaver · ⑩ · Womble Carlyle Sandridge & Rice · One West Fourth Street · Winston-Salem, NC 27101 · 336-721-3600

Ronald R. Davis · Womble Carlyle Sandridge & Rice · One West Fourth Street · Winston-Salem, NC 27101 · 336-721-3600

William Kearns Davis · ⑩ · Bell, Davis & Pitt · http://www.belldavispitt.com · Century Plaza, Suite 600 · 100 North Cherry Street · P.O. Box 21029 · Winston-Salem, NC 27120 · 336-722-3700

James R. Fox · ⑩ · Bell, Davis & Pitt · http://www.belldavispitt.com · Century Plaza, Suite 600 · 100 North Cherry Street · P.O. Box 21029 · Winston-Salem, NC 27120 · 336-722-3700

Ellen M. Gregg · Womble Carlyle Sandridge & Rice · One West Fourth Street · Winston-Salem, NC 27101 · 336-721-3600

James H. Kelly, Jr. · ⑩ · Kilpatrick Stockton · 1001 West Fourth Street · Winston-Salem, NC 27101-2400 · 336-607-7300

Richard J. Keshian · Kilpatrick Stockton · 1001 West Fourth Street · Winston-Salem, NC 27101-2400 · 336-607-7300

Robert J. Lawing · ⑩ · Robinson & Lawing · http://www.robinson-lawing.com · 101 North Cherry Street, Suite 720 · Winston-Salem, NC 27101 · 336-631-8500

George L. Little, Jr. · ⑩ · Kilpatrick Stockton · 1001 West Fourth Street · Winston-Salem, NC 27101-2400 · 336-607-7300

Michael E. Ray · Womble Carlyle Sandridge & Rice · One West Fourth Street · Winston-Salem, NC 27101 · 336-721-3600

Michael L. Robinson · Robinson & Lawing · http://www.robinson-lawing.com · 101 North Cherry Street, Suite 720 · Winston-Salem, NC 27101 · 336-631-8500

Norwood Robinson · ⑳ · Robinson & Lawing · http://www.robinson-lawing.com · 101 North Cherry Street, Suite 720 · Winston-Salem, NC 27101 · 336-631-8500

Alan M. Ruley · Bell, Davis & Pitt · http://www.belldavispitt.com · Century Plaza, Suite 600 · 100 North Cherry Street · P.O. Box 21029 · Winston-Salem, NC 27120 · 336-722-3700

Stephen M. Russell · Bell, Davis & Pitt · http://www.belldavispitt.com · Century Plaza, Suite 600 · 100 North Cherry Street · P.O. Box 21029 · Winston-Salem, NC 27120 · 336-722-3700

David C. Smith · Kilpatrick Stockton · 1001 West Fourth Street · Winston-Salem, NC 27101-2400 · 336-607-7300

Daniel R. Taylor, Jr. · Kilpatrick Stockton · 1001 West Fourth Street · Winston-Salem, NC 27101-2400 · 336-607-7300

Keith W. Vaughan · ⑩ · Womble Carlyle Sandridge & Rice · One West Fourth Street · Winston-Salem, NC 27101 · 336-721-3600

G. Gray Wilson · ⑩ · Wilson & Coffey · 110 Oakwood Drive, Suite 400 · Winston-Salem, NC 27103 · 336-631-8866

William F. Womble, Jr. · ⑩ · Womble Carlyle Sandridge & Rice · One West Fourth Street · Winston-Salem, NC 27101 · 336-721-3600

Charlot F. Wood · Bell, Davis & Pitt · http://www.belldavispitt.com · Century Plaza, Suite 600 · 100 North Cherry Street · P.O. Box 21029 · Winston-Salem, NC 27120 · 336-722-3700

COMMUNICATIONS LAW

Charlotte

James H. Jeffries IV · Moore & Van Allen · Bank of America Corporate Center, Suite 4700 · 100 North Tryon Street · Charlotte, NC 28202-4003 · 704-331-1000

Raleigh

Henry C. Campen, Jr. · Parker Poe Adams & Bernstein · http://www.parkerpoe.com · Wachovia Capitol Center, Suite 1400 · 150 Fayetteville Street · Raleigh, NC 27601 · 919-828-0564

Daniel C. Higgins · Burns, Day & Presnell · 2626 Glenwood Avenue, Suite 560 · P.O. Box 10867 · Raleigh, NC 27605 · 919-782-1441

CONSTRUCTION LAW

Asheville

Jones P. Byrd, Sr. · The Van Winkle Law Firm · 11 North Market Street · P.O. Box 7376 · Asheville, NC 28801-7376 · 828-258-2991

Charlotte

Greg C. Ahlum · Johnston, Allison & Hord · 1065 East Morehead Street · P.O. Box 36469 · Charlotte, NC 28236 · 704-332-1181

Robert L. Burchette · Johnston, Allison & Hord · 1065 East Morehead Street · P.O. Box 36469 · Charlotte, NC 28236 · 704-332-1181

Jeffrey J. Davis · Jeffrey J. Davis · 400 North Church Street, Suite 222 · Charlotte, NC 28202 · 704-331-1037

Fred W. DeVore III · DeVore Acton & Stafford · 1321 East Morehead Street · Charlotte, NC 28204-2913 704-377-5242

David B. Hamilton · Hamilton Moon Stephens Steele & Martin · 201 South College Street, Suite 2020 · Charlotte, NC 28244-2020 · 704-344-1117

Edward F. Hennessey IV · Robinson, Bradshaw & Hinson · http://www.rbh.com · 101 North Tryon Street, Suite 1900 · Charlotte, NC 28246-1900 · 704-377-2536

Wayne P. Huckel · K&L Gates · Hearst Tower, 47th Floor · 214 North Tryon Street · Charlotte, NC 28202 · 704-331-7400

Bentford E. Martin · Hamilton Moon Stephens Steele & Martin · 201 South College Street, Suite 2020 · Charlotte, NC 28244-2020 · 704-344-1117

Kiran H. Mehta · K&L Gates · Hearst Tower, 47th Floor · 214 North Tryon Street · Charlotte, NC 28202 704-331-7400

Roy H. Michaux, Jr. · K&L Gates · Hearst Tower, 47th Floor · 214 North Tryon Street · Charlotte, NC 28202 · 704-331-7400

Robert C. Sink · ⑩ · Robinson, Bradshaw & Hinson · http://www.rbh.com · 101 North Tryon Street, Suite 1900 · Charlotte, NC 28246-1900 · 704-377-2536

Robert C. Stephens · Hamilton Moon Stephens Steele & Martin · 201 South College Street, Suite 2020 · Charlotte, NC 28244-2020 · 704-344-1117

John B. Taylor · Taylor, Riemann · LakePointe Corporate Center II, Suite 360 · 2359 Perimeter Pointe Parkway · Charlotte, NC 28208 · 704-424-2900

Gary Welch · Johnston, Allison & Hord · 1065 East Morehead Street · P.O. Box 36469 · Charlotte, NC 28236 · 704-332-1181

Richard W. Wilson · Nexsen Pruet · http://www.nexsenpruet.com · 201 South Tryon Street, Suite 1200 · Charlotte, NC 28202 · 704-339-0304

Steele B. Windle III · Shumaker, Loop & Kendrick · First Citizen's Bank Building, Suite 1800 · 128 South Tryon Street · Charlotte, NC 28202-1675 · 704-375-0057

Durham

John E. Bugg · Bugg & Wolf · University Office Park, Suite 170 · 411 Andrews Road · Durham, NC 27705 · 919-383-9431

Greensboro

Bruce Ashley · Smith Moore Leatherwood · http://www.smithmoorelaw.com · 300 North Greene Street, Suite 1400 · P.O. Box 21927 · Greensboro, NC 27420-1927 · 336-378-5200

Richard D. Conner · Conner Gwyn Schenck · http://www.cgspllc.com · 306 East Market Street, Suite One · P.O. Box 20744 · Greensboro, NC 27420 · 336-691-9222

Allen Holt Gwyn · Conner Gwyn Schenck · http://www.cgspllc.com · 306 East Market Street, Suite One · P.O. Box 20744 · Greensboro, NC 27420 · 336-691-9222

R. Harper Heckman · Nexsen Pruet · http://www.nexsenpruet.com · 701 Green Valley Road, Suite 100 · Greensboro, NC 27408 · 336-373-1600

David A. Senter · Nexsen Pruet · http://www.nexsenpruet.com · 701 Green Valley Road, Suite 100 · Greensboro, NC 27408 · 336-373-1600

Greenville

Donalt J. Eglinton · Ward and Smith · http://www.wardandsmith.com · 120 West Fire Tower Road · P.O. Box 8088 · Greenville, NC 27835-8088 · 252-215-4000

Morrisville

David E. Fox · Moore & Van Allen · 430 Davis Drive, Suite 500 · P.O. Box 13706 · Morrisville, NC 27709 919-286-8000

New Bern

Ryal W. Tayloe · Ward and Smith · http://www.wardandsmith.com · 1001 College Court · P.O. Box 867 · New Bern, NC 28563-0867 · 252-672-5400

Raleigh

Daniel K. Bryson · Lewis & Roberts · 3700 Glenwood Avenue, Suite 410 · P.O. Box 17529 · Raleigh, NC 27619-7529 · 919-981-0191

George K. Freeman, Jr. · Poyner & Spruill · http://www.poynerspruill.com · 3600 Glenwood Avenue · P.O. Box 10096 · Raleigh, NC 27605-0096 · 919-783-6400

William H. Gammon · Nelson Mullins Riley & Scarborough · GlenLake One, Suite 200 · 4140 Parklake Avenue · P.O. Box 30519 · Raleigh, NC 27622-0519 · 919-877-3800

C. Hamilton Jarrett · Conner Gwyn Schenck · http://www.cgspllc.com · 3141 John Humphries Wynd, Suite 100 · P.O. Box 30933 · Raleigh, NC 27622 · 919-789-9242

Russell B. Killen · Parker Poe Adams & Bernstein · http://www.parkerpoe.com · Wachovia Capitol Center, Suite 1400 · 150 Fayetteville Street · Raleigh, NC 27601 · 919-828-0564

John I. Mabe, Jr. · Williams Mullen · http://www.williamsmullen.com · Highwoods Tower One, Suite 500 · 3200 Beechleaf Court · P.O. Drawer 19764 · Raleigh, NC 27619-9764 · 919-981-4000

Peter J. Marino · Smith, Anderson, Blount, Dorsett, Mitchell & Jernigan · http://www.smithlaw.com · 2500 Wachovia Capitol Center · P.O. Box 2611 · Raleigh, NC 27602-2611 · 919-821-1220

J. Anthony Penry · Taylor, Riemann · 510 Glenwood Avenue, Suite 319 · Raleigh, NC 27603 · 919-833-9449

James A. Roberts III · Lewis & Roberts · 3700 Glenwood Avenue, Suite 410 · P.O. Box 17529 · Raleigh, NC 27619-7529 · 919-981-0191

James S. Schenck IV · Conner Gwyn Schenck · http://www.cgspllc.com · 3141 John Humphries Wynd, Suite 100 · P.O. Box 30933 · Raleigh, NC 27622 · 919-789-9242

John L. Shaw · Poyner & Spruill · http://www.poynerspruill.com · 3600 Glenwood Avenue · P.O. Box 10096 · Raleigh, NC 27605-0096 · 919-783-6400

A. Graham Shirley · Shirley & Adams · 150 Fayetteville Street, Suite 520 · Raleigh, NC 27601 · 919-899-6278

Wilmington

Daniel Lee Brawley · ⑩ · Williams Mullen · http://www.williamsmullen.com · 300 North Third Street, Suite 420 · Wilmington, NC 28401 · 910-256-5135

Winston-Salem

Karen E. Carey · Womble Carlyle Sandridge & Rice · One West Fourth Street · Winston-Salem, NC 27101 · 336-721-3600

D. Anderson Carmen · Bell, Davis & Pitt · http://www.belldavispitt.com · Century Plaza, Suite 600 · 100 North Cherry Street · P.O. Box 21029 · Winston-Salem, NC 27120 · 336-722-3700

Dudley Humphrey · Kilpatrick Stockton · 1001 West Fourth Street · Winston-Salem, NC 27101-2400 · 336-607-7300

CORPORATE GOVERNANCE AND COMPLIANCE LAW

Charlotte

Garza Baldwin III · ⑩ · Womble Carlyle Sandridge & Rice · One Wachovia Center, Suite 3500 · 301 South College Street · Charlotte, NC 28202-6037 · 704-331-4900

Patrick S. Bryant · Robinson, Bradshaw & Hinson · http://www.rbh.com · 101 North Tryon Street, Suite 1900 · Charlotte, NC 28246-1900 · 704-377-2536

Peter C. Buck · Robinson, Bradshaw & Hinson · http://www.rbh.com · 101 North Tryon Street, Suite 1900 · Charlotte, NC 28246-1900 · 704-377-2536

Boyd C. Campbell, Jr. · ⑩ · McGuireWoods · http://www.mcguirewoods.com · 201 North Tryon Street, Suite 3000 · P.O. Box 31247 · Charlotte, NC 28231 · 704-343-2000

Matthew S. Churchill · Robinson, Bradshaw & Hinson · http://www.rbh.com · 101 North Tryon Street, Suite 1900 · Charlotte, NC 28246-1900 · 704-377-2536

Stephen D. Hope · Moore & Van Allen · Bank of America Corporate Center, Suite 4700 · 100 North Tryon Street · Charlotte, NC 28202-4003 · 704-331-1000

Sean M. Jones · K&L Gates · Hearst Tower, 47th Floor · 214 North Tryon Street · Charlotte, NC 28202 · 704-331-7400

Stephen M. Lynch · Robinson, Bradshaw & Hinson · http://www.rbh.com · 101 North Tryon Street, Suite 1900 · Charlotte, NC 28246-1900 · 704-377-2536

Eugene C. Pridgen · K&L Gates · Hearst Tower, 47th Floor · 214 North Tryon Street · Charlotte, NC 28202 · 704-331-7400

J. Norfleet Pruden III · K&L Gates · Hearst Tower, 47th Floor · 214 North Tryon Street · Charlotte, NC 28202 · 704-331-7400

Henry H. Ralston · Robinson, Bradshaw & Hinson · http://www.rbh.com · 101 North Tryon Street, Suite 1900 · Charlotte, NC 28246-1900 · 704-377-2536

Stephen K. Rhyne · K&L Gates · Hearst Tower, 47th Floor · 214 North Tryon Street · Charlotte, NC 28202 · 704-331-7400

A. Zachary Smith III · K&L Gates · Hearst Tower, 47th Floor · 214 North Tryon Street · Charlotte, NC 28202 · 704-331-7400

Raleigh

D. Scott Coward · K&L Gates · 4350 Lassiter at North Hills Avenue, Suite 300 · Raleigh, NC 27609 · 919-743-7300

Winston-Salem

W. Randy Eaddy · ⑩ · Kilpatrick Stockton · 1001 West Fourth Street · Winston-Salem, NC 27101-2400 · 336-607-7300

CORPORATE LAW

Asheville

John S. Stevens · Roberts & Stevens · BB&T Building, Suite 1100 · One West Pack Square · P.O. Box 7647 · Asheville, NC 28802 · 828-252-6600

Charlotte

John D. Allison · K&L Gates · Hearst Tower, 47th Floor · 214 North Tryon Street · Charlotte, NC 28202 704-331-7400

Benjamin W. Baldwin · Robinson, Bradshaw & Hinson · http://www.rbh.com · 101 North Tryon Street, Suite 1900 · Charlotte, NC 28246-1900 · 704-377-2536

Garza Baldwin III · ⑩ · Womble Carlyle Sandridge & Rice · One Wachovia Center, Suite 3500 · 301 South College Street · Charlotte, NC 28202-6037 · 704-331-4900

Jonathan A. Barrett · Mayer Brown · 214 North Tryon Street, Suite 2200 · Charlotte, NC 28202 · 704-444-3561

Francis J. Blanchfield, Jr. · ⑩ · Mayer Brown · 214 North Tryon Street, Suite 2200 · Charlotte, NC 28202 · 704-444-3561

Patrick S. Bryant · Robinson, Bradshaw & Hinson · http://www.rbh.com · 101 North Tryon Street, Suite 1900 · Charlotte, NC 28246-1900 · 704-377-2536

Peter C. Buck · Robinson, Bradshaw & Hinson · http://www.rbh.com · 101 North Tryon Street, Suite 1900 · Charlotte, NC 28246-1900 · 704-377-2536

Boyd C. Campbell, Jr. · ⑩ · McGuireWoods · http://www.mcguirewoods.com · 201 North Tryon Street, Suite 3000 · P.O. Box 31247 · Charlotte, NC 28231 · 704-343-2000

Larry J. Dagenhart · ⑩ · McGuireWoods · http://www.mcguirewoods.com · 201 North Tryon Street, Suite 3000 · P.O. Box 31247 · Charlotte, NC 28231 · 704-343-2000

J. Carlton Fleming · ⑳ · Womble Carlyle Sandridge & Rice · One Wachovia Center, Suite 3500 · 301 South College Street · Charlotte, NC 28202-6037 · 704-331-4900

T. Richard Giovannelli · K&L Gates · Hearst Tower, 47th Floor · 214 North Tryon Street · Charlotte, NC 28202 · 704-331-7400

Robert G. Griffin · Robinson, Bradshaw & Hinson · http://www.rbh.com · 101 North Tryon Street, Suite 1900 · Charlotte, NC 28246-1900 · 704-377-2536

Michael S. Hawley · K&L Gates · Hearst Tower, 47th Floor · 214 North Tryon Street · Charlotte, NC 28202 · 704-331-7400

Jeffrey S. Hay · Womble Carlyle Sandridge & Rice · One Wachovia Center, Suite 3500 · 301 South College Street · Charlotte, NC 28202-6037 · 704-331-4900

Robin L. Hinson · ⑩ · Robinson, Bradshaw & Hinson · http://www.rbh.com · 101 North Tryon Street, Suite 1900 · Charlotte, NC 28246-1900 · 704-377-2536

Stephen D. Hope · Moore & Van Allen · Bank of America Corporate Center, Suite 4700 · 100 North Tryon Street · Charlotte, NC 28202-4003 · 704-331-1000

H. Bryan Ives III · Alston + Bird · http://www.alston.com · Bank of America Plaza, Suite 4000 · 101 South Tryon Street · Charlotte, NC 28280-4000 · 704-444-1000

Gary C. Ivey · Alston + Bird · http://www.alston.com · Bank of America Plaza, Suite 4000 · 101 South Tryon Street · Charlotte, NC 28280-4000 · 704-444-1000

Cyrus M. Johnson, Jr. · Womble Carlyle Sandridge & Rice · One Wachovia Center, Suite 3500 · 301 South College Street · Charlotte, NC 28202-6037 · 704-331-4900

Sean M. Jones · K&L Gates · Hearst Tower, 47th Floor · 214 North Tryon Street · Charlotte, NC 28202 · 704-331-7400

Donald C. Lampe · Womble Carlyle Sandridge & Rice · One Wachovia Center, Suite 3500 · 301 South College Street · Charlotte, NC 28202-6037 · 704-331-4900

Haynes P. Lea · Robinson, Bradshaw & Hinson · http://www.rbh.com · 101 North Tryon Street, Suite 1900 · Charlotte, NC 28246-1900 · 704-377-2536

Hal A. Levinson · Moore & Van Allen · Bank of America Corporate Center, Suite 4700 · 100 North Tryon Street · Charlotte, NC 28202-4003 · 704-331-1000

Stephen M. Lynch · Robinson, Bradshaw & Hinson · http://www.rbh.com · 101 North Tryon Street, Suite 1900 · Charlotte, NC 28246-1900 · 704-377-2536

E. Lynwood Mallard · ⑩ · McGuireWoods · http://www.mcguirewoods.com · 201 North Tryon Street, Suite 3000 · P.O. Box 31247 · Charlotte, NC 28231 · 704-343-2000

Harrison L. Marshall, Jr. · McGuireWoods · http://www.mcguirewoods.com · 201 North Tryon Street, Suite 3000 · P.O. Box 31247 · Charlotte, NC 28231 · 704-343-2000

Kent J. McCready · Robinson, Bradshaw & Hinson · http://www.rbh.com · 101 North Tryon Street, Suite 1900 · Charlotte, NC 28246-1900 · 704-377-2536

Robert S. McLean · Robinson, Bradshaw & Hinson · http://www.rbh.com · 101 North Tryon Street, Suite 1900 · Charlotte, NC 28246-1900 · 704-377-2536

John R. Miller · Robinson, Bradshaw & Hinson · http://www.rbh.com · 101 North Tryon Street, Suite 1900 · Charlotte, NC 28246-1900 · 704-377-2536

Eugene C. Pridgen · K&L Gates · Hearst Tower, 47th Floor · 214 North Tryon Street · Charlotte, NC 28202 · 704-331-7400

J. Norfleet Pruden III · K&L Gates · Hearst Tower, 47th Floor · 214 North Tryon Street · Charlotte, NC 28202 · 704-331-7400

Henry H. Ralston · Robinson, Bradshaw & Hinson · http://www.rbh.com · 101 North Tryon Street, Suite 1900 · Charlotte, NC 28246-1900 · 704-377-2536

C. Richard Rayburn, Jr. · ⑩ · Rayburn, Cooper & Durham · 227 West Trade Street, Suite 1200 · Charlotte, NC 28202-1672 · 704-334-0891

Stephen K. Rhyne · K&L Gates · Hearst Tower, 47th Floor · 214 North Tryon Street · Charlotte, NC 28202 · 704-331-7400

Russell M. Robinson II · ㉕ · Robinson, Bradshaw & Hinson · http://www.rbh.com · 101 North Tryon Street, Suite 1900 · Charlotte, NC 28246-1900 · 704-377-2536

Richard K. Schell · Parker Poe Adams & Bernstein · http://www.parkerpoe.com · Three Wachovia Center, Suite 3000 · 401 South Tryon Street · Charlotte, NC 28202-1935 · 704-372-9000

Roy L. Smart III · Parker Poe Adams & Bernstein · http://www.parkerpoe.com · Three Wachovia Center, Suite 3000 · 401 South Tryon Street · Charlotte, NC 28202-1935 · 704-372-9000

A. Zachary Smith III · K&L Gates · Hearst Tower, 47th Floor · 214 North Tryon Street · Charlotte, NC 28202 · 704-331-7400

Edward W. Wellman, Jr. · Parker Poe Adams & Bernstein · http://www.parkerpoe.com · Three Wachovia Center, Suite 3000 · 401 South Tryon Street · Charlotte, NC 28202-1935 · 704-372-9000

Elizabeth G. Wren · McGuireWoods · http://www.mcguirewoods.com · Bank of America Corporate Center, Suite 2900 · 100 North Tryon Street · Charlotte, NC 28202-4011 · 704-373-8999

Greensboro

Michael R. Abel · ⑩ · Schell Bray Aycock Abel & Livingston · http://www.sbaal.com · Renaissance Plaza, Suite 1500 · 230 North Elm Street · Greensboro, NC 27401 · 336-370-8800

E. Kent Auberry · Smith Moore Leatherwood · http://www.smithmoorelaw.com · 300 North Greene Street, Suite 1400 · P.O. Box 21927 · Greensboro, NC 27420-1927 · 336-378-5200

W. Alexander Audilet · Smith Moore Leatherwood · http://www.smithmoorelaw.com · 300 North Greene Street, Suite 1400 · P.O. Box 21927 · Greensboro, NC 27420-1927 · 336-378-5200

Robert G. Baynes · Nexsen Pruet · http://www.nexsenpruet.com · 701 Green Valley Road, Suite 100 · Greensboro, NC 27408 · 336-373-1600

Marc D. Bishop · Brooks, Pierce, McLendon, Humphrey & Leonard · http://www.brookspierce.com · 2000 Renaissance Plaza · 230 North Elm Street · Greensboro, NC 27401 · 336-373-8850

Doris R. Bray · ⑳ · Schell Bray Aycock Abel & Livingston · http://www.sbaal.com · Renaissance Plaza, Suite 1500 · 230 North Elm Street · Greensboro, NC 27401 · 336-370-8800

Mark Davidson · Brooks, Pierce, McLendon, Humphrey & Leonard · http://www.brookspierce.com · 2000 Renaissance Plaza · 230 North Elm Street · Greensboro, NC 27401 · 336-373-8850

Herbert O. Davis · ⑩ · Smith Moore Leatherwood · http://www.smithmoorelaw.com · 300 North Greene Street, Suite 1400 · P.O. Box 21927 · Greensboro, NC 27420-1927 · 336-378-5200

Garland G. Graham · Schell Bray Aycock Abel & Livingston · http://www.sbaal.com · Renaissance Plaza, Suite 1500 · 230 North Elm Street · Greensboro, NC 27401 · 336-370-8800

Wayne E. Tumlin · Tuggle Duggins & Meschan · http://www.tuggleduggins.com · 100 North Greene Street, Suite 600 · P.O. Box 2888 · Greensboro, NC 27402-2888 · 336-378-1431

Thomas C. Watkins · ⑩ · Schell Bray Aycock Abel & Livingston · http://www.sbaal.com · Renaissance Plaza, Suite 1500 · 230 North Elm Street · Greensboro, NC 27401 · 336-370-8800

High Point

Charles E. Lynch, Jr. · Keziah, Gates & Samet · High Point Bank & Trust Building, Suite 400 · 300 North Main Street · P.O. Box 2608 · High Point, NC 27261-2608 · 336-889-6900

Morrisville

Reich L. Welborn · Moore & Van Allen · 430 Davis Drive, Suite 500 · P.O. Box 13706 · Morrisville, NC 27709 · 919-286-8000

New Bern

J. Troy Smith, Jr. · ⑳ · Ward and Smith · http://www.wardandsmith.com · 1001 College Court · P.O. Box 867 · New Bern, NC 28563-0867 · 252-672-5400

David L. Ward, Jr. · ㉕ · Ward and Smith · http://www.wardandsmith.com · 1001 College Court · P.O. Box 867 · New Bern, NC 28563-0867 · 252-672-5400

Raleigh

R. Marks Arnold · Smith, Anderson, Blount, Dorsett, Mitchell & Jernigan · http://www.smithlaw.com · 2500 Wachovia Capitol Center · P.O. Box 2611 · Raleigh, NC 27602-2611 · 919-821-1220

Martin H. Brinkley · Smith, Anderson, Blount, Dorsett, Mitchell & Jernigan · http://www.smithlaw.com · 2500 Wachovia Capitol Center · P.O. Box 2611 · Raleigh, NC 27602-2611 · 919-821-1220

Christopher B. Capel · Smith, Anderson, Blount, Dorsett, Mitchell & Jernigan · http://www.smithlaw.com · 2500 Wachovia Capitol Center · P.O. Box 2611 · Raleigh, NC 27602-2611 · 919-821-1220

Kent F. Christison · K&L Gates · 4350 Lassiter at North Hills Avenue, Suite 300 · Raleigh, NC 27609 · 919-743-7300

Walter E. Daniels · Ward and Smith · http://www.wardandsmith.com · Wade II, Suite 400 · 5430 Wade Park Boulevard · P.O. Box 33009 · Raleigh, NC 27636-3009 · 919-277-9100

William M. Flynn · Hunton & Williams · One Bank Of America Plaza, Suite 1400 · 421 Fayetteville Street · P.O. Box 109 · Raleigh, NC 27602 · 919-899-3000

William B. Gwyn, Jr. · Williams Mullen · http://www.williamsmullen.com · Highwoods Tower One, Suite 500 · 3200 Beechleaf Court · P.O. Drawer 19764 · Raleigh, NC 27619-9764 · 919-981-4000

Wade H. Hargrove · ⑩ · Brooks, Pierce, McLendon, Humphrey & Leonard · http://www.brookspierce.com · 1600 Wachovia Capitol Center · 150 Fayetteville Street · Raleigh, NC 27601 · 919-839-0300

Fred D. Hutchison · Hutchison Law Group · http://www.hutchlaw.com · 5410 Trinity Road, Suite 400 · Raleigh, NC 27607 · 919-829-9600

John L. Jernigan · ⑩ · Smith, Anderson, Blount, Dorsett, Mitchell & Jernigan · http://www.smithlaw.com 2500 Wachovia Capitol Center · P.O. Box 2611 · Raleigh, NC 27602-2611 · 919-821-1220

Byron B. Kirkland · Smith, Anderson, Blount, Dorsett, Mitchell & Jernigan · http://www.smithlaw.com · 2500 Wachovia Capitol Center · P.O. Box 2611 · Raleigh, NC 27602-2611 · 919-821-1220

Helga L. Leftwich · Hutchison Law Group · http://www.hutchlaw.com · 5410 Trinity Road, Suite 400 · Raleigh, NC 27607 · 919-829-9600

J. Christopher Lynch · Wyrick Robbins Yates & Ponton · http://www.wyrick.com · The Summit, Suite 300 · 4101 Lake Boone Trail · P.O. Drawer 17803 · Raleigh, NC 27607-7506 · 919-781-4000

Brad S. Markoff · DLA Piper · 4141 Parklake Avenue, Suite 300 · Raleigh, NC 27612-2350 · 919-786-2000

Henry A. Mitchell, Jr. · ⑳ · Smith, Anderson, Blount, Dorsett, Mitchell & Jernigan · http://www.smithlaw.com · 2500 Wachovia Capitol Center · P.O. Box 2611 · Raleigh, NC 27602-2611 · 919-821-1220

Samuel T. Oliver · ⑩ · Manning, Fulton & Skinner · http://www.manningfulton.com · 3605 Glenwood Avenue, Suite 500 · P.O. Box 20389 · Raleigh, NC 27619-0389 · 919-787-8880

William G. Pappas · Parker Poe Adams & Bernstein · http://www.parkerpoe.com · Wachovia Capitol Center, Suite 1400 · 150 Fayetteville Street · Raleigh, NC 27601 · 919-828-0564

William S. Patterson · Hunton & Williams · One Bank Of America Plaza, Suite 1400 · 421 Fayetteville Street · P.O. Box 109 · Raleigh, NC 27602 · 919-899-3000

Gerald F. Roach · Smith, Anderson, Blount, Dorsett, Mitchell & Jernigan · http://www.smithlaw.com · 2500 Wachovia Capitol Center · P.O. Box 2611 · Raleigh, NC 27602-2611 · 919-821-1220

Larry E. Robbins · Wyrick Robbins Yates & Ponton · http://www.wyrick.com · The Summit, Suite 300 · 4101 Lake Boone Trail · P.O. Drawer 17803 · Raleigh, NC 27607-7506 · 919-781-4000

James F. Verdonik · ⑩ · Ward and Smith · http://www.wardandsmith.com · Wade II, Suite 400 · 5430 Wade Park Boulevard · P.O. Box 33009 · Raleigh, NC 27636-3009 · 919-277-9100

Robert B. Womble · K&L Gates · 4350 Lassiter at North Hills Avenue, Suite 300 · Raleigh, NC 27609 · 919-743-7300

James J. Yates, Jr. · Wyrick Robbins Yates & Ponton · http://www.wyrick.com · The Summit, Suite 300 · 4101 Lake Boone Trail · P.O. Drawer 17803 · Raleigh, NC 27607-7506 · 919-781-4000

Research Triangle Park

Kenneth G. Carroll · Womble Carlyle Sandridge & Rice · 2530 Meridian Parkway, Suite 400 · P.O. Box 13069 · Research Triangle Park, NC 27709-3069 · 919-484-2300

Wilmington

George Rountree III · ⑩ · Rountree Losee & Baldwin · 2419 Market Street · P.O. Box 1409 · Wilmington, NC 28403 · 910-763-3404

Winston-Salem

John W. Babcock · Wall Esleeck Babcock · http://www.webllp.com · 1076 West Fourth Street, Suite 100 · Winston-Salem, NC 27101 · 336-722-6300

Peter S. Brunstetter · Womble Carlyle Sandridge & Rice · One West Fourth Street · Winston-Salem, NC 27101 · 336-721-3600

Linwood L. Davis · ㉕ · Womble Carlyle Sandridge & Rice · One West Fourth Street · Winston-Salem, NC 27101 · 336-721-3600

W. Randy Eaddy · ⑩ · Kilpatrick Stockton · 1001 West Fourth Street · Winston-Salem, NC 27101-2400 · 336-607-7300

Robert E. Esleeck · Wall Esleeck Babcock · http://www.webllp.com · 1076 West Fourth Street, Suite 100 Winston-Salem, NC 27101 · 336-722-6300

Murray C. Greason, Jr. · ㉕ · Womble Carlyle Sandridge & Rice · One West Fourth Street · Winston-Salem, NC 27101 · 336-721-3600

Michael D. Gunter · ⑩ · Womble Carlyle Sandridge & Rice · One West Fourth Street · Winston-Salem, NC 27101 · 336-721-3600

Richard B. Howington · ⑩ · Nelson Mullins Riley & Scarborough · The Knollwood, Suite 530 · 380 Knollwood Street · Winston-Salem, NC 27103 · 336-774-3300

Jeffrey C. Howland · ⑩ · Womble Carlyle Sandridge & Rice · One West Fourth Street · Winston-Salem, NC 27101 · 336-721-3600

Dudley Humphrey · Kilpatrick Stockton · 1001 West Fourth Street · Winston-Salem, NC 27101-2400 · 336-607-7300

Greg L. Smith · ⑩ · Womble Carlyle Sandridge & Rice · One West Fourth Street · Winston-Salem, NC 27101 · 336-721-3600

DERIVATIVES LAW

Charlotte

Joseph B. Buonanno · Hunton & Williams · Bank of America Plaza, Suite 3500 · 101 South Tryon Street Charlotte, NC 28280 · 704-378-4700

Francisco J. Linares · Cadwalader, Wickersham & Taft · http://www.cadwalader.com · 227 West Trade Street · Charlotte, NC 28202 · 704-348-5100

Kristin P. Manzano · Alston + Bird · http://www.alston.com · Bank of America Plaza, Suite 4000 · 101 South Tryon Street · Charlotte, NC 28280-4000 · 704-444-1000

DUI/DWI DEFENSE

Charlotte

George V. Laughrun II · Goodman, Carr, Laughrun, Levine, Murray & Greene · Cameron Brown Building, Suite 602 · 301 South McDowell Street · Charlotte, NC 28204 · 704-372-2770

Fayetteville

Ronnie M. Mitchell · ⑩ · Mitchell Brewer Richardson · 255 Ray Avenue · Fayetteville, NC 28304 · 910-678-7100

New Bern

Marcus W. Chesnutt · Chesnutt, Clemmons & Peacock · 225-C Broad Street · P. O. Box 12530 · New Bern, NC 28561 · 252-633-6868

Raleigh

John K. Fanney · Bass, Bryant & Fanney · 16 West Martin Street, Suite 900 · P.O. Drawer 909 · Raleigh, NC 27602 · 919-832-9661

Smithfield

John P. O'Hale · ⑩ · Narron, O'Hale & Whittington · 102 South Third Street · P.O. Box 1567 · Smithfield, NC 27577 · 919-934-6021

EDUCATION LAW

Charlotte

Jim D. Cooley · Womble Carlyle Sandridge & Rice · One Wachovia Center, Suite 3500 · 301 South College Street · Charlotte, NC 28202-6037 · 704-331-4900

Greensboro

James T. Williams, Jr. · ⑩ · Brooks, Pierce, McLendon, Humphrey & Leonard · http://www.brookspierce.com · 2000 Renaissance Plaza · 230 North Elm Street · Greensboro, NC 27401 · 336-373-8850

Jill R. Wilson · Brooks, Pierce, McLendon, Humphrey & Leonard · http://www.brookspierce.com · 2000 Renaissance Plaza · 230 North Elm Street · Greensboro, NC 27401 · 336-373-8850

Raleigh

Donna R. Rascoe · Cranfill, Sumner & Hartzog · http://www.cshlaw.com · 5420 Wade Park Boulevard · P.O. Box 27808 · Raleigh, NC 27611-7808 · 919-828-5100

ELDER LAW

Black Mountain

Wendy A. Craig · Wendy A. Craig · 207 East State Street · Black Mountain, NC 28711 · 828-273-0345

Boone

Carole L. Spainhour · Carole L. Spainhour · 379 New Market Boulevard, Suite Two · Boone, NC 28607 828-265-0200

Charlotte

Elizabeth J. Caviness · Caviness Law Firm · 225 East Kingston Avenue · Charlotte, NC 28203-4743 · 704-529-0646

Laura L. Yaeger · Laura L. Yaeger · 401 North Tryon Street, 10th Floor · Charlotte, NC 28202-2108 · 704-358-4984

Cornelius

Nicole Vandiver Bryan · Vandiver & Bryan · http://www.vbfirm.com · 18809 West Catawba Avenue, Suite 102 · Cornelius, NC 28031 · 704-892-9355

Durham

Larry H. Rocamora · McPherson & Rocamora · 3211 Shannon Road, Suite 620 · Durham, NC 27707 · 919-493-0584

Greensboro

A. Frank Johns · Booth, Harrington & Johns · 239 North Edgeworth Street · P.O. Box 3585 · Greensboro, NC 27402 · 336-275-9567

Raleigh

J. Gregory Wallace · Monroe, Wyne & Wallace · 3225 Blue Ridge Road, Suite 117 · Raleigh, NC 27612 · 919-876-1400

EMINENT DOMAIN AND CONDEMNATION LAW

Asheville

Jones P. Byrd, Sr. · The Van Winkle Law Firm · 11 North Market Street · P.O. Box 7376 · Asheville, NC 28801-7376 · 828-258-2991

Charlotte

Mark W. Merritt · ⑩ · Robinson, Bradshaw & Hinson · http://www.rbh.com · 101 North Tryon Street, Suite 1900 · Charlotte, NC 28246-1900 · 704-377-2536

Durham

Jay H. Ferguson · Thomas, Ferguson & Mullins · 119 East Main Street · Durham, NC 27701 · 919-682-5648

Greensboro

M. Jay DeVaney · Nexsen Pruet · http://www.nexsenpruet.com · 701 Green Valley Road, Suite 100 · Greensboro, NC 27408 · 336-373-1600

Raleigh

George B. Autry, Jr. · Cranfill, Sumner & Hartzog · http://www.cshlaw.com · 5420 Wade Park Boulevard P.O. Box 27808 · Raleigh, NC 27611-7808 · 919-828-5100

Stephanie H. Autry · Cranfill, Sumner & Hartzog · http://www.cshlaw.com · 5420 Wade Park Boulevard · P.O. Box 27808 · Raleigh, NC 27611-7808 · 919-828-5100

Emmett Boney Haywood · Emmett Boney Haywood · 3700 National Drive, Suite 112 · Raleigh, NC 27612 · 919-781-1371

John B. McMillan · Manning, Fulton & Skinner · http://www.manningfulton.com · 3605 Glenwood Avenue, Suite 500 · P.O. Box 20389 · Raleigh, NC 27619-0389 · 919-787-8880

Winston-Salem

Michael J. Lewis · ⑩ · Lewis & Daggett · 285 Executive Park Boulevard · Winston-Salem, NC 27103 · 336-765-7777

EMPLOYEE BENEFITS LAW

Asheville

Michael L. Miller · ⑩ · Michael L. Miller · Ninety Southside Avenue, Suite 100 · P.O. Box 2953 · Asheville, NC 28802 · 828-281-2100

Burlington

Charles F. Royster III · Tuggle & Royster · 3011 South Church Street · Burlington, NC 27215 · 336-524-0183

Charlotte

Jeffrey R. Capwell · ⑩ · McGuireWoods · http://www.mcguirewoods.com · Bank of America Corporate Center, Suite 2900 · 100 North Tryon Street · Charlotte, NC 28202-4011 · 704-373-8999

James E. Daniel · Womble Carlyle Sandridge & Rice · One Wachovia Center, Suite 3500 · 301 South College Street · Charlotte, NC 28202-6037 · 704-331-4900

James E. Earle · K&L Gates · Hearst Tower, 47th Floor · 214 North Tryon Street · Charlotte, NC 28202 704-331-7400

Richard W. Gibson, Jr. · Robinson, Bradshaw & Hinson · http://www.rbh.com · 101 North Tryon Street, Suite 1900 · Charlotte, NC 28246-1900 · 704-377-2536

Eugene S. Griggs · Poyner & Spruill · http://www.poynerspruill.com · One Wachovia Center, Suite 2300 · 301 South College Street · Charlotte, NC 28202-6021 · 704-342-5250

Carl E. Johnson, Jr. · Robinson, Bradshaw & Hinson · http://www.rbh.com · 101 North Tryon Street, Suite 1900 · Charlotte, NC 28246-1900 · 704-377-2536

Lee W. Movius · K&L Gates · Hearst Tower, 47th Floor · 214 North Tryon Street · Charlotte, NC 28202 704-331-7400

Raleigh A. Shoemaker · ⑳ · K&L Gates · Hearst Tower, 47th Floor · 214 North Tryon Street · Charlotte, NC 28202 · 704-331-7400

Mary Turk-Meena · K&L Gates · Hearst Tower, 47th Floor · 214 North Tryon Street · Charlotte, NC 28202 · 704-331-7400

Greensboro

Michael R. Abel · ⑩ · Schell Bray Aycock Abel & Livingston · http://www.sbaal.com · Renaissance Plaza, Suite 1500 · 230 North Elm Street · Greensboro, NC 27401 · 336-370-8800

Raleigh

Craig B. Wheaton · ⑩ · Kilpatrick Stockton · 3737 Glenwood Avenue, Suite 400 · Raleigh, NC 27612-5515 · 919-420-1700

Winston-Salem

Michael D. Gunter · ⑩ · Womble Carlyle Sandridge & Rice · One West Fourth Street · Winston-Salem, NC 27101 · 336-721-3600

William R. Whitehurst · Womble Carlyle Sandridge & Rice · One West Fourth Street · Winston-Salem, NC 27101 · 336-721-3600

ENERGY LAW

Charlotte

W. Edward Poe, Jr. · Parker Poe Adams & Bernstein · http://www.parkerpoe.com · Three Wachovia Center, Suite 3000 · 401 South Tryon Street · Charlotte, NC 28202-1935 · 704-372-9000

Raleigh

Wade H. Hargrove · ⑩ · Brooks, Pierce, McLendon, Humphrey & Leonard · http://www.brookspierce.com · 1600 Wachovia Capitol Center · 150 Fayetteville Street · Raleigh, NC 27601 · 919-839-0300

M. Keith Kapp · Williams Mullen · http://www.williamsmullen.com · Highwoods Tower One, Suite 500 · 3200 Beechleaf Court · P.O. Drawer 19764 · Raleigh, NC 27619-9764 · 919-981-4000

Robert W. Kaylor · Robert W. Kaylor · 225 Hillsborough Street, Suite 480 · Raleigh, NC 27603 · 919-828-5250

M. Gray Styers, Jr. · Blanchard, Miller, Lewis & Styers · http://www.bjmls-law.com · 1117 Hillsborough Street · Raleigh, NC 27603 · 919-755-3993

ENTERTAINMENT LAW

Charlotte

Stokely G. Caldwell, Jr. · Robinson, Bradshaw & Hinson · http://www.rbh.com · 101 North Tryon Street, Suite 1900 · Charlotte, NC 28246-1900 · 704-377-2536

Raleigh

Richard Noel Gusler · The Law Offices of Richard Noel Gusler · http://www.gusler.com · 107 Glenwood Avenue · Raleigh, NC 27602 · 919-582-2150

ENVIRONMENTAL LAW

Asheville

William Clarke · ⑩ · Roberts & Stevens · BB&T Building, Suite 1100 · One West Pack Square · P.O. Box 7647 · Asheville, NC 28802 · 828-252-6600

Charlotte

Bradford A. De Vore · Womble Carlyle Sandridge & Rice · One Wachovia Center, Suite 3500 · 301 South College Street · Charlotte, NC 28202-6037 · 704-331-4900

David A. Franchina · K&L Gates · Hearst Tower, 47th Floor · 214 North Tryon Street · Charlotte, NC 28202 · 704-331-7400

Thomas N. Griffin III · Parker Poe Adams & Bernstein · http://www.parkerpoe.com · Three Wachovia Center, Suite 3000 · 401 South Tryon Street · Charlotte, NC 28202-1935 · 704-372-9000

Benne C. Hutson · ⑩ · McGuireWoods · http://www.mcguirewoods.com · 201 North Tryon Street, Suite 3000 · P.O. Box 31247 · Charlotte, NC 28231 · 704-343-2000

Max E. Justice · ⑩ · Parker Poe Adams & Bernstein · http://www.parkerpoe.com · Three Wachovia Center, Suite 3000 · 401 South Tryon Street · Charlotte, NC 28202-1935 · 704-372-9000

T. Richard Kane · Poyner & Spruill · http://www.poynerspruill.com · One Wachovia Center, Suite 2300 · 301 South College Street · Charlotte, NC 28202-6021 · 704-342-5250

Richard E. Morton · Womble Carlyle Sandridge & Rice · One Wachovia Center, Suite 3500 · 301 South College Street · Charlotte, NC 28202-6037 · 704-331-4900

William W. Toole · Robinson, Bradshaw & Hinson · http://www.rbh.com · 101 North Tryon Street, Suite 1900 · Charlotte, NC 28246-1900 · 704-377-2536

Carolyn A. Jones Van Buren · Van Buren Law · 5950 Fairview Road, Suite 600 · Charlotte, NC 28210 · 704-556-2285

Edenton

Lars P. Simonsen · Simonsen Law Firm · http://www.simonsenlawfirm.com · 106 East Queen Street · P. O. Box 848 · Edenton, NC 27932 · 252-482-2175

Greensboro

Harold N. Bynum · ⓴ · Smith Moore Leatherwood · http://www.smithmoorelaw.com · 300 North Greene Street, Suite 1400 · P.O. Box 21927 · Greensboro, NC 27420-1927 · 336-378-5200

Stephen W. Earp · ⑩ · Smith Moore Leatherwood · http://www.smithmoorelaw.com · 300 North Greene Street, Suite 1400 · P.O. Box 21927 · Greensboro, NC 27420-1927 · 336-378-5200

George W. House · ⓴ · Brooks, Pierce, McLendon, Humphrey & Leonard · http://www.brookspierce.com · 2000 Renaissance Plaza · 230 North Elm Street · Greensboro, NC 27401 · 336-373-8850

V. Randall Tinsley · Brooks, Pierce, McLendon, Humphrey & Leonard · http://www.brookspierce.com · 2000 Renaissance Plaza · 230 North Elm Street · Greensboro, NC 27401 · 336-373-8850

Greenville

James F. Hopf · Hopf & Higley · 1694 East Arlington Boulevard, Suite E · Greenville, NC 27858 · 252-756-1883

New Bern

Frank H. Sheffield, Jr. · ⑩ · Ward and Smith · http://www.wardandsmith.com · 1001 College Court · P.O. Box 867 · New Bern, NC 28563-0867 · 252-672-5400

I. Clark Wright, Jr. · ⑩ · Davis Hartman Wright · 209 Pollock Street · New Bern, NC 28560 · 252-514-2828

Raleigh

Stanford D. Baird · K&L Gates · 4350 Lassiter at North Hills Avenue, Suite 300 · Raleigh, NC 27609 · 919-743-7300

Craig A. Bromby · ⑩ · Hunton & Williams · One Bank Of America Plaza, Suite 1400 · 421 Fayetteville Street · P.O. Box 109 · Raleigh, NC 27602 · 919-899-3000

John J. Butler · Parker Poe Adams & Bernstein · http://www.parkerpoe.com · Wachovia Capitol Center, Suite 1400 · 150 Fayetteville Street · Raleigh, NC 27601 · 919-828-0564

Charles S. Carter · Troutman Sanders · Two Hannover Square, Suite 1900 · 434 Fayetteville Street · P.O. Box 1389 · Raleigh, NC 27602-1389 · 919-835-4100

Charles D. Case · ⓴ · Hunton & Williams · One Bank Of America Plaza, Suite 1400 · 421 Fayetteville Street · P.O. Box 109 · Raleigh, NC 27602 · 919-899-3000

Amos C. Dawson III · ⓴ · Williams Mullen · http://www.williamsmullen.com · Highwoods Tower One, Suite 500 · 3200 Beechleaf Court · P.O. Drawer 19764 · Raleigh, NC 27619-9764 · 919-981-4000

H. Glenn Dunn · ⑳ · Poyner & Spruill · http://www.poynerspruill.com · 3600 Glenwood Avenue · P.O. Box 10096 · Raleigh, NC 27605-0096 · 919-783-6400

Keith H. Johnson · Poyner & Spruill · http://www.poynerspruill.com · 3600 Glenwood Avenue · P.O. Box 10096 · Raleigh, NC 27605-0096 · 919-783-6400

William F. Lane · Kilpatrick Stockton · 3737 Glenwood Avenue, Suite 400 · Raleigh, NC 27612-5515 · 919-420-1700

Steven J. Levitas · Kilpatrick Stockton · 3737 Glenwood Avenue, Suite 400 · Raleigh, NC 27612-5515 · 919-420-1700

Alan H. McConnell · Kilpatrick Stockton · 3737 Glenwood Avenue, Suite 400 · Raleigh, NC 27612-5515 · 919-420-1700

Kurt J. Olson · Kurt J. Olson · 3737 Glenwood Avenue, Suite 100 · Raleigh, NC 27607-3146 · 919-573-6172

Stephen T. Parascandola · Smith, Anderson, Blount, Dorsett, Mitchell & Jernigan · http://www.smithlaw.com · 2500 Wachovia Capitol Center · P.O. Box 2611 · Raleigh, NC 27602-2611 · 919-821-1220

Timothy P. Sullivan · Poyner & Spruill · http://www.poynerspruill.com · 3600 Glenwood Avenue · P.O. Box 10096 · Raleigh, NC 27605-0096 · 919-783-6400

Wilmington

William A. Raney, Jr. · ⑩ · Wessel & Raney · 107-B North Second Street · P.O. Box 1049 · Wilmington, NC 28402 · 910-762-7475

Winston-Salem

Stephen R. Berlin · Kilpatrick Stockton · 1001 West Fourth Street · Winston-Salem, NC 27101-2400 · 336-607-7300

Stanley B. Green · Womble Carlyle Sandridge & Rice · One West Fourth Street · Winston-Salem, NC 27101 · 336-721-3600

Lori Privette Hinnant · Womble Carlyle Sandridge & Rice · One West Fourth Street · Winston-Salem, NC 27101 · 336-721-3600

EQUIPMENT FINANCE LAW

Charlotte

Robert V. Baker · Moore & Van Allen · Bank of America Corporate Center, Suite 4700 · 100 North Tryon Street · Charlotte, NC 28202-4003 · 704-331-1000

Robert I. Kenny · Moore & Van Allen · Bank of America Corporate Center, Suite 4700 · 100 North Tryon Street · Charlotte, NC 28202-4003 · 704-331-1000

Greensboro

Kenneth M. Greene · ⑩ · Carruthers & Roth · http://www.crlaw.com · 235 North Edgeworth Street · P.O. Box 540 · Greensboro, NC 27402 · 336-379-8651

Morrisville

Joseph D. Joyner, Jr. · Moore & Van Allen · 430 Davis Drive, Suite 500 · P.O. Box 13706 · Morrisville, NC 27709 · 919-286-8000

FAMILY LAW

Asheville

Michael W. Drye · Law Offices of Michael W. Drye · 510 Swannanoa River Road · Asheville, NC 28801 · 828-298-1484

Howard L. Gum · ⑩ · Gum, Hillier and McCroskey · http://www.gumandhillier.com · 47 North Market Street · P.O. Box 3235 · Asheville, NC 28802 · 828-258-3368

Patrick McCroskey · Gum, Hillier and McCroskey · http://www.gumandhillier.com · 47 North Market Street · P.O. Box 3235 · Asheville, NC 28802 · 828-258-3368

William B. Parker · Long, Parker, Warren & Anderson · 14 South Pack Square, Suite 600 · P.O. Box 7216 Asheville, NC 28802 · 828-258-2296

Robert E. Riddle · ㉕ · Robert E. Riddle · 10 North Dogwood Road · Asheville, NC 28804 · 828-253-1723

Burlington

J. Wade Harrison · Wishart, Norris, Henninger & Pittman · 3120 South Church Street · P.O. Box 1998 · Burlington, NC 27216-1998 · 336-584-3388

Wiley P. Wooten · Vernon Law · 522 South Lexington Avenue · P.O. Drawer 2958 · Burlington, NC 27216-2958 · 336-227-8851

Charlotte

L. Stanley Brown · Hamilton Moon Stephens Steele & Martin · 201 South College Street, Suite 2020 · Charlotte, NC 28244-2020 · 704-344-1117

Thomas R. Cannon · ⑩ · Horack, Talley, Pharr & Lowndes · http://www.horacktalley.com · 2600 One Wachovia Center · 301 South College Street · Charlotte, NC 28202 · 704-377-2500

Nelson M. Casstevens, Jr. · ⑩ · Casstevens, Hanner, Gunter, Riopel & Wofford · 602 East Morehead Street · P.O. Box 34607 · Charlotte, NC 28234 · 704-372-2140

William K. Diehl, Jr. · ⑳ · James, McElroy & Diehl · 600 South College Street, Suite 3000 · Charlotte, NC 28202 · 704-372-9870

Dorian H. Gunter · Casstevens, Hanner, Gunter, Riopel & Wofford · 602 East Morehead Street · P.O. Box 34607 · Charlotte, NC 28234 · 704-372-2140

Fred A. Hicks · ⑩ · Katten Muchin Rosenman · 401 South Tryon Street, Suite 2600 · Charlotte, NC 28202-1935 · 704-444-2000

Elizabeth T. Hodges · Horack, Talley, Pharr & Lowndes · http://www.horacktalley.com · 2600 One Wachovia Center · 301 South College Street · Charlotte, NC 28202 · 704-377-2500

Katie S. Holliday · James, McElroy & Diehl · 600 South College Street, Suite 3000 · Charlotte, NC 28202 · 704-372-9870

Gena G. Morris · Horack, Talley, Pharr & Lowndes · http://www.horacktalley.com · 2600 One Wachovia Center · 301 South College Street · Charlotte, NC 28202 · 704-377-2500

Richard D. Stephens · 20 · Dozier, Miller, Pollard & Murphy · Cameron-Brown Building, Suite 700 · 301 South McDowell Street · Charlotte, NC 28204 · 704-372-6373

Tate K. Sterrett · Horack, Talley, Pharr & Lowndes · http://www.horacktalley.com · 2600 One Wachovia Center · 301 South College Street · Charlotte, NC 28202 · 704-377-2500

Durham

N. Joanne Foil · Foil Law Offices · 112 East Main Street · Durham, NC 27701 · 919-688-9631

James B. Maxwell · 20 · Maxwell, Freeman & Bowman · 2741 University Drive · P.O. Box 52396 · Durham, NC 27717-2396 · 919-493-6464

Fayetteville

Renny W. Deese · Reid, Lewis, Deese, Nance & Person · 330 Dick Street · P.O. Drawer 1358 · Fayetteville, NC 28302 · 910-323-3500

Goldsboro

Shelby D. Benton · Hollowell & Benton · 130 South John Street · Goldsboro, NC 27533 · 919-736-3076

S. Reed Warren · S. Reed Warren · 660 North Spence Avenue · Goldsboro, NC 27534 · 919-778-3877

Greensboro

Trudy A. Ennis · 10 · Nexsen Pruet · http://www.nexsenpruet.com · 701 Green Valley Road, Suite 100 · Greensboro, NC 27408 · 336-373-1600

Marilyn Feuchs-Marker · Smith Moore Leatherwood · http://www.smithmoorelaw.com · 300 North Greene Street, Suite 1400 · P.O. Box 21927 · Greensboro, NC 27420-1927 · 336-378-5200

William Welch Jordan · 10 · Hill, Evans, Jordan & Beatty · 1400 Renaissance Plaza · 230 North Elm Street · P.O. Box 989 · Greensboro, NC 27402 · 336-379-1390

Barbara R. Morgenstern · 10 · Morgenstern & Bonuomo · 419 North Edgeworth Street · Greensboro, NC 27401 · 336-379-5006

Carolyn J. Woodruff · Woodruff Law Firm · http://www.woodrufflawfirm.com · 420 West Market Street · Greensboro, NC 27401 · 336-272-9122

Greenville

Dallas Clark, Jr. · Colombo, Kitchin, Dunn, Ball & Porter · 1698 East Arlington Boulevard · Greenville, NC 27858 · 252-321-2020

High Point

A. Doyle Early, Jr. · 10 · Wyatt, Early, Harris, Wheeler · 1912 East Chester Drive, Suite 400 · P.O. Drawer 2086 · High Point, NC 27261-2086 · 336-884-4444

Jacksonville

Lana S. Warlick · 20 · Law Office of Lana S. Warlick · 410 New Bridge Street, Suite 1-A · P.O. Box 1393 · Jacksonville, NC 28541-1393 · 910-347-4400

Morrisville

William O. King · ⑩ · Moore & Van Allen · 430 Davis Drive, Suite 500 · P.O. Box 13706 · Morrisville, NC 27709 · 919-286-8000

New Bern

J. Randal Hunter · Law Office of J. Randal Hunter · 310 George Street · P.O. Box 567 · New Bern, NC 28563 · 252-638-3222

Charles William Kafer · ⑩ · Charles William Kafer · 209 Pollock Street · P.O. Box 947 · New Bern, NC 28563 · 252-636-3788

Raleigh

John Maclachlan Boxley · ⑳ · Boxley, Bolton, Garber & Haywood · The Nash Square Building · 227 West Martin Street · P.O. Drawer 1429 · Raleigh, NC 27602 · 919-832-3915

Kimberly Bryan · Cheshire, Parker, Schneider, Bryan & Vitale · http://www.cheshirepark.com · 133 Fayetteville Street, Suite 500 · P.O. Box 1029 · Raleigh, NC 27602-1029 · 919-833-3114

Lynn P. Burleson · ⑩ · Tharrington Smith · http://www.tharringtonsmith.com · 209 Fayetteville Street · P.O. Box 1151 · Raleigh, NC 27602-1151 · 919-821-4711

Charles W. Clanton · Wyrick Robbins Yates & Ponton · http://www.wyrick.com · The Summit, Suite 300 4101 Lake Boone Trail · P.O. Drawer 17803 · Raleigh, NC 27607-7506 · 919-781-4000

Carole S. Gailor · Gailor, Wallis & Hunt · http://www.gailorwallishunt.com · The 1903 Building, Suite 201 · 1101 Haynes Street · Raleigh, NC 27604 · 919-832-8488

Jaye P. Meyer · Tharrington Smith · http://www.tharringtonsmith.com · 209 Fayetteville Street · P.O. Box 1151 · Raleigh, NC 27602-1151 · 919-821-4711

Fred Morelock · Tharrington Smith · http://www.tharringtonsmith.com · 209 Fayetteville Street · P.O. Box 1151 · Raleigh, NC 27602-1151 · 919-821-4711

John W. Narron · Smith Debnam Narron Wyche Saintsing & Myers · The Landmark Center, Suite 400 · 4601 Six Forks Road · P.O. Drawer 26268 · Raleigh, NC 27611-6268 · 919-250-2000

John Hill Parker · ⑳ · Cheshire, Parker, Schneider, Bryan & Vitale · http://www.cheshirepark.com · 133 Fayetteville Street, Suite 500 · P.O. Box 1029 · Raleigh, NC 27602-1029 · 919-833-3114

Robert A. Ponton, Jr. · Wyrick Robbins Yates & Ponton · http://www.wyrick.com · The Summit, Suite 300 · 4101 Lake Boone Trail · P.O. Drawer 17803 · Raleigh, NC 27607-7506 · 919-781-4000

Carlyn G. Poole · ⑩ · Tharrington Smith · http://www.tharringtonsmith.com · 209 Fayetteville Street · P.O. Box 1151 · Raleigh, NC 27602-1151 · 919-821-4711

Michael F. Schilawski · Wake Family Law Group · 4350 Lassiter at North Hills Avenue, Suite 360 · Raleigh, NC 27609 · 919-787-4040

Marc W. Sokol · Wake Family Law Group · 4350 Lassiter at North Hills Avenue, Suite 360 · Raleigh, NC 27609 · 919-787-4040

Rose H. Stout · Smith Debnam Narron Wyche Saintsing & Myers · The Landmark Center, Suite 400 · 4601 Six Forks Road · P.O. Drawer 26268 · Raleigh, NC 27611-6268 · 919-250-2000

Lorion M. Vitale · Cheshire, Parker, Schneider, Bryan & Vitale · http://www.cheshirepark.com · 133 Fayetteville Street, Suite 500 · P.O. Box 1029 · Raleigh, NC 27602-1029 · 919-833-3114

Rocky Mount

Katherine Wiggins Fisher · Battle, Winslow, Scott & Wiley · 2343 Professional Drive · P.O. Box 7100 · Rocky Mount, NC 27804-0100 · 252-937-2200

Smithfield

Marcia H. Armstrong · ⑩ · Armstrong & Armstrong · 602 South Third Street · P.O. Box 27 · Smithfield, NC 27577 · 919-934-1575

Stephen C. Woodard, Jr. · ⑩ · Daughtry, Woodard, Lawrence & Starling · 405 East Market Street · P.O. Drawer 1960 · Smithfield, NC 27577-1960 · 919-934-5012

Wilmington

James W. Lea III · Lea Rhine & Associates · 314 Walnut Street, Suites 1000 & 2000 · Wilmington, NC 28403 · 910-772-9960

Carlton S. Prickett, Jr. · ⑩ · Carlton S. Prickett, Jr. · Seven South Fifth Street · Wilmington, NC 28401 · 910-762-1845

Wilson

Thomas R. Sallenger · Sallenger & Brown · 701 West Nash Street · Wilson, NC 27893 · 252-243-7800

Winston-Salem

Jimmy H. Barnhill · ⑩ · Womble Carlyle Sandridge & Rice · One West Fourth Street · Winston-Salem, NC 27101 · 336-721-3600

Loretta C. Biggs · Davis & Harwell · 380 Knollwood Street, Suite 720 · Winston-Salem, NC 27103 · 336-722-1534

Fred G. Crumpler, Jr. · ㉕ · Crumpler Freedman Parker & Witt · 301 North Main Street, Suite 1100 · Winston-Salem, NC 27101 · 336-725-1304

Joslin Davis · ⑩ · Davis & Harwell · 380 Knollwood Street, Suite 720 · Winston-Salem, NC 27103 · 336-722-1534

C. Ray Grantham, Jr. · Robinson & Lawing · http://www.robinson-lawing.com · 101 North Cherry Street, Suite 720 · Winston-Salem, NC 27101 · 336-631-8500

Jon B. Kurtz · Tash & Kurtz · http://www.tashkurtzlaw.com · 3305 Healy Drive · P.O. Box 25744 · Winston-Salem, NC 27114-5744 · 336-768-1515

John F. Morrow · ⑩ · Morrow Alexander · 3890 Vest Mill Road · P.O. Box 25226 · Winston-Salem, NC 27114-5226 · 336-760-1400

G. Edgar Parker · Crumpler Freedman Parker & Witt · 301 North Main Street, Suite 1100 · Winston-Salem, NC 27101 · 336-725-1304

David C. Pishko · Elliot Pishko Morgan · 426 Old Salem Road · Winston-Salem, NC 27101 · 336-724-2828

Robin J. Stinson · Bell, Davis & Pitt · http://www.belldavispitt.com · Century Plaza, Suite 600 · 100 North Cherry Street · P.O. Box 21029 · Winston-Salem, NC 27120 · 336-722-3700

Gary B. Tash · ⑩ · Tash & Kurtz · http://www.tashkurtzlaw.com · 3305 Healy Drive · P.O. Box 25744 · Winston-Salem, NC 27114-5744 · 336-768-1515

FAMILY LAW MEDIATION

Asheville

Michael W. Drye · Law Offices of Michael W. Drye · 510 Swannanoa River Road · Asheville, NC 28801 · 828-298-1484

Morrisville

William O. King · ⑩ · Moore & Van Allen · 430 Davis Drive, Suite 500 · P.O. Box 13706 · Morrisville, NC 27709 · 919-286-8000

FIRST AMENDMENT LAW

Cary

Richard W. Ellis · ⑩ · Ellis & Winters · http://www.elliswinters.com · 1100 Crescent Green, Suite 200 · Cary, NC 27518 · 919-865-7000

Charlotte

E. Osborne Ayscue, Jr. · ⑳ · McGuireWoods · http://www.mcguirewoods.com · 201 North Tryon Street, Suite 3000 · P.O. Box 31247 · Charlotte, NC 28231 · 704-343-2000

Jonathan E. Buchan · ⑩ · McGuireWoods · http://www.mcguirewoods.com · 201 North Tryon Street, Suite 3000 · P.O. Box 31247 · Charlotte, NC 28231 · 704-343-2000

John W. Gresham · ⑩ · Ferguson Stein Chambers Gresham & Sumter · 741 Kenilworth Avenue, Suite 300 · Charlotte, NC 28204 · 704-375-8461

John H. Hasty · ⑩ · Guthrie, Davis, Henderson & Staton · 719 East Boulevard · Charlotte, NC 28203 · 704-372-5600

Greensboro

Alan W. Duncan · ⑩ · Smith Moore Leatherwood · http://www.smithmoorelaw.com · 300 North Greene Street, Suite 1400 · P.O. Box 21927 · Greensboro, NC 27420-1927 · 336-378-5200

Norman B. Smith · ㉕ · Smith, James, Rowlett & Cohen · 101 South Elm Street, Suite 310 · P.O. Box 990 Greensboro, NC 27402 · 336-274-2992

Allison O. Van Laningham · Smith Moore Leatherwood · http://www.smithmoorelaw.com · 300 North Greene Street, Suite 1400 · P.O. Box 21927 · Greensboro, NC 27420-1927 · 336-378-5200

Raleigh

John A. Bussian III · The Bussian Law Firm · Wachovia Capitol Center, 16th Floor · 150 Fayetteville Street · Raleigh, NC 27601 · 919-829-4900

Wade H. Hargrove · ⑩ · Brooks, Pierce, McLendon, Humphrey & Leonard · http://www.brookspierce.com · 1600 Wachovia Capitol Center · 150 Fayetteville Street · Raleigh, NC 27601 · 919-839-0300

C. Amanda Martin · Everett, Gaskins, Hancock & Stevens · The Professional Building, Suite 600 · 127 West Hargett Street · P.O. Box 911 · Raleigh, NC 27602-0911 · 919-755-0025

Mark J. Prak · ⑩ · Brooks, Pierce, McLendon, Humphrey & Leonard · http://www.brookspierce.com · 1600 Wachovia Capitol Center · 150 Fayetteville Street · Raleigh, NC 27601 · 919-839-0300

Hugh Stevens · ⑩ · Everett, Gaskins, Hancock & Stevens · The Professional Building, Suite 600 · 127 West Hargett Street · P.O. Box 911 · Raleigh, NC 27602-0911 · 919-755-0025

Marcus W. Trathen · Brooks, Pierce, McLendon, Humphrey & Leonard · http://www.brookspierce.com · 1600 Wachovia Capitol Center · 150 Fayetteville Street · Raleigh, NC 27601 · 919-839-0300

Winston-Salem

W. Andrew Copenhaver · ⑩ · Womble Carlyle Sandridge & Rice · One West Fourth Street · Winston-Salem, NC 27101 · 336-721-3600

GOVERNMENT RELATIONS LAW

Charlotte

Jefferson W. Brown · King & Spalding · 227 West Trade Street, Suite 600 · Charlotte, NC 28202 · 704-503-2600

Bailey Patrick, Jr. · ⑳ · K&L Gates · Hearst Tower, 47th Floor · 214 North Tryon Street · Charlotte, NC 28202 · 704-331-7400

Raleigh

John T. Bode · Bode, Call & Stroupe · 3105 Glenwood Avenue, Suite 300 · P.O. Box 6338 · Raleigh, NC 27628-6338 · 919-881-0338

B. Davis Horne, Jr. · Smith, Anderson, Blount, Dorsett, Mitchell & Jernigan · http://www.smithlaw.com · 2500 Wachovia Capitol Center · P.O. Box 2611 · Raleigh, NC 27602-2611 · 919-821-1220

John B. McMillan · Manning, Fulton & Skinner · http://www.manningfulton.com · 3605 Glenwood Avenue, Suite 500 · P.O. Box 20389 · Raleigh, NC 27619-0389 · 919-787-8880

Alexander P. Sands III · Womble Carlyle Sandridge & Rice · 150 Fayetteville Street, Suite 2100 · P.O. Box 831 · Raleigh, NC 27601-0831 · 919-755-2100

William G. Scoggin · K&L Gates · 4350 Lassiter at North Hills Avenue, Suite 300 · Raleigh, NC 27609 · 919-743-7300

Dana E. Simpson · Smith, Anderson, Blount, Dorsett, Mitchell & Jernigan · http://www.smithlaw.com · 2500 Wachovia Capitol Center · P.O. Box 2611 · Raleigh, NC 27602-2611 · 919-821-1220

George M. Teague · Nelson Mullins Riley & Scarborough · GlenLake One, Suite 200 · 4140 Parklake Avenue · P.O. Box 30519 · Raleigh, NC 27622-0519 · 919-877-3800

R. Bruce Thompson II · Parker Poe Adams & Bernstein · http://www.parkerpoe.com · Wachovia Capitol Center, Suite 1400 · 150 Fayetteville Street · Raleigh, NC 27601 · 919-828-0564

HEALTH CARE LAW

Charlotte

James W. Allison · Johnston, Allison & Hord · 1065 East Morehead Street · P.O. Box 36469 · Charlotte, NC 28236 · 704-332-1181

Everett J. Bowman · Robinson, Bradshaw & Hinson · http://www.rbh.com · 101 North Tryon Street, Suite 1900 · Charlotte, NC 28246-1900 · 704-377-2536

Karen A. Gledhill · Robinson, Bradshaw & Hinson · http://www.rbh.com · 101 North Tryon Street, Suite 1900 · Charlotte, NC 28246-1900 · 704-377-2536

Joy M. Hord · Parker Poe Adams & Bernstein · http://www.parkerpoe.com · Three Wachovia Center, Suite 3000 · 401 South Tryon Street · Charlotte, NC 28202-1935 · 704-372-9000

Mark J. Horoschak · Womble Carlyle Sandridge & Rice · One Wachovia Center, Suite 3500 · 301 South College Street · Charlotte, NC 28202-6037 · 704-331-4900

Raboteau T. Wilder, Jr. · Womble Carlyle Sandridge & Rice · One Wachovia Center, Suite 3500 · 301 South College Street · Charlotte, NC 28202-6037 · 704-331-4900

Greensboro

Thomas E. Cone · Ott Cone & Redpath · 1501 Highwoods Boulevard, Suite 101 · P.O. Box 160 · Greensboro, NC 27402 · 336-373-1300

Terrill Johnson Harris · Smith Moore Leatherwood · http://www.smithmoorelaw.com · 300 North Greene Street, Suite 1400 · P.O. Box 21927 · Greensboro, NC 27420-1927 · 336-378-5200

Maureen Demarest Murray · ⑩ · Smith Moore Leatherwood · http://www.smithmoorelaw.com · 300 North Greene Street, Suite 1400 · P.O. Box 21927 · Greensboro, NC 27420-1927 · 336-378-5200

Wendell H. Ott · ⑩ · Ott Cone & Redpath · 1501 Highwoods Boulevard, Suite 101 · P.O. Box 160 · Greensboro, NC 27402 · 336-373-1300

Randolph A. Redpath · ⑩ · Ott Cone & Redpath · 1501 Highwoods Boulevard, Suite 101 · P.O. Box 160 · Greensboro, NC 27402 · 336-373-1300

Thomas S. Stukes · ⑩ · Womble Carlyle Sandridge & Rice · 300 North Greene Street, Suite 1900 · Greensboro, NC 27401 · 336-574-8030

Raleigh

Barry D. Alexander · Nelson Mullins Riley & Scarborough · GlenLake One, Suite 200 · 4140 Parklake Avenue · P.O. Box 30519 · Raleigh, NC 27622-0519 · 919-877-3800

Julian D. Bobbitt, Jr. · ⑩ · Smith, Anderson, Blount, Dorsett, Mitchell & Jernigan · http://www.smithlaw.com · 2500 Wachovia Capitol Center · P.O. Box 2611 · Raleigh, NC 27602-2611 · 919-821-1220

Kenneth L. Burgess · Poyner & Spruill · http://www.poynerspruill.com · 3600 Glenwood Avenue · P.O. Box 10096 · Raleigh, NC 27605-0096 · 919-783-6400

John L. Crill · Parker Poe Adams & Bernstein · http://www.parkerpoe.com · Wachovia Capitol Center, Suite 1400 · 150 Fayetteville Street · Raleigh, NC 27601 · 919-828-0564

Wallace C. Chuck Hollowell III · Nelson Mullins Riley & Scarborough · GlenLake One, Suite 200 · 4140 Parklake Avenue · P.O. Box 30519 · Raleigh, NC 27622-0519 · 919-877-3800

Noah H. Huffstetler III · ⑩ · Nelson Mullins Riley & Scarborough · GlenLake One, Suite 200 · 4140 Parklake Avenue · P.O. Box 30519 · Raleigh, NC 27622-0519 · 919-877-3800

Patricia A. Markus · Smith Moore Leatherwood · http://www.smithmoorelaw.com · Two Hannover Square, Suite 2800 · P.O. Box 27525 · Raleigh, NC 27611 · 919-755-8700

Renee J. Montgomery · Parker Poe Adams & Bernstein · http://www.parkerpoe.com · Wachovia Capitol Center, Suite 1400 · 150 Fayetteville Street · Raleigh, NC 27601 · 919-828-0564

William R. Shenton · Poyner & Spruill · http://www.poynerspruill.com · 3600 Glenwood Avenue · P.O. Box 10096 · Raleigh, NC 27605-0096 · 919-783-6400

Samuel O. Southern · Smith Moore Leatherwood · http://www.smithmoorelaw.com · Two Hannover Square, Suite 2800 · P.O. Box 27525 · Raleigh, NC 27611 · 919-755-8700

Sean A. Timmons · Smith, Anderson, Blount, Dorsett, Mitchell & Jernigan · http://www.smithlaw.com · 2500 Wachovia Capitol Center · P.O. Box 2611 · Raleigh, NC 27602-2611 · 919-821-1220

Robert L. Wilson, Jr. · ⑩ · Smith Moore Leatherwood · http://www.smithmoorelaw.com · Two Hannover Square, Suite 2800 · P.O. Box 27525 · Raleigh, NC 27611 · 919-755-8700

Research Triangle Park

Arlene J. Diosegy · Williams Mullen · http://www.williamsmullen.com · 4721 Emperor Boulevard, Suite 400 · P.O. Box 12109 · Research Triangle Park, NC 27709-2109 · 919-361-4900

Mary Beth Johnston · ⑩ · K&L Gates · P.O. Box 14210 · Research Triangle Park, NC 27709 · 919-466-1190

Patricia T. Meador · ⑩ · K&L Gates · P.O. Box 14210 · Research Triangle Park, NC 27709 · 919-466-1190

Gary S. Qualls · K&L Gates · P.O. Box 14210 · Research Triangle Park, NC 27709 · 919-466-1190

Wilmington

Michael Murchison · Murchison, Taylor & Gibson · 16 North Fifth Avenue · Wilmington, NC 28401 · 910-763-2426

Winston-Salem

Anthony H. Brett · ⑩ · Womble Carlyle Sandridge & Rice · One West Fourth Street · Winston-Salem, NC 27101 · 336-721-3600

Peter S. Brunstetter · Womble Carlyle Sandridge & Rice · One West Fourth Street · Winston-Salem, NC 27101 · 336-721-3600

Denise M. Gunter · Nelson Mullins Riley & Scarborough · The Knollwood, Suite 530 · 380 Knollwood Street · Winston-Salem, NC 27103 · 336-774-3300

Richard B. Howington · ⑩ · Nelson Mullins Riley & Scarborough · The Knollwood, Suite 530 · 380 Knollwood Street · Winston-Salem, NC 27103 · 336-774-3300

Greg L. Smith · ⑩ · Womble Carlyle Sandridge & Rice · One West Fourth Street · Winston-Salem, NC 27101 · 336-721-3600

James D. Wall · Wall Esleeck Babcock · http://www.webllp.com · 1076 West Fourth Street, Suite 100 · Winston-Salem, NC 27101 · 336-722-6300

IMMIGRATION LAW

Charlotte

Cynthia A. Aziz · Aziz Law Firm · 1804 East Boulevard · Charlotte, NC 28203 · 704-347-1808

Elizabeth R. Edwards · Aziz Law Firm · 1804 East Boulevard · Charlotte, NC 28203 · 704-347-1808

Steven H. Garfinkel · Garfinkel Immigration Law Firm · http://www.garfinkelimmigration.com · 6230 Fairview Road, Suite 105 · Charlotte, NC 28210 · 704-442-8000

Alan S. Gordon · ⑩ · Alan Gordon Immigration Law · http://www.greencards.com · 1018 East Boulevard, Suite Seven · Charlotte, NC 28203 · 704-332-2555

Howard L. Kushner · ⑩ · Kushner & Kushner · 6739 Fairview Road, Second Floor · Charlotte, NC 28210 · 704-362-1106

Felicia A. Washington · K&L Gates · Hearst Tower, 47th Floor · 214 North Tryon Street · Charlotte, NC 28202 · 704-331-7400

Greensboro

Laura Deddish Burton · Smith Moore Leatherwood · http://www.smithmoorelaw.com · 300 North Greene Street, Suite 1400 · P.O. Box 21927 · Greensboro, NC 27420-1927 · 336-378-5200

Gerard M. Chapman · Chapman Law Firm · 403 North Elm Street, Suite A · Greensboro, NC 27401 · 336-334-0034

Jeremy L. McKinney · McKinney & Justice · 910 North Elm Street · Greensboro, NC 27401 · 336-275-5885

Jamestown

David J. Long · Long, Chang & Associates · 4915 Piedmont Parkway, Suite 103 · Jamestown, NC 27282 · 336-855-5700

Raleigh

Murali Bashyam · Bashyam Spiro & Edgerton · The Summit Building, Suite 200 · 4101 Lake Boone Trail Raleigh, NC 27607 · 919-833-0840

C. Lynn Calder · ⑩ · Allen & Pinnix · 333 Fayetteville Street, Suite 1200 · P.O. Drawer 1270 · Raleigh, NC 27602-1270 · 919-755-0505

Laura Edgerton · Bashyam Spiro & Edgerton · The Summit Building, Suite 200 · 4101 Lake Boone Trail Raleigh, NC 27607 · 919-833-0840

John L. Pinnix · ⑩ · Allen & Pinnix · 333 Fayetteville Street, Suite 1200 · P.O. Drawer 1270 · Raleigh, NC 27602-1270 · 919-755-0505

Todd M. Rubin · Parker Poe Adams & Bernstein · http://www.parkerpoe.com · Wachovia Capitol Center, Suite 1400 · 150 Fayetteville Street · Raleigh, NC 27601 · 919-828-0564

Winston-Salem

Penni P. Bradshaw · Constangy, Brooks & Smith · http://www.constangy.com · 100 North Cherry Street, Suite 300 · Winston-Salem, NC 27101-4016 · 336-721-1001

Charlotte

Josephine H. Hicks · Parker Poe Adams & Bernstein · http://www.parkerpoe.com · Three Wachovia Center, Suite 3000 · 401 South Tryon Street · Charlotte, NC 28202-1935 · 704-372-9000

L. D. Simmons II · McGuireWoods · http://www.mcguirewoods.com · 201 North Tryon Street, Suite 3000 P.O. Box 31247 · Charlotte, NC 28231 · 704-343-2000

Harold C. Spears · Caudle & Spears · Interstate Tower, Suite 2600 · 121 West Trade Street · Charlotte, NC 28202 · 704-377-1200

Greensboro

David L. Brown · Pinto Coates Kyre & Brown · 3203 Brassfield Road · P.O. Box 4848 · Greensboro, NC 27404 · 336-282-8848

Paul D. Coates · Pinto Coates Kyre & Brown · 3203 Brassfield Road · P.O. Box 4848 · Greensboro, NC 27404 · 336-282-8848

Richard L. Pinto · Pinto Coates Kyre & Brown · 3203 Brassfield Road · P.O. Box 4848 · Greensboro, NC 27404 · 336-282-8848

Raleigh

Walter E. Brock, Jr. · Young, Moore & Henderson · 3101 Glenwood Avenue · P.O. Box 31627 · Raleigh, NC 27622-1627 · 919-782-6860

R. Scott Brown · Brown, Crump, Vanore & Tierney · 421 Fayetteville Street, Suite 1203 · P.O. Box 1729 · Raleigh, NC 27602 · 919-835-0909

Susan K. Burkhart · Cranfill, Sumner & Hartzog · http://www.cshlaw.com · 5420 Wade Park Boulevard · P.O. Box 27808 · Raleigh, NC 27611-7808 · 919-828-5100

David S. Coats · Bailey & Dixon · 2500 Two Hannover Square · P.O. Box 1351 · Raleigh, NC 27602-1351 919-828-0731

Garth A. Gersten · Womble Carlyle Sandridge & Rice · 150 Fayetteville Street, Suite 2100 · P.O. Box 831 Raleigh, NC 27601-0831 · 919-755-2100

Theodore B. Smyth · Smyth & Cioffi · 3221 Blue Ridge Road, Suite 101 · Raleigh, NC 27612 · 919-782-2000

Barbara B. Weyher · Yates, McLamb & Weyher · One Bank of America Plaza, Suite 1200 · 421 Fayetteville Street · P.O. Box 2889 · Raleigh, NC 27602-2889 · 919-835-0900

Winston-Salem

Reid C. Adams, Jr. · Womble Carlyle Sandridge & Rice · One West Fourth Street · Winston-Salem, NC 27101 · 336-721-3600

Richard V. Bennett · ⑩ · Bennett & Guthrie · 1560 Westbrook Plaza Drive · Winston-Salem, NC 27103-1328 · 336-765-3121

Susan H. Boyles · Kilpatrick Stockton · 1001 West Fourth Street · Winston-Salem, NC 27101-2400 · 336-607-7300

James H. Kelly, Jr. · ⑩ · Kilpatrick Stockton · 1001 West Fourth Street · Winston-Salem, NC 27101-2400 · 336-607-7300

Richard T. Rice · Womble Carlyle Sandridge & Rice · One West Fourth Street · Winston-Salem, NC 27101 · 336-721-3600

INTELLECTUAL PROPERTY LAW

Charlotte

Albert P. Allan · Summa, Allan & Additon · Ballantyne Coporate Park, Suite 200 · 11610 North Community House Road · Charlotte, NC 28277-2199 · 704-945-6700

William M. Atkinson · Alston + Bird · http://www.alston.com · Bank of America Plaza, Suite 4000 · 101 South Tryon Street · Charlotte, NC 28280-4000 · 704-444-1000

John J. Barnhardt III · Summa, Allan & Additon · Ballantyne Coporate Park, Suite 200 · 11610 North Community House Road · Charlotte, NC 28277-2199 · 704-945-6700

Michael S. Connor · Alston + Bird · http://www.alston.com · Bank of America Plaza, Suite 4000 · 101 South Tryon Street · Charlotte, NC 28280-4000 · 704-444-1000

Jason P. Cooper · Alston + Bird · http://www.alston.com · Bank of America Plaza, Suite 4000 · 101 South Tryon Street · Charlotte, NC 28280-4000 · 704-444-1000

Brian M. Davis · Alston + Bird · http://www.alston.com · Bank of America Plaza, Suite 4000 · 101 South Tryon Street · Charlotte, NC 28280-4000 · 704-444-1000

Charles B. Elderkin · Alston + Bird · http://www.alston.com · Bank of America Plaza, Suite 4000 · 101 South Tryon Street · Charlotte, NC 28280-4000 · 704-444-1000

Guy R. Gosnell · Alston + Bird · http://www.alston.com · Bank of America Plaza, Suite 4000 · 101 South Tryon Street · Charlotte, NC 28280-4000 · 704-444-1000

Susan Serad Jackson · K&L Gates · Hearst Tower, 47th Floor · 214 North Tryon Street · Charlotte, NC 28202 · 704-331-7400

Dickson M. Lupo · Moore & Van Allen · Bank of America Corporate Center, Suite 4700 · 100 North Tryon Street · Charlotte, NC 28202-4003 · 704-331-1000

Francis M. Pinckney · ⑩ · K&L Gates · Hearst Tower, 47th Floor · 214 North Tryon Street · Charlotte, NC 28202 · 704-331-7400

Karl S. Sawyer, Jr. · K&L Gates · Hearst Tower, 47th Floor · 214 North Tryon Street · Charlotte, NC 28202 · 704-331-7400

Dalbert U. Shefte · K&L Gates · Hearst Tower, 47th Floor · 214 North Tryon Street · Charlotte, NC 28202 · 704-331-7400

John L. Sullivan, Jr. · Alston + Bird · http://www.alston.com · Bank of America Plaza, Suite 4000 · 101 South Tryon Street · Charlotte, NC 28280-4000 · 704-444-1000

Philip Summa · Summa, Allan & Additon · Ballantyne Coporate Park, Suite 200 · 11610 North Community House Road · Charlotte, NC 28277-2199 · 704-945-6700

Michael A. Tobin · K&L Gates · Hearst Tower, 47th Floor · 214 North Tryon Street · Charlotte, NC 28202 · 704-331-7400

Greensboro

Jack B. Hicks · Womble Carlyle Sandridge & Rice · 300 North Greene Street, Suite 1900 · Greensboro, NC 27401 · 336-574-8030

James A. Medford · Smith Moore Leatherwood · http://www.smithmoorelaw.com · 300 North Greene Street, Suite 1400 · P.O. Box 21927 · Greensboro, NC 27420-1927 · 336-378-5200

C. Robert Rhodes · Womble Carlyle Sandridge & Rice · 300 North Greene Street, Suite 1900 · Greensboro, NC 27401 · 336-574-8030

David W. Sar · Brooks, Pierce, McLendon, Humphrey & Leonard · http://www.brookspierce.com · 2000 Renaissance Plaza · 230 North Elm Street · Greensboro, NC 27401 · 336-373-8850

Morrisville

Allen R. Baum · Brinks Hofer Gilson & Lione · 2801 Slater Road, Suite 120 · Morrisville, NC 27560 · 919-481-1111

Raleigh

Mitchell S. Bigel · Myers Bigel Sibley & Sajovec · 4140 Parklake Avenue, Suite 600 · P.O. Box 37428 · Raleigh, NC 27627 · 919-854-1400

James R. Cannon · Myers Bigel Sibley & Sajovec · 4140 Parklake Avenue, Suite 600 · P.O. Box 37428 · Raleigh, NC 27627 · 919-854-1400

Robert W. Glatz · Myers Bigel Sibley & Sajovec · 4140 Parklake Avenue, Suite 600 · P.O. Box 37428 · Raleigh, NC 27627 · 919-854-1400

Kenneth D. Sibley · Myers Bigel Sibley & Sajovec · 4140 Parklake Avenue, Suite 600 · P.O. Box 37428 · Raleigh, NC 27627 · 919-854-1400

Robert W. Spearman · ⑩ · Parker Poe Adams & Bernstein · http://www.parkerpoe.com · Wachovia Capitol Center, Suite 1400 · 150 Fayetteville Street · Raleigh, NC 27601 · 919-828-0564

W. Murray Spruill, Jr. · Alston + Bird · http://www.alston.com · 3201 Beechleaf Court, Suite 600 · Raleigh, NC 27604-1062 · 919-862-2210

Winston-Salem

Julia C. Archer · Enns & Archer · http://www.ennsandarcher.com · 939 Burke Street · Winston-Salem, NC 27101 · 336-723-5180

Charles W. Calkins · Kilpatrick Stockton · 1001 West Fourth Street · Winston-Salem, NC 27101-2400 · 336-607-7300

Steven Gardner · Kilpatrick Stockton · 1001 West Fourth Street · Winston-Salem, NC 27101-2400 · 336-607-7300

George L. Little, Jr. · ⑩ · Kilpatrick Stockton · 1001 West Fourth Street · Winston-Salem, NC 27101-2400 · 336-607-7300

Michael E. Ray · Womble Carlyle Sandridge & Rice · One West Fourth Street · Winston-Salem, NC 27101 · 336-721-3600

INTERNATIONAL TRADE AND FINANCE LAW

Charlotte

John D. Allison · K&L Gates · Hearst Tower, 47th Floor · 214 North Tryon Street · Charlotte, NC 28202 704-331-7400

Peter C. Buck · Robinson, Bradshaw & Hinson · http://www.rbh.com · 101 North Tryon Street, Suite 1900 · Charlotte, NC 28246-1900 · 704-377-2536

Ernest W. Reigel · Moore & Van Allen · Bank of America Corporate Center, Suite 4700 · 100 North Tryon Street · Charlotte, NC 28202-4003 · 704-331-1000

Russell M. Robinson II · ㉕ · Robinson, Bradshaw & Hinson · http://www.rbh.com · 101 North Tryon Street, Suite 1900 · Charlotte, NC 28246-1900 · 704-377-2536

Greensboro

James A. Medford · Smith Moore Leatherwood · http://www.smithmoorelaw.com · 300 North Greene Street, Suite 1400 · P.O. Box 21927 · Greensboro, NC 27420-1927 · 336-378-5200

New Bern

David L. Ward, Jr. · ㉕ · Ward and Smith · http://www.wardandsmith.com · 1001 College Court · P.O. Box 867 · New Bern, NC 28563-0867 · 252-672-5400

LABOR AND EMPLOYMENT LAW

Beaufort

John B. Meuser · ⑩ · Law Offices of John Meuser · 112-B Straits Road · Beaufort, NC 28516 · 252-728-2570

Charlotte

Mason G. Alexander · Fisher & Phillips · http://www.laborlawyers.com · 227 West Trade Street, Suite 2020 · Charlotte, NC 28202 · 704-334-4565

Louis A. Bledsoe III · Robinson, Bradshaw & Hinson · http://www.rbh.com · 101 North Tryon Street, Suite 1900 · Charlotte, NC 28246-1900 · 704-377-2536

Julius Chambers · Ferguson Stein Chambers Gresham & Sumter · 741 Kenilworth Avenue, Suite 300 · Charlotte, NC 28204 · 704-375-8461

Edward G. Connette III · Essex Richards · 1701 South Boulevard · Charlotte, NC 28203 · 704-377-4300

Jonathan M. Crotty · Parker Poe Adams & Bernstein · http://www.parkerpoe.com · Three Wachovia Center, Suite 3000 · 401 South Tryon Street · Charlotte, NC 28202-1935 · 704-372-9000

C. Margaret Errington · Ferguson Stein Chambers Gresham & Sumter · 741 Kenilworth Avenue, Suite 300 · Charlotte, NC 28204 · 704-375-8461

Julie H. Fosbinder · Law Office of Julie H. Fosbinder · 1307 West Morehead Street, Suite 201 · Charlotte, NC 28209 · 704-333-1428

John W. Gresham · ⑩ · Ferguson Stein Chambers Gresham & Sumter · 741 Kenilworth Avenue, Suite 300 · Charlotte, NC 28204 · 704-375-8461

Ann Groninger · Patterson Harkavy · 521 East Boulevard · Charlotte, NC 28203 · 704-200-2009

Charles E. Johnson · Robinson, Bradshaw & Hinson · http://www.rbh.com · 101 North Tryon Street, Suite 1900 · Charlotte, NC 28246-1900 · 704-377-2536

Richard F. Kane · Moore & Van Allen · Bank of America Corporate Center, Suite 4700 · 100 North Tryon Street · Charlotte, NC 28202-4003 · 704-331-1000

Sarah J. Kromer · Sarah J. Kromer · 6525 Morrison Boulevard, Suite 400 · Charlotte, NC 28211 · 704-688-5040

Louis L. Lesesne, Jr. · ⑩ · Essex Richards · 1701 South Boulevard · Charlotte, NC 28203 · 704-377-4300

Paul M. Navarro · McGuireWoods · http://www.mcguirewoods.com · 201 North Tryon Street, Suite 3000 P.O. Box 31247 · Charlotte, NC 28231 · 704-343-2000

Richard L. Rainey · Womble Carlyle Sandridge & Rice · One Wachovia Center, Suite 3500 · 301 South College Street · Charlotte, NC 28202-6037 · 704-331-4900

Russell F. Sizemore · K&L Gates · Hearst Tower, 47th Floor · 214 North Tryon Street · Charlotte, NC 28202 · 704-331-7400

James B. Spears, Jr. · ⑩ · Ogletree Deakins · http://www.ogletreedeakins.com · 201 South College Street, Suite 2300 · Charlotte, NC 28244 · 704-342-2588

William H. Sturges · Shumaker, Loop & Kendrick · First Citizen's Bank Building, Suite 1800 · 128 South Tryon Street · Charlotte, NC 28202-1675 · 704-375-0057

Geraldine Sumter · Ferguson Stein Chambers Gresham & Sumter · 741 Kenilworth Avenue, Suite 300 · Charlotte, NC 28204 · 704-375-8461

Philip M. Van Hoy · ⑩ · Van Hoy, Reutlinger, Adams & Dunn · 737 East Boulevard · Charlotte, NC 28203 · 704-375-6022

Felicia A. Washington · K&L Gates · Hearst Tower, 47th Floor · 214 North Tryon Street · Charlotte, NC 28202 · 704-331-7400

Keith M. Weddington · Parker Poe Adams & Bernstein · http://www.parkerpoe.com · Three Wachovia Center, Suite 3000 · 401 South Tryon Street · Charlotte, NC 28202-1935 · 704-372-9000

John R. Wester · ⑩ · Robinson, Bradshaw & Hinson · http://www.rbh.com · 101 North Tryon Street, Suite 1900 · Charlotte, NC 28246-1900 · 704-377-2536

Stacy K. Wood · Parker Poe Adams & Bernstein · http://www.parkerpoe.com · Three Wachovia Center, Suite 3000 · 401 South Tryon Street · Charlotte, NC 28202-1935 · 704-372-9000

David C. Wright III · Robinson, Bradshaw & Hinson · http://www.rbh.com · 101 North Tryon Street, Suite 1900 · Charlotte, NC 28246-1900 · 704-377-2536

Julian H. Wright, Jr. · Robinson, Bradshaw & Hinson · http://www.rbh.com · 101 North Tryon Street, Suite 1900 · Charlotte, NC 28246-1900 · 704-377-2536

Durham

Stewart W. Fisher · Glenn, Mills & Fisher · 709 Southbank Building · 400 West Main Street · P.O. Box 3865 · Durham, NC 27702-3865 · 919-683-2135

Greensboro

William P. H. Cary · ⑩ · Brooks, Pierce, McLendon, Humphrey & Leonard · http://www.brookspierce.com · 2000 Renaissance Plaza · 230 North Elm Street · Greensboro, NC 27401 · 336-373-8850

Seth R. Cohen · Smith, James, Rowlett & Cohen · 101 South Elm Street, Suite 310 · P.O. Box 990 · Greensboro, NC 27402 · 336-274-2992

Martin N. Erwin · ⑳ · Smith Moore Leatherwood · http://www.smithmoorelaw.com · 300 North Greene Street, Suite 1400 · P.O. Box 21927 · Greensboro, NC 27420-1927 · 336-378-5200

Jonathan Ross Harkavy · ㉕ · Patterson Harkavy · 101 South Elm Street · P.O. Box 29269 · Greensboro, NC 27429-9269 · 336-370-4200

Nahomi Harkavy · ⑩ · Patterson Harkavy · 101 South Elm Street · P.O. Box 29269 · Greensboro, NC 27429-9269 · 336-370-4200

J. David James · ⑩ · Smith, James, Rowlett & Cohen · 101 South Elm Street, Suite 310 · P.O. Box 990 · Greensboro, NC 27402 · 336-274-2992

Alexander Maultsby · Smith Moore Leatherwood · http://www.smithmoorelaw.com · 300 North Greene Street, Suite 1400 · P.O. Box 21927 · Greensboro, NC 27420-1927 · 336-378-5200

M. Daniel McGinn · ⑩ · Brooks, Pierce, McLendon, Humphrey & Leonard · http://www.brookspierce.com · 2000 Renaissance Plaza · 230 North Elm Street · Greensboro, NC 27401 · 336-373-8850

James M. Powell · Womble Carlyle Sandridge & Rice · 300 North Greene Street, Suite 1900 · Greensboro, NC 27401 · 336-574-8030

Norman B. Smith · ㉕ · Smith, James, Rowlett & Cohen · 101 South Elm Street, Suite 310 · P.O. Box 990 Greensboro, NC 27402 · 336-274-2992

Julianna C. Theall · ⑩ · Smith Moore Leatherwood · http://www.smithmoorelaw.com · 300 North Greene Street, Suite 1400 · P.O. Box 21927 · Greensboro, NC 27420-1927 · 336-378-5200

Marion

C. Frank Goldsmith, Jr. · Goldsmith, Goldsmith & Dews · 57 South Main Street · P.O. Box 1107 · Marion, NC 28752 · 828-652-3000

Raleigh

Rodolfo R. Agraz · Ogletree Deakins · http://www.ogletreedeakins.com · 2301 Sugar Bush Road, Suite 600 · Raleigh, NC 27612 · 919-787-9700

Randall D. Avram · Kilpatrick Stockton · 3737 Glenwood Avenue, Suite 400 · Raleigh, NC 27612-5515 · 919-420-1700

Albert R. Bell, Jr. · ⑩ · Ward and Smith · http://www.wardandsmith.com · Wade II, Suite 400 · 5430 Wade Park Boulevard · P.O. Box 33009 · Raleigh, NC 27636-3009 · 919-277-9100

John S. Burgin · Ogletree Deakins · http://www.ogletreedeakins.com · 2301 Sugar Bush Road, Suite 600 · Raleigh, NC 27612 · 919-787-9700

Burton Craige · Patterson Harkavy · 414 West Jones Street · P.O. Box 27927 · Raleigh, NC 27603 · 919-755-1812

Gretchen W. Ewalt · Ogletree Deakins · http://www.ogletreedeakins.com · 2301 Sugar Bush Road, Suite 600 · Raleigh, NC 27612 · 919-787-9700

Thomas A. Farr · ⑩ · Ogletree Deakins · http://www.ogletreedeakins.com · 2301 Sugar Bush Road, Suite 600 · Raleigh, NC 27612 · 919-787-9700

Susanna K. Gibbons · Poyner & Spruill · http://www.poynerspruill.com · 3600 Glenwood Avenue · P.O. Box 10096 · Raleigh, NC 27605-0096 · 919-783-6400

Lisa Grafstein · Law Office of Lisa Grafstein · 410 North Boylan Avenue · Raleigh, NC 27603 · 919-256-3796

Cecil W. Harrison · ⑩ · Poyner & Spruill · http://www.poynerspruill.com · 3600 Glenwood Avenue · P.O. Box 10096 · Raleigh, NC 27605-0096 · 919-783-6400

Patricia L. Holland · Cranfill, Sumner & Hartzog · http://www.cshlaw.com · 5420 Wade Park Boulevard · P.O. Box 27808 · Raleigh, NC 27611-7808 · 919-828-5100

C. Matthew Keen · Ogletree Deakins · http://www.ogletreedeakins.com · 2301 Sugar Bush Road, Suite 600 · Raleigh, NC 27612 · 919-787-9700

Kimberly J. Korando · Smith, Anderson, Blount, Dorsett, Mitchell & Jernigan · http://www.smithlaw.com · 2500 Wachovia Capitol Center · P.O. Box 2611 · Raleigh, NC 27602-2611 · 919-821-1220

Michael C. Lord · ⑩ · Williams Mullen · http://www.williamsmullen.com · Highwoods Tower One, Suite 500 · 3200 Beechleaf Court · P.O. Drawer 19764 · Raleigh, NC 27619-9764 · 919-981-4000

Michael G. Okun · ⑳ · Patterson Harkavy · 414 West Jones Street · P.O. Box 27927 · Raleigh, NC 27603 919-755-1812

George J. Oliver · Smith Moore Leatherwood · http://www.smithmoorelaw.com · Two Hannover Square, Suite 2800 · P.O. Box 27525 · Raleigh, NC 27611 · 919-755-8700

M. Travis Payne · Edelstein & Payne · 315 East Jones Street · P.O. Box 28186 · Raleigh, NC 27611-8186 919-828-1456

Bruce A. Petesch · Ogletree Deakins · http://www.ogletreedeakins.com · 2301 Sugar Bush Road, Suite 600 · Raleigh, NC 27612 · 919-787-9700

Kerry A. Shad · Smith, Anderson, Blount, Dorsett, Mitchell & Jernigan · http://www.smithlaw.com · 2500 Wachovia Capitol Center · P.O. Box 2611 · Raleigh, NC 27602-2611 · 919-821-1220

Phillip J. Strach · Ogletree Deakins · http://www.ogletreedeakins.com · 2301 Sugar Bush Road, Suite 600 Raleigh, NC 27612 · 919-787-9700

Mark S. Thomas · Williams Mullen · http://www.williamsmullen.com · Highwoods Tower One, Suite 500 3200 Beechleaf Court · P.O. Drawer 19764 · Raleigh, NC 27619-9764 · 919-981-4000

Frank P. Ward, Jr. · ⑳ · Williams Mullen · http://www.williamsmullen.com · Highwoods Tower One, Suite 500 · 3200 Beechleaf Court · P.O. Drawer 19764 · Raleigh, NC 27619-9764 · 919-981-4000

Wilmington

Michael Murchison · Murchison, Taylor & Gibson · 16 North Fifth Avenue · Wilmington, NC 28401 · 910-763-2426

Penni P. Bradshaw · Constangy, Brooks & Smith · http://www.constangy.com · 100 North Cherry Street, Suite 300 · Winston-Salem, NC 27101-4016 · 336-721-1001

Kenneth P. Carlson, Jr. · Constangy, Brooks & Smith · http://www.constangy.com · 100 North Cherry Street, Suite 300 · Winston-Salem, NC 27101-4016 · 336-721-1001

Terry A. Clark · Constangy, Brooks & Smith · http://www.constangy.com · 100 North Cherry Street, Suite 300 · Winston-Salem, NC 27101-4016 · 336-721-1001

Louis W. Doherty · Kilpatrick Stockton · 1001 West Fourth Street · Winston-Salem, NC 27101-2400 · 336-607-7300

John J. Doyle, Jr. · (20) · Constangy, Brooks & Smith · http://www.constangy.com · 100 North Cherry Street, Suite 300 · Winston-Salem, NC 27101-4016 · 336-721-1001

Charles A. Edwards · Womble Carlyle Sandridge & Rice · One West Fourth Street · Winston-Salem, NC 27101 · 336-721-3600

Robert M. Elliot · (10) · Elliot Pishko Morgan · 426 Old Salem Road · Winston-Salem, NC 27101 · 336-724-2828

W. Randolph Loftis, Jr. · (20) · Constangy, Brooks & Smith · http://www.constangy.com · 100 North Cherry Street, Suite 300 · Winston-Salem, NC 27101-4016 · 336-721-1001

J. Griffin Morgan · (10) · Elliot Pishko Morgan · 426 Old Salem Road · Winston-Salem, NC 27101 · 336-724-2828

James R. Morgan, Jr. · Womble Carlyle Sandridge & Rice · One West Fourth Street · Winston-Salem, NC 27101 · 336-721-3600

David C. Pishko · Elliot Pishko Morgan · 426 Old Salem Road · Winston-Salem, NC 27101 · 336-724-2828

LAND USE & ZONING LAW

Asheville

W. Louis Bissette, Jr. · McGuire, Wood & Bissette · Drhumor Building · 48 Patton Avenue · P.O. Box 3180 · Asheville, NC 28802-3180 · 828-254-8800

Sarah Patterson Brison · Roberts & Stevens · BB&T Building, Suite 1100 · One West Pack Square · P.O. Box 7647 · Asheville, NC 28802 · 828-252-6600

Craig D. Justus · The Van Winkle Law Firm · 11 North Market Street · P.O. Box 7376 · Asheville, NC 28801-7376 · 828-258-2991

Chapel Hill

Michael B. Brough · The Brough Law Firm · 1829 East Franklin Street, Suite 800-A · Chapel Hill, NC 27514 · 919-929-3905

Charlotte

Jefferson W. Brown · King & Spalding · 227 West Trade Street, Suite 600 · Charlotte, NC 28202 · 704-503-2600

John H. Carmichael · K&L Gates · Hearst Tower, 47th Floor · 214 North Tryon Street · Charlotte, NC 28202 · 704-331-7400

Anthony Fox · Parker Poe Adams & Bernstein · http://www.parkerpoe.com · Three Wachovia Center, Suite 3000 · 401 South Tryon Street · Charlotte, NC 28202-1935 · 704-372-9000

Glen B. Hardymon · K&L Gates · Hearst Tower, 47th Floor · 214 North Tryon Street · Charlotte, NC 28202 · 704-331-7400

Robert E. Henderson · Guthrie, Davis, Henderson & Staton · 719 East Boulevard · Charlotte, NC 28203 704-372-5600

Stephen R. McCrae, Jr. · K&L Gates · Hearst Tower, 47th Floor · 214 North Tryon Street · Charlotte, NC 28202 · 704-331-7400

J. Christopher Oates · Moore & Van Allen · Bank of America Corporate Center, Suite 4700 · 100 North Tryon Street · Charlotte, NC 28202-4003 · 704-331-1000

Bailey Patrick, Jr. · ⑳ · K&L Gates · Hearst Tower, 47th Floor · 214 North Tryon Street · Charlotte, NC 28202 · 704-331-7400

William H. Sturges · Shumaker, Loop & Kendrick · First Citizen's Bank Building, Suite 1800 · 128 South Tryon Street · Charlotte, NC 28202-1675 · 704-375-0057

Greensboro

Derek J. Allen · Brooks, Pierce, McLendon, Humphrey & Leonard · http://www.brookspierce.com · 2000 Renaissance Plaza · 230 North Elm Street · Greensboro, NC 27401 · 336-373-8850

Michael S. Fox · Tuggle Duggins & Meschan · http://www.tuggleduggins.com · 100 North Greene Street, Suite 600 · P.O. Box 2888 · Greensboro, NC 27402-2888 · 336-378-1431

Henry H. Isaacson · Isaacson Isaacson & Sheridan · Bank of America Building, Suite 400 · 101 West Friendly Avenue · P.O. Box 1888 · Greensboro, NC 27402 · 336-275-7626

Marc L. Isaacson · Isaacson Isaacson & Sheridan · Bank of America Building, Suite 400 · 101 West Friendly Avenue · P.O. Box 1888 · Greensboro, NC 27402 · 336-275-7626

Charles E. Melvin, Jr. · ⑳ · Smith Moore Leatherwood · http://www.smithmoorelaw.com · 300 North Greene Street, Suite 1400 · P.O. Box 21927 · Greensboro, NC 27420-1927 · 336-378-5200

Thomas E. Terrell, Jr. · Smith Moore Leatherwood · http://www.smithmoorelaw.com · 300 North Greene Street, Suite 1400 · P.O. Box 21927 · Greensboro, NC 27420-1927 · 336-378-5200

Raleigh

Robin Tatum Currin · Poyner & Spruill · http://www.poynerspruill.com · 3600 Glenwood Avenue · P.O. Box 10096 · Raleigh, NC 27605-0096 · 919-783-6400

Clyde Holt III · Smith Moore Leatherwood · http://www.smithmoorelaw.com · Two Hannover Square, Suite 2800 · P.O. Box 27525 · Raleigh, NC 27611 · 919-755-8700

Mack A. Paul IV · K&L Gates · 4350 Lassiter at North Hills Avenue, Suite 300 · Raleigh, NC 27609 · 919-743-7300

Lacy H. Reaves · Smith, Anderson, Blount, Dorsett, Mitchell & Jernigan · http://www.smithlaw.com · 2500 Wachovia Capitol Center · P.O. Box 2611 · Raleigh, NC 27602-2611 · 919-821-1220

M. Gray Styers, Jr. · Blanchard, Miller, Lewis & Styers · http://www.bjmls-law.com · 1117 Hillsborough Street · Raleigh, NC 27603 · 919-755-3993

R. Bruce Thompson II · Parker Poe Adams & Bernstein · http://www.parkerpoe.com · Wachovia Capitol Center, Suite 1400 · 150 Fayetteville Street · Raleigh, NC 27601 · 919-828-0564

Elizabeth C. Trahos · Smith Moore Leatherwood · http://www.smithmoorelaw.com · Two Hannover Square, Suite 2800 · P.O. Box 27525 · Raleigh, NC 27611 · 919-755-8700

Thomas C. Worth · Thomas C. Worth · 127 West Hargett Street, Suite 500 · P. O. Box 1799 · Raleigh, NC 27602 · 919-831-1125

David L. York · Smith Moore Leatherwood · http://www.smithmoorelaw.com · Two Hannover Square, Suite 2800 · P.O. Box 27525 · Raleigh, NC 27611 · 919-755-8700

Research Triangle Park

Eric M. Braun · K&L Gates · P.O. Box 14210 · Research Triangle Park, NC 27709 · 919-466-1190

John E. Markham, Jr. · K&L Gates · P.O. Box 14210 · Research Triangle Park, NC 27709 · 919-466-1190

Wilmington

John C. Wessel III · Wessel & Raney · 107-B North Second Street · P.O. Box 1049 · Wilmington, NC 28402 · 910-762-7475

LEGAL MALPRACTICE LAW

Chapel Hill

Grover C. McCain, Jr. · Grover C. McCain, Jr. · 1414 Raleigh Road, Suite 330 · Chapel Hill, NC 27517 · 919-967-0811

Charlotte

E. Fitzgerald Parnell III · ⑩ · Poyner & Spruill · http://www.poynerspruill.com · One Wachovia Center, Suite 2300 · 301 South College Street · Charlotte, NC 28202-6021 · 704-342-5250

New Bern

Thomas E. Harris · ⑳ · Harris, Creech, Ward & Blackerby · 325 Pollock Street · P.O. Drawer 1168 · New Bern, NC 28563-1168 · 252-638-6666

Raleigh

Gary S. Parsons · Troutman Sanders · Two Hannover Square, Suite 1900 · 434 Fayetteville Street · P.O. Box 1389 · Raleigh, NC 27602-1389 · 919-835-4100

Winston-Salem

David C. Pishko · Elliot Pishko Morgan · 426 Old Salem Road · Winston-Salem, NC 27101 · 336-724-2828

Stephen M. Russell · Bell, Davis & Pitt · http://www.belldavispitt.com · Century Plaza, Suite 600 · 100 North Cherry Street · P.O. Box 21029 · Winston-Salem, NC 27120 · 336-722-3700

LEVERAGED BUYOUTS AND PRIVATE EQUITY LAW

Charlotte

Peter C. Buck · Robinson, Bradshaw & Hinson · http://www.rbh.com · 101 North Tryon Street, Suite 1900 · Charlotte, NC 28246-1900 · 704-377-2536

H. Bryan Ives III · Alston + Bird · http://www.alston.com · Bank of America Plaza, Suite 4000 · 101 South Tryon Street · Charlotte, NC 28280-4000 · 704-444-1000

C. Mark Kelly · Alston + Bird · http://www.alston.com · Bank of America Plaza, Suite 4000 · 101 South Tryon Street · Charlotte, NC 28280-4000 · 704-444-1000

Haynes P. Lea · Robinson, Bradshaw & Hinson · http://www.rbh.com · 101 North Tryon Street, Suite 1900 · Charlotte, NC 28246-1900 · 704-377-2536

Kevin P. Stichter · K&L Gates · Hearst Tower, 47th Floor · 214 North Tryon Street · Charlotte, NC 28202 · 704-331-7400

Greensboro

Wayne E. Tumlin · Tuggle Duggins & Meschan · http://www.tuggleduggins.com · 100 North Greene Street, Suite 600 · P.O. Box 2888 · Greensboro, NC 27402-2888 · 336-378-1431

Raleigh

Curtis C. Brewer IV · K&L Gates · 4350 Lassiter at North Hills Avenue, Suite 300 · Raleigh, NC 27609 · 919-743-7300

Robert B. Womble · K&L Gates · 4350 Lassiter at North Hills Avenue, Suite 300 · Raleigh, NC 27609 · 919-743-7300

Research Triangle Park

Kenneth N. Shelton · Womble Carlyle Sandridge & Rice · 2530 Meridian Parkway, Suite 400 · P.O. Box 13069 · Research Triangle Park, NC 27709-3069 · 919-484-2300

MARITIME LAW

Beaufort

Stevenson L. Weeks · Wheatly, Wheatly, Weeks & Lupton · 710 Cedar Street · P.O. Box 360 · Beaufort, NC 28516 · 252-728-3158

Fletcher

J. Harold Seagle · Law Office of J. Harold Seagle · 311 Bradenton Knoll · Fletcher, NC 28732 · 828-628-2777

Wilmington

Daniel Lee Brawley · ⑩ · Williams Mullen · http://www.williamsmullen.com · 300 North Third Street, Suite 420 · Wilmington, NC 28401 · 910-256-5135

Don T. Evans, Jr. · Clark, Newton, Evans & Bryan · 509 Princess Street · Wilmington, NC 28401 · 910-762-8743

Geoffrey A. Losee · Rountree Losee & Baldwin · 2419 Market Street · P.O. Box 1409 · Wilmington, NC 28403 · 910-763-3404

John Richard Newton · 10 · Clark, Newton, Evans & Bryan · 509 Princess Street · Wilmington, NC 28401 · 910-762-8743

George Rountree III · 10 · Rountree Losee & Baldwin · 2419 Market Street · P.O. Box 1409 · Wilmington, NC 28403 · 910-763-3404

MASS TORT LITIGATION

Charlotte

David Neal Allen · Parker Poe Adams & Bernstein · http://www.parkerpoe.com · Three Wachovia Center, Suite 3000 · 401 South Tryon Street · Charlotte, NC 28202-1935 · 704-372-9000

Douglas W. Ey, Jr. · McGuireWoods · http://www.mcguirewoods.com · 201 North Tryon Street, Suite 3000 · P.O. Box 31247 · Charlotte, NC 28231 · 704-343-2000

Robert R. Marcus · Smith Moore Leatherwood · http://www.smithmoorelaw.com · 525 North Tryon Street, Suite 1400 · Charlotte, NC 28202 · 704-384-2600

Greensboro

Janet Ward Black · Ward Black Law · 208 West Wendover Avenue · Greensboro, NC 27401 · 336-273-3812

J. Donald Cowan, Jr. · 20 · Ellis & Winters · http://www.elliswinters.com · 100 North Greene Street, Suite 102 · Greensboro, NC 27401 · 336-217-4193

Raleigh

Robert E. Fields III · Womble Carlyle Sandridge & Rice · 150 Fayetteville Street, Suite 2100 · P.O. Box 831 · Raleigh, NC 27601-0831 · 919-755-2100

Marilyn R. Forbes · Womble Carlyle Sandridge & Rice · 150 Fayetteville Street, Suite 2100 · P.O. Box 831 · Raleigh, NC 27601-0831 · 919-755-2100

H. Forest Horne, Jr. · Martin & Jones · http://www.martinandjones.com · 410 Glenwood Avenue, Suite 200 · Raleigh, NC 27603 · 919-821-0005

E. Spencer Parris · Martin & Jones · http://www.martinandjones.com · 410 Glenwood Avenue, Suite 200 · Raleigh, NC 27603 · 919-821-0005

Wilmington

Gary K. Shipman · Shipman & Wright · 575 Military Cutoff Road, Suite 106 · Wilmington, NC 28405 · 910-762-1990

Winston-Salem

R. Michael Leonard · Womble Carlyle Sandridge & Rice · One West Fourth Street · Winston-Salem, NC 27101 · 336-721-3600

MEDIA LAW

Raleigh

Wade H. Hargrove · ⑩ · Brooks, Pierce, McLendon, Humphrey & Leonard · http://www.brookspierce.com · 1600 Wachovia Capitol Center · 150 Fayetteville Street · Raleigh, NC 27601 · 919-839-0300

MEDICAL MALPRACTICE LAW

Asheville

Robert B. Long, Jr. · ⑩ · Long, Parker, Warren & Anderson · 14 South Pack Square, Suite 600 · P.O. Box 7216 · Asheville, NC 28802 · 828-258-2296

Isaac N. Northup, Jr. · ⑩ · Northup McConnell & Sizemore · 123 Biltmore Avenue · Asheville, NC 28801 · 828-232-4481

James W. Williams · ⑩ · Roberts & Stevens · BB&T Building, Suite 1100 · One West Pack Square · P.O. Box 7647 · Asheville, NC 28802 · 828-252-6600

Cary

Alex J. Hagan · Ellis & Winters · http://www.elliswinters.com · 1100 Crescent Green, Suite 200 · Cary, NC 27518 · 919-865-7000

Chapel Hill

Adam Stein · ⑩ · Ferguson Stein Chambers Gresham & Sumter · Franklin Suites, Suite Two · 312 West Franklin Street · Chapel Hill, NC 27516 · 919-933-5300

Charlotte

David Neal Allen · Parker Poe Adams & Bernstein · http://www.parkerpoe.com · Three Wachovia Center, Suite 3000 · 401 South Tryon Street · Charlotte, NC 28202-1935 · 704-372-9000

James P. Cooney III · ⑩ · Womble Carlyle Sandridge & Rice · One Wachovia Center, Suite 3500 · 301 South College Street · Charlotte, NC 28202-6037 · 704-331-4900

Harvey L. Cosper, Jr. · ⑩ · Parker Poe Adams & Bernstein · http://www.parkerpoe.com · Three Wachovia Center, Suite 3000 · 401 South Tryon Street · Charlotte, NC 28202-1935 · 704-372-9000

James E. Ferguson II · ㉕ · Ferguson Stein Chambers Gresham & Sumter · 741 Kenilworth Avenue, Suite 300 · Charlotte, NC 28204 · 704-375-8461

John G. Golding · ⑳ · Golding Holden & Pope · 3325 Springbank Lane, Suite 304 · Charlotte, NC 28226 · 704-374-1600

Gary S. Hemric · James, McElroy & Diehl · 600 South College Street, Suite 3000 · Charlotte, NC 28202 · 704-372-9870

Scott M. Stevenson · Shumaker, Loop & Kendrick · First Citizen's Bank Building, Suite 1800 · 128 South Tryon Street · Charlotte, NC 28202-1675 · 704-375-0057

Durham

James B. Maxwell · ⑳ · Maxwell, Freeman & Bowman · 2741 University Drive · P.O. Box 52396 · Durham, NC 27717-2396 · 919-493-6464

Fayetteville

Wade E. Byrd · ⑩ · Law Offices of Wade E. Byrd · 232 Person Street · P.O. Drawer 2797 · Fayetteville, NC 28302-2797 · 910-401-3590

Joe McLeod · ⑳ · The McLeod Law Firm · 1318 Raeford Road, Suite One · P.O. Box 53390 · Fayetteville, NC 28305-3390 · 910-323-1425

Goldsboro

Robert D. Walker, Jr. · ⑩ · Walker, Allen Trial Attorneys · 1407 West Grantham Street · P.O. Box 2047 · Goldsboro, NC 27533-2047 · 919-734-6565

Greensboro

J. Donald Cowan, Jr. · ⑳ · Ellis & Winters · http://www.elliswinters.com · 100 North Greene Street, Suite 102 · Greensboro, NC 27401 · 336-217-4193

Alan W. Duncan · ⑩ · Smith Moore Leatherwood · http://www.smithmoorelaw.com · 300 North Greene Street, Suite 1400 · P.O. Box 21927 · Greensboro, NC 27420-1927 · 336-378-5200

Sally A. Lawing · ⑩ · The Lawing Firm · Battleground Corporate Park, Suite 210 · 3859 Battleground Avenue · Greensboro, NC 27410 · 336-288-0808

Joseph M. Stavola · Sharpless & Stavola · 200 South Elm Street · P.O. Box 22106 · Greensboro, NC 27420 · 336-333-6400

Richard L. Vanore · Carruthers & Roth · http://www.crlaw.com · 235 North Edgeworth Street · P.O. Box 540 · Greensboro, NC 27402 · 336-379-8651

Greenville

A. Charles Ellis · ⑩ · Ward and Smith · http://www.wardandsmith.com · 120 West Fire Tower Road · P.O. Box 8088 · Greenville, NC 27835-8088 · 252-215-4000

Jacksonville

William J. Morgan · William J. Morgan · 127 Chaney Avenue · P.O. Drawer 700 · Jacksonville, NC 28541-0700 · 910-989-1234

John Drew Warlick, Jr. · ⑳ · Law Offices of John Drew Warlick · 313 New Bridge Street · P.O. Drawer 1006 · Jacksonville, NC 28541-1006 · 910-455-7700

Marion

Charles E. Burgin · ⑩ · Dameron, Burgin, Parker, Lorenz & Jackson · 26 West Court Street · P.O. Drawer 1049 · Marion, NC 28752 · 828-652-2441

New Bern

C. David Creech · Harris, Creech, Ward & Blackerby · 325 Pollock Street · P.O. Drawer 1168 · New Bern, NC 28563-1168 · 252-638-6666

Thomas E. Harris · ⑳ · Harris, Creech, Ward & Blackerby · 325 Pollock Street · P.O. Drawer 1168 · New Bern, NC 28563-1168 · 252-638-6666

Raleigh

Mark E. Anderson · McGuireWoods · http://www.mcguirewoods.com · Two Hannover Square, Suite 2600 · P.O. Box 27507 · Raleigh, NC 27601 · 704-343-2000

David H. Batten · Cranfill, Sumner & Hartzog · http://www.cshlaw.com · 5420 Wade Park Boulevard · P.O. Box 27808 · Raleigh, NC 27611-7808 · 919-828-5100

Donald H. Beskind · ⑩ · Twiggs, Beskind, Strickland & Rabenau · Wachovia Capitol Center, Suite 1100 150 Fayetteville Street · Raleigh, NC 27601 · 919-828-4357

James G. Billings · ⑳ · The Law Office of James G. Billings · 3737 Glenwood Avenue, Suite 100 · Raleigh, NC 27612 · 919-573-1890

M. Lee Cheney · Troutman Sanders · Two Hannover Square, Suite 1900 · 434 Fayetteville Street · P.O. Box 1389 · Raleigh, NC 27602-1389 · 919-835-4100

Robert M. Clay · ㉕ · Young, Moore & Henderson · 3101 Glenwood Avenue · P.O. Box 31627 · Raleigh, NC 27622-1627 · 919-782-6860

Burton Craige · Patterson Harkavy · 414 West Jones Street · P.O. Box 27927 · Raleigh, NC 27603 · 919-755-1812

C. Mark Holt · Kirby & Holt · 3201 Glenwood Avenue, Suite 100 · P.O. Box 31665 · Raleigh, NC 27622 · 919-881-2111

John Alan Jones · Martin & Jones · http://www.martinandjones.com · 410 Glenwood Avenue, Suite 200 · Raleigh, NC 27603 · 919-821-0005

David F. Kirby · Kirby & Holt · 3201 Glenwood Avenue, Suite 100 · P.O. Box 31665 · Raleigh, NC 27622 919-881-2111

Elizabeth F. Kuniholm · ⑩ · Kuniholm Law Firm · 1500 Sunday Drive, Suite 208 · P.O. Box 30303 · Raleigh, NC 27622 · 919-854-4454

Timothy P. Lehan · Smith, Anderson, Blount, Dorsett, Mitchell & Jernigan · http://www.smithlaw.com · 2500 Wachovia Capitol Center · P.O. Box 2611 · Raleigh, NC 27602-2611 · 919-821-1220

John D. Madden · Smith, Anderson, Blount, Dorsett, Mitchell & Jernigan · http://www.smithlaw.com · 2500 Wachovia Capitol Center · P.O. Box 2611 · Raleigh, NC 27602-2611 · 919-821-1220

Dan J. McLamb · ⑩ · Yates, McLamb & Weyher · One Bank of America Plaza, Suite 1200 · 421 Fayetteville Street · P.O. Box 2889 · Raleigh, NC 27602-2889 · 919-835-0900

William H. Moss · Smith, Anderson, Blount, Dorsett, Mitchell & Jernigan · http://www.smithlaw.com · 2500 Wachovia Capitol Center · P.O. Box 2611 · Raleigh, NC 27602-2611 · 919-821-1220

Karen Rabenau · Twiggs, Beskind, Strickland & Rabenau · Wachovia Capitol Center, Suite 1100 · 150 Fayetteville Street · Raleigh, NC 27601 · 919-828-4357

Samuel G. Thompson · Smith, Anderson, Blount, Dorsett, Mitchell & Jernigan · http://www.smithlaw.com · 2500 Wachovia Capitol Center · P.O. Box 2611 · Raleigh, NC 27602-2611 · 919-821-1220

David D. Ward · Cranfill, Sumner & Hartzog · http://www.cshlaw.com · 5420 Wade Park Boulevard · P.O. Box 27808 · Raleigh, NC 27611-7808 · 919-828-5100

Wilmington

John D. Martin · Cranfill, Sumner & Hartzog · http://www.cshlaw.com · Culbreth Center, Suite 200 · 1209 Culbreth Drive · Wilmington, NC 28405 · 910-509-9778

Gary K. Shipman · Shipman & Wright · 575 Military Cutoff Road, Suite 106 · Wilmington, NC 28405 · 910-762-1990

Winston-Salem

J. Dennis Bailey · Carruthers & Bailey · 155 Sunnynoll Court, Suite 102 · Winston-Salem, NC 27106 · 336-714-1220

Richard V. Bennett · ⑩ · Bennett & Guthrie · 1560 Westbrook Plaza Drive · Winston-Salem, NC 27103-1328 · 336-765-3121

Clifford Britt · Comerford & Britt · 250 West First Street, Suite 200 · Winston-Salem, NC 27101-4010 · 336-631-8510

Joseph T. Carruthers · ⑩ · Carruthers & Bailey · 155 Sunnynoll Court, Suite 102 · Winston-Salem, NC 27106 · 336-714-1220

Tamura Coffey · Wilson & Coffey · 110 Oakwood Drive, Suite 400 · Winston-Salem, NC 27103 · 336-631-8866

W. Thompson Comerford, Jr. · Comerford & Britt · 250 West First Street, Suite 200 · Winston-Salem, NC 27101-4010 · 336-631-8510

William Kearns Davis · ⑩ · Bell, Davis & Pitt · http://www.belldavispitt.com · Century Plaza, Suite 600 · 100 North Cherry Street · P.O. Box 21029 · Winston-Salem, NC 27120 · 336-722-3700

G. Gray Wilson · ⑩ · Wilson & Coffey · 110 Oakwood Drive, Suite 400 · Winston-Salem, NC 27103 · 336-631-8866

MERGERS & ACQUISITIONS LAW

Charlotte

Peter C. Buck · Robinson, Bradshaw & Hinson · http://www.rbh.com · 101 North Tryon Street, Suite 1900 · Charlotte, NC 28246-1900 · 704-377-2536

Boyd C. Campbell, Jr. · ⑩ · McGuireWoods · http://www.mcguirewoods.com · 201 North Tryon Street, Suite 3000 · P.O. Box 31247 · Charlotte, NC 28231 · 704-343-2000

T. Richard Giovannelli · K&L Gates · Hearst Tower, 47th Floor · 214 North Tryon Street · Charlotte, NC 28202 · 704-331-7400

Robert G. Griffin · Robinson, Bradshaw & Hinson · http://www.rbh.com · 101 North Tryon Street, Suite 1900 · Charlotte, NC 28246-1900 · 704-377-2536

Robin L. Hinson · ⑩ · Robinson, Bradshaw & Hinson · http://www.rbh.com · 101 North Tryon Street, Suite 1900 · Charlotte, NC 28246-1900 · 704-377-2536

Stephen D. Hope · Moore & Van Allen · Bank of America Corporate Center, Suite 4700 · 100 North Tryon Street · Charlotte, NC 28202-4003 · 704-331-1000

H. Bryan Ives III · Alston + Bird · http://www.alston.com · Bank of America Plaza, Suite 4000 · 101 South Tryon Street · Charlotte, NC 28280-4000 · 704-444-1000

Gary C. Ivey · Alston + Bird · http://www.alston.com · Bank of America Plaza, Suite 4000 · 101 South Tryon Street · Charlotte, NC 28280-4000 · 704-444-1000

Sean M. Jones · K&L Gates · Hearst Tower, 47th Floor · 214 North Tryon Street · Charlotte, NC 28202 · 704-331-7400

Stephen M. Lynch · Robinson, Bradshaw & Hinson · http://www.rbh.com · 101 North Tryon Street, Suite 1900 · Charlotte, NC 28246-1900 · 704-377-2536

E. Lynwood Mallard · ⑩ · McGuireWoods · http://www.mcguirewoods.com · 201 North Tryon Street, Suite 3000 · P.O. Box 31247 · Charlotte, NC 28231 · 704-343-2000

Kent J. McCready · Robinson, Bradshaw & Hinson · http://www.rbh.com · 101 North Tryon Street, Suite 1900 · Charlotte, NC 28246-1900 · 704-377-2536

John R. Miller · Robinson, Bradshaw & Hinson · http://www.rbh.com · 101 North Tryon Street, Suite 1900 · Charlotte, NC 28246-1900 · 704-377-2536

Eugene C. Pridgen · K&L Gates · Hearst Tower, 47th Floor · 214 North Tryon Street · Charlotte, NC 28202 · 704-331-7400

J. Norfleet Pruden III · K&L Gates · Hearst Tower, 47th Floor · 214 North Tryon Street · Charlotte, NC 28202 · 704-331-7400

Russell M. Robinson II · ㉕ · Robinson, Bradshaw & Hinson · http://www.rbh.com · 101 North Tryon Street, Suite 1900 · Charlotte, NC 28246-1900 · 704-377-2536

Richard K. Schell · Parker Poe Adams & Bernstein · http://www.parkerpoe.com · Three Wachovia Center, Suite 3000 · 401 South Tryon Street · Charlotte, NC 28202-1935 · 704-372-9000

Roy L. Smart III · Parker Poe Adams & Bernstein · http://www.parkerpoe.com · Three Wachovia Center, Suite 3000 · 401 South Tryon Street · Charlotte, NC 28202-1935 · 704-372-9000

Paul A. Steffens · K&L Gates · Hearst Tower, 47th Floor · 214 North Tryon Street · Charlotte, NC 28202 · 704-331-7400

Edward W. Wellman, Jr. · Parker Poe Adams & Bernstein · http://www.parkerpoe.com · Three Wachovia Center, Suite 3000 · 401 South Tryon Street · Charlotte, NC 28202-1935 · 704-372-9000

Greensboro

Doris R. Bray · ⑳ · Schell Bray Aycock Abel & Livingston · http://www.sbaal.com · Renaissance Plaza, Suite 1500 · 230 North Elm Street · Greensboro, NC 27401 · 336-370-8800

Mark Davidson · Brooks, Pierce, McLendon, Humphrey & Leonard · http://www.brookspierce.com · 2000 Renaissance Plaza · 230 North Elm Street · Greensboro, NC 27401 · 336-373-8850

Randall A. Hanson · Womble Carlyle Sandridge & Rice · 300 North Greene Street, Suite 1900 · Greensboro, NC 27401 · 336-574-8030

Robert A. Singer · Brooks, Pierce, McLendon, Humphrey & Leonard · http://www.brookspierce.com · 2000 Renaissance Plaza · 230 North Elm Street · Greensboro, NC 27401 · 336-373-8850

Wayne E. Tumlin · Tuggle Duggins & Meschan · http://www.tuggleduggins.com · 100 North Greene Street, Suite 600 · P.O. Box 2888 · Greensboro, NC 27402-2888 · 336-378-1431

Raleigh

R. Marks Arnold · Smith, Anderson, Blount, Dorsett, Mitchell & Jernigan · http://www.smithlaw.com · 2500 Wachovia Capitol Center · P.O. Box 2611 · Raleigh, NC 27602-2611 · 919-821-1220

Curtis C. Brewer IV · K&L Gates · 4350 Lassiter at North Hills Avenue, Suite 300 · Raleigh, NC 27609 · 919-743-7300

Martin H. Brinkley · Smith, Anderson, Blount, Dorsett, Mitchell & Jernigan · http://www.smithlaw.com · 2500 Wachovia Capitol Center · P.O. Box 2611 · Raleigh, NC 27602-2611 · 919-821-1220

Christopher B. Capel · Smith, Anderson, Blount, Dorsett, Mitchell & Jernigan · http://www.smithlaw.com · 2500 Wachovia Capitol Center · P.O. Box 2611 · Raleigh, NC 27602-2611 · 919-821-1220

Kent F. Christison · K&L Gates · 4350 Lassiter at North Hills Avenue, Suite 300 · Raleigh, NC 27609 · 919-743-7300

Wade H. Hargrove · (10) · Brooks, Pierce, McLendon, Humphrey & Leonard · http://www.brookspierce.com · 1600 Wachovia Capitol Center · 150 Fayetteville Street · Raleigh, NC 27601 · 919-839-0300

John L. Jernigan · (10) · Smith, Anderson, Blount, Dorsett, Mitchell & Jernigan · http://www.smithlaw.com 2500 Wachovia Capitol Center · P.O. Box 2611 · Raleigh, NC 27602-2611 · 919-821-1220

Byron B. Kirkland · Smith, Anderson, Blount, Dorsett, Mitchell & Jernigan · http://www.smithlaw.com · 2500 Wachovia Capitol Center · P.O. Box 2611 · Raleigh, NC 27602-2611 · 919-821-1220

Gerald F. Roach · Smith, Anderson, Blount, Dorsett, Mitchell & Jernigan · http://www.smithlaw.com · 2500 Wachovia Capitol Center · P.O. Box 2611 · Raleigh, NC 27602-2611 · 919-821-1220

Research Triangle Park

Kenneth G. Carroll · Womble Carlyle Sandridge & Rice · 2530 Meridian Parkway, Suite 400 · P.O. Box 13069 · Research Triangle Park, NC 27709-3069 · 919-484-2300

Winston-Salem

John W. Babcock · Wall Esleeck Babcock · http://www.webllp.com · 1076 West Fourth Street, Suite 100 · Winston-Salem, NC 27101 · 336-722-6300

Michael L. Drye · Womble Carlyle Sandridge & Rice · One West Fourth Street · Winston-Salem, NC 27101 · 336-721-3600

Murray C. Greason, Jr. · (25) · Womble Carlyle Sandridge & Rice · One West Fourth Street · Winston-Salem, NC 27101 · 336-721-3600

Michael D. Gunter · (10) · Womble Carlyle Sandridge & Rice · One West Fourth Street · Winston-Salem, NC 27101 · 336-721-3600

MINING LAW

Greensboro

George W. House · (20) · Brooks, Pierce, McLendon, Humphrey & Leonard · http://www.brookspierce.com · 2000 Renaissance Plaza · 230 North Elm Street · Greensboro, NC 27401 · 336-373-8850

MUNICIPAL LAW

Winston-Salem

Gusti W. Frankel · Womble Carlyle Sandridge & Rice · One West Fourth Street · Winston-Salem, NC 27101 · 336-721-3600

MUTUAL FUNDS LAW

Charlotte

R. Douglas Harmon · Parker Poe Adams & Bernstein · http://www.parkerpoe.com · Three Wachovia Center, Suite 3000 · 401 South Tryon Street · Charlotte, NC 28202-1935 · 704-372-9000

NATURAL RESOURCES LAW

Asheville

William Clarke · ⑩ · Roberts & Stevens · BB&T Building, Suite 1100 · One West Pack Square · P.O. Box 7647 · Asheville, NC 28802 · 828-252-6600

Charlotte

William W. Toole · Robinson, Bradshaw & Hinson · http://www.rbh.com · 101 North Tryon Street, Suite 1900 · Charlotte, NC 28246-1900 · 704-377-2536

Greensboro

George W. House · ⑳ · Brooks, Pierce, McLendon, Humphrey & Leonard · http://www.brookspierce.com · 2000 Renaissance Plaza · 230 North Elm Street · Greensboro, NC 27401 · 336-373-8850

Winston-Salem

R. Michael Leonard · Womble Carlyle Sandridge & Rice · One West Fourth Street · Winston-Salem, NC 27101 · 336-721-3600

NON-PROFIT/CHARITIES LAW

Greensboro

David L. Kyger · Smith Moore Leatherwood · http://www.smithmoorelaw.com · 300 North Greene Street, Suite 1400 · P.O. Box 21927 · Greensboro, NC 27420-1927 · 336-378-5200

Robert B. Lloyd, Jr. · ㉕ · Hunter Higgins · P.O. Box 20570 · Greensboro, NC 27420-0570 · 336-373-5991

Robert W. Saunders · Brooks, Pierce, McLendon, Humphrey & Leonard · http://www.brookspierce.com 2000 Renaissance Plaza · 230 North Elm Street · Greensboro, NC 27401 · 336-373-8850

Winston-Salem

Linwood L. Davis · ㉕ · Womble Carlyle Sandridge & Rice · One West Fourth Street · Winston-Salem, NC 27101 · 336-721-3600

NON-WHITE-COLLAR CRIMINAL DEFENSE

Asheboro

Charles T. Browne · ⑳ · Bell and Browne · 151 North Fayetteville Street · Asheboro, NC 27203 · 336-625-2111

Asheville

Robert B. Long, Jr. · ⑩ · Long, Parker, Warren & Anderson · 14 South Pack Square, Suite 600 · P.O. Box 7216 · Asheville, NC 28802 · 828-258-2296

Chapel Hill

M. Gordon Widenhouse, Jr. · Rudolf Widenhouse & Fialko · http://www.rwf-law.com · 312 West Franklin Street · Chapel Hill, NC 27516 · 919-967-4900

Charlotte

Peter C. Anderson · Anderson Terpening · 409 East Boulevard · Charlotte, NC 28203 · 704-372-7370

James P. Cooney III · ⑩ · Womble Carlyle Sandridge & Rice · One Wachovia Center, Suite 3500 · 301 South College Street · Charlotte, NC 28202-6037 · 704-331-4900

James E. Ferguson II · ㉕ · Ferguson Stein Chambers Gresham & Sumter · 741 Kenilworth Avenue, Suite 300 · Charlotte, NC 28204 · 704-375-8461

Christopher C. Fialko · Rudolf Widenhouse & Fialko · http://www.rwf-law.com · 1800 Camden Road, Suite 105 · Charlotte, NC 28203 · 704-333-9945

Eben T. Rawls III · Rawls, Dickinson & Scheer · 1011 East Morehead Street, Suite 300 · Charlotte, NC 28204 · 704-376-3200

David S. Rudolf · ⑩ · Rudolf Widenhouse & Fialko · http://www.rwf-law.com · 1800 Camden Road, Suite 105 · Charlotte, NC 28203 · 704-333-9945

James F. Wyatt III · ⑩ · Wyatt & Blake · 435 East Morehead Street · Charlotte, NC 28202-2609 · 704-331-0767

Clinton

W. Douglas Parsons · ⑩ · Johnson, Parsons & Hobson · 500 College Street · P.O. Drawer 1049 · Clinton, NC 28329 · 910-592-7066

Durham

William J. Thomas II · Thomas, Ferguson & Mullins · 119 East Main Street · Durham, NC 27701 · 919-682-5648

Fayetteville

H. Gerald Beaver · ⑩ · Beaver, Holt, Sternlicht & Courie · 230 Green Street · P.O. Box 2275 · Fayetteville, NC 28302 · 910-323-4600

Greensboro

Locke T. Clifford · ⑳ · Clifford, Clendenin & O'Hale · 415 West Friendly Avenue · Greensboro, NC 27401 · 336-378-1212

Charles A. Lloyd · ⑩ · Charles A. Lloyd · 301 South Greene Street, Suite 100 · Greensboro, NC 27401 · 336-275-9358

H. Davis North III · ⑩ · Cahoon, Swisher, North, Cooke and Landreth · First Citizen Bank Building, Suite 300 · 100 South Elm Street · P.O. Box 520 · Greensboro, NC 27401 · 336-275-1231

High Point

C. Richard Tate, Jr. · ㉕ · C. Richard Tate, Jr. · 115 West High Avenue · P.O. Box 2726 · High Point, NC 27261 · 336-885-0176

New Bern

Norman B. Kellum, Jr. · ⑩ · Kellum Law Firm · 219 Broad Street · P.O. Box 866 · New Bern, NC 28563 252-633-2550

Pinehurst

James R. Van Camp · ㉕ · Van Camp, Meacham & Newman · Two Regional Circle · P.O. Box 1389 · Pinehurst, NC 28370 · 910-295-2525

Raleigh

R. Daniel Boyce · Boyce & Isley · Lawyers Weekly Building, Suite 100 · 107 Fayetteville Street Mall · P.O. Box 1990 · Raleigh, NC 27602-1990 · 919-833-7373

Joseph B. Cheshire V · ㉕ · Cheshire, Parker, Schneider, Bryan & Vitale · http://www.cheshirepark.com · 133 Fayetteville Street, Suite 500 · P.O. Box 1029 · Raleigh, NC 27602-1029 · 919-833-3114

Russell W. DeMent, Jr. · ㉕ · DeMent, Askew, Gammon & DeMent · 333 Fayetteville Street Mall, Suite 1513 · P.O. Box 711 · Raleigh, NC 27602 · 919-833-5555

David W. Long · ⑳ · Poyner & Spruill · http://www.poynerspruill.com · 3600 Glenwood Avenue · P.O. Box 10096 · Raleigh, NC 27605-0096 · 919-783-6400

Thomas Courtland Manning · ⑩ · Manning & Crouch · http://www.manningandcrouchlaw.com · 727 West Hargett Street, Suite 205 · P.O. Box 350 · Raleigh, NC 27602 · 919-828-5778

Duncan A. McMillan · ⑩ · McMillan, Smith & Plyler · 205 West Martin Street · P.O. Box 150 · Raleigh, NC 27602 · 919-821-5124

Robert L. McMillan, Jr. · ㉕ · McMillan, Smith & Plyler · 205 West Martin Street · P.O. Box 150 · Raleigh, NC 27602 · 919-821-5124

Roger W. Smith, Sr. · ㉕ · Tharrington Smith · http://www.tharringtonsmith.com · 209 Fayetteville Street P.O. Box 1151 · Raleigh, NC 27602-1151 · 919-821-4711

Wade M. Smith · ㉕ · Tharrington Smith · http://www.tharringtonsmith.com · 209 Fayetteville Street · P.O. Box 1151 · Raleigh, NC 27602-1151 · 919-821-4711

Joseph E. Zeszotarski · Poyner & Spruill · http://www.poynerspruill.com · 3600 Glenwood Avenue · P.O. Box 10096 · Raleigh, NC 27605-0096 · 919-783-6400

Smithfield

John P. O'Hale · (10) · Narron, O'Hale & Whittington · 102 South Third Street · P.O. Box 1567 · Smithfield, NC 27577 · 919-934-6021

Southern Pines

Bruce T. Cunningham · Law Office of Bruce T. Cunningham, Jr. · 225 North Bennett Street · Southern Pines, NC 28387 · 910-693-3999

Wilson

Allen G. Thomas · Thomas & Farris · 104 West Nash Street · P.O. Box 2848 · Wilson, NC 27894 · 252-243-3000

Winston-Salem

Charles J. Alexander II · Morrow Alexander · 3890 Vest Mill Road · P.O. Box 25226 · Winston-Salem, NC 27114-5226 · 336-760-1400

Fred G. Crumpler, Jr. · (25) · Crumpler Freedman Parker & Witt · 301 North Main Street, Suite 1100 · Winston-Salem, NC 27101 · 336-725-1304

David B. Freedman · Crumpler Freedman Parker & Witt · 301 North Main Street, Suite 1100 · Winston-Salem, NC 27101 · 336-725-1304

Donald Tisdale · Grace Holton Tisdale & Clifton · 301 North Main Street, Suite 100 · Winston-Salem, NC 27101 · 336-725-9428

PERSONAL INJURY LITIGATION

Asheville

Jones P. Byrd, Sr. · The Van Winkle Law Firm · 11 North Market Street · P.O. Box 7376 · Asheville, NC 28801-7376 · 828-258-2991

George Ward Hendon · Adams, Hendon, Carson, Crow & Saenger · http://www.adamsfirm.com · 72 Patton Avenue · P.O. Box 2714 · Asheville, NC 28802 · 828-252-7381

Robert B. Long, Jr. · (10) · Long, Parker, Warren & Anderson · 14 South Pack Square, Suite 600 · P.O. Box 7216 · Asheville, NC 28802 · 828-258-2296

Larry S. McDevitt · The Van Winkle Law Firm · 11 North Market Street · P.O. Box 7376 · Asheville, NC 28801-7376 · 828-258-2991

Isaac N. Northup, Jr. · (10) · Northup McConnell & Sizemore · 123 Biltmore Avenue · Asheville, NC 28801 · 828-232-4481

Steve R. Warren · Long, Parker, Warren & Anderson · 14 South Pack Square, Suite 600 · P.O. Box 7216 · Asheville, NC 28802 · 828-258-2296

James W. Williams · (10) · Roberts & Stevens · BB&T Building, Suite 1100 · One West Pack Square · P.O. Box 7647 · Asheville, NC 28802 · 828-252-6600

Cary

Alex J. Hagan · Ellis & Winters · http://www.elliswinters.com · 1100 Crescent Green, Suite 200 · Cary, NC 27518 · 919-865-7000

Leslie C. O'Toole · Ellis & Winters · http://www.elliswinters.com · 1100 Crescent Green, Suite 200 · Cary, NC 27518 · 919-865-7000

Chapel Hill

Adam Stein · ⑩ · Ferguson Stein Chambers Gresham & Sumter · Franklin Suites, Suite Two · 312 West Franklin Street · Chapel Hill, NC 27516 · 919-933-5300

Charlotte

David Neal Allen · Parker Poe Adams & Bernstein · http://www.parkerpoe.com · Three Wachovia Center, Suite 3000 · 401 South Tryon Street · Charlotte, NC 28202-1935 · 704-372-9000

Martin L. Brackett, Jr. · ⑩ · Robinson, Bradshaw & Hinson · http://www.rbh.com · 101 North Tryon Street, Suite 1900 · Charlotte, NC 28246-1900 · 704-377-2536

James P. Cooney III · ⑩ · Womble Carlyle Sandridge & Rice · One Wachovia Center, Suite 3500 · 301 South College Street · Charlotte, NC 28202-6037 · 704-331-4900

Harvey L. Cosper, Jr. · ⑩ · Parker Poe Adams & Bernstein · http://www.parkerpoe.com · Three Wachovia Center, Suite 3000 · 401 South Tryon Street · Charlotte, NC 28202-1935 · 704-372-9000

James E. Ferguson II · ㉕ · Ferguson Stein Chambers Gresham & Sumter · 741 Kenilworth Avenue, Suite 300 · Charlotte, NC 28204 · 704-375-8461

John G. Golding · ⑳ · Golding Holden & Pope · 3325 Springbank Lane, Suite 304 · Charlotte, NC 28226 · 704-374-1600

Gary S. Hemric · James, McElroy & Diehl · 600 South College Street, Suite 3000 · Charlotte, NC 28202 · 704-372-9870

C. Byron Holden · Golding Holden & Pope · 3325 Springbank Lane, Suite 304 · Charlotte, NC 28226 · 704-374-1600

Bradley R. Kutrow · McGuireWoods · http://www.mcguirewoods.com · 201 North Tryon Street, Suite 3000 · P.O. Box 31247 · Charlotte, NC 28231 · 704-343-2000

Raymond E. Owens, Jr. · ⑩ · K&L Gates · Hearst Tower, 47th Floor · 214 North Tryon Street · Charlotte, NC 28202 · 704-331-7400

William Benjamin Smith · Price, Smith, Hargett, Petho & Anderson · 1430 Elizabeth Avenue · Charlotte, NC 28204 · 704-372-2160

Scott M. Stevenson · Shumaker, Loop & Kendrick · First Citizen's Bank Building, Suite 1800 · 128 South Tryon Street · Charlotte, NC 28202-1675 · 704-375-0057

Davidson

James C. Fuller · ⑳ · The McIntosh Law Firm · The Historic Davidson Cotton Mill, Suite 203 · 209 Delburg Street · P.O. Box 2270 · Davidson, NC 28036-2270 · 704-892-1699

Durham

Guy W. Crabtree · Pulley, Watson, King & Lischer · Brightleaf Square, Suite 21-F · 905 West Main Street · P.O. Drawer 3600 · Durham, NC 27702 · 919-682-9691

James B. Maxwell · ⑳ · Maxwell, Freeman & Bowman · 2741 University Drive · P.O. Box 52396 · Durham, NC 27717-2396 · 919-493-6464

William S. Mills · Glenn, Mills & Fisher · 709 Southbank Building · 400 West Main Street · P.O. Box 3865 · Durham, NC 27702-3865 · 919-683-2135

Richard N. Watson · Pulley, Watson, King & Lischer · Brightleaf Square, Suite 21-F · 905 West Main Street · P.O. Drawer 3600 · Durham, NC 27702 · 919-682-9691

Elizabeth City

L. P. Hornthal, Jr. · Hornthal, Riley, Ellis & Maland · 301 East Main Street · P.O. Box 220 · Elizabeth City, NC 27907 · 252-335-0871

Fayetteville

Wade E. Byrd · ⑩ · Law Offices of Wade E. Byrd · 232 Person Street · P.O. Drawer 2797 · Fayetteville, NC 28302-2797 · 910-401-3590

Joe McLeod · ⑳ · The McLeod Law Firm · 1318 Raeford Road, Suite One · P.O. Box 53390 · Fayetteville, NC 28305-3390 · 910-323-1425

Mark A. Sternlicht · Beaver, Holt, Sternlicht & Courie · 230 Green Street · P.O. Box 2275 · Fayetteville, NC 28302 · 910-323-4600

Goldsboro

Robert D. Walker, Jr. · ⑩ · Walker, Allen Trial Attorneys · 1407 West Grantham Street · P.O. Box 2047 · Goldsboro, NC 27533-2047 · 919-734-6565

Greensboro

Jonathan A. Berkelhammer · Smith Moore Leatherwood · http://www.smithmoorelaw.com · 300 North Greene Street, Suite 1400 · P.O. Box 21927 · Greensboro, NC 27420-1927 · 336-378-5200

Janet Ward Black · Ward Black Law · 208 West Wendover Avenue · Greensboro, NC 27401 · 336-273-3812

Andrew S. Chamberlin · Ellis & Winters · http://www.elliswinters.com · 100 North Greene Street, Suite 102 · Greensboro, NC 27401 · 336-217-4193

Stephen W. Coles · ⑩ · Nexsen Pruet · http://www.nexsenpruet.com · 701 Green Valley Road, Suite 100 · Greensboro, NC 27408 · 336-373-1600

J. Donald Cowan, Jr. · ⑳ · Ellis & Winters · http://www.elliswinters.com · 100 North Greene Street, Suite 102 · Greensboro, NC 27401 · 336-217-4193

Alan W. Duncan · ⑩ · Smith Moore Leatherwood · http://www.smithmoorelaw.com · 300 North Greene Street, Suite 1400 · P.O. Box 21927 · Greensboro, NC 27420-1927 · 336-378-5200

William F. Horsley · ⑩ · Law Offices of William F. Horsley · http://www.horsleylawfirm.com · 500-D State Street · Greensboro, NC 27405 · 336-691-0077

Sally A. Lawing · ⑩ · The Lawing Firm · Battleground Corporate Park, Suite 210 · 3859 Battleground Avenue · Greensboro, NC 27410 · 336-288-0808

D. Clark Smith, Jr. · ⑩ · Smith Moore Leatherwood · http://www.smithmoorelaw.com · 300 North Greene Street, Suite 1400 · P.O. Box 21927 · Greensboro, NC 27420-1927 · 336-378-5200

Allison O. Van Laningham · Smith Moore Leatherwood · http://www.smithmoorelaw.com · 300 North Greene Street, Suite 1400 · P.O. Box 21927 · Greensboro, NC 27420-1927 · 336-378-5200

Richard L. Vanore · Carruthers & Roth · http://www.crlaw.com · 235 North Edgeworth Street · P.O. Box 540 · Greensboro, NC 27402 · 336-379-8651

Greenville

A. Charles Ellis · ⑩ · Ward and Smith · http://www.wardandsmith.com · 120 West Fire Tower Road · P.O. Box 8088 · Greenville, NC 27835-8088 · 252-215-4000

John M. Martin · ⑩ · Ward and Smith · http://www.wardandsmith.com · 120 West Fire Tower Road · P.O. Box 8088 · Greenville, NC 27835-8088 · 252-215-4000

High Point

Arch K. Schoch IV · ㉕ · Schoch and Schoch · 500 East Green Drive · P.O. Box 1893 · High Point, NC 27261 · 336-884-4151

Jacksonville

William J. Morgan · William J. Morgan · 127 Chaney Avenue · P.O. Drawer 700 · Jacksonville, NC 28541-0700 · 910-989-1234

John Drew Warlick, Jr. · ⑳ · Law Offices of John Drew Warlick · 313 New Bridge Street · P.O. Drawer 1006 · Jacksonville, NC 28541-1006 · 910-455-7700

Marion

Charles E. Burgin · ⑩ · Dameron, Burgin, Parker, Lorenz & Jackson · 26 West Court Street · P.O. Drawer 1049 · Marion, NC 28752 · 828-652-2441

New Bern

Thomas E. Harris · ⑳ · Harris, Creech, Ward & Blackerby · 325 Pollock Street · P.O. Drawer 1168 · New Bern, NC 28563-1168 · 252-638-6666

Gary J. Rickner · ⑩ · Ward and Smith · http://www.wardandsmith.com · 1001 College Court · P.O. Box 867 · New Bern, NC 28563-0867 · 252-672-5400

Raleigh

Douglas B. Abrams · Abrams and Abrams · http://www.abramslawfirm.com · 2021 Fairview Road · P.O. Box 6509 · Raleigh, NC 27628 · 919-755-9166

Mark E. Anderson · McGuireWoods · http://www.mcguirewoods.com · Two Hannover Square, Suite 2600 · P.O. Box 27507 · Raleigh, NC 27601 · 704-343-2000

David H. Batten · Cranfill, Sumner & Hartzog · http://www.cshlaw.com · 5420 Wade Park Boulevard · P.O. Box 27808 · Raleigh, NC 27611-7808 · 919-828-5100

Charles L. Becton · ⑩ · Becton, Slifkin & Bell · 4000 Westchase Boulevard, Suite 500 · Raleigh, NC 27607 · 919-755-1068

Asa L. Bell, Jr. · Becton, Slifkin & Bell · 4000 Westchase Boulevard, Suite 500 · Raleigh, NC 27607 · 919-755-1068

Donald H. Beskind · ⑩ · Twiggs, Beskind, Strickland & Rabenau · Wachovia Capitol Center, Suite 1100 150 Fayetteville Street · Raleigh, NC 27601 · 919-828-4357

James G. Billings · ⑳ · The Law Office of James G. Billings · 3737 Glenwood Avenue, Suite 100 · Raleigh, NC 27612 · 919-573-1890

Robert M. Clay · ㉕ · Young, Moore & Henderson · 3101 Glenwood Avenue · P.O. Box 31627 · Raleigh, NC 27622-1627 · 919-782-6860

Burton Craige · Patterson Harkavy · 414 West Jones Street · P.O. Box 27927 · Raleigh, NC 27603 · 919-755-1812

Ronald C. Dilthey · ⑳ · Patterson, Dilthey, Clay & Bryson · 4020 Westchase Boulevard, Suite 550 · Raleigh, NC 27607 · 919-821-4020

Dan M. Hartzog · Cranfill, Sumner & Hartzog · http://www.cshlaw.com · 5420 Wade Park Boulevard · P.O. Box 27808 · Raleigh, NC 27611-7808 · 919-828-5100

C. Mark Holt · Kirby & Holt · 3201 Glenwood Avenue, Suite 100 · P.O. Box 31665 · Raleigh, NC 27622 · 919-881-2111

Patricia P. Kerner · Troutman Sanders · Two Hannover Square, Suite 1900 · 434 Fayetteville Street · P.O. Box 1389 · Raleigh, NC 27602-1389 · 919-835-4100

David F. Kirby · Kirby & Holt · 3201 Glenwood Avenue, Suite 100 · P.O. Box 31665 · Raleigh, NC 27622 919-881-2111

Elizabeth F. Kuniholm · ⑩ · Kuniholm Law Firm · 1500 Sunday Drive, Suite 208 · P.O. Box 30303 · Raleigh, NC 27622 · 919-854-4454

Timothy P. Lehan · Smith, Anderson, Blount, Dorsett, Mitchell & Jernigan · http://www.smithlaw.com · 2500 Wachovia Capitol Center · P.O. Box 2611 · Raleigh, NC 27602-2611 · 919-821-1220

Dan J. McLamb · ⑩ · Yates, McLamb & Weyher · One Bank of America Plaza, Suite 1200 · 421 Fayetteville Street · P.O. Box 2889 · Raleigh, NC 27602-2889 · 919-835-0900

Joseph C. Moore III · Allen & Moore · 3700 Computer Drive, Suite 320 · Raleigh, NC 27609-6505 · 919-783-8023

Gary S. Parsons · Troutman Sanders · Two Hannover Square, Suite 1900 · 434 Fayetteville Street · P.O. Box 1389 · Raleigh, NC 27602-1389 · 919-835-4100

Lacy M. Presnell III · Burns, Day & Presnell · 2626 Glenwood Avenue, Suite 560 · P.O. Box 10867 · Raleigh, NC 27605 · 919-782-1441

Karen Rabenau · Twiggs, Beskind, Strickland & Rabenau · Wachovia Capitol Center, Suite 1100 · 150 Fayetteville Street · Raleigh, NC 27601 · 919-828-4357

James A. Roberts III · Lewis & Roberts · 3700 Glenwood Avenue, Suite 410 · P.O. Box 17529 · Raleigh, NC 27619-7529 · 919-981-0191

Anne R. Slifkin · ⑩ · Becton, Slifkin & Bell · 4000 Westchase Boulevard, Suite 500 · Raleigh, NC 27607 · 919-755-1068

Theodore B. Smyth · Smyth & Cioffi · 3221 Blue Ridge Road, Suite 101 · Raleigh, NC 27612 · 919-782-2000

Donald R. Strickland · Twiggs, Beskind, Strickland & Rabenau · Wachovia Capitol Center, Suite 1100 · 150 Fayetteville Street · Raleigh, NC 27601 · 919-828-4357

Robert W. Sumner · Cranfill, Sumner & Hartzog · http://www.cshlaw.com · 5420 Wade Park Boulevard · P.O. Box 27808 · Raleigh, NC 27611-7808 · 919-828-5100

Hoyt G. Tessener · Martin & Jones · http://www.martinandjones.com · 410 Glenwood Avenue, Suite 200 · Raleigh, NC 27603 · 919-821-0005

Samuel G. Thompson · Smith, Anderson, Blount, Dorsett, Mitchell & Jernigan · http://www.smithlaw.com · 2500 Wachovia Capitol Center · P.O. Box 2611 · Raleigh, NC 27602-2611 · 919-821-1220

Sanford Thompson IV · Sanford W. Thompson · http://www.sthompsonlaw.com · 4800 Six Forks Road, Suite 100 · Raleigh, NC 27609 · 919-784-9007

Jerome Paul Trehy, Jr. · Twiggs, Beskind, Strickland & Rabenau · Wachovia Capitol Center, Suite 1100 150 Fayetteville Street · Raleigh, NC 27601 · 919-828-4357

Howard F. Twiggs · ⑳ · Twiggs, Beskind, Strickland & Rabenau · Wachovia Capitol Center, Suite 1100 · 150 Fayetteville Street · Raleigh, NC 27601 · 919-828-4357

David D. Ward · Cranfill, Sumner & Hartzog · http://www.cshlaw.com · 5420 Wade Park Boulevard · P.O. Box 27808 · Raleigh, NC 27611-7808 · 919-828-5100

Rocky Mount

Marshall Aubrey Gallop, Jr. · Battle, Winslow, Scott & Wiley · 2343 Professional Drive · P.O. Box 7100 · Rocky Mount, NC 27804-0100 · 252-937-2200

Wilmington

Daniel Lee Brawley · ⑩ · Williams Mullen · http://www.williamsmullen.com · 300 North Third Street, Suite 420 · Wilmington, NC 28401 · 910-256-5135

John D. Martin · Cranfill, Sumner & Hartzog · http://www.cshlaw.com · Culbreth Center, Suite 200 · 1209 Culbreth Drive · Wilmington, NC 28405 · 910-509-9778

Gary K. Shipman · Shipman & Wright · 575 Military Cutoff Road, Suite 106 · Wilmington, NC 28405 · 910-762-1990

Lonnie B. Williams, Sr. · ⑳ · Marshall, Williams & Gorham · 14 South Fifth Street · P.O. Box 2088 · Wilmington, NC 28402-2088 · 910-763-9891

Winston-Salem

Reid C. Adams, Jr. · Womble Carlyle Sandridge & Rice · One West Fourth Street · Winston-Salem, NC 27101 · 336-721-3600

J. Dennis Bailey · Carruthers & Bailey · 155 Sunnynoll Court, Suite 102 · Winston-Salem, NC 27106 · 336-714-1220

H. Grady Barnhill, Jr. · ㉕ · Womble Carlyle Sandridge & Rice · One West Fourth Street · Winston-Salem, NC 27101 · 336-721-3600

Richard V. Bennett · ⑩ · Bennett & Guthrie · 1560 Westbrook Plaza Drive · Winston-Salem, NC 27103-1328 · 336-765-3121

Susan H. Boyles · Kilpatrick Stockton · 1001 West Fourth Street · Winston-Salem, NC 27101-2400 · 336-607-7300

Clifford Britt · Comerford & Britt · 250 West First Street, Suite 200 · Winston-Salem, NC 27101-4010 · 336-631-8510

Joseph T. Carruthers · ⑩ · Carruthers & Bailey · 155 Sunnynoll Court, Suite 102 · Winston-Salem, NC 27106 · 336-714-1220

W. Thompson Comerford, Jr. · Comerford & Britt · 250 West First Street, Suite 200 · Winston-Salem, NC 27101-4010 · 336-631-8510

Fred G. Crumpler, Jr. · ㉕ · Crumpler Freedman Parker & Witt · 301 North Main Street, Suite 1100 · Winston-Salem, NC 27101 · 336-725-1304

William Kearns Davis · ⑩ · Bell, Davis & Pitt · http://www.belldavispitt.com · Century Plaza, Suite 600 · 100 North Cherry Street · P.O. Box 21029 · Winston-Salem, NC 27120 · 336-722-3700

Gusti W. Frankel · Womble Carlyle Sandridge & Rice · One West Fourth Street · Winston-Salem, NC 27101 · 336-721-3600

Allan R. Gitter · ⑳ · Womble Carlyle Sandridge & Rice · One West Fourth Street · Winston-Salem, NC 27101 · 336-721-3600

Jane C. Jackson · Robinson & Lawing · http://www.robinson-lawing.com · 101 North Cherry Street, Suite 720 · Winston-Salem, NC 27101 · 336-631-8500

James H. Kelly, Jr. · ⑩ · Kilpatrick Stockton · 1001 West Fourth Street · Winston-Salem, NC 27101-2400 · 336-607-7300

Robert J. Lawing · ⑩ · Robinson & Lawing · http://www.robinson-lawing.com · 101 North Cherry Street, Suite 720 · Winston-Salem, NC 27101 · 336-631-8500

Michael J. Lewis · ⑩ · Lewis & Daggett · 285 Executive Park Boulevard · Winston-Salem, NC 27103 · 336-765-7777

Richard T. Rice · Womble Carlyle Sandridge & Rice · One West Fourth Street · Winston-Salem, NC 27101 · 336-721-3600

Stephen M. Russell · Bell, Davis & Pitt · http://www.belldavispitt.com · Century Plaza, Suite 600 · 100 North Cherry Street · P.O. Box 21029 · Winston-Salem, NC 27120 · 336-722-3700

Keith W. Vaughan · ⑩ · Womble Carlyle Sandridge & Rice · One West Fourth Street · Winston-Salem, NC 27101 · 336-721-3600

G. Gray Wilson · ⑩ · Wilson & Coffey · 110 Oakwood Drive, Suite 400 · Winston-Salem, NC 27103 · 336-631-8866

William F. Womble, Jr. · ⑩ · Womble Carlyle Sandridge & Rice · One West Fourth Street · Winston-Salem, NC 27101 · 336-721-3600

PRIVATE FUNDS LAW

Charlotte

Kristin P. Manzano · Alston + Bird · http://www.alston.com · Bank of America Plaza, Suite 4000 · 101 South Tryon Street · Charlotte, NC 28280-4000 · 704-444-1000

Raleigh

Curtis C. Brewer IV · K&L Gates · 4350 Lassiter at North Hills Avenue, Suite 300 · Raleigh, NC 27609 · 919-743-7300

Robert B. Womble · K&L Gates · 4350 Lassiter at North Hills Avenue, Suite 300 · Raleigh, NC 27609 · 919-743-7300

Research Triangle Park

Kenneth N. Shelton · Womble Carlyle Sandridge & Rice · 2530 Meridian Parkway, Suite 400 · P.O. Box 13069 · Research Triangle Park, NC 27709-3069 · 919-484-2300

PRODUCT LIABILITY LITIGATION

Cary

Richard W. Ellis · ⑩ · Ellis & Winters · http://www.elliswinters.com · 1100 Crescent Green, Suite 200 · Cary, NC 27518 · 919-865-7000

Leslie C. O'Toole · Ellis & Winters · http://www.elliswinters.com · 1100 Crescent Green, Suite 200 · Cary, NC 27518 · 919-865-7000

Charlotte

David Neal Allen · Parker Poe Adams & Bernstein · http://www.parkerpoe.com · Three Wachovia Center, Suite 3000 · 401 South Tryon Street · Charlotte, NC 28202-1935 · 704-372-9000

Douglas W. Ey, Jr. · McGuireWoods · http://www.mcguirewoods.com · 201 North Tryon Street, Suite 3000 · P.O. Box 31247 · Charlotte, NC 28231 · 704-343-2000

John E. Grupp · Parker Poe Adams & Bernstein · http://www.parkerpoe.com · Three Wachovia Center, Suite 3000 · 401 South Tryon Street · Charlotte, NC 28202-1935 · 704-372-9000

Josephine H. Hicks · Parker Poe Adams & Bernstein · http://www.parkerpoe.com · Three Wachovia Center, Suite 3000 · 401 South Tryon Street · Charlotte, NC 28202-1935 · 704-372-9000

Bradley R. Kutrow · McGuireWoods · http://www.mcguirewoods.com · 201 North Tryon Street, Suite 3000 · P.O. Box 31247 · Charlotte, NC 28231 · 704-343-2000

David C. Wright III · Robinson, Bradshaw & Hinson · http://www.rbh.com · 101 North Tryon Street, Suite 1900 · Charlotte, NC 28246-1900 · 704-377-2536

Greensboro

Jonathan A. Berkelhammer · Smith Moore Leatherwood · http://www.smithmoorelaw.com · 300 North Greene Street, Suite 1400 · P.O. Box 21927 · Greensboro, NC 27420-1927 · 336-378-5200

Andrew S. Chamberlin · Ellis & Winters · http://www.elliswinters.com · 100 North Greene Street, Suite 102 · Greensboro, NC 27401 · 336-217-4193

J. Donald Cowan, Jr. · ⑳ · Ellis & Winters · http://www.elliswinters.com · 100 North Greene Street, Suite 102 · Greensboro, NC 27401 · 336-217-4193

Allison O. Van Laningham · Smith Moore Leatherwood · http://www.smithmoorelaw.com · 300 North Greene Street, Suite 1400 · P.O. Box 21927 · Greensboro, NC 27420-1927 · 336-378-5200

New Bern

Thomas E. Harris · ⑳ · Harris, Creech, Ward & Blackerby · 325 Pollock Street · P.O. Drawer 1168 · New Bern, NC 28563-1168 · 252-638-6666

Raleigh

Douglas B. Abrams · Abrams and Abrams · http://www.abramslawfirm.com · 2021 Fairview Road · P.O. Box 6509 · Raleigh, NC 27628 · 919-755-9166

Ronald C. Dilthey · ⑳ · Patterson, Dilthey, Clay & Bryson · 4020 Westchase Boulevard, Suite 550 · Raleigh, NC 27607 · 919-821-4020

John Alan Jones · Martin & Jones · http://www.martinandjones.com · 410 Glenwood Avenue, Suite 200 · Raleigh, NC 27603 · 919-821-0005

Frederick W. Rom · Womble Carlyle Sandridge & Rice · 150 Fayetteville Street, Suite 2100 · P.O. Box 831 · Raleigh, NC 27601-0831 · 919-755-2100

Robert W. Sumner · Cranfill, Sumner & Hartzog · http://www.cshlaw.com · 5420 Wade Park Boulevard · P.O. Box 27808 · Raleigh, NC 27611-7808 · 919-828-5100

Hoyt G. Tessener · Martin & Jones · http://www.martinandjones.com · 410 Glenwood Avenue, Suite 200 · Raleigh, NC 27603 · 919-821-0005

Jerome Paul Trehy, Jr. · Twiggs, Beskind, Strickland & Rabenau · Wachovia Capitol Center, Suite 1100 150 Fayetteville Street · Raleigh, NC 27601 · 919-828-4357

Kirk G. Warner · Smith, Anderson, Blount, Dorsett, Mitchell & Jernigan · http://www.smithlaw.com · 2500 Wachovia Capitol Center · P.O. Box 2611 · Raleigh, NC 27602-2611 · 919-821-1220

Winston-Salem

Clifford Britt · Comerford & Britt · 250 West First Street, Suite 200 · Winston-Salem, NC 27101-4010 · 336-631-8510

W. Thompson Comerford, Jr. · Comerford & Britt · 250 West First Street, Suite 200 · Winston-Salem, NC 27101-4010 · 336-631-8510

Hada de Varona Haulsee · Womble Carlyle Sandridge & Rice · One West Fourth Street · Winston-Salem, NC 27101 · 336-721-3600

Richard J. Keshian · Kilpatrick Stockton · 1001 West Fourth Street · Winston-Salem, NC 27101-2400 · 336-607-7300

Richard T. Rice · Womble Carlyle Sandridge & Rice · One West Fourth Street · Winston-Salem, NC 27101 · 336-721-3600

Keith W. Vaughan · ⑩ · Womble Carlyle Sandridge & Rice · One West Fourth Street · Winston-Salem, NC 27101 · 336-721-3600

Erna A. P. Womble · Womble Carlyle Sandridge & Rice · One West Fourth Street · Winston-Salem, NC 27101 · 336-721-3600

William F. Womble, Jr. · ⑩ · Womble Carlyle Sandridge & Rice · One West Fourth Street · Winston-Salem, NC 27101 · 336-721-3600

PROFESSIONAL MALPRACTICE LAW

Charlotte

Harvey L. Cosper, Jr. · ⑩ · Parker Poe Adams & Bernstein · http://www.parkerpoe.com · Three Wachovia Center, Suite 3000 · 401 South Tryon Street · Charlotte, NC 28202-1935 · 704-372-9000

Gary S. Hemric · James, McElroy & Diehl · 600 South College Street, Suite 3000 · Charlotte, NC 28202 · 704-372-9870

Durham

James B. Maxwell · ⑳ · Maxwell, Freeman & Bowman · 2741 University Drive · P.O. Box 52396 · Durham, NC 27717-2396 · 919-493-6464

Goldsboro

Robert D. Walker, Jr. · ⑩ · Walker, Allen Trial Attorneys · 1407 West Grantham Street · P.O. Box 2047 · Goldsboro, NC 27533-2047 · 919-734-6565

Greensboro

Sally A. Lawing · ⑩ · The Lawing Firm · Battleground Corporate Park, Suite 210 · 3859 Battleground Avenue · Greensboro, NC 27410 · 336-288-0808

Richard L. Vanore · Carruthers & Roth · http://www.crlaw.com · 235 North Edgeworth Street · P.O. Box 540 · Greensboro, NC 27402 · 336-379-8651

New Bern

Thomas E. Harris · ⑳ · Harris, Creech, Ward & Blackerby · 325 Pollock Street · P.O. Drawer 1168 · New Bern, NC 28563-1168 · 252-638-6666

Raleigh

Mark E. Anderson · McGuireWoods · http://www.mcguirewoods.com · Two Hannover Square, Suite 2600 · P.O. Box 27507 · Raleigh, NC 27601 · 704-343-2000

Donald H. Beskind · ⑩ · Twiggs, Beskind, Strickland & Rabenau · Wachovia Capitol Center, Suite 1100 150 Fayetteville Street · Raleigh, NC 27601 · 919-828-4357

Burton Craige · Patterson Harkavy · 414 West Jones Street · P.O. Box 27927 · Raleigh, NC 27603 · 919-755-1812

Ronald C. Dilthey · ⑳ · Patterson, Dilthey, Clay & Bryson · 4020 Westchase Boulevard, Suite 550 · Raleigh, NC 27607 · 919-821-4020

Timothy P. Lehan · Smith, Anderson, Blount, Dorsett, Mitchell & Jernigan · http://www.smithlaw.com · 2500 Wachovia Capitol Center · P.O. Box 2611 · Raleigh, NC 27602-2611 · 919-821-1220

Dan J. McLamb · ⑩ · Yates, McLamb & Weyher · One Bank of America Plaza, Suite 1200 · 421 Fayetteville Street · P.O. Box 2889 · Raleigh, NC 27602-2889 · 919-835-0900

Joseph C. Moore III · Allen & Moore · 3700 Computer Drive, Suite 320 · Raleigh, NC 27609-6505 · 919-783-8023

Robert W. Spearman · ⑩ · Parker Poe Adams & Bernstein · http://www.parkerpoe.com · Wachovia Capitol Center, Suite 1400 · 150 Fayetteville Street · Raleigh, NC 27601 · 919-828-0564

Winston-Salem

Allan R. Gitter · ⑳ · Womble Carlyle Sandridge & Rice · One West Fourth Street · Winston-Salem, NC 27101 · 336-721-3600

Richard T. Rice · Womble Carlyle Sandridge & Rice · One West Fourth Street · Winston-Salem, NC 27101 · 336-721-3600

Stephen M. Russell · Bell, Davis & Pitt · http://www.belldavispitt.com · Century Plaza, Suite 600 · 100 North Cherry Street · P.O. Box 21029 · Winston-Salem, NC 27120 · 336-722-3700

PROJECT FINANCE LAW

Charlotte

John D. Allison · K&L Gates · Hearst Tower, 47th Floor · 214 North Tryon Street · Charlotte, NC 28202 704-331-7400

PUBLIC FINANCE LAW

Charlotte

Alice Pinckney Adams · Robinson, Bradshaw & Hinson · http://www.rbh.com · 101 North Tryon Street, Suite 1900 · Charlotte, NC 28246-1900 · 704-377-2536

Stephen L. Cordell · McGuireWoods · http://www.mcguirewoods.com · 201 North Tryon Street, Suite 3000 · P.O. Box 31247 · Charlotte, NC 28231 · 704-343-2000

Amy K. Johnson · Moore & Van Allen · Bank of America Corporate Center, Suite 4700 · 100 North Tryon Street · Charlotte, NC 28202-4003 · 704-331-1000

Scott E. Leo · Parker Poe Adams & Bernstein · http://www.parkerpoe.com · Three Wachovia Center, Suite 3000 · 401 South Tryon Street · Charlotte, NC 28202-1935 · 704-372-9000

Edwin F. Lucas · Robinson, Bradshaw & Hinson · http://www.rbh.com · 101 North Tryon Street, Suite 1900 · Charlotte, NC 28246-1900 · 704-377-2536

Josiah C. T. Lucas · McGuireWoods · http://www.mcguirewoods.com · Bank of America Corporate Center, Suite 2900 · 100 North Tryon Street · Charlotte, NC 28202-4011 · 704-373-8999

Allen K. Robertson · Robinson, Bradshaw & Hinson · http://www.rbh.com · 101 North Tryon Street, Suite 1900 · Charlotte, NC 28246-1900 · 704-377-2536

Caroline Wannamaker Sink · Robinson, Bradshaw & Hinson · http://www.rbh.com · 101 North Tryon Street, Suite 1900 · Charlotte, NC 28246-1900 · 704-377-2536

Donald P. Ubell · Parker Poe Adams & Bernstein · http://www.parkerpoe.com · Three Wachovia Center, Suite 3000 · 401 South Tryon Street · Charlotte, NC 28202-1935 · 704-372-9000

Raleigh

Paul H. Billow · Womble Carlyle Sandridge & Rice · 150 Fayetteville Street, Suite 2100 · P.O. Box 831 · Raleigh, NC 27601-0831 · 919-755-2100

G. Thomas Lee · Womble Carlyle Sandridge & Rice · 150 Fayetteville Street, Suite 2100 · P.O. Box 831 · Raleigh, NC 27601-0831 · 919-755-2100

William H. McBride · Hunton & Williams · One Bank Of America Plaza, Suite 1400 · 421 Fayetteville Street · P.O. Box 109 · Raleigh, NC 27602 · 919-899-3000

Mary Nash K. Rusher · Hunton & Williams · One Bank Of America Plaza, Suite 1400 · 421 Fayetteville Street · P.O. Box 109 · Raleigh, NC 27602 · 919-899-3000

RAILROAD LAW

Greensboro

L. P. McLendon, Jr. · Brooks, Pierce, McLendon, Humphrey & Leonard · http://www.brookspierce.com 2000 Renaissance Plaza · 230 North Elm Street · Greensboro, NC 27401 · 336-373-8850

Raleigh

Jeffrey A. Bandini · Parker Poe Adams & Bernstein · http://www.parkerpoe.com · Wachovia Capitol Center, Suite 1400 · 150 Fayetteville Street · Raleigh, NC 27601 · 919-828-0564

Gilbert C. Laite III · Williams Mullen · http://www.williamsmullen.com · Highwoods Tower One, Suite 500 · 3200 Beechleaf Court · P.O. Drawer 19764 · Raleigh, NC 27619-9764 · 919-981-4000

REAL ESTATE LAW

Asheville

Cynthia W. Eller · The Van Winkle Law Firm · 11 North Market Street · P.O. Box 7376 · Asheville, NC 28801-7376 · 828-258-2991

Sheryl Howell Williams · Roberts & Stevens · BB&T Building, Suite 1100 · One West Pack Square · P.O. Box 7647 · Asheville, NC 28802 · 828-252-6600

Cary

Charles N. Anderson, Jr. · Ellis & Winters · http://www.elliswinters.com · 1100 Crescent Green, Suite 200 · Cary, NC 27518 · 919-865-7000

Donna K. Blumberg · Ellis & Winters · http://www.elliswinters.com · 1100 Crescent Green, Suite 200 · Cary, NC 27518 · 919-865-7000

Michael G. Winters · Ellis & Winters · http://www.elliswinters.com · 1100 Crescent Green, Suite 200 · Cary, NC 27518 · 919-865-7000

Chapel Hill

Holly H. Alderman · Schell Bray Aycock Abel & Livingston · http://www.sbaal.com · 100 Europa Drive, Suite 360 · Chapel Hill, NC 27517 · 919-929-0990

Jefferson W. Brown · King & Spalding · 227 West Trade Street, Suite 600 · Charlotte, NC 28202 · 704-503-2600

John H. Carmichael · K&L Gates · Hearst Tower, 47th Floor · 214 North Tryon Street · Charlotte, NC 28202 · 704-331-7400

James P. Carroll · Cadwalader, Wickersham & Taft · http://www.cadwalader.com · 227 West Trade Street · Charlotte, NC 28202 · 704-348-5100

G. Lee Cory, Jr. · K&L Gates · Hearst Tower, 47th Floor · 214 North Tryon Street · Charlotte, NC 28202 · 704-331-7400

Thomas D. Eatman, Jr. · ⑩ · Poyner & Spruill · http://www.poynerspruill.com · One Wachovia Center, Suite 2300 · 301 South College Street · Charlotte, NC 28202-6021 · 704-342-5250

Brian P. Evans · K&L Gates · Hearst Tower, 47th Floor · 214 North Tryon Street · Charlotte, NC 28202 704-331-7400

B. D. Farmer III · ⑩ · K&L Gates · Hearst Tower, 47th Floor · 214 North Tryon Street · Charlotte, NC 28202 · 704-331-7400

Walter D. Fisher, Jr. · K&L Gates · Hearst Tower, 47th Floor · 214 North Tryon Street · Charlotte, NC 28202 · 704-331-7400

Glen B. Hardymon · K&L Gates · Hearst Tower, 47th Floor · 214 North Tryon Street · Charlotte, NC 28202 · 704-331-7400

Hayden Harrell · Katten Muchin Rosenman · 401 South Tryon Street, Suite 2600 · Charlotte, NC 28202-1935 · 704-444-2000

William N. Harris · K&L Gates · Hearst Tower, 47th Floor · 214 North Tryon Street · Charlotte, NC 28202 · 704-331-7400

Ashley L. Hogewood, Jr. · ⑳ · Parker Poe Adams & Bernstein · http://www.parkerpoe.com · Three Wachovia Center, Suite 3000 · 401 South Tryon Street · Charlotte, NC 28202-1935 · 704-372-9000

Daniel S. Huffenus · Katten Muchin Rosenman · 401 South Tryon Street, Suite 2600 · Charlotte, NC 28202-1935 · 704-444-2000

David H. Jones · K&L Gates · Hearst Tower, 47th Floor · 214 North Tryon Street · Charlotte, NC 28202 704-331-7400

William B. Kirk, Jr. · Kirk Palmer & Thigpen · 1100 Kenilworth Avenue, Suite 200 · Charlotte, NC 28204 · 704-332-8000

Christopher W. Loeb · Robinson, Bradshaw & Hinson · http://www.rbh.com · 101 North Tryon Street, Suite 1900 · Charlotte, NC 28246-1900 · 704-377-2536

Stephen R. McCrae, Jr. · K&L Gates · Hearst Tower, 47th Floor · 214 North Tryon Street · Charlotte, NC 28202 · 704-331-7400

Charles H. McCreary III · ⑩ · Womble Carlyle Sandridge & Rice · One Wachovia Center, Suite 3500 · 301 South College Street · Charlotte, NC 28202-6037 · 704-331-4900

Peter McLean III · K&L Gates · Hearst Tower, 47th Floor · 214 North Tryon Street · Charlotte, NC 28202 · 704-331-7400

Roy H. Michaux, Jr. · K&L Gates · Hearst Tower, 47th Floor · 214 North Tryon Street · Charlotte, NC 28202 · 704-331-7400

Brent M. Milgrom, Jr. · Parker Poe Adams & Bernstein · http://www.parkerpoe.com · Three Wachovia Center, Suite 3000 · 401 South Tryon Street · Charlotte, NC 28202-1935 · 704-372-9000

J. Christopher Oates · Moore & Van Allen · Bank of America Corporate Center, Suite 4700 · 100 North Tryon Street · Charlotte, NC 28202-4003 · 704-331-1000

Bailey Patrick, Jr. · ⓴ · K&L Gates · Hearst Tower, 47th Floor · 214 North Tryon Street · Charlotte, NC 28202 · 704-331-7400

William F. Potts, Jr. · McGuireWoods · http://www.mcguirewoods.com · 201 North Tryon Street, Suite 3000 · P.O. Box 31247 · Charlotte, NC 28231 · 704-343-2000

E. Allen Prichard · ❿ · K&L Gates · Hearst Tower, 47th Floor · 214 North Tryon Street · Charlotte, NC 28202 · 704-331-7400

T. Edmund Rast · Moore & Van Allen · Bank of America Corporate Center, Suite 4700 · 100 North Tryon Street · Charlotte, NC 28202-4003 · 704-331-1000

Jane S. Ratteree · Robinson, Bradshaw & Hinson · http://www.rbh.com · 101 North Tryon Street, Suite 1900 · Charlotte, NC 28246-1900 · 704-377-2536

Patrick L. Ridinger · K&L Gates · Hearst Tower, 47th Floor · 214 North Tryon Street · Charlotte, NC 28202 · 704-331-7400

Michael E. Robbe · Robbe Law · 3915 Oldfield Road · Charlotte, NC 28226 · 704-887-3533

Carlton A. Shannon, Jr. · Katten Muchin Rosenman · 401 South Tryon Street, Suite 2600 · Charlotte, NC 28202-1935 · 704-444-2000

Robert Wayne Simmons · McGuireWoods · http://www.mcguirewoods.com · 201 North Tryon Street, Suite 3000 · P.O. Box 31247 · Charlotte, NC 28231 · 704-343-2000

Caroline Wannamaker Sink · Robinson, Bradshaw & Hinson · http://www.rbh.com · 101 North Tryon Street, Suite 1900 · Charlotte, NC 28246-1900 · 704-377-2536

Robert C. Sink · ❿ · Robinson, Bradshaw & Hinson · http://www.rbh.com · 101 North Tryon Street, Suite 1900 · Charlotte, NC 28246-1900 · 704-377-2536

Skottowe W. Smith · Moore & Van Allen · Bank of America Corporate Center, Suite 4700 · 100 North Tryon Street · Charlotte, NC 28202-4003 · 704-331-1000

Gary W. Swindell · ❿ · The Law Offices of Gary W. Swindell · 227 West Trade Street, Suite 2030 · Charlotte, NC 28202 · 704-376-1390

Maynard E. Tipps · ❿ · K&L Gates · Hearst Tower, 47th Floor · 214 North Tryon Street · Charlotte, NC 28202 · 704-331-7400

Brent A. Torstrick · Robinson, Bradshaw & Hinson · http://www.rbh.com · 101 North Tryon Street, Suite 1900 · Charlotte, NC 28246-1900 · 704-377-2536

W. Samuel Woodard · ❿ · Parker Poe Adams & Bernstein · http://www.parkerpoe.com · Three Wachovia Center, Suite 3000 · 401 South Tryon Street · Charlotte, NC 28202-1935 · 704-372-9000

Durham

Robert O. Belo · Kennon, Craver, Belo, Craig & McKee · 4011 University Drive, Suite 300 · P.O. Box 51579 · Durham, NC 27717-1579 · 919-490-0500

Greensboro

William P. Aycock II · ⑳ · Schell Bray Aycock Abel & Livingston · http://www.sbaal.com · Renaissance Plaza, Suite 1500 · 230 North Elm Street · Greensboro, NC 27401 · 336-370-8800

Howard L. Borum · Carruthers & Roth · http://www.crlaw.com · 235 North Edgeworth Street · P.O. Box 540 · Greensboro, NC 27402 · 336-379-8651

Margaret Shea Burnham · Nexsen Pruet · http://www.nexsenpruet.com · 701 Green Valley Road, Suite 100 · Greensboro, NC 27408 · 336-373-1600

Brian W. Byrd · Smith Moore Leatherwood · http://www.smithmoorelaw.com · 300 North Greene Street, Suite 1400 · P.O. Box 21927 · Greensboro, NC 27420-1927 · 336-378-5200

Barbara R. Christy · Schell Bray Aycock Abel & Livingston · http://www.sbaal.com · Renaissance Plaza, Suite 1500 · 230 North Elm Street · Greensboro, NC 27401 · 336-370-8800

M. Jay DeVaney · Nexsen Pruet · http://www.nexsenpruet.com · 701 Green Valley Road, Suite 100 · Greensboro, NC 27408 · 336-373-1600

Charles E. Melvin, Jr. · ⑳ · Smith Moore Leatherwood · http://www.smithmoorelaw.com · 300 North Greene Street, Suite 1400 · P.O. Box 21927 · Greensboro, NC 27420-1927 · 336-378-5200

Christopher J. Vaughn · Carruthers & Roth · http://www.crlaw.com · 235 North Edgeworth Street · P.O. Box 540 · Greensboro, NC 27402 · 336-379-8651

E. Garrett Walker · ⑩ · Smith Moore Leatherwood · http://www.smithmoorelaw.com · 300 North Greene Street, Suite 1400 · P.O. Box 21927 · Greensboro, NC 27420-1927 · 336-378-5200

Morrisville

Reich L. Welborn · Moore & Van Allen · 430 Davis Drive, Suite 500 · P.O. Box 13706 · Morrisville, NC 27709 · 919-286-8000

New Bern

James Lee Davis · ⑩ · Ward and Smith · http://www.wardandsmith.com · 1001 College Court · P.O. Box 867 · New Bern, NC 28563-0867 · 252-672-5400

C. H. Pope, Jr. · ⑩ · Ward and Smith · http://www.wardandsmith.com · 1001 College Court · P.O. Box 867 · New Bern, NC 28563-0867 · 252-672-5400

Clint D. Routson · Ward and Smith · http://www.wardandsmith.com · 1001 College Court · P.O. Box 867 · New Bern, NC 28563-0867 · 252-672-5400

Pinehurst

John M. May · Robbins, May & Rich · Turnberry Wood · 120 Applecross Road · Pinehurst, NC 28374 · 910-692-4900

Raleigh

Francis C. Bagbey · Smith, Anderson, Blount, Dorsett, Mitchell & Jernigan · http://www.smithlaw.com · 2500 Wachovia Capitol Center · P.O. Box 2611 · Raleigh, NC 27602-2611 · 919-821-1220

Jeffrey A. Benson · Kilpatrick Stockton · 3737 Glenwood Avenue, Suite 400 · Raleigh, NC 27612-5515 · 919-420-1700

J. Clark Brewer · 10 · Young, Moore & Henderson · 3101 Glenwood Avenue · P.O. Box 31627 · Raleigh, NC 27622-1627 · 919-782-6860

William S. Cherry, Jr. · Poyner & Spruill · http://www.poynerspruill.com · 3600 Glenwood Avenue · P.O. Box 10096 · Raleigh, NC 27605-0096 · 919-783-6400

Reuben G. Clark III · Williams Mullen · http://www.williamsmullen.com · Highwoods Tower One, Suite 500 · 3200 Beechleaf Court · P.O. Drawer 19764 · Raleigh, NC 27619-9764 · 919-981-4000

Joseph B. Dempster, Jr. · Poyner & Spruill · http://www.poynerspruill.com · 3600 Glenwood Avenue · P.O. Box 10096 · Raleigh, NC 27605-0096 · 919-783-6400

Donald A. Donadio · 10 · Womble Carlyle Sandridge & Rice · 150 Fayetteville Street, Suite 2100 · P.O. Box 831 · Raleigh, NC 27601-0831 · 919-755-2100

David R. Dorton · 10 · Williams Mullen · http://www.williamsmullen.com · Highwoods Tower One, Suite 500 · 3200 Beechleaf Court · P.O. Drawer 19764 · Raleigh, NC 27619-9764 · 919-981-4000

Gary K. Joyner · Kilpatrick Stockton · 3737 Glenwood Avenue, Suite 400 · Raleigh, NC 27612-5515 · 919-420-1700

Michael F. King · K&L Gates · 4350 Lassiter at North Hills Avenue, Suite 300 · Raleigh, NC 27609 · 919-743-7300

Barry D. Mann · 10 · Manning, Fulton & Skinner · http://www.manningfulton.com · 3605 Glenwood Avenue, Suite 500 · P.O. Box 20389 · Raleigh, NC 27619-0389 · 919-787-8880

C. Steven Mason · 10 · Smith, Anderson, Blount, Dorsett, Mitchell & Jernigan · http://www.smithlaw.com 2500 Wachovia Capitol Center · P.O. Box 2611 · Raleigh, NC 27602-2611 · 919-821-1220

William C. Matthews, Jr. · Womble Carlyle Sandridge & Rice · 150 Fayetteville Street, Suite 2100 · P.O. Box 831 · Raleigh, NC 27601-0831 · 919-755-2100

Samuel T. Oliver · 10 · Manning, Fulton & Skinner · http://www.manningfulton.com · 3605 Glenwood Avenue, Suite 500 · P.O. Box 20389 · Raleigh, NC 27619-0389 · 919-787-8880

Alan H. Peterson · K&L Gates · 4350 Lassiter at North Hills Avenue, Suite 300 · Raleigh, NC 27609 · 919-743-7300

Lacy H. Reaves · Smith, Anderson, Blount, Dorsett, Mitchell & Jernigan · http://www.smithlaw.com · 2500 Wachovia Capitol Center · P.O. Box 2611 · Raleigh, NC 27602-2611 · 919-821-1220

Ronald R. Rogers · Williams Mullen · http://www.williamsmullen.com · Highwoods Tower One, Suite 500 · 3200 Beechleaf Court · P.O. Drawer 19764 · Raleigh, NC 27619-9764 · 919-981-4000

Research Triangle Park

William J. Brian, Jr. · K&L Gates · P.O. Box 14210 · Research Triangle Park, NC 27709 · 919-466-1190

Leslie E. Browder · 20 · Womble Carlyle Sandridge & Rice · 2530 Meridian Parkway, Suite 400 · P.O. Box 13069 · Research Triangle Park, NC 27709-3069 · 919-484-2300

John E. Markham, Jr. · K&L Gates · P.O. Box 14210 · Research Triangle Park, NC 27709 · 919-466-1190

Wilmington

David E. Huffine · McGuireWoods · http://www.mcguirewoods.com · 300 North Third Street, Suite 400 · P.O. Box 599 · Wilmington, NC 28402 · 910-254-3800

Kenneth A. Shanklin · Shanklin & Nichols · 214 Market Street · P.O. Box 1347 · Wilmington, NC 28402-1347 · 910-762-9400

Wilson

Reginald W. Harrison, Jr. · Narron & Holdford · 204 North Tarboro Street · P.O. Drawer 279 · Wilson, NC 27894 · 252-237-3153

Winston-Salem

Alfred G. Adams · ⑳ · Womble Carlyle Sandridge & Rice · One West Fourth Street · Winston-Salem, NC 27101 · 336-721-3600

Frank M. Bell, Jr. · ⑳ · Bell, Davis & Pitt · http://www.belldavispitt.com · Century Plaza, Suite 600 · 100 North Cherry Street · P.O. Box 21029 · Winston-Salem, NC 27120 · 336-722-3700

R. Brandt Deal · Hatfield, Mountcastle, Deal, VanZandt & Mann · Bethesda Oaks, Suite 605 · 2990 Bethesda Place · Winston-Salem, NC 27103 · 336-768-1842

Hardin G. Halsey · Womble Carlyle Sandridge & Rice · One West Fourth Street · Winston-Salem, NC 27101 · 336-721-3600

Kenneth A. Moser · ⑩ · Womble Carlyle Sandridge & Rice · One West Fourth Street · Winston-Salem, NC 27101 · 336-721-3600

Donald M. VonCannon · Allman Spry Leggett & Crumpler · 380 Knollwood Street, Suite 700 · P.O. Drawer 5129 · Winston-Salem, NC 27103-4152 · 336-722-2300

SECURITIES LAW

Charlotte

Garza Baldwin III · ⑩ · Womble Carlyle Sandridge & Rice · One Wachovia Center, Suite 3500 · 301 South College Street · Charlotte, NC 28202-6037 · 704-331-4900

Patrick S. Bryant · Robinson, Bradshaw & Hinson · http://www.rbh.com · 101 North Tryon Street, Suite 1900 · Charlotte, NC 28246-1900 · 704-377-2536

Peter C. Buck · Robinson, Bradshaw & Hinson · http://www.rbh.com · 101 North Tryon Street, Suite 1900 · Charlotte, NC 28246-1900 · 704-377-2536

George C. Covington · King & Spalding · 227 West Trade Street, Suite 600 · Charlotte, NC 28202 · 704-503-2600

R. Douglas Harmon · Parker Poe Adams & Bernstein · http://www.parkerpoe.com · Three Wachovia Center, Suite 3000 · 401 South Tryon Street · Charlotte, NC 28202-1935 · 704-372-9000

Stephen D. Hope · Moore & Van Allen · Bank of America Corporate Center, Suite 4700 · 100 North Tryon Street · Charlotte, NC 28202-4003 · 704-331-1000

Gary C. Ivey · Alston + Bird · http://www.alston.com · Bank of America Plaza, Suite 4000 · 101 South Tryon Street · Charlotte, NC 28280-4000 · 704-444-1000

Sean M. Jones · K&L Gates · Hearst Tower, 47th Floor · 214 North Tryon Street · Charlotte, NC 28202 · 704-331-7400

Stephen M. Lynch · Robinson, Bradshaw & Hinson · http://www.rbh.com · 101 North Tryon Street, Suite 1900 · Charlotte, NC 28246-1900 · 704-377-2536

J. Norfleet Pruden III · K&L Gates · Hearst Tower, 47th Floor · 214 North Tryon Street · Charlotte, NC 28202 · 704-331-7400

Elizabeth G. Wren · McGuireWoods · http://www.mcguirewoods.com · Bank of America Corporate Center, Suite 2900 · 100 North Tryon Street · Charlotte, NC 28202-4011 · 704-373-8999

Greensboro

E. Kent Auberry · Smith Moore Leatherwood · http://www.smithmoorelaw.com · 300 North Greene Street, Suite 1400 · P.O. Box 21927 · Greensboro, NC 27420-1927 · 336-378-5200

Doris R. Bray · ⑳ · Schell Bray Aycock Abel & Livingston · http://www.sbaal.com · Renaissance Plaza, Suite 1500 · 230 North Elm Street · Greensboro, NC 27401 · 336-370-8800

Mark Davidson · Brooks, Pierce, McLendon, Humphrey & Leonard · http://www.brookspierce.com · 2000 Renaissance Plaza · 230 North Elm Street · Greensboro, NC 27401 · 336-373-8850

Wayne E. Tumlin · Tuggle Duggins & Meschan · http://www.tuggleduggins.com · 100 North Greene Street, Suite 600 · P.O. Box 2888 · Greensboro, NC 27402-2888 · 336-378-1431

Raleigh

Amy M. Batten · Smith, Anderson, Blount, Dorsett, Mitchell & Jernigan · http://www.smithlaw.com · 2500 Wachovia Capitol Center · P.O. Box 2611 · Raleigh, NC 27602-2611 · 919-821-1220

Christopher B. Capel · Smith, Anderson, Blount, Dorsett, Mitchell & Jernigan · http://www.smithlaw.com · 2500 Wachovia Capitol Center · P.O. Box 2611 · Raleigh, NC 27602-2611 · 919-821-1220

John L. Jernigan · ⑩ · Smith, Anderson, Blount, Dorsett, Mitchell & Jernigan · http://www.smithlaw.com 2500 Wachovia Capitol Center · P.O. Box 2611 · Raleigh, NC 27602-2611 · 919-821-1220

Byron B. Kirkland · Smith, Anderson, Blount, Dorsett, Mitchell & Jernigan · http://www.smithlaw.com · 2500 Wachovia Capitol Center · P.O. Box 2611 · Raleigh, NC 27602-2611 · 919-821-1220

J. Christopher Lynch · Wyrick Robbins Yates & Ponton · http://www.wyrick.com · The Summit, Suite 300 · 4101 Lake Boone Trail · P.O. Drawer 17803 · Raleigh, NC 27607-7506 · 919-781-4000

Brad S. Markoff · DLA Piper · 4141 Parklake Avenue, Suite 300 · Raleigh, NC 27612-2350 · 919-786-2000

Merrill M. Mason · Smith, Anderson, Blount, Dorsett, Mitchell & Jernigan · http://www.smithlaw.com · 2500 Wachovia Capitol Center · P.O. Box 2611 · Raleigh, NC 27602-2611 · 919-821-1220

Gerald F. Roach · Smith, Anderson, Blount, Dorsett, Mitchell & Jernigan · http://www.smithlaw.com · 2500 Wachovia Capitol Center · P.O. Box 2611 · Raleigh, NC 27602-2611 · 919-821-1220

Winston-Salem

W. Randy Eaddy · ⑩ · Kilpatrick Stockton · 1001 West Fourth Street · Winston-Salem, NC 27101-2400 · 336-607-7300

Jeffrey C. Howland · ⑩ · Womble Carlyle Sandridge & Rice · One West Fourth Street · Winston-Salem, NC 27101 · 336-721-3600

SPORTS LAW

Charlotte

Stokely G. Caldwell, Jr. · Robinson, Bradshaw & Hinson · http://www.rbh.com · 101 North Tryon Street, Suite 1900 · Charlotte, NC 28246-1900 · 704-377-2536

Gregory H. Gach · Gach Law Firm · 6000 Monroe Road, Suite 350 · Charlotte, NC 28212 · 704-531-9355

D. Blaine Sanders · Robinson, Bradshaw & Hinson · http://www.rbh.com · 101 North Tryon Street, Suite 1900 · Charlotte, NC 28246-1900 · 704-377-2536

TAX LAW

Asheville

Jackson D. Hamilton · Roberts & Stevens · BB&T Building, Suite 1100 · One West Pack Square · P.O. Box 7647 · Asheville, NC 28802 · 828-252-6600

Brian F. D. Lavelle · ⑳ · The Van Winkle Law Firm · 11 North Market Street · P.O. Box 7376 · Asheville, NC 28801-7376 · 828-258-2991

Michael L. Miller · ⑩ · Michael L. Miller · Ninety Southside Avenue, Suite 100 · P.O. Box 2953 · Asheville, NC 28802 · 828-281-2100

Charlotte

Robert V. Baker · Moore & Van Allen · Bank of America Corporate Center, Suite 4700 · 100 North Tryon Street · Charlotte, NC 28202-4003 · 704-331-1000

Francis J. Blanchfield, Jr. · ⑩ · Mayer Brown · 214 North Tryon Street, Suite 2200 · Charlotte, NC 28202 · 704-444-3561

Hayden D. Brown · Mayer Brown · 214 North Tryon Street, Suite 2200 · Charlotte, NC 28202 · 704-444-3561

Jeffrey P. Cantrell · Mayer Brown · 214 North Tryon Street, Suite 2200 · Charlotte, NC 28202 · 704-444-3561

John J. Carpenter · Culp, Elliott & Carpenter · 4401 Barclay Downs Drive, Suite 200 · Charlotte, NC 28209 · 704-372-6322

Bernard B. Clark · Moore & Van Allen · Bank of America Corporate Center, Suite 4700 · 100 North Tryon Street · Charlotte, NC 28202-4003 · 704-331-1000

Robert T. Duffy · Kilpatrick Stockton · 214 North Tryon Street, Suite 2500 · Charlotte, NC 28202-2381 · 704-338-5000

W. Curtis Elliott · Culp, Elliott & Carpenter · 4401 Barclay Downs Drive, Suite 200 · Charlotte, NC 28209 · 704-372-6322

James N. Greene III · Parker Poe Adams & Bernstein · http://www.parkerpoe.com · Three Wachovia Center, Suite 3000 · 401 South Tryon Street · Charlotte, NC 28202-1935 · 704-372-9000

Warren P. Kean · K&L Gates · Hearst Tower, 47th Floor · 214 North Tryon Street · Charlotte, NC 28202 · 704-331-7400

Neill G. McBryde · ㉕ · Moore & Van Allen · Bank of America Corporate Center, Suite 4700 · 100 North Tryon Street · Charlotte, NC 28202-4003 · 704-331-1000

E. Graham McGoogan, Jr. · McGuireWoods · http://www.mcguirewoods.com · 201 North Tryon Street, Suite 3000 · P.O. Box 31247 · Charlotte, NC 28231 · 704-343-2000

Robert L. Mendenhall · Mayer Brown · 214 North Tryon Street, Suite 2200 · Charlotte, NC 28202 · 704-444-3561

Herman Spence III · Robinson, Bradshaw & Hinson · http://www.rbh.com · 101 North Tryon Street, Suite 1900 · Charlotte, NC 28246-1900 · 704-377-2536

J. Michael Wilson · McGuireWoods · http://www.mcguirewoods.com · 201 North Tryon Street, Suite 3000 · P.O. Box 31247 · Charlotte, NC 28231 · 704-343-2000

Greensboro

Michael R. Abel · ⑩ · Schell Bray Aycock Abel & Livingston · http://www.sbaal.com · Renaissance Plaza, Suite 1500 · 230 North Elm Street · Greensboro, NC 27401 · 336-370-8800

E. Kent Auberry · Smith Moore Leatherwood · http://www.smithmoorelaw.com · 300 North Greene Street, Suite 1400 · P.O. Box 21927 · Greensboro, NC 27420-1927 · 336-378-5200

W. B. Rodman Davis · Hagan Davis Mangum Barrett Langley & Hale · Wachovia Tower, Suite 200 · 300 North Greene Street · Greensboro, NC 27401 · 336-232-0650

James N. Duggins, Jr. · ⑩ · Tuggle Duggins & Meschan · http://www.tuggleduggins.com · 100 North Greene Street, Suite 600 · P.O. Box 2888 · Greensboro, NC 27402-2888 · 336-378-1431

William G. McNairy · ⑩ · Brooks, Pierce, McLendon, Humphrey & Leonard · http://www.brookspierce.com · 2000 Renaissance Plaza · 230 North Elm Street · Greensboro, NC 27401 · 336-373-8850

H. Vaughn Ramsey · Tuggle Duggins & Meschan · http://www.tuggleduggins.com · 100 North Greene Street, Suite 600 · P.O. Box 2888 · Greensboro, NC 27402-2888 · 336-378-1431

Barbara C. Ruby · Smith Moore Leatherwood · http://www.smithmoorelaw.com · 300 North Greene Street, Suite 1400 · P.O. Box 21927 · Greensboro, NC 27420-1927 · 336-378-5200

Desmond G. Sheridan · Isaacson Isaacson & Sheridan · Bank of America Building, Suite 400 · 101 West Friendly Avenue · P.O. Box 1888 · Greensboro, NC 27402 · 336-275-7626

Richard J. Tuggle, Sr. · ㉕ · Tuggle Duggins & Meschan · http://www.tuggleduggins.com · 100 North Greene Street, Suite 600 · P.O. Box 2888 · Greensboro, NC 27402-2888 · 336-378-1431

Michael J. Wenig · Tuggle Duggins & Meschan · http://www.tuggleduggins.com · 100 North Greene Street, Suite 600 · P.O. Box 2888 · Greensboro, NC 27402-2888 · 336-378-1431

William M. Wilcox IV · Nexsen Pruet · http://www.nexsenpruet.com · 701 Green Valley Road, Suite 100 · Greensboro, NC 27408 · 336-373-1600

Howard L. Williams · Brooks, Pierce, McLendon, Humphrey & Leonard · http://www.brookspierce.com 2000 Renaissance Plaza · 230 North Elm Street · Greensboro, NC 27401 · 336-373-8850

Keith A. Wood · Carruthers & Roth · http://www.crlaw.com · 235 North Edgeworth Street · P.O. Box 540 Greensboro, NC 27402 · 336-379-8651

Greenville

Michael A. Colombo · Colombo, Kitchin, Dunn, Ball & Porter · 1698 East Arlington Boulevard · Greenville, NC 27858 · 252-321-2020

High Point

S. Perry Keziah · ⑩ · Keziah, Gates & Samet · High Point Bank & Trust Building, Suite 400 · 300 North Main Street · P.O. Box 2608 · High Point, NC 27261-2608 · 336-889-6900

Charles E. Lynch, Jr. · Keziah, Gates & Samet · High Point Bank & Trust Building, Suite 400 · 300 North Main Street · P.O. Box 2608 · High Point, NC 27261-2608 · 336-889-6900

Raleigh

Thomas H. Cook, Jr. · Wyrick Robbins Yates & Ponton · http://www.wyrick.com · The Summit, Suite 300 · 4101 Lake Boone Trail · P.O. Drawer 17803 · Raleigh, NC 27607-7506 · 919-781-4000

Jasper L. Cummings, Jr. · Alston + Bird · http://www.alston.com · 3201 Beechleaf Court, Suite 600 · Raleigh, NC 27604-1062 · 919-862-2210

Lemuel H. Gibbons III · Poyner & Spruill · http://www.poynerspruill.com · 3600 Glenwood Avenue · P.O. Box 10096 · Raleigh, NC 27605-0096 · 919-783-6400

R. Donavon Munford, Jr. · Smith, Anderson, Blount, Dorsett, Mitchell & Jernigan · http://www.smithlaw.com · 2500 Wachovia Capitol Center · P.O. Box 2611 · Raleigh, NC 27602-2611 · 919-821-1220

Charles Neely · Williams Mullen · http://www.williamsmullen.com · Highwoods Tower One, Suite 500 · 3200 Beechleaf Court · P.O. Drawer 19764 · Raleigh, NC 27619-9764 · 919-981-4000

William W. Nelson · Smith, Anderson, Blount, Dorsett, Mitchell & Jernigan · http://www.smithlaw.com · 2500 Wachovia Capitol Center · P.O. Box 2611 · Raleigh, NC 27602-2611 · 919-821-1220

Walter R. Rogers, Jr. · Smith, Anderson, Blount, Dorsett, Mitchell & Jernigan · http://www.smithlaw.com · 2500 Wachovia Capitol Center · P.O. Box 2611 · Raleigh, NC 27602-2611 · 919-821-1220

W. Gerald Thornton · ⑳ · Manning, Fulton & Skinner · http://www.manningfulton.com · 3605 Glenwood Avenue, Suite 500 · P.O. Box 20389 · Raleigh, NC 27619-0389 · 919-787-8880

Rocky Mount

Frank P. Meadows, Jr. · ⑩ · Poyner & Spruill · http://www.poynerspruill.com · 130 South Franklin Street P.O. Box 353 · Rocky Mount, NC 27802-0353 · 252-446-2341

Winston-Salem

Jeffrey T. Lawyer · Womble Carlyle Sandridge & Rice · One West Fourth Street · Winston-Salem, NC 27101 · 336-721-3600

Greg L. Smith · ⑩ · Womble Carlyle Sandridge & Rice · One West Fourth Street · Winston-Salem, NC 27101 · 336-721-3600

Robert C. Vaughn, Jr. · ㉕ · Vaughn Perkinson Ehlinger Moxley & Stogner · 4505 Country Club Road, Suite 210 · P.O. Box 25715 · Winston-Salem, NC 27114 · 336-794-6000

C. Mark Wiley · ⑩ · Womble Carlyle Sandridge & Rice · One West Fourth Street · Winston-Salem, NC 27101 · 336-721-3600

TECHNOLOGY LAW

Raleigh

Fred D. Hutchison · Hutchison Law Group · http://www.hutchlaw.com · 5410 Trinity Road, Suite 400 · Raleigh, NC 27607 · 919-829-9600

James F. Verdonik · ⑩ · Ward and Smith · http://www.wardandsmith.com · Wade II, Suite 400 · 5430 Wade Park Boulevard · P.O. Box 33009 · Raleigh, NC 27636-3009 · 919-277-9100

Winston-Salem

Jeffrey C. Howland · ⑩ · Womble Carlyle Sandridge & Rice · One West Fourth Street · Winston-Salem, NC 27101 · 336-721-3600

TIMBER LAW

Research Triangle Park

Kenneth N. Shelton · Womble Carlyle Sandridge & Rice · 2530 Meridian Parkway, Suite 400 · P.O. Box 13069 · Research Triangle Park, NC 27709-3069 · 919-484-2300

Winston-Salem

Hardin G. Halsey · Womble Carlyle Sandridge & Rice · One West Fourth Street · Winston-Salem, NC 27101 · 336-721-3600

TRUSTS AND ESTATES

Asheville

Robert H. Haggard · The Van Winkle Law Firm · 11 North Market Street · P.O. Box 7376 · Asheville, NC 28801-7376 · 828-258-2991

Barry B. Kempson · ⑳ · The Van Winkle Law Firm · 11 North Market Street · P.O. Box 7376 · Asheville, NC 28801-7376 · 828-258-2991

Brian F. D. Lavelle · ⑳ · The Van Winkle Law Firm · 11 North Market Street · P.O. Box 7376 · Asheville, NC 28801-7376 · 828-258-2991

John W. Mason · Roberts & Stevens · BB&T Building, Suite 1100 · One West Pack Square · P.O. Box 7647 · Asheville, NC 28802 · 828-252-6600

Michael L. Miller · ⑩ · Michael L. Miller · Ninety Southside Avenue, Suite 100 · P.O. Box 2953 · Asheville, NC 28802 · 828-281-2100

Charlotte

William T. Belcher · Poyner & Spruill · http://www.poynerspruill.com · One Wachovia Center, Suite 2300 301 South College Street · Charlotte, NC 28202-6021 · 704-342-5250

Richard A. Bigger, Jr. · Wishart, Norris, Henninger & Pittman · 6832 Morrison Boulevard · Charlotte, NC 28211 · 704-364-0010

Herbert H. Browne, Jr. · ⑩ · McGuireWoods · http://www.mcguirewoods.com · 201 North Tryon Street, Suite 3000 · P.O. Box 31247 · Charlotte, NC 28231 · 704-343-2000

Cornelius W. Coghill III · Womble Carlyle Sandridge & Rice · One Wachovia Center, Suite 3500 · 301 South College Street · Charlotte, NC 28202-6037 · 704-331-4900

W. Curtis Elliott · Culp, Elliott & Carpenter · 4401 Barclay Downs Drive, Suite 200 · Charlotte, NC 28209 · 704-372-6322

Ray S. Farris · Johnston, Allison & Hord · 1065 East Morehead Street · P.O. Box 36469 · Charlotte, NC 28236 · 704-332-1181

Debra L. Foster · Foster Kelly · 200 Providence Road, Suite 206 · Charlotte, NC 28207 · 704-375-0600

Meg D. Goldstein · ⑩ · Poyner & Spruill · http://www.poynerspruill.com · One Wachovia Center, Suite 2300 · 301 South College Street · Charlotte, NC 28202-6021 · 704-342-5250

Julie Zydron Griggs · ⑩ · Robinson, Bradshaw & Hinson · http://www.rbh.com · 101 North Tryon Street, Suite 1900 · Charlotte, NC 28246-1900 · 704-377-2536

Graham D. Holding, Jr. · ⑩ · Robinson, Bradshaw & Hinson · http://www.rbh.com · 101 North Tryon Street, Suite 1900 · Charlotte, NC 28246-1900 · 704-377-2536

Neill G. McBryde · ㉕ · Moore & Van Allen · Bank of America Corporate Center, Suite 4700 · 100 North Tryon Street · Charlotte, NC 28202-4003 · 704-331-1000

Susan McCrory · Robinson, Bradshaw & Hinson · http://www.rbh.com · 101 North Tryon Street, Suite 1900 · Charlotte, NC 28246-1900 · 704-377-2536

Sherri L. McGirt · McNair Law Firm · http://www.mcnair.net · Two Wachovia Center, Suite 1615 · 301 South Tryon Street · Charlotte, NC 28282 · 704-347-1170

E. Graham McGoogan, Jr. · McGuireWoods · http://www.mcguirewoods.com · 201 North Tryon Street, Suite 3000 · P.O. Box 31247 · Charlotte, NC 28231 · 704-343-2000

Christy Eve Reid · ⑩ · Robinson, Bradshaw & Hinson · http://www.rbh.com · 101 North Tryon Street, Suite 1900 · Charlotte, NC 28246-1900 · 704-377-2536

Carolyn Gilmer Shaw · K&L Gates · Hearst Tower, 47th Floor · 214 North Tryon Street · Charlotte, NC 28202 · 704-331-7400

Laura L. Yaeger · Laura L. Yaeger · 401 North Tryon Street, 10th Floor · Charlotte, NC 28202-2108 · 704-358-4984

Durham

Larry H. Rocamora · McPherson & Rocamora · 3211 Shannon Road, Suite 620 · Durham, NC 27707 · 919-493-0584

Goldsboro

John C. Hine · Baddour Parker & Hine · 208 South William Street · P.O. Box 916 · Goldsboro, NC 27533-0916 · 919-735-7275

Greensboro

J. Stanley Atwell · Carruthers & Roth · http://www.crlaw.com · 235 North Edgeworth Street · P.O. Box 540 · Greensboro, NC 27402 · 336-379-8651

Carole W. Bruce · Smith Moore Leatherwood · http://www.smithmoorelaw.com · 300 North Greene Street, Suite 1400 · P.O. Box 21927 · Greensboro, NC 27420-1927 · 336-378-5200

W. Erwin Fuller, Jr. · Brooks, Pierce, McLendon, Humphrey & Leonard · http://www.brookspierce.com 2000 Renaissance Plaza · 230 North Elm Street · Greensboro, NC 27401 · 336-373-8850

Michael H. Godwin · Schell Bray Aycock Abel & Livingston · http://www.sbaal.com · Renaissance Plaza, Suite 1500 · 230 North Elm Street · Greensboro, NC 27401 · 336-370-8800

Paul H. Livingston, Jr. · ⑩ · Schell Bray Aycock Abel & Livingston · http://www.sbaal.com · Renaissance Plaza, Suite 1500 · 230 North Elm Street · Greensboro, NC 27401 · 336-370-8800

Robert B. Lloyd, Jr. · ㉕ · Hunter Higgins · P.O. Box 20570 · Greensboro, NC 27420-0570 · 336-373-5991

William G. McNairy · ⑩ · Brooks, Pierce, McLendon, Humphrey & Leonard · http://www.brookspierce.com · 2000 Renaissance Plaza · 230 North Elm Street · Greensboro, NC 27401 · 336-373-8850

Greenville

Michael A. Colombo · Colombo, Kitchin, Dunn, Ball & Porter · 1698 East Arlington Boulevard · Greenville, NC 27858 · 252-321-2020

Hickory

Charles D. Dixon · Patrick, Harper & Dixon · Centura Bank Building · 34 Second Street, NW · P.O. Box 218 · Hickory, NC 28603 · 828-322-7741

High Point

Ann E. Hanks · Ann E. Hanks · 202 West Lexington Avenue · P.O. Box 5064 · High Point, NC 27262 · 336-812-3073

S. Perry Keziah · ⑩ · Keziah, Gates & Samet · High Point Bank & Trust Building, Suite 400 · 300 North Main Street · P.O. Box 2608 · High Point, NC 27261-2608 · 336-889-6900

Kinston

C. Gray Johnsey · ⑩ · White & Allen · 106 South McLewean Street · P.O. Box 3169 · Kinston, NC 28502 252-527-8000

Mocksville

Henry P. Van Hoy II · Martin & Van Hoy · 10 Court Square · Mocksville, NC 27028-2415 · 336-751-2171

Raleigh

Madison E. Bullard, Jr. · Wyrick Robbins Yates & Ponton · http://www.wyrick.com · The Summit, Suite 300 · 4101 Lake Boone Trail · P.O. Drawer 17803 · Raleigh, NC 27607-7506 · 919-781-4000

Jean Gordon Carter · Hunton & Williams · One Bank Of America Plaza, Suite 1400 · 421 Fayetteville Street · P.O. Box 109 · Raleigh, NC 27602 · 919-899-3000

Stuart B. Dorsett · Ward and Smith · http://www.wardandsmith.com · Wade II, Suite 400 · 5430 Wade Park Boulevard · P.O. Box 33009 · Raleigh, NC 27636-3009 · 919-277-9100

Carl W. Hibbert · ⑩ · Kilpatrick Stockton · 3737 Glenwood Avenue, Suite 400 · Raleigh, NC 27612-5515 919-420-1700

Deborah L. Hildebran-Bachofen · Manning, Fulton & Skinner · http://www.manningfulton.com · 3605 Glenwood Avenue, Suite 500 · P.O. Box 20389 · Raleigh, NC 27619-0389 · 919-787-8880

Maria M. Lynch · ⑩ · Lynch & Eatman · Carolina Corporate Center, Suite 201 · 5400 Glennwood Avenue P.O. Box 30515 · Raleigh, NC 27622-0515 · 919-571-3332

R. Donavon Munford, Jr. · Smith, Anderson, Blount, Dorsett, Mitchell & Jernigan · http://www.smithlaw.com · 2500 Wachovia Capitol Center · P.O. Box 2611 · Raleigh, NC 27602-2611 · 919-821-1220

Rudy L. Ogburn · Young, Moore & Henderson · 3101 Glenwood Avenue · P.O. Box 31627 · Raleigh, NC 27622-1627 · 919-782-6860

Walter R. Rogers, Jr. · Smith, Anderson, Blount, Dorsett, Mitchell & Jernigan · http://www.smithlaw.com · 2500 Wachovia Capitol Center · P.O. Box 2611 · Raleigh, NC 27602-2611 · 919-821-1220

Rocky Mount

Michael S. Batts · Batts, Batts & Bell · 103 Candlewood Road · P.O. Box 8228 · Rocky Mount, NC 27804-1228 · 252-977-6450

Smithfield

James W. Narron · ⑩ · Narron, O'Hale & Whittington · 102 South Third Street · P.O. Box 1567 · Smithfield, NC 27577 · 919-934-6021

Wilmington

G. Stephen Diab · Murchison, Taylor & Gibson · 16 North Fifth Avenue · Wilmington, NC 28401 · 910-763-2426

Winston-Salem

Jean Taylor Adams · Womble Carlyle Sandridge & Rice · One West Fourth Street · Winston-Salem, NC 27101 · 336-721-3600

C. Penn Craver, Jr. · Kilpatrick Stockton · 1001 West Fourth Street · Winston-Salem, NC 27101-2400 · 336-607-7300

Robert Leon Edwards · Kilpatrick Stockton · 1001 West Fourth Street · Winston-Salem, NC 27101-2400 336-607-7300

Gordon W. Jenkins · Wells Jenkins Lucas & Jenkins · 155 Sunnynoll Court, Suite 200 · Winston-Salem, NC 27106 · 336-725-2900

Elizabeth L. Quick · ⑳ · Womble Carlyle Sandridge & Rice · One West Fourth Street · Winston-Salem, NC 27101 · 336-721-3600

George A. Ragland · ⑩ · Womble Carlyle Sandridge & Rice · One West Fourth Street · Winston-Salem, NC 27101 · 336-721-3600

Amy K. Smith · Bell, Davis & Pitt · http://www.belldavispitt.com · Century Plaza, Suite 600 · 100 North Cherry Street · P.O. Box 21029 · Winston-Salem, NC 27120 · 336-722-3700

Kimberly H. Stogner · Vaughn Perkinson Ehlinger Moxley & Stogner · 4505 Country Club Road, Suite 210 · P.O. Box 25715 · Winston-Salem, NC 27114 · 336-794-6000

Neal E. Tackabery · Blanco Tackabery Combs & Matamoros · Stratford Point Building, Fifth Floor · 110 South Stratford Road · Winston-Salem, NC 27104-4299 · 336-293-9000

Robert C. Vaughn, Jr. · ㉕ · Vaughn Perkinson Ehlinger Moxley & Stogner · 4505 Country Club Road, Suite 210 · P.O. Box 25715 · Winston-Salem, NC 27114 · 336-794-6000

VENTURE CAPITAL LAW

Charlotte

T. Richard Giovannelli · K&L Gates · Hearst Tower, 47th Floor · 214 North Tryon Street · Charlotte, NC 28202 · 704-331-7400

Jeffrey S. Hay · Womble Carlyle Sandridge & Rice · One Wachovia Center, Suite 3500 · 301 South College Street · Charlotte, NC 28202-6037 · 704-331-4900

Haynes P. Lea · Robinson, Bradshaw & Hinson · http://www.rbh.com · 101 North Tryon Street, Suite 1900 · Charlotte, NC 28246-1900 · 704-377-2536

Harrison L. Marshall, Jr. · McGuireWoods · http://www.mcguirewoods.com · 201 North Tryon Street, Suite 3000 · P.O. Box 31247 · Charlotte, NC 28231 · 704-343-2000

Thomas A. Price · Womble Carlyle Sandridge & Rice · One Wachovia Center, Suite 3500 · 301 South College Street · Charlotte, NC 28202-6037 · 704-331-4900

Richard S. Starling · Robinson, Bradshaw & Hinson · http://www.rbh.com · 101 North Tryon Street, Suite 1900 · Charlotte, NC 28246-1900 · 704-377-2536

Paul A. Steffens · K&L Gates · Hearst Tower, 47th Floor · 214 North Tryon Street · Charlotte, NC 28202 · 704-331-7400

Kevin P. Stichter · K&L Gates · Hearst Tower, 47th Floor · 214 North Tryon Street · Charlotte, NC 28202 · 704-331-7400

Raleigh

Christopher B. Capel · Smith, Anderson, Blount, Dorsett, Mitchell & Jernigan · http://www.smithlaw.com · 2500 Wachovia Capitol Center · P.O. Box 2611 · Raleigh, NC 27602-2611 · 919-821-1220

Kenneth E. Eheman, Jr. · Wyrick Robbins Yates & Ponton · http://www.wyrick.com · The Summit, Suite 300 · 4101 Lake Boone Trail · P.O. Drawer 17803 · Raleigh, NC 27607-7506 · 919-781-4000

Byron B. Kirkland · Smith, Anderson, Blount, Dorsett, Mitchell & Jernigan · http://www.smithlaw.com · 2500 Wachovia Capitol Center · P.O. Box 2611 · Raleigh, NC 27602-2611 · 919-821-1220

J. Christopher Lynch · Wyrick Robbins Yates & Ponton · http://www.wyrick.com · The Summit, Suite 300 · 4101 Lake Boone Trail · P.O. Drawer 17803 · Raleigh, NC 27607-7506 · 919-781-4000

Merrill M. Mason · Smith, Anderson, Blount, Dorsett, Mitchell & Jernigan · http://www.smithlaw.com · 2500 Wachovia Capitol Center · P.O. Box 2611 · Raleigh, NC 27602-2611 · 919-821-1220

Gerald F. Roach · Smith, Anderson, Blount, Dorsett, Mitchell & Jernigan · http://www.smithlaw.com · 2500 Wachovia Capitol Center · P.O. Box 2611 · Raleigh, NC 27602-2611 · 919-821-1220

Larry E. Robbins · Wyrick Robbins Yates & Ponton · http://www.wyrick.com · The Summit, Suite 300 · 4101 Lake Boone Trail · P.O. Drawer 17803 · Raleigh, NC 27607-7506 · 919-781-4000

James F. Verdonik · ⑩ · Ward and Smith · http://www.wardandsmith.com · Wade II, Suite 400 · 5430 Wade Park Boulevard · P.O. Box 33009 · Raleigh, NC 27636-3009 · 919-277-9100

Winston-Salem

Jeffrey C. Howland · ⑩ · Womble Carlyle Sandridge & Rice · One West Fourth Street · Winston-Salem, NC 27101 · 336-721-3600

WATER LAW

Greensboro

George W. House · ⑳ · Brooks, Pierce, McLendon, Humphrey & Leonard · http://www.brookspierce.com · 2000 Renaissance Plaza · 230 North Elm Street · Greensboro, NC 27401 · 336-373-8850

Raleigh

H. Glenn Dunn · ⑳ · Poyner & Spruill · http://www.poynerspruill.com · 3600 Glenwood Avenue · P.O. Box 10096 · Raleigh, NC 27605-0096 · 919-783-6400

WHITE-COLLAR CRIMINAL DEFENSE

Asheville

Robert B. Long, Jr. · ⑩ · Long, Parker, Warren & Anderson · 14 South Pack Square, Suite 600 · P.O. Box 7216 · Asheville, NC 28802 · 828-258-2296

Chapel Hill

M. Gordon Widenhouse, Jr. · Rudolf Widenhouse & Fialko · http://www.rwf-law.com · 312 West Franklin Street · Chapel Hill, NC 27516 · 919-967-4900

Charlotte

Kenneth D. Bell · Hunton & Williams · Bank of America Plaza, Suite 3500 · 101 South Tryon Street · Charlotte, NC 28280 · 704-378-4700

Martin L. Brackett, Jr. · ⑩ · Robinson, Bradshaw & Hinson · http://www.rbh.com · 101 North Tryon Street, Suite 1900 · Charlotte, NC 28246-1900 · 704-377-2536

Mark T. Calloway · Alston + Bird · http://www.alston.com · Bank of America Plaza, Suite 4000 · 101 South Tryon Street · Charlotte, NC 28280-4000 · 704-444-1000

James P. Cooney III · ⑩ · Womble Carlyle Sandridge & Rice · One Wachovia Center, Suite 3500 · 301 South College Street · Charlotte, NC 28202-6037 · 704-331-4900

James E. Ferguson II · ㉕ · Ferguson Stein Chambers Gresham & Sumter · 741 Kenilworth Avenue, Suite 300 · Charlotte, NC 28204 · 704-375-8461

Christopher C. Fialko · Rudolf Widenhouse & Fialko · http://www.rwf-law.com · 1800 Camden Road, Suite 105 · Charlotte, NC 28203 · 704-333-9945

Richard S. Glaser, Jr. · Parker Poe Adams & Bernstein · http://www.parkerpoe.com · Three Wachovia Center, Suite 3000 · 401 South Tryon Street · Charlotte, NC 28202-1935 · 704-372-9000

Edward T. Hinson, Jr. · James, McElroy & Diehl · 600 South College Street, Suite 3000 · Charlotte, NC 28202 · 704-372-9870

E. Fitzgerald Parnell III · ⑩ · Poyner & Spruill · http://www.poynerspruill.com · One Wachovia Center, Suite 2300 · 301 South College Street · Charlotte, NC 28202-6021 · 704-342-5250

Eben T. Rawls III · Rawls, Dickinson & Scheer · 1011 East Morehead Street, Suite 300 · Charlotte, NC 28204 · 704-376-3200

David S. Rudolf · ⑩ · Rudolf Widenhouse & Fialko · http://www.rwf-law.com · 1800 Camden Road, Suite 105 · Charlotte, NC 28203 · 704-333-9945

Anne M. Tompkins · Alston + Bird · http://www.alston.com · Bank of America Plaza, Suite 4000 · 101 South Tryon Street · Charlotte, NC 28280-4000 · 704-444-1000

Thomas G. Walker · Alston + Bird · http://www.alston.com · Bank of America Plaza, Suite 4000 · 101 South Tryon Street · Charlotte, NC 28280-4000 · 704-444-1000

James F. Wyatt III · ⑩ · Wyatt & Blake · 435 East Morehead Street · Charlotte, NC 28202-2609 · 704-331-0767

Clinton

W. Douglas Parsons · ⑩ · Johnson, Parsons & Hobson · 500 College Street · P.O. Drawer 1049 · Clinton, NC 28329 · 910-592-7066

Fayetteville

H. Gerald Beaver · ⑩ · Beaver, Holt, Sternlicht & Courie · 230 Green Street · P.O. Box 2275 · Fayetteville, NC 28302 · 910-323-4600

Greensboro

Locke T. Clifford · ⑳ · Clifford, Clendenin & O'Hale · 415 West Friendly Avenue · Greensboro, NC 27401 · 336-378-1212

Charles A. Lloyd · ⑩ · Charles A. Lloyd · 301 South Greene Street, Suite 100 · Greensboro, NC 27401 · 336-275-9358

H. Davis North III · ⑩ · Cahoon, Swisher, North, Cooke and Landreth · First Citizen Bank Building, Suite 300 · 100 South Elm Street · P.O. Box 520 · Greensboro, NC 27401 · 336-275-1231

Greenville

Myron T. Hill, Jr. · Browning & Hill · 200 East Fourth Street · Greenville, NC 27858 · 252-758-1403

High Point

C. Richard Tate, Jr. · ㉕ · C. Richard Tate, Jr. · 115 West High Avenue · P.O. Box 2726 · High Point, NC 27261 · 336-885-0176

Pinehurst

James R. Van Camp · ㉕ · Van Camp, Meacham & Newman · Two Regional Circle · P.O. Box 1389 · Pinehurst, NC 28370 · 910-295-2525

Raleigh

R. Daniel Boyce · Boyce & Isley · Lawyers Weekly Building, Suite 100 · 107 Fayetteville Street Mall · P.O. Box 1990 · Raleigh, NC 27602-1990 · 919-833-7373

Joseph B. Cheshire V · ㉕ · Cheshire, Parker, Schneider, Bryan & Vitale · http://www.cheshirepark.com · 133 Fayetteville Street, Suite 500 · P.O. Box 1029 · Raleigh, NC 27602-1029 · 919-833-3114

Douglas E. Kingsbery · Tharrington Smith · http://www.tharringtonsmith.com · 209 Fayetteville Street · P.O. Box 1151 · Raleigh, NC 27602-1151 · 919-821-4711

David W. Long · ⑳ · Poyner & Spruill · http://www.poynerspruill.com · 3600 Glenwood Avenue · P.O. Box 10096 · Raleigh, NC 27605-0096 · 919-783-6400

Thomas Courtland Manning · ⑩ · Manning & Crouch · http://www.manningandcrouchlaw.com · 727 West Hargett Street, Suite 205 · P.O. Box 350 · Raleigh, NC 27602 · 919-828-5778

Roger W. Smith, Sr. · ㉕ · Tharrington Smith · http://www.tharringtonsmith.com · 209 Fayetteville Street P.O. Box 1151 · Raleigh, NC 27602-1151 · 919-821-4711

Stephen T. Smith · ⑩ · McMillan, Smith & Plyler · 205 West Martin Street · P.O. Box 150 · Raleigh, NC 27602 · 919-821-5124

Wade M. Smith · ㉕ · Tharrington Smith · http://www.tharringtonsmith.com · 209 Fayetteville Street · P.O. Box 1151 · Raleigh, NC 27602-1151 · 919-821-4711

Joseph E. Zeszotarski · Poyner & Spruill · http://www.poynerspruill.com · 3600 Glenwood Avenue · P.O. Box 10096 · Raleigh, NC 27605-0096 · 919-783-6400

Smithfield

John P. O'Hale · ⑩ · Narron, O'Hale & Whittington · 102 South Third Street · P.O. Box 1567 · Smithfield, NC 27577 · 919-934-6021

Wilson

Allen G. Thomas · Thomas & Farris · 104 West Nash Street · P.O. Box 2848 · Wilson, NC 27894 · 252-243-3000

Winston-Salem

Fred G. Crumpler, Jr. · ㉕ · Crumpler Freedman Parker & Witt · 301 North Main Street, Suite 1100 · Winston-Salem, NC 27101 · 336-725-1304

David B. Freedman · Crumpler Freedman Parker & Witt · 301 North Main Street, Suite 1100 · Winston-Salem, NC 27101 · 336-725-1304

Asheville

Sandra M. King · Russell & King · 17 North Market Street · P.O. Box 7668 · Asheville, NC 28802 · 828-252-7651

J. William Russell · ⑩ · Russell & King · 17 North Market Street · P.O. Box 7668 · Asheville, NC 28802 · 828-252-7651

Cary

R. James Lore · ⑩ · R. James Lore · 102 Commonwealth Court, Suite I · Cary, NC 27511 · 919-833-4509

Chapel Hill

Leto Copeley · Patterson Harkavy · 100 Europa Drive, Suite 250 · Chapel Hill, NC 27517 · 919-942-5200

Valerie A. Johnson · Patterson Harkavy · 100 Europa Drive, Suite 250 · Chapel Hill, NC 27517 · 919-942-5200

Henry N. Patterson, Jr. · ㉕ · Patterson Harkavy · 100 Europa Drive, Suite 250 · Chapel Hill, NC 27517 · 919-942-5200

Charlotte

M. Andrew Avram · Cranfill, Sumner & Hartzog · http://www.cshlaw.com · 2907 Providence Road, Suite 200 · P.O. Box 30787 · Charlotte, NC 28202 · 704-332-8300

Bobby L. Bollinger, Jr. · Bollinger & Piemonte · http://www.bollingerandpiemonte.com · 601 East Fifth Street, Suite 250 · Charlotte, NC 28202-3095 · 704-373-1777

Henry C. Byrum, Jr. · Stiles, Byrum & Horne · The Arlington, Suite 650 · 325 Arlington Avenue · Charlotte, NC 28203 · 704-332-2830

Jack A. Gardner III · ⑩ · Hedrick, Gardner, Kincheloe & Garofalo · 6000 Fairview Road, Suite 1000 · P.O. Box 30397 · Charlotte, NC 28230 · 704-366-1101

Hatcher B. Kincheloe · Hedrick, Gardner, Kincheloe & Garofalo · 6000 Fairview Road, Suite 1000 · P.O. Box 30397 · Charlotte, NC 28230 · 704-366-1101

Robert G. Spratt III · Jones, Hewson & Woolard · The Addison Building, Suite 560 · 831 East Morehead Street · Charlotte, NC 28202 · 704-372-6541

Mark T. Sumwalt · ⑩ · The Sumwalt Law Firm · 1114 East Boulevard · Charlotte, NC 28203 · 704-377-3770

Vernon Sumwalt · The Sumwalt Law Firm · 1114 East Boulevard · Charlotte, NC 28203 · 704-377-3770

Gastonia

H. Randolph Sumner · Mullen, Holland & Cooper · 301 South York Street · P.O. Box 488 · Gastonia, NC 28053-0488 · 704-864-2634

Greensboro

Harry H. Clendenin III · Clifford, Clendenin & O'Hale · 415 West Friendly Avenue · Greensboro, NC 27401 · 336-378-1212

Jay A. Gervasi, Jr. · Jay A. Gervasi · 910 North Elm Street · Greensboro, NC 27401 · 336-574-0174

Caroline Hudson Lock · Smith Moore Leatherwood · http://www.smithmoorelaw.com · 300 North Greene Street, Suite 1400 · P.O. Box 21927 · Greensboro, NC 27420-1927 · 336-378-5200

Margaret F. Rowlett · Smith, James, Rowlett & Cohen · 101 South Elm Street, Suite 310 · P.O. Box 990 · Greensboro, NC 27402 · 336-274-2992

Jeri L. Whitfield · ⑩ · Smith Moore Leatherwood · http://www.smithmoorelaw.com · 300 North Greene Street, Suite 1400 · P.O. Box 21927 · Greensboro, NC 27420-1927 · 336-378-5200

New Bern

S. McKinley Gray III · Ward and Smith · http://www.wardandsmith.com · 1001 College Court · P.O. Box 867 · New Bern, NC 28563-0867 · 252-672-5400

Raleigh

William J. Austin, Jr. · Ward and Smith · http://www.wardandsmith.com · Wade II, Suite 400 · 5430 Wade Park Boulevard · P.O. Box 33009 · Raleigh, NC 27636-3009 · 919-277-9100

P. Collins Barwick III · Cranfill, Sumner & Hartzog · http://www.cshlaw.com · 5420 Wade Park Boulevard · P.O. Box 27808 · Raleigh, NC 27611-7808 · 919-828-5100

Paul L. Cranfill · ⑩ · Cranfill, Sumner & Hartzog · http://www.cshlaw.com · 5420 Wade Park Boulevard · P.O. Box 27808 · Raleigh, NC 27611-7808 · 919-828-5100

George W. Dennis III · ⑩ · Teague, Campbell, Dennis & Gorham · 4800 Six Forks Road, Suite 300 · P.O. Box 19207 · Raleigh, NC 27619-9207 · 919-873-0166

N. Victor Farah · The Jernigan Law Firm · Wachovia Capitol Center, Suite 1910 · 150 Fayetteville Street P.O. Box 847 · Raleigh, NC 27602-0847 · 919-833-1283

Dayle A. Flammia · Teague, Campbell, Dennis & Gorham · 4800 Six Forks Road, Suite 300 · P.O. Box 19207 · Raleigh, NC 27619-9207 · 919-873-0166

W. Scott Fuller · Cranfill, Sumner & Hartzog · http://www.cshlaw.com · 5420 Wade Park Boulevard · P.O. Box 27808 · Raleigh, NC 27611-7808 · 919-828-5100

Bruce Alan Hamilton · Teague, Campbell, Dennis & Gorham · 4800 Six Forks Road, Suite 300 · P.O. Box 19207 · Raleigh, NC 27619-9207 · 919-873-0166

Charles R. Hassell, Jr. · Charles R. Hassell · 115 South St. Marys Street · Raleigh, NC 27603-1617 · 919-828-8746

Jack Spain Holmes · McAngus, Goudelock & Courie · 5400 Glenwood Avenue, Suite G-02 · P.O. Box 30516 · Raleigh, NC 27622 · 919-719-8200

Leonard T. Jernigan, Jr. · ⑩ · The Jernigan Law Firm · Wachovia Capitol Center, Suite 1910 · 150 Fayetteville Street · P.O. Box 847 · Raleigh, NC 27602-0847 · 919-833-1283

Robert C. Kerner · Teague, Campbell, Dennis & Gorham · 4800 Six Forks Road, Suite 300 · P.O. Box 19207 · Raleigh, NC 27619-9207 · 919-873-0166

Kirk D. Kuhns · Cranfill, Sumner & Hartzog · http://www.cshlaw.com · 5420 Wade Park Boulevard · P.O. Box 27808 · Raleigh, NC 27611-7808 · 919-828-5100

Brian D. Lake · Lewis & Roberts · 3700 Glenwood Avenue, Suite 410 · P.O. Box 17529 · Raleigh, NC 27619-7529 · 919-981-0191

George W. Lennon · Lennon & Camak · 425 North Boylan Avenue · Raleigh, NC 27603 · 919-856-9000

Richard M. Lewis · ⑩ · Lewis & Roberts · 3700 Glenwood Avenue, Suite 410 · P.O. Box 17529 · Raleigh, NC 27619-7529 · 919-981-0191

Tamara Nance · Teague, Campbell, Dennis & Gorham · 4800 Six Forks Road, Suite 300 · P.O. Box 19207 Raleigh, NC 27619-9207 · 919-873-0166

C. D. Taylor Pace · Cranfill, Sumner & Hartzog · http://www.cshlaw.com · 5420 Wade Park Boulevard · P.O. Box 27808 · Raleigh, NC 27611-7808 · 919-828-5100

Winston L. Page, Jr. · ⑩ · Lewis & Roberts · 3700 Glenwood Avenue, Suite 410 · P.O. Box 17529 · Raleigh, NC 27619-7529 · 919-981-0191

Timothy S. Riordan · Lewis & Roberts · 3700 Glenwood Avenue, Suite 410 · P.O. Box 17529 · Raleigh, NC 27619-7529 · 919-981-0191

Samuel A. Scudder · Scudder & Hedrick · 5104-D Western Boulevard · Raleigh, NC 27606 · 919-851-3311

Robin H. Terry · Cranfill, Sumner & Hartzog · http://www.cshlaw.com · 5420 Wade Park Boulevard · P.O. Box 27808 · Raleigh, NC 27611-7808 · 919-828-5100

Rockingham

Woodrow W. Gunter II · ⑩ · Woodrow W. Gunter, II · 219 East Franklin Street · P.O. Drawer 249 · Rockingham, NC 28380 · 910-997-5558

Rocky Mount

Ralph G. Willey III · Ralph G. Willey · 3202 Sunset Avenue, Suite A · P.O. Box 7846 · Rocky Mount, NC 27804 · 252-443-1117

Sylva

Richard B. Harper · Richard B. Harper · 1336 Savannah Drive · P.O. Box 395 · Sylva, NC 28779 · 828-586-3305

Wilmington

Kathleen S. Glancy · Law Firms of Kathleen Shannon Glancy · 114 South Front Street · Wilmington, NC 28401 · 910-762-6091

Winston-Salem

Maureen Geraghty · The Geraghty Law Firm · 426 Old Salem Road · Winston-Salem, NC 27101 · 336-714-1199

Celeste M. Harris · Maynard & Harris · The Stratford Oaks Building · 514 South Stratford Road · Winston-Salem, NC 27103 · 336-777-1411

Jane C. Jackson · Robinson & Lawing · http://www.robinson-lawing.com · 101 North Cherry Street, Suite 720 · Winston-Salem, NC 27101 · 336-631-8500

J. Griffin Morgan · ⑩ · Elliot Pishko Morgan · 426 Old Salem Road · Winston-Salem, NC 27101 · 336-724-2828

Charlot F. Wood · Bell, Davis & Pitt · http://www.belldavispitt.com · Century Plaza, Suite 600 · 100 North Cherry Street · P.O. Box 21029 · Winston-Salem, NC 27120 · 336-722-3700

NORTH DAKOTA

ADMINISTRATIVE LAW

Bismarck

Joel W. Gilbertson · Vogel Law Firm · 200 North Third Street, Suite 201 · P.O. Box 2097 · Bismarck, ND 58502-2097 · 701-258-7899

ALTERNATIVE DISPUTE RESOLUTION

Bismarck

Rebecca S. Thiem · a · Zuger Kirmis & Smith · Provident Life Building · 316 North Fifth Street · P.O. Box 1695 · Bismarck, ND 58502-1695 · 701-223-2711

Fargo

Jack G. Marcil · 2) · Serkland Law Firm · 10 Roberts Street · P.O. Box 6017 · Fargo, ND 58108-6017 · 701-232-8957

Roger J. Minch · a · Serkland Law Firm · 10 Roberts Street · P.O. Box 6017 · Fargo, ND 58108-6017 · 701-232-8957

BANKING LAW

Grand Forks

John S. Foster · 2) · Zimney, Foster, Johnson, Dittus & Flaten · 3100 South Columbia Road, Suite 200 · P.O. Box 13417 · Grand Forks, ND 58208-3417 · 701-772-8111

Minot

Richard P. Olson · 2) · Olson, Burns & Lee · 17 First Avenue, SE · P.O. Box 1180 · Minot, ND 58702-1180 · 701-839-1740

BANKRUPTCY AND CREDITOR-DEBTOR RIGHTS LAW

Bismarck

LaRoy Baird III · a · LaRoy Baird · 109 North Fourth Street, Suite 300 · P.O. Box 913 · Bismarck, ND 58502-0913 · 701-223-6400

Jack McDonald · a · Wheeler Wolf · 220 North Fourth Street · P.O. Box 1776 · Bismarck, ND 58502-1776 · 701-751-1776

Sean O. Smith · Tschider & Smith · 418 East Rosser Avenue, Suite 200 · Bismarck, ND 58501-4046 · 701-258-4000

Fargo

Lowell P. Bottrell · a · Anderson & Bottrell · 4132 Thirtieth Avenue South, Suite 100 · P.O. Box 10247 · Fargo, ND 58106-0247 · 701-235-3300

Jon R. Brakke · a · Vogel Law Firm · 218 NP Avenue · P.O. Box 1389 · Fargo, ND 58107-1389 · 701-237-6983

David L. Johnson · a · McNair, Larson & Carlson · Dakota Center Building, Suite 600 · 51 Broadway · P.O. Box 2189 · Fargo, ND 58108-2189 · 701-293-9190

Roger J. Minch · a · Serkland Law Firm · 10 Roberts Street · P.O. Box 6017 · Fargo, ND 58108-6017 · 701-232-8957

Grand Forks

John S. Foster · 2) · Zimney, Foster, Johnson, Dittus & Flaten · 3100 South Columbia Road, Suite 200 · P.O. Box 13417 · Grand Forks, ND 58208-3417 · 701-772-8111

Minot

Richard P. Olson · 2) · Olson, Burns & Lee · 17 First Avenue, SE · P.O. Box 1180 · Minot, ND 58702-1180 · 701-839-1740

COMMERCIAL LITIGATION

Bismarck

Malcolm H. Brown · 2) · Malcolm H. Brown · 209 East Broadway Avenue · P.O. Box 2692 · Bismarck, ND 58502-2692 · 701-224-8825

Lyle W. Kirmis · 2) · Zuger Kirmis & Smith · Provident Life Building · 316 North Fifth Street · P.O. Box 1695 · Bismarck, ND 58502-1695 · 701-223-2711

David S. Maring · Maring Williams · 400 East Broadway, Suite 307 · Bismarck, ND 58501-0795 · 701-224-0430

Steven A. Storslee · a · Storslee Law Firm · 1900 Burnt Boat Drive, Suite 101 · P.O. Box 4007 · Bismarck, ND 58502-4007 · 701-222-1315

Rebecca S. Thiem · a · Zuger Kirmis & Smith · Provident Life Building · 316 North Fifth Street · P.O. Box 1695 · Bismarck, ND 58502-1695 · 701-223-2711

H. Patrick Weir, Sr. · a · Vogel Law Firm · 200 North Third Street, Suite 201 · P.O. Box 2097 · Bismarck, ND 58502-2097 · 701-258-7899

Fargo

Bruce H. Carlson · McNair, Larson & Carlson · Dakota Center Building, Suite 600 · 51 Broadway · P.O. Box 2189 · Fargo, ND 58108-2189 · 701-293-9190

Ronald H. McLean · Serkland Law Firm · 10 Roberts Street · P.O. Box 6017 · Fargo, ND 58108-6017 · 701-232-8957

Roger J. Minch · a · Serkland Law Firm · 10 Roberts Street · P.O. Box 6017 · Fargo, ND 58108-6017 · 701-232-8957

Stephen W. Plambeck · a · Nilles Law Firm · 1800 Radisson Tower · 201 North Fifth Street · P.O. Box 2626 · Fargo, ND 58108 · 701-237-5544

Todd E. Zimmerman · Dorsey & Whitney · Dakota Center, Suite 402 · 51B North Broadway · Fargo, ND 58107-1344 · 701-235-6000

Grand Forks

Ronald F. Fischer · Pearson Christensen & Clapp · 24 North Fourth Street · P.O. Box 5758 · Grand Forks, ND 58206-5758 · 701-775-0521

John S. Foster · 2) · Zimney, Foster, Johnson, Dittus & Flaten · 3100 South Columbia Road, Suite 200 · P.O. Box 13417 · Grand Forks, ND 58208-3417 · 701-772-8111

Minot

Richard P. Olson · 2) · Olson, Burns & Lee · 17 First Avenue, SE · P.O. Box 1180 · Minot, ND 58702-1180 · 701-839-1740

CORPORATE LAW

Bismarck

Malcolm H. Brown · 2) · Malcolm H. Brown · 209 East Broadway Avenue · P.O. Box 2692 · Bismarck, ND 58502-2692 · 701-224-8825

Lyle W. Kirmis · 2) · Zuger Kirmis & Smith · Provident Life Building · 316 North Fifth Street · P.O. Box 1695 · Bismarck, ND 58502-1695 · 701-223-2711

William P. Pearce · 2) · Fredrikson & Byron · 200 North Third Street, Suite 150 · Bismarck, ND 58501-3879 · 701-221-4020

Sean O. Smith · Tschider & Smith · 418 East Rosser Avenue, Suite 200 · Bismarck, ND 58501-4046 · 701-258-4000

Fargo

Steve A. Johnson · Vogel Law Firm · 218 NP Avenue · P.O. Box 1389 · Fargo, ND 58107-1389 · 701-237-6983

William A. Schlossman, Jr. · Vogel Law Firm · 218 NP Avenue · P.O. Box 1389 · Fargo, ND 58107-1389 701-237-6983

Brad A. Sinclair · Serkland Law Firm · 10 Roberts Street · P.O. Box 6017 · Fargo, ND 58108-6017 · 701-232-8957

Jon E. Strinden · Dorsey & Whitney · Dakota Center, Suite 402 · 51B North Broadway · Fargo, ND 58107-1344 · 701-235-6000

Michael M. Thomas · Conmy Feste · 200 Wells Fargo Center · 406 Main Avenue · P.O. Box 2686 · Fargo, ND 58103 · 701-293-9911

Grand Forks

Garry A. Pearson · 2) · Pearson Christensen & Clapp · 24 North Fourth Street · P.O. Box 5758 · Grand Forks, ND 58206-5758 · 701-775-0521

Minot

Richard P. Olson · 2) · Olson, Burns & Lee · 17 First Avenue, SE · P.O. Box 1180 · Minot, ND 58702-1180 · 701-839-1740

DUI/DWI DEFENSE

Fargo

Bruce Douglas Quick · a · Vogel Law Firm · 218 NP Avenue · P.O. Box 1389 · Fargo, ND 58107-1389 · 701-237-6983

EMPLOYEE BENEFITS LAW

Fargo

C. Nicholas Vogel · 2) · Vogel Law Firm · 218 NP Avenue · P.O. Box 1389 · Fargo, ND 58107-1389 · 701-237-6983

ENERGY LAW

Bismarck

Lawrence X. Bender · Fredrikson & Byron · 200 North Third Street, Suite 150 · Bismarck, ND 58501-3879 · 701-221-4020

John W. Morrison, Jr. · a · Fleck, Mather & Strutz · Wells Fargo Bank Building, Suite 600 · 400 East Broadway · P.O. Box 2798 · Bismarck, ND 58502-2798 · 701-223-6585

William P. Pearce · 2) · Fredrikson & Byron · 200 North Third Street, Suite 150 · Bismarck, ND 58501-3879 · 701-221-4020

Williston

Fred C. Rathert · 2) · Crowley, Haughey, Hanson, Toole & Dietrich · http://www.crowleylaw.com · 111 East Broadway · P.O. Box 1206 · Williston, ND 58802-1206 · 701-572-2200

ENVIRONMENTAL LAW

Fargo

Tami Norgard · Vogel Law Firm · 218 NP Avenue · P.O. Box 1389 · Fargo, ND 58107-1389 · 701-237-6983

FAMILY LAW

Fargo

Wayne T. Anderson · a · Wayne T. Anderson · 2108 South University Drive, Suite 103 · Fargo, ND 58103-5348 · 701-293-3400

James R. Brothers · 2) · Wold Johnson · 500 Second Avenue North, Suite 400 · P.O. Box 1680 · Fargo, ND 58107 · 701-235-5515

Maureen Holman · a · Serkland Law Firm · 10 Roberts Street · P.O. Box 6017 · Fargo, ND 58108-6017 · 701-232-8957

Grand Forks

Scott D. Jensen · Camrud, Maddock, Olson & Larson · 401 DeMers Avenue, Suite 500 · P.O. Box 5849 · Grand Forks, ND 58206-5849 · 701-775-5595

FIRST AMENDMENT LAW

Bismarck

Patrick W. Durick · a · Pearce & Durick · 314 East Thayer Avenue, Third Floor · P.O. Box 400 · Bismarck, ND 58502 · 701-223-2890

Jack McDonald · a · Wheeler Wolf · 220 North Fourth Street · P.O. Box 1776 · Bismarck, ND 58502-1776 · 701-751-1776

GOVERNMENT RELATIONS LAW

Bismarck

Joel W. Gilbertson · Vogel Law Firm · 200 North Third Street, Suite 201 · P.O. Box 2097 · Bismarck, ND 58502-2097 · 701-258-7899

John M. Olson · John M. Olson · 418 East Broadway Avenue, Suite Nine · Bismarck, ND 58501 · 701-222-3485

HEALTH CARE LAW

Bismarck

Michael C. Waller · Fleck, Mather & Strutz · Wells Fargo Bank Building, Suite 600 · 400 East Broadway · P.O. Box 2798 · Bismarck, ND 58502-2798 · 701-223-6585

H. Patrick Weir, Sr. · a · Vogel Law Firm · 200 North Third Street, Suite 201 · P.O. Box 2097 · Bismarck, ND 58502-2097 · 701-258-7899

Fargo

Angela E. Lord · Vogel Law Firm · 218 NP Avenue · P.O. Box 1389 · Fargo, ND 58107-1389 · 701-237-6983

INSURANCE LAW

Fargo

Carlton J. Hunke · 2) · Vogel Law Firm · 218 NP Avenue · P.O. Box 1389 · Fargo, ND 58107-1389 · 701-237-6983

LABOR AND EMPLOYMENT LAW

Bismarck

Patrick J. Ward · a · Zuger Kirmis & Smith · Provident Life Building · 316 North Fifth Street · P.O. Box 1695 · Bismarck, ND 58502-1695 · 701-223-2711

Fargo

Michelle M. Donarski · Anderson & Bottrell · 4132 Thirtieth Avenue South, Suite 100 · P.O. Box 10247 · Fargo, ND 58106-0247 · 701-235-3300

Sarah A. Herman · a · Dorsey & Whitney · Dakota Center, Suite 402 · 51B North Broadway · Fargo, ND 58107-1344 · 701-235-6000

Daniel E. Phillips · Solberg, Stewart, Miller & Tjon · 1129 Fifth Avenue South · P.O. Box 1897 · Fargo, ND 58107-1897 · 701-237-3166

Benjamin Eugene Thomas · Wold Johnson · 500 Second Avenue North, Suite 400 · P.O. Box 1680 · Fargo, ND 58107 · 701-235-5515

LEGAL MALPRACTICE LAW

Grand Forks

Randall S. Hanson · Camrud, Maddock, Olson & Larson · 401 DeMers Avenue, Suite 500 · P.O. Box 5849 · Grand Forks, ND 58206-5849 · 701-775-5595

MEDICAL MALPRACTICE LAW

Bismarck

Brenda L. Blazer · Vogel Law Firm · 200 North Third Street, Suite 201 · P.O. Box 2097 · Bismarck, ND 58502-2097 · 701-258-7899

Lance D. Schreiner · a · Zuger Kirmis & Smith · Provident Life Building · 316 North Fifth Street · P.O. Box 1695 · Bismarck, ND 58502-1695 · 701-223-2711

Grand Forks

Randall S. Hanson · Camrud, Maddock, Olson & Larson · 401 DeMers Avenue, Suite 500 · P.O. Box 5849 · Grand Forks, ND 58206-5849 · 701-775-5595

Patrick J. Maddock · a · Camrud, Maddock, Olson & Larson · 401 DeMers Avenue, Suite 500 · P.O. Box 5849 · Grand Forks, ND 58206-5849 · 701-775-5595

MERGERS & ACQUISITIONS LAW

Bismarck

Sean O. Smith · Tschider & Smith · 418 East Rosser Avenue, Suite 200 · Bismarck, ND 58501-4046 · 701-258-4000

Fargo

Steve A. Johnson · Vogel Law Firm · 218 NP Avenue · P.O. Box 1389 · Fargo, ND 58107-1389 · 701-237-6983

William A. Schlossman, Jr. · Vogel Law Firm · 218 NP Avenue · P.O. Box 1389 · Fargo, ND 58107-1389 701-237-6983

Brad A. Sinclair · Serkland Law Firm · 10 Roberts Street · P.O. Box 6017 · Fargo, ND 58108-6017 · 701-232-8957

Michael M. Thomas · Conmy Feste · 200 Wells Fargo Center · 406 Main Avenue · P.O. Box 2686 · Fargo, ND 58103 · 701-293-9911

NATURAL RESOURCES LAW

Bismarck

Lawrence X. Bender · Fredrikson & Byron · 200 North Third Street, Suite 150 · Bismarck, ND 58501-3879 · 701-221-4020

Brian R. Bjella · Fleck, Mather & Strutz · Wells Fargo Bank Building, Suite 600 · 400 East Broadway · P.O. Box 2798 · Bismarck, ND 58502-2798 · 701-223-6585

John W. Morrison, Jr. · a · Fleck, Mather & Strutz · Wells Fargo Bank Building, Suite 600 · 400 East Broadway · P.O. Box 2798 · Bismarck, ND 58502-2798 · 701-223-6585

William P. Pearce · 2) · Fredrikson & Byron · 200 North Third Street, Suite 150 · Bismarck, ND 58501-3879 · 701-221-4020

Williston

Fred C. Rathert · 2) · Crowley, Haughey, Hanson, Toole & Dietrich · http://www.crowleylaw.com · 111 East Broadway · P.O. Box 1206 · Williston, ND 58802-1206 · 701-572-2200

NON-WHITE-COLLAR CRIMINAL DEFENSE

Bismarck

Thomas A. Dickson · a · Dickson Law Office · Tuscany Square, Suite 150 · 107 West Main Street · P.O. Box 1896 · Bismarck, ND 58502-1896 · 701-222-4400

Michael R. Hoffman · a · Michael R. Hoffman · 120 North Third Street, Suite 100 · P.O. Box 1056 · Bismarck, ND 58502-1056 · 701-355-0900

Irvin B. Nodland · 2) · Nodland Law Offices · 109 North Fourth Street, Suite 300 · P.O. Box 640 · Bismarck, ND 58502 · 701-222-3030

Ralph A. Vinje · 2) · Vinje Law Firm · 523 North Fourth Street, Suite Three · Bismarck, ND 58501-4055 · 701-258-9475

Fargo

Bruce Douglas Quick · a · Vogel Law Firm · 218 NP Avenue · P.O. Box 1389 · Fargo, ND 58107-1389 · 701-237-6983

OIL & GAS LAW

Bismarck

Lawrence X. Bender · Fredrikson & Byron · 200 North Third Street, Suite 150 · Bismarck, ND 58501-3879 · 701-221-4020

John W. Morrison, Jr. · a · Fleck, Mather & Strutz · Wells Fargo Bank Building, Suite 600 · 400 East Broadway · P.O. Box 2798 · Bismarck, ND 58502-2798 · 701-223-6585

William P. Pearce · 2) · Fredrikson & Byron · 200 North Third Street, Suite 150 · Bismarck, ND 58501-3879 · 701-221-4020

Williston

Fred C. Rathert · 2) · Crowley, Haughey, Hanson, Toole & Dietrich · http://www.crowleylaw.com · 111 East Broadway · P.O. Box 1206 · Williston, ND 58802-1206 · 701-572-2200

PERSONAL INJURY LITIGATION

Bismarck

Thomas A. Dickson · a · Dickson Law Office · Tuscany Square, Suite 150 · 107 West Main Street · P.O. Box 1896 · Bismarck, ND 58502-1896 · 701-222-4400

B. Timothy Durick · 2) · Pearce & Durick · 314 East Thayer Avenue, Third Floor · P.O. Box 400 · Bismarck, ND 58502 · 701-223-2890

Patrick W. Durick · a · Pearce & Durick · 314 East Thayer Avenue, Third Floor · P.O. Box 400 · Bismarck, ND 58502 · 701-223-2890

James S. Hill · a · Zuger Kirmis & Smith · Provident Life Building · 316 North Fifth Street · P.O. Box 1695 · Bismarck, ND 58502-1695 · 701-223-2711

Irvin B. Nodland · 2) · Nodland Law Offices · 109 North Fourth Street, Suite 300 · P.O. Box 640 · Bismarck, ND 58502 · 701-222-3030

Lance D. Schreiner · a · Zuger Kirmis & Smith · Provident Life Building · 316 North Fifth Street · P.O. Box 1695 · Bismarck, ND 58502-1695 · 701-223-2711

Steven A. Storslee · a · Storslee Law Firm · 1900 Burnt Boat Drive, Suite 101 · P.O. Box 4007 · Bismarck, ND 58502-4007 · 701-222-1315

Patrick J. Ward · a · Zuger Kirmis & Smith · Provident Life Building · 316 North Fifth Street · P.O. Box 1695 · Bismarck, ND 58502-1695 · 701-223-2711

H. Patrick Weir, Sr. · a · Vogel Law Firm · 200 North Third Street, Suite 201 · P.O. Box 2097 · Bismarck, ND 58502-2097 · 701-258-7899

Fargo

David R. Bossart · 2) · David R. Bossart · 1220 Main Avenue, Suite 105 · P.O. Box 2187 · Fargo, ND 58108-2187 · 701-271-8030

Carlton J. Hunke · 2) · Vogel Law Firm · 218 NP Avenue · P.O. Box 1389 · Fargo, ND 58107-1389 · 701-237-6983

Duane H. Ilvedson · 2) · Nilles Law Firm · 1800 Radisson Tower · 201 North Fifth Street · P.O. Box 2626 Fargo, ND 58108 · 701-237-5544

Jack G. Marcil · 2) · Serkland Law Firm · 10 Roberts Street · P.O. Box 6017 · Fargo, ND 58108-6017 · 701-232-8957

Grand Forks

Richard A. Clapp · Pearson Christensen & Clapp · 24 North Fourth Street · P.O. Box 5758 · Grand Forks, ND 58206-5758 · 701-775-0521

Ronald F. Fischer · Pearson Christensen & Clapp · 24 North Fourth Street · P.O. Box 5758 · Grand Forks, ND 58206-5758 · 701-775-0521

Randall S. Hanson · Camrud, Maddock, Olson & Larson · 401 DeMers Avenue, Suite 500 · P.O. Box 5849 · Grand Forks, ND 58206-5849 · 701-775-5595

Patrick J. Maddock · a · Camrud, Maddock, Olson & Larson · 401 DeMers Avenue, Suite 500 · P.O. Box 5849 · Grand Forks, ND 58206-5849 · 701-775-5595

Minot

Richard H. McGee II · a · McGee, Hankla, Backes & Dobrovolny · Wells Fargo Bank Center, Suite 305 15 Second Avenue, SW · P.O. Box 998 · Minot, ND 58702-0998 · 701-852-2544

PRODUCT LIABILITY LITIGATION

Bismarck

Patrick W. Durick · a · Pearce & Durick · 314 East Thayer Avenue, Third Floor · P.O. Box 400 · Bismarck, ND 58502 · 701-223-2890

Dickinson

Paul F. Ebeltoft, Jr. · Mackoff, Kellogg, Kirby & Kloster · 46 West Second Street · P.O. Box 1097 · Dickinson, ND 58602-1097 · 701-227-1841

Fargo

Jack G. Marcil · 2) · Serkland Law Firm · 10 Roberts Street · P.O. Box 6017 · Fargo, ND 58108-6017 · 701-232-8957

M. Daniel Vogel · Vogel Law Firm · 218 NP Avenue · P.O. Box 1389 · Fargo, ND 58107-1389 · 701-237-6983

Todd E. Zimmerman · Dorsey & Whitney · Dakota Center, Suite 402 · 51B North Broadway · Fargo, ND 58107-1344 · 701-235-6000

PROFESSIONAL MALPRACTICE LAW

Bismarck

Michael C. Waller · Fleck, Mather & Strutz · Wells Fargo Bank Building, Suite 600 · 400 East Broadway · P.O. Box 2798 · Bismarck, ND 58502-2798 · 701-223-6585

Fargo

M. Daniel Vogel · Vogel Law Firm · 218 NP Avenue · P.O. Box 1389 · Fargo, ND 58107-1389 · 701-237-6983

REAL ESTATE LAW

Bismarck

Jack McDonald · a · Wheeler Wolf · 220 North Fourth Street · P.O. Box 1776 · Bismarck, ND 58502-1776 · 701-751-1776

Fargo

Daniel A. Bueide · Vogel Law Firm · 218 NP Avenue · P.O. Box 1389 · Fargo, ND 58107-1389 · 701-237-6983

Paul M. Hubbard · 2) · Conmy Feste · 200 Wells Fargo Center · 406 Main Avenue · P.O. Box 2686 · Fargo, ND 58103 · 701-293-9911

J. Philip Johnson · a · Wold Johnson · 500 Second Avenue North, Suite 400 · P.O. Box 1680 · Fargo, ND 58107 · 701-235-5515

Dean A. Rindy · Stroup & Rindy · 3137 Thirty-Second Avenue, SW, Suite 212 · Fargo, ND 58103 · 701-271-8500

Robert L. Stroup II · 2) · Stroup & Rindy · 3137 Thirty-Second Avenue, SW, Suite 212 · Fargo, ND 58103 · 701-271-8500

West Fargo

David L. Wanner · Ohnstad Twichell · 901 Thirteenth Avenue East, Suite B · P.O. Box 458 · West Fargo, ND 58078-0458 · 701-282-3249

TAX LAW

Fargo

C. Nicholas Vogel · 2) · Vogel Law Firm · 218 NP Avenue · P.O. Box 1389 · Fargo, ND 58107-1389 · 701-237-6983

Grand Forks

Jon J. Jensen · Pearson Christensen & Clapp · 24 North Fourth Street · P.O. Box 5758 · Grand Forks, ND 58206-5758 · 701-775-0521

Garry A. Pearson · 2) · Pearson Christensen & Clapp · 24 North Fourth Street · P.O. Box 5758 · Grand Forks, ND 58206-5758 · 701-775-0521

TRUSTS AND ESTATES

Fargo

C. Nicholas Vogel · 2) · Vogel Law Firm · 218 NP Avenue · P.O. Box 1389 · Fargo, ND 58107-1389 · 701-237-6983

Grand Forks

Garry A. Pearson · 2) · Pearson Christensen & Clapp · 24 North Fourth Street · P.O. Box 5758 · Grand Forks, ND 58206-5758 · 701-775-0521

West Fargo

Robert E. Rosenvold · a · Ohnstad Twichell · 901 Thirteenth Avenue East, Suite B · P.O. Box 458 · West Fargo, ND 58078-0458 · 701-282-3249

David L. Wanner · Ohnstad Twichell · 901 Thirteenth Avenue East, Suite B · P.O. Box 458 · West Fargo, ND 58078-0458 · 701-282-3249

WHITE-COLLAR CRIMINAL DEFENSE

Bismarck

Thomas A. Dickson · a · Dickson Law Office · Tuscany Square, Suite 150 · 107 West Main Street · P.O. Box 1896 · Bismarck, ND 58502-1896 · 701-222-4400

Michael R. Hoffman · a · Michael R. Hoffman · 120 North Third Street, Suite 100 · P.O. Box 1056 · Bismarck, ND 58502-1056 · 701-355-0900

Irvin B. Nodland · 2) · Nodland Law Offices · 109 North Fourth Street, Suite 300 · P.O. Box 640 · Bismarck, ND 58502 · 701-222-3030

Ralph A. Vinje · 2) · Vinje Law Firm · 523 North Fourth Street, Suite Three · Bismarck, ND 58501-4055 701-258-9475

Fargo

Bruce Douglas Quick · a · Vogel Law Firm · 218 NP Avenue · P.O. Box 1389 · Fargo, ND 58107-1389 · 701-237-6983

Bismarck

Kathryn L. Dietz · a · Dietz & Little Lawyers · Gateway Office Building, Suite 302 · 2718 Gateway Avenue · Bismarck, ND 58503-0585 · 701-222-1761

Lawrence A. Dopson · Zuger Kirmis & Smith · Provident Life Building · 316 North Fifth Street · P.O. Box 1695 · Bismarck, ND 58502-1695 · 701-223-2711

Stephen D. Little · a · Dietz & Little Lawyers · Gateway Office Building, Suite 302 · 2718 Gateway Avenue · Bismarck, ND 58503-0585 · 701-222-1761

Fargo

Mark G. Schneider · a · Schneider, Schneider & Schneider · 815 Third Avenue South · Fargo, ND 58103 · 701-235-4481

Steven C. Schneider · a · Schneider, Schneider & Schneider · 815 Third Avenue South · Fargo, ND 58103 · 701-235-4481

OHIO

ADMINISTRATIVE LAW

Chagrin Falls

Dennis A. Roth · a · Dennis A. Roth · 110 Farwood Drive · Chagrin Falls, OH 44022-6582 · 216-952-8649

Cincinnati

John W. Fischer III · Peck, Shaffer · 201 East Fifth Street, Suite 900 · Cincinnati, OH 45202 · 513-621-3394

Cleveland

Harry M. Brown · a · Benesch, Friedlander, Coplan & Aronoff · BP Tower, Suite 2300 · 200 Public Square · Cleveland, OH 44114-2378 · 216-363-4500

Eric M. Simon · Taft Stettinius & Hollister · http://www.taftlaw.com · BP Tower, Suite 3500 · 200 Public Square · Cleveland, OH 44114-2302 · 216-241-2838

Columbus

Donald C. Brey · Chester Willcox & Saxbe · http://www.cwslaw.com · 65 East State Street, Suite 1000 · Columbus, OH 43215 · 614-221-4000

Beth Collis · Collis Smiles & Collis · http://www.collislaw.com · 1650 Lake Shore Drive, Suite 225 · Columbus, OH 43204 · 614-486-3909

N. Victor Goodman · 2% · Benesch, Friedlander, Coplan & Aronoff · 41 South High Street, Suite 2600 · Columbus, OH 43215 · 614-223-9300

Thomas W. Hess · a · Dinsmore & Shohl · http://www.dinslaw.com · 191 West Nationwide Boulevard, Suite 300 · Columbus, OH 43215 · 614-221-8448

C. David Paragas · Benesch, Friedlander, Coplan & Aronoff · 41 South High Street, Suite 2600 · Columbus, OH 43215 · 614-223-9300

Alex Shumate · a · Squire Sanders · http://www.ssd.com · 1300 Huntington Center · 41 South High Street · Columbus, OH 43215-6197 · 614-365-2700

ADVERTISING LAW

Cincinnati

Stephen E. Gillen · Greenebaum Doll & McDonald · http://www.gdm.com · Chemed Center, Suite 2900 255 East Fifth Street · Cincinnati, OH 45202 · 513-455-7600

Richard M. Goehler · a · Frost Brown Todd · http://www.frostbrowntodd.com · PNC Center, Suite 2200 201 East Fifth Street · Cincinnati, OH 45202-4182 · 513-651-6800

Lori E. Krafte · Greenebaum Doll & McDonald · http://www.gdm.com · Chemed Center, Suite 2900 · 255 East Fifth Street · Cincinnati, OH 45202 · 513-455-7600

Dayton

D. Jeffrey Ireland, Jr. · Faruki Ireland & Cox · Courthouse Plaza, SW, Suite 500 · 10 North Ludlow Street · Dayton, OH 45402 · 937-227-3700

ALTERNATIVE DISPUTE RESOLUTION

Beachwood

Jeffrey A. Belkin · 2) · Jeffrey A. Belkin · 23240 Chagrin Boulevard, Suite 450 · Beachwood, OH 44122 · 216-292-0560

Canton

Jeffrey S. Wilkof · Attorneys Mediation Services · 124 Fifteenth Street, NW · Canton, OH 44703 · 330-453-6344

Chagrin Falls

Thomas G. Repicky · Thomas Repicky · 100 North Main Street · Chagrin Falls, OH 44022 · 440-247-3898

Cincinnati

Todd H. Bailey · Frost Brown Todd · http://www.frostbrowntodd.com · PNC Center, Suite 2200 · 201 East Fifth Street · Cincinnati, OH 45202-4182 · 513-651-6800

Stephen P. Calardo · Calardo Mediation Services · 5608 Harrison Avenue · Cincinnati, OH 45248-2314 · 513-598-5000

Paul B. Calico · Strauss & Troy · http://www.strausstroy.com · The Federal Reserve Building · 150 East Fourth Street · Cincinnati, OH 45202-4018 · 513-621-2120

W. Roger Fry · Rendigs, Fry, Kiely & Dennis · One West Fourth Street, Suite 900 · Cincinnati, OH 45202-3688 · 513-381-9200

Michael W. Hawkins · 2) · Dinsmore & Shohl · http://www.dinslaw.com · 255 East Fifth Street, Suite 1900 · Cincinnati, OH 45202-3172 · 513-977-8200

Robert S. Kaiser · Robert S. Kaiser · 100 East Fifth Street, Room 331 · Cincinnati, OH 45202 · 513-564-7330

Bea V. Larsen · 2) · Center for Resolution of Disputes · Eight West Ninth Street · Cincinnati, OH 45202-2036 · 513-721-4466

James K. L. Lawrence · 2) · Frost Brown Todd · http://www.frostbrowntodd.com · PNC Center, Suite 2200 · 201 East Fifth Street · Cincinnati, OH 45202-4182 · 513-651-6800

Jerry H. Lawson · Center for Resolution of Disputes · Eight West Ninth Street · Cincinnati, OH 45202-2036 · 513-721-4466

David Wade Peck · Barron Peck Bennie & Schlemmer · http://www.bpbattorneys.com · 3074 Madison Road · Cincinnati, OH 45209-1723 · 513-721-1350

John B. Pinney · Graydon, Head & Ritchey · 1900 Fifth Third Center · 511 Walnut Street · Cincinnati, OH 45202 · 513-621-6464

James B. Robinson · a · Robinson Law Firm · http://www.jimrobinsonlaw.com · 119 Court Street, Suite 213 · Cincinnati, OH 45202 · 513-381-3525

Robert G. Stachler · 2% · Taft Stettinius & Hollister · http://www.taftlaw.com · 425 Walnut Street, Suite 1800 · Cincinnati, OH 45202-3957 · 513-381-2838

John A. West · Greenebaum Doll & McDonald · http://www.gdm.com · Chemed Center, Suite 2900 · 255 East Fifth Street · Cincinnati, OH 45202 · 513-455-7600

Cleveland

Deborah A. Coleman · Hahn Loeser & Parks · BP Tower, Suite 2800 · 200 Public Square · Cleveland, OH 44114-2301 · 216-621-0150

Michael Diamant · Taft Stettinius & Hollister · http://www.taftlaw.com · BP Tower, Suite 3500 · 200 Public Square · Cleveland, OH 44114-2302 · 216-241-2838

Michael J. Jordan · Walter & Haverfield · http://www.walterhav.com · The Tower at Erieview, Suite 3500 · 1301 East Ninth Street · Cleveland, OH 44114 · 216-781-1212

Marvin L. Karp · 2% · Ulmer & Berne · Skylight Office Tower, Suite 1100 · 1660 West Second Street · Cleveland, OH 44113-1448 · 216-583-7000

Thomas S. Kilbane · 2) · Squire Sanders · http://www.ssd.com · 4900 Key Tower · 127 Public Square · Cleveland, OH 44114-1304 · 216-479-8500

Thomas D. Lambros · Janik Dorman & Winter · http://www.janiklaw.com · 9200 South Hills Boulevard, Suite 300 · Cleveland, OH 44147-3521 · 440-838-7600

William B. Leahy · Buckingham, Doolittle & Burroughs · http://www.bdblaw.com · 1375 East Ninth Street, Suite 1700 · Cleveland, OH 44114 · 216-621-5300

John D. Liber · 2) · Spangenberg, Shibley & Liber · 1900 East Ninth Street, Suite 2400 · Cleveland, OH 44114-3400 · 216-696-3232

James J. McMonagle · Vorys, Sater, Seymour and Pease · 2100 One Cleveland Center · 1375 East Ninth Street · Cleveland, OH 44114-1724 · 216-479-6100

Richard W. Pogue · Jones Day · North Point · 901 Lakeside Avenue · Cleveland, OH 44114-1190 · 216-586-3939

Susan Grody Ruben · Susan Grody Ruben · 30799 Pinetree Road, Suite 226 · Cleveland, OH 44124 · 216-464-4060

David A. Schaefer · McCarthy, Lebit, Crystal & Liffman · http://www.mccarthylebit.com · The Midland Building, Suite 1800 · 101 West Prospect Avenue · Cleveland, OH 44115 · 216-696-1422

Niki Z. Schwartz · a · Schwartz, Downey and Company · Guildhall Building, Suite 1616 · 45 West Prospect Avenue · Cleveland, OH 44115 · 216-696-7100

Gregory P. Szuter · Gregory P. Szuter · Am Trust Center, Suite 1310 · 1801 East Ninth Street · Cleveland, OH 44114 · 216-861-0503

Jerome F. Weiss · Mediation Inc. · http://www.mediate.com/mediationinc · Midland Building, Suite 1600 101 Prospect Avenue West · Cleveland, OH 44115-1027 · 216-589-9995

James R. Wooley · Baker Hostetler · http://www.bakerlaw.com · National City Center, Suite 3200 · 1900 East Ninth Street · Cleveland, OH 44114-3485 · 216-621-0200

Daniel George Zeiser · Law Office of Daniel G. Zeiser · P.O. Box 43280 · Cleveland, OH 44143-0280 · 440-449-9311

Columbus

Sandra J. Anderson · a · Vorys, Sater, Seymour and Pease · 52 East Gay Street · P.O. Box 1008 · Columbus, OH 43216-1008 · 614-464-6400

David C. Patterson · Patterson Law Office · 10 West Broad Street, Suite 1900 · Columbus, OH 43215-3420 · 614-221-7610

James A. Readey · Readey & Patterson · 37 West Broad Street, Suite 420 · Columbus, OH 43215-3610 · 614-221-4799

Suzanne K. Richards · Vorys, Sater, Seymour and Pease · 52 East Gay Street · P.O. Box 1008 · Columbus, OH 43216-1008 · 614-464-6400

North Olmsted

John E. Martindale · a · John E. Martindale · 26031 Butternut Ridge Road · North Olmsted, OH 44070-4514 · 216-272-7750

Northfield Center

Mitchell B. Goldberg · Mitchell B. Goldberg · 253 East Aurora Road · Northfield Center, OH 44067-2012 · 330-468-5303

Toledo

Peter R. Silverman · Shumaker, Loop & Kendrick · North Courthouse Square · 1000 Jackson Street · Toledo, OH 43604-5573 · 419-241-9000

Cincinnati

Stephen J. Butler · Thompson Hine · 312 Walnut Street, 14th Floor · Cincinnati, OH 45202-4089 · 513-352-6700

Jeanne M. Cors · Taft Stettinius & Hollister · http://www.taftlaw.com · 425 Walnut Street, Suite 1800 · Cincinnati, OH 45202-3957 · 513-381-2838

G. Jack Donson, Jr. · Taft Stettinius & Hollister · http://www.taftlaw.com · 425 Walnut Street, Suite 1800 · Cincinnati, OH 45202-3957 · 513-381-2838

Thomas C. Hill · Taft Stettinius & Hollister · http://www.taftlaw.com · 425 Walnut Street, Suite 1800 · Cincinnati, OH 45202-3957 · 513-381-2838

William J. Seitz · Taft Stettinius & Hollister · http://www.taftlaw.com · 425 Walnut Street, Suite 1800 · Cincinnati, OH 45202-3957 · 513-381-2838

Mark L. Silbersack · Dinsmore & Shohl · http://www.dinslaw.com · 255 East Fifth Street, Suite 1900 · Cincinnati, OH 45202-3172 · 513-977-8200

Cleveland

John J. Eklund · Calfee, Halter & Griswold · http://www.calfee.com · 1400 KeyBank Center · 800 Superior Avenue · Cleveland, OH 44114-2688 · 216-622-8200

Leslie W. Jacobs · Thompson Hine · Key Center, Suite 3900 · 127 Public Square · Cleveland, OH 44114-1291 · 216-566-5500

James B. Niehaus · Frantz Ward · http://www.frantzward.com · Public Square, Suite 127 · 2500 Key Center · Cleveland, OH 44114-1230 · 216-515-1660

M. Neal Rains · Frantz Ward · http://www.frantzward.com · Public Square, Suite 127 · 2500 Key Center · Cleveland, OH 44114-1230 · 216-515-1660

Donald S. Scherzer · Roetzel & Andress · http://www.ralaw.com · One Cleveland Center, Ninth Floor · 1375 East Ninth Street · Cleveland, OH 44114 · 216-623-0150

Stephen J. Squeri · Jones Day · North Point · 901 Lakeside Avenue · Cleveland, OH 44114-1190 · 216-586-3939

Columbus

Michael J. Canter · Vorys, Sater, Seymour and Pease · 52 East Gay Street · P.O. Box 1008 · Columbus, OH 43216-1008 · 614-464-6400

Robert G. Cohen · Kegler, Brown, Hill & Ritter · http://www.keglerbrown.com · Capitol Square, Suite 1800 · 65 East State Street · Columbus, OH 43215-4294 · 614-462-5400

James P. Kennedy · Vorys, Sater, Seymour and Pease · 52 East Gay Street · P.O. Box 1008 · Columbus, OH 43216-1008 · 614-464-6400

Edward A. Matto · Steptoe & Johnson · http://www.steptoe-johnson.com · Huntington Center, Suite 2200 · 41 South High Street · Columbus, OH 43215 · 614-221-5100

James A. Wilson · Vorys, Sater, Seymour and Pease · 52 East Gay Street · P.O. Box 1008 · Columbus, OH 43216-1008 · 614-464-6400

Dayton

William J. Leibold · Dinsmore & Shohl · http://www.dinslaw.com · One Dayton Centre, Suite 1300 · One South Main Street · Dayton, OH 45402 · 937-449-6400

Toledo

Michael M. Briley · Shumaker, Loop & Kendrick · North Courthouse Square · 1000 Jackson Street · Toledo, OH 43604-5573 · 419-241-9000

APPELLATE LAW

Cincinnati

John B. Nalbandian · Taft Stettinius & Hollister · http://www.taftlaw.com · 425 Walnut Street, Suite 1800 · Cincinnati, OH 45202-3957 · 513-381-2838

William T. Robinson III · a · Frost Brown Todd · http://www.frostbrowntodd.com · PNC Center, Suite 2200 · 201 East Fifth Street · Cincinnati, OH 45202-4182 · 513-651-6800

Russell S. Sayre · Taft Stettinius & Hollister · http://www.taftlaw.com · 425 Walnut Street, Suite 1800 · Cincinnati, OH 45202-3957 · 513-381-2838

Robert G. Stachler · 2% · Taft Stettinius & Hollister · http://www.taftlaw.com · 425 Walnut Street, Suite 1800 · Cincinnati, OH 45202-3957 · 513-381-2838

Mark A. Vander Laan · Dinsmore & Shohl · http://www.dinslaw.com · 255 East Fifth Street, Suite 1900 · Cincinnati, OH 45202-3172 · 513-977-8200

John A. West · Greenebaum Doll & McDonald · http://www.gdm.com · Chemed Center, Suite 2900 · 255 East Fifth Street · Cincinnati, OH 45202 · 513-455-7600

Cleveland

Irene Keyse-Walker · a · Tucker Ellis & West · Huntington Building, Suite 1150 · 925 Euclid Avenue · Cleveland, OH 44115-1475 · 216-592-5000

Clifford C. Masch · Reminger Attorneys At Law · 1400 Midland Building · 101 Prospect Avenue West · Cleveland, OH 44115-1093 · 216-687-1311

Andrew S. Pollis · Hahn Loeser & Parks · BP Tower, Suite 2800 · 200 Public Square · Cleveland, OH 44114-2301 · 216-621-0150

Thomas D. Warren · Baker Hostetler · http://www.bakerlaw.com · National City Center, Suite 3200 · 1900 East Ninth Street · Cleveland, OH 44114-3485 · 216-621-0200

Columbus

Stewart R. Jaffy · a · Stewart Jaffy & Associates · 306 East Gay Street · Columbus, OH 43215-3247 · 614-228-6148

Chad A. Readler · Jones Day · 325 John H. McConnell Boulevard, Suite 600 · P.O. Box 165017 · Columbus, OH 43216-5017 · 614-469-3939

Geoffrey Stern · Kegler, Brown, Hill & Ritter · http://www.keglerbrown.com · Capitol Square, Suite 1800 65 East State Street · Columbus, OH 43215-4294 · 614-462-5400

Mark D. Tucker · Benesch, Friedlander, Coplan & Aronoff · 41 South High Street, Suite 2600 · Columbus, OH 43215 · 614-223-9300

John F. Winkler · Winkler & Winkler · 326 South High Street, Suite 400 · Columbus, OH 43215 · 614-559-3841

BANKING LAW

Akron

Stephen M. Hammersmith · a · Buckingham, Doolittle & Burroughs · http://www.bdblaw.com · 3800 Embassy Parkway, Suite 300 · P.O. Box 1500 · Akron, OH 44309-1500 · 330-376-5300

David M. Hunter · a · Brouse McDowell · 388 South Main Street, Suite 500 · Akron, OH 44311 · 330-535-5711

Philip A. Lloyd · a · Vorys, Sater, Seymour and Pease · First National Tower, Suite 1100 · 106 South Main Street · Akron, OH 44308-1417 · 330-208-1000

Brian J. Moore · Roetzel & Andress · http://www.ralaw.com · 222 South Main Street · Akron, OH 44308-2098 · 330-376-2700

James L. Rench · a · Stark & Knoll · http://www.stark-knoll.com · 3475 Ridgewood Road · Akron, OH 44333-3163 · 330-376-3300

Thomas R. Trotter · a · Vorys, Sater, Seymour and Pease · First National Tower, Suite 1100 · 106 South Main Street · Akron, OH 44308-1417 · 330-208-1000

Avon Lake

Philip E. Langer · a · Philip E. Langer · 32397 Regency Court · Avon Lake, OH 44012-2501 · 440-714-1290

Canton

Sam O. Simmerman · Krugliak, Wilkins, Griffiths & Dougherty · http://www.kwgd.com · 4775 Munson Street, NW · P.O. Box 36963 · Canton, OH 44735-6963 · 330-497-0700

Cincinnati

James J. Barresi · Squire Sanders · http://www.ssd.com · 221 East Fourth Street, Suite 2900 · Cincinnati, OH 45202-4026 · 513-361-1200

Melvin A. Bedree · Vorys, Sater, Seymour and Pease · Atrium Two, Suite 2000 · 221 East Fourth Street · P.O. Box 0236 · Cincinnati, OH 45201-0236 · 513-723-4000

David S. Bence · Frost Brown Todd · http://www.frostbrowntodd.com · PNC Center, Suite 2200 · 201 East Fifth Street · Cincinnati, OH 45202-4182 · 513-651-6800

J. Michael Debbeler · Graydon, Head & Ritchey · 1900 Fifth Third Center · 511 Walnut Street · Cincinnati, OH 45202 · 513-621-6464

Daniel H. Demmerle II · Strauss & Troy · http://www.strausstroy.com · The Federal Reserve Building · 150 East Fourth Street · Cincinnati, OH 45202-4018 · 513-621-2120

Gerald S. Greenberg · Taft Stettinius & Hollister · http://www.taftlaw.com · 425 Walnut Street, Suite 1800 · Cincinnati, OH 45202-3957 · 513-381-2838

Hani R. Kallas · Vorys, Sater, Seymour and Pease · Atrium Two, Suite 2000 · 221 East Fourth Street · P.O. Box 0236 · Cincinnati, OH 45201-0236 · 513-723-4000

P. Reid Lemasters · Frost Brown Todd · http://www.frostbrowntodd.com · PNC Center, Suite 2200 · 201 East Fifth Street · Cincinnati, OH 45202-4182 · 513-651-6800

Timothy Matthews · Keating Muething & Klekamp · http://www.kmklaw.com · One East Fourth Street, Suite 1400 · Cincinnati, OH 45202 · 513-579-6400

Kimberly K. Mauer · Frost Brown Todd · http://www.frostbrowntodd.com · PNC Center, Suite 2200 · 201 East Fifth Street · Cincinnati, OH 45202-4182 · 513-651-6800

Tracey A. Puthoff · Taft Stettinius & Hollister · http://www.taftlaw.com · 425 Walnut Street, Suite 1800 · Cincinnati, OH 45202-3957 · 513-381-2838

Jeffrey L. Rohr · Graydon, Head & Ritchey · 1900 Fifth Third Center · 511 Walnut Street · Cincinnati, OH 45202 · 513-621-6464

Jeffery R. Rush · a · Frost Brown Todd · http://www.frostbrowntodd.com · PNC Center, Suite 2200 · 201 East Fifth Street · Cincinnati, OH 45202-4182 · 513-651-6800

Jeffrey S. Schloemer · Taft Stettinius & Hollister · http://www.taftlaw.com · 425 Walnut Street, Suite 1800 · Cincinnati, OH 45202-3957 · 513-381-2838

Thomas J. Sherman · Dinsmore & Shohl · http://www.dinslaw.com · 255 East Fifth Street, Suite 1900 · Cincinnati, OH 45202-3172 · 513-977-8200

Melvin S. Shotten · Taft Stettinius & Hollister · http://www.taftlaw.com · 425 Walnut Street, Suite 1800 · Cincinnati, OH 45202-3957 · 513-381-2838

Susan B. Zaunbrecher · Dinsmore & Shohl · http://www.dinslaw.com · 255 East Fifth Street, Suite 1900 · Cincinnati, OH 45202-3172 · 513-977-8200

Cleveland

Kevin D. Barnes · a · Taft Stettinius & Hollister · http://www.taftlaw.com · BP Tower, Suite 3500 · 200 Public Square · Cleveland, OH 44114-2302 · 216-241-2838

Brett P. Barragate · Jones Day · North Point · 901 Lakeside Avenue · Cleveland, OH 44114-1190 · 216-586-3939

Karl S. Beus · Calfee, Halter & Griswold · http://www.calfee.com · 1400 KeyBank Center · 800 Superior Avenue · Cleveland, OH 44114-2688 · 216-622-8200

Thomas A. Cicarella · a · Calfee, Halter & Griswold · http://www.calfee.com · 1400 KeyBank Center · 800 Superior Avenue · Cleveland, OH 44114-2688 · 216-622-8200

Shelly G. Dedmon · Calfee, Halter & Griswold · http://www.calfee.com · 1400 KeyBank Center · 800 Superior Avenue · Cleveland, OH 44114-2688 · 216-622-8200

Mark S. Edelman · McGlinchey Stafford · http://www.mcglinchey.com · 25550 Chagrin Boulevard, Suite 406 · Cleveland, OH 44122-4640 · 216-378-9905

Martin S. Gates · Calfee, Halter & Griswold · http://www.calfee.com · 1400 KeyBank Center · 800 Superior Avenue · Cleveland, OH 44114-2688 · 216-622-8200

Guy F. Guinn · a · Squire Sanders · http://www.ssd.com · 4900 Key Tower · 127 Public Square · Cleveland, OH 44114-1304 · 216-479-8500

Kenneth M. Lapine · a · Roetzel & Andress · http://www.ralaw.com · One Cleveland Center, Ninth Floor · 1375 East Ninth Street · Cleveland, OH 44114 · 216-623-0150

Craig R. Martahus · a · Thompson Hine · Key Center, Suite 3900 · 127 Public Square · Cleveland, OH 44114-1291 · 216-566-5500

Osborne Mills, Jr. · a · Squire Sanders · http://www.ssd.com · 4900 Key Tower · 127 Public Square · Cleveland, OH 44114-1304 · 216-479-8500

JoEllen M. Minchak · Squire Sanders · http://www.ssd.com · 4900 Key Tower · 127 Public Square · Cleveland, OH 44114-1304 · 216-479-8500

Leslee W. Miraldi · Thompson Hine · Key Center, Suite 3900 · 127 Public Square · Cleveland, OH 44114-1291 · 216-566-5500

David J. Naftzinger · Thompson Hine · Key Center, Suite 3900 · 127 Public Square · Cleveland, OH 44114-1291 · 216-566-5500

Thomas W. Ostrowski · Ulmer & Berne · Skylight Office Tower, Suite 1100 · 1660 West Second Street · Cleveland, OH 44113-1448 · 216-583-7000

Lee D. Powar · a · Hahn Loeser & Parks · BP Tower, Suite 2800 · 200 Public Square · Cleveland, OH 44114-2301 · 216-621-0150

Rachel L. Rawson · Jones Day · North Point · 901 Lakeside Avenue · Cleveland, OH 44114-1190 · 216-586-3939

Ronald J. Teplitzky · Benesch, Friedlander, Coplan & Aronoff · BP Tower, Suite 2300 · 200 Public Square · Cleveland, OH 44114-2378 · 216-363-4500

Columbus

Richard A. Barnhart · Schottenstein, Zox & Dunn · http://www.szd.com · 250 West Street, Suite 700 · Columbus, OH 43215-2538 · 614-462-2700

James P. Botti · Porter, Wright, Morris & Arthur · http://www.porterwright.com · Huntington Center · 41 South High Street · Columbus, OH 43215-6194 · 614-227-2000

S. Ronald Cook · a · Porter, Wright, Morris & Arthur · http://www.porterwright.com · Huntington Center · 41 South High Street · Columbus, OH 43215-6194 · 614-227-2000

John C. Deal · a · Winkler & Winkler · 326 South High Street, Suite 400 · Columbus, OH 43215 · 614-559-3841

Charles S. DeRousie · a · Vorys, Sater, Seymour and Pease · 52 East Gay Street · P.O. Box 1008 · Columbus, OH 43216-1008 · 614-464-6400

Darrell L. Dreher · a · Dreher Langer & Tomkies · http://www.dltlaw.com · Huntington Center, Suite 2250 · 41 South High Street · Columbus, OH 43215 · 614-628-8000

Patrick J. Dugan · Squire Sanders · http://www.ssd.com · 1300 Huntington Center · 41 South High Street Columbus, OH 43215-6197 · 614-365-2700

Timothy E. Grady · a · Porter, Wright, Morris & Arthur · http://www.porterwright.com · Huntington Center · 41 South High Street · Columbus, OH 43215-6194 · 614-227-2000

John C. Hartranft, Sr. · a · Porter, Wright, Morris & Arthur · http://www.porterwright.com · Huntington Center · 41 South High Street · Columbus, OH 43215-6194 · 614-227-2000

Gordon W. Johnston · a · Bricker & Eckler · http://www.bricker.com · 100 South Third Street · Columbus, OH 43215-4291 · 614-227-2300

Jennifer T. Mills · Porter, Wright, Morris & Arthur · http://www.porterwright.com · Huntington Center · 41 South High Street · Columbus, OH 43215-6194 · 614-227-2000

John D. Robinett · Schottenstein, Zox & Dunn · http://www.szd.com · 250 West Street, Suite 700 · Columbus, OH 43215-2538 · 614-462-2700

Thomas O. Ruby · a · Vorys, Sater, Seymour and Pease · 52 East Gay Street · P.O. Box 1008 · Columbus, OH 43216-1008 · 614-464-6400

James G. Ryan · Bailey Cavalieri · One Columbus Building, Suite 2100 · 10 West Broad Street · Columbus, OH 43215-3422 · 614-221-3155

H. Grant Stephenson · Porter, Wright, Morris & Arthur · http://www.porterwright.com · Huntington Center · 41 South High Street · Columbus, OH 43215-6194 · 614-227-2000

John C. Vorys · Vorys, Sater, Seymour and Pease · 52 East Gay Street · P.O. Box 1008 · Columbus, OH 43216-1008 · 614-464-6400

John B. Weimer · a · Vorys, Sater, Seymour and Pease · 52 East Gay Street · P.O. Box 1008 · Columbus, OH 43216-1008 · 614-464-6400

Dayton

Lawrence T. Burick · a · Thompson Hine · 2000 Courthouse Plaza, NE · 10 West Second Street · P.O. Box 8801 · Dayton, OH 45401-8801 · 937-443-6600

Ronald S. Pretekin · a · Coolidge Wall Co. · http://www.coollaw.com · 33 West First Street, Suite 600 · Dayton, OH 45402 · 937-223-8177

Arik A. Sherk · a · Thompson Hine · 2000 Courthouse Plaza, NE · 10 West Second Street · P.O. Box 8801 · Dayton, OH 45401-8801 · 937-443-6600

Charles D. Shook · Bieser, Greer & Landis · http://www.biesergreer.com · National City Center, Suite 400 · Six North Main Street · Dayton, OH 45402-1908 · 937-223-3277

Toledo

Thomas C. Blank · Shumaker, Loop & Kendrick · North Courthouse Square · 1000 Jackson Street · Toledo, OH 43604-5573 · 419-241-9000

Henry N. Heuerman · Eastman & Smith · One Seagate, 24th Floor · P.O. Box 10032 · Toledo, OH 43699-0032 · 419-241-6000

John W. Hilbert II · a · Shumaker, Loop & Kendrick · North Courthouse Square · 1000 Jackson Street · Toledo, OH 43604-5573 · 419-241-9000

John N. MacKay · Shumaker, Loop & Kendrick · North Courthouse Square · 1000 Jackson Street · Toledo, OH 43604-5573 · 419-241-9000

Martin D. Werner · Shumaker, Loop & Kendrick · North Courthouse Square · 1000 Jackson Street · Toledo, OH 43604-5573 · 419-241-9000

Akron

John J. Guy · 2) · Law Offices of Guy & Lammert · First National Tower, Suite 2210 · 106 South Main Street · Akron, OH 44308-1457 · 330-535-2151

David M. Hunter · a · Brouse McDowell · 388 South Main Street, Suite 500 · Akron, OH 44311 · 330-535-5711

Patrick J. Keating · a · Buckingham, Doolittle & Burroughs · http://www.bdblaw.com · 3800 Embassy Parkway, Suite 300 · P.O. Box 1500 · Akron, OH 44309-1500 · 330-376-5300

Philip A. Lloyd · a · Vorys, Sater, Seymour and Pease · First National Tower, Suite 1100 · 106 South Main Street · Akron, OH 44308-1417 · 330-208-1000

Marc B. Merklin · Brouse McDowell · 388 South Main Street, Suite 500 · Akron, OH 44311 · 330-535-5711

Roger J. Stevenson · Roetzel & Andress · http://www.ralaw.com · 222 South Main Street · Akron, OH 44308-2098 · 330-376-2700

Avon Lake

Philip E. Langer · a · Philip E. Langer · 32397 Regency Court · Avon Lake, OH 44012-2501 · 440-714-1290

Canton

Joel K. Dayton · Black, McCuskey, Souers & Arbaugh · 220 Market Avenue South, Suite 1000 · Canton, OH 44702 · 330-456-8341

Cincinnati

Richard Boydston · Greenebaum Doll & McDonald · http://www.gdm.com · Chemed Center, Suite 2900 255 East Fifth Street · Cincinnati, OH 45202 · 513-455-7600

J. Michael Debbeler · Graydon, Head & Ritchey · 1900 Fifth Third Center · 511 Walnut Street · Cincinnati, OH 45202 · 513-621-6464

Ronald E. Gold · Frost Brown Todd · http://www.frostbrowntodd.com · PNC Center, Suite 2200 · 201 East Fifth Street · Cincinnati, OH 45202-4182 · 513-651-6800

Timothy J. Hurley · a · Taft Stettinius & Hollister · http://www.taftlaw.com · 425 Walnut Street, Suite 1800 · Cincinnati, OH 45202-3957 · 513-381-2838

Kevin E. Irwin · a · Keating Muething & Klekamp · http://www.kmklaw.com · One East Fourth Street, Suite 1400 · Cincinnati, OH 45202 · 513-579-6400

Monica V. Kindt · Cohen, Todd, Kite & Stanford · 250 East Fifth Street, Suite 1200 · Cincinnati, OH 45202-4139 · 513-421-4020

Stephen D. Lerner · a · Squire Sanders · http://www.ssd.com · 221 East Fourth Street, Suite 2900 · Cincinnati, OH 45202-4026 · 513-361-1200

Kim Martin Lewis · Dinsmore & Shohl · http://www.dinslaw.com · 255 East Fifth Street, Suite 1900 · Cincinnati, OH 45202-3172 · 513-977-8200

Douglas L. Lutz · Frost Brown Todd · http://www.frostbrowntodd.com · PNC Center, Suite 2200 · 201 East Fifth Street · Cincinnati, OH 45202-4182 · 513-651-6800

Jeffrey A. Marks · Squire Sanders · http://www.ssd.com · 221 East Fourth Street, Suite 2900 · Cincinnati, OH 45202-4026 · 513-361-1200

Henry E. Menninger, Jr. · Wood & Lamping · 600 Vine Street, Suite 2500 · Cincinnati, OH 45202 · 513-852-6000

W. Timothy Miller · Taft Stettinius & Hollister · http://www.taftlaw.com · 425 Walnut Street, Suite 1800 · Cincinnati, OH 45202-3957 · 513-381-2838

Richard D. Nelson · Cohen, Todd, Kite & Stanford · 250 East Fifth Street, Suite 1200 · Cincinnati, OH 45202-4139 · 513-421-4020

Michael J. O'Grady · Frost Brown Todd · http://www.frostbrowntodd.com · PNC Center, Suite 2200 · 201 East Fifth Street · Cincinnati, OH 45202-4182 · 513-651-6800

Donald J. Rafferty · Cohen, Todd, Kite & Stanford · 250 East Fifth Street, Suite 1200 · Cincinnati, OH 45202-4139 · 513-421-4020

Robert G. Sanker · Keating Muething & Klekamp · http://www.kmklaw.com · One East Fourth Street, Suite 1400 · Cincinnati, OH 45202 · 513-579-6400

Louis F. Solimine · a · Thompson Hine · 312 Walnut Street, 14th Floor · Cincinnati, OH 45202-4089 · 513-352-6700

Cleveland

Jeffrey Baddeley · Baker Hostetler · http://www.bakerlaw.com · National City Center, Suite 3200 · 1900 East Ninth Street · Cleveland, OH 44114-3485 · 216-621-0200

Brian A. Bash · Baker Hostetler · http://www.bakerlaw.com · National City Center, Suite 3200 · 1900 East Ninth Street · Cleveland, OH 44114-3485 · 216-621-0200

Richard A. Baumgart · 2) · Dettelbach, Sicherman & Baumgart · Am Trust Bank Center, Suite 1100 · 1801 East Ninth Street · Cleveland, OH 44114-3169 · 216-696-6000

Daniel A. DeMarco · Hahn Loeser & Parks · BP Tower, Suite 2800 · 200 Public Square · Cleveland, OH 44114-2301 · 216-621-0150

Bryan J. Farkas · Vorys, Sater, Seymour and Pease · 2100 One Cleveland Center · 1375 East Ninth Street Cleveland, OH 44114-1724 · 216-479-6100

M. Colette Gibbons · Schottenstein, Zox & Dunn · http://www.szd.com · U.S. Bank Centre, Suite 1400 · 1350 Euclid Avenue · Cleveland, OH 44115 · 216-621-6501

Matthew R. Goldman · a · Baker Hostetler · http://www.bakerlaw.com · National City Center, Suite 3200 · 1900 East Ninth Street · Cleveland, OH 44114-3485 · 216-621-0200

Harry W. Greenfield · Buckley King · 1400 Fifth Third Center · 600 Superior Avenue · Cleveland, OH 44114-2652 · 216-363-1400

Richard G. Hardy · Ulmer & Berne · Skylight Office Tower, Suite 1100 · 1660 West Second Street · Cleveland, OH 44113-1448 · 216-583-7000

David G. Heiman · 2% · Jones Day · North Point · 901 Lakeside Avenue · Cleveland, OH 44114-1190 · 216-586-3939

Joseph F. Hutchinson, Jr. · Baker Hostetler · http://www.bakerlaw.com · National City Center, Suite 3200 · 1900 East Ninth Street · Cleveland, OH 44114-3485 · 216-621-0200

Alan S. Kopit · Hahn Loeser & Parks · BP Tower, Suite 2800 · 200 Public Square · Cleveland, OH 44114-2301 · 216-621-0150

James M. Lawniczak · Calfee, Halter & Griswold · http://www.calfee.com · 1400 KeyBank Center · 800 Superior Avenue · Cleveland, OH 44114-2688 · 216-622-8200

Heather Lennox · Jones Day · North Point · 901 Lakeside Avenue · Cleveland, OH 44114-1190 · 216-586-3939

Alan R. Lepene · a · Thompson Hine · Key Center, Suite 3900 · 127 Public Square · Cleveland, OH 44114-1291 · 216-566-5500

G. Christopher Meyer · a · Squire Sanders · http://www.ssd.com · 4900 Key Tower · 127 Public Square · Cleveland, OH 44114-1304 · 216-479-8500

Lawrence E. Oscar · Hahn Loeser & Parks · BP Tower, Suite 2800 · 200 Public Square · Cleveland, OH 44114-2301 · 216-621-0150

Drew T. Parobek · Vorys, Sater, Seymour and Pease · 2100 One Cleveland Center · 1375 East Ninth Street · Cleveland, OH 44114-1724 · 216-479-6100

Lee D. Powar · a · Hahn Loeser & Parks · BP Tower, Suite 2800 · 200 Public Square · Cleveland, OH 44114-2301 · 216-621-0150

Mary Ann Rabin · Rabin & Rabin · 55 Public Square, Suite 1510 · Cleveland, OH 44113 · 216-771-8084

Shawn M. Riley · McDonald Hopkins · 600 Superior Avenue East, Suite 2100 · Cleveland, OH 44114-2653 · 216-348-5400

Jean R. Robertson · Calfee, Halter & Griswold · http://www.calfee.com · 1400 KeyBank Center · 800 Superior Avenue · Cleveland, OH 44114-2688 · 216-622-8200

William E. Schonberg · Benesch, Friedlander, Coplan & Aronoff · BP Tower, Suite 2300 · 200 Public Square · Cleveland, OH 44114-2378 · 216-363-4500

Marvin A. Sicherman · 2% · Dettelbach, Sicherman & Baumgart · Am Trust Bank Center, Suite 1100 · 1801 East Ninth Street · Cleveland, OH 44114-3169 · 216-696-6000

David O. Simon · David O. Simon · 450 Standard Building · 1370 Ontario Street · Cleveland, OH 44113-1744 · 216-621-6201

Michael S. Tucker · Ulmer & Berne · Skylight Office Tower, Suite 1100 · 1660 West Second Street · Cleveland, OH 44113-1448 · 216-583-7000

Mary K. Whitmer · a · Kohrman, Jackson & Krantz · One Cleveland Center, 20th Floor · 1375 East Ninth Street · Cleveland, OH 44114-1739 · 216-696-8700

Columbus

Thomas R. Allen · a · Allen Kuehnle Stovall & Newman · 21 West Broad Street, Suite 400 · Columbus, OH 43215 · 614-221-8500

Nick V. Cavalieri · 2% · Bailey Cavalieri · One Columbus Building, Suite 2100 · 10 West Broad Street · Columbus, OH 43215-3422 · 614-221-3155

Kenneth R. Cookson · Kegler, Brown, Hill & Ritter · http://www.keglerbrown.com · Capitol Square, Suite 1800 · 65 East State Street · Columbus, OH 43215-4294 · 614-462-5400

E. James Hopple · 2) · Schottenstein, Zox & Dunn · http://www.szd.com · 250 West Street, Suite 700 · Columbus, OH 43215-2538 · 614-462-2700

Reginald W. Jackson · a · Vorys, Sater, Seymour and Pease · 52 East Gay Street · P.O. Box 1008 · Columbus, OH 43216-1008 · 614-464-6400

Kenneth C. Johnson · Bricker & Eckler · http://www.bricker.com · 100 South Third Street · Columbus, OH 43215-4291 · 614-227-2300

W. Mark Jump · Koffel & Jump · http://www.kjlaws.com · 2130 Arlington Avenue · Columbus, OH 43221 · 614-481-4480

Randall D. LaTour · a · Vorys, Sater, Seymour and Pease · 52 East Gay Street · P.O. Box 1008 · Columbus, OH 43216-1008 · 614-464-6400

William B. Logan, Jr. · 2) · Luper, Neidenthal & Logan · LeVeque Tower, Suite 1200 · 50 West Broad Street · Columbus, OH 43215-3374 · 614-221-7663

Frederick M. Luper · a · Luper, Neidenthal & Logan · LeVeque Tower, Suite 1200 · 50 West Broad Street · Columbus, OH 43215-3374 · 614-221-7663

Jack R. Pigman · 2% · Porter, Wright, Morris & Arthur · http://www.porterwright.com · Huntington Center 41 South High Street · Columbus, OH 43215-6194 · 614-227-2000

Victoria E. Powers · Schottenstein, Zox & Dunn · http://www.szd.com · 250 West Street, Suite 700 · Columbus, OH 43215-2538 · 614-462-2700

Robert J. Sidman · 2) · Vorys, Sater, Seymour and Pease · 52 East Gay Street · P.O. Box 1008 · Columbus, OH 43216-1008 · 614-464-6400

Richard K. Stovall · Allen Kuehnle Stovall & Newman · 21 West Broad Street, Suite 400 · Columbus, OH 43215 · 614-221-8500

Daniel R. Swetnam · Schottenstein, Zox & Dunn · http://www.szd.com · 250 West Street, Suite 700 · Columbus, OH 43215-2538 · 614-462-2700

David M. Whittaker · a · Bricker & Eckler · http://www.bricker.com · 100 South Third Street · Columbus, OH 43215-4291 · 614-227-2300

Alec Wightman · a · Baker Hostetler · http://www.bakerlaw.com · Capitol Square, Suite 2100 · 65 East State Street · Columbus, OH 43215-4260 · 614-228-1541

Dayton

Lawrence T. Burick · a · Thompson Hine · 2000 Courthouse Plaza, NE · 10 West Second Street · P.O. Box 8801 · Dayton, OH 45401-8801 · 937-443-6600

Dennis L. Patterson · 2) · Dennis L. Patterson · 131 North Ludlow Street, Suite 1200 · Dayton, OH 45402-1737 · 937-226-1200

Ronald S. Pretekin · a · Coolidge Wall Co. · http://www.coollaw.com · 33 West First Street, Suite 600 · Dayton, OH 45402 · 937-223-8177

Walter Reynolds · Porter, Wright, Morris & Arthur · http://www.porterwright.com · One Dayton Centre, Suite 1600 · One South Main Street · Dayton, OH 45402-2028 · 937-449-6810

Ira Rubin · a · Goldman, Rubin & Shapiro · 1340 Woodman Drive · Dayton, OH 45432-3441 · 937-254-4455

Charles D. Shook · Bieser, Greer & Landis · http://www.biesergreer.com · National City Center, Suite 400 · Six North Main Street · Dayton, OH 45402-1908 · 937-223-3277

Lester R. Thompson · Thompson & DeVeny · 1340 Woodman Drive · Dayton, OH 45432 · 937-252-2030

Toledo

Kenneth C. Baker · a · Eastman & Smith · One Seagate, 24th Floor · P.O. Box 10032 · Toledo, OH 43699-0032 · 419-241-6000

H. Buswell Roberts, Jr. · 2) · Shumaker, Loop & Kendrick · North Courthouse Square · 1000 Jackson Street · Toledo, OH 43604-5573 · 419-241-9000

Thomas J. Schank · a · Hunter & Schank · One Canton Square · 1700 Canton Avenue · Toledo, OH 43624-1378 · 419-255-4300

Youngstown

Michael A. Gallo, Jr. · 2% · Nadler, Nadler & Burdman · 20 Federal Plaza West, Suite 600 · Youngstown, OH 44503 · 330-744-0247

BET-THE-COMPANY LITIGATION

Akron

John F. Hill · Hill Hardman Oldfield · http://www.hillhardmanoldfield.com · One Cascade Plaza, Suite 2000 · Akron, OH 44308 · 330-253-4000

Ronald S. Kopp · Roetzel & Andress · http://www.ralaw.com · 222 South Main Street · Akron, OH 44308-2098 · 330-376-2700

Orville L. Reed III · 2) · Buckingham, Doolittle & Burroughs · http://www.bdblaw.com · 3800 Embassy Parkway, Suite 300 · P.O. Box 1500 · Akron, OH 44309-1500 · 330-376-5300

Canton

Mark J. Skakun III · a · Buckingham, Doolittle & Burroughs · http://www.bdblaw.com · 4518 Fulton Drive, NW · P.O. Box 35548 · Canton, OH 44735-5548 · 330-492-8717

Cincinnati

Daniel J. Buckley · Vorys, Sater, Seymour and Pease · Atrium Two, Suite 2000 · 221 East Fourth Street · P.O. Box 0236 · Cincinnati, OH 45201-0236 · 513-723-4000

James E. Burke · Keating Muething & Klekamp · http://www.kmklaw.com · One East Fourth Street, Suite 1400 · Cincinnati, OH 45202 · 513-579-6400

L. Clifford Craig · a · Taft Stettinius & Hollister · http://www.taftlaw.com · 425 Walnut Street, Suite 1800 · Cincinnati, OH 45202-3957 · 513-381-2838

Michael D. Eagen · a · Dinsmore & Shohl · http://www.dinslaw.com · 255 East Fifth Street, Suite 1900 · Cincinnati, OH 45202-3172 · 513-977-8200

David P. Kamp · White, Getgey & Meyer · Fourth & Vine Tower, Suite 1700 · One West Fourth Street · Cincinnati, OH 45202-3621 · 513-241-3685

R. Joseph Parker · a · Taft Stettinius & Hollister · http://www.taftlaw.com · 425 Walnut Street, Suite 1800 · Cincinnati, OH 45202-3957 · 513-381-2838

Robert A. Pitcairn, Jr. · a · Katz, Teller, Brant & Hild · http://www.katzteller.com · 255 East Fifth Street, Suite 2400 · Cincinnati, OH 45202-4724 · 513-721-4532

Mark A. Vander Laan · Dinsmore & Shohl · http://www.dinslaw.com · 255 East Fifth Street, Suite 1900 · Cincinnati, OH 45202-3172 · 513-977-8200

Glenn V. Whitaker · 2) · Vorys, Sater, Seymour and Pease · Atrium Two, Suite 2000 · 221 East Fourth Street · P.O. Box 0236 · Cincinnati, OH 45201-0236 · 513-723-4000

Frank C. Woodside III · a · Dinsmore & Shohl · http://www.dinslaw.com · 255 East Fifth Street, Suite 1900 · Cincinnati, OH 45202-3172 · 513-977-8200

Cleveland

David J. Hooker · Thompson Hine · Key Center, Suite 3900 · 127 Public Square · Cleveland, OH 44114-1291 · 216-566-5500

Marvin L. Karp · 2% · Ulmer & Berne · Skylight Office Tower, Suite 1100 · 1660 West Second Street · Cleveland, OH 44113-1448 · 216-583-7000

John M. Newman, Jr. · Jones Day · North Point · 901 Lakeside Avenue · Cleveland, OH 44114-1190 · 216-586-3939

Mark O'Neill · 2% · Weston Hurd · The Tower at Erieview, Suite 1900 · 1301 East Ninth Street · Cleveland, OH 44114-1862 · 216-241-6602

Niki Z. Schwartz · a · Schwartz, Downey and Company · Guildhall Building, Suite 1616 · 45 West Prospect Avenue · Cleveland, OH 44115 · 216-696-7100

Stephen G. Sozio · Jones Day · North Point · 901 Lakeside Avenue · Cleveland, OH 44114-1190 · 216-586-3939

Hugh M. Stanley, Jr. · a · Tucker Ellis & West · Huntington Building, Suite 1150 · 925 Euclid Avenue · Cleveland, OH 44115-1475 · 216-592-5000

Robert C. Tucker · Tucker Ellis & West · Huntington Building, Suite 1150 · 925 Euclid Avenue · Cleveland, OH 44115-1475 · 216-592-5000

James R. Wooley · Baker Hostetler · http://www.bakerlaw.com · National City Center, Suite 3200 · 1900 East Ninth Street · Cleveland, OH 44114-3485 · 216-621-0200

Columbus

Sandra J. Anderson · a · Vorys, Sater, Seymour and Pease · 52 East Gay Street · P.O. Box 1008 · Columbus, OH 43216-1008 · 614-464-6400

Michael H. Carpenter · a · Carpenter Lipps & Leland · http://www.carpenterlipps.com · 280 Plaza, Suite 1300 · 280 North High Street · Columbus, OH 43215 · 614-365-4100

Thomas W. Hill · a · Kegler, Brown, Hill & Ritter · http://www.keglerbrown.com · Capitol Square, Suite 1800 · 65 East State Street · Columbus, OH 43215-4294 · 614-462-5400

John C. McDonald · a · Schottenstein, Zox & Dunn · http://www.szd.com · 250 West Street, Suite 700 · Columbus, OH 43215-2538 · 614-462-2700

Frank A. Ray · 2) · Chester Willcox & Saxbe · http://www.cwslaw.com · 65 East State Street, Suite 1000 · Columbus, OH 43215 · 614-221-4000

Thomas B. Ridgley · 2% · Vorys, Sater, Seymour and Pease · 52 East Gay Street · P.O. Box 1008 · Columbus, OH 43216-1008 · 614-464-6400

Robert W. Trafford · a · Porter, Wright, Morris & Arthur · http://www.porterwright.com · Huntington Center · 41 South High Street · Columbus, OH 43215-6194 · 614-227-2000

Dayton

Charles J. Faruki · 2) · Faruki Ireland & Cox · Courthouse Plaza, SW, Suite 500 · 10 North Ludlow Street · Dayton, OH 45402 · 937-227-3700

Neil F. Freund · a · Freund, Freeze & Arnold · One Dayton Centre, Suite 1800 · One South Main Street Dayton, OH 45402-2017 · 937-222-2424

David C. Greer · 2% · Bieser, Greer & Landis · http://www.biesergreer.com · National City Center, Suite 400 · Six North Main Street · Dayton, OH 45402-1908 · 937-223-3277

Toledo

Frederick Byers · a · Fritz Byers · The Spitzer Building, Suite 824 · 520 Madison Avenue · Toledo, OH 43604-1343 · 419-241-8013

Cary Cooper · 2) · Cooper & Walinski · 900 Adams Street · Toledo, OH 43604 · 419-241-1200

Richard S. Walinski · a · Cooper & Walinski · 900 Adams Street · Toledo, OH 43604 · 419-241-1200

BIOTECHNOLOGY LAW

Cleveland

John T. Wiedemann · Calfee, Halter & Griswold · http://www.calfee.com · 1400 KeyBank Center · 800 Superior Avenue · Cleveland, OH 44114-2688 · 216-622-8200

CIVIL RIGHTS LAW

Cincinnati

Alphonse A. Gerhardstein · a · Gerhardstein & Branch · 617 Vine Street, Suite 1409 · Cincinnati, OH 45202 · 513-621-9100

Lisa Meeks · Newman & Meeks · 215 East Ninth Street, Suite 650 · Cincinnati, OH 45202-2143 · 513-639-7000

Marc D. Mezibov · 2) · Mezibov & Jenkins · 401 East Court Street, Suite 600 · Cincinnati, OH 45202 · 513-621-8800

Robert B. Newman · a · Newman & Meeks · 215 East Ninth Street, Suite 650 · Cincinnati, OH 45202-2143 · 513-639-7000

Akron

Mark W. Bernlohr · Bernlohr Wertz · The Nantucket Building, Third Floor · 23 South Main Street · Akron, OH 44308 · 330-434-1000

Douglas N. Godshall · Hanna, Campbell & Powell · 3737 Embassy Parkway, Suite 100 · P.O. Box 5521 · Akron, OH 44334 · 330-670-7300

David W. Hilkert · Buckingham, Doolittle & Burroughs · http://www.bdblaw.com · 3800 Embassy Parkway, Suite 300 · P.O. Box 1500 · Akron, OH 44309-1500 · 330-376-5300

John F. Hill · Hill Hardman Oldfield · http://www.hillhardmanoldfield.com · One Cascade Plaza, Suite 2000 · Akron, OH 44308 · 330-253-4000

Patrick J. Keating · a · Buckingham, Doolittle & Burroughs · http://www.bdblaw.com · 3800 Embassy Parkway, Suite 300 · P.O. Box 1500 · Akron, OH 44309-1500 · 330-376-5300

Ronald S. Kopp · Roetzel & Andress · http://www.ralaw.com · 222 South Main Street · Akron, OH 44308-2098 · 330-376-2700

Robert W. Malone · 2) · Buckingham, Doolittle & Burroughs · http://www.bdblaw.com · 3800 Embassy Parkway, Suite 300 · P.O. Box 1500 · Akron, OH 44309-1500 · 330-376-5300

Orville L. Reed III · 2) · Buckingham, Doolittle & Burroughs · http://www.bdblaw.com · 3800 Embassy Parkway, Suite 300 · P.O. Box 1500 · Akron, OH 44309-1500 · 330-376-5300

John L. Reyes · Buckingham, Doolittle & Burroughs · http://www.bdblaw.com · 3800 Embassy Parkway, Suite 300 · P.O. Box 1500 · Akron, OH 44309-1500 · 330-376-5300

Thomas R. Trotter · a · Vorys, Sater, Seymour and Pease · First National Tower, Suite 1100 · 106 South Main Street · Akron, OH 44308-1417 · 330-208-1000

Canton

Lee J. Bell · Buckingham, Doolittle & Burroughs · http://www.bdblaw.com · 4518 Fulton Drive, NW · P.O. Box 35548 · Canton, OH 44735-5548 · 330-492-8717

Todd S. Bundy · Black, McCuskey, Souers & Arbaugh · 220 Market Avenue South, Suite 1000 · Canton, OH 44702 · 330-456-8341

Mark J. Skakun III · a · Buckingham, Doolittle & Burroughs · http://www.bdblaw.com · 4518 Fulton Drive, NW · P.O. Box 35548 · Canton, OH 44735-5548 · 330-492-8717

Michael A. Thompson · Michael A. Thompson · 4571 Stephen Circle, NW, Suite 130 · Canton, OH 44718-3633 · 330-499-1016

Cincinnati

Todd H. Bailey · Frost Brown Todd · http://www.frostbrowntodd.com · PNC Center, Suite 2200 · 201 East Fifth Street · Cincinnati, OH 45202-4182 · 513-651-6800

Kent A. Britt · Vorys, Sater, Seymour and Pease · Atrium Two, Suite 2000 · 221 East Fourth Street · P.O. Box 0236 · Cincinnati, OH 45201-0236 · 513-723-4000

Daniel J. Buckley · Vorys, Sater, Seymour and Pease · Atrium Two, Suite 2000 · 221 East Fourth Street · P.O. Box 0236 · Cincinnati, OH 45201-0236 · 513-723-4000

James E. Burke · Keating Muething & Klekamp · http://www.kmklaw.com · One East Fourth Street, Suite 1400 · Cincinnati, OH 45202 · 513-579-6400

Stephen J. Butler · Thompson Hine · 312 Walnut Street, 14th Floor · Cincinnati, OH 45202-4089 · 513-352-6700

Eric K. Combs · Taft Stettinius & Hollister · http://www.taftlaw.com · 425 Walnut Street, Suite 1800 · Cincinnati, OH 45202-3957 · 513-381-2838

Grant S. Cowan · Frost Brown Todd · http://www.frostbrowntodd.com · PNC Center, Suite 2200 · 201 East Fifth Street · Cincinnati, OH 45202-4182 · 513-651-6800

L. Clifford Craig · a · Taft Stettinius & Hollister · http://www.taftlaw.com · 425 Walnut Street, Suite 1800 · Cincinnati, OH 45202-3957 · 513-381-2838

G. Jack Donson, Jr. · Taft Stettinius & Hollister · http://www.taftlaw.com · 425 Walnut Street, Suite 1800 · Cincinnati, OH 45202-3957 · 513-381-2838

W. Stuart Dornette · a · Taft Stettinius & Hollister · http://www.taftlaw.com · 425 Walnut Street, Suite 1800 · Cincinnati, OH 45202-3957 · 513-381-2838

Michael D. Eagen · a · Dinsmore & Shohl · http://www.dinslaw.com · 255 East Fifth Street, Suite 1900 · Cincinnati, OH 45202-3172 · 513-977-8200

W. Roger Fry · Rendigs, Fry, Kiely & Dennis · One West Fourth Street, Suite 900 · Cincinnati, OH 45202-3688 · 513-381-9200

Cynthia L. Gibson · Katz, Teller, Brant & Hild · http://www.katzteller.com · 255 East Fifth Street, Suite 2400 · Cincinnati, OH 45202-4724 · 513-721-4532

John C. Greiner · Graydon, Head & Ritchey · 1900 Fifth Third Center · 511 Walnut Street · Cincinnati, OH 45202 · 513-621-6464

D. Scott Gurney · Frost Brown Todd · http://www.frostbrowntodd.com · PNC Center, Suite 2200 · 201 East Fifth Street · Cincinnati, OH 45202-4182 · 513-651-6800

Adam P. Hall · Frost Brown Todd · http://www.frostbrowntodd.com · PNC Center, Suite 2200 · 201 East Fifth Street · Cincinnati, OH 45202-4182 · 513-651-6800

James B. Helmer, Jr. · 2) · Helmer, Martins, Rice & Popham · 600 Vine Street, Suite 2704 · Cincinnati, OH 45202 · 513-421-2400

Brian E. Hurley · Crabbe, Brown & James · 30 Garfield Place, Suite 740 · Cincinnati, OH 45202 · 513-784-1525

Timothy J. Hurley · a · Taft Stettinius & Hollister · http://www.taftlaw.com · 425 Walnut Street, Suite 1800 · Cincinnati, OH 45202-3957 · 513-381-2838

David P. Kamp · White, Getgey & Meyer · Fourth & Vine Tower, Suite 1700 · One West Fourth Street · Cincinnati, OH 45202-3621 · 513-241-3685

Robert A. Klingler · Robert A. Klingler · 525 Vine Street, Suite 2320 · Cincinnati, OH 45202 · 513-665-9500

John J. Kropp · Graydon, Head & Ritchey · 1900 Fifth Third Center · 511 Walnut Street · Cincinnati, OH 45202 · 513-621-6464

Nathaniel Lampley, Jr. · Vorys, Sater, Seymour and Pease · Atrium Two, Suite 2000 · 221 East Fourth Street · P.O. Box 0236 · Cincinnati, OH 45201-0236 · 513-723-4000

Nancy A. Lawson · Dinsmore & Shohl · http://www.dinslaw.com · 255 East Fifth Street, Suite 1900 · Cincinnati, OH 45202-3172 · 513-977-8200

John D. Luken · Dinsmore & Shohl · http://www.dinslaw.com · 255 East Fifth Street, Suite 1900 · Cincinnati, OH 45202-3172 · 513-977-8200

Earle Jay Maiman · Thompson Hine · 312 Walnut Street, 14th Floor · Cincinnati, OH 45202-4089 · 513-352-6700

Paul B. Martins · Helmer, Martins, Rice & Popham · 600 Vine Street, Suite 2704 · Cincinnati, OH 45202 513-421-2400

James McCarthy III · Katz, Teller, Brant & Hild · http://www.katzteller.com · 255 East Fifth Street, Suite 2400 · Cincinnati, OH 45202-4724 · 513-721-4532

David C. Olson · Frost Brown Todd · http://www.frostbrowntodd.com · PNC Center, Suite 2200 · 201 East Fifth Street · Cincinnati, OH 45202-4182 · 513-651-6800

R. Joseph Parker · a · Taft Stettinius & Hollister · http://www.taftlaw.com · 425 Walnut Street, Suite 1800 · Cincinnati, OH 45202-3957 · 513-381-2838

Jeffrey F. Peck · Ulmer & Berne · 600 Vine Street, Suite 2800 · Cincinnati, OH 45202-2409 · 513-698-5000

John B. Pinney · Graydon, Head & Ritchey · 1900 Fifth Third Center · 511 Walnut Street · Cincinnati, OH 45202 · 513-621-6464

Robert A. Pitcairn, Jr. · a · Katz, Teller, Brant & Hild · http://www.katzteller.com · 255 East Fifth Street, Suite 2400 · Cincinnati, OH 45202-4724 · 513-721-4532

Donald J. Rafferty · Cohen, Todd, Kite & Stanford · 250 East Fifth Street, Suite 1200 · Cincinnati, OH 45202-4139 · 513-421-4020

William T. Robinson III · a · Frost Brown Todd · http://www.frostbrowntodd.com · PNC Center, Suite 2200 · 201 East Fifth Street · Cincinnati, OH 45202-4182 · 513-651-6800

Mark J. Ruehlmann · Squire Sanders · http://www.ssd.com · 221 East Fourth Street, Suite 2900 · Cincinnati, OH 45202-4026 · 513-361-1200

Russell S. Sayre · Taft Stettinius & Hollister · http://www.taftlaw.com · 425 Walnut Street, Suite 1800 · Cincinnati, OH 45202-3957 · 513-381-2838

Thomas R. Schuck · Taft Stettinius & Hollister · http://www.taftlaw.com · 425 Walnut Street, Suite 1800 Cincinnati, OH 45202-3957 · 513-381-2838

Kenneth F. Seibel · Jacobs, Kleiman, Seibel & McNally · Kroger Building, Suite 2300 · 1014 Vine Street · Cincinnati, OH 45202-1116 · 513-381-6600

Robert G. Stachler · 2% · Taft Stettinius & Hollister · http://www.taftlaw.com · 425 Walnut Street, Suite 1800 · Cincinnati, OH 45202-3957 · 513-381-2838

Thomas L. Stachler · Strauss & Troy · http://www.strausstroy.com · The Federal Reserve Building · 150 East Fourth Street · Cincinnati, OH 45202-4018 · 513-621-2120

Robert A. Steinberg · Waite, Schneider, Bayless & Chesley · 1513 Fourth and Vine Tower · Cincinnati, OH 45202 · 513-621-0267

Carl J. Stich, Jr. · White, Getgey & Meyer · Fourth & Vine Tower, Suite 1700 · One West Fourth Street Cincinnati, OH 45202-3621 · 513-241-3685

Timothy C. Sullivan · Taft Stettinius & Hollister · http://www.taftlaw.com · 425 Walnut Street, Suite 1800 · Cincinnati, OH 45202-3957 · 513-381-2838

Gregory M. Utter · Keating Muething & Klekamp · http://www.kmklaw.com · One East Fourth Street, Suite 1400 · Cincinnati, OH 45202 · 513-579-6400

Mark A. Vander Laan · Dinsmore & Shohl · http://www.dinslaw.com · 255 East Fifth Street, Suite 1900 · Cincinnati, OH 45202-3172 · 513-977-8200

Richard S. Wayne · Strauss & Troy · http://www.strausstroy.com · The Federal Reserve Building · 150 East Fourth Street · Cincinnati, OH 45202-4018 · 513-621-2120

W. Breck Weigel · Vorys, Sater, Seymour and Pease · Atrium Two, Suite 2000 · 221 East Fourth Street · P.O. Box 0236 · Cincinnati, OH 45201-0236 · 513-723-4000

Gerald V. Weigle, Jr. · Dinsmore & Shohl · http://www.dinslaw.com · 255 East Fifth Street, Suite 1900 · Cincinnati, OH 45202-3172 · 513-977-8200

John A. West · Greenebaum Doll & McDonald · http://www.gdm.com · Chemed Center, Suite 2900 · 255 East Fifth Street · Cincinnati, OH 45202 · 513-455-7600

Glenn V. Whitaker · 2) · Vorys, Sater, Seymour and Pease · Atrium Two, Suite 2000 · 221 East Fourth Street · P.O. Box 0236 · Cincinnati, OH 45201-0236 · 513-723-4000

Frank C. Woodside III · a · Dinsmore & Shohl · http://www.dinslaw.com · 255 East Fifth Street, Suite 1900 · Cincinnati, OH 45202-3172 · 513-977-8200

Cleveland

Brett K. Bacon · Frantz Ward · http://www.frantzward.com · Public Square, Suite 127 · 2500 Key Center · Cleveland, OH 44114-1230 · 216-515-1660

Mitchell G. Blair · Calfee, Halter & Griswold · http://www.calfee.com · 1400 KeyBank Center · 800 Superior Avenue · Cleveland, OH 44114-2688 · 216-622-8200

Kathleen B. Burke · Jones Day · North Point · 901 Lakeside Avenue · Cleveland, OH 44114-1190 · 216-586-3939

Ralph E. Cascarilla · Walter & Haverfield · http://www.walterhav.com · The Tower at Erieview, Suite 3500 · 1301 East Ninth Street · Cleveland, OH 44114 · 216-781-1212

Joseph A. Castrodale · Ulmer & Berne · Skylight Office Tower, Suite 1100 · 1660 West Second Street · Cleveland, OH 44113-1448 · 216-583-7000

George S. Coakley · Reminger Attorneys At Law · 1400 Midland Building · 101 Prospect Avenue West · Cleveland, OH 44115-1093 · 216-687-1311

Harry D. Cornett, Jr. · a · Tucker Ellis & West · Huntington Building, Suite 1150 · 925 Euclid Avenue · Cleveland, OH 44115-1475 · 216-592-5000

Wayne C. Dabb, Jr. · Baker Hostetler · http://www.bakerlaw.com · National City Center, Suite 3200 · 1900 East Ninth Street · Cleveland, OH 44114-3485 · 216-621-0200

Robert J. Fogarty · Hahn Loeser & Parks · BP Tower, Suite 2800 · 200 Public Square · Cleveland, OH 44114-2301 · 216-621-0150

Steven A. Friedman · Squire Sanders · http://www.ssd.com · 4900 Key Tower · 127 Public Square · Cleveland, OH 44114-1304 · 216-479-8500

Steven A. Goldfarb · Hahn Loeser & Parks · BP Tower, Suite 2800 · 200 Public Square · Cleveland, OH 44114-2301 · 216-621-0150

Theodore M. Grossman · Jones Day · North Point · 901 Lakeside Avenue · Cleveland, OH 44114-1190 · 216-586-3939

Richard S. Gurbst · Squire Sanders · http://www.ssd.com · 4900 Key Tower · 127 Public Square · Cleveland, OH 44114-1304 · 216-479-8500

Anthony J. Hartman · Hermann, Cahn & Schneider · http://www.hcsattys.com · 1301 East Ninth Street, Suite 500 · Cleveland, OH 44114 · 216-781-5515

Bruce G. Hearey · Ogletree Deakins · http://www.ogletreedeakins.com · Key Tower, Suite 4130 · 127 Public Square · Cleveland, OH 44114 · 216-241-6100

David J. Hooker · Thompson Hine · Key Center, Suite 3900 · 127 Public Square · Cleveland, OH 44114-1291 · 216-566-5500

Ronald H. Isroff · Ulmer & Berne · Skylight Office Tower, Suite 1100 · 1660 West Second Street · Cleveland, OH 44113-1448 · 216-583-7000

Steven G. Janik · a · Janik Dorman & Winter · http://www.janiklaw.com · 9200 South Hills Boulevard, Suite 300 · Cleveland, OH 44147-3521 · 440-838-7600

Marvin L. Karp · 2% · Ulmer & Berne · Skylight Office Tower, Suite 1100 · 1660 West Second Street · Cleveland, OH 44113-1448 · 216-583-7000

Steven S. Kaufman · Thompson Hine · Key Center, Suite 3900 · 127 Public Square · Cleveland, OH 44114-1291 · 216-566-5500

Irene Keyse-Walker · a · Tucker Ellis & West · Huntington Building, Suite 1150 · 925 Euclid Avenue · Cleveland, OH 44115-1475 · 216-592-5000

Thomas S. Kilbane · 2) · Squire Sanders · http://www.ssd.com · 4900 Key Tower · 127 Public Square · Cleveland, OH 44114-1304 · 216-479-8500

Alan S. Kopit · Hahn Loeser & Parks · BP Tower, Suite 2800 · 200 Public Square · Cleveland, OH 44114-2301 · 216-621-0150

David A. Kutik · Jones Day · North Point · 901 Lakeside Avenue · Cleveland, OH 44114-1190 · 216-586-3939

Thomas R. Lucchesi · Baker Hostetler · http://www.bakerlaw.com · National City Center, Suite 3200 · 1900 East Ninth Street · Cleveland, OH 44114-3485 · 216-621-0200

Damond R. Mace · Squire Sanders · http://www.ssd.com · 4900 Key Tower · 127 Public Square · Cleveland, OH 44114-1304 · 216-479-8500

Patrick F. McCartan · 2% · Jones Day · North Point · 901 Lakeside Avenue · Cleveland, OH 44114-1190 · 216-586-3939

George L. McGaughey, Jr. · McDonald Hopkins · 600 Superior Avenue East, Suite 2100 · Cleveland, OH 44114-2653 · 216-348-5400

Hugh E. McKay · Porter, Wright, Morris & Arthur · http://www.porterwright.com · 925 Euclid Avenue, Suite 1700 · Cleveland, OH 44115-1483 · 216-443-9000

Patrick M. McLaughlin · McLaughlin & McCaffrey · Eaton Center, Suite 1350 · 1111 Superior Avenue · Cleveland, OH 44114-2500 · 216-623-0900

George J. Moscarino · Jones Day · North Point · 901 Lakeside Avenue · Cleveland, OH 44114-1190 · 216-586-3939

Frederick R. Nance · Squire Sanders · http://www.ssd.com · 4900 Key Tower · 127 Public Square · Cleveland, OH 44114-1304 · 216-479-8500

John M. Newman, Jr. · Jones Day · North Point · 901 Lakeside Avenue · Cleveland, OH 44114-1190 · 216-586-3939

Howard J. C. Nicols · Squire Sanders · http://www.ssd.com · 4900 Key Tower · 127 Public Square · Cleveland, OH 44114-1304 · 216-479-8500

James B. Niehaus · Frantz Ward · http://www.frantzward.com · Public Square, Suite 127 · 2500 Key Center · Cleveland, OH 44114-1230 · 216-515-1660

Stephen M. O'Bryan · Taft Stettinius & Hollister · http://www.taftlaw.com · BP Tower, Suite 3500 · 200 Public Square · Cleveland, OH 44114-2302 · 216-241-2838

Anthony J. O'Malley · Vorys, Sater, Seymour and Pease · 2100 One Cleveland Center · 1375 East Ninth Street · Cleveland, OH 44114-1724 · 216-479-6100

Mark O'Neill · 2% · Weston Hurd · The Tower at Erieview, Suite 1900 · 1301 East Ninth Street · Cleveland, OH 44114-1862 · 216-241-6602

John D. Parker · Baker Hostetler · http://www.bakerlaw.com · National City Center, Suite 3200 · 1900 East Ninth Street · Cleveland, OH 44114-3485 · 216-621-0200

M. Neal Rains · Frantz Ward · http://www.frantzward.com · Public Square, Suite 127 · 2500 Key Center · Cleveland, OH 44114-1230 · 216-515-1660

John Winship Read · Vorys, Sater, Seymour and Pease · 2100 One Cleveland Center · 1375 East Ninth Street · Cleveland, OH 44114-1724 · 216-479-6100

Harold H. Reader · Ulmer & Berne · Skylight Office Tower, Suite 1100 · 1660 West Second Street · Cleveland, OH 44113-1448 · 216-583-7000

Carole S. Rendon · Giffen & Kaminsky · 1717 East Ninth Street, Suite 2100 · Cleveland, OH 44114 · 216-621-5161

James D. Robenalt · Thompson Hine · Key Center, Suite 3900 · 127 Public Square · Cleveland, OH 44114-1291 · 216-566-5500

Nicholas D. Satullo · Reminger Attorneys At Law · 1400 Midland Building · 101 Prospect Avenue West · Cleveland, OH 44115-1093 · 216-687-1311

David A. Schaefer · McCarthy, Lebit, Crystal & Liffman · http://www.mccarthylebit.com · The Midland Building, Suite 1800 · 101 West Prospect Avenue · Cleveland, OH 44115 · 216-696-1422

Donald S. Scherzer · Roetzel & Andress · http://www.ralaw.com · One Cleveland Center, Ninth Floor · 1375 East Ninth Street · Cleveland, OH 44114 · 216-623-0150

Niki Z. Schwartz · a · Schwartz, Downey and Company · Guildhall Building, Suite 1616 · 45 West Prospect Avenue · Cleveland, OH 44115 · 216-696-7100

Randall L. Solomon · a · Baker Hostetler · http://www.bakerlaw.com · National City Center, Suite 3200 1900 East Ninth Street · Cleveland, OH 44114-3485 · 216-621-0200

Stephen G. Sozio · Jones Day · North Point · 901 Lakeside Avenue · Cleveland, OH 44114-1190 · 216-586-3939

Hugh M. Stanley, Jr. · ⑩ · Tucker Ellis & West · Huntington Building, Suite 1150 · 925 Euclid Avenue · Cleveland, OH 44115-1475 · 216-592-5000

Robert C. Tucker · Tucker Ellis & West · Huntington Building, Suite 1150 · 925 Euclid Avenue · Cleveland, OH 44115-1475 · 216-592-5000

Michael N. Ungar · Ulmer & Berne · Skylight Office Tower, Suite 1100 · 1660 West Second Street · Cleveland, OH 44113-1448 · 216-583-7000

Robert Valerian · Taft Stettinius & Hollister · http://www.taftlaw.com · BP Tower, Suite 3500 · 200 Public Square · Cleveland, OH 44114-2302 · 216-241-2838

Ernest E. Vargo · Baker Hostetler · http://www.bakerlaw.com · National City Center, Suite 3200 · 1900 East Ninth Street · Cleveland, OH 44114-3485 · 216-621-0200

F. Thomas Vickers · Ulmer & Berne · Skylight Office Tower, Suite 1100 · 1660 West Second Street · Cleveland, OH 44113-1448 · 216-583-7000

Robert S. Walker · Jones Day · North Point · 901 Lakeside Avenue · Cleveland, OH 44114-1190 · 216-586-3939

David H. Wallace · Taft Stettinius & Hollister · http://www.taftlaw.com · BP Tower, Suite 3500 · 200 Public Square · Cleveland, OH 44114-2302 · 216-241-2838

Mark I. Wallach · ⑩ · Calfee, Halter & Griswold · http://www.calfee.com · 1400 KeyBank Center · 800 Superior Avenue · Cleveland, OH 44114-2688 · 216-622-8200

Daniel R. Warren · Baker Hostetler · http://www.bakerlaw.com · National City Center, Suite 3200 · 1900 East Ninth Street · Cleveland, OH 44114-3485 · 216-621-0200

Robin G. Weaver · Squire Sanders · http://www.ssd.com · 4900 Key Tower · 127 Public Square · Cleveland, OH 44114-1304 · 216-479-8500

David C. Weiner · ⑩ · Squire Sanders · http://www.ssd.com · 4900 Key Tower · 127 Public Square · Cleveland, OH 44114-1304 · 216-479-8500

Richard B. Whitney · Jones Day · North Point · 901 Lakeside Avenue · Cleveland, OH 44114-1190 · 216-586-3939

James R. Wooley · Baker Hostetler · http://www.bakerlaw.com · National City Center, Suite 3200 · 1900 East Ninth Street · Cleveland, OH 44114-3485 · 216-621-0200

Barbara F. Yaksic · McGlinchey Stafford · http://www.mcglinchey.com · 25550 Chagrin Boulevard, Suite 406 · Cleveland, OH 44122-4640 · 216-378-9905

Kevin M. Young · Tucker Ellis & West · Huntington Building, Suite 1150 · 925 Euclid Avenue · Cleveland, OH 44115-1475 · 216-592-5000

Columbus

David W. Alexander · ⑩ · Squire Sanders · http://www.ssd.com · 1300 Huntington Center · 41 South High Street · Columbus, OH 43215-6197 · 614-365-2700

Sandra J. Anderson · ⑩ · Vorys, Sater, Seymour and Pease · 52 East Gay Street · P.O. Box 1008 · Columbus, OH 43216-1008 · 614-464-6400

James E. Arnold · James E. Arnold & Company · http://www.arnlaw.com · 471 East Broad Street, Suite 1400 · Columbus, OH 43215 · 614-460-1600

Michael H. Carpenter · a · Carpenter Lipps & Leland · http://www.carpenterlipps.com · 280 Plaza, Suite 1300 · 280 North High Street · Columbus, OH 43215 · 614-365-4100

Stephen E. Chappelear · a · Hahn Loeser & Parks · 65 East State Street, Suite 1400 · Columbus, OH 43215 · 614-221-0240

John J. Chester, Sr. · 2% · Chester Willcox & Saxbe · http://www.cwslaw.com · 65 East State Street, Suite 1000 · Columbus, OH 43215 · 614-221-4000

J. Kevin Cogan · Jones Day · 325 John H. McConnell Boulevard, Suite 600 · P.O. Box 165017 · Columbus, OH 43216-5017 · 614-469-3939

Dan L. Cvetanovich · a · Bailey Cavalieri · One Columbus Building, Suite 2100 · 10 West Broad Street · Columbus, OH 43215-3422 · 614-221-3155

Philomena M. Dane · Squire Sanders · http://www.ssd.com · 1300 Huntington Center · 41 South High Street · Columbus, OH 43215-6197 · 614-365-2700

James E. Davidson · Schottenstein, Zox & Dunn · http://www.szd.com · 250 West Street, Suite 700 · Columbus, OH 43215-2538 · 614-462-2700

Philip F. Downey · Vorys, Sater, Seymour and Pease · 52 East Gay Street · P.O. Box 1008 · Columbus, OH 43216-1008 · 614-464-6400

Mason Evans IV · Porter, Wright, Morris & Arthur · http://www.porterwright.com · Huntington Center · 41 South High Street · Columbus, OH 43215-6194 · 614-227-2000

Mary Ellen Fairfield · a · Vorys, Sater, Seymour and Pease · 52 East Gay Street · P.O. Box 1008 · Columbus, OH 43216-1008 · 614-464-6400

Stephen C. Fitch · a · Chester Willcox & Saxbe · http://www.cwslaw.com · 65 East State Street, Suite 1000 · Columbus, OH 43215 · 614-221-4000

John R. Gall · a · Squire Sanders · http://www.ssd.com · 1300 Huntington Center · 41 South High Street Columbus, OH 43215-6197 · 614-365-2700

John P. Gilligan · Schottenstein, Zox & Dunn · http://www.szd.com · 250 West Street, Suite 700 · Columbus, OH 43215-2538 · 614-462-2700

Thomas W. Hill · a · Kegler, Brown, Hill & Ritter · http://www.keglerbrown.com · Capitol Square, Suite 1800 · 65 East State Street · Columbus, OH 43215-4294 · 614-462-5400

Fordham E. Huffman · Jones Day · 325 John H. McConnell Boulevard, Suite 600 · P.O. Box 165017 · Columbus, OH 43216-5017 · 614-469-3939

Robert M. Kincaid, Jr. · Baker Hostetler · http://www.bakerlaw.com · Capitol Square, Suite 2100 · 65 East State Street · Columbus, OH 43215-4260 · 614-228-1541

Mark Landes · Isaac, Brant, Ledman & Teetor · The Midland Building, Suite 900 · 250 East Broad Street Columbus, OH 43215-3742 · 614-221-2121

John L. Landolfi · Vorys, Sater, Seymour and Pease · 52 East Gay Street · P.O. Box 1008 · Columbus, OH 43216-1008 · 614-464-6400

Jeffrey A. Lipps · Carpenter Lipps & Leland · http://www.carpenterlipps.com · 280 Plaza, Suite 1300 · 280 North High Street · Columbus, OH 43215 · 614-365-4100

Michael G. Long · Vorys, Sater, Seymour and Pease · 52 East Gay Street · P.O. Box 1008 · Columbus, OH 43216-1008 · 614-464-6400

Thomas L. Long · a · Baker Hostetler · http://www.bakerlaw.com · Capitol Square, Suite 2100 · 65 East State Street · Columbus, OH 43215-4260 · 614-228-1541

Kevin R. McDermott · Schottenstein, Zox & Dunn · http://www.szd.com · 250 West Street, Suite 700 · Columbus, OH 43215-2538 · 614-462-2700

John C. McDonald · a · Schottenstein, Zox & Dunn · http://www.szd.com · 250 West Street, Suite 700 · Columbus, OH 43215-2538 · 614-462-2700

Joel H. Mirman · Adams, Babner & Gitlitz · 5003 Horizons Drive, Suite 200 · Columbus, OH 43220 · 614-451-4227

William G. Porter II · Vorys, Sater, Seymour and Pease · 52 East Gay Street · P.O. Box 1008 · Columbus, OH 43216-1008 · 614-464-6400

Alan T. Radnor · 2) · Vorys, Sater, Seymour and Pease · 52 East Gay Street · P.O. Box 1008 · Columbus, OH 43216-1008 · 614-464-6400

Frank A. Ray · 2) · Chester Willcox & Saxbe · http://www.cwslaw.com · 65 East State Street, Suite 1000 · Columbus, OH 43215 · 614-221-4000

Thomas B. Ridgley · 2% · Vorys, Sater, Seymour and Pease · 52 East Gay Street · P.O. Box 1008 · Columbus, OH 43216-1008 · 614-464-6400

Charles R. Saxbe · a · Chester Willcox & Saxbe · http://www.cwslaw.com · 65 East State Street, Suite 1000 · Columbus, OH 43215 · 614-221-4000

Alan G. Starkoff · Schottenstein, Zox & Dunn · http://www.szd.com · 250 West Street, Suite 700 · Columbus, OH 43215-2538 · 614-462-2700

Roger P. Sugarman · Kegler, Brown, Hill & Ritter · http://www.keglerbrown.com · Capitol Square, Suite 1800 · 65 East State Street · Columbus, OH 43215-4294 · 614-462-5400

Kathleen McManus Trafford · a · Porter, Wright, Morris & Arthur · http://www.porterwright.com · Huntington Center · 41 South High Street · Columbus, OH 43215-6194 · 614-227-2000

Robert W. Trafford · a · Porter, Wright, Morris & Arthur · http://www.porterwright.com · Huntington Center · 41 South High Street · Columbus, OH 43215-6194 · 614-227-2000

Melvin D. Weinstein · Kegler, Brown, Hill & Ritter · http://www.keglerbrown.com · Capitol Square, Suite 1800 · 65 East State Street · Columbus, OH 43215-4294 · 614-462-5400

William C. Wilkinson · Thompson Hine · 10 West Broad Street, Suite 700 · Columbus, OH 43215-3435 · 614-469-3200

C. Craig Woods · Squire Sanders · http://www.ssd.com · 1300 Huntington Center · 41 South High Street · Columbus, OH 43215-6197 · 614-365-2700

John W. Zeiger · 2) · Zeiger, Tigges & Little · http://www.litohio.com · Huntington Center, Suite 3500 · 41 South High Street · Columbus, OH 43215 · 614-365-9900

Dayton

Thomas L. Czechowski · Dinsmore & Shohl · http://www.dinslaw.com · Courthouse Plaza, SW, Suite 1100 · 10 North Ludlow Street · Dayton, OH 45402 · 937-449-2800

Terence L. Fague · Coolidge Wall Co. · http://www.coollaw.com · 33 West First Street, Suite 600 · Dayton, OH 45402 · 937-223-8177

Charles J. Faruki · 2) · Faruki Ireland & Cox · Courthouse Plaza, SW, Suite 500 · 10 North Ludlow Street · Dayton, OH 45402 · 937-227-3700

Neil F. Freund · a · Freund, Freeze & Arnold · One Dayton Centre, Suite 1800 · One South Main Street Dayton, OH 45402-2017 · 937-222-2424

David C. Greer · 2% · Bieser, Greer & Landis · http://www.biesergreer.com · National City Center, Suite 400 · Six North Main Street · Dayton, OH 45402-1908 · 937-223-3277

Paul G. Hallinan · Porter, Wright, Morris & Arthur · http://www.porterwright.com · One Dayton Centre, Suite 1600 · One South Main Street · Dayton, OH 45402-2028 · 937-449-6810

Nicholas C. Hollenkamp · a · Dinsmore & Shohl · http://www.dinslaw.com · One Dayton Centre, Suite 1300 · One South Main Street · Dayton, OH 45402 · 937-449-6400

D. Jeffrey Ireland, Jr. · Faruki Ireland & Cox · Courthouse Plaza, SW, Suite 500 · 10 North Ludlow Street · Dayton, OH 45402 · 937-227-3700

Michael W. Krumholtz · Bieser, Greer & Landis · http://www.biesergreer.com · National City Center, Suite 400 · Six North Main Street · Dayton, OH 45402-1908 · 937-223-3277

Roger J. Makley · 2) · Boucher & Boucher · 12 West Monument Avenue, Suite 200 · Dayton, OH 45402-1202 · 937-223-0122

Thomas P. Whelley II · Dinsmore & Shohl · http://www.dinslaw.com · Courthouse Plaza, SW, Suite 1100 10 North Ludlow Street · Dayton, OH 45402 · 937-449-2800

David P. Williamson · Bieser, Greer & Landis · http://www.biesergreer.com · National City Center, Suite 400 · Six North Main Street · Dayton, OH 45402-1908 · 937-223-3277

North Olmsted

John E. Martindale · a · John E. Martindale · 26031 Butternut Ridge Road · North Olmsted, OH 44070-4514 · 216-272-7750

Toledo

John C. Barron · Shumaker, Loop & Kendrick · North Courthouse Square · 1000 Jackson Street · Toledo, OH 43604-5573 · 419-241-9000

Frederick Byers · a · Fritz Byers · The Spitzer Building, Suite 824 · 520 Madison Avenue · Toledo, OH 43604-1343 · 419-241-8013

Cary Cooper · 2) · Cooper & Walinski · 900 Adams Street · Toledo, OH 43604 · 419-241-1200

Thomas P. Dillon · Shumaker, Loop & Kendrick · North Courthouse Square · 1000 Jackson Street · Toledo, OH 43604-5573 · 419-241-9000

Robert J. Gilmer, Jr. · Eastman & Smith · One Seagate, 24th Floor · P.O. Box 10032 · Toledo, OH 43699-0032 · 419-241-6000

Henry N. Heuerman · Eastman & Smith · One Seagate, 24th Floor · P.O. Box 10032 · Toledo, OH 43699-0032 · 419-241-6000

Reginald S. Jackson, Jr. · Connelly, Jackson & Collier · 405 Madison Avenue, Suite 1600 · Toledo, OH 43604 · 419-243-2100

James R. Jeffery · a · Spengler Nathanson · 608 Madison Avenue, Suite 1000 · Toledo, OH 43604-1169 · 419-241-2201

Richard M. Kerger · a · Kerger & Associates · 33 South Michigan Street, Suite 100 · Toledo, OH 43602 · 419-255-5990

Gerald R. Kowalski · Cooper & Walinski · 900 Adams Street · Toledo, OH 43604 · 419-241-1200

James F. Nooney · Eastman & Smith · One Seagate, 24th Floor · P.O. Box 10032 · Toledo, OH 43699-0032 · 419-241-6000

Thomas G. Pletz · Shumaker, Loop & Kendrick · North Courthouse Square · 1000 Jackson Street · Toledo, OH 43604-5573 · 419-241-9000

Stephen A. Rothschild · Shumaker, Loop & Kendrick · North Courthouse Square · 1000 Jackson Street · Toledo, OH 43604-5573 · 419-241-9000

Theodore M. Rowen · 2% · Spengler Nathanson · 608 Madison Avenue, Suite 1000 · Toledo, OH 43604-1169 · 419-241-2201

Michael G. Sanderson · Shumaker, Loop & Kendrick · North Courthouse Square · 1000 Jackson Street · Toledo, OH 43604-5573 · 419-241-9000

Joseph P. Thacker · Cooper & Walinski · 900 Adams Street · Toledo, OH 43604 · 419-241-1200

Richard S. Walinski · a · Cooper & Walinski · 900 Adams Street · Toledo, OH 43604 · 419-241-1200

David Wicklund · Shumaker, Loop & Kendrick · North Courthouse Square · 1000 Jackson Street · Toledo, OH 43604-5573 · 419-241-9000

COMMUNICATIONS LAW

Cleveland

David L. Marburger · a · Baker Hostetler · http://www.bakerlaw.com · National City Center, Suite 3200 · 1900 East Ninth Street · Cleveland, OH 44114-3485 · 216-621-0200

Columbus

John W. Bentine · a · Chester Willcox & Saxbe · http://www.cwslaw.com · 65 East State Street, Suite 1000 · Columbus, OH 43215 · 614-221-4000

Daniel R. Conway · Porter, Wright, Morris & Arthur · http://www.porterwright.com · Huntington Center · 41 South High Street · Columbus, OH 43215-6194 · 614-227-2000

Gregory J. Dunn · Schottenstein, Zox & Dunn · http://www.szd.com · 250 West Street, Suite 700 · Columbus, OH 43215-2538 · 614-462-2700

Frederick M. Gittes · 2) · Fred Gittes · 723 Oak Street · Columbus, OH 43205 · 614-222-4735

Marion H. Little, Jr. · Zeiger, Tigges & Little · http://www.litohio.com · Huntington Center, Suite 3500 · 41 South High Street · Columbus, OH 43215 · 614-365-9900

Thomas E. Lodge · Thompson Hine · 10 West Broad Street, Suite 700 · Columbus, OH 43215-3435 · 614-469-3200

Thomas J. O'Brien · Bricker & Eckler · http://www.bricker.com · 100 South Third Street · Columbus, OH 43215-4291 · 614-227-2300

Stephen J. Smith, Sr. · Schottenstein, Zox & Dunn · http://www.szd.com · 250 West Street, Suite 700 · Columbus, OH 43215-2538 · 614-462-2700

John W. Zeiger · 2) · Zeiger, Tigges & Little · http://www.litohio.com · Huntington Center, Suite 3500 · 41 South High Street · Columbus, OH 43215 · 614-365-9900

Toledo

Frederick Byers · a · Fritz Byers · The Spitzer Building, Suite 824 · 520 Madison Avenue · Toledo, OH 43604-1343 · 419-241-8013

CONSTRUCTION LAW

Akron

Nicholas T. George · Buckingham, Doolittle & Burroughs · http://www.bdblaw.com · 3800 Embassy Parkway, Suite 300 · P.O. Box 1500 · Akron, OH 44309-1500 · 330-376-5300

Canton

Richard J. Lolli · Buckingham, Doolittle & Burroughs · http://www.bdblaw.com · 4518 Fulton Drive, NW P.O. Box 35548 · Canton, OH 44735-5548 · 330-492-8717

John C. Ross · Buckingham, Doolittle & Burroughs · http://www.bdblaw.com · 4518 Fulton Drive, NW · P.O. Box 35548 · Canton, OH 44735-5548 · 330-492-8717

Randolph L. Snow · Black, McCuskey, Souers & Arbaugh · 220 Market Avenue South, Suite 1000 · Canton, OH 44702 · 330-456-8341

Cincinnati

Mark C. Bissinger · a · Dinsmore & Shohl · http://www.dinslaw.com · 255 East Fifth Street, Suite 1900 · Cincinnati, OH 45202-3172 · 513-977-8200

James A. Comodeca · Dinsmore & Shohl · http://www.dinslaw.com · 255 East Fifth Street, Suite 1900 · Cincinnati, OH 45202-3172 · 513-977-8200

Thomas L. Gabelman · Vorys, Sater, Seymour and Pease · Atrium Two, Suite 2000 · 221 East Fourth Street · P.O. Box 0236 · Cincinnati, OH 45201-0236 · 513-723-4000

D. Scott Gurney · Frost Brown Todd · http://www.frostbrowntodd.com · PNC Center, Suite 2200 · 201 East Fifth Street · Cincinnati, OH 45202-4182 · 513-651-6800

Cleveland

Jeffrey R. Appelbaum · a · Thompson Hine · Key Center, Suite 3900 · 127 Public Square · Cleveland, OH 44114-1291 · 216-566-5500

Joseph E. Cavasinni · Reminger Attorneys At Law · 1400 Midland Building · 101 Prospect Avenue West · Cleveland, OH 44115-1093 · 216-687-1311

Steven A. Friedman · Squire Sanders · http://www.ssd.com · 4900 Key Tower · 127 Public Square · Cleveland, OH 44114-1304 · 216-479-8500

David H. Gunning II · Roetzel & Andress · http://www.ralaw.com · One Cleveland Center, Ninth Floor · 1375 East Ninth Street · Cleveland, OH 44114 · 216-623-0150

Robert A. Hager · Buckingham, Doolittle & Burroughs · http://www.bdblaw.com · 1375 East Ninth Street, Suite 1700 · Cleveland, OH 44114 · 216-621-5300

William B. Leahy · Buckingham, Doolittle & Burroughs · http://www.bdblaw.com · 1375 East Ninth Street, Suite 1700 · Cleveland, OH 44114 · 216-621-5300

Barry J. Miller · Benesch, Friedlander, Coplan & Aronoff · BP Tower, Suite 2300 · 200 Public Square · Cleveland, OH 44114-2378 · 216-363-4500

Andrew J. Natale · Frantz Ward · http://www.frantzward.com · Public Square, Suite 127 · 2500 Key Center · Cleveland, OH 44114-1230 · 216-515-1660

Royce R. Remington · Hahn Loeser & Parks · BP Tower, Suite 2800 · 200 Public Square · Cleveland, OH 44114-2301 · 216-621-0150

James D. Robenalt · Thompson Hine · Key Center, Suite 3900 · 127 Public Square · Cleveland, OH 44114-1291 · 216-566-5500

Patrick J. Sweeney · Thompson Hine · Key Center, Suite 3900 · 127 Public Square · Cleveland, OH 44114-1291 · 216-566-5500

Columbus

Michael W. Currie · Thompson Hine · 10 West Broad Street, Suite 700 · Columbus, OH 43215-3435 · 614-469-3200

Daniel F. Edwards · Thompson Hine · 10 West Broad Street, Suite 700 · Columbus, OH 43215-3435 · 614-469-3200

Donald W. Gregory · Kegler, Brown, Hill & Ritter · http://www.keglerbrown.com · Capitol Square, Suite 1800 · 65 East State Street · Columbus, OH 43215-4294 · 614-462-5400

Donald B. Leach, Jr. · Dinsmore & Shohl · http://www.dinslaw.com · 191 West Nationwide Boulevard, Suite 300 · Columbus, OH 43215 · 614-221-8448

John J. Petro · Williams & Petro Company · 338 South High Street, Second Floor · Columbus, OH 43215-4546 · 614-224-0531

Jack Rosati, Jr. · Bricker & Eckler · http://www.bricker.com · 100 South Third Street · Columbus, OH 43215-4291 · 614-227-2300

Michael D. Tarullo · Schottenstein, Zox & Dunn · http://www.szd.com · 250 West Street, Suite 700 · Columbus, OH 43215-2538 · 614-462-2700

Peter D. Welin · Thompson Hine · 10 West Broad Street, Suite 700 · Columbus, OH 43215-3435 · 614-469-3200

CORPORATE GOVERNANCE AND COMPLIANCE LAW

Akron

J. Bret Treier · Vorys, Sater, Seymour and Pease · First National Tower, Suite 1100 · 106 South Main Street · Akron, OH 44308-1417 · 330-208-1000

Cincinnati

Gerald S. Greenberg · Taft Stettinius & Hollister · http://www.taftlaw.com · 425 Walnut Street, Suite 1800 · Cincinnati, OH 45202-3957 · 513-381-2838

William T. Hayden · Katz, Teller, Brant & Hild · http://www.katzteller.com · 255 East Fifth Street, Suite 2400 · Cincinnati, OH 45202-4724 · 513-721-4532

Charles F. Hertlein · Dinsmore & Shohl · http://www.dinslaw.com · 255 East Fifth Street, Suite 1900 · Cincinnati, OH 45202-3172 · 513-977-8200

William G. Kohlhepp · a · Cors & Bassett · 537 East Pete Rose Way, Suite 400 · Cincinnati, OH 45202-3502 · 513-852-8200

Mark H. Longenecker, Jr. · Porter, Wright, Morris & Arthur · http://www.porterwright.com · 250 East Fifth Street, Suite 2200 · Cincinnati, OH 45202-5118 · 513-381-4700

Clifford A. Roe, Jr. · 2) · Dinsmore & Shohl · http://www.dinslaw.com · 255 East Fifth Street, Suite 1900 Cincinnati, OH 45202-3172 · 513-977-8200

George H. Vincent · Dinsmore & Shohl · http://www.dinslaw.com · 255 East Fifth Street, Suite 1900 · Cincinnati, OH 45202-3172 · 513-977-8200

Thomas J. Westerfield · Dinsmore & Shohl · http://www.dinslaw.com · 255 East Fifth Street, Suite 1900 · Cincinnati, OH 45202-3172 · 513-977-8200

Cleveland

James R. Carlson · a · Thompson Hine · Key Center, Suite 3900 · 127 Public Square · Cleveland, OH 44114-1291 · 216-566-5500

Lyle G. Ganske · Jones Day · North Point · 901 Lakeside Avenue · Cleveland, OH 44114-1190 · 216-586-3939

Frances Floriano Goins · Ulmer & Berne · Skylight Office Tower, Suite 1100 · 1660 West Second Street Cleveland, OH 44113-1448 · 216-583-7000

Craig Owen White · Hahn Loeser & Parks · BP Tower, Suite 2800 · 200 Public Square · Cleveland, OH 44114-2301 · 216-621-0150

Columbus

John P. Beavers · 2% · Bricker & Eckler · http://www.bricker.com · 100 South Third Street · Columbus, OH 43215-4291 · 614-227-2300

William J. Kelly, Jr. · Porter, Wright, Morris & Arthur · http://www.porterwright.com · Huntington Center · 41 South High Street · Columbus, OH 43215-6194 · 614-227-2000

Christopher J. Weber · Kegler, Brown, Hill & Ritter · http://www.keglerbrown.com · Capitol Square, Suite 1800 · 65 East State Street · Columbus, OH 43215-4294 · 614-462-5400

CORPORATE LAW

Akron

Ronald C. Allan · Buckingham, Doolittle & Burroughs · http://www.bdblaw.com · 3800 Embassy Parkway, Suite 300 · P.O. Box 1500 · Akron, OH 44309-1500 · 330-376-5300

Robert W. Briggs · Buckingham, Doolittle & Burroughs · http://www.bdblaw.com · 3800 Embassy Parkway, Suite 300 · P.O. Box 1500 · Akron, OH 44309-1500 · 330-376-5300

Nicholas T. George · Buckingham, Doolittle & Burroughs · http://www.bdblaw.com · 3800 Embassy Parkway, Suite 300 · P.O. Box 1500 · Akron, OH 44309-1500 · 330-376-5300

David M. Hunter · a · Brouse McDowell · 388 South Main Street, Suite 500 · Akron, OH 44311 · 330-535-5711

Duane L. Isham · 2) · Roetzel & Andress · http://www.ralaw.com · 222 South Main Street · Akron, OH 44308-2098 · 330-376-2700

David Kern · Buckingham, Doolittle & Burroughs · http://www.bdblaw.com · 3800 Embassy Parkway, Suite 300 · P.O. Box 1500 · Akron, OH 44309-1500 · 330-376-5300

Thomas G. Knoll · a · Stark & Knoll · http://www.stark-knoll.com · 3475 Ridgewood Road · Akron, OH 44333-3163 · 330-376-3300

James D. Kraus · Buckingham, Doolittle & Burroughs · http://www.bdblaw.com · 3800 Embassy Parkway, Suite 300 · P.O. Box 1500 · Akron, OH 44309-1500 · 330-376-5300

Craig S. Marshall · Buckingham, Doolittle & Burroughs · http://www.bdblaw.com · 3800 Embassy Parkway, Suite 300 · P.O. Box 1500 · Akron, OH 44309-1500 · 330-376-5300

J. Bret Treier · Vorys, Sater, Seymour and Pease · First National Tower, Suite 1100 · 106 South Main Street · Akron, OH 44308-1417 · 330-208-1000

Canton

Fred J. Haupt · Krugliak, Wilkins, Griffiths & Dougherty · http://www.kwgd.com · 4775 Munson Street, NW · P.O. Box 36963 · Canton, OH 44735-6963 · 330-497-0700

Randall C. Hunt · Krugliak, Wilkins, Griffiths & Dougherty · http://www.kwgd.com · 4775 Munson Street, NW · P.O. Box 36963 · Canton, OH 44735-6963 · 330-497-0700

Cincinnati

Andrew R. Berger · Katz, Teller, Brant & Hild · http://www.katzteller.com · 255 East Fifth Street, Suite 2400 · Cincinnati, OH 45202-4724 · 513-721-4532

Robert E. Brant · Katz, Teller, Brant & Hild · http://www.katzteller.com · 255 East Fifth Street, Suite 2400 · Cincinnati, OH 45202-4724 · 513-721-4532

James E. Burke · Keating Muething & Klekamp · http://www.kmklaw.com · One East Fourth Street, Suite 1400 · Cincinnati, OH 45202 · 513-579-6400

Robert E. Coletti · Keating Muething & Klekamp · http://www.kmklaw.com · One East Fourth Street, Suite 1400 · Cincinnati, OH 45202 · 513-579-6400

Martiné R. Dunn · Dinsmore & Shohl · http://www.dinslaw.com · 255 East Fifth Street, Suite 1900 · Cincinnati, OH 45202-3172 · 513-977-8200

Neil Ganulin · Frost Brown Todd · http://www.frostbrowntodd.com · PNC Center, Suite 2200 · 201 East Fifth Street · Cincinnati, OH 45202-4182 · 513-651-6800

John R. Gierl · Katz, Teller, Brant & Hild · http://www.katzteller.com · 255 East Fifth Street, Suite 2400 · Cincinnati, OH 45202-4724 · 513-721-4532

Gerald S. Greenberg · Taft Stettinius & Hollister · http://www.taftlaw.com · 425 Walnut Street, Suite 1800 · Cincinnati, OH 45202-3957 · 513-381-2838

Theodore D. Grosser · Porter, Wright, Morris & Arthur · http://www.porterwright.com · 250 East Fifth Street, Suite 2200 · Cincinnati, OH 45202-5118 · 513-381-4700

Bradley G. Haas · Katz, Teller, Brant & Hild · http://www.katzteller.com · 255 East Fifth Street, Suite 2400 · Cincinnati, OH 45202-4724 · 513-721-4532

Charles F. Hertlein · Dinsmore & Shohl · http://www.dinslaw.com · 255 East Fifth Street, Suite 1900 · Cincinnati, OH 45202-3172 · 513-977-8200

Michael A. Hirschfeld · a · Graydon, Head & Ritchey · 1900 Fifth Third Center · 511 Walnut Street · Cincinnati, OH 45202 · 513-621-6464

Timothy E. Hoberg · 2) · Taft Stettinius & Hollister · http://www.taftlaw.com · 425 Walnut Street, Suite 1800 · Cincinnati, OH 45202-3957 · 513-381-2838

Mark J. Jahnke · a · Katz, Teller, Brant & Hild · http://www.katzteller.com · 255 East Fifth Street, Suite 2400 · Cincinnati, OH 45202-4724 · 513-721-4532

Thomas W. Kahle · Baker Hostetler · http://www.bakerlaw.com · 312 Walnut Street, Suite 3200 · Cincinnati, OH 45202-4074 · 513-929-3400

Reuven J. Katz · 2% · Katz, Teller, Brant & Hild · http://www.katzteller.com · 255 East Fifth Street, Suite 2400 · Cincinnati, OH 45202-4724 · 513-721-4532

William J. Keating, Jr. · Keating Muething & Klekamp · http://www.kmklaw.com · One East Fourth Street, Suite 1400 · Cincinnati, OH 45202 · 513-579-6400

Donald P. Klekamp · a · Keating Muething & Klekamp · http://www.kmklaw.com · One East Fourth Street, Suite 1400 · Cincinnati, OH 45202 · 513-579-6400

William G. Kohlhepp · a · Cors & Bassett · 537 East Pete Rose Way, Suite 400 · Cincinnati, OH 45202-3502 · 513-852-8200

Gary P. Kreider · 2) · Keating Muething & Klekamp · http://www.kmklaw.com · One East Fourth Street, Suite 1400 · Cincinnati, OH 45202 · 513-579-6400

Richard T. LaJeunesse · Graydon, Head & Ritchey · 1900 Fifth Third Center · 511 Walnut Street · Cincinnati, OH 45202 · 513-621-6464

Roger E. Lautzenhiser, Jr. · a · Vorys, Sater, Seymour and Pease · Atrium Two, Suite 2000 · 221 East Fourth Street · P.O. Box 0236 · Cincinnati, OH 45201-0236 · 513-723-4000

Margaret A. Lawson · Taft Stettinius & Hollister · http://www.taftlaw.com · 425 Walnut Street, Suite 1800 · Cincinnati, OH 45202-3957 · 513-381-2838

Mark H. Longenecker, Jr. · Porter, Wright, Morris & Arthur · http://www.porterwright.com · 250 East Fifth Street, Suite 2200 · Cincinnati, OH 45202-5118 · 513-381-4700

Paul R. Mattingly · Dinsmore & Shohl · http://www.dinslaw.com · 255 East Fifth Street, Suite 1900 · Cincinnati, OH 45202-3172 · 513-977-8200

John J. McCoy · Taft Stettinius & Hollister · http://www.taftlaw.com · 425 Walnut Street, Suite 1800 · Cincinnati, OH 45202-3957 · 513-381-2838

George D. Molinsky · Taft Stettinius & Hollister · http://www.taftlaw.com · 425 Walnut Street, Suite 1800 · Cincinnati, OH 45202-3957 · 513-381-2838

Paul V. Muething · Keating Muething & Klekamp · http://www.kmklaw.com · One East Fourth Street, Suite 1400 · Cincinnati, OH 45202 · 513-579-6400

Clifford A. Roe, Jr. · 2) · Dinsmore & Shohl · http://www.dinslaw.com · 255 East Fifth Street, Suite 1900 Cincinnati, OH 45202-3172 · 513-977-8200

Jeffrey L. Rohr · Graydon, Head & Ritchey · 1900 Fifth Third Center · 511 Walnut Street · Cincinnati, OH 45202 · 513-621-6464

Jeffery R. Rush · a · Frost Brown Todd · http://www.frostbrowntodd.com · PNC Center, Suite 2200 · 201 East Fifth Street · Cincinnati, OH 45202-4182 · 513-651-6800

Jeffrey S. Schloemer · Taft Stettinius & Hollister · http://www.taftlaw.com · 425 Walnut Street, Suite 1800 · Cincinnati, OH 45202-3957 · 513-381-2838

Richard G. Schmalzl · Graydon, Head & Ritchey · 1900 Fifth Third Center · 511 Walnut Street · Cincinnati, OH 45202 · 513-621-6464

Melvin S. Shotten · Taft Stettinius & Hollister · http://www.taftlaw.com · 425 Walnut Street, Suite 1800 · Cincinnati, OH 45202-3957 · 513-381-2838

Patricia Mann Smitson · Thompson Hine · 312 Walnut Street, 14th Floor · Cincinnati, OH 45202-4089 · 513-352-6700

Edward E. Steiner · Keating Muething & Klekamp · http://www.kmklaw.com · One East Fourth Street, Suite 1400 · Cincinnati, OH 45202 · 513-579-6400

John S. Stith · a · Porter, Wright, Morris & Arthur · http://www.porterwright.com · 250 East Fifth Street, Suite 2200 · Cincinnati, OH 45202-5118 · 513-381-4700

George H. Vincent · Dinsmore & Shohl · http://www.dinslaw.com · 255 East Fifth Street, Suite 1900 · Cincinnati, OH 45202-3172 · 513-977-8200

Cleveland

Albert T. Adams · a · Baker Hostetler · http://www.bakerlaw.com · National City Center, Suite 3200 · 1900 East Ninth Street · Cleveland, OH 44114-3485 · 216-621-0200

Thomas A. Aldrich · Thompson Hine · Key Center, Suite 3900 · 127 Public Square · Cleveland, OH 44114-1291 · 216-566-5500

George N. Aronoff · 2% · Benesch, Friedlander, Coplan & Aronoff · BP Tower, Suite 2300 · 200 Public Square · Cleveland, OH 44114-2378 · 216-363-4500

Malvin E. Bank · 2% · Thompson Hine · Key Center, Suite 3900 · 127 Public Square · Cleveland, OH 44114-1291 · 216-566-5500

Lawrence M. Bell · 2% · Benesch, Friedlander, Coplan & Aronoff · BP Tower, Suite 2300 · 200 Public Square · Cleveland, OH 44114-2378 · 216-363-4500

Daniel G. Berick · Squire Sanders · http://www.ssd.com · 4900 Key Tower · 127 Public Square · Cleveland, OH 44114-1304 · 216-479-8500

Irv Berliner · Taft Stettinius & Hollister · http://www.taftlaw.com · BP Tower, Suite 3500 · 200 Public Square · Cleveland, OH 44114-2302 · 216-241-2838

Howard Bobrow · Taft Stettinius & Hollister · http://www.taftlaw.com · BP Tower, Suite 3500 · 200 Public Square · Cleveland, OH 44114-2302 · 216-241-2838

Carolyn J. Buller · Squire Sanders · http://www.ssd.com · 4900 Key Tower · 127 Public Square · Cleveland, OH 44114-1304 · 216-479-8500

James R. Carlson · a · Thompson Hine · Key Center, Suite 3900 · 127 Public Square · Cleveland, OH 44114-1291 · 216-566-5500

Elizabeth A. Dellinger · Benesch, Friedlander, Coplan & Aronoff · BP Tower, Suite 2300 · 200 Public Square · Cleveland, OH 44114-2378 · 216-363-4500

Dominic A. DiPuccio · Taft Stettinius & Hollister · http://www.taftlaw.com · BP Tower, Suite 3500 · 200 Public Square · Cleveland, OH 44114-2302 · 216-241-2838

Michael A. Ellis · Porter, Wright, Morris & Arthur · http://www.porterwright.com · 925 Euclid Avenue, Suite 1700 · Cleveland, OH 44115-1483 · 216-443-9000

Stephen C. Ellis · a · Tucker Ellis & West · Huntington Building, Suite 1150 · 925 Euclid Avenue · Cleveland, OH 44115-1475 · 216-592-5000

Lyle G. Ganske · Jones Day · North Point · 901 Lakeside Avenue · Cleveland, OH 44114-1190 · 216-586-3939

Allan Goldner · Benesch, Friedlander, Coplan & Aronoff · BP Tower, Suite 2300 · 200 Public Square · Cleveland, OH 44114-2378 · 216-363-4500

Douglas E. Haas · Benesch, Friedlander, Coplan & Aronoff · BP Tower, Suite 2300 · 200 Public Square · Cleveland, OH 44114-2378 · 216-363-4500

Suzanne K. Hanselman · Baker Hostetler · http://www.bakerlaw.com · National City Center, Suite 3200 · 1900 East Ninth Street · Cleveland, OH 44114-3485 · 216-621-0200

Charles W. Hardin, Jr. · Jones Day · North Point · 901 Lakeside Avenue · Cleveland, OH 44114-1190 · 216-586-3939

Christopher J. Hewitt · Jones Day · North Point · 901 Lakeside Avenue · Cleveland, OH 44114-1190 · 216-586-3939

James M. Hill · Benesch, Friedlander, Coplan & Aronoff · BP Tower, Suite 2300 · 200 Public Square · Cleveland, OH 44114-2378 · 216-363-4500

John J. Jenkins · Calfee, Halter & Griswold · http://www.calfee.com · 1400 KeyBank Center · 800 Superior Avenue · Cleveland, OH 44114-2688 · 216-622-8200

Mary Ann Jorgenson · a · Squire Sanders · http://www.ssd.com · 4900 Key Tower · 127 Public Square · Cleveland, OH 44114-1304 · 216-479-8500

Gordon S. Kaiser, Jr. · a · Squire Sanders · http://www.ssd.com · 4900 Key Tower · 127 Public Square · Cleveland, OH 44114-1304 · 216-479-8500

Ira C. Kaplan · Benesch, Friedlander, Coplan & Aronoff · BP Tower, Suite 2300 · 200 Public Square · Cleveland, OH 44114-2378 · 216-363-4500

Christopher M. Kelly · Jones Day · North Point · 901 Lakeside Avenue · Cleveland, OH 44114-1190 · 216-586-3939

Craig R. Martahus · a · Thompson Hine · Key Center, Suite 3900 · 127 Public Square · Cleveland, OH 44114-1291 · 216-566-5500

Thomas F. McKee · a · Calfee, Halter & Griswold · http://www.calfee.com · 1400 KeyBank Center · 800 Superior Avenue · Cleveland, OH 44114-2688 · 216-622-8200

Harry D. Mercer · a · Hahn Loeser & Parks · BP Tower, Suite 2800 · 200 Public Square · Cleveland, OH 44114-2301 · 216-621-0150

Donald H. Messinger · a · Thompson Hine · Key Center, Suite 3900 · 127 Public Square · Cleveland, OH 44114-1291 · 216-566-5500

Glenn E. Morrical · Tucker Ellis & West · Huntington Building, Suite 1150 · 925 Euclid Avenue · Cleveland, OH 44115-1475 · 216-592-5000

F. Ronald O'Keefe · a · Hahn Loeser & Parks · BP Tower, Suite 2800 · 200 Public Square · Cleveland, OH 44114-2301 · 216-621-0150

Brian M. O'Neill · Ulmer & Berne · Skylight Office Tower, Suite 1100 · 1660 West Second Street · Cleveland, OH 44113-1448 · 216-583-7000

Stephen P. Owendoff · a · Hahn Loeser & Parks · BP Tower, Suite 2800 · 200 Public Square · Cleveland, OH 44114-2301 · 216-621-0150

David P. Porter · Jones Day · North Point · 901 Lakeside Avenue · Cleveland, OH 44114-1190 · 216-586-3939

Edward G. Ptaszek, Jr. · a · Baker Hostetler · http://www.bakerlaw.com · National City Center, Suite 3200 · 1900 East Ninth Street · Cleveland, OH 44114-3485 · 216-621-0200

Richard S. Rivitz · Taft Stettinius & Hollister · http://www.taftlaw.com · BP Tower, Suite 3500 · 200 Public Square · Cleveland, OH 44114-2302 · 216-241-2838

John M. Saada, Jr. · Jones Day · North Point · 901 Lakeside Avenue · Cleveland, OH 44114-1190 · 216-586-3939

Lawrence N. Schultz · Calfee, Halter & Griswold · http://www.calfee.com · 1400 KeyBank Center · 800 Superior Avenue · Cleveland, OH 44114-2688 · 216-622-8200

David R. Tavolier · Taft Stettinius & Hollister · http://www.taftlaw.com · BP Tower, Suite 3500 · 200 Public Square · Cleveland, OH 44114-2302 · 216-241-2838

Thomas E. Wagner · Calfee, Halter & Griswold · http://www.calfee.com · 1400 KeyBank Center · 800 Superior Avenue · Cleveland, OH 44114-2688 · 216-622-8200

Richard T. Watson · 2) · Spieth, Bell, McCurdy & Newell · Huntington Building, Suite 2000 · 925 Euclid Avenue · Cleveland, OH 44115-1496 · 216-696-4700

David A. Zagore · Squire Sanders · http://www.ssd.com · 4900 Key Tower · 127 Public Square · Cleveland, OH 44114-1304 · 216-479-8500

Columbus

William E. Arthur · 2% · Porter, Wright, Morris & Arthur · http://www.porterwright.com · Huntington Center · 41 South High Street · Columbus, OH 43215-6194 · 614-227-2000

Dan A. Bailey · Bailey Cavalieri · One Columbus Building, Suite 2100 · 10 West Broad Street · Columbus, OH 43215-3422 · 614-221-3155

James H. Balthaser · Thompson Hine · 10 West Broad Street, Suite 700 · Columbus, OH 43215-3435 · 614-469-3200

Richard A. Barnhart · Schottenstein, Zox & Dunn · http://www.szd.com · 250 West Street, Suite 700 · Columbus, OH 43215-2538 · 614-462-2700

John P. Beavers · 2% · Bricker & Eckler · http://www.bricker.com · 100 South Third Street · Columbus, OH 43215-4291 · 614-227-2300

John C. Beeler · Porter, Wright, Morris & Arthur · http://www.porterwright.com · Huntington Center · 41 South High Street · Columbus, OH 43215-6194 · 614-227-2000

Jack A. Bjerke · Baker Hostetler · http://www.bakerlaw.com · Capitol Square, Suite 2100 · 65 East State Street · Columbus, OH 43215-4260 · 614-228-1541

James J. Chester · Chester Willcox & Saxbe · http://www.cwslaw.com · 65 East State Street, Suite 1000 · Columbus, OH 43215 · 614-221-4000

Michael A. Cline · a · Vorys, Sater, Seymour and Pease · 52 East Gay Street · P.O. Box 1008 · Columbus, OH 43216-1008 · 614-464-6400

John W. Cook III · Bricker & Eckler · http://www.bricker.com · 100 South Third Street · Columbus, OH 43215-4291 · 614-227-2300

Jay R. Dingledy · Schottenstein, Zox & Dunn · http://www.szd.com · 250 West Street, Suite 700 · Columbus, OH 43215-2538 · 614-462-2700

Patrick J. Dugan · Squire Sanders · http://www.ssd.com · 1300 Huntington Center · 41 South High Street Columbus, OH 43215-6197 · 614-365-2700

J. Richard Emens · 2% · Chester Willcox & Saxbe · http://www.cwslaw.com · 65 East State Street, Suite 1000 · Columbus, OH 43215 · 614-221-4000

James H. Gross · Vorys, Sater, Seymour and Pease · 52 East Gay Street · P.O. Box 1008 · Columbus, OH 43216-1008 · 614-464-6400

Jeffrey T. Hayes · Porter, Wright, Morris & Arthur · http://www.porterwright.com · Huntington Center · 41 South High Street · Columbus, OH 43215-6194 · 614-227-2000

Bruce R. Henke · Vorys, Sater, Seymour and Pease · 52 East Gay Street · P.O. Box 1008 · Columbus, OH 43216-1008 · 614-464-6400

Harry L. Henning · Porter, Wright, Morris & Arthur · http://www.porterwright.com · Huntington Center · 41 South High Street · Columbus, OH 43215-6194 · 614-227-2000

David L. Johnson · Taft Stettinius & Hollister · http://www.taftlaw.com · 21 East State Street, Suite 1200 Columbus, OH 43215-2007 · 614-221-2838

William J. Kelly, Jr. · Porter, Wright, Morris & Arthur · http://www.porterwright.com · Huntington Center · 41 South High Street · Columbus, OH 43215-6194 · 614-227-2000

Steven R. Kerber · Bricker & Eckler · http://www.bricker.com · 100 South Third Street · Columbus, OH 43215-4291 · 614-227-2300

James A. King · Porter, Wright, Morris & Arthur · http://www.porterwright.com · Huntington Center · 41 South High Street · Columbus, OH 43215-6194 · 614-227-2000

James R. King · a · Jones Day · 325 John H. McConnell Boulevard, Suite 600 · P.O. Box 165017 · Columbus, OH 43216-5017 · 614-469-3939

J. Anthony Kington · Chester Willcox & Saxbe · http://www.cwslaw.com · 65 East State Street, Suite 1000 · Columbus, OH 43215 · 614-221-4000

Curtis A. Loveland · a · Porter, Wright, Morris & Arthur · http://www.porterwright.com · Huntington Center · 41 South High Street · Columbus, OH 43215-6194 · 614-227-2000

Daniel M. Maher · Squire Sanders · http://www.ssd.com · 1300 Huntington Center · 41 South High Street Columbus, OH 43215-6197 · 614-365-2700

Michael P. Mahoney · Bailey Cavalieri · One Columbus Building, Suite 2100 · 10 West Broad Street · Columbus, OH 43215-3422 · 614-221-3155

Richard C. McQuown · Porter, Wright, Morris & Arthur · http://www.porterwright.com · Huntington Center · 41 South High Street · Columbus, OH 43215-6194 · 614-227-2000

Dixon F. Miller · Porter, Wright, Morris & Arthur · http://www.porterwright.com · Huntington Center · 41 South High Street · Columbus, OH 43215-6194 · 614-227-2000

Douglas S. Morgan · Calfee, Halter & Griswold · http://www.calfee.com · 1100 Fifth Third Center · 21 East State Street · Columbus, OH 43215-4243 · 614-621-1500

Richard R. Murphey, Jr. · 2% · Squire Sanders · http://www.ssd.com · 1300 Huntington Center · 41 South High Street · Columbus, OH 43215-6197 · 614-365-2700

Robert R. Ouellette · Schottenstein, Zox & Dunn · http://www.szd.com · 250 West Street, Suite 700 · Columbus, OH 43215-2538 · 614-462-2700

Susan D. Rector · Schottenstein, Zox & Dunn · http://www.szd.com · 250 West Street, Suite 700 · Columbus, OH 43215-2538 · 614-462-2700

Paul D. Ritter, Jr. · a · Kegler, Brown, Hill & Ritter · http://www.keglerbrown.com · Capitol Square, Suite 1800 · 65 East State Street · Columbus, OH 43215-4294 · 614-462-5400

Ronald A. Robins, Jr. · Vorys, Sater, Seymour and Pease · 52 East Gay Street · P.O. Box 1008 · Columbus, OH 43216-1008 · 614-464-6400

Russell R. Rosler · Vorys, Sater, Seymour and Pease · 52 East Gay Street · P.O. Box 1008 · Columbus, OH 43216-1008 · 614-464-6400

Richard W. Rubenstein · a · Squire Sanders · http://www.ssd.com · 1300 Huntington Center · 41 South High Street · Columbus, OH 43215-6197 · 614-365-2700

James A. Rutledge · Bricker & Eckler · http://www.bricker.com · 100 South Third Street · Columbus, OH 43215-4291 · 614-227-2300

James G. Ryan · Bailey Cavalieri · One Columbus Building, Suite 2100 · 10 West Broad Street · Columbus, OH 43215-3422 · 614-221-3155

Alex Shumate · a · Squire Sanders · http://www.ssd.com · 1300 Huntington Center · 41 South High Street · Columbus, OH 43215-6197 · 614-365-2700

Richard C. Simpson · Bricker & Eckler · http://www.bricker.com · 100 South Third Street · Columbus, OH 43215-4291 · 614-227-2300

S. Martijn Steger · Kegler, Brown, Hill & Ritter · http://www.keglerbrown.com · Capitol Square, Suite 1800 · 65 East State Street · Columbus, OH 43215-4294 · 614-462-5400

Gregory W. Stype · Squire Sanders · http://www.ssd.com · 1300 Huntington Center · 41 South High Street · Columbus, OH 43215-6197 · 614-365-2700

Robert J. Tannous · Porter, Wright, Morris & Arthur · http://www.porterwright.com · Huntington Center 41 South High Street · Columbus, OH 43215-6194 · 614-227-2000

John R. Thomas · 2% · Kegler, Brown, Hill & Ritter · http://www.keglerbrown.com · Capitol Square, Suite 1800 · 65 East State Street · Columbus, OH 43215-4294 · 614-462-5400

John C. Vorys · Vorys, Sater, Seymour and Pease · 52 East Gay Street · P.O. Box 1008 · Columbus, OH 43216-1008 · 614-464-6400

Randall M. Walters · Jones Day · 325 John H. McConnell Boulevard, Suite 600 · P.O. Box 165017 · Columbus, OH 43216-5017 · 614-469-3939

Roger T. Whitaker · Luper, Neidenthal & Logan · LeVeque Tower, Suite 1200 · 50 West Broad Street · Columbus, OH 43215-3374 · 614-221-7663

Roderick H. Willcox · a · Chester Willcox & Saxbe · http://www.cwslaw.com · 65 East State Street, Suite 1000 · Columbus, OH 43215 · 614-221-4000

Dayton

Glenn L. Bower · a · Coolidge Wall Co. · http://www.coollaw.com · 33 West First Street, Suite 600 · Dayton, OH 45402 · 937-223-8177

Richard A. Broock · a · Dinsmore & Shohl · http://www.dinslaw.com · Courthouse Plaza, SW, Suite 1100 · 10 North Ludlow Street · Dayton, OH 45402 · 937-449-2800

Richard J. Chernesky · a · Dinsmore & Shohl · http://www.dinslaw.com · Courthouse Plaza, SW, Suite 1100 · 10 North Ludlow Street · Dayton, OH 45402 · 937-449-2800

Andrew K. Cherney · Dinsmore & Shohl · http://www.dinslaw.com · Courthouse Plaza, SW, Suite 1100 · 10 North Ludlow Street · Dayton, OH 45402 · 937-449-2800

Jonas J. Gruenberg · Coolidge Wall Co. · http://www.coollaw.com · 33 West First Street, Suite 600 · Dayton, OH 45402 · 937-223-8177

J. Michael Herr · a · Thompson Hine · 2000 Courthouse Plaza, NE · 10 West Second Street · P.O. Box 8801 · Dayton, OH 45401-8801 · 937-443-6600

Ralph E. Heyman · 2) · Dinsmore & Shohl · http://www.dinslaw.com · Courthouse Plaza, SW, Suite 1100 10 North Ludlow Street · Dayton, OH 45402 · 937-449-2800

Thomas A. Holton · a · Porter, Wright, Morris & Arthur · http://www.porterwright.com · One Dayton Centre, Suite 1600 · One South Main Street · Dayton, OH 45402-2028 · 937-449-6810

Charles Y. Kidwell · Porter, Wright, Morris & Arthur · http://www.porterwright.com · One Dayton Centre, Suite 1600 · One South Main Street · Dayton, OH 45402-2028 · 937-449-6810

Edward M. Kress · a · Dinsmore & Shohl · http://www.dinslaw.com · Courthouse Plaza, SW, Suite 1100 · 10 North Ludlow Street · Dayton, OH 45402 · 937-449-2800

David A. Neuhardt · a · Thompson Hine · 2000 Courthouse Plaza, NE · 10 West Second Street · P.O. Box 8801 · Dayton, OH 45401-8801 · 937-443-6600

Sharen Swartz Neuhardt · Thompson Hine · 2000 Courthouse Plaza, NE · 10 West Second Street · P.O. Box 8801 · Dayton, OH 45401-8801 · 937-443-6600

Joseph M. Rigot · Thompson Hine · 2000 Courthouse Plaza, NE · 10 West Second Street · P.O. Box 8801 Dayton, OH 45401-8801 · 937-443-6600

Richard A. Schwartz · Coolidge Wall Co. · http://www.coollaw.com · 33 West First Street, Suite 600 · Dayton, OH 45402 · 937-223-8177

Edward L. Shank · 2) · Bieser, Greer & Landis · http://www.biesergreer.com · National City Center, Suite 400 · Six North Main Street · Dayton, OH 45402-1908 · 937-223-3277

Beverly F. Shillito · Sebaly, Shillito & Dyer · Kettering Tower, Suite 1900 · 40 North Main Street · Dayton, OH 45423-1013 · 937-222-2520

Steven R. Watts · Dinsmore & Shohl · http://www.dinslaw.com · Courthouse Plaza, SW, Suite 1100 · 10 North Ludlow Street · Dayton, OH 45402 · 937-449-2800

Merle F. Wilberding · Coolidge Wall Co. · http://www.coollaw.com · 33 West First Street, Suite 600 · Dayton, OH 45402 · 937-223-8177

Dublin

Kenneth J. Warren · Kenneth J. Warren · 5134 Paul G. Blazer Parkway · Dublin, OH 43017-8751 · 614-766-1960

Toledo

John W. Hilbert II · a · Shumaker, Loop & Kendrick · North Courthouse Square · 1000 Jackson Street · Toledo, OH 43604-5573 · 419-241-9000

Michael S. McGowan · a · Shumaker, Loop & Kendrick · North Courthouse Square · 1000 Jackson Street · Toledo, OH 43604-5573 · 419-241-9000

Mary Ellen Pisanelli · Shumaker, Loop & Kendrick · North Courthouse Square · 1000 Jackson Street · Toledo, OH 43604-5573 · 419-241-9000

James I. Rothschild · Shumaker, Loop & Kendrick · North Courthouse Square · 1000 Jackson Street · Toledo, OH 43604-5573 · 419-241-9000

Lyman F. Spitzer · Shumaker, Loop & Kendrick · North Courthouse Square · 1000 Jackson Street · Toledo, OH 43604-5573 · 419-241-9000

Ronald J. Tice · Eastman & Smith · One Seagate, 24th Floor · P.O. Box 10032 · Toledo, OH 43699-0032 419-241-6000

David F. Waterman · 2) · Shumaker, Loop & Kendrick · North Courthouse Square · 1000 Jackson Street · Toledo, OH 43604-5573 · 419-241-9000

Thomas I. Webb, Jr. · Shumaker, Loop & Kendrick · North Courthouse Square · 1000 Jackson Street · Toledo, OH 43604-5573 · 419-241-9000

James F. White, Jr. · 2% · Shumaker, Loop & Kendrick · North Courthouse Square · 1000 Jackson Street · Toledo, OH 43604-5573 · 419-241-9000

Youngstown

Jay M. Skolnick · a · Nadler, Nadler & Burdman · 20 Federal Plaza West, Suite 600 · Youngstown, OH 44503 · 330-744-0247

DUI/DWI DEFENSE

Columbus

Bradley P. Koffel · Koffel & Jump · http://www.kjlaws.com · 2130 Arlington Avenue · Columbus, OH 43221 · 614-481-4480

Toledo

Richard C. Hasbrook · Richard C. Hasbrook · 608 Madison Avenue, Suite 1400 · Toledo, OH 43604-1121 · 419-242-1400

Akron

Susan McGown · McGown, Markling & Whalen · 1894 North Cleveland Massillon Road · Akron, OH 44333 · 330-670-0005

Cleveland

W. Michael Hanna · a · Squire Sanders · http://www.ssd.com · 4900 Key Tower · 127 Public Square · Cleveland, OH 44114-1304 · 216-479-8500

Susan C. Hastings · Squire Sanders · http://www.ssd.com · 4900 Key Tower · 127 Public Square · Cleveland, OH 44114-1304 · 216-479-8500

David J. Millstone · a · Squire Sanders · http://www.ssd.com · 4900 Key Tower · 127 Public Square · Cleveland, OH 44114-1304 · 216-479-8500

Timothy J. Sheeran · Squire Sanders · http://www.ssd.com · 4900 Key Tower · 127 Public Square · Cleveland, OH 44114-1304 · 216-479-8500

Nessa G. Siegel · Siegel & Agins Company · 4070 Mayfield Road · Cleveland, OH 44121 · 216-291-1300

David Kane Smith · Britton, Smith, Peters & Kalail · http://www.ohioedlaw.com · Three Summit Park Drive, Suite 400 · Cleveland, OH 44131 · 216-503-5055

Columbus

Kimball H. Carey · Bricker & Eckler · http://www.bricker.com · 100 South Third Street · Columbus, OH 43215-4291 · 614-227-2300

Susan M. DiMickele · Squire Sanders · http://www.ssd.com · 1300 Huntington Center · 41 South High Street · Columbus, OH 43215-6197 · 614-365-2700

Dane A. Gaschen · Bricker & Eckler · http://www.bricker.com · 100 South Third Street · Columbus, OH 43215-4291 · 614-227-2300

Michael J. Melliere · Peck, Shaffer · 175 South Third Street, Suite 600 · Columbus, OH 43215 · 614-224-5205

William A. Nolan · Squire Sanders · http://www.ssd.com · 1300 Huntington Center · 41 South High Street Columbus, OH 43215-6197 · 614-365-2700

Dayton

Janet K. Cooper · Cooper & Gentile · Talbott Tower, Suite 850 · 118 West First Street · Dayton, OH 45402 · 937-224-5300

Nicholas E. Subashi · Subashi, Wildermuth & Ballato · The Greene Town Center, Suite 230 · 50 Chestnut Street · Dayton, OH 45440 · 973-427-8800

Middletown

Thomas B. Allen · Frost Brown Todd · http://www.frostbrowntodd.com · 300 North Main Street, Suite 200 · Middletown, OH 45042-1919 · 513-422-2001

ELDER LAW

Canton

James F. Contini II · Krugliak, Wilkins, Griffiths & Dougherty · http://www.kwgd.com · 4775 Munson Street, NW · P.O. Box 36963 · Canton, OH 44735-6963 · 330-497-0700

Richard E. Davis · Krugliak, Wilkins, Griffiths & Dougherty · http://www.kwgd.com · 4775 Munson Street, NW · P.O. Box 36963 · Canton, OH 44735-6963 · 330-497-0700

Cleveland

Sandra J. Buzney · Hickman & Lowder · 1300 East Ninth Street, Suite 1020 · Cleveland, OH 44114 · 216-861-0360

Janet L. Lowder · Hickman & Lowder · 1300 East Ninth Street, Suite 1020 · Cleveland, OH 44114 · 216-861-0360

Columbus

Richard T. Taps · Richard T. Taps · 713 South Front Street · Columbus, OH 43206 · 614-443-8000

Elyria

David A. Myers · Hickman & Lowder · 374 Broad Street, Suite Two · Elyria, OH 44035 · 440-323-1111

Toledo

Nirakar C. Thakur · Nirakar C. Thakur · 416 North Erie Street, Suite 200 · Toledo, OH 43624 · 419-242-8900

EMINENT DOMAIN AND CONDEMNATION LAW

Beachwood

Sheldon Berns · a · Berns, Ockner & Greenberger · 3733 Park East Drive, Suite 200 · Beachwood, OH 44122-4334 · 216-831-8838

Columbus

Craig B. Paynter · Chester Willcox & Saxbe · http://www.cwslaw.com · 65 East State Street, Suite 1000 · Columbus, OH 43215 · 614-221-4000

EMPLOYEE BENEFITS LAW

Akron

Cathy C. Godshall · Buckingham, Doolittle & Burroughs · http://www.bdblaw.com · 3800 Embassy Parkway, Suite 300 · P.O. Box 1500 · Akron, OH 44309-1500 · 330-376-5300

Richard P. Rohrich · Buckingham, Doolittle & Burroughs · http://www.bdblaw.com · 3800 Embassy Parkway, Suite 300 · P.O. Box 1500 · Akron, OH 44309-1500 · 330-376-5300

George H. Rosin · Buckingham, Doolittle & Burroughs · http://www.bdblaw.com · 3800 Embassy Parkway, Suite 300 · P.O. Box 1500 · Akron, OH 44309-1500 · 330-376-5300

Eleanor J. Tschugunov · Buckingham, Doolittle & Burroughs · http://www.bdblaw.com · 3800 Embassy Parkway, Suite 300 · P.O. Box 1500 · Akron, OH 44309-1500 · 330-376-5300

Cincinnati

John H. Appel · a · Frost Brown Todd · http://www.frostbrowntodd.com · PNC Center, Suite 2200 · 201 East Fifth Street · Cincinnati, OH 45202-4182 · 513-651-6800

Robert E. Brant · Katz, Teller, Brant & Hild · http://www.katzteller.com · 255 East Fifth Street, Suite 2400 · Cincinnati, OH 45202-4724 · 513-721-4532

Thomas A. Breitenbach · Graydon, Head & Ritchey · 1900 Fifth Third Center · 511 Walnut Street · Cincinnati, OH 45202 · 513-621-6464

Timothy R. Brown · a · Thompson Hine · 312 Walnut Street, 14th Floor · Cincinnati, OH 45202-4089 · 513-352-6700

Jerold A. Fink · 2) · Taft Stettinius & Hollister · http://www.taftlaw.com · 425 Walnut Street, Suite 1800 · Cincinnati, OH 45202-3957 · 513-381-2838

William M. Freedman · 2% · Dinsmore & Shohl · http://www.dinslaw.com · 255 East Fifth Street, Suite 1900 · Cincinnati, OH 45202-3172 · 513-977-8200

Stephen M. Goodson · Keating Muething & Klekamp · http://www.kmklaw.com · One East Fourth Street, Suite 1400 · Cincinnati, OH 45202 · 513-579-6400

Steve Kisling · Katz, Teller, Brant & Hild · http://www.katzteller.com · 255 East Fifth Street, Suite 2400 · Cincinnati, OH 45202-4724 · 513-721-4532

Michael A. Laing · a · Taft Stettinius & Hollister · http://www.taftlaw.com · 425 Walnut Street, Suite 1800 · Cincinnati, OH 45202-3957 · 513-381-2838

Robert R. Saelinger · Graydon, Head & Ritchey · 1900 Fifth Third Center · 511 Walnut Street · Cincinnati, OH 45202 · 513-621-6464

Mark A. Stiebel · a · Graf & Stiebel · US Bank Tower, Suite 2400 · 425 Walnut Street · Cincinnati, OH 45202-3954 · 513-618-7800

Cleveland

Carol F. Dakin · Squire Sanders · http://www.ssd.com · 4900 Key Tower · 127 Public Square · Cleveland, OH 44114-1304 · 216-479-8500

Carl A. Draucker · Squire Sanders · http://www.ssd.com · 4900 Key Tower · 127 Public Square · Cleveland, OH 44114-1304 · 216-479-8500

Daniel C. Hagen · Jones Day · North Point · 901 Lakeside Avenue · Cleveland, OH 44114-1190 · 216-586-3939

Thomas A. Jorgensen · 2) · Calfee, Halter & Griswold · http://www.calfee.com · 1400 KeyBank Center · 800 Superior Avenue · Cleveland, OH 44114-2688 · 216-622-8200

Ronald L. Kahn · a · Ulmer & Berne · Skylight Office Tower, Suite 1100 · 1660 West Second Street · Cleveland, OH 44113-1448 · 216-583-7000

Raymond M. Malone · Baker Hostetler · http://www.bakerlaw.com · National City Center, Suite 3200 · 1900 East Ninth Street · Cleveland, OH 44114-3485 · 216-621-0200

John J. McGowan, Jr. · Baker Hostetler · http://www.bakerlaw.com · National City Center, Suite 3200 · 1900 East Ninth Street · Cleveland, OH 44114-3485 · 216-621-0200

Robert A. Miller · Calfee, Halter & Griswold · http://www.calfee.com · 1400 KeyBank Center · 800 Superior Avenue · Cleveland, OH 44114-2688 · 216-622-8200

W. James Ollinger · 2) · Baker Hostetler · http://www.bakerlaw.com · National City Center, Suite 3200 · 1900 East Ninth Street · Cleveland, OH 44114-3485 · 216-621-0200

Mary M. Reil · Jones Day · North Point · 901 Lakeside Avenue · Cleveland, OH 44114-1190 · 216-586-3939

Russell C. Shaw · a · Walter & Haverfield · http://www.walterhav.com · The Tower at Erieview, Suite 3500 · 1301 East Ninth Street · Cleveland, OH 44114 · 216-781-1212

Patricia A. Shlonsky · Ulmer & Berne · Skylight Office Tower, Suite 1100 · 1660 West Second Street · Cleveland, OH 44113-1448 · 216-583-7000

Ronald C. Stansbury · Ulmer & Berne · Skylight Office Tower, Suite 1100 · 1660 West Second Street · Cleveland, OH 44113-1448 · 216-583-7000

Gregory J. Viviani · Squire Sanders · http://www.ssd.com · 4900 Key Tower · 127 Public Square · Cleveland, OH 44114-1304 · 216-479-8500

Dale R. Vlasek · McDonald Hopkins · 600 Superior Avenue East, Suite 2100 · Cleveland, OH 44114-2653 · 216-348-5400

Karen D. Youngstrom · Thompson Hine · Key Center, Suite 3900 · 127 Public Square · Cleveland, OH 44114-1291 · 216-566-5500

Columbus

Marc Gertner · 2) · Gertner & Gertner · 175 South Third Street, Suite 505 · Columbus, OH 43215 · 614-463-9393

Richard J. Helmreich · Porter, Wright, Morris & Arthur · http://www.porterwright.com · Huntington Center · 41 South High Street · Columbus, OH 43215-6194 · 614-227-2000

Linda R. Mendel · Vorys, Sater, Seymour and Pease · 52 East Gay Street · P.O. Box 1008 · Columbus, OH 43216-1008 · 614-464-6400

Paul D. Ritter, Jr. · a · Kegler, Brown, Hill & Ritter · http://www.keglerbrown.com · Capitol Square, Suite 1800 · 65 East State Street · Columbus, OH 43215-4294 · 614-462-5400

Thomas J. Sigmund · a · Kegler, Brown, Hill & Ritter · http://www.keglerbrown.com · Capitol Square, Suite 1800 · 65 East State Street · Columbus, OH 43215-4294 · 614-462-5400

John Terakedis, Jr. · 2% · Schottenstein, Zox & Dunn · http://www.szd.com · 250 West Street, Suite 700 · Columbus, OH 43215-2538 · 614-462-2700

Sheldon Mike Young · Walter & Haverfield · http://www.walterhav.com · 4776 Smoketalk Lane · Columbus, OH 43081 · 614-898-1096

Dayton

Richard F. Carlile · a · Thompson Hine · 2000 Courthouse Plaza, NE · 10 West Second Street · P.O. Box 8801 · Dayton, OH 45401-8801 · 937-443-6600

Mark S. Feuer · Dinsmore & Shohl · http://www.dinslaw.com · Courthouse Plaza, SW, Suite 1100 · 10 North Ludlow Street · Dayton, OH 45402 · 937-449-2800

Allen R. Norris · Thompson Hine · 2000 Courthouse Plaza, NE · 10 West Second Street · P.O. Box 8801 · Dayton, OH 45401-8801 · 937-443-6600

Steven C. Scudder · Scudder & Esler · 2912 Springboro West, Suite 105 · Dayton, OH 45439 · 937-298-0008

Toledo

Eric D. Britton · Shumaker, Loop & Kendrick · North Courthouse Square · 1000 Jackson Street · Toledo, OH 43604-5573 · 419-241-9000

Gary Diesing · Shumaker, Loop & Kendrick · North Courthouse Square · 1000 Jackson Street · Toledo, OH 43604-5573 · 419-241-9000

Vivian Folk · Shumaker, Loop & Kendrick · North Courthouse Square · 1000 Jackson Street · Toledo, OH 43604-5573 · 419-241-9000

ENERGY LAW

Cleveland

Glenn S. Krassen · Bricker & Eckler · http://www.bricker.com · 1375 East Ninth Street, Suite 1500 · Cleveland, OH 44114-1718 · 216-523-5405

Columbus

John W. Bentine · a · Chester Willcox & Saxbe · http://www.cwslaw.com · 65 East State Street, Suite 1000 · Columbus, OH 43215 · 614-221-4000

Sally W. Bloomfield · a · Bricker & Eckler · http://www.bricker.com · 100 South Third Street · Columbus, OH 43215-4291 · 614-227-2300

Daniel R. Conway · Porter, Wright, Morris & Arthur · http://www.porterwright.com · Huntington Center · 41 South High Street · Columbus, OH 43215-6194 · 614-227-2000

Gretchen J. Hummel · McNees Wallace & Nurick · Fifth Third Center, Suite 1700 · 21 East State Street Columbus, OH 43215-4228 · 614-469-8000

Benita A. Kahn · a · Vorys, Sater, Seymour and Pease · 52 East Gay Street · P.O. Box 1008 · Columbus, OH 43216-1008 · 614-464-6400

Thomas E. Lodge · Thompson Hine · 10 West Broad Street, Suite 700 · Columbus, OH 43215-3435 · 614-469-3200

William S. Newcomb, Jr. · a · Vorys, Sater, Seymour and Pease · 52 East Gay Street · P.O. Box 1008 · Columbus, OH 43216-1008 · 614-464-6400

Thomas J. O'Brien · Bricker & Eckler · http://www.bricker.com · 100 South Third Street · Columbus, OH 43215-4291 · 614-227-2300

M. Howard Petricoff · a · Vorys, Sater, Seymour and Pease · 52 East Gay Street · P.O. Box 1008 · Columbus, OH 43216-1008 · 614-464-6400

Samuel C. Randazzo · a · McNees Wallace & Nurick · Fifth Third Center, Suite 1700 · 21 East State Street · Columbus, OH 43215-4228 · 614-469-8000

Barth Royer · Bell Royer & Sanders · 33 South Grant Avenue · Columbus, OH 43215-3927 · 614-228-0704

Roger P. Sugarman · Kegler, Brown, Hill & Ritter · http://www.keglerbrown.com · Capitol Square, Suite 1800 · 65 East State Street · Columbus, OH 43215-4294 · 614-462-5400

Dayton

Charles J. Faruki · 2) · Faruki Ireland & Cox · Courthouse Plaza, SW, Suite 500 · 10 North Ludlow Street · Dayton, OH 45402 · 937-227-3700

ENTERTAINMENT LAW

Akron

David P. Bertsch · Buckingham, Doolittle & Burroughs · http://www.bdblaw.com · 3800 Embassy Parkway, Suite 300 · P.O. Box 1500 · Akron, OH 44309-1500 · 330-376-5300

Cleveland

Jack S. Kluznik · Weston Hurd · The Tower at Erieview, Suite 1900 · 1301 East Ninth Street · Cleveland, OH 44114-1862 · 216-241-6602

ENVIRONMENTAL LAW

Akron

William L. Caplan · Buckingham, Doolittle & Burroughs · http://www.bdblaw.com · 3800 Embassy Parkway, Suite 300 · P.O. Box 1500 · Akron, OH 44309-1500 · 330-376-5300

Shane A. Farolino · Roetzel & Andress · http://www.ralaw.com · 222 South Main Street · Akron, OH 44308-2098 · 330-376-2700

Terrence S. Finn · Roetzel & Andress · http://www.ralaw.com · 222 South Main Street · Akron, OH 44308-2098 · 330-376-2700

Thomas M. Skove · Roetzel & Andress · http://www.ralaw.com · 222 South Main Street · Akron, OH 44308-2098 · 330-376-2700

Canton

Jacqueline Bollas Caldwell · Krugliak, Wilkins, Griffiths & Dougherty · http://www.kwgd.com · 4775 Munson Street, NW · P.O. Box 36963 · Canton, OH 44735-6963 · 330-497-0700

Cincinnati

Brian M. Babb · Keating Muething & Klekamp · http://www.kmklaw.com · One East Fourth Street, Suite 1400 · Cincinnati, OH 45202 · 513-579-6400

Kim K. Burke · a · Taft Stettinius & Hollister · http://www.taftlaw.com · 425 Walnut Street, Suite 1800 · Cincinnati, OH 45202-3957 · 513-381-2838

Stephen P. Calardo · Calardo Mediation Services · 5608 Harrison Avenue · Cincinnati, OH 45248-2314 · 513-598-5000

Paul W. Casper, Jr. · Frost Brown Todd · http://www.frostbrowntodd.com · PNC Center, Suite 2200 · 201 East Fifth Street · Cincinnati, OH 45202-4182 · 513-651-6800

Christopher S. Habel · Frost Brown Todd · http://www.frostbrowntodd.com · PNC Center, Suite 2200 · 201 East Fifth Street · Cincinnati, OH 45202-4182 · 513-651-6800

Stephen N. Haughey · Frost Brown Todd · http://www.frostbrowntodd.com · PNC Center, Suite 2200 · 201 East Fifth Street · Cincinnati, OH 45202-4182 · 513-651-6800

William D. Hayes · Vorys, Sater, Seymour and Pease · Atrium Two, Suite 2000 · 221 East Fourth Street · P.O. Box 0236 · Cincinnati, OH 45201-0236 · 513-723-4000

Kevin J. Hopper · Kevin J. Hopper · Southampton Square · 7434 Jager Court · Cincinnati, OH 45230-9924 · 513-232-7578

Andrew L. Kolesar III · Thompson Hine · 312 Walnut Street, 14th Floor · Cincinnati, OH 45202-4089 · 513-352-6700

Kevin N. McMurray · Frost Brown Todd · http://www.frostbrowntodd.com · PNC Center, Suite 2200 · 201 East Fifth Street · Cincinnati, OH 45202-4182 · 513-651-6800

Mark A. Norman · Vorys, Sater, Seymour and Pease · Atrium Two, Suite 2000 · 221 East Fourth Street · P.O. Box 0236 · Cincinnati, OH 45201-0236 · 513-723-4000

Laura A. Ringenbach · a · Taft Stettinius & Hollister · http://www.taftlaw.com · 425 Walnut Street, Suite 1800 · Cincinnati, OH 45202-3957 · 513-381-2838

Philip J. Schworer · Frost Brown Todd · http://www.frostbrowntodd.com · PNC Center, Suite 2200 · 201 East Fifth Street · Cincinnati, OH 45202-4182 · 513-651-6800

Vincent B. Stamp · Dinsmore & Shohl · http://www.dinslaw.com · 255 East Fifth Street, Suite 1900 · Cincinnati, OH 45202-3172 · 513-977-8200

Thomas T. Terp · 2) · Taft Stettinius & Hollister · http://www.taftlaw.com · 425 Walnut Street, Suite 1800 · Cincinnati, OH 45202-3957 · 513-381-2838

A. Christian Worrell III · Graydon, Head & Ritchey · 1900 Fifth Third Center · 511 Walnut Street · Cincinnati, OH 45202 · 513-621-6464

Cleveland

Heather A. Austin · Thompson Hine · Key Center, Suite 3900 · 127 Public Square · Cleveland, OH 44114-1291 · 216-566-5500

Geoffrey K. Barnes · a · Squire Sanders · http://www.ssd.com · 4900 Key Tower · 127 Public Square · Cleveland, OH 44114-1304 · 216-479-8500

Maureen A. Brennan · Baker Hostetler · http://www.bakerlaw.com · National City Center, Suite 3200 · 1900 East Ninth Street · Cleveland, OH 44114-3485 · 216-621-0200

David W. Burchmore · Squire Sanders · http://www.ssd.com · 4900 Key Tower · 127 Public Square · Cleveland, OH 44114-1304 · 216-479-8500

Van Carson · a · Squire Sanders · http://www.ssd.com · 4900 Key Tower · 127 Public Square · Cleveland, OH 44114-1304 · 216-479-8500

Robert B. Casarona · Roetzel & Andress · http://www.ralaw.com · One Cleveland Center, Ninth Floor · 1375 East Ninth Street · Cleveland, OH 44114 · 216-623-0150

Ralph E. Cascarilla · Walter & Haverfield · http://www.walterhav.com · The Tower at Erieview, Suite 3500 · 1301 East Ninth Street · Cleveland, OH 44114 · 216-781-1212

Michael A. Cyphert · 2) · Walter & Haverfield · http://www.walterhav.com · The Tower at Erieview, Suite 3500 · 1301 East Ninth Street · Cleveland, OH 44114 · 216-781-1212

Gregory J. Degulis · McMahon DeGulis · The Caxton Building, Suite 650 · 812 Huron Road · Cleveland, OH 44115-1126 · 216-621-1312

Keven D. Eiber · Brouse McDowell · 1001 Lakeside Avenue, Suite 1600 · Cleveland, OH 44114 · 216-830-6830

Stephen Q. Giblin · Jones Day · North Point · 901 Lakeside Avenue · Cleveland, OH 44114-1190 · 216-586-3939

Heidi B. Goldstein · Thompson Hine · Key Center, Suite 3900 · 127 Public Square · Cleveland, OH 44114-1291 · 216-566-5500

Michael L. Hardy · 2) · Thompson Hine · Key Center, Suite 3900 · 127 Public Square · Cleveland, OH 44114-1291 · 216-566-5500

Ronald R. Janke · a · Jones Day · North Point · 901 Lakeside Avenue · Cleveland, OH 44114-1190 · 216-586-3939

Wendlene M. Lavey · Squire Sanders · http://www.ssd.com · 4900 Key Tower · 127 Public Square · Cleveland, OH 44114-1304 · 216-479-8500

Kevin D. Margolis · Benesch, Friedlander, Coplan & Aronoff · BP Tower, Suite 2300 · 200 Public Square Cleveland, OH 44114-2378 · 216-363-4500

Louis L. McMahon · Thompson Hine · Key Center, Suite 3900 · 127 Public Square · Cleveland, OH 44114-1291 · 216-566-5500

Michael S. McMahon · McMahon DeGulis · The Caxton Building, Suite 650 · 812 Huron Road · Cleveland, OH 44115-1126 · 216-621-1312

Douglas A. McWilliams · Squire Sanders · http://www.ssd.com · 4900 Key Tower · 127 Public Square · Cleveland, OH 44114-1304 · 216-479-8500

Kenneth C. Moore · 2) · Squire Sanders · http://www.ssd.com · 4900 Key Tower · 127 Public Square · Cleveland, OH 44114-1304 · 216-479-8500

David E. Nash · a · McMahon DeGulis · The Caxton Building, Suite 650 · 812 Huron Road · Cleveland, OH 44115-1126 · 216-621-1312

Stephen M. O'Bryan · Taft Stettinius & Hollister · http://www.taftlaw.com · BP Tower, Suite 3500 · 200 Public Square · Cleveland, OH 44114-2302 · 216-241-2838

John A. Rego · Jones Day · North Point · 901 Lakeside Avenue · Cleveland, OH 44114-1190 · 216-586-3939

Columbus

Theodore A. Boggs · Vorys, Sater, Seymour and Pease · 52 East Gay Street · P.O. Box 1008 · Columbus, OH 43216-1008 · 614-464-6400

Robert L. Brubaker · a · Porter, Wright, Morris & Arthur · http://www.porterwright.com · Huntington Center · 41 South High Street · Columbus, OH 43215-6194 · 614-227-2000

Richard P. Fahey · a · Vorys, Sater, Seymour and Pease · 52 East Gay Street · P.O. Box 1008 · Columbus, OH 43216-1008 · 614-464-6400

Robert J. Karl · Ulmer & Berne · 88 East Broad Street, Suite 1600 · Columbus, OH 43215-3581 · 614-229-0000

J. Jeffrey McNealey · 2) · Porter, Wright, Morris & Arthur · http://www.porterwright.com · Huntington Center · 41 South High Street · Columbus, OH 43215-6194 · 614-227-2000

Frank L. Merrill · Bricker & Eckler · http://www.bricker.com · 100 South Third Street · Columbus, OH 43215-4291 · 614-227-2300

Katerina M. Eftimoff Milenkovski · Steptoe & Johnson · http://www.steptoe-johnson.com · Huntington Center, Suite 2200 · 41 South High Street · Columbus, OH 43215 · 614-221-5100

David E. Northrop · a · Porter, Wright, Morris & Arthur · http://www.porterwright.com · Huntington Center · 41 South High Street · Columbus, OH 43215-6194 · 614-227-2000

Joseph Reidy · Schottenstein, Zox & Dunn · http://www.szd.com · 250 West Street, Suite 700 · Columbus, OH 43215-2538 · 614-462-2700

Stephen P. Samuels · Schottenstein, Zox & Dunn · http://www.szd.com · 250 West Street, Suite 700 · Columbus, OH 43215-2538 · 614-462-2700

Robert J. Schmidt, Jr. · Porter, Wright, Morris & Arthur · http://www.porterwright.com · Huntington Center · 41 South High Street · Columbus, OH 43215-6194 · 614-227-2000

Christopher R. Schraff · a · Porter, Wright, Morris & Arthur · http://www.porterwright.com · Huntington Center · 41 South High Street · Columbus, OH 43215-6194 · 614-227-2000

Martin S. Seltzer · a · Porter, Wright, Morris & Arthur · http://www.porterwright.com · Huntington Center · 41 South High Street · Columbus, OH 43215-6194 · 614-227-2000

J. Gregory Smith · Ulmer & Berne · 88 East Broad Street, Suite 1600 · Columbus, OH 43215-3581 · 614-229-0000

Craig A. Sturtz · Squire Sanders · http://www.ssd.com · 1300 Huntington Center · 41 South High Street · Columbus, OH 43215-6197 · 614-365-2700

Jack A. Van Kley · Van Kley & Walker · 132 Northwoods Boulevard, Suite C-1 · Columbus, OH 43235 · 614-431-8900

Charles H. Waterman III · a · Bricker & Eckler · http://www.bricker.com · 100 South Third Street · Columbus, OH 43215-4291 · 614-227-2300

Kristin L. Watt · Vorys, Sater, Seymour and Pease · 52 East Gay Street · P.O. Box 1008 · Columbus, OH 43216-1008 · 614-464-6400

Karen A. Winters · Squire Sanders · http://www.ssd.com · 1300 Huntington Center · 41 South High Street · Columbus, OH 43215-6197 · 614-365-2700

Dayton

Stephen J. Axtell · Thompson Hine · 2000 Courthouse Plaza, NE · 10 West Second Street · P.O. Box 8801 · Dayton, OH 45401-8801 · 937-443-6600

J. Wray Blattner · a · Thompson Hine · 2000 Courthouse Plaza, NE · 10 West Second Street · P.O. Box 8801 · Dayton, OH 45401-8801 · 937-443-6600

Timothy D. Hoffman · Dinsmore & Shohl · http://www.dinslaw.com · Courthouse Plaza, SW, Suite 1100 · 10 North Ludlow Street · Dayton, OH 45402 · 937-449-2800

Toledo

Douglas G. Haynam · a · Shumaker, Loop & Kendrick · North Courthouse Square · 1000 Jackson Street Toledo, OH 43604-5573 · 419-241-9000

William L. Patberg · Shumaker, Loop & Kendrick · North Courthouse Square · 1000 Jackson Street · Toledo, OH 43604-5573 · 419-241-9000

Richard T. Sargeant · 2) · Eastman & Smith · One Seagate, 24th Floor · P.O. Box 10032 · Toledo, OH 43699-0032 · 419-241-6000

Joseph S. Simpson · Shumaker, Loop & Kendrick · North Courthouse Square · 1000 Jackson Street · Toledo, OH 43604-5573 · 419-241-9000

Louis E. Tosi · 2) · Shumaker, Loop & Kendrick · North Courthouse Square · 1000 Jackson Street · Toledo, OH 43604-5573 · 419-241-9000

EQUIPMENT FINANCE LAW

Cleveland

David G. Heiman · 2% · Jones Day · North Point · 901 Lakeside Avenue · Cleveland, OH 44114-1190 · 216-586-3939

Harry D. Mercer · a · Hahn Loeser & Parks · BP Tower, Suite 2800 · 200 Public Square · Cleveland, OH 44114-2301 · 216-621-0150

Lee D. Powar · a · Hahn Loeser & Parks · BP Tower, Suite 2800 · 200 Public Square · Cleveland, OH 44114-2301 · 216-621-0150

Columbus

James P. Botti · Porter, Wright, Morris & Arthur · http://www.porterwright.com · Huntington Center · 41 South High Street · Columbus, OH 43215-6194 · 614-227-2000

Timothy E. Grady · a · Porter, Wright, Morris & Arthur · http://www.porterwright.com · Huntington Center · 41 South High Street · Columbus, OH 43215-6194 · 614-227-2000

Gordon W. Johnston · a · Bricker & Eckler · http://www.bricker.com · 100 South Third Street · Columbus, OH 43215-4291 · 614-227-2300

James H. Prior · Porter, Wright, Morris & Arthur · http://www.porterwright.com · Huntington Center · 41 South High Street · Columbus, OH 43215-6194 · 614-227-2000

Thomas O. Ruby · a · Vorys, Sater, Seymour and Pease · 52 East Gay Street · P.O. Box 1008 · Columbus, OH 43216-1008 · 614-464-6400

H. Grant Stephenson · Porter, Wright, Morris & Arthur · http://www.porterwright.com · Huntington Center · 41 South High Street · Columbus, OH 43215-6194 · 614-227-2000

John B. Weimer · a · Vorys, Sater, Seymour and Pease · 52 East Gay Street · P.O. Box 1008 · Columbus, OH 43216-1008 · 614-464-6400

FAMILY LAW

Canton

Francis G. Centrone · Black, McCuskey, Souers & Arbaugh · 220 Market Avenue South, Suite 1000 · Canton, OH 44702 · 330-456-8341

James G. Mannos · Tzangas, Plakas, Mannos & Raies · 220 Market Avenue South, Eigth Floor · Canton, OH 44702 · 330-455-6112

Cincinnati

Gregory L. Adams · Croswell & Adams · Olde Sycamore Square · 1208 Sycamore Street · Cincinnati, OH 45202 · 513-241-5670

Randal S. Bloch · a · Wagner & Bloch · 2345 Ashland Avenue · Cincinnati, OH 45206-2204 · 513-751-4420

Phyllis G. Bossin · a · Phyllis G. Bossin · http://www.bossinlaw.com · 105 East Fourth Street, Suite 1300 Cincinnati, OH 45202 · 513-421-4420

William A. DeCenso · Santen & Hughes · 600 Vine Street, Suite 2700 · Cincinnati, OH 45202 · 513-721-4450

Ralph P. Ginocchio · Schimpf, Ginocchio & Mullins · 36 East Seventh Street, Suite 2600 · Cincinnati, OH 45202 · 513-977-5570

Guy M. Hild · 2) · Katz, Teller, Brant & Hild · http://www.katzteller.com · 255 East Fifth Street, Suite 2400 · Cincinnati, OH 45202-4724 · 513-721-4532

William L. Martin, Jr. · Martin & Wharton · 10101 Alliance Road, Suite 220 · Cincinnati, OH 45242 · 513-322-6811

David Wade Peck · Barron Peck Bennie & Schlemmer · http://www.bpbattorneys.com · 3074 Madison Road · Cincinnati, OH 45209-1723 · 513-721-1350

Beth Silverman · a · Beth Silverman · http://www.bethsilverman.com · 30 Garfield Place, Suite 920 · Cincinnati, OH 45202 · 513-241-9844

Sherri Goren Slovin · a · Sherri Goren Slovin Company · http://www.slovinlaw.com · 30 Garfield Place, Suite 920 · Cincinnati, OH 45202-4322 · 513-241-9844

Jerome S. Teller · 2% · Katz, Teller, Brant & Hild · http://www.katzteller.com · 255 East Fifth Street, Suite 2400 · Cincinnati, OH 45202-4724 · 513-721-4532

Timothy A. Tepe · Dinsmore & Shohl · http://www.dinslaw.com · 255 East Fifth Street, Suite 1900 · Cincinnati, OH 45202-3172 · 513-977-8200

Cleveland

Deborah Akers-Parry · 2) · Wolf & Akers · 2200 One Cleveland Center · 1375 East Ninth Steet · Cleveland, OH 44114 · 216-623-9999

James S. Cahn · ⑩ · Hermann, Cahn & Schneider · http://www.hcsattys.com · 1301 East Ninth Street, Suite 500 · Cleveland, OH 44114 · 216-781-5515

Rosemary Grdina Gold · Rosemary Grdina Gold · 33000 Pine Tree Road · Cleveland, OH 44124 · 216-593-0001

Thomas J. LaFond · ⑩ · Schneider, Smeltz, Ranney & LaFond · 1111 Superior Avenue, Suite 1000 · Cleveland, OH 44114-2568 · 216-696-4200

James A. Loeb · Baker Hostetler · http://www.bakerlaw.com · National City Center, Suite 3200 · 1900 East Ninth Street · Cleveland, OH 44114-3485 · 216-621-0200

Carl A. Murway · Taft Stettinius & Hollister · http://www.taftlaw.com · BP Tower, Suite 3500 · 200 Public Square · Cleveland, OH 44114-2302 · 216-241-2838

James R. Skirbunt · ⑩ · Skirbunt, Skirbunt & Wirtz · http://www.skirbuntlaw.com · One Cleveland Center, Suite 3150 · 1375 East Ninth Street · Cleveland, OH 44114-1001 · 216-363-1313

Andrew A. Zashin · Zashin & Rich · http://www.zrlaw.com · 55 Public Square, Fourth Floor · Cleveland, OH 44113 · 216-696-4441

Columbus

William S. Friedman · ㉕ · Friedman & Mirman · 1320 Dublin Road, Suite 101 · Columbus, OH 43215-1188 · 614-221-0090

Jeffrey A. Grossman · ㉕ · Grossman Law Offices · http://www.grossmanlawoffices.com · 32 West Hoster Street, Suite 100 · Columbus, OH 43215-5763 · 614-221-7711

Frederick M. Isaac · Isaac, Brant, Ledman & Teetor · The Midland Building, Suite 900 · 250 East Broad Street · Columbus, OH 43215-3742 · 614-221-2121

Eugene B. Lewis · Chester Willcox & Saxbe · http://www.cwslaw.com · 65 East State Street, Suite 1000 · Columbus, OH 43215 · 614-221-4000

Cuyahoga Falls

Randal A. Lowry · ⑩ · Weick, Gibson & Lowry · 234 Portage Trail · P.O. Box 535 · Cuyahoga Falls, OH 44222 · 330-929-0507

Dayton

Keith R. Kearney · Rogers & Greenberg · Kettering Tower, Suite 2160 · Dayton, OH 45423 · 937-223-8171

James R. Kirkland · James R. Kirkland & Associates · 111 West First Street, Suite 518 · Dayton, OH 45402-1131 · 937-223-0697

Charles D. Lowe · ⑳ · Law Offices of Charles D. Lowe · Kettering Tower, Suite 1500 · 40 North Main Street · Dayton, OH 45423 · 937-222-8091

Lancaster

Norman J. Ogilvie, Jr. · Dagger, Johnston, Miller, Ogilvie & Hampson · http://www.daggerlaw.com · 144 East Main Street · P.O. Box 667 · Lancaster, OH 43130-0667 · 740-653-6464

Sylvania

Ron L. Rimelspach · 2) · Law Office of Ron L. Rimelspach · 5800 Monroe Street, Building C · Sylvania, OH 43560-2263 · 419-885-2153

Toledo

Jude T. Aubry · 2) · Jude T. Aubry · Fifth Third Center, Suite 1400 · 608 Madison Avenue · Toledo, OH 43604-1121 · 419-242-1400

Henry B. Herschel · Herschel, Accettola, Bloom, Mills & Manore · 615 Adams Street · Toledo, OH 43604-1419 · 419-241-1150

Peter L. Moran · 2) · Moran & Moran · Louisville Building, Suite 300 · 626 Madison Avenue · Toledo, OH 43604 · 419-241-8171

Melvin G. Nusbaum · 2) · Law Office of Melvin G. Nusbaum · Spitzer Building, Suite 840 · 520 Madison Avenue · Toledo, OH 43604-1387 · 419-255-6070

John L. Straub · a · Shumaker, Loop & Kendrick · North Courthouse Square · 1000 Jackson Street · Toledo, OH 43604-5573 · 419-241-9000

Warren

William R. Biviano · Biviano Law Firm · Huntington Bank Tower, Suite 700 · 108 Main Avenue, SW · Warren, OH 44481-1089 · 330-392-5000

FAMILY LAW MEDIATION

Cincinnati

Sherry L. Davis · Sherry L. Davis · Eight West Ninth Street · Cincinnati, OH 45202 · 513-721-4555

Bea V. Larsen · 2) · Center for Resolution of Disputes · Eight West Ninth Street · Cincinnati, OH 45202-2036 · 513-721-4466

David Wade Peck · Barron Peck Bennie & Schlemmer · http://www.bpbattorneys.com · 3074 Madison Road · Cincinnati, OH 45209-1723 · 513-721-1350

Sherri Goren Slovin · a · Sherri Goren Slovin Company · http://www.slovinlaw.com · 30 Garfield Place, Suite 920 · Cincinnati, OH 45202-4322 · 513-241-9844

FIRST AMENDMENT LAW

Cincinnati

Lawrence Barbiere · Schroeder, Maundrell, Barbiere & Powers · Governor's Knoll, Suite 110 · 11935 Mason Road · Cincinnati, OH 45249 · 513-583-4200

Richard M. Goehler · a · Frost Brown Todd · http://www.frostbrowntodd.com · PNC Center, Suite 2200 201 East Fifth Street · Cincinnati, OH 45202-4182 · 513-651-6800

Scott T. Greenwood · a · Scott T. Greenwood · One Liberty House · P.O. Box 54400 · Cincinnati, OH 45254-0400 · 513-943-4200

John C. Greiner · Graydon, Head & Ritchey · 1900 Fifth Third Center · 511 Walnut Street · Cincinnati, OH 45202 · 513-621-6464

Marc D. Mezibov · 2) · Mezibov & Jenkins · 401 East Court Street, Suite 600 · Cincinnati, OH 45202 · 513-621-8800

Robert B. Newman · a · Newman & Meeks · 215 East Ninth Street, Suite 650 · Cincinnati, OH 45202-2143 · 513-639-7000

H. Louis Sirkin · a · Sirkin, Pinales & Schwartz · 105 West Fourth Street · Cincinnati, OH 45202-2726 · 513-721-4876

Cleveland

Louis A. Colombo · a · Baker Hostetler · http://www.bakerlaw.com · National City Center, Suite 3200 · 1900 East Ninth Street · Cleveland, OH 44114-3485 · 216-621-0200

David L. Marburger · a · Baker Hostetler · http://www.bakerlaw.com · National City Center, Suite 3200 · 1900 East Ninth Street · Cleveland, OH 44114-3485 · 216-621-0200

J. Michael Murray · a · Berkman, Gordon, Murray & DeVan · 55 Public Square, Suite 2200 · Cleveland, OH 44113-1972 · 216-781-5245

Columbus

Susan B. Gellman · a · Wolman & Genshaft · 88 East Broad Street, Suite 1590 · Columbus, OH 43215-3506 · 614-280-1000

Frederick M. Gittes · 2) · Fred Gittes · 723 Oak Street · Columbus, OH 43205 · 614-222-4735

Marion H. Little, Jr. · Zeiger, Tigges & Little · http://www.litohio.com · Huntington Center, Suite 3500 · 41 South High Street · Columbus, OH 43215 · 614-365-9900

John W. Zeiger · 2) · Zeiger, Tigges & Little · http://www.litohio.com · Huntington Center, Suite 3500 · 41 South High Street · Columbus, OH 43215 · 614-365-9900

Toledo

Frederick Byers · a · Fritz Byers · The Spitzer Building, Suite 824 · 520 Madison Avenue · Toledo, OH 43604-1343 · 419-241-8013

John Czarnecki · a · Cooper & Walinski · 900 Adams Street · Toledo, OH 43604 · 419-241-1200

FRANCHISE LAW

Cincinnati

Melvin A. Bedree · Vorys, Sater, Seymour and Pease · Atrium Two, Suite 2000 · 221 East Fourth Street · P.O. Box 0236 · Cincinnati, OH 45201-0236 · 513-723-4000

Paul R. Mattingly · Dinsmore & Shohl · http://www.dinslaw.com · 255 East Fifth Street, Suite 1900 · Cincinnati, OH 45202-3172 · 513-977-8200

Columbus

Stephen R. Buchenroth · a · Vorys, Sater, Seymour and Pease · 52 East Gay Street · P.O. Box 1008 · Columbus, OH 43216-1008 · 614-464-6400

Herbert A. Hedden · a · Vorys, Sater, Seymour and Pease · 52 East Gay Street · P.O. Box 1008 · Columbus, OH 43216-1008 · 614-464-6400

Dublin

Nancy L. Sponseller · a · Law Offices of Nancy L. Sponseller · http://www.sponsellerlaw.com · 5890 Sawmill Road, Suite 110 · Dublin, OH 43017 · 614-764-0423

Toledo

Kathleen A. Kress · Shumaker, Loop & Kendrick · North Courthouse Square · 1000 Jackson Street · Toledo, OH 43604-5573 · 419-241-9000

Brian N. McMahon · Shumaker, Loop & Kendrick · North Courthouse Square · 1000 Jackson Street · Toledo, OH 43604-5573 · 419-241-9000

Peter R. Silverman · Shumaker, Loop & Kendrick · North Courthouse Square · 1000 Jackson Street · Toledo, OH 43604-5573 · 419-241-9000

GAMING LAW

Cleveland

Irv Berliner · Taft Stettinius & Hollister · http://www.taftlaw.com · BP Tower, Suite 3500 · 200 Public Square · Cleveland, OH 44114-2302 · 216-241-2838

GOVERNMENT RELATIONS LAW

Columbus

Daniel J. Massey · Porter, Wright, Morris & Arthur · http://www.porterwright.com · Huntington Center · 41 South High Street · Columbus, OH 43215-6194 · 614-227-2000

C. David Paragas · Benesch, Friedlander, Coplan & Aronoff · 41 South High Street, Suite 2600 · Columbus, OH 43215 · 614-223-9300

Charles R. Saxbe · a · Chester Willcox & Saxbe · http://www.cwslaw.com · 65 East State Street, Suite 1000 · Columbus, OH 43215 · 614-221-4000

Alex Shumate · a · Squire Sanders · http://www.ssd.com · 1300 Huntington Center · 41 South High Street · Columbus, OH 43215-6197 · 614-365-2700

HEALTH CARE LAW

Canton

Joseph J. Feltes · Buckingham, Doolittle & Burroughs · http://www.bdblaw.com · 4518 Fulton Drive, NW · P.O. Box 35548 · Canton, OH 44735-5548 · 330-492-8717

Chagrin Falls

Dennis A. Roth · a · Dennis A. Roth · 110 Farwood Drive · Chagrin Falls, OH 44022-6582 · 216-952-8649

Cincinnati

Thomas D. Anthony · Frost Brown Todd · http://www.frostbrowntodd.com · PNC Center, Suite 2200 · 201 East Fifth Street · Cincinnati, OH 45202-4182 · 513-651-6800

William M. Freedman · 2% · Dinsmore & Shohl · http://www.dinslaw.com · 255 East Fifth Street, Suite 1900 · Cincinnati, OH 45202-3172 · 513-977-8200

Cynthia L. Gibson · Katz, Teller, Brant & Hild · http://www.katzteller.com · 255 East Fifth Street, Suite 2400 · Cincinnati, OH 45202-4724 · 513-721-4532

Thomas W. Kahle · Baker Hostetler · http://www.bakerlaw.com · 312 Walnut Street, Suite 3200 · Cincinnati, OH 45202-4074 · 513-929-3400

John J. Kropp · Graydon, Head & Ritchey · 1900 Fifth Third Center · 511 Walnut Street · Cincinnati, OH 45202 · 513-621-6464

Deborah R. Lydon · Dinsmore & Shohl · http://www.dinslaw.com · 255 East Fifth Street, Suite 1900 · Cincinnati, OH 45202-3172 · 513-977-8200

John J. McCoy · Taft Stettinius & Hollister · http://www.taftlaw.com · 425 Walnut Street, Suite 1800 · Cincinnati, OH 45202-3957 · 513-381-2838

Robert E. Rich · Taft Stettinius & Hollister · http://www.taftlaw.com · 425 Walnut Street, Suite 1800 · Cincinnati, OH 45202-3957 · 513-381-2838

Melvin S. Shotten · Taft Stettinius & Hollister · http://www.taftlaw.com · 425 Walnut Street, Suite 1800 · Cincinnati, OH 45202-3957 · 513-381-2838

Frank C. Woodside III · a · Dinsmore & Shohl · http://www.dinslaw.com · 255 East Fifth Street, Suite 1900 · Cincinnati, OH 45202-3172 · 513-977-8200

Cleveland

Gregory G. Binford · a · Benesch, Friedlander, Coplan & Aronoff · BP Tower, Suite 2300 · 200 Public Square · Cleveland, OH 44114-2378 · 216-363-4500

Harry M. Brown · a · Benesch, Friedlander, Coplan & Aronoff · BP Tower, Suite 2300 · 200 Public Square · Cleveland, OH 44114-2378 · 216-363-4500

Arthur L. Cobb · a · Hahn Loeser & Parks · BP Tower, Suite 2800 · 200 Public Square · Cleveland, OH 44114-2301 · 216-621-0150

Richard S. Cooper · a · McDonald Hopkins · 600 Superior Avenue East, Suite 2100 · Cleveland, OH 44114-2653 · 216-348-5400

Steven A. Eisenberg · Baker Hostetler · http://www.bakerlaw.com · National City Center, Suite 3200 · 1900 East Ninth Street · Cleveland, OH 44114-3485 · 216-621-0200

Ira S. Goffman · a · Rolf & Goffman · Corporate Circle, Suite 350 · 30100 Chagrin Boulevard · Cleveland, OH 44124-5705 · 216-514-1100

Michael J. Jordan · Walter & Haverfield · http://www.walterhav.com · The Tower at Erieview, Suite 3500 · 1301 East Ninth Street · Cleveland, OH 44114 · 216-781-1212

Jeffrey L. Kapp · Jones Day · North Point · 901 Lakeside Avenue · Cleveland, OH 44114-1190 · 216-586-3939

Paul A. Lang · Rolf & Goffman · Corporate Circle, Suite 350 · 30100 Chagrin Boulevard · Cleveland, OH 44124-5705 · 216-514-1100

Amy S. Leopard · Walter & Haverfield · http://www.walterhav.com · The Tower at Erieview, Suite 3500 · 1301 East Ninth Street · Cleveland, OH 44114 · 216-781-1212

John T. Mulligan · McDonald Hopkins · 600 Superior Avenue East, Suite 2100 · Cleveland, OH 44114-2653 · 216-348-5400

Thomas J. Onusko · a · Vorys, Sater, Seymour and Pease · 2100 One Cleveland Center · 1375 East Ninth Street · Cleveland, OH 44114-1724 · 216-479-6100

Carol Rolf · a · Rolf & Goffman · Corporate Circle, Suite 350 · 30100 Chagrin Boulevard · Cleveland, OH 44124-5705 · 216-514-1100

Alan E. Schabes · Benesch, Friedlander, Coplan & Aronoff · BP Tower, Suite 2300 · 200 Public Square · Cleveland, OH 44114-2378 · 216-363-4500

Isaac Schulz · Ulmer & Berne · Skylight Office Tower, Suite 1100 · 1660 West Second Street · Cleveland, OH 44113-1448 · 216-583-7000

Eric M. Simon · Taft Stettinius & Hollister · http://www.taftlaw.com · BP Tower, Suite 3500 · 200 Public Square · Cleveland, OH 44114-2302 · 216-241-2838

Christopher J. Swift · a · Baker Hostetler · http://www.bakerlaw.com · National City Center, Suite 3200 1900 East Ninth Street · Cleveland, OH 44114-3485 · 216-621-0200

Columbus

Donald A. Antrim · a · Dinsmore & Shohl · http://www.dinslaw.com · 191 West Nationwide Boulevard, Suite 300 · Columbus, OH 43215 · 614-221-8448

Catherine M. Ballard · a · Bricker & Eckler · http://www.bricker.com · 100 South Third Street · Columbus, OH 43215-4291 · 614-227-2300

Martha Post Baxter · a · Bricker & Eckler · http://www.bricker.com · 100 South Third Street · Columbus, OH 43215-4291 · 614-227-2300

Frank Carsonie · Benesch, Friedlander, Coplan & Aronoff · 41 South High Street, Suite 2600 · Columbus, OH 43215 · 614-223-9300

Donald A. Davies · a · Bailey Cavalieri · One Columbus Building, Suite 2100 · 10 West Broad Street · Columbus, OH 43215-3422 · 614-221-3155

Kris M. Dawley · Schottenstein, Zox & Dunn · http://www.szd.com · 250 West Street, Suite 700 · Columbus, OH 43215-2538 · 614-462-2700

Lloyd DePew · Porter, Wright, Morris & Arthur · http://www.porterwright.com · Huntington Center · 41 South High Street · Columbus, OH 43215-6194 · 614-227-2000

Catherine T. Dunlay · Schottenstein, Zox & Dunn · http://www.szd.com · 250 West Street, Suite 700 · Columbus, OH 43215-2538 · 614-462-2700

Thomas E. Dutton · a · Jones Day · 325 John H. McConnell Boulevard, Suite 600 · P.O. Box 165017 · Columbus, OH 43216-5017 · 614-469-3939

Janet K. Feldkamp · Benesch, Friedlander, Coplan & Aronoff · 41 South High Street, Suite 2600 · Columbus, OH 43215 · 614-223-9300

James F. Flynn · Bricker & Eckler · http://www.bricker.com · 100 South Third Street · Columbus, OH 43215-4291 · 614-227-2300

Lisa Ge Shang Han · Schottenstein, Zox & Dunn · http://www.szd.com · 250 West Street, Suite 700 · Columbus, OH 43215-2538 · 614-462-2700

Michael K. Gire · a · Bricker & Eckler · http://www.bricker.com · 100 South Third Street · Columbus, OH 43215-4291 · 614-227-2300

David W. Grauer · Squire Sanders · http://www.ssd.com · 1300 Huntington Center · 41 South High Street Columbus, OH 43215-6197 · 614-365-2700

Thomas W. Hess · a · Dinsmore & Shohl · http://www.dinslaw.com · 191 West Nationwide Boulevard, Suite 300 · Columbus, OH 43215 · 614-221-8448

James R. King · a · Jones Day · 325 John H. McConnell Boulevard, Suite 600 · P.O. Box 165017 · Columbus, OH 43216-5017 · 614-469-3939

John M. Kirsner · Squire Sanders · http://www.ssd.com · 1300 Huntington Center · 41 South High Street Columbus, OH 43215-6197 · 614-365-2700

Kevin D. Lyles · Jones Day · 325 John H. McConnell Boulevard, Suite 600 · P.O. Box 165017 · Columbus, OH 43216-5017 · 614-469-3939

Peter A. Pavarini · a · Schottenstein, Zox & Dunn · http://www.szd.com · 250 West Street, Suite 700 · Columbus, OH 43215-2538 · 614-462-2700

Eric J. Plinke · Dinsmore & Shohl · http://www.dinslaw.com · 191 West Nationwide Boulevard, Suite 300 Columbus, OH 43215 · 614-221-8448

Diane M. Signoracci · a · Bricker & Eckler · http://www.bricker.com · 100 South Third Street · Columbus, OH 43215-4291 · 614-227-2300

Terri-Lynne Smiles · Collis Smiles & Collis · http://www.collislaw.com · 1650 Lake Shore Drive, Suite 225 · Columbus, OH 43204 · 614-486-3909

David C. Spialter · Bricker & Eckler · http://www.bricker.com · 100 South Third Street · Columbus, OH 43215-4291 · 614-227-2300

Elisabeth A. Squeglia · Bricker & Eckler · http://www.bricker.com · 100 South Third Street · Columbus, OH 43215-4291 · 614-227-2300

Martha J. Sweterlitsch · Benesch, Friedlander, Coplan & Aronoff · 41 South High Street, Suite 2600 · Columbus, OH 43215 · 614-223-9300

William M. Todd · a · Benesch, Friedlander, Coplan & Aronoff · 41 South High Street, Suite 2600 · Columbus, OH 43215 · 614-223-9300

Geoffrey Webster · Geoffrey E. Webster · Two Miranova Place, Suite 310 · Columbus, OH 43215-3413 · 614-461-1156

Dayton

John L. Green · Coolidge Wall Co. · http://www.coollaw.com · 33 West First Street, Suite 600 · Dayton, OH 45402 · 937-223-8177

Toledo

Jenifer A. Belt · Shumaker, Loop & Kendrick · North Courthouse Square · 1000 Jackson Street · Toledo, OH 43604-5573 · 419-241-9000

Edwin G. Emerson · a · Shumaker, Loop & Kendrick · North Courthouse Square · 1000 Jackson Street · Toledo, OH 43604-5573 · 419-241-9000

David L. Kuhl · a · Eastman & Smith · One Seagate, 24th Floor · P.O. Box 10032 · Toledo, OH 43699-0032 · 419-241-6000

Dennis P. Witherell · a · Shumaker, Loop & Kendrick · North Courthouse Square · 1000 Jackson Street · Toledo, OH 43604-5573 · 419-241-9000

West Chester

Claire Turcotte · Bricker & Eckler · http://www.bricker.com · 9277 Centre Pointe Drive, Suite 100 · West Chester, OH 45069 · 513-870-6700

IMMIGRATION LAW

Cincinnati

Gregory P. Adams · a · Dinsmore & Shohl · http://www.dinslaw.com · 255 East Fifth Street, Suite 1900 · Cincinnati, OH 45202-3172 · 513-977-8200

Douglas J. Halpert · a · Dinsmore & Shohl · http://www.dinslaw.com · 255 East Fifth Street, Suite 1900 · Cincinnati, OH 45202-3172 · 513-977-8200

Douglas S. Weigle · a · Bartlett & Weigle · 432 Walnut Street, Suite 1100 · Cincinnati, OH 45202 · 513-241-3992

Michael J. Zavatsky · a · Taft Stettinius & Hollister · http://www.taftlaw.com · 425 Walnut Street, Suite 1800 · Cincinnati, OH 45202-3957 · 513-381-2838

Cleveland

Anikó T. Kálnoki · Sharon & Kálnoki · 55 Public Square, Suite 750 · Cleveland, OH 44113 · 216-348-9878

David W. Leopold · David Wolfe Leopold & Associates · 2000 East Ninth Street, Suite 300 · Cleveland, OH 44115 · 216-696-4676

Karen G. Moss · Rosner & Associates · The Caxton Building, Suite 601 · 812 Huron Road · Cleveland, OH 44115 · 216-771-5588

William R. Rosner · a · Rosner & Associates · The Caxton Building, Suite 601 · 812 Huron Road · Cleveland, OH 44115 · 216-771-5588

Columbus

David S. Bloomfield · a · Bloomfield & Kempf · 175 South Third Street, Suite 505 · Columbus, OH 43215-5188 · 614-224-9221

Robert H. Cohen · a · Porter, Wright, Morris & Arthur · http://www.porterwright.com · Huntington Center · 41 South High Street · Columbus, OH 43215-6194 · 614-227-2000

Christopher J. Kempf · a · Bloomfield & Kempf · 175 South Third Street, Suite 505 · Columbus, OH 43215-5188 · 614-224-9221

Toledo

Regina M. Joseph · Shumaker, Loop & Kendrick · North Courthouse Square · 1000 Jackson Street · Toledo, OH 43604-5573 · 419-241-9000

William G. Meyer · a · William G. Meyer · 608 Madison Avenue, Suite 1400 · Toledo, OH 43604-1121 · 419-246-5722

Mary Ellen Pisanelli · Shumaker, Loop & Kendrick · North Courthouse Square · 1000 Jackson Street · Toledo, OH 43604-5573 · 419-241-9000

Mechelle Zarou · Shumaker, Loop & Kendrick · North Courthouse Square · 1000 Jackson Street · Toledo, OH 43604-5573 · 419-241-9000

INFORMATION TECHNOLOGY LAW

Cincinnati

Todd H. Bailey · Frost Brown Todd · http://www.frostbrowntodd.com · PNC Center, Suite 2200 · 201 East Fifth Street · Cincinnati, OH 45202-4182 · 513-651-6800

Cleveland

Michael D. Stovsky · Ulmer & Berne · Skylight Office Tower, Suite 1100 · 1660 West Second Street · Cleveland, OH 44113-1448 · 216-583-7000

Columbus

Dino Tsibouris · Tsibouris & Associates · http://www.tsibouris.com · 88 East Broad Street, Suite 1560 · Columbus, OH 43215 · 614-228-9707

INSURANCE LAW

Akron

Laura Faust · Roetzel & Andress · http://www.ralaw.com · 222 South Main Street · Akron, OH 44308-2098 · 330-376-2700

David W. Hilkert · Buckingham, Doolittle & Burroughs · http://www.bdblaw.com · 3800 Embassy Parkway, Suite 300 · P.O. Box 1500 · Akron, OH 44309-1500 · 330-376-5300

Canton

David L. Dingwell · Tzangas, Plakas, Mannos & Raies · 220 Market Avenue South, Eigth Floor · Canton, OH 44702 · 330-455-6112

Merle D. Evans III · Day Ketterer · Millennium Centre, Suite 300 · 200 Market Avenue North · P.O. Box 24213 · Canton, OH 44701-4213 · 330-455-0173

John A. Murphy, Jr. · Day Ketterer · Millennium Centre, Suite 300 · 200 Market Avenue North · P.O. Box 24213 · Canton, OH 44701-4213 · 330-455-0173

Cincinnati

Alan H. Abes · Dinsmore & Shohl · http://www.dinslaw.com · 255 East Fifth Street, Suite 1900 · Cincinnati, OH 45202-3172 · 513-977-8200

Christopher M. Bechhold · Thompson Hine · 312 Walnut Street, 14th Floor · Cincinnati, OH 45202-4089 · 513-352-6700

Scott R. Brown · Frost Brown Todd · http://www.frostbrowntodd.com · PNC Center, Suite 2200 · 201 East Fifth Street · Cincinnati, OH 45202-4182 · 513-651-6800

Thomas B. Bruns · Freund, Freeze & Arnold · Fourth & Walnut Centre, Suite 1400 · 105 East Fourth Street · Cincinnati, OH 45202-4035 · 513-665-3500

Gregory A. Harrison · Dinsmore & Shohl · http://www.dinslaw.com · 255 East Fifth Street, Suite 1900 · Cincinnati, OH 45202-3172 · 513-977-8200

Paul W. McCartney · Rendigs, Fry, Kiely & Dennis · One West Fourth Street, Suite 900 · Cincinnati, OH 45202-3688 · 513-381-9200

John F. McLaughlin · Rendigs, Fry, Kiely & Dennis · One West Fourth Street, Suite 900 · Cincinnati, OH 45202-3688 · 513-381-9200

Arthur E. Phelps, Jr. · Rendigs, Fry, Kiely & Dennis · One West Fourth Street, Suite 900 · Cincinnati, OH 45202-3688 · 513-381-9200

Carl J. Stich, Jr. · White, Getgey & Meyer · Fourth & Vine Tower, Suite 1700 · One West Fourth Street Cincinnati, OH 45202-3621 · 513-241-3685

Gerald V. Weigle, Jr. · Dinsmore & Shohl · http://www.dinslaw.com · 255 East Fifth Street, Suite 1900 · Cincinnati, OH 45202-3172 · 513-977-8200

Cleveland

Robert D. Anderle · Seeley, Savidge, Ebert & Gourash · 26600 Detroit Road · Cleveland, OH 44114-2655 · 216-566-8200

Michael Brittain · Calfee, Halter & Griswold · http://www.calfee.com · 1400 KeyBank Center · 800 Superior Avenue · Cleveland, OH 44114-2688 · 216-622-8200

Carolyn M. Cappel · Weston Hurd · The Tower at Erieview, Suite 1900 · 1301 East Ninth Street · Cleveland, OH 44114-1862 · 216-241-6602

Andrew J. Dorman · Janik Dorman & Winter · http://www.janiklaw.com · 9200 South Hills Boulevard, Suite 300 · Cleveland, OH 44147-3521 · 440-838-7600

Keven D. Eiber · Brouse McDowell · 1001 Lakeside Avenue, Suite 1600 · Cleveland, OH 44114 · 216-830-6830

David J. Fagnilli · Davis and Young · 1200 Fifth Third Center · 600 Superior Avenue East · Cleveland, OH 44114-2654 · 216-348-1700

Daniel F. Gourash · Seeley, Savidge, Ebert & Gourash · 26600 Detroit Road · Cleveland, OH 44114-2655 · 216-566-8200

Steven G. Janik · a · Janik Dorman & Winter · http://www.janiklaw.com · 9200 South Hills Boulevard, Suite 300 · Cleveland, OH 44147-3521 · 440-838-7600

Timothy D. Johnson · Weston Hurd · The Tower at Erieview, Suite 1900 · 1301 East Ninth Street · Cleveland, OH 44114-1862 · 216-241-6602

Michael J. Jordan · Walter & Haverfield · http://www.walterhav.com · The Tower at Erieview, Suite 3500 · 1301 East Ninth Street · Cleveland, OH 44114 · 216-781-1212

David L. Lester · Ulmer & Berne · Skylight Office Tower, Suite 1100 · 1660 West Second Street · Cleveland, OH 44113-1448 · 216-583-7000

Mark O'Neill · 2% · Weston Hurd · The Tower at Erieview, Suite 1900 · 1301 East Ninth Street · Cleveland, OH 44114-1862 · 216-241-6602

Harold H. Reader · Ulmer & Berne · Skylight Office Tower, Suite 1100 · 1660 West Second Street · Cleveland, OH 44113-1448 · 216-583-7000

Ronald A. Rispo · Weston Hurd · The Tower at Erieview, Suite 1900 · 1301 East Ninth Street · Cleveland, OH 44114-1862 · 216-241-6602

Hilary S. Taylor · Weston Hurd · The Tower at Erieview, Suite 1900 · 1301 East Ninth Street · Cleveland, OH 44114-1862 · 216-241-6602

Columbus

John M. Kirsner · Squire Sanders · http://www.ssd.com · 1300 Huntington Center · 41 South High Street Columbus, OH 43215-6197 · 614-365-2700

William J. Pohlman · Vorys, Sater, Seymour and Pease · 52 East Gay Street · P.O. Box 1008 · Columbus, OH 43216-1008 · 614-464-6400

Faith M. Williams · Bricker & Eckler · http://www.bricker.com · 100 South Third Street · Columbus, OH 43215-4291 · 614-227-2300

Dayton

Christopher W. Carrigg · Freund, Freeze & Arnold · One Dayton Centre, Suite 1800 · One South Main Street · Dayton, OH 45402-2017 · 937-222-2424

Christopher F. Johnson · Freund, Freeze & Arnold · One Dayton Centre, Suite 1800 · One South Main Street · Dayton, OH 45402-2017 · 937-222-2424

Scott G. Oxley · Jenks, Pyper & Oxley · Courthouse Plaza, SW, Suite 901 · 10 North Ludlow Street · Dayton, OH 45402 · 937-223-3001

Thomas H. Pyper · Jenks, Pyper & Oxley · Courthouse Plaza, SW, Suite 901 · 10 North Ludlow Street · Dayton, OH 45402 · 937-223-3001

North Canton

Gregory A. Beck · Baker, Dublikar, Beck, Wiley & Mathews · 400 South Main Street · North Canton, OH 44720 · 330-499-6000

James F. Mathews · Baker, Dublikar, Beck, Wiley & Mathews · 400 South Main Street · North Canton, OH 44720 · 330-499-6000

Toledo

Edwin A. Coy · Coy, Konieczny & Peppel · 405 Madison Avenue, Suite 700 · Toledo, OH 43604 · 419-724-5252

Joseph P. Thacker · Cooper & Walinski · 900 Adams Street · Toledo, OH 43604 · 419-241-1200

Akron

Mark A. Watkins · Hahn Loeser & Parks · One GOJO Plaza, Suite 300 · 501 South Main Street · Akron, OH 44311-1076 · 330-864-5550

Ray L. Weber · a · Renner, Kenner, Greive, Bobak, Taylor & Weber · First National Tower, Fourth Floor · Akron, OH 44308 · 330-376-1242

Canton

Lee J. Bell · Buckingham, Doolittle & Burroughs · http://www.bdblaw.com · 4518 Fulton Drive, NW · P.O. Box 35548 · Canton, OH 44735-5548 · 330-492-8717

Mark J. Skakun III · a · Buckingham, Doolittle & Burroughs · http://www.bdblaw.com · 4518 Fulton Drive, NW · P.O. Box 35548 · Canton, OH 44735-5548 · 330-492-8717

Cincinnati

Gregory F. Ahrens · Wood, Herron & Evans · http://www.whepatent.com · Carew Tower, Suite 2700 · 441 Vine Street · Cincinnati, OH 45202-2917 · 513-241-2324

Todd H. Bailey · Frost Brown Todd · http://www.frostbrowntodd.com · PNC Center, Suite 2200 · 201 East Fifth Street · Cincinnati, OH 45202-4182 · 513-651-6800

Bruce O. Baumgartner · Baker Hostetler · http://www.bakerlaw.com · 312 Walnut Street, Suite 3200 · Cincinnati, OH 45202-4074 · 513-929-3400

J. Robert Chambers · a · Wood, Herron & Evans · http://www.whepatent.com · Carew Tower, Suite 2700 · 441 Vine Street · Cincinnati, OH 45202-2917 · 513-241-2324

Thomas W. Flynn · Wood, Herron & Evans · http://www.whepatent.com · Carew Tower, Suite 2700 · 441 Vine Street · Cincinnati, OH 45202-2917 · 513-241-2324

Donald F. Frei, Sr. · a · Wood, Herron & Evans · http://www.whepatent.com · Carew Tower, Suite 2700 441 Vine Street · Cincinnati, OH 45202-2917 · 513-241-2324

Karen K. Gaunt · Greenebaum Doll & McDonald · http://www.gdm.com · Chemed Center, Suite 2900 · 255 East Fifth Street · Cincinnati, OH 45202 · 513-455-7600

Kenneth B. Germain · a · Greenebaum Doll & McDonald · http://www.gdm.com · Chemed Center, Suite 2900 · 255 East Fifth Street · Cincinnati, OH 45202 · 513-455-7600

Stephen E. Gillen · Greenebaum Doll & McDonald · http://www.gdm.com · Chemed Center, Suite 2900 255 East Fifth Street · Cincinnati, OH 45202 · 513-455-7600

Steven J. Goldstein · a · Frost Brown Todd · http://www.frostbrowntodd.com · PNC Center, Suite 2200 · 201 East Fifth Street · Cincinnati, OH 45202-4182 · 513-651-6800

Kurt L. Grossman · Wood, Herron & Evans · http://www.whepatent.com · Carew Tower, Suite 2700 · 441 Vine Street · Cincinnati, OH 45202-2917 · 513-241-2324

Patricia B. Hogan · Keating Muething & Klekamp · http://www.kmklaw.com · One East Fourth Street, Suite 1400 · Cincinnati, OH 45202 · 513-579-6400

David J. Josephic · a · Wood, Herron & Evans · http://www.whepatent.com · Carew Tower, Suite 2700 · 441 Vine Street · Cincinnati, OH 45202-2917 · 513-241-2324

Holly D. Kozlowski · Porter, Wright, Morris & Arthur · http://www.porterwright.com · 250 East Fifth Street, Suite 2200 · Cincinnati, OH 45202-5118 · 513-381-4700

Lynda E. Roesch · a · Dinsmore & Shohl · http://www.dinslaw.com · 255 East Fifth Street, Suite 1900 · Cincinnati, OH 45202-3172 · 513-977-8200

David E. Schmit · Frost Brown Todd · http://www.frostbrowntodd.com · PNC Center, Suite 2200 · 201 East Fifth Street · Cincinnati, OH 45202-4182 · 513-651-6800

David S. Stallard · a · Wood, Herron & Evans · http://www.whepatent.com · Carew Tower, Suite 2700 · 441 Vine Street · Cincinnati, OH 45202-2917 · 513-241-2324

Bruce Tittel · a · Wood, Herron & Evans · http://www.whepatent.com · Carew Tower, Suite 2700 · 441 Vine Street · Cincinnati, OH 45202-2917 · 513-241-2324

Cleveland

Kenneth R. Adamo · a · Jones Day · North Point · 901 Lakeside Avenue · Cleveland, OH 44114-1190 · 216-586-3939

Steven M. Auvil · Benesch, Friedlander, Coplan & Aronoff · BP Tower, Suite 2300 · 200 Public Square · Cleveland, OH 44114-2378 · 216-363-4500

Armand P. Boisselle · a · Renner, Otto, Boisselle & Sklar · 1621 Euclid Avenue, 19th Floor · Cleveland, OH 44115-2107 · 216-621-1113

Robert P. Ducatman · Jones Day · North Point · 901 Lakeside Avenue · Cleveland, OH 44114-1190 · 216-586-3939

Regan J. Fay · a · Jones Day · North Point · 901 Lakeside Avenue · Cleveland, OH 44114-1190 · 216-586-3939

Calvin P. Griffith · Jones Day · North Point · 901 Lakeside Avenue · Cleveland, OH 44114-1190 · 216-586-3939

Robert C. Kahrl · Jones Day · North Point · 901 Lakeside Avenue · Cleveland, OH 44114-1190 · 216-586-3939

Charles B. Lyon · a · Calfee, Halter & Griswold · http://www.calfee.com · 1400 KeyBank Center · 800 Superior Avenue · Cleveland, OH 44114-2688 · 216-622-8200

Timothy O'Hearn · Jones Day · North Point · 901 Lakeside Avenue · Cleveland, OH 44114-1190 · 216-586-3939

James L. Wamsley III · Jones Day · North Point · 901 Lakeside Avenue · Cleveland, OH 44114-1190 · 216-586-3939

Columbus

Edwin M. Baranowski · a · Porter, Wright, Morris & Arthur · http://www.porterwright.com · Huntington Center · 41 South High Street · Columbus, OH 43215-6194 · 614-227-2000

Joseph R. Dreitler · Bricker & Eckler · http://www.bricker.com · 100 South Third Street · Columbus, OH 43215-4291 · 614-227-2300

T. Earl LeVere · Schottenstein, Zox & Dunn · http://www.szd.com · 250 West Street, Suite 700 · Columbus, OH 43215-2538 · 614-462-2700

Susan D. Rector · Schottenstein, Zox & Dunn · http://www.szd.com · 250 West Street, Suite 700 · Columbus, OH 43215-2538 · 614-462-2700

Donna M. Ruscitti · Porter, Wright, Morris & Arthur · http://www.porterwright.com · Huntington Center · 41 South High Street · Columbus, OH 43215-6194 · 614-227-2000

Dayton

James E. Beyer · Dinsmore & Shohl · http://www.dinslaw.com · One Dayton Centre, Suite 1300 · One South Main Street · Dayton, OH 45402 · 937-449-6400

Kimberly Gambrel · Dinsmore & Shohl · http://www.dinslaw.com · One Dayton Centre, Suite 1300 · One South Main Street · Dayton, OH 45402 · 937-449-6400

James F. Gottman · Dinsmore & Shohl · http://www.dinslaw.com · One Dayton Centre, Suite 1300 · One South Main Street · Dayton, OH 45402 · 937-449-6400

Timothy W. Hagan · a · Dinsmore & Shohl · http://www.dinslaw.com · One Dayton Centre, Suite 1300 · One South Main Street · Dayton, OH 45402 · 937-449-6400

Richard A. Killworth · a · Dinsmore & Shohl · http://www.dinslaw.com · One Dayton Centre, Suite 1300 · One South Main Street · Dayton, OH 45402 · 937-449-6400

Mark P. Levy · a · Thompson Hine · 2000 Courthouse Plaza, NE · 10 West Second Street · P.O. Box 8801 · Dayton, OH 45401-8801 · 937-443-6600

Theodore D. Lienesch · Thompson Hine · 2000 Courthouse Plaza, NE · 10 West Second Street · P.O. Box 8801 · Dayton, OH 45401-8801 · 937-443-6600

B. Joseph Schaeff · Dinsmore & Shohl · http://www.dinslaw.com · One Dayton Centre, Suite 1300 · One South Main Street · Dayton, OH 45402 · 937-449-6400

Toledo

Ted C. Gillespie · MacMillan, Sobanski & Todd · One Maritime Plaza, Fifth Floor · 720 Water Street · Toledo, OH 43604-0001 · 419-255-5900

INTERNATIONAL ARBITRATION

Cincinnati

Joseph J. Dehner · Frost Brown Todd · http://www.frostbrowntodd.com · PNC Center, Suite 2200 · 201 East Fifth Street · Cincinnati, OH 45202-4182 · 513-651-6800

John B. Pinney · Graydon, Head & Ritchey · 1900 Fifth Third Center · 511 Walnut Street · Cincinnati, OH 45202 · 513-621-6464

INTERNATIONAL TRADE AND FINANCE LAW

Cincinnati

Paul Allaer · Thompson Hine · 312 Walnut Street, 14th Floor · Cincinnati, OH 45202-4089 · 513-352-6700

Joseph J. Dehner · Frost Brown Todd · http://www.frostbrowntodd.com · PNC Center, Suite 2200 · 201 East Fifth Street · Cincinnati, OH 45202-4182 · 513-651-6800

Ross E. Wales · Taft Stettinius & Hollister · http://www.taftlaw.com · 425 Walnut Street, Suite 1800 · Cincinnati, OH 45202-3957 · 513-381-2838

LABOR AND EMPLOYMENT LAW

Akron

Harley M. Kastner · Kastner Westman & Wilkins · 3480 West Market Street, Suite 300 · Akron, OH 44333 · 330-867-9998

Gary W. Spring · a · Roetzel & Andress · http://www.ralaw.com · 222 South Main Street · Akron, OH 44308-2098 · 330-376-2700

Brecksville

Steven D. Bell · Steven D. Bell Company · http://www.stevebell-law.com · 8803 Brecksville Road, Suite 11 · Brecksville, OH 44141 · 330-294-0347

Canton

James R. Blake · Day Ketterer · Millennium Centre, Suite 300 · 200 Market Avenue North · P.O. Box 24213 · Canton, OH 44701-4213 · 330-455-0173

John Bogniard · Krugliak, Wilkins, Griffiths & Dougherty · http://www.kwgd.com · 4775 Munson Street, NW · P.O. Box 36963 · Canton, OH 44735-6963 · 330-497-0700

William B. Gore · 2) · Macala, Gore & Piatt · 4150 Belden Village, NW, Suite 602 · Canton, OH 44718 · 330-493-1570

Leslie I. Kuntz · Krugliak, Wilkins, Griffiths & Dougherty · http://www.kwgd.com · 4775 Munson Street, NW · P.O. Box 36963 · Canton, OH 44735-6963 · 330-497-0700

Sheila Markley-Black · Day Ketterer · Millennium Centre, Suite 300 · 200 Market Avenue North · P.O. Box 24213 · Canton, OH 44701-4213 · 330-455-0173

Karen S. McQueen · Krugliak, Wilkins, Griffiths & Dougherty · http://www.kwgd.com · 4775 Munson Street, NW · P.O. Box 36963 · Canton, OH 44735-6963 · 330-497-0700

Robert C. Meyer · Buckingham, Doolittle & Burroughs · http://www.bdblaw.com · 4518 Fulton Drive, NW · P.O. Box 35548 · Canton, OH 44735-5548 · 330-492-8717

Tod T. Morrow · Buckingham, Doolittle & Burroughs · http://www.bdblaw.com · 4518 Fulton Drive, NW P.O. Box 35548 · Canton, OH 44735-5548 · 330-492-8717

Paul J. Pusateri · Buckingham, Doolittle & Burroughs · http://www.bdblaw.com · 4518 Fulton Drive, NW · P.O. Box 35548 · Canton, OH 44735-5548 · 330-492-8717

Elizabeth A. Raies · Tzangas, Plakas, Mannos & Raies · 220 Market Avenue South, Eigth Floor · Canton, OH 44702 · 330-455-6112

Mary E. Reynolds · Buckingham, Doolittle & Burroughs · http://www.bdblaw.com · 4518 Fulton Drive, NW · P.O. Box 35548 · Canton, OH 44735-5548 · 330-492-8717

Cincinnati

Deborah S. Adams · 2% · Frost Brown Todd · http://www.frostbrowntodd.com · PNC Center, Suite 2200 · 201 East Fifth Street · Cincinnati, OH 45202-4182 · 513-651-6800

G. Randall Ayers · Frost Brown Todd · http://www.frostbrowntodd.com · PNC Center, Suite 2200 · 201 East Fifth Street · Cincinnati, OH 45202-4182 · 513-651-6800

Lawrence J. Barty · Taft Stettinius & Hollister · http://www.taftlaw.com · 425 Walnut Street, Suite 1800 · Cincinnati, OH 45202-3957 · 513-381-2838

Louise S. Brock · Dinsmore & Shohl · http://www.dinslaw.com · 255 East Fifth Street, Suite 1900 · Cincinnati, OH 45202-3172 · 513-977-8200

Daniel E. Burke · Graydon, Head & Ritchey · 1900 Fifth Third Center · 511 Walnut Street · Cincinnati, OH 45202 · 513-621-6464

Mark J. Byrne · a · Jacobs, Kleiman, Seibel & McNally · Kroger Building, Suite 2300 · 1014 Vine Street · Cincinnati, OH 45202-1116 · 513-381-6600

Doreen Canton · a · Taft Stettinius & Hollister · http://www.taftlaw.com · 425 Walnut Street, Suite 1800 Cincinnati, OH 45202-3957 · 513-381-2838

David T. Croall · Porter, Wright, Morris & Arthur · http://www.porterwright.com · 250 East Fifth Street, Suite 2200 · Cincinnati, OH 45202-5118 · 513-381-4700

Deborah DeLong · Dinsmore & Shohl · http://www.dinslaw.com · 255 East Fifth Street, Suite 1900 · Cincinnati, OH 45202-3172 · 513-977-8200

Robert A. Dimling · Frost Brown Todd · http://www.frostbrowntodd.com · PNC Center, Suite 2200 · 201 East Fifth Street · Cincinnati, OH 45202-4182 · 513-651-6800

Paul D. Dorger · Keating Muething & Klekamp · http://www.kmklaw.com · One East Fourth Street, Suite 1400 · Cincinnati, OH 45202 · 513-579-6400

Randolph H. Freking · a · Freking & Betz · 525 Vine Street, Suite 600 · Cincinnati, OH 45202 · 513-721-1975

Alphonse A. Gerhardstein · a · Gerhardstein & Branch · 617 Vine Street, Suite 1409 · Cincinnati, OH 45202 · 513-621-9100

Cynthia L. Gibson · Katz, Teller, Brant & Hild · http://www.katzteller.com · 255 East Fifth Street, Suite 2400 · Cincinnati, OH 45202-4724 · 513-721-4532

Michael S. Glassman · Dinsmore & Shohl · http://www.dinslaw.com · 255 East Fifth Street, Suite 1900 · Cincinnati, OH 45202-3172 · 513-977-8200

Gary L. Greenberg · Denlinger, Rosenthal & Greenberg · http://www.drgfirm.com · 425 Walnut Street, Suite 2300 · Cincinnati, OH 45202-3918 · 513-621-3440

Michael W. Hawkins · 2) · Dinsmore & Shohl · http://www.dinslaw.com · 255 East Fifth Street, Suite 1900 · Cincinnati, OH 45202-3172 · 513-977-8200

James B. Helmer, Jr. · 2) · Helmer, Martins, Rice & Popham · 600 Vine Street, Suite 2704 · Cincinnati, OH 45202 · 513-421-2400

Robert A. Klingler · Robert A. Klingler · 525 Vine Street, Suite 2320 · Cincinnati, OH 45202 · 513-665-9500

James K. L. Lawrence · 2) · Frost Brown Todd · http://www.frostbrowntodd.com · PNC Center, Suite 2200 · 201 East Fifth Street · Cincinnati, OH 45202-4182 · 513-651-6800

Sorrell Logothetis · 2% · Cook Portune & Logothetis · 22 West Ninth Street · Cincinnati, OH 45202 · 513-721-0444

Mark E. Lutz · Denlinger, Rosenthal & Greenberg · http://www.drgfirm.com · 425 Walnut Street, Suite 2300 · Cincinnati, OH 45202-3918 · 513-621-3440

David S. Mann · Mann & Mann · 1900 Kroger Building · 1014 Vine Street · Cincinnati, OH 45202-1141 · 513-721-6266

Robert W. Maxwell II · a · Keating Muething & Klekamp · http://www.kmklaw.com · One East Fourth Street, Suite 1400 · Cincinnati, OH 45202 · 513-579-6400

Martin McHenry · Haverkamp, Rebold & Riehl · 5856 Glenway Avenue · Cincinnati, OH 45238-2007 · 513-922-3200

Marc D. Mezibov · 2) · Mezibov & Jenkins · 401 East Court Street, Suite 600 · Cincinnati, OH 45202 · 513-621-8800

David K. Montgomery · Keating Muething & Klekamp · http://www.kmklaw.com · One East Fourth Street, Suite 1400 · Cincinnati, OH 45202 · 513-579-6400

Kelly Mulloy Myers · Freking & Betz · 525 Vine Street, Suite 600 · Cincinnati, OH 45202 · 513-721-1975

Michael J. Newman · Dinsmore & Shohl · http://www.dinslaw.com · 255 East Fifth Street, Suite 1900 · Cincinnati, OH 45202-3172 · 513-977-8200

Robert B. Newman · a · Newman & Meeks · 215 East Ninth Street, Suite 650 · Cincinnati, OH 45202-2143 · 513-639-7000

David Hamilton Peck · Taft Stettinius & Hollister · http://www.taftlaw.com · 425 Walnut Street, Suite 1800 · Cincinnati, OH 45202-3957 · 513-381-2838

Bruce I. Petrie, Jr. · Graydon, Head & Ritchey · 1900 Fifth Third Center · 511 Walnut Street · Cincinnati, OH 45202 · 513-621-6464

Robert A. Pitcairn, Jr. · a · Katz, Teller, Brant & Hild · http://www.katzteller.com · 255 East Fifth Street, Suite 2400 · Cincinnati, OH 45202-4724 · 513-721-4532

Timothy P. Reilly · a · Taft Stettinius & Hollister · http://www.taftlaw.com · 425 Walnut Street, Suite 1800 · Cincinnati, OH 45202-3957 · 513-381-2838

James B. Robinson · a · Robinson Law Firm · http://www.jimrobinsonlaw.com · 119 Court Street, Suite 213 · Cincinnati, OH 45202 · 513-381-3525

Charles M. Roesch · Dinsmore & Shohl · http://www.dinslaw.com · 255 East Fifth Street, Suite 1900 · Cincinnati, OH 45202-3172 · 513-977-8200

Gregory Parker Rogers · Taft Stettinius & Hollister · http://www.taftlaw.com · 425 Walnut Street, Suite 1800 · Cincinnati, OH 45202-3957 · 513-381-2838

Daniel G. Rosenthal · a · Denlinger, Rosenthal & Greenberg · http://www.drgfirm.com · 425 Walnut Street, Suite 2300 · Cincinnati, OH 45202-3918 · 513-621-3440

Jerry S. Sallee · Dinsmore & Shohl · http://www.dinslaw.com · 255 East Fifth Street, Suite 1900 · Cincinnati, OH 45202-3172 · 513-977-8200

Jeffrey S. Shoskin · Frost Brown Todd · http://www.frostbrowntodd.com · PNC Center, Suite 2200 · 201 East Fifth Street · Cincinnati, OH 45202-4182 · 513-651-6800

David A. Skidmore, Jr. · Frost Brown Todd · http://www.frostbrowntodd.com · PNC Center, Suite 2200 · 201 East Fifth Street · Cincinnati, OH 45202-4182 · 513-651-6800

Sheila M. Smith · Freking & Betz · 525 Vine Street, Suite 600 · Cincinnati, OH 45202 · 513-721-1975

Keith P. Spiller · Thompson Hine · 312 Walnut Street, 14th Floor · Cincinnati, OH 45202-4089 · 513-352-6700

Mark J. Stepaniak · a · Taft Stettinius & Hollister · http://www.taftlaw.com · 425 Walnut Street, Suite 1800 · Cincinnati, OH 45202-3957 · 513-381-2838

Paul H. Tobias · a · Tobias, Kraus & Torchia · Mercantile Library Building, Suite 911 · 414 Walnut Street · Cincinnati, OH 45202 · 513-241-8137

David G. Torchia · a · Tobias, Kraus & Torchia · Mercantile Library Building, Suite 911 · 414 Walnut Street · Cincinnati, OH 45202 · 513-241-8137

George E. Yund · a · Frost Brown Todd · http://www.frostbrowntodd.com · PNC Center, Suite 2200 · 201 East Fifth Street · Cincinnati, OH 45202-4182 · 513-651-6800

Cleveland

Keith A. Ashmus · Frantz Ward · http://www.frantzward.com · Public Square, Suite 127 · 2500 Key Center · Cleveland, OH 44114-1230 · 216-515-1660

Elliot S. Azoff · Baker Hostetler · http://www.bakerlaw.com · National City Center, Suite 3200 · 1900 East Ninth Street · Cleveland, OH 44114-3485 · 216-621-0200

Thomas H. Barnard · a · Ogletree Deakins · http://www.ogletreedeakins.com · Key Tower, Suite 4130 · 127 Public Square · Cleveland, OH 44114 · 216-241-6100

Barbara Kaye Besser · Elfvin & Besser · 4070 Mayfield Road · Cleveland, OH 44121-3031 · 216-382-2500

John T. Billick · Littler Mendelson · 1100 Superior Avenue, 20th Floor · Cleveland, OH 44114 · 216-696-7600

Barton A. Bixenstine · Ogletree Deakins · http://www.ogletreedeakins.com · Key Tower, Suite 4130 · 127 Public Square · Cleveland, OH 44114 · 216-241-6100

Frank W. Buck · a · Littler Mendelson · 1100 Superior Avenue, 20th Floor · Cleveland, OH 44114 · 216-696-7600

Maynard A. Buck · Benesch, Friedlander, Coplan & Aronoff · BP Tower, Suite 2300 · 200 Public Square · Cleveland, OH 44114-2378 · 216-363-4500

T. Merritt Bumpass · Frantz Ward · http://www.frantzward.com · Public Square, Suite 127 · 2500 Key Center · Cleveland, OH 44114-1230 · 216-515-1660

Sue Marie Douglas · Littler Mendelson · 1100 Superior Avenue, 20th Floor · Cleveland, OH 44114 · 216-696-7600

Robert P. Duvin · 2% · Littler Mendelson · 1100 Superior Avenue, 20th Floor · Cleveland, OH 44114 · 216-696-7600

William D. Edwards · Ulmer & Berne · Skylight Office Tower, Suite 1100 · 1660 West Second Street · Cleveland, OH 44113-1448 · 216-583-7000

Bruce B. Elfvin · a · Elfvin & Besser · 4070 Mayfield Road · Cleveland, OH 44121-3031 · 216-382-2500

Michael J. Frantz · Frantz Ward · http://www.frantzward.com · Public Square, Suite 127 · 2500 Key Center · Cleveland, OH 44114-1230 · 216-515-1660

Wade M. Fricke · Ogletree Deakins · http://www.ogletreedeakins.com · Key Tower, Suite 4130 · 127 Public Square · Cleveland, OH 44114 · 216-241-6100

Amy S. Glesius · The Law Office of Amy S. Glesius · The Lorenzo Carter Building, Suite 310 · 1360 West Ninth Street · Cleveland, OH 44113 · 216-241-6882

Joyce Goldstein · a · Joyce Goldstein & Associates · The Leader Building, Suite 1040 · 526 Superior Avenue East · Cleveland, OH 44114-1401 · 216-771-6633

Caryn M. Groedel · Caryn Groedel & Associates · 5910 Landerbrook Drive, Suite 200 · Cleveland, OH 44124 · 440-544-1122

W. Michael Hanna · a · Squire Sanders · http://www.ssd.com · 4900 Key Tower · 127 Public Square · Cleveland, OH 44114-1304 · 216-479-8500

Susan C. Hastings · Squire Sanders · http://www.ssd.com · 4900 Key Tower · 127 Public Square · Cleveland, OH 44114-1304 · 216-479-8500

Lee J. Hutton · Littler Mendelson · 1100 Superior Avenue, 20th Floor · Cleveland, OH 44114 · 216-696-7600

Ronald H. Isroff · Ulmer & Berne · Skylight Office Tower, Suite 1100 · 1660 West Second Street · Cleveland, OH 44113-1448 · 216-583-7000

Mark D. Katz · Ulmer & Berne · Skylight Office Tower, Suite 1100 · 1660 West Second Street · Cleveland, OH 44113-1448 · 216-583-7000

Jack S. Kluznik · Weston Hurd · The Tower at Erieview, Suite 1900 · 1301 East Ninth Street · Cleveland, OH 44114-1862 · 216-241-6602

James D. Kurek · Millisor & Nobil · 9150 South Hills Boulevard, Suite 300 · Cleveland, OH 44147-3599 · 440-838-8800

Barbara J. Leukart · Jones Day · North Point · 901 Lakeside Avenue · Cleveland, OH 44114-1190 · 216-586-3939

Richard H. Leukart II · Baker Hostetler · http://www.bakerlaw.com · National City Center, Suite 3200 · 1900 East Ninth Street · Cleveland, OH 44114-3485 · 216-621-0200

John B. Lewis · a · Baker Hostetler · http://www.bakerlaw.com · National City Center, Suite 3200 · 1900 East Ninth Street · Cleveland, OH 44114-3485 · 216-621-0200

Stephen A. Markus · Ulmer & Berne · Skylight Office Tower, Suite 1100 · 1660 West Second Street · Cleveland, OH 44113-1448 · 216-583-7000

Eben O. McNair IV · Schwarzwald McNair & Fusco · Penton Media Building, Suite 616 · 1300 East Ninth Street · Cleveland, OH 44114-1503 · 216-566-1600

Gregory V. Mersol · Baker Hostetler · http://www.bakerlaw.com · National City Center, Suite 3200 · 1900 East Ninth Street · Cleveland, OH 44114-3485 · 216-621-0200

Andrew C. Meyer · Littler Mendelson · 1100 Superior Avenue, 20th Floor · Cleveland, OH 44114 · 216-696-7600

Kenneth R. Millisor · 2% · Millisor & Nobil · 9150 South Hills Boulevard, Suite 300 · Cleveland, OH 44147-3599 · 440-838-8800

David J. Millstone · a · Squire Sanders · http://www.ssd.com · 4900 Key Tower · 127 Public Square · Cleveland, OH 44114-1304 · 216-479-8500

Steven M. Moss · Taft Stettinius & Hollister · http://www.taftlaw.com · BP Tower, Suite 3500 · 200 Public Square · Cleveland, OH 44114-2302 · 216-241-2838

Steven M. Nobil · a · Millisor & Nobil · 9150 South Hills Boulevard, Suite 300 · Cleveland, OH 44147-3599 · 440-838-8800

Suellen Oswald · Littler Mendelson · 1100 Superior Avenue, 20th Floor · Cleveland, OH 44114 · 216-696-7600

Stanley Dan Pace · Ogletree Deakins · http://www.ogletreedeakins.com · Key Tower, Suite 4130 · 127 Public Square · Cleveland, OH 44114 · 216-241-6100

Richard T. Prasse · Hahn Loeser & Parks · BP Tower, Suite 2800 · 200 Public Square · Cleveland, OH 44114-2301 · 216-621-0150

James A. Rydzel · Jones Day · North Point · 901 Lakeside Avenue · Cleveland, OH 44114-1190 · 216-586-3939

David E. Schreiner · Millisor & Nobil · 9150 South Hills Boulevard, Suite 300 · Cleveland, OH 44147-3599 · 440-838-8800

Timothy J. Sheeran · Squire Sanders · http://www.ssd.com · 4900 Key Tower · 127 Public Square · Cleveland, OH 44114-1304 · 216-479-8500

Ellen S. Simon · a · The Simon Law Firm · 1717 Penton Media Building · 1300 East Ninth Street · Cleveland, OH 44114-1503 · 216-575-1002

Stephen C. Sutton · Baker Hostetler · http://www.bakerlaw.com · National City Center, Suite 3200 · 1900 East Ninth Street · Cleveland, OH 44114-3485 · 216-621-0200

Christopher P. Thorman · Thorman & Hardin-Levine · 1220 West Sixth Street, Suite 307 · Cleveland, OH 44113 · 216-621-9767

Robert Valerian · Taft Stettinius & Hollister · http://www.taftlaw.com · BP Tower, Suite 3500 · 200 Public Square · Cleveland, OH 44114-2302 · 216-241-2838

Daniel A. Ward · Frantz Ward · http://www.frantzward.com · Public Square, Suite 127 · 2500 Key Center · Cleveland, OH 44114-1230 · 216-515-1660

Robert M. Wolff · Littler Mendelson · 1100 Superior Avenue, 20th Floor · Cleveland, OH 44114 · 216-696-7600

Martin T. Wymer · Baker Hostetler · http://www.bakerlaw.com · National City Center, Suite 3200 · 1900 East Ninth Street · Cleveland, OH 44114-3485 · 216-621-0200

Columbus

Sandra J. Anderson · a · Vorys, Sater, Seymour and Pease · 52 East Gay Street · P.O. Box 1008 · Columbus, OH 43216-1008 · 614-464-6400

Gary S. Batke · Bailey Cavalieri · One Columbus Building, Suite 2100 · 10 West Broad Street · Columbus, OH 43215-3422 · 614-221-3155

G. Ross Bridgman · a · Vorys, Sater, Seymour and Pease · 52 East Gay Street · P.O. Box 1008 · Columbus, OH 43216-1008 · 614-464-6400

Wanda L. Carter · Moots, Carter & Hogan · 3600 Olentangy River Road, Building 501 · Columbus, OH 43214-3913 · 614-459-4140

D. Lewis Clark, Jr. · Squire Sanders · http://www.ssd.com · 1300 Huntington Center · 41 South High Street · Columbus, OH 43215-6197 · 614-365-2700

Frederick G. Cloppert, Jr. · a · Cloppert, Latanick, Sauter & Washburn · 225 East Broad Street · Columbus, OH 43215 · 614-564-0059

Susan A. Cohen · Vorys, Sater, Seymour and Pease · 52 East Gay Street · P.O. Box 1008 · Columbus, OH 43216-1008 · 614-464-6400

James E. Davidson · Schottenstein, Zox & Dunn · http://www.szd.com · 250 West Street, Suite 700 · Columbus, OH 43215-2538 · 614-462-2700

Susan M. DiMickele · Squire Sanders · http://www.ssd.com · 1300 Huntington Center · 41 South High Street · Columbus, OH 43215-6197 · 614-365-2700

Mary Ellen Fairfield · a · Vorys, Sater, Seymour and Pease · 52 East Gay Street · P.O. Box 1008 · Columbus, OH 43216-1008 · 614-464-6400

Lawrence F. Feheley · Kegler, Brown, Hill & Ritter · http://www.keglerbrown.com · Capitol Square, Suite 1800 · 65 East State Street · Columbus, OH 43215-4294 · 614-462-5400

Frederick M. Gittes · 2) · Fred Gittes · 723 Oak Street · Columbus, OH 43205 · 614-222-4735

N. Victor Goodman · 2% · Benesch, Friedlander, Coplan & Aronoff · 41 South High Street, Suite 2600 · Columbus, OH 43215 · 614-223-9300

Dennis D. Grant · 2) · Bailey Cavalieri · One Columbus Building, Suite 2100 · 10 West Broad Street · Columbus, OH 43215-3422 · 614-221-3155

Kevin E. Griffith · Porter, Wright, Morris & Arthur · http://www.porterwright.com · Huntington Center · 41 South High Street · Columbus, OH 43215-6194 · 614-227-2000

Robert K. Handelman · Barkan Neff Handelman Meizlish · 360 South Grant Avenue · P.O. Box 1989 · Columbus, OH 43216-1989 · 614-221-4221

David P. Hiller · Millisor & Nobil · 9150 South Hills Boulevard, Suite 300 · Columbus, OH 44147-3599 · 440-838-8800

Stewart R. Jaffy · a · Stewart Jaffy & Associates · 306 East Gay Street · Columbus, OH 43215-3247 · 614-228-6148

Donald R. Keller · Bricker & Eckler · http://www.bricker.com · 100 South Third Street · Columbus, OH 43215-4291 · 614-227-2300

G. Roger King · 2) · Jones Day · 325 John H. McConnell Boulevard, Suite 600 · P.O. Box 165017 · Columbus, OH 43216-5017 · 614-469-3939

Mark A. Knueve · Vorys, Sater, Seymour and Pease · 52 East Gay Street · P.O. Box 1008 · Columbus, OH 43216-1008 · 614-464-6400

Ronald G. Linville · a · Baker Hostetler · http://www.bakerlaw.com · Capitol Square, Suite 2100 · 65 East State Street · Columbus, OH 43215-4260 · 614-228-1541

John S. Marshall · a · Marshall and Morrow · http://www.marshallandmorrow.com · 111 West Rich Street, Suite 430 · Columbus, OH 43215-5296 · 614-463-9790

Alvin J. McKenna · 2) · Porter, Wright, Morris & Arthur · http://www.porterwright.com · Huntington Center · 41 South High Street · Columbus, OH 43215-6194 · 614-227-2000

Philip R. Moots · Moots, Carter & Hogan · 3600 Olentangy River Road, Building 501 · Columbus, OH 43214-3913 · 614-459-4140

William A. Nolan · Squire Sanders · http://www.ssd.com · 1300 Huntington Center · 41 South High Street Columbus, OH 43215-6197 · 614-365-2700

Jonathan M. Norman · Vorys, Sater, Seymour and Pease · 52 East Gay Street · P.O. Box 1008 · Columbus, OH 43216-1008 · 614-464-6400

Christopher J. North · Vorys, Sater, Seymour and Pease · 52 East Gay Street · P.O. Box 1008 · Columbus, OH 43216-1008 · 614-464-6400

Adele E. O'Conner · Porter, Wright, Morris & Arthur · http://www.porterwright.com · Huntington Center 41 South High Street · Columbus, OH 43215-6194 · 614-227-2000

Susan Porter · Schottenstein, Zox & Dunn · http://www.szd.com · 250 West Street, Suite 700 · Columbus, OH 43215-2538 · 614-462-2700

Fred G. Pressley, Jr. · Porter, Wright, Morris & Arthur · http://www.porterwright.com · Huntington Center · 41 South High Street · Columbus, OH 43215-6194 · 614-227-2000

Diane C. Reichwein · Porter, Wright, Morris & Arthur · http://www.porterwright.com · Huntington Center · 41 South High Street · Columbus, OH 43215-6194 · 614-227-2000

Suzanne K. Richards · Vorys, Sater, Seymour and Pease · 52 East Gay Street · P.O. Box 1008 · Columbus, OH 43216-1008 · 614-464-6400

Roger L. Sabo · a · Schottenstein, Zox & Dunn · http://www.szd.com · 250 West Street, Suite 700 · Columbus, OH 43215-2538 · 614-462-2700

Robert W. Sauter · a · Cloppert, Latanick, Sauter & Washburn · 225 East Broad Street · Columbus, OH 43215 · 614-564-0059

Gregory B. Scott · Scott, Scriven & Wahoff · 50 West Broad Street, Suite 2500 · Columbus, OH 43215 · 614-222-8686

Bradd N. Siegel · 2) · Porter, Wright, Morris & Arthur · http://www.porterwright.com · Huntington Center 41 South High Street · Columbus, OH 43215-6194 · 614-227-2000

Andrew C. Smith · Vorys, Sater, Seymour and Pease · 52 East Gay Street · P.O. Box 1008 · Columbus, OH 43216-1008 · 614-464-6400

Alexander M. Spater · 2) · Alexander M. Spater · 360 South Grant Avenue · Columbus, OH 43215 · 614-222-4734

Elizabeth M. Stanton · Chester Willcox & Saxbe · http://www.cwslaw.com · 65 East State Street, Suite 1000 · Columbus, OH 43215 · 614-221-4000

Mark S. Stemm · Porter, Wright, Morris & Arthur · http://www.porterwright.com · Huntington Center · 41 South High Street · Columbus, OH 43215-6194 · 614-227-2000

John M. Stephen · Porter, Wright, Morris & Arthur · http://www.porterwright.com · Huntington Center · 41 South High Street · Columbus, OH 43215-6194 · 614-227-2000

Betsy A. Swift · Bricker & Eckler · http://www.bricker.com · 100 South Third Street · Columbus, OH 43215-4291 · 614-227-2300

Thomas Tarpy · Vorys, Sater, Seymour and Pease · 52 East Gay Street · P.O. Box 1008 · Columbus, OH 43216-1008 · 614-464-6400

Mark D. Tucker · Benesch, Friedlander, Coplan & Aronoff · 41 South High Street, Suite 2600 · Columbus, OH 43215 · 614-223-9300

Michael J. Underwood · Porter, Wright, Morris & Arthur · http://www.porterwright.com · Huntington Center · 41 South High Street · Columbus, OH 43215-6194 · 614-227-2000

Felix C. Wade · Schottenstein, Zox & Dunn · http://www.szd.com · 250 West Street, Suite 700 · Columbus, OH 43215-2538 · 614-462-2700

Charles C. Warner · a · Porter, Wright, Morris & Arthur · http://www.porterwright.com · Huntington Center · 41 South High Street · Columbus, OH 43215-6194 · 614-227-2000

Robert D. Weisman · Schottenstein, Zox & Dunn · http://www.szd.com · 250 West Street, Suite 700 · Columbus, OH 43215-2538 · 614-462-2700

Thomas V. Williams · Frost Brown Todd · http://www.frostbrowntodd.com · One Columbus, Suite 2300 · 10 West Broad Street · Columbus, OH 43215-3467 · 614-464-1211

Dayton

Robert J. Brown · 2) · Thompson Hine · 2000 Courthouse Plaza, NE · 10 West Second Street · P.O. Box 8801 · Dayton, OH 45401-8801 · 937-443-6600

Karen T. Dunlevey · Bieser, Greer & Landis · http://www.biesergreer.com · National City Center, Suite 400 · Six North Main Street · Dayton, OH 45402-1908 · 937-223-3277

Marc L. Fleishauer · Porter, Wright, Morris & Arthur · http://www.porterwright.com · One Dayton Centre, Suite 1600 · One South Main Street · Dayton, OH 45402-2028 · 937-449-6810

Julie C. Ford · Doll, Jansen & Ford · 111 West First Street, Suite 1100 · Dayton, OH 45402 · 937-461-5310

Teresa D. Jones · Thompson Hine · 2000 Courthouse Plaza, NE · 10 West Second Street · P.O. Box 8801 Dayton, OH 45401-8801 · 937-443-6600

C. Mark Kingseed · Coolidge Wall Co. · http://www.coollaw.com · 33 West First Street, Suite 600 · Dayton, OH 45402 · 937-223-8177

Jeffrey A. Mullins · Taft Stettinius & Hollister · http://www.taftlaw.com · Fifth Third Center, Suite 900 · 110 North Main Street · Dayton, OH 45402-1786 · 937-228-2838

Jeffrey M. Silverstein · Jeffrey M. Silverstein and Associates · 627 South Edwin C. Moses Boulevard, Suite 2-C · Dayton, OH 45408 · 937-228-3731

Thomas P. Whelley II · Dinsmore & Shohl · http://www.dinslaw.com · Courthouse Plaza, SW, Suite 1100 10 North Ludlow Street · Dayton, OH 45402 · 937-449-2800

Reynoldsburg

Leonard S. Sigall · 2) · The Law Offices of Leonard S. Sigall · 6470 East Main Street · Reynoldsburg, OH 43068-2349 · 614-866-4025

Toledo

Joseph J. Allotta · Allotta, Farley & Woodman · 2222 Centennial Road · Toledo, OH 43617 · 419-535-0075

Paul T. Belazis · Paul T. Belazis · 1822 Cherry Street · Toledo, OH 43608-2801 · 419-241-2200

R. Kevin Greenfield · Franklin & Greenfield · 420 Madison Avenue, Suite 1101 · Toledo, OH 43604 · 419-243-9005

Justice G. Johnson, Jr. · 2) · Marshall & Melhorn · Four Seagate, Eighth Floor · Toledo, OH 43604 · 419-249-7100

Patrick J. Johnson · 2) · Eastman & Smith · One Seagate, 24th Floor · P.O. Box 10032 · Toledo, OH 43699-0032 · 419-241-6000

John T. Landwehr · a · Eastman & Smith · One Seagate, 24th Floor · P.O. Box 10032 · Toledo, OH 43699-0032 · 419-241-6000

Margaret J. Lockhart · Cooper & Walinski · 900 Adams Street · Toledo, OH 43604 · 419-241-1200

C. Thomas McCarter · a · C. Thomas McCarter · 421 North Michigan Street, Suite D · Toledo, OH 43624-1606 · 419-255-9100

Timothy C. McCarthy · a · Shumaker, Loop & Kendrick · North Courthouse Square · 1000 Jackson Street · Toledo, OH 43604-5573 · 419-241-9000

Donald M. Mewhort, Jr. · 2% · Shumaker, Loop & Kendrick · North Courthouse Square · 1000 Jackson Street · Toledo, OH 43604-5573 · 419-241-9000

Stephen J. Stanford · Robison, Curphey & O'Connell · Four Seagate, Ninth Floor · Toledo, OH 43604 · 419-249-7900

Joan M. Torzewski · a · Harris · Reny · Torzewski · Two Maritime Plaza, Third Floor · Toledo, OH 43604-1803 · 419-243-1105

LAND USE & ZONING LAW

Beachwood

Sheldon Berns · a · Berns, Ockner & Greenberger · 3733 Park East Drive, Suite 200 · Beachwood, OH 44122-4334 · 216-831-8838

Cincinnati

C. Francis Barrett · Barrett & Weber · Fourth & Walnut Centre, Suite 500 · 105 East Fourth Street · Cincinnati, OH 45202-4015 · 513-721-2120

Timothy M. Burke · Manley Burke · 225 West Court Street · Cincinnati, OH 45202 · 513-721-5525

Gary E. Powell · Gary E. Powell · 1014 Vine Street, Suite 1919 · Cincinnati, OH 45202-1116 · 513-608-6225

Richard B. Tranter · Dinsmore & Shohl · http://www.dinslaw.com · 255 East Fifth Street, Suite 1900 · Cincinnati, OH 45202-3172 · 513-977-8200

Joseph L. Trauth, Jr. · Keating Muething & Klekamp · http://www.kmklaw.com · One East Fourth Street, Suite 1400 · Cincinnati, OH 45202 · 513-579-6400

Cleveland

Thomas A. Mason · 2% · Thompson Hine · Key Center, Suite 3900 · 127 Public Square · Cleveland, OH 44114-1291 · 216-566-5500

Richard C. Brahm · Plank & Brahm · 145 East Rich Street, Suite 400 · Columbus, OH 42315-5240 · 614-228-4546

Jeffrey L. Brown · Smith & Hale · 37 West Broad Street, Suite 725 · Columbus, OH 43215-4199 · 614-221-4255

Glen A. Dugger · Smith & Hale · 37 West Broad Street, Suite 725 · Columbus, OH 43215-4199 · 614-221-4255

Ben W. Hale · Smith & Hale · 37 West Broad Street, Suite 725 · Columbus, OH 43215-4199 · 614-221-4255

Richard L. Loveland · 2) · Loveland & Brosius · 50 West Broad Street, Suite 3300 · Columbus, OH 43215-5917 · 614-464-3563

J. Jeffrey McNealey · 2) · Porter, Wright, Morris & Arthur · http://www.porterwright.com · Huntington Center · 41 South High Street · Columbus, OH 43215-6194 · 614-227-2000

Robert A. Meyer, Jr. · Porter, Wright, Morris & Arthur · http://www.porterwright.com · Huntington Center · 41 South High Street · Columbus, OH 43215-6194 · 614-227-2000

Daniel H. Schoedinger · Vorys, Sater, Seymour and Pease · 52 East Gay Street · P.O. Box 1008 · Columbus, OH 43216-1008 · 614-464-6400

Elizabeth M. Stanton · Chester Willcox & Saxbe · http://www.cwslaw.com · 65 East State Street, Suite 1000 · Columbus, OH 43215 · 614-221-4000

Jill S. Tangeman · Vorys, Sater, Seymour and Pease · 52 East Gay Street · P.O. Box 1008 · Columbus, OH 43216-1008 · 614-464-6400

Dayton

John C. Chambers · a · Coolidge Wall Co. · http://www.coollaw.com · 33 West First Street, Suite 600 · Dayton, OH 45402 · 937-223-8177

Barry W. Mancz · Rogers & Greenberg · Kettering Tower, Suite 2160 · Dayton, OH 45423 · 937-223-8171

Toledo

Jerome R. Parker · 2) · Gressley, Kaplin & Parker · One SeaGate, Suite 1645 · Toledo, OH 43604-1584 · 419-244-8336

Joseph A. Rideout · 2) · Shumaker, Loop & Kendrick · North Courthouse Square · 1000 Jackson Street · Toledo, OH 43604-5573 · 419-241-9000

Mark H. Rose · Marshall & Melhorn · Four Seagate, Eighth Floor · Toledo, OH 43604 · 419-249-7100

Barton L. Wagenman · 2% · Shumaker, Loop & Kendrick · North Courthouse Square · 1000 Jackson Street · Toledo, OH 43604-5573 · 419-241-9000

LEGAL MALPRACTICE LAW

Cleveland

Harry D. Cornett, Jr. · a · Tucker Ellis & West · Huntington Building, Suite 1150 · 925 Euclid Avenue · Cleveland, OH 44115-1475 · 216-592-5000

Murray K. Lenson · Ulmer & Berne · Skylight Office Tower, Suite 1100 · 1660 West Second Street · Cleveland, OH 44113-1448 · 216-583-7000

William A. Meadows · Reminger Attorneys At Law · 1400 Midland Building · 101 Prospect Avenue West Cleveland, OH 44115-1093 · 216-687-1311

Ronald A. Rispo · Weston Hurd · The Tower at Erieview, Suite 1900 · 1301 East Ninth Street · Cleveland, OH 44114-1862 · 216-241-6602

Jason Winter · Janik Dorman & Winter · http://www.janiklaw.com · 9200 South Hills Boulevard, Suite 300 · Cleveland, OH 44147-3521 · 440-838-7600

Columbus

Timothy J. Boone · Timothy J. Boone · 1349 East Broad Street, Second Floor · Columbus, OH 43205-1503 · 614-228-0200

Marion H. Little, Jr. · Zeiger, Tigges & Little · http://www.litohio.com · Huntington Center, Suite 3500 · 41 South High Street · Columbus, OH 43215 · 614-365-9900

Geoffrey Stern · Kegler, Brown, Hill & Ritter · http://www.keglerbrown.com · Capitol Square, Suite 1800 65 East State Street · Columbus, OH 43215-4294 · 614-462-5400

Gerald J. Todaro · a · Arnold, Todaro & Welch · 2075 Marble Cliff Office Park · Columbus, OH 43215-1053 · 614-485-1800

Dayton

Neil F. Freund · a · Freund, Freeze & Arnold · One Dayton Centre, Suite 1800 · One South Main Street Dayton, OH 45402-2017 · 937-222-2424

LEVERAGED BUYOUTS AND PRIVATE EQUITY LAW

Cincinnati

Paul R. Mattingly · Dinsmore & Shohl · http://www.dinslaw.com · 255 East Fifth Street, Suite 1900 · Cincinnati, OH 45202-3172 · 513-977-8200

Clifford A. Roe, Jr. · 2) · Dinsmore & Shohl · http://www.dinslaw.com · 255 East Fifth Street, Suite 1900 Cincinnati, OH 45202-3172 · 513-977-8200

George H. Vincent · Dinsmore & Shohl · http://www.dinslaw.com · 255 East Fifth Street, Suite 1900 · Cincinnati, OH 45202-3172 · 513-977-8200

Cleveland

Daniel G. Berick · Squire Sanders · http://www.ssd.com · 4900 Key Tower · 127 Public Square · Cleveland, OH 44114-1304 · 216-479-8500

Craig R. Martahus · a · Thompson Hine · Key Center, Suite 3900 · 127 Public Square · Cleveland, OH 44114-1291 · 216-566-5500

MARITIME LAW

Cleveland

Henry E. Billingsley II · Tucker Ellis & West · Huntington Building, Suite 1150 · 925 Euclid Avenue · Cleveland, OH 44115-1475 · 216-592-5000

Richard C. Binzley · a · Thompson Hine · Key Center, Suite 3900 · 127 Public Square · Cleveland, OH 44114-1291 · 216-566-5500

Julia R. Brouhard · Ray, Robinson, Carle & Davies · 1717 East Ninth Street, Suite 1650 · Cleveland, OH 44114-2878 · 216-861-4533

David G. Davies · 2) · Ray, Robinson, Carle & Davies · 1717 East Ninth Street, Suite 1650 · Cleveland, OH 44114-2878 · 216-861-4533

Gene B. George · Ray, Robinson, Carle & Davies · 1717 East Ninth Street, Suite 1650 · Cleveland, OH 44114-2878 · 216-861-4533

Harold W. Henderson · Thompson Hine · Key Center, Suite 3900 · 127 Public Square · Cleveland, OH 44114-1291 · 216-566-5500

MASS TORT LITIGATION

Akron

Susan S. Box · Roetzel & Andress · http://www.ralaw.com · 222 South Main Street · Akron, OH 44308-2098 · 330-376-2700

Ronald B. Lee · Roetzel & Andress · http://www.ralaw.com · 222 South Main Street · Akron, OH 44308-2098 · 330-376-2700

Cincinnati

Stanley M. Chesley · 2) · Waite, Schneider, Bayless & Chesley · 1513 Fourth and Vine Tower · Cincinnati, OH 45202 · 513-621-0267

James A. Comodeca · Dinsmore & Shohl · http://www.dinslaw.com · 255 East Fifth Street, Suite 1900 · Cincinnati, OH 45202-3172 · 513-977-8200

K.C. Green · Dinsmore & Shohl · http://www.dinslaw.com · 255 East Fifth Street, Suite 1900 · Cincinnati, OH 45202-3172 · 513-977-8200

Jack B. Harrison · Frost Brown Todd · http://www.frostbrowntodd.com · PNC Center, Suite 2200 · 201 East Fifth Street · Cincinnati, OH 45202-4182 · 513-651-6800

M. Gabrielle Hils · Dinsmore & Shohl · http://www.dinslaw.com · 255 East Fifth Street, Suite 1900 · Cincinnati, OH 45202-3172 · 513-977-8200

Richard S. Wayne · Strauss & Troy · http://www.strausstroy.com · The Federal Reserve Building · 150 East Fourth Street · Cincinnati, OH 45202-4018 · 513-621-2120

Frank C. Woodside III · a · Dinsmore & Shohl · http://www.dinslaw.com · 255 East Fifth Street, Suite 1900 · Cincinnati, OH 45202-3172 · 513-977-8200

Cleveland

Thomas E. Dover · Gallagher Sharp Attorneys · Bulkley Building, Sixth Floor · 1501 Euclid Avenue · Cleveland, OH 44115 · 216-241-5310

S. Stuart Eilers · Thompson Hine · Key Center, Suite 3900 · 127 Public Square · Cleveland, OH 44114-1291 · 216-566-5500

Elizabeth B. Wright · Thompson Hine · Key Center, Suite 3900 · 127 Public Square · Cleveland, OH 44114-1291 · 216-566-5500

MEDIA LAW

Cincinnati

Susan Grogan Faller · a · Frost Brown Todd · http://www.frostbrowntodd.com · PNC Center, Suite 2200 201 East Fifth Street · Cincinnati, OH 45202-4182 · 513-651-6800

Richard M. Goehler · a · Frost Brown Todd · http://www.frostbrowntodd.com · PNC Center, Suite 2200 201 East Fifth Street · Cincinnati, OH 45202-4182 · 513-651-6800

Jill P. Meyer · Frost Brown Todd · http://www.frostbrowntodd.com · PNC Center, Suite 2200 · 201 East Fifth Street · Cincinnati, OH 45202-4182 · 513-651-6800

Cleveland

David L. Marburger · a · Baker Hostetler · http://www.bakerlaw.com · National City Center, Suite 3200 · 1900 East Ninth Street · Cleveland, OH 44114-3485 · 216-621-0200

Columbus

Marion H. Little, Jr. · Zeiger, Tigges & Little · http://www.litohio.com · Huntington Center, Suite 3500 · 41 South High Street · Columbus, OH 43215 · 614-365-9900

Toledo

Frederick Byers · a · Fritz Byers · The Spitzer Building, Suite 824 · 520 Madison Avenue · Toledo, OH 43604-1343 · 419-241-8013

MEDICAL MALPRACTICE LAW

Akron

David M. Best · David M. Best Co. · 4900 West Bath Road · Akron, OH 44333 · 330-665-1855

Kevin P. Hardman · Hill Hardman Oldfield · http://www.hillhardmanoldfield.com · One Cascade Plaza, Suite 2000 · Akron, OH 44308 · 330-253-4000

Michael J. Hudak · Roetzel & Andress · http://www.ralaw.com · 222 South Main Street · Akron, OH 44308-2098 · 330-376-2700

Gregory T. Rossi · Hanna, Campbell & Powell · 3737 Embassy Parkway, Suite 100 · P.O. Box 5521 · Akron, OH 44334 · 330-670-7300

Jeffrey E. Schobert · Hanna, Campbell & Powell · 3737 Embassy Parkway, Suite 100 · P.O. Box 5521 · Akron, OH 44334 · 330-670-7300

Thomas A. Treadon · Roetzel & Andress · http://www.ralaw.com · 222 South Main Street · Akron, OH 44308-2098 · 330-376-2700

Canton

Stephen P. Griffin · Buckingham, Doolittle & Burroughs · http://www.bdblaw.com · 4518 Fulton Drive, NW · P.O. Box 35548 · Canton, OH 44735-5548 · 330-492-8717

Brian R. Wilson · Nicodemo & Wilson · 124 Fifteenth Street, NW · Canton, OH 44703-3208 · 330-452-8832

Cincinnati

James A. Comodeca · Dinsmore & Shohl · http://www.dinslaw.com · 255 East Fifth Street, Suite 1900 · Cincinnati, OH 45202-3172 · 513-977-8200

John D. Holschuh, Jr. · a · Santen & Hughes · 600 Vine Street, Suite 2700 · Cincinnati, OH 45202 · 513-721-4450

David S. Lockemeyer · Triona, Calderhead & Lockemeyer · The Adam Riddle House · 2021 Auburn Avenue · Cincinnati, OH 45219 · 513-576-1060

James H. Scheper · Shea & Associates · Chiquita Center, Suite 444 · 250 East Fifth Street · Cincinnati, OH 45202-4119 · 513-621-8333

Joseph W. Shea III · a · Shea & Associates · Chiquita Center, Suite 444 · 250 East Fifth Street · Cincinnati, OH 45202-4119 · 513-621-8333

James P. Triona · Triona, Calderhead & Lockemeyer · The Adam Riddle House · 2021 Auburn Avenue · Cincinnati, OH 45219 · 513-576-1060

Frank C. Woodside III · a · Dinsmore & Shohl · http://www.dinslaw.com · 255 East Fifth Street, Suite 1900 · Cincinnati, OH 45202-3172 · 513-977-8200

Cleveland

Richard J. Berris · Weisman, Kennedy & Berris · Midland Building, Suite 1600 · 101 West Prospect Avenue · Cleveland, OH 44115 · 216-781-1111

William D. Bonezzi · Bonezzi Switzer Murphy Polito & Hupp · http://www.bsmph.com · 1300 East Ninth Street, Suite 1950 · Cleveland, OH 44114-1501 · 216-875-2767

Anna M. Carulas · Roetzel & Andress · http://www.ralaw.com · One Cleveland Center, Ninth Floor · 1375 East Ninth Street · Cleveland, OH 44114 · 216-623-0150

William Martin Greene · a · Greene & Eisen · 1300 East Ninth Street, Suite 1801 · Cleveland, OH 44114 · 216-687-0900

William Hawal · Spangenberg, Shibley & Liber · 1900 East Ninth Street, Suite 2400 · Cleveland, OH 44114-3400 · 216-696-3232

R. Mark Jones · Roetzel & Andress · http://www.ralaw.com · One Cleveland Center, Ninth Floor · 1375 East Ninth Street · Cleveland, OH 44114 · 216-623-0150

R. Eric Kennedy · 2) · Weisman, Kennedy & Berris · Midland Building, Suite 1600 · 101 West Prospect Avenue · Cleveland, OH 44115 · 216-781-1111

Andrew P. Krembs · Andrew P. Krembs & Associates · 55 Public Square, Suite 1700 · Cleveland, OH 44113-1021 · 216-875-7500

John A. Lancione, Jr. · Lancione & Lancione · 200 Public Square, Suite 2955 · Cleveland, OH 44114 · 216-623-4949

John G. Lancione · a · Lancione & Lancione · 200 Public Square, Suite 2955 · Cleveland, OH 44114 · 216-623-4949

Dennis R. Lansdowne · Spangenberg, Shibley & Liber · 1900 East Ninth Street, Suite 2400 · Cleveland, OH 44114-3400 · 216-696-3232

William A. Meadows · Reminger Attorneys At Law · 1400 Midland Building · 101 Prospect Avenue West Cleveland, OH 44115-1093 · 216-687-1311

Christopher M. Mellino · Mellino Law Firm · 200 Public Square, Suite 2900 · Cleveland, OH 44113 · 216-241-1901

J. Michael Monteleone · a · Jeffries, Kube, Forrest & Monteleone · Midland Building, Suite 1650 · 101 Prospect Avenue West · Cleveland, OH 44115-1027 · 216-771-4050

Patrick J. Murphy · Bonezzi Switzer Murphy Polito & Hupp · http://www.bsmph.com · 1300 East Ninth Street, Suite 1950 · Cleveland, OH 44114-1501 · 216-875-2767

John S. Polito · Bonezzi Switzer Murphy Polito & Hupp · http://www.bsmph.com · 1300 East Ninth Street, Suite 1950 · Cleveland, OH 44114-1501 · 216-875-2767

Dirk E. Riemenschneider · Buckingham, Doolittle & Burroughs · http://www.bdblaw.com · 1375 East Ninth Street, Suite 1700 · Cleveland, OH 44114 · 216-621-5300

Kent B. Schneider · a · Hermann, Cahn & Schneider · http://www.hcsattys.com · 1301 East Ninth Street, Suite 500 · Cleveland, OH 44114 · 216-781-5515

Donald H. Switzer · Bonezzi Switzer Murphy Polito & Hupp · http://www.bsmph.com · 1300 East Ninth Street, Suite 1950 · Cleveland, OH 44114-1501 · 216-875-2767

Robert C. Tucker · Tucker Ellis & West · Huntington Building, Suite 1150 · 925 Euclid Avenue · Cleveland, OH 44115-1475 · 216-592-5000

Stephen E. Walters · a · Reminger Attorneys At Law · 1400 Midland Building · 101 Prospect Avenue West · Cleveland, OH 44115-1093 · 216-687-1311

Peter H. Weinberger · Spangenberg, Shibley & Liber · 1900 East Ninth Street, Suite 2400 · Cleveland, OH 44114-3400 · 216-696-3232

Columbus

John F. Birath, Jr. · Bricker & Eckler · http://www.bricker.com · 100 South Third Street · Columbus, OH 43215-4291 · 614-227-2300

Thomas A. Dillon · Roetzel & Andress · http://www.ralaw.com · National City Plaza, 12th Floor · 155 East Broad Street · Columbus, OH 43215 · 614-723-2002

Gregory B. Foliano · Arnold, Todaro & Welch · 2075 Marble Cliff Office Park · Columbus, OH 43215-1053 · 614-485-1800

Robert E. Hanson · Scherner, Hanson & Cornwell · 130 Northwoods Boulevard · Columbus, OH 43215 · 614-431-7200

James S. Oliphant · 2) · Porter, Wright, Morris & Arthur · http://www.porterwright.com · Huntington Center · 41 South High Street · Columbus, OH 43215-6194 · 614-227-2000

Alan T. Radnor · 2) · Vorys, Sater, Seymour and Pease · 52 East Gay Street · P.O. Box 1008 · Columbus, OH 43216-1008 · 614-464-6400

Gregory D. Rankin · Lane, Alton & Horst · Two Miranova Place, Suite 500 · Columbus, OH 43215-7052 614-228-6885

Michael Romanello · a · Reminger Attorneys At Law · Capitol Square Office Building, Fourth Floor · 65 East State Street · Columbus, OH 43215 · 614-228-1311

Michael J. Rourke · a · Rourke & Blumenthal · 495 South High Street, Suite 450 · Columbus, OH 43215 · 614-220-9200

Hans Scherner · 2) · Scherner, Hanson & Cornwell · 130 Northwoods Boulevard · Columbus, OH 43215 · 614-431-7200

Mark L. Schumacher · Freund, Freeze & Arnold · Capitol Square Office Building, Suite 800 · 65 East State Street · Columbus, OH 43215 · 614-827-7300

Maryellen C. Spirito · Arnold, Todaro & Welch · 2075 Marble Cliff Office Park · Columbus, OH 43215-1053 · 614-485-1800

Richard D. Topper · Richard D. Topper · 5132 Olentangy River Road · Columbus, OH 43235 · 614-442-5784

Daniel R. Volkema · Volkema Thomas · 140 East Town Street, Suite 1100 · Columbus, OH 43215 · 614-221-4400

Marilena R. Walters · Dinsmore & Shohl · http://www.dinslaw.com · 191 West Nationwide Boulevard, Suite 300 · Columbus, OH 43215 · 614-221-8448

Dayton

Susan Blasik-Miller · Freund, Freeze & Arnold · One Dayton Centre, Suite 1800 · One South Main Street · Dayton, OH 45402-2017 · 937-222-2424

Neil F. Freund · a · Freund, Freeze & Arnold · One Dayton Centre, Suite 1800 · One South Main Street Dayton, OH 45402-2017 · 937-222-2424

Gregory C. Gibson · Gibson & O'Keefe · 40 North Main Street, Suite 2810 · Dayton, OH 45423 · 937-643-0600

John F. Haviland, Jr. · Bieser, Greer & Landis · http://www.biesergreer.com · National City Center, Suite 400 · Six North Main Street · Dayton, OH 45402-1908 · 937-223-3277

Howard Penn Krisher II · a · Bieser, Greer & Landis · http://www.biesergreer.com · National City Center, Suite 400 · Six North Main Street · Dayton, OH 45402-1908 · 937-223-3277

John B. Welch · Arnold, Todaro & Welch · 580 Lincoln Park Boulevard, Suite 222 · Dayton, OH 45429 · 937-296-1600

Toledo

Elizabeth E. Baer · Marshall & Melhorn · Four Seagate, Eighth Floor · Toledo, OH 43604 · 419-249-7100

John C. Barron · Shumaker, Loop & Kendrick · North Courthouse Square · 1000 Jackson Street · Toledo, OH 43604-5573 · 419-241-9000

Steven P. Collier · a · Connelly, Jackson & Collier · 405 Madison Avenue, Suite 1600 · Toledo, OH 43604 · 419-243-2100

Jay Harris · a · Harris · Reny · Torzewski · Two Maritime Plaza, Third Floor · Toledo, OH 43604-1803 · 419-243-1105

E. Thomas Maguire · a · Robison, Curphey & O'Connell · Four Seagate, Ninth Floor · Toledo, OH 43604 · 419-249-7900

Warren

Charles L. Richards · a · Law Office of Charles L. Richards · 8600 East Market Street, Suite One · Warren, OH 44484-2375 · 330-373-1000

Martin F. White · Martin F. White Co. · 156 Park Avenue, NE · P.O. Box 1150 · Warren, OH 44481-1218 330-394-9692

Youngstown

Thomas J. Wilson · a · Comstock, Springer & Wilson · 100 Federal Plaza East, Suite 926 · Youngstown, OH 44503 · 330-746-5643

Zanesville

Michael J. Micheli · Micheli, Baldwin, Northrup · 3808 James Court, Suite Two · P.O. Box 788 · Zanesville, OH 43702 · 740-454-2545

MERGERS & ACQUISITIONS LAW

Akron

Craig S. Marshall · Buckingham, Doolittle & Burroughs · http://www.bdblaw.com · 3800 Embassy Parkway, Suite 300 · P.O. Box 1500 · Akron, OH 44309-1500 · 330-376-5300

Canton

Randall C. Hunt · Krugliak, Wilkins, Griffiths & Dougherty · http://www.kwgd.com · 4775 Munson Street, NW · P.O. Box 36963 · Canton, OH 44735-6963 · 330-497-0700

Daniel A. Minkler · Day Ketterer · Millennium Centre, Suite 300 · 200 Market Avenue North · P.O. Box 24213 · Canton, OH 44701-4213 · 330-455-0173

Terry A. Moore · Krugliak, Wilkins, Griffiths & Dougherty · http://www.kwgd.com · 4775 Munson Street, NW · P.O. Box 36963 · Canton, OH 44735-6963 · 330-497-0700

Bruce M. Soares · Black, McCuskey, Souers & Arbaugh · 220 Market Avenue South, Suite 1000 · Canton, OH 44702 · 330-456-8341

John M. Tucker · Krugliak, Wilkins, Griffiths & Dougherty · http://www.kwgd.com · 4775 Munson Street, NW · P.O. Box 36963 · Canton, OH 44735-6963 · 330-497-0700

Cincinnati

Gerald S. Greenberg · Taft Stettinius & Hollister · http://www.taftlaw.com · 425 Walnut Street, Suite 1800 · Cincinnati, OH 45202-3957 · 513-381-2838

Theodore D. Grosser · Porter, Wright, Morris & Arthur · http://www.porterwright.com · 250 East Fifth Street, Suite 2200 · Cincinnati, OH 45202-5118 · 513-381-4700

Michael A. Hirschfeld · a · Graydon, Head & Ritchey · 1900 Fifth Third Center · 511 Walnut Street · Cincinnati, OH 45202 · 513-621-6464

Mark J. Jahnke · a · Katz, Teller, Brant & Hild · http://www.katzteller.com · 255 East Fifth Street, Suite 2400 · Cincinnati, OH 45202-4724 · 513-721-4532

Gary P. Kreider · 2) · Keating Muething & Klekamp · http://www.kmklaw.com · One East Fourth Street, Suite 1400 · Cincinnati, OH 45202 · 513-579-6400

Clifford A. Roe, Jr. · 2) · Dinsmore & Shohl · http://www.dinslaw.com · 255 East Fifth Street, Suite 1900 Cincinnati, OH 45202-3172 · 513-977-8200

Edward E. Steiner · Keating Muething & Klekamp · http://www.kmklaw.com · One East Fourth Street, Suite 1400 · Cincinnati, OH 45202 · 513-579-6400

George H. Vincent · Dinsmore & Shohl · http://www.dinslaw.com · 255 East Fifth Street, Suite 1900 · Cincinnati, OH 45202-3172 · 513-977-8200

Susan B. Zaunbrecher · Dinsmore & Shohl · http://www.dinslaw.com · 255 East Fifth Street, Suite 1900 · Cincinnati, OH 45202-3172 · 513-977-8200

Cleveland

Daniel G. Berick · Squire Sanders · http://www.ssd.com · 4900 Key Tower · 127 Public Square · Cleveland, OH 44114-1304 · 216-479-8500

James R. Carlson · a · Thompson Hine · Key Center, Suite 3900 · 127 Public Square · Cleveland, OH 44114-1291 · 216-566-5500

Stephen C. Ellis · a · Tucker Ellis & West · Huntington Building, Suite 1150 · 925 Euclid Avenue · Cleveland, OH 44115-1475 · 216-592-5000

Lyle G. Ganske · Jones Day · North Point · 901 Lakeside Avenue · Cleveland, OH 44114-1190 · 216-586-3939

Allan Goldner · Benesch, Friedlander, Coplan & Aronoff · BP Tower, Suite 2300 · 200 Public Square · Cleveland, OH 44114-2378 · 216-363-4500

Mary Ann Jorgenson · a · Squire Sanders · http://www.ssd.com · 4900 Key Tower · 127 Public Square · Cleveland, OH 44114-1304 · 216-479-8500

Gordon S. Kaiser, Jr. · a · Squire Sanders · http://www.ssd.com · 4900 Key Tower · 127 Public Square · Cleveland, OH 44114-1304 · 216-479-8500

Ira C. Kaplan · Benesch, Friedlander, Coplan & Aronoff · BP Tower, Suite 2300 · 200 Public Square · Cleveland, OH 44114-2378 · 216-363-4500

David P. Porter · Jones Day · North Point · 901 Lakeside Avenue · Cleveland, OH 44114-1190 · 216-586-3939

David A. Zagore · Squire Sanders · http://www.ssd.com · 4900 Key Tower · 127 Public Square · Cleveland, OH 44114-1304 · 216-479-8500

Columbus

Dan A. Bailey · Bailey Cavalieri · One Columbus Building, Suite 2100 · 10 West Broad Street · Columbus, OH 43215-3422 · 614-221-3155

John P. Beavers · 2% · Bricker & Eckler · http://www.bricker.com · 100 South Third Street · Columbus, OH 43215-4291 · 614-227-2300

Patrick J. Dugan · Squire Sanders · http://www.ssd.com · 1300 Huntington Center · 41 South High Street Columbus, OH 43215-6197 · 614-365-2700

Douglas S. Morgan · Calfee, Halter & Griswold · http://www.calfee.com · 1100 Fifth Third Center · 21 East State Street · Columbus, OH 43215-4243 · 614-621-1500

Robert R. Ouellette · Schottenstein, Zox & Dunn · http://www.szd.com · 250 West Street, Suite 700 · Columbus, OH 43215-2538 · 614-462-2700

Fred A. Summer · Squire Sanders · http://www.ssd.com · 1300 Huntington Center · 41 South High Street Columbus, OH 43215-6197 · 614-365-2700

Randall M. Walters · Jones Day · 325 John H. McConnell Boulevard, Suite 600 · P.O. Box 165017 · Columbus, OH 43216-5017 · 614-469-3939

Dayton

Richard J. Chernesky · a · Dinsmore & Shohl · http://www.dinslaw.com · Courthouse Plaza, SW, Suite 1100 · 10 North Ludlow Street · Dayton, OH 45402 · 937-449-2800

Charles Y. Kidwell · Porter, Wright, Morris & Arthur · http://www.porterwright.com · One Dayton Centre, Suite 1600 · One South Main Street · Dayton, OH 45402-2028 · 937-449-6810

Toledo

Scott Aubry · Shumaker, Loop & Kendrick · North Courthouse Square · 1000 Jackson Street · Toledo, OH 43604-5573 · 419-241-9000

James I. Rothschild · Shumaker, Loop & Kendrick · North Courthouse Square · 1000 Jackson Street · Toledo, OH 43604-5573 · 419-241-9000

David F. Waterman · 2) · Shumaker, Loop & Kendrick · North Courthouse Square · 1000 Jackson Street · Toledo, OH 43604-5573 · 419-241-9000

James F. White, Jr. · 2% · Shumaker, Loop & Kendrick · North Courthouse Square · 1000 Jackson Street · Toledo, OH 43604-5573 · 419-241-9000

MUNICIPAL LAW

Cincinnati

Richard D. Spoor · Keating Muething & Klekamp · http://www.kmklaw.com · One East Fourth Street, Suite 1400 · Cincinnati, OH 45202 · 513-579-6400

Cleveland

Charles T. Riehl · Walter & Haverfield · http://www.walterhav.com · The Tower at Erieview, Suite 3500 · 1301 East Ninth Street · Cleveland, OH 44114 · 216-781-1212

Hilary S. Taylor · Weston Hurd · The Tower at Erieview, Suite 1900 · 1301 East Ninth Street · Cleveland, OH 44114-1862 · 216-241-6602

Columbus

John W. Bentine · a · Chester Willcox & Saxbe · http://www.cwslaw.com · 65 East State Street, Suite 1000 · Columbus, OH 43215 · 614-221-4000

Gregory J. Dunn · Schottenstein, Zox & Dunn · http://www.szd.com · 250 West Street, Suite 700 · Columbus, OH 43215-2538 · 614-462-2700

Stephen J. Smith, Sr. · Schottenstein, Zox & Dunn · http://www.szd.com · 250 West Street, Suite 700 · Columbus, OH 43215-2538 · 614-462-2700

NATURAL RESOURCES LAW

Columbus

April R. Bott · Chester Willcox & Saxbe · http://www.cwslaw.com · 65 East State Street, Suite 1000 · Columbus, OH 43215 · 614-221-4000

J. Richard Emens · 2% · Chester Willcox & Saxbe · http://www.cwslaw.com · 65 East State Street, Suite 1000 · Columbus, OH 43215 · 614-221-4000

NON-PROFIT/CHARITIES LAW

Cincinnati

Barbara S. Bromberg · Dinsmore & Shohl · http://www.dinslaw.com · 255 East Fifth Street, Suite 1900 · Cincinnati, OH 45202-3172 · 513-977-8200

Ronald C. Christian · Taft Stettinius & Hollister · http://www.taftlaw.com · 425 Walnut Street, Suite 1800 · Cincinnati, OH 45202-3957 · 513-381-2838

John E. Christopher · Dinsmore & Shohl · http://www.dinslaw.com · 255 East Fifth Street, Suite 1900 · Cincinnati, OH 45202-3172 · 513-977-8200

Douglas D. Thomson · Frost Brown Todd · http://www.frostbrowntodd.com · PNC Center, Suite 2200 · 201 East Fifth Street · Cincinnati, OH 45202-4182 · 513-651-6800

Cleveland

Malvin E. Bank · 2% · Thompson Hine · Key Center, Suite 3900 · 127 Public Square · Cleveland, OH 44114-1291 · 216-566-5500

Michael J. Horvitz · Jones Day · North Point · 901 Lakeside Avenue · Cleveland, OH 44114-1190 · 216-586-3939

Stephen J. Knerly, Jr. · Hahn Loeser & Parks · BP Tower, Suite 2800 · 200 Public Square · Cleveland, OH 44114-2301 · 216-621-0150

Columbus

James R. King · a · Jones Day · 325 John H. McConnell Boulevard, Suite 600 · P.O. Box 165017 · Columbus, OH 43216-5017 · 614-469-3939

Terri-Lynne Smiles · Collis Smiles & Collis · http://www.collislaw.com · 1650 Lake Shore Drive, Suite 225 · Columbus, OH 43204 · 614-486-3909

Martha J. Sweterlitsch · Benesch, Friedlander, Coplan & Aronoff · 41 South High Street, Suite 2600 · Columbus, OH 43215 · 614-223-9300

Mark E. Vannatta · Vorys, Sater, Seymour and Pease · 52 East Gay Street · P.O. Box 1008 · Columbus, OH 43216-1008 · 614-464-6400

Dayton

Irvin G. Bieser, Jr. · Bieser, Greer & Landis · http://www.biesergreer.com · National City Center, Suite 400 · Six North Main Street · Dayton, OH 45402-1908 · 937-223-3277

Charles Y. Kidwell · Porter, Wright, Morris & Arthur · http://www.porterwright.com · One Dayton Centre, Suite 1600 · One South Main Street · Dayton, OH 45402-2028 · 937-449-6810

NON-WHITE-COLLAR CRIMINAL DEFENSE

Akron

James L. Burdon · 2) · James L. Burdon, Attorney at Law · http://www.ohio-lawyer-criminal-defense.com The Delaware Building, Suite 201 · 137 South Main Street · Akron, OH 44308 · 330-253-7171

Cincinnati

Perry L. Ancona · Perry L. Ancona · The Nathaniel Ropes Building, Second Floor · 917 Main Street · Cincinnati, OH 45202-1314 · 513-721-1997

R. Scott Croswell III · a · Croswell & Adams · Olde Sycamore Square · 1208 Sycamore Street · Cincinnati, OH 45202 · 513-241-5670

Richard J. Goldberg · Schuh & Goldberg · 2662 Madison Road · Cincinnati, OH 45208 · 513-321-2662

Edward C. Perry · Edward C. Perry · 810 Sycamore Street, Sixth Floor · Cincinnati, OH 45202-2508 · 513-621-0442

James N. Perry · 2) · James N. Perry · 810 Sycamore Street, Sixth Floor · Cincinnati, OH 45202-2508 · 513-621-0442

Martin S. Pinales · 2) · Sirkin, Pinales & Schwartz · 105 West Fourth Street · Cincinnati, OH 45202-2726 513-721-4876

Jack C. Rubenstein · 2) · Rubenstein & Thurman · 125 East Court Street, Suite 1000 · Cincinnati, OH 45202 · 513-241-7460

Cleveland

William D. Beyer · Wuliger, Fadel & Beyer · The Brownell Building · 1340 Sumner Court · Cleveland, OH 44115 · 216-781-7777

Mark R. DeVan · Berkman, Gordon, Murray & DeVan · 55 Public Square, Suite 2200 · Cleveland, OH 44113-1972 · 216-781-5245

Gerald S. Gold · 2% · Gold and Pyle · Leader Building, Suite 1140 · 526 Superior Avenue East · Cleveland, OH 44114-1498 · 216-696-6122

Henry J. Hilow · McGinty, Hilow & Spellacy · 614 West Superior Avenue, Suite 1300 · Cleveland, OH 44113 · 216-344-9220

Richard G. Lillie · Lillie & Holderman · 75 Public Square, Suite 1313 · Cleveland, OH 44113-2011 · 216-861-1313

John F. McCaffrey · McLaughlin & McCaffrey · Eaton Center, Suite 1350 · 1111 Superior Avenue · Cleveland, OH 44114-2500 · 216-623-0900

John S. Pyle · a · Gold and Pyle · Leader Building, Suite 1140 · 526 Superior Avenue East · Cleveland, OH 44114-1498 · 216-696-6122

Robert J. Rotatori · 2% · Rotatori, Bender, Gragel, Stoper & Alexander · http://www.rotatori.com · 800 Leader Building · 526 Superior Avenue East · Cleveland, OH 44114-1498 · 216-928-1010

Niki Z. Schwartz · a · Schwartz, Downey and Company · Guildhall Building, Suite 1616 · 45 West Prospect Avenue · Cleveland, OH 44115 · 216-696-7100

Columbus

R. William Meeks · 2) · R. William Meeks · 511 South High Street · Columbus, OH 43215-5601 · 614-228-4141

S. Michael Miller · Kegler, Brown, Hill & Ritter · http://www.keglerbrown.com · Capitol Square, Suite 1800 · 65 East State Street · Columbus, OH 43215-4294 · 614-462-5400

Samuel H. Shamansky · a · Samuel H. Shamansky · 511 South High Street · Columbus, OH 43215-5602 614-228-4141

Terry K. Sherman · a · Terry K. Sherman · 52 West Whittier Street · Columbus, OH 43206 · 614-444-8800

Thomas M. Tyack · 2% · Tyack, Blackmore & Liston · 536 South High Street · Columbus, OH 43215-5605 · 614-221-1341

Samuel B. Weiner · 2) · Samuel B. Weiner · 743 South Front Street · Columbus, OH 43206-1991 · 614-443-6581

Dayton

Dennis A. Lieberman · 2) · Flanagan, Lieberman, Hoffman & Swaim · 318 West Fourth Street · Dayton, OH 45402-1437 · 937-223-5200

John H. Rion · 2% · Rion, Rion & Rion · One First National Plaza, Suite 2150 · 130 West Second Street · P.O. Box 10126 · Dayton, OH 45402 · 937-223-9133

Jon Paul Rion · Rion, Rion & Rion · One First National Plaza, Suite 2150 · 130 West Second Street · P.O. Box 10126 · Dayton, OH 45402 · 937-223-9133

Toledo

William M. Connelly · 2) · Connelly, Jackson & Collier · 405 Madison Avenue, Suite 1600 · Toledo, OH 43604 · 419-243-2100

John Czarnecki · a · Cooper & Walinski · 900 Adams Street · Toledo, OH 43604 · 419-241-1200

Robert Zachary Kaplan · a · Robert Zachary Kaplan · The Spitzer Building, Suite 830 · 520 Madison Avenue · Toledo, OH 43604 · 419-241-6168

Richard M. Kerger · a · Kerger & Associates · 33 South Michigan Street, Suite 100 · Toledo, OH 43602 · 419-255-5990

Alan S. Konop · a · Alan S. Konop · 413 North Michigan Street · Toledo, OH 43604 · 419-255-0571

John F. Potts · John F. Potts · National City Bank Building, Suite 1010 · 405 Madison Avenue · Toledo, OH 43604-1211 · 419-255-2800

Jon D. Richardson · 2% · Jon D. Richardson · The Spitzer Building, Suite 830 · 520 Madison Avenue · Toledo, OH 43604 · 419-241-6168

Youngstown

J. Gerald Ingram, Jr. · a · J. Gerald Ingram · 7330 Market Street · Youngstown, OH 44512-5622 · 330-758-2308

OIL & GAS LAW

Canton

William G. Williams · Krugliak, Wilkins, Griffiths & Dougherty · http://www.kwgd.com · 4775 Munson Street, NW · P.O. Box 36963 · Canton, OH 44735-6963 · 330-497-0700

Cleveland

Glenn S. Krassen · Bricker & Eckler · http://www.bricker.com · 1375 East Ninth Street, Suite 1500 · Cleveland, OH 44114-1718 · 216-523-5405

Columbus

W. Jonathon Airey · Vorys, Sater, Seymour and Pease · 52 East Gay Street · P.O. Box 1008 · Columbus, OH 43216-1008 · 614-464-6400

John W. Bentine · a · Chester Willcox & Saxbe · http://www.cwslaw.com · 65 East State Street, Suite 1000 · Columbus, OH 43215 · 614-221-4000

J. Richard Emens · 2% · Chester Willcox & Saxbe · http://www.cwslaw.com · 65 East State Street, Suite 1000 · Columbus, OH 43215 · 614-221-4000

John K. Keller · Vorys, Sater, Seymour and Pease · 52 East Gay Street · P.O. Box 1008 · Columbus, OH 43216-1008 · 614-464-6400

PERSONAL INJURY LITIGATION

Akron

Charles E. Grisi · Grisi & Riegler · 159 South Main Street, Suite 1030 · Akron, OH 44308 · 330-535-8171

John F. Hill · Hill Hardman Oldfield · http://www.hillhardmanoldfield.com · One Cascade Plaza, Suite 2000 · Akron, OH 44308 · 330-253-4000

Paul G. Perantinides · a · Perantinides & Nolan · http://www.perantinides.com · 80 South Summit Street · Akron, OH 44308-1736 · 866-611-1381

Orville L. Reed III · 2) · Buckingham, Doolittle & Burroughs · http://www.bdblaw.com · 3800 Embassy Parkway, Suite 300 · P.O. Box 1500 · Akron, OH 44309-1500 · 330-376-5300

Timothy F. Scanlon · 2) · Scanlon & Gearinger · 50 South Main Street, Suite 1200 · Akron, OH 44308-1463 · 330-376-4558

Amelia

Carl W. Zugelter · Law Office of Carl W. Zugelter · 1285 West Ohio Pike · Amelia, OH 45102-1242 · 513-752-2338

Canton

Lee J. Bell · Buckingham, Doolittle & Burroughs · http://www.bdblaw.com · 4518 Fulton Drive, NW · P.O. Box 35548 · Canton, OH 44735-5548 · 330-492-8717

Lee E. Plakas · Tzangas, Plakas, Mannos & Raies · 220 Market Avenue South, Eigth Floor · Canton, OH 44702 · 330-455-6112

Allen Schulman, Jr. · a · Allen Schulman & Associates · Carnegie Building · 236 Third Street, SW · Canton, OH 44702 · 330-456-4400

Chagrin Falls

John R. Liber II · Liber & Associates · 100 North Main Street, Suite 350 · Chagrin Falls, OH 44022 · 440-247-5078

Cincinnati

James F. Brockman · Lindhorst & Dreidame · 312 Walnut Street, Suite 3100 · Cincinnati, OH 45202-4048 · 513-421-6630

Daniel J. Buckley · Vorys, Sater, Seymour and Pease · Atrium Two, Suite 2000 · 221 East Fourth Street · P.O. Box 0236 · Cincinnati, OH 45201-0236 · 513-723-4000

Nicholas Bunch · White, Getgey & Meyer · Fourth & Vine Tower, Suite 1700 · One West Fourth Street · Cincinnati, OH 45202-3621 · 513-241-3685

Mark J. Byrne · a · Jacobs, Kleiman, Seibel & McNally · Kroger Building, Suite 2300 · 1014 Vine Street · Cincinnati, OH 45202-1116 · 513-381-6600

Stanley M. Chesley · 2) · Waite, Schneider, Bayless & Chesley · 1513 Fourth and Vine Tower · Cincinnati, OH 45202 · 513-621-0267

Michael D. Eagen · a · Dinsmore & Shohl · http://www.dinslaw.com · 255 East Fifth Street, Suite 1900 · Cincinnati, OH 45202-3172 · 513-977-8200

Michael F. Gehrig · Michael F. Gehrig · 938 Mercantile Library Building · 414 Walnut Street · Cincinnati, OH 45202-3908 · 513-421-9010

Alphonse A. Gerhardstein · a · Gerhardstein & Branch · 617 Vine Street, Suite 1409 · Cincinnati, OH 45202 · 513-621-9100

Louis F. Gilligan · 2) · Keating Muething & Klekamp · http://www.kmklaw.com · One East Fourth Street, Suite 1400 · Cincinnati, OH 45202 · 513-579-6400

Brett Goodson · Goodson & Company · 110 East Eighth Street, Suite 200 · Cincinnati, OH 45202 · 513-621-5631

Walter E. Haggerty · Frost Brown Todd · http://www.frostbrowntodd.com · PNC Center, Suite 2200 · 201 East Fifth Street · Cincinnati, OH 45202-4182 · 513-651-6800

John D. Holschuh, Jr. · a · Santen & Hughes · 600 Vine Street, Suite 2700 · Cincinnati, OH 45202 · 513-721-4450

Brian E. Hurley · Crabbe, Brown & James · 30 Garfield Place, Suite 740 · Cincinnati, OH 45202 · 513-784-1525

Barbara Bison Jacobson · a · Vorys, Sater, Seymour and Pease · Atrium Two, Suite 2000 · 221 East Fourth Street · P.O. Box 0236 · Cincinnati, OH 45201-0236 · 513-723-4000

David P. Kamp · White, Getgey & Meyer · Fourth & Vine Tower, Suite 1700 · One West Fourth Street · Cincinnati, OH 45202-3621 · 513-241-3685

Mark A. Macdonald · Freund, Freeze & Arnold · Fourth & Walnut Centre, Suite 1400 · 105 East Fourth Street · Cincinnati, OH 45202-4035 · 513-665-3500

Bruce B. McIntosh · a · McIntosh & McIntosh · 15 East Eighth Street, Suite 300-W · Cincinnati, OH 45202 · 513-929-4040

R. Joseph Parker · a · Taft Stettinius & Hollister · http://www.taftlaw.com · 425 Walnut Street, Suite 1800 · Cincinnati, OH 45202-3957 · 513-381-2838

Gerald J. Rapien · Taft Stettinius & Hollister · http://www.taftlaw.com · 425 Walnut Street, Suite 1800 · Cincinnati, OH 45202-3957 · 513-381-2838

William T. Robinson III · a · Frost Brown Todd · http://www.frostbrowntodd.com · PNC Center, Suite 2200 · 201 East Fifth Street · Cincinnati, OH 45202-4182 · 513-651-6800

James H. Scheper · Shea & Associates · Chiquita Center, Suite 444 · 250 East Fifth Street · Cincinnati, OH 45202-4119 · 513-621-8333

Joseph W. Shea III · a · Shea & Associates · Chiquita Center, Suite 444 · 250 East Fifth Street · Cincinnati, OH 45202-4119 · 513-621-8333

Gregory M. Utter · Keating Muething & Klekamp · http://www.kmklaw.com · One East Fourth Street, Suite 1400 · Cincinnati, OH 45202 · 513-579-6400

Glenn V. Whitaker · 2) · Vorys, Sater, Seymour and Pease · Atrium Two, Suite 2000 · 221 East Fourth Street · P.O. Box 0236 · Cincinnati, OH 45201-0236 · 513-723-4000

Frank C. Woodside III · a · Dinsmore & Shohl · http://www.dinslaw.com · 255 East Fifth Street, Suite 1900 · Cincinnati, OH 45202-3172 · 513-977-8200

Cleveland

Richard J. Berris · Weisman, Kennedy & Berris · Midland Building, Suite 1600 · 101 West Prospect Avenue · Cleveland, OH 44115 · 216-781-1111

Peter J. Brodhead · Spangenberg, Shibley & Liber · 1900 East Ninth Street, Suite 2400 · Cleveland, OH 44114-3400 · 216-696-3232

Mario C. Ciano · a · Reminger Attorneys At Law · 1400 Midland Building · 101 Prospect Avenue West · Cleveland, OH 44115-1093 · 216-687-1311

Charles F. Clarke · 2) · Squire Sanders · http://www.ssd.com · 4900 Key Tower · 127 Public Square · Cleveland, OH 44114-1304 · 216-479-8500

George S. Coakley · Reminger Attorneys At Law · 1400 Midland Building · 101 Prospect Avenue West · Cleveland, OH 44115-1093 · 216-687-1311

Thomas E. Dover · Gallagher Sharp Attorneys · Bulkley Building, Sixth Floor · 1501 Euclid Avenue · Cleveland, OH 44115 · 216-241-5310

Paul Eklund · Davis and Young · 1200 Fifth Third Center · 600 Superior Avenue East · Cleveland, OH 44114-2654 · 216-348-1700

Gary H. Goldwasser · a · Reminger Attorneys At Law · 1400 Midland Building · 101 Prospect Avenue West · Cleveland, OH 44115-1093 · 216-687-1311

William Martin Greene · a · Greene & Eisen · 1300 East Ninth Street, Suite 1801 · Cleveland, OH 44114 · 216-687-0900

Steven G. Janik · a · Janik Dorman & Winter · http://www.janiklaw.com · 9200 South Hills Boulevard, Suite 300 · Cleveland, OH 44147-3521 · 440-838-7600

Charles Kampinski · 2) · Kampinski Schneider · 1301 East Ninth Street, Suite 500 · Cleveland, OH 44114 · 216-781-4110

R. Eric Kennedy · 2) · Weisman, Kennedy & Berris · Midland Building, Suite 1600 · 101 West Prospect Avenue · Cleveland, OH 44115 · 216-781-1111

Andrew P. Krembs · Andrew P. Krembs & Associates · 55 Public Square, Suite 1700 · Cleveland, OH 44113-1021 · 216-875-7500

John G. Lancione · a · Lancione & Lancione · 200 Public Square, Suite 2955 · Cleveland, OH 44114 · 216-623-4949

Dennis R. Lansdowne · Spangenberg, Shibley & Liber · 1900 East Ninth Street, Suite 2400 · Cleveland, OH 44114-3400 · 216-696-3232

James A. Lowe · a · Lowe Eklund Wakefield & Mulvihill · http://www.lewm.com · Tower City Center, Suite 610 · Skylight Office Tower · 1660 West Second Street · Cleveland, OH 44113-1454 · 216-781-2600

James L. Malone · a · Reminger Attorneys At Law · 1400 Midland Building · 101 Prospect Avenue West Cleveland, OH 44115-1093 · 216-687-1311

Patrick F. McCartan · 2% · Jones Day · North Point · 901 Lakeside Avenue · Cleveland, OH 44114-1190 · 216-586-3939

Mark F. Mccarthy · Tucker Ellis & West · Huntington Building, Suite 1150 · 925 Euclid Avenue · Cleveland, OH 44115-1475 · 216-592-5000

C. Richard McDonald · Davis and Young · 1200 Fifth Third Center · 600 Superior Avenue East · Cleveland, OH 44114-2654 · 216-348-1700

J. Michael Monteleone · a · Jeffries, Kube, Forrest & Monteleone · Midland Building, Suite 1650 · 101 Prospect Avenue West · Cleveland, OH 44115-1027 · 216-771-4050

Martin J. Murphy · a · Davis and Young · 1200 Fifth Third Center · 600 Superior Avenue East · Cleveland, OH 44114-2654 · 216-348-1700

Mark O'Neill · ㉕ · Weston Hurd · The Tower at Erieview, Suite 1900 · 1301 East Ninth Street · Cleveland, OH 44114-1862 · 216-241-6602

David M. Paris · Nurenberg, Plevin, Heller & McCarthy · 1370 Ontario Street, Suite 100 · Cleveland, OH 44113-1792 · 216-621-2300

Kent B. Schneider · ⑩ · Hermann, Cahn & Schneider · http://www.hcsattys.com · 1301 East Ninth Street, Suite 500 · Cleveland, OH 44114 · 216-781-5515

Scott E. Stewart · Stewart and DeChant · 1370 Ontario Street, Suite 1440 · Cleveland, OH 44113-1701 · 216-781-2258

Robert C. Tucker · Tucker Ellis & West · Huntington Building, Suite 1150 · 925 Euclid Avenue · Cleveland, OH 44115-1475 · 216-592-5000

S. Peter Voudouris · Tucker Ellis & West · Huntington Building, Suite 1150 · 925 Euclid Avenue · Cleveland, OH 44115-1475 · 216-592-5000

Stephen E. Walters · ⑩ · Reminger Attorneys At Law · 1400 Midland Building · 101 Prospect Avenue West · Cleveland, OH 44115-1093 · 216-687-1311

Robin G. Weaver · Squire Sanders · http://www.ssd.com · 4900 Key Tower · 127 Public Square · Cleveland, OH 44114-1304 · 216-479-8500

Peter H. Weinberger · Spangenberg, Shibley & Liber · 1900 East Ninth Street, Suite 2400 · Cleveland, OH 44114-3400 · 216-696-3232

Mitchell A. Weisman · Weisman, Kennedy & Berris · Midland Building, Suite 1600 · 101 West Prospect Avenue · Cleveland, OH 44115 · 216-781-1111

Fred Wendel III · Stewart and DeChant · 1370 Ontario Street, Suite 1440 · Cleveland, OH 44113-1701 · 216-781-2258

Columbus

Sandra J. Anderson · ⑩ · Vorys, Sater, Seymour and Pease · 52 East Gay Street · P.O. Box 1008 · Columbus, OH 43216-1008 · 614-464-6400

James E. Arnold · James E. Arnold & Company · http://www.arnlaw.com · 471 East Broad Street, Suite 1400 · Columbus, OH 43215 · 614-460-1600

Craig D. Barclay · ⑩ · Alton & Barclay · 175 South Third Street, Suite 360 · Columbus, OH 43215 · 614-221-1770

Mary Barley-McBride · Lane, Alton & Horst · Two Miranova Place, Suite 500 · Columbus, OH 43215-7052 · 614-228-6885

John F. Birath, Jr. · Bricker & Eckler · http://www.bricker.com · 100 South Third Street · Columbus, OH 43215-4291 · 614-227-2300

James B. Blumenstiel · ⑩ · Blumenstiel, Huhn, Adams & Evans · 261 West Johnstown Road · Columbus, OH 43230-2732 · 614-475-9511

Kenneth S. Blumenthal · Rourke & Blumenthal · 495 South High Street, Suite 450 · Columbus, OH 43215 · 614-220-9200

Timothy J. Boone · Timothy J. Boone · 1349 East Broad Street, Second Floor · Columbus, OH 43205-1503 · 614-228-0200

Michael H. Carpenter · a · Carpenter Lipps & Leland · http://www.carpenterlipps.com · 280 Plaza, Suite 1300 · 280 North High Street · Columbus, OH 43215 · 614-365-4100

Charles H. Cooper, Jr. · Cooper & Elliott · 2175 Riverside Drive · Columbus, OH 43221 · 614-481-6000

Thomas A. Dillon · Roetzel & Andress · http://www.ralaw.com · National City Plaza, 12th Floor · 155 East Broad Street · Columbus, OH 43215 · 614-723-2002

Rex H. Elliott · Cooper & Elliott · 2175 Riverside Drive · Columbus, OH 43221 · 614-481-6000

Mary Ellen Fairfield · a · Vorys, Sater, Seymour and Pease · 52 East Gay Street · P.O. Box 1008 · Columbus, OH 43216-1008 · 614-464-6400

Gregory B. Foliano · Arnold, Todaro & Welch · 2075 Marble Cliff Office Park · Columbus, OH 43215-1053 · 614-485-1800

Joseph A. Gerling · Lane, Alton & Horst · Two Miranova Place, Suite 500 · Columbus, OH 43215-7052 · 614-228-6885

Jeffrey W. Hutson · a · Lane, Alton & Horst · Two Miranova Place, Suite 500 · Columbus, OH 43215-7052 · 614-228-6885

Robert Kerpsack · Robert W. Kerpsack · Metrocenter V, Suite 255 · 655 Metro Place South · Columbus, OH 43017-5389 · 614-766-2000

Mark M. Kitrick · Kitrick, Lewis & Harris · http://www.kitricklaw.com · 515 East Main Street, Suite 515 · Columbus, OH 43215-5398 · 614-224-7711

William D. Kloss, Jr. · Vorys, Sater, Seymour and Pease · 52 East Gay Street · P.O. Box 1008 · Columbus, OH 43216-1008 · 614-464-6400

William W. Lamkin · a · Lamkin, Van Eman, Trimble, Beals & Dougherty · 500 South Front Street, Suite 200 · Columbus, OH 43215 · 614-224-8187

Gerald S. Leeseberg · a · Leeseberg & Valentine · 175 South Third Street, Penthouse One · Columbus, OH 43215 · 614-221-2223

Mark Lewis · Kitrick, Lewis & Harris · http://www.kitricklaw.com · 515 East Main Street, Suite 515 · Columbus, OH 43215-5398 · 614-224-7711

D. Andrew List · Clark, Perdue & List · 471 East Broad Street, Suite 1550 · Columbus, OH 43215 · 614-469-1400

Richard S. Lovering · Bricker & Eckler · http://www.bricker.com · 100 South Third Street · Columbus, OH 43215-4291 · 614-227-2300

Terrance M. Miller · 2) · Porter, Wright, Morris & Arthur · http://www.porterwright.com · Huntington Center · 41 South High Street · Columbus, OH 43215-6194 · 614-227-2000

Joel H. Mirman · Adams, Babner & Gitlitz · 5003 Horizons Drive, Suite 200 · Columbus, OH 43220 · 614-451-4227

James S. Oliphant · 2) · Porter, Wright, Morris & Arthur · http://www.porterwright.com · Huntington Center · 41 South High Street · Columbus, OH 43215-6194 · 614-227-2000

Robert G. Palmer · a · Robert Gray Palmer Company · http://www.rgpalmerlaw.com · 140 East Town Street, Suite 1200 · Columbus, OH 43215 · 614-484-1200

Dale K. Perdue · Clark, Perdue & List · 471 East Broad Street, Suite 1550 · Columbus, OH 43215 · 614-469-1400

Alan T. Radnor · 2) · Vorys, Sater, Seymour and Pease · 52 East Gay Street · P.O. Box 1008 · Columbus, OH 43216-1008 · 614-464-6400

Frank A. Ray · 2) · Chester Willcox & Saxbe · http://www.cwslaw.com · 65 East State Street, Suite 1000 · Columbus, OH 43215 · 614-221-4000

Thomas B. Ridgley · 2% · Vorys, Sater, Seymour and Pease · 52 East Gay Street · P.O. Box 1008 · Columbus, OH 43216-1008 · 614-464-6400

Michael Romanello · a · Reminger Attorneys At Law · Capitol Square Office Building, Fourth Floor · 65 East State Street · Columbus, OH 43215 · 614-228-1311

Michael J. Rourke · a · Rourke & Blumenthal · 495 South High Street, Suite 450 · Columbus, OH 43215 · 614-220-9200

Joseph W. Ryan, Jr. · Porter, Wright, Morris & Arthur · http://www.porterwright.com · Huntington Center · 41 South High Street · Columbus, OH 43215-6194 · 614-227-2000

Hans Scherner · 2) · Scherner, Hanson & Cornwell · 130 Northwoods Boulevard · Columbus, OH 43215 · 614-431-7200

Mark L. Schumacher · Freund, Freeze & Arnold · Capitol Square Office Building, Suite 800 · 65 East State Street · Columbus, OH 43215 · 614-827-7300

Paul O. Scott · a · Paul O. Scott Company · 471 East Broad Street, Suite 1400 · Columbus, OH 43215 · 614-460-1633

Bradley L. Snyder · Roetzel & Andress · http://www.ralaw.com · National City Plaza, 12th Floor · 155 East Broad Street · Columbus, OH 43215 · 614-723-2002

Maryellen C. Spirito · Arnold, Todaro & Welch · 2075 Marble Cliff Office Park · Columbus, OH 43215-1053 · 614-485-1800

Frank E. Todaro · a · The Law Firm of Todaro & Wagoner · 471 East Broad Street, Suite 1303 · Columbus, OH 43215-4228 · 614-242-4333

Gerald J. Todaro · a · Arnold, Todaro & Welch · 2075 Marble Cliff Office Park · Columbus, OH 43215-1053 · 614-485-1800

Richard D. Topper · Richard D. Topper · 5132 Olentangy River Road · Columbus, OH 43235 · 614-442-5784

Thomas M. Tyack · 2% · Tyack, Blackmore & Liston · 536 South High Street · Columbus, OH 43215-5605 · 614-221-1341

Anne M. Valentine · Leeseberg & Valentine · 175 South Third Street, Penthouse One · Columbus, OH 43215 · 614-221-2223

Dayton

Gordon D. Arnold · Freund, Freeze & Arnold · One Dayton Centre, Suite 1800 · One South Main Street Dayton, OH 45402-2017 · 937-222-2424

Susan Blasik-Miller · Freund, Freeze & Arnold · One Dayton Centre, Suite 1800 · One South Main Street · Dayton, OH 45402-2017 · 937-222-2424

Christopher W. Carrigg · Freund, Freeze & Arnold · One Dayton Centre, Suite 1800 · One South Main Street · Dayton, OH 45402-2017 · 937-222-2424

Steven K. Dankof, Sr. · Skilken, Lowe & Dankof · 40 North Main Street · 1500 Kettering Tower · Dayton, OH 45423-1001 · 937-223-1500

Stephen V. Freeze · Freund, Freeze & Arnold · One Dayton Centre, Suite 1800 · One South Main Street Dayton, OH 45402-2017 · 937-222-2424

Neil F. Freund · a · Freund, Freeze & Arnold · One Dayton Centre, Suite 1800 · One South Main Street Dayton, OH 45402-2017 · 937-222-2424

David C. Greer · 2% · Bieser, Greer & Landis · http://www.biesergreer.com · National City Center, Suite 400 · Six North Main Street · Dayton, OH 45402-1908 · 937-223-3277

Thomas E. Jenks · 2) · Jenks, Pyper & Oxley · Courthouse Plaza, SW, Suite 901 · 10 North Ludlow Street Dayton, OH 45402 · 937-223-3001

Christopher F. Johnson · Freund, Freeze & Arnold · One Dayton Centre, Suite 1800 · One South Main Street · Dayton, OH 45402-2017 · 937-222-2424

Leo F. Krebs · a · Bieser, Greer & Landis · http://www.biesergreer.com · National City Center, Suite 400 Six North Main Street · Dayton, OH 45402-1908 · 937-223-3277

Howard Penn Krisher II · a · Bieser, Greer & Landis · http://www.biesergreer.com · National City Center, Suite 400 · Six North Main Street · Dayton, OH 45402-1908 · 937-223-3277

Charles D. Lowe · 2) · Law Offices of Charles D. Lowe · Kettering Tower, Suite 1500 · 40 North Main Street · Dayton, OH 45423 · 937-222-8091

Elyria

Michael F. Becker · Becker & Mishkind · Becker Haynes Building · 134 Middle Avenue · Elyria, OH 44035 · 440-328-8803

Lima

Lawrence S. Huffman, Sr. · Huffman, Kelley, Becker & Brock · 540 West Market Street · P.O. Box 546 · Lima, OH 45802 · 419-227-3423

North Olmsted

John E. Martindale · a · John E. Martindale · 26031 Butternut Ridge Road · North Olmsted, OH 44070-4514 · 216-272-7750

Toledo

John F. Bodie, Jr. · Marshall & Melhorn · Four Seagate, Eighth Floor · Toledo, OH 43604 · 419-249-7100

Steven P. Collier · a · Connelly, Jackson & Collier · 405 Madison Avenue, Suite 1600 · Toledo, OH 43604 · 419-243-2100

William M. Connelly · 2) · Connelly, Jackson & Collier · 405 Madison Avenue, Suite 1600 · Toledo, OH 43604 · 419-243-2100

Edwin A. Coy · Coy, Konieczny & Peppel · 405 Madison Avenue, Suite 700 · Toledo, OH 43604 · 419-724-5252

Richard F. Ellenberger · Anspach Meeks Ellenberger · 300 Madison Avenue, Suite 1600 · Toledo, OH 43604-2633 · 419-246-5757

Jack G. Fynes · Shumaker, Loop & Kendrick · North Courthouse Square · 1000 Jackson Street · Toledo, OH 43604-5573 · 419-241-9000

Thomas W. Gallagher · Williams, Jilek, Lafferty, Gallagher & Scott · Toledo Legal Building, Suite 500 · 416 North Erie Street · Toledo, OH 43604-6301 · 419-241-7700

Jay Harris · a · Harris · Reny · Torzewski · Two Maritime Plaza, Third Floor · Toledo, OH 43604-1803 · 419-243-1105

James R. Jeffery · a · Spengler Nathanson · 608 Madison Avenue, Suite 1000 · Toledo, OH 43604-1169 · 419-241-2201

Gerald R. Kowalski · Cooper & Walinski · 900 Adams Street · Toledo, OH 43604 · 419-241-1200

E. Thomas Maguire · a · Robison, Curphey & O'Connell · Four Seagate, Ninth Floor · Toledo, OH 43604 · 419-249-7900

Gary W. Osborne · Gary W. Osborne & Associates · http://www.garyosbornelaw.com · 2754 Centennial Road · Toledo, OH 43617 · 419-842-8200

Martin W. Williams · 2) · Williams, Jilek, Lafferty, Gallagher & Scott · Toledo Legal Building, Suite 500 416 North Erie Street · Toledo, OH 43604-6301 · 419-241-7700

Warren

Charles L. Richards · a · Law Office of Charles L. Richards · 8600 East Market Street, Suite One · Warren, OH 44484-2375 · 330-373-1000

Martin F. White · Martin F. White Co. · 156 Park Avenue, NE · P.O. Box 1150 · Warren, OH 44481-1218 330-394-9692

Westerville

Edwin J. Hollern · Hollern & Associates · 77 North State Street · Westerville, OH 43081-2115 · 614-839-5700

Youngstown

Marshall D. Buck · Comstock, Springer & Wilson · 100 Federal Plaza East, Suite 926 · Youngstown, OH 44503 · 330-746-5643

Thomas J. Wilson · a · Comstock, Springer & Wilson · 100 Federal Plaza East, Suite 926 · Youngstown, OH 44503 · 330-746-5643

PRODUCT LIABILITY LITIGATION

Akron

Susan S. Box · Roetzel & Andress · http://www.ralaw.com · 222 South Main Street · Akron, OH 44308-2098 · 330-376-2700

Jeffrey J. Casto · Roetzel & Andress · http://www.ralaw.com · 222 South Main Street · Akron, OH 44308-2098 · 330-376-2700

Ronald B. Lee · Roetzel & Andress · http://www.ralaw.com · 222 South Main Street · Akron, OH 44308-2098 · 330-376-2700

Aaron E. McQueen · Roetzel & Andress · http://www.ralaw.com · 222 South Main Street · Akron, OH 44308-2098 · 330-376-2700

Randall J. Moore · Roetzel & Andress · http://www.ralaw.com · 222 South Main Street · Akron, OH 44308-2098 · 330-376-2700

Robert A. Royer · Scanlon & Gearinger · 50 South Main Street, Suite 1200 · Akron, OH 44308-1463 · 330-376-4558

Canton

Allen Schulman, Jr. · a · Allen Schulman & Associates · Carnegie Building · 236 Third Street, SW · Canton, OH 44702 · 330-456-4400

Cincinnati

Bruce M. Allman · Thompson Hine · 312 Walnut Street, 14th Floor · Cincinnati, OH 45202-4089 · 513-352-6700

J. David Brittingham · Dinsmore & Shohl · http://www.dinslaw.com · 255 East Fifth Street, Suite 1900 · Cincinnati, OH 45202-3172 · 513-977-8200

James A. Comodeca · Dinsmore & Shohl · http://www.dinslaw.com · 255 East Fifth Street, Suite 1900 · Cincinnati, OH 45202-3172 · 513-977-8200

Michael D. Eagen · a · Dinsmore & Shohl · http://www.dinslaw.com · 255 East Fifth Street, Suite 1900 · Cincinnati, OH 45202-3172 · 513-977-8200

Louis F. Gilligan · 2) · Keating Muething & Klekamp · http://www.kmklaw.com · One East Fourth Street, Suite 1400 · Cincinnati, OH 45202 · 513-579-6400

K.C. Green · Dinsmore & Shohl · http://www.dinslaw.com · 255 East Fifth Street, Suite 1900 · Cincinnati, OH 45202-3172 · 513-977-8200

M. Gabrielle Hils · Dinsmore & Shohl · http://www.dinslaw.com · 255 East Fifth Street, Suite 1900 · Cincinnati, OH 45202-3172 · 513-977-8200

Jeffrey F. Peck · Ulmer & Berne · 600 Vine Street, Suite 2800 · Cincinnati, OH 45202-2409 · 513-698-5000

Gina M. Saelinger · Ulmer & Berne · 600 Vine Street, Suite 2800 · Cincinnati, OH 45202-2409 · 513-698-5000

Frederick X. Shadley · Ulmer & Berne · 600 Vine Street, Suite 2800 · Cincinnati, OH 45202-2409 · 513-698-5000

Michael J. Suffern · Ulmer & Berne · 600 Vine Street, Suite 2800 · Cincinnati, OH 45202-2409 · 513-698-5000

Carolyn A. Taggart · Porter, Wright, Morris & Arthur · http://www.porterwright.com · 250 East Fifth Street, Suite 2200 · Cincinnati, OH 45202-5118 · 513-381-4700

Joseph P. Thomas · Ulmer & Berne · 600 Vine Street, Suite 2800 · Cincinnati, OH 45202-2409 · 513-698-5000

Frank C. Woodside III · a · Dinsmore & Shohl · http://www.dinslaw.com · 255 East Fifth Street, Suite 1900 · Cincinnati, OH 45202-3172 · 513-977-8200

Cleveland

Carolyn M. Cappel · Weston Hurd · The Tower at Erieview, Suite 1900 · 1301 East Ninth Street · Cleveland, OH 44114-1862 · 216-241-6602

Paul G. Crist · Jones Day · North Point · 901 Lakeside Avenue · Cleveland, OH 44114-1190 · 216-586-3939

S. Stuart Eilers · Thompson Hine · Key Center, Suite 3900 · 127 Public Square · Cleveland, OH 44114-1291 · 216-566-5500

James A. Lowe · a · Lowe Eklund Wakefield & Mulvihill · http://www.lewm.com · Tower City Center, Suite 610 · Skylight Office Tower · 1660 West Second Street · Cleveland, OH 44113-1454 · 216-781-2600

Damond R. Mace · Squire Sanders · http://www.ssd.com · 4900 Key Tower · 127 Public Square · Cleveland, OH 44114-1304 · 216-479-8500

James L. McCrystal, Jr. · Brzytwa, Quick & McCrystal · 1660 West Second Street, Suite 900 · Cleveland, OH 44113-1411 · 216-664-6900

Kent B. Schneider · a · Hermann, Cahn & Schneider · http://www.hcsattys.com · 1301 East Ninth Street, Suite 500 · Cleveland, OH 44114 · 216-781-5515

Randall L. Solomon · a · Baker Hostetler · http://www.bakerlaw.com · National City Center, Suite 3200 1900 East Ninth Street · Cleveland, OH 44114-3485 · 216-621-0200

S. Peter Voudouris · Tucker Ellis & West · Huntington Building, Suite 1150 · 925 Euclid Avenue · Cleveland, OH 44115-1475 · 216-592-5000

Robin G. Weaver · Squire Sanders · http://www.ssd.com · 4900 Key Tower · 127 Public Square · Cleveland, OH 44114-1304 · 216-479-8500

Elizabeth B. Wright · Thompson Hine · Key Center, Suite 3900 · 127 Public Square · Cleveland, OH 44114-1291 · 216-566-5500

Columbus

John M. Alton · John M. Alton Co. · 175 South Third Street, Suite 360 · Columbus, OH 43215 · 614-221-6751

Mary Ellen Fairfield · a · Vorys, Sater, Seymour and Pease · 52 East Gay Street · P.O. Box 1008 · Columbus, OH 43216-1008 · 614-464-6400

Joseph A. Gerling · Lane, Alton & Horst · Two Miranova Place, Suite 500 · Columbus, OH 43215-7052 · 614-228-6885

Terrance M. Miller · 2) · Porter, Wright, Morris & Arthur · http://www.porterwright.com · Huntington Center · 41 South High Street · Columbus, OH 43215-6194 · 614-227-2000

Alan T. Radnor · 2) · Vorys, Sater, Seymour and Pease · 52 East Gay Street · P.O. Box 1008 · Columbus, OH 43216-1008 · 614-464-6400

Thomas B. Ridgley · 2% · Vorys, Sater, Seymour and Pease · 52 East Gay Street · P.O. Box 1008 · Columbus, OH 43216-1008 · 614-464-6400

Toledo

Jay Harris · a · Harris · Reny · Torzewski · Two Maritime Plaza, Third Floor · Toledo, OH 43604-1803 · 419-243-1105

Gerald R. Kowalski · Cooper & Walinski · 900 Adams Street · Toledo, OH 43604 · 419-241-1200

PROFESSIONAL MALPRACTICE LAW

Cleveland

Mario C. Ciano · a · Reminger Attorneys At Law · 1400 Midland Building · 101 Prospect Avenue West · Cleveland, OH 44115-1093 · 216-687-1311

Timothy D. Johnson · Weston Hurd · The Tower at Erieview, Suite 1900 · 1301 East Ninth Street · Cleveland, OH 44114-1862 · 216-241-6602

Murray K. Lenson · Ulmer & Berne · Skylight Office Tower, Suite 1100 · 1660 West Second Street · Cleveland, OH 44113-1448 · 216-583-7000

David Ross · Reminger Attorneys At Law · 1400 Midland Building · 101 Prospect Avenue West · Cleveland, OH 44115-1093 · 216-687-1311

Columbus

John M. Alton · John M. Alton Co. · 175 South Third Street, Suite 360 · Columbus, OH 43215 · 614-221-6751

Timothy J. Boone · Timothy J. Boone · 1349 East Broad Street, Second Floor · Columbus, OH 43205-1503 · 614-228-0200

Rick E. Marsh · Lane, Alton & Horst · Two Miranova Place, Suite 500 · Columbus, OH 43215-7052 · 614-228-6885

Terrance M. Miller · 2) · Porter, Wright, Morris & Arthur · http://www.porterwright.com · Huntington Center · 41 South High Street · Columbus, OH 43215-6194 · 614-227-2000

Frank A. Ray · 2) · Chester Willcox & Saxbe · http://www.cwslaw.com · 65 East State Street, Suite 1000 · Columbus, OH 43215 · 614-221-4000

Hans Scherner · 2) · Scherner, Hanson & Cornwell · 130 Northwoods Boulevard · Columbus, OH 43215 · 614-431-7200

Geoffrey Stern · Kegler, Brown, Hill & Ritter · http://www.keglerbrown.com · Capitol Square, Suite 1800 65 East State Street · Columbus, OH 43215-4294 · 614-462-5400

Frank E. Todaro · a · The Law Firm of Todaro & Wagoner · 471 East Broad Street, Suite 1303 · Columbus, OH 43215-4228 · 614-242-4333

Gerald J. Todaro · a · Arnold, Todaro & Welch · 2075 Marble Cliff Office Park · Columbus, OH 43215-1053 · 614-485-1800

Christopher J. Weber · Kegler, Brown, Hill & Ritter · http://www.keglerbrown.com · Capitol Square, Suite 1800 · 65 East State Street · Columbus, OH 43215-4294 · 614-462-5400

PROJECT FINANCE LAW

Cincinnati

Daniel H. Demmerle II · Strauss & Troy · http://www.strausstroy.com · The Federal Reserve Building · 150 East Fourth Street · Cincinnati, OH 45202-4018 · 513-621-2120

Joanne M. Schreiner · Dinsmore & Shohl · http://www.dinslaw.com · 255 East Fifth Street, Suite 1900 · Cincinnati, OH 45202-3172 · 513-977-8200

Pete A. Smith · Strauss & Troy · http://www.strausstroy.com · The Federal Reserve Building · 150 East Fourth Street · Cincinnati, OH 45202-4018 · 513-621-2120

Daniel P. Utt · Katz, Teller, Brant & Hild · http://www.katzteller.com · 255 East Fifth Street, Suite 2400 · Cincinnati, OH 45202-4724 · 513-721-4532

Herbert B. Weiss · 2% · Keating Muething & Klekamp · http://www.kmklaw.com · One East Fourth Street, Suite 1400 · Cincinnati, OH 45202 · 513-579-6400

PUBLIC FINANCE LAW

Cincinnati

John W. Fischer III · Peck, Shaffer · 201 East Fifth Street, Suite 900 · Cincinnati, OH 45202 · 513-621-3394

John Weld Peck · Peck, Shaffer · 201 East Fifth Street, Suite 900 · Cincinnati, OH 45202 · 513-621-3394

Robert A. Selak · Thompson Hine · 312 Walnut Street, 14th Floor · Cincinnati, OH 45202-4089 · 513-352-6700

Cleveland

Virginia D. Benjamin · Calfee, Halter & Griswold · http://www.calfee.com · 1400 KeyBank Center · 800 Superior Avenue · Cleveland, OH 44114-2688 · 216-622-8200

Jeffrey A. Bomberger · Squire Sanders · http://www.ssd.com · 4900 Key Tower · 127 Public Square · Cleveland, OH 44114-1304 · 216-479-8500

Ernie K. Demanelis · Squire Sanders · http://www.ssd.com · 4900 Key Tower · 127 Public Square · Cleveland, OH 44114-1304 · 216-479-8500

D. Bruce Gabriel · Squire Sanders · http://www.ssd.com · 4900 Key Tower · 127 Public Square · Cleveland, OH 44114-1304 · 216-479-8500

David S. Goodman · Squire Sanders · http://www.ssd.com · 4900 Key Tower · 127 Public Square · Cleveland, OH 44114-1304 · 216-479-8500

Pamela I. Hanover · Squire Sanders · http://www.ssd.com · 4900 Key Tower · 127 Public Square · Cleveland, OH 44114-1304 · 216-479-8500

Barbara L. Hawley · Squire Sanders · http://www.ssd.com · 4900 Key Tower · 127 Public Square · Cleveland, OH 44114-1304 · 216-479-8500

F. Barry Keefe · Squire Sanders · http://www.ssd.com · 4900 Key Tower · 127 Public Square · Cleveland, OH 44114-1304 · 216-479-8500

Robert Labes · Squire Sanders · http://www.ssd.com · 4900 Key Tower · 127 Public Square · Cleveland, OH 44114-1304 · 216-479-8500

Richard Manoloff · Squire Sanders · http://www.ssd.com · 4900 Key Tower · 127 Public Square · Cleveland, OH 44114-1304 · 216-479-8500

Kurt J. von Boeselager · Hurtuk & Daroff · Parkland Terrace, Suite 100 · 6120 Parkland Boulevard · Cleveland, OH 44124 · 440-605-6660

Columbus

Edward Cavezza · Peck, Shaffer · 175 South Third Street, Suite 600 · Columbus, OH 43215 · 614-224-5205

William T. Conard II · Bricker & Eckler · http://www.bricker.com · 100 South Third Street · Columbus, OH 43215-4291 · 614-227-2300

Christopher J. Franzmann · Squire Sanders · http://www.ssd.com · 1300 Huntington Center · 41 South High Street · Columbus, OH 43215-6197 · 614-365-2700

Jason L. George · Peck, Shaffer · 175 South Third Street, Suite 600 · Columbus, OH 43215 · 614-224-5205

Stephen P. Grassbaugh · Peck, Shaffer · 175 South Third Street, Suite 600 · Columbus, OH 43215 · 614-224-5205

Richard F. Kane · Bricker & Eckler · http://www.bricker.com · 100 South Third Street · Columbus, OH 43215-4291 · 614-227-2300

Michael J. Melliere · Peck, Shaffer · 175 South Third Street, Suite 600 · Columbus, OH 43215 · 614-224-5205

Randall E. Moore · Bricker & Eckler · http://www.bricker.com · 100 South Third Street · Columbus, OH 43215-4291 · 614-227-2300

Glendon B. Pratt · Peck, Shaffer · 175 South Third Street, Suite 600 · Columbus, OH 43215 · 614-224-5205

David A. Rogers · Bricker & Eckler · http://www.bricker.com · 100 South Third Street · Columbus, OH 43215-4291 · 614-227-2300

Dennis G. Schwallie · Peck, Shaffer · 175 South Third Street, Suite 600 · Columbus, OH 43215 · 614-224-5205

Richard C. Simpson · Bricker & Eckler · http://www.bricker.com · 100 South Third Street · Columbus, OH 43215-4291 · 614-227-2300

Gregory W. Stype · Squire Sanders · http://www.ssd.com · 1300 Huntington Center · 41 South High Street · Columbus, OH 43215-6197 · 614-365-2700

RAILROAD LAW

Cincinnati

James F. Brockman · Lindhorst & Dreidame · 312 Walnut Street, Suite 3100 · Cincinnati, OH 45202-4048 · 513-421-6630

Walter E. Haggerty · Frost Brown Todd · http://www.frostbrowntodd.com · PNC Center, Suite 2200 · 201 East Fifth Street · Cincinnati, OH 45202-4182 · 513-651-6800

James L. O'Connell · a · Lindhorst & Dreidame · 312 Walnut Street, Suite 3100 · Cincinnati, OH 45202-4048 · 513-421-6630

Steven H. Ray · Dinsmore & Shohl · http://www.dinslaw.com · 255 East Fifth Street, Suite 1900 · Cincinnati, OH 45202-3172 · 513-977-8200

Cleveland

Thomas E. Dover · Gallagher Sharp Attorneys · Bulkley Building, Sixth Floor · 1501 Euclid Avenue · Cleveland, OH 44115 · 216-241-5310

Columbus

R. Leland Evans · Porter, Wright, Morris & Arthur · http://www.porterwright.com · Huntington Center · 41 South High Street · Columbus, OH 43215-6194 · 614-227-2000

Toledo

Richard F. Ellenberger · Anspach Meeks Ellenberger · 300 Madison Avenue, Suite 1600 · Toledo, OH 43604-2633 · 419-246-5757

REAL ESTATE LAW

Akron

Edward V. Buehrle · Buckingham, Doolittle & Burroughs · http://www.bdblaw.com · 3800 Embassy Parkway, Suite 300 · P.O. Box 1500 · Akron, OH 44309-1500 · 330-376-5300

John M. Coyne · Roetzel & Andress · http://www.ralaw.com · 222 South Main Street · Akron, OH 44308-2098 · 330-376-2700

Nicholas T. George · Buckingham, Doolittle & Burroughs · http://www.bdblaw.com · 3800 Embassy Parkway, Suite 300 · P.O. Box 1500 · Akron, OH 44309-1500 · 330-376-5300

Brian J. Moore · Roetzel & Andress · http://www.ralaw.com · 222 South Main Street · Akron, OH 44308-2098 · 330-376-2700

Jay P. Porter · a · Vorys, Sater, Seymour and Pease · First National Tower, Suite 1100 · 106 South Main Street · Akron, OH 44308-1417 · 330-208-1000

David W. Woodburn · Buckingham, Doolittle & Burroughs · http://www.bdblaw.com · 3800 Embassy Parkway, Suite 300 · P.O. Box 1500 · Akron, OH 44309-1500 · 330-376-5300

Beachwood

Sheldon Berns · a · Berns, Ockner & Greenberger · 3733 Park East Drive, Suite 200 · Beachwood, OH 44122-4334 · 216-831-8838

Troy R. Brown · Singerman, Mills, Desberg & Kauntz · 3401 Enterprise Parkway, Suite 200 · Beachwood, OH 44122 · 216-292-5807

Gary S. Desberg · Singerman, Mills, Desberg & Kauntz · 3401 Enterprise Parkway, Suite 200 · Beachwood, OH 44122 · 216-292-5807

Gary W. Melsher · a · Singerman, Mills, Desberg & Kauntz · 3401 Enterprise Parkway, Suite 200 · Beachwood, OH 44122 · 216-292-5807

Paul J. Singerman · Singerman, Mills, Desberg & Kauntz · 3401 Enterprise Parkway, Suite 200 · Beachwood, OH 44122 · 216-292-5807

Canal Winchester

John M. Kantner · John Kantner · Five West Waterloo Street · Canal Winchester, OH 43110-1139 · 614-834-5917

Cincinnati

Charles C. Bissinger, Jr. · Vorys, Sater, Seymour and Pease · Atrium Two, Suite 2000 · 221 East Fourth Street · P.O. Box 0236 · Cincinnati, OH 45201-0236 · 513-723-4000

Martin C. Butler · Strauss & Troy · http://www.strausstroy.com · The Federal Reserve Building · 150 East Fourth Street · Cincinnati, OH 45202-4018 · 513-621-2120

Daniel H. Demmerle II · Strauss & Troy · http://www.strausstroy.com · The Federal Reserve Building · 150 East Fourth Street · Cincinnati, OH 45202-4018 · 513-621-2120

Edward D. Diller · 2) · Taft Stettinius & Hollister · http://www.taftlaw.com · 425 Walnut Street, Suite 1800 · Cincinnati, OH 45202-3957 · 513-381-2838

Andrew R. Giannella · Strauss & Troy · http://www.strausstroy.com · The Federal Reserve Building · 150 East Fourth Street · Cincinnati, OH 45202-4018 · 513-621-2120

Stephen M. Griffith, Jr. · a · Taft Stettinius & Hollister · http://www.taftlaw.com · 425 Walnut Street, Suite 1800 · Cincinnati, OH 45202-3957 · 513-381-2838

Stephen R. Hunt · Aronoff, Rosen & Hunt · U.S. Bank Tower, Suite 2200 · 425 Walnut Street · Cincinnati, OH 45202-3954 · 513-241-0400

Scott P. Kadish · Ulmer & Berne · 600 Vine Street, Suite 2800 · Cincinnati, OH 45202-2409 · 513-698-5000

Stephen M. King · Thompson Hine · 312 Walnut Street, 14th Floor · Cincinnati, OH 45202-4089 · 513-352-6700

Monica Donath Kohnen · Graydon, Head & Ritchey · 1900 Fifth Third Center · 511 Walnut Street · Cincinnati, OH 45202 · 513-621-6464

Kenneth P. Kreider · Keating Muething & Klekamp · http://www.kmklaw.com · One East Fourth Street, Suite 1400 · Cincinnati, OH 45202 · 513-579-6400

Richard T. LaJeunesse · Graydon, Head & Ritchey · 1900 Fifth Third Center · 511 Walnut Street · Cincinnati, OH 45202 · 513-621-6464

William L. Martin, Jr. · Martin & Wharton · 10101 Alliance Road, Suite 220 · Cincinnati, OH 45242 · 513-322-6811

E. Richard Oberschmidt · a · Frost Brown Todd · http://www.frostbrowntodd.com · PNC Center, Suite 2200 · 201 East Fifth Street · Cincinnati, OH 45202-4182 · 513-651-6800

Joanne M. Schreiner · Dinsmore & Shohl · http://www.dinslaw.com · 255 East Fifth Street, Suite 1900 · Cincinnati, OH 45202-3172 · 513-977-8200

Charles E. Schroer · Frost Brown Todd · http://www.frostbrowntodd.com · PNC Center, Suite 2200 · 201 East Fifth Street · Cincinnati, OH 45202-4182 · 513-651-6800

Thomas J. Sherman · Dinsmore & Shohl · http://www.dinslaw.com · 255 East Fifth Street, Suite 1900 · Cincinnati, OH 45202-3172 · 513-977-8200

Andrew M. Shott · Strauss & Troy · http://www.strausstroy.com · The Federal Reserve Building · 150 East Fourth Street · Cincinnati, OH 45202-4018 · 513-621-2120

Donald J. Shuller · Vorys, Sater, Seymour and Pease · Atrium Two, Suite 2000 · 221 East Fourth Street · P.O. Box 0236 · Cincinnati, OH 45201-0236 · 513-723-4000

Steven R. Smith · Greenebaum Doll & McDonald · http://www.gdm.com · Chemed Center, Suite 2900 · 255 East Fifth Street · Cincinnati, OH 45202 · 513-455-7600

Richard B. Tranter · Dinsmore & Shohl · http://www.dinslaw.com · 255 East Fifth Street, Suite 1900 · Cincinnati, OH 45202-3172 · 513-977-8200

Joseph L. Trauth, Jr. · Keating Muething & Klekamp · http://www.kmklaw.com · One East Fourth Street, Suite 1400 · Cincinnati, OH 45202 · 513-579-6400

Daniel P. Utt · Katz, Teller, Brant & Hild · http://www.katzteller.com · 255 East Fifth Street, Suite 2400 · Cincinnati, OH 45202-4724 · 513-721-4532

Mark J. Weber · Keating Muething & Klekamp · http://www.kmklaw.com · One East Fourth Street, Suite 1400 · Cincinnati, OH 45202 · 513-579-6400

Steven W. Weeks · a · Taft Stettinius & Hollister · http://www.taftlaw.com · 425 Walnut Street, Suite 1800 · Cincinnati, OH 45202-3957 · 513-381-2838

Herbert B. Weiss · 2% · Keating Muething & Klekamp · http://www.kmklaw.com · One East Fourth Street, Suite 1400 · Cincinnati, OH 45202 · 513-579-6400

W. Russell Wilson · Frost Brown Todd · http://www.frostbrowntodd.com · PNC Center, Suite 2200 · 201 East Fifth Street · Cincinnati, OH 45202-4182 · 513-651-6800

Cleveland

Jeffrey R. Appelbaum · a · Thompson Hine · Key Center, Suite 3900 · 127 Public Square · Cleveland, OH 44114-1291 · 216-566-5500

James B. Aronoff · Thompson Hine · Key Center, Suite 3900 · 127 Public Square · Cleveland, OH 44114-1291 · 216-566-5500

Brent D. Ballard · Calfee, Halter & Griswold · http://www.calfee.com · 1400 KeyBank Center · 800 Superior Avenue · Cleveland, OH 44114-2688 · 216-622-8200

Arthur L. Cobb · a · Hahn Loeser & Parks · BP Tower, Suite 2800 · 200 Public Square · Cleveland, OH 44114-2301 · 216-621-0150

Dianne Coscarelli · Thompson Hine · Key Center, Suite 3900 · 127 Public Square · Cleveland, OH 44114-1291 · 216-566-5500

Thomas J. Coyne · Thompson Hine · Key Center, Suite 3900 · 127 Public Square · Cleveland, OH 44114-1291 · 216-566-5500

Charles Daroff II · Hurtuk & Daroff · Parkland Terrace, Suite 100 · 6120 Parkland Boulevard · Cleveland, OH 44124 · 440-605-6660

Carl J. Dyczek · Walter & Haverfield · http://www.walterhav.com · The Tower at Erieview, Suite 3500 · 1301 East Ninth Street · Cleveland, OH 44114 · 216-781-1212

Harold E. Friedman · 2% · Ulmer & Berne · Skylight Office Tower, Suite 1100 · 1660 West Second Street Cleveland, OH 44113-1448 · 216-583-7000

Robert A. Fuerst · Taft Stettinius & Hollister · http://www.taftlaw.com · BP Tower, Suite 3500 · 200 Public Square · Cleveland, OH 44114-2302 · 216-241-2838

Bill J. Gagliano · Ulmer & Berne · Skylight Office Tower, Suite 1100 · 1660 West Second Street · Cleveland, OH 44113-1448 · 216-583-7000

Lynn M. Gattozzi · Squire Sanders · http://www.ssd.com · 4900 Key Tower · 127 Public Square · Cleveland, OH 44114-1304 · 216-479-8500

Bruce E. Gaynor · Taft Stettinius & Hollister · http://www.taftlaw.com · BP Tower, Suite 3500 · 200 Public Square · Cleveland, OH 44114-2302 · 216-241-2838

Bernard D. Goodman · 2) · Benesch, Friedlander, Coplan & Aronoff · BP Tower, Suite 2300 · 200 Public Square · Cleveland, OH 44114-2378 · 216-363-4500

Norman W. Gutmacher · a · Benesch, Friedlander, Coplan & Aronoff · BP Tower, Suite 2300 · 200 Public Square · Cleveland, OH 44114-2378 · 216-363-4500

Kevin M. Hinkel · Kadish, Hinkel & Weibel · http://www.khwlaw.com · 1717 East Ninth Street, Suite 2112 · Cleveland, OH 44114 · 216-696-3030

Edward A. Hurtuk · Hurtuk & Daroff · Parkland Terrace, Suite 100 · 6120 Parkland Boulevard · Cleveland, OH 44124 · 440-605-6660

Kenneth M. Lapine · a · Roetzel & Andress · http://www.ralaw.com · One Cleveland Center, Ninth Floor · 1375 East Ninth Street · Cleveland, OH 44114 · 216-623-0150

Kenneth B. Liffman · McCarthy, Lebit, Crystal & Liffman · http://www.mccarthylebit.com · The Midland Building, Suite 1800 · 101 West Prospect Avenue · Cleveland, OH 44115 · 216-696-1422

Lawrence V. Lindberg · Baker Hostetler · http://www.bakerlaw.com · National City Center, Suite 3200 · 1900 East Ninth Street · Cleveland, OH 44114-3485 · 216-621-0200

David Linder · Ulmer & Berne · Skylight Office Tower, Suite 1100 · 1660 West Second Street · Cleveland, OH 44113-1448 · 216-583-7000

Mary Lovett · Ulmer & Berne · Skylight Office Tower, Suite 1100 · 1660 West Second Street · Cleveland, OH 44113-1448 · 216-583-7000

Steven A. Marrer · Taft Stettinius & Hollister · http://www.taftlaw.com · BP Tower, Suite 3500 · 200 Public Square · Cleveland, OH 44114-2302 · 216-241-2838

Thomas A. Mason · 2% · Thompson Hine · Key Center, Suite 3900 · 127 Public Square · Cleveland, OH 44114-1291 · 216-566-5500

Stephen C. Mixter · Jones Day · North Point · 901 Lakeside Avenue · Cleveland, OH 44114-1190 · 216-586-3939

Patricia J. O'Donnell · a · Baker Hostetler · http://www.bakerlaw.com · National City Center, Suite 3200 1900 East Ninth Street · Cleveland, OH 44114-3485 · 216-621-0200

Brian M. O'Neill · Ulmer & Berne · Skylight Office Tower, Suite 1100 · 1660 West Second Street · Cleveland, OH 44113-1448 · 216-583-7000

Robert C. Ondak, Jr. · Benesch, Friedlander, Coplan & Aronoff · BP Tower, Suite 2300 · 200 Public Square · Cleveland, OH 44114-2378 · 216-363-4500

Michael S. Owendoff · Jones Day · North Point · 901 Lakeside Avenue · Cleveland, OH 44114-1190 · 216-586-3939

Stephen P. Owendoff · a · Hahn Loeser & Parks · BP Tower, Suite 2800 · 200 Public Square · Cleveland, OH 44114-2301 · 216-621-0150

Zachary T. Paris · a · Jones Day · North Point · 901 Lakeside Avenue · Cleveland, OH 44114-1190 · 216-586-3939

Samuel S. Pearlman · a · Squire Sanders · http://www.ssd.com · 4900 Key Tower · 127 Public Square · Cleveland, OH 44114-1304 · 216-479-8500

William M. Phillips · Taft Stettinius & Hollister · http://www.taftlaw.com · BP Tower, Suite 3500 · 200 Public Square · Cleveland, OH 44114-2302 · 216-241-2838

Richard L. Reppert · a · Jones Day · North Point · 901 Lakeside Avenue · Cleveland, OH 44114-1190 · 216-586-3939

Richard S. Rivitz · Taft Stettinius & Hollister · http://www.taftlaw.com · BP Tower, Suite 3500 · 200 Public Square · Cleveland, OH 44114-2302 · 216-241-2838

Richard A. Rosner · 2% · Taft Stettinius & Hollister · http://www.taftlaw.com · BP Tower, Suite 3500 · 200 Public Square · Cleveland, OH 44114-2302 · 216-241-2838

Suzanne K. Saganich · Roetzel & Andress · http://www.ralaw.com · One Cleveland Center, Ninth Floor · 1375 East Ninth Street · Cleveland, OH 44114 · 216-623-0150

John P. Slagter · Buckingham, Doolittle & Burroughs · http://www.bdblaw.com · 1375 East Ninth Street, Suite 1700 · Cleveland, OH 44114 · 216-621-5300

William K. Smith · Ulmer & Berne · Skylight Office Tower, Suite 1100 · 1660 West Second Street · Cleveland, OH 44113-1448 · 216-583-7000

Howard A. Steindler · 2) · Benesch, Friedlander, Coplan & Aronoff · BP Tower, Suite 2300 · 200 Public Square · Cleveland, OH 44114-2378 · 216-363-4500

David J. Strauss · a · Baker Hostetler · http://www.bakerlaw.com · National City Center, Suite 3200 · 1900 East Ninth Street · Cleveland, OH 44114-3485 · 216-621-0200

Linda A. Striefsky · a · Thompson Hine · Key Center, Suite 3900 · 127 Public Square · Cleveland, OH 44114-1291 · 216-566-5500

Michael K. Swearengen · Benesch, Friedlander, Coplan & Aronoff · BP Tower, Suite 2300 · 200 Public Square · Cleveland, OH 44114-2378 · 216-363-4500

Patrick J. Sweeney · Thompson Hine · Key Center, Suite 3900 · 127 Public Square · Cleveland, OH 44114-1291 · 216-566-5500

Terence L. Thomas · Squire Sanders · http://www.ssd.com · 4900 Key Tower · 127 Public Square · Cleveland, OH 44114-1304 · 216-479-8500

William R. Weir · Porter, Wright, Morris & Arthur · http://www.porterwright.com · 925 Euclid Avenue, Suite 1700 · Cleveland, OH 44115-1483 · 216-443-9000

Jeffrey J. Wild · Benesch, Friedlander, Coplan & Aronoff · BP Tower, Suite 2300 · 200 Public Square · Cleveland, OH 44114-2378 · 216-363-4500

Randall S. Arndt · a · Schottenstein, Zox & Dunn · http://www.szd.com · 250 West Street, Suite 700 · Columbus, OH 43215-2538 · 614-462-2700

David G. Baker · 2) · Bricker & Eckler · http://www.bricker.com · 100 South Third Street · Columbus, OH 43215-4291 · 614-227-2300

James M. Ball · Vorys, Sater, Seymour and Pease · 52 East Gay Street · P.O. Box 1008 · Columbus, OH 43216-1008 · 614-464-6400

John E. Brady · Porter, Wright, Morris & Arthur · http://www.porterwright.com · Huntington Center · 41 South High Street · Columbus, OH 43215-6194 · 614-227-2000

Michael D. Bridges · Baker Hostetler · http://www.bakerlaw.com · Capitol Square, Suite 2100 · 65 East State Street · Columbus, OH 43215-4260 · 614-228-1541

Stephen D. Browning · Vorys, Sater, Seymour and Pease · 52 East Gay Street · P.O. Box 1008 · Columbus, OH 43216-1008 · 614-464-6400

Stephen R. Buchenroth · a · Vorys, Sater, Seymour and Pease · 52 East Gay Street · P.O. Box 1008 · Columbus, OH 43216-1008 · 614-464-6400

Bruce H. Burkholder · a · Wiles, Boyle, Burkholder & Bringardner · 300 Spruce Street, First Floor · Columbus, OH 43215 · 614-221-5216

John I. Cadwallader · a · Frost Brown Todd · http://www.frostbrowntodd.com · One Columbus, Suite 2300 · 10 West Broad Street · Columbus, OH 43215-3467 · 614-464-1211

David K. Conrad · a · Bricker & Eckler · http://www.bricker.com · 100 South Third Street · Columbus, OH 43215-4291 · 614-227-2300

Gary E. Davis · a · Vorys, Sater, Seymour and Pease · 52 East Gay Street · P.O. Box 1008 · Columbus, OH 43216-1008 · 614-464-6400

Ronald E. Davis · Folkerth, Haddow & Davis · 250 Civic Center Drive, Suite 460 · Columbus, OH 43215-5086 · 614-228-2945

Steven P. Elliott · Wiles, Boyle, Burkholder & Bringardner · 300 Spruce Street, First Floor · Columbus, OH 43215 · 614-221-5216

David W. Fisher · Kephart & Fisher · 207 North Fourth Street · Columbus, OH 43215-2510 · 614-469-1882

Herbert R. Godby · Schottenstein, Zox & Dunn · http://www.szd.com · 250 West Street, Suite 700 · Columbus, OH 43215-2538 · 614-462-2700

Kenneth A. Golonka, Jr. · Vorys, Sater, Seymour and Pease · 52 East Gay Street · P.O. Box 1008 · Columbus, OH 43216-1008 · 614-464-6400

Howard J. Haddow · 2% · Folkerth, Haddow & Davis · 250 Civic Center Drive, Suite 460 · Columbus, OH 43215-5086 · 614-228-2945

Craig A. Haddox · Bricker & Eckler · http://www.bricker.com · 100 South Third Street · Columbus, OH 43215-4291 · 614-227-2300

Stephen Intihar · Bricker & Eckler · http://www.bricker.com · 100 South Third Street · Columbus, OH 43215-4291 · 614-227-2300

Donald W. Jordan · Porter, Wright, Morris & Arthur · http://www.porterwright.com · Huntington Center 41 South High Street · Columbus, OH 43215-6194 · 614-227-2000

John J. Joseph · a · Joseph & Joseph · http://www.josephandjoseph.com · 931 South Front Street · Columbus, OH 43206 · 614-449-8282

Daniel Kayne · Kayne Law Group · 612 Park Street, Suite 200 · Columbus, OH 43215 · 614-223-8800

Robert C. Kiger · 2% · Porter, Wright, Morris & Arthur · http://www.porterwright.com · Huntington Center · 41 South High Street · Columbus, OH 43215-6194 · 614-227-2000

Kenton L. Kuehnle · 2) · Allen Kuehnle Stovall & Newman · 21 West Broad Street, Suite 400 · Columbus, OH 43215 · 614-221-8500

Rick A. Lavinsky · Dinsmore & Shohl · http://www.dinslaw.com · 191 West Nationwide Boulevard, Suite 300 · Columbus, OH 43215 · 614-221-8448

Donald B. Leach, Jr. · Dinsmore & Shohl · http://www.dinslaw.com · 191 West Nationwide Boulevard, Suite 300 · Columbus, OH 43215 · 614-221-8448

Jack S. Levey · Plunkett Cooney · 300 East Broad Street, Suite 590 · Columbus, OH 43215 · 614-629-3000

Richard L. Levine · Richard L. Levine · 460 East Main Street · Columbus, OH 43215-5344 · 614-227-0300

Richard L. Loveland · 2) · Loveland & Brosius · 50 West Broad Street, Suite 3300 · Columbus, OH 43215-5917 · 614-464-3563

Daniel J. Minor · Vorys, Sater, Seymour and Pease · 52 East Gay Street · P.O. Box 1008 · Columbus, OH 43216-1008 · 614-464-6400

William E. Nakasian · Jones Day · 325 John H. McConnell Boulevard, Suite 600 · P.O. Box 165017 · Columbus, OH 43216-5017 · 614-469-3939

Harlan W. Robins · Baker Hostetler · http://www.bakerlaw.com · Capitol Square, Suite 2100 · 65 East State Street · Columbus, OH 43215-4260 · 614-228-1541

John B. Rohyans · a · Porter, Wright, Morris & Arthur · http://www.porterwright.com · Huntington Center · 41 South High Street · Columbus, OH 43215-6194 · 614-227-2000

Richard W. Rubenstein · a · Squire Sanders · http://www.ssd.com · 1300 Huntington Center · 41 South High Street · Columbus, OH 43215-6197 · 614-365-2700

Michael D. Saad · a · Squire Sanders · http://www.ssd.com · 1300 Huntington Center · 41 South High Street · Columbus, OH 43215-6197 · 614-365-2700

Daniel H. Schoedinger · Vorys, Sater, Seymour and Pease · 52 East Gay Street · P.O. Box 1008 · Columbus, OH 43216-1008 · 614-464-6400

Dirken T. Voelker · a · Voelker & Voelker · 1635 West First Avenue · Columbus, OH 43212 · 614-481-6500

Dow T. Voelker · Voelker & Voelker · 1635 West First Avenue · Columbus, OH 43212 · 614-481-6500

John P. Wellner · a · Vorys, Sater, Seymour and Pease · 52 East Gay Street · P.O. Box 1008 · Columbus, OH 43216-1008 · 614-464-6400

Robert W. Werth · a · Vorys, Sater, Seymour and Pease · 52 East Gay Street · P.O. Box 1008 · Columbus, OH 43216-1008 · 614-464-6400

Nancy B. Young · a · Porter, Wright, Morris & Arthur · http://www.porterwright.com · Huntington Center · 41 South High Street · Columbus, OH 43215-6194 · 614-227-2000

Michael E. Zatezalo · Kegler, Brown, Hill & Ritter · http://www.keglerbrown.com · Capitol Square, Suite 1800 · 65 East State Street · Columbus, OH 43215-4294 · 614-462-5400

Dayton

Karen R. Adams · Dinsmore & Shohl · http://www.dinslaw.com · One Dayton Centre, Suite 1300 · One South Main Street · Dayton, OH 45402 · 937-449-6400

John C. Chambers · a · Coolidge Wall Co. · http://www.coollaw.com · 33 West First Street, Suite 600 · Dayton, OH 45402 · 937-223-8177

Robert M. Curry · 2) · Thompson Hine · 2000 Courthouse Plaza, NE · 10 West Second Street · P.O. Box 8801 · Dayton, OH 45401-8801 · 937-443-6600

William G. Deas · a · Porter, Wright, Morris & Arthur · http://www.porterwright.com · One Dayton Centre, Suite 1600 · One South Main Street · Dayton, OH 45402-2028 · 937-449-6810

Jonas J. Gruenberg · Coolidge Wall Co. · http://www.coollaw.com · 33 West First Street, Suite 600 · Dayton, OH 45402 · 937-223-8177

Timothy J. Hackert · a · Thompson Hine · 2000 Courthouse Plaza, NE · 10 West Second Street · P.O. Box 8801 · Dayton, OH 45401-8801 · 937-443-6600

J. Stephen Herbert · 2) · Coolidge Wall Co. · http://www.coollaw.com · 33 West First Street, Suite 600 · Dayton, OH 45402 · 937-223-8177

Edward M. Kress · a · Dinsmore & Shohl · http://www.dinslaw.com · Courthouse Plaza, SW, Suite 1100 · 10 North Ludlow Street · Dayton, OH 45402 · 937-449-2800

Joan H. Roddy · a · Thompson Hine · 2000 Courthouse Plaza, NE · 10 West Second Street · P.O. Box 8801 · Dayton, OH 45401-8801 · 937-443-6600

Alan B. Schaeffer · Pickrel, Schaeffer & Ebeling · Kettering Tower, 27th Floor · 40 North Main Street · Dayton, OH 45423 · 937-223-1130

Edward L. Shank · 2) · Bieser, Greer & Landis · http://www.biesergreer.com · National City Center, Suite 400 · Six North Main Street · Dayton, OH 45402-1908 · 937-223-3277

Merideth A. Trott · Dinsmore & Shohl · http://www.dinslaw.com · One Dayton Centre, Suite 1300 · One South Main Street · Dayton, OH 45402 · 937-449-6400

Merle F. Wilberding · Coolidge Wall Co. · http://www.coollaw.com · 33 West First Street, Suite 600 · Dayton, OH 45402 · 937-223-8177

North Canton

Thomas Winkhart, Jr. · Winkhart & Rambacher · 825 South Main Street · North Canton, OH 44720 · 330-433-6700

Toledo

Thomas W. Heintschel · Frederickson, Heintschel & King · National City Bank Building, Suite 1212 · 405 Madison Avenue · Toledo, OH 43604-1108 · 419-242-5100

Timothy Konieczny · Coy, Konieczny & Peppel · 405 Madison Avenue, Suite 700 · Toledo, OH 43604 · 419-724-5252

Jerome R. Parker · 2) · Gressley, Kaplin & Parker · One SeaGate, Suite 1645 · Toledo, OH 43604-1584 · 419-244-8336

Steven Reinbolt · Eastman & Smith · One Seagate, 24th Floor · P.O. Box 10032 · Toledo, OH 43699-0032 · 419-241-6000

Cynthia L. Rerucha · a · Shumaker, Loop & Kendrick · North Courthouse Square · 1000 Jackson Street · Toledo, OH 43604-5573 · 419-241-9000

Joseph A. Rideout · 2) · Shumaker, Loop & Kendrick · North Courthouse Square · 1000 Jackson Street · Toledo, OH 43604-5573 · 419-241-9000

Gregory S. Shumaker · a · Shumaker, Loop & Kendrick · North Courthouse Square · 1000 Jackson Street · Toledo, OH 43604-5573 · 419-241-9000

Barton L. Wagenman · 2% · Shumaker, Loop & Kendrick · North Courthouse Square · 1000 Jackson Street · Toledo, OH 43604-5573 · 419-241-9000

SECURITIES LAW

Cincinnati

Andrew R. Berger · Katz, Teller, Brant & Hild · http://www.katzteller.com · 255 East Fifth Street, Suite 2400 · Cincinnati, OH 45202-4724 · 513-721-4532

Neil Ganulin · Frost Brown Todd · http://www.frostbrowntodd.com · PNC Center, Suite 2200 · 201 East Fifth Street · Cincinnati, OH 45202-4182 · 513-651-6800

Charles F. Hertlein · Dinsmore & Shohl · http://www.dinslaw.com · 255 East Fifth Street, Suite 1900 · Cincinnati, OH 45202-3172 · 513-977-8200

Timothy E. Hoberg · 2) · Taft Stettinius & Hollister · http://www.taftlaw.com · 425 Walnut Street, Suite 1800 · Cincinnati, OH 45202-3957 · 513-381-2838

Paul V. Muething · Keating Muething & Klekamp · http://www.kmklaw.com · One East Fourth Street, Suite 1400 · Cincinnati, OH 45202 · 513-579-6400

Clifford A. Roe, Jr. · 2) · Dinsmore & Shohl · http://www.dinslaw.com · 255 East Fifth Street, Suite 1900 Cincinnati, OH 45202-3172 · 513-977-8200

George H. Vincent · Dinsmore & Shohl · http://www.dinslaw.com · 255 East Fifth Street, Suite 1900 · Cincinnati, OH 45202-3172 · 513-977-8200

Susan B. Zaunbrecher · Dinsmore & Shohl · http://www.dinslaw.com · 255 East Fifth Street, Suite 1900 · Cincinnati, OH 45202-3172 · 513-977-8200

Cleveland

George N. Aronoff · 2% · Benesch, Friedlander, Coplan & Aronoff · BP Tower, Suite 2300 · 200 Public Square · Cleveland, OH 44114-2378 · 216-363-4500

Daniel G. Berick · Squire Sanders · http://www.ssd.com · 4900 Key Tower · 127 Public Square · Cleveland, OH 44114-1304 · 216-479-8500

Irv Berliner · Taft Stettinius & Hollister · http://www.taftlaw.com · BP Tower, Suite 3500 · 200 Public Square · Cleveland, OH 44114-2302 · 216-241-2838

Frances Floriano Goins · Ulmer & Berne · Skylight Office Tower, Suite 1100 · 1660 West Second Street Cleveland, OH 44113-1448 · 216-583-7000

Thomas F. McKee · a · Calfee, Halter & Griswold · http://www.calfee.com · 1400 KeyBank Center · 800 Superior Avenue · Cleveland, OH 44114-2688 · 216-622-8200

Megan L. Mehalko · Benesch, Friedlander, Coplan & Aronoff · BP Tower, Suite 2300 · 200 Public Square Cleveland, OH 44114-2378 · 216-363-4500

Donald H. Messinger · a · Thompson Hine · Key Center, Suite 3900 · 127 Public Square · Cleveland, OH 44114-1291 · 216-566-5500

Glenn E. Morrical · Tucker Ellis & West · Huntington Building, Suite 1150 · 925 Euclid Avenue · Cleveland, OH 44115-1475 · 216-592-5000

Frederick R. Nance · Squire Sanders · http://www.ssd.com · 4900 Key Tower · 127 Public Square · Cleveland, OH 44114-1304 · 216-479-8500

Lawrence N. Schultz · Calfee, Halter & Griswold · http://www.calfee.com · 1400 KeyBank Center · 800 Superior Avenue · Cleveland, OH 44114-2688 · 216-622-8200

Columbus

Dan A. Bailey · Bailey Cavalieri · One Columbus Building, Suite 2100 · 10 West Broad Street · Columbus, OH 43215-3422 · 614-221-3155

John P. Beavers · 2% · Bricker & Eckler · http://www.bricker.com · 100 South Third Street · Columbus, OH 43215-4291 · 614-227-2300

Gregory W. Stype · Squire Sanders · http://www.ssd.com · 1300 Huntington Center · 41 South High Street · Columbus, OH 43215-6197 · 614-365-2700

Roger P. Sugarman · Kegler, Brown, Hill & Ritter · http://www.keglerbrown.com · Capitol Square, Suite 1800 · 65 East State Street · Columbus, OH 43215-4294 · 614-462-5400

Dayton

Joseph M. Rigot · Thompson Hine · 2000 Courthouse Plaza, NE · 10 West Second Street · P.O. Box 8801 Dayton, OH 45401-8801 · 937-443-6600

Toledo

Lyman F. Spitzer · Shumaker, Loop & Kendrick · North Courthouse Square · 1000 Jackson Street · Toledo, OH 43604-5573 · 419-241-9000

Thomas I. Webb, Jr. · Shumaker, Loop & Kendrick · North Courthouse Square · 1000 Jackson Street · Toledo, OH 43604-5573 · 419-241-9000

SPORTS LAW

Akron

David P. Bertsch · Buckingham, Doolittle & Burroughs · http://www.bdblaw.com · 3800 Embassy Parkway, Suite 300 · P.O. Box 1500 · Akron, OH 44309-1500 · 330-376-5300

Cleveland

Frederick R. Nance · Squire Sanders · http://www.ssd.com · 4900 Key Tower · 127 Public Square · Cleveland, OH 44114-1304 · 216-479-8500

STRUCTURED FINANCE LAW

Cincinnati

Joanne M. Schreiner · Dinsmore & Shohl · http://www.dinslaw.com · 255 East Fifth Street, Suite 1900 · Cincinnati, OH 45202-3172 · 513-977-8200

TAX LAW

Akron

Steven A. Dimengo · Buckingham, Doolittle & Burroughs · http://www.bdblaw.com · 3800 Embassy Parkway, Suite 300 · P.O. Box 1500 · Akron, OH 44309-1500 · 330-376-5300

Cathy C. Godshall · Buckingham, Doolittle & Burroughs · http://www.bdblaw.com · 3800 Embassy Parkway, Suite 300 · P.O. Box 1500 · Akron, OH 44309-1500 · 330-376-5300

David Kern · Buckingham, Doolittle & Burroughs · http://www.bdblaw.com · 3800 Embassy Parkway, Suite 300 · P.O. Box 1500 · Akron, OH 44309-1500 · 330-376-5300

Jeffrey W. Leonard · Roetzel & Andress · http://www.ralaw.com · 222 South Main Street · Akron, OH 44308-2098 · 330-376-2700

Frank A. Lettieri · 2) · Brennan, Manna & Diamond · The Carnegie Building · 75 East Market Street · Akron, OH 44308 · 330-253-5060

David J. Lewis · Buckingham, Doolittle & Burroughs · http://www.bdblaw.com · 3800 Embassy Parkway, Suite 300 · P.O. Box 1500 · Akron, OH 44309-1500 · 330-376-5300

Robert W. Malone · 2) · Buckingham, Doolittle & Burroughs · http://www.bdblaw.com · 3800 Embassy Parkway, Suite 300 · P.O. Box 1500 · Akron, OH 44309-1500 · 330-376-5300

Cincinnati

Henry G. Alexander · Graydon, Head & Ritchey · 1900 Fifth Third Center · 511 Walnut Street · Cincinnati, OH 45202 · 513-621-6464

Mark H. Berliant · 2% · Strauss & Troy · http://www.strausstroy.com · The Federal Reserve Building · 150 East Fourth Street · Cincinnati, OH 45202-4018 · 513-621-2120

Joel S. Brant · Katz, Teller, Brant & Hild · http://www.katzteller.com · 255 East Fifth Street, Suite 2400 · Cincinnati, OH 45202-4724 · 513-721-4532

Robert E. Brant · Katz, Teller, Brant & Hild · http://www.katzteller.com · 255 East Fifth Street, Suite 2400 · Cincinnati, OH 45202-4724 · 513-721-4532

Alan S. Fershtman · Keating Muething & Klekamp · http://www.kmklaw.com · One East Fourth Street, Suite 1400 · Cincinnati, OH 45202 · 513-579-6400

William M. Freedman · 2% · Dinsmore & Shohl · http://www.dinslaw.com · 255 East Fifth Street, Suite 1900 · Cincinnati, OH 45202-3172 · 513-977-8200

Patrick J. Mitchell · Taft Stettinius & Hollister · http://www.taftlaw.com · 425 Walnut Street, Suite 1800 · Cincinnati, OH 45202-3957 · 513-381-2838

Martin E. Mooney · a · Frost Brown Todd · http://www.frostbrowntodd.com · PNC Center, Suite 2200 · 201 East Fifth Street · Cincinnati, OH 45202-4182 · 513-651-6800

Stephen M. Nechemias · 2% · Taft Stettinius & Hollister · http://www.taftlaw.com · 425 Walnut Street, Suite 1800 · Cincinnati, OH 45202-3957 · 513-381-2838

Robert E. Rich · Taft Stettinius & Hollister · http://www.taftlaw.com · 425 Walnut Street, Suite 1800 · Cincinnati, OH 45202-3957 · 513-381-2838

Howard L. Richshafer · a · Statman, Harris & Eyrich · 441 Vine Street, Suite 3700 · Cincinnati, OH 45202 · 513-621-2666

Thomas C. Rink · Strauss & Troy · http://www.strausstroy.com · The Federal Reserve Building · 150 East Fourth Street · Cincinnati, OH 45202-4018 · 513-621-2120

Stanley L. Ruby · Schwartz, Manes, Ruby & Slovin · Carew Tower, Suite 2900 · 441 Vine Street · Cincinnati, OH 45202-3090 · 513-579-1414

William F. Russo · a · Katz, Teller, Brant & Hild · http://www.katzteller.com · 255 East Fifth Street, Suite 2400 · Cincinnati, OH 45202-4724 · 513-721-4532

Michael G. Schwartz · Vorys, Sater, Seymour and Pease · Atrium Two, Suite 2000 · 221 East Fourth Street · P.O. Box 0236 · Cincinnati, OH 45201-0236 · 513-723-4000

Samuel M. Scoggins · Frost Brown Todd · http://www.frostbrowntodd.com · PNC Center, Suite 2200 · 201 East Fifth Street · Cincinnati, OH 45202-4182 · 513-651-6800

Mark E. Sims · a · Keating Muething & Klekamp · http://www.kmklaw.com · One East Fourth Street, Suite 1400 · Cincinnati, OH 45202 · 513-579-6400

Scott M. Slovin · Schwartz, Manes, Ruby & Slovin · Carew Tower, Suite 2900 · 441 Vine Street · Cincinnati, OH 45202-3090 · 513-579-1414

Cleveland

Joseph Paul Alexander · Rotatori, Bender, Gragel, Stoper & Alexander · http://www.rotatori.com · 800 Leader Building · 526 Superior Avenue East · Cleveland, OH 44114-1498 · 216-928-1010

Malvin E. Bank · 2% · Thompson Hine · Key Center, Suite 3900 · 127 Public Square · Cleveland, OH 44114-1291 · 216-566-5500

Lewis T. Barr · 2) · Ulmer & Berne · Skylight Office Tower, Suite 1100 · 1660 West Second Street · Cleveland, OH 44113-1448 · 216-583-7000

J. Timothy Bender · a · Rotatori, Bender, Gragel, Stoper & Alexander · http://www.rotatori.com · 800 Leader Building · 526 Superior Avenue East · Cleveland, OH 44114-1498 · 216-928-1010

Stephen L. Buescher · a · Thompson Hine · Key Center, Suite 3900 · 127 Public Square · Cleveland, OH 44114-1291 · 216-566-5500

Thomas J. Callahan · Thompson Hine · Key Center, Suite 3900 · 127 Public Square · Cleveland, OH 44114-1291 · 216-566-5500

John D. Currivan · a · Jones Day · North Point · 901 Lakeside Avenue · Cleveland, OH 44114-1190 · 216-586-3939

Alan S. Doris · 2) · Squire Sanders · http://www.ssd.com · 4900 Key Tower · 127 Public Square · Cleveland, OH 44114-1304 · 216-479-8500

Robert J. Eidnier · a · Squire Sanders · http://www.ssd.com · 4900 Key Tower · 127 Public Square · Cleveland, OH 44114-1304 · 216-479-8500

Jeffry J. Erney · Baker Hostetler · http://www.bakerlaw.com · National City Center, Suite 3200 · 1900 East Ninth Street · Cleveland, OH 44114-3485 · 216-621-0200

Brian W. FitzSimons · a · Tucker Ellis & West · Huntington Building, Suite 1150 · 925 Euclid Avenue · Cleveland, OH 44115-1475 · 216-592-5000

Harvey L. Frutkin · a · Cavitch, Familo, Durkin & Frutkin · 1717 East Ninth Street, 14th Floor · Cleveland, OH 44114 · 216-621-7860

John C. Goheen · a · Ulmer & Berne · Skylight Office Tower, Suite 1100 · 1660 West Second Street · Cleveland, OH 44113-1448 · 216-583-7000

Carl M. Jenks · a · Jones Day · North Point · 901 Lakeside Avenue · Cleveland, OH 44114-1190 · 216-586-3939

Stephen L. Kadish · 2% · Kadish, Hinkel & Weibel · http://www.khwlaw.com · 1717 East Ninth Street, Suite 2112 · Cleveland, OH 44114 · 216-696-3030

Kimon P. Karas · McCarthy, Lebit, Crystal & Liffman · http://www.mccarthylebit.com · The Midland Building, Suite 1800 · 101 West Prospect Avenue · Cleveland, OH 44115 · 216-696-1422

James C. Koenig · Thompson Hine · Key Center, Suite 3900 · 127 Public Square · Cleveland, OH 44114-1291 · 216-566-5500

Stephen P. Kresnye · Calfee, Halter & Griswold · http://www.calfee.com · 1400 KeyBank Center · 800 Superior Avenue · Cleveland, OH 44114-2688 · 216-622-8200

Michael G. Meissner · a · Squire Sanders · http://www.ssd.com · 4900 Key Tower · 127 Public Square · Cleveland, OH 44114-1304 · 216-479-8500

Ronald H. Neill · Calfee, Halter & Griswold · http://www.calfee.com · 1400 KeyBank Center · 800 Superior Avenue · Cleveland, OH 44114-2688 · 216-622-8200

Jeffrey H. Paravano · Baker Hostetler · http://www.bakerlaw.com · National City Center, Suite 3200 · 1900 East Ninth Street · Cleveland, OH 44114-3485 · 216-621-0200

Terrence G. Perris · 2) · Squire Sanders · http://www.ssd.com · 4900 Key Tower · 127 Public Square · Cleveland, OH 44114-1304 · 216-479-8500

Edward G. Ptaszek, Jr. · a · Baker Hostetler · http://www.bakerlaw.com · National City Center, Suite 3200 · 1900 East Ninth Street · Cleveland, OH 44114-3485 · 216-621-0200

Deborah Z. Read · Thompson Hine · Key Center, Suite 3900 · 127 Public Square · Cleveland, OH 44114-1291 · 216-566-5500

Hewitt B. Shaw · a · Baker Hostetler · http://www.bakerlaw.com · National City Center, Suite 3200 · 1900 East Ninth Street · Cleveland, OH 44114-3485 · 216-621-0200

Christopher J. Swift · a · Baker Hostetler · http://www.bakerlaw.com · National City Center, Suite 3200 1900 East Ninth Street · Cleveland, OH 44114-3485 · 216-621-0200

David R. Tavolier · Taft Stettinius & Hollister · http://www.taftlaw.com · BP Tower, Suite 3500 · 200 Public Square · Cleveland, OH 44114-2302 · 216-241-2838

Mitchell S. Thompson · Squire Sanders · http://www.ssd.com · 4900 Key Tower · 127 Public Square · Cleveland, OH 44114-1304 · 216-479-8500

William M. Toomajian · 2) · Baker Hostetler · http://www.bakerlaw.com · National City Center, Suite 3200 · 1900 East Ninth Street · Cleveland, OH 44114-3485 · 216-621-0200

Jeffry L. Weiler · 2) · Benesch, Friedlander, Coplan & Aronoff · BP Tower, Suite 2300 · 200 Public Square · Cleveland, OH 44114-2378 · 216-363-4500

Frederick N. Widen · Ulmer & Berne · Skylight Office Tower, Suite 1100 · 1660 West Second Street · Cleveland, OH 44113-1448 · 216-583-7000

Gary A. Zwick · Walter & Haverfield · http://www.walterhav.com · The Tower at Erieview, Suite 3500 · 1301 East Ninth Street · Cleveland, OH 44114 · 216-781-1212

Columbus

Jerry O. Allen · Bricker & Eckler · http://www.bricker.com · 100 South Third Street · Columbus, OH 43215-4291 · 614-227-2300

Raymond D. Anderson · Vorys, Sater, Seymour and Pease · 52 East Gay Street · P.O. Box 1008 · Columbus, OH 43216-1008 · 614-464-6400

Michael R. Becker · 2) · Becker & Lilly · http://www.beckerlilly.com · 100 East Broad Street, Suite 2320 · Columbus, OH 43215 · 614-469-4778

Harvey Dunn · a · Schottenstein, Zox & Dunn · http://www.szd.com · 250 West Street, Suite 700 · Columbus, OH 43215-2538 · 614-462-2700

Maryann B. Gall · a · Jones Day · 325 John H. McConnell Boulevard, Suite 600 · P.O. Box 165017 · Columbus, OH 43216-5017 · 614-469-3939

Terrence A. Grady · a · Terrence A. Grady & Associates Company · 100 East Broad Street, Suite 2310 · Columbus, OH 43215 · 614-849-0378

Edward C. Hertenstein · a · Roetzel & Andress · http://www.ralaw.com · National City Plaza, 12th Floor 155 East Broad Street · Columbus, OH 43215 · 614-723-2002

Richard Holz · Schottenstein, Zox & Dunn · http://www.szd.com · 250 West Street, Suite 700 · Columbus, OH 43215-2538 · 614-462-2700

Dan L. Jaffe · Vorys, Sater, Seymour and Pease · 52 East Gay Street · P.O. Box 1008 · Columbus, OH 43216-1008 · 614-464-6400

Charles J. Kegler · a · Kegler, Brown, Hill & Ritter · http://www.keglerbrown.com · Capitol Square, Suite 1800 · 65 East State Street · Columbus, OH 43215-4294 · 614-462-5400

James R. King · a · Jones Day · 325 John H. McConnell Boulevard, Suite 600 · P.O. Box 165017 · Columbus, OH 43216-5017 · 614-469-3939

Gordon F. Litt · Bricker & Eckler · http://www.bricker.com · 100 South Third Street · Columbus, OH 43215-4291 · 614-227-2300

Steven F. Mount · Squire Sanders · http://www.ssd.com · 1300 Huntington Center · 41 South High Street Columbus, OH 43215-6197 · 614-365-2700

Aaron P. Rosenfeld · Vorys, Sater, Seymour and Pease · 52 East Gay Street · P.O. Box 1008 · Columbus, OH 43216-1008 · 614-464-6400

Ronald L. Rowland · 2% · Vorys, Sater, Seymour and Pease · 52 East Gay Street · P.O. Box 1008 · Columbus, OH 43216-1008 · 614-464-6400

Fredric L. Smith · 2) · Squire Sanders · http://www.ssd.com · 1300 Huntington Center · 41 South High Street · Columbus, OH 43215-6197 · 614-365-2700

John Terakedis, Jr. · 2% · Schottenstein, Zox & Dunn · http://www.szd.com · 250 West Street, Suite 700 · Columbus, OH 43215-2538 · 614-462-2700

David A. Tumen · Porter, Wright, Morris & Arthur · http://www.porterwright.com · Huntington Center · 41 South High Street · Columbus, OH 43215-6194 · 614-227-2000

Mark E. Vannatta · Vorys, Sater, Seymour and Pease · 52 East Gay Street · P.O. Box 1008 · Columbus, OH 43216-1008 · 614-464-6400

Lee A. Wendel · Squire Sanders · http://www.ssd.com · 1300 Huntington Center · 41 South High Street · Columbus, OH 43215-6197 · 614-365-2700

Dayton

Frederick J. Caspar · a · Dinsmore & Shohl · http://www.dinslaw.com · Courthouse Plaza, SW, Suite 1100 · 10 North Ludlow Street · Dayton, OH 45402 · 937-449-2800

Thomas E. DeBrosse · Thompson Hine · 2000 Courthouse Plaza, NE · 10 West Second Street · P.O. Box 8801 · Dayton, OH 45401-8801 · 937-443-6600

Francesco A. Ferrante · Thompson Hine · 2000 Courthouse Plaza, NE · 10 West Second Street · P.O. Box 8801 · Dayton, OH 45401-8801 · 937-443-6600

Ralph E. Heyman · 2) · Dinsmore & Shohl · http://www.dinslaw.com · Courthouse Plaza, SW, Suite 1100 10 North Ludlow Street · Dayton, OH 45402 · 937-449-2800

Sam Warwar · a · Coolidge Wall Co. · http://www.coollaw.com · 33 West First Street, Suite 600 · Dayton, OH 45402 · 937-223-8177

Maumee

Robert V. Sterling · a · Weber & Sterling · 1721 Indian Wood Circle, Suite One · Maumee, OH 43537-4065 · 419-893-3360

Dennis P. Williams · a · Weber & Sterling · 1721 Indian Wood Circle, Suite One · Maumee, OH 43537-4065 · 419-893-3360

Toledo

Morton Bobowick · 2% · Eastman & Smith · One Seagate, 24th Floor · P.O. Box 10032 · Toledo, OH 43699-0032 · 419-241-6000

Craig F. Frederickson · a · Frederickson, Heintschel & King · National City Bank Building, Suite 1212 · 405 Madison Avenue · Toledo, OH 43604-1108 · 419-242-5100

Gary M. Harden · a · Eastman & Smith · One Seagate, 24th Floor · P.O. Box 10032 · Toledo, OH 43699-0032 · 419-241-6000

Michael S. McGowan · a · Shumaker, Loop & Kendrick · North Courthouse Square · 1000 Jackson Street · Toledo, OH 43604-5573 · 419-241-9000

David F. Waterman · 2) · Shumaker, Loop & Kendrick · North Courthouse Square · 1000 Jackson Street · Toledo, OH 43604-5573 · 419-241-9000

Worthington

Steven A. Martin · a · Blaugrund, Herbert & Martin · 300 West Wilson Bridge Road, Suite 100 · Worthington, OH 43085 · 614-764-0681

TECHNOLOGY LAW

Cincinnati

Todd H. Bailey · Frost Brown Todd · http://www.frostbrowntodd.com · PNC Center, Suite 2200 · 201 East Fifth Street · Cincinnati, OH 45202-4182 · 513-651-6800

Stephen E. Gillen · Greenebaum Doll & McDonald · http://www.gdm.com · Chemed Center, Suite 2900 255 East Fifth Street · Cincinnati, OH 45202 · 513-455-7600

TRANSPORTATION LAW

Akron

Bradley A. Wright · Roetzel & Andress · http://www.ralaw.com · 222 South Main Street · Akron, OH 44308-2098 · 330-376-2700

Cincinnati

Gary E. Becker · Dinsmore & Shohl · http://www.dinslaw.com · 255 East Fifth Street, Suite 1900 · Cincinnati, OH 45202-3172 · 513-977-8200

Jeffrey P. Hinebaugh · Dinsmore & Shohl · http://www.dinslaw.com · 255 East Fifth Street, Suite 1900 · Cincinnati, OH 45202-3172 · 513-977-8200

Cleveland

Kenneth P. Abbarno · Reminger Attorneys At Law · 1400 Midland Building · 101 Prospect Avenue West Cleveland, OH 44115-1093 · 216-687-1311

Hunter S. Havens · Hermann, Cahn & Schneider · http://www.hcsattys.com · 1301 East Ninth Street, Suite 500 · Cleveland, OH 44114 · 216-781-5515

Frank Leonetti III · Reminger Attorneys At Law · 1400 Midland Building · 101 Prospect Avenue West · Cleveland, OH 44115-1093 · 216-687-1311

Richard A. Plewacki · Roetzel & Andress · http://www.ralaw.com · One Cleveland Center, Ninth Floor · 1375 East Ninth Street · Cleveland, OH 44114 · 216-623-0150

James J. Turek · Reminger Attorneys At Law · 1400 Midland Building · 101 Prospect Avenue West · Cleveland, OH 44115-1093 · 216-687-1311

Eric Larson Zalud · Benesch, Friedlander, Coplan & Aronoff · BP Tower, Suite 2300 · 200 Public Square Cleveland, OH 44114-2378 · 216-363-4500

Columbus

Eric W. Beery · Beery & Spurlock · 275 East State Street · Columbus, OH 43215 · 614-228-8575

Marc S. Blubaugh · Benesch, Friedlander, Coplan & Aronoff · 41 South High Street, Suite 2600 · Columbus, OH 43215 · 614-223-9300

Robert C. Buchbinder · Crabbe, Brown & James · 500 South Front Street, Suite 1200 · Columbus, OH 43215 · 614-228-5511

Michael Spurlock · Beery & Spurlock · 275 East State Street · Columbus, OH 43215 · 614-228-8575

TRUSTS AND ESTATES

Akron

Richard W. Burke · a · Brennan, Manna & Diamond · The Carnegie Building · 75 East Market Street · Akron, OH 44308 · 330-253-5060

Steven St. L. Cox · Roetzel & Andress · http://www.ralaw.com · 222 South Main Street · Akron, OH 44308-2098 · 330-376-2700

Richard H. Harris III · Brouse McDowell · 388 South Main Street, Suite 500 · Akron, OH 44311 · 330-535-5711

Philip S. Kaufmann · a · Buckingham, Doolittle & Burroughs · http://www.bdblaw.com · 3800 Embassy Parkway, Suite 300 · P.O. Box 1500 · Akron, OH 44309-1500 · 330-376-5300

David Kern · Buckingham, Doolittle & Burroughs · http://www.bdblaw.com · 3800 Embassy Parkway, Suite 300 · P.O. Box 1500 · Akron, OH 44309-1500 · 330-376-5300

David J. Lewis · Buckingham, Doolittle & Burroughs · http://www.bdblaw.com · 3800 Embassy Parkway, Suite 300 · P.O. Box 1500 · Akron, OH 44309-1500 · 330-376-5300

Patricia A. Pacenta · 2) · Buckingham, Doolittle & Burroughs · http://www.bdblaw.com · 3800 Embassy Parkway, Suite 300 · P.O. Box 1500 · Akron, OH 44309-1500 · 330-376-5300

Michael L. Stark · 2) · Stark & Knoll · http://www.stark-knoll.com · 3475 Ridgewood Road · Akron, OH 44333-3163 · 330-376-3300

Michael A. Sweeney · a · Brouse McDowell · 388 South Main Street, Suite 500 · Akron, OH 44311 · 330-535-5711

Patrick J. Weschler · a · Buckingham, Doolittle & Burroughs · http://www.bdblaw.com · 3800 Embassy Parkway, Suite 300 · P.O. Box 1500 · Akron, OH 44309-1500 · 330-376-5300

David W. Woodburn · Buckingham, Doolittle & Burroughs · http://www.bdblaw.com · 3800 Embassy Parkway, Suite 300 · P.O. Box 1500 · Akron, OH 44309-1500 · 330-376-5300

Canton

Dianne Blocker Braun · Buckingham, Doolittle & Burroughs · http://www.bdblaw.com · 4518 Fulton Drive, NW · P.O. Box 35548 · Canton, OH 44735-5548 · 330-492-8717

John D. Clark · Krugliak, Wilkins, Griffiths & Dougherty · http://www.kwgd.com · 4775 Munson Street, NW · P.O. Box 36963 · Canton, OH 44735-6963 · 330-497-0700

James F. Contini II · Krugliak, Wilkins, Griffiths & Dougherty · http://www.kwgd.com · 4775 Munson Street, NW · P.O. Box 36963 · Canton, OH 44735-6963 · 330-497-0700

Richard E. Davis · Krugliak, Wilkins, Griffiths & Dougherty · http://www.kwgd.com · 4775 Munson Street, NW · P.O. Box 36963 · Canton, OH 44735-6963 · 330-497-0700

Jeffrey A. Halm · Buckingham, Doolittle & Burroughs · http://www.bdblaw.com · 4518 Fulton Drive, NW · P.O. Box 35548 · Canton, OH 44735-5548 · 330-492-8717

James P. Kamerer · Black, McCuskey, Souers & Arbaugh · 220 Market Avenue South, Suite 1000 · Canton, OH 44702 · 330-456-8341

David J. Simmons · a · David J. Simmons & Associates · 4690 Munson Street, NW, Suite B · Canton, OH 44718-3636 · 330-499-8899

Cincinnati

William J. Baechtold · Graydon, Head & Ritchey · 1900 Fifth Third Center · 511 Walnut Street · Cincinnati, OH 45202 · 513-621-6464

Joel S. Brant · Katz, Teller, Brant & Hild · http://www.katzteller.com · 255 East Fifth Street, Suite 2400 · Cincinnati, OH 45202-4724 · 513-721-4532

Joseph A. Brant · 2) · Katz, Teller, Brant & Hild · http://www.katzteller.com · 255 East Fifth Street, Suite 2400 · Cincinnati, OH 45202-4724 · 513-721-4532

Christina A. Buttress · Graydon, Head & Ritchey · 1900 Fifth Third Center · 511 Walnut Street · Cincinnati, OH 45202 · 513-621-6464

Bonnie G. Camden · Dinsmore & Shohl · http://www.dinslaw.com · 255 East Fifth Street, Suite 1900 · Cincinnati, OH 45202-3172 · 513-977-8200

John L. Campbell · Kohnen & Patton · http://www.kohnenpatton.com · 201 East Fifth Street, Suite 800 · Cincinnati, OH 45202 · 513-381-0656

James Chalfie · Santen & Hughes · 600 Vine Street, Suite 2700 · Cincinnati, OH 45202 · 513-721-4450

J. Michael Cooney · a · Dinsmore & Shohl · http://www.dinslaw.com · 255 East Fifth Street, Suite 1900 · Cincinnati, OH 45202-3172 · 513-977-8200

John W. Eilers · a · Wood & Lamping · 600 Vine Street, Suite 2500 · Cincinnati, OH 45202 · 513-852-6000

William R. Graf · Graf & Stiebel · US Bank Tower, Suite 2400 · 425 Walnut Street · Cincinnati, OH 45202-3954 · 513-618-7800

David A. Groenke · Vorys, Sater, Seymour and Pease · Atrium Two, Suite 2000 · 221 East Fourth Street · P.O. Box 0236 · Cincinnati, OH 45201-0236 · 513-723-4000

Mary J. Healy · a · Dinsmore & Shohl · http://www.dinslaw.com · 255 East Fifth Street, Suite 1900 · Cincinnati, OH 45202-3172 · 513-977-8200

Daniel J. Hoffheimer · Taft Stettinius & Hollister · http://www.taftlaw.com · 425 Walnut Street, Suite 1800 · Cincinnati, OH 45202-3957 · 513-381-2838

Jon Hoffheimer · 2% · Jon Hoffheimer · Mercantile Library Building, Suite 1200 · 414 Walnut Street · Cincinnati, OH 45202-3912 · 513-421-7666

Brenda Mayes Kloos · a · Thompson Hine · 312 Walnut Street, 14th Floor · Cincinnati, OH 45202-4089 513-352-6700

Suzanne P. Land · Greenebaum Doll & McDonald · http://www.gdm.com · Chemed Center, Suite 2900 · 255 East Fifth Street · Cincinnati, OH 45202 · 513-455-7600

Patricia D. Laub · a · Frost Brown Todd · http://www.frostbrowntodd.com · PNC Center, Suite 2200 · 201 East Fifth Street · Cincinnati, OH 45202-4182 · 513-651-6800

Marilyn J. Maag · Strauss & Troy · http://www.strausstroy.com · The Federal Reserve Building · 150 East Fourth Street · Cincinnati, OH 45202-4018 · 513-621-2120

Bernard L. McKay · Frost Brown Todd · http://www.frostbrowntodd.com · PNC Center, Suite 2200 · 201 East Fifth Street · Cincinnati, OH 45202-4182 · 513-651-6800

Julia B. Meister · Taft Stettinius & Hollister · http://www.taftlaw.com · 425 Walnut Street, Suite 1800 · Cincinnati, OH 45202-3957 · 513-381-2838

Keith D. Meyer · Kohnen & Patton · http://www.kohnenpatton.com · 201 East Fifth Street, Suite 800 · Cincinnati, OH 45202 · 513-381-0656

Michael R. Miller · Graydon, Head & Ritchey · 1900 Fifth Third Center · 511 Walnut Street · Cincinnati, OH 45202 · 513-621-6464

William L. Montague · Greenebaum Doll & McDonald · http://www.gdm.com · Chemed Center, Suite 2900 · 255 East Fifth Street · Cincinnati, OH 45202 · 513-455-7600

T. Stephen Phillips · 2) · Frost Brown Todd · http://www.frostbrowntodd.com · PNC Center, Suite 2200 · 201 East Fifth Street · Cincinnati, OH 45202-4182 · 513-651-6800

Ruth I. Rounding · a · Ruth Rounding · http://www.roundinglaw.com · 810 Sycamore Street, Sixth Floor Cincinnati, OH 45202 · 513-621-8700

Stanley L. Ruby · Schwartz, Manes, Ruby & Slovin · Carew Tower, Suite 2900 · 441 Vine Street · Cincinnati, OH 45202-3090 · 513-579-1414

William F. Russo · a · Katz, Teller, Brant & Hild · http://www.katzteller.com · 255 East Fifth Street, Suite 2400 · Cincinnati, OH 45202-4724 · 513-721-4532

Mary L. Rust · Taft Stettinius & Hollister · http://www.taftlaw.com · 425 Walnut Street, Suite 1800 · Cincinnati, OH 45202-3957 · 513-381-2838

Michael G. Schwartz · Vorys, Sater, Seymour and Pease · Atrium Two, Suite 2000 · 221 East Fourth Street · P.O. Box 0236 · Cincinnati, OH 45201-0236 · 513-723-4000

Scott M. Slovin · Schwartz, Manes, Ruby & Slovin · Carew Tower, Suite 2900 · 441 Vine Street · Cincinnati, OH 45202-3090 · 513-579-1414

Stuart R. Susskind · Ulmer & Berne · 600 Vine Street, Suite 2800 · Cincinnati, OH 45202-2409 · 513-698-5000

Stanton H. Vollman · Cohen, Todd, Kite & Stanford · 250 East Fifth Street, Suite 1200 · Cincinnati, OH 45202-4139 · 513-421-4020

Susan E. Wheatley · Taft Stettinius & Hollister · http://www.taftlaw.com · 425 Walnut Street, Suite 1800 Cincinnati, OH 45202-3957 · 513-381-2838

Cleveland

Oakley V. Andrews · 2) · Baker Hostetler · http://www.bakerlaw.com · National City Center, Suite 3200 · 1900 East Ninth Street · Cleveland, OH 44114-3485 · 216-621-0200

Gary B. Bilchik · Benesch, Friedlander, Coplan & Aronoff · BP Tower, Suite 2300 · 200 Public Square · Cleveland, OH 44114-2378 · 216-363-4500

Herbert L. Braverman · Walter & Haverfield · http://www.walterhav.com · The Tower at Erieview, Suite 3500 · 1301 East Ninth Street · Cleveland, OH 44114 · 216-781-1212

James R. Bright · Spieth, Bell, McCurdy & Newell · Huntington Building, Suite 2000 · 925 Euclid Avenue · Cleveland, OH 44115-1496 · 216-696-4700

J. Donald Cairns · 2) · Spieth, Bell, McCurdy & Newell · Huntington Building, Suite 2000 · 925 Euclid Avenue · Cleveland, OH 44115-1496 · 216-696-4700

Jeffrey P. Consolo · McDonald Hopkins · 600 Superior Avenue East, Suite 2100 · Cleveland, OH 44114-2653 · 216-348-5400

M. Patricia Culler · Hahn Loeser & Parks · BP Tower, Suite 2800 · 200 Public Square · Cleveland, OH 44114-2301 · 216-621-0150

Rebecca Holloway Dent · Spieth, Bell, McCurdy & Newell · Huntington Building, Suite 2000 · 925 Euclid Avenue · Cleveland, OH 44115-1496 · 216-696-4700

James G. Dickinson · a · Cavitch, Familo, Durkin & Frutkin · 1717 East Ninth Street, 14th Floor · Cleveland, OH 44114 · 216-621-7860

Gary L. Dinner · a · Tucker Ellis & West · Huntington Building, Suite 1150 · 925 Euclid Avenue · Cleveland, OH 44115-1475 · 216-592-5000

Christina D'Eramo Evans · Hahn Loeser & Parks · BP Tower, Suite 2800 · 200 Public Square · Cleveland, OH 44114-2301 · 216-621-0150

Andrew L. Fabens III · 2) · Thompson Hine · Key Center, Suite 3900 · 127 Public Square · Cleveland, OH 44114-1291 · 216-566-5500

Robert B. Ford · a · Thompson Hine · Key Center, Suite 3900 · 127 Public Square · Cleveland, OH 44114-1291 · 216-566-5500

Adam Fried · Reminger Attorneys At Law · 1400 Midland Building · 101 Prospect Avenue West · Cleveland, OH 44115-1093 · 216-687-1311

Robert R. Galloway · Baker Hostetler · http://www.bakerlaw.com · National City Center, Suite 3200 · 1900 East Ninth Street · Cleveland, OH 44114-3485 · 216-621-0200

Stephen H. Gariepy · Hahn Loeser & Parks · BP Tower, Suite 2800 · 200 Public Square · Cleveland, OH 44114-2301 · 216-621-0150

James A. Goldsmith · Ulmer & Berne · Skylight Office Tower, Suite 1100 · 1660 West Second Street · Cleveland, OH 44113-1448 · 216-583-7000

Joan M. Gross · Hahn Loeser & Parks · BP Tower, Suite 2800 · 200 Public Square · Cleveland, OH 44114-2301 · 216-621-0150

Kenneth G. Hochman · 2) · Jones Day · North Point · 901 Lakeside Avenue · Cleveland, OH 44114-1190 · 216-586-3939

Barbara Janovitz · Reminger Attorneys At Law · 1400 Midland Building · 101 Prospect Avenue West · Cleveland, OH 44115-1093 · 216-687-1311

Brian J. Jereb · McDonald Hopkins · 600 Superior Avenue East, Suite 2100 · Cleveland, OH 44114-2653 216-348-5400

Matthew F. Kadish · Kadish, Hinkel & Weibel · http://www.khwlaw.com · 1717 East Ninth Street, Suite 2112 · Cleveland, OH 44114 · 216-696-3030

Kimon P. Karas · McCarthy, Lebit, Crystal & Liffman · http://www.mccarthylebit.com · The Midland Building, Suite 1800 · 101 West Prospect Avenue · Cleveland, OH 44115 · 216-696-1422

Bernard L. Karr · a · McDonald Hopkins · 600 Superior Avenue East, Suite 2100 · Cleveland, OH 44114-2653 · 216-348-5400

Roy Krall · Weston Hurd · The Tower at Erieview, Suite 1900 · 1301 East Ninth Street · Cleveland, OH 44114-1862 · 216-241-6602

Robert K. Lease · a · Baker Hostetler · http://www.bakerlaw.com · National City Center, Suite 3200 · 1900 East Ninth Street · Cleveland, OH 44114-3485 · 216-621-0200

Janet L. Lowder · Hickman & Lowder · 1300 East Ninth Street, Suite 1020 · Cleveland, OH 44114 · 216-861-0360

Ginger Fuller Mlakar · Thompson Hine · Key Center, Suite 3900 · 127 Public Square · Cleveland, OH 44114-1291 · 216-566-5500

James P. Oliver · Squire Sanders · http://www.ssd.com · 4900 Key Tower · 127 Public Square · Cleveland, OH 44114-1304 · 216-479-8500

Susan L. Racey · Tucker Ellis & West · Huntington Building, Suite 1150 · 925 Euclid Avenue · Cleveland, OH 44115-1475 · 216-592-5000

Michael G. Riley · McDonald Hopkins · 600 Superior Avenue East, Suite 2100 · Cleveland, OH 44114-2653 · 216-348-5400

Kevin G. Robertson · Baker Hostetler · http://www.bakerlaw.com · National City Center, Suite 3200 · 1900 East Ninth Street · Cleveland, OH 44114-3485 · 216-621-0200

John F. Shelley · Squire Sanders · http://www.ssd.com · 4900 Key Tower · 127 Public Square · Cleveland, OH 44114-1304 · 216-479-8500

Roger L. Shumaker · a · McDonald Hopkins · 600 Superior Avenue East, Suite 2100 · Cleveland, OH 44114-2653 · 216-348-5400

Mark F. Swary · a · Hahn Loeser & Parks · BP Tower, Suite 2800 · 200 Public Square · Cleveland, OH 44114-2301 · 216-621-0150

David G. Weibel · Kadish, Hinkel & Weibel · http://www.khwlaw.com · 1717 East Ninth Street, Suite 2112 · Cleveland, OH 44114 · 216-696-3030

Jeffry L. Weiler · 2) · Benesch, Friedlander, Coplan & Aronoff · BP Tower, Suite 2300 · 200 Public Square · Cleveland, OH 44114-2378 · 216-363-4500

Leon A. Weiss · 2) · Reminger Attorneys At Law · 1400 Midland Building · 101 Prospect Avenue West · Cleveland, OH 44115-1093 · 216-687-1311

Marcia J. Wexberg · Calfee, Halter & Griswold · http://www.calfee.com · 1400 KeyBank Center · 800 Superior Avenue · Cleveland, OH 44114-2688 · 216-622-8200

J. Talbot Young, Jr. · a · Spieth, Bell, McCurdy & Newell · Huntington Building, Suite 2000 · 925 Euclid Avenue · Cleveland, OH 44115-1496 · 216-696-4700

Columbus

Alan S. Acker · Alan S. Acker · 145 East Rich Street, Fourth Floor · Columbus, OH 43215 · 614-220-8877

Robert B. Barnett, Jr. · Carlile Patchen & Murphy · http://www.cpmlaw.com · 366 East Broad Street · Columbus, OH 43215 · 614-228-6135

William W. Brown · William W. Brown · 2999 East Dublin-Granville Road, Suite 217 · Columbus, OH 43231 · 614-890-9099

Robert R. Dunn · Bailey Cavalieri · One Columbus Building, Suite 2100 · 10 West Broad Street · Columbus, OH 43215-3422 · 614-221-3155

Lloyd E. Fisher, Jr. · 2% · Porter, Wright, Morris & Arthur · http://www.porterwright.com · Huntington Center · 41 South High Street · Columbus, OH 43215-6194 · 614-227-2000

Edward C. Hertenstein · a · Roetzel & Andress · http://www.ralaw.com · National City Plaza, 12th Floor 155 East Broad Street · Columbus, OH 43215 · 614-723-2002

Charles J. Kegler · a · Kegler, Brown, Hill & Ritter · http://www.keglerbrown.com · Capitol Square, Suite 1800 · 65 East State Street · Columbus, OH 43215-4294 · 614-462-5400

Lori-Lou Kimm · Porter, Wright, Morris & Arthur · http://www.porterwright.com · Huntington Center · 41 South High Street · Columbus, OH 43215-6194 · 614-227-2000

J. Anthony Kington · Chester Willcox & Saxbe · http://www.cwslaw.com · 65 East State Street, Suite 1000 · Columbus, OH 43215 · 614-221-4000

Phillip G. Lilly · Becker & Lilly · http://www.beckerlilly.com · 100 East Broad Street, Suite 2320 · Columbus, OH 43215 · 614-469-4778

Gordon F. Litt · Bricker & Eckler · http://www.bricker.com · 100 South Third Street · Columbus, OH 43215-4291 · 614-227-2300

Karen M. Moore · a · Bricker & Eckler · http://www.bricker.com · 100 South Third Street · Columbus, OH 43215-4291 · 614-227-2300

Robert C. Rafferty · Bricker & Eckler · http://www.bricker.com · 100 South Third Street · Columbus, OH 43215-4291 · 614-227-2300

Barry R. Robinson · a · Baker Hostetler · http://www.bakerlaw.com · Capitol Square, Suite 2100 · 65 East State Street · Columbus, OH 43215-4260 · 614-228-1541

Ronald L. Rowland · 2% · Vorys, Sater, Seymour and Pease · 52 East Gay Street · P.O. Box 1008 · Columbus, OH 43216-1008 · 614-464-6400

Edward M. Segelken · Porter, Wright, Morris & Arthur · http://www.porterwright.com · Huntington Center · 41 South High Street · Columbus, OH 43215-6194 · 614-227-2000

Thomas J. Sigmund · a · Kegler, Brown, Hill & Ritter · http://www.keglerbrown.com · Capitol Square, Suite 1800 · 65 East State Street · Columbus, OH 43215-4294 · 614-462-5400

David A. Swift · a · Vorys, Sater, Seymour and Pease · 52 East Gay Street · P.O. Box 1008 · Columbus, OH 43216-1008 · 614-464-6400

J. Troy Terakedis · Calfee, Halter & Griswold · http://www.calfee.com · 1100 Fifth Third Center · 21 East State Street · Columbus, OH 43215-4243 · 614-621-1500

John Terakedis, Jr. · 2% · Schottenstein, Zox & Dunn · http://www.szd.com · 250 West Street, Suite 700 · Columbus, OH 43215-2538 · 614-462-2700

Mark E. Vannatta · Vorys, Sater, Seymour and Pease · 52 East Gay Street · P.O. Box 1008 · Columbus, OH 43216-1008 · 614-464-6400

Lee A. Wendel · Squire Sanders · http://www.ssd.com · 1300 Huntington Center · 41 South High Street · Columbus, OH 43215-6197 · 614-365-2700

Roderick H. Willcox · a · Chester Willcox & Saxbe · http://www.cwslaw.com · 65 East State Street, Suite 1000 · Columbus, OH 43215 · 614-221-4000

R. Douglas Wrightsel · a · Wrightsel & Wrightsel · 3300 Riverside Drive, Suite 100 · Columbus, OH 43221-1726 · 614-255-3388

Dayton

R. Scott Blackburn · a · Coolidge Wall Co. · http://www.coollaw.com · 33 West First Street, Suite 600 · Dayton, OH 45402 · 937-223-8177

Frederick J. Caspar · a · Dinsmore & Shohl · http://www.dinslaw.com · Courthouse Plaza, SW, Suite 1100 · 10 North Ludlow Street · Dayton, OH 45402 · 937-449-2800

Mark A. Conway · Thompson Hine · 2000 Courthouse Plaza, NE · 10 West Second Street · P.O. Box 8801 · Dayton, OH 45401-8801 · 937-443-6600

Ralph E. Heyman · 2) · Dinsmore & Shohl · http://www.dinslaw.com · Courthouse Plaza, SW, Suite 1100 10 North Ludlow Street · Dayton, OH 45402 · 937-449-2800

C. Terry Johnson · 2) · Porter, Wright, Morris & Arthur · http://www.porterwright.com · One Dayton Centre, Suite 1600 · One South Main Street · Dayton, OH 45402-2028 · 937-449-6810

Crofford J. Macklin, Jr. · 2) · Thompson Hine · 2000 Courthouse Plaza, NE · 10 West Second Street · P.O. Box 8801 · Dayton, OH 45401-8801 · 937-443-6600

Donald G. Schweller · 2% · Pickrel, Schaeffer & Ebeling · Kettering Tower, 27th Floor · 40 North Main Street · Dayton, OH 45423 · 937-223-1130

Jeffrey A. Winwood · Winwood Rutledge Company · 580 Lincoln Park Boulevard, Suite 388 · Dayton, OH 45429 · 937-294-5270

Maumee

Robert V. Sterling · a · Weber & Sterling · 1721 Indian Wood Circle, Suite One · Maumee, OH 43537-4065 · 419-893-3360

Dennis P. Williams · a · Weber & Sterling · 1721 Indian Wood Circle, Suite One · Maumee, OH 43537-4065 · 419-893-3360

Piqua

William B. McNeil · a · McCulloch, Felger, Fite & Gutmann · 123 Market Street, Second Floor · P.O. Drawer 910 · Piqua, OH 45356-0910 · 937-773-3212

Toledo

William F. Bates · a · Watkins, Bates & Carey · National City Bank Building, Suite 1900 · 405 Madison Avenue · Toledo, OH 43604-1207 · 419-241-2100

Morton Bobowick · 2% · Eastman & Smith · One Seagate, 24th Floor · P.O. Box 10032 · Toledo, OH 43699-0032 · 419-241-6000

John H. Boggs · Eastman & Smith · One Seagate, 24th Floor · P.O. Box 10032 · Toledo, OH 43699-0032 419-241-6000

John H. Burson · a · Shumaker, Loop & Kendrick · North Courthouse Square · 1000 Jackson Street · Toledo, OH 43604-5573 · 419-241-9000

Craig F. Frederickson · a · Frederickson, Heintschel & King · National City Bank Building, Suite 1212 · 405 Madison Avenue · Toledo, OH 43604-1108 · 419-242-5100

William Gosline · Shumaker, Loop & Kendrick · North Courthouse Square · 1000 Jackson Street · Toledo, OH 43604-5573 · 419-241-9000

David C. Krock · Eastman & Smith · One Seagate, 24th Floor · P.O. Box 10032 · Toledo, OH 43699-0032 · 419-241-6000

David J. Rectenwald · Shumaker, Loop & Kendrick · North Courthouse Square · 1000 Jackson Street · Toledo, OH 43604-5573 · 419-241-9000

Nirakar C. Thakur · Nirakar C. Thakur · 416 North Erie Street, Suite 200 · Toledo, OH 43624 · 419-242-8900

Joseph L. Wittenberg · a · Joseph L. Wittenberg · 2727 North Holland-Sylvania Road, Suite G · Toledo, OH 43615-1800 · 419-535-7544

Kathryn J. Woodward · Shumaker, Loop & Kendrick · North Courthouse Square · 1000 Jackson Street · Toledo, OH 43604-5573 · 419-241-9000

Wooster

Ralph E. Lehman · Logee, Hostetler, Stutzman & Lehman · 2171-B Eagle Pass · Wooster, OH 44691 · 330-264-6115

Worthington

Fredrick L. Fisher · a · Fisher Law Office · 6711 Elmer's Court · Worthington, OH 43085 · 614-746-9028

William A. Morse · William A. Morse · 933 High Street, Suite 140 · Worthington, OH 43085 · 614-436-8010

VENTURE CAPITAL LAW

Cincinnati

Gerald S. Greenberg · Taft Stettinius & Hollister · http://www.taftlaw.com · 425 Walnut Street, Suite 1800 · Cincinnati, OH 45202-3957 · 513-381-2838

George D. Molinsky · Taft Stettinius & Hollister · http://www.taftlaw.com · 425 Walnut Street, Suite 1800 · Cincinnati, OH 45202-3957 · 513-381-2838

David J. Willbrand · Thompson Hine · 312 Walnut Street, 14th Floor · Cincinnati, OH 45202-4089 · 513-352-6700

Cleveland

John Paul Batt · Calfee, Halter & Griswold · http://www.calfee.com · 1400 KeyBank Center · 800 Superior Avenue · Cleveland, OH 44114-2688 · 216-622-8200

Howard Bobrow · Taft Stettinius & Hollister · http://www.taftlaw.com · BP Tower, Suite 3500 · 200 Public Square · Cleveland, OH 44114-2302 · 216-241-2838

Warren Goldenberg · Hahn Loeser & Parks · BP Tower, Suite 2800 · 200 Public Square · Cleveland, OH 44114-2301 · 216-621-0150

Ira C. Kaplan · Benesch, Friedlander, Coplan & Aronoff · BP Tower, Suite 2300 · 200 Public Square · Cleveland, OH 44114-2378 · 216-363-4500

Craig R. Martahus · a · Thompson Hine · Key Center, Suite 3900 · 127 Public Square · Cleveland, OH 44114-1291 · 216-566-5500

Westlake

Kevin P. Gluntz · Carney, Gluntz & Associates · http://www.carneygluntzlaw.com · 2001 Crocker Road, Suite 530 · Westlake, OH 44145-6966 · 440-249-0850

WATER LAW

Cincinnati

Kevin J. Hopper · Kevin J. Hopper · Southampton Square · 7434 Jager Court · Cincinnati, OH 45230-9924 · 513-232-7578

Cleveland

Ronald R. Janke · a · Jones Day · North Point · 901 Lakeside Avenue · Cleveland, OH 44114-1190 · 216-586-3939

Columbus

John W. Bentine · a · Chester Willcox & Saxbe · http://www.cwslaw.com · 65 East State Street, Suite 1000 · Columbus, OH 43215 · 614-221-4000

Sally W. Bloomfield · a · Bricker & Eckler · http://www.bricker.com · 100 South Third Street · Columbus, OH 43215-4291 · 614-227-2300

Thomas J. O'Brien · Bricker & Eckler · http://www.bricker.com · 100 South Third Street · Columbus, OH 43215-4291 · 614-227-2300

Robert J. Schmidt, Jr. · Porter, Wright, Morris & Arthur · http://www.porterwright.com · Huntington Center · 41 South High Street · Columbus, OH 43215-6194 · 614-227-2000

Dayton

Stephen J. Axtell · Thompson Hine · 2000 Courthouse Plaza, NE · 10 West Second Street · P.O. Box 8801 · Dayton, OH 45401-8801 · 937-443-6600

Toledo

Richard T. Sargeant · 2) · Eastman & Smith · One Seagate, 24th Floor · P.O. Box 10032 · Toledo, OH 43699-0032 · 419-241-6000

WHITE-COLLAR CRIMINAL DEFENSE

Akron

James L. Burdon · 2) · James L. Burdon, Attorney at Law · http://www.ohio-lawyer-criminal-defense.com The Delaware Building, Suite 201 · 137 South Main Street · Akron, OH 44308 · 330-253-7171

Peter T. Cahoon · Buckingham, Doolittle & Burroughs · http://www.bdblaw.com · 3800 Embassy Parkway, Suite 300 · P.O. Box 1500 · Akron, OH 44309-1500 · 330-376-5300

Canton

Mark J. Skakun III · a · Buckingham, Doolittle & Burroughs · http://www.bdblaw.com · 4518 Fulton Drive, NW · P.O. Box 35548 · Canton, OH 44735-5548 · 330-492-8717

Cincinnati

R. Scott Croswell III · a · Croswell & Adams · Olde Sycamore Square · 1208 Sycamore Street · Cincinnati, OH 45202 · 513-241-5670

Richard J. Goldberg · Schuh & Goldberg · 2662 Madison Road · Cincinnati, OH 45208 · 513-321-2662

Edward C. Perry · Edward C. Perry · 810 Sycamore Street, Sixth Floor · Cincinnati, OH 45202-2508 · 513-621-0442

James N. Perry · 2) · James N. Perry · 810 Sycamore Street, Sixth Floor · Cincinnati, OH 45202-2508 · 513-621-0442

Martin S. Pinales · 2) · Sirkin, Pinales & Schwartz · 105 West Fourth Street · Cincinnati, OH 45202-2726 513-721-4876

Jack C. Rubenstein · 2) · Rubenstein & Thurman · 125 East Court Street, Suite 1000 · Cincinnati, OH 45202 · 513-241-7460

Thomas R. Smith · a · Haverkamp, Rebold & Riehl · 5856 Glenway Avenue · Cincinnati, OH 45238-2007 · 513-922-3200

Glenn V. Whitaker · 2) · Vorys, Sater, Seymour and Pease · Atrium Two, Suite 2000 · 221 East Fourth Street · P.O. Box 0236 · Cincinnati, OH 45201-0236 · 513-723-4000

Cleveland

William D. Beyer · Wuliger, Fadel & Beyer · The Brownell Building · 1340 Sumner Court · Cleveland, OH 44115 · 216-781-7777

Ralph E. Cascarilla · Walter & Haverfield · http://www.walterhav.com · The Tower at Erieview, Suite 3500 · 1301 East Ninth Street · Cleveland, OH 44114 · 216-781-1212

Harry D. Cornett, Jr. · a · Tucker Ellis & West · Huntington Building, Suite 1150 · 925 Euclid Avenue · Cleveland, OH 44115-1475 · 216-592-5000

Mark R. DeVan · Berkman, Gordon, Murray & DeVan · 55 Public Square, Suite 2200 · Cleveland, OH 44113-1972 · 216-781-5245

Gerald S. Gold · 2% · Gold and Pyle · Leader Building, Suite 1140 · 526 Superior Avenue East · Cleveland, OH 44114-1498 · 216-696-6122

Henry J. Hilow · McGinty, Hilow & Spellacy · 614 West Superior Avenue, Suite 1300 · Cleveland, OH 44113 · 216-344-9220

Richard G. Lillie · Lillie & Holderman · 75 Public Square, Suite 1313 · Cleveland, OH 44113-2011 · 216-861-1313

John F. McCaffrey · McLaughlin & McCaffrey · Eaton Center, Suite 1350 · 1111 Superior Avenue · Cleveland, OH 44114-2500 · 216-623-0900

Patrick M. McLaughlin · McLaughlin & McCaffrey · Eaton Center, Suite 1350 · 1111 Superior Avenue · Cleveland, OH 44114-2500 · 216-623-0900

J. Michael Murray · a · Berkman, Gordon, Murray & DeVan · 55 Public Square, Suite 2200 · Cleveland, OH 44113-1972 · 216-781-5245

John S. Pyle · a · Gold and Pyle · Leader Building, Suite 1140 · 526 Superior Avenue East · Cleveland, OH 44114-1498 · 216-696-6122

Carole S. Rendon · Giffen & Kaminsky · 1717 East Ninth Street, Suite 2100 · Cleveland, OH 44114 · 216-621-5161

Robert J. Rotatori · 2% · Rotatori, Bender, Gragel, Stoper & Alexander · http://www.rotatori.com · 800 Leader Building · 526 Superior Avenue East · Cleveland, OH 44114-1498 · 216-928-1010

Niki Z. Schwartz · a · Schwartz, Downey and Company · Guildhall Building, Suite 1616 · 45 West Prospect Avenue · Cleveland, OH 44115 · 216-696-7100

Stephen G. Sozio · Jones Day · North Point · 901 Lakeside Avenue · Cleveland, OH 44114-1190 · 216-586-3939

Daniel R. Warren · Baker Hostetler · http://www.bakerlaw.com · National City Center, Suite 3200 · 1900 East Ninth Street · Cleveland, OH 44114-3485 · 216-621-0200

James R. Wooley · Baker Hostetler · http://www.bakerlaw.com · National City Center, Suite 3200 · 1900 East Ninth Street · Cleveland, OH 44114-3485 · 216-621-0200

Columbus

R. William Meeks · 2) · R. William Meeks · 511 South High Street · Columbus, OH 43215-5601 · 614-228-4141

S. Michael Miller · Kegler, Brown, Hill & Ritter · http://www.keglerbrown.com · Capitol Square, Suite 1800 · 65 East State Street · Columbus, OH 43215-4294 · 614-462-5400

James E. Phillips · Vorys, Sater, Seymour and Pease · 52 East Gay Street · P.O. Box 1008 · Columbus, OH 43216-1008 · 614-464-6400

Samuel H. Shamansky · a · Samuel H. Shamansky · 511 South High Street · Columbus, OH 43215-5602 614-228-4141

Thomas M. Tyack · 2% · Tyack, Blackmore & Liston · 536 South High Street · Columbus, OH 43215-5605 · 614-221-1341

Samuel B. Weiner · 2) · Samuel B. Weiner · 743 South Front Street · Columbus, OH 43206-1991 · 614-443-6581

Cuyahoga Falls

George G. Keith · Keith, Godward & Clark · 135 Portage Trail · P.O. Box 374 · Cuyahoga Falls, OH 44222-0008 · 330-929-3168

Dayton

Charles J. Faruki · 2) · Faruki Ireland & Cox · Courthouse Plaza, SW, Suite 500 · 10 North Ludlow Street · Dayton, OH 45402 · 937-227-3700

David C. Greer · 2% · Bieser, Greer & Landis · http://www.biesergreer.com · National City Center, Suite 400 · Six North Main Street · Dayton, OH 45402-1908 · 937-223-3277

Lawrence J. Greger · Greger Law Office · 120 West Second Street, Suite 1100 · Dayton, OH 45402-1657 937-223-3153

Nicholas C. Hollenkamp · a · Dinsmore & Shohl · http://www.dinslaw.com · One Dayton Centre, Suite 1300 · One South Main Street · Dayton, OH 45402 · 937-449-6400

Michael W. Krumholtz · Bieser, Greer & Landis · http://www.biesergreer.com · National City Center, Suite 400 · Six North Main Street · Dayton, OH 45402-1908 · 937-223-3277

Dennis A. Lieberman · 2) · Flanagan, Lieberman, Hoffman & Swaim · 318 West Fourth Street · Dayton, OH 45402-1437 · 937-223-5200

Roger J. Makley · 2) · Boucher & Boucher · 12 West Monument Avenue, Suite 200 · Dayton, OH 45402-1202 · 937-223-0122

Daniel J. O'Brien · 2% · Daniel J. O'Brien · Talbott Tower, Suite 1210 · 131 North Ludlow Street · Dayton, OH 45402 · 937-228-6001

John H. Rion · 2% · Rion, Rion & Rion · One First National Plaza, Suite 2150 · 130 West Second Street · P.O. Box 10126 · Dayton, OH 45402 · 937-223-9133

Jon Paul Rion · Rion, Rion & Rion · One First National Plaza, Suite 2150 · 130 West Second Street · P.O. Box 10126 · Dayton, OH 45402 · 937-223-9133

Toledo

Frederick Byers · a · Fritz Byers · The Spitzer Building, Suite 824 · 520 Madison Avenue · Toledo, OH 43604-1343 · 419-241-8013

William M. Connelly · 2) · Connelly, Jackson & Collier · 405 Madison Avenue, Suite 1600 · Toledo, OH 43604 · 419-243-2100

John Czarnecki · a · Cooper & Walinski · 900 Adams Street · Toledo, OH 43604 · 419-241-1200

Reginald S. Jackson, Jr. · Connelly, Jackson & Collier · 405 Madison Avenue, Suite 1600 · Toledo, OH 43604 · 419-243-2100

Robert Zachary Kaplan · a · Robert Zachary Kaplan · The Spitzer Building, Suite 830 · 520 Madison Avenue · Toledo, OH 43604 · 419-241-6168

Richard M. Kerger · a · Kerger & Associates · 33 South Michigan Street, Suite 100 · Toledo, OH 43602 · 419-255-5990

Alan S. Konop · a · Alan S. Konop · 413 North Michigan Street · Toledo, OH 43604 · 419-255-0571

John F. Potts · John F. Potts · National City Bank Building, Suite 1010 · 405 Madison Avenue · Toledo, OH 43604-1211 · 419-255-2800

Jon D. Richardson · 2% · Jon D. Richardson · The Spitzer Building, Suite 830 · 520 Madison Avenue · Toledo, OH 43604 · 419-241-6168

Theodore M. Rowen · 2% · Spengler Nathanson · 608 Madison Avenue, Suite 1000 · Toledo, OH 43604-1169 · 419-241-2201

Willoughby

Albert L. Purola · a · Albert L. Purola · 38108 Third Street · Willoughby, OH 44094-6140 · 440-951-2323

Youngstown

J. Gerald Ingram, Jr. · a · J. Gerald Ingram · 7330 Market Street · Youngstown, OH 44512-5622 · 330-758-2308

WORKERS' COMPENSATION LAW

Akron

F. Daniel Balmert · a · Vorys, Sater, Seymour and Pease · First National Tower, Suite 1100 · 106 South Main Street · Akron, OH 44308-1417 · 330-208-1000

Thomas E. Davis · Barrett & Davis · Key Building, Suite 510 · 159 South Main Street · Akron, OH 44308-1399 · 330-762-6281

George H. Rosin · Buckingham, Doolittle & Burroughs · http://www.bdblaw.com · 3800 Embassy Parkway, Suite 300 · P.O. Box 1500 · Akron, OH 44309-1500 · 330-376-5300

Eleanor J. Tschugunov · Buckingham, Doolittle & Burroughs · http://www.bdblaw.com · 3800 Embassy Parkway, Suite 300 · P.O. Box 1500 · Akron, OH 44309-1500 · 330-376-5300

Canton

Barbara A. Knapic · Buckingham, Doolittle & Burroughs · http://www.bdblaw.com · 4518 Fulton Drive, NW · P.O. Box 35548 · Canton, OH 44735-5548 · 330-492-8717

Robert C. Meyer · Buckingham, Doolittle & Burroughs · http://www.bdblaw.com · 4518 Fulton Drive, NW · P.O. Box 35548 · Canton, OH 44735-5548 · 330-492-8717

Tod T. Morrow · Buckingham, Doolittle & Burroughs · http://www.bdblaw.com · 4518 Fulton Drive, NW P.O. Box 35548 · Canton, OH 44735-5548 · 330-492-8717

Edward D. Murray · Krugliak, Wilkins, Griffiths & Dougherty · http://www.kwgd.com · 4775 Munson Street, NW · P.O. Box 36963 · Canton, OH 44735-6963 · 330-497-0700

Mary E. Reynolds · Buckingham, Doolittle & Burroughs · http://www.bdblaw.com · 4518 Fulton Drive, NW · P.O. Box 35548 · Canton, OH 44735-5548 · 330-492-8717

Cincinnati

Christopher A. Benintendi · Dinsmore & Shohl · http://www.dinslaw.com · 255 East Fifth Street, Suite 1900 · Cincinnati, OH 45202-3172 · 513-977-8200

Eric G. Bruestle · a · Roetzel & Andress · http://www.ralaw.com · Chiquita Center, Suite 310 · 250 East Fifth Street · Cincinnati, OH 45202 · 513-361-0200

Daniel E. Burke · Graydon, Head & Ritchey · 1900 Fifth Third Center · 511 Walnut Street · Cincinnati, OH 45202 · 513-621-6464

William E. Clements · a · Clements, Mahin & Cohen · 35 East Seventh Street, Suite 710 · Cincinnati, OH 45202 · 513-721-6500

Samuel M. Duran · Taft Stettinius & Hollister · http://www.taftlaw.com · 425 Walnut Street, Suite 1800 · Cincinnati, OH 45202-3957 · 513-381-2838

Louis J. Finkelmeier · a · Finkelmeier & Farrell · http://www.cincinnatiworkerscompensationlawyers.com · 36 East Seventh Street, Suite 1660 · Cincinnati, OH 45202-4459 · 513-621-9921

Bernard C. Fox, Jr. · Fox & Fox · 2407 Ashland Avenue · Cincinnati, OH 45206 · 513-961-6644

Jerald David Harris · a · Harris & Burgin · 9545 Kenwood Road · Cincinnati, OH 45242 · 513-891-3270

Glenda M. Hertzman · White, Getgey & Meyer · Fourth & Vine Tower, Suite 1700 · One West Fourth Street · Cincinnati, OH 45202-3621 · 513-241-3685

Brian P. Perry · Dinsmore & Shohl · http://www.dinslaw.com · 255 East Fifth Street, Suite 1900 · Cincinnati, OH 45202-3172 · 513-977-8200

William D. Snyder · a · William D. Snyder · 2115 Luray Avenue · Cincinnati, OH 45206 · 513-281-1544

Catharin R. Taylor · Clements, Mahin & Cohen · 35 East Seventh Street, Suite 710 · Cincinnati, OH 45202 · 513-721-6500

Joan M. Verchot · Dinsmore & Shohl · http://www.dinslaw.com · 255 East Fifth Street, Suite 1900 · Cincinnati, OH 45202-3172 · 513-977-8200

George B. Wilkinson · a · Dinsmore & Shohl · http://www.dinslaw.com · 255 East Fifth Street, Suite 1900 · Cincinnati, OH 45202-3172 · 513-977-8200

Hilla M. Zerbst · Frost Brown Todd · http://www.frostbrowntodd.com · PNC Center, Suite 2200 · 201 East Fifth Street · Cincinnati, OH 45202-4182 · 513-651-6800

Cleveland

Charles P. Alusheff · Reminger Attorneys At Law · 1400 Midland Building · 101 Prospect Avenue West · Cleveland, OH 44115-1093 · 216-687-1311

W. Michael Hanna · a · Squire Sanders · http://www.ssd.com · 4900 Key Tower · 127 Public Square · Cleveland, OH 44114-1304 · 216-479-8500

James D. Kendis · a · Kendis & Associates · Rockefeller Building, 15th Floor · 614 Superior Avenue West · Cleveland, OH 44113-1306 · 216-621-3346

Robert D. Kendis · a · Kendis & Associates · Rockefeller Building, 15th Floor · 614 Superior Avenue West · Cleveland, OH 44113-1306 · 216-621-3346

Donald E. Lampert · a · Calfee, Halter & Griswold · http://www.calfee.com · 1400 KeyBank Center · 800 Superior Avenue · Cleveland, OH 44114-2688 · 216-622-8200

William L. S. Ross · Calfee, Halter & Griswold · http://www.calfee.com · 1400 KeyBank Center · 800 Superior Avenue · Cleveland, OH 44114-2688 · 216-622-8200

David G. Schmidt · a · Schmidt Legal Group · 614 West Superior Avenue, Suite 1500 · Cleveland, OH 44113-1398 · 216-621-6752

Deborah Sesek · a · Buckingham, Doolittle & Burroughs · http://www.bdblaw.com · 1375 East Ninth Street, Suite 1700 · Cleveland, OH 44114 · 216-621-5300

Jeffrey Wedel · Squire Sanders · http://www.ssd.com · 4900 Key Tower · 127 Public Square · Cleveland, OH 44114-1304 · 216-479-8500

Columbus

Thomas H. Bainbridge · Ward, Kaps, Bainbridge, Maurer & Melvin · 580 South High Street, Suite 100 · Columbus, OH 43215 · 614-224-9223

David B. Barnhart · a · Philip J. Fulton Law Office · 89 East Nationwide Boulevard, Suite 300 · Columbus, OH 43215 · 614-441-9828

Philip J. Fulton · a · Philip J. Fulton Law Office · 89 East Nationwide Boulevard, Suite 300 · Columbus, OH 43215 · 614-441-9828

Preston J. Garvin · a · Garvin & Hickey · 181 East Livingston Avenue · Columbus, OH 43215 · 614-225-9000

J. Miles Gibson · a · Gibson Law Offices · 673 Mohawk Street, Fourth Floor · Columbus, OH 43206-2154 · 614-445-5858

Jonathan H. Goodman · Heinzerling & Goodman · 5900 Roche Drive, Fourth Floor · Columbus, OH 43229 · 614-436-4882

Richard A. Hernandez · Dinsmore & Shohl · http://www.dinslaw.com · 191 West Nationwide Boulevard, Suite 300 · Columbus, OH 43215 · 614-221-8448

Michael J. Hickey · a · Garvin & Hickey · 181 East Livingston Avenue · Columbus, OH 43215 · 614-225-9000

Paulette Ivan · Reminger Attorneys At Law · Capitol Square Office Building, Fourth Floor · 65 East State Street · Columbus, OH 43215 · 614-228-1311

Stewart R. Jaffy · a · Stewart Jaffy & Associates · 306 East Gay Street · Columbus, OH 43215-3247 · 614-228-6148

Ronald J. Koltak · Koltak & Gibson · Five East Long Street, Suite 100 · Columbus, OH 43215-2915 · 614-221-7382

Gavin R. Larrimer · a · Larrimer & Larrimer · 165 North High Street · Columbus, OH 43215 · 614-221-7548

Terrence W. Larrimer · a · Larrimer & Larrimer · 165 North High Street · Columbus, OH 43215 · 614-221-7548

Brett L. Miller · a · Dinsmore & Shohl · http://www.dinslaw.com · 191 West Nationwide Boulevard, Suite 300 · Columbus, OH 43215 · 614-221-8448

Robert Allen Minor · a · Vorys, Sater, Seymour and Pease · 52 East Gay Street · P.O. Box 1008 · Columbus, OH 43216-1008 · 614-464-6400

Adele E. O'Conner · Porter, Wright, Morris & Arthur · http://www.porterwright.com · Huntington Center 41 South High Street · Columbus, OH 43215-6194 · 614-227-2000

Robert M. Robenalt · Schottenstein, Zox & Dunn · http://www.szd.com · 250 West Street, Suite 700 · Columbus, OH 43215-2538 · 614-462-2700

Christopher C. Russell · Porter, Wright, Morris & Arthur · http://www.porterwright.com · Huntington Center · 41 South High Street · Columbus, OH 43215-6194 · 614-227-2000

Barbara A. Sentz · a · Barbara A. Sentz · Five East Long Street, Suite 100 · Columbus, OH 43215 · 614-221-1444

Bradley K. Sinnott · a · Vorys, Sater, Seymour and Pease · 52 East Gay Street · P.O. Box 1008 · Columbus, OH 43216-1008 · 614-464-6400

Michael L. Squillace · Dinsmore & Shohl · http://www.dinslaw.com · 191 West Nationwide Boulevard, Suite 300 · Columbus, OH 43215 · 614-221-8448

Stanley Stein · Stanley R. Stein · 280 North High Street, Suite 220 · Columbus, OH 43215 · 614-224-7077

H. Toney Stroud · Steptoe & Johnson · http://www.steptoe-johnson.com · Huntington Center, Suite 2200 41 South High Street · Columbus, OH 43215 · 614-221-5100

Elizabeth Whedon · Lee Smith & Associates · 929 Harrison Avenue, Suite 300 · Columbus, OH 43215 · 614-464-1626

Michael L. Williams · Dinsmore & Shohl · http://www.dinslaw.com · 191 West Nationwide Boulevard, Suite 300 · Columbus, OH 43215 · 614-221-8448

Marysville

Robert L. Bridges · Cannizzaro, Fraser, Bridges, Jillisky & Streng · 302 South Main Street · Marysville, OH 43040 · 937-644-9125

Toledo

Theodore A. Bowman · a · Gallon, Takacs, Boissoneault & Schaffer · The Jack Gallon Building · 3516 Granite Circle · P.O. Box 352018 · Toledo, OH 43617 · 419-843-2001

Scott G. Deller · Shumaker, Loop & Kendrick · North Courthouse Square · 1000 Jackson Street · Toledo, OH 43604-5573 · 419-241-9000

Gregory B. Denny · a · Bugbee & Conkle · National City Bank Building, Suite 1300 · 405 Madison Avenue · Toledo, OH 43604-1238 · 419-244-6788

George N. Fell II · a · Fell & Marcus · 6545 West Central Avenue, Suite 202 · Toledo, OH 43617-1034 · 419-537-6610

John T. Landwehr · a · Eastman & Smith · One Seagate, 24th Floor · P.O. Box 10032 · Toledo, OH 43699-0032 · 419-241-6000

John J. Siciliano · Shumaker, Loop & Kendrick · North Courthouse Square · 1000 Jackson Street · Toledo, OH 43604-5573 · 419-241-9000

Joan M. Torzewski · a · Harris · Reny · Torzewski · Two Maritime Plaza, Third Floor · Toledo, OH 43604-1803 · 419-243-1105

Warrensville Heights

Alan J. Shapiro · a · Shapiro, Shapiro and Shapiro · http://www.theshapirolaw.com · 4469 Renaissance Parkway · Warrensville Heights, OH 44128 · 216-927-2030

Geoffrey J. Shapiro · Shapiro, Shapiro and Shapiro · http://www.theshapirolaw.com · 4469 Renaissance Parkway · Warrensville Heights, OH 44128 · 216-927-2030

OKLAHOMA

ADMINISTRATIVE LAW

Oklahoma City

J. Angela Ables · Kerr, Irvine, Rhodes & Ables · 201 Robert S. Kerr Avenue, Suite 600 · Oklahoma City, OK 73102-4267 · 405-272-9221

Robert G. McCampbell · Crowe & Dunlevy · http://www.crowedunlevy.com · 20 North Broadway, Suite 1800 · Oklahoma City, OK 73102-8273 · 405-235-7700

ALTERNATIVE DISPUTE RESOLUTION

Durant

Michael Burrage · Burrage Law Firm · First United Center, Suite 100 · 115 North Washington · P.O. Box 1727 · Durant, OK 74702-1727 · 580-920-0700

Oklahoma City

Steven L. Barghols · GableGotwals · http://www.gablelaw.com · One Leadership Square, 15th Floor · 211 North Robinson · Oklahoma City, OK 73102-7101 · 405-235-5500

Peter B. Bradford · 25 · Conner & Winters · http://www.cwlaw.com · One Leadership Square, Suite 1700 211 North Robinson Avenue · Oklahoma City, OK 73102-7101 · 405-272-5711

Gary W. Davis · 10 · Crowe & Dunlevy · http://www.crowedunlevy.com · 20 North Broadway, Suite 1800 · Oklahoma City, OK 73102-8273 · 405-235-7700

Robert C. Margo · 10 · Robert C. Margo · 5655 Classen Boulevard · Oklahoma City, OK 73118 · 405-286-3636

Kenneth N. McKinney · 25 · Tomlinson & O'Connell · Two Leadership Square, Suite 450 · 211 North Robinson Avenue · Oklahoma City, OK 73102 · 405-606-3350

Earl D. Mills · 20 · The Mills Law Firm · 119 North Robinson Avenue, Suite 500 · Oklahoma City, OK 73102 · 405-239-2501

William G. Paul · Crowe & Dunlevy · http://www.crowedunlevy.com · 20 North Broadway, Suite 1800 · Oklahoma City, OK 73102-8273 · 405-235-7700

Tulsa

Thomas R. Brett · Givens & Givens · 1010 Williams Center, Tower I · Tulsa, OK 74103 · 918-728-7121

John A. Gladd, Sr. · 20 · Dispute Resolution Consultants, Inc. · 1602 South Main Street · Tulsa, OK 74119 · 918-382-0300

Joseph W. Morris · 10 · GableGotwals · http://www.gablelaw.com · ONEOK Plaza, Suite 1100 · 100 West Fifth Street · Tulsa, OK 74103-4217 · 918-595-4800

ANTITRUST LAW

Oklahoma City

Eric S. Eissenstat · Fellers, Snider, Blankenship, Bailey & Tippens · http://www.fellerssnider.com · Chase Tower, Suite 1700 · 100 North Broadway · Oklahoma City, OK 73102-8820 · 405-232-0621

D. Kent Meyers · ㉕ · Crowe & Dunlevy · http://www.crowedunlevy.com · 20 North Broadway, Suite 1800 Oklahoma City, OK 73102-8273 · 405-235-7700

Mack J. Morgan III · Crowe & Dunlevy · http://www.crowedunlevy.com · 20 North Broadway, Suite 1800 Oklahoma City, OK 73102-8273 · 405-235-7700

Drew Neville, Jr. · ⑩ · Hartzog Conger Cason & Neville · http://www.hartzoglaw.com · Bank of Oklahoma Plaza, Suite 1600 · 201 Robert S. Kerr Avenue · Oklahoma City, OK 73102 · 405-235-7000

Reid E. Robison · ⑩ · McAfee & Taft · http://www.mcafeetaft.com · Two Leadership Square, 10th Floor 211 North Robinson · Oklahoma City, OK 73102 · 405-235-9621

Tulsa

James M. Sturdivant · ㉕ · GableGotwals · http://www.gablelaw.com · ONEOK Plaza, Suite 1100 · 100 West Fifth Street · Tulsa, OK 74103-4217 · 918-595-4800

Joel L. Wohlgemuth · ⑩ · Norman Wohlgemuth Chandler & Dowdell · Mid-Continent Tower, Suite 2900 · 401 South Boston Avenue · Tulsa, OK 74103 · 918-583-7571

APPELLATE LAW

Oklahoma City

Harvey D. Ellis, Jr. · Crowe & Dunlevy · http://www.crowedunlevy.com · 20 North Broadway, Suite 1800 Oklahoma City, OK 73102-8273 · 405-235-7700

Clyde A. Muchmore · ⑳ · Crowe & Dunlevy · http://www.crowedunlevy.com · 20 North Broadway, Suite 1800 · Oklahoma City, OK 73102-8273 · 405-235-7700

Tulsa

Amelia A. Fogleman · GableGotwals · http://www.gablelaw.com · ONEOK Plaza, Suite 1100 · 100 West Fifth Street · Tulsa, OK 74103-4217 · 918-595-4800

J. Michael Medina · Frederic Dorwart · Old City Hall · 124 East Fourth Street · Tulsa, OK 74103-5010 · 918-583-9922

BANKING LAW

Norman

Marion C. Bauman · ⑩ · Marion C. Bauman · 2600 Van Buren Street, Suite 2604 · Norman, OK 73072 · 405-329-9101

Oklahoma City

C. Bruce Crum · ⑩ · McAfee & Taft · http://www.mcafeetaft.com · Two Leadership Square, 10th Floor · 211 North Robinson · Oklahoma City, OK 73102 · 405-235-9621

Michael R. Ford · Fellers, Snider, Blankenship, Bailey & Tippens · http://www.fellerssnider.com · Chase Tower, Suite 1700 · 100 North Broadway · Oklahoma City, OK 73102-8820 · 405-232-0621

Robert T. Luttrell III · McAfee & Taft · http://www.mcafeetaft.com · Two Leadership Square, 10th Floor · 211 North Robinson · Oklahoma City, OK 73102 · 405-235-9621

James A. McCaffrey · Phillips McFall McCaffrey McVay & Murrah · http://www.phillipsmcfall.com · Corporate Tower, 13th Floor · 101 North Robinson · Oklahoma City, OK 73102 · 405-235-4100

Fred H. Miller · Phillips McFall McCaffrey McVay & Murrah · http://www.phillipsmcfall.com · Corporate Tower, 13th Floor · 101 North Robinson · Oklahoma City, OK 73102 · 405-235-4100

Sally Mock · ㉕ · McAfee & Taft · http://www.mcafeetaft.com · Two Leadership Square, 10th Floor · 211 North Robinson · Oklahoma City, OK 73102 · 405-235-9621

Michael M. Stewart · ⑩ · Crowe & Dunlevy · http://www.crowedunlevy.com · 20 North Broadway, Suite 1800 · Oklahoma City, OK 73102-8273 · 405-235-7700

Terry W. Tippens · ㉕ · Fellers, Snider, Blankenship, Bailey & Tippens · http://www.fellerssnider.com · Chase Tower, Suite 1700 · 100 North Broadway · Oklahoma City, OK 73102-8820 · 405-232-0621

Tulsa

Gary L. Betow · ⑩ · Conner & Winters · http://www.cwlaw.com · One Williams Center, Suite 4000 · Tulsa, OK 74172 · 918-586-5711

Charles Greenough · McAfee & Taft · http://www.mcafeetaft.com · ONEOK Plaza, Suite 500 · 100 West Fifth Street · Tulsa, OK 74103 · 918-587-0000

Jeffrey D. Hassell · GableGotwals · http://www.gablelaw.com · ONEOK Plaza, Suite 1100 · 100 West Fifth Street · Tulsa, OK 74103-4217 · 918-595-4800

Gary R. McSpadden · ⑩ · Crowe & Dunlevy · http://www.crowedunlevy.com · Kennedy Building, Suite 500 · 321 South Boston Avenue · Tulsa, OK 74103-3313 · 918-592-9800

Barry Reynolds · Titus Hillis Reynolds Love Dickman & McCalmon · First Place Tower, Suite 3700 · 15 East Fifth Street · Tulsa, OK 74103 · 918-587-6800

Gentra A. Sorem · Conner & Winters · http://www.cwlaw.com · One Williams Center, Suite 4000 · Tulsa, OK 74172 · 918-586-5711

BANKRUPTCY AND CREDITOR-DEBTOR RIGHTS LAW

Edmond

Michael A. Rubenstein · Rubenstein, McCormick & Pitts · 1503 East 19th Street · Edmond, OK 73013 · 405-340-1900

Oklahoma City

Larry G. Ball · Hall Estill · http://www.hallestill.com · Chase Tower, Suite 2900 · 100 North Broadway · Oklahoma City, OK 73102-8865 · 405-553-2828

Gary A. Bryant · 20 · Mock, Schwabe, Waldo, Elder, Reeves & Bryant · http://www.mswerb.com · Two Leadership Square, 14th Floor · 211 North Robinson Avenue · Oklahoma City, OK 73102 · 405-235-1110

Steven W. Bugg · McAfee & Taft · http://www.mcafeetaft.com · Two Leadership Square, 10th Floor · 211 North Robinson · Oklahoma City, OK 73102 · 405-235-9621

Sarah Alexander Hall · Mock, Schwabe, Waldo, Elder, Reeves & Bryant · http://www.mswerb.com · Two Leadership Square, 14th Floor · 211 North Robinson Avenue · Oklahoma City, OK 73102 · 405-235-1110

William H. Hoch III · Crowe & Dunlevy · http://www.crowedunlevy.com · 20 North Broadway, Suite 1800 · Oklahoma City, OK 73102-8273 · 405-235-7700

Doneen Douglas Jones · Fellers, Snider, Blankenship, Bailey & Tippens · http://www.fellerssnider.com · Chase Tower, Suite 1700 · 100 North Broadway · Oklahoma City, OK 73102-8820 · 405-232-0621

Timothy D. Kline · 20 · Kline, Kline, Elliott & Bryant · 720 Northeast 63rd Street · Oklahoma City, OK 73105 · 405-848-4448

D. Kent Meyers · 25 · Crowe & Dunlevy · http://www.crowedunlevy.com · 20 North Broadway, Suite 1800 Oklahoma City, OK 73102-8273 · 405-235-7700

Fred S. Morgan · 10 · Reynolds, Ridings, Vogt & Morgan · First National Center, Suite 2200 · 120 North Robinson Avenue · Oklahoma City, OK 73102-7400 · 405-232-8131

Judy Hamilton Morse · 10 · Crowe & Dunlevy · http://www.crowedunlevy.com · 20 North Broadway, Suite 1800 · Oklahoma City, OK 73102-8273 · 405-235-7700

Ross A. Plourde · McAfee & Taft · http://www.mcafeetaft.com · Two Leadership Square, 10th Floor · 211 North Robinson · Oklahoma City, OK 73102 · 405-235-9621

Louis J. Price · 20 · McAfee & Taft · http://www.mcafeetaft.com · Two Leadership Square, 10th Floor · 211 North Robinson · Oklahoma City, OK 73102 · 405-235-9621

G. Blaine Schwabe III · 25 · Mock, Schwabe, Waldo, Elder, Reeves & Bryant · http://www.mswerb.com · Two Leadership Square, 14th Floor · 211 North Robinson Avenue · Oklahoma City, OK 73102 · 405-235-1110

John W. Swinford, Jr. · 20 · Calvert Law Firm · 1041 Northwest Grand Boulevard · Oklahoma City, OK 73118 · 405-848-5000

Jerry Tubb · 20 · Fuller, Tubb, Pomeroy & Stokes · 201 Robert S. Kerr Avenue, Suite 1000 · Oklahoma City, OK 73102 · 405-235-2575

James W. Vogt · 10 · Reynolds, Ridings, Vogt & Morgan · First National Center, Suite 2200 · 120 North Robinson Avenue · Oklahoma City, OK 73102-7400 · 405-232-8131

Tulsa

Sam G. Bratton II · 20 · Doerner, Saunders, Daniel & Anderson · http://www.dsda.com · 320 South Boston Avenue, Suite 500 · Tulsa, OK 74103-3725 · 918-582-1211

Mark A. Craige · Morrel, Saffa, Craige, Hicks, Barnhart & Brunton · 3501 South Yale Avenue · Tulsa, OK 74135-8014 · 918-664-0800

Thomas A. Creekmore III · Hall Estill · http://www.hallestill.com · 320 South Boston Avenue, Suite 200 · Tulsa, OK 74103-3706 · 918-594-0400

Robert S. Glass · ⑩ · GlassWilkin · 1515 South Utica Avenue, Suite 250 · Tulsa, OK 74104 · 918-582-7100

Charles Greenough · McAfee & Taft · http://www.mcafeetaft.com · ONEOK Plaza, Suite 500 · 100 West Fifth Street · Tulsa, OK 74103 · 918-587-0000

Jeffrey D. Hassell · GableGotwals · http://www.gablelaw.com · ONEOK Plaza, Suite 1100 · 100 West Fifth Street · Tulsa, OK 74103-4217 · 918-595-4800

John E. Howland · Rosenstein, Fist & Ringold · Park Centre, Suite 700 · 525 South Main Street · Tulsa, OK 74103-4508 · 918-585-9211

Gary M. McDonald · ⑳ · Doerner, Saunders, Daniel & Anderson · http://www.dsda.com · 320 South Boston Avenue, Suite 500 · Tulsa, OK 74103-3725 · 918-582-1211

Patrick D. O'Connor · Moyers, Martin, Santee & Imel · Mid-Continent Tower, Suite 1100 · 401 South Boston Avenue · Tulsa, OK 74103 · 918-582-5281

Leonard I. Pataki · Doerner, Saunders, Daniel & Anderson · http://www.dsda.com · 320 South Boston Avenue, Suite 500 · Tulsa, OK 74103-3725 · 918-582-1211

Steven W. Soule · Hall Estill · http://www.hallestill.com · 320 South Boston Avenue, Suite 200 · Tulsa, OK 74103-3706 · 918-594-0400

Sidney K. Swinson · GableGotwals · http://www.gablelaw.com · ONEOK Plaza, Suite 1100 · 100 West Fifth Street · Tulsa, OK 74103-4217 · 918-595-4800

Terry M. Thomas · Crowe & Dunlevy · http://www.crowedunlevy.com · Kennedy Building, Suite 500 · 321 South Boston Avenue · Tulsa, OK 74103-3313 · 918-592-9800

Neal Tomlins · Hall Estill · http://www.hallestill.com · 320 South Boston Avenue, Suite 200 · Tulsa, OK 74103-3706 · 918-594-0400

Andrew R. Turner · Conner & Winters · http://www.cwlaw.com · One Williams Center, Suite 4000 · Tulsa, OK 74172 · 918-586-5711

BET-THE-COMPANY LITIGATION

Oklahoma City

George S. Corbyn, Jr. · ⑩ · Corbyn Hampton · One Leadership Square, Suite 1910 · 211 North Robinson Avenue · Oklahoma City, OK 73102-7115 · 405-239-7055

Gary W. Davis · ⑩ · Crowe & Dunlevy · http://www.crowedunlevy.com · 20 North Broadway, Suite 1800 · Oklahoma City, OK 73102-8273 · 405-235-7700

Jimmy K. Goodman · Crowe & Dunlevy · http://www.crowedunlevy.com · 20 North Broadway, Suite 1800 · Oklahoma City, OK 73102-8273 · 405-235-7700

John N. Hermes · ⑩ · McAfee & Taft · http://www.mcafeetaft.com · Two Leadership Square, 10th Floor 211 North Robinson · Oklahoma City, OK 73102 · 405-235-9621

Kenneth N. McKinney · ㉕ · Tomlinson & O'Connell · Two Leadership Square, Suite 450 · 211 North Robinson Avenue · Oklahoma City, OK 73102 · 405-606-3350

D. Kent Meyers · ㉕ · Crowe & Dunlevy · http://www.crowedunlevy.com · 20 North Broadway, Suite 1800 Oklahoma City, OK 73102-8273 · 405-235-7700

Clyde A. Muchmore · ⑳ · Crowe & Dunlevy · http://www.crowedunlevy.com · 20 North Broadway, Suite 1800 · Oklahoma City, OK 73102-8273 · 405-235-7700

Drew Neville, Jr. · ⑩ · Hartzog Conger Cason & Neville · http://www.hartzoglaw.com · Bank of Oklahoma Plaza, Suite 1600 · 201 Robert S. Kerr Avenue · Oklahoma City, OK 73102 · 405-235-7000

Patrick M. Ryan · Ryan, Whaley & Coldiron · 900 Robinson Renaissance · 119 North Robinson · Oklahoma City, OK 73102 · 405-239-6040

Terry W. Tippens · ㉕ · Fellers, Snider, Blankenship, Bailey & Tippens · http://www.fellerssnider.com · Chase Tower, Suite 1700 · 100 North Broadway · Oklahoma City, OK 73102-8820 · 405-232-0621

Tulsa

William C. Anderson · ⑳ · Doerner, Saunders, Daniel & Anderson · http://www.dsda.com · 320 South Boston Avenue, Suite 500 · Tulsa, OK 74103-3725 · 918-582-1211

David L. Bryant · GableGotwals · http://www.gablelaw.com · ONEOK Plaza, Suite 1100 · 100 West Fifth Street · Tulsa, OK 74103-4217 · 918-595-4800

J. Patrick Cremin · ⑳ · Hall Estill · http://www.hallestill.com · 320 South Boston Avenue, Suite 200 · Tulsa, OK 74103-3706 · 918-594-0400

Oliver S. Howard · ⑩ · GableGotwals · http://www.gablelaw.com · ONEOK Plaza, Suite 1100 · 100 West Fifth Street · Tulsa, OK 74103-4217 · 918-595-4800

James L. Kincaid · ⑳ · Crowe & Dunlevy · http://www.crowedunlevy.com · Kennedy Building, Suite 500 321 South Boston Avenue · Tulsa, OK 74103-3313 · 918-592-9800

Graydon Dean Luthey, Jr. · Hall Estill · http://www.hallestill.com · 320 South Boston Avenue, Suite 200 Tulsa, OK 74103-3706 · 918-594-0400

James M. Sturdivant · ㉕ · GableGotwals · http://www.gablelaw.com · ONEOK Plaza, Suite 1100 · 100 West Fifth Street · Tulsa, OK 74103-4217 · 918-595-4800

John H. Tucker · ⑩ · Rhodes, Hieronymus, Jones, Tucker & Gable · http://www.rhodesokla.com · 100 West Fifth Street, Suite 400 · P.O. Box 21100 · Tulsa, OK 74121-1100 · 918-582-1173

COMMERCIAL LITIGATION

Norman

Mary Robertson · Crowe & Dunlevy · http://www.crowedunlevy.com · The HiPoint Office Building, Suite 140 · 2500 South McGee Avenue · Norman, OK 73072-6705 · 405-321-7317

Oklahoma City

Steven L. Barghols · GableGotwals · http://www.gablelaw.com · One Leadership Square, 15th Floor · 211 North Robinson · Oklahoma City, OK 73102-7101 · 405-235-5500

Warren F. Bickford · Fellers, Snider, Blankenship, Bailey & Tippens · http://www.fellerssnider.com · Chase Tower, Suite 1700 · 100 North Broadway · Oklahoma City, OK 73102-8820 · 405-232-0621

Joseph H. Bocock · McAfee & Taft · http://www.mcafeetaft.com · Two Leadership Square, 10th Floor · 211 North Robinson · Oklahoma City, OK 73102 · 405-235-9621

Peter B. Bradford · ㉕ · Conner & Winters · http://www.cwlaw.com · One Leadership Square, Suite 1700 211 North Robinson Avenue · Oklahoma City, OK 73102-7101 · 405-272-5711

James Chaney · Kirk & Chaney · 101 Park Avenue, Suite 800 · Oklahoma City, OK 73102 · 405-235-1333

Gary S. Chilton · Holladay, Chilton & DeGiusti · City Place, Suite 1550 · 204 North Robinson Avenue · Oklahoma City, OK 73102 · 405-236-2343

Andrew M. Coats · ㉕ · Crowe & Dunlevy · http://www.crowedunlevy.com · 20 North Broadway, Suite 1800 · Oklahoma City, OK 73102-8273 · 405-235-7700

George S. Corbyn, Jr. · ⑩ · Corbyn Hampton · One Leadership Square, Suite 1910 · 211 North Robinson Avenue · Oklahoma City, OK 73102-7115 · 405-239-7055

Gary W. Davis · ⑩ · Crowe & Dunlevy · http://www.crowedunlevy.com · 20 North Broadway, Suite 1800 · Oklahoma City, OK 73102-8273 · 405-235-7700

James F. Davis · ㉕ · Andrews Davis · 100 North Broadway, Suite 3300 · Oklahoma City, OK 73102-8812 405-272-9241

Stephen L. DeGiusti · Crowe & Dunlevy · http://www.crowedunlevy.com · 20 North Broadway, Suite 1800 · Oklahoma City, OK 73102-8273 · 405-235-7700

Sidney G. Dunagan · ⑳ · GableGotwals · http://www.gablelaw.com · One Leadership Square, 15th Floor · 211 North Robinson · Oklahoma City, OK 73102-7101 · 405-235-5500

Eric S. Eissenstat · Fellers, Snider, Blankenship, Bailey & Tippens · http://www.fellerssnider.com · Chase Tower, Suite 1700 · 100 North Broadway · Oklahoma City, OK 73102-8820 · 405-232-0621

Charles E. Geister III · Hartzog Conger Cason & Neville · http://www.hartzoglaw.com · Bank of Oklahoma Plaza, Suite 1600 · 201 Robert S. Kerr Avenue · Oklahoma City, OK 73102 · 405-235-7000

Robert H. Gilliland, Jr. · ㉕ · McAfee & Taft · http://www.mcafeetaft.com · Two Leadership Square, 10th Floor · 211 North Robinson · Oklahoma City, OK 73102 · 405-235-9621

Jimmy K. Goodman · Crowe & Dunlevy · http://www.crowedunlevy.com · 20 North Broadway, Suite 1800 · Oklahoma City, OK 73102-8273 · 405-235-7700

Mark S. Grossman · Crowe & Dunlevy · http://www.crowedunlevy.com · 20 North Broadway, Suite 1800 Oklahoma City, OK 73102-8273 · 405-235-7700

Joe M. Hampton · Hampton Law Firm · 211 North Robinson, Suite 1910 · Oklahoma City, OK 73120 · 405-702-4344

John N. Hermes · ⑩ · McAfee & Taft · http://www.mcafeetaft.com · Two Leadership Square, 10th Floor 211 North Robinson · Oklahoma City, OK 73102 · 405-235-9621

William H. Hoch III · Crowe & Dunlevy · http://www.crowedunlevy.com · 20 North Broadway, Suite 1800 · Oklahoma City, OK 73102-8273 · 405-235-7700

Don G. Holladay · Holladay, Chilton & DeGiusti · City Place, Suite 1550 · 204 North Robinson Avenue · Oklahoma City, OK 73102 · 405-236-2343

John A. Kenney · McAfee & Taft · http://www.mcafeetaft.com · Two Leadership Square, 10th Floor · 211 North Robinson · Oklahoma City, OK 73102 · 405-235-9621

James A. Kirk · ㉕ · Kirk & Chaney · 101 Park Avenue, Suite 800 · Oklahoma City, OK 73102 · 405-235-1333

Robert G. McCampbell · Crowe & Dunlevy · http://www.crowedunlevy.com · 20 North Broadway, Suite 1800 · Oklahoma City, OK 73102-8273 · 405-235-7700

Kenneth N. McKinney · ㉕ · Tomlinson & O'Connell · Two Leadership Square, Suite 450 · 211 North Robinson Avenue · Oklahoma City, OK 73102 · 405-606-3350

D. Kent Meyers · ㉕ · Crowe & Dunlevy · http://www.crowedunlevy.com · 20 North Broadway, Suite 1800 Oklahoma City, OK 73102-8273 · 405-235-7700

Mack J. Morgan III · Crowe & Dunlevy · http://www.crowedunlevy.com · 20 North Broadway, Suite 1800 Oklahoma City, OK 73102-8273 · 405-235-7700

Judy Hamilton Morse · ⑩ · Crowe & Dunlevy · http://www.crowedunlevy.com · 20 North Broadway, Suite 1800 · Oklahoma City, OK 73102-8273 · 405-235-7700

Clyde A. Muchmore · ⑳ · Crowe & Dunlevy · http://www.crowedunlevy.com · 20 North Broadway, Suite 1800 · Oklahoma City, OK 73102-8273 · 405-235-7700

Brooke S. Murphy · Crowe & Dunlevy · http://www.crowedunlevy.com · 20 North Broadway, Suite 1800 Oklahoma City, OK 73102-8273 · 405-235-7700

Drew Neville, Jr. · ⑩ · Hartzog Conger Cason & Neville · http://www.hartzoglaw.com · Bank of Oklahoma Plaza, Suite 1600 · 201 Robert S. Kerr Avenue · Oklahoma City, OK 73102 · 405-235-7000

Reid E. Robison · ⑩ · McAfee & Taft · http://www.mcafeetaft.com · Two Leadership Square, 10th Floor 211 North Robinson · Oklahoma City, OK 73102 · 405-235-9621

Anton J. Rupert · Crowe & Dunlevy · http://www.crowedunlevy.com · 20 North Broadway, Suite 1800 · Oklahoma City, OK 73102-8273 · 405-235-7700

Patrick M. Ryan · Ryan, Whaley & Coldiron · 900 Robinson Renaissance · 119 North Robinson · Oklahoma City, OK 73102 · 405-239-6040

G. Blaine Schwabe III · ㉕ · Mock, Schwabe, Waldo, Elder, Reeves & Bryant · http://www.mswerb.com · Two Leadership Square, 14th Floor · 211 North Robinson Avenue · Oklahoma City, OK 73102 · 405-235-1110

Stephen R. Stephens · Fellers, Snider, Blankenship, Bailey & Tippens · http://www.fellerssnider.com · Chase Tower, Suite 1700 · 100 North Broadway · Oklahoma City, OK 73102-8820 · 405-232-0621

Todd P. Taylor · Todd Taylor, Attorney at Law · 5761 Northwest 132nd Street · Oklahoma City, OK 73142 · 405-470-6649

John M. Thompson · Crowe & Dunlevy · http://www.crowedunlevy.com · 20 North Broadway, Suite 1800 · Oklahoma City, OK 73102-8273 · 405-235-7700

Terry W. Tippens · ㉕ · Fellers, Snider, Blankenship, Bailey & Tippens · http://www.fellerssnider.com · Chase Tower, Suite 1700 · 100 North Broadway · Oklahoma City, OK 73102-8820 · 405-232-0621

Jeremy Tubb · Crowe & Dunlevy · http://www.crowedunlevy.com · 20 North Broadway, Suite 1800 · Oklahoma City, OK 73102-8273 · 405-235-7700

Daniel G. Webber, Jr. · Ryan, Whaley & Coldiron · 900 Robinson Renaissance · 119 North Robinson · Oklahoma City, OK 73102 · 405-239-6040

Phillip G. Whaley · Ryan, Whaley & Coldiron · 900 Robinson Renaissance · 119 North Robinson · Oklahoma City, OK 73102 · 405-239-6040

Thomas G. Wolfe · Phillips McFall McCaffrey McVay & Murrah · http://www.phillipsmcfall.com · Corporate Tower, 13th Floor · 101 North Robinson · Oklahoma City, OK 73102 · 405-235-4100

Harry A. Woods, Jr. · ⑳ · Crowe & Dunlevy · http://www.crowedunlevy.com · 20 North Broadway, Suite 1800 · Oklahoma City, OK 73102-8273 · 405-235-7700

Tulsa

William C. Anderson · ⑳ · Doerner, Saunders, Daniel & Anderson · http://www.dsda.com · 320 South Boston Avenue, Suite 500 · Tulsa, OK 74103-3725 · 918-582-1211

Mark K. Blongewicz · Hall Estill · http://www.hallestill.com · 320 South Boston Avenue, Suite 200 · Tulsa, OK 74103-3706 · 918-594-0400

Steven A. Broussard · Hall Estill · http://www.hallestill.com · 320 South Boston Avenue, Suite 200 · Tulsa, OK 74103-3706 · 918-594-0400

David L. Bryant · GableGotwals · http://www.gablelaw.com · ONEOK Plaza, Suite 1100 · 100 West Fifth Street · Tulsa, OK 74103-4217 · 918-595-4800

Dennis C. Cameron · GableGotwals · http://www.gablelaw.com · ONEOK Plaza, Suite 1100 · 100 West Fifth Street · Tulsa, OK 74103-4217 · 918-595-4800

Timothy A. Carney · GableGotwals · http://www.gablelaw.com · ONEOK Plaza, Suite 1100 · 100 West Fifth Street · Tulsa, OK 74103-4217 · 918-595-4800

J. Patrick Cremin · ⑳ · Hall Estill · http://www.hallestill.com · 320 South Boston Avenue, Suite 200 · Tulsa, OK 74103-3706 · 918-594-0400

Samuel P. Daniel · ㉕ · Doerner, Saunders, Daniel & Anderson · http://www.dsda.com · 320 South Boston Avenue, Suite 500 · Tulsa, OK 74103-3725 · 918-582-1211

Reuben Davis · McAfee & Taft · http://www.mcafeetaft.com · ONEOK Plaza, Suite 500 · 100 West Fifth Street · Tulsa, OK 74103 · 918-587-0000

Tom Q. Ferguson · Doerner, Saunders, Daniel & Anderson · http://www.dsda.com · 320 South Boston Avenue, Suite 500 · Tulsa, OK 74103-3725 · 918-582-1211

Amelia A. Fogleman · GableGotwals · http://www.gablelaw.com · ONEOK Plaza, Suite 1100 · 100 West Fifth Street · Tulsa, OK 74103-4217 · 918-595-4800

Michael J. Gibbens · ⑩ · Crowe & Dunlevy · http://www.crowedunlevy.com · Kennedy Building, Suite 500 · 321 South Boston Avenue · Tulsa, OK 74103-3313 · 918-592-9800

Jack R. Givens · ⑩ · Givens & Givens · 1010 Williams Center, Tower I · Tulsa, OK 74103 · 918-728-7121

James E. Green, Jr. · Conner & Winters · http://www.cwlaw.com · One Williams Center, Suite 4000 · Tulsa, OK 74172 · 918-586-5711

James C. T. Hardwick · ⑳ · Hall Estill · http://www.hallestill.com · 320 South Boston Avenue, Suite 200 · Tulsa, OK 74103-3706 · 918-594-0400

Jeffrey D. Hassell · GableGotwals · http://www.gablelaw.com · ONEOK Plaza, Suite 1100 · 100 West Fifth Street · Tulsa, OK 74103-4217 · 918-595-4800

J. Kevin Hayes · Hall Estill · http://www.hallestill.com · 320 South Boston Avenue, Suite 200 · Tulsa, OK 74103-3706 · 918-594-0400

Richard P. Hix · Doerner, Saunders, Daniel & Anderson · http://www.dsda.com · 320 South Boston Avenue, Suite 500 · Tulsa, OK 74103-3725 · 918-582-1211

Oliver S. Howard · ⑩ · GableGotwals · http://www.gablelaw.com · ONEOK Plaza, Suite 1100 · 100 West Fifth Street · Tulsa, OK 74103-4217 · 918-595-4800

John M. Imel · ㉕ · Moyers, Martin, Santee & Imel · Mid-Continent Tower, Suite 1100 · 401 South Boston Avenue · Tulsa, OK 74103 · 918-582-5281

Michael T. Keester · Hall Estill · http://www.hallestill.com · 320 South Boston Avenue, Suite 200 · Tulsa, OK 74103-3706 · 918-594-0400

David E. Keglovits · GableGotwals · http://www.gablelaw.com · ONEOK Plaza, Suite 1100 · 100 West Fifth Street · Tulsa, OK 74103-4217 · 918-595-4800

James L. Kincaid · ⑳ · Crowe & Dunlevy · http://www.crowedunlevy.com · Kennedy Building, Suite 500 321 South Boston Avenue · Tulsa, OK 74103-3313 · 918-592-9800

G. Michael Lewis · Doerner, Saunders, Daniel & Anderson · http://www.dsda.com · 320 South Boston Avenue, Suite 500 · Tulsa, OK 74103-3725 · 918-582-1211

Graydon Dean Luthey, Jr. · Hall Estill · http://www.hallestill.com · 320 South Boston Avenue, Suite 200 Tulsa, OK 74103-3706 · 918-594-0400

Victor E. Morgan · Crowe & Dunlevy · http://www.crowedunlevy.com · Kennedy Building, Suite 500 · 321 South Boston Avenue · Tulsa, OK 74103-3313 · 918-592-9800

Richard B. Noulles · GableGotwals · http://www.gablelaw.com · ONEOK Plaza, Suite 1100 · 100 West Fifth Street · Tulsa, OK 74103-4217 · 918-595-4800

Terry D. Ragsdale · GableGotwals · http://www.gablelaw.com · ONEOK Plaza, Suite 1100 · 100 West Fifth Street · Tulsa, OK 74103-4217 · 918-595-4800

Phil R. Richards · Richards & Connor · Park Centre Building, 12th Floor · 525 South Main · Tulsa, OK 74103-4509 · 918-585-2394

Tracy W. Robinett · Robinett & Murphy · 624 South Boston Avenue, Suite 900 · Tulsa, OK 74119 · 918-592-3699

Scott R. Rowland · ⑩ · GableGotwals · http://www.gablelaw.com · ONEOK Plaza, Suite 1100 · 100 West Fifth Street · Tulsa, OK 74103-4217 · 918-595-4800

James W. Rusher · Albright, Rusher & Hardcastle · Bank of America Center, Suite 2600 · 15 West Sixth Street · Tulsa, OK 74119-5434 · 918-583-5800

James M. Sturdivant · ㉕ · GableGotwals · http://www.gablelaw.com · ONEOK Plaza, Suite 1100 · 100 West Fifth Street · Tulsa, OK 74103-4217 · 918-595-4800

Terry M. Thomas · Crowe & Dunlevy · http://www.crowedunlevy.com · Kennedy Building, Suite 500 · 321 South Boston Avenue · Tulsa, OK 74103-3313 · 918-592-9800

John H. Tucker · ⑩ · Rhodes, Hieronymus, Jones, Tucker & Gable · http://www.rhodesokla.com · 100 West Fifth Street, Suite 400 · P.O. Box 21100 · Tulsa, OK 74121-1100 · 918-582-1173

Randall G. Vaughan · Pray, Walker, Jackman, Williamson & Marlar · ONEOK Plaza, Suite 900 · 100 West Fifth Street · Tulsa, OK 74103-4218 · 918-581-5500

Joel L. Wohlgemuth · ⑩ · Norman Wohlgemuth Chandler & Dowdell · Mid-Continent Tower, Suite 2900 · 401 South Boston Avenue · Tulsa, OK 74103 · 918-583-7571

COMMUNICATIONS LAW

Tulsa

Michael D. Cooke · Hall Estill · http://www.hallestill.com · 320 South Boston Avenue, Suite 200 · Tulsa, OK 74103-3706 · 918-594-0400

James J. Proszek · Hall Estill · http://www.hallestill.com · 320 South Boston Avenue, Suite 200 · Tulsa, OK 74103-3706 · 918-594-0400

CONSTRUCTION LAW

Oklahoma City

Sally A. Hasenfratz · Phillips McFall McCaffrey McVay & Murrah · http://www.phillipsmcfall.com · Corporate Tower, 13th Floor · 101 North Robinson · Oklahoma City, OK 73102 · 405-235-4100

Henry D. Hoss · McAfee & Taft · http://www.mcafeetaft.com · Two Leadership Square, 10th Floor · 211 North Robinson · Oklahoma City, OK 73102 · 405-235-9621

Michael S. Laird · Crowe & Dunlevy · http://www.crowedunlevy.com · 20 North Broadway, Suite 1800 · Oklahoma City, OK 73102-8273 · 405-235-7700

Anton J. Rupert · Crowe & Dunlevy · http://www.crowedunlevy.com · 20 North Broadway, Suite 1800 · Oklahoma City, OK 73102-8273 · 405-235-7700

John M. Thompson · Crowe & Dunlevy · http://www.crowedunlevy.com · 20 North Broadway, Suite 1800 · Oklahoma City, OK 73102-8273 · 405-235-7700

CORPORATE GOVERNANCE AND COMPLIANCE LAW

Oklahoma City

David J. Ketelsleger · McAfee & Taft · http://www.mcafeetaft.com · Two Leadership Square, 10th Floor 211 North Robinson · Oklahoma City, OK 73102 · 405-235-9621

Kenni B. Merritt · ⑩ · Crowe & Dunlevy · http://www.crowedunlevy.com · 20 North Broadway, Suite 1800 · Oklahoma City, OK 73102-8273 · 405-235-7700

Armand Paliotta · Hartzog Conger Cason & Neville · http://www.hartzoglaw.com · Bank of Oklahoma Plaza, Suite 1600 · 201 Robert S. Kerr Avenue · Oklahoma City, OK 73102 · 405-235-7000

Michael M. Stewart · ⑩ · Crowe & Dunlevy · http://www.crowedunlevy.com · 20 North Broadway, Suite 1800 · Oklahoma City, OK 73102-8273 · 405-235-7700

Roger A. Stong · ⑩ · Crowe & Dunlevy · http://www.crowedunlevy.com · 20 North Broadway, Suite 1800 Oklahoma City, OK 73102-8273 · 405-235-7700

Jerry A. Warren · McAfee & Taft · http://www.mcafeetaft.com · Two Leadership Square, 10th Floor · 211 North Robinson · Oklahoma City, OK 73102 · 405-235-9621

Tulsa

Graydon Dean Luthey, Jr. · Hall Estill · http://www.hallestill.com · 320 South Boston Avenue, Suite 200 Tulsa, OK 74103-3706 · 918-594-0400

Oklahoma City

J. Edward Barth · (25) · Andrews Davis · 100 North Broadway, Suite 3300 · Oklahoma City, OK 73102-8812 · 405-272-9241

T. Michael Blake · McAfee & Taft · http://www.mcafeetaft.com · Two Leadership Square, 10th Floor · 211 North Robinson · Oklahoma City, OK 73102 · 405-235-9621

Tom Blalock · Commercial Law Group · Oklahoma Tower, Suite 700 · 210 Park Avenue · Oklahoma City, OK 73102 · 405-232-3001

Len Cason · (10) · Hartzog Conger Cason & Neville · http://www.hartzoglaw.com · Bank of Oklahoma Plaza, Suite 1600 · 201 Robert S. Kerr Avenue · Oklahoma City, OK 73102 · 405-235-7000

W. Chris Coleman · McAfee & Taft · http://www.mcafeetaft.com · Two Leadership Square, 10th Floor · 211 North Robinson · Oklahoma City, OK 73102 · 405-235-9621

C. Bruce Crum · (10) · McAfee & Taft · http://www.mcafeetaft.com · Two Leadership Square, 10th Floor · 211 North Robinson · Oklahoma City, OK 73102 · 405-235-9621

James F. Davis · (25) · Andrews Davis · 100 North Broadway, Suite 3300 · Oklahoma City, OK 73102-8812 405-272-9241

Gary W. Derrick · (10) · Derrick & Briggs · Chase Tower, 28th Floor · 100 North Broadway Avenue · Oklahoma City, OK 73102-8806 · 405-235-1900

Theodore M. Elam · (20) · McAfee & Taft · http://www.mcafeetaft.com · Two Leadership Square, 10th Floor · 211 North Robinson · Oklahoma City, OK 73102 · 405-235-9621

Michael R. Ford · Fellers, Snider, Blankenship, Bailey & Tippens · http://www.fellerssnider.com · Chase Tower, Suite 1700 · 100 North Broadway · Oklahoma City, OK 73102-8820 · 405-232-0621

Gary F. Fuller · (20) · McAfee & Taft · http://www.mcafeetaft.com · Two Leadership Square, 10th Floor · 211 North Robinson · Oklahoma City, OK 73102 · 405-235-9621

Robert L. Garbrecht · McAfee & Taft · http://www.mcafeetaft.com · Two Leadership Square, 10th Floor 211 North Robinson · Oklahoma City, OK 73102 · 405-235-9621

Michael E. Joseph · (10) · McAfee & Taft · http://www.mcafeetaft.com · Two Leadership Square, 10th Floor · 211 North Robinson · Oklahoma City, OK 73102 · 405-235-9621

David J. Ketelsleger · McAfee & Taft · http://www.mcafeetaft.com · Two Leadership Square, 10th Floor 211 North Robinson · Oklahoma City, OK 73102 · 405-235-9621

Timothy M. Larason · (25) · Andrews Davis · 100 North Broadway, Suite 3300 · Oklahoma City, OK 73102-8812 · 405-272-9241

D. Keith McFall · McAfee & Taft · http://www.mcafeetaft.com · Two Leadership Square, 10th Floor · 211 North Robinson · Oklahoma City, OK 73102 · 405-235-9621

John McHenry Mee · (20) · McAfee & Taft · http://www.mcafeetaft.com · Two Leadership Square, 10th Floor · 211 North Robinson · Oklahoma City, OK 73102 · 405-235-9621

Kenni B. Merritt · (10) · Crowe & Dunlevy · http://www.crowedunlevy.com · 20 North Broadway, Suite 1800 · Oklahoma City, OK 73102-8273 · 405-235-7700

Randall D. Mock · ㉕ · Mock, Schwabe, Waldo, Elder, Reeves & Bryant · http://www.mswerb.com · Two Leadership Square, 14th Floor · 211 North Robinson Avenue · Oklahoma City, OK 73102 · 405-235-1110

Richard D. Nix · McAfee & Taft · http://www.mcafeetaft.com · Two Leadership Square, 10th Floor · 211 North Robinson · Oklahoma City, OK 73102 · 405-235-9621

Armand Paliotta · Hartzog Conger Cason & Neville · http://www.hartzoglaw.com · Bank of Oklahoma Plaza, Suite 1600 · 201 Robert S. Kerr Avenue · Oklahoma City, OK 73102 · 405-235-7000

Frank L. Polk · McAfee & Taft · http://www.mcafeetaft.com · Two Leadership Square, 10th Floor · 211 North Robinson · Oklahoma City, OK 73102 · 405-235-9621

Lynn A. Pringle · ⑩ · Pringle & Pringle · 4101 North Classen Boulevard, Suite A · Oklahoma City, OK 73118-2432 · 405-848-4810

Karen S. Rieger · ⑩ · Crowe & Dunlevy · http://www.crowedunlevy.com · 20 North Broadway, Suite 1800 · Oklahoma City, OK 73102-8273 · 405-235-7700

John D. Robertson · Hartzog Conger Cason & Neville · http://www.hartzoglaw.com · Bank of Oklahoma Plaza, Suite 1600 · 201 Robert S. Kerr Avenue · Oklahoma City, OK 73102 · 405-235-7000

D. Joe Rockett · ⑳ · Andrews Davis · 100 North Broadway, Suite 3300 · Oklahoma City, OK 73102-8812 405-272-9241

Shannon T. Self · Commercial Law Group · Oklahoma Tower, Suite 700 · 210 Park Avenue · Oklahoma City, OK 73102 · 405-232-3001

Irwin H. Steinhorn · Conner & Winters · http://www.cwlaw.com · One Leadership Square, Suite 1700 · 211 North Robinson Avenue · Oklahoma City, OK 73102-7101 · 405-272-5711

Michael M. Stewart · ⑩ · Crowe & Dunlevy · http://www.crowedunlevy.com · 20 North Broadway, Suite 1800 · Oklahoma City, OK 73102-8273 · 405-235-7700

Roger A. Stong · ⑩ · Crowe & Dunlevy · http://www.crowedunlevy.com · 20 North Broadway, Suite 1800 Oklahoma City, OK 73102-8273 · 405-235-7700

N. Martin Stringer · McAfee & Taft · http://www.mcafeetaft.com · Two Leadership Square, 10th Floor · 211 North Robinson · Oklahoma City, OK 73102 · 405-235-9621

Tulsa

Lawrence T. Chambers, Jr. · Doerner, Saunders, Daniel & Anderson · http://www.dsda.com · 320 South Boston Avenue, Suite 500 · Tulsa, OK 74103-3725 · 918-582-1211

Michael D. Cooke · Hall Estill · http://www.hallestill.com · 320 South Boston Avenue, Suite 200 · Tulsa, OK 74103-3706 · 918-594-0400

H. Wayne Cooper · Doerner, Saunders, Daniel & Anderson · http://www.dsda.com · 320 South Boston Avenue, Suite 500 · Tulsa, OK 74103-3725 · 918-582-1211

B. Kenneth Cox, Jr. · Hall Estill · http://www.hallestill.com · 320 South Boston Avenue, Suite 200 · Tulsa, OK 74103-3706 · 918-594-0400

Robert A. Curry · ⑩ · Conner & Winters · http://www.cwlaw.com · One Williams Center, Suite 4000 · Tulsa, OK 74172 · 918-586-5711

Kenneth E. Dornblaser · Johnson, Jones, Dornblaser, Coffman & Shorb · Bank Of America Building, Suite 2200 · 15 West Sixth Street · Tulsa, OK 74119 · 918-584-6644

Lon Foster III · 20 · Fellers, Snider, Blankenship, Bailey & Tippens · http://www.fellerssnider.com · The Kennedy Building, Suite 800 · 321 South Boston Avenue · Tulsa, OK 74103-3318 · 918-599-0621

Lawrence Hall · Conner & Winters · http://www.cwlaw.com · One Williams Center, Suite 4000 · Tulsa, OK 74172 · 918-586-5711

David A. Johnson · Boesche McDermott · 610 South Main, Suite 300 · Tulsa, OK 74119 · 918-583-1777

John B. Johnson, Jr. · 25 · Johnson, Jones, Dornblaser, Coffman & Shorb · Bank Of America Building, Suite 2200 · 15 West Sixth Street · Tulsa, OK 74119 · 918-584-6644

Robert J. Melgaard · Conner & Winters · http://www.cwlaw.com · One Williams Center, Suite 4000 · Tulsa, OK 74172 · 918-586-5711

Lynnwood R. Moore, Jr. · 10 · Conner & Winters · http://www.cwlaw.com · One Williams Center, Suite 4000 · Tulsa, OK 74172 · 918-586-5711

Thomas P. Nally · Hall Estill · http://www.hallestill.com · 320 South Boston Avenue, Suite 200 · Tulsa, OK 74103-3706 · 918-594-0400

P. David Newsome, Jr. · Cooper Newsome & Woosley · 401 South Boston Avenue, Suite 3300 · Tulsa, OK 74103-4070 · 918-592-3300

C. Raymond Patton, Jr. · Conner & Winters · http://www.cwlaw.com · One Williams Center, Suite 4000 · Tulsa, OK 74172 · 918-586-5711

William F. Riggs · Doerner, Saunders, Daniel & Anderson · http://www.dsda.com · 320 South Boston Avenue, Suite 500 · Tulsa, OK 74103-3725 · 918-582-1211

Patrick O. Waddel · 25 · Sneed Lang · Williams Center Tower One, Suite 1700 · One West Third Street · Tulsa, OK 74103-3552 · 918-583-3145

EDUCATION LAW

Lawton

Charles E. Wade, Jr. · Wade and Mackey Law Firm · 431 South West C Avenue, Suite 100 · P.O. Box 2515 · Lawton, OK 73502 · 580-357-7700

Norman

Robert L. Pendarvis · Crowe & Dunlevy · http://www.crowedunlevy.com · The HiPoint Office Building, Suite 140 · 2500 South McGee Avenue · Norman, OK 73072-6705 · 405-321-7317

Mary Robertson · Crowe & Dunlevy · http://www.crowedunlevy.com · The HiPoint Office Building, Suite 140 · 2500 South McGee Avenue · Norman, OK 73072-6705 · 405-321-7317

Tulsa

Andrea R. Kunkel · Rosenstein, Fist & Ringold · Park Centre, Suite 700 · 525 South Main Street · Tulsa, OK 74103-4508 · 918-585-9211

Karen L. Long · 10 · Rosenstein, Fist & Ringold · Park Centre, Suite 700 · 525 South Main Street · Tulsa, OK 74103-4508 · 918-585-9211

J. Douglas Mann · Rosenstein, Fist & Ringold · Park Centre, Suite 700 · 525 South Main Street · Tulsa, OK 74103-4508 · 918-585-9211

John G. Moyer, Jr. · Rosenstein, Fist & Ringold · Park Centre, Suite 700 · 525 South Main Street · Tulsa, OK 74103-4508 · 918-585-9211

Eric P. Nelson · Rosenstein, Fist & Ringold · Park Centre, Suite 700 · 525 South Main Street · Tulsa, OK 74103-4508 · 918-585-9211

ELDER LAW

Oklahoma City

Lee M. Holmes · Holmes, Holmes & Neisent · 501 Northwest 13th Street · Oklahoma City, OK 73103 · 405-235-8455

Tracy S. Neisent · Holmes, Holmes & Neisent · 501 Northwest 13th Street · Oklahoma City, OK 73103 · 405-235-8455

Martin Postic, Jr. · Postic & Bates · 2212 Shadowlake Drive · Oklahoma City, OK 73159-7440 · 405-691-5080

EMINENT DOMAIN AND CONDEMNATION LAW

Oklahoma City

James R. Waldo · Mock, Schwabe, Waldo, Elder, Reeves & Bryant · http://www.mswerb.com · Two Leadership Square, 14th Floor · 211 North Robinson Avenue · Oklahoma City, OK 73102 · 405-235-1110

Tulsa

Robert J. Nichols · Robert J. Nichols · 400 Petroleum Club Building · 601 South Boulder Avenue · Tulsa, OK 74119 · 918-582-3222

EMPLOYEE BENEFITS LAW

Oklahoma City

James H. Holloman, Jr. · 25 · Crowe & Dunlevy · http://www.crowedunlevy.com · 20 North Broadway, Suite 1800 · Oklahoma City, OK 73102-8273 · 405-235-7700

James Dudley Hyde · 10 · McAfee & Taft · http://www.mcafeetaft.com · Two Leadership Square, 10th Floor · 211 North Robinson · Oklahoma City, OK 73102 · 405-235-9621

Kenni B. Merritt · 10 · Crowe & Dunlevy · http://www.crowedunlevy.com · 20 North Broadway, Suite 1800 · Oklahoma City, OK 73102-8273 · 405-235-7700

Richard D. Nix · McAfee & Taft · http://www.mcafeetaft.com · Two Leadership Square, 10th Floor · 211 North Robinson · Oklahoma City, OK 73102 · 405-235-9621

John A. Papahronis · McAfee & Taft · http://www.mcafeetaft.com · Two Leadership Square, 10th Floor 211 North Robinson · Oklahoma City, OK 73102 · 405-235-9621

Mark H. Price · Mark H. Price · 2929 West Wilshire · Oklahoma City, OK 73116 · 405-842-1888

James C. Prince · McAfee & Taft · http://www.mcafeetaft.com · Two Leadership Square, 10th Floor · 211 North Robinson · Oklahoma City, OK 73102 · 405-235-9621

Jon H. Trudgeon · ⑩ · Hartzog Conger Cason & Neville · http://www.hartzoglaw.com · Bank of Oklahoma Plaza, Suite 1600 · 201 Robert S. Kerr Avenue · Oklahoma City, OK 73102 · 405-235-7000

Tulsa

Debbie L. Blackwell · ⑩ · Concordia Benefits Group · http://www.concordiabenefits.com · 320 South Boston Avenue, Suite 2000 · Tulsa, OK 74103 · 918-583-5700

Paul E. Braden · Conner & Winters · http://www.cwlaw.com · One Williams Center, Suite 4000 · Tulsa, OK 74172 · 918-586-5711

Steven W. McGrath · ⑩ · Conner & Winters · http://www.cwlaw.com · One Williams Center, Suite 4000 · Tulsa, OK 74172 · 918-586-5711

David B. McKinney · ⑩ · GableGotwals · http://www.gablelaw.com · ONEOK Plaza, Suite 1100 · 100 West Fifth Street · Tulsa, OK 74103-4217 · 918-595-4800

Sheppard F. Miers, Jr. · GableGotwals · http://www.gablelaw.com · ONEOK Plaza, Suite 1100 · 100 West Fifth Street · Tulsa, OK 74103-4217 · 918-595-4800

Eric Smith · Concordia Benefits Group · http://www.concordiabenefits.com · 320 South Boston Avenue, Suite 2000 · Tulsa, OK 74103 · 918-583-5700

Martin R. Wing · Conner & Winters · http://www.cwlaw.com · One Williams Center, Suite 4000 · Tulsa, OK 74172 · 918-586-5711

ENERGY LAW

Oklahoma City

Ronald Comingdeer · ⑩ · Comingdeer & Associates · 6011 North Robinson Avenue · Oklahoma City, OK 73118 · 405-848-5534

Jack P. Fite · ⑩ · White, Coffey & Fite · 1001 Northwest 63rd Street, Suite 100 · Oklahoma City, OK 73116-7335 · 405-842-7545

Robert H. Gilliland, Jr. · ㉕ · McAfee & Taft · http://www.mcafeetaft.com · Two Leadership Square, 10th Floor · 211 North Robinson · Oklahoma City, OK 73102 · 405-235-9621

Philip D. Hart · ⑳ · McAfee & Taft · http://www.mcafeetaft.com · Two Leadership Square, 10th Floor · 211 North Robinson · Oklahoma City, OK 73102 · 405-235-9621

Rob F. Robertson · GableGotwals · http://www.gablelaw.com · One Leadership Square, 15th Floor · 211 North Robinson · Oklahoma City, OK 73102-7101 · 405-235-5500

Paul D. Trimble · Crowe & Dunlevy · http://www.crowedunlevy.com · 20 North Broadway, Suite 1800 · Oklahoma City, OK 73102-8273 · 405-235-7700

Cody B. Waddell · ⑩ · Cody B. Waddell · 19 Northeast 50th Street · Oklahoma City, OK 73075 · 405-822-3311

L. Mark Walker · Crowe & Dunlevy · http://www.crowedunlevy.com · 20 North Broadway, Suite 1800 · Oklahoma City, OK 73102-8273 · 405-235-7700

Tulsa

Mark Banner · Hall Estill · http://www.hallestill.com · 320 South Boston Avenue, Suite 200 · Tulsa, OK 74103-3706 · 918-594-0400

Shelton L. Benedict · ⑩ · Shelton L. Benedict · North Mezzanine Beacon Building · 406 South Boulder Avenue · Tulsa, OK 74103-3821 · 918-585-2090

John A. Gaberino, Jr. · GableGotwals · http://www.gablelaw.com · ONEOK Plaza, Suite 1100 · 100 West Fifth Street · Tulsa, OK 74103-4217 · 918-595-4800

J. Kevin Hayes · Hall Estill · http://www.hallestill.com · 320 South Boston Avenue, Suite 200 · Tulsa, OK 74103-3706 · 918-594-0400

Terry D. Ragsdale · GableGotwals · http://www.gablelaw.com · ONEOK Plaza, Suite 1100 · 100 West Fifth Street · Tulsa, OK 74103-4217 · 918-595-4800

James D. Satrom · Hall Estill · http://www.hallestill.com · 320 South Boston Avenue, Suite 200 · Tulsa, OK 74103-3706 · 918-594-0400

Donald S. Smith · Pray, Walker, Jackman, Williamson & Marlar · ONEOK Plaza, Suite 900 · 100 West Fifth Street · Tulsa, OK 74103-4218 · 918-581-5500

ENVIRONMENTAL LAW

Edmond

Connie M. Bryan · Rubenstein, McCormick & Pitts · 1503 East 19th Street · Edmond, OK 73013 · 405-340-1900

Oklahoma City

Robert N. Barnes · ⑩ · Barnes & Lewis · 208 Northwest 60th Street · Oklahoma City, OK 73118 · 405-843-0363

LeAnne Burnett · Crowe & Dunlevy · http://www.crowedunlevy.com · 20 North Broadway, Suite 1800 · Oklahoma City, OK 73102-8273 · 405-235-7700

Allan DeVore · ⑩ · The DeVore Law Firm · 5709 Northwest 132nd Street · Oklahoma City, OK 73142 · 405-603-8585

Kenneth N. McKinney · ㉕ · Tomlinson & O'Connell · Two Leadership Square, Suite 450 · 211 North Robinson Avenue · Oklahoma City, OK 73102 · 405-606-3350

Mary Ellen Ternes · McAfee & Taft · http://www.mcafeetaft.com · Two Leadership Square, 10th Floor · 211 North Robinson · Oklahoma City, OK 73102 · 405-235-9621

L. Mark Walker · Crowe & Dunlevy · http://www.crowedunlevy.com · 20 North Broadway, Suite 1800 · Oklahoma City, OK 73102-8273 · 405-235-7700

Tulsa

Gerald L. Hilsher · McAfee & Taft · http://www.mcafeetaft.com · ONEOK Plaza, Suite 500 · 100 West Fifth Street · Tulsa, OK 74103 · 918-587-0000

Linda Crook Martin · Doerner, Saunders, Daniel & Anderson · http://www.dsda.com · 320 South Boston Avenue, Suite 500 · Tulsa, OK 74103-3725 · 918-582-1211

EQUIPMENT FINANCE LAW

Oklahoma City

Alan Durbin · Andrews Davis · 100 North Broadway, Suite 3300 · Oklahoma City, OK 73102-8812 · 405-272-9241

Preston G. Gaddis II · Crowe & Dunlevy · http://www.crowedunlevy.com · 20 North Broadway, Suite 1800 · Oklahoma City, OK 73102-8273 · 405-235-7700

Jack P. Gilchrist · DeBee Gilchrist · 100 North Broadway Avenue, Suite 1500 · Oklahoma City, OK 73102 · 405-232-7777

Susan H. Haught · Daugherty, Fowler, Peregrin Haught & Jenson · 204 North Robinson, Suite 900 · Oklahoma City, OK 73102-6800 · 405-232-0003

J. Robert Kalsu · Crowe & Dunlevy · http://www.crowedunlevy.com · 20 North Broadway, Suite 1800 · Oklahoma City, OK 73102-8273 · 405-235-7700

Scott D. McCreary · McAfee & Taft · http://www.mcafeetaft.com · Two Leadership Square, 10th Floor · 211 North Robinson · Oklahoma City, OK 73102 · 405-235-9621

Robert M. Peregrin · Daugherty, Fowler, Peregrin Haught & Jenson · 204 North Robinson, Suite 900 · Oklahoma City, OK 73102-6800 · 405-232-0003

Frank L. Polk · McAfee & Taft · http://www.mcafeetaft.com · Two Leadership Square, 10th Floor · 211 North Robinson · Oklahoma City, OK 73102 · 405-235-9621

Erin M. Van Laanen · McAfee & Taft · http://www.mcafeetaft.com · Two Leadership Square, 10th Floor 211 North Robinson · Oklahoma City, OK 73102 · 405-235-9621

Tulsa

Gary L. Betow · ⑩ · Conner & Winters · http://www.cwlaw.com · One Williams Center, Suite 4000 · Tulsa, OK 74172 · 918-586-5711

Gary R. McSpadden · ⑩ · Crowe & Dunlevy · http://www.crowedunlevy.com · Kennedy Building, Suite 500 · 321 South Boston Avenue · Tulsa, OK 74103-3313 · 918-592-9800

FAMILY LAW

Edmond

Arnold D. Fagin · ㉕ · Arnold D. Fagin · LeChene Office Park, Suite Three · 1218 East Ninth Street · Edmond, OK 73034 · 405-341-6565

Norman

Catherine H. Petersen · ⑩ · Petersen Henson & Meadows · 314 East Comanche Street, Suite 102 · P.O. Box 1243 · Norman, OK 73070 · 405-329-3307

Oklahoma City

Allen Campbell · Kirk & Chaney · 101 Park Avenue, Suite 800 · Oklahoma City, OK 73102 · 405-235-1333

Jon L. Hester · ⑳ · Hester, Schem, Hester & Batson · 16311 Sonoma Park Drive · Oklahoma City, OK 73113 · 405-705-5900

James A. Kirk · ㉕ · Kirk & Chaney · 101 Park Avenue, Suite 800 · Oklahoma City, OK 73102 · 405-235-1333

Laura McConnell-Corbyn · Hartzog Conger Cason & Neville · http://www.hartzoglaw.com · Bank of Oklahoma Plaza, Suite 1600 · 201 Robert S. Kerr Avenue · Oklahoma City, OK 73102 · 405-235-7000

Michael Mullins · Mullins Hirsch and Jones · http://www.mullinshirschjones.com · 100 Park Avenue, Suite 400 · Oklahoma City, OK 73102 · 405-235-2335

Carolyn S. Thompson · ⑩ · Ramsey & Gray · 700 Corporate Tower · 101 North Robinson · Oklahoma City, OK 73102 · 405-239-2393

Pryor

Paul E. Blevins · Blevins Law Office · 110 North Adair · P.O. Box 870 · Pryor, OK 74362 · 918-341-9050

Stillwater

Christopher D. Szlichta · ⑩ · Szlichta & Ramsey · Eight Main Place · P.O. Box 1206 · Stillwater, OK 74076 · 405-377-3393

Tulsa

Samuel P. Daniel · ㉕ · Doerner, Saunders, Daniel & Anderson · http://www.dsda.com · 320 South Boston Avenue, Suite 500 · Tulsa, OK 74103-3725 · 918-582-1211

Jack R. Givens · ⑩ · Givens & Givens · 1010 Williams Center, Tower I · Tulsa, OK 74103 · 918-728-7121

James R. Gotwals · ⑩ · James R. Gotwals and Associates · 525 South Main Street, Suite 1130 · Tulsa, OK 74103-4512 · 918-599-7088

Bradley A. Grundy · Hall Estill · http://www.hallestill.com · 320 South Boston Avenue, Suite 200 · Tulsa, OK 74103-3706 · 918-594-0400

Richard A. Wagner II · ⑩ · Wagner Law Firm · 2000 Bank of America Center · 15 West Sixth Street · Tulsa, OK 74119-5414 · 918-587-2547

Don E. Williams · ⑳ · Naylor, Williams & Tracy · 1701 South Boston Avenue · Tulsa, OK 74119-4895 · 918-582-8000

FIRST AMENDMENT LAW

Oklahoma City

Jon A. Epstein · Hall Estill · http://www.hallestill.com · Chase Tower, Suite 2900 · 100 North Broadway · Oklahoma City, OK 73102-8865 · 405-553-2828

Michael Minnis · ⑩ · Doerner, Saunders, Daniel & Anderson · http://www.dsda.com · 201 Robert S. Kerr Avenue, Suite 700 · Oklahoma City, OK 73102 · 405-319-3500

Clyde A. Muchmore · ⑳ · Crowe & Dunlevy · http://www.crowedunlevy.com · 20 North Broadway, Suite 1800 · Oklahoma City, OK 73102-8273 · 405-235-7700

Robert D. Nelon · ⑩ · Hall Estill · http://www.hallestill.com · Chase Tower, Suite 2900 · 100 North Broadway · Oklahoma City, OK 73102-8865 · 405-553-2828

Tulsa

S. Douglas Dodd · ⑩ · Doerner, Saunders, Daniel & Anderson · http://www.dsda.com · 320 South Boston Avenue, Suite 500 · Tulsa, OK 74103-3725 · 918-582-1211

J. Schaad Titus · ⑩ · Titus Hillis Reynolds Love Dickman & McCalmon · First Place Tower, Suite 3700 15 East Fifth Street · Tulsa, OK 74103 · 918-587-6800

FRANCHISE LAW

Oklahoma City

Michael E. Joseph · ⑩ · McAfee & Taft · http://www.mcafeetaft.com · Two Leadership Square, 10th Floor · 211 North Robinson · Oklahoma City, OK 73102 · 405-235-9621

Judy Hamilton Morse · ⑩ · Crowe & Dunlevy · http://www.crowedunlevy.com · 20 North Broadway, Suite 1800 · Oklahoma City, OK 73102-8273 · 405-235-7700

Todd P. Taylor · Todd Taylor, Attorney at Law · 5761 Northwest 132nd Street · Oklahoma City, OK 73142 · 405-470-6649

Tulsa

Frederick K. Slicker · Slicker Law Firm · http://www.slickerlawfirm.com · 4444 East 66th Street, Suite 201 · Tulsa, OK 74136-4206 · 918-496-9020

GAMING LAW

Ada

Jesse D. Green · Green Law Firm · 301 East Main Street · Ada, OK 74820 · 580-436-1946

Oklahoma City

Michael S. Laird · Crowe & Dunlevy · http://www.crowedunlevy.com · 20 North Broadway, Suite 1800 · Oklahoma City, OK 73102-8273 · 405-235-7700

Michael M. Stewart · ⑩ · Crowe & Dunlevy · http://www.crowedunlevy.com · 20 North Broadway, Suite 1800 · Oklahoma City, OK 73102-8273 · 405-235-7700

Tulsa

Graydon Dean Luthey, Jr. · Hall Estill · http://www.hallestill.com · 320 South Boston Avenue, Suite 200 Tulsa, OK 74103-3706 · 918-594-0400

GOVERNMENT RELATIONS LAW

Oklahoma City

Larry Derryberry · Derryberry & Naifeh · 4800 North Lincoln Boulevard · Oklahoma City, OK 73105 · 405-528-6569

Robert G. McCampbell · Crowe & Dunlevy · http://www.crowedunlevy.com · 20 North Broadway, Suite 1800 · Oklahoma City, OK 73102-8273 · 405-235-7700

Lee Slater · Lee Slater · 2601 Northwest Expressway, Suite 210 West · P.O. Box 14785 · Oklahoma City, OK 73113-0785 · 405-608-0914

Michael C. Turpen · Riggs, Abney, Neal, Turpen, Orbison & Lewis · The Paragon Building, Suite 101 · 5801 Broadway Extension · Oklahoma City, OK 73118-7489 · 405-843-9909

HEALTH CARE LAW

Oklahoma City

Laura L. Cross · ⑩ · Scoggins & Cross · 3100 City Place Building · 204 North Robinson · Oklahoma City, OK 73102 · 405-239-4300

S. Gregory Frogge · ⑩ · McAfee & Taft · http://www.mcafeetaft.com · Two Leadership Square, 10th Floor · 211 North Robinson · Oklahoma City, OK 73102 · 405-235-9621

Kevin D. Gordon · Crowe & Dunlevy · http://www.crowedunlevy.com · 20 North Broadway, Suite 1800 · Oklahoma City, OK 73102-8273 · 405-235-7700

Michael E. Joseph · ⑩ · McAfee & Taft · http://www.mcafeetaft.com · Two Leadership Square, 10th Floor · 211 North Robinson · Oklahoma City, OK 73102 · 405-235-9621

Michael F. Lauderdale · ⑩ · McAfee & Taft · http://www.mcafeetaft.com · Two Leadership Square, 10th Floor · 211 North Robinson · Oklahoma City, OK 73102 · 405-235-9621

M. Richard Mullins · McAfee & Taft · http://www.mcafeetaft.com · Two Leadership Square, 10th Floor · 211 North Robinson · Oklahoma City, OK 73102 · 405-235-9621

J. Michael Nordin · McAfee & Taft · http://www.mcafeetaft.com · Two Leadership Square, 10th Floor · 211 North Robinson · Oklahoma City, OK 73102 · 405-235-9621

James C. Prince · McAfee & Taft · http://www.mcafeetaft.com · Two Leadership Square, 10th Floor · 211 North Robinson · Oklahoma City, OK 73102 · 405-235-9621

Karen S. Rieger · ⑩ · Crowe & Dunlevy · http://www.crowedunlevy.com · 20 North Broadway, Suite 1800 · Oklahoma City, OK 73102-8273 · 405-235-7700

Patricia A. Rogers · McAfee & Taft · http://www.mcafeetaft.com · Two Leadership Square, 10th Floor · 211 North Robinson · Oklahoma City, OK 73102 · 405-235-9621

Linda G. Scoggins · ⑩ · Scoggins & Cross · 3100 City Place Building · 204 North Robinson · Oklahoma City, OK 73102 · 405-239-4300

Elizabeth Tyrrell · McAfee & Taft · http://www.mcafeetaft.com · Two Leadership Square, 10th Floor · 211 North Robinson · Oklahoma City, OK 73102 · 405-235-9621

Tulsa

Gary L. Betow · ⑩ · Conner & Winters · http://www.cwlaw.com · One Williams Center, Suite 4000 · Tulsa, OK 74172 · 918-586-5711

Elise Dunitz Brennan · ⑩ · Doerner, Saunders, Daniel & Anderson · http://www.dsda.com · 320 South Boston Avenue, Suite 500 · Tulsa, OK 74103-3725 · 918-582-1211

Teresa Meinders Burkett · ⑩ · Conner & Winters · http://www.cwlaw.com · One Williams Center, Suite 4000 · Tulsa, OK 74172 · 918-586-5711

Robert S. Glass · ⑩ · GlassWilkin · 1515 South Utica Avenue, Suite 250 · Tulsa, OK 74104 · 918-582-7100

David J. Hyman · Sneed Lang · Williams Center Tower One, Suite 1700 · One West Third Street · Tulsa, OK 74103-3552 · 918-583-3145

David B. McKinney · ⑩ · GableGotwals · http://www.gablelaw.com · ONEOK Plaza, Suite 1100 · 100 West Fifth Street · Tulsa, OK 74103-4217 · 918-595-4800

A. F. Ringold · ⑩ · Rosenstein, Fist & Ringold · Park Centre, Suite 700 · 525 South Main Street · Tulsa, OK 74103-4508 · 918-585-9211

Barry L. Smith · McAfee & Taft · http://www.mcafeetaft.com · ONEOK Plaza, Suite 500 · 100 West Fifth Street · Tulsa, OK 74103 · 918-587-0000

IMMIGRATION LAW

Oklahoma City

Rance G. Stein · Winningham & Stein · 2200 Northwest 50th Street, Suite 240 · Oklahoma City, OK 73112-8044 · 405-843-1037

T. Douglas Stump · Stump & Associates · http://www.usvisagroup.com · 50 Penn Place, Suite 1320 · 1900 Northwest Expressway · Oklahoma City, OK 73118 · 405-879-0800

E. Vance Winningham · ⑩ · Winningham & Stein · 2200 Northwest 50th Street, Suite 240 · Oklahoma City, OK 73112-8044 · 405-843-1037

INFORMATION TECHNOLOGY LAW

Oklahoma City

Phillip L. Free, Jr. · Crowe & Dunlevy · http://www.crowedunlevy.com · 20 North Broadway, Suite 1800 Oklahoma City, OK 73102-8273 · 405-235-7700

INSURANCE LAW

Oklahoma City

J. Angela Ables · Kerr, Irvine, Rhodes & Ables · 201 Robert S. Kerr Avenue, Suite 600 · Oklahoma City, OK 73102-4267 · 405-272-9221

Gary S. Chilton · Holladay, Chilton & DeGiusti · City Place, Suite 1550 · 204 North Robinson Avenue · Oklahoma City, OK 73102 · 405-236-2343

Gerald E. Durbin II · ⑩ · Durbin, Larimore & Bialick · http://www.dlb.net · 920 North Harvey Avenue · Oklahoma City, OK 73102-2610 · 405-235-9584

Eric S. Eissenstat · Fellers, Snider, Blankenship, Bailey & Tippens · http://www.fellerssnider.com · Chase Tower, Suite 1700 · 100 North Broadway · Oklahoma City, OK 73102-8820 · 405-232-0621

Richard C. Ford · Crowe & Dunlevy · http://www.crowedunlevy.com · 20 North Broadway, Suite 1800 · Oklahoma City, OK 73102-8273 · 405-235-7700

Charles E. Geister III · Hartzog Conger Cason & Neville · http://www.hartzoglaw.com · Bank of Oklahoma Plaza, Suite 1600 · 201 Robert S. Kerr Avenue · Oklahoma City, OK 73102 · 405-235-7000

Kevin D. Gordon · Crowe & Dunlevy · http://www.crowedunlevy.com · 20 North Broadway, Suite 1800 · Oklahoma City, OK 73102-8273 · 405-235-7700

Brooke S. Murphy · Crowe & Dunlevy · http://www.crowedunlevy.com · 20 North Broadway, Suite 1800 Oklahoma City, OK 73102-8273 · 405-235-7700

Timila S. Rother · Crowe & Dunlevy · http://www.crowedunlevy.com · 20 North Broadway, Suite 1800 · Oklahoma City, OK 73102-8273 · 405-235-7700

Tulsa

Ann E. Allison · Rhodes, Hieronymus, Jones, Tucker & Gable · http://www.rhodesokla.com · 100 West Fifth Street, Suite 400 · P.O. Box 21100 · Tulsa, OK 74121-1100 · 918-582-1173

Mark K. Blongewicz · Hall Estill · http://www.hallestill.com · 320 South Boston Avenue, Suite 200 · Tulsa, OK 74103-3706 · 918-594-0400

Timothy A. Carney · GableGotwals · http://www.gablelaw.com · ONEOK Plaza, Suite 1100 · 100 West Fifth Street · Tulsa, OK 74103-4217 · 918-595-4800

James E. Green, Jr. · Conner & Winters · http://www.cwlaw.com · One Williams Center, Suite 4000 · Tulsa, OK 74172 · 918-586-5711

Phil R. Richards · Richards & Connor · Park Centre Building, 12th Floor · 525 South Main · Tulsa, OK 74103-4509 · 918-585-2394

INTELLECTUAL PROPERTY LAW

Oklahoma City

Clifford C. Dougherty III · ⑩ · McAfee & Taft · http://www.mcafeetaft.com · Two Leadership Square, 10th Floor · 211 North Robinson · Oklahoma City, OK 73102 · 405-235-9621

Phillip L. Free, Jr. · Crowe & Dunlevy · http://www.crowedunlevy.com · 20 North Broadway, Suite 1800 Oklahoma City, OK 73102-8273 · 405-235-7700

E. Harrison Gilbert III · ⑩ · McAfee & Taft · http://www.mcafeetaft.com · Two Leadership Square, 10th Floor · 211 North Robinson · Oklahoma City, OK 73102 · 405-235-9621

John A. Kenney · McAfee & Taft · http://www.mcafeetaft.com · Two Leadership Square, 10th Floor · 211 North Robinson · Oklahoma City, OK 73102 · 405-235-9621

Michael J. LaBrie · McAfee & Taft · http://www.mcafeetaft.com · Two Leadership Square, 10th Floor · 211 North Robinson · Oklahoma City, OK 73102 · 405-235-9621

Bill D. McCarthy · Fellers, Snider, Blankenship, Bailey & Tippens · http://www.fellerssnider.com · Chase Tower, Suite 1700 · 100 North Broadway · Oklahoma City, OK 73102-8820 · 405-232-0621

Randall K. McCarthy · Fellers, Snider, Blankenship, Bailey & Tippens · http://www.fellerssnider.com · Chase Tower, Suite 1700 · 100 North Broadway · Oklahoma City, OK 73102-8820 · 405-232-0621

Anthony L. Rahhal · McAfee & Taft · http://www.mcafeetaft.com · Two Leadership Square, 10th Floor · 211 North Robinson · Oklahoma City, OK 73102 · 405-235-9621

David M. Sullivan · Crowe & Dunlevy · http://www.crowedunlevy.com · 20 North Broadway, Suite 1800 · Oklahoma City, OK 73102-8273 · 405-235-7700

Tulsa

Rachel Blue · Doerner, Saunders, Daniel & Anderson · http://www.dsda.com · 320 South Boston Avenue, Suite 500 · Tulsa, OK 74103-3725 · 918-582-1211

Roy C. Breedlove · Fellers, Snider, Blankenship, Bailey & Tippens · http://www.fellerssnider.com · The Kennedy Building, Suite 800 · 321 South Boston Avenue · Tulsa, OK 74103-3318 · 918-599-0621

Dennis D. Brown · Fellers, Snider, Blankenship, Bailey & Tippens · http://www.fellerssnider.com · The Kennedy Building, Suite 800 · 321 South Boston Avenue · Tulsa, OK 74103-3318 · 918-599-0621

Paul H. Johnson · GableGotwals · http://www.gablelaw.com · ONEOK Plaza, Suite 1100 · 100 West Fifth Street · Tulsa, OK 74103-4217 · 918-595-4800

R. Alan Weeks · Fellers, Snider, Blankenship, Bailey & Tippens · http://www.fellerssnider.com · The Kennedy Building, Suite 800 · 321 South Boston Avenue · Tulsa, OK 74103-3318 · 918-599-0621

LABOR AND EMPLOYMENT LAW

Oklahoma City

Gayle L. Barrett · ⑩ · Crowe & Dunlevy · http://www.crowedunlevy.com · 20 North Broadway, Suite 1800 · Oklahoma City, OK 73102-8273 · 405-235-7700

H. Leonard Court · ⑳ · Crowe & Dunlevy · http://www.crowedunlevy.com · 20 North Broadway, Suite 1800 · Oklahoma City, OK 73102-8273 · 405-235-7700

Kevin R. Donelson · Fellers, Snider, Blankenship, Bailey & Tippens · http://www.fellerssnider.com · Chase Tower, Suite 1700 · 100 North Broadway · Oklahoma City, OK 73102-8820 · 405-232-0621

Rand C. Eddy · Eddy & Jones · 228 Robert S. Kerr Avenue, Suite 220 · Oklahoma City, OK 73102 · 405-239-2524

Sam R. Fulkerson · McAfee & Taft · http://www.mcafeetaft.com · Two Leadership Square, 10th Floor · 211 North Robinson · Oklahoma City, OK 73102 · 405-235-9621

George J. McCaffrey · ㉕ · McCaffrey & Associates · 6301 Waterford Boulevard, Suite 401 · Oklahoma City, OK 73118 · 405-767-3300

James R. Moore · ⑳ · Moore & Vernier · 301 Northwest 63rd Street, Suite 550 · Oklahoma City, OK 73116 · 405-843-9675

Jim T. Priest · ⑩ · Whitten, Burrage, Priest, Fulmer, Anderson & Eisel · One Leadership Square, Suite 1350 · 211 North Robinson Avenue · Oklahoma City, OK 73102 · 405-516-7800

Tony G. Puckett · ⑩ · McAfee & Taft · http://www.mcafeetaft.com · Two Leadership Square, 10th Floor 211 North Robinson · Oklahoma City, OK 73102 · 405-235-9621

Jeremy Tubb · Crowe & Dunlevy · http://www.crowedunlevy.com · 20 North Broadway, Suite 1800 · Oklahoma City, OK 73102-8273 · 405-235-7700

Peter T. Van Dyke · ⑳ · McAfee & Taft · http://www.mcafeetaft.com · Two Leadership Square, 10th Floor · 211 North Robinson · Oklahoma City, OK 73102 · 405-235-9621

Nathan Whatley · McAfee & Taft · http://www.mcafeetaft.com · Two Leadership Square, 10th Floor · 211 North Robinson · Oklahoma City, OK 73102 · 405-235-9621

Elizabeth Scott Wood · McAfee & Taft · http://www.mcafeetaft.com · Two Leadership Square, 10th Floor · 211 North Robinson · Oklahoma City, OK 73102 · 405-235-9621

Tulsa

Donald M. Bingham · ⑩ · Riggs, Abney, Neal, Turpen, Orbison & Lewis · The Frisco Building · 502 West Sixth Street · Tulsa, OK 74119 · 918-587-3161

Steven A. Broussard · Hall Estill · http://www.hallestill.com · 320 South Boston Avenue, Suite 200 · Tulsa, OK 74103-3706 · 918-594-0400

Louis W. Bullock · ⑳ · Bullock Bullock & Blakemore · 110 West Seventh Street, Suite 707 · Tulsa, OK 74119 · 918-584-2001

David R. Cordell · Conner & Winters · http://www.cwlaw.com · One Williams Center, Suite 4000 · Tulsa, OK 74172 · 918-586-5711

J. Patrick Cremin · ⑳ · Hall Estill · http://www.hallestill.com · 320 South Boston Avenue, Suite 200 · Tulsa, OK 74103-3706 · 918-594-0400

Kevin P. Doyle · Pray, Walker, Jackman, Williamson & Marlar · ONEOK Plaza, Suite 900 · 100 West Fifth Street · Tulsa, OK 74103-4218 · 918-581-5500

Karen L. Long · ⑩ · Rosenstein, Fist & Ringold · Park Centre, Suite 700 · 525 South Main Street · Tulsa, OK 74103-4508 · 918-585-9211

Kimberly Lambert Love · Titus Hillis Reynolds Love Dickman & McCalmon · First Place Tower, Suite 3700 · 15 East Fifth Street · Tulsa, OK 74103 · 918-587-6800

Kathy R. Neal · Eldridge Cooper Steichen & Leach · http://www.ecslok.com · 110 West Seventh Street, Suite 200 · Tulsa, OK 74119 · 918-388-5555

J. Ronald Petrikin · ⑩ · Conner & Winters · http://www.cwlaw.com · One Williams Center, Suite 4000 · Tulsa, OK 74172 · 918-586-5711

Charles S. Plumb · ⑩ · McAfee & Taft · http://www.mcafeetaft.com · ONEOK Plaza, Suite 500 · 100 West Fifth Street · Tulsa, OK 74103 · 918-587-0000

Randall J. Snapp · Crowe & Dunlevy · http://www.crowedunlevy.com · Kennedy Building, Suite 500 · 321 South Boston Avenue · Tulsa, OK 74103-3313 · 918-592-9800

David E. Strecker · ⑳ · Strecker & Associates · 2150 Mid-Continent Tower · 401 South Boston Avenue · Tulsa, OK 74103-4009 · 918-582-1716

W. Kirk Turner · Newton, O'Connor, Turner & Ketchum · 15 West Sixth Street, Suite 2700 · Tulsa, OK 74119-5423 · 918-587-0101

LAND USE & ZONING LAW

Oklahoma City

Michael S. Laird · Crowe & Dunlevy · http://www.crowedunlevy.com · 20 North Broadway, Suite 1800 · Oklahoma City, OK 73102-8273 · 405-235-7700

Tulsa

Kevin C. Coutant · Doerner, Saunders, Daniel & Anderson · http://www.dsda.com · 320 South Boston Avenue, Suite 500 · Tulsa, OK 74103-3725 · 918-582-1211

Charles E. Norman · Norman Wohlgemuth Chandler & Dowdell · Mid-Continent Tower, Suite 2900 · 401 South Boston Avenue · Tulsa, OK 74103 · 918-583-7571

Malcolm E. Rosser IV · Crowe & Dunlevy · http://www.crowedunlevy.com · Kennedy Building, Suite 500 · 321 South Boston Avenue · Tulsa, OK 74103-3313 · 918-592-9800

LEGAL MALPRACTICE LAW

McAlester

W. G. Steidley, Jr. · Steidley & Neal · 100 East Carl Albert Parkway · P.O. Box 1165 · McAlester, OK 74502 · 918-423-4611

Oklahoma City

Murray E. Abowitz · ⑩ · Abowitz, Timberlake & Dahnke · The Hightower Building, Tenth Floor · 105 North Hudson · P.O. Box 1937 · Oklahoma City, OK 73101 · 405-236-4645

Reid E. Robison · ⑩ · McAfee & Taft · http://www.mcafeetaft.com · Two Leadership Square, 10th Floor 211 North Robinson · Oklahoma City, OK 73102 · 405-235-9621

Tulsa

Joseph R. Farris · ⑩ · Feldman, Franden, Woodard & Farris · Park Centre, Suite 1000 · 525 South Main Street · Tulsa, OK 74103 · 918-583-7129

MASS TORT LITIGATION

Oklahoma City

Richard C. Ford · Crowe & Dunlevy · http://www.crowedunlevy.com · 20 North Broadway, Suite 1800 · Oklahoma City, OK 73102-8273 · 405-235-7700

Harry A. Woods, Jr. · ⑳ · Crowe & Dunlevy · http://www.crowedunlevy.com · 20 North Broadway, Suite 1800 · Oklahoma City, OK 73102-8273 · 405-235-7700

MEDICAL MALPRACTICE LAW

Oklahoma City

Benjamin Butts · Butts & Marrs · 5655 Classen Boulevard · Oklahoma City, OK 73114 · 405-608-0098

Steven E. Clark · Clark & Mitchell · 101 Park Avenue, Suite 210 · Oklahoma City, OK 73102 · 405-235-8488

Robert C. Margo · ⑩ · Robert C. Margo · 5655 Classen Boulevard · Oklahoma City, OK 73118 · 405-286-3636

Perry Thomas Marrs, Jr. · Butts & Marrs · 5655 Classen Boulevard · Oklahoma City, OK 73114 · 405-608-0098

Larry A. Tawwater · The Tawwater Law Firm · http://www.tawlaw.com · One Leadership Square, Suite 1950 · 211 North Robinson · Oklahoma City, OK 73102 · 405-319-7300

John E. Wiggins · ⑩ · Wiggins Sewell & Ogletree · Oklahoma Tower, Suite 3100 · 210 Park Avenue · Oklahoma City, OK 73102 · 405-232-1211

Tulsa

Michael P. Atkinson · ⑩ · Atkinson, Haskins, Nellis, Brittingham, Gladd & Carwile · 1500 Park Centre · 525 South Main Street · Tulsa, OK 74103-4524 · 918-582-8877

Timothy G. Best · Best & Sharp · 100 West Fifth Street, Suite 808 · Tulsa, OK 74103-4225 · 918-582-1234

Clark O. Brewster · Brewster & DeAngelis · 2617 East 21st Street · Tulsa, OK 74114 · 918-742-2021

Karen L. Callahan · Rodolf & Todd · 401 South Boston Avenue, Suite 2000 · Tulsa, OK 74103 · 918-295-2100

James W. Connor, Jr. · Richards & Connor · Park Centre Building, 12th Floor · 525 South Main · Tulsa, OK 74103-4509 · 918-585-2394

Phil R. Richards · Richards & Connor · Park Centre Building, 12th Floor · 525 South Main · Tulsa, OK 74103-4509 · 918-585-2394

Stephen J. Rodolf · ⑩ · Rodolf & Todd · 401 South Boston Avenue, Suite 2000 · Tulsa, OK 74103 · 918-295-2100

MERGERS & ACQUISITIONS LAW

Oklahoma City

Tom Blalock · Commercial Law Group · Oklahoma Tower, Suite 700 · 210 Park Avenue · Oklahoma City, OK 73102 · 405-232-3001

Michael R. Ford · Fellers, Snider, Blankenship, Bailey & Tippens · http://www.fellerssnider.com · Chase Tower, Suite 1700 · 100 North Broadway · Oklahoma City, OK 73102-8820 · 405-232-0621

Armand Paliotta · Hartzog Conger Cason & Neville · http://www.hartzoglaw.com · Bank of Oklahoma Plaza, Suite 1600 · 201 Robert S. Kerr Avenue · Oklahoma City, OK 73102 · 405-235-7000

John D. Robertson · Hartzog Conger Cason & Neville · http://www.hartzoglaw.com · Bank of Oklahoma Plaza, Suite 1600 · 201 Robert S. Kerr Avenue · Oklahoma City, OK 73102 · 405-235-7000

D. Joe Rockett · ⑳ · Andrews Davis · 100 North Broadway, Suite 3300 · Oklahoma City, OK 73102-8812 405-272-9241

Shannon T. Self · Commercial Law Group · Oklahoma Tower, Suite 700 · 210 Park Avenue · Oklahoma City, OK 73102 · 405-232-3001

Michael M. Stewart · ⑩ · Crowe & Dunlevy · http://www.crowedunlevy.com · 20 North Broadway, Suite 1800 · Oklahoma City, OK 73102-8273 · 405-235-7700

Roger A. Stong · ⑩ · Crowe & Dunlevy · http://www.crowedunlevy.com · 20 North Broadway, Suite 1800 Oklahoma City, OK 73102-8273 · 405-235-7700

N. Martin Stringer · McAfee & Taft · http://www.mcafeetaft.com · Two Leadership Square, 10th Floor · 211 North Robinson · Oklahoma City, OK 73102 · 405-235-9621

Tulsa

Gary L. Betow · ⑩ · Conner & Winters · http://www.cwlaw.com · One Williams Center, Suite 4000 · Tulsa, OK 74172 · 918-586-5711

Kenneth E. Dornblaser · Johnson, Jones, Dornblaser, Coffman & Shorb · Bank Of America Building, Suite 2200 · 15 West Sixth Street · Tulsa, OK 74119 · 918-584-6644

Terry R. Doverspike · Pray, Walker, Jackman, Williamson & Marlar · ONEOK Plaza, Suite 900 · 100 West Fifth Street · Tulsa, OK 74103-4218 · 918-581-5500

Lon Foster III · ⑳ · Fellers, Snider, Blankenship, Bailey & Tippens · http://www.fellerssnider.com · The Kennedy Building, Suite 800 · 321 South Boston Avenue · Tulsa, OK 74103-3318 · 918-599-0621

John B. Johnson, Jr. · ㉕ · Johnson, Jones, Dornblaser, Coffman & Shorb · Bank Of America Building, Suite 2200 · 15 West Sixth Street · Tulsa, OK 74119 · 918-584-6644

Douglas J. May · GableGotwals · http://www.gablelaw.com · ONEOK Plaza, Suite 1100 · 100 West Fifth Street · Tulsa, OK 74103-4217 · 918-595-4800

Frederick K. Slicker · Slicker Law Firm · http://www.slickerlawfirm.com · 4444 East 66th Street, Suite 201 · Tulsa, OK 74136-4206 · 918-496-9020

MUNICIPAL LAW

Norman

Robert L. Pendarvis · Crowe & Dunlevy · http://www.crowedunlevy.com · The HiPoint Office Building, Suite 140 · 2500 South McGee Avenue · Norman, OK 73072-6705 · 405-321-7317

NATIVE AMERICAN LAW

Ada

Jesse D. Green · Green Law Firm · 301 East Main Street · Ada, OK 74820 · 580-436-1946

Oklahoma City

Kennis Bellmard · Andrews Davis · 100 North Broadway, Suite 3300 · Oklahoma City, OK 73102-8812 · 405-272-9241

Jennifer H. McBee · Andrews Davis · 100 North Broadway, Suite 3300 · Oklahoma City, OK 73102-8812 405-272-9241

Pawhuska

Geoffrey M. Standing Bear · Geoffrey M. Standing Bear · http://www.ndnlawyer.com · 715 Kihekah Avenue · P.O. Box 1049 · Pawhuska, OK 74056 · 918-287-4700

Tulsa

Graydon Dean Luthey, Jr. · Hall Estill · http://www.hallestill.com · 320 South Boston Avenue, Suite 200 Tulsa, OK 74103-3706 · 918-594-0400

D. Michael McBride III · Crowe & Dunlevy · http://www.crowedunlevy.com · Kennedy Building, Suite 500 · 321 South Boston Avenue · Tulsa, OK 74103-3313 · 918-592-9800

NATURAL RESOURCES LAW

Guymon

David K. Petty · David Petty Law Office · 301 West Fifth Street · P.O. Box 1187 · Guymon, OK 73942 · 580-338-5484

Oklahoma City

Terry R. Barrett · McAfee & Taft · http://www.mcafeetaft.com · Two Leadership Square, 10th Floor · 211 North Robinson · Oklahoma City, OK 73102 · 405-235-9621

Mark D. Christiansen · ⑩ · Crowe & Dunlevy · http://www.crowedunlevy.com · 20 North Broadway, Suite 1800 · Oklahoma City, OK 73102-8273 · 405-235-7700

Gary W. Davis · ⑩ · Crowe & Dunlevy · http://www.crowedunlevy.com · 20 North Broadway, Suite 1800 · Oklahoma City, OK 73102-8273 · 405-235-7700

Allan DeVore · ⑩ · The DeVore Law Firm · 5709 Northwest 132nd Street · Oklahoma City, OK 73142 · 405-603-8585

James W. George · ⑩ · Crowe & Dunlevy · http://www.crowedunlevy.com · 20 North Broadway, Suite 1800 · Oklahoma City, OK 73102-8273 · 405-235-7700

John J. Griffin, Jr. · Crowe & Dunlevy · http://www.crowedunlevy.com · 20 North Broadway, Suite 1800 Oklahoma City, OK 73102-8273 · 405-235-7700

Robert G. Gum · Gum, Puckett & Mackechnie · 105 North Hudson, Suite 900 · Oklahoma City, OK 73102 · 405-488-1212

Philip D. Hart · ⑳ · McAfee & Taft · http://www.mcafeetaft.com · Two Leadership Square, 10th Floor · 211 North Robinson · Oklahoma City, OK 73102 · 405-235-9621

John C. Moricoli, Jr. · ⑩ · Moricoli & Schovanec · Two Leadership Square, Suite 1200 · 211 North Robinson Avenue · Oklahoma City, OK 73102-7114 · 405-235-3357

David E. Pepper · Hartzog Conger Cason & Neville · http://www.hartzoglaw.com · Bank of Oklahoma Plaza, Suite 1600 · 201 Robert S. Kerr Avenue · Oklahoma City, OK 73102 · 405-235-7000

John R. Reeves · Mock, Schwabe, Waldo, Elder, Reeves & Bryant · http://www.mswerb.com · Two Leadership Square, 14th Floor · 211 North Robinson Avenue · Oklahoma City, OK 73102 · 405-235-1110

C. David Stinson · ⑩ · McAfee & Taft · http://www.mcafeetaft.com · Two Leadership Square, 10th Floor 211 North Robinson · Oklahoma City, OK 73102 · 405-235-9621

Steven R. Welch · McAfee & Taft · http://www.mcafeetaft.com · Two Leadership Square, 10th Floor · 211 North Robinson · Oklahoma City, OK 73102 · 405-235-9621

Tulsa

James C. T. Hardwick · 20 · Hall Estill · http://www.hallestill.com · 320 South Boston Avenue, Suite 200 · Tulsa, OK 74103-3706 · 918-594-0400

Joseph W. Morris · 10 · GableGotwals · http://www.gablelaw.com · ONEOK Plaza, Suite 1100 · 100 West Fifth Street · Tulsa, OK 74103-4217 · 918-595-4800

Richard B. Noulles · GableGotwals · http://www.gablelaw.com · ONEOK Plaza, Suite 1100 · 100 West Fifth Street · Tulsa, OK 74103-4217 · 918-595-4800

M. Benjamin Singletary · 10 · GableGotwals · http://www.gablelaw.com · ONEOK Plaza, Suite 1100 · 100 West Fifth Street · Tulsa, OK 74103-4217 · 918-595-4800

W. Bland Williamson, Jr. · 10 · Pray, Walker, Jackman, Williamson & Marlar · ONEOK Plaza, Suite 900 · 100 West Fifth Street · Tulsa, OK 74103-4218 · 918-581-5500

NON-PROFIT/CHARITIES LAW

Oklahoma City

Jennifer H. Callahan · McAfee & Taft · http://www.mcafeetaft.com · Two Leadership Square, 10th Floor 211 North Robinson · Oklahoma City, OK 73102 · 405-235-9621

Steven C. Davis · 10 · Hartzog Conger Cason & Neville · http://www.hartzoglaw.com · Bank of Oklahoma Plaza, Suite 1600 · 201 Robert S. Kerr Avenue · Oklahoma City, OK 73102 · 405-235-7000

James H. Holloman, Jr. · 25 · Crowe & Dunlevy · http://www.crowedunlevy.com · 20 North Broadway, Suite 1800 · Oklahoma City, OK 73102-8273 · 405-235-7700

Randall D. Mock · 25 · Mock, Schwabe, Waldo, Elder, Reeves & Bryant · http://www.mswerb.com · Two Leadership Square, 14th Floor · 211 North Robinson Avenue · Oklahoma City, OK 73102 · 405-235-1110

Cynda C. Ottaway · 20 · Crowe & Dunlevy · http://www.crowedunlevy.com · 20 North Broadway, Suite 1800 · Oklahoma City, OK 73102-8273 · 405-235-7700

NON-WHITE-COLLAR CRIMINAL DEFENSE

Claremore

Jack Gordon, Jr. · Gordon & Gordon · 111 South Muskogee · P.O. Box 1167 · Claremore, OK 74018 · 918-341-7322

Enid

Stephen Jones · 10 · Jones, Otjen, Davis & Nixon · 114 East Broadway Avenue, Suite 1100 · P.O. Box 472 Enid, OK 73702 · 580-242-5500

McAlester

P. Warren Gotcher · 25 · Gotcher & Belote · 2626 South 14th Street · P.O. Box 160 · McAlester, OK 74502 · 918-423-0412

Oklahoma City

John W. Coyle III · ⑩ · Coyle Law Firm · 125 Park Avenue, First Floor · Oklahoma City, OK 73102 · 405-232-1988

Garvin A. Isaacs · ⑩ · Garvin A. Isaacs · Rainy Mountain Building · 123 Northwest Eighth Street · Oklahoma City, OK 73102 · 405-232-2060

Gary J. James · Gary J. James & Associates · 701 North Broadway, Suite 410 · Oklahoma City, OK 73101 405-521-9900

Mack K. Martin · ⑩ · Martin Law Office · 125 Park Avenue, Fifth Floor · Oklahoma City, OK 73102 · 405-236-8888

D. C. Thomas · ㉕ · D. C. Thomas · One Leadership Square, Suite 900 · 211 North Robinson Avenue · Oklahoma City, OK 73102 · 405-235-4300

Robert L. Wyatt · Wyatt Law Office · http://www.wyattlaw.com · 501 North Walker Avenue, Suite 110 · P.O. Box 1947 · Oklahoma City, OK 73101 · 405-234-5500

Tulsa

Clark O. Brewster · Brewster & DeAngelis · 2617 East 21st Street · Tulsa, OK 74114 · 918-742-2021

Allen M. Smallwood · Allen Smallwood · 1310 South Denver Avenue · Tulsa, OK 74119 · 918-582-1993

OIL & GAS LAW

Edmond

Richard A. Grimes · Grimes Anderson & Day · 609 South Kelly Avenue, Suite K4 · Edmond, OK 73003 · 405-330-0700

Oklahoma City

Steven L. Barghols · GableGotwals · http://www.gablelaw.com · One Leadership Square, 15th Floor · 211 North Robinson · Oklahoma City, OK 73102-7101 · 405-235-5500

Terry R. Barrett · McAfee & Taft · http://www.mcafeetaft.com · Two Leadership Square, 10th Floor · 211 North Robinson · Oklahoma City, OK 73102 · 405-235-9621

Mark D. Christiansen · ⑩ · Crowe & Dunlevy · http://www.crowedunlevy.com · 20 North Broadway, Suite 1800 · Oklahoma City, OK 73102-8273 · 405-235-7700

Stanley L. Cunningham · ⑳ · McAfee & Taft · http://www.mcafeetaft.com · Two Leadership Square, 10th Floor · 211 North Robinson · Oklahoma City, OK 73102 · 405-235-9621

Gary W. Davis · ⑩ · Crowe & Dunlevy · http://www.crowedunlevy.com · 20 North Broadway, Suite 1800 · Oklahoma City, OK 73102-8273 · 405-235-7700

James W. George · ⑩ · Crowe & Dunlevy · http://www.crowedunlevy.com · 20 North Broadway, Suite 1800 · Oklahoma City, OK 73102-8273 · 405-235-7700

John J. Griffin, Jr. · Crowe & Dunlevy · http://www.crowedunlevy.com · 20 North Broadway, Suite 1800 Oklahoma City, OK 73102-8273 · 405-235-7700

Philip D. Hart · (20) · McAfee & Taft · http://www.mcafeetaft.com · Two Leadership Square, 10th Floor · 211 North Robinson · Oklahoma City, OK 73102 · 405-235-9621

Eric R. King · GableGotwals · http://www.gablelaw.com · One Leadership Square, 15th Floor · 211 North Robinson · Oklahoma City, OK 73102-7101 · 405-235-5500

John C. Moricoli, Jr. · (10) · Moricoli & Schovanec · Two Leadership Square, Suite 1200 · 211 North Robinson Avenue · Oklahoma City, OK 73102-7114 · 405-235-3357

David E. Pepper · Hartzog Conger Cason & Neville · http://www.hartzoglaw.com · Bank of Oklahoma Plaza, Suite 1600 · 201 Robert S. Kerr Avenue · Oklahoma City, OK 73102 · 405-235-7000

John R. Reeves · Mock, Schwabe, Waldo, Elder, Reeves & Bryant · http://www.mswerb.com · Two Leadership Square, 14th Floor · 211 North Robinson Avenue · Oklahoma City, OK 73102 · 405-235-1110

Harry H. Selph II · Fellers, Snider, Blankenship, Bailey & Tippens · http://www.fellerssnider.com · Chase Tower, Suite 1700 · 100 North Broadway · Oklahoma City, OK 73102-8820 · 405-232-0621

C. David Stinson · (10) · McAfee & Taft · http://www.mcafeetaft.com · Two Leadership Square, 10th Floor 211 North Robinson · Oklahoma City, OK 73102 · 405-235-9621

Steven R. Welch · McAfee & Taft · http://www.mcafeetaft.com · Two Leadership Square, 10th Floor · 211 North Robinson · Oklahoma City, OK 73102 · 405-235-9621

Tulsa

James C. T. Hardwick · (20) · Hall Estill · http://www.hallestill.com · 320 South Boston Avenue, Suite 200 · Tulsa, OK 74103-3706 · 918-594-0400

Oliver S. Howard · (10) · GableGotwals · http://www.gablelaw.com · ONEOK Plaza, Suite 1100 · 100 West Fifth Street · Tulsa, OK 74103-4217 · 918-595-4800

James D. Satrom · Hall Estill · http://www.hallestill.com · 320 South Boston Avenue, Suite 200 · Tulsa, OK 74103-3706 · 918-594-0400

Tom Schroedter · Hall Estill · http://www.hallestill.com · 320 South Boston Avenue, Suite 200 · Tulsa, OK 74103-3706 · 918-594-0400

W. Bland Williamson, Jr. · (10) · Pray, Walker, Jackman, Williamson & Marlar · ONEOK Plaza, Suite 900 · 100 West Fifth Street · Tulsa, OK 74103-4218 · 918-581-5500

PERSONAL INJURY LITIGATION

Bartlesville

Alan R. Carlson · Garrison, Brown, Carlson & Buchanan · 530 Southeast Delaware · P.O. Box 1217 · Bartlesville, OK 74005 · 918-336-2520

Broken Arrow

Eugene Robinson · The Robinson Law Firm · 1820 North 15th Street · Broken Arrow, OK 74012 · 918-587-2311

Claremore

Sean Burrage · Taylor, Burrage, Foster, Mallett, Downs & Ramsey · 400 West Fourth Street · P.O. Box 309 · Claremore, OK 74018 · 918-343-4100

Edmond

Robert W. Nelson · Nelson, Roselius, Terry, O'Hara & Morton · 3540 South Boulevard, Suite 300 · Edmond, OK 73013 · 405-705-3600

Guymon

David K. Petty · David Petty Law Office · 301 West Fifth Street · P.O. Box 1187 · Guymon, OK 73942 · 580-338-5484

Lawton

John P. Zelbst · John P. Zelbst Law Firm · 411 Southwest Sixth Street · P.O. Box 365 · Lawton, OK 73502-0365 · 580-248-4844

Norman

Stanley M. Ward · Stanley M. Ward · 1821 Imhoff Road · Norman, OK 73071 · 405-360-9700

Oklahoma City

Ed Abel · ⑳ · Abel Law Firm · http://www.abellawfirm.com · The White House · 900 Northeast 63rd Street · Oklahoma City, OK 73105 · 405-239-7046

Murray E. Abowitz · ⑩ · Abowitz, Timberlake & Dahnke · The Hightower Building, Tenth Floor · 105 North Hudson · P.O. Box 1937 · Oklahoma City, OK 73101 · 405-236-4645

Howard K. Berry III · Berry Law Firm · http://www.berrylawok.com · 1923 North Classen Boulevard · Oklahoma City, OK 73106 · 405-524-1041

Mark E. Bialick · Durbin, Larimore & Bialick · http://www.dlb.net · 920 North Harvey Avenue · Oklahoma City, OK 73102-2610 · 405-235-9584

Steven E. Clark · Clark & Mitchell · 101 Park Avenue, Suite 210 · Oklahoma City, OK 73102 · 405-235-8488

Gerald E. Durbin II · ⑩ · Durbin, Larimore & Bialick · http://www.dlb.net · 920 North Harvey Avenue · Oklahoma City, OK 73102-2610 · 405-235-9584

Gerald P. Green · Pierce Couch Hendrickson Baysinger & Green · 1109 North Francis Avenue · P.O. Box 26350 · Oklahoma City, OK 73126 · 405-235-1611

Duke Halley · Duke Halley Law Firm · 500 Colcord Drive · Oklahoma City, OK 73102 · 405-602-8600

Garvin A. Isaacs · ⑩ · Garvin A. Isaacs · Rainy Mountain Building · 123 Northwest Eighth Street · Oklahoma City, OK 73102 · 405-232-2060

Robert C. Margo · ⑩ · Robert C. Margo · 5655 Classen Boulevard · Oklahoma City, OK 73118 · 405-286-3636

Kenneth N. McKinney · ㉕ · Tomlinson & O'Connell · Two Leadership Square, Suite 450 · 211 North Robinson Avenue · Oklahoma City, OK 73102 · 405-606-3350

Earl D. Mills · ⑳ · The Mills Law Firm · 119 North Robinson Avenue, Suite 500 · Oklahoma City, OK 73102 · 405-239-2501

John W. Norman · ⑳ · Norman & Edem · Renaissance Centre East · 127 Northwest 10th Street · Oklahoma City, OK 73103-4927 · 405-272-0200

Larry A. Tawwater · The Tawwater Law Firm · http://www.tawlaw.com · One Leadership Square, Suite 1950 · 211 North Robinson · Oklahoma City, OK 73102 · 405-319-7300

Reggie N. Whitten · ⑩ · Whitten, Burrage, Priest, Fulmer, Anderson & Eisel · One Leadership Square, Suite 1350 · 211 North Robinson Avenue · Oklahoma City, OK 73102 · 405-516-7800

John E. Wiggins · ⑩ · Wiggins Sewell & Ogletree · Oklahoma Tower, Suite 3100 · 210 Park Avenue · Oklahoma City, OK 73102 · 405-232-1211

Shawnee

Terry W. West · ⑩ · The West Law Firm · 124 West Highland Street · P.O. Box 698 · Shawnee, OK 74802-0698 · 405-275-0040

Tulsa

Edwin W. Ash · ⑩ · The Ash Law Firm · Mid-Continent Tower, Suite 2500 · 401 South Boston Avenue · Tulsa, OK 74103-4016 · 918-599-0001

Michael P. Atkinson · ⑩ · Atkinson, Haskins, Nellis, Brittingham, Gladd & Carwile · 1500 Park Centre · 525 South Main Street · Tulsa, OK 74103-4524 · 918-582-8877

Timothy G. Best · Best & Sharp · 100 West Fifth Street, Suite 808 · Tulsa, OK 74103-4225 · 918-582-1234

Clark O. Brewster · Brewster & DeAngelis · 2617 East 21st Street · Tulsa, OK 74114 · 918-742-2021

James W. Connor, Jr. · Richards & Connor · Park Centre Building, 12th Floor · 525 South Main · Tulsa, OK 74103-4509 · 918-585-2394

E. Terril Corley · ⑩ · Corley Ganem & Bolt · 1809 East 15th Street · Tulsa, OK 74104 · 918-745-9200

James E. Frasier · ⑳ · Frasier, Frasier & Hickman · 1700 Southwest Boulevard · P.O. Box 799 · Tulsa, OK 74101 · 918-584-4724

Richard D. Gibbon · ⑳ · Gibbon, Barron & Barron · Two West Sixth Street, Suite 320 · Tulsa, OK 74119 918-745-0687

John A. Gladd, Sr. · ⑳ · Dispute Resolution Consultants, Inc. · 1602 South Main Street · Tulsa, OK 74119 · 918-382-0300

Walter D. Haskins · Atkinson, Haskins, Nellis, Brittingham, Gladd & Carwile · 1500 Park Centre · 525 South Main Street · Tulsa, OK 74103-4524 · 918-582-8877

Amy E. Kempfert · Best & Sharp · 100 West Fifth Street, Suite 808 · Tulsa, OK 74103-4225 · 918-582-1234

G. Michael Lewis · Doerner, Saunders, Daniel & Anderson · http://www.dsda.com · 320 South Boston Avenue, Suite 500 · Tulsa, OK 74103-3725 · 918-582-1211

John F. McCormick · Pray, Walker, Jackman, Williamson & Marlar · ONEOK Plaza, Suite 900 · 100 West Fifth Street · Tulsa, OK 74103-4218 · 918-581-5500

James E. Poe · ㉕ · Covington & Poe · 111 West Fifth Street, Suite 740 · Tulsa, OK 74103-4267 · 918-585-5537

Phil R. Richards · Richards & Connor · Park Centre Building, 12th Floor · 525 South Main · Tulsa, OK 74103-4509 · 918-585-2394

Gary L. Richardson · ⑩ · Richardson Law Firm · 6450 South Lewis, Suite 300 · Tulsa, OK 74136 · 918-492-7674

Stephen J. Rodolf · ⑩ · Rodolf & Todd · 401 South Boston Avenue, Suite 2000 · Tulsa, OK 74103 · 918-295-2100

Ted C. Sherwood · Ted C. Sherwood · 15 West Sixth Street, Suite 2112 · Tulsa, OK 74119 · 918-592-1144

A. Mark Smiling · Smiling, Miller & Vaughn · Bradford Place, Suite 150 · 9175 South Yale Avenue · Tulsa, OK 74137 · 918-477-7500

John H. Tucker · ⑩ · Rhodes, Hieronymus, Jones, Tucker & Gable · http://www.rhodesokla.com · 100 West Fifth Street, Suite 400 · P.O. Box 21100 · Tulsa, OK 74121-1100 · 918-582-1173

John R. Woodard III · ⑩ · Feldman, Franden, Woodard & Farris · Park Centre, Suite 1000 · 525 South Main Street · Tulsa, OK 74103 · 918-583-7129

PRODUCT LIABILITY LITIGATION

Oklahoma City

Richard C. Ford · Crowe & Dunlevy · http://www.crowedunlevy.com · 20 North Broadway, Suite 1800 · Oklahoma City, OK 73102-8273 · 405-235-7700

Jimmy K. Goodman · Crowe & Dunlevy · http://www.crowedunlevy.com · 20 North Broadway, Suite 1800 · Oklahoma City, OK 73102-8273 · 405-235-7700

Robert D. Looney, Jr. · Hall Estill · http://www.hallestill.com · Chase Tower, Suite 2900 · 100 North Broadway · Oklahoma City, OK 73102-8865 · 405-553-2828

Robert C. Margo · ⑩ · Robert C. Margo · 5655 Classen Boulevard · Oklahoma City, OK 73118 · 405-286-3636

Larry A. Tawwater · The Tawwater Law Firm · http://www.tawlaw.com · One Leadership Square, Suite 1950 · 211 North Robinson · Oklahoma City, OK 73102 · 405-319-7300

Harry A. Woods, Jr. · ⑳ · Crowe & Dunlevy · http://www.crowedunlevy.com · 20 North Broadway, Suite 1800 · Oklahoma City, OK 73102-8273 · 405-235-7700

Tulsa

Dennis C. Cameron · GableGotwals · http://www.gablelaw.com · ONEOK Plaza, Suite 1100 · 100 West Fifth Street · Tulsa, OK 74103-4217 · 918-595-4800

James W. Connor, Jr. · Richards & Connor · Park Centre Building, 12th Floor · 525 South Main · Tulsa, OK 74103-4509 · 918-585-2394

Mary Quinn Cooper · Eldridge Cooper Steichen & Leach · http://www.ecslok.com · 110 West Seventh Street, Suite 200 · Tulsa, OK 74119 · 918-388-5555

Reuben Davis · McAfee & Taft · http://www.mcafeetaft.com · ONEOK Plaza, Suite 500 · 100 West Fifth Street · Tulsa, OK 74103 · 918-587-0000

John R. Woodard III · ⑩ · Feldman, Franden, Woodard & Farris · Park Centre, Suite 1000 · 525 South Main Street · Tulsa, OK 74103 · 918-583-7129

PROJECT FINANCE LAW

Oklahoma City

Allan A. Brooks III · The Public Finance Law Group · 1900 First National Center West · 120 North Robinson · Oklahoma City, OK 73102 · 405-235-3413

Michael E. Joseph · ⑩ · McAfee & Taft · http://www.mcafeetaft.com · Two Leadership Square, 10th Floor · 211 North Robinson · Oklahoma City, OK 73102 · 405-235-9621

PUBLIC FINANCE LAW

Oklahoma City

Allan A. Brooks III · The Public Finance Law Group · 1900 First National Center West · 120 North Robinson · Oklahoma City, OK 73102 · 405-235-3413

Gary M. Bush · The Public Finance Law Group · 1900 First National Center West · 120 North Robinson Oklahoma City, OK 73102 · 405-235-3413

Mark F. Selvidge · Kutak Rock · 6305 Waterford Boulevard, Suite 475 · Oklahoma City, OK 73118-1116 · 405-848-2475

Earl A. Skarky · Crowe & Dunlevy · http://www.crowedunlevy.com · 20 North Broadway, Suite 1800 · Oklahoma City, OK 73102-8273 · 405-235-7700

Tulsa

Eric P. Nelson · Rosenstein, Fist & Ringold · Park Centre, Suite 700 · 525 South Main Street · Tulsa, OK 74103-4508 · 918-585-9211

REAL ESTATE LAW

Norman

John D. Hastie · ㉕ · Phillips McFall McCaffrey McVay & Murrah · http://www.phillipsmcfall.com · 401 West Main, Suite 444 · Norman, OK 73072 · 405-292-4445

Oklahoma City

Zachary W. Allen · Mock, Schwabe, Waldo, Elder, Reeves & Bryant · http://www.mswerb.com · Two Leadership Square, 14th Floor · 211 North Robinson Avenue · Oklahoma City, OK 73102 · 405-235-1110

James C. Elder · ㉕ · Mock, Schwabe, Waldo, Elder, Reeves & Bryant · http://www.mswerb.com · Two Leadership Square, 14th Floor · 211 North Robinson Avenue · Oklahoma City, OK 73102 · 405-235-1110

Lloyd T. Hardin, Jr. · Phillips McFall McCaffrey McVay & Murrah · http://www.phillipsmcfall.com · Corporate Tower, 13th Floor · 101 North Robinson · Oklahoma City, OK 73102 · 405-235-4100

Frank D. Hill · ㉕ · McAfee & Taft · http://www.mcafeetaft.com · Two Leadership Square, 10th Floor · 211 North Robinson · Oklahoma City, OK 73102 · 405-235-9621

Robert M. Johnson · ㉕ · Crowe & Dunlevy · http://www.crowedunlevy.com · 20 North Broadway, Suite 1800 · Oklahoma City, OK 73102-8273 · 405-235-7700

David D. Kennedy · ⑩ · Spradling, Kennedy & McPhail · The Tower, Suite 1750 · 1601 Northwest Expressway · Oklahoma City, OK 73118 · 405-418-2700

Michael S. Laird · Crowe & Dunlevy · http://www.crowedunlevy.com · 20 North Broadway, Suite 1800 · Oklahoma City, OK 73102-8273 · 405-235-7700

Sally Mock · ㉕ · McAfee & Taft · http://www.mcafeetaft.com · Two Leadership Square, 10th Floor · 211 North Robinson · Oklahoma City, OK 73102 · 405-235-9621

J. Michael Nordin · McAfee & Taft · http://www.mcafeetaft.com · Two Leadership Square, 10th Floor · 211 North Robinson · Oklahoma City, OK 73102 · 405-235-9621

Henry P. Rheinberger · ㉕ · Crowe & Dunlevy · http://www.crowedunlevy.com · 20 North Broadway, Suite 1800 · Oklahoma City, OK 73102-8273 · 405-235-7700

Richard A. Riggs · ㉕ · McAfee & Taft · http://www.mcafeetaft.com · Two Leadership Square, 10th Floor 211 North Robinson · Oklahoma City, OK 73102 · 405-235-9621

John E. Sargent · McAfee & Taft · http://www.mcafeetaft.com · Two Leadership Square, 10th Floor · 211 North Robinson · Oklahoma City, OK 73102 · 405-235-9621

T. Scott Spradling · ㉕ · Spradling, Kennedy & McPhail · The Tower, Suite 1750 · 1601 Northwest Expressway · Oklahoma City, OK 73118 · 405-418-2700

Tulsa

Gary L. Betow · ⑩ · Conner & Winters · http://www.cwlaw.com · One Williams Center, Suite 4000 · Tulsa, OK 74172 · 918-586-5711

Kevin C. Coutant · Doerner, Saunders, Daniel & Anderson · http://www.dsda.com · 320 South Boston Avenue, Suite 500 · Tulsa, OK 74103-3725 · 918-582-1211

B. Kenneth Cox, Jr. · Hall Estill · http://www.hallestill.com · 320 South Boston Avenue, Suite 200 · Tulsa, OK 74103-3706 · 918-594-0400

William B. Jones · ㉕ · Jones, Gotcher & Bogan · 3800 First Place Tower · 15 East Fifth Street · Tulsa, OK 74103-4309 · 918-581-8200

Elizabeth R. Muratet · GableGotwals · http://www.gablelaw.com · ONEOK Plaza, Suite 1100 · 100 West Fifth Street · Tulsa, OK 74103-4217 · 918-595-4800

Eric P. Nelson · Rosenstein, Fist & Ringold · Park Centre, Suite 700 · 525 South Main Street · Tulsa, OK 74103-4508 · 918-585-9211

Coleman L. Robison · Rosenstein, Fist & Ringold · Park Centre, Suite 700 · 525 South Main Street · Tulsa, OK 74103-4508 · 918-585-9211

Malcolm E. Rosser IV · Crowe & Dunlevy · http://www.crowedunlevy.com · Kennedy Building, Suite 500 · 321 South Boston Avenue · Tulsa, OK 74103-3313 · 918-592-9800

Stephen A. Schuller · GableGotwals · http://www.gablelaw.com · ONEOK Plaza, Suite 1100 · 100 West Fifth Street · Tulsa, OK 74103-4217 · 918-595-4800

Steven A. Stecher · Moyers, Martin, Santee & Imel · Mid-Continent Tower, Suite 1100 · 401 South Boston Avenue · Tulsa, OK 74103 · 918-582-5281

Oklahoma City

Douglas A. Branch · Phillips McFall McCaffrey McVay & Murrah · http://www.phillipsmcfall.com · Corporate Tower, 13th Floor · 101 North Robinson · Oklahoma City, OK 73102 · 405-235-4100

David J. Ketelsleger · McAfee & Taft · http://www.mcafeetaft.com · Two Leadership Square, 10th Floor 211 North Robinson · Oklahoma City, OK 73102 · 405-235-9621

James W. Larimore · Crowe & Dunlevy · http://www.crowedunlevy.com · 20 North Broadway, Suite 1800 · Oklahoma City, OK 73102-8273 · 405-235-7700

Armand Paliotta · Hartzog Conger Cason & Neville · http://www.hartzoglaw.com · Bank of Oklahoma Plaza, Suite 1600 · 201 Robert S. Kerr Avenue · Oklahoma City, OK 73102 · 405-235-7000

John D. Robertson · Hartzog Conger Cason & Neville · http://www.hartzoglaw.com · Bank of Oklahoma Plaza, Suite 1600 · 201 Robert S. Kerr Avenue · Oklahoma City, OK 73102 · 405-235-7000

Michael M. Stewart · ⑩ · Crowe & Dunlevy · http://www.crowedunlevy.com · 20 North Broadway, Suite 1800 · Oklahoma City, OK 73102-8273 · 405-235-7700

Roger A. Stong · ⑩ · Crowe & Dunlevy · http://www.crowedunlevy.com · 20 North Broadway, Suite 1800 Oklahoma City, OK 73102-8273 · 405-235-7700

Terry W. Tippens · ㉕ · Fellers, Snider, Blankenship, Bailey & Tippens · http://www.fellerssnider.com · Chase Tower, Suite 1700 · 100 North Broadway · Oklahoma City, OK 73102-8820 · 405-232-0621

Jerry A. Warren · McAfee & Taft · http://www.mcafeetaft.com · Two Leadership Square, 10th Floor · 211 North Robinson · Oklahoma City, OK 73102 · 405-235-9621

Tulsa

Robert A. Curry · ⑩ · Conner & Winters · http://www.cwlaw.com · One Williams Center, Suite 4000 · Tulsa, OK 74172 · 918-586-5711

Kenneth E. Dornblaser · Johnson, Jones, Dornblaser, Coffman & Shorb · Bank Of America Building, Suite 2200 · 15 West Sixth Street · Tulsa, OK 74119 · 918-584-6644

Lon Foster III · ⑳ · Fellers, Snider, Blankenship, Bailey & Tippens · http://www.fellerssnider.com · The Kennedy Building, Suite 800 · 321 South Boston Avenue · Tulsa, OK 74103-3318 · 918-599-0621

John B. Johnson, Jr. · ㉕ · Johnson, Jones, Dornblaser, Coffman & Shorb · Bank Of America Building, Suite 2200 · 15 West Sixth Street · Tulsa, OK 74119 · 918-584-6644

Lynnwood R. Moore, Jr. · ⑩ · Conner & Winters · http://www.cwlaw.com · One Williams Center, Suite 4000 · Tulsa, OK 74172 · 918-586-5711

P. David Newsome, Jr. · Cooper Newsome & Woosley · 401 South Boston Avenue, Suite 3300 · Tulsa, OK 74103-4070 · 918-592-3300

James M. Sturdivant · ㉕ · GableGotwals · http://www.gablelaw.com · ONEOK Plaza, Suite 1100 · 100 West Fifth Street · Tulsa, OK 74103-4217 · 918-595-4800

Norman

Steven T. Ledgerwood · Steven Ledgerwood · 1800 North Interstate Drive, Suite 100 · P.O. Box 722397 · Norman, OK 73070 · 405-701-2846

Oklahoma City

Cynthia L. Andrews · Crowe & Dunlevy · http://www.crowedunlevy.com · 20 North Broadway, Suite 1800 · Oklahoma City, OK 73102-8273 · 405-235-7700

Mark H. Bennett · Conner & Winters · http://www.cwlaw.com · One Leadership Square, Suite 1700 · 211 North Robinson Avenue · Oklahoma City, OK 73102-7101 · 405-272-5711

T. Michael Blake · McAfee & Taft · http://www.mcafeetaft.com · Two Leadership Square, 10th Floor · 211 North Robinson · Oklahoma City, OK 73102 · 405-235-9621

Len Cason · (10) · Hartzog Conger Cason & Neville · http://www.hartzoglaw.com · Bank of Oklahoma Plaza, Suite 1600 · 201 Robert S. Kerr Avenue · Oklahoma City, OK 73102 · 405-235-7000

Richard D. Craig · McAfee & Taft · http://www.mcafeetaft.com · Two Leadership Square, 10th Floor · 211 North Robinson · Oklahoma City, OK 73102 · 405-235-9621

Steven C. Davis · (10) · Hartzog Conger Cason & Neville · http://www.hartzoglaw.com · Bank of Oklahoma Plaza, Suite 1600 · 201 Robert S. Kerr Avenue · Oklahoma City, OK 73102 · 405-235-7000

Gary F. Fuller · (20) · McAfee & Taft · http://www.mcafeetaft.com · Two Leadership Square, 10th Floor · 211 North Robinson · Oklahoma City, OK 73102 · 405-235-9621

Terry Hanna · (10) · Crowe & Dunlevy · http://www.crowedunlevy.com · 20 North Broadway, Suite 1800 · Oklahoma City, OK 73102-8273 · 405-235-7700

James H. Holloman, Jr. · (25) · Crowe & Dunlevy · http://www.crowedunlevy.com · 20 North Broadway, Suite 1800 · Oklahoma City, OK 73102-8273 · 405-235-7700

Richard B. Kells, Jr. · (20) · Hartzog Conger Cason & Neville · http://www.hartzoglaw.com · Bank of Oklahoma Plaza, Suite 1600 · 201 Robert S. Kerr Avenue · Oklahoma City, OK 73102 · 405-235-7000

Timothy M. Larason · (25) · Andrews Davis · 100 North Broadway, Suite 3300 · Oklahoma City, OK 73102-8812 · 405-272-9241

Randall D. Mock · (25) · Mock, Schwabe, Waldo, Elder, Reeves & Bryant · http://www.mswerb.com · Two Leadership Square, 14th Floor · 211 North Robinson Avenue · Oklahoma City, OK 73102 · 405-235-1110

Robert O. O'Bannon · Phillips McFall McCaffrey McVay & Murrah · http://www.phillipsmcfall.com · Corporate Tower, 13th Floor · 101 North Robinson · Oklahoma City, OK 73102 · 405-235-4100

Dee A. Replogle · (10) · McAfee & Taft · http://www.mcafeetaft.com · Two Leadership Square, 10th Floor 211 North Robinson · Oklahoma City, OK 73102 · 405-235-9621

Tulsa

Kenneth F. Albright · Albright, Rusher & Hardcastle · Bank of America Center, Suite 2600 · 15 West Sixth Street · Tulsa, OK 74119-5434 · 918-583-5800

William E. Farrior · Barrows & Grimm · 110 West Seventh Street, Suite 900 · Tulsa, OK 74119-1044 · 918-584-1600

Kenneth L. Hunt · Hall Estill · http://www.hallestill.com · 320 South Boston Avenue, Suite 200 · Tulsa, OK 74103-3706 · 918-594-0400

Sheppard F. Miers, Jr. · GableGotwals · http://www.gablelaw.com · ONEOK Plaza, Suite 1100 · 100 West Fifth Street · Tulsa, OK 74103-4217 · 918-595-4800

Thomas G. Potts · ⑩ · James, Potts & Wulfers · http://www.jpwlaw.com · 2600 Mid Continent Tower · 401 South Boston Avenue · Tulsa, OK 74103-4016 · 918-584-0881

Douglas M. Rather · ⑩ · Conner & Winters · http://www.cwlaw.com · One Williams Center, Suite 4000 · Tulsa, OK 74172 · 918-586-5711

Gail R. Runnels · Holliman, Langholz & Runnels · 10 East Third Street, Suite 400 · Tulsa, OK 74103 · 918-584-1471

Randy R. Shorb · Johnson, Jones, Dornblaser, Coffman & Shorb · Bank Of America Building, Suite 2200 15 West Sixth Street · Tulsa, OK 74119 · 918-584-6644

Varley H. Taylor, Jr. · Doerner, Saunders, Daniel & Anderson · http://www.dsda.com · 320 South Boston Avenue, Suite 500 · Tulsa, OK 74103-3725 · 918-582-1211

John B. Turner · ㉕ · Stuart & Biolchini · First Place Tower, Suite 3300 · 15 East Fifth Street · Tulsa, OK 74136 · 918-582-3311

Henry G. Will · ㉕ · Conner & Winters · http://www.cwlaw.com · One Williams Center, Suite 4000 · Tulsa, OK 74172 · 918-586-5711

Andrew M. Wolov · ㉕ · Hall Estill · http://www.hallestill.com · 320 South Boston Avenue, Suite 200 · Tulsa, OK 74103-3706 · 918-594-0400

TECHNOLOGY LAW

Tulsa

Sarah E. Hansel · Hall Estill · http://www.hallestill.com · 320 South Boston Avenue, Suite 200 · Tulsa, OK 74103-3706 · 918-594-0400

TRUSTS AND ESTATES

Edmond

Lloyd McAlister · ⑩ · McAlister, McAlister, McKinnis & Tuggle · Kirkpatrick Bank Building, Suite 200 · 15 East 15th Street · P.O. Box 3735 · Edmond, OK 73013 · 405-359-0701

El Reno

James C. Bass · Bass Law Firm · 104 North Rock Island Avenue · El Reno, OK 73036 · 405-262-4040

Enid

G. L. Brown III · Brown & Associates · One Grand Center, Suite 301 · 201 North Grand · Enid, OK 73701 · 580-234-6600

Richard L. McKnight · Gungoll, Jackson, Collins, Box & Devoll · 323 West Broadway · P.O. Box 1549 · Enid, OK 73701 · 580-234-0436

Oklahoma City

Elizabeth K. Brown · Phillips McFall McCaffrey McVay & Murrah · http://www.phillipsmcfall.com · Corporate Tower, 13th Floor · 101 North Robinson · Oklahoma City, OK 73102 · 405-235-4100

Len Cason · ⑩ · Hartzog Conger Cason & Neville · http://www.hartzoglaw.com · Bank of Oklahoma Plaza, Suite 1600 · 201 Robert S. Kerr Avenue · Oklahoma City, OK 73102 · 405-235-7000

Richard D. Craig · McAfee & Taft · http://www.mcafeetaft.com · Two Leadership Square, 10th Floor · 211 North Robinson · Oklahoma City, OK 73102 · 405-235-9621

James F. Davis · ㉕ · Andrews Davis · 100 North Broadway, Suite 3300 · Oklahoma City, OK 73102-8812 405-272-9241

Steven C. Davis · ⑩ · Hartzog Conger Cason & Neville · http://www.hartzoglaw.com · Bank of Oklahoma Plaza, Suite 1600 · 201 Robert S. Kerr Avenue · Oklahoma City, OK 73102 · 405-235-7000

Allen D. Evans · ㉕ · Crowe & Dunlevy · http://www.crowedunlevy.com · 20 North Broadway, Suite 1800 Oklahoma City, OK 73102-8273 · 405-235-7700

James H. Holloman, Jr. · ㉕ · Crowe & Dunlevy · http://www.crowedunlevy.com · 20 North Broadway, Suite 1800 · Oklahoma City, OK 73102-8273 · 405-235-7700

Richard B. Kells, Jr. · ⑳ · Hartzog Conger Cason & Neville · http://www.hartzoglaw.com · Bank of Oklahoma Plaza, Suite 1600 · 201 Robert S. Kerr Avenue · Oklahoma City, OK 73102 · 405-235-7000

Randall D. Mock · ㉕ · Mock, Schwabe, Waldo, Elder, Reeves & Bryant · http://www.mswerb.com · Two Leadership Square, 14th Floor · 211 North Robinson Avenue · Oklahoma City, OK 73102 · 405-235-1110

Cynda C. Ottaway · ⑳ · Crowe & Dunlevy · http://www.crowedunlevy.com · 20 North Broadway, Suite 1800 · Oklahoma City, OK 73102-8273 · 405-235-7700

Mark H. Price · Mark H. Price · 2929 West Wilshire · Oklahoma City, OK 73116 · 405-842-1888

John N. Schaefer · McAfee & Taft · http://www.mcafeetaft.com · Two Leadership Square, 10th Floor · 211 North Robinson · Oklahoma City, OK 73102 · 405-235-9621

Susan B. Shields · McAfee & Taft · http://www.mcafeetaft.com · Two Leadership Square, 10th Floor · 211 North Robinson · Oklahoma City, OK 73102 · 405-235-9621

Amy J. Sine · Hartzog Conger Cason & Neville · http://www.hartzoglaw.com · Bank of Oklahoma Plaza, Suite 1600 · 201 Robert S. Kerr Avenue · Oklahoma City, OK 73102 · 405-235-7000

Stacey D. Spivey · Crowe & Dunlevy · http://www.crowedunlevy.com · 20 North Broadway, Suite 1800 · Oklahoma City, OK 73102-8273 · 405-235-7700

Michael W. Thom · ⑳ · Michael W. Thom Law Office · 4301 Northwest 63rd Street, Suite 109 · Oklahoma City, OK 73116 · 405-848-6600

Jon H. Trudgeon · ⑩ · Hartzog Conger Cason & Neville · http://www.hartzoglaw.com · Bank of Oklahoma Plaza, Suite 1600 · 201 Robert S. Kerr Avenue · Oklahoma City, OK 73102 · 405-235-7000

Stillwater

Hal WM Ellis · Ellis & Drummond · 711 South Husband Street · Stillwater, OK 74074 · 405-743-3770

Tulsa

Erin Donovan · Erin Donovan · 1921 South Boston Avenue · Tulsa, OK 74119 · 918-747-3788

David F. James · ⑩ · James, Potts & Wulfers · http://www.jpwlaw.com · 2600 Mid Continent Tower · 401 South Boston Avenue · Tulsa, OK 74103-4016 · 918-584-0881

John B. Johnson, Jr. · ㉕ · Johnson, Jones, Dornblaser, Coffman & Shorb · Bank Of America Building, Suite 2200 · 15 West Sixth Street · Tulsa, OK 74119 · 918-584-6644

Michael L. Nemec · Hall Estill · http://www.hallestill.com · 320 South Boston Avenue, Suite 200 · Tulsa, OK 74103-3706 · 918-594-0400

John B. Turner · ㉕ · Stuart & Biolchini · First Place Tower, Suite 3300 · 15 East Fifth Street · Tulsa, OK 74136 · 918-582-3311

Henry G. Will · ㉕ · Conner & Winters · http://www.cwlaw.com · One Williams Center, Suite 4000 · Tulsa, OK 74172 · 918-586-5711

Andrew M. Wolov · ㉕ · Hall Estill · http://www.hallestill.com · 320 South Boston Avenue, Suite 200 · Tulsa, OK 74103-3706 · 918-594-0400

Jerry Zimmerman · Rosenstein, Fist & Ringold · Park Centre, Suite 700 · 525 South Main Street · Tulsa, OK 74103-4508 · 918-585-9211

Vinita

Mark W. Curnutte · Logan & Lowry · 101 South Wilson Street · P.O. Box 558 · Vinita, OK 74301-0558 · 918-256-7511

VENTURE CAPITAL LAW

Oklahoma City

Douglas A. Branch · Phillips McFall McCaffrey McVay & Murrah · http://www.phillipsmcfall.com · Corporate Tower, 13th Floor · 101 North Robinson · Oklahoma City, OK 73102 · 405-235-4100

D. Joe Rockett · ⑳ · Andrews Davis · 100 North Broadway, Suite 3300 · Oklahoma City, OK 73102-8812 405-272-9241

Michael M. Stewart · ⑩ · Crowe & Dunlevy · http://www.crowedunlevy.com · 20 North Broadway, Suite 1800 · Oklahoma City, OK 73102-8273 · 405-235-7700

Roger A. Stong · ⑩ · Crowe & Dunlevy · http://www.crowedunlevy.com · 20 North Broadway, Suite 1800 Oklahoma City, OK 73102-8273 · 405-235-7700

WATER LAW

Oklahoma City

John J. Griffin, Jr. · Crowe & Dunlevy · http://www.crowedunlevy.com · 20 North Broadway, Suite 1800 Oklahoma City, OK 73102-8273 · 405-235-7700

L. Mark Walker · Crowe & Dunlevy · http://www.crowedunlevy.com · 20 North Broadway, Suite 1800 · Oklahoma City, OK 73102-8273 · 405-235-7700

Claremore

Jack Gordon, Jr. · Gordon & Gordon · 111 South Muskogee · P.O. Box 1167 · Claremore, OK 74018 · 918-341-7322

Edmond

Carl D. Hughes · ⑩ · Hughes, Joseph & Hughes · 1218 East Ninth Street, Suite Eight · Edmond, OK 73034 · 405-848-0111

Enid

Stephen Jones · ⑩ · Jones, Otjen, Davis & Nixon · 114 East Broadway Avenue, Suite 1100 · P.O. Box 472 Enid, OK 73702 · 580-242-5500

McAlester

P. Warren Gotcher · ㉕ · Gotcher & Belote · 2626 South 14th Street · P.O. Box 160 · McAlester, OK 74502 · 918-423-0412

Oklahoma City

John W. Coyle III · ⑩ · Coyle Law Firm · 125 Park Avenue, First Floor · Oklahoma City, OK 73102 · 405-232-1988

Garvin A. Isaacs · ⑩ · Garvin A. Isaacs · Rainy Mountain Building · 123 Northwest Eighth Street · Oklahoma City, OK 73102 · 405-232-2060

Mack K. Martin · ⑩ · Martin Law Office · 125 Park Avenue, Fifth Floor · Oklahoma City, OK 73102 · 405-236-8888

Robert G. McCampbell · Crowe & Dunlevy · http://www.crowedunlevy.com · 20 North Broadway, Suite 1800 · Oklahoma City, OK 73102-8273 · 405-235-7700

Drew Neville, Jr. · ⑩ · Hartzog Conger Cason & Neville · http://www.hartzoglaw.com · Bank of Oklahoma Plaza, Suite 1600 · 201 Robert S. Kerr Avenue · Oklahoma City, OK 73102 · 405-235-7000

D. C. Thomas · ㉕ · D. C. Thomas · One Leadership Square, Suite 900 · 211 North Robinson Avenue · Oklahoma City, OK 73102 · 405-235-4300

Robert L. Wyatt · Wyatt Law Office · http://www.wyattlaw.com · 501 North Walker Avenue, Suite 110 · P.O. Box 1947 · Oklahoma City, OK 73101 · 405-234-5500

Tulsa

Clark O. Brewster · Brewster & DeAngelis · 2617 East 21st Street · Tulsa, OK 74114 · 918-742-2021

Allen M. Smallwood · Allen Smallwood · 1310 South Denver Avenue · Tulsa, OK 74119 · 918-582-1993

Norman

Richard A. Bell · The Bell Law Firm · 1225 West Main Street, Suite 201 · P.O. Box 1529 · Norman, OK 73070 · 405-329-6850

Oklahoma City

Jacque Brawner · McAfee & Taft · http://www.mcafeetaft.com · Two Leadership Square, 10th Floor · 211 North Robinson · Oklahoma City, OK 73102 · 405-235-9621

Arlen Fielden · Crowe & Dunlevy · http://www.crowedunlevy.com · 20 North Broadway, Suite 1800 · Oklahoma City, OK 73102-8273 · 405-235-7700

John A. McCaleb · ⑩ · Fenton, Fenton, Smith, Reneau & Moon · 211 North Robinson Avenue, Suite 800 North · Oklahoma City, OK 73102 · 405-235-4671

John S. Oldfield · ⑩ · Oldfield & Graves · 4808 North Classen Boulevard · Oklahoma City, OK 73118 · 405-840-0555

Tulsa

Jack D. Crews · ⑩ · Jack D. Crews · Pecan Tree Place · 5508 South Lewis Avenue · Tulsa, OK 74105-7105 · 918-742-0282

Madalene A. B. Witterholt · Crowe & Dunlevy · http://www.crowedunlevy.com · Kennedy Building, Suite 500 · 321 South Boston Avenue · Tulsa, OK 74103-3313 · 918-592-9800

OREGON

ADMINISTRATIVE LAW

Eugene

William F. Gary · Harrang Long Gary Rudnick · http://www.harrang.com · 360 East 10th Avenue, Suite 300 · Eugene, OR 97401-3248 · 541-485-0220

Glenn Klein · Harrang Long Gary Rudnick · http://www.harrang.com · 360 East 10th Avenue, Suite 300 · Eugene, OR 97401-3248 · 541-485-0220

Portland

Jeffrey G. Condit · Miller Nash · 3400 U.S. Bancorp Tower · 111 Southwest Fifth Avenue · Portland, OR 97204-3699 · 503-224-5858

John Junkin · Bullivant Houser Bailey · 888 Southwest Fifth Avenue, Suite 300 · Portland, OR 97204-2089 · 503-228-6351

James M. Kennedy · Kennedy & Kennedy · 601 Southwest Second Avenue, Suite 2050 · Portland, OR 97204 · 503-226-6555

Rhonda W. Kennedy · Kennedy & Kennedy · 601 Southwest Second Avenue, Suite 2050 · Portland, OR 97204 · 503-226-6555

Michael M. Morgan · a · Tonkon Torp · http://www.tonkon.com · Pioneer Tower, Suite 1600 · 888 Southwest Fifth Avenue · Portland, OR 97204-2099 · 503-221-1440

Lisa F. Rackner · McDowell & Rackner · 520 Southwest Sixth Avenue, Suite 830 · Portland, OR 97204 · 503-595-3922

Mark Trinchero · Davis Wright Tremaine · 1300 Southwest Fifth Avenue, Suite 2300 · Portland, OR 97201-5630 · 503-241-2300

ADVERTISING LAW

Portland

Benjamin H. Kaminash · Kaminash & Associates · 805 Southwest Broadway, Suite 2440 · Portland, OR 97205 · 503-224-3241

Jere M. Webb · ⑩ · Stoel Rives · http://www.stoel.com · 900 Southwest Fifth Avenue, Suite 2600 · Portland, OR 97204-1268 · 503-224-3380

ALTERNATIVE DISPUTE RESOLUTION

Carlton

Sidney A. Brockley · Sid Brockley Mediation · http://www.sidbrockley.com · P.O. Box 899 · Carlton, OR 97111 · 503-852-6196

Lake Oswego

Larry T. Coady · Larry T. Coady · Three Monroe Parkway, Suite P · P.O. Box 452 · Lake Oswego, OR 97035 · 503-227-7357

Portland

John R. Barker · Barker Law Firm · 1000 Southwest Broadway, Suite 1700 · Portland, OR 97205 · 503-227-6300

Jeffrey M. Batchelor · Markowitz, Herbold, Glade & Mehlhaf · http://www.mhgm.com · Pacwest Center, Suite 3000 · 1211 Southwest Fifth Avenue · Portland, OR 97204 · 503-295-3085

James J. Damis · Law Office of James J. Damis · 620 Southwest Fifth Avenue, Suite 1010 · Portland, OR 97204 · 503-226-3109

Cynthia M. Fraser · Garvey Schubert Barer · 121 Southwest Morrison Street, 11th Floor · Portland, OR 97204-3141 · 503-228-3939

William N. Gross · William N. Gross · 117 Southwest Taylor Street, Suite 200 · Portland, OR 97204 · 503-417-0478

Susan M. Hammer · Susan M. Hammer Dispute Resolution Services · 25 Northwest 23rd Place, Suite 6-473 · Portland, OR 97210-5599 · 503-222-5949

Samuel J. Imperati · Samuel J. Imperati · 11524 Southwest Vacuna Court · Portland, OR 97219 · 503-244-1174

Joshua D. Kadish · Meyer & Wyse · 621 Southwest Morrison Street, Suite 1300 · Portland, OR 97205 · 503-228-8448

James L. Knoll · James L. Knoll · http://www.knollmediation.com · 1500 Southwest Taylor Street · Portland, OR 97205 · 503-222-9000

Eric B. Lindauer · Eric Lindauer · 1000 Southwest Broadway, Suite 2400 · Portland, OR 97205 · 503-223-2300

Daniel H. Skerritt · Tonkon Torp · http://www.tonkon.com · Pioneer Tower, Suite 1600 · 888 Southwest Fifth Avenue · Portland, OR 97204-2099 · 503-221-1440

Richard G. Spier · Richard G. Spier · http://www.spier-mediate.com · 2536 Northeast 28th Avenue · Portland, OR 97212 · 503-284-2511

Jacob B. Tanzer · Jacob B. Tanzer · 4405 Southwest Warrens Way · Portland, OR 97221 · 503-274-0017

Sharon Williams · Sharon A. Williams · http://www.portlandfamilymediator.com · 520 Southwest Yamhill, Suite 1015 · Portland, OR 97205 · 503-224-5775

Salem

Susan M. Leeson · Susan M. Leeson · 1795 Cottage Street, NE · Salem, OR 97301 · 503-588-0535

ANTITRUST LAW

Portland

John F. McGrory · Davis Wright Tremaine · 1300 Southwest Fifth Avenue, Suite 2300 · Portland, OR 97201-5630 · 503-241-2300

Milo P. Petranovich · Lane Powell · http://www.lanepowell.com · 601 Southwest Second Avenue, Suite 2100 · Portland, OR 97204-3158 · 503-778-2100

Philip S. Van Der Weele · K&L Gates · 222 Southwest Columbia Street, Suite 1400 · Portland, OR 97201 · 503-228-3200

E. Walter Van Valkenburg · Stoel Rives · http://www.stoel.com · 900 Southwest Fifth Avenue, Suite 2600 · Portland, OR 97204-1268 · 503-224-3380

APPELLATE LAW

Eugene

William F. Gary · Harrang Long Gary Rudnick · http://www.harrang.com · 360 East 10th Avenue, Suite 300 · Eugene, OR 97401-3248 · 541-485-0220

Sharon A. Rudnick · Harrang Long Gary Rudnick · http://www.harrang.com · 360 East 10th Avenue, Suite 300 · Eugene, OR 97401-3248 · 541-485-0220

Portland

Jeffrey M. Batchelor · Markowitz, Herbold, Glade & Mehlhaf · http://www.mhgm.com · Pacwest Center, Suite 3000 · 1211 Southwest Fifth Avenue · Portland, OR 97204 · 503-295-3085

Thomas W. Brown · Cosgrave Vergeer Kester · 805 Southwest Broadway Street, Eighth Floor · Portland, OR 97205 · 503-323-9000

Thomas M. Christ · a · Cosgrave Vergeer Kester · 805 Southwest Broadway Street, Eighth Floor · Portland, OR 97205 · 503-323-9000

James S. Coon · Swanson Thomas & Coon · 820 Southwest Second Avenue, Suite 200 · Portland, OR 97204 · 503-228-5222

John Paul Graff · a · Graff & O'Neil · 2121 Southwest Broadway · Portland, OR 97201 · 503-222-4545

Charles F. Hinkle · a · Stoel Rives · http://www.stoel.com · 900 Southwest Fifth Avenue, Suite 2600 · Portland, OR 97204-1268 · 503-224-3380

Lindsey H. Hughes · Keating Jones Bildstein & Hughes · 800 Benjamin Franklin Plaza · One SouthWest Columbia · Portland, OR 97258-2095 · 503-222-9955

Maureen Leonard · Maureen Leonard · 520 Southwest Sixth Avenue, Suite 920 · Portland, OR 97204 · 503-224-0212

R. Daniel Lindahl · Lindahl Law Firm · 121 Southwest Morrison Street, Suite 1100 · Portland, OR 97204 503-241-4099

Susan D. Marmaduke · Harrang Long Gary Rudnick · http://www.harrang.com · 1001 Southwest Fifth Avenue, Suite 1600 · Portland, OR 97204-1116 · 503-242-0000

James E. Mountain, Jr. · Harrang Long Gary Rudnick · http://www.harrang.com · 1001 Southwest Fifth Avenue, Suite 1600 · Portland, OR 97204-1116 · 503-242-0000

Janet M. Schroer · Hoffman, Hart & Wagner · 1000 Southwest Broadway, 20th Floor · Portland, OR 97205 · 503-222-4499

Michael H. Simon · a · Perkins Coie · http://www.perkinscoie.com · 1120 Northwest Couch Street, 10th Floor · Portland, OR 97209-4128 · 503-727-2000

Thomas W. Sondag · Lane Powell · http://www.lanepowell.com · 601 Southwest Second Avenue, Suite 2100 · Portland, OR 97204-3158 · 503-778-2100

James N. Westwood · a · Stoel Rives · http://www.stoel.com · 900 Southwest Fifth Avenue, Suite 2600 · Portland, OR 97204-1268 · 503-224-3380

Salem

J. Michael Alexander · Swanson, Lathen, Alexander & McCann · 388 State Street, Suite 1000 · Salem, OR 97304 · 503-581-2421

BANKING LAW

Portland

Gordon E. Crim · Foster Pepper · 601 Southwest Second Avenue, Suite 1800 · Portland, OR 97204-3171 503-221-0607

Mary Ann Frantz · Miller Nash · 3400 U.S. Bancorp Tower · 111 Southwest Fifth Avenue · Portland, OR 97204-3699 · 503-224-5858

Carol Dey Hibbs · a · Tonkon Torp · http://www.tonkon.com · Pioneer Tower, Suite 1600 · 888 Southwest Fifth Avenue · Portland, OR 97204-2099 · 503-221-1440

William R. Miller, Jr. · Davis Wright Tremaine · 1300 Southwest Fifth Avenue, Suite 2300 · Portland, OR 97201-5630 · 503-241-2300

Kenneth E. Roberts, Jr. · a · Foster Pepper · 601 Southwest Second Avenue, Suite 1800 · Portland, OR 97204-3171 · 503-221-0607

Kenneth D. Stephens · a · Tonkon Torp · http://www.tonkon.com · Pioneer Tower, Suite 1600 · 888 Southwest Fifth Avenue · Portland, OR 97204-2099 · 503-221-1440

Salem

Kenneth Sherman, Jr. · Sherman, Sherman, Johnnie & Hoyt · 693 Chemeketa Street, NE · P.O. Box 2247 · Salem, OR 97301 · 503-364-2281

BANKRUPTCY AND CREDITOR-DEBTOR RIGHTS LAW

Eugene

David B. Mills · a · Hammons & Mills · 115 West Eighth Avenue, Suite 280 · Eugene, OR 97401 · 541-484-1216

Wilson C. Muhlheim · 2) · Muhlheim Boyd · 88 East Broadway · Eugene, OR 97401 · 541-868-8005

Portland

Steve Hedberg · Perkins Coie · http://www.perkinscoie.com · 1120 Northwest Couch Street, 10th Floor · Portland, OR 97209-4128 · 503-727-2000

Louis G. Henry · a · Miller Nash · 3400 U.S. Bancorp Tower · 111 Southwest Fifth Avenue · Portland, OR 97204-3699 · 503-224-5858

David W. Hercher · Miller Nash · 3400 U.S. Bancorp Tower · 111 Southwest Fifth Avenue · Portland, OR 97204-3699 · 503-224-5858

Albert N. Kennedy · 2) · Tonkon Torp · http://www.tonkon.com · Pioneer Tower, Suite 1600 · 888 Southwest Fifth Avenue · Portland, OR 97204-2099 · 503-221-1440

Leon Simson · 2) · Tonkon Torp · http://www.tonkon.com · Pioneer Tower, Suite 1600 · 888 Southwest Fifth Avenue · Portland, OR 97204-2099 · 503-221-1440

Brad T. Summers · Ball Janik · One Main Place, Suite 1100 · 101 Southwest Main Street · Portland, OR 97204 · 503-228-2525

James C. Waggoner · Davis Wright Tremaine · 1300 Southwest Fifth Avenue, Suite 2300 · Portland, OR 97201-5630 · 503-241-2300

BET-THE-COMPANY LITIGATION

Portland

Steven K. Blackhurst · Ater Wynne · http://www.aterwynne.com · KOIN Center, Suite 1800 · 222 Southwest Columbia Street · Portland, OR 97201-6618 · 503-226-1191

Barnes H. Ellis · 2) · Stoel Rives · http://www.stoel.com · 900 Southwest Fifth Avenue, Suite 2600 · Portland, OR 97204-1268 · 503-224-3380

Stephen F. English · Bullivant Houser Bailey · 888 Southwest Fifth Avenue, Suite 300 · Portland, OR 97204-2089 · 503-228-6351

David B. Markowitz · a · Markowitz, Herbold, Glade & Mehlhaf · http://www.mhgm.com · Pacwest Center, Suite 3000 · 1211 Southwest Fifth Avenue · Portland, OR 97204 · 503-295-3085

Thomas H. Tongue · Dunn Carney Allen Higgins & Tongue · http://www.dunn-carney.com · 851 Southwest Sixth Avenue, Suite 1500 · Portland, OR 97204 · 503-224-6440

CIVIL RIGHTS LAW

Portland

Elden M. Rosenthal · a · Rosenthal & Greene · 121 Southwest Salmon Street, Suite 1090 · Portland, OR 97204 · 503-228-3015

COLLABORATIVE LAW: FAMILY LAW

Eugene

Laura Parrish · Laura A. Parrish · 777 High Street, Suite 102 · Eugene, OR 97401 · 541-485-6162

COMMERCIAL LITIGATION

Eugene

William F. Gary · Harrang Long Gary Rudnick · http://www.harrang.com · 360 East 10th Avenue, Suite 300 · Eugene, OR 97401-3248 · 541-485-0220

William H. Martin · Gleaves, Swearingen, Potter & Scott · http://www.gleaveslaw.com · 975 Oak Street, Eighth Floor · P.O. Box 1147 · Eugene, OR 97440-1147 · 541-686-8833

K. Patrick Neill · 2) · Hershner Hunter · http://www.hershnerhunter.com · 180 East 11th Avenue · P.O. Box 1475 · Eugene, OR 97440 · 541-686-8511

Dennis W. Percell · a · Arnold Gallagher Saydack Percell Roberts & Potter · http://www.arnoldgallagher.com · 800 Willamette Street, Suite 800 · P.O. Box 1758 · Eugene, OR 97440-1758 · 541-484-0188

Rohn M. Roberts · Arnold Gallagher Saydack Percell Roberts & Potter · http://www.arnoldgallagher.com 800 Willamette Street, Suite 800 · P.O. Box 1758 · Eugene, OR 97440-1758 · 541-484-0188

William G. Wheatley · 2% · Jaqua & Wheatley · 825 East Park Street · Eugene, OR 97401-2909 · 541-686-8485

Portland

David H. Angeli · Hoffman Angeli · 1000 Southwest Broadway, Suite 1500 · Portland, OR 97205 · 503-222-1125

Joseph C. Arellano · Kennedy, Watts, Arellano & Ricks · 1211 Southwest Fifth Avenue, Suite 2850 · Portland, OR 97204-3733 · 503-228-6191

Jeffrey M. Batchelor · Markowitz, Herbold, Glade & Mehlhaf · http://www.mhgm.com · Pacwest Center, Suite 3000 · 1211 Southwest Fifth Avenue · Portland, OR 97204 · 503-295-3085

Gary M. Berne · Stoll Berne · http://www.stollberne.com · 209 Southwest Oak Street, Suite 500 · Portland, OR 97204 · 503-227-1600

Steven K. Blackhurst · Ater Wynne · http://www.aterwynne.com · KOIN Center, Suite 1800 · 222 Southwest Columbia Street · Portland, OR 97201-6618 · 503-226-1191

David A. Bledsoe · Perkins Coie · http://www.perkinscoie.com · 1120 Northwest Couch Street, 10th Floor Portland, OR 97209-4128 · 503-727-2000

William B. Crow · a · Schwabe, Williamson & Wyatt · Pacwest Center, Suite 1900 · 1211 Southwest Fifth Avenue · Portland, OR 97204-3795 · 503-222-9981

Austin W. Crowe, Jr. · Perkins Coie · http://www.perkinscoie.com · 1120 Northwest Couch Street, 10th Floor · Portland, OR 97209-4128 · 503-727-2000

Thomas V. Dulcich · Schwabe, Williamson & Wyatt · Pacwest Center, Suite 1900 · 1211 Southwest Fifth Avenue · Portland, OR 97204-3795 · 503-222-9981

Barnes H. Ellis · 2) · Stoel Rives · http://www.stoel.com · 900 Southwest Fifth Avenue, Suite 2600 · Portland, OR 97204-1268 · 503-224-3380

Stephen F. English · Bullivant Houser Bailey · 888 Southwest Fifth Avenue, Suite 300 · Portland, OR 97204-2089 · 503-228-6351

Michael J. Esler · Esler, Stephens & Buckley · 700 Pioneer Tower · 888 Fifth Avenue South West · Portland, OR 97204-2021 · 503-223-1510

Paul T. Fortino · a · Perkins Coie · http://www.perkinscoie.com · 1120 Northwest Couch Street, 10th Floor · Portland, OR 97209-4128 · 503-727-2000

Randolph C. Foster · Stoel Rives · http://www.stoel.com · 900 Southwest Fifth Avenue, Suite 2600 · Portland, OR 97204-1268 · 503-224-3380

James H. Gidley · Perkins Coie · http://www.perkinscoie.com · 1120 Northwest Couch Street, 10th Floor Portland, OR 97209-4128 · 503-727-2000

Peter H. Glade · Markowitz, Herbold, Glade & Mehlhaf · http://www.mhgm.com · Pacwest Center, Suite 3000 · 1211 Southwest Fifth Avenue · Portland, OR 97204 · 503-295-3085

S. Ward Greene · a · Greene & Markley · The 1515 Building, Suite 600 · 1515 Southwest Fifth Avenue · Portland, OR 97201 · 503-295-2668

David G. Hosenpud · Lane Powell · http://www.lanepowell.com · 601 Southwest Second Avenue, Suite 2100 · Portland, OR 97204-3158 · 503-778-2100

Chris Kent · Kent & Johnson · 1500 Southwest Taylor Street · Portland, OR 97215 · 503-220-0717

Keith A. Ketterling · Stoll Berne · http://www.stollberne.com · 209 Southwest Oak Street, Suite 500 · Portland, OR 97204 · 503-227-1600

George L. Kirklin · a · Kirklin Folawn · 522 Southwest Fifth Avenue, Suite 1100 · Portland, OR 97204 · 503-222-1640

Rodney E. Lewis · Davis Wright Tremaine · 1300 Southwest Fifth Avenue, Suite 2300 · Portland, OR 97201-5630 · 503-241-2300

David B. Markowitz · a · Markowitz, Herbold, Glade & Mehlhaf · http://www.mhgm.com · Pacwest Center, Suite 3000 · 1211 Southwest Fifth Avenue · Portland, OR 97204 · 503-295-3085

James P. Martin · Hoffman, Hart & Wagner · 1000 Southwest Broadway, 20th Floor · Portland, OR 97205 · 503-222-4499

William F. Martson, Jr. · Tonkon Torp · http://www.tonkon.com · Pioneer Tower, Suite 1600 · 888 Southwest Fifth Avenue · Portland, OR 97204-2099 · 503-221-1440

William N. Mehlhaf · Markowitz, Herbold, Glade & Mehlhaf · http://www.mhgm.com · Pacwest Center, Suite 3000 · 1211 Southwest Fifth Avenue · Portland, OR 97204 · 503-295-3085

Gregory R. Mowe · a · Stoel Rives · http://www.stoel.com · 900 Southwest Fifth Avenue, Suite 2600 · Portland, OR 97204-1268 · 503-224-3380

Joel A. Mullin · Stoel Rives · http://www.stoel.com · 900 Southwest Fifth Avenue, Suite 2600 · Portland, OR 97204-1268 · 503-224-3380

Robert D. Newell · Davis Wright Tremaine · 1300 Southwest Fifth Avenue, Suite 2300 · Portland, OR 97201-5630 · 503-241-2300

Daniel E. O'Leary · 2% · Davis Wright Tremaine · 1300 Southwest Fifth Avenue, Suite 2300 · Portland, OR 97201-5630 · 503-241-2300

Milo P. Petranovich · Lane Powell · http://www.lanepowell.com · 601 Southwest Second Avenue, Suite 2100 · Portland, OR 97204-3158 · 503-778-2100

Per A. Ramfjord · Stoel Rives · http://www.stoel.com · 900 Southwest Fifth Avenue, Suite 2600 · Portland, OR 97204-1268 · 503-224-3380

Dennis P. Rawlinson · Miller Nash · 3400 U.S. Bancorp Tower · 111 Southwest Fifth Avenue · Portland, OR 97204-3699 · 503-224-5858

Peter C. Richter · a · Miller Nash · 3400 U.S. Bancorp Tower · 111 Southwest Fifth Avenue · Portland, OR 97204-3699 · 503-224-5858

Lois O. Rosenbaum · Stoel Rives · http://www.stoel.com · 900 Southwest Fifth Avenue, Suite 2600 · Portland, OR 97204-1268 · 503-224-3380

Thomas C. Sand · Miller Nash · 3400 U.S. Bancorp Tower · 111 Southwest Fifth Avenue · Portland, OR 97204-3699 · 503-224-5858

Kerry J. Shepherd · Markowitz, Herbold, Glade & Mehlhaf · http://www.mhgm.com · Pacwest Center, Suite 3000 · 1211 Southwest Fifth Avenue · Portland, OR 97204 · 503-295-3085

Robert A. Shlachter · Stoll Berne · http://www.stollberne.com · 209 Southwest Oak Street, Suite 500 · Portland, OR 97204 · 503-227-1600

Michael H. Simon · a · Perkins Coie · http://www.perkinscoie.com · 1120 Northwest Couch Street, 10th Floor · Portland, OR 97209-4128 · 503-727-2000

Daniel H. Skerritt · Tonkon Torp · http://www.tonkon.com · Pioneer Tower, Suite 1600 · 888 Southwest Fifth Avenue · Portland, OR 97204-2099 · 503-221-1440

N. Robert Stoll · Stoll Berne · http://www.stollberne.com · 209 Southwest Oak Street, Suite 500 · Portland, OR 97204 · 503-227-1600

Thomas H. Tongue · Dunn Carney Allen Higgins & Tongue · http://www.dunn-carney.com · 851 Southwest Sixth Avenue, Suite 1500 · Portland, OR 97204 · 503-224-6440

Jay Waldron · Schwabe, Williamson & Wyatt · Pacwest Center, Suite 1900 · 1211 Southwest Fifth Avenue · Portland, OR 97204-3795 · 503-222-9981

Robert C. Weaver, Jr. · a · Garvey Schubert Barer · 121 Southwest Morrison Street, 11th Floor · Portland, OR 97204-3141 · 503-228-3939

James N. Westwood · a · Stoel Rives · http://www.stoel.com · 900 Southwest Fifth Avenue, Suite 2600 · Portland, OR 97204-1268 · 503-224-3380

COMMUNICATIONS LAW

Portland

Lisa F. Rackner · McDowell & Rackner · 520 Southwest Sixth Avenue, Suite 830 · Portland, OR 97204 · 503-595-3922

Mark Trinchero · Davis Wright Tremaine · 1300 Southwest Fifth Avenue, Suite 2300 · Portland, OR 97201-5630 · 503-241-2300

James M. Van Nostrand · a · Perkins Coie · http://www.perkinscoie.com · 1120 Northwest Couch Street, 10th Floor · Portland, OR 97209-4128 · 503-727-2000

CONSTRUCTION LAW

Eugene

William R. Turnbow · WIlliam R. Turnbow · 800 Willamette Street, Suite 600 · Eugene, OR 97401 · 541-677-6121

Portland

Richard E. Alexander · Stoel Rives · http://www.stoel.com · 900 Southwest Fifth Avenue, Suite 2600 · Portland, OR 97204-1268 · 503-224-3380

Eric A. Grasberger · Stoel Rives · http://www.stoel.com · 900 Southwest Fifth Avenue, Suite 2600 · Portland, OR 97204-1268 · 503-224-3380

Arnold L. Gray · Stewart Sokol & Gray · http://www.lawssg.com · 2300 Southwest First Avenue, Suite 200 · Portland, OR 97201-5047 · 503-221-0699

Martha J. Hodgkinson · Hoffman, Hart & Wagner · 1000 Southwest Broadway, 20th Floor · Portland, OR 97205 · 503-222-4499

Daniel F. Knox · Schwabe, Williamson & Wyatt · Pacwest Center, Suite 1900 · 1211 Southwest Fifth Avenue · Portland, OR 97204-3795 · 503-222-9981

Guy A. Randles · Stoel Rives · http://www.stoel.com · 900 Southwest Fifth Avenue, Suite 2600 · Portland, OR 97204-1268 · 503-224-3380

Tigard

Michael J. Scott · Scott Hookland · http://www.scott-hookland.com · 9185 Southwest Burnham · P.O. Box 23414 · Tigard, OR 97281 · 503-620-4540

CORPORATE GOVERNANCE AND COMPLIANCE LAW

Portland

Ruth A. Beyer · Stoel Rives · http://www.stoel.com · 900 Southwest Fifth Avenue, Suite 2600 · Portland, OR 97204-1268 · 503-224-3380

Henry H. Hewitt · 2% · Stoel Rives · http://www.stoel.com · 900 Southwest Fifth Avenue, Suite 2600 · Portland, OR 97204-1268 · 503-224-3380

Margaret Hill Noto · a · Stoel Rives · http://www.stoel.com · 900 Southwest Fifth Avenue, Suite 2600 · Portland, OR 97204-1268 · 503-224-3380

Gregory E. Struxness · Ater Wynne · http://www.aterwynne.com · KOIN Center, Suite 1800 · 222 Southwest Columbia Street · Portland, OR 97201-6618 · 503-226-1191

Eugene

Donald A. Gallagher, Jr. · a · Arnold Gallagher Saydack Percell Roberts & Potter · http://www.arnoldgallagher.com · 800 Willamette Street, Suite 800 · P.O. Box 1758 · Eugene, OR 97440-1758 · 541-484-0188

Norman LeCompte, Jr. · a · Hershner Hunter · http://www.hershnerhunter.com · 180 East 11th Avenue P.O. Box 1475 · Eugene, OR 97440 · 541-686-8511

Standlee G. Potter · a · Gleaves, Swearingen, Potter & Scott · http://www.gleaveslaw.com · 975 Oak Street, Eighth Floor · P.O. Box 1147 · Eugene, OR 97440-1147 · 541-686-8833

William R. Potter · a · Arnold Gallagher Saydack Percell Roberts & Potter · http://www.arnoldgallagher.com · 800 Willamette Street, Suite 800 · P.O. Box 1758 · Eugene, OR 97440-1758 · 541-484-0188

Roger M. Saydack · a · Arnold Gallagher Saydack Percell Roberts & Potter · http://www.arnoldgallagher.com · 800 Willamette Street, Suite 800 · P.O. Box 1758 · Eugene, OR 97440-1758 · 541-484-0188

R. Sande Tomlinson · a · Watkinson Laird Rubenstein Baldwin & Burgess · 101 East Broadway, Suite 200 · P.O. Box 10567 · Eugene, OR 97440 · 541-484-2277

Portland

Todd A. Bauman · Stoel Rives · http://www.stoel.com · 900 Southwest Fifth Avenue, Suite 2600 · Portland, OR 97204-1268 · 503-224-3380

Ruth A. Beyer · Stoel Rives · http://www.stoel.com · 900 Southwest Fifth Avenue, Suite 2600 · Portland, OR 97204-1268 · 503-224-3380

Owen D. Blank · Tonkon Torp · http://www.tonkon.com · Pioneer Tower, Suite 1600 · 888 Southwest Fifth Avenue · Portland, OR 97204-2099 · 503-221-1440

Brian G. Booth · 2) · Tonkon Torp · http://www.tonkon.com · Pioneer Tower, Suite 1600 · 888 Southwest Fifth Avenue · Portland, OR 97204-2099 · 503-221-1440

Jason M. Brauser · Stoel Rives · http://www.stoel.com · 900 Southwest Fifth Avenue, Suite 2600 · Portland, OR 97204-1268 · 503-224-3380

William C. Campbell · Ater Wynne · http://www.aterwynne.com · KOIN Center, Suite 1800 · 222 Southwest Columbia Street · Portland, OR 97201-6618 · 503-226-1191

Stuart Chestler · Stoel Rives · http://www.stoel.com · 900 Southwest Fifth Avenue, Suite 2600 · Portland, OR 97204-1268 · 503-224-3380

Edward L. Epstein · 2) · Stoel Rives · http://www.stoel.com · 900 Southwest Fifth Avenue, Suite 2600 · Portland, OR 97204-1268 · 503-224-3380

Mary Ann Frantz · Miller Nash · 3400 U.S. Bancorp Tower · 111 Southwest Fifth Avenue · Portland, OR 97204-3699 · 503-224-5858

Ronald L. Greenman · a · Tonkon Torp · http://www.tonkon.com · Pioneer Tower, Suite 1600 · 888 Southwest Fifth Avenue · Portland, OR 97204-2099 · 503-221-1440

John J. Halle · Stoel Rives · http://www.stoel.com · 900 Southwest Fifth Avenue, Suite 2600 · Portland, OR 97204-1268 · 503-224-3380

Henry H. Hewitt · 2% · Stoel Rives · http://www.stoel.com · 900 Southwest Fifth Avenue, Suite 2600 · Portland, OR 97204-1268 · 503-224-3380

Carol Dey Hibbs · a · Tonkon Torp · http://www.tonkon.com · Pioneer Tower, Suite 1600 · 888 Southwest Fifth Avenue · Portland, OR 97204-2099 · 503-221-1440

James M. Kennedy · Kennedy & Kennedy · 601 Southwest Second Avenue, Suite 2050 · Portland, OR 97204 · 503-226-6555

Erich W. Merrill, Jr. · Miller Nash · 3400 U.S. Bancorp Tower · 111 Southwest Fifth Avenue · Portland, OR 97204-3699 · 503-224-5858

Robert J. Moorman · Stoel Rives · http://www.stoel.com · 900 Southwest Fifth Avenue, Suite 2600 · Portland, OR 97204-1268 · 503-224-3380

Andrew J. Morrow, Jr. · Foster Pepper · 601 Southwest Second Avenue, Suite 1800 · Portland, OR 97204-3171 · 503-221-0607

Margaret Hill Noto · a · Stoel Rives · http://www.stoel.com · 900 Southwest Fifth Avenue, Suite 2600 · Portland, OR 97204-1268 · 503-224-3380

George C. Spencer · a · Tonkon Torp · http://www.tonkon.com · Pioneer Tower, Suite 1600 · 888 Southwest Fifth Avenue · Portland, OR 97204-2099 · 503-221-1440

Kenneth D. Stephens · a · Tonkon Torp · http://www.tonkon.com · Pioneer Tower, Suite 1600 · 888 Southwest Fifth Avenue · Portland, OR 97204-2099 · 503-221-1440

Gregory E. Struxness · Ater Wynne · http://www.aterwynne.com · KOIN Center, Suite 1800 · 222 Southwest Columbia Street · Portland, OR 97201-6618 · 503-226-1191

John R. Thomas · Perkins Coie · http://www.perkinscoie.com · 1120 Northwest Couch Street, 10th Floor Portland, OR 97209-4128 · 503-727-2000

Roy W. Tucker · Perkins Coie · http://www.perkinscoie.com · 1120 Northwest Couch Street, 10th Floor · Portland, OR 97209-4128 · 503-727-2000

Mark A. von Bergen · Holland & Knight · http://www.hklaw.com · U.S. Bancorp Tower, Suite 2300 · 111 Southwest Fifth Avenue · Portland, OR 97204 · 503-243-2300

DUI/DWI DEFENSE

Oregon City

John Henry Hingson III · a · John Henry Hingson III · 409 Center Street · P.O. Box 1448 · Oregon City, OR 97045-2211 · 503-656-0355

EDUCATION LAW

Oregon City

Nancy Hungerford · Hungerford Law Firm · P.O. Box 3010 · Oregon City, OR 97045 · 503-650-7990

Portland

Jeffrey G. Condit · Miller Nash · 3400 U.S. Bancorp Tower · 111 Southwest Fifth Avenue · Portland, OR 97204-3699 · 503-224-5858

ELDER LAW

Springfield

Janice E. Hatton · Thorp Purdy Jewett Urness & Wilkinson · 1011 Harlow Road, Suite 300 · Springfield, OR 97477 · 541-747-3354

John C. Urness · Thorp Purdy Jewett Urness & Wilkinson · 1011 Harlow Road, Suite 300 · Springfield, OR 97477 · 541-747-3354

EMINENT DOMAIN AND CONDEMNATION LAW

Portland

Jill S. Gelineau · Schwabe, Williamson & Wyatt · Pacwest Center, Suite 1900 · 1211 Southwest Fifth Avenue · Portland, OR 97204-3795 · 503-222-9981

John Junkin · Bullivant Houser Bailey · 888 Southwest Fifth Avenue, Suite 300 · Portland, OR 97204-2089 · 503-228-6351

Robert E. Maloney, Jr. · Lane Powell · http://www.lanepowell.com · 601 Southwest Second Avenue, Suite 2100 · Portland, OR 97204-3158 · 503-778-2100

Gregory R. Mowe · a · Stoel Rives · http://www.stoel.com · 900 Southwest Fifth Avenue, Suite 2600 · Portland, OR 97204-1268 · 503-224-3380

John R. Osburn · Bullivant Houser Bailey · 888 Southwest Fifth Avenue, Suite 300 · Portland, OR 97204-2089 · 503-228-6351

Donald Joe Willis · Schwabe, Williamson & Wyatt · Pacwest Center, Suite 1900 · 1211 Southwest Fifth Avenue · Portland, OR 97204-3795 · 503-222-9981

EMPLOYEE BENEFITS LAW

Eugene

Jeff Kirtner · Hershner Hunter · http://www.hershnerhunter.com · 180 East 11th Avenue · P.O. Box 1475 Eugene, OR 97440 · 541-686-8511

Stephen O. Lane · a · Gleaves, Swearingen, Potter & Scott · http://www.gleaveslaw.com · 975 Oak Street, Eighth Floor · P.O. Box 1147 · Eugene, OR 97440-1147 · 541-686-8833

Walter W. Miller · Gleaves, Swearingen, Potter & Scott · http://www.gleaveslaw.com · 975 Oak Street, Eighth Floor · P.O. Box 1147 · Eugene, OR 97440-1147 · 541-686-8833

Everett R. Moreland · Hershner Hunter · http://www.hershnerhunter.com · 180 East 11th Avenue · P.O. Box 1475 · Eugene, OR 97440 · 541-686-8511

Craig A. Smith · a · Hershner Hunter · http://www.hershnerhunter.com · 180 East 11th Avenue · P.O. Box 1475 · Eugene, OR 97440 · 541-686-8511

Portland

James F. Ambrose · Davis Wright Tremaine · 1300 Southwest Fifth Avenue, Suite 2300 · Portland, OR 97201-5630 · 503-241-2300

Ray R. Benner · a · Schwabe, Williamson & Wyatt · Pacwest Center, Suite 1900 · 1211 Southwest Fifth Avenue · Portland, OR 97204-3795 · 503-222-9981

Donald A. Burns · a · Miller Nash · 3400 U.S. Bancorp Tower · 111 Southwest Fifth Avenue · Portland, OR 97204-3699 · 503-224-5858

Vincent P. Cacciottoli · a · Garvey Schubert Barer · 121 Southwest Morrison Street, 11th Floor · Portland, OR 97204-3141 · 503-228-3939

Ronald S. Grossmann · a · Stoel Rives · http://www.stoel.com · 900 Southwest Fifth Avenue, Suite 2600 Portland, OR 97204-1268 · 503-224-3380

Stuart C. Harris · Davis Wright Tremaine · 1300 Southwest Fifth Avenue, Suite 2300 · Portland, OR 97201-5630 · 503-241-2300

Jeffrey W. Knapp · Lane Powell · http://www.lanepowell.com · 601 Southwest Second Avenue, Suite 2100 · Portland, OR 97204-3158 · 503-778-2100

Thomas I. Kramer · Bullard Smith Jernstedt Wilson · http://www.bullardlaw.com · 1000 Southwest Broadway, Suite 1900 · Portland, OR 97205 · 503-248-1134

Jeffrey M. Krueger · Stoel Rives · http://www.stoel.com · 900 Southwest Fifth Avenue, Suite 2600 · Portland, OR 97204-1268 · 503-224-3380

Dennis Leybold · Stoel Rives · http://www.stoel.com · 900 Southwest Fifth Avenue, Suite 2600 · Portland, OR 97204-1268 · 503-224-3380

Gregory H. Macpherson · a · Stoel Rives · http://www.stoel.com · 900 Southwest Fifth Avenue, Suite 2600 · Portland, OR 97204-1268 · 503-224-3380

Victoria L. Macpherson · Miller Nash · 3400 U.S. Bancorp Tower · 111 Southwest Fifth Avenue · Portland, OR 97204-3699 · 503-224-5858

Darcy M. Norville · Tonkon Torp · http://www.tonkon.com · Pioneer Tower, Suite 1600 · 888 Southwest Fifth Avenue · Portland, OR 97204-2099 · 503-221-1440

Joseph L. Reinhart · Zalutsky, Klarquist & Reinhart · http://www.erisalaw.com · The Waldo Block,Third Floor · 215 Southwest Washington Street · Portland, OR 97204 · 503-248-0300

Leigh D. Stephenson-Kuhn · a · Lane Powell · http://www.lanepowell.com · 601 Southwest Second Avenue, Suite 2100 · Portland, OR 97204-3158 · 503-778-2100

Jack Walsh · Lane Powell · http://www.lanepowell.com · 601 Southwest Second Avenue, Suite 2100 · Portland, OR 97204-3158 · 503-778-2100

Morton H. Zalutsky · 2) · Zalutsky, Klarquist & Reinhart · http://www.erisalaw.com · The Waldo Block,Third Floor · 215 Southwest Washington Street · Portland, OR 97204 · 503-248-0300

Salem

Randall W. Cook · Saalfeld Griggs · Park Place, Suite 300 · 250 Church Street, SE · Salem, OR 97301 · 503-399-1070

Clark B. Williams · a · Heltzel, Upjohn, Williams, Yandell, Roth, Smith & Petersen · Pioneer Trust Building, Fourth Floor · 117 Commercial Street, NE · P.O. Box 1048 · Salem, OR 97308 · 503-585-4422

ENERGY LAW

Portland

James E. Benedict · Cable Huston Benedict Haagensen & Lloyd · 1001 Southwest Fifth Avenue, Suite 2000 · Portland, OR 97204-1136 · 503-224-3092

John A. Cameron, Jr. · Davis Wright Tremaine · 1300 Southwest Fifth Avenue, Suite 2300 · Portland, OR 97201-5630 · 503-241-2300

Kirk H. Gibson · Ater Wynne · http://www.aterwynne.com · KOIN Center, Suite 1800 · 222 Southwest Columbia Street · Portland, OR 97201-6618 · 503-226-1191

Richard M. Glick · Davis Wright Tremaine · 1300 Southwest Fifth Avenue, Suite 2300 · Portland, OR 97201-5630 · 503-241-2300

William H. Holmes · Stoel Rives · http://www.stoel.com · 900 Southwest Fifth Avenue, Suite 2600 · Portland, OR 97204-1268 · 503-224-3380

Karen E. Jones · Stoel Rives · http://www.stoel.com · 900 Southwest Fifth Avenue, Suite 2600 · Portland, OR 97204-1268 · 503-224-3380

Katherine A. McDowell · a · McDowell & Rackner · 520 Southwest Sixth Avenue, Suite 830 · Portland, OR 97204 · 503-595-3922

Michael M. Morgan · a · Tonkon Torp · http://www.tonkon.com · Pioneer Tower, Suite 1600 · 888 Southwest Fifth Avenue · Portland, OR 97204-2099 · 503-221-1440

Ronald L. Saxton · Ater Wynne · http://www.aterwynne.com · KOIN Center, Suite 1800 · 222 Southwest Columbia Street · Portland, OR 97201-6618 · 503-226-1191

James M. Van Nostrand · a · Perkins Coie · http://www.perkinscoie.com · 1120 Northwest Couch Street, 10th Floor · Portland, OR 97209-4128 · 503-727-2000

Marcus Wood · a · Stoel Rives · http://www.stoel.com · 900 Southwest Fifth Avenue, Suite 2600 · Portland, OR 97204-1268 · 503-224-3380

ENVIRONMENTAL LAW

Portland

David F. Bartz, Jr. · Schwabe, Williamson & Wyatt · Pacwest Center, Suite 1900 · 1211 Southwest Fifth Avenue · Portland, OR 97204-3795 · 503-222-9981

James E. Benedict · Cable Huston Benedict Haagensen & Lloyd · 1001 Southwest Fifth Avenue, Suite 2000 · Portland, OR 97204-1136 · 503-224-3092

David A. Bledsoe · Perkins Coie · http://www.perkinscoie.com · 1120 Northwest Couch Street, 10th Floor Portland, OR 97209-4128 · 503-727-2000

David L. Blount · 2) · Landye Bennett Blumstein · 1300 Southwest Fifth Avenue, Suite 3500 · Portland, OR 97201 · 503-224-4100

Michael R. Campbell · Stoel Rives · http://www.stoel.com · 900 Southwest Fifth Avenue, Suite 2600 · Portland, OR 97204-1268 · 503-224-3380

Patricia M. Dost · Schwabe, Williamson & Wyatt · Pacwest Center, Suite 1900 · 1211 Southwest Fifth Avenue · Portland, OR 97204-3795 · 503-222-9981

David E. Filippi · Stoel Rives · http://www.stoel.com · 900 Southwest Fifth Avenue, Suite 2600 · Portland, OR 97204-1268 · 503-224-3380

Richard M. Glick · Davis Wright Tremaine · 1300 Southwest Fifth Avenue, Suite 2300 · Portland, OR 97201-5630 · 503-241-2300

Donald A. Haagensen · Cable Huston Benedict Haagensen & Lloyd · 1001 Southwest Fifth Avenue, Suite 2000 · Portland, OR 97204-1136 · 503-224-3092

Christopher R. Hermann · Stoel Rives · http://www.stoel.com · 900 Southwest Fifth Avenue, Suite 2600 Portland, OR 97204-1268 · 503-224-3380

William H. Holmes · Stoel Rives · http://www.stoel.com · 900 Southwest Fifth Avenue, Suite 2600 · Portland, OR 97204-1268 · 503-224-3380

Tom E. Lindley · a · Perkins Coie · http://www.perkinscoie.com · 1120 Northwest Couch Street, 10th Floor · Portland, OR 97209-4128 · 503-727-2000

Max M. Miller, Jr. · Tonkon Torp · http://www.tonkon.com · Pioneer Tower, Suite 1600 · 888 Southwest Fifth Avenue · Portland, OR 97204-2099 · 503-221-1440

J. Mark Morford · a · Stoel Rives · http://www.stoel.com · 900 Southwest Fifth Avenue, Suite 2600 · Portland, OR 97204-1268 · 503-224-3380

Claudia K. Powers · Ater Wynne · http://www.aterwynne.com · KOIN Center, Suite 1800 · 222 Southwest Columbia Street · Portland, OR 97201-6618 · 503-226-1191

Joan P. Snyder · Stoel Rives · http://www.stoel.com · 900 Southwest Fifth Avenue, Suite 2600 · Portland, OR 97204-1268 · 503-224-3380

Thomas R. Wood · Stoel Rives · http://www.stoel.com · 900 Southwest Fifth Avenue, Suite 2600 · Portland, OR 97204-1268 · 503-224-3380

EQUIPMENT FINANCE LAW

Portland

Gary R. Barnum · Stoel Rives · http://www.stoel.com · 900 Southwest Fifth Avenue, Suite 2600 · Portland, OR 97204-1268 · 503-224-3380

ETHICS AND PROFESSIONAL RESPONSIBILITY LAW

Portland

Mark J. Fucile · Fucile & Reising · 115 Northwest First aven, Suite 401 · Portland, OR 97209-4024 · 503-224-4895

FAMILY LAW

Portland

David C. Gearing · Gearing, Rackner & Engel · 811 Southwest Naito Parkway, Suite 600 · Portland, OR 97204 · 503-222-9116

William J. Howe III · Gevurtz, Menashe, Larson & Howe · http://www.gevurtzmenashe.com · The US Bancorp Tower, Suite 900 · 111 Southwest Fifth Avenue · Portland, OR 97204-3604 · 503-227-1515

Eric C. Larson · Gevurtz, Menashe, Larson & Howe · http://www.gevurtzmenashe.com · The US Bancorp Tower, Suite 900 · 111 Southwest Fifth Avenue · Portland, OR 97204-3604 · 503-227-1515

Albert A. Menashe · 20 · Gevurtz, Menashe, Larson & Howe · http://www.gevurtzmenashe.com · The US Bancorp Tower, Suite 900 · 111 Southwest Fifth Avenue · Portland, OR 97204-3604 · 503-227-1515

Ruth Pekelder · Gevurtz, Menashe, Larson & Howe · http://www.gevurtzmenashe.com · The US Bancorp Tower, Suite 900 · 111 Southwest Fifth Avenue · Portland, OR 97204-3604 · 503-227-1515

Laura E. Rackner · Gearing, Rackner & Engel · 811 Southwest Naito Parkway, Suite 600 · Portland, OR 97204 · 503-222-9116

Ted E. Runstein · Kell Alterman & Runstein · 520 Southwest Yamhill Street, Suite 600 · Portland, OR 97204-1329 · 503-222-3531

William F. Schulte, Jr. · Schulte, Anderson, Downes, Aronson & Bittner · 811 Southwest Naito Parkway, Suite 500 · Portland, OR 97204-3379 · 503-223-4131

Michael A. Yates · Yates, Matthews & Eaton · http://www.yatesmatthews.com · Umpqua Bank Plaza, Suite 1800 · One Southwest Columbia Street · Portland, OR 97258 · 503-224-7077

Gary J. Zimmer · 20 · Zimmer & Bunch · One Southwest Columbia Street, Suite 680 · Portland, OR 97258 · 503-295-6191

Salem

William C. Crothers · 10 · Crothers Hansen · 750 Front Street, NE, Suite 100 · Salem, OR 97301 · 503-378-0225

Gilbert B. Feibleman · Feibleman & Case · http://www.feibleman-law.com · The Geer House · 1815 Commercial Street, SE · Salem, OR 97302 · 503-399-9218

Paul E. Saucy · Saucy Law Offices · 265 State Street, Suite 210 · Salem, OR 97301 · 503-362-9330

FAMILY LAW MEDIATION

Portland

J. Michael Dwyer · Dwyer & Miller · http://www.dwyermiller.com · 215 Southwest Washington Street, Suite 200 · Portland, OR 97204 · 503-241-9456

Joshua D. Kadish · Meyer & Wyse · 621 Southwest Morrison Street, Suite 1300 · Portland, OR 97205 · 503-228-8448

James O'Connor · Jim O'Connor · 3939 Northeast Hancock Avenue, Suite 309 · Portland, OR 97212 · 503-473-8242

Sharon Williams · Sharon A. Williams · http://www.portlandfamilymediator.com · 520 Southwest Yamhill, Suite 1015 · Portland, OR 97205 · 503-224-5775

FIRST AMENDMENT LAW

Portland

Thomas M. Christ · ⑩ · Cosgrave Vergeer Kester · 805 Southwest Broadway Street, Eighth Floor · Portland, OR 97205 · 503-323-9000

John Paul Graff · ⑩ · Graff & O'Neil · 2121 Southwest Broadway · Portland, OR 97201 · 503-222-4545

Charles F. Hinkle · ⑩ · Stoel Rives · http://www.stoel.com · 900 Southwest Fifth Avenue, Suite 2600 · Portland, OR 97204-1268 · 503-224-3380

Bernard Jolles · ⑩ · Bernard Jolles · 721 Southwest Oak Street, Second Floor · Portland, OR 97205-3791 503-228-6474

Roy Pulvers · Hinshaw & Culbertson · http://www.hinshawlaw.com · 1000 SW Broadway · Portland, OR 97205-3078 · 503-243-7696

Michael H. Simon · ⑩ · Perkins Coie · http://www.perkinscoie.com · 1120 Northwest Couch Street, 10th Floor · Portland, OR 97209-4128 · 503-727-2000

FRANCHISE LAW

Portland

Kevin E. Brannon · Schwabe, Williamson & Wyatt · Pacwest Center, Suite 1900 · 1211 Southwest Fifth Avenue · Portland, OR 97204-3795 · 503-222-9981

GOVERNMENT RELATIONS LAW

Portland

Jeffrey G. Condit · Miller Nash · 3400 U.S. Bancorp Tower · 111 Southwest Fifth Avenue · Portland, OR 97204-3699 · 503-224-5858

Paul S. Cosgrove · Lindsay, Hart, Neil & Weigler · 1300 Southwest Fifth Avenue, Suite 3400 · Portland, OR 97201 · 503-226-7677

Jack Isselmann · Tonkon Torp · http://www.tonkon.com · Pioneer Tower, Suite 1600 · 888 Southwest Fifth Avenue · Portland, OR 97204-2099 · 503-221-1440

John Junkin · Bullivant Houser Bailey · 888 Southwest Fifth Avenue, Suite 300 · Portland, OR 97204-2089 · 503-228-6351

John R. Osburn · Bullivant Houser Bailey · 888 Southwest Fifth Avenue, Suite 300 · Portland, OR 97204-2089 · 503-228-6351

Loren D. Podwill · Bullivant Houser Bailey · 888 Southwest Fifth Avenue, Suite 300 · Portland, OR 97204-2089 · 503-228-6351

HEALTH CARE LAW

Eugene

Jeff Kirtner · Hershner Hunter · http://www.hershnerhunter.com · 180 East 11th Avenue · P.O. Box 1475 Eugene, OR 97440 · 541-686-8511

Donald R. Laird · Watkinson Laird Rubenstein Baldwin & Burgess · 101 East Broadway, Suite 200 · P.O. Box 10567 · Eugene, OR 97440 · 541-484-2277

Craig A. Smith · a · Hershner Hunter · http://www.hershnerhunter.com · 180 East 11th Avenue · P.O. Box 1475 · Eugene, OR 97440 · 541-686-8511

Lake Oswego

Thomas E. Cooney, Sr. · a · Cooney & Crew · 4949 Meadows Road, Suite 460 · Lake Oswego, OR 97035-3158 · 503-224-7600

Michael D. Crew · Cooney & Crew · 4949 Meadows Road, Suite 460 · Lake Oswego, OR 97035-3158 · 503-224-7600

Portland

Ingrid Brydolf · Davis Wright Tremaine · 1300 Southwest Fifth Avenue, Suite 2300 · Portland, OR 97201-5630 · 503-241-2300

Edward L. Epstein · 2) · Stoel Rives · http://www.stoel.com · 900 Southwest Fifth Avenue, Suite 2600 · Portland, OR 97204-1268 · 503-224-3380

Eric A. Lindenauer · Garvey Schubert Barer · 121 Southwest Morrison Street, 11th Floor · Portland, OR 97204-3141 · 503-228-3939

Barbara L. Nay · Stoel Rives · http://www.stoel.com · 900 Southwest Fifth Avenue, Suite 2600 · Portland, OR 97204-1268 · 503-224-3380

IMMIGRATION LAW

Portland

Turid L. Owren · Tonkon Torp · http://www.tonkon.com · Pioneer Tower, Suite 1600 · 888 Southwest Fifth Avenue · Portland, OR 97204-2099 · 503-221-1440

INFORMATION TECHNOLOGY LAW

Portland

Stuart K. Cohen · Landye Bennett Blumstein · 1300 Southwest Fifth Avenue, Suite 3500 · Portland, OR 97201 · 503-224-4100

Randolph C. Foster · Stoel Rives · http://www.stoel.com · 900 Southwest Fifth Avenue, Suite 2600 · Portland, OR 97204-1268 · 503-224-3380

Gary W. Glisson · Stoel Rives · http://www.stoel.com · 900 Southwest Fifth Avenue, Suite 2600 · Portland, OR 97204-1268 · 503-224-3380

Paula Holm Jensen · Holm Jensen Law · P.O. Box 4825 · Portland, OR 97208 · 503-490-0265

Jere M. Webb · ⑩ · Stoel Rives · http://www.stoel.com · 900 Southwest Fifth Avenue, Suite 2600 · Portland, OR 97204-1268 · 503-224-3380

INSURANCE LAW

Portland

Thomas M. Christ · ⑩ · Cosgrave Vergeer Kester · 805 Southwest Broadway Street, Eighth Floor · Portland, OR 97205 · 503-323-9000

Ronald Clark · Bullivant Houser Bailey · 888 Southwest Fifth Avenue, Suite 300 · Portland, OR 97204-2089 · 503-228-6351

Stephen F. English · Bullivant Houser Bailey · 888 Southwest Fifth Avenue, Suite 300 · Portland, OR 97204-2089 · 503-228-6351

Douglas G. Houser · Bullivant Houser Bailey · 888 Southwest Fifth Avenue, Suite 300 · Portland, OR 97204-2089 · 503-228-6351

Rhonda W. Kennedy · Kennedy & Kennedy · 601 Southwest Second Avenue, Suite 2050 · Portland, OR 97204 · 503-226-6555

Margaret Van Valkenburg · Bullivant Houser Bailey · 888 Southwest Fifth Avenue, Suite 300 · Portland, OR 97204-2089 · 503-228-6351

INTELLECTUAL PROPERTY LAW

Portland

Paul S. Angello · ⑩ · Stoel Rives · http://www.stoel.com · 900 Southwest Fifth Avenue, Suite 2600 · Portland, OR 97204-1268 · 503-224-3380

Al AuYeung · Schwabe, Williamson & Wyatt · Pacwest Center, Suite 1900 · 1211 Southwest Fifth Avenue Portland, OR 97204-3795 · 503-222-9981

Craig D. Bachman · Lane Powell · http://www.lanepowell.com · 601 Southwest Second Avenue, Suite 2100 · Portland, OR 97204-3158 · 503-778-2100

Vicki A. Ballou · Tonkon Torp · http://www.tonkon.com · Pioneer Tower, Suite 1600 · 888 Southwest Fifth Avenue · Portland, OR 97204-2099 · 503-221-1440

Timothy S. DeJong · Stoll Berne · http://www.stollberne.com · 209 Southwest Oak Street, Suite 500 · Portland, OR 97204 · 503-227-1600

Randolph C. Foster · Stoel Rives · http://www.stoel.com · 900 Southwest Fifth Avenue, Suite 2600 · Portland, OR 97204-1268 · 503-224-3380

William O. Geny · Chernoff, Vilhauer, McClung & Stenzel · http://www.chernofflaw.com · ODS Tower, Suite 1600 · 601 Southwest Second Avenue · Portland, OR 97204-3157 · 503-227-5631

Anne W. Glazer · Stoel Rives · http://www.stoel.com · 900 Southwest Fifth Avenue, Suite 2600 · Portland, OR 97204-1268 · 503-224-3380

Peter E. Heuser · Kolisch Hartwell · Pacific Building, Suite 200 · 520 Southwest Yamhill Street · Portland, OR 97204 · 503-224-6655

Ramon A. Klitzke II · Klarquist Sparkman · One World Trade Center, Suite 1600 · 121 Southwest Salmon Street · Portland, OR 97204 · 503-595-5300

James S. Leigh · a · Klarquist Sparkman · One World Trade Center, Suite 1600 · 121 Southwest Salmon Street · Portland, OR 97204 · 503-595-5300

Steven T. Lovett · Stoel Rives · http://www.stoel.com · 900 Southwest Fifth Avenue, Suite 2600 · Portland, OR 97204-1268 · 503-224-3380

Don H. Marmaduke · Tonkon Torp · http://www.tonkon.com · Pioneer Tower, Suite 1600 · 888 Southwest Fifth Avenue · Portland, OR 97204-2099 · 503-221-1440

Alan T. McCollom · Marger Johnson & McCollom · http://www.techlaw.com · 210 Southwest Morrison Street, Suite 400 · Portland, OR 97204 · 503-222-3613

Nancy J. Moriarty · Chernoff, Vilhauer, McClung & Stenzel · http://www.chernofflaw.com · ODS Tower, Suite 1600 · 601 Southwest Second Avenue · Portland, OR 97204-3157 · 503-227-5631

Robert A. Shlachter · Stoll Berne · http://www.stollberne.com · 209 Southwest Oak Street, Suite 500 · Portland, OR 97204 · 503-227-1600

J. Peter Staples · Chernoff, Vilhauer, McClung & Stenzel · http://www.chernofflaw.com · ODS Tower, Suite 1600 · 601 Southwest Second Avenue · Portland, OR 97204-3157 · 503-227-5631

Dennis E. Stenzel · Chernoff, Vilhauer, McClung & Stenzel · http://www.chernofflaw.com · ODS Tower, Suite 1600 · 601 Southwest Second Avenue · Portland, OR 97204-3157 · 503-227-5631

Micah D. Stolowitz · Stolowitz Ford Cowger · 621 Southwest Morrison Street, Suite 600 · Portland, OR 97205 · 503-224-2170

E. Walter Van Valkenburg · Stoel Rives · http://www.stoel.com · 900 Southwest Fifth Avenue, Suite 2600 · Portland, OR 97204-1268 · 503-224-3380

John D. Vandenberg · Klarquist Sparkman · One World Trade Center, Suite 1600 · 121 Southwest Salmon Street · Portland, OR 97204 · 503-595-5300

Jacob E. Vilhauer, Jr. · a · Chernoff, Vilhauer, McClung & Stenzel · http://www.chernofflaw.com · ODS Tower, Suite 1600 · 601 Southwest Second Avenue · Portland, OR 97204-3157 · 503-227-5631

Jere M. Webb · a · Stoel Rives · http://www.stoel.com · 900 Southwest Fifth Avenue, Suite 2600 · Portland, OR 97204-1268 · 503-224-3380

LABOR AND EMPLOYMENT LAW

Eugene

Andrew G. Lewis · Hershner Hunter · http://www.hershnerhunter.com · 180 East 11th Avenue · P.O. Box 1475 · Eugene, OR 97440 · 541-686-8511

Lake Oswego

Kathy A. Peck · Williams, Zografos & Peck · 334 Third Street · P.O. Box 547 · Lake Oswego, OR 97034 · 503-699-1300

Larry K. Amburgey · a · Littler Mendelson · 1750 Southwest Harbor Way, Suite 450 · Portland, OR 97201 · 503-221-0309

Courtney W. Angeli · Buchanan Angeli Altschul & Sullivan · 321 Southwest Fourth Avenue, Suite 600 · Portland, OR 97204 · 503-974-5015

Paula A. Barran · a · Barran Liebman · http://www.barran.com · 601 Southwest Second Avenue, Suite 2300 · Portland, OR 97204-3159 · 503-228-0500

Clarence Belnavis · Fisher & Phillips · http://www.laborlawyers.com · 111 Southwest Fifth Avenue, Suite 1250 · Portland, OR 97204 · 503-242-4262

Carol J. Bernick · Davis Wright Tremaine · 1300 Southwest Fifth Avenue, Suite 2300 · Portland, OR 97201-5630 · 503-241-2300

Harlan Bernstein · 2) · Harlan Bernstein · 721 Southwest Oak Street, Suite 200 · Portland, OR 97205 · 503-228-6477

Steve L. Brischetto · a · Stephen L. Brischetto · 621 Southwest Morrison, Suite 1025 · Portland, OR 97205 · 503-223-5814

Paul C. Buchanan · Buchanan Angeli Altschul & Sullivan · 321 Southwest Fourth Avenue, Suite 600 · Portland, OR 97204 · 503-974-5015

Richard C. Busse, Jr. · 2) · Busse & Hunt · American Bank Building, Suite 521 · 621 Southwest Morrison Street · Portland, OR 97205 · 503-248-0504

Robert L. Carey · Tonkon Torp · http://www.tonkon.com · Pioneer Tower, Suite 1600 · 888 Southwest Fifth Avenue · Portland, OR 97204-2099 · 503-221-1440

Clay Creps · Bullivant Houser Bailey · 888 Southwest Fifth Avenue, Suite 300 · Portland, OR 97204-2089 503-228-6351

Corbett Gordon · Fisher & Phillips · http://www.laborlawyers.com · 111 Southwest Fifth Avenue, Suite 1250 · Portland, OR 97204 · 503-242-4262

Dan Grinfas · Buchanan Angeli Altschul & Sullivan · 321 Southwest Fourth Avenue, Suite 600 · Portland, OR 97204 · 503-974-5015

Edwin A. Harnden · Barran Liebman · http://www.barran.com · 601 Southwest Second Avenue, Suite 2300 · Portland, OR 97204-3159 · 503-228-0500

Paul C. Hays · Carney, Buckley, Hays & Marsh · 1500 Southwest First Avenue, Suite 1015 · Portland, OR 97201 · 503-221-0611

Kathryn M. Hindman · Bullard Smith Jernstedt Wilson · http://www.bullardlaw.com · 1000 Southwest Broadway, Suite 1900 · Portland, OR 97205 · 503-248-1134

David G. Hosenpud · Lane Powell · http://www.lanepowell.com · 601 Southwest Second Avenue, Suite 2100 · Portland, OR 97204-3158 · 503-778-2100

Scott N. Hunt · Busse & Hunt · American Bank Building, Suite 521 · 621 Southwest Morrison Street · Portland, OR 97205 · 503-248-0504

Jathan W. Janove · Ater Wynne · http://www.aterwynne.com · KOIN Center, Suite 1800 · 222 Southwest Columbia Street · Portland, OR 97201-6618 · 503-226-1191

Kenneth E. Jernstedt · 2% · Bullard Smith Jernstedt Wilson · http://www.bullardlaw.com · 1000 Southwest Broadway, Suite 1900 · Portland, OR 97205 · 503-248-1134

Bernard Jolles · a · Bernard Jolles · 721 Southwest Oak Street, Second Floor · Portland, OR 97205-3791 503-228-6474

Calvin L. Keith · Perkins Coie · http://www.perkinscoie.com · 1120 Northwest Couch Street, 10th Floor · Portland, OR 97209-4128 · 503-727-2000

Victor J. Kisch · Stoel Rives · http://www.stoel.com · 900 Southwest Fifth Avenue, Suite 2600 · Portland, OR 97204-1268 · 503-224-3380

Christine Kitchel · a · Stoel Rives · http://www.stoel.com · 900 Southwest Fifth Avenue, Suite 2600 · Portland, OR 97204-1268 · 503-224-3380

Wayne D. Landsverk · Newcomb, Sabin, Schwartz & Landsverk · http://www.nsslaw.com · 111 Southwest Fifth Avenue, Suite 4040 · Portland, OR 97204 · 503-228-8446

Tamsen L. Leachman · Dunn Carney Allen Higgins & Tongue · http://www.dunn-carney.com · 851 Southwest Sixth Avenue, Suite 1500 · Portland, OR 97204 · 503-224-6440

Richard F. Liebman · a · Barran Liebman · http://www.barran.com · 601 Southwest Second Avenue, Suite 2300 · Portland, OR 97204-3159 · 503-228-0500

Chrys A. Martin · Bullivant Houser Bailey · 888 Southwest Fifth Avenue, Suite 300 · Portland, OR 97204-2089 · 503-228-6351

Charles J. Merten · Charles J. Merten · 320 Southwest Stark Street, Suite 205 · Portland, OR 97204 · 503-227-2405

Douglas S. Parker · Littler Mendelson · 1750 Southwest Harbor Way, Suite 450 · Portland, OR 97201 · 503-221-0309

Amy Joseph Pedersen · Stoel Rives · http://www.stoel.com · 900 Southwest Fifth Avenue, Suite 2600 · Portland, OR 97204-1268 · 503-224-3380

Edward J. Reeves · Stoel Rives · http://www.stoel.com · 900 Southwest Fifth Avenue, Suite 2600 · Portland, OR 97204-1268 · 503-224-3380

Elden M. Rosenthal · a · Rosenthal & Greene · 121 Southwest Salmon Street, Suite 1090 · Portland, OR 97204 · 503-228-3015

Howard Rubin · Littler Mendelson · 1750 Southwest Harbor Way, Suite 450 · Portland, OR 97201 · 503-221-0309

Lester V. Smith, Jr. · 2% · Bullard Smith Jernstedt Wilson · http://www.bullardlaw.com · 1000 Southwest Broadway, Suite 1900 · Portland, OR 97205 · 503-248-1134

Judy D. Snyder · Law Offices of Judy Snyder · 1000 Southwest Broadway, Suite 2400 · Portland, OR 97205 · 503-228-5027

Bradley F. Tellam · Stoel Rives · http://www.stoel.com · 900 Southwest Fifth Avenue, Suite 2600 · Portland, OR 97204-1268 · 503-224-3380

Thomas M. Triplett · Schwabe, Williamson & Wyatt · Pacwest Center, Suite 1900 · 1211 Southwest Fifth Avenue · Portland, OR 97204-3795 · 503-222-9981

David H. Wilson, Jr. · Bullard Smith Jernstedt Wilson · http://www.bullardlaw.com · 1000 Southwest Broadway, Suite 1900 · Portland, OR 97205 · 503-248-1134

Maryann Yelnosky · Bullard Smith Jernstedt Wilson · http://www.bullardlaw.com · 1000 Southwest Broadway, Suite 1900 · Portland, OR 97205 · 503-248-1134

LAND USE & ZONING LAW

Eugene

James W. Spickerman · Gleaves, Swearingen, Potter & Scott · http://www.gleaveslaw.com · 975 Oak Street, Eighth Floor · P.O. Box 1147 · Eugene, OR 97440-1147 · 541-686-8833

Paul V. Vaughan · Hershner Hunter · http://www.hershnerhunter.com · 180 East 11th Avenue · P.O. Box 1475 · Eugene, OR 97440 · 541-686-8511

Lake Oswego

Timothy V. Ramis · Jordan Schrader Ramis · Two Centerpointe Drive, Sixth Floor · Lake Oswego, OR 97035 · 503-598-7070

Portland

Steven W. Abel · Stoel Rives · http://www.stoel.com · 900 Southwest Fifth Avenue, Suite 2600 · Portland, OR 97204-1268 · 503-224-3380

Jeffrey G. Condit · Miller Nash · 3400 U.S. Bancorp Tower · 111 Southwest Fifth Avenue · Portland, OR 97204-3699 · 503-224-5858

Phillip E. Grillo · Miller Nash · 3400 U.S. Bancorp Tower · 111 Southwest Fifth Avenue · Portland, OR 97204-3699 · 503-224-5858

Stephen Thomas Janik · 2% · Ball Janik · One Main Place, Suite 1100 · 101 Southwest Main Street · Portland, OR 97204 · 503-228-2525

Steven L. Pfeiffer · Perkins Coie · http://www.perkinscoie.com · 1120 Northwest Couch Street, 10th Floor Portland, OR 97209-4128 · 503-727-2000

Michael C. Robinson · Perkins Coie · http://www.perkinscoie.com · 1120 Northwest Couch Street, 10th Floor · Portland, OR 97209-4128 · 503-727-2000

Edward J. Sullivan · Garvey Schubert Barer · 121 Southwest Morrison Street, 11th Floor · Portland, OR 97204-3141 · 503-228-3939

Robert D. Van Brocklin · Stoel Rives · http://www.stoel.com · 900 Southwest Fifth Avenue, Suite 2600 · Portland, OR 97204-1268 · 503-224-3380

Mark Whitlow · Perkins Coie · http://www.perkinscoie.com · 1120 Northwest Couch Street, 10th Floor · Portland, OR 97209-4128 · 503-727-2000

LEGAL MALPRACTICE LAW

Portland

John S. Folawn · a · Kirklin Folawn · 522 Southwest Fifth Avenue, Suite 1100 · Portland, OR 97204 · 503-222-1640

Michael A. Greene · a · Rosenthal & Greene · 121 Southwest Salmon Street, Suite 1090 · Portland, OR 97204 · 503-228-3015

LEVERAGED BUYOUTS AND PRIVATE EQUITY LAW

Portland

Todd A. Bauman · Stoel Rives · http://www.stoel.com · 900 Southwest Fifth Avenue, Suite 2600 · Portland, OR 97204-1268 · 503-224-3380

MARITIME LAW

Portland

John M. Coletti · Paulson Coletti Trial Attorneys · http://www.paulsoncoletti.com · 1000 Southwest Broadway, Suite 1660 · Portland, OR 97205-3068 · 503-226-6361

Dean D. DeChaine · 2) · Miller Nash · 3400 U.S. Bancorp Tower · 111 Southwest Fifth Avenue · Portland, OR 97204-3699 · 503-224-5858

Daniel C. Dziuba · Tichenor & Dziuba · Standard Plaza, Suite 1450 · 1100 Southwest Sixth Avenue · Portland, OR 97204 · 503-224-3333

Michael E. Haglund · a · Haglund, Kelley, Horngren & Jones · One Main Place, Suite 1800 · 101 Southwest Main Street · Portland, OR 97204-3226 · 503-225-0777

Daniel F. Knox · Schwabe, Williamson & Wyatt · Pacwest Center, Suite 1900 · 1211 Southwest Fifth Avenue · Portland, OR 97204-3795 · 503-222-9981

Thomas E. McDermott · Lindsay, Hart, Neil & Weigler · 1300 Southwest Fifth Avenue, Suite 3400 · Portland, OR 97201 · 503-226-7677

Craig C. Murphy · a · Murphy Arbitration and Mediation · 1211 Southwest Fifth Avenue, Suite 2330 · Portland, OR 97204 · 503-227-5594

Carl R. Neil · a · Lindsay, Hart, Neil & Weigler · 1300 Southwest Fifth Avenue, Suite 3400 · Portland, OR 97201 · 503-226-7677

C. Kent Roberts · Schwabe, Williamson & Wyatt · Pacwest Center, Suite 1900 · 1211 Southwest Fifth Avenue · Portland, OR 97204-3795 · 503-222-9981

Robert I. Sanders · a · Wood Tatum · 6915 Southwest Macadam Avenue, Suite 115 · Portland, OR 97219 · 503-224-5430

MASS TORT LITIGATION

Portland

Gary M. Berne · Stoll Berne · http://www.stollberne.com · 209 Southwest Oak Street, Suite 500 · Portland, OR 97204 · 503-227-1600

David G. Hosenpud · Lane Powell · http://www.lanepowell.com · 601 Southwest Second Avenue, Suite 2100 · Portland, OR 97204-3158 · 503-778-2100

N. Robert Stoll · Stoll Berne · http://www.stollberne.com · 209 Southwest Oak Street, Suite 500 · Portland, OR 97204 · 503-227-1600

Michael L. Williams · a · Williams Love O'Leary Craine & Powers · 9755 Southwest Barnes Road, Suite 450 · Portland, OR 97225 · 503-295-2924

Eugene

Windsor Calkins · Calkins & Calkins · 101 East 14th Avenue · Eugene, OR 97401-3517 · 541-345-0371

Don Corson · The Corson & Johnson Law Firm · http://www.corsonjohnsonlaw.com · 101 East Broadway, Suite 303 · Eugene, OR 97401 · 541-484-2525

William G. Wheatley · 2% · Jaqua & Wheatley · 825 East Park Street · Eugene, OR 97401-2909 · 541-686-8485

Hillsboro

Larry A. Brisbee · a · Brisbee and Stockton · 139 Northeast Lincoln Street · P.O. Box 567 · Hillsboro, OR 97123 · 503-648-6677

Drake A. Hood · Brisbee and Stockton · 139 Northeast Lincoln Street · P.O. Box 567 · Hillsboro, OR 97123 · 503-648-6677

Lake Oswego

Thomas E. Cooney, Sr. · a · Cooney & Crew · 4949 Meadows Road, Suite 460 · Lake Oswego, OR 97035-3158 · 503-224-7600

Newport

William A. Barton · a · Barton & Strever · 214 South West Coast Highway · P.O. Box 870 · Newport, OR 97365 · 541-265-5377

Portland

Paul R. Duden · Williams Kastner · Pioneer Office Tower, Suite 600 · 888 Southwest Fifth Avenue · Portland, OR 97204-2025 · 503-228-7967

Linda K. Eyerman · Gaylord Eyerman Bradley · http://www.gaylordeyerman.com · 1400 Southwest Montgomery Street · Portland, OR 97201 · 503-222-3526

William A. Gaylord · Gaylord Eyerman Bradley · http://www.gaylordeyerman.com · 1400 Southwest Montgomery Street · Portland, OR 97201 · 503-222-3526

John E. Hart · 2) · Hoffman, Hart & Wagner · 1000 Southwest Broadway, 20th Floor · Portland, OR 97205 · 503-222-4499

Steven P. Jones · Keating Jones Bildstein & Hughes · 800 Benjamin Franklin Plaza · One SouthWest Columbia · Portland, OR 97258-2095 · 503-222-9955

David C. Landis · a · David C. Landis · 1515 Southwest Fifth Avenue, Suite 844 · Portland, OR 97201 · 503-224-5680

James P. Martin · Hoffman, Hart & Wagner · 1000 Southwest Broadway, 20th Floor · Portland, OR 97205 · 503-222-4499

Eric J. Neiman · Williams Kastner · Pioneer Office Tower, Suite 600 · 888 Southwest Fifth Avenue · Portland, OR 97204-2025 · 503-228-7967

Charles P. A. Paulson · 2% · Paulson Coletti Trial Attorneys · http://www.paulsoncoletti.com · 1000 Southwest Broadway, Suite 1660 · Portland, OR 97205-3068 · 503-226-6361

Jane Paulson · Paulson Coletti Trial Attorneys · http://www.paulsoncoletti.com · 1000 Southwest Broadway, Suite 1660 · Portland, OR 97205-3068 · 503-226-6361

Elden M. Rosenthal · a · Rosenthal & Greene · 121 Southwest Salmon Street, Suite 1090 · Portland, OR 97204 · 503-228-3015

Larry N. Sokol · a · Sokol and Associates · Strowbridge Building, Second Floor · 735 Southwest First Avenue · Portland, OR 97204 · 503-228-6469

Jeffrey R. Street · Hoffman, Hart & Wagner · 1000 Southwest Broadway, 20th Floor · Portland, OR 97205 · 503-222-4499

Keith Tichenor · Tichenor & Dziuba · Standard Plaza, Suite 1450 · 1100 Southwest Sixth Avenue · Portland, OR 97204 · 503-224-3333

Jeffrey B. Wihtol · Law Office of Jeffrey Wihtol · 620 Southwest Main Street, Suite 602 · Portland, OR 97205-3024 · 503-228-1210

D. Lawrence Wobbrock · a · Lawrence Wobbrock · Jackson Tower, 10th Floor · 806 Southwest Broadway · Portland, OR 97205 · 503-228-6600

MERGERS & ACQUISITIONS LAW

Portland

Todd A. Bauman · Stoel Rives · http://www.stoel.com · 900 Southwest Fifth Avenue, Suite 2600 · Portland, OR 97204-1268 · 503-224-3380

Ruth A. Beyer · Stoel Rives · http://www.stoel.com · 900 Southwest Fifth Avenue, Suite 2600 · Portland, OR 97204-1268 · 503-224-3380

William C. Campbell · Ater Wynne · http://www.aterwynne.com · KOIN Center, Suite 1800 · 222 Southwest Columbia Street · Portland, OR 97201-6618 · 503-226-1191

Stuart Chestler · Stoel Rives · http://www.stoel.com · 900 Southwest Fifth Avenue, Suite 2600 · Portland, OR 97204-1268 · 503-224-3380

Edward L. Epstein · 2) · Stoel Rives · http://www.stoel.com · 900 Southwest Fifth Avenue, Suite 2600 · Portland, OR 97204-1268 · 503-224-3380

Rhonda W. Kennedy · Kennedy & Kennedy · 601 Southwest Second Avenue, Suite 2050 · Portland, OR 97204 · 503-226-6555

Margaret B. Kushner · Stoel Rives · http://www.stoel.com · 900 Southwest Fifth Avenue, Suite 2600 · Portland, OR 97204-1268 · 503-224-3380

Robert J. Moorman · Stoel Rives · http://www.stoel.com · 900 Southwest Fifth Avenue, Suite 2600 · Portland, OR 97204-1268 · 503-224-3380

Margaret Hill Noto · a · Stoel Rives · http://www.stoel.com · 900 Southwest Fifth Avenue, Suite 2600 · Portland, OR 97204-1268 · 503-224-3380

Kurt W. Ruttum · Tonkon Torp · http://www.tonkon.com · Pioneer Tower, Suite 1600 · 888 Southwest Fifth Avenue · Portland, OR 97204-2099 · 503-221-1440

Patrick J. Simpson · Perkins Coie · http://www.perkinscoie.com · 1120 Northwest Couch Street, 10th Floor · Portland, OR 97209-4128 · 503-727-2000

John R. Thomas · Perkins Coie · http://www.perkinscoie.com · 1120 Northwest Couch Street, 10th Floor Portland, OR 97209-4128 · 503-727-2000

Roy W. Tucker · Perkins Coie · http://www.perkinscoie.com · 1120 Northwest Couch Street, 10th Floor · Portland, OR 97209-4128 · 503-727-2000

MINING LAW

Portland

Jerry R. Fish · 2) · Stoel Rives · http://www.stoel.com · 900 Southwest Fifth Avenue, Suite 2600 · Portland, OR 97204-1268 · 503-224-3380

Mark A. Norby · 2) · Stoel Rives · http://www.stoel.com · 900 Southwest Fifth Avenue, Suite 2600 · Portland, OR 97204-1268 · 503-224-3380

MUNICIPAL LAW

Eugene

Glenn Klein · Harrang Long Gary Rudnick · http://www.harrang.com · 360 East 10th Avenue, Suite 300 · Eugene, OR 97401-3248 · 541-485-0220

Jerome S. Lidz · Harrang Long Gary Rudnick · http://www.harrang.com · 360 East 10th Avenue, Suite 300 · Eugene, OR 97401-3248 · 541-485-0220

Portland

Pamela J. Beery · Beery & Elsner · 1750 Southwest Harbor Way, Suite 380 · Portland, OR 97201 · 503-226-7191

Jeffrey G. Condit · Miller Nash · 3400 U.S. Bancorp Tower · 111 Southwest Fifth Avenue · Portland, OR 97204-3699 · 503-224-5858

Paul C. Elsner · Beery & Elsner · 1750 Southwest Harbor Way, Suite 380 · Portland, OR 97201 · 503-226-7191

Harvey W. Rogers · K&L Gates · 222 Southwest Columbia Street, Suite 1400 · Portland, OR 97201 · 503-228-3200

James P. Shannon · Mersereau & Shannon · One Southwest Columbia Street, Suite 1600 · Portland, OR 97258 · 503-226-6400

Tom Sponsler · Beery & Elsner · 1750 Southwest Harbor Way, Suite 380 · Portland, OR 97201 · 503-226-7191

NATIVE AMERICAN LAW

Bend

Howard G. Arnett · Karnopp Petersen · 1201 Northwest Wall Street, Suite 300 · Bend, OR 97701 · 541-382-3011

Portland

John M. Schultz · Ater Wynne · http://www.aterwynne.com · KOIN Center, Suite 1800 · 222 Southwest Columbia Street · Portland, OR 97201-6618 · 503-226-1191

NATURAL RESOURCES LAW

Portland

Barbara D. Craig · Stoel Rives · http://www.stoel.com · 900 Southwest Fifth Avenue, Suite 2600 · Portland, OR 97204-1268 · 503-224-3380

David E. Filippi · Stoel Rives · http://www.stoel.com · 900 Southwest Fifth Avenue, Suite 2600 · Portland, OR 97204-1268 · 503-224-3380

Jerry R. Fish · 2) · Stoel Rives · http://www.stoel.com · 900 Southwest Fifth Avenue, Suite 2600 · Portland, OR 97204-1268 · 503-224-3380

Donald A. Haagensen · Cable Huston Benedict Haagensen & Lloyd · 1001 Southwest Fifth Avenue, Suite 2000 · Portland, OR 97204-1136 · 503-224-3092

Mark A. Norby · 2) · Stoel Rives · http://www.stoel.com · 900 Southwest Fifth Avenue, Suite 2600 · Portland, OR 97204-1268 · 503-224-3380

NON-PROFIT/CHARITIES LAW

Portland

Conrad L. Moore · 2) · Thede Culpepper Moore Munro & Silliman · U.S. Bancorp Tower, Suite 3675 · 111 Southwest Fifth Avenue · Portland, OR 97204 · 503-416-6160

Terrence R. Pancoast · Stoel Rives · http://www.stoel.com · 900 Southwest Fifth Avenue, Suite 2600 · Portland, OR 97204-1268 · 503-224-3380

Pendleton Hamlet Serrurier · Stoel Rives · http://www.stoel.com · 900 Southwest Fifth Avenue, Suite 2600 · Portland, OR 97204-1268 · 503-224-3380

Jeffrey C. Thede · a · Thede Culpepper Moore Munro & Silliman · U.S. Bancorp Tower, Suite 3675 · 111 Southwest Fifth Avenue · Portland, OR 97204 · 503-416-6160

NON-WHITE-COLLAR CRIMINAL DEFENSE

Eugene

Donald D. Diment, Jr. · 2) · Diment & Walker · 767 Willamette Street, Suite 208 · Eugene, OR 97401 · 541-484-2422

Hubert G. Duvall, Jr. · Clark & Duvall · 856 Olive Street, Suite 101 · Eugene, OR 97401 · 541-345-4500

Robert J. McCrea · 2) · McCrea · 1147 High Street · Eugene, OR 97401-3270 · 541-485-1182

Shaun S. McCrea · a · McCrea · 1147 High Street · Eugene, OR 97401-3270 · 541-485-1182

Gregory E. Veralrud · Veralrud & Associates · Citizens Building, Suite 625 · 975 Oak Street · Eugene, OR 97401 · 541-345-3333

Terri Wood · Law Office of Terri Wood · http://www.terriwoodlawoffice.com · 730 Van Buren Street · Eugene, OR 97402 · 541-484-4171

Newport

William A. Barton · ⑩ · Barton & Strever · 214 South West Coast Highway · P.O. Box 870 · Newport, OR 97365 · 541-265-5377

Oregon City

John Henry Hingson III · ⑩ · John Henry Hingson III · 409 Center Street · P.O. Box 1448 · Oregon City, OR 97045-2211 · 503-656-0355

Wayne Mackeson · Wayne Mackeson · 409 Center Street · Oregon City, OR 97045 · 503-656-8300

Portland

Patrick M. Birmingham · ⑩ · Patrick M. Birmingham · http://www.patbirminghamlaw.com · 1001 Southwest Fifth Avenue, Suite 2175 · Portland, OR 97204 · 503-224-2310

Marc D. Blackman · ㉕ · Ransom Blackman · Congress Center, Suite 1400 · 1001 Southwest Fifth Avenue Portland, OR 97204-1144 · 503-228-0487

Whitney P. Boise · Hoevet, Boise & Olson · 1000 Southwest Broadway, Suite 1500 · Portland, OR 97205 503-228-0497

Ronald H. Hoevet · ⑳ · Hoevet, Boise & Olson · 1000 Southwest Broadway, Suite 1500 · Portland, OR 97205 · 503-228-0497

Janet Lee Hoffman · ⑩ · Hoffman Angeli · 1000 Southwest Broadway, Suite 1500 · Portland, OR 97205 · 503-222-1125

Stephen A. Houze · ⑳ · Stephen A. Houze · 1240 Pacwest Center · 1211 Southwest Fifth Avenue · Portland, OR 97204 · 503-299-6426

Kenneth Lerner · Kenneth Lerner · 3439 Northeast Sandy Boulevard, Suite 286 · Portland, OR 97232 · 503-223-0442

Lawrence Matasar · ⑩ · Lawrence Matasar · 621 Southwest Morrison Street, Suite 1025 · Portland, OR 97205 · 503-222-9830

David T. McDonald · David T. McDonald · 510 Southwest Third Avenue, Suite 400 · Portland, OR 97204 · 503-226-0188

John S. Ransom · ㉕ · Ransom Blackman · Congress Center, Suite 1400 · 1001 Southwest Fifth Avenue · Portland, OR 97204-1144 · 503-228-0487

Emily Simon · Emily Simon · 26 Northeast 11th Avenue · Portland, OR 97232 · 503-239-6101

Robert G. Thuemmel · ⑩ · Thuemmel & Uhle · 210 Southwest Morrison Street, Suite 600 · Portland, OR 97204-3109 · 503-227-4601

Robert C. Weaver, Jr. · ⑩ · Garvey Schubert Barer · 121 Southwest Morrison Street, 11th Floor · Portland, OR 97204-3141 · 503-228-3939

Salem

Walter J. Todd · a · Walter J. Todd · 1250 Cannon Street, SE · Salem, OR 97302 · 503-588-3088

OIL & GAS LAW

Portland

Jerry R. Fish · 2) · Stoel Rives · http://www.stoel.com · 900 Southwest Fifth Avenue, Suite 2600 · Portland, OR 97204-1268 · 503-224-3380

Kirk H. Gibson · Ater Wynne · http://www.aterwynne.com · KOIN Center, Suite 1800 · 222 Southwest Columbia Street · Portland, OR 97201-6618 · 503-226-1191

Mark A. Norby · 2) · Stoel Rives · http://www.stoel.com · 900 Southwest Fifth Avenue, Suite 2600 · Portland, OR 97204-1268 · 503-224-3380

PERSONAL INJURY LITIGATION

Eugene

Windsor Calkins · Calkins & Calkins · 101 East 14th Avenue · Eugene, OR 97401-3517 · 541-345-0371

Don Corson · The Corson & Johnson Law Firm · http://www.corsonjohnsonlaw.com · 101 East Broadway, Suite 303 · Eugene, OR 97401 · 541-484-2525

Arthur C. Johnson · 2) · Johnson, Clifton, Larson & Schaller · 975 Oak Street, Suite 1050 · Eugene, OR 97401-3176 · 541-484-2434

Dennis W. Percell · a · Arnold Gallagher Saydack Percell Roberts & Potter · http://www.arnoldgallagher.com · 800 Willamette Street, Suite 800 · P.O. Box 1758 · Eugene, OR 97440-1758 · 541-484-0188

William G. Wheatley · 2% · Jaqua & Wheatley · 825 East Park Street · Eugene, OR 97401-2909 · 541-686-8485

William H. Wiswall · Wiswall & Walsh · 151 West Seventh Avenue, Suite 550 · P.O. Box 11736 · Eugene, OR 97440-3936 · 541-484-6630

Hillsboro

Larry A. Brisbee · a · Brisbee and Stockton · 139 Northeast Lincoln Street · P.O. Box 567 · Hillsboro, OR 97123 · 503-648-6677

William H. Stockton · a · Brisbee and Stockton · 139 Northeast Lincoln Street · P.O. Box 567 · Hillsboro, OR 97123 · 503-648-6677

Lake Oswego

Mark R. Bocci · Mark R. Bocci · 385 First Street, Suite 215 · Lake Oswego, OR 97034 · 503-607-0222

Thomas E. Cooney, Sr. · a · Cooney & Crew · 4949 Meadows Road, Suite 460 · Lake Oswego, OR 97035-3158 · 503-224-7600

Newport

William A. Barton · a · Barton & Strever · 214 South West Coast Highway · P.O. Box 870 · Newport, OR 97365 · 541-265-5377

Kevin K. Strever · Barton & Strever · 214 South West Coast Highway · P.O. Box 870 · Newport, OR 97365 · 541-265-5377

Oregon City

James Tait · Tait & Associates · 294 Warner Milne Road · Oregon City, OR 97045 · 503-657-8144

Portland

Jan Thomas Baisch · a · Law Offices of Jan Baisch · 1000 Southwest Broadway, Suite 2450 · Portland, OR 97205 · 503-226-3636

Jeffrey M. Batchelor · Markowitz, Herbold, Glade & Mehlhaf · http://www.mhgm.com · Pacwest Center, Suite 3000 · 1211 Southwest Fifth Avenue · Portland, OR 97204 · 503-295-3085

Todd A. Bradley · Gaylord Eyerman Bradley · http://www.gaylordeyerman.com · 1400 Southwest Montgomery Street · Portland, OR 97201 · 503-222-3526

John M. Coletti · Paulson Coletti Trial Attorneys · http://www.paulsoncoletti.com · 1000 Southwest Broadway, Suite 1660 · Portland, OR 97205-3068 · 503-226-6361

Daniel C. Dziuba · Tichenor & Dziuba · Standard Plaza, Suite 1450 · 1100 Southwest Sixth Avenue · Portland, OR 97204 · 503-224-3333

Linda K. Eyerman · Gaylord Eyerman Bradley · http://www.gaylordeyerman.com · 1400 Southwest Montgomery Street · Portland, OR 97201 · 503-222-3526

Jeffrey P. Foote · Foote Webster · 1515 Southwest Fifth Avenue, Suite 808 · Portland, OR 97201 · 503-228-1133

William A. Gaylord · Gaylord Eyerman Bradley · http://www.gaylordeyerman.com · 1400 Southwest Montgomery Street · Portland, OR 97201 · 503-222-3526

John E. Hart · 2) · Hoffman, Hart & Wagner · 1000 Southwest Broadway, 20th Floor · Portland, OR 97205 · 503-222-4499

Jonathan M. Hoffman · Martin Bischoff Templeton Langslet & Hoffman · 900 Pioneer Tower · 888 Southwest Fifth Avenue · Portland, OR 97204 · 503-224-3113

Bernard Jolles · a · Bernard Jolles · 721 Southwest Oak Street, Second Floor · Portland, OR 97205-3791 503-228-6474

Garry L. Kahn · a · Kahn & Kahn · 1210 Cascade Building · 520 Southwest Sixth Avenue · Portland, OR 97204-1510 · 503-227-4488

George L. Kirklin · a · Kirklin Folawn · 522 Southwest Fifth Avenue, Suite 1100 · Portland, OR 97204 · 503-222-1640

Jan K. Kitchel · Schwabe, Williamson & Wyatt · Pacwest Center, Suite 1900 · 1211 Southwest Fifth Avenue · Portland, OR 97204-3795 · 503-222-9981

David C. Landis · a · David C. Landis · 1515 Southwest Fifth Avenue, Suite 844 · Portland, OR 97201 · 503-224-5680

Richard A. Lane · Lawrence Wobbrock · Jackson Tower, 10th Floor · 806 Southwest Broadway · Portland, OR 97205 · 503-228-6600

James P. Martin · Hoffman, Hart & Wagner · 1000 Southwest Broadway, 20th Floor · Portland, OR 97205 · 503-222-4499

Jeffrey S. Mutnick · Law Office of Jeffrey S. Mutnick · 737 Southwest Vista Avenue · Portland, OR 97205 · 503-595-1033

Robert J. Neuberger · Robert J. Neuberger · http://www.robertneuberger.com · 700 Jackson Tower · 806 Southwest Broadway · Portland, OR 97205 · 503-228-1221

Daniel E. O'Leary · 2% · Davis Wright Tremaine · 1300 Southwest Fifth Avenue, Suite 2300 · Portland, OR 97201-5630 · 503-241-2300

Charles P. A. Paulson · 2% · Paulson Coletti Trial Attorneys · http://www.paulsoncoletti.com · 1000 Southwest Broadway, Suite 1660 · Portland, OR 97205-3068 · 503-226-6361

Jane Paulson · Paulson Coletti Trial Attorneys · http://www.paulsoncoletti.com · 1000 Southwest Broadway, Suite 1660 · Portland, OR 97205-3068 · 503-226-6361

Elden M. Rosenthal · a · Rosenthal & Greene · 121 Southwest Salmon Street, Suite 1090 · Portland, OR 97204 · 503-228-3015

Larry N. Sokol · a · Sokol and Associates · Strowbridge Building, Second Floor · 735 Southwest First Avenue · Portland, OR 97204 · 503-228-6469

Walter H. Sweek · a · Cosgrave Vergeer Kester · 805 Southwest Broadway Street, Eighth Floor · Portland, OR 97205 · 503-323-9000

Keith Tichenor · Tichenor & Dziuba · Standard Plaza, Suite 1450 · 1100 Southwest Sixth Avenue · Portland, OR 97204 · 503-224-3333

Michael L. Williams · a · Williams Love O'Leary Craine & Powers · 9755 Southwest Barnes Road, Suite 450 · Portland, OR 97225 · 503-295-2924

D. Lawrence Wobbrock · a · Lawrence Wobbrock · Jackson Tower, 10th Floor · 806 Southwest Broadway · Portland, OR 97205 · 503-228-6600

Salem

J. Michael Alexander · Swanson, Lathen, Alexander & McCann · 388 State Street, Suite 1000 · Salem, OR 97304 · 503-581-2421

Neil F. Lathen · Swanson, Lathen, Alexander & McCann · 388 State Street, Suite 1000 · Salem, OR 97304 · 503-581-2421

Michael C. McClinton · a · McClinton & Troutt · 698 Twelfth Street, SE, Suite 210 · Salem, OR 97301 503-361-3910

Ralph C. Spooner · Spooner & Much · 530 Center Street, NE, Suite 722 · Salem, OR 97301 · 503-378-7777

D. Keith Swanson · Swanson, Lathen, Alexander & McCann · 388 State Street, Suite 1000 · Salem, OR 97304 · 503-581-2421

Eugene

Don Corson · The Corson & Johnson Law Firm · http://www.corsonjohnsonlaw.com · 101 East Broadway, Suite 303 · Eugene, OR 97401 · 541-484-2525

Arthur C. Johnson · 2) · Johnson, Clifton, Larson & Schaller · 975 Oak Street, Suite 1050 · Eugene, OR 97401-3176 · 541-484-2434

Derek C. Johnson · Johnson, Clifton, Larson & Schaller · 975 Oak Street, Suite 1050 · Eugene, OR 97401-3176 · 541-484-2434

William G. Wheatley · 2% · Jaqua & Wheatley · 825 East Park Street · Eugene, OR 97401-2909 · 541-686-8485

Lake Oswego

Mark R. Bocci · Mark R. Bocci · 385 First Street, Suite 215 · Lake Oswego, OR 97034 · 503-607-0222

Portland

Lawrence Baron · Law Office of Lawrence Baron · 1515 SW Fifth Avenue, Suite 808 · Portland, OR 97201 · 503-417-1117

John M. Coletti · Paulson Coletti Trial Attorneys · http://www.paulsoncoletti.com · 1000 Southwest Broadway, Suite 1660 · Portland, OR 97205-3068 · 503-226-6361

William B. Crow · a · Schwabe, Williamson & Wyatt · Pacwest Center, Suite 1900 · 1211 Southwest Fifth Avenue · Portland, OR 97204-3795 · 503-222-9981

Paul R. Duden · Williams Kastner · Pioneer Office Tower, Suite 600 · 888 Southwest Fifth Avenue · Portland, OR 97204-2025 · 503-228-7967

Jeffrey S. Eden · Bullivant Houser Bailey · 888 Southwest Fifth Avenue, Suite 300 · Portland, OR 97204-2089 · 503-228-6351

Stephen F. English · Bullivant Houser Bailey · 888 Southwest Fifth Avenue, Suite 300 · Portland, OR 97204-2089 · 503-228-6351

Jeffrey P. Foote · Foote Webster · 1515 Southwest Fifth Avenue, Suite 808 · Portland, OR 97201 · 503-228-1133

David R. Foster · Bullivant Houser Bailey · 888 Southwest Fifth Avenue, Suite 300 · Portland, OR 97204-2089 · 503-228-6351

William A. Gaylord · Gaylord Eyerman Bradley · http://www.gaylordeyerman.com · 1400 Southwest Montgomery Street · Portland, OR 97201 · 503-222-3526

Jonathan M. Hoffman · Martin Bischoff Templeton Langslet & Hoffman · 900 Pioneer Tower · 888 Southwest Fifth Avenue · Portland, OR 97204 · 503-224-3113

Margaret Hoffmann · Schwabe, Williamson & Wyatt · Pacwest Center, Suite 1900 · 1211 Southwest Fifth Avenue · Portland, OR 97204-3795 · 503-222-9981

Frank V. Langfitt · Ater Wynne · http://www.aterwynne.com · KOIN Center, Suite 1800 · 222 Southwest Columbia Street · Portland, OR 97201-6618 · 503-226-1191

Steven O. Rosen · The Rosen Law Firm · Old Federal Courthouse, Suite 702 · 620 Southwest Main Street · Portland, OR 97205 · 503-525-2525

Ronald G. Stephenson · Bullivant Houser Bailey · 888 Southwest Fifth Avenue, Suite 300 · Portland, OR 97204-2089 · 503-228-6351

Raymond F. Thomas · Swanson Thomas & Coon · 820 Southwest Second Avenue, Suite 200 · Portland, OR 97204 · 503-228-5222

Michael L. Williams · a · Williams Love O'Leary Craine & Powers · 9755 Southwest Barnes Road, Suite 450 · Portland, OR 97225 · 503-295-2924

PROFESSIONAL MALPRACTICE LAW

Eugene

Arthur C. Johnson · 2) · Johnson, Clifton, Larson & Schaller · 975 Oak Street, Suite 1050 · Eugene, OR 97401-3176 · 541-484-2434

William G. Wheatley · 2% · Jaqua & Wheatley · 825 East Park Street · Eugene, OR 97401-2909 · 541-686-8485

Hillsboro

James M. Daigle · Brisbee and Stockton · 139 Northeast Lincoln Street · P.O. Box 567 · Hillsboro, OR 97123 · 503-648-6677

Drake A. Hood · Brisbee and Stockton · 139 Northeast Lincoln Street · P.O. Box 567 · Hillsboro, OR 97123 · 503-648-6677

Portland

Richard E. Alexander · Stoel Rives · http://www.stoel.com · 900 Southwest Fifth Avenue, Suite 2600 · Portland, OR 97204-1268 · 503-224-3380

Daniel F. Knox · Schwabe, Williamson & Wyatt · Pacwest Center, Suite 1900 · 1211 Southwest Fifth Avenue · Portland, OR 97204-3795 · 503-222-9981

Richard J. Kuhn · Hoffman, Hart & Wagner · 1000 Southwest Broadway, 20th Floor · Portland, OR 97205 · 503-222-4499

Frank A. Moscato · Harrang Long Gary Rudnick · http://www.harrang.com · 1001 Southwest Fifth Avenue, Suite 1600 · Portland, OR 97204-1116 · 503-242-0000

Joel Wilson · Bullivant Houser Bailey · 888 Southwest Fifth Avenue, Suite 300 · Portland, OR 97204-2089 · 503-228-6351

PROJECT FINANCE LAW

Portland

Robert R. Griffith · Garvey Schubert Barer · 121 Southwest Morrison Street, 11th Floor · Portland, OR 97204-3141 · 503-228-3939

Karen M. Williams · Lane Powell · http://www.lanepowell.com · 601 Southwest Second Avenue, Suite 2100 · Portland, OR 97204-3158 · 503-778-2100

PUBLIC FINANCE LAW

Portland

Edward D. Einowski · Stoel Rives · http://www.stoel.com · 900 Southwest Fifth Avenue, Suite 2600 · Portland, OR 97204-1268 · 503-224-3380

Townsend Hyatt · Orrick, Herrington & Sutcliffe · 1120 Northwest Couch Street, Suite 200 · Portland, OR 97209 · 503-943-4800

Edward A. McCullough · K&L Gates · 222 Southwest Columbia Street, Suite 1400 · Portland, OR 97201 503-228-3200

Harvey W. Rogers · K&L Gates · 222 Southwest Columbia Street, Suite 1400 · Portland, OR 97201 · 503-228-3200

Scott Schickli · Orrick, Herrington & Sutcliffe · 1120 Northwest Couch Street, Suite 200 · Portland, OR 97209 · 503-943-4800

Catherine A. Shaw · Miller Nash · 3400 U.S. Bancorp Tower · 111 Southwest Fifth Avenue · Portland, OR 97204-3699 · 503-224-5858

Ann L. Sherman · K&L Gates · 222 Southwest Columbia Street, Suite 1400 · Portland, OR 97201 · 503-228-3200

REAL ESTATE LAW

Eugene

William R. Potter · a · Arnold Gallagher Saydack Percell Roberts & Potter · http://www.arnoldgallagher.com · 800 Willamette Street, Suite 800 · P.O. Box 1758 · Eugene, OR 97440-1758 · 541-484-0188

Malcolm H. Scott · a · Gleaves, Swearingen, Potter & Scott · http://www.gleaveslaw.com · 975 Oak Street, Eighth Floor · P.O. Box 1147 · Eugene, OR 97440-1147 · 541-686-8833

John C. Watkinson · a · Watkinson Laird Rubenstein Baldwin & Burgess · 101 East Broadway, Suite 200 · P.O. Box 10567 · Eugene, OR 97440 · 541-484-2277

Lake Oswego

Timothy V. Ramis · Jordan Schrader Ramis · Two Centerpointe Drive, Sixth Floor · Lake Oswego, OR 97035 · 503-598-7070

Portland

Kenneth S. Antell · Dunn Carney Allen Higgins & Tongue · http://www.dunn-carney.com · 851 Southwest Sixth Avenue, Suite 1500 · Portland, OR 97204 · 503-224-6440

Randall B. Bateman · Bateman Seidel Miner Blomgren Chellis & Gram · 888 Southwest Fifth Avenue, Suite 1250 · Portland, OR 97204 · 503-972-9920

J. David Bennett · Landye Bennett Blumstein · 1300 Southwest Fifth Avenue, Suite 3500 · Portland, OR 97201 · 503-224-4100

Owen D. Blank · Tonkon Torp · http://www.tonkon.com · Pioneer Tower, Suite 1600 · 888 Southwest Fifth Avenue · Portland, OR 97204-2099 · 503-221-1440

Richard A. Cantlin · 2) · Perkins Coie · http://www.perkinscoie.com · 1120 Northwest Couch Street, 10th Floor · Portland, OR 97209-4128 · 503-727-2000

Don G. Carter · McEwen Gisvold · Standard Plaza, Suite 1600 · 1100 Southwest Sixth Avenue · Portland, OR 97204 · 503-226-7321

Howard M. Feuerstein · 2% · Stoel Rives · http://www.stoel.com · 900 Southwest Fifth Avenue, Suite 2600 · Portland, OR 97204-1268 · 503-224-3380

Valerie D. Fisher · Ater Wynne · http://www.aterwynne.com · KOIN Center, Suite 1800 · 222 Southwest Columbia Street · Portland, OR 97201-6618 · 503-226-1191

Eugene A. Frassetto · Stoel Rives · http://www.stoel.com · 900 Southwest Fifth Avenue, Suite 2600 · Portland, OR 97204-1268 · 503-224-3380

Morris J. Galen · Tonkon Torp · http://www.tonkon.com · Pioneer Tower, Suite 1600 · 888 Southwest Fifth Avenue · Portland, OR 97204-2099 · 503-221-1440

Dean P. Gisvold · a · McEwen Gisvold · Standard Plaza, Suite 1600 · 1100 Southwest Sixth Avenue · Portland, OR 97204 · 503-226-7321

Jonathon L. Goodling · Miller Nash · 3400 U.S. Bancorp Tower · 111 Southwest Fifth Avenue · Portland, OR 97204-3699 · 503-224-5858

Eugene L. Grant · Davis Wright Tremaine · 1300 Southwest Fifth Avenue, Suite 2300 · Portland, OR 97201-5630 · 503-241-2300

David W. Green · a · Stoel Rives · http://www.stoel.com · 900 Southwest Fifth Avenue, Suite 2600 · Portland, OR 97204-1268 · 503-224-3380

John D. Guinasso · Schwabe, Williamson & Wyatt · Pacwest Center, Suite 1900 · 1211 Southwest Fifth Avenue · Portland, OR 97204-3795 · 503-222-9981

Terry C. Hauck · 2) · Schwabe, Williamson & Wyatt · Pacwest Center, Suite 1900 · 1211 Southwest Fifth Avenue · Portland, OR 97204-3795 · 503-222-9981

Stephen Thomas Janik · 2% · Ball Janik · One Main Place, Suite 1100 · 101 Southwest Main Street · Portland, OR 97204 · 503-228-2525

Don K. Lloyd · Cable Huston Benedict Haagensen & Lloyd · 1001 Southwest Fifth Avenue, Suite 2000 · Portland, OR 97204-1136 · 503-224-3092

David A. Lokting · Stoll Berne · http://www.stollberne.com · 209 Southwest Oak Street, Suite 500 · Portland, OR 97204 · 503-227-1600

Mark Manulik · Schwabe, Williamson & Wyatt · Pacwest Center, Suite 1900 · 1211 Southwest Fifth Avenue · Portland, OR 97204-3795 · 503-222-9981

Bradley S. Miller · Ball Janik · One Main Place, Suite 1100 · 101 Southwest Main Street · Portland, OR 97204 · 503-228-2525

Thomas R. Page · a · Stoel Rives · http://www.stoel.com · 900 Southwest Fifth Avenue, Suite 2600 · Portland, OR 97204-1268 · 503-224-3380

Gilbert E. Parker · Dunn Carney Allen Higgins & Tongue · http://www.dunn-carney.com · 851 Southwest Sixth Avenue, Suite 1500 · Portland, OR 97204 · 503-224-6440

Bryan E. Powell · Lane Powell · http://www.lanepowell.com · 601 Southwest Second Avenue, Suite 2100 Portland, OR 97204-3158 · 503-778-2100

Barbara W. Radler · Ball Janik · One Main Place, Suite 1100 · 101 Southwest Main Street · Portland, OR 97204 · 503-228-2525

Stanley M. Samuels · 2% · Bateman Seidel Miner Blomgren Chellis & Gram · 888 Southwest Fifth Avenue, Suite 1250 · Portland, OR 97204 · 503-972-9920

Mark A. Stayer · Schwabe, Williamson & Wyatt · Pacwest Center, Suite 1900 · 1211 Southwest Fifth Avenue · Portland, OR 97204-3795 · 503-222-9981

Joseph S. Voboril · a · Tonkon Torp · http://www.tonkon.com · Pioneer Tower, Suite 1600 · 888 Southwest Fifth Avenue · Portland, OR 97204-2099 · 503-221-1440

SECURITIES LAW

Portland

Jason M. Brauser · Stoel Rives · http://www.stoel.com · 900 Southwest Fifth Avenue, Suite 2600 · Portland, OR 97204-1268 · 503-224-3380

Stuart Chestler · Stoel Rives · http://www.stoel.com · 900 Southwest Fifth Avenue, Suite 2600 · Portland, OR 97204-1268 · 503-224-3380

Ronald L. Greenman · a · Tonkon Torp · http://www.tonkon.com · Pioneer Tower, Suite 1600 · 888 Southwest Fifth Avenue · Portland, OR 97204-2099 · 503-221-1440

John J. Halle · Stoel Rives · http://www.stoel.com · 900 Southwest Fifth Avenue, Suite 2600 · Portland, OR 97204-1268 · 503-224-3380

Robert J. Moorman · Stoel Rives · http://www.stoel.com · 900 Southwest Fifth Avenue, Suite 2600 · Portland, OR 97204-1268 · 503-224-3380

Margaret Hill Noto · a · Stoel Rives · http://www.stoel.com · 900 Southwest Fifth Avenue, Suite 2600 · Portland, OR 97204-1268 · 503-224-3380

Thomas P. Palmer · Tonkon Torp · http://www.tonkon.com · Pioneer Tower, Suite 1600 · 888 Southwest Fifth Avenue · Portland, OR 97204-2099 · 503-221-1440

Patrick J. Simpson · Perkins Coie · http://www.perkinscoie.com · 1120 Northwest Couch Street, 10th Floor · Portland, OR 97209-4128 · 503-727-2000

Kenneth D. Stephens · a · Tonkon Torp · http://www.tonkon.com · Pioneer Tower, Suite 1600 · 888 Southwest Fifth Avenue · Portland, OR 97204-2099 · 503-221-1440

John R. Thomas · Perkins Coie · http://www.perkinscoie.com · 1120 Northwest Couch Street, 10th Floor Portland, OR 97209-4128 · 503-727-2000

Roy W. Tucker · Perkins Coie · http://www.perkinscoie.com · 1120 Northwest Couch Street, 10th Floor · Portland, OR 97209-4128 · 503-727-2000

TAX LAW

Portland

Larry Brant · Garvey Schubert Barer · 121 Southwest Morrison Street, 11th Floor · Portland, OR 97204-3141 · 503-228-3939

David C. Culpepper · Thede Culpepper Moore Munro & Silliman · U.S. Bancorp Tower, Suite 3675 · 111 Southwest Fifth Avenue · Portland, OR 97204 · 503-416-6160

Joyle C. Dahl · Schwabe, Williamson & Wyatt · Pacwest Center, Suite 1900 · 1211 Southwest Fifth Avenue · Portland, OR 97204-3795 · 503-222-9981

John H. Gadon · Lane Powell · http://www.lanepowell.com · 601 Southwest Second Avenue, Suite 2100 · Portland, OR 97204-3158 · 503-778-2100

Christopher K. Heuer · Stoel Rives · http://www.stoel.com · 900 Southwest Fifth Avenue, Suite 2600 · Portland, OR 97204-1268 · 503-224-3380

Lewis M. Horowitz · Lane Powell · http://www.lanepowell.com · 601 Southwest Second Avenue, Suite 2100 · Portland, OR 97204-3158 · 503-778-2100

Neil D. Kimmelfield · Lane Powell · http://www.lanepowell.com · 601 Southwest Second Avenue, Suite 2100 · Portland, OR 97204-3158 · 503-778-2100

Mark F. LeRoux · Tonkon Torp · http://www.tonkon.com · Pioneer Tower, Suite 1600 · 888 Southwest Fifth Avenue · Portland, OR 97204-2099 · 503-221-1440

David A. Lokting · Stoll Berne · http://www.stollberne.com · 209 Southwest Oak Street, Suite 500 · Portland, OR 97204 · 503-227-1600

Robert T. Manicke · Stoel Rives · http://www.stoel.com · 900 Southwest Fifth Avenue, Suite 2600 · Portland, OR 97204-1268 · 503-224-3380

William S. Manne · Miller Nash · 3400 U.S. Bancorp Tower · 111 Southwest Fifth Avenue · Portland, OR 97204-3699 · 503-224-5858

Ingolf Noto · Tonkon Torp · http://www.tonkon.com · Pioneer Tower, Suite 1600 · 888 Southwest Fifth Avenue · Portland, OR 97204-2099 · 503-221-1440

Peter L. Osborne · Schwabe, Williamson & Wyatt · Pacwest Center, Suite 1900 · 1211 Southwest Fifth Avenue · Portland, OR 97204-3795 · 503-222-9981

Marc K. Sellers · Schwabe, Williamson & Wyatt · Pacwest Center, Suite 1900 · 1211 Southwest Fifth Avenue · Portland, OR 97204-3795 · 503-222-9981

Merritt S. Yoelin · Samuels Yoelin Kantor Seymour & Spinrad · 4640 Southwest Macadam Avenue, Suite 200 · Portland, OR 97239 · 503-226-2966

TIMBER LAW

Portland

Kirk Johansen · Schwabe, Williamson & Wyatt · Pacwest Center, Suite 1900 · 1211 Southwest Fifth Avenue · Portland, OR 97204-3795 · 503-222-9981

Mark A. Norby · Stoel Rives · http://www.stoel.com · 900 Southwest Fifth Avenue, Suite 2600 · Portland, OR 97204-1268 · 503-224-3380

Mark A. Stayer · Schwabe, Williamson & Wyatt · Pacwest Center, Suite 1900 · 1211 Southwest Fifth Avenue · Portland, OR 97204-3795 · 503-222-9981

Bend

James E. Petersen · a · Karnopp Petersen · 1201 Northwest Wall Street, Suite 300 · Bend, OR 97701 · 541-382-3011

Thomas J. Sayeg · Karnopp Petersen · 1201 Northwest Wall Street, Suite 300 · Bend, OR 97701 · 541-382-3011

Coos Bay

John W. Whitty · Foss, Whitty, Littlefield, McDaniel & Bodkin · 444 North Fourth Street · P.O. Box 1120 · Coos Bay, OR 97420 · 541-267-2156

Eugene

David N. Andrews · 2% · Hershner Hunter · http://www.hershnerhunter.com · 180 East 11th Avenue · P.O. Box 1475 · Eugene, OR 97440 · 541-686-8511

William D. Brewer · Hershner Hunter · http://www.hershnerhunter.com · 180 East 11th Avenue · P.O. Box 1475 · Eugene, OR 97440 · 541-686-8511

Arthur J. Clark · Hershner Hunter · http://www.hershnerhunter.com · 180 East 11th Avenue · P.O. Box 1475 · Eugene, OR 97440 · 541-686-8511

Howard F. Feinman · Gleaves, Swearingen, Potter & Scott · http://www.gleaveslaw.com · 975 Oak Street, Eighth Floor · P.O. Box 1147 · Eugene, OR 97440-1147 · 541-686-8833

Stephen O. Lane · a · Gleaves, Swearingen, Potter & Scott · http://www.gleaveslaw.com · 975 Oak Street, Eighth Floor · P.O. Box 1147 · Eugene, OR 97440-1147 · 541-686-8833

Douglas A. Nelson · Gartland, Nelson, McCleery, Wade & Walloch · 44 Club Road, Suite 200 · P.O. Box 11230 · Eugene, OR 97440 · 541-344-2174

Standlee G. Potter · a · Gleaves, Swearingen, Potter & Scott · http://www.gleaveslaw.com · 975 Oak Street, Eighth Floor · P.O. Box 1147 · Eugene, OR 97440-1147 · 541-686-8833

Barry Rubenstein · Watkinson Laird Rubenstein Baldwin & Burgess · 101 East Broadway, Suite 200 · P.O. Box 10567 · Eugene, OR 97440 · 541-484-2277

Portland

Christine Brown · Garvey Schubert Barer · 121 Southwest Morrison Street, 11th Floor · Portland, OR 97204-3141 · 503-228-3939

Nancy L. Cowgill · 2) · Stoel Rives · http://www.stoel.com · 900 Southwest Fifth Avenue, Suite 2600 · Portland, OR 97204-1268 · 503-224-3380

Robert D. Dayton · 2) · Schwabe, Williamson & Wyatt · Pacwest Center, Suite 1900 · 1211 Southwest Fifth Avenue · Portland, OR 97204-3795 · 503-222-9981

Patrick J. Green · a · Davis Wright Tremaine · 1300 Southwest Fifth Avenue, Suite 2300 · Portland, OR 97201-5630 · 503-241-2300

Joseph J. Hanna, Jr. · 2% · Hanna Strader · 1300 Southwest Sixth Avenue, Suite 300 · Portland, OR 97201 · 503-273-2700

Nikki C. Hatton · Schwabe, Williamson & Wyatt · Pacwest Center, Suite 1900 · 1211 Southwest Fifth Avenue · Portland, OR 97204-3795 · 503-222-9981

Robert T. Huston · Cable Huston Benedict Haagensen & Lloyd · 1001 Southwest Fifth Avenue, Suite 2000 · Portland, OR 97204-1136 · 503-224-3092

J. Alan Jensen · a · Holland & Knight · http://www.hklaw.com · U.S. Bancorp Tower, Suite 2300 · 111 Southwest Fifth Avenue · Portland, OR 97204 · 503-243-2300

Philip N. Jones · Duffy Kekel · Standard Plaza, Suite 1200 · 1100 Southwest Sixth Avenue · Portland, OR 97204 · 503-226-1371

Emily V. Karr · Stoel Rives · http://www.stoel.com · 900 Southwest Fifth Avenue, Suite 2600 · Portland, OR 97204-1268 · 503-224-3380

Kenneth S. Klarquist, Jr. · Zalutsky, Klarquist & Reinhart · http://www.erisalaw.com · The Waldo Block,Third Floor · 215 Southwest Washington Street · Portland, OR 97204 · 503-248-0300

Stephen J. Klarquist · Zalutsky, Klarquist & Reinhart · http://www.erisalaw.com · The Waldo Block,Third Floor · 215 Southwest Washington Street · Portland, OR 97204 · 503-248-0300

D. Charles Mauritz · a · Duffy Kekel · Standard Plaza, Suite 1200 · 1100 Southwest Sixth Avenue · Portland, OR 97204 · 503-226-1371

Carolyn W. Miller · a · Carolyn W. Miller · The River Forum, Suite 525 · 4380 Southwest Macadam Avenue · Portland, OR 97239 · 503-241-2801

Conrad L. Moore · 2) · Thede Culpepper Moore Munro & Silliman · U.S. Bancorp Tower, Suite 3675 · 111 Southwest Fifth Avenue · Portland, OR 97204 · 503-416-6160

Donna M. Muehleck · Duffy Kekel · Standard Plaza, Suite 1200 · 1100 Southwest Sixth Avenue · Portland, OR 97204 · 503-226-1371

Terrence R. Pancoast · Stoel Rives · http://www.stoel.com · 900 Southwest Fifth Avenue, Suite 2600 · Portland, OR 97204-1268 · 503-224-3380

John H. Rosenfeld · a · Tonkon Torp · http://www.tonkon.com · Pioneer Tower, Suite 1600 · 888 Southwest Fifth Avenue · Portland, OR 97204-2099 · 503-221-1440

Pendleton Hamlet Serrurier · Stoel Rives · http://www.stoel.com · 900 Southwest Fifth Avenue, Suite 2600 · Portland, OR 97204-1268 · 503-224-3380

Timothy R. Strader · Hanna Strader · 1300 Southwest Sixth Avenue, Suite 300 · Portland, OR 97201 · 503-273-2700

Jeffrey C. Thede · a · Thede Culpepper Moore Munro & Silliman · U.S. Bancorp Tower, Suite 3675 · 111 Southwest Fifth Avenue · Portland, OR 97204 · 503-416-6160

Timothy J. Wachter · Duffy Kekel · Standard Plaza, Suite 1200 · 1100 Southwest Sixth Avenue · Portland, OR 97204 · 503-226-1371

Merritt S. Yoelin · Samuels Yoelin Kantor Seymour & Spinrad · 4640 Southwest Macadam Avenue, Suite 200 · Portland, OR 97239 · 503-226-2966

Salem

James G. Heltzel · a · Heltzel, Upjohn, Williams, Yandell, Roth, Smith & Petersen · Pioneer Trust Building, Fourth Floor · 117 Commercial Street, NE · P.O. Box 1048 · Salem, OR 97308 · 503-585-4422

Robert J. Saalfeld · a · Saalfeld Griggs · Park Place, Suite 300 · 250 Church Street, SE · Salem, OR 97301 · 503-399-1070

Springfield

Janice E. Hatton · Thorp Purdy Jewett Urness & Wilkinson · 1011 Harlow Road, Suite 300 · Springfield, OR 97477 · 541-747-3354

John C. Urness · Thorp Purdy Jewett Urness & Wilkinson · 1011 Harlow Road, Suite 300 · Springfield, OR 97477 · 541-747-3354

VENTURE CAPITAL LAW

Portland

Todd A. Bauman · Stoel Rives · http://www.stoel.com · 900 Southwest Fifth Avenue, Suite 2600 · Portland, OR 97204-1268 · 503-224-3380

William C. Campbell · Ater Wynne · http://www.aterwynne.com · KOIN Center, Suite 1800 · 222 Southwest Columbia Street · Portland, OR 97201-6618 · 503-226-1191

Neil M. Nathanson · Perkins Coie · http://www.perkinscoie.com · 1120 Northwest Couch Street, 10th Floor · Portland, OR 97209-4128 · 503-727-2000

Roy W. Tucker · Perkins Coie · http://www.perkinscoie.com · 1120 Northwest Couch Street, 10th Floor · Portland, OR 97209-4128 · 503-727-2000

WATER LAW

Portland

Michael R. Campbell · Stoel Rives · http://www.stoel.com · 900 Southwest Fifth Avenue, Suite 2600 · Portland, OR 97204-1268 · 503-224-3380

David E. Filippi · Stoel Rives · http://www.stoel.com · 900 Southwest Fifth Avenue, Suite 2600 · Portland, OR 97204-1268 · 503-224-3380

Richard M. Glick · Davis Wright Tremaine · 1300 Southwest Fifth Avenue, Suite 2300 · Portland, OR 97201-5630 · 503-241-2300

Douglas W. MacDougal · Schwabe, Williamson & Wyatt · Pacwest Center, Suite 1900 · 1211 Southwest Fifth Avenue · Portland, OR 97204-3795 · 503-222-9981

Salem

Martha O. Pagel · Schwabe, Williamson & Wyatt · The Equitable Center, Suite 400 · 530 Center Street, NE · Salem, OR 97301 · 503-540-4262

WHITE-COLLAR CRIMINAL DEFENSE

Eugene

Donald D. Diment, Jr. · 2) · Diment & Walker · 767 Willamette Street, Suite 208 · Eugene, OR 97401 · 541-484-2422

Robert J. McCrea · ⑳ · McCrea · 1147 High Street · Eugene, OR 97401-3270 · 541-485-1182

Shaun S. McCrea · ⑩ · McCrea · 1147 High Street · Eugene, OR 97401-3270 · 541-485-1182

Gregory E. Veralrud · Veralrud & Associates · Citizens Building, Suite 625 · 975 Oak Street · Eugene, OR 97401 · 541-345-3333

Terri Wood · Law Office of Terri Wood · http://www.terriwoodlawoffice.com · 730 Van Buren Street · Eugene, OR 97402 · 541-484-4171

Newport

William A. Barton · ⑩ · Barton & Strever · 214 South West Coast Highway · P.O. Box 870 · Newport, OR 97365 · 541-265-5377

Oregon City

John Henry Hingson III · ⑩ · John Henry Hingson III · 409 Center Street · P.O. Box 1448 · Oregon City, OR 97045-2211 · 503-656-0355

Wayne Mackeson · Wayne Mackeson · 409 Center Street · Oregon City, OR 97045 · 503-656-8300

Portland

David H. Angeli · Hoffman Angeli · 1000 Southwest Broadway, Suite 1500 · Portland, OR 97205 · 503-222-1125

Patrick M. Birmingham · ⑩ · Patrick M. Birmingham · http://www.patbirminghamlaw.com · 1001 Southwest Fifth Avenue, Suite 2175 · Portland, OR 97204 · 503-224-2310

Marc D. Blackman · ㉕ · Ransom Blackman · Congress Center, Suite 1400 · 1001 Southwest Fifth Avenue Portland, OR 97204-1144 · 503-228-0487

Whitney P. Boise · Hoevet, Boise & Olson · 1000 Southwest Broadway, Suite 1500 · Portland, OR 97205 503-228-0497

Ronald H. Hoevet · ⑳ · Hoevet, Boise & Olson · 1000 Southwest Broadway, Suite 1500 · Portland, OR 97205 · 503-228-0497

Janet Lee Hoffman · ⑩ · Hoffman Angeli · 1000 Southwest Broadway, Suite 1500 · Portland, OR 97205 · 503-222-1125

Stephen A. Houze · ⑳ · Stephen A. Houze · 1240 Pacwest Center · 1211 Southwest Fifth Avenue · Portland, OR 97204 · 503-299-6426

Kenneth Lerner · Kenneth Lerner · 3439 Northeast Sandy Boulevard, Suite 286 · Portland, OR 97232 · 503-223-0442

Lawrence Matasar · ⑩ · Lawrence Matasar · 621 Southwest Morrison Street, Suite 1025 · Portland, OR 97205 · 503-222-9830

Per A. Ramfjord · Stoel Rives · http://www.stoel.com · 900 Southwest Fifth Avenue, Suite 2600 · Portland, OR 97204-1268 · 503-224-3380

John S. Ransom · ㉕ · Ransom Blackman · Congress Center, Suite 1400 · 1001 Southwest Fifth Avenue · Portland, OR 97204-1144 · 503-228-0487

Norman Sepenuk · 2% · Norman Sepenuk · 520 Southwest Yamhill Street, Suite 600 · Portland, OR 97204 503-221-1633

Emily Simon · Emily Simon · 26 Northeast 11th Avenue · Portland, OR 97232 · 503-239-6101

Robert G. Thuemmel · a · Thuemmel & Uhle · 210 Southwest Morrison Street, Suite 600 · Portland, OR 97204-3109 · 503-227-4601

Steven B. Ungar · Lane Powell · http://www.lanepowell.com · 601 Southwest Second Avenue, Suite 2100 Portland, OR 97204-3158 · 503-778-2100

Robert C. Weaver, Jr. · a · Garvey Schubert Barer · 121 Southwest Morrison Street, 11th Floor · Portland, OR 97204-3141 · 503-228-3939

Salem

Walter J. Todd · a · Walter J. Todd · 1250 Cannon Street, SE · Salem, OR 97302 · 503-588-3088

WORKERS' COMPENSATION LAW

Eugene

Evohl F. Malagon · a · Malagon, Moore & Jensen · 678 Country Club Road · P.O. Box 7788 · Eugene, OR 97401 · 541-484-7022

Christopher D. Moore · a · Malagon, Moore & Jensen · 678 Country Club Road · P.O. Box 7788 · Eugene, OR 97401 · 541-484-7022

Portland

David A. Hytowitz · Law Offices of Robert S Dorband · 16505 Southwest 72nd Avenue, Suite 200 · Portland, OR 97224 · 503-697-6747

Scott H. Terrall · Terrall & Terrall · 909 Southwest Saint Clair Avenue, Suite One · Portland, OR 97205 · 503-224-2625

PENNSYLVANIA

ALTERNATIVE DISPUTE RESOLUTION

Philadelphia

Arlin M. Adams · Schnader Harrison Segal & Lewis · http://www.schnader.com · 1600 Market Street, Suite 3600 · Philadelphia, PA 19103-7286 · 215-751-2000

Steven A. Arbittier · Ballard Spahr Andrews & Ingersoll · 1735 Market Street, 51st Floor · Philadelphia, PA 19103-7599 · 215-665-8500

Louis C. Bechtle · Conrad O'Brien Gellman & Rohn · http://www.cogr.com · 1515 Market Street, 16th Floor · Philadelphia, PA 19102-1916 · 215-864-9600

Edward N. Cahn · Blank Rome · One Logan Square · 130 North 18th Street · Philadelphia, PA 19103-6998 · 215-569-5500

Louis Coffey · WolfBlock · http://wolfblock.com · 1650 Arch Street, 22nd Floor · Philadelphia, PA 19103-2097 · 215-977-2000

Edward L. Edelstein · ADR Options · http://www.adroptions.com · Two Commerce Square, Suite 1100 · 2001 Market Street · Philadelphia, PA 19103-7044 · 215-564-1775

William H. Ewing · Eckert Seamans Cherin & Mellott · Two Liberty Place, 22nd Floor · 50 South 16th Street · Philadelphia, PA 19102 · 215-851-8400

Abraham J. Gafni · ADR Options · http://www.adroptions.com · Two Commerce Square, Suite 1100 · 2001 Market Street · Philadelphia, PA 19103-7044 · 215-564-1775

William Hangley · a · Hangley Aronchick Segal & Pudlin · http://www.hangley.com · One Logan Square, 27th Floor · 18th and Cherry Street · Philadelphia, PA 19103-6933 · 215-568-6200

John G. Harkins, Jr. · 2% · Harkins Cunningham · http://www.harkinscunningham.com · 2800 One Commerce Square · 2005 Market Street · Philadelphia, PA 19103-7042 · 215-851-6700

Robert C. Heim · ⑩ · Dechert · Cira Centre · 2929 Arch Street · Philadelphia, PA 19104-2808 · 215-994-4000

Barbara W. Mather · Pepper Hamilton · http://www.pepperlaw.com · Two Logan Square, Suite 3000 · 18th and Arch Street · Philadelphia, PA 19103-2799 · 215-981-4000

Judith P. Meyer · ADR Options · http://www.adroptions.com · Two Commerce Square, Suite 1100 · 2001 Market Street · Philadelphia, PA 19103-7044 · 215-564-1775

Edwin E. Naythons · ADR Options · http://www.adroptions.com · Two Commerce Square, Suite 1100 · 2001 Market Street · Philadelphia, PA 19103-7044 · 215-564-1775

Bennett G. Picker · Stradley, Ronon, Stevens & Young · 2600 One Commerce Square · Philadelphia, PA 19103-7098 · 215-564-8000

Andrew S. Price · Andrew S. Price Associates · 121 South Broad Street, Suite 1700 · Philadelphia, PA 19107 · 610-566-4500

Thomas Raup · ADR Options · http://www.adroptions.com · Two Commerce Square, Suite 1100 · 2001 Market Street · Philadelphia, PA 19103-7044 · 215-564-1775

Thomas B. Rutter · ADR Options · http://www.adroptions.com · Two Commerce Square, Suite 1100 · 2001 Market Street · Philadelphia, PA 19103-7044 · 215-564-1775

Ronald H. Sherr · ADR Options · http://www.adroptions.com · Two Commerce Square, Suite 1100 · 2001 Market Street · Philadelphia, PA 19103-7044 · 215-564-1775

Jerome J. Shestack · ⑩ · WolfBlock · http://wolfblock.com · 1650 Arch Street, 22nd Floor · Philadelphia, PA 19103-2097 · 215-977-2000

Howard D. Venzie, Jr. · Venzie, Phillips & Warshawer · 2032 Chancellor Street · Philadelphia, PA 19103 215-567-3322

Diane M. Welsh · JAMS · Bell Atlantic Tower, Suite 4010 · 1717 Arch Street · Philadelphia, PA 19103 · 215-246-9494

Pittsburgh

Albert Bates, Jr. · Duane Morris · 600 Grant Street, Suite 5010 · Pittsburgh, PA 15219-2811 · 412-497-1000

James B. Brown · Cohen & Grigsby · 625 Liberty Avenue · Pittsburgh, PA 15222-3152 · 412-297-4900

Robert A. Creo · Impartial Dispute Resolution Services · 1807 Jancey Street, First Floor · Pittsburgh, PA 15206-1065 · 412-361-7983

Louis B. Kushner · ⑳ · Rothman Gordon · Grant Building, Third Floor · 310 Grant Street · Pittsburgh, PA 15219-2202 · 412-338-1100

Roslyn M. Litman · ㉕ · Litman Law Firm · One Oxford Centre, 34th Floor · 301 Grant Street · Pittsburgh, PA 15219-1407 · 412-456-2000

Philadelphia

Steven A. Asher · Weinstein Kitchenoff & Asher · http://www.wka-law.com · 1845 Walnut Street, Suite 1100 · Philadelphia, PA 19103 · 215-545-7200

Steven E. Bizar · Buchanan Ingersoll & Rooney · http://www.bipc.com · 1835 Market Street, 14th Floor · Philadelphia, PA 19103-2985 · 215-665-8700

Allen D. Black · Fine, Kaplan and Black · 1835 Market Street, 28th Floor · Philadelphia, PA 19103 · 215-567-6565

Stephen D. Brown · Dechert · Cira Centre · 2929 Arch Street · Philadelphia, PA 19104-2808 · 215-994-4000

Merill G. Davidoff · Berger & Montague · 1622 Locust Street · Philadelphia, PA 19103 · 215-875-3000

Mark P. Edwards · Morgan Lewis & Bockius · 1701 Market Street · Philadelphia, PA 19103-2921 · 215-963-5000

Joseph B. G. Fay · Morgan Lewis & Bockius · 1701 Market Street · Philadelphia, PA 19103-2921 · 215-963-5000

Nancy J. Gellman · a · Conrad O'Brien Gellman & Rohn · http://www.cogr.com · 1515 Market Street, 16th Floor · Philadelphia, PA 19102-1916 · 215-864-9600

George G. Gordon · Dechert · Cira Centre · 2929 Arch Street · Philadelphia, PA 19104-2808 · 215-994-4000

John G. Harkins, Jr. · 2% · Harkins Cunningham · http://www.harkinscunningham.com · 2800 One Commerce Square · 2005 Market Street · Philadelphia, PA 19103-7042 · 215-851-6700

Robert C. Heim · a · Dechert · Cira Centre · 2929 Arch Street · Philadelphia, PA 19104-2808 · 215-994-4000

Joseph C. Kohn · Kohn, Swift & Graf · One South Broad Street, Suite 2100 · Philadelphia, PA 19107 · 215-238-1700

Robert J. LaRocca · Kohn, Swift & Graf · One South Broad Street, Suite 2100 · Philadelphia, PA 19107 · 215-238-1700

Christine C. Levin · Dechert · Cira Centre · 2929 Arch Street · Philadelphia, PA 19104-2808 · 215-994-4000

Roberta D. Liebenberg · Fine, Kaplan and Black · 1835 Market Street, 28th Floor · Philadelphia, PA 19103 · 215-567-6565

Barbara W. Mather · Pepper Hamilton · http://www.pepperlaw.com · Two Logan Square, Suite 3000 · 18th and Arch Street · Philadelphia, PA 19103-2799 · 215-981-4000

H. Laddie Montague, Jr. · Berger & Montague · 1622 Locust Street · Philadelphia, PA 19103 · 215-875-3000

Francis Patrick Newell · Harkins Cunningham · http://www.harkinscunningham.com · 2800 One Commerce Square · 2005 Market Street · Philadelphia, PA 19103-7042 · 215-851-6700

William J. O'Brien · a · Conrad O'Brien Gellman & Rohn · http://www.cogr.com · 1515 Market Street, 16th Floor · Philadelphia, PA 19102-1916 · 215-864-9600

Steven A. Reed · Harkins Cunningham · http://www.harkinscunningham.com · 2800 One Commerce Square · 2005 Market Street · Philadelphia, PA 19103-7042 · 215-851-6700

James J. Rodgers · Dilworth Paxson · 3200 Mellon Bank Center · 1735 Market Street · Philadelphia, PA 19103-7595 · 215-575-7000

Howard J. Sedran · Levin, Fishbein, Sedran & Berman · 510 Walnut Street, Suite 500 · Philadelphia, PA 19106-3697 · 215-592-1500

Laurence Z. Shiekman · Pepper Hamilton · http://www.pepperlaw.com · Two Logan Square, Suite 3000 · 18th and Arch Street · Philadelphia, PA 19103-2799 · 215-981-4000

Barbara T. Sicalides · Pepper Hamilton · http://www.pepperlaw.com · Two Logan Square, Suite 3000 · 18th and Arch Street · Philadelphia, PA 19103-2799 · 215-981-4000

Joseph A. Tate · a · Dechert · Cira Centre · 2929 Arch Street · Philadelphia, PA 19104-2808 · 215-994-4000

Pittsburgh

Thomas L. Allen · Reed Smith · 435 Sixth Avenue · Pittsburgh, PA 15219-1886 · 412-288-3131

Daniel I. Booker · a · Reed Smith · 435 Sixth Avenue · Pittsburgh, PA 15219-1886 · 412-288-3131

Debra H. Dermody · Reed Smith · 435 Sixth Avenue · Pittsburgh, PA 15219-1886 · 412-288-3131

David J. Hickton · Burns, White & Hickton · http://www.bwhllc.com · Four Northshore Center · 106 Isabella Street · Pittsburgh, PA 15212 · 412-995-3000

David L. McClenahan · a · K&L Gates · Henry W. Oliver Building · 535 Smithfield Street · Pittsburgh, PA 15222-2312 · 412-355-6500

Wendelynne J. Newton · Buchanan Ingersoll & Rooney · http://www.bipc.com · One Oxford Centre, 20th Floor · 301 Grant Street · Pittsburgh, PA 15219-1410 · 412-562-8800

Thomas L. VanKirk · Buchanan Ingersoll & Rooney · http://www.bipc.com · One Oxford Centre, 20th Floor · 301 Grant Street · Pittsburgh, PA 15219-1410 · 412-562-8800

APPELLATE LAW

Ardmore

Peter Goldberger · a · Peter Goldberger · 50 Rittenhouse Place · Ardmore, PA 19003 · 610-649-8200

Philadelphia

Arlin M. Adams · Schnader Harrison Segal & Lewis · http://www.schnader.com · 1600 Market Street, Suite 3600 · Philadelphia, PA 19103-7286 · 215-751-2000

Jules Epstein · a · Kairys, Rudovsky, Messing & Feinberg · The Cast Iron Building, Suite 501 South · 718 Arch Street · Philadelphia, PA 19106 · 215-925-4400

Gregory M. Harvey · a · Montgomery, McCracken, Walker & Rhoads · 123 South Broad Street · Avenue Of The Arts · Philadelphia, PA 19109-1029 · 215-772-1500

David H. Marion · a · Montgomery, McCracken, Walker & Rhoads · 123 South Broad Street · Avenue Of The Arts · Philadelphia, PA 19109-1029 · 215-772-1500

Bruce P. Merenstein · Schnader Harrison Segal & Lewis · http://www.schnader.com · 1600 Market Street, Suite 3600 · Philadelphia, PA 19103-7286 · 215-751-2000

Alfred W. Putnam, Jr. · Drinker Biddle & Reath · One Logan Square · 18th and Cherry Streets · Philadelphia, PA 19103-6996 · 215-988-2700

Deena Jo Schneider · Schnader Harrison Segal & Lewis · http://www.schnader.com · 1600 Market Street, Suite 3600 · Philadelphia, PA 19103-7286 · 215-751-2000

Jerome J. Shestack · a · WolfBlock · http://wolfblock.com · 1650 Arch Street, 22nd Floor · Philadelphia, PA 19103-2097 · 215-977-2000

Carl A. Solano · Schnader Harrison Segal & Lewis · http://www.schnader.com · 1600 Market Street, Suite 3600 · Philadelphia, PA 19103-7286 · 215-751-2000

Nancy Winkelman · Schnader Harrison Segal & Lewis · http://www.schnader.com · 1600 Market Street, Suite 3600 · Philadelphia, PA 19103-7286 · 215-751-2000

Pittsburgh

David A. Brownlee · a · K&L Gates · Henry W. Oliver Building · 535 Smithfield Street · Pittsburgh, PA 15222-2312 · 412-355-6500

Robert L. Byer · Duane Morris · 600 Grant Street, Suite 5010 · Pittsburgh, PA 15219-2811 · 412-497-1000

James C. Martin · Reed Smith · 435 Sixth Avenue · Pittsburgh, PA 15219-1886 · 412-288-3131

W. Thomas McGough, Jr. · a · Reed Smith · 435 Sixth Avenue · Pittsburgh, PA 15219-1886 · 412-288-3131

Richard B. Tucker III · Tucker Arensberg · http://www.tuckerlaw.com · 1500 One PPG Place · Pittsburgh, PA 15222-5401 · 412-566-1212

Kim M. Watterson · Reed Smith · 435 Sixth Avenue · Pittsburgh, PA 15219-1886 · 412-288-3131

BANKING LAW

Carlisle

John B. Lampi · Saidis Flower & Lindsay · 26 West High Street · Carlisle, PA 17013 · 717-243-6222

Harrisburg

Charles J. Ferry · Rhoads & Sinon · M & T Bank Building, 12th Floor · One South Market Square · P.O. Box 1146 · Harrisburg, PA 17108-1146 · 717-233-5731

Daniel J. Malpezzi · McNees Wallace & Nurick · 100 Pine Street · P.O. Box 1166 · Harrisburg, PA 17108-1166 · 717-232-8000

Henry W. Rhoads · a · Rhoads & Sinon · M & T Bank Building, 12th Floor · One South Market Square · P.O. Box 1146 · Harrisburg, PA 17108-1146 · 717-233-5731

Malvern

David F. Scranton · a · Stradley, Ronon, Stevens & Young · Great Valley Corporate Center · 30 Valley Stream Parkway · Malvern, PA 19355-1481 · 610-640-5800

Philadelphia

Lawrence F. Flick II · Blank Rome · One Logan Square · 130 North 18th Street · Philadelphia, PA 19103-6998 · 215-569-5500

Harvey I. Forman · a · Blank Rome · One Logan Square · 130 North 18th Street · Philadelphia, PA 19103-6998 · 215-569-5500

Carl H. Fridy · a · Ballard Spahr Andrews & Ingersoll · 1735 Market Street, 51st Floor · Philadelphia, PA 19103-7599 · 215-665-8500

John F. Horstmann III · a · Duane Morris · 30 South 17th Street · Philadelphia, PA 19103-4196 · 215-979-1000

James A. Hunter, Jr. · Morgan Lewis & Bockius · 1701 Market Street · Philadelphia, PA 19103-2921 · 215-963-5000

Lisa D. Kabnick · Reed Smith · 2500 One Liberty Place · 1650 Market Street · Philadelphia, PA 19103 · 215-851-8100

Alan S. Kaplinsky · Ballard Spahr Andrews & Ingersoll · 1735 Market Street, 51st Floor · Philadelphia, PA 19103-7599 · 215-665-8500

Bruce R. Lesser · WolfBlock · http://wolfblock.com · 1650 Arch Street, 22nd Floor · Philadelphia, PA 19103-2097 · 215-977-2000

Richard S. Perelman · Ballard Spahr Andrews & Ingersoll · 1735 Market Street, 51st Floor · Philadelphia, PA 19103-7599 · 215-665-8500

Mark I. Rabinowitz · Blank Rome · One Logan Square · 130 North 18th Street · Philadelphia, PA 19103-6998 · 215-569-5500

Jeremy T. Rosenblum · Ballard Spahr Andrews & Ingersoll · 1735 Market Street, 51st Floor · Philadelphia, PA 19103-7599 · 215-665-8500

Joan N. Stern · Blank Rome · One Logan Square · 130 North 18th Street · Philadelphia, PA 19103-6998 · 215-569-5500

Stephen D. Teaford · a · Duane Morris · 30 South 17th Street · Philadelphia, PA 19103-4196 · 215-979-1000

Pittsburgh

Bruce I. Booken · Buchanan Ingersoll & Rooney · http://www.bipc.com · One Oxford Centre, 20th Floor 301 Grant Street · Pittsburgh, PA 15219-1410 · 412-562-8800

Jeffrey J. Conn · Thorp, Reed & Armstrong · One Oxford Centre, 14th Floor · 301 Grant Street · Pittsburgh, PA 15219-1425 · 412-394-7711

Thomas S. Galey · Buchanan Ingersoll & Rooney · http://www.bipc.com · One Oxford Centre, 20th Floor 301 Grant Street · Pittsburgh, PA 15219-1410 · 412-562-8800

Frank T. Guadagnino · Reed Smith · 435 Sixth Avenue · Pittsburgh, PA 15219-1886 · 412-288-3131

Calvin R. Harvey · 2) · Buchanan Ingersoll & Rooney · http://www.bipc.com · One Oxford Centre, 20th Floor · 301 Grant Street · Pittsburgh, PA 15219-1410 · 412-562-8800

Craig S. Heryford · Buchanan Ingersoll & Rooney · http://www.bipc.com · One Oxford Centre, 20th Floor · 301 Grant Street · Pittsburgh, PA 15219-1410 · 412-562-8800

Alan E. London · a · Reed Smith · 435 Sixth Avenue · Pittsburgh, PA 15219-1886 · 412-288-3131

David A. Murdoch · a · K&L Gates · Henry W. Oliver Building · 535 Smithfield Street · Pittsburgh, PA 15222-2312 · 412-355-6500

Daniel J. Perry · Tucker Arensberg · http://www.tuckerlaw.com · 1500 One PPG Place · Pittsburgh, PA 15222-5401 · 412-566-1212

Thomas Todd · a · Reed Smith · 435 Sixth Avenue · Pittsburgh, PA 15219-1886 · 412-288-3131

Joel M. Walker · Duane Morris · 600 Grant Street, Suite 5010 · Pittsburgh, PA 15219-2811 · 412-497-1000

BANKRUPTCY AND CREDITOR-DEBTOR RIGHTS LAW

Erie

Guy C. Fustine · a · Knox McLaughlin Gornall & Sennett · 120 West 10th Street · Erie, PA 16501-1461 · 814-459-2800

Harrisburg

Robert E. Chernicoff · a · Cunningham & Chernicoff · http://www.cclawpc.com · 2320 North Second Street · P.O. Box 60457 · Harrisburg, PA 17106-0457 · 717-238-6570

Leon P. Haller · 2% · Purcell, Krug & Haller · 1719 North Front Street · Harrisburg, PA 17102-2392 · 717-234-4178

Robert L. Knupp · 2% · Knupp Kodak & Imblum · Cameron Mansion · 407 North Front Street · P.O. Box 630 · Harrisburg, PA 17108-1848 · 717-238-7151

Philadelphia

Leon R. Barson · Pepper Hamilton · http://www.pepperlaw.com · Two Logan Square, Suite 3000 · 18th and Arch Street · Philadelphia, PA 19103-2799 · 215-981-4000

Thomas E. Biron · a · Blank Rome · One Logan Square · 130 North 18th Street · Philadelphia, PA 19103-6998 · 215-569-5500

Michael A. Bloom · Morgan Lewis & Bockius · 1701 Market Street · Philadelphia, PA 19103-2921 · 215-963-5000

Myron A. Bloom · Hangley Aronchick Segal & Pudlin · http://www.hangley.com · One Logan Square, 27th Floor · 18th and Cherry Street · Philadelphia, PA 19103-6933 · 215-568-6200

Morton R. Branzburg · Klehr, Harrison, Harvey, Branzburg & Ellers · 260 South Broad Street, Suite 400 · Philadelphia, PA 19102-5003 · 215-568-6060

Barry E. Bressler · Schnader Harrison Segal & Lewis · http://www.schnader.com · 1600 Market Street, Suite 3600 · Philadelphia, PA 19103-7286 · 215-751-2000

Peter S. Clark II · Reed Smith · 2500 One Liberty Place · 1650 Market Street · Philadelphia, PA 19103 · 215-851-8100

Neal D. Colton · 2) · Cozen O'Connor · The Atrium · 1900 Market Street · Philadelphia, PA 19103 · 215-665-2000

Joseph A. Dworetzky · Hangley Aronchick Segal & Pudlin · http://www.hangley.com · One Logan Square, 27th Floor · 18th and Cherry Street · Philadelphia, PA 19103-6933 · 215-568-6200

Bonnie G. Fatell · Blank Rome · One Logan Square · 130 North 18th Street · Philadelphia, PA 19103-6998 · 215-569-5500

Harvey I. Forman · a · Blank Rome · One Logan Square · 130 North 18th Street · Philadelphia, PA 19103-6998 · 215-569-5500

Robert M. Greenbaum · Saul Ewing · Centre Square West, 38th Floor · 1500 Market Street · Philadelphia, PA 19102-2186 · 215-972-7777

John F. Horstmann III · a · Duane Morris · 30 South 17th Street · Philadelphia, PA 19103-4196 · 215-979-1000

Andrew C. Kassner · Drinker Biddle & Reath · One Logan Square · 18th and Cherry Streets · Philadelphia, PA 19103-6996 · 215-988-2700

Regina Stango Kelbon · Blank Rome · One Logan Square · 130 North 18th Street · Philadelphia, PA 19103-6998 · 215-569-5500

Barry D. Kleban · McElroy, Deutsch, Mulvaney & Carpenter · http://www.mdmc-law.com · One Penn Center, Suite 1500 · 1617 JFK Boulevard · Philadelphia, PA 19103-1815 · 215-557-2900

Lawrence J. Kotler · Duane Morris · 30 South 17th Street · Philadelphia, PA 19103-4196 · 215-979-1000

Robert Lapowsky · Stevens & Lee · 1818 Market Street, 29th Floor · Philadelphia, PA 19103 · 215-575-0100

Francis J. Lawall · Pepper Hamilton · http://www.pepperlaw.com · Two Logan Square, Suite 3000 · 18th and Arch Street · Philadelphia, PA 19103-2799 · 215-981-4000

Vincent J. Marriott III · Ballard Spahr Andrews & Ingersoll · 1735 Market Street, 51st Floor · Philadelphia, PA 19103-7599 · 215-665-8500

James M. Matour · Hangley Aronchick Segal & Pudlin · http://www.hangley.com · One Logan Square, 27th Floor · 18th and Cherry Street · Philadelphia, PA 19103-6933 · 215-568-6200

Lawrence G. McMichael · Dilworth Paxson · 3200 Mellon Bank Center · 1735 Market Street · Philadelphia, PA 19103-7595 · 215-575-7000

J. Gregg Miller · Pepper Hamilton · http://www.pepperlaw.com · Two Logan Square, Suite 3000 · 18th and Arch Street · Philadelphia, PA 19103-2799 · 215-981-4000

Paul A. Patterson · Stradley, Ronon, Stevens & Young · 2600 One Commerce Square · Philadelphia, PA 19103-7098 · 215-564-8000

David L. Pollack · Ballard Spahr Andrews & Ingersoll · 1735 Market Street, 51st Floor · Philadelphia, PA 19103-7599 · 215-665-8500

Margery N. Reed · Duane Morris · 30 South 17th Street · Philadelphia, PA 19103-4196 · 215-979-1000

Michael H. Reed · Pepper Hamilton · http://www.pepperlaw.com · Two Logan Square, Suite 3000 · 18th and Arch Street · Philadelphia, PA 19103-2799 · 215-981-4000

William H. Schorling · Buchanan Ingersoll & Rooney · http://www.bipc.com · 1835 Market Street, 14th Floor · Philadelphia, PA 19103-2985 · 215-665-8700

Raymond L. Shapiro · 25 · Blank Rome · One Logan Square · 130 North 18th Street · Philadelphia, PA 19103-6998 · 215-569-5500

Henry J. Sommer · Henry J. Sommers · 7118 McCallum Street · Philadelphia, PA 19119 · 215-242-8639

Claudia Z. Springer · Reed Smith · 2500 One Liberty Place · 1650 Market Street · Philadelphia, PA 19103 · 215-851-8100

David T. Sykes · ⑳ · Duane Morris · 30 South 17th Street · Philadelphia, PA 19103-4196 · 215-979-1000

Michael L. Temin · ㉕ · WolfBlock · http://wolfblock.com · 1650 Arch Street, 22nd Floor · Philadelphia, PA 19103-2097 · 215-977-2000

Steven D. Usdin · Cohen Seglias Pallas Greenhall & Furman · United Plaza, 19th Floor · 30 South 17th Street · Philadelphia, PA 19103 · 215-564-1700

Pittsburgh

Philip E. Beard, Sr. · ㉕ · Stonecipher, Cunningham, Beard & Schmitt · 125 First Avenue · Pittsburgh, PA 15222-1590 · 412-391-8510

Robert S. Bernstein · Bernstein Law Firm · Gulf Tower, Suite 2200 · Pittsburgh, PA 15219 · 800-693-4013

Douglas A. Campbell · ㉕ · Campbell & Levine · http://www.camlev.com · 1700 Grant Building · 330 Grant Street · Pittsburgh, PA 15219 · 412-261-0310

George L. Cass · ㉕ · Buchanan Ingersoll & Rooney · http://www.bipc.com · One Oxford Centre, 20th Floor · 301 Grant Street · Pittsburgh, PA 15219-1410 · 412-562-8800

Mark E. Freedlander · McGuireWoods · http://www.mcguirewoods.com · Dominion Tower, 23rd Floor · 625 Liberty Avenue · Pittsburgh, PA 15222-3142 · 412-667-6000

Norman E. Gilkey · Babst, Calland, Clements and Zomnir · http://www.bccz.com · Two Gateway Center, Eighth Floor · 603 Stanwix Street · Pittsburgh, PA 15222 · 412-394-5400

Joel M. Helmrich · Meyer, Unkovic & Scott · http://www.muslaw.com · 1300 Oliver Building · 535 Smithfield Street · Pittsburgh, PA 15222 · 412-456-2800

Stanley E. Levine · ⑳ · Campbell & Levine · http://www.camlev.com · 1700 Grant Building · 330 Grant Street · Pittsburgh, PA 15219 · 412-261-0310

Beverly Weiss Manne · Tucker Arensberg · http://www.tuckerlaw.com · 1500 One PPG Place · Pittsburgh, PA 15222-5401 · 412-566-1212

Joseph McDonough · ⑩ · Manion, McDonough & Lucas · USX Tower, Suite 1414 · 600 Grant Street · Pittsburgh, PA 15219 · 412-232-0200

Philip E. Milch · Campbell & Levine · http://www.camlev.com · 1700 Grant Building · 330 Grant Street · Pittsburgh, PA 15219 · 412-261-0310

David A. Murdoch · ⑩ · K&L Gates · Henry W. Oliver Building · 535 Smithfield Street · Pittsburgh, PA 15222-2312 · 412-355-6500

Gary Philip Nelson · Sherrard, German & Kelly · Two PNC Plaza, 28th Floor · 620 Liberty Avenue · Pittsburgh, PA 15222 · 412-355-0200

Ronald B. Roteman · Campbell & Levine · http://www.camlev.com · 1700 Grant Building · 330 Grant Street · Pittsburgh, PA 15219 · 412-261-0310

David K. Rudov · Rudov & Stein · First and Market Building, Suite 500 · 100 First Avenue · Pittsburgh, PA 15222-1504 · 412-281-7300

Robert G. Sable · 2% · McGuireWoods · http://www.mcguirewoods.com · Dominion Tower, 23rd Floor · 625 Liberty Avenue · Pittsburgh, PA 15222-3142 · 412-667-6000

David B. Salzman · a · Campbell & Levine · http://www.camlev.com · 1700 Grant Building · 330 Grant Street · Pittsburgh, PA 15219 · 412-261-0310

Eric A. Schaffer · Reed Smith · 435 Sixth Avenue · Pittsburgh, PA 15219-1886 · 412-288-3131

Paul M. Singer · 2) · Reed Smith · 435 Sixth Avenue · Pittsburgh, PA 15219-1886 · 412-288-3131

George T. Snyder · Stonecipher, Cunningham, Beard & Schmitt · 125 First Avenue · Pittsburgh, PA 15222-1590 · 412-391-8510

Joel M. Walker · Duane Morris · 600 Grant Street, Suite 5010 · Pittsburgh, PA 15219-2811 · 412-497-1000

BET-THE-COMPANY LITIGATION

Harrisburg

David E. Lehman · McNees Wallace & Nurick · 100 Pine Street · P.O. Box 1166 · Harrisburg, PA 17108-1166 · 717-232-8000

Jack M. Stover · Buchanan Ingersoll & Rooney · http://www.bipc.com · One South Market Square, Third Floor · 213 Market Street · P.O. Box 12023 · Harrisburg, PA 17108 · 717-237-4800

Philadelphia

Mark A. Aronchick · Hangley Aronchick Segal & Pudlin · http://www.hangley.com · One Logan Square, 27th Floor · 18th and Cherry Street · Philadelphia, PA 19103-6933 · 215-568-6200

Nancy J. Gellman · a · Conrad O'Brien Gellman & Rohn · http://www.cogr.com · 1515 Market Street, 16th Floor · Philadelphia, PA 19102-1916 · 215-864-9600

William Hangley · a · Hangley Aronchick Segal & Pudlin · http://www.hangley.com · One Logan Square, 27th Floor · 18th and Cherry Street · Philadelphia, PA 19103-6933 · 215-568-6200

John G. Harkins, Jr. · 2% · Harkins Cunningham · http://www.harkinscunningham.com · 2800 One Commerce Square · 2005 Market Street · Philadelphia, PA 19103-7042 · 215-851-6700

Robert C. Heim · a · Dechert · Cira Centre · 2929 Arch Street · Philadelphia, PA 19104-2808 · 215-994-4000

David H. Marion · a · Montgomery, McCracken, Walker & Rhoads · 123 South Broad Street · Avenue Of The Arts · Philadelphia, PA 19109-1029 · 215-772-1500

Barbara W. Mather · Pepper Hamilton · http://www.pepperlaw.com · Two Logan Square, Suite 3000 · 18th and Arch Street · Philadelphia, PA 19103-2799 · 215-981-4000

William J. O'Brien · a · Conrad O'Brien Gellman & Rohn · http://www.cogr.com · 1515 Market Street, 16th Floor · Philadelphia, PA 19102-1916 · 215-864-9600

Dennis R. Suplee · Schnader Harrison Segal & Lewis · http://www.schnader.com · 1600 Market Street, Suite 3600 · Philadelphia, PA 19103-7286 · 215-751-2000

Joseph A. Tate · a · Dechert · Cira Centre · 2929 Arch Street · Philadelphia, PA 19104-2808 · 215-994-4000

Pittsburgh

Thomas L. Allen · Reed Smith · 435 Sixth Avenue · Pittsburgh, PA 15219-1886 · 412-288-3131

David J. Armstrong · 2% · Dickie, McCamey & Chilcote · http://www.dmclaw.com · Two PPG Place, Suite 400 · Pittsburgh, PA 15222-5402 · 412-281-7272

Daniel I. Booker · a · Reed Smith · 435 Sixth Avenue · Pittsburgh, PA 15219-1886 · 412-288-3131

David B. Fawcett · 2% · Dickie, McCamey & Chilcote · http://www.dmclaw.com · Two PPG Place, Suite 400 · Pittsburgh, PA 15222-5402 · 412-281-7272

Peter J. Kalis · a · K&L Gates · Henry W. Oliver Building · 535 Smithfield Street · Pittsburgh, PA 15222-2312 · 412-355-6500

David L. McClenahan · a · K&L Gates · Henry W. Oliver Building · 535 Smithfield Street · Pittsburgh, PA 15222-2312 · 412-355-6500

W. Thomas McGough, Jr. · a · Reed Smith · 435 Sixth Avenue · Pittsburgh, PA 15219-1886 · 412-288-3131

William A. Pietragallo II · a · Pietragallo Gordon Alfano Bosick & Raspanti · One Oxford Centre, 38th Floor · Pittsburgh, PA 15219 · 412-263-2000

William M. Wycoff · a · Thorp, Reed & Armstrong · One Oxford Centre, 14th Floor · 301 Grant Street · Pittsburgh, PA 15219-1425 · 412-394-7711

BIOTECHNOLOGY LAW

Berwyn

Jeffrey P. Libson · Pepper Hamilton · http://www.pepperlaw.com · 400 Berwyn Park · 899 Cassatt Road · Berwyn, PA 19312-1183 · 610-640-7800

Philadelphia

James A. Lebovitz · Dechert · Cira Centre · 2929 Arch Street · Philadelphia, PA 19104-2808 · 215-994-4000

COMMERCIAL LITIGATION

Harrisburg

Alan R. Boynton, Jr. · McNees Wallace & Nurick · 100 Pine Street · P.O. Box 1166 · Harrisburg, PA 17108-1166 · 717-232-8000

James P. DeAngelo · McNees Wallace & Nurick · 100 Pine Street · P.O. Box 1166 · Harrisburg, PA 17108-1166 · 717-232-8000

James J. Kutz · Post & Schell · 17 North Second Street, 12th Floor · Harrisburg, PA 17101-1601 · 717-731-1970

James W. Kutz · McNees Wallace & Nurick · 100 Pine Street · P.O. Box 1166 · Harrisburg, PA 17108-1166 · 717-232-8000

David E. Lehman · McNees Wallace & Nurick · 100 Pine Street · P.O. Box 1166 · Harrisburg, PA 17108-1166 · 717-232-8000

Daniel J. Malpezzi · McNees Wallace & Nurick · 100 Pine Street · P.O. Box 1166 · Harrisburg, PA 17108-1166 · 717-232-8000

James G. Morgan, Jr. · Tucker Arensberg · http://www.tuckerlaw.com · 111 North Front Street · P.O. Box 889 · Harrisburg, PA 17108-0889 · 717-234-4121

Jack M. Stover · Buchanan Ingersoll & Rooney · http://www.bipc.com · One South Market Square, Third Floor · 213 Market Street · P.O. Box 12023 · Harrisburg, PA 17108 · 717-237-4800

Jayson R. Wolfgang · Buchanan Ingersoll & Rooney · http://www.bipc.com · One South Market Square, Third Floor · 213 Market Street · P.O. Box 12023 · Harrisburg, PA 17108 · 717-237-4800

Lancaster

Joseph F. Roda · Roda & Nast · 801 Estelle Drive · Lancaster, PA 17601-2130 · 717-892-3000

Philadelphia

Elizabeth K. Ainslie · Schnader Harrison Segal & Lewis · http://www.schnader.com · 1600 Market Street, Suite 3600 · Philadelphia, PA 19103-7286 · 215-751-2000

Steven A. Arbittier · Ballard Spahr Andrews & Ingersoll · 1735 Market Street, 51st Floor · Philadelphia, PA 19103-7599 · 215-665-8500

Mark A. Aronchick · Hangley Aronchick Segal & Pudlin · http://www.hangley.com · One Logan Square, 27th Floor · 18th and Cherry Street · Philadelphia, PA 19103-6933 · 215-568-6200

Michael L. Banks · Morgan Lewis & Bockius · 1701 Market Street · Philadelphia, PA 19103-2921 · 215-963-5000

Allen D. Black · Fine, Kaplan and Black · 1835 Market Street, 28th Floor · Philadelphia, PA 19103 · 215-567-6565

James M. Brogan · DLA Piper · One Liberty Place, Suite 4900 · 1650 Market Street · Philadelphia, PA 19103-7300 · 215-656-3300

Carl M. Buchholz · Blank Rome · One Logan Square · 130 North 18th Street · Philadelphia, PA 19103-6998 · 215-569-5500

Jay H. Calvert, Jr. · Morgan Lewis & Bockius · 1701 Market Street · Philadelphia, PA 19103-2921 · 215-963-5000

J. Gordon Cooney, Jr. · Morgan Lewis & Bockius · 1701 Market Street · Philadelphia, PA 19103-2921 · 215-963-5000

Joseph C. Crawford · Pepper Hamilton · http://www.pepperlaw.com · Two Logan Square, Suite 3000 · 18th and Arch Street · Philadelphia, PA 19103-2799 · 215-981-4000

André L. Dennis · Stradley, Ronon, Stevens & Young · 2600 One Commerce Square · Philadelphia, PA 19103-7098 · 215-564-8000

Francis P. Devine III · a · Pepper Hamilton · http://www.pepperlaw.com · Two Logan Square, Suite 3000 · 18th and Arch Street · Philadelphia, PA 19103-2799 · 215-981-4000

Thomas J. Duffy · Duffy + Partners · http://www.duffyfirm.com · One Liberty Place, 55th Floor · Philadelphia, PA 19103 · 215-238-8700

Steven B. Feirson · Dechert · Cira Centre · 2929 Arch Street · Philadelphia, PA 19104-2808 · 215-994-4000

H. Robert Fiebach · a · Cozen O'Connor · The Atrium · 1900 Market Street · Philadelphia, PA 19103 · 215-665-2000

Brian Flaherty · WolfBlock · http://wolfblock.com · 1650 Arch Street, 22nd Floor · Philadelphia, PA 19103-2097 · 215-977-2000

Lawrence J. Fox · Drinker Biddle & Reath · One Logan Square · 18th and Cherry Streets · Philadelphia, PA 19103-6996 · 215-988-2700

Louis W. Fryman · Conrad O'Brien Gellman & Rohn · http://www.cogr.com · 1515 Market Street, 16th Floor · Philadelphia, PA 19102-1916 · 215-864-9600

Rudolph Garcia · Buchanan Ingersoll & Rooney · http://www.bipc.com · 1835 Market Street, 14th Floor · Philadelphia, PA 19103-2985 · 215-665-8700

Nancy J. Gellman · a · Conrad O'Brien Gellman & Rohn · http://www.cogr.com · 1515 Market Street, 16th Floor · Philadelphia, PA 19102-1916 · 215-864-9600

M. Norman Goldberger · Hangley Aronchick Segal & Pudlin · http://www.hangley.com · One Logan Square, 27th Floor · 18th and Cherry Street · Philadelphia, PA 19103-6933 · 215-568-6200

William Hangley · a · Hangley Aronchick Segal & Pudlin · http://www.hangley.com · One Logan Square, 27th Floor · 18th and Cherry Street · Philadelphia, PA 19103-6933 · 215-568-6200

John G. Harkins, Jr. · 2% · Harkins Cunningham · http://www.harkinscunningham.com · 2800 One Commerce Square · 2005 Market Street · Philadelphia, PA 19103-7042 · 215-851-6700

Robert C. Heim · a · Dechert · Cira Centre · 2929 Arch Street · Philadelphia, PA 19104-2808 · 215-994-4000

Robert L. Hickok · Pepper Hamilton · http://www.pepperlaw.com · Two Logan Square, Suite 3000 · 18th and Arch Street · Philadelphia, PA 19103-2799 · 215-981-4000

Alexander Kerr · McCarter & English · Mellon Bank Center Building, Suite 700 · 1735 Market Street · Philadelphia, PA 19103 · 215-979-3800

Dana B. Klinges · WolfBlock · http://wolfblock.com · 1650 Arch Street, 22nd Floor · Philadelphia, PA 19103-2097 · 215-977-2000

Mary E. Kohart · Drinker Biddle & Reath · One Logan Square · 18th and Cherry Streets · Philadelphia, PA 19103-6996 · 215-988-2700

Ann Blair Laupheimer · Blank Rome · One Logan Square · 130 North 18th Street · Philadelphia, PA 19103-6998 · 215-569-5500

Roberta D. Liebenberg · Fine, Kaplan and Black · 1835 Market Street, 28th Floor · Philadelphia, PA 19103 · 215-567-6565

S. Gerald Litvin · 2% · Morgan Lewis & Bockius · 1701 Market Street · Philadelphia, PA 19103-2921 · 215-963-5000

Fred T. Magaziner · Dechert · Cira Centre · 2929 Arch Street · Philadelphia, PA 19104-2808 · 215-994-4000

Arthur Makadon · Ballard Spahr Andrews & Ingersoll · 1735 Market Street, 51st Floor · Philadelphia, PA 19103-7599 · 215-665-8500

Edward F. Mannino · a · Akin Gump Strauss Hauer & Feld · One Commerce Square, Suite 2100 · 2005 Market Street · Philadelphia, PA 19103-7013 · 215-965-1200

David H. Marion · a · Montgomery, McCracken, Walker & Rhoads · 123 South Broad Street · Avenue Of The Arts · Philadelphia, PA 19109-1029 · 215-772-1500

Barbara W. Mather · Pepper Hamilton · http://www.pepperlaw.com · Two Logan Square, Suite 3000 · 18th and Arch Street · Philadelphia, PA 19103-2799 · 215-981-4000

J. Bruce McKissock · Marshall, Dennehey, Warner, Coleman & Goggin · 1845 Walnut Street · Philadelphia, PA 19103-4707 · 215-575-2600

Arthur Newbold · Dechert · Cira Centre · 2929 Arch Street · Philadelphia, PA 19104-2808 · 215-994-4000

William J. O'Brien · a · Conrad O'Brien Gellman & Rohn · http://www.cogr.com · 1515 Market Street, 16th Floor · Philadelphia, PA 19102-1916 · 215-864-9600

Patrick J. O'Connor · Cozen O'Connor · The Atrium · 1900 Market Street · Philadelphia, PA 19103 · 215-665-2000

David H. Pittinsky · Ballard Spahr Andrews & Ingersoll · 1735 Market Street, 51st Floor · Philadelphia, PA 19103-7599 · 215-665-8500

Edward Posner · Drinker Biddle & Reath · One Logan Square · 18th and Cherry Streets · Philadelphia, PA 19103-6996 · 215-988-2700

Alfred W. Putnam, Jr. · Drinker Biddle & Reath · One Logan Square · 18th and Cherry Streets · Philadelphia, PA 19103-6996 · 215-988-2700

Steven A. Reed · Harkins Cunningham · http://www.harkinscunningham.com · 2800 One Commerce Square · 2005 Market Street · Philadelphia, PA 19103-7042 · 215-851-6700

Abraham C. Reich · Fox Rothschild · 2000 Market Street, 10th Floor · Philadelphia, PA 19103-3291 · 215-299-2000

Douglas E. Ress · Kaufman, Coren & Ress · http://www.kcr-law.com · 1717 Arch Street, Suite 3710 · Philadelphia, PA 19103 · 215-735-8700

James J. Rohn · Conrad O'Brien Gellman & Rohn · http://www.cogr.com · 1515 Market Street, 16th Floor Philadelphia, PA 19102-1916 · 215-864-9600

Howard D. Scher · Buchanan Ingersoll & Rooney · http://www.bipc.com · 1835 Market Street, 14th Floor Philadelphia, PA 19103-2985 · 215-665-8700

Ronald P. Schiller · DLA Piper · One Liberty Place, Suite 4900 · 1650 Market Street · Philadelphia, PA 19103-7300 · 215-656-3300

Samuel W. Silver · Schnader Harrison Segal & Lewis · http://www.schnader.com · 1600 Market Street, Suite 3600 · Philadelphia, PA 19103-7286 · 215-751-2000

Eric W. Sitarchuk · Morgan Lewis & Bockius · 1701 Market Street · Philadelphia, PA 19103-2921 · 215-963-5000

David Smith · Schnader Harrison Segal & Lewis · http://www.schnader.com · 1600 Market Street, Suite 3600 · Philadelphia, PA 19103-7286 · 215-751-2000

James T. Smith · Blank Rome · One Logan Square · 130 North 18th Street · Philadelphia, PA 19103-6998 215-569-5500

Marc J. Sonnenfeld · a · Morgan Lewis & Bockius · 1701 Market Street · Philadelphia, PA 19103-2921 · 215-963-5000

John S. Summers · Hangley Aronchick Segal & Pudlin · http://www.hangley.com · One Logan Square, 27th Floor · 18th and Cherry Street · Philadelphia, PA 19103-6933 · 215-568-6200

Dennis R. Suplee · Schnader Harrison Segal & Lewis · http://www.schnader.com · 1600 Market Street, Suite 3600 · Philadelphia, PA 19103-7286 · 215-751-2000

Joseph A. Tate · a · Dechert · Cira Centre · 2929 Arch Street · Philadelphia, PA 19104-2808 · 215-994-4000

Jeffrey G. Weil · Dechert · Cira Centre · 2929 Arch Street · Philadelphia, PA 19104-2808 · 215-994-4000

Ralph G. Wellington · Schnader Harrison Segal & Lewis · http://www.schnader.com · 1600 Market Street, Suite 3600 · Philadelphia, PA 19103-7286 · 215-751-2000

William J. Winning · a · Cozen O'Connor · The Atrium · 1900 Market Street · Philadelphia, PA 19103 · 215-665-2000

David N. Zeehandelaar · Blank Rome · One Logan Square · 130 North 18th Street · Philadelphia, PA 19103-6998 · 215-569-5500

Pittsburgh

Thomas L. Allen · Reed Smith · 435 Sixth Avenue · Pittsburgh, PA 15219-1886 · 412-288-3131

David J. Armstrong · 2% · Dickie, McCamey & Chilcote · http://www.dmclaw.com · Two PPG Place, Suite 400 · Pittsburgh, PA 15222-5402 · 412-281-7272

Thomas E. Birsic · K&L Gates · Henry W. Oliver Building · 535 Smithfield Street · Pittsburgh, PA 15222-2312 · 412-355-6500

Frederick W. Bode III · Dickie, McCamey & Chilcote · http://www.dmclaw.com · Two PPG Place, Suite 400 · Pittsburgh, PA 15222-5402 · 412-281-7272

Daniel I. Booker · a · Reed Smith · 435 Sixth Avenue · Pittsburgh, PA 15219-1886 · 412-288-3131

David A. Brownlee · a · K&L Gates · Henry W. Oliver Building · 535 Smithfield Street · Pittsburgh, PA 15222-2312 · 412-355-6500

Michael W. Burns · Burns, White & Hickton · http://www.bwhllc.com · Four Northshore Center · 106 Isabella Street · Pittsburgh, PA 15212 · 412-995-3000

Robert L. Byer · Duane Morris · 600 Grant Street, Suite 5010 · Pittsburgh, PA 15219-2811 · 412-497-1000

William R. Caroselli · a · Caroselli, Beachler, McTiernan & Conboy · http://www.cbmclaw.com · 20 Stanwix Street, Seventh Floor · Pittsburgh, PA 15222-4802 · 412-391-9860

Joseph S. D. Christof II · Dickie, McCamey & Chilcote · http://www.dmclaw.com · Two PPG Place, Suite 400 · Pittsburgh, PA 15222-5402 · 412-281-7272

William D. Clifford · Dickie, McCamey & Chilcote · http://www.dmclaw.com · Two PPG Place, Suite 400 · Pittsburgh, PA 15222-5402 · 412-281-7272

Walter P. DeForest III · 2% · DeForest Koscelnik Yokitis Kaplan & Berardinelli · Koppers Building, 30th Floor · 436 Seventh Avenue · Pittsburgh, PA 15219 · 412-227-3100

John R. Dingess · K&L Gates · Henry W. Oliver Building · 535 Smithfield Street · Pittsburgh, PA 15222-2312 · 412-355-6500

Patricia L. Dodge · Meyer, Unkovic & Scott · http://www.muslaw.com · 1300 Oliver Building · 535 Smithfield Street · Pittsburgh, PA 15222 · 412-456-2800

Larry K. Elliott · Cohen & Grigsby · 625 Liberty Avenue · Pittsburgh, PA 15222-3152 · 412-297-4900

Laura E. Ellsworth · Jones Day · One Mellon Center, Suite 4500 · 500 Grant Street · Pittsburgh, PA 15219-2502 · 412-391-3939

David B. Fawcett · ㉕ · Dickie, McCamey & Chilcote · http://www.dmclaw.com · Two PPG Place, Suite 400 · Pittsburgh, PA 15222-5402 · 412-281-7272

David B. Fawcett III · ⑩ · Buchanan Ingersoll & Rooney · http://www.bipc.com · One Oxford Centre, 20th Floor · 301 Grant Street · Pittsburgh, PA 15219-1410 · 412-562-8800

Maria Greco Danaher · Ogletree Deakins · http://www.ogletreedeakins.com · Four Gateway Center, Suite 400 · 444 Liberty Avenue · Pittsburgh, PA 15222-1237 · 412-394-3333

John E. Hall · Eckert Seamans Cherin & Mellott · U.S. Steel Tower, 44th Floor · 600 Grant Street · Pittsburgh, PA 15219 · 412-566-6000

David J. Hickton · Burns, White & Hickton · http://www.bwhllc.com · Four Northshore Center · 106 Isabella Street · Pittsburgh, PA 15212 · 412-995-3000

Richard W. Hosking · ⑩ · K&L Gates · Henry W. Oliver Building · 535 Smithfield Street · Pittsburgh, PA 15222-2312 · 412-355-6500

Gary P. Hunt · Tucker Arensberg · http://www.tuckerlaw.com · 1500 One PPG Place · Pittsburgh, PA 15222-5401 · 412-566-1212

Peter J. Kalis · ⑩ · K&L Gates · Henry W. Oliver Building · 535 Smithfield Street · Pittsburgh, PA 15222-2312 · 412-355-6500

Robert A. King · ⑩ · Reed Smith · 435 Sixth Avenue · Pittsburgh, PA 15219-1886 · 412-288-3131

Edwin L. Klett · ⑩ · Buchanan Ingersoll & Rooney · http://www.bipc.com · One Oxford Centre, 20th Floor · 301 Grant Street · Pittsburgh, PA 15219-1410 · 412-562-8800

Jeffrey J. Leech · Tucker Arensberg · http://www.tuckerlaw.com · 1500 One PPG Place · Pittsburgh, PA 15222-5401 · 412-566-1212

Harry Litman · Litman Law Firm · One Oxford Centre, 34th Floor · 301 Grant Street · Pittsburgh, PA 15219-1407 · 412-456-2000

Roslyn M. Litman · ㉕ · Litman Law Firm · One Oxford Centre, 34th Floor · 301 Grant Street · Pittsburgh, PA 15219-1407 · 412-456-2000

Kevin Lucas · Manion, McDonough & Lucas · USX Tower, Suite 1414 · 600 Grant Street · Pittsburgh, PA 15219 · 412-232-0200

Paul A. Manion · ⑩ · Manion, McDonough & Lucas · USX Tower, Suite 1414 · 600 Grant Street · Pittsburgh, PA 15219 · 412-232-0200

Leonard J. Marsico · McGuireWoods · http://www.mcguirewoods.com · Dominion Tower, 23rd Floor · 625 Liberty Avenue · Pittsburgh, PA 15222-3142 · 412-667-6000

David L. McClenahan · ⑩ · K&L Gates · Henry W. Oliver Building · 535 Smithfield Street · Pittsburgh, PA 15222-2312 · 412-355-6500

Jerry S. McDevitt · K&L Gates · Henry W. Oliver Building · 535 Smithfield Street · Pittsburgh, PA 15222-2312 · 412-355-6500

Joseph McDonough · ⑩ · Manion, McDonough & Lucas · USX Tower, Suite 1414 · 600 Grant Street · Pittsburgh, PA 15219 · 412-232-0200

John McGinley · Eckert Seamans Cherin & Mellott · U.S. Steel Tower, 44th Floor · 600 Grant Street · Pittsburgh, PA 15219 · 412-566-6000

W. Thomas McGough, Jr. · ⑩ · Reed Smith · 435 Sixth Avenue · Pittsburgh, PA 15219-1886 · 412-288-3131

J. Frank McKenna · Reed Smith · 435 Sixth Avenue · Pittsburgh, PA 15219-1886 · 412-288-3131

Dennis St. J. Mulvihill · ⑩ · Robb Leonard Mulvihill · 2300 One Mellon Center, 23rd Floor · 500 Grant Street · Pittsburgh, PA 15219 · 412-281-5431

John J. Myers · Eckert Seamans Cherin & Mellott · U.S. Steel Tower, 44th Floor · 600 Grant Street · Pittsburgh, PA 15219 · 412-566-6000

Richard R. Nelson II · Cohen & Grigsby · 625 Liberty Avenue · Pittsburgh, PA 15222-3152 · 412-297-4900

Mark F. Nowak · Thorp, Reed & Armstrong · One Oxford Centre, 14th Floor · 301 Grant Street · Pittsburgh, PA 15219-1425 · 412-394-7711

Russell J. Ober, Jr. · Meyer, Unkovic & Scott · http://www.muslaw.com · 1300 Oliver Building · 535 Smithfield Street · Pittsburgh, PA 15222 · 412-456-2800

David G. Oberdick · Meyer, Unkovic & Scott · http://www.muslaw.com · 1300 Oliver Building · 535 Smithfield Street · Pittsburgh, PA 15222 · 412-456-2800

Christopher R. Opalinski · Eckert Seamans Cherin & Mellott · U.S. Steel Tower, 44th Floor · 600 Grant Street · Pittsburgh, PA 15219 · 412-566-6000

Anthony P. Picadio · ⑩ · Picadio Sneath Miller & Norton · 4710 U.S. Steel Tower · 600 Grant Street · Pittsburgh, PA 15219-2702 · 412-288-4000

William A. Pietragallo II · ⑩ · Pietragallo Gordon Alfano Bosick & Raspanti · One Oxford Centre, 38th Floor · Pittsburgh, PA 15219 · 412-263-2000

Paul M. Pohl · Jones Day · One Mellon Center, Suite 4500 · 500 Grant Street · Pittsburgh, PA 15219-2502 · 412-391-3939

Thomas M. Reiter · K&L Gates · Henry W. Oliver Building · 535 Smithfield Street · Pittsburgh, PA 15222-2312 · 412-355-6500

James J. Restivo, Jr. · ⑩ · Reed Smith · 435 Sixth Avenue · Pittsburgh, PA 15219-1886 · 412-288-3131

John A. Robb, Jr. · Robb Leonard Mulvihill · 2300 One Mellon Center, 23rd Floor · 500 Grant Street · Pittsburgh, PA 15219 · 412-281-5431

Timothy P. Ryan · Eckert Seamans Cherin & Mellott · U.S. Steel Tower, 44th Floor · 600 Grant Street · Pittsburgh, PA 15219 · 412-566-6000

Mark D. Shepard · Babst, Calland, Clements and Zomnir · http://www.bccz.com · Two Gateway Center, Eighth Floor · 603 Stanwix Street · Pittsburgh, PA 15222 · 412-394-5400

Stanley M. Stein · Feldstein, Grinberg, Stein & McKee · 428 Boulevard of the Allies · Pittsburgh, PA 15219 · 412-471-0677

E. J. Strassburger · Strassburger, McKenna, Gutnick & Potter · Four Gateway Center, Suite 2200 · 444 Liberty Avenue · Pittsburgh, PA 15222 · 412-281-5423

Arthur H. Stroyd · Del Sole Cavanaugh · The Waterfront Building, Suite 300 · 200 First Avenue · Pittsburgh, PA 15222 · 412-261-2393

Paul H. Titus · Schnader Harrison Segal & Lewis · http://www.schnader.com · Fifth Avenue Place, Suite 2700 · 120 Fifth Avenue · Pittsburgh, PA 15222-3001 · 412-577-5200

Thomas L. VanKirk · Buchanan Ingersoll & Rooney · http://www.bipc.com · One Oxford Centre, 20th Floor · 301 Grant Street · Pittsburgh, PA 15219-1410 · 412-562-8800

Jeffrey P. Ward · Cohen & Grigsby · 625 Liberty Avenue · Pittsburgh, PA 15222-3152 · 412-297-4900

William F. Ward · Thieman & Ward · Koppers Building, Suite 2312 · 436 Seventh Avenue · Pittsburgh, PA 15219 · 412-395-1245

William M. Wycoff · ⑩ · Thorp, Reed & Armstrong · One Oxford Centre, 14th Floor · 301 Grant Street · Pittsburgh, PA 15219-1425 · 412-394-7711

Susan Yohe · Buchanan Ingersoll & Rooney · http://www.bipc.com · One Oxford Centre, 20th Floor · 301 Grant Street · Pittsburgh, PA 15219-1410 · 412-562-8800

Michael G. Zanic · K&L Gates · Henry W. Oliver Building · 535 Smithfield Street · Pittsburgh, PA 15222-2312 · 412-355-6500

C. James Zeszutek · Dinsmore & Shohl · http://www.dinslaw.com · One Oxford Centre, Suite 2800 · 301 Grant Street · Pittsburgh, PA 15219 · 412-281-5000

Steven W. Zoffer · Dickie, McCamey & Chilcote · http://www.dmclaw.com · Two PPG Place, Suite 400 · Pittsburgh, PA 15222-5402 · 412-281-7272

COMMUNICATIONS LAW

Harrisburg

Daniel P. Delaney · K&L Gates · 17 North Second Street, 18th Floor · Harrisburg, PA 17101-1507 · 717-231-4500

Alan C. Kohler · WolfBlock · http://wolfblock.com · 213 Market Street, Ninth Floor · P.O. Box 865 · Harrisburg, PA 17108-0865 · 717-237-7160

John F. Povilaitis · Ryan Russell Ogden & Seltzer · http://www.ryanrussell.com · 800 North Third Street, Suite 101 · Harrisburg, PA 17102-2025 · 717-236-7714

Wyomissing

Jeffrey A. Franklin · Ryan Russell Ogden & Seltzer · http://www.ryanrussell.com · 1150 Berkshire Boulevard, Suite 210 · Wyomissing, PA 19610-1208 · 610-372-4761

Harrisburg

C. Grainger Bowman · K&L Gates · 17 North Second Street, 18th Floor · Harrisburg, PA 17101-1507 · 717-231-4500

Kenneth W. Lee · Tucker Arensberg · http://www.tuckerlaw.com · 111 North Front Street · P.O. Box 889 Harrisburg, PA 17108-0889 · 717-234-4121

Diane M. Tokarsky · McNees Wallace & Nurick · 100 Pine Street · P.O. Box 1166 · Harrisburg, PA 17108-1166 · 717-232-8000

Philadelphia

Steven A. Arbittier · Ballard Spahr Andrews & Ingersoll · 1735 Market Street, 51st Floor · Philadelphia, PA 19103-7599 · 215-665-8500

Lynn R. Axelroth · Ballard Spahr Andrews & Ingersoll · 1735 Market Street, 51st Floor · Philadelphia, PA 19103-7599 · 215-665-8500

David P. Bruton · Drinker Biddle & Reath · One Logan Square · 18th and Cherry Streets · Philadelphia, PA 19103-6996 · 215-988-2700

Bruce W. Ficken · Pepper Hamilton · http://www.pepperlaw.com · Two Logan Square, Suite 3000 · 18th and Arch Street · Philadelphia, PA 19103-2799 · 215-981-4000

Rudolph Garcia · Buchanan Ingersoll & Rooney · http://www.bipc.com · 1835 Market Street, 14th Floor · Philadelphia, PA 19103-2985 · 215-665-8700

F. Warren Jacoby · Cozen O'Connor · The Atrium · 1900 Market Street · Philadelphia, PA 19103 · 215-665-2000

B. Christopher Lee · Jacoby Donner · http://www.jacobydonner.com · 1700 Market Street, Suite 3100 · Philadelphia, PA 19103 · 215-563-2400

George E. Rahn, Jr. · Saul Ewing · Centre Square West, 38th Floor · 1500 Market Street · Philadelphia, PA 19102-2186 · 215-972-7777

Howard D. Venzie, Jr. · Venzie, Phillips & Warshawer · 2032 Chancellor Street · Philadelphia, PA 19103 215-567-3322

Pittsburgh

Albert Bates, Jr. · Duane Morris · 600 Grant Street, Suite 5010 · Pittsburgh, PA 15219-2811 · 412-497-1000

Amy E. Bentz · Bentz Law Firm · The Washington Center Building, Suite 200 · 680 Washington Road · Pittsburgh, PA 15228 · 412-563-4500

Robert J. Blumling · Blumling & Gusky · 1200 Koppers Building · Pittsburgh, PA 15219 · 412-227-2500

Scott D. Cessar · Eckert Seamans Cherin & Mellott · U.S. Steel Tower, 44th Floor · 600 Grant Street · Pittsburgh, PA 15219 · 412-566-6000

William D. Clifford · Dickie, McCamey & Chilcote · http://www.dmclaw.com · Two PPG Place, Suite 400 · Pittsburgh, PA 15222-5402 · 412-281-7272

John R. Dingess · K&L Gates · Henry W. Oliver Building · 535 Smithfield Street · Pittsburgh, PA 15222-2312 · 412-355-6500

Mark J. Gesk · Wayman, Irvin & McAuley · 1624 Frick Building · 437 Grant Street · Pittsburgh, PA 15219 · 412-566-2970

Gary P. Hunt · Tucker Arensberg · http://www.tuckerlaw.com · 1500 One PPG Place · Pittsburgh, PA 15222-5401 · 412-566-1212

D. Matthew Jameson III · Babst, Calland, Clements and Zomnir · http://www.bccz.com · Two Gateway Center, Eighth Floor · 603 Stanwix Street · Pittsburgh, PA 15222 · 412-394-5400

Robert A. King · a · Reed Smith · 435 Sixth Avenue · Pittsburgh, PA 15219-1886 · 412-288-3131

Richard G. Kotarba · a · Meyer, Unkovic & Scott · http://www.muslaw.com · 1300 Oliver Building · 535 Smithfield Street · Pittsburgh, PA 15222 · 412-456-2800

James R. Mall · Meyer, Unkovic & Scott · http://www.muslaw.com · 1300 Oliver Building · 535 Smithfield Street · Pittsburgh, PA 15222 · 412-456-2800

Ralph F. Manning · Tucker Arensberg · http://www.tuckerlaw.com · 1500 One PPG Place · Pittsburgh, PA 15222-5401 · 412-566-1212

J. Frank McKenna · Reed Smith · 435 Sixth Avenue · Pittsburgh, PA 15219-1886 · 412-288-3131

K. Bradley Mellor · Blumling & Gusky · 1200 Koppers Building · Pittsburgh, PA 15219 · 412-227-2500

Christopher R. Opalinski · Eckert Seamans Cherin & Mellott · U.S. Steel Tower, 44th Floor · 600 Grant Street · Pittsburgh, PA 15219 · 412-566-6000

W. Alan Torrance · Dickie, McCamey & Chilcote · http://www.dmclaw.com · Two PPG Place, Suite 400 Pittsburgh, PA 15222-5402 · 412-281-7272

CORPORATE GOVERNANCE AND COMPLIANCE LAW

Harrisburg

Stephen A. Moore · McNees Wallace & Nurick · 100 Pine Street · P.O. Box 1166 · Harrisburg, PA 17108-1166 · 717-232-8000

Philadelphia

Barry M. Abelson · a · Pepper Hamilton · http://www.pepperlaw.com · Two Logan Square, Suite 3000 · 18th and Arch Street · Philadelphia, PA 19103-2799 · 215-981-4000

Henry N. Nassau · Dechert · Cira Centre · 2929 Arch Street · Philadelphia, PA 19104-2808 · 215-994-4000

Alan Singer · Morgan Lewis & Bockius · 1701 Market Street · Philadelphia, PA 19103-2921 · 215-963-5000

Barton J. Winokur · 2) · Dechert · Cira Centre · 2929 Arch Street · Philadelphia, PA 19104-2808 · 215-994-4000

Pittsburgh

Marlee S. Myers · Morgan Lewis & Bockius · One Oxford Centre, 32nd Floor · 301 Grant Street · Pittsburgh, PA 15219-6401 · 412-560-3300

Exton

Michael S. Harrington · Fox Rothschild · 747 Constitution Drive, Suite 100 · Exton, PA 19341-0673 · 610-458-7500

Harrisburg

Shaun R. Eisenhauer · McNees Wallace & Nurick · 100 Pine Street · P.O. Box 1166 · Harrisburg, PA 17108-1166 · 717-232-8000

Bradley J. Gunnison · a · Buchanan Ingersoll & Rooney · http://www.bipc.com · One South Market Square, Third Floor · 213 Market Street · P.O. Box 12023 · Harrisburg, PA 17108 · 717-237-4800

Michael Hund · Buchanan Ingersoll & Rooney · http://www.bipc.com · One South Market Square, Third Floor · 213 Market Street · P.O. Box 12023 · Harrisburg, PA 17108 · 717-237-4800

Daniel J. Malpezzi · McNees Wallace & Nurick · 100 Pine Street · P.O. Box 1166 · Harrisburg, PA 17108-1166 · 717-232-8000

John P. Manbeck · a · Rhoads & Sinon · M & T Bank Building, 12th Floor · One South Market Square · P.O. Box 1146 · Harrisburg, PA 17108-1146 · 717-233-5731

Richard W. Stevenson · 2) · McNees Wallace & Nurick · 100 Pine Street · P.O. Box 1166 · Harrisburg, PA 17108-1166 · 717-232-8000

Lancaster

John O. Shirk · a · Barley Snyder · 126 East King Street · Lancaster, PA 17602-2893 · 717-299-5201

Mechanicsburg

Wayne M. Pecht · Pecht & Associates · http://www.pechtlaw.com · 1205 Manor Drive, Suite 200 · Mechanicsburg, PA 17055 · 717-691-9808

Philadelphia

Barry M. Abelson · a · Pepper Hamilton · http://www.pepperlaw.com · Two Logan Square, Suite 3000 · 18th and Arch Street · Philadelphia, PA 19103-2799 · 215-981-4000

Fred Blume · Blank Rome · One Logan Square · 130 North 18th Street · Philadelphia, PA 19103-6998 · 215-569-5500

Sheldon M. Bonovitz · 2% · Duane Morris · 30 South 17th Street · Philadelphia, PA 19103-4196 · 215-979-1000

Richard J. Braemer · Ballard Spahr Andrews & Ingersoll · 1735 Market Street, 51st Floor · Philadelphia, PA 19103-7599 · 215-665-8500

William H. Clark, Jr. · a · Drinker Biddle & Reath · One Logan Square · 18th and Cherry Streets · Philadelphia, PA 19103-6996 · 215-988-2700

Albert S. Dandridge III · Schnader Harrison Segal & Lewis · http://www.schnader.com · 1600 Market Street, Suite 3600 · Philadelphia, PA 19103-7286 · 215-751-2000

Stephen M. Foxman · Eckert Seamans Cherin & Mellott · Two Liberty Place, 22nd Floor · 50 South 16th Street · Philadelphia, PA 19102 · 215-851-8400

Michael H. Friedman · Pepper Hamilton · http://www.pepperlaw.com · Two Logan Square, Suite 3000 · 18th and Arch Street · Philadelphia, PA 19103-2799 · 215-981-4000

Louis W. Fryman · Conrad O'Brien Gellman & Rohn · http://www.cogr.com · 1515 Market Street, 16th Floor · Philadelphia, PA 19102-1916 · 215-864-9600

Barry H. Genkin · Blank Rome · One Logan Square · 130 North 18th Street · Philadelphia, PA 19103-6998 · 215-569-5500

Henry A. Gladstone · a · Cozen O'Connor · The Atrium · 1900 Market Street · Philadelphia, PA 19103 · 215-665-2000

Stephen M. Goodman · a · Morgan Lewis & Bockius · 1701 Market Street · Philadelphia, PA 19103-2921 · 215-963-5000

Stephen J. Harmelin · 2) · Dilworth Paxson · 3200 Mellon Bank Center · 1735 Market Street · Philadelphia, PA 19103-7595 · 215-575-7000

Joseph H. Jacovini · Dilworth Paxson · 3200 Mellon Bank Center · 1735 Market Street · Philadelphia, PA 19103-7595 · 215-575-7000

Christopher G. Karras · Dechert · Cira Centre · 2929 Arch Street · Philadelphia, PA 19104-2808 · 215-994-4000

Justin P. Klein · Ballard Spahr Andrews & Ingersoll · 1735 Market Street, 51st Floor · Philadelphia, PA 19103-7599 · 215-665-8500

Henry M. Kuller · Blank Rome · One Logan Square · 130 North 18th Street · Philadelphia, PA 19103-6998 · 215-569-5500

James A. Lebovitz · Dechert · Cira Centre · 2929 Arch Street · Philadelphia, PA 19104-2808 · 215-994-4000

Frederick D. Lipman · 2) · Blank Rome · One Logan Square · 130 North 18th Street · Philadelphia, PA 19103-6998 · 215-569-5500

Timothy Maxwell · Morgan Lewis & Bockius · 1701 Market Street · Philadelphia, PA 19103-2921 · 215-963-5000

James W. McKenzie, Jr. · Morgan Lewis & Bockius · 1701 Market Street · Philadelphia, PA 19103-2921 215-963-5000

H. John Michel, Jr. · Drinker Biddle & Reath · One Logan Square · 18th and Cherry Streets · Philadelphia, PA 19103-6996 · 215-988-2700

Steven J. Molitor · Dechert · Cira Centre · 2929 Arch Street · Philadelphia, PA 19104-2808 · 215-994-4000

Henry N. Nassau · Dechert · Cira Centre · 2929 Arch Street · Philadelphia, PA 19104-2808 · 215-994-4000

G. Daniel O'Donnell · Dechert · Cira Centre · 2929 Arch Street · Philadelphia, PA 19104-2808 · 215-994-4000

F. Douglas Raymond III · Drinker Biddle & Reath · One Logan Square · 18th and Cherry Streets · Philadelphia, PA 19103-6996 · 215-988-2700

Carmen J. Romano · Dechert · Cira Centre · 2929 Arch Street · Philadelphia, PA 19104-2808 · 215-994-4000

William R. Sasso · Stradley, Ronon, Stevens & Young · 2600 One Commerce Square · Philadelphia, PA 19103-7098 · 215-564-8000

Jason M. Shargel · WolfBlock · http://wolfblock.com · 1650 Arch Street, 22nd Floor · Philadelphia, PA 19103-2097 · 215-977-2000

Kathleen M. Shay · Duane Morris · 30 South 17th Street · Philadelphia, PA 19103-4196 · 215-979-1000

Alan Singer · Morgan Lewis & Bockius · 1701 Market Street · Philadelphia, PA 19103-2921 · 215-963-5000

Edward D. Slevin · ⑩ · Ballard Spahr Andrews & Ingersoll · 1735 Market Street, 51st Floor · Philadelphia, PA 19103-7599 · 215-665-8500

Joanne R. Soslow · Morgan Lewis & Bockius · 1701 Market Street · Philadelphia, PA 19103-2921 · 215-963-5000

Barton J. Winokur · ⑳ · Dechert · Cira Centre · 2929 Arch Street · Philadelphia, PA 19104-2808 · 215-994-4000

Lawrence R. Wiseman · Blank Rome · One Logan Square · 130 North 18th Street · Philadelphia, PA 19103-6998 · 215-569-5500

Alan L. Zeiger · Blank Rome · One Logan Square · 130 North 18th Street · Philadelphia, PA 19103-6998 · 215-569-5500

Pittsburgh

Ronald Basso · Buchanan Ingersoll & Rooney · http://www.bipc.com · One Oxford Centre, 20th Floor · 301 Grant Street · Pittsburgh, PA 15219-1410 · 412-562-8800

Bruce I. Booken · Buchanan Ingersoll & Rooney · http://www.bipc.com · One Oxford Centre, 20th Floor 301 Grant Street · Pittsburgh, PA 15219-1410 · 412-562-8800

Daniel I. Booker · ⑩ · Reed Smith · 435 Sixth Avenue · Pittsburgh, PA 15219-1886 · 412-288-3131

James D. Chiafullo · Cohen & Grigsby · 625 Liberty Avenue · Pittsburgh, PA 15222-3152 · 412-297-4900

Charles C. Cohen · ⑩ · Cohen & Grigsby · 625 Liberty Avenue · Pittsburgh, PA 15222-3152 · 412-297-4900

David L. DeNinno · ⑩ · Reed Smith · 435 Sixth Avenue · Pittsburgh, PA 15219-1886 · 412-288-3131

Jack W. Elliott · Cohen & Grigsby · 625 Liberty Avenue · Pittsburgh, PA 15222-3152 · 412-297-4900

Jeremiah G. Garvey · Buchanan Ingersoll & Rooney · http://www.bipc.com · One Oxford Centre, 20th Floor · 301 Grant Street · Pittsburgh, PA 15219-1410 · 412-562-8800

Robert T. Harper · ⑩ · Buchanan Ingersoll & Rooney · http://www.bipc.com · One Oxford Centre, 20th Floor · 301 Grant Street · Pittsburgh, PA 15219-1410 · 412-562-8800

David J. Lehman · K&L Gates · Henry W. Oliver Building · 535 Smithfield Street · Pittsburgh, PA 15222-2312 · 412-355-6500

Michael C. McLean · ㉕ · K&L Gates · Henry W. Oliver Building · 535 Smithfield Street · Pittsburgh, PA 15222-2312 · 412-355-6500

Marlee S. Myers · Morgan Lewis & Bockius · One Oxford Centre, 32nd Floor · 301 Grant Street · Pittsburgh, PA 15219-6401 · 412-560-3300

Carl E. Rothenberger, Jr. · Buchanan Ingersoll & Rooney · http://www.bipc.com · One Oxford Centre, 20th Floor · 301 Grant Street · Pittsburgh, PA 15219-1410 · 412-562-8800

W. Henry Snyder · K&L Gates · Henry W. Oliver Building · 535 Smithfield Street · Pittsburgh, PA 15222-2312 · 412-355-6500

Thomas M. Thompson · a · Buchanan Ingersoll & Rooney · http://www.bipc.com · One Oxford Centre, 20th Floor · 301 Grant Street · Pittsburgh, PA 15219-1410 · 412-562-8800

Ted Wesolowski · Babst, Calland, Clements and Zomnir · http://www.bccz.com · Two Gateway Center, Eighth Floor · 603 Stanwix Street · Pittsburgh, PA 15222 · 412-394-5400

Ronald D. West · K&L Gates · Henry W. Oliver Building · 535 Smithfield Street · Pittsburgh, PA 15222-2312 · 412-355-6500

EDUCATION LAW

Harrisburg

Jeffrey F. Champagne · McNees Wallace & Nurick · 100 Pine Street · P.O. Box 1166 · Harrisburg, PA 17108-1166 · 717-232-8000

Philadelphia

Wendy Beetlestone · Hangley Aronchick Segal & Pudlin · http://www.hangley.com · One Logan Square, 27th Floor · 18th and Cherry Street · Philadelphia, PA 19103-6933 · 215-568-6200

Neil J. Hamburg · Hamburg & Golden · 1601 Market Street, Suite 3310 · Philadelphia, PA 19103-1443 · 215-255-8590

Pittsburgh

W. Theodore Brooks · Tucker Arensberg · http://www.tuckerlaw.com · 1500 One PPG Place · Pittsburgh, PA 15222-5401 · 412-566-1212

Carolyn D. Duronio · Reed Smith · 435 Sixth Avenue · Pittsburgh, PA 15219-1886 · 412-288-3131

Matthew M. Hoffman · Tucker Arensberg · http://www.tuckerlaw.com · 1500 One PPG Place · Pittsburgh, PA 15222-5401 · 412-566-1212

Martha H. Munsch · a · Reed Smith · 435 Sixth Avenue · Pittsburgh, PA 15219-1886 · 412-288-3131

Thomas P. Peterson · Tucker Arensberg · http://www.tuckerlaw.com · 1500 One PPG Place · Pittsburgh, PA 15222-5401 · 412-566-1212

ELDER LAW

Coraopolis

Julian E. Gray · Springer Bush & Perry · 500 Cherrington Parkway, Suite 420 · Coraopolis, PA 15108 · 412-269-4200

Harrisburg

Marielle F. Hazen · Hazen Elder Law · 2000 Linglestown Road, Suite 202 · Harrisburg, PA 17110 · 717-540-4332

Jersey Shore

Jeffrey A. Marshall · Marshall, Parker & Associates · 303 Allegheny Street · Jersey Shore, PA 17740 · 570-398-7603

Media

Linda M. Anderson · Anderson Elder Law · 216 South Orange Street · Media, PA 19063 · 610-566-4700

Pittsburgh

Carol Sikov Gross · Sikov and Love · Lawyers Building, Suite 1400 · 428 Forbes Avenue · Pittsburgh, PA 15219-1684 · 412-261-4202

Gary J. Gushard · Tucker Arensberg · http://www.tuckerlaw.com · 1500 One PPG Place · Pittsburgh, PA 15222-5401 · 412-566-1212

Stephen P. Paschall · Lovett Bookman Harmon Marks · Fifth Avenue Place, Suite 2900 · 120 Fifth Avenue · Pittsburgh, PA 15222 · 412-392-2220

Frank A. Petrich · Petrich & Sykes · 615 Washington Road, Suite 304 · Pittsburgh, PA 15228 · 412-531-7123

State College

H. Amos Goodall · Goodall & Yurchak · http://www.centrelaw.com · 328 South Atherton Street · State College, PA 16801 · 814-237-4100

Titusville

Kemp Scales · The Elder Law Office of Kemp Scales · 115 South Washington Street · P.O. Box 346 · Titusville, PA 16354 · 814-827-2788

York

Robert Clofine · Law Offices of Robert Clofine · 120 Pine Grove Commons · York, PA 17403-5151 · 717-747-5995

EMINENT DOMAIN AND CONDEMNATION LAW

Pittsburgh

William P. Bresnahan · a · Hollinshead, Mendelson, Bresnahan & Nixon · 2901 Grant Building · 310 Grant Street · Pittsburgh, PA 15219 · 412-355-7070

Thomas J. Dempsey, Sr. · 2% · Thomas J. Dempsey · 618 Frick Building · 437 Grant Street · Pittsburgh, PA 15219 · 412-281-2442

Andrea Geraghty · Geraghty & Associates · Two Gateway Center, Suite 2050 · 603 Stanwix Street · Pittsburgh, PA 15222 · 412-232-7070

Harvey E. Robins · Brennan, Robins & Daley · Fort Pitt Commons, Suite 500 · 445 Fort Pitt Boulevard · Pittsburgh, PA 15219-1322 · 412-281-0776

Harrisburg

Stephen R. Kern · McNees Wallace & Nurick · 100 Pine Street · P.O. Box 1166 · Harrisburg, PA 17108-1166 · 717-232-8000

Drake D. Nicholas · a · Rhoads & Sinon · M & T Bank Building, 12th Floor · One South Market Square P.O. Box 1146 · Harrisburg, PA 17108-1146 · 717-233-5731

Jenkintown

Robert A. Bildersee · 2) · Bildersee & Silbert · 101 West Avenue, Suite 110 · Jenkintown, PA 19046 · 215-914-0414

Marc M. Silbert · a · Bildersee & Silbert · 101 West Avenue, Suite 110 · Jenkintown, PA 19046 · 215-914-0414

Philadelphia

Robert L. Abramowitz · a · Morgan Lewis & Bockius · 1701 Market Street · Philadelphia, PA 19103-2921 · 215-963-5000

John Marley Bernard · Ballard Spahr Andrews & Ingersoll · 1735 Market Street, 51st Floor · Philadelphia, PA 19103-7599 · 215-665-8500

Joseph J. Costello · Morgan Lewis & Bockius · 1701 Market Street · Philadelphia, PA 19103-2921 · 215-963-5000

Brian J. Dougherty · Post & Schell · Four Penn Center, 14th Floor · 1600 John F. Kennedy Boulevard · Philadelphia, PA 19103-2808 · 215-587-1000

I. Lee Falk · Morgan Lewis & Bockius · 1701 Market Street · Philadelphia, PA 19103-2921 · 215-963-5000

Susan Katz Hoffman · a · Littler Mendelson · Three Parkway, Suite 1400 · 1601 Cherry Street · Philadelphia, PA 19102-1321 · 267-402-3000

Joel E. Horowitz · McCarter & English · Mellon Bank Center Building, Suite 700 · 1735 Market Street · Philadelphia, PA 19103 · 215-979-3800

David F. Jones · Dechert · Cira Centre · 2929 Arch Street · Philadelphia, PA 19104-2808 · 215-994-4000

Paul S. Kimbol · 2) · Dechert · Cira Centre · 2929 Arch Street · Philadelphia, PA 19104-2808 · 215-994-4000

Edward I. Leeds · Ballard Spahr Andrews & Ingersoll · 1735 Market Street, 51st Floor · Philadelphia, PA 19103-7599 · 215-665-8500

Deborah M. Lerner · Willig, Williams & Davidson · 1845 Walnut Street, 24th Floor · Philadelphia, PA 19103 · 215-656-3600

Robert J. Lichtenstein · a · Morgan Lewis & Bockius · 1701 Market Street · Philadelphia, PA 19103-2921 · 215-963-5000

William Scott Magargee III · 2) · Dechert · Cira Centre · 2929 Arch Street · Philadelphia, PA 19104-2808 215-994-4000

Brian T. Ortelere · Morgan Lewis & Bockius · 1701 Market Street · Philadelphia, PA 19103-2921 · 215-963-5000

Andrew J. Rudolph · a · Pepper Hamilton · http://www.pepperlaw.com · Two Logan Square, Suite 3000 18th and Arch Street · Philadelphia, PA 19103-2799 · 215-981-4000

Steven D. Spencer · Morgan Lewis & Bockius · 1701 Market Street · Philadelphia, PA 19103-2921 · 215-963-5000

Mims Maynard Zabriskie · a · Morgan Lewis & Bockius · 1701 Market Street · Philadelphia, PA 19103-2921 · 215-963-5000

Kathleen Ziga · a · Dechert · Cira Centre · 2929 Arch Street · Philadelphia, PA 19104-2808 · 215-994-4000

Pittsburgh

Dennis R. Bonessa · Reed Smith · 435 Sixth Avenue · Pittsburgh, PA 15219-1886 · 412-288-3131

Kathryn A. English · Eckert Seamans Cherin & Mellott · U.S. Steel Tower, 44th Floor · 600 Grant Street Pittsburgh, PA 15219 · 412-566-6000

John G. Ferreira · Morgan Lewis & Bockius · One Oxford Centre, 32nd Floor · 301 Grant Street · Pittsburgh, PA 15219-6401 · 412-560-3300

Hollis T. Hurd · a · The Benefits Department · Three Penn Center West, Suite 120 · Pittsburgh, PA 15276 · 412-788-2334

Robert A. Johnson · 2) · Buchanan Ingersoll & Rooney · http://www.bipc.com · One Oxford Centre, 20th Floor · 301 Grant Street · Pittsburgh, PA 15219-1410 · 412-562-8800

Susan Foreman Jordan · Fox Rothschild · 625 Liberty Avenue, 29th Floor · Pittsburgh, PA 15222-3115 · 412-391-1334

Lauren B. Licastro · Morgan Lewis & Bockius · One Oxford Centre, 32nd Floor · 301 Grant Street · Pittsburgh, PA 15219-6401 · 412-560-3300

Michael E. Lloyd · Williams, Coulson, Johnson, Lloyd, Parker & Tedesco · One Gateway Center, 16th Floor · Pittsburgh, PA 15219 · 412-454-0200

William H. Powderly III · 2) · Tucker Arensberg · http://www.tuckerlaw.com · 1500 One PPG Place · Pittsburgh, PA 15222-5401 · 412-566-1212

Charles R. Smith, Jr. · 2) · K&L Gates · Henry W. Oliver Building · 535 Smithfield Street · Pittsburgh, PA 15222-2312 · 412-355-6500

R. Randall Tracht · Morgan Lewis & Bockius · One Oxford Centre, 32nd Floor · 301 Grant Street · Pittsburgh, PA 15219-6401 · 412-560-3300

John H. Wilson · Buchanan Ingersoll & Rooney · http://www.bipc.com · One Oxford Centre, 20th Floor · 301 Grant Street · Pittsburgh, PA 15219-1410 · 412-562-8800

Cher E. Wynkoop · Reed Smith · 435 Sixth Avenue · Pittsburgh, PA 15219-1886 · 412-288-3131

ENERGY LAW

Harrisburg

Daniel Clearfield · WolfBlock · http://wolfblock.com · 213 Market Street, Ninth Floor · P.O. Box 865 · Harrisburg, PA 17108-0865 · 717-237-7160

Daniel P. Delaney · K&L Gates · 17 North Second Street, 18th Floor · Harrisburg, PA 17101-1507 · 717-231-4500

Michael W. Gang · Post & Schell · 17 North Second Street, 12th Floor · Harrisburg, PA 17101-1601 · 717-731-1970

David M. Kleppinger · a · McNees Wallace & Nurick · 100 Pine Street · P.O. Box 1166 · Harrisburg, PA 17108-1166 · 717-232-8000

John F. Povilaitis · Ryan Russell Ogden & Seltzer · http://www.ryanrussell.com · 800 North Third Street, Suite 101 · Harrisburg, PA 17102-2025 · 717-236-7714

John M. Quain · Buchanan Ingersoll & Rooney · http://www.bipc.com · 17 North Second Street, 15th Floor · Harrisburg, PA 17101-1503 · 717-237-4800

Charles E. Thomas, Jr. · a · Thomas, Thomas, Armstrong & Niesen · 212 Locust Street, Suite 500 · P.O. Box 9500 · Harrisburg, PA 17108-9500 · 717-255-7600

D. Mark Thomas · a · Thomas, Thomas, Armstrong & Niesen · 212 Locust Street, Suite 500 · P.O. Box 9500 · Harrisburg, PA 17108-9500 · 717-255-7600

Derrick Price Williamson · McNees Wallace & Nurick · 100 Pine Street · P.O. Box 1166 · Harrisburg, PA 17108-1166 · 717-232-8000

Philadelphia

Thomas P. Gadsden · a · Morgan Lewis & Bockius · 1701 Market Street · Philadelphia, PA 19103-2921 · 215-963-5000

David B. MacGregor · a · Post & Schell · Four Penn Center, 14th Floor · 1600 John F. Kennedy Boulevard · Philadelphia, PA 19103-2808 · 215-587-1000

Wyomissing

W. Edwin Ogden · Ryan Russell Ogden & Seltzer · http://www.ryanrussell.com · 1150 Berkshire Boulevard, Suite 210 · Wyomissing, PA 19610-1208 · 610-372-4761

Alan Michael Seltzer · a · Ryan Russell Ogden & Seltzer · http://www.ryanrussell.com · 1150 Berkshire Boulevard, Suite 210 · Wyomissing, PA 19610-1208 · 610-372-4761

ENTERTAINMENT LAW

Philadelphia

James E. Elam IV · Elam Law Firm · 1616 Walnut Street, Suite 700 · Philadelphia, PA 19103 · 215-545-9870

Corey Field · Ballard Spahr Andrews & Ingersoll · 1735 Market Street, 51st Floor · Philadelphia, PA 19103-7599 · 215-665-8500

Lloyd Z. Remick · Lloyd Zane Remick · http://www.zanemanagement.com · One Liberty Place, 21st Floor · 1650 Market Street · Philadelphia, PA 19103 · 215-575-3804

ENVIRONMENTAL LAW

Bala Cynwyd

Bart E. Cassidy · Manko, Gold, Katcher & Fox · http://www.mgkflaw.com · 401 City Avenue, Suite 500 · Bala Cynwyd, PA 19004 · 484-430-5700

Robert D. Fox · a · Manko, Gold, Katcher & Fox · http://www.mgkflaw.com · 401 City Avenue, Suite 500 · Bala Cynwyd, PA 19004 · 484-430-5700

Marc E. Gold · 2) · Manko, Gold, Katcher & Fox · http://www.mgkflaw.com · 401 City Avenue, Suite 500 Bala Cynwyd, PA 19004 · 484-430-5700

Brenda Hustis Gotanda · Manko, Gold, Katcher & Fox · http://www.mgkflaw.com · 401 City Avenue, Suite 500 · Bala Cynwyd, PA 19004 · 484-430-5700

Jill H. Kaplan · Manko, Gold, Katcher & Fox · http://www.mgkflaw.com · 401 City Avenue, Suite 500 · Bala Cynwyd, PA 19004 · 484-430-5700

Joseph M. Manko · a · Manko, Gold, Katcher & Fox · http://www.mgkflaw.com · 401 City Avenue, Suite 500 · Bala Cynwyd, PA 19004 · 484-430-5700

Michael M. Meloy · Manko, Gold, Katcher & Fox · http://www.mgkflaw.com · 401 City Avenue, Suite 500 · Bala Cynwyd, PA 19004 · 484-430-5700

Jonathan Rinde · Manko, Gold, Katcher & Fox · http://www.mgkflaw.com · 401 City Avenue, Suite 500 · Bala Cynwyd, PA 19004 · 484-430-5700

Jonathan H. Spergel · Manko, Gold, Katcher & Fox · http://www.mgkflaw.com · 401 City Avenue, Suite 500 · Bala Cynwyd, PA 19004 · 484-430-5700

Neil S. Witkes · Manko, Gold, Katcher & Fox · http://www.mgkflaw.com · 401 City Avenue, Suite 500 · Bala Cynwyd, PA 19004 · 484-430-5700

Berwyn

David J. Brooman · a · Drinker Biddle & Reath · 1000 Westlakes Drive · Berwyn, PA 19312-2409 · 610-993-2200

John P. Judge · Montgomery, McCracken, Walker & Rhoads · 1235 Westlakes Drive, Suite 200 · Berwyn, PA 19312 · 610-889-2210

Erie

Matthew Wolford · Wolford Law Firm · 638 West Sixth Street · Erie, PA 16507 · 814-459-9600

Harrisburg

Terry R. Bossert · Post & Schell · 17 North Second Street, 12th Floor · Harrisburg, PA 17101-1601 · 717-731-1970

Brian J. Clark · Buchanan Ingersoll & Rooney · http://www.bipc.com · One South Market Square, Third Floor · 213 Market Street · P.O. Box 12023 · Harrisburg, PA 17108 · 717-237-4800

Eugene E. Dice · 2) · Buchanan Ingersoll & Rooney · http://www.bipc.com · One South Market Square, Third Floor · 213 Market Street · P.O. Box 12023 · Harrisburg, PA 17108 · 717-237-4800

Richard H. Friedman · McNees Wallace & Nurick · 100 Pine Street · P.O. Box 1166 · Harrisburg, PA 17108-1166 · 717-232-8000

Scott A. Gould · McNees Wallace & Nurick · 100 Pine Street · P.O. Box 1166 · Harrisburg, PA 17108-1166 · 717-232-8000

John P. Krill, Jr. · a · K&L Gates · 17 North Second Street, 18th Floor · Harrisburg, PA 17101-1507 · 717-231-4500

R. Timothy Weston · a · K&L Gates · 17 North Second Street, 18th Floor · Harrisburg, PA 17101-1507 · 717-231-4500

Maxine M. Woelfling · Morgan Lewis & Bockius · 17 North Second Street, Fourteenth Floor · Harrisburg, PA 17101-1601 · 717-237-5000

Norristown

Kenneth R. Myers · 2) · High Swartz · 40 East Airy Street · P.O. Box 671 · Norristown, PA 19404 · 610-275-0700

Philadelphia

Bonnie A. Barnett · Drinker Biddle & Reath · One Logan Square · 18th and Cherry Streets · Philadelphia, PA 19103-6996 · 215-988-2700

Timothy J. Bergère · Montgomery, McCracken, Walker & Rhoads · 123 South Broad Street · Avenue Of The Arts · Philadelphia, PA 19109-1029 · 215-772-1500

Michael A. Bogdonoff · Dechert · Cira Centre · 2929 Arch Street · Philadelphia, PA 19104-2808 · 215-994-4000

Abbi L. Cohen · Dechert · Cira Centre · 2929 Arch Street · Philadelphia, PA 19104-2808 · 215-994-4000

Robert L. Collings · 2) · Schnader Harrison Segal & Lewis · http://www.schnader.com · 1600 Market Street, Suite 3600 · Philadelphia, PA 19103-7286 · 215-751-2000

Brendan K. Collins · Ballard Spahr Andrews & Ingersoll · 1735 Market Street, 51st Floor · Philadelphia, PA 19103-7599 · 215-665-8500

Carl B. Everett · a · Saul Ewing · Centre Square West, 38th Floor · 1500 Market Street · Philadelphia, PA 19102-2186 · 215-972-7777

Andrew S. Levine · Stradley, Ronon, Stevens & Young · 2600 One Commerce Square · Philadelphia, PA 19103-7098 · 215-564-8000

David G. Mandelbaum · Ballard Spahr Andrews & Ingersoll · 1735 Market Street, 51st Floor · Philadelphia, PA 19103-7599 · 215-665-8500

John J. McAleese III · Morgan Lewis & Bockius · 1701 Market Street · Philadelphia, PA 19103-2921 · 215-963-5000

Robert B. Mckinstry, Jr. · Ballard Spahr Andrews & Ingersoll · 1735 Market Street, 51st Floor · Philadelphia, PA 19103-7599 · 215-665-8500

Steven T. Miano · Hangley Aronchick Segal & Pudlin · http://www.hangley.com · One Logan Square, 27th Floor · 18th and Cherry Street · Philadelphia, PA 19103-6933 · 215-568-6200

Kermit L. Rader · WolfBlock · http://wolfblock.com · 1650 Arch Street, 22nd Floor · Philadelphia, PA 19103-2097 · 215-977-2000

Ronald A. Sarachan · Ballard Spahr Andrews & Ingersoll · 1735 Market Street, 51st Floor · Philadelphia, PA 19103-7599 · 215-665-8500

Mark A. Stevens · Langsam Stevens & Silver · 1616 Walnut Street, Suite 1700 · Philadelphia, PA 19103-5319 · 215-732-3255

Benjamin G. Stonelake, Jr. · a · Blank Rome · One Logan Square · 130 North 18th Street · Philadelphia, PA 19103-6998 · 215-569-5500

John F. Stoviak · a · Saul Ewing · Centre Square West, 38th Floor · 1500 Market Street · Philadelphia, PA 19102-2186 · 215-972-7777

Glen R. Stuart · Morgan Lewis & Bockius · 1701 Market Street · Philadelphia, PA 19103-2921 · 215-963-5000

Glenn L. Unterberger · Ballard Spahr Andrews & Ingersoll · 1735 Market Street, 51st Floor · Philadelphia, PA 19103-7599 · 215-665-8500

Kenneth J. Warren · a · Hangley Aronchick Segal & Pudlin · http://www.hangley.com · One Logan Square, 27th Floor · 18th and Cherry Street · Philadelphia, PA 19103-6933 · 215-568-6200

Pittsburgh

Chester R. Babst III · a · Babst, Calland, Clements and Zomnir · http://www.bccz.com · Two Gateway Center, Eighth Floor · 603 Stanwix Street · Pittsburgh, PA 15222 · 412-394-5400

Donald C. Bluedorn II · Babst, Calland, Clements and Zomnir · http://www.bccz.com · Two Gateway Center, Eighth Floor · 603 Stanwix Street · Pittsburgh, PA 15222 · 412-394-5400

Dean A. Calland · a · Babst, Calland, Clements and Zomnir · http://www.bccz.com · Two Gateway Center, Eighth Floor · 603 Stanwix Street · Pittsburgh, PA 15222 · 412-394-5400

Kevin J. Garber · Babst, Calland, Clements and Zomnir · http://www.bccz.com · Two Gateway Center, Eighth Floor · 603 Stanwix Street · Pittsburgh, PA 15222 · 412-394-5400

Lindsay P. Howard · Babst, Calland, Clements and Zomnir · http://www.bccz.com · Two Gateway Center, Eighth Floor · 603 Stanwix Street · Pittsburgh, PA 15222 · 412-394-5400

Alan S. Miller · Picadio Sneath Miller & Norton · 4710 U.S. Steel Tower · 600 Grant Street · Pittsburgh, PA 15219-2702 · 412-288-4000

Louis A. Naugle · a · Reed Smith · 435 Sixth Avenue · Pittsburgh, PA 15219-1886 · 412-288-3131

Anthony P. Picadio · a · Picadio Sneath Miller & Norton · 4710 U.S. Steel Tower · 600 Grant Street · Pittsburgh, PA 15219-2702 · 412-288-4000

Joseph K. Reinhart · Babst, Calland, Clements and Zomnir · http://www.bccz.com · Two Gateway Center, Eighth Floor · 603 Stanwix Street · Pittsburgh, PA 15222 · 412-394-5400

Harley N. Trice II · 2) · Reed Smith · 435 Sixth Avenue · Pittsburgh, PA 15219-1886 · 412-288-3131

John W. Ubinger, Jr. · Jones Day · One Mellon Center, Suite 4500 · 500 Grant Street · Pittsburgh, PA 15219-2502 · 412-391-3939

Howard J. Wein · Buchanan Ingersoll & Rooney · http://www.bipc.com · One Oxford Centre, 20th Floor · 301 Grant Street · Pittsburgh, PA 15219-1410 · 412-562-8800

Warrington

M. Joel Bolstein · Fox Rothschild · 2700 Kelly Road, Suite 300 · Warrington, PA 18976-3624 · 215-345-7500

EQUIPMENT FINANCE LAW

Philadelphia

E. Carolan Berkley · Stradley, Ronon, Stevens & Young · 2600 One Commerce Square · Philadelphia, PA 19103-7098 · 215-564-8000

Lawrence F. Flick II · Blank Rome · One Logan Square · 130 North 18th Street · Philadelphia, PA 19103-6998 · 215-569-5500

Harvey I. Forman · a · Blank Rome · One Logan Square · 130 North 18th Street · Philadelphia, PA 19103-6998 · 215-569-5500

Carl H. Fridy · a · Ballard Spahr Andrews & Ingersoll · 1735 Market Street, 51st Floor · Philadelphia, PA 19103-7599 · 215-665-8500

ETHICS AND PROFESSIONAL RESPONSIBILITY LAW

Philadelphia

Patrick Matusky · WolfBlock · http://wolfblock.com · 1650 Arch Street, 22nd Floor · Philadelphia, PA 19103-2097 · 215-977-2000

FAMILY LAW

Blue Bell

Mason Avrigian, Sr. · 2) · Wisler Perlstine · 484 Norristown Road, Suite 100 · Blue Bell, PA 19422 · 610-825-8400

Jack A. Rounick · Flamm, Boroff & Bacine · 794 Penllyn Pike · Blue Bell, PA 19422 · 267-419-1500

Camp Hill

Maria P. Cognetti · Cognetti & Associates · 210 Grandview Avenue, Suite 102 · Camp Hill, PA 17011 · 717-909-4060

Doylestown

Jeffrey M. Williams · Jeffrey M. Williams · 43 North Pine Street · Doylestown, PA 18901 · 215-340-2207

Harrisburg

J. Paul Helvy · McNees Wallace & Nurick · 100 Pine Street · P.O. Box 1166 · Harrisburg, PA 17108-1166 717-232-8000

John C. Howett, Jr. · 2) · Howett, Kissinger & Holst · 130 Walnut Street · P.O. Box 810 · Harrisburg, PA 17108 · 717-234-2616

Sandra L. Meilton · Daley, Zucker, Meilton, Miner & Gingrich · 1029 Scenery Drive · Harrisburg, PA 17109 · 717-657-4795

Lansdale

Mark B. Dischell · a · Dischell, Bartle, Yanoff & Dooley · http://dbyd.com · 1800 Pennbrook Parkway, Suite 200 · P.O. Box 107 · Lansdale, PA 19446-0107 · 215-362-2474

Media

Michael A. Raffaele · Raffaele & Puppio · 19 West Third Street · Media, PA 19063 · 610-891-6710

Michael R. Sweeney · 2) · Sweeney & Neary · 200 North Jackson Street · Media, PA 19063 · 610-892-7500

Norristown

Mary Cushing Doherty · a · High Swartz · 40 East Airy Street · P.O. Box 671 · Norristown, PA 19404 · 610-275-0700

Philadelphia

Leonard Dubin · 2% · Blank Rome · One Logan Square · 130 North 18th Street · Philadelphia, PA 19103-6998 · 215-569-5500

Michael E. Fingerman · 2) · Michael E. Fingerman · http://www.mfingerman.com · Two Penn Center Plaza, Suite 1040 · 1500 JFK Boulelvard · Philadelphia, PA 19102 · 215-731-1300

David N. Hofstein · Hofstein Weiner & Levit · 1760 Market Street, Suite 1300 · Philadelphia, PA 19103 · 215-561-1100

Neil Hurowitz · 2% · Astor, Weiss, Kaplan & Mandel · The Bellevue, Sixth Floor · 200 South Broad Street Philadelphia, PA 19102 · 215-790-0100

Saul Levit · 2% · Hofstein Weiner & Levit · 1760 Market Street, Suite 1300 · Philadelphia, PA 19103 · 215-561-1100

Albert Momjian · 2% · Schnader Harrison Segal & Lewis · http://www.schnader.com · 1600 Market Street, Suite 3600 · Philadelphia, PA 19103-7286 · 215-751-2000

Mark A. Momjian · Schnader Harrison Segal & Lewis · http://www.schnader.com · 1600 Market Street, Suite 3600 · Philadelphia, PA 19103-7286 · 215-751-2000

David S. Rasner · a · Fox Rothschild · 2000 Market Street, 10th Floor · Philadelphia, PA 19103-3291 · 215-299-2000

Charles C. Shainberg · 2% · Shainberg & Viola · One South Broad Street, Suite 1820 · Philadelphia, PA 19107 · 215-988-9700

Ann G. Verber · Obermayer Rebmann Maxwell & Hippel · http://www.obermayer.com · One Penn Center, 19th Floor · 1617 John F. Kennedy Boulevard · Philadelphia, PA 19103-1895 · 215-665-3000

Robert I. Whitelaw · a · Obermayer Rebmann Maxwell & Hippel · http://www.obermayer.com · One Penn Center, 19th Floor · 1617 John F. Kennedy Boulevard · Philadelphia, PA 19103-1895 · 215-665-3000

Cheryl L. Young · Hangley Aronchick Segal & Pudlin · http://www.hangley.com · One Logan Square, 27th Floor · 18th and Cherry Street · Philadelphia, PA 19103-6933 · 215-568-6200

James L. Beck · Gillotti, Capristo & Beck · The Grant Building, Suite 215 · 310 Grant Street · Pittsburgh, PA 15219-2201 · 412-391-4242

Todd M. Begg · Pollock Begg Komar Glasser · Frick Building, Suite 501 · 437 Grant Street · Pittsburgh, PA 15219-6003 · 412-471-9000

Carol A. Behers · Raphael, Ramsden & Behers · 1200 Frick Building · 437 Grant Street · Pittsburgh, PA 15219 · 412-471-8822

Jay A. Blechman · Steiner & Blechman · 310 Grant Street, Suite 3220 · Pittsburgh, PA 15219-2203 · 412-263-3700

Robert C. Capristo · a · Gillotti, Capristo & Beck · The Grant Building, Suite 215 · 310 Grant Street · Pittsburgh, PA 15219-2201 · 412-391-4242

Frederick N. Frank · a · Frank, Bails, Murcko, Gubinsky & Gale · Gulf Tower, Suite 3300 · 707 Grant Street · Pittsburgh, PA 15219 · 412-471-3000

Gary G. Gentile · a · Goldberg, Gruener, Gentile, Horoho & Avalli · The Grant Building, Suite 230 · 310 Grant Street · Pittsburgh, PA 15219-2201 · 412-261-9900

Chris F. Gillotti · 2% · Gillotti, Capristo & Beck · The Grant Building, Suite 215 · 310 Grant Street · Pittsburgh, PA 15219-2201 · 412-391-4242

Mark J. Goldberg · 2% · Goldberg, Gruener, Gentile, Horoho & Avalli · The Grant Building, Suite 230 · 310 Grant Street · Pittsburgh, PA 15219-2201 · 412-261-9900

Harry J. Gruener · 2) · Goldberg, Gruener, Gentile, Horoho & Avalli · The Grant Building, Suite 230 · 310 Grant Street · Pittsburgh, PA 15219-2201 · 412-261-9900

Kenneth J. Horoho, Jr. · Goldberg, Gruener, Gentile, Horoho & Avalli · The Grant Building, Suite 230 · 310 Grant Street · Pittsburgh, PA 15219-2201 · 412-261-9900

Margaret P. Joy · McCarthy, McDonald, Schulberg & Joy · 1111 Oliver Building · 535 Smithfield Street · Pittsburgh, PA 15222-2307 · 412-471-9900

Candice L. Komar · Pollock Begg Komar Glasser · Frick Building, Suite 501 · 437 Grant Street · Pittsburgh, PA 15219-6003 · 412-471-9000

James E. Mahood · Wilder & Mahood · Koppers Building, 10th Floor · 436 Seventh Avenue · Pittsburgh, PA 15219 · 412-261-4040

Carol S. McCarthy · McCarthy, McDonald, Schulberg & Joy · 1111 Oliver Building · 535 Smithfield Street · Pittsburgh, PA 15222-2307 · 412-471-9900

Thomas M. Mulroy · Bauman, Bundy, Mulroy & Schultz · 223 Fourth Avenue, Suite 500 · Pittsburgh, PA 15222 · 412-471-3300

Mary Sue Ramsden · Raphael, Ramsden & Behers · 1200 Frick Building · 437 Grant Street · Pittsburgh, PA 15219 · 412-471-8822

Melaine S. Rothey · Jones, Gregg, Creehan & Gerace · 411 Seventh Avenue, Suite 1200 · Pittsburgh, PA 15219-1905 · 412-261-6400

William L. Steiner · a · Steiner & Blechman · 310 Grant Street, Suite 3220 · Pittsburgh, PA 15219-2203 · 412-263-3700

Joanne Ross Wilder · 2% · Wilder & Mahood · Koppers Building, 10th Floor · 436 Seventh Avenue · Pittsburgh, PA 15219 · 412-261-4040

FAMILY LAW MEDIATION

Harrisburg

Sandra L. Meilton · Daley, Zucker, Meilton, Miner & Gingrich · 1029 Scenery Drive · Harrisburg, PA 17109 · 717-657-4795

King of Prussia

Kathleen Bilotta Vetrano · Vetrano & Vetrano · 455 South Gulph Road, Suite 410 · King of Prussia, PA 19406 · 610-265-4441

Philadelphia

Edward Blumstein · Edward Blumstein · 1528 Walnut Street, Suite 1100 · Philadelphia, PA 19102-3419 · 215-790-9666

Michael E. Fingerman · 2) · Michael E. Fingerman · http://www.mfingerman.com · Two Penn Center Plaza, Suite 1040 · 1500 JFK Boulelvard · Philadelphia, PA 19102 · 215-731-1300

Ann G. Verber · Obermayer Rebmann Maxwell & Hippel · http://www.obermayer.com · One Penn Center, 19th Floor · 1617 John F. Kennedy Boulevard · Philadelphia, PA 19103-1895 · 215-665-3000

Pittsburgh

Ann L. Begler · Frank, Bails, Murcko, Gubinsky & Gale · Gulf Tower, Suite 3300 · 707 Grant Street · Pittsburgh, PA 15219 · 412-471-3000

Maureen B. Cohon · Buchanan Ingersoll & Rooney · http://www.bipc.com · One Oxford Centre, 20th Floor · 301 Grant Street · Pittsburgh, PA 15219-1410 · 412-562-8800

FIRST AMENDMENT LAW

Conway

Scott L. Melton · a · Conte, Melton & D'Antonio · 300 Ninth Street · Conway, PA 15027-1696 · 724-869-2164

Philadelphia

Joseph C. Crawford · Pepper Hamilton · http://www.pepperlaw.com · Two Logan Square, Suite 3000 · 18th and Arch Street · Philadelphia, PA 19103-2799 · 215-981-4000

Amy B. Ginensky · Pepper Hamilton · http://www.pepperlaw.com · Two Logan Square, Suite 3000 · 18th and Arch Street · Philadelphia, PA 19103-2799 · 215-981-4000

Gregory M. Harvey · a · Montgomery, McCracken, Walker & Rhoads · 123 South Broad Street · Avenue Of The Arts · Philadelphia, PA 19109-1029 · 215-772-1500

David H. Marion · a · Montgomery, McCracken, Walker & Rhoads · 123 South Broad Street · Avenue Of The Arts · Philadelphia, PA 19109-1029 · 215-772-1500

William J. O'Brien · a · Conrad O'Brien Gellman & Rohn · http://www.cogr.com · 1515 Market Street, 16th Floor · Philadelphia, PA 19102-1916 · 215-864-9600

Burt M. Rublin · a · Ballard Spahr Andrews & Ingersoll · 1735 Market Street, 51st Floor · Philadelphia, PA 19103-7599 · 215-665-8500

Daniel Segal · Hangley Aronchick Segal & Pudlin · http://www.hangley.com · One Logan Square, 27th Floor · 18th and Cherry Street · Philadelphia, PA 19103-6933 · 215-568-6200

Jerome J. Shestack · a · WolfBlock · http://wolfblock.com · 1650 Arch Street, 22nd Floor · Philadelphia, PA 19103-2097 · 215-977-2000

Carl A. Solano · Schnader Harrison Segal & Lewis · http://www.schnader.com · 1600 Market Street, Suite 3600 · Philadelphia, PA 19103-7286 · 215-751-2000

Richard A. Sprague · 2% · Sprague & Sprague · The Wellington Building, Suite 400 · 135 South 19th Street · Philadelphia, PA 19103 · 215-561-7681

Pittsburgh

Walter P. DeForest III · 2% · DeForest Koscelnik Yokitis Kaplan & Berardinelli · Koppers Building, 30th Floor · 436 Seventh Avenue · Pittsburgh, PA 15219 · 412-227-3100

Scott E. Henderson · a · Thorp, Reed & Armstrong · One Oxford Centre, 14th Floor · 301 Grant Street · Pittsburgh, PA 15219-1425 · 412-394-7711

Gregory B. Jordan · a · Reed Smith · 435 Sixth Avenue · Pittsburgh, PA 15219-1886 · 412-288-3131

Roslyn M. Litman · 2% · Litman Law Firm · One Oxford Centre, 34th Floor · 301 Grant Street · Pittsburgh, PA 15219-1407 · 412-456-2000

W. Thomas McGough, Jr. · a · Reed Smith · 435 Sixth Avenue · Pittsburgh, PA 15219-1886 · 412-288-3131

FRANCHISE LAW

Harrisburg

Michael A. Doctrow · McNees Wallace & Nurick · 100 Pine Street · P.O. Box 1166 · Harrisburg, PA 17108-1166 · 717-232-8000

Horsham

Harris J. Chernow · Chernow Katz · 721 Dresher Road, Suite 1100 · Horsham, PA 19044 · 215-659-3600

Philadelphia

Constantine T. Fournaris · Wiggin and Dana · http://www.wiggin.com · One Liberty Place, 36th Floor · 1650 Market Street · Philadelphia, PA 19103 · 610-834-2400

Pittsburgh

Jeffrey Letwin · Schnader Harrison Segal & Lewis · http://www.schnader.com · Fifth Avenue Place, Suite 2700 · 120 Fifth Avenue · Pittsburgh, PA 15222-3001 · 412-577-5200

GAMING LAW

Harrisburg

Alan C. Kohler · WolfBlock · http://wolfblock.com · 213 Market Street, Ninth Floor · P.O. Box 865 · Harrisburg, PA 17108-0865 · 717-237-7160

Philadelphia

Robert P. Krauss · Ballard Spahr Andrews & Ingersoll · 1735 Market Street, 51st Floor · Philadelphia, PA 19103-7599 · 215-665-8500

Howell J. Reeves · WolfBlock · http://wolfblock.com · 1650 Arch Street, 22nd Floor · Philadelphia, PA 19103-2097 · 215-977-2000

Stephen D. Schrier · Blank Rome · One Logan Square · 130 North 18th Street · Philadelphia, PA 19103-6998 · 215-569-5500

GOVERNMENT RELATIONS LAW

Blue Bell

Stewart J. Greenleaf, Sr. · Elliott Greenleaf & Siedzikowski · 925 Harvest Drive · P.O. Box 3010 · Blue Bell, PA 19422 · 215-977-1000

Harrisburg

Karen S. Ball · Buchanan Ingersoll & Rooney · http://www.bipc.com · One South Market Square, Third Floor · 213 Market Street · P.O. Box 12023 · Harrisburg, PA 17108 · 717-237-4800

Daniel E. Beren · Buchanan Ingersoll & Rooney · http://www.bipc.com · One South Market Square, Third Floor · 213 Market Street · P.O. Box 12023 · Harrisburg, PA 17108 · 717-237-4800

Richard J. Gmerek · Wolf Block Government Relations · The Locust Court Building, Suite 600 · 212 Locust Street · Harrisburg, PA 17101 · 717-234-8525

Laura J. Kuller · Buchanan Ingersoll & Rooney · http://www.bipc.com · 17 North Second Street, 15th Floor · Harrisburg, PA 17101-1503 · 717-237-4800

Thomas G. Paese · Buchanan Ingersoll & Rooney · http://www.bipc.com · 17 North Second Street, 15th Floor · Harrisburg, PA 17101-1503 · 717-237-4800

John M. Quain · Buchanan Ingersoll & Rooney · http://www.bipc.com · 17 North Second Street, 15th Floor · Harrisburg, PA 17101-1503 · 717-237-4800

Philadelphia

Carl M. Buchholz · Blank Rome · One Logan Square · 130 North 18th Street · Philadelphia, PA 19103-6998 · 215-569-5500

HEALTH CARE LAW

Exton

Ernest L. Tsoules, Jr. · Tsoules, Sweeney, Martin & Orr · Lionville Professional Center · 29 Dowlin Forge Road · Exton, PA 19341 · 610-423-4200

Harrisburg

Mark M. Van Blargan · McNees Wallace & Nurick · 100 Pine Street · P.O. Box 1166 · Harrisburg, PA 17108-1166 · 717-232-8000

Jonathan Vipond III · a · Buchanan Ingersoll & Rooney · http://www.bipc.com · One South Market Square, Third Floor · 213 Market Street · P.O. Box 12023 · Harrisburg, PA 17108 · 717-237-4800

Haverford

Jennifer A. Stiller · Law Offices of Jennifer A. Stiller · http://www.healthregs.com · 625 Haydock Lane · Haverford, PA 19041-1207 · 610-642-3366

Mechanicsburg

Kimber Latsha · Latsha Davis Yohe & McKenna · 1700 Bent Creek Boulevard, Suite 140 · Mechanicsburg, PA 17050 · 717-620-2424

Philadelphia

Lawrence J. Beaser · a · Blank Rome · One Logan Square · 130 North 18th Street · Philadelphia, PA 19103-6998 · 215-569-5500

Mark H. Gallant · Cozen O'Connor · The Atrium · 1900 Market Street · Philadelphia, PA 19103 · 215-665-2000

Alice G. Gosfield · a · Alice G. Gosfield & Associates · 2309 Delancey Place · Philadelphia, PA 19103 · 215-735-2384

Roland Morris · a · Duane Morris · 30 South 17th Street · Philadelphia, PA 19103-4196 · 215-979-1000

Brian M. Peters · Post & Schell · Four Penn Center, 14th Floor · 1600 John F. Kennedy Boulevard · Philadelphia, PA 19103-2808 · 215-587-1000

Marc S. Raspanti · Pietragallo Gordon Alfano Bosick & Raspanti · 1818 Market Street, Suite 3402 · Philadelphia, PA 19103 · 215-320-6200

Edward F. Shay · a · Post & Schell · Four Penn Center, 14th Floor · 1600 John F. Kennedy Boulevard · Philadelphia, PA 19103-2808 · 215-587-1000

Eric W. Sitarchuk · Morgan Lewis & Bockius · 1701 Market Street · Philadelphia, PA 19103-2921 · 215-963-5000

Thomas M. Tammany · Buchanan Ingersoll & Rooney · http://www.bipc.com · 1835 Market Street, 14th Floor · Philadelphia, PA 19103-2985 · 215-665-8700

Karl A. Thallner, Jr. · a · Reed Smith · 2500 One Liberty Place · 1650 Market Street · Philadelphia, PA 19103 · 215-851-8100

John R. Washlick · Cozen O'Connor · The Atrium · 1900 Market Street · Philadelphia, PA 19103 · 215-665-2000

Pittsburgh

Barbara A. Blackmond · a · Horty, Springer & Mattern · 4614 Fifth Avenue · Pittsburgh, PA 15213 · 412-687-7677

Thomas E. Boyle · a · Buchanan Ingersoll & Rooney · http://www.bipc.com · One Oxford Centre, 20th Floor · 301 Grant Street · Pittsburgh, PA 15219-1410 · 412-562-8800

Henry M. Casale · Horty, Springer & Mattern · 4614 Fifth Avenue · Pittsburgh, PA 15213 · 412-687-7677

Michael A. Cassidy · Tucker Arensberg · http://www.tuckerlaw.com · 1500 One PPG Place · Pittsburgh, PA 15222-5401 · 412-566-1212

Rosemary L. Corsetti · Buchanan Ingersoll & Rooney · http://www.bipc.com · One Oxford Centre, 20th Floor · 301 Grant Street · Pittsburgh, PA 15219-1410 · 412-562-8800

J. Kent Culley · Tucker Arensberg · http://www.tuckerlaw.com · 1500 One PPG Place · Pittsburgh, PA 15222-5401 · 412-566-1212

Robert G. Geeseman · Fox Rothschild · 625 Liberty Avenue, 29th Floor · Pittsburgh, PA 15222-3115 · 412-391-1334

Linda Haddad · a · Horty, Springer & Mattern · 4614 Fifth Avenue · Pittsburgh, PA 15213 · 412-687-7677

Robert T. Harper · a · Buchanan Ingersoll & Rooney · http://www.bipc.com · One Oxford Centre, 20th Floor · 301 Grant Street · Pittsburgh, PA 15219-1410 · 412-562-8800

John F. Horty · a · Horty, Springer & Mattern · 4614 Fifth Avenue · Pittsburgh, PA 15213 · 412-687-7677

John D. Houston II · Houston Harbaugh · Three Gateway Center, 22nd Floor · 401 Liberty Avenue · Pittsburgh, PA 15222-1005 · 412-281-5060

Edward J. Kabala · a · Fox Rothschild · 625 Liberty Avenue, 29th Floor · Pittsburgh, PA 15222-3115 · 412-391-1334

William H. Maruca · Fox Rothschild · 625 Liberty Avenue, 29th Floor · Pittsburgh, PA 15222-3115 · 412-391-1334

David L. McClenahan · a · K&L Gates · Henry W. Oliver Building · 535 Smithfield Street · Pittsburgh, PA 15222-2312 · 412-355-6500

Daniel M. Mulholland III · a · Horty, Springer & Mattern · 4614 Fifth Avenue · Pittsburgh, PA 15213 · 412-687-7677

Anne D. Mullaney · Thorp, Reed & Armstrong · One Oxford Centre, 14th Floor · 301 Grant Street · Pittsburgh, PA 15219-1425 · 412-394-7711

Deborah J. Robinson · Houston Harbaugh · Three Gateway Center, 22nd Floor · 401 Liberty Avenue · Pittsburgh, PA 15222-1005 · 412-281-5060

Edward V. Weisgerber · a · K&L Gates · Henry W. Oliver Building · 535 Smithfield Street · Pittsburgh, PA 15222-2312 · 412-355-6500

Williamsport

David R. Bahl · McCormick Law Firm · 835 West Fourth Street · P.O. Box 577 · Williamsport, PA 17703 570-326-5131

Jenkintown

Jane W. Goldblum · Goldblum & Hess · Jenkintown Plaza, Suite 380 · 101 Greenwood Avenue · Jenkintown, PA 19046 · 215-885-3600

Wendy Castor Hess · Goldblum & Hess · Jenkintown Plaza, Suite 380 · 101 Greenwood Avenue · Jenkintown, PA 19046 · 215-885-3600

Philadelphia

Peter T. Baumann · ⑩ · Baumann, DeSeve & Landau · Penn Mutual Towers Building, Suite 1340 · 510 Walnut Street · Philadelphia, PA 19106 · 215-925-0705

H. Ronald Klasko · ⑩ · Klasko, Rulon, Stock & Seltzer · 1800 John F. Kennedy Boulevard, Suite 1700 · Philadelphia, PA 19103 · 215-825-8600

Jon Landau · Baumann, DeSeve & Landau · Penn Mutual Towers Building, Suite 1340 · 510 Walnut Street · Philadelphia, PA 19106 · 215-925-0705

Steven A. Morley · ⑩ · Morley Surin & Griffin · Constitution Place, Suite 1305-P · 325 Chestnut Street · Philadelphia, PA 19106 · 215-925-4435

James J. Orlow · ⑩ · Orlow, Kaplan & Hohenstein · Public Ledger Building, Suite 656 · 620 Chestnut Street · P.O. Box 40017 · Philadelphia, PA 19106 · 215-922-1183

Frances P. Rayer · Buchanan Ingersoll & Rooney · http://www.bipc.com · 1835 Market Street, 14th Floor Philadelphia, PA 19103-2985 · 215-665-8700

Ann A. Ruben · Steel, Rudnick & Ruben · 1608 Walnut Street, Suite 1500 · Philadelphia, PA 19103 · 215-546-4333

Lawrence H. Rudnick · ⑩ · Steel, Rudnick & Ruben · 1608 Walnut Street, Suite 1500 · Philadelphia, PA 19103 · 215-546-4333

Richard R. Rulon · Klasko, Rulon, Stock & Seltzer · 1800 John F. Kennedy Boulevard, Suite 1700 · Philadelphia, PA 19103 · 215-825-8600

Suzanne B. Seltzer · Klasko, Rulon, Stock & Seltzer · 1800 John F. Kennedy Boulevard, Suite 1700 · Philadelphia, PA 19103 · 215-825-8600

Richard D. Steel · ⑩ · Steel, Rudnick & Ruben · 1608 Walnut Street, Suite 1500 · Philadelphia, PA 19103 · 215-546-4333

William A. Stock · Klasko, Rulon, Stock & Seltzer · 1800 John F. Kennedy Boulevard, Suite 1700 · Philadelphia, PA 19103 · 215-825-8600

Pittsburgh

Barbara L. Bower · ⑩ · K&L Gates · Henry W. Oliver Building · 535 Smithfield Street · Pittsburgh, PA 15222-2312 · 412-355-6500

John S. Brendel · Cohen & Grigsby · 625 Liberty Avenue · Pittsburgh, PA 15222-3152 · 412-297-4900

Lawrence M. Lebowitz · ⑩ · Cohen & Grigsby · 625 Liberty Avenue · Pittsburgh, PA 15222-3152 · 412-297-4900

Joel Pfeffer · Meyer, Unkovic & Scott · http://www.muslaw.com · 1300 Oliver Building · 535 Smithfield Street · Pittsburgh, PA 15222 · 412-456-2800

Matthew T. Phillips · Cohen & Grigsby · 625 Liberty Avenue · Pittsburgh, PA 15222-3152 · 412-297-4900

Robert S. Whitehill · ⑩ · Fox Rothschild · 625 Liberty Avenue, 29th Floor · Pittsburgh, PA 15222-3115 · 412-391-1334

York

Stephen D. Converse · Anderson Converse & Fennick · 1423 East Market Street · York, PA 17403-1264 · 717-846-7100

INFORMATION TECHNOLOGY LAW

Philadelphia

Barbara Murphy Melby · Morgan Lewis & Bockius · 1701 Market Street · Philadelphia, PA 19103-2921 · 215-963-5000

Pittsburgh

Gary L. Kaplan · DeForest Koscelnik Yokitis Kaplan & Berardinelli · Koppers Building, 30th Floor · 436 Seventh Avenue · Pittsburgh, PA 15219 · 412-227-3100

Stanton D. Levenson · ⑩ · Stanton D. Levenson · http://www.seriousdefense.com · 1715 Gulf Tower · Pittsburgh, PA 15219 · 412-355-0650

Steven B. Silverman · Tucker Arensberg · http://www.tuckerlaw.com · 1500 One PPG Place · Pittsburgh, PA 15222-5401 · 412-566-1212

INSURANCE LAW

Harrisburg

P. Kevin Brobson · Buchanan Ingersoll & Rooney · http://www.bipc.com · One South Market Square, Third Floor · 213 Market Street · P.O. Box 12023 · Harrisburg, PA 17108 · 717-237-4800

Michael F. Consedine · Saul Ewing · Penn National Insurance Plaza, Seventh Floor · Two North Second Street · Harrisburg, PA 17101-1619 · 717-257-7500

Constance B. Foster · Saul Ewing · Penn National Insurance Plaza, Seventh Floor · Two North Second Street · Harrisburg, PA 17101-1619 · 717-257-7500

Heidi B. Hamman Shakely · Eckert Seamans Cherin & Mellott · One South Market Square Building, Eighth Floor · 213 Market Street · Harrisburg, PA 17101 · 717-237-6000

Michael R. Kelley · McNees Wallace & Nurick · 100 Pine Street · P.O. Box 1166 · Harrisburg, PA 17108-1166 · 717-232-8000

Robert E. Kelly, Jr. · Kelly, Parker & Cohen · Commerce Towers, 10th Floor · 300 North Second Street · Harrisburg, PA 17106-2003 · 717-920-8100

Lancaster

Joseph F. Roda · Roda & Nast · 801 Estelle Drive · Lancaster, PA 17601-2130 · 717-892-3000

Philadelphia

Samuel J. Arena, Jr. · Stradley, Ronon, Stevens & Young · 2600 One Commerce Square · Philadelphia, PA 19103-7098 · 215-564-8000

Stephen A. Cozen · Cozen O'Connor · The Atrium · 1900 Market Street · Philadelphia, PA 19103 · 215-665-2000

Paul M. Hummer · Saul Ewing · Centre Square West, 38th Floor · 1500 Market Street · Philadelphia, PA 19102-2186 · 215-972-7777

Ann Blair Laupheimer · Blank Rome · One Logan Square · 130 North 18th Street · Philadelphia, PA 19103-6998 · 215-569-5500

Jay M. Levin · Reed Smith · 2500 One Liberty Place · 1650 Market Street · Philadelphia, PA 19103 · 215-851-8100

Joann M. Lytle · McCarter & English · Mellon Bank Center Building, Suite 700 · 1735 Market Street · Philadelphia, PA 19103 · 215-979-3800

Randy Maniloff · White and Williams · 1800 One Liberty Place · Philadelphia, PA 19103-7395 · 215-864-7000

Richard F. McMenamin · Morgan Lewis & Bockius · 1701 Market Street · Philadelphia, PA 19103-2921 · 215-963-5000

Deborah M. Minkoff · Cozen O'Connor · The Atrium · 1900 Market Street · Philadelphia, PA 19103 · 215-665-2000

R. Bruce Morrison · Marshall, Dennehey, Warner, Coleman & Goggin · 1845 Walnut Street · Philadelphia, PA 19103-4707 · 215-575-2600

Ronald P. Schiller · DLA Piper · One Liberty Place, Suite 4900 · 1650 Market Street · Philadelphia, PA 19103-7300 · 215-656-3300

William P. Shelley · Cozen O'Connor · The Atrium · 1900 Market Street · Philadelphia, PA 19103 · 215-665-2000

John F. Smith III · Reed Smith · 2500 One Liberty Place · 1650 Market Street · Philadelphia, PA 19103 · 215-851-8100

Douglas R. Widin · Reed Smith · 2500 One Liberty Place · 1650 Market Street · Philadelphia, PA 19103 · 215-851-8100

Pittsburgh

David J. Armstrong · 2% · Dickie, McCamey & Chilcote · http://www.dmclaw.com · Two PPG Place, Suite 400 · Pittsburgh, PA 15222-5402 · 412-281-7272

Neal R. Brendel · K&L Gates · Henry W. Oliver Building · 535 Smithfield Street · Pittsburgh, PA 15222-2312 · 412-355-6500

Douglas E. Cameron · Reed Smith · 435 Sixth Avenue · Pittsburgh, PA 15219-1886 · 412-288-3131

David B. Fawcett · 2% · Dickie, McCamey & Chilcote · http://www.dmclaw.com · Two PPG Place, Suite 400 · Pittsburgh, PA 15222-5402 · 412-281-7272

Lawrence E. Flatley · Reed Smith · 435 Sixth Avenue · Pittsburgh, PA 15219-1886 · 412-288-3131

Courtney C.T. Horrigan · Reed Smith · 435 Sixth Avenue · Pittsburgh, PA 15219-1886 · 412-288-3131

Peter J. Kalis · a · K&L Gates · Henry W. Oliver Building · 535 Smithfield Street · Pittsburgh, PA 15222-2312 · 412-355-6500

David F. McGonigle · K&L Gates · Henry W. Oliver Building · 535 Smithfield Street · Pittsburgh, PA 15222-2312 · 412-355-6500

J. W. Montgomery III · Jones Day · One Mellon Center, Suite 4500 · 500 Grant Street · Pittsburgh, PA 15219-2502 · 412-391-3939

Wilbur McCoy Otto · a · Dickie, McCamey & Chilcote · http://www.dmclaw.com · Two PPG Place, Suite 400 · Pittsburgh, PA 15222-5402 · 412-281-7272

Thomas M. Reiter · K&L Gates · Henry W. Oliver Building · 535 Smithfield Street · Pittsburgh, PA 15222-2312 · 412-355-6500

James J. Restivo, Jr. · a · Reed Smith · 435 Sixth Avenue · Pittsburgh, PA 15219-1886 · 412-288-3131

James R. Segerdahl · K&L Gates · Henry W. Oliver Building · 535 Smithfield Street · Pittsburgh, PA 15222-2312 · 412-355-6500

Donald E. Seymour · K&L Gates · Henry W. Oliver Building · 535 Smithfield Street · Pittsburgh, PA 15222-2312 · 412-355-6500

Daniel P. Stefko · Dickie, McCamey & Chilcote · http://www.dmclaw.com · Two PPG Place, Suite 400 · Pittsburgh, PA 15222-5402 · 412-281-7272

George L. Stewart · Reed Smith · 435 Sixth Avenue · Pittsburgh, PA 15219-1886 · 412-288-3131

John M. Sylvester · K&L Gates · Henry W. Oliver Building · 535 Smithfield Street · Pittsburgh, PA 15222-2312 · 412-355-6500

Michael G. Zanic · K&L Gates · Henry W. Oliver Building · 535 Smithfield Street · Pittsburgh, PA 15222-2312 · 412-355-6500

Scranton

Timothy G. Lenahan · Lenahan & Dempsey · The Kane Building, Suite 400 · 116 North Washington Avenue · P.O. Box 234 · Scranton, PA 18501-0234 · 570-346-2097

INTELLECTUAL PROPERTY LAW

Berwyn

John Jay Marshall · Drinker Biddle & Reath · 1000 Westlakes Drive · Berwyn, PA 19312-2409 · 610-993-2200

Harrisburg

Michael A. Doctrow · McNees Wallace & Nurick · 100 Pine Street · P.O. Box 1166 · Harrisburg, PA 17108-1166 · 717-232-8000

Malvern

Kevin R. Casey · Stradley, Ronon, Stevens & Young · Great Valley Corporate Center · 30 Valley Stream Parkway · Malvern, PA 19355-1481 · 610-640-5800

Keith R. Dutill · Stradley, Ronon, Stevens & Young · Great Valley Corporate Center · 30 Valley Stream Parkway · Malvern, PA 19355-1481 · 610-640-5800

Philadelphia

Martin G. Belisario · Panitch Schwarze Belisario & Nadel · One Commerce Square, Suite 2200 · 2005 Market Street · Philadelphia, PA 19103-7013 · 215-965-1330

Alan H. Bernstein · Caesar, Rivise, Bernstein, Cohen & Pokotilow · 1635 Market Street, 11th Floor · Philadelphia, PA 19103-2212 · 215-567-2010

Jamie B. Bischoff · Ballard Spahr Andrews & Ingersoll · 1735 Market Street, 51st Floor · Philadelphia, PA 19103-7599 · 215-665-8500

Stanley H. Cohen · Caesar, Rivise, Bernstein, Cohen & Pokotilow · 1635 Market Street, 11th Floor · Philadelphia, PA 19103-2212 · 215-567-2010

John P. Donohue · Woodcock Washburn · Cira Centre, 12th Floor · 2929 Arch Street · Philadelphia, PA 19104-2891 · 215-568-3100

John Charles Dorfman · a · Dann, Dorfman, Herrell & Skillman · 1601 Market Street, Suite 2400 · Philadelphia, PA 19103-2307 · 215-563-4100

Kathryn R. Doyle · Drinker Biddle & Reath · One Logan Square · 18th and Cherry Streets · Philadelphia, PA 19103-6996 · 215-988-2700

Dianne B. Elderkin · Woodcock Washburn · Cira Centre, 12th Floor · 2929 Arch Street · Philadelphia, PA 19104-2891 · 215-568-3100

Martin L. Faigus · Caesar, Rivise, Bernstein, Cohen & Pokotilow · 1635 Market Street, 11th Floor · Philadelphia, PA 19103-2212 · 215-567-2010

Kevin M. Flannery · Dechert · Cira Centre · 2929 Arch Street · Philadelphia, PA 19104-2808 · 215-994-4000

Glenn A. Gundersen · Dechert · Cira Centre · 2929 Arch Street · Philadelphia, PA 19104-2808 · 215-994-4000

Patrick J. Hagan · Dann, Dorfman, Herrell & Skillman · 1601 Market Street, Suite 2400 · Philadelphia, PA 19103-2307 · 215-563-4100

Louis M. Heidelberger · a · Gibbons · http://www.gibbonslaw.com · 1700 Two Logan Square · 18th & Arch Streets · Philadelphia, PA 19103-2769 · 215-665-0400

Dale M. Heist · Woodcock Washburn · Cira Centre, 12th Floor · 2929 Arch Street · Philadelphia, PA 19104-2891 · 215-568-3100

Roger W. Herrell · Dann, Dorfman, Herrell & Skillman · 1601 Market Street, Suite 2400 · Philadelphia, PA 19103-2307 · 215-563-4100

Randolph J. Huis · Volpe and Koenig · United Plaza, Suite 1600 · 30 South 17th Street · Philadelphia, PA 19103 · 215-568-6400

Roberta Jacobs-Meadway · Eckert Seamans Cherin & Mellott · Two Liberty Place, 22nd Floor · 50 South 16th Street · Philadelphia, PA 19102 · 215-851-8400

C. Frederick Koenig III · Volpe and Koenig · United Plaza, Suite 1600 · 30 South 17th Street · Philadelphia, PA 19103 · 215-568-6400

Robert A. Koons, Jr. · Drinker Biddle & Reath · One Logan Square · 18th and Cherry Streets · Philadelphia, PA 19103-6996 · 215-988-2700

Eric Kraeutler · Morgan Lewis & Bockius · 1701 Market Street · Philadelphia, PA 19103-2921 · 215-963-5000

Gregory J. Lavorgna · Drinker Biddle & Reath · One Logan Square · 18th and Cherry Streets · Philadelphia, PA 19103-6996 · 215-988-2700

Gary H. Levin · Woodcock Washburn · Cira Centre, 12th Floor · 2929 Arch Street · Philadelphia, PA 19104-2891 · 215-568-3100

Lynn A. Malinoski · Woodcock Washburn · Cira Centre, 12th Floor · 2929 Arch Street · Philadelphia, PA 19104-2891 · 215-568-3100

Eric S. Marzluf · Caesar, Rivise, Bernstein, Cohen & Pokotilow · 1635 Market Street, 11th Floor · Philadelphia, PA 19103-2212 · 215-567-2010

James R. Meyer · Schnader Harrison Segal & Lewis · http://www.schnader.com · 1600 Market Street, Suite 3600 · Philadelphia, PA 19103-7286 · 215-751-2000

Daniel A. Monaco · Drinker Biddle & Reath · One Logan Square · 18th and Cherry Streets · Philadelphia, PA 19103-6996 · 215-988-2700

Lynn B. Morreale · Woodcock Washburn · Cira Centre, 12th Floor · 2929 Arch Street · Philadelphia, PA 19104-2891 · 215-568-3100

William H. Murray · Duane Morris · 30 South 17th Street · Philadelphia, PA 19103-4196 · 215-979-1000

Alan S. Nadel · Panitch Schwarze Belisario & Nadel · One Commerce Square, Suite 2200 · 2005 Market Street · Philadelphia, PA 19103-7013 · 215-965-1330

Ronald L. Panitch · Panitch Schwarze Belisario & Nadel · One Commerce Square, Suite 2200 · 2005 Market Street · Philadelphia, PA 19103-7013 · 215-965-1330

Henrik D. Parker · Woodcock Washburn · Cira Centre, 12th Floor · 2929 Arch Street · Philadelphia, PA 19104-2891 · 215-568-3100

Donald R. Piper, Jr. · Dann, Dorfman, Herrell & Skillman · 1601 Market Street, Suite 2400 · Philadelphia, PA 19103-2307 · 215-563-4100

Manny D. Pokotilow · Caesar, Rivise, Bernstein, Cohen & Pokotilow · 1635 Market Street, 11th Floor · Philadelphia, PA 19103-2212 · 215-567-2010

Steven J. Rocci · Woodcock Washburn · Cira Centre, 12th Floor · 2929 Arch Street · Philadelphia, PA 19104-2891 · 215-568-3100

Lynn E. Rzonca · Ballard Spahr Andrews & Ingersoll · 1735 Market Street, 51st Floor · Philadelphia, PA 19103-7599 · 215-665-8500

Steven B. Samuels · Woodcock Washburn · Cira Centre, 12th Floor · 2929 Arch Street · Philadelphia, PA 19104-2891 · 215-568-3100

William W. Schwarze · Panitch Schwarze Belisario & Nadel · One Commerce Square, Suite 2200 · 2005 Market Street · Philadelphia, PA 19103-7013 · 215-965-1330

Arthur H. Seidel · Drinker Biddle & Reath · One Logan Square · 18th and Cherry Streets · Philadelphia, PA 19103-6996 · 215-988-2700

Joseph J. Serritella · Pepper Hamilton · http://www.pepperlaw.com · Two Logan Square, Suite 3000 · 18th and Arch Street · Philadelphia, PA 19103-2799 · 215-981-4000

Barry A. Stein · Caesar, Rivise, Bernstein, Cohen & Pokotilow · 1635 Market Street, 11th Floor · Philadelphia, PA 19103-2212 · 215-567-2010

Anthony S. Volpe · Volpe and Koenig · United Plaza, Suite 1600 · 30 South 17th Street · Philadelphia, PA 19103 · 215-568-6400

David Wolfsohn · Woodcock Washburn · Cira Centre, 12th Floor · 2929 Arch Street · Philadelphia, PA 19104-2891 · 215-568-3100

Pittsburgh

Lynn J. Alstadt · Buchanan Ingersoll & Rooney · http://www.bipc.com · One Oxford Centre, 20th Floor · 301 Grant Street · Pittsburgh, PA 15219-1410 · 412-562-8800

Paul A. Beck · ⑩ · Beck & Thomas · 1575 McFarland Road, Suite 100 · Pittsburgh, PA 15216 · 412-343-9700

Richard L. Byrne · The Webb Law Firm · 700 Koppers Building · 436 Seventh Avenue · Pittsburgh, PA 15219 · 412-471-8815

Frederick H. Colen · ⑩ · Reed Smith · 435 Sixth Avenue · Pittsburgh, PA 15219-1886 · 412-288-3131

Christine R. Ethridge · K&L Gates · Henry W. Oliver Building · 535 Smithfield Street · Pittsburgh, PA 15222-2312 · 412-355-6500

James R. Kyper · K&L Gates · Henry W. Oliver Building · 535 Smithfield Street · Pittsburgh, PA 15222-2312 · 412-355-6500

Robert O. Lindefjeld · Jones Day · One Mellon Center, Suite 4500 · 500 Grant Street · Pittsburgh, PA 15219-2502 · 412-391-3939

David G. Oberdick · Meyer, Unkovic & Scott · http://www.muslaw.com · 1300 Oliver Building · 535 Smithfield Street · Pittsburgh, PA 15222 · 412-456-2800

Gene A. Tabachnick · Reed Smith · 435 Sixth Avenue · Pittsburgh, PA 15219-1886 · 412-288-3131

Thomas C. Wettach · Cohen & Grigsby · 625 Liberty Avenue · Pittsburgh, PA 15222-3152 · 412-297-4900

Robert D. Yeager · ⑩ · K&L Gates · Henry W. Oliver Building · 535 Smithfield Street · Pittsburgh, PA 15222-2312 · 412-355-6500

Valley Forge

Kenneth N. Nigon · RatnerPrestia · 1235 Westlakes Drive, Suite 301 · P.O. Box 980 · Valley Forge, PA 19482 · 610-407-0700

Paul F. Prestia · RatnerPrestia · 1235 Westlakes Drive, Suite 301 · P.O. Box 980 · Valley Forge, PA 19482 610-407-0700

INTERNATIONAL TRADE AND FINANCE LAW

Pittsburgh

V. Susanne Cook · Cohen & Grigsby · 625 Liberty Avenue · Pittsburgh, PA 15222-3152 · 412-297-4900

Ronald W. Frank · Reed Smith · 435 Sixth Avenue · Pittsburgh, PA 15219-1886 · 412-288-3131

David A. Murdoch · ⑩ · K&L Gates · Henry W. Oliver Building · 535 Smithfield Street · Pittsburgh, PA 15222-2312 · 412-355-6500

David P. Pusateri · McGuireWoods · http://www.mcguirewoods.com · Dominion Tower, 23rd Floor · 625 Liberty Avenue · Pittsburgh, PA 15222-3142 · 412-667-6000

Dennis Unkovic · Meyer, Unkovic & Scott · http://www.muslaw.com · 1300 Oliver Building · 535 Smithfield Street · Pittsburgh, PA 15222 · 412-456-2800

LABOR AND EMPLOYMENT LAW

Ardmore

Anna M. Durbin · Law Offices of Anna M. Durbin · 50 Rittenhouse Place · Ardmore, PA 19003 · 610-649-8200

Berwyn

Jonathan A. Kane · ⑩ · Pepper Hamilton · http://www.pepperlaw.com · 400 Berwyn Park · 899 Cassatt Road · Berwyn, PA 19312-1183 · 610-640-7800

Camphill

Charles W. Johnston · ⑩ · Charles W. Johnston · 150 Corporate Center Drive, Suite 203 · Camphill, PA 17011 · 717-975-5500

Harrisburg

Irwin W. Aronson · ⑳ · Willig, Williams & Davidson · 212 Locust Street, Suite 504 · Harrisburg, PA 17101-1510 · 717-221-1000

William J. Flannery · ⑩ · Post & Schell · 17 North Second Street, 12th Floor · Harrisburg, PA 17101-1601 · 717-731-1970

Brian F. Jackson · McNees Wallace & Nurick · 100 Pine Street · P.O. Box 1166 · Harrisburg, PA 17108-1166 · 717-232-8000

Ira H. Weinstock · ㉕ · Ira H. Weinstock · 800 North Second Street, Suite 100 · Harrisburg, PA 17102 · 717-238-1657

Lehigh Valley

R. Michael Carr · Stevens & Lee · 190 Brodhead Road, Suite 200 · P.O. Box 20830 · Lehigh Valley, PA 18002-0830 · 610-691-7111

John S. Hayes · ㉕ · Stevens & Lee · 190 Brodhead Road, Suite 200 · P.O. Box 20830 · Lehigh Valley, PA 18002-0830 · 610-691-7111

Alice W. Ballard · 2) · Alice W. Ballard · 1616 Walnut Street, Suite 2205 · Philadelphia, PA 19103 · 215-893-9708

Michael L. Banks · Morgan Lewis & Bockius · 1701 Market Street · Philadelphia, PA 19103-2921 · 215-963-5000

James S. Beall · Willig, Williams & Davidson · 1845 Walnut Street, 24th Floor · Philadelphia, PA 19103 · 215-656-3600

Alan D. Berkowitz · Dechert · Cira Centre · 2929 Arch Street · Philadelphia, PA 19104-2808 · 215-994-4000

Mark Blondman · Blank Rome · One Logan Square · 130 North 18th Street · Philadelphia, PA 19103-6998 · 215-569-5500

Warren J. Borish · 2) · Spear Wilderman · 230 South Broad Street, Suite 1400 · Philadelphia, PA 19102 · 215-732-0101

Jeffrey L. Braff · Cozen O'Connor · The Atrium · 1900 Market Street · Philadelphia, PA 19103 · 215-665-2000

William H. Brown III · Schnader Harrison Segal & Lewis · http://www.schnader.com · 1600 Market Street, Suite 3600 · Philadelphia, PA 19103-7286 · 215-751-2000

Hope A. Comisky · Pepper Hamilton · http://www.pepperlaw.com · Two Logan Square, Suite 3000 · 18th and Arch Street · Philadelphia, PA 19103-2799 · 215-981-4000

Stephen G. Console · Console Law Offices · 1525 Locust Street, Ninth Floor · Philadelphia, PA 19102 · 215-545-7676

Joseph J. Costello · Morgan Lewis & Bockius · 1701 Market Street · Philadelphia, PA 19103-2921 · 215-963-5000

Alfred J. D'Angelo, Jr. · 2) · Buchanan Ingersoll & Rooney · http://www.bipc.com · 1835 Market Street, 14th Floor · Philadelphia, PA 19103-2985 · 215-665-8700

Stuart W. Davidson · a · Willig, Williams & Davidson · 1845 Walnut Street, 24th Floor · Philadelphia, PA 19103 · 215-656-3600

Doreen S. Davis · a · Morgan Lewis & Bockius · 1701 Market Street · Philadelphia, PA 19103-2921 · 215-963-5000

Mark S. Dichter · 2) · Morgan Lewis & Bockius · 1701 Market Street · Philadelphia, PA 19103-2921 · 215-963-5000

Edward T. Ellis · Montgomery, McCracken, Walker & Rhoads · 123 South Broad Street · Avenue Of The Arts · Philadelphia, PA 19109-1029 · 215-772-1500

Alan B. Epstein · a · Spector Gadon & Rosen · http://www.lawsgr.com · Seven Penn Center, Seventh Floor · 1635 Market Street · Philadelphia, PA 19103 · 215-241-8888

Howard R. Flaxman · a · Fox Rothschild · 2000 Market Street, 10th Floor · Philadelphia, PA 19103-3291 · 215-299-2000

Mark J. Foley · Cozen O'Connor · The Atrium · 1900 Market Street · Philadelphia, PA 19103 · 215-665-2000

Karl A. Fritton · a · Reed Smith · 2500 One Liberty Place · 1650 Market Street · Philadelphia, PA 19103 215-851-8100

Sidney L. Gold · Sidney L. Gold & Associates · http://www.discrimlaw.net · 1835 Market Street, Suite 515 · Philadelphia, PA 19103 · 215-569-1999

Robert M. Goldich · Greenberg Traurig · http://www.gtlaw.com · Two Commerce Square, Suite 2700 · 2001 Market Street · Philadelphia, PA 19103 · 215-988-7800

Neal Goldstein · a · Freedman & Lorry · 1601 Market Street, Second Floor · Philadelphia, PA 19103 · 215-925-8400

Harold I. Goodman · Raynes McCarty · http://www.raynesmccarty.com · 1845 Walnut Street, 20th Floor · Philadelphia, PA 19103 · 215-568-6190

Anthony B. Haller · Blank Rome · One Logan Square · 130 North 18th Street · Philadelphia, PA 19103-6998 · 215-569-5500

Michael J. Hanlon · Blank Rome · One Logan Square · 130 North 18th Street · Philadelphia, PA 19103-6998 · 215-569-5500

Judith E. Harris · Morgan Lewis & Bockius · 1701 Market Street · Philadelphia, PA 19103-2921 · 215-963-5000

Robert S. Hawkins · Buchanan Ingersoll & Rooney · http://www.bipc.com · 1835 Market Street, 14th Floor · Philadelphia, PA 19103-2985 · 215-665-8700

Jerome A. Hoffman · Dechert · Cira Centre · 2929 Arch Street · Philadelphia, PA 19104-2808 · 215-994-4000

Stephen J. Holroyd · Jennings Sigmond · The Penn Mutual Tower, 16th Floor · Independence Square · 510 Walnut Street · Philadelphia, PA 19106-3683 · 215-922-6700

John Freedley Hunsicker, Jr. · a · Drinker Biddle & Reath · One Logan Square · 18th and Cherry Streets · Philadelphia, PA 19103-6996 · 215-988-2700

Kenneth M. Jarin · a · Ballard Spahr Andrews & Ingersoll · 1735 Market Street, 51st Floor · Philadelphia, PA 19103-7599 · 215-665-8500

Thomas W. Jennings · 2% · Jennings Sigmond · The Penn Mutual Tower, 16th Floor · Independence Square · 510 Walnut Street · Philadelphia, PA 19106-3683 · 215-922-6700

Sarah A. Kelly · Cozen O'Connor · The Atrium · 1900 Market Street · Philadelphia, PA 19103 · 215-665-2000

Raymond A. Kresge · Cozen O'Connor · The Atrium · 1900 Market Street · Philadelphia, PA 19103 · 215-665-2000

Theodore M. Lieverman · Spector, Roseman & Kodroff · 1818 Market Street, Suite 2500 · Philadelphia, PA 19103 · 215-496-0300

S. Gerald Litvin · 2% · Morgan Lewis & Bockius · 1701 Market Street · Philadelphia, PA 19103-2921 · 215-963-5000

Gail Lopez-Henriquez · Freedman & Lorry · 1601 Market Street, Second Floor · Philadelphia, PA 19103 215-925-8400

Carol A. Mager · Mager & Goldstein · 1818 Market Street, Suite 3710 · Philadelphia, PA 19103 · 215-640-3280

Richard Henry Markowitz · 2% · Markowitz & Richman · North American Building, Suite 1100 · 121 South Broad Street · Philadelphia, PA 19107 · 215-875-3100

James A. Matthews III · Fox Rothschild · 2000 Market Street, 10th Floor · Philadelphia, PA 19103-3291 · 215-299-2000

Francis M. Milone · a · Morgan Lewis & Bockius · 1701 Market Street · Philadelphia, PA 19103-2921 · 215-963-5000

Dennis J. Morikawa · Morgan Lewis & Bockius · 1701 Market Street · Philadelphia, PA 19103-2921 · 215-963-5000

Timothy P. O'Reilly · 2) · Morgan Lewis & Bockius · 1701 Market Street · Philadelphia, PA 19103-2921 · 215-963-5000

Michael J. Ossip · Morgan Lewis & Bockius · 1701 Market Street · Philadelphia, PA 19103-2921 · 215-963-5000

Jeffrey Ivan Pasek · Cozen O'Connor · The Atrium · 1900 Market Street · Philadelphia, PA 19103 · 215-665-2000

Brian D. Pedrow · Ballard Spahr Andrews & Ingersoll · 1735 Market Street, 51st Floor · Philadelphia, PA 19103-7599 · 215-665-8500

Vincent J. Pentima · Buchanan Ingersoll & Rooney · http://www.bipc.com · 1835 Market Street, 14th Floor · Philadelphia, PA 19103-2985 · 215-665-8700

Patricia V. Pierce · a · Willig, Williams & Davidson · 1845 Walnut Street, 24th Floor · Philadelphia, PA 19103 · 215-656-3600

Stephen C. Richman · Markowitz & Richman · North American Building, Suite 1100 · 121 South Broad Street · Philadelphia, PA 19107 · 215-875-3100

Richard B. Sigmond · 2) · Jennings Sigmond · The Penn Mutual Tower, 16th Floor · Independence Square · 510 Walnut Street · Philadelphia, PA 19106-3683 · 215-922-6700

Barry Simon · Ogletree Deakins · http://www.ogletreedeakins.com · 1600 Market Street, Suite 2020 · Philadelphia, PA 19103-7218 · 215-419-6530

Ralph J. Teti · Willig, Williams & Davidson · 1845 Walnut Street, 24th Floor · Philadelphia, PA 19103 · 215-656-3600

Anthony F. Visco, Jr. · Ballard Spahr Andrews & Ingersoll · 1735 Market Street, 51st Floor · Philadelphia, PA 19103-7599 · 215-665-8500

Steven R. Wall · Morgan Lewis & Bockius · 1701 Market Street · Philadelphia, PA 19103-2921 · 215-963-5000

Marguerite S. Walsh · Littler Mendelson · Three Parkway, Suite 1400 · 1601 Cherry Street · Philadelphia, PA 19102-1321 · 267-402-3000

Alaine S. Williams · Willig, Williams & Davidson · 1845 Walnut Street, 24th Floor · Philadelphia, PA 19103 · 215-656-3600

Deborah R. Willig · 2) · Willig, Williams & Davidson · 1845 Walnut Street, 24th Floor · Philadelphia, PA 19103 · 215-656-3600

Ronald J. Andrykovitch · Cohen & Grigsby · 625 Liberty Avenue · Pittsburgh, PA 15222-3152 · 412-297-4900

Richard J. Antonelli · Babst, Calland, Clements and Zomnir · http://www.bccz.com · Two Gateway Center, Eighth Floor · 603 Stanwix Street · Pittsburgh, PA 15222 · 412-394-5400

William Bevan III · ⑳ · Reed Smith · 435 Sixth Avenue · Pittsburgh, PA 15219-1886 · 412-288-3131

Cathy Bissoon · Cohen & Grigsby · 625 Liberty Avenue · Pittsburgh, PA 15222-3152 · 412-297-4900

Alan C. Blanco · Rothman Gordon · Grant Building, Third Floor · 310 Grant Street · Pittsburgh, PA 15219-2202 · 412-338-1100

Laura A. Candris · Meyer, Unkovic & Scott · http://www.muslaw.com · 1300 Oliver Building · 535 Smithfield Street · Pittsburgh, PA 15222 · 412-456-2800

Edmund M. Carney · Dinsmore & Shohl · http://www.dinslaw.com · One Oxford Centre, Suite 2800 · 301 Grant Street · Pittsburgh, PA 15219 · 412-281-5000

James W. Carroll, Jr. · Rothman Gordon · Grant Building, Third Floor · 310 Grant Street · Pittsburgh, PA 15219-2202 · 412-338-1100

John Cerilli · Littler Mendelson · Dominion Tower, 26th Floor · 625 Liberty Avenue · Pittsburgh, PA 15222-3110 · 412-201-7600

Eugene K. Connors · Reed Smith · 435 Sixth Avenue · Pittsburgh, PA 15219-1886 · 412-288-3131

Samuel J. Cordes · Ogg, Cordes, Murphy & Ignelzi · Riverview Place, Fourth Floor · 245 Fort Pitt Boulevard · Pittsburgh, PA 15222-1511 · 412-471-8500

Robert B. Cottington · Cohen & Grigsby · 625 Liberty Avenue · Pittsburgh, PA 15222-3152 · 412-297-4900

Walter P. DeForest III · ㉕ · DeForest Koscelnik Yokitis Kaplan & Berardinelli · Koppers Building, 30th Floor · 436 Seventh Avenue · Pittsburgh, PA 15219 · 412-227-3100

Robert A. Eberle · Jubelirer, Pass & Intrieri · 219 Fort Pitt Boulevard · Pittsburgh, PA 15222-1505 · 412-281-3850

Thomas S. Giotto · Buchanan Ingersoll & Rooney · http://www.bipc.com · One Oxford Centre, 20th Floor · 301 Grant Street · Pittsburgh, PA 15219-1410 · 412-562-8800

Maria Greco Danaher · Ogletree Deakins · http://www.ogletreedeakins.com · Four Gateway Center, Suite 400 · 444 Liberty Avenue · Pittsburgh, PA 15222-1237 · 412-394-3333

James R. Haggerty · Cohen & Grigsby · 625 Liberty Avenue · Pittsburgh, PA 15222-3152 · 412-297-4900

W. Scott Hardy · Cohen & Grigsby · 625 Liberty Avenue · Pittsburgh, PA 15222-3152 · 412-297-4900

Michael J. Healey · Healey & Hornack · The Pennsylvanian, Suite C-2 · 1100 Liberty Avenue · Pittsburgh, PA 15222 · 412-391-7711

Mark R. Hornak · Buchanan Ingersoll & Rooney · http://www.bipc.com · One Oxford Centre, 20th Floor 301 Grant Street · Pittsburgh, PA 15219-1410 · 412-562-8800

Stephen H. Jordan · ⑩ · Rothman Gordon · Grant Building, Third Floor · 310 Grant Street · Pittsburgh, PA 15219-2202 · 412-338-1100

Maureen P. Kelly · Babst, Calland, Clements and Zomnir · http://www.bccz.com · Two Gateway Center, Eighth Floor · 603 Stanwix Street · Pittsburgh, PA 15222 · 412-394-5400

Jacqueline A. Koscelnik · ⑩ · DeForest Koscelnik Yokitis Kaplan & Berardinelli · Koppers Building, 30th Floor · 436 Seventh Avenue · Pittsburgh, PA 15219 · 412-227-3100

Louis B. Kushner · ⑳ · Rothman Gordon · Grant Building, Third Floor · 310 Grant Street · Pittsburgh, PA 15219-2202 · 412-338-1100

David J. Laurent · Buchanan Ingersoll & Rooney · http://www.bipc.com · One Oxford Centre, 20th Floor 301 Grant Street · Pittsburgh, PA 15219-1410 · 412-562-8800

Thomas H. May · Dickie, McCamey & Chilcote · http://www.dmclaw.com · Two PPG Place, Suite 400 · Pittsburgh, PA 15222-5402 · 412-281-7272

David J. McAllister · Reed Smith · 435 Sixth Avenue · Pittsburgh, PA 15219-1886 · 412-288-3131

Robert L. McTiernan · Tucker Arensberg · http://www.tuckerlaw.com · 1500 One PPG Place · Pittsburgh, PA 15222-5401 · 412-566-1212

Kurt A. Miller · Thorp, Reed & Armstrong · One Oxford Centre, 14th Floor · 301 Grant Street · Pittsburgh, PA 15219-1425 · 412-394-7711

Martha H. Munsch · ⑩ · Reed Smith · 435 Sixth Avenue · Pittsburgh, PA 15219-1886 · 412-288-3131

Terrence H. Murphy · Buchanan Ingersoll & Rooney · http://www.bipc.com · One Oxford Centre, 20th Floor · 301 Grant Street · Pittsburgh, PA 15219-1410 · 412-562-8800

John J. Myers · Eckert Seamans Cherin & Mellott · U.S. Steel Tower, 44th Floor · 600 Grant Street · Pittsburgh, PA 15219 · 412-566-6000

Stephen M. Olson · ⑩ · K&L Gates · Henry W. Oliver Building · 535 Smithfield Street · Pittsburgh, PA 15222-2312 · 412-355-6500

Ernest B. Orsatti · Jubelirer, Pass & Intrieri · 219 Fort Pitt Boulevard · Pittsburgh, PA 15222-1505 · 412-281-3850

Lynn C. Outwater · Jackson Lewis · http://www.jacksonlewis.com · One PPG Place, 28th Floor · Pittsburgh, PA 15222 · 412-232-0404

Joseph J. Pass, Jr. · ㉕ · Jubelirer, Pass & Intrieri · 219 Fort Pitt Boulevard · Pittsburgh, PA 15222-1505 · 412-281-3850

Peter D. Post · ⑩ · Ogletree Deakins · http://www.ogletreedeakins.com · Four Gateway Center, Suite 400 444 Liberty Avenue · Pittsburgh, PA 15222-1237 · 412-394-3333

Robert F. Prorok · Cohen & Grigsby · 625 Liberty Avenue · Pittsburgh, PA 15222-3152 · 412-297-4900

Patrick W. Ritchey · ⑳ · Reed Smith · 435 Sixth Avenue · Pittsburgh, PA 15219-1886 · 412-288-3131

Catherine S. Ryan · Reed Smith · 435 Sixth Avenue · Pittsburgh, PA 15219-1886 · 412-288-3131

Hayes C. Stover · ⑳ · K&L Gates · Henry W. Oliver Building · 535 Smithfield Street · Pittsburgh, PA 15222-2312 · 412-355-6500

John C. Unkovic · 2) · Reed Smith · 435 Sixth Avenue · Pittsburgh, PA 15219-1886 · 412-288-3131

Scott F. Zimmerman · 2% · Reed Smith · 435 Sixth Avenue · Pittsburgh, PA 15219-1886 · 412-288-3131

West Chester

Loralyn McKinley · McKinley & Ryan · 238 West Miner Street · West Chester, PA 19382 · 610-436-6060

LAND USE & ZONING LAW

Blue Bell

Marc B. Kaplin · Kaplin Stewart Meloff Reiter & Stein · Union Meeting Corporate Center · 910 Harvest Drive · P.O. Box 3037 · Blue Bell, PA 19422-1900 · 610-260-6000

Doylestown

John A. VanLuvanee · Eastburn and Gray · 60 East Court Street · P.O. Box 1389 · Doylestown, PA 18901-0137 · 215-345-7000

Harrisburg

Ronald M. Lucas · Stevens & Lee · 208 North Third Street, Suite 310 · P.O. Box 12090 · Harrisburg, PA 17108-2090 · 717-234-1250

Philadelphia

Carl S. Primavera · Klehr, Harrison, Harvey, Branzburg & Ellers · 260 South Broad Street, Suite 400 · Philadelphia, PA 19102-5003 · 215-568-6060

Pittsburgh

Joel P. Aaronson · Reed Smith · 435 Sixth Avenue · Pittsburgh, PA 15219-1886 · 412-288-3131

W. Theodore Brooks · Tucker Arensberg · http://www.tuckerlaw.com · 1500 One PPG Place · Pittsburgh, PA 15222-5401 · 412-566-1212

Vincent J. Grogan · 2% · Grogan Graffam · http://www.grogangraffam.com · Four Gateway Center, 12th Floor · Pittsburgh, PA 15222-1009 · 412-553-6300

Clifford B. Levine · Thorp, Reed & Armstrong · One Oxford Centre, 14th Floor · 301 Grant Street · Pittsburgh, PA 15219-1425 · 412-394-7711

Blaine A. Lucas · Babst, Calland, Clements and Zomnir · http://www.bccz.com · Two Gateway Center, Eighth Floor · 603 Stanwix Street · Pittsburgh, PA 15222 · 412-394-5400

Kevin F. McKeegan · Meyer, Unkovic & Scott · http://www.muslaw.com · 1300 Oliver Building · 535 Smithfield Street · Pittsburgh, PA 15222 · 412-456-2800

James H. Roberts · Eckert Seamans Cherin & Mellott · U.S. Steel Tower, 44th Floor · 600 Grant Street · Pittsburgh, PA 15219 · 412-566-6000

Blue Bell

John M. Elliott · Elliott Greenleaf & Siedzikowski · 925 Harvest Drive · P.O. Box 3010 · Blue Bell, PA 19422 · 215-977-1000

Philadelphia

Steven E. Angstreich · Levy, Angstreich, Finney, Baldante, Rubenstein & Coren · 1616 Walnut Street, Fifth Floor · Philadelphia, PA 19103 · 215-735-1616

H. Robert Fiebach · a · Cozen O'Connor · The Atrium · 1900 Market Street · Philadelphia, PA 19103 · 215-665-2000

Nancy J. Gellman · a · Conrad O'Brien Gellman & Rohn · http://www.cogr.com · 1515 Market Street, 16th Floor · Philadelphia, PA 19102-1916 · 215-864-9600

Arthur W. Lefco · Marshall, Dennehey, Warner, Coleman & Goggin · 1845 Walnut Street · Philadelphia, PA 19103-4707 · 215-575-2600

Jeffrey R. Lerman · a · Montgomery, McCracken, Walker & Rhoads · 123 South Broad Street · Avenue Of The Arts · Philadelphia, PA 19109-1029 · 215-772-1500

David H. Marion · a · Montgomery, McCracken, Walker & Rhoads · 123 South Broad Street · Avenue Of The Arts · Philadelphia, PA 19109-1029 · 215-772-1500

Jeffrey B. McCarron · Swartz Campbell · Two Liberty Place, 28th Floor · 50 South 16th Street · Philadelphia, PA 19102 · 215-564-5190

James C. Schwartzman · Stevens & Lee · 1818 Market Street, 29th Floor · Philadelphia, PA 19103 · 215-575-0100

Richard A. Sprague · 2% · Sprague & Sprague · The Wellington Building, Suite 400 · 135 South 19th Street · Philadelphia, PA 19103 · 215-561-7681

Philip B. Toran · Marshall, Dennehey, Warner, Coleman & Goggin · 1845 Walnut Street · Philadelphia, PA 19103-4707 · 215-575-2600

Pittsburgh

Vincent J. Grogan · 2% · Grogan Graffam · http://www.grogangraffam.com · Four Gateway Center, 12th Floor · Pittsburgh, PA 15222-1009 · 412-553-6300

Dennis St. J. Mulvihill · a · Robb Leonard Mulvihill · 2300 One Mellon Center, 23rd Floor · 500 Grant Street · Pittsburgh, PA 15219 · 412-281-5431

Dennis J. Roman · Marshall, Dennehey, Warner, Coleman & Goggin · USX Tower, Suite 2900 · 600 Grant Street · Pittsburgh, PA 15219 · 412-803-1140

James R. Schadel · a · Weinheimer, Schadel & Haber · Law and Finance Building, Suite 602 · 429 Fourth Avenue · Pittsburgh, PA 15219-1501 · 412-765-3399

Henry M. Sneath · Picadio Sneath Miller & Norton · 4710 U.S. Steel Tower · 600 Grant Street · Pittsburgh, PA 15219-2702 · 412-288-4000

LEVERAGED BUYOUTS AND PRIVATE EQUITY LAW

Philadelphia

Craig L. Godshall · Dechert · Cira Centre · 2929 Arch Street · Philadelphia, PA 19104-2808 · 215-994-4000

Richard P. Jaffe · Ballard Spahr Andrews & Ingersoll · 1735 Market Street, 51st Floor · Philadelphia, PA 19103-7599 · 215-665-8500

Christopher G. Karras · Dechert · Cira Centre · 2929 Arch Street · Philadelphia, PA 19104-2808 · 215-994-4000

James A. Lebovitz · Dechert · Cira Centre · 2929 Arch Street · Philadelphia, PA 19104-2808 · 215-994-4000

G. Daniel O'Donnell · Dechert · Cira Centre · 2929 Arch Street · Philadelphia, PA 19104-2808 · 215-994-4000

Carmen J. Romano · Dechert · Cira Centre · 2929 Arch Street · Philadelphia, PA 19104-2808 · 215-994-4000

Geraldine A. Sinatra · Dechert · Cira Centre · 2929 Arch Street · Philadelphia, PA 19104-2808 · 215-994-4000

Barton J. Winokur · 2) · Dechert · Cira Centre · 2929 Arch Street · Philadelphia, PA 19104-2808 · 215-994-4000

Pittsburgh

David A. Gerson · Morgan Lewis & Bockius · One Oxford Centre, 32nd Floor · 301 Grant Street · Pittsburgh, PA 15219-6401 · 412-560-3300

Robert T. Harper · a · Buchanan Ingersoll & Rooney · http://www.bipc.com · One Oxford Centre, 20th Floor · 301 Grant Street · Pittsburgh, PA 15219-1410 · 412-562-8800

MARITIME LAW

Philadelphia

Alfred J. Kuffler · Montgomery, McCracken, Walker & Rhoads · 123 South Broad Street · Avenue Of The Arts · Philadelphia, PA 19109-1029 · 215-772-1500

MASS TORT LITIGATION

Lancaster

Dianne M. Nast · Roda & Nast · 801 Estelle Drive · Lancaster, PA 17601-2130 · 717-892-3000

Philadelphia

Lee Balefsky · Kline & Specter · http://www.klinespecter.com · 1525 Locust Street, 19th Floor · Philadelphia, PA 19102 · 215-772-1000

Lawrence R. Cohan · Anapol Schwartz · 1710 Spruce Street · Philadelphia, PA 19103 · 215-735-1130

Stewart L. Cohen · Cohen, Placitella & Roth · Two Commerce Square, Suite 2900 · 2001 Market Street · Philadelphia, PA 19103 · 215-567-3500

J. Gordon Cooney, Jr. · Morgan Lewis & Bockius · 1701 Market Street · Philadelphia, PA 19103-2921 · 215-963-5000

Michael D. Fishbein · Levin, Fishbein, Sedran & Berman · 510 Walnut Street, Suite 500 · Philadelphia, PA 19106-3697 · 215-592-1500

Hope S. Freiwald · Dechert · Cira Centre · 2929 Arch Street · Philadelphia, PA 19104-2808 · 215-994-4000

Robert C. Heim · a · Dechert · Cira Centre · 2929 Arch Street · Philadelphia, PA 19104-2808 · 215-994-4000

Howard M. Klein · Conrad O'Brien Gellman & Rohn · http://www.cogr.com · 1515 Market Street, 16th Floor · Philadelphia, PA 19102-1916 · 215-864-9600

Arnold Levin · Levin, Fishbein, Sedran & Berman · 510 Walnut Street, Suite 500 · Philadelphia, PA 19106-3697 · 215-592-1500

Robert A. Limbacher · Dechert · Cira Centre · 2929 Arch Street · Philadelphia, PA 19104-2808 · 215-994-4000

Fred T. Magaziner · Dechert · Cira Centre · 2929 Arch Street · Philadelphia, PA 19104-2808 · 215-994-4000

Ellen R. Rogoff · Stradley, Ronon, Stevens & Young · 2600 One Commerce Square · Philadelphia, PA 19103-7098 · 215-564-8000

Benjamin P. Shein · Shein Law Center · 121 South Broad Street, 21st Floor · Philadelphia, PA 19107 · 215-735-6677

Shanin Specter · a · Kline & Specter · http://www.klinespecter.com · 1525 Locust Street, 19th Floor · Philadelphia, PA 19102 · 215-772-1000

Sean P. Wajert · Dechert · Cira Centre · 2929 Arch Street · Philadelphia, PA 19104-2808 · 215-994-4000

Sol H. Weiss · Anapol Schwartz · 1900 Delancey Place · Philadelphia, PA 19103 · 215-735-1130

Pittsburgh

Richard K. Dandrea · Eckert Seamans Cherin & Mellott · U.S. Steel Tower, 44th Floor · 600 Grant Street · Pittsburgh, PA 15219 · 412-566-6000

Joel Persky · Goldberg, Persky & White · 1030 Fifth Avenue · Pittsburgh, PA 15219 · 412-471-3980

Richard C. Polley · Dickie, McCamey & Chilcote · http://www.dmclaw.com · Two PPG Place, Suite 400 Pittsburgh, PA 15222-5402 · 412-281-7272

Arthur H. Stroyd · Del Sole Cavanaugh · The Waterfront Building, Suite 300 · 200 First Avenue · Pittsburgh, PA 15222 · 412-261-2393

C. James Zeszutek · Dinsmore & Shohl · http://www.dinslaw.com · One Oxford Centre, Suite 2800 · 301 Grant Street · Pittsburgh, PA 15219 · 412-281-5000

MEDIA LAW

Pittsburgh

Michael W. Burns · Burns, White & Hickton · http://www.bwhllc.com · Four Northshore Center · 106 Isabella Street · Pittsburgh, PA 15212 · 412-995-3000

Walter P. DeForest III · 2% · DeForest Koscelnik Yokitis Kaplan & Berardinelli · Koppers Building, 30th Floor · 436 Seventh Avenue · Pittsburgh, PA 15219 · 412-227-3100

Scott E. Henderson · a · Thorp, Reed & Armstrong · One Oxford Centre, 14th Floor · 301 Grant Street · Pittsburgh, PA 15219-1425 · 412-394-7711

David A. Strassburger · Strassburger, McKenna, Gutnick & Potter · Four Gateway Center, Suite 2200 · 444 Liberty Avenue · Pittsburgh, PA 15222 · 412-281-5423

Reading

Daniel B. Huyett · Stevens & Lee · 111 North Sixth Street · P.O. Box 679 · Reading, PA 19603-0679 · 610-478-2000

MEDICAL MALPRACTICE LAW

Harrisburg

Sarah W. Arosell · Thomas, Thomas & Hafer · http://www.tthlaw.com · 305 North Front Street, Sixth Floor · P.O. Box 999 · Harrisburg, PA 17108 · 717-237-7100

Evan Black · Thomas, Thomas & Hafer · http://www.tthlaw.com · 305 North Front Street, Sixth Floor · P.O. Box 999 · Harrisburg, PA 17108 · 717-237-7100

Joseph P. Hafer · 2) · Thomas, Thomas & Hafer · http://www.tthlaw.com · 305 North Front Street, Sixth Floor · P.O. Box 999 · Harrisburg, PA 17108 · 717-237-7100

Arthur K. Hoffman · Thomas, Thomas & Hafer · http://www.tthlaw.com · 305 North Front Street, Sixth Floor · P.O. Box 999 · Harrisburg, PA 17108 · 717-237-7100

Lancaster

Willam A. Atlee, Jr. · a · Atlee, Hall & Brookhart · http://www.atleehall.com · Eight North Queen Street P.O. Box 449 · Lancaster, PA 17608-0449 · 717-393-9596

Thomas W. Hall · Atlee, Hall & Brookhart · http://www.atleehall.com · Eight North Queen Street · P.O. Box 449 · Lancaster, PA 17608-0449 · 717-393-9596

Lebanon

Wiley P. Parker · Henry & Beaver · 937 Willow Street · P.O. Box 1140 · Lebanon, PA 17042-1140 · 717-274-3644

Philadelphia

Thomas A. Brophy · Marshall, Dennehey, Warner, Coleman & Goggin · 1845 Walnut Street · Philadelphia, PA 19103-4707 · 215-575-2600

James Lewis Griffith · 2) · Fox Rothschild · 2000 Market Street, 10th Floor · Philadelphia, PA 19103-3291 · 215-299-2000

Howard M. Klein · Conrad O'Brien Gellman & Rohn · http://www.cogr.com · 1515 Market Street, 16th Floor · Philadelphia, PA 19102-1916 · 215-864-9600

Thomas R. Kline · a · Kline & Specter · http://www.klinespecter.com · 1525 Locust Street, 19th Floor · Philadelphia, PA 19102 · 215-772-1000

Slade H. McLaughlin · The Beasley Firm · The Beasley Building · 1125 Walnut Street · Philadelphia, PA 19107 · 215-592-1000

Roberta Pichini · Feldman Shepherd Wohlgelernter Tanner & Weinstock · 1845 Walnut Street, 25th Floor · Philadelphia, PA 19103 · 215-567-8300

Shanin Specter · a · Kline & Specter · http://www.klinespecter.com · 1525 Locust Street, 19th Floor · Philadelphia, PA 19102 · 215-772-1000

Charles G. Young III · a · Young Ricchiuti Caldwell & Heller · 1600 Market Street, Suite 3800 · Philadelphia, PA 19103 · 267-546-1000

Pittsburgh

Joshua Berger · Berger & Lagnese · 310 Grant Steet, Suite 720 · Pittsburgh, PA 15219 · 412-471-4300

Frederick W. Bode III · Dickie, McCamey & Chilcote · http://www.dmclaw.com · Two PPG Place, Suite 400 · Pittsburgh, PA 15222-5402 · 412-281-7272

John A. Caputo · a · Caputo Cox, Schwarzwaelder & Melton · Three Gateway Center, Fifth Floor · 401 Liberty Avenue · Pittsburgh, PA 15222 · 412-391-4990

William R. Caroselli · a · Caroselli, Beachler, McTiernan & Conboy · http://www.cbmclaw.com · 20 Stanwix Street, Seventh Floor · Pittsburgh, PA 15222-4802 · 412-391-9860

Harry S. Cohen · Harry S. Cohen & Associates · Two Chatham Center, Suite 985 · Pittsburgh, PA 15219 412-281-3000

John C. Conti · Dickie, McCamey & Chilcote · http://www.dmclaw.com · Two PPG Place, Suite 400 · Pittsburgh, PA 15222-5402 · 412-281-7272

James A. Dattilo · a · Dattilo & Associates · 100 Ross Street, Suite 103 · Pittsburgh, PA 15219 · 412-391-6300

Michael C. George · The Law Office of Michael C. George · The Grant Building, Suite 712 · 330 Grant Street · Pittsburgh, PA 15219 · 412-566-2299

Paula A. Koczan · Weber Gallagher Simpson Stapleton Fires & Newby · http://www.wglaw.com · Two Gateway Center, Suite 1450 · 603 Stanwix Street · Pittsburgh, PA 15222 · 412-281-4541

Paul Lagnese · Berger & Lagnese · 310 Grant Steet, Suite 720 · Pittsburgh, PA 15219 · 412-471-4300

David J. Lozier · Harry S. Cohen & Associates · Two Chatham Center, Suite 985 · Pittsburgh, PA 15219 · 412-281-3000

Jerry I. Meyers · Meyers, Kenrick, Giuffre & Evans · U.S. Steel Tower, Suite 4800 · 600 Grant Street · Pittsburgh, PA 15219-6003 · 412-281-4100

Wilbur McCoy Otto · a · Dickie, McCamey & Chilcote · http://www.dmclaw.com · Two PPG Place, Suite 400 · Pittsburgh, PA 15222-5402 · 412-281-7272

Jon Perry · Rosen Louik & Perry · http://www.caringlawyers.com · The Frick Building, Suite 200 · 437 Grant Street · Pittsburgh, PA 15219-6003 · 412-281-4200

Neil R. Rosen · Rosen Louik & Perry · http://www.caringlawyers.com · The Frick Building, Suite 200 · 437 Grant Street · Pittsburgh, PA 15219-6003 · 412-281-4200

Paul Kenneth Vey · Pietragallo Gordon Alfano Bosick & Raspanti · One Oxford Centre, 38th Floor · Pittsburgh, PA 15219 · 412-263-2000

David B. White · Burns, White & Hickton · http://www.bwhllc.com · Four Northshore Center · 106 Isabella Street · Pittsburgh, PA 15212 · 412-995-3000

Washington

William D. Phillips · a · Phillips & Faldowski · 29 East Beau Street · Washington, PA 15301 · 724-225-9933

MERGERS & ACQUISITIONS LAW

Harrisburg

John S. Oyler · 2) · McNees Wallace & Nurick · 100 Pine Street · P.O. Box 1166 · Harrisburg, PA 17108-1166 · 717-232-8000

Philadelphia

Barry M. Abelson · a · Pepper Hamilton · http://www.pepperlaw.com · Two Logan Square, Suite 3000 · 18th and Arch Street · Philadelphia, PA 19103-2799 · 215-981-4000

Richard J. Braemer · Ballard Spahr Andrews & Ingersoll · 1735 Market Street, 51st Floor · Philadelphia, PA 19103-7599 · 215-665-8500

Michael H. Friedman · Pepper Hamilton · http://www.pepperlaw.com · Two Logan Square, Suite 3000 · 18th and Arch Street · Philadelphia, PA 19103-2799 · 215-981-4000

Justin P. Klein · Ballard Spahr Andrews & Ingersoll · 1735 Market Street, 51st Floor · Philadelphia, PA 19103-7599 · 215-665-8500

James A. Lebovitz · Dechert · Cira Centre · 2929 Arch Street · Philadelphia, PA 19104-2808 · 215-994-4000

Henry N. Nassau · Dechert · Cira Centre · 2929 Arch Street · Philadelphia, PA 19104-2808 · 215-994-4000

G. Daniel O'Donnell · Dechert · Cira Centre · 2929 Arch Street · Philadelphia, PA 19104-2808 · 215-994-4000

F. Douglas Raymond III · Drinker Biddle & Reath · One Logan Square · 18th and Cherry Streets · Philadelphia, PA 19103-6996 · 215-988-2700

Carmen J. Romano · Dechert · Cira Centre · 2929 Arch Street · Philadelphia, PA 19104-2808 · 215-994-4000

Jason M. Shargel · WolfBlock · http://wolfblock.com · 1650 Arch Street, 22nd Floor · Philadelphia, PA 19103-2097 · 215-977-2000

Kathleen M. Shay · Duane Morris · 30 South 17th Street · Philadelphia, PA 19103-4196 · 215-979-1000

Alan Singer · Morgan Lewis & Bockius · 1701 Market Street · Philadelphia, PA 19103-2921 · 215-963-5000

Barton J. Winokur · ⑳ · Dechert · Cira Centre · 2929 Arch Street · Philadelphia, PA 19104-2808 · 215-994-4000

Pittsburgh

David L. DeNinno · ⑩ · Reed Smith · 435 Sixth Avenue · Pittsburgh, PA 15219-1886 · 412-288-3131

Jack W. Elliott · Cohen & Grigsby · 625 Liberty Avenue · Pittsburgh, PA 15222-3152 · 412-297-4900

Jeremiah G. Garvey · Buchanan Ingersoll & Rooney · http://www.bipc.com · One Oxford Centre, 20th Floor · 301 Grant Street · Pittsburgh, PA 15219-1410 · 412-562-8800

David A. Gerson · Morgan Lewis & Bockius · One Oxford Centre, 32nd Floor · 301 Grant Street · Pittsburgh, PA 15219-6401 · 412-560-3300

Robert T. Harper · ⑩ · Buchanan Ingersoll & Rooney · http://www.bipc.com · One Oxford Centre, 20th Floor · 301 Grant Street · Pittsburgh, PA 15219-1410 · 412-562-8800

Marlee S. Myers · Morgan Lewis & Bockius · One Oxford Centre, 32nd Floor · 301 Grant Street · Pittsburgh, PA 15219-6401 · 412-560-3300

W. Henry Snyder · K&L Gates · Henry W. Oliver Building · 535 Smithfield Street · Pittsburgh, PA 15222-2312 · 412-355-6500

Thomas M. Thompson · ⑩ · Buchanan Ingersoll & Rooney · http://www.bipc.com · One Oxford Centre, 20th Floor · 301 Grant Street · Pittsburgh, PA 15219-1410 · 412-562-8800

Ronald D. West · K&L Gates · Henry W. Oliver Building · 535 Smithfield Street · Pittsburgh, PA 15222-2312 · 412-355-6500

MINING LAW

Indiana

John A. Bonya · ⑩ · Bonya, Gazza & DeGory · 134 South Sixth Street · Indiana, PA 15701-2736 · 724-465-5535

Pittsburgh

Edmund M. Carney · Dinsmore & Shohl · http://www.dinslaw.com · One Oxford Centre, Suite 2800 · 301 Grant Street · Pittsburgh, PA 15219 · 412-281-5000

R. Henry Moore · Jackson Kelly · Three Gateway Center, Suite 1340 · 401 Liberty Avenue · Pittsburgh, PA 15222 · 412-434-8055

Thomas C. Reed · Dinsmore & Shohl · http://www.dinslaw.com · One Oxford Centre, Suite 2800 · 301 Grant Street · Pittsburgh, PA 15219 · 412-281-5000

MUNICIPAL LAW

Pittsburgh

Patrick J. Clair · Goehring, Rutter & Boehm · Frick Building, Suite 1424 · 437 Grant Street · Pittsburgh, PA 15219 · 412-281-0587

Gary J. Gushard · Tucker Arensberg · http://www.tuckerlaw.com · 1500 One PPG Place · Pittsburgh, PA 15222-5401 · 412-566-1212

Blaine A. Lucas · Babst, Calland, Clements and Zomnir · http://www.bccz.com · Two Gateway Center, Eighth Floor · 603 Stanwix Street · Pittsburgh, PA 15222 · 412-394-5400

Robert L. McTiernan · Tucker Arensberg · http://www.tuckerlaw.com · 1500 One PPG Place · Pittsburgh, PA 15222-5401 · 412-566-1212

MUTUAL FUNDS LAW

Philadelphia

Bruce G. Leto · Stradley, Ronon, Stevens & Young · 2600 One Commerce Square · Philadelphia, PA 19103-7098 · 215-564-8000

Michael P. Malloy · Drinker Biddle & Reath · One Logan Square · 18th and Cherry Streets · Philadelphia, PA 19103-6996 · 215-988-2700

William H. Rheiner · Stradley, Ronon, Stevens & Young · 2600 One Commerce Square · Philadelphia, PA 19103-7098 · 215-564-8000

Pittsburgh

Stephen A. Keen · Reed Smith · 435 Sixth Avenue · Pittsburgh, PA 15219-1886 · 412-288-3131

NATURAL RESOURCES LAW

Indiana

John A. Bonya · a · Bonya, Gazza & DeGory · 134 South Sixth Street · Indiana, PA 15701-2736 · 724-465-5535

Pittsburgh

Samuel L. Douglass · 2) · Rothman Gordon · Grant Building, Third Floor · 310 Grant Street · Pittsburgh, PA 15219-2202 · 412-338-1100

Donald P. Eriksen · Tucker Arensberg · http://www.tuckerlaw.com · 1500 One PPG Place · Pittsburgh, PA 15222-5401 · 412-566-1212

David J. Laurent · Buchanan Ingersoll & Rooney · http://www.bipc.com · One Oxford Centre, 20th Floor 301 Grant Street · Pittsburgh, PA 15219-1410 · 412-562-8800

R. Henry Moore · Jackson Kelly · Three Gateway Center, Suite 1340 · 401 Liberty Avenue · Pittsburgh, PA 15222 · 412-434-8055

Thomas C. Reed · Dinsmore & Shohl · http://www.dinslaw.com · One Oxford Centre, Suite 2800 · 301 Grant Street · Pittsburgh, PA 15219 · 412-281-5000

NON-PROFIT/CHARITIES LAW

Bala Cynwyd

Joseph E. Lundy · Lundy & Flynn · Two Bala Plaza, Suite 300 · Bala Cynwyd, PA 19004 · 610-660-7788

Harrisburg

Stanley A. Smith · Rhoads & Sinon · M & T Bank Building, 12th Floor · One South Market Square · P.O. Box 1146 · Harrisburg, PA 17108-1146 · 717-233-5731

Philadelphia

Frederick J. Gerhart · Dechert · Cira Centre · 2929 Arch Street · Philadelphia, PA 19104-2808 · 215-994-4000

Pittsburgh

Carolyn D. Duronio · Reed Smith · 435 Sixth Avenue · Pittsburgh, PA 15219-1886 · 412-288-3131

Christopher F. Farrell · Cohen & Grigsby · 625 Liberty Avenue · Pittsburgh, PA 15222-3152 · 412-297-4900

Robert A. Johnson · ⑳ · Buchanan Ingersoll & Rooney · http://www.bipc.com · One Oxford Centre, 20th Floor · 301 Grant Street · Pittsburgh, PA 15219-1410 · 412-562-8800

NON-WHITE-COLLAR CRIMINAL DEFENSE

Ardmore

Anna M. Durbin · Law Offices of Anna M. Durbin · 50 Rittenhouse Place · Ardmore, PA 19003 · 610-649-8200

Doylestown

William L. Goldman, Jr. · Goldman Law Office · 90 East State Street · P.O. Box 1989 · Doylestown, PA 18901 · 215-348-2605

Erie

Leonard G. Ambrose III · ⑩ · The Ambrose Law Firm · 319 West Eighth Street · Erie, PA 16502 · 814-459-5900

Greensburg

Richard H. Galloway · Quatrini Rafferty Galloway · 550 East Pittsburgh Street · Greensburg, PA 15601 · 724-837-0080

Robert I. Johnson · Belden Law · Belden Building · 117 North Main Street · Greensburg, PA 15601 · 724-834-0300

Jeffrey D. Monzo · Belden Law · Belden Building · 117 North Main Street · Greensburg, PA 15601 · 724-834-0300

Harrisburg

William J. Fulton · William J. Fulton · 106 Walnut Street · Harrisburg, PA 17101 · 717-233-5133

Joshua D. Lock · Goldberg Katzman · Strawberry Square · 320 Market Street · P.O. Box 1268 · Harrisburg, PA 17108-1268 · 717-234-4161

Lemoyne

William C. Costopoulos · 2% · Costopoulos, Foster & Fields · 831 Market Street · P.O. Box 222 · Lemoyne, PA 17043-0222 · 717-761-2121

Malvern

Thomas A. Bergstrom · a · Thomas A. Bergstrom · 138 Davis Road · Malvern, PA 19355 · 610-251-9260

Media

Arthur T. Donato, Jr. · a · Arthur T. Donato, Jr. · 211-213 North Olive Street · Media, PA 19063-2810 · 610-565-4747

New Kensington

Thomas R. Ceraso · a · Thomas R. Ceraso · 425 Finnin Road · New Kensington, PA 15068-2506 · 412-558-3699

Philadelphia

Ellen C. Brotman · Montgomery, McCracken, Walker & Rhoads · 123 South Broad Street · Avenue Of The Arts · Philadelphia, PA 19109-1029 · 215-772-1500

Dennis J. Cogan · a · Dennis J. Cogan · http://www.denniscogan.com · 2000 Market Street, Suite 2925 · Philadelphia, PA 19103 · 215-545-2400

Frank De Simone · Frank De Simone · 1880 John F. Kennedy Boulevard, Suite 600 · Philadelphia, PA 19103 · 215-567-3507

Jules Epstein · a · Kairys, Rudovsky, Messing & Feinberg · The Cast Iron Building, Suite 501 South · 718 Arch Street · Philadelphia, PA 19106 · 215-925-4400

Stephen R. LaCheen · a · LaCheen Dixon Wittels & Greenberg · 1429 Walnut Street, 13th Floor · Philadelphia, PA 19102 · 215-735-5900

Gregory P. Miller · Drinker Biddle & Reath · One Logan Square · 18th and Cherry Streets · Philadelphia, PA 19103-6996 · 215-988-2700

Catherine M. Recker · Welsh & Recker · 2000 Market Street, Suite 2903 · Philadelphia, PA 19103 · 215-972-6430

Richard A. Sprague · 2% · Sprague & Sprague · The Wellington Building, Suite 400 · 135 South 19th Street · Philadelphia, PA 19103 · 215-561-7681

Christopher D. Warren · Christopher D. Warren · 1500 Walnut Street, Suite 1500 · Philadelphia, PA 19102 · 215-546-3750

Pittsburgh

Paul D. Boas · a · The Law Office of Paul D. Boas · Law and Finance Building, Fifth Floor · 429 Fourth Avenue · Pittsburgh, PA 15219 · 412-391-7707

Robert G. Del Greco, Jr. · Dickie, McCamey & Chilcote · http://www.dmclaw.com · Two PPG Place, Suite 400 · Pittsburgh, PA 15222-5402 · 412-281-7272

Thomas J. Farrell · Dreier · 1000 Koppers Building · 436 Seventh Avenue · Pittsburgh, PA 15219 · 412-894-1380

J. Alan Johnson · a · Johnson & Eddy · 1720 Gulf Tower · 707 Grant Street · Pittsburgh, PA 15219 · 412-338-4790

Mark Lancaster · Mark Lancaster · 445 Fort Pitt Boulevard, Suite 100 · Pittsburgh, PA 15219 · 412-355-0915

Stanton D. Levenson · a · Stanton D. Levenson · http://www.seriousdefense.com · 1715 Gulf Tower · Pittsburgh, PA 15219 · 412-355-0650

Charles J. Porter · Brucker, Schneider & Porter · 300 Weyman Road, Suite 320 · Pittsburgh, PA 15236 · 412-881-6620

Caroline M. Roberto · a · Law Office of Caroline M. Roberto · Law and Finance Building, Fifth Floor · 429 Fourth Avenue · Pittsburgh, PA 15219 · 412-391-4071

Gary B. Zimmerman · Gary B. Zimmerman · 100 Ross Street, Suite 304 · Pittsburgh, PA 15219-2013 · 412-566-2133

West Chester

Robert J. Donatoni · Donatoni & Kratsa · 200 North High Street, Suite 301 · West Chester, PA 19380 · 610-719-0500

OIL & GAS LAW

Greensburg

Sean Cassidy · Sean Cassidy · 118 North Main Street · Greensburg, PA 15601 · 724-836-4900

Meadville

Russel Schetroma · Culbertson, Weiss, Schetroma and Schug · 201 Chestnut Street, Suite 200 · Meadville, PA 16335-2629 · 814-336-6400

Pittsburgh

Donald P. Eriksen · Tucker Arensberg · http://www.tuckerlaw.com · 1500 One PPG Place · Pittsburgh, PA 15222-5401 · 412-566-1212

PERSONAL INJURY LITIGATION

Bethlehem

Peter J. Curry · a · Thomas, Thomas & Hafer · http://www.tthlaw.com · CrownePointe Corp Center, Suite 301 · 3101 Emrick Boulevard · Bethlehem, PA 18020 · 610-868-1675

Erie

Andrew J. Conner · 2) · Conner Riley Friedman & Weichler · The Bell Telephone Building · 17 West 10th Street · P.O. Box 860 · Erie, PA 16512-0860 · 814-453-3343

Steven E. Riley, Jr. · Conner Riley Friedman & Weichler · The Bell Telephone Building · 17 West 10th Street · P.O. Box 860 · Erie, PA 16512-0860 · 814-453-3343

Greensburg

Richard H. Galloway · Quatrini Rafferty Galloway · 550 East Pittsburgh Street · Greensburg, PA 15601 · 724-837-0080

Harrisburg

Richard C. Angino · 2% · Angino & Rovner · http://www.angino-rovner.com · 4503 North Front Street · Harrisburg, PA 17110-1708 · 717-238-6791

Joseph P. Hafer · 2) · Thomas, Thomas & Hafer · http://www.tthlaw.com · 305 North Front Street, Sixth Floor · P.O. Box 999 · Harrisburg, PA 17108 · 717-237-7100

Dave L. Lutz · Angino & Rovner · http://www.angino-rovner.com · 4503 North Front Street · Harrisburg, PA 17110-1708 · 717-238-6791

Joseph M. Melillo · Angino & Rovner · http://www.angino-rovner.com · 4503 North Front Street · Harrisburg, PA 17110-1708 · 717-238-6791

Neil J. Rovner · a · Angino & Rovner · http://www.angino-rovner.com · 4503 North Front Street · Harrisburg, PA 17110-1708 · 717-238-6791

Lee C. Swartz · a · Tucker Arensberg · http://www.tuckerlaw.com · 111 North Front Street · P.O. Box 889 · Harrisburg, PA 17108-0889 · 717-234-4121

James K. Thomas II · Thomas, Thomas & Hafer · http://www.tthlaw.com · 305 North Front Street, Sixth Floor · P.O. Box 999 · Harrisburg, PA 17108 · 717-237-7100

Richard H. Wix · a · Wix, Wenger & Weidner · 4705 Duke Street · Harrisburg, PA 17109-3099 · 717-652-8455

King of Prussia

Robert St. Leger Goggin · a · Marshall, Dennehey, Warner, Coleman & Goggin · 620 Freedom Business Center, Suite 300 · King of Prussia, PA 19406-1330 · 610-354-8250

Daniel J. Sherry · Marshall, Dennehey, Warner, Coleman & Goggin · 620 Freedom Business Center, Suite 300 · King of Prussia, PA 19406-1330 · 610-354-8250

Kingston

Joseph A. Quinn, Jr. · 2) · Hourigan, Kluger & Quinn · http://www.hkqpc.com · 600 Third Avenue · Kingston, PA 18704-5815 · 570-287-3000

Lancaster

Willam A. Atlee, Jr. · a · Atlee, Hall & Brookhart · http://www.atleehall.com · Eight North Queen Street P.O. Box 449 · Lancaster, PA 17608-0449 · 717-393-9596

Thomas W. Hall · Atlee, Hall & Brookhart · http://www.atleehall.com · Eight North Queen Street · P.O. Box 449 · Lancaster, PA 17608-0449 · 717-393-9596

Christopher W. Mattson · a · Barley Snyder · 126 East King Street · Lancaster, PA 17602-2893 · 717-299-5201

Dianne M. Nast · Roda & Nast · 801 Estelle Drive · Lancaster, PA 17601-2130 · 717-892-3000

Latrobe

Ned J. Nakles, Jr. · Nakles & Nakles · Lincoln Professional Building · 1714 Lincoln Avenue · Latrobe, PA 15650-3097 · 724-539-1291

Lebanon

Wiley P. Parker · Henry & Beaver · 937 Willow Street · P.O. Box 1140 · Lebanon, PA 17042-1140 · 717-274-3644

Lemoyne

Jeffrey B. Rettig · Johnson, Duffie, Stewart & Weidner · 301 Market Street · P.O. Box 109 · Lemoyne, PA 17043-0109 · 717-761-4540

Media

Joseph M. Fioravanti · Joseph M. Fioravanti · 217 North Monroe Street · P.O. Box 1826 · Media, PA 19063 · 610-892-7370

Philadelphia

John Barrett, Jr. · Buchanan Ingersoll & Rooney · http://www.bipc.com · 1835 Market Street, 14th Floor Philadelphia, PA 19103-2985 · 215-665-8700

Larry Bendesky · Saltz Mongeluzzi Barrett & Bendesky · One Liberty Place, 52nd Floor · 1650 Market Street · Philadelphia, PA 19103 · 215-496-8282

Martin K. Brigham · Raynes McCarty · http://www.raynesmccarty.com · 1845 Walnut Street, 20th Floor · Philadelphia, PA 19103 · 215-568-6190

Robert M. Britton · Post & Schell · Four Penn Center, 14th Floor · 1600 John F. Kennedy Boulevard · Philadelphia, PA 19103-2808 · 215-587-1000

Thomas A. Brophy · Marshall, Dennehey, Warner, Coleman & Goggin · 1845 Walnut Street · Philadelphia, PA 19103-4707 · 215-575-2600

Stewart L. Cohen · Cohen, Placitella & Roth · Two Commerce Square, Suite 2900 · 2001 Market Street · Philadelphia, PA 19103 · 215-567-3500

Robert J. Coleman · Marshall, Dennehey, Warner, Coleman & Goggin · 1845 Walnut Street · Philadelphia, PA 19103-4707 · 215-575-2600

A. Roy Decaro · Raynes McCarty · http://www.raynesmccarty.com · 1845 Walnut Street, 20th Floor · Philadelphia, PA 19103 · 215-568-6190

Thomas J. Duffy · Duffy + Partners · http://www.duffyfirm.com · One Liberty Place, 55th Floor · Philadelphia, PA 19103 · 215-238-8700

Edward L. Edelstein · ADR Options · http://www.adroptions.com · Two Commerce Square, Suite 1100 · 2001 Market Street · Philadelphia, PA 19103-7044 · 215-564-1775

Keith S. Erbstein · Young Ricchiuti Caldwell & Heller · 1600 Market Street, Suite 3800 · Philadelphia, PA 19103 · 267-546-1000

Joseph H. Foster · 2% · White and Williams · 1800 One Liberty Place · Philadelphia, PA 19103-7395 · 215-864-7000

Joseph W. Fullem, Jr. · a · Thorp, Reed & Armstrong · 400 Market Street, Suite 200 · Philadelphia, PA 19106 · 215-829-9900

Allan H. Gordon · Kolsby, Gordon, Robin, Shore & Bezar · 2000 Market Street, 28th Floor · Philadelphia, PA 19103 · 215-851-9700

James Lewis Griffith · 2) · Fox Rothschild · 2000 Market Street, 10th Floor · Philadelphia, PA 19103-3291 · 215-299-2000

Peter J. Hoffman · a · Eckert Seamans Cherin & Mellott · Two Liberty Place, 22nd Floor · 50 South 16th Street · Philadelphia, PA 19102 · 215-851-8400

Thomas R. Kline · a · Kline & Specter · http://www.klinespecter.com · 1525 Locust Street, 19th Floor · Philadelphia, PA 19102 · 215-772-1000

Arnold Levin · Levin, Fishbein, Sedran & Berman · 510 Walnut Street, Suite 500 · Philadelphia, PA 19106-3697 · 215-592-1500

S. Gerald Litvin · 2% · Morgan Lewis & Bockius · 1701 Market Street · Philadelphia, PA 19103-2921 · 215-963-5000

Gerald A. McHugh, Jr. · Raynes McCarty · http://www.raynesmccarty.com · 1845 Walnut Street, 20th Floor · Philadelphia, PA 19103 · 215-568-6190

J. Bruce McKissock · Marshall, Dennehey, Warner, Coleman & Goggin · 1845 Walnut Street · Philadelphia, PA 19103-4707 · 215-575-2600

Slade H. McLaughlin · The Beasley Firm · The Beasley Building · 1125 Walnut Street · Philadelphia, PA 19107 · 215-592-1000

Peter S. Miller · Marshall, Dennehey, Warner, Coleman & Goggin · 1845 Walnut Street · Philadelphia, PA 19103-4707 · 215-575-2600

Robert J. Mongeluzzi · Saltz Mongeluzzi Barrett & Bendesky · One Liberty Place, 52nd Floor · 1650 Market Street · Philadelphia, PA 19103 · 215-496-8282

William J. O'Brien · a · Conrad O'Brien Gellman & Rohn · http://www.cogr.com · 1515 Market Street, 16th Floor · Philadelphia, PA 19102-1916 · 215-864-9600

Roberta Pichini · Feldman Shepherd Wohlgelernter Tanner & Weinstock · 1845 Walnut Street, 25th Floor · Philadelphia, PA 19103 · 215-567-8300

Rosemary Pinto · Feldman & Pinto · 1604 Locust Street, Second Floor · Philadelphia, PA 19103 · 215-546-2604

Thomas Raup · ADR Options · http://www.adroptions.com · Two Commerce Square, Suite 1100 · 2001 Market Street · Philadelphia, PA 19103-7044 · 215-564-1775

Stephen Edward Raynes · Raynes McCarty · http://www.raynesmccarty.com · 1845 Walnut Street, 20th Floor · Philadelphia, PA 19103 · 215-568-6190

Harry M. Roth · Cohen, Placitella & Roth · Two Commerce Square, Suite 2900 · 2001 Market Street · Philadelphia, PA 19103 · 215-567-3500

Daniel J. Ryan, Jr. · Marshall, Dennehey, Warner, Coleman & Goggin · 1845 Walnut Street · Philadelphia, PA 19103-4707 · 215-575-2600

Ronald H. Sherr · ADR Options · http://www.adroptions.com · Two Commerce Square, Suite 1100 · 2001 Market Street · Philadelphia, PA 19103-7044 · 215-564-1775

Shanin Specter · a · Kline & Specter · http://www.klinespecter.com · 1525 Locust Street, 19th Floor · Philadelphia, PA 19102 · 215-772-1000

Wayne R. Spivey · a · Shrager, Spivey & Sachs · http://www.shragerlaw.com · Two Commerce Square, 32nd Floor · 2001 Market Street · Philadelphia, PA 19103 · 215-568-7771

Andrew J. Stern · Kline & Specter · http://www.klinespecter.com · 1525 Locust Street, 19th Floor · Philadelphia, PA 19102 · 215-772-1000

Philip B. Toran · Marshall, Dennehey, Warner, Coleman & Goggin · 1845 Walnut Street · Philadelphia, PA 19103-4707 · 215-575-2600

Eric A. Weiss · Marshall, Dennehey, Warner, Coleman & Goggin · 1845 Walnut Street · Philadelphia, PA 19103-4707 · 215-575-2600

Charles G. Young III · a · Young Ricchiuti Caldwell & Heller · 1600 Market Street, Suite 3800 · Philadelphia, PA 19103 · 267-546-1000

Pittsburgh

Edward J. Balzarini, Sr. · 2% · Balzarini & Watson · 3303 Grant Building · 310 Grant Street · Pittsburgh, PA 15219-2394 · 412-471-1200

Edwin H. Beachler · a · Caroselli, Beachler, McTiernan & Conboy · http://www.cbmclaw.com · 20 Stanwix Street, Seventh Floor · Pittsburgh, PA 15222-4802 · 412-391-9860

Thomas A. Berret · Meyer, Unkovic & Scott · http://www.muslaw.com · 1300 Oliver Building · 535 Smithfield Street · Pittsburgh, PA 15222 · 412-456-2800

John A. Caputo · a · Caputo Cox, Schwarzwaelder & Melton · Three Gateway Center, Fifth Floor · 401 Liberty Avenue · Pittsburgh, PA 15222 · 412-391-4990

William R. Caroselli · a · Caroselli, Beachler, McTiernan & Conboy · http://www.cbmclaw.com · 20 Stanwix Street, Seventh Floor · Pittsburgh, PA 15222-4802 · 412-391-9860

John C. Conti · Dickie, McCamey & Chilcote · http://www.dmclaw.com · Two PPG Place, Suite 400 · Pittsburgh, PA 15222-5402 · 412-281-7272

James A. Dattilo · a · Dattilo & Associates · 100 Ross Street, Suite 103 · Pittsburgh, PA 15219 · 412-391-6300

Carl A. Eck · 2) · Meyer, Darragh, Buckler, Bebenek & Eck · U.S. Steel Tower, Suite 4850 · 600 Grant Street · Pittsburgh, PA 15219 · 412-261-6600

Charles E. Evans · a · Meyers, Kenrick, Giuffre & Evans · U.S. Steel Tower, Suite 4800 · 600 Grant Street · Pittsburgh, PA 15219-6003 · 412-281-4100

David B. Fawcett · 2% · Dickie, McCamey & Chilcote · http://www.dmclaw.com · Two PPG Place, Suite 400 · Pittsburgh, PA 15222-5402 · 412-281-7272

Craig Fishman · Shenderovich, Shenderovich & Fishman · http://www.ssf-lawfirm.com · Law & Finance Building, Suite 1600 · 429 Fourth Avenue · Pittsburgh, PA 15219 · 412-391-7610

William F. Goodrich · Goodrich & Goodrich · http://goodlazlaw.com · Law & Finance Building, Suite 900 · 429 Fourth Avenue · Pittsburgh, PA 15219 · 412-281-1455

Dennis C. Harrington · 2% · The McClelland Law Group · 100 Ross Street, Suite 102 · Pittsburgh, PA 15219-2013 · 412-391-7343

Philip A. Ignelzi · ⑩ · Ogg, Cordes, Murphy & Ignelzi · Riverview Place, Fourth Floor · 245 Fort Pitt Boulevard · Pittsburgh, PA 15222-1511 · 412-471-8500

George M. Kontos · Swensen, Perer & Kontos · One Oxford Centre, Suite 2501 · Pittsburgh, PA 15219 · 412-281-1970

Arthur J. Leonard · Robb Leonard Mulvihill · 2300 One Mellon Center, 23rd Floor · 500 Grant Street · Pittsburgh, PA 15219 · 412-281-5431

Joseph L. Luvara · Dickie, McCamey & Chilcote · http://www.dmclaw.com · Two PPG Place, Suite 400 · Pittsburgh, PA 15222-5402 · 412-281-7272

Michael L. Magulick · Wayman, Irvin & McAuley · 1624 Frick Building · 437 Grant Street · Pittsburgh, PA 15219 · 412-566-2970

Robert J. Marino · Dickie, McCamey & Chilcote · http://www.dmclaw.com · Two PPG Place, Suite 400 · Pittsburgh, PA 15222-5402 · 412-281-7272

Regis M. McClelland · The McClelland Law Group · 100 Ross Street, Suite 102 · Pittsburgh, PA 15219-2013 · 412-391-7343

Renee A. Metal · Rosen Louik & Perry · http://www.caringlawyers.com · The Frick Building, Suite 200 · 437 Grant Street · Pittsburgh, PA 15219-6003 · 412-281-4200

Jerry I. Meyers · Meyers, Kenrick, Giuffre & Evans · U.S. Steel Tower, Suite 4800 · 600 Grant Street · Pittsburgh, PA 15219-6003 · 412-281-4100

James R. Miller · ⑩ · Dickie, McCamey & Chilcote · http://www.dmclaw.com · Two PPG Place, Suite 400 · Pittsburgh, PA 15222-5402 · 412-281-7272

Dennis St. J. Mulvihill · ⑩ · Robb Leonard Mulvihill · 2300 One Mellon Center, 23rd Floor · 500 Grant Street · Pittsburgh, PA 15219 · 412-281-5431

David J. Obermeier · Dickie, McCamey & Chilcote · http://www.dmclaw.com · Two PPG Place, Suite 400 · Pittsburgh, PA 15222-5402 · 412-281-7272

Gary J. Ogg · Ogg, Cordes, Murphy & Ignelzi · Riverview Place, Fourth Floor · 245 Fort Pitt Boulevard · Pittsburgh, PA 15222-1511 · 412-471-8500

Wilbur McCoy Otto · ⑩ · Dickie, McCamey & Chilcote · http://www.dmclaw.com · Two PPG Place, Suite 400 · Pittsburgh, PA 15222-5402 · 412-281-7272

Alan H. Perer · Swensen, Perer & Kontos · One Oxford Centre, Suite 2501 · Pittsburgh, PA 15219 · 412-281-1970

Jon Perry · Rosen Louik & Perry · http://www.caringlawyers.com · The Frick Building, Suite 200 · 437 Grant Street · Pittsburgh, PA 15219-6003 · 412-281-4200

Anthony P. Picadio · ⑩ · Picadio Sneath Miller & Norton · 4710 U.S. Steel Tower · 600 Grant Street · Pittsburgh, PA 15219-2702 · 412-288-4000

William A. Pietragallo II · ⑩ · Pietragallo Gordon Alfano Bosick & Raspanti · One Oxford Centre, 38th Floor · Pittsburgh, PA 15219 · 412-263-2000

John T. Pion · Dickie, McCamey & Chilcote · http://www.dmclaw.com · Two PPG Place, Suite 400 · Pittsburgh, PA 15222-5402 · 412-281-7272

John E. Quinn · Portnoy & Quinn · http://www.paqlawyers.com · One Oxford Centre, 36th Floor · 301 Grant Street · Pittsburgh, PA 15219-6401 · 412-765-3800

John A. Robb, Jr. · Robb Leonard Mulvihill · 2300 One Mellon Center, 23rd Floor · 500 Grant Street · Pittsburgh, PA 15219 · 412-281-5431

Neil R. Rosen · Rosen Louik & Perry · http://www.caringlawyers.com · The Frick Building, Suite 200 · 437 Grant Street · Pittsburgh, PA 15219-6003 · 412-281-4200

Richard J. Schubert · Alpern Schubert · 2727 Grant Building · 330 Grant Street · Pittsburgh, PA 15219 · 412-434-7790

Henry M. Sneath · Picadio Sneath Miller & Norton · 4710 U.S. Steel Tower · 600 Grant Street · Pittsburgh, PA 15219-2702 · 412-288-4000

Louis M. Tarasi, Jr. · Tarasi & Tarasi · 510 Third Avenue · Pittsburgh, PA 15219 · 412-391-7135

John Edward Wall · Dickie, McCamey & Chilcote · http://www.dmclaw.com · Two PPG Place, Suite 400 Pittsburgh, PA 15222-5402 · 412-281-7272

Henry H. Wallace · Wallace Barozzini Harvey & Zimmaro · 310 Grant Street, Suite 2220 · Pittsburgh, PA 15219 · 412-391-6666

David B. White · Burns, White & Hickton · http://www.bwhllc.com · Four Northshore Center · 106 Isabella Street · Pittsburgh, PA 15212 · 412-995-3000

William M. Wycoff · a · Thorp, Reed & Armstrong · One Oxford Centre, 14th Floor · 301 Grant Street · Pittsburgh, PA 15219-1425 · 412-394-7711

Scranton

John R. Lenahan, Jr. · a · Lenahan & Dempsey · The Kane Building, Suite 400 · 116 North Washington Avenue · P.O. Box 234 · Scranton, PA 18501-0234 · 570-346-2097

Joseph P. Lenahan · Lenahan & Dempsey · The Kane Building, Suite 400 · 116 North Washington Avenue · P.O. Box 234 · Scranton, PA 18501-0234 · 570-346-2097

Robert W. Munley · a · Munley, Munley and Cartwright · Forum Plaza · 227 Penn Avenue · Scranton, PA 18503 · 570-346-7401

State College

Robert L. Martin · McNees Wallace & Nurick · 330 Innovation Boulevard, Suite 301 · State College, PA 16803 · 814-867-8500

Washington

William D. Phillips · a · Phillips & Faldowski · 29 East Beau Street · Washington, PA 15301 · 724-225-9933

PRIVATE FUNDS LAW

Philadelphia

Steven B. King · Ballard Spahr Andrews & Ingersoll · 1735 Market Street, 51st Floor · Philadelphia, PA 19103-7599 · 215-665-8500

G. Daniel O'Donnell · Dechert · Cira Centre · 2929 Arch Street · Philadelphia, PA 19104-2808 · 215-994-4000

Malvern

Joseph J. McHale · Stradley, Ronon, Stevens & Young · Great Valley Corporate Center · 30 Valley Stream Parkway · Malvern, PA 19355-1481 · 610-640-5800

Philadelphia

Martin K. Brigham · Raynes McCarty · http://www.raynesmccarty.com · 1845 Walnut Street, 20th Floor · Philadelphia, PA 19103 · 215-568-6190

Hope S. Freiwald · Dechert · Cira Centre · 2929 Arch Street · Philadelphia, PA 19104-2808 · 215-994-4000

Andrew R. Gaddes · Dechert · Cira Centre · 2929 Arch Street · Philadelphia, PA 19104-2808 · 215-994-4000

James Lewis Griffith · 2) · Fox Rothschild · 2000 Market Street, 10th Floor · Philadelphia, PA 19103-3291 · 215-299-2000

Joseph K. Hetrick · Dechert · Cira Centre · 2929 Arch Street · Philadelphia, PA 19104-2808 · 215-994-4000

Thomas R. Kline · a · Kline & Specter · http://www.klinespecter.com · 1525 Locust Street, 19th Floor · Philadelphia, PA 19102 · 215-772-1000

John P. Lavelle, Jr. · Ballard Spahr Andrews & Ingersoll · 1735 Market Street, 51st Floor · Philadelphia, PA 19103-7599 · 215-665-8500

Robert A. Limbacher · Dechert · Cira Centre · 2929 Arch Street · Philadelphia, PA 19104-2808 · 215-994-4000

Fred T. Magaziner · Dechert · Cira Centre · 2929 Arch Street · Philadelphia, PA 19104-2808 · 215-994-4000

Stephen J. McConnell · Dechert · Cira Centre · 2929 Arch Street · Philadelphia, PA 19104-2808 · 215-994-4000

Beatrice O'Donnell · Duane Morris · 30 South 17th Street · Philadelphia, PA 19103-4196 · 215-979-1000

James D. Pagliaro · Morgan Lewis & Bockius · 1701 Market Street · Philadelphia, PA 19103-2921 · 215-963-5000

Rosemary Pinto · Feldman & Pinto · 1604 Locust Street, Second Floor · Philadelphia, PA 19103 · 215-546-2604

William J. Ricci · Lavin, O'Neil, Ricci, Cedrone & DiSipio · 190 North Independence Mall West, Suite 500 · Philadelphia, PA 19106 · 215-627-0303

Ronald H. Sherr · ADR Options · http://www.adroptions.com · Two Commerce Square, Suite 1100 · 2001 Market Street · Philadelphia, PA 19103-7044 · 215-564-1775

Madeline M. Sherry · Gibbons · http://www.gibbonslaw.com · 1700 Two Logan Square · 18th & Arch Streets · Philadelphia, PA 19103-2769 · 215-665-0400

Shanin Specter · a · Kline & Specter · http://www.klinespecter.com · 1525 Locust Street, 19th Floor · Philadelphia, PA 19102 · 215-772-1000

Andrew J. Trevelise · Reed Smith · 2500 One Liberty Place · 1650 Market Street · Philadelphia, PA 19103 · 215-851-8100

Sean P. Wajert · Dechert · Cira Centre · 2929 Arch Street · Philadelphia, PA 19104-2808 · 215-994-4000

Eric A. Weiss · Marshall, Dennehey, Warner, Coleman & Goggin · 1845 Walnut Street · Philadelphia, PA 19103-4707 · 215-575-2600

Pittsburgh

Frederick W. Bode III · Dickie, McCamey & Chilcote · http://www.dmclaw.com · Two PPG Place, Suite 400 · Pittsburgh, PA 15222-5402 · 412-281-7272

William R. Caroselli · a · Caroselli, Beachler, McTiernan & Conboy · http://www.cbmclaw.com · 20 Stanwix Street, Seventh Floor · Pittsburgh, PA 15222-4802 · 412-391-9860

Craig E. Coleman · Caroselli, Beachler, McTiernan & Conboy · http://www.cbmclaw.com · 20 Stanwix Street, Seventh Floor · Pittsburgh, PA 15222-4802 · 412-391-9860

Richard K. Dandrea · Eckert Seamans Cherin & Mellott · U.S. Steel Tower, 44th Floor · 600 Grant Street · Pittsburgh, PA 15219 · 412-566-6000

Patricia L. Dodge · Meyer, Unkovic & Scott · http://www.muslaw.com · 1300 Oliver Building · 535 Smithfield Street · Pittsburgh, PA 15222 · 412-456-2800

John E. Hall · Eckert Seamans Cherin & Mellott · U.S. Steel Tower, 44th Floor · 600 Grant Street · Pittsburgh, PA 15219 · 412-566-6000

Paul M. Pohl · Jones Day · One Mellon Center, Suite 4500 · 500 Grant Street · Pittsburgh, PA 15219-2502 · 412-391-3939

Arthur H. Stroyd · Del Sole Cavanaugh · The Waterfront Building, Suite 300 · 200 First Avenue · Pittsburgh, PA 15222 · 412-261-2393

Thomas J. Sweeney · Eckert Seamans Cherin & Mellott · U.S. Steel Tower, 44th Floor · 600 Grant Street Pittsburgh, PA 15219 · 412-566-6000

John Edward Wall · Dickie, McCamey & Chilcote · http://www.dmclaw.com · Two PPG Place, Suite 400 Pittsburgh, PA 15222-5402 · 412-281-7272

C. James Zeszutek · Dinsmore & Shohl · http://www.dinslaw.com · One Oxford Centre, Suite 2800 · 301 Grant Street · Pittsburgh, PA 15219 · 412-281-5000

Wayne

William J. Conroy · Campbell Campbell Edwards & Conroy · Chesterbrook Corporate Center, Suite 300 690 Lee Road · Wayne, PA 19087 · 610-964-1900

PROFESSIONAL MALPRACTICE LAW

Harrisburg

Joseph P. Hafer · 2) · Thomas, Thomas & Hafer · http://www.tthlaw.com · 305 North Front Street, Sixth Floor · P.O. Box 999 · Harrisburg, PA 17108 · 717-237-7100

Lancaster

Willam A. Atlee, Jr. · a · Atlee, Hall & Brookhart · http://www.atleehall.com · Eight North Queen Street P.O. Box 449 · Lancaster, PA 17608-0449 · 717-393-9596

Philadelphia

Laura Feldman · Feldman & Pinto · 1604 Locust Street, Second Floor · Philadelphia, PA 19103 · 215-546-2604

James Lewis Griffith · 2) · Fox Rothschild · 2000 Market Street, 10th Floor · Philadelphia, PA 19103-3291 · 215-299-2000

Peter J. Hoffman · a · Eckert Seamans Cherin & Mellott · Two Liberty Place, 22nd Floor · 50 South 16th Street · Philadelphia, PA 19102 · 215-851-8400

Arthur W. Lefco · Marshall, Dennehey, Warner, Coleman & Goggin · 1845 Walnut Street · Philadelphia, PA 19103-4707 · 215-575-2600

Beatrice O'Donnell · Duane Morris · 30 South 17th Street · Philadelphia, PA 19103-4196 · 215-979-1000

Philip B. Toran · Marshall, Dennehey, Warner, Coleman & Goggin · 1845 Walnut Street · Philadelphia, PA 19103-4707 · 215-575-2600

Pittsburgh

Michael L. Magulick · Wayman, Irvin & McAuley · 1624 Frick Building · 437 Grant Street · Pittsburgh, PA 15219 · 412-566-2970

PROJECT FINANCE LAW

Pittsburgh

Charles E. Harris III · K&L Gates · Henry W. Oliver Building · 535 Smithfield Street · Pittsburgh, PA 15222-2312 · 412-355-6500

Daniel J. Perry · Tucker Arensberg · http://www.tuckerlaw.com · 1500 One PPG Place · Pittsburgh, PA 15222-5401 · 412-566-1212

PUBLIC FINANCE LAW

Harrisburg

Jens H. Damgaard · Rhoads & Sinon · M & T Bank Building, 12th Floor · One South Market Square · P.O. Box 1146 · Harrisburg, PA 17108-1146 · 717-233-5731

Philadelphia

Kevin R. Cunningham · Ballard Spahr Andrews & Ingersoll · 1735 Market Street, 51st Floor · Philadelphia, PA 19103-7599 · 215-665-8500

Dianne Coady Fisher · Greenberg Traurig · http://www.gtlaw.com · Two Commerce Square, Suite 2700 · 2001 Market Street · Philadelphia, PA 19103 · 215-988-7800

David A. Franklin · Pepper Hamilton · http://www.pepperlaw.com · Two Logan Square, Suite 3000 · 18th and Arch Street · Philadelphia, PA 19103-2799 · 215-981-4000

Michael L. Lehr · Greenberg Traurig · http://www.gtlaw.com · Two Commerce Square, Suite 2700 · 2001 Market Street · Philadelphia, PA 19103 · 215-988-7800

George T. Magnatta · Saul Ewing · Centre Square West, 38th Floor · 1500 Market Street · Philadelphia, PA 19102-2186 · 215-972-7777

J. Douglas Rollow III · Ballard Spahr Andrews & Ingersoll · 1735 Market Street, 51st Floor · Philadelphia, PA 19103-7599 · 215-665-8500

Joan N. Stern · Blank Rome · One Logan Square · 130 North 18th Street · Philadelphia, PA 19103-6998 · 215-569-5500

Pittsburgh

Margaret B. Angel · Buchanan Ingersoll & Rooney · http://www.bipc.com · One Oxford Centre, 20th Floor · 301 Grant Street · Pittsburgh, PA 15219-1410 · 412-562-8800

Peter H. Beaman · Buchanan Ingersoll & Rooney · http://www.bipc.com · One Oxford Centre, 20th Floor 301 Grant Street · Pittsburgh, PA 15219-1410 · 412-562-8800

Christopher B. Brewer · Dinsmore & Shohl · http://www.dinslaw.com · One Oxford Centre, Suite 2800 · 301 Grant Street · Pittsburgh, PA 15219 · 412-281-5000

Charles R. Brodbeck · Cohen & Grigsby · 625 Liberty Avenue · Pittsburgh, PA 15222-3152 · 412-297-4900

Dean F. Richardson · Eckert Seamans Cherin & Mellott · U.S. Steel Tower, 44th Floor · 600 Grant Street · Pittsburgh, PA 15219 · 412-566-6000

James H. Webster · Houston Harbaugh · Three Gateway Center, 22nd Floor · 401 Liberty Avenue · Pittsburgh, PA 15222-1005 · 412-281-5060

RAILROAD LAW

Pittsburgh

Michael W. Burns · Burns, White & Hickton · http://www.bwhllc.com · Four Northshore Center · 106 Isabella Street · Pittsburgh, PA 15212 · 412-995-3000

David A. Damico · Burns, White & Hickton · http://www.bwhllc.com · Four Northshore Center · 106 Isabella Street · Pittsburgh, PA 15212 · 412-995-3000

Daniel B. Donahoe · Burns, White & Hickton · http://www.bwhllc.com · Four Northshore Center · 106 Isabella Street · Pittsburgh, PA 15212 · 412-995-3000

J. Lawson Johnston · Dickie, McCamey & Chilcote · http://www.dmclaw.com · Two PPG Place, Suite 400 · Pittsburgh, PA 15222-5402 · 412-281-7272

REAL ESTATE LAW

Harrisburg

Robert M. Cherry · ⑩ · McNees Wallace & Nurick · 100 Pine Street · P.O. Box 1166 · Harrisburg, PA 17108-1166 · 717-232-8000

Dean A. Weidner · a · Wix, Wenger & Weidner · 508 North Second Street · P.O. Box 845 · Harrisburg, PA 17108-0845 · 717-234-4182

Steven J. Weingarten · McNees Wallace & Nurick · 100 Pine Street · P.O. Box 1166 · Harrisburg, PA 17108-1166 · 717-232-8000

Lancaster

John O. Shirk · a · Barley Snyder · 126 East King Street · Lancaster, PA 17602-2893 · 717-299-5201

Media

Richard M. Heller · Richard M. Heller · 300 West State Street, Suite 206 · Media, PA 19063 · 610-565-9260

Philadelphia

Stephen S. Aichele · Saul Ewing · Centre Square West, 38th Floor · 1500 Market Street · Philadelphia, PA 19102-2186 · 215-972-7777

David C. Auten · 2% · Reed Smith · 2500 One Liberty Place · 1650 Market Street · Philadelphia, PA 19103 · 215-851-8100

Lynn R. Axelroth · Ballard Spahr Andrews & Ingersoll · 1735 Market Street, 51st Floor · Philadelphia, PA 19103-7599 · 215-665-8500

John Joseph Broderick · Morgan Lewis & Bockius · 1701 Market Street · Philadelphia, PA 19103-2921 · 215-963-5000

James S. Burns · a · WolfBlock · http://wolfblock.com · 1650 Arch Street, 22nd Floor · Philadelphia, PA 19103-2097 · 215-977-2000

Harry S. Cherken, Jr. · a · Drinker Biddle & Reath · One Logan Square · 18th and Cherry Streets · Philadelphia, PA 19103-6996 · 215-988-2700

Morris J. Dean · 2% · Blank Rome · One Logan Square · 130 North 18th Street · Philadelphia, PA 19103-6998 · 215-569-5500

Alvin H. Dorsky · 2% · WolfBlock · http://wolfblock.com · 1650 Arch Street, 22nd Floor · Philadelphia, PA 19103-2097 · 215-977-2000

David A. Ebby · Drinker Biddle & Reath · One Logan Square · 18th and Cherry Streets · Philadelphia, PA 19103-6996 · 215-988-2700

Stuart F. Ebby · 2% · Hangley Aronchick Segal & Pudlin · http://www.hangley.com · One Logan Square, 27th Floor · 18th and Cherry Street · Philadelphia, PA 19103-6933 · 215-568-6200

Herman C. Fala · a · WolfBlock · http://wolfblock.com · 1650 Arch Street, 22nd Floor · Philadelphia, PA 19103-2097 · 215-977-2000

Joseph S. Finkelstein · Blank Rome · One Logan Square · 130 North 18th Street · Philadelphia, PA 19103-6998 · 215-569-5500

David W. Forti · Dechert · Cira Centre · 2929 Arch Street · Philadelphia, PA 19104-2808 · 215-994-4000

David B. Gifford · Ballard Spahr Andrews & Ingersoll · 1735 Market Street, 51st Floor · Philadelphia, PA 19103-7599 · 215-665-8500

Ronald B. Glazer · 2% · WolfBlock · http://wolfblock.com · 1650 Arch Street, 22nd Floor · Philadelphia, PA 19103-2097 · 215-977-2000

Richard R. Goldberg · Ballard Spahr Andrews & Ingersoll · 1735 Market Street, 51st Floor · Philadelphia, PA 19103-7599 · 215-665-8500

Gregory G. Gosfield · Klehr, Harrison, Harvey, Branzburg & Ellers · 260 South Broad Street, Suite 400 · Philadelphia, PA 19102-5003 · 215-568-6060

Rush T. Haines II · Drinker Biddle & Reath · One Logan Square · 18th and Cherry Streets · Philadelphia, PA 19103-6996 · 215-988-2700

Richard D. Jones · Dechert · Cira Centre · 2929 Arch Street · Philadelphia, PA 19104-2808 · 215-994-4000

Philip B. Korb · Ballard Spahr Andrews & Ingersoll · 1735 Market Street, 51st Floor · Philadelphia, PA 19103-7599 · 215-665-8500

Marilyn Z. Kutler · a · Schnader Harrison Segal & Lewis · http://www.schnader.com · 1600 Market Street, Suite 3600 · Philadelphia, PA 19103-7286 · 215-751-2000

Bernard Lee · WolfBlock · http://wolfblock.com · 1650 Arch Street, 22nd Floor · Philadelphia, PA 19103-2097 · 215-977-2000

Diana C. Liu · WolfBlock · http://wolfblock.com · 1650 Arch Street, 22nd Floor · Philadelphia, PA 19103-2097 · 215-977-2000

G. Craig Lord · Blank Rome · One Logan Square · 130 North 18th Street · Philadelphia, PA 19103-6998 · 215-569-5500

Stephen M. Lyons III · a · Reed Smith · 2500 One Liberty Place · 1650 Market Street · Philadelphia, PA 19103 · 215-851-8100

Tina R. Makoulian · Ballard Spahr Andrews & Ingersoll · 1735 Market Street, 51st Floor · Philadelphia, PA 19103-7599 · 215-665-8500

Bart I. Mellits · Ballard Spahr Andrews & Ingersoll · 1735 Market Street, 51st Floor · Philadelphia, PA 19103-7599 · 215-665-8500

Henry F. Miller · 2% · WolfBlock · http://wolfblock.com · 1650 Arch Street, 22nd Floor · Philadelphia, PA 19103-2097 · 215-977-2000

David L. Pollack · Ballard Spahr Andrews & Ingersoll · 1735 Market Street, 51st Floor · Philadelphia, PA 19103-7599 · 215-665-8500

Michael Pollack · Blank Rome · One Logan Square · 130 North 18th Street · Philadelphia, PA 19103-6998 · 215-569-5500

Carl S. Primavera · Klehr, Harrison, Harvey, Branzburg & Ellers · 260 South Broad Street, Suite 400 · Philadelphia, PA 19102-5003 · 215-568-6060

Julian P. Rackow · 2) · Blank Rome · One Logan Square · 130 North 18th Street · Philadelphia, PA 19103-6998 · 215-569-5500

Alan S. Ritterband · Ballard Spahr Andrews & Ingersoll · 1735 Market Street, 51st Floor · Philadelphia, PA 19103-7599 · 215-665-8500

Kenneth I. Rosenberg · 2) · Schnader Harrison Segal & Lewis · http://www.schnader.com · 1600 Market Street, Suite 3600 · Philadelphia, PA 19103-7286 · 215-751-2000

Jeffrey B. Rotwitt · Obermayer Rebmann Maxwell & Hippel · http://www.obermayer.com · One Penn Center, 19th Floor · 1617 John F. Kennedy Boulevard · Philadelphia, PA 19103-1895 · 215-665-3000

Robert M. Segal · ㉕ · WolfBlock · http://wolfblock.com · 1650 Arch Street, 22nd Floor · Philadelphia, PA 19103-2097 · 215-977-2000

Nina Segre · Montgomery, McCracken, Walker & Rhoads · 123 South Broad Street · Avenue Of The Arts Philadelphia, PA 19109-1029 · 215-772-1500

Robert A. Silverman · WolfBlock · http://wolfblock.com · 1650 Arch Street, 22nd Floor · Philadelphia, PA 19103-2097 · 215-977-2000

Michael Sklaroff · ⑩ · Ballard Spahr Andrews & Ingersoll · 1735 Market Street, 51st Floor · Philadelphia, PA 19103-7599 · 215-665-8500

Eric L. Stern · Morgan Lewis & Bockius · 1701 Market Street · Philadelphia, PA 19103-2921 · 215-963-5000

Frederick D. Strober · Saul Ewing · Centre Square West, 38th Floor · 1500 Market Street · Philadelphia, PA 19102-2186 · 215-972-7777

Clifford H. Swain · ⑩ · Drinker Biddle & Reath · One Logan Square · 18th and Cherry Streets · Philadelphia, PA 19103-6996 · 215-988-2700

James R. Williams · WolfBlock · http://wolfblock.com · 1650 Arch Street, 22nd Floor · Philadelphia, PA 19103-2097 · 215-977-2000

Pittsburgh

Alan L. Ackerman · ㉕ · Alan L. Ackerman · 1515 Allegheny Building · 429 Forbes Avenue · Pittsburgh, PA 15219 · 412-338-9944

John A. Barbour · Buchanan Ingersoll & Rooney · http://www.bipc.com · One Oxford Centre, 20th Floor 301 Grant Street · Pittsburgh, PA 15219-1410 · 412-562-8800

Joseph J. Barnes · ⑩ · Marcus & Shapira · One Oxford Centre, 35th Floor · 301 Grant Street · Pittsburgh, PA 15219 · 412-471-3490

Raymond N. Baum · ⑩ · Pepper Hamilton · http://www.pepperlaw.com · 500 Grant Street, 50th Floor · Pittsburgh, PA 15219-2502 · 412-454-5000

William P. Bresnahan · ⑩ · Hollinshead, Mendelson, Bresnahan & Nixon · 2901 Grant Building · 310 Grant Street · Pittsburgh, PA 15219 · 412-355-7070

Charles R. Brodbeck · Cohen & Grigsby · 625 Liberty Avenue · Pittsburgh, PA 15222-3152 · 412-297-4900

W. Theodore Brooks · Tucker Arensberg · http://www.tuckerlaw.com · 1500 One PPG Place · Pittsburgh, PA 15222-5401 · 412-566-1212

Thomas J. Dempsey, Sr. · ㉕ · Thomas J. Dempsey · 618 Frick Building · 437 Grant Street · Pittsburgh, PA 15219 · 412-281-2442

Samuel L. Douglass · ⑳ · Rothman Gordon · Grant Building, Third Floor · 310 Grant Street · Pittsburgh, PA 15219-2202 · 412-338-1100

Andrea Geraghty · Geraghty & Associates · Two Gateway Center, Suite 2050 · 603 Stanwix Street · Pittsburgh, PA 15222 · 412-232-7070

Alan B. Gordon · McGuireWoods · http://www.mcguirewoods.com · Dominion Tower, 23rd Floor · 625 Liberty Avenue · Pittsburgh, PA 15222-3142 · 412-667-6000

Vincent J. Grogan · 2% · Grogan Graffam · http://www.grogangraffam.com · Four Gateway Center, 12th Floor · Pittsburgh, PA 15222-1009 · 412-553-6300

Ronald G. Hartman · a · Reed Smith · 435 Sixth Avenue · Pittsburgh, PA 15219-1886 · 412-288-3131

Calvin R. Harvey · 2) · Buchanan Ingersoll & Rooney · http://www.bipc.com · One Oxford Centre, 20th Floor · 301 Grant Street · Pittsburgh, PA 15219-1410 · 412-562-8800

Scott W. Irmscher · Buchanan Ingersoll & Rooney · http://www.bipc.com · One Oxford Centre, 20th Floor · 301 Grant Street · Pittsburgh, PA 15219-1410 · 412-562-8800

Dusty Elias Kirk · Pepper Hamilton · http://www.pepperlaw.com · 500 Grant Street, 50th Floor · Pittsburgh, PA 15219-2502 · 412-454-5000

Charles G. Knox · a · Buchanan Ingersoll & Rooney · http://www.bipc.com · One Oxford Centre, 20th Floor · 301 Grant Street · Pittsburgh, PA 15219-1410 · 412-562-8800

Richard G. Kotarba · a · Meyer, Unkovic & Scott · http://www.muslaw.com · 1300 Oliver Building · 535 Smithfield Street · Pittsburgh, PA 15222 · 412-456-2800

Rebecca Livingston Lando · Buchanan Ingersoll & Rooney · http://www.bipc.com · One Oxford Centre, 20th Floor · 301 Grant Street · Pittsburgh, PA 15219-1410 · 412-562-8800

Robert Mauro · a · Meyer, Unkovic & Scott · http://www.muslaw.com · 1300 Oliver Building · 535 Smithfield Street · Pittsburgh, PA 15222 · 412-456-2800

Kevin F. McKeegan · Meyer, Unkovic & Scott · http://www.muslaw.com · 1300 Oliver Building · 535 Smithfield Street · Pittsburgh, PA 15222 · 412-456-2800

Robert L. Murphy · Papernick & Gefsky · One Oxford Centre, 34th Floor · 301 Grant Street · Pittsburgh, PA 15219 · 412-765-2212

David L. Nixon · a · Hollinshead, Mendelson, Bresnahan & Nixon · 2901 Grant Building · 310 Grant Street · Pittsburgh, PA 15219 · 412-355-7070

Alan Papernick · a · Papernick & Gefsky · One Oxford Centre, 34th Floor · 301 Grant Street · Pittsburgh, PA 15219 · 412-765-2212

W. Grant Scott · Meyer, Unkovic & Scott · http://www.muslaw.com · 1300 Oliver Building · 535 Smithfield Street · Pittsburgh, PA 15222 · 412-456-2800

Edward W. Seifert · 2% · Reed Smith · 435 Sixth Avenue · Pittsburgh, PA 15219-1886 · 412-288-3131

Margaret K. Sitko · Sitko, Rodella & Bruno · 2006 East Carson Street · Pittsburgh, PA 15203 · 412-431-7490

Thomas R. Solomich · a · Rothman Gordon · Grant Building, Third Floor · 310 Grant Street · Pittsburgh, PA 15219-2202 · 412-338-1100

William J. Staley · 2) · Tucker Arensberg · http://www.tuckerlaw.com · 1500 One PPG Place · Pittsburgh, PA 15222-5401 · 412-566-1212

Patrick E. Sweeney · a · Sitko, Rodella & Bruno · 2006 East Carson Street · Pittsburgh, PA 15203 · 412-431-7490

Michael H. Syme · Cohen & Grigsby · 625 Liberty Avenue · Pittsburgh, PA 15222-3152 · 412-297-4900

William R. Taxay · Cohen & Grigsby · 625 Liberty Avenue · Pittsburgh, PA 15222-3152 · 412-297-4900

York

William F. Hoffmeyer · Hoffmeyer & Semmelman · 30 North George Street · York, PA 17401-1280 · 717-846-8846

SECURITIES LAW

Harrisburg

Michael Hund · Buchanan Ingersoll & Rooney · http://www.bipc.com · One South Market Square, Third Floor · 213 Market Street · P.O. Box 12023 · Harrisburg, PA 17108 · 717-237-4800

Philadelphia

Barry M. Abelson · ⑩ · Pepper Hamilton · http://www.pepperlaw.com · Two Logan Square, Suite 3000 · 18th and Arch Street · Philadelphia, PA 19103-2799 · 215-981-4000

Stephen M. Foxman · Eckert Seamans Cherin & Mellott · Two Liberty Place, 22nd Floor · 50 South 16th Street · Philadelphia, PA 19102 · 215-851-8400

Barry H. Genkin · Blank Rome · One Logan Square · 130 North 18th Street · Philadelphia, PA 19103-6998 · 215-569-5500

Gerald J. Guarcini · Ballard Spahr Andrews & Ingersoll · 1735 Market Street, 51st Floor · Philadelphia, PA 19103-7599 · 215-665-8500

Christopher G. Karras · Dechert · Cira Centre · 2929 Arch Street · Philadelphia, PA 19104-2808 · 215-994-4000

Michael L. Kichline · Dechert · Cira Centre · 2929 Arch Street · Philadelphia, PA 19104-2808 · 215-994-4000

Justin P. Klein · Ballard Spahr Andrews & Ingersoll · 1735 Market Street, 51st Floor · Philadelphia, PA 19103-7599 · 215-665-8500

James A. Lebovitz · Dechert · Cira Centre · 2929 Arch Street · Philadelphia, PA 19104-2808 · 215-994-4000

Steven J. Molitor · Dechert · Cira Centre · 2929 Arch Street · Philadelphia, PA 19104-2808 · 215-994-4000

William P. Quinn, Jr. · Morgan Lewis & Bockius · 1701 Market Street · Philadelphia, PA 19103-2921 · 215-963-5000

Alan Singer · Morgan Lewis & Bockius · 1701 Market Street · Philadelphia, PA 19103-2921 · 215-963-5000

Joanne R. Soslow · Morgan Lewis & Bockius · 1701 Market Street · Philadelphia, PA 19103-2921 · 215-963-5000

Pittsburgh

Ronald Basso · Buchanan Ingersoll & Rooney · http://www.bipc.com · One Oxford Centre, 20th Floor · 301 Grant Street · Pittsburgh, PA 15219-1410 · 412-562-8800

Lewis U. Davis, Jr. · Buchanan Ingersoll & Rooney · http://www.bipc.com · One Oxford Centre, 20th Floor · 301 Grant Street · Pittsburgh, PA 15219-1410 · 412-562-8800

Jeremiah G. Garvey · Buchanan Ingersoll & Rooney · http://www.bipc.com · One Oxford Centre, 20th Floor · 301 Grant Street · Pittsburgh, PA 15219-1410 · 412-562-8800

David A. Gerson · Morgan Lewis & Bockius · One Oxford Centre, 32nd Floor · 301 Grant Street · Pittsburgh, PA 15219-6401 · 412-560-3300

Janice C. Hartman · K&L Gates · Henry W. Oliver Building · 535 Smithfield Street · Pittsburgh, PA 15222-2312 · 412-355-6500

Marlee S. Myers · Morgan Lewis & Bockius · One Oxford Centre, 32nd Floor · 301 Grant Street · Pittsburgh, PA 15219-6401 · 412-560-3300

Ronald D. West · K&L Gates · Henry W. Oliver Building · 535 Smithfield Street · Pittsburgh, PA 15222-2312 · 412-355-6500

SPORTS LAW

Philadelphia

Lloyd Z. Remick · Lloyd Zane Remick · http://www.zanemanagement.com · One Liberty Place, 21st Floor · 1650 Market Street · Philadelphia, PA 19103 · 215-575-3804

STRUCTURED FINANCE LAW

Philadelphia

Richard R. Goldberg · Ballard Spahr Andrews & Ingersoll · 1735 Market Street, 51st Floor · Philadelphia, PA 19103-7599 · 215-665-8500

Steven J. Molitor · Dechert · Cira Centre · 2929 Arch Street · Philadelphia, PA 19104-2808 · 215-994-4000

Pittsburgh

Jeffrey J. Conn · Thorp, Reed & Armstrong · One Oxford Centre, 14th Floor · 301 Grant Street · Pittsburgh, PA 15219-1425 · 412-394-7711

Charles E. Harris III · K&L Gates · Henry W. Oliver Building · 535 Smithfield Street · Pittsburgh, PA 15222-2312 · 412-355-6500

Daniel J. Perry · Tucker Arensberg · http://www.tuckerlaw.com · 1500 One PPG Place · Pittsburgh, PA 15222-5401 · 412-566-1212

Harrisburg

James L. Fritz · McNees Wallace & Nurick · 100 Pine Street · P.O. Box 1166 · Harrisburg, PA 17108-1166 · 717-232-8000

Bradley J. Gunnison · a · Buchanan Ingersoll & Rooney · http://www.bipc.com · One South Market Square, Third Floor · 213 Market Street · P.O. Box 12023 · Harrisburg, PA 17108 · 717-237-4800

Gerald K. Morrison · 2) · McNees Wallace & Nurick · 100 Pine Street · P.O. Box 1166 · Harrisburg, PA 17108-1166 · 717-232-8000

John S. Oyler · 2) · McNees Wallace & Nurick · 100 Pine Street · P.O. Box 1166 · Harrisburg, PA 17108-1166 · 717-232-8000

Richard W. Stevenson · 2) · McNees Wallace & Nurick · 100 Pine Street · P.O. Box 1166 · Harrisburg, PA 17108-1166 · 717-232-8000

Lemoyne

Elyse E. Rogers · a · Keefer Wood Allen & Rahal · 635 North 12th Street · Lemoyne, PA 17043 · 717-612-5800

Philadelphia

Joan C. Arnold · Pepper Hamilton · http://www.pepperlaw.com · Two Logan Square, Suite 3000 · 18th and Arch Street · Philadelphia, PA 19103-2799 · 215-981-4000

Daniel R. Blickman · Blank Rome · One Logan Square · 130 North 18th Street · Philadelphia, PA 19103-6998 · 215-569-5500

Sheldon M. Bonovitz · 2% · Duane Morris · 30 South 17th Street · Philadelphia, PA 19103-4196 · 215-979-1000

C. VanLeer Davis III · a · Dechert · Cira Centre · 2929 Arch Street · Philadelphia, PA 19104-2808 · 215-994-4000

Thomas J. Gallagher III · a · WolfBlock · http://wolfblock.com · 1650 Arch Street, 22nd Floor · Philadelphia, PA 19103-2097 · 215-977-2000

Stephen D. D. Hamilton · a · Drinker Biddle & Reath · One Logan Square · 18th and Cherry Streets · Philadelphia, PA 19103-6996 · 215-988-2700

Victor F. Keen · Duane Morris · 30 South 17th Street · Philadelphia, PA 19103-4196 · 215-979-1000

Wendi Kotzen · Ballard Spahr Andrews & Ingersoll · 1735 Market Street, 51st Floor · Philadelphia, PA 19103-7599 · 215-665-8500

Stephen P. Magowan · Steiker, Fischer, Edwards & Greenapple · 10 Shurs Lane, Suite 102 · Philadelphia, PA 19127 · 215-508-1500

Carolyn S. Nachmias · Schnader Harrison Segal & Lewis · http://www.schnader.com · 1600 Market Street, Suite 3600 · Philadelphia, PA 19103-7286 · 215-751-2000

William S. Pilling III · Stradley, Ronon, Stevens & Young · 2600 One Commerce Square · Philadelphia, PA 19103-7098 · 215-564-8000

David B. Pudlin · Hangley Aronchick Segal & Pudlin · http://www.hangley.com · One Logan Square, 27th Floor · 18th and Cherry Street · Philadelphia, PA 19103-6933 · 215-568-6200

Joseph M. Sedlack · ⑩ · Reed Smith · 2500 One Liberty Place · 1650 Market Street · Philadelphia, PA 19103 · 215-851-8100

David Shechtman · Drinker Biddle & Reath · One Logan Square · 18th and Cherry Streets · Philadelphia, PA 19103-6996 · 215-988-2700

Kyle O. Sollie · Reed Smith · 2500 One Liberty Place · 1650 Market Street · Philadelphia, PA 19103 · 215-851-8100

Stewart M. Weintraub · Schnader Harrison Segal & Lewis · http://www.schnader.com · 1600 Market Street, Suite 3600 · Philadelphia, PA 19103-7286 · 215-751-2000

Ronald M. Wiener · ㉕ · WolfBlock · http://wolfblock.com · 1650 Arch Street, 22nd Floor · Philadelphia, PA 19103-2097 · 215-977-2000

Richard P. Wild · ⑳ · Dechert · Cira Centre · 2929 Arch Street · Philadelphia, PA 19104-2808 · 215-994-4000

Lee A. Zoeller · Reed Smith · 2500 One Liberty Place · 1650 Market Street · Philadelphia, PA 19103 · 215-851-8100

Pittsburgh

Thomas D. Arbogast · ⑳ · Schnader Harrison Segal & Lewis · http://www.schnader.com · Fifth Avenue Place, Suite 2700 · 120 Fifth Avenue · Pittsburgh, PA 15222-3001 · 412-577-5200

J. Stephen Barge · K&L Gates · Henry W. Oliver Building · 535 Smithfield Street · Pittsburgh, PA 15222-2312 · 412-355-6500

Jeffrey S. Blum · ⑩ · Deloitte & Touche · 2500 One PPG Place · Pittsburgh, PA 15222-5401 · 412-338-7200

Carolyn D. Duronio · Reed Smith · 435 Sixth Avenue · Pittsburgh, PA 15219-1886 · 412-288-3131

Christopher F. Farrell · Cohen & Grigsby · 625 Liberty Avenue · Pittsburgh, PA 15222-3152 · 412-297-4900

Alan H. Finegold · ㉕ · Alan H. Finegold · Six PPG Place, Suite 1150 · Pittsburgh, PA 15222 · 412-471-2548

Leo N. Hitt · ⑩ · Reed Smith · 435 Sixth Avenue · Pittsburgh, PA 15219-1886 · 412-288-3131

Susan Foreman Jordan · Fox Rothschild · 625 Liberty Avenue, 29th Floor · Pittsburgh, PA 15222-3115 · 412-391-1334

Mark C. Larson · Eckert Seamans Cherin & Mellott · U.S. Steel Tower, 44th Floor · 600 Grant Street · Pittsburgh, PA 15219 · 412-566-6000

Steven J. Lynch · Williams, Coulson, Johnson, Lloyd, Parker & Tedesco · One Gateway Center, 16th Floor · Pittsburgh, PA 15219 · 412-454-0200

Francis A. Muracca II · Jones Day · One Mellon Center, Suite 4500 · 500 Grant Street · Pittsburgh, PA 15219-2502 · 412-391-3939

Larry E. Phillips · ⑳ · Buchanan Ingersoll & Rooney · http://www.bipc.com · One Oxford Centre, 20th Floor · 301 Grant Street · Pittsburgh, PA 15219-1410 · 412-562-8800

Louis A. Prosperi · Louis A. Prosperi & Associates · 310 Grant Street, Suite 3601 · Pittsburgh, PA 15234 · 412-281-0566

John C. Rodney · ⑩ · Thorp, Reed & Armstrong · One Oxford Centre, 14th Floor · 301 Grant Street · Pittsburgh, PA 15219-1425 · 412-394-7711

W. Henry Snyder · K&L Gates · Henry W. Oliver Building · 535 Smithfield Street · Pittsburgh, PA 15222-2312 · 412-355-6500

Raymond C. Vogliano · Eckert Seamans Cherin & Mellott · U.S. Steel Tower, 44th Floor · 600 Grant Street · Pittsburgh, PA 15219 · 412-566-6000

Robert B. Williams · ⑳ · Williams, Coulson, Johnson, Lloyd, Parker & Tedesco · One Gateway Center, 16th Floor · Pittsburgh, PA 15219 · 412-454-0200

TECHNOLOGY LAW

Harrisburg

Michael A. Doctrow · McNees Wallace & Nurick · 100 Pine Street · P.O. Box 1166 · Harrisburg, PA 17108-1166 · 717-232-8000

Pittsburgh

David J. Kalson · Cohen & Grigsby · 625 Liberty Avenue · Pittsburgh, PA 15222-3152 · 412-297-4900

Eric D. Kline · Morgan Lewis & Bockius · One Oxford Centre, 32nd Floor · 301 Grant Street · Pittsburgh, PA 15219-6401 · 412-560-3300

Marlee S. Myers · Morgan Lewis & Bockius · One Oxford Centre, 32nd Floor · 301 Grant Street · Pittsburgh, PA 15219-6401 · 412-560-3300

TRUSTS AND ESTATES

Bala Cynwyd

Ann T. Loftus · Zateeny Loftus · Two Bala Plaza, Suite 604 · Bala Cynwyd, PA 19004 · 610-660-6110

Berwyn

Edward M. Watters III · ⑩ · Pepper Hamilton · http://www.pepperlaw.com · 400 Berwyn Park · 899 Cassatt Road · Berwyn, PA 19312-1183 · 610-640-7800

Bethlehem

Kirby G. Upright · King, Spry, Herman, Freund & Faul · One West Broad Street, Suite 700 · Bethlehem, PA 18018-5716 · 610-332-0390

Erie

James D. Cullen · ⑩ · MacDonald, Illig, Jones & Britton · 100 State Street, Suite 700 · Erie, PA 16507-1459 · 814-870-7600

Fort Washington

Thomas A. Boulden · Timoney Knox · http://www.timoneyknox.com · 400 Maryland Drive · Fort Washington, PA 19034-7544 · 215-646-6000

Harrisburg

Robert Church · Keefer Wood Allen & Rahal · Walnut Court Building · 210 Walnut Street · P.O. Box 11963 · Harrisburg, PA 17108-1963 · 717-255-8000

Neil E. Hendershot · Goldberg Katzman · Strawberry Square · 320 Market Street · P.O. Box 1268 · Harrisburg, PA 17108-1268 · 717-234-4161

Howell C. Mette · 2) · Mette, Evans & Woodside · 3401 North Front Street · P.O. Box 5950 · Harrisburg, PA 17110-0950 · 717-232-5000

Elizabeth P. Mullaugh · McNees Wallace & Nurick · 100 Pine Street · P.O. Box 1166 · Harrisburg, PA 17108-1166 · 717-232-8000

Henry W. Rhoads · a · Rhoads & Sinon · M & T Bank Building, 12th Floor · One South Market Square · P.O. Box 1146 · Harrisburg, PA 17108-1146 · 717-233-5731

Stanley A. Smith · Rhoads & Sinon · M & T Bank Building, 12th Floor · One South Market Square · P.O. Box 1146 · Harrisburg, PA 17108-1146 · 717-233-5731

Jenkintown

Richard W. Stevens · Richard W. Stevens · 115 West Avenue, Suite 108 · Jenkintown, PA 19046-2031 · 215-887-4600

King of Prussia

James F. Mannion · Mannion Prior · 840 First Avenue, Suite 100 · King of Prussia, PA 19406-1459 · 610-265-7800

Langhorne

Michael J. Saile · Saile & Saile · 405 Executive Drive · Langhorne, PA 19047 · 215-860-5800

Lemoyne

Elyse E. Rogers · a · Keefer Wood Allen & Rahal · 635 North 12th Street · Lemoyne, PA 17043 · 717-612-5800

Mechanicsburg

Wayne M. Pecht · Pecht & Associates · http://www.pechtlaw.com · 1205 Manor Drive, Suite 200 · Mechanicsburg, PA 17055 · 717-691-9808

Media

Stephen Carroll · Carroll & Karagelian · 15 West Front Street · P.O. Box 1440 · Media, PA 19063 · 610-892-9800

S. Jonathan Emerson · 2% · S. Jonathan Emerson · Monroe Professional Building · 117 North Monroe Street · Media, PA 19063 · 610-566-8007

Terrance A. Kline · Terrence A. Kline · 200 East State Street, Suite 308 · P.O. Box A · Media, PA 19063 · 610-566-3330

Joseph E. Lastowka, Jr. · Abbott, Lastowka & Overholt · The Madison Building · 108 Chesley Drive · Media, PA 19063-1712 · 610-565-0330

Norristown

J. Brooke Aker · 2% · Smith, Aker, Grossman & Hollinger · 60 East Penn Street · P.O. Box 150 · Norristown, PA 19404 · 610-275-8200

Richard L. Grossman · 2) · Smith, Aker, Grossman & Hollinger · 60 East Penn Street · P.O. Box 150 · Norristown, PA 19404 · 610-275-8200

James L. Hollinger · 2) · Smith, Aker, Grossman & Hollinger · 60 East Penn Street · P.O. Box 150 · Norristown, PA 19404 · 610-275-8200

Philadelphia

Mary Jane Barrett · Harkins and Harkins · 123 South Broad Street, Suite 2102 · Philadelphia, PA 19109-1090 · 215-546-2653

Edwin R. Boynton · Stradley, Ronon, Stevens & Young · 2600 One Commerce Square · Philadelphia, PA 19103-7098 · 215-564-8000

Beverly R. Budin · a · Ballard Spahr Andrews & Ingersoll · 1735 Market Street, 51st Floor · Philadelphia, PA 19103-7599 · 215-665-8500

William C. Bullitt · 2) · Drinker Biddle & Reath · One Logan Square · 18th and Cherry Streets · Philadelphia, PA 19103-6996 · 215-988-2700

Leonard J. Cooper · a · WolfBlock · http://wolfblock.com · 1650 Arch Street, 22nd Floor · Philadelphia, PA 19103-2097 · 215-977-2000

Robert L. Freedman · a · Dechert · Cira Centre · 2929 Arch Street · Philadelphia, PA 19104-2808 · 215-994-4000

Robert I. Friedman · WolfBlock · http://wolfblock.com · 1650 Arch Street, 22nd Floor · Philadelphia, PA 19103-2097 · 215-977-2000

Kevin P. Gilboy · Teeters, Harvey, Gilboy · Eleven Penn Center · 1835 Market Street · Philadelphia, PA 19103-2968 · 215-567-2030

Eugene H. Gillin · a · Harkins and Harkins · 123 South Broad Street, Suite 2102 · Philadelphia, PA 19109-1090 · 215-546-2653

Bernard Glassman · Blank Rome · One Logan Square · 130 North 18th Street · Philadelphia, PA 19103-6998 · 215-569-5500

David R. Glyn · WolfBlock · http://wolfblock.com · 1650 Arch Street, 22nd Floor · Philadelphia, PA 19103-2097 · 215-977-2000

Edmund L. Harvey, Jr. · a · Teeters, Harvey, Gilboy · Eleven Penn Center · 1835 Market Street · Philadelphia, PA 19103-2968 · 215-567-2030

Paul C. Heintz · 2) · Obermayer Rebmann Maxwell & Hippel · http://www.obermayer.com · One Penn Center, 19th Floor · 1617 John F. Kennedy Boulevard · Philadelphia, PA 19103-1895 · 215-665-3000

John C. Hook · Stradley, Ronon, Stevens & Young · 2600 One Commerce Square · Philadelphia, PA 19103-7098 · 215-564-8000

Matthew H. Kamens · a · WolfBlock · http://wolfblock.com · 1650 Arch Street, 22nd Floor · Philadelphia, PA 19103-2097 · 215-977-2000

John J. Lombard, Jr. · 2% · McCarter & English · Mellon Bank Center Building, Suite 700 · 1735 Market Street · Philadelphia, PA 19103 · 215-979-3800

Clifford Scott Meyer · Montgomery, McCracken, Walker & Rhoads · 123 South Broad Street · Avenue Of The Arts · Philadelphia, PA 19109-1029 · 215-772-1500

Francis J. Mirabello · a · Morgan Lewis & Bockius · 1701 Market Street · Philadelphia, PA 19103-2921 · 215-963-5000

Benjamin R. Neilson · a · Ballard Spahr Andrews & Ingersoll · 1735 Market Street, 51st Floor · Philadelphia, PA 19103-7599 · 215-665-8500

Morey S. Rosenbloom · Blank Rome · One Logan Square · 130 North 18th Street · Philadelphia, PA 19103-6998 · 215-569-5500

Bruce A. Rosenfield · a · Schnader Harrison Segal & Lewis · http://www.schnader.com · 1600 Market Street, Suite 3600 · Philadelphia, PA 19103-7286 · 215-751-2000

Daniel R. Ross · Ross & McCrea · 7169 Germantown Avenue, Second Floor · Philadelphia, PA 19119 · 215-247-3550

Marilyn C. Sanborne · Ballard Spahr Andrews & Ingersoll · 1735 Market Street, 51st Floor · Philadelphia, PA 19103-7599 · 215-665-8500

Arthur R. G. Solmssen, Jr. · Dechert · Cira Centre · 2929 Arch Street · Philadelphia, PA 19104-2808 · 215-994-4000

Nina B. Stryker · Obermayer Rebmann Maxwell & Hippel · http://www.obermayer.com · One Penn Center, 19th Floor · 1617 John F. Kennedy Boulevard · Philadelphia, PA 19103-1895 · 215-665-3000

John R. Suria · Saul Ewing · Centre Square West, 38th Floor · 1500 Market Street · Philadelphia, PA 19102-2186 · 215-972-7777

Ralph N. Teeters · a · Teeters, Harvey, Gilboy · Eleven Penn Center · 1835 Market Street · Philadelphia, PA 19103-2968 · 215-567-2030

Regina O'Brien Thomas · 2) · Ballard Spahr Andrews & Ingersoll · 1735 Market Street, 51st Floor · Philadelphia, PA 19103-7599 · 215-665-8500

Margaret Gallagher Thompson · Cozen O'Connor · The Atrium · 1900 Market Street · Philadelphia, PA 19103 · 215-665-2000

M. Howard Vigderman · Montgomery, McCracken, Walker & Rhoads · 123 South Broad Street · Avenue Of The Arts · Philadelphia, PA 19109-1029 · 215-772-1500

Robert J. Weinberg · Pepper Hamilton · http://www.pepperlaw.com · Two Logan Square, Suite 3000 · 18th and Arch Street · Philadelphia, PA 19103-2799 · 215-981-4000

Larissa R. Whitman · Montgomery, McCracken, Walker & Rhoads · 123 South Broad Street · Avenue Of The Arts · Philadelphia, PA 19109-1029 · 215-772-1500

Pittsburgh

Charles J. Avalli · Goldberg, Gruener, Gentile, Horoho & Avalli · The Grant Building, Suite 230 · 310 Grant Street · Pittsburgh, PA 15219-2201 · 412-261-9900

Mark Bookman · ⑩ · Lovett Bookman Harmon Marks · Fifth Avenue Place, Suite 2900 · 120 Fifth Avenue · Pittsburgh, PA 15222 · 412-392-2220

Timothy F. Burke, Jr. · ⑩ · Tener, Van Kirk, Wolf & Moore · Oliver Building, Suite 920 · 535 Smithfield Street · Pittsburgh, PA 15222-2305 · 412-281-5580

R. Michael Daniel · ⑩ · Cohen & Grigsby · 625 Liberty Avenue · Pittsburgh, PA 15222-3152 · 412-297-4900

R. Douglas DeNardo · Rothman Gordon · Grant Building, Third Floor · 310 Grant Street · Pittsburgh, PA 15219-2202 · 412-338-1100

Linda Rhone Enion · Lovett Bookman Harmon Marks · Fifth Avenue Place, Suite 2900 · 120 Fifth Avenue · Pittsburgh, PA 15222 · 412-392-2220

Christopher F. Farrell · Cohen & Grigsby · 625 Liberty Avenue · Pittsburgh, PA 15222-3152 · 412-297-4900

Andrew L. Gespass · K&L Gates · Henry W. Oliver Building · 535 Smithfield Street · Pittsburgh, PA 15222-2312 · 412-355-6500

Samuel J. Gonez · Jones Day · One Mellon Center, Suite 4500 · 500 Grant Street · Pittsburgh, PA 15219-2502 · 412-391-3939

John C. Harmon · ⑩ · Lovett Bookman Harmon Marks · Fifth Avenue Place, Suite 2900 · 120 Fifth Avenue · Pittsburgh, PA 15222 · 412-392-2220

Daniel P. Johnson · Williams, Coulson, Johnson, Lloyd, Parker & Tedesco · One Gateway Center, 16th Floor · Pittsburgh, PA 15219 · 412-454-0200

Susan Foreman Jordan · Fox Rothschild · 625 Liberty Avenue, 29th Floor · Pittsburgh, PA 15222-3115 · 412-391-1334

Kenneth E. Lewis · ⑩ · Fox Rothschild · 625 Liberty Avenue, 29th Floor · Pittsburgh, PA 15222-3115 · 412-391-1334

Robert G. Lovett · ⑩ · Lovett Bookman Harmon Marks · Fifth Avenue Place, Suite 2900 · 120 Fifth Avenue · Pittsburgh, PA 15222 · 412-392-2220

E. David Margolis · Buchanan Ingersoll & Rooney · http://www.bipc.com · One Oxford Centre, 20th Floor · 301 Grant Street · Pittsburgh, PA 15219-1410 · 412-562-8800

Jan A. Marks · Lovett Bookman Harmon Marks · Fifth Avenue Place, Suite 2900 · 120 Fifth Avenue · Pittsburgh, PA 15222 · 412-392-2220

John F. Meck · ⑩ · Eckert Seamans Cherin & Mellott · U.S. Steel Tower, 44th Floor · 600 Grant Street · Pittsburgh, PA 15219 · 412-566-6000

K. Sidney Neuman · ㉕ · Rothman Gordon · Grant Building, Third Floor · 310 Grant Street · Pittsburgh, PA 15219-2202 · 412-338-1100

Raymond P. Parker · Williams, Coulson, Johnson, Lloyd, Parker & Tedesco · One Gateway Center, 16th Floor · Pittsburgh, PA 15219 · 412-454-0200

C. Eric Pfeil · Cohen & Grigsby · 625 Liberty Avenue · Pittsburgh, PA 15222-3152 · 412-297-4900

John W. Powell · Meyer, Unkovic & Scott · http://www.muslaw.com · 1300 Oliver Building · 535 Smithfield Street · Pittsburgh, PA 15222 · 412-456-2800

Nancy L. Rackoff · Tener, Van Kirk, Wolf & Moore · Oliver Building, Suite 920 · 535 Smithfield Street · Pittsburgh, PA 15222-2305 · 412-281-5580

Jonathan M. Schmerling · ⑩ · Cohen & Grigsby · 625 Liberty Avenue · Pittsburgh, PA 15222-3152 · 412-297-4900

Paul W. Schwendeman · K&L Gates · Henry W. Oliver Building · 535 Smithfield Street · Pittsburgh, PA 15222-2312 · 412-355-6500

James W. Ummer · Rothman Gordon · Grant Building, Third Floor · 310 Grant Street · Pittsburgh, PA 15219-2202 · 412-338-1100

Charles J. Vater · Tucker Arensberg · http://www.tuckerlaw.com · 1500 One PPG Place · Pittsburgh, PA 15222-5401 · 412-566-1212

Keith H. West · Thorp, Reed & Armstrong · One Oxford Centre, 14th Floor · 301 Grant Street · Pittsburgh, PA 15219-1425 · 412-394-7711

Robert B. Williams · ⑳ · Williams, Coulson, Johnson, Lloyd, Parker & Tedesco · One Gateway Center, 16th Floor · Pittsburgh, PA 15219 · 412-454-0200

Edward P. Wojnaroski, Jr. · Williams, Coulson, Johnson, Lloyd, Parker & Tedesco · One Gateway Center, 16th Floor · Pittsburgh, PA 15219 · 412-454-0200

Robert B. Wolf · ⑩ · Tener, Van Kirk, Wolf & Moore · Oliver Building, Suite 920 · 535 Smithfield Street Pittsburgh, PA 15222-2305 · 412-281-5580

Radnor

Christopher H. Gadsden · ⑳ · Gadsden Schneider & Woodward · 201 King Of Prussia Road, Suite 100 · Radnor, PA 19087-5152 · 484-683-2600

Pam H. Schneider · ⑩ · Gadsden Schneider & Woodward · 201 King Of Prussia Road, Suite 100 · Radnor, PA 19087-5152 · 484-683-2600

W. Steven Woodward · Gadsden Schneider & Woodward · 201 King Of Prussia Road, Suite 100 · Radnor, PA 19087-5152 · 484-683-2600

Reading

C. Thomas Work · ⑩ · Stevens & Lee · 111 North Sixth Street · P.O. Box 679 · Reading, PA 19603-0679 610-478-2000

West Conshohocken

Kim D. Fetrow · Heckscher Teillon Terrill & Sager · 100 Four Falls, Suite 300 · West Conshohocken, PA 19428-2983 · 610-940-2600

Jill R. Fowler · Heckscher Teillon Terrill & Sager · 100 Four Falls, Suite 300 · West Conshohocken, PA 19428-2983 · 610-940-2600

Martin A. Heckscher · ㉕ · Heckscher Teillon Terrill & Sager · 100 Four Falls, Suite 300 · West Conshohocken, PA 19428-2983 · 610-940-2600

Thomas O. Hiscott · Heckscher Teillon Terrill & Sager · 100 Four Falls, Suite 300 · West Conshohocken, PA 19428-2983 · 610-940-2600

Margaret E. W. Sager · a · Heckscher Teillon Terrill & Sager · 100 Four Falls, Suite 300 · West Conshohocken, PA 19428-2983 · 610-940-2600

L. Pierre Teillon, Jr. · a · Heckscher Teillon Terrill & Sager · 100 Four Falls, Suite 300 · West Conshohocken, PA 19428-2983 · 610-940-2600

John A. Terrill II · a · Heckscher Teillon Terrill & Sager · 100 Four Falls, Suite 300 · West Conshohocken, PA 19428-2983 · 610-940-2600

VENTURE CAPITAL LAW

Berwyn

Jeffrey P. Libson · Pepper Hamilton · http://www.pepperlaw.com · 400 Berwyn Park · 899 Cassatt Road · Berwyn, PA 19312-1183 · 610-640-7800

Philadelphia

Stephen M. Goodman · a · Morgan Lewis & Bockius · 1701 Market Street · Philadelphia, PA 19103-2921 · 215-963-5000

Michael J. Heller · Cozen O'Connor · The Atrium · 1900 Market Street · Philadelphia, PA 19103 · 215-665-2000

Richard P. Jaffe · Ballard Spahr Andrews & Ingersoll · 1735 Market Street, 51st Floor · Philadelphia, PA 19103-7599 · 215-665-8500

WATER LAW

Erie

Matthew Wolford · Wolford Law Firm · 638 West Sixth Street · Erie, PA 16507 · 814-459-9600

Harrisburg

Brian J. Clark · Buchanan Ingersoll & Rooney · http://www.bipc.com · One South Market Square, Third Floor · 213 Market Street · P.O. Box 12023 · Harrisburg, PA 17108 · 717-237-4800

R. Timothy Weston · a · K&L Gates · 17 North Second Street, 18th Floor · Harrisburg, PA 17101-1507 · 717-231-4500

Philadelphia

David G. Mandelbaum · Ballard Spahr Andrews & Ingersoll · 1735 Market Street, 51st Floor · Philadelphia, PA 19103-7599 · 215-665-8500

Pittsburgh

Donald C. Bluedorn II · Babst, Calland, Clements and Zomnir · http://www.bccz.com · Two Gateway Center, Eighth Floor · 603 Stanwix Street · Pittsburgh, PA 15222 · 412-394-5400

Kevin J. Garber · Babst, Calland, Clements and Zomnir · http://www.bccz.com · Two Gateway Center, Eighth Floor · 603 Stanwix Street · Pittsburgh, PA 15222 · 412-394-5400

Ardmore

Peter Goldberger · a · Peter Goldberger · 50 Rittenhouse Place · Ardmore, PA 19003 · 610-649-8200

Doylestown

William L. Goldman, Jr. · Goldman Law Office · 90 East State Street · P.O. Box 1989 · Doylestown, PA 18901 · 215-348-2605

Erie

Leonard G. Ambrose III · a · The Ambrose Law Firm · 319 West Eighth Street · Erie, PA 16502 · 814-459-5900

Greensburg

Richard H. Galloway · Quatrini Rafferty Galloway · 550 East Pittsburgh Street · Greensburg, PA 15601 · 724-837-0080

Harrisburg

Joshua D. Lock · Goldberg Katzman · Strawberry Square · 320 Market Street · P.O. Box 1268 · Harrisburg, PA 17108-1268 · 717-234-4161

Lemoyne

William C. Costopoulos · 2% · Costopoulos, Foster & Fields · 831 Market Street · P.O. Box 222 · Lemoyne, PA 17043-0222 · 717-761-2121

Malvern

Thomas A. Bergstrom · a · Thomas A. Bergstrom · 138 Davis Road · Malvern, PA 19355 · 610-251-9260

Media

Arthur T. Donato, Jr. · a · Arthur T. Donato, Jr. · 211-213 North Olive Street · Media, PA 19063-2810 · 610-565-4747

New Kensington

Thomas R. Ceraso · a · Thomas R. Ceraso · 425 Finnin Road · New Kensington, PA 15068-2506 · 412-558-3699

Philadelphia

James M. Becker · Saul Ewing · Centre Square West, 38th Floor · 1500 Market Street · Philadelphia, PA 19102-2186 · 215-972-7777

Creed C. Black, Jr. · a · Creed C. Black, Jr. · 1700 Market Street, Suite 3025 · Philadelphia, PA 19103 · 215-564-4060

Stephen D. Brown · Dechert · Cira Centre · 2929 Arch Street · Philadelphia, PA 19104-2808 · 215-994-4000

John Rogers Carroll · 2% · Law Office of John Rogers Carroll · One Liberty Place, 55th Floor · 1650 Market Street · Philadelphia, PA 19103-7301 · 215-925-4100

Dennis J. Cogan · a · Dennis J. Cogan · http://www.denniscogan.com · 2000 Market Street, Suite 2925 · Philadelphia, PA 19103 · 215-545-2400

Ian M. Comisky · Blank Rome · One Logan Square · 130 North 18th Street · Philadelphia, PA 19103-6998 · 215-569-5500

Frank De Simone · Frank De Simone · 1880 John F. Kennedy Boulevard, Suite 600 · Philadelphia, PA 19103 · 215-567-3507

William A. DeStefano · Buchanan Ingersoll & Rooney · http://www.bipc.com · 1835 Market Street, 14th Floor · Philadelphia, PA 19103-2985 · 215-665-8700

John C. Dodds · Morgan Lewis & Bockius · 1701 Market Street · Philadelphia, PA 19103-2921 · 215-963-5000

Jules Epstein · a · Kairys, Rudovsky, Messing & Feinberg · The Cast Iron Building, Suite 501 South · 718 Arch Street · Philadelphia, PA 19106 · 215-925-4400

Donald J. Goldberg · 2% · Ballard Spahr Andrews & Ingersoll · 1735 Market Street, 51st Floor · Philadelphia, PA 19103-7599 · 215-665-8500

Jack Gruenstein · Vaira & Riley · 1600 Market Street, Suite 2650 · Philadelphia, PA 19103-7226 · 215-789-9405

David M. Howard · Dechert · Cira Centre · 2929 Arch Street · Philadelphia, PA 19104-2808 · 215-994-4000

Howard Bruce Klein · Law Offices of Howard Bruce Klein · http://www.hbklein.com · 1700 Market Street, Suite 3025 · Philadelphia, PA 19103 · 215-972-1411

Eric Kraeutler · Morgan Lewis & Bockius · 1701 Market Street · Philadelphia, PA 19103-2921 · 215-963-5000

Stephen R. LaCheen · a · LaCheen Dixon Wittels & Greenberg · 1429 Walnut Street, 13th Floor · Philadelphia, PA 19102 · 215-735-5900

Thomas H. Lee II · Dechert · Cira Centre · 2929 Arch Street · Philadelphia, PA 19104-2808 · 215-994-4000

Catherine M. Recker · Welsh & Recker · 2000 Market Street, Suite 2903 · Philadelphia, PA 19103 · 215-972-6430

James J. Rohn · Conrad O'Brien Gellman & Rohn · http://www.cogr.com · 1515 Market Street, 16th Floor Philadelphia, PA 19102-1916 · 215-864-9600

Eric W. Sitarchuk · Morgan Lewis & Bockius · 1701 Market Street · Philadelphia, PA 19103-2921 · 215-963-5000

Richard A. Sprague · 2% · Sprague & Sprague · The Wellington Building, Suite 400 · 135 South 19th Street · Philadelphia, PA 19103 · 215-561-7681

Joseph A. Tate · a · Dechert · Cira Centre · 2929 Arch Street · Philadelphia, PA 19104-2808 · 215-994-4000

Christopher D. Warren · Christopher D. Warren · 1500 Walnut Street, Suite 1500 · Philadelphia, PA 19102 · 215-546-3750

Robert E. Welsh, Jr. · a · Welsh & Recker · 2000 Market Street, Suite 2903 · Philadelphia, PA 19103 · 215-972-6430

William J. Winning · a · Cozen O'Connor · The Atrium · 1900 Market Street · Philadelphia, PA 19103 · 215-665-2000

Pittsburgh

David J. Armstrong · 2% · Dickie, McCamey & Chilcote · http://www.dmclaw.com · Two PPG Place, Suite 400 · Pittsburgh, PA 15222-5402 · 412-281-7272

Paul D. Boas · a · The Law Office of Paul D. Boas · Law and Finance Building, Fifth Floor · 429 Fourth Avenue · Pittsburgh, PA 15219 · 412-391-7707

Charles A. De Monaco · Dickie, McCamey & Chilcote · http://www.dmclaw.com · Two PPG Place, Suite 400 · Pittsburgh, PA 15222-5402 · 412-281-7272

Cynthia Reed Eddy · Johnson & Eddy · 1720 Gulf Tower · 707 Grant Street · Pittsburgh, PA 15219 · 412-338-4790

Thomas J. Farrell · Dreier · 1000 Koppers Building · 436 Seventh Avenue · Pittsburgh, PA 15219 · 412-894-1380

Efrem M. Grail · Reed Smith · 435 Sixth Avenue · Pittsburgh, PA 15219-1886 · 412-288-3131

Stanley W. Greenfield · 2) · Greenfield & Kraut · Greenfield Court · 1040 Fifth Avenue · Pittsburgh, PA 15219 · 412-261-4466

Philip A. Ignelzi · a · Ogg, Cordes, Murphy & Ignelzi · Riverview Place, Fourth Floor · 245 Fort Pitt Boulevard · Pittsburgh, PA 15222-1511 · 412-471-8500

J. Alan Johnson · a · Johnson & Eddy · 1720 Gulf Tower · 707 Grant Street · Pittsburgh, PA 15219 · 412-338-4790

Stanton D. Levenson · a · Stanton D. Levenson · http://www.seriousdefense.com · 1715 Gulf Tower · Pittsburgh, PA 15219 · 412-355-0650

Harry Litman · Litman Law Firm · One Oxford Centre, 34th Floor · 301 Grant Street · Pittsburgh, PA 15219-1407 · 412-456-2000

W. Thomas McGough, Jr. · a · Reed Smith · 435 Sixth Avenue · Pittsburgh, PA 15219-1886 · 412-288-3131

Caroline M. Roberto · a · Law Office of Caroline M. Roberto · Law and Finance Building, Fifth Floor · 429 Fourth Avenue · Pittsburgh, PA 15219 · 412-391-4071

William F. Ward · Thieman & Ward · Koppers Building, Suite 2312 · 436 Seventh Avenue · Pittsburgh, PA 15219 · 412-395-1245

Gary B. Zimmerman · Gary B. Zimmerman · 100 Ross Street, Suite 304 · Pittsburgh, PA 15219-2013 · 412-566-2133

Sewickley

William F. Manifesto · 2% · William F. Manifesto · 139 Willow Ridge Road · Sewickley, PA 15143 · 412-471-8893

Beaver

Bruce E. Woodske · a · Bruce E. Woodske · 255 College Avenue · Beaver, PA 15009 · 724-775-9955

California

Lisa J. Buday · Lisa J. Buday · 200 Third Street · P.O. Box 488 · California, PA 15419 · 724-938-1355

Greensburg

Vincent J. Quatrini, Jr. · a · Quatrini Rafferty Galloway · 550 East Pittsburgh Street · Greensburg, PA 15601 · 724-837-0080

Harrisburg

Shannon P. Fellin · Marshall, Dennehey, Warner, Coleman & Goggin · 4200 Crums Mill Road, Suite B · Harrisburg, PA 17112 · 717-651-3500

Edward H. Jordan, Jr. · Thomas, Thomas & Hafer · http://www.tthlaw.com · 305 North Front Street, Sixth Floor · P.O. Box 999 · Harrisburg, PA 17108 · 717-237-7100

Dennis R. Sheaffer · Tucker Arensberg · http://www.tuckerlaw.com · 111 North Front Street · P.O. Box 889 · Harrisburg, PA 17108-0889 · 717-234-4121

Jason Weinstock · Ira H. Weinstock · 800 North Second Street, Suite 100 · Harrisburg, PA 17102 · 717-238-1657

Lisa M. B. Woodburn · Angino & Rovner · http://www.angino-rovner.com · 4503 North Front Street · Harrisburg, PA 17110-1708 · 717-238-6791

Johnstown

John J. Bagnato · a · Spence, Custer, Saylor, Wolfe & Rose · 216 Franklin Street, Suite 400 · P.O. Box 280 · Johnstown, PA 15907-0280 · 814-536-0735

Norristown

William J. McKee · a · The Chartwell Law Offices · Valley Forge Corporate Center · 2621 Van Buren Avenue · Norristown, PA 19403 · 610-666-7700

Philadelphia

Thomas R. Bond · Marshall, Dennehey, Warner, Coleman & Goggin · 1845 Walnut Street · Philadelphia, PA 19103-4707 · 215-575-2600

Paul M. Fires · Weber Gallagher Simpson Stapleton Fires & Newby · http://www.wglaw.com · 2000 Market Street, Suite 1300 · Philadelphia, PA 19103 · 215-972-7900

Jeffrey S. Gross · Jeffrey S. Gross · Two Penn Center Plaza, Suite 1312 · 1500 John F. Kennedy Boulevard · Philadelphia, PA 19102 · 215-512-1500

Jason Krasno · Krasno, Krasno & Onwudinjo · 2000 Market Street, Suite 1805 · Philadelphia, PA 19103-3205 · 215-223-6718

George Martin · a · Martin, Banks, Pond, Lehocky & Wilson · 1818 Market Street, 35th Floor · Philadelphia, PA 19103 · 215-587-8400

Samuel H. Pond · Martin, Banks, Pond, Lehocky & Wilson · 1818 Market Street, 35th Floor · Philadelphia, PA 19103 · 215-587-8400

Stephen T. Potako · Post & Schell · Four Penn Center, 14th Floor · 1600 John F. Kennedy Boulevard · Philadelphia, PA 19103-2808 · 215-587-1000

Peter J. Weber · a · Weber Gallagher Simpson Stapleton Fires & Newby · http://www.wglaw.com · 2000 Market Street, Suite 1300 · Philadelphia, PA 19103 · 215-972-7900

Pittsburgh

Edward Jaffee Abes · a · Abes Baumann · 810 Penn Avenue, Fifth Floor · Pittsburgh, PA 15222-3614 · 412-765-2772

Jonathan C. Ascher · Post & Schell · One Oxford Centre, Suite 4300 · 301 Grant Street · Pittsburgh, PA 15219 · 412-577-2972

Lawrence J. Baldasare · a · Dapper, Baldasare, Benson, Behling & Kane · Four Gateway Center, 10th Floor · 444 Liberty Avenue · Pittsburgh, PA 15222-1225 · 412-456-5555

Thomas C. Baumann · Abes Baumann · 810 Penn Avenue, Fifth Floor · Pittsburgh, PA 15222-3614 · 412-765-2772

Edwin H. Beachler · a · Caroselli, Beachler, McTiernan & Conboy · http://www.cbmclaw.com · 20 Stanwix Street, Seventh Floor · Pittsburgh, PA 15222-4802 · 412-391-9860

Stuart W. Benson III · a · Dapper, Baldasare, Benson, Behling & Kane · Four Gateway Center, 10th Floor · 444 Liberty Avenue · Pittsburgh, PA 15222-1225 · 412-456-5555

Sylvester A. Beozzo · Marcus & Shapira · One Oxford Centre, 35th Floor · 301 Grant Street · Pittsburgh, PA 15219 · 412-471-3490

Daniel K. Bricmont · Caroselli, Beachler, McTiernan & Conboy · http://www.cbmclaw.com · 20 Stanwix Street, Seventh Floor · Pittsburgh, PA 15222-4802 · 412-391-9860

Charles G. Brown · Dickie, McCamey & Chilcote · http://www.dmclaw.com · Two PPG Place, Suite 400 Pittsburgh, PA 15222-5402 · 412-281-7272

William R. Caroselli · a · Caroselli, Beachler, McTiernan & Conboy · http://www.cbmclaw.com · 20 Stanwix Street, Seventh Floor · Pittsburgh, PA 15222-4802 · 412-391-9860

Lawrence R. Chaban · a · Alpern Schubert · 2727 Grant Building · 330 Grant Street · Pittsburgh, PA 15219 · 412-434-7790

G. Timothy Conboy · a · Caroselli, Beachler, McTiernan & Conboy · http://www.cbmclaw.com · 20 Stanwix Street, Seventh Floor · Pittsburgh, PA 15222-4802 · 412-391-9860

William M. Conwell · Swartz Campbell · 4750 US Steel Tower · 600 Grant Street · Pittsburgh, PA 15219 412-232-9800

David H. Dille · a · Dapper, Baldasare, Benson, Behling & Kane · Four Gateway Center, 10th Floor · 444 Liberty Avenue · Pittsburgh, PA 15222-1225 · 412-456-5555

Shelly W. Elovitz · a · Rothman Gordon · Grant Building, Third Floor · 310 Grant Street · Pittsburgh, PA 15219-2202 · 412-338-1100

Eugene A. Giotto · Buchanan Ingersoll & Rooney · http://www.bipc.com · One Oxford Centre, 20th Floor · 301 Grant Street · Pittsburgh, PA 15219-1410 · 412-562-8800

Mark Gordon · a · Pietragallo Gordon Alfano Bosick & Raspanti · One Oxford Centre, 38th Floor · Pittsburgh, PA 15219 · 412-263-2000

Harry J. Klucher · Dapper, Baldasare, Benson, Behling & Kane · Four Gateway Center, 10th Floor · 444 Liberty Avenue · Pittsburgh, PA 15222-1225 · 412-456-5555

Maureen Kowalski · Dickie, McCamey & Chilcote · http://www.dmclaw.com · Two PPG Place, Suite 400 Pittsburgh, PA 15222-5402 · 412-281-7272

Paul S. Mazeski · Buchanan Ingersoll & Rooney · http://www.bipc.com · One Oxford Centre, 20th Floor · 301 Grant Street · Pittsburgh, PA 15219-1410 · 412-562-8800

John W. McTiernan · a · Caroselli, Beachler, McTiernan & Conboy · http://www.cbmclaw.com · 20 Stanwix Street, Seventh Floor · Pittsburgh, PA 15222-4802 · 412-391-9860

Francis E. Pipak, Jr. · a · Pietragallo Gordon Alfano Bosick & Raspanti · One Oxford Centre, 38th Floor Pittsburgh, PA 15219 · 412-263-2000

Leta V. Pittman · Poerio, Walter & Mason · 1119 Penn Avenue, Suite 303 · Pittsburgh, PA 15222 · 412-246-0506

James M. Poerio · Poerio, Walter & Mason · 1119 Penn Avenue, Suite 303 · Pittsburgh, PA 15222 · 412-246-0506

Ralph J. Saunders, Jr. · Dickie, McCamey & Chilcote · http://www.dmclaw.com · Two PPG Place, Suite 400 · Pittsburgh, PA 15222-5402 · 412-281-7272

Thomas G. Smith · Caroselli, Beachler, McTiernan & Conboy · http://www.cbmclaw.com · 20 Stanwix Street, Seventh Floor · Pittsburgh, PA 15222-4802 · 412-391-9860

Fred Soilis · Caroselli, Beachler, McTiernan & Conboy · http://www.cbmclaw.com · 20 Stanwix Street, Seventh Floor · Pittsburgh, PA 15222-4802 · 412-391-9860

James D. Strader · a · Dickie, McCamey & Chilcote · http://www.dmclaw.com · Two PPG Place, Suite 400 · Pittsburgh, PA 15222-5402 · 412-281-7272

Paul E. Sutter · Thompson Calkins & Sutter · Frick Building, Suite 510 · 437 Grant Street · Pittsburgh, PA 15219-6160 · 412-261-4050

Edward H. Walter · Jubelirer, Pass & Intrieri · 219 Fort Pitt Boulevard · Pittsburgh, PA 15222-1505 · 412-281-3850

James A. Welker · Jubelirer, Pass & Intrieri · 219 Fort Pitt Boulevard · Pittsburgh, PA 15222-1505 · 412-281-3850

Douglas A. Williams · Abes Baumann · 810 Penn Avenue, Fifth Floor · Pittsburgh, PA 15222-3614 · 412-765-2772

Jeffrey R. Wilson · Buchanan Ingersoll & Rooney · http://www.bipc.com · One Oxford Centre, 20th Floor 301 Grant Street · Pittsburgh, PA 15219-1410 · 412-562-8800

John W. Zatkos, Jr. · Rothman Gordon · Grant Building, Third Floor · 310 Grant Street · Pittsburgh, PA 15219-2202 · 412-338-1100

Scranton

Todd J. O'Malley · O'Malley & Langen · 426 Mulberry Street, Suite 104 · Scranton, PA 18503 · 570-344-2667

Eric P. Betzner · Yablonski, Costello & Leckie · 505 Washington Trust Building · 30 East Beau Street · Washington, PA 15301 · 724-225-9130

Benjamin L. Costello · a · Yablonski, Costello & Leckie · 505 Washington Trust Building · 30 East Beau Street · Washington, PA 15301 · 724-225-9130

J. Scott Leckie · a · Yablonski, Costello & Leckie · 505 Washington Trust Building · 30 East Beau Street Washington, PA 15301 · 724-225-9130

RHODE ISLAND

ADMINISTRATIVE LAW

Providence

Richard R. Beretta · Adler Pollock & Sheehan · One Citizens Plaza, Eighth Floor · Providence, RI 02903-1345 · 401-274-7200

Stephen D. Zubiago · Nixon Peabody · One Citizens Plaza, Suite 500 · Providence, RI 02903 · 401-454-1000

ALTERNATIVE DISPUTE RESOLUTION

Providence

John E. Bulman · Little Medeiros Kinder Bulman & Whitney · http://www.lmkbw.com · 72 Pine Street · Providence, RI 02903 · 401-272-8080

Paul V. Curcio · Adler Pollock & Sheehan · One Citizens Plaza, Eighth Floor · Providence, RI 02903-1345 · 401-274-7200

Peter Lawson Kennedy · Adler Pollock & Sheehan · One Citizens Plaza, Eighth Floor · Providence, RI 02903-1345 · 401-274-7200

William A. Poore · Poore & Rosenbaum · The Commerce Center, 30 Exchange Terrace · Providence, RI 02901-1117 · 401-831-2600

ANTITRUST LAW

Providence

Joseph V. Cavanagh, Jr. · ㉕ · Blish & Cavanagh · Commerce Center · 30 Exchange Terrace · Providence, RI 02903 · 401-831-8900

Matthew F. Medeiros · ⑳ · Little Medeiros Kinder Bulman & Whitney · http://www.lmkbw.com · 72 Pine Street · Providence, RI 02903 · 401-272-8080

Steven E. Snow · Partridge Snow & Hahn · 180 South Main Street · Providence, RI 02903 · 401-861-8200

Patricia A. Sullivan · Edwards Angell Palmer & Dodge · 2800 Financial Plaza · Providence, RI 02903 · 401-274-9200

APPELLATE LAW

Johnston

Thomas M. Dickinson · Law Offices of Thomas M. Dickinson · 1312 Atwood Avenue · Johnston, RI 02919 · 401-490-8083

Providence

Thomas R. Bender · Hanson Curran · http://www.hansoncurran.com · The Francis Building · 146 Westminster Street · Providence, RI 02903 · 401-421-2154

Lauren E. Jones · Jones Associates · 72 South Main Street · Providence, RI 02903 · 401-274-4446

John A. MacFadyen III · ⑳ · MacFadyen, Gescheidt & O'Brien · The Owen Building · 101 Dyer Street · Providence, RI 02903 · 401-751-5090

Mark S. Mandell · Mandell, Schwartz & Boisclair · http://www.mandellschwartzboisclair.com · One Park Row · Providence, RI 02903 · 401-273-8330

John A. Tarantino · Adler Pollock & Sheehan · One Citizens Plaza, Eighth Floor · Providence, RI 02903-1345 · 401-274-7200

BANKING LAW

Providence

Andrew J. Chlebus · ⑩ · Edwards Angell Palmer & Dodge · 2800 Financial Plaza · Providence, RI 02903 401-274-9200

Joseph P. Curran · ⑩ · Hinckley, Allen & Snyder · http://www.haslaw.com · 50 Kennedy Plaza, Suite 1500 · Providence, RI 02903-3293 · 401-274-2000

Joseph M. DiOrio · Law Office of Joseph M. DiOrio · 10 Dorrance Street, Suite 1200 · Providence, RI 02903 · 401-632-0911

Malcolm Farmer III · ⑩ · Hinckley, Allen & Snyder · http://www.haslaw.com · 50 Kennedy Plaza, Suite 1500 · Providence, RI 02903-3293 · 401-274-2000

David M. Gilden · ⑩ · Partridge Snow & Hahn · 180 South Main Street · Providence, RI 02903 · 401-861-8200

Michael R. Goldenberg · ⑩ · Winograd, Shine & Zacks · 123 Dyer Street, Suite Two · Providence, RI 02903-3980 · 401-273-8300

Christopher D. Graham · ⑩ · Edwards Angell Palmer & Dodge · 2800 Financial Plaza · Providence, RI 02903 · 401-274-9200

V. Duncan Johnson · ⑩ · Edwards Angell Palmer & Dodge · 2800 Financial Plaza · Providence, RI 02903 · 401-274-9200

Matthew T. Marcello III · ⑩ · Hinckley, Allen & Snyder · http://www.haslaw.com · 50 Kennedy Plaza, Suite 1500 · Providence, RI 02903-3293 · 401-274-2000

Gail E. McCann · ⑩ · Edwards Angell Palmer & Dodge · 2800 Financial Plaza · Providence, RI 02903 · 401-274-9200

Robert A. Migliaccio · ⑩ · Cameron & Mittleman · 56 Exchange Terrace · Providence, RI 02903 · 401-331-5700

BANKRUPTCY AND CREDITOR-DEBTOR RIGHTS LAW

Providence

Joseph A. Avanzato · Adler Pollock & Sheehan · One Citizens Plaza, Eighth Floor · Providence, RI 02903-1345 · 401-274-7200

Edward J. Bertozzi, Jr. · ⑳ · Edwards Angell Palmer & Dodge · 2800 Financial Plaza · Providence, RI 02903 · 401-274-9200

John Boyajian · Boyajian, Harrington & Richardson · 182 Waterman Street · Providence, RI 02906 · 401-273-9600

Joseph M. DiOrio · Law Office of Joseph M. DiOrio · 10 Dorrance Street, Suite 1200 · Providence, RI 02903 · 401-632-0911

Diane Finkle · Winograd, Shine & Zacks · 123 Dyer Street, Suite Two · Providence, RI 02903-3980 · 401-273-8300

Matthew J. McGowan · Salter McGowan Sylvia & Leonard · The Heritage Building · 321 South Main Street · Providence, RI 02903 · 401-274-0300

Richard S. Mittleman · ⑩ · Cameron & Mittleman · 56 Exchange Terrace · Providence, RI 02903 · 401-331-5700

Andrew S. Richardson · Boyajian, Harrington & Richardson · 182 Waterman Street · Providence, RI 02906 · 401-273-9600

Allan M. Shine · ㉕ · Winograd, Shine & Zacks · 123 Dyer Street, Suite Two · Providence, RI 02903-3980 401-273-8300

BET-THE-COMPANY LITIGATION

Providence

Joseph V. Cavanagh, Jr. · ㉕ · Blish & Cavanagh · Commerce Center · 30 Exchange Terrace · Providence, RI 02903 · 401-831-8900

John A. Tarantino · Adler Pollock & Sheehan · One Citizens Plaza, Eighth Floor · Providence, RI 02903-1345 · 401-274-7200

Jamestown

A. Lauriston Parks · ⑩ · A. Lauriston Parks · 53 Narragansett Avenue · Jamestown, RI 02835 · 401-423-8900

Providence

Joseph V. Cavanagh, Jr. · ㉕ · Blish & Cavanagh · Commerce Center · 30 Exchange Terrace · Providence, RI 02903 · 401-831-8900

Michael P. DeFanti · ⑳ · Hinckley, Allen & Snyder · http://www.haslaw.com · 50 Kennedy Plaza, Suite 1500 · Providence, RI 02903-3293 · 401-274-2000

Mark O. Denehy · Adler Pollock & Sheehan · One Citizens Plaza, Eighth Floor · Providence, RI 02903-1345 · 401-274-7200

Robert M. Duffy · Duffy Sweeney & Scott · One Turks Head Place, Suite 1200 · Providence, RI 02903 · 401-455-0700

Mark W. Freel · Edwards Angell Palmer & Dodge · 2800 Financial Plaza · Providence, RI 02903 · 401-274-9200

William R. Grimm · ⑩ · Hinckley, Allen & Snyder · http://www.haslaw.com · 50 Kennedy Plaza, Suite 1500 · Providence, RI 02903-3293 · 401-274-2000

Lauren E. Jones · Jones Associates · 72 South Main Street · Providence, RI 02903 · 401-274-4446

Peter Lawson Kennedy · Adler Pollock & Sheehan · One Citizens Plaza, Eighth Floor · Providence, RI 02903-1345 · 401-274-7200

George E. Lieberman · Vetter & White · http://www.vetterandwhite.com · 20 Washington Place, Third Floor · Providence, RI 02903 · 401-421-3060

John A. MacFadyen III · ⑳ · MacFadyen, Gescheidt & O'Brien · The Owen Building · 101 Dyer Street · Providence, RI 02903 · 401-751-5090

Matthew F. Medeiros · ⑳ · Little Medeiros Kinder Bulman & Whitney · http://www.lmkbw.com · 72 Pine Street · Providence, RI 02903 · 401-272-8080

Howard A. Merten · Partridge Snow & Hahn · 180 South Main Street · Providence, RI 02903 · 401-861-8200

Anthony F. Muri · ⑩ · Muri Associates · http://www.murilaw.com · 10 Weybosset Street · Providence, RI 02903 · 401-421-7300

Karen A. Pelczarski · Blish & Cavanagh · Commerce Center · 30 Exchange Terrace · Providence, RI 02903 · 401-831-8900

Gerald J. Petros · Hinckley, Allen & Snyder · http://www.haslaw.com · 50 Kennedy Plaza, Suite 1500 · Providence, RI 02903-3293 · 401-274-2000

Mark A. Pogue · Edwards Angell Palmer & Dodge · 2800 Financial Plaza · Providence, RI 02903 · 401-274-9200

R. Daniel Prentiss · ⑩ · The Prentiss Law Firm · One Turks Head Place, Suite 380 · Providence, RI 02903 · 401-824-5150

Patricia K. Rocha · Adler Pollock & Sheehan · One Citizens Plaza, Eighth Floor · Providence, RI 02903-1345 · 401-274-7200

Deming E. Sherman · ⑩ · Edwards Angell Palmer & Dodge · 2800 Financial Plaza · Providence, RI 02903 · 401-274-9200

Steven E. Snow · Partridge Snow & Hahn · 180 South Main Street · Providence, RI 02903 · 401-861-8200

Patricia A. Sullivan · Edwards Angell Palmer & Dodge · 2800 Financial Plaza · Providence, RI 02903 · 401-274-9200

John A. Tarantino · Adler Pollock & Sheehan · One Citizens Plaza, Eighth Floor · Providence, RI 02903-1345 · 401-274-7200

Benjamin V. White · ⑩ · Vetter & White · http://www.vetterandwhite.com · 20 Washington Place, Third Floor · Providence, RI 02903 · 401-421-3060

David A. Wollin · Adler Pollock & Sheehan · One Citizens Plaza, Eighth Floor · Providence, RI 02903-1345 · 401-274-7200

CONSTRUCTION LAW

Providence

John E. Bulman · Little Medeiros Kinder Bulman & Whitney · http://www.lmkbw.com · 72 Pine Street · Providence, RI 02903 · 401-272-8080

Thomas W. Heald · Heald & LeBoeuf · One Turks Head Place, Suite 600 · 76 Westminster Street · Providence, RI 02903-2817 · 401-421-1500

Peter Lawson Kennedy · Adler Pollock & Sheehan · One Citizens Plaza, Eighth Floor · Providence, RI 02903-1345 · 401-274-7200

Christopher H. Little · Little Medeiros Kinder Bulman & Whitney · http://www.lmkbw.com · 72 Pine Street · Providence, RI 02903 · 401-272-8080

Christopher C. Whitney · Little Medeiros Kinder Bulman & Whitney · http://www.lmkbw.com · 72 Pine Street · Providence, RI 02903 · 401-272-8080

CORPORATE GOVERNANCE AND COMPLIANCE LAW

Providence

Gary R. Pannone · Pannone, Lopes & Devereaux · http://www.pldlaw.com · 317 Iron Horse Way, Suite 301 · Providence, RI 02908 · 401-824-5100

John J. Partridge · Partridge Snow & Hahn · 180 South Main Street · Providence, RI 02903 · 401-861-8200

CORPORATE LAW

Providence

E. Colby Cameron · ⑩ · Cameron & Mittleman · 56 Exchange Terrace · Providence, RI 02903 · 401-331-5700

Stephen J. Carlotti · ⑩ · Hinckley, Allen & Snyder · http://www.haslaw.com · 50 Kennedy Plaza, Suite 1500 · Providence, RI 02903-3293 · 401-274-2000

John F. Corrigan · ⑩ · John F. Corrigan · 90 Elm Street · Providence, RI 02903 · 401-276-8350

David K. Duffell · ⑩ · Weil Gotshal & Manges · 50 Kennedy Plaza, 11th Floor · Providence, RI 02903 · 401-278-4700

Malcolm Farmer III · ⑩ · Hinckley, Allen & Snyder · http://www.haslaw.com · 50 Kennedy Plaza, Suite 1500 · Providence, RI 02903-3293 · 401-274-2000

Margaret D. Farrell · Hinckley, Allen & Snyder · http://www.haslaw.com · 50 Kennedy Plaza, Suite 1500 Providence, RI 02903-3293 · 401-274-2000

Christopher D. Graham · ⑩ · Edwards Angell Palmer & Dodge · 2800 Financial Plaza · Providence, RI 02903 · 401-274-9200

James H. Hahn · Partridge Snow & Hahn · 180 South Main Street · Providence, RI 02903 · 401-861-8200

V. Duncan Johnson · ⑩ · Edwards Angell Palmer & Dodge · 2800 Financial Plaza · Providence, RI 02903 · 401-274-9200

E. Hans Lundsten · Adler Pollock & Sheehan · One Citizens Plaza, Eighth Floor · Providence, RI 02903-1345 · 401-274-7200

Gary R. Pannone · Pannone, Lopes & Devereaux · http://www.pldlaw.com · 317 Iron Horse Way, Suite 301 · Providence, RI 02908 · 401-824-5100

John J. Partridge · Partridge Snow & Hahn · 180 South Main Street · Providence, RI 02903 · 401-861-8200

Walter G. D. Reed · Edwards Angell Palmer & Dodge · 2800 Financial Plaza · Providence, RI 02903 · 401-274-9200

Richard G. Small · ⑩ · Edwards Angell Palmer & Dodge · 2800 Financial Plaza · Providence, RI 02903 · 401-274-9200

Michael F. Sweeney · Duffy Sweeney & Scott · One Turks Head Place, Suite 1200 · Providence, RI 02903 · 401-455-0700

Joseph F. Whinery · Cameron & Mittleman · 56 Exchange Terrace · Providence, RI 02903 · 401-331-5700

EMPLOYEE BENEFITS LAW

Providence

Frederick P. McClure · ⑳ · Hinckley, Allen & Snyder · http://www.haslaw.com · 50 Kennedy Plaza, Suite 1500 · Providence, RI 02903-3293 · 401-274-2000

ENERGY LAW

Providence

Peter V. Lacouture · Nixon Peabody · One Citizens Plaza, Suite 500 · Providence, RI 02903 · 401-454-1000

Gerald J. Petros · Hinckley, Allen & Snyder · http://www.haslaw.com · 50 Kennedy Plaza, Suite 1500 · Providence, RI 02903-3293 · 401-274-2000

ENVIRONMENTAL LAW

Providence

Sean O. Coffey · ⑩ · Burns & Levinson · http://www.burnslev.com · One Citizens Plaza, Suite 1100 · Providence, RI 02903 · 401-831-8330

Mark O. Denehy · Adler Pollock & Sheehan · One Citizens Plaza, Eighth Floor · Providence, RI 02903-1345 · 401-274-7200

Dennis H. Esposito · Adler Pollock & Sheehan · One Citizens Plaza, Eighth Floor · Providence, RI 02903-1345 · 401-274-7200

Robin L. Main · Hinckley, Allen & Snyder · http://www.haslaw.com · 50 Kennedy Plaza, Suite 1500 · Providence, RI 02903-3293 · 401-274-2000

Gerald J. Petros · Hinckley, Allen & Snyder · http://www.haslaw.com · 50 Kennedy Plaza, Suite 1500 · Providence, RI 02903-3293 · 401-274-2000

Deming E. Sherman · ⑩ · Edwards Angell Palmer & Dodge · 2800 Financial Plaza · Providence, RI 02903 · 401-274-9200

Kristen W. Sherman · Adler Pollock & Sheehan · One Citizens Plaza, Eighth Floor · Providence, RI 02903-1345 · 401-274-7200

Richard A. Sherman · Edwards Angell Palmer & Dodge · 2800 Financial Plaza · Providence, RI 02903 · 401-274-9200

FAMILY LAW

Cranston

Alfred Factor · ⑳ · Kirshenbaum & Kirshenbaum · 888 Reservoir Avenue · Cranston, RI 02910 · 401-946-3200

John E. McCann III · Kirshenbaum & Kirshenbaum · 888 Reservoir Avenue · Cranston, RI 02910 · 401-946-3200

Providence

Jerry L. McIntyre · ㉕ · McIntyre Tate & Lynch · 321 South Main Street, Suite 400 · Providence, RI 02903-7109 · 401-351-7700

Deborah M. Tate · McIntyre Tate & Lynch · 321 South Main Street, Suite 400 · Providence, RI 02903-7109 · 401-351-7700

Warwick

John D. Lynch, Sr. · Lynch & Friel · 600 Toll Gate Road · Warwick, RI 02886 · 401-739-8500

FIRST AMENDMENT LAW

Providence

Joseph V. Cavanagh, Jr. · ㉕ · Blish & Cavanagh · Commerce Center · 30 Exchange Terrace · Providence, RI 02903 · 401-831-8900

John W. Dineen · John W. Dineen · 305 South Main Street · Providence, RI 02903-7133 · 401-223-2397

Lynette Labinger · Roney & Labinger · 344 Wickenden Street · Providence, RI 02903-4469 · 401-421-9794

Howard A. Merten · Partridge Snow & Hahn · 180 South Main Street · Providence, RI 02903 · 401-861-8200

Warwick

Sandra A. Lanni · Sandra A. Lanni · 33 College Hill Road, Suite 20D · Warwick, RI 02886 · 401-737-4300

GOVERNMENT RELATIONS LAW

Providence

Richard R. Beretta · Adler Pollock & Sheehan · One Citizens Plaza, Eighth Floor · Providence, RI 02903-1345 · 401-274-7200

Richard A. Licht · Adler Pollock & Sheehan · One Citizens Plaza, Eighth Floor · Providence, RI 02903-1345 · 401-274-7200

HEALTH CARE LAW

Providence

Susan Leach DeBlasio · ⑩ · Tillinghast Licht · 10 Weybosset Street · Providence, RI 02903 · 401-456-1200

Gerard R. Goulet · ⑩ · Hinckley, Allen & Snyder · http://www.haslaw.com · 50 Kennedy Plaza, Suite 1500 · Providence, RI 02903-3293 · 401-274-2000

Patricia K. Rocha · Adler Pollock & Sheehan · One Citizens Plaza, Eighth Floor · Providence, RI 02903-1345 · 401-274-7200

Michael G. Tauber · Hinckley, Allen & Snyder · http://www.haslaw.com · 50 Kennedy Plaza, Suite 1500 · Providence, RI 02903-3293 · 401-274-2000

Cynthia J. Warren · Cameron & Mittleman · 56 Exchange Terrace · Providence, RI 02903 · 401-331-5700

Don E. Wineberg · Chace Ruttenberg & Freedman · One Park Row, Suite 300 · Providence, RI 02903 · 401-453-6400

INSURANCE LAW

Providence

Stephen D. Zubiago · Nixon Peabody · One Citizens Plaza, Suite 500 · Providence, RI 02903 · 401-454-1000

INTELLECTUAL PROPERTY LAW

Providence

William R. Grimm · ⑩ · Hinckley, Allen & Snyder · http://www.haslaw.com · 50 Kennedy Plaza, Suite 1500 · Providence, RI 02903-3293 · 401-274-2000

Stephen J. Holmes · Barlow, Josephs & Holmes · 101 Dyer Street, Fifth Floor · Providence, RI 02903 · 401-273-4446

Roger W. Hood · Duffy Sweeney & Scott · One Turks Head Place, Suite 1200 · Providence, RI 02903 · 401-455-0700

David R. Josephs · Barlow, Josephs & Holmes · 101 Dyer Street, Fifth Floor · Providence, RI 02903 · 401-273-4446

Craig M. Scott · Duffy Sweeney & Scott · One Turks Head Place, Suite 1200 · Providence, RI 02903 · 401-455-0700

LABOR AND EMPLOYMENT LAW

North Kingstown

Marc B. Gursky · ⑩ · Gursky Law Associates · 420 Scrabbletown Road, Suite C · North Kingstown, RI 02852 · 401-294-4700

Providence

Robert P. Brooks · Adler Pollock & Sheehan · One Citizens Plaza, Eighth Floor · Providence, RI 02903-1345 · 401-274-7200

Richard L.E. Jocelyn · Hinckley, Allen & Snyder · http://www.haslaw.com · 50 Kennedy Plaza, Suite 1500 · Providence, RI 02903-3293 · 401-274-2000

Jeffrey W. Kasle · St. Peter & Kasle · Four Richmond Square · Providence, RI 02906 · 401-453-4330

Daniel K. Kinder · Little Medeiros Kinder Bulman & Whitney · http://www.lmkbw.com · 72 Pine Street · Providence, RI 02903 · 401-272-8080

Charles S. Kirwan · Charles S. Kirwan & Associates · 204 King Phillip Street · Providence, RI 02909 · 401-272-6800

Lynette Labinger · Roney & Labinger · 344 Wickenden Street · Providence, RI 02903-4469 · 401-421-9794

Neal J. McNamara · Nixon Peabody · One Citizens Plaza, Suite 500 · Providence, RI 02903 · 401-454-1000

Andrew B. Prescott · Nixon Peabody · One Citizens Plaza, Suite 500 · Providence, RI 02903 · 401-454-1000

Patricia K. Rocha · Adler Pollock & Sheehan · One Citizens Plaza, Eighth Floor · Providence, RI 02903-1345 · 401-274-7200

Gary R. St. Peter · ⑩ · St. Peter & Kasle · Four Richmond Square · Providence, RI 02906 · 401-453-4330

Joseph D. Whelan · Hinckley, Allen & Snyder · http://www.haslaw.com · 50 Kennedy Plaza, Suite 1500 · Providence, RI 02903-3293 · 401-274-2000

Warwick

Sandra A. Lanni · Sandra A. Lanni · 33 College Hill Road, Suite 20D · Warwick, RI 02886 · 401-737-4300

LAND USE & ZONING LAW

Providence

William R. Landry · Blish & Cavanagh · Commerce Center · 30 Exchange Terrace · Providence, RI 02903 · 401-831-8900

Elizabeth M. Noonan · Adler Pollock & Sheehan · One Citizens Plaza, Eighth Floor · Providence, RI 02903-1345 · 401-274-7200

Andrew M. Teitz · Ursillo, Teitz & Ritch · http://www.utrlaw.com · Two Williams Street · Providence, RI 02903 · 401-331-2222

LEGAL MALPRACTICE LAW

Providence

John T. Walsh, Jr. · Higgins, Cavanaugh & Cooney · The Hay Building, Fourth Floor · 123 Dyer Street · Providence, RI 02903 · 401-272-3500

LEVERAGED BUYOUTS AND PRIVATE EQUITY LAW

Providence

John F. Corrigan · ⑩ · John F. Corrigan · 90 Elm Street · Providence, RI 02903 · 401-276-8350

David K. Duffell · ⑩ · Weil Gotshal & Manges · 50 Kennedy Plaza, 11th Floor · Providence, RI 02903 · 401-278-4700

Richard G. Small · ⑩ · Edwards Angell Palmer & Dodge · 2800 Financial Plaza · Providence, RI 02903 · 401-274-9200

MASS TORT LITIGATION

Providence

Mark O. Denehy · Adler Pollock & Sheehan · One Citizens Plaza, Eighth Floor · Providence, RI 02903-1345 · 401-274-7200

Fidelma L. Fitzpatrick · Motley Rice · 321 South Main Street · P.O. Box 6067 · Providence, RI 02940 · 401-457-7700

Peter Lawson Kennedy · Adler Pollock & Sheehan · One Citizens Plaza, Eighth Floor · Providence, RI 02903-1345 · 401-274-7200

John J. McConnell, Jr. · Motley Rice · 321 South Main Street · P.O. Box 6067 · Providence, RI 02940 · 401-457-7700

Robert R. McConnell · Motley Rice · 321 South Main Street · P.O. Box 6067 · Providence, RI 02940 · 401-457-7700

John A. Tarantino · Adler Pollock & Sheehan · One Citizens Plaza, Eighth Floor · Providence, RI 02903-1345 · 401-274-7200

MEDICAL MALPRACTICE LAW

Providence

Joseph V. Cavanagh, Jr. · ㉕ · Blish & Cavanagh · Commerce Center · 30 Exchange Terrace · Providence, RI 02903 · 401-831-8900

Leonard Decof · ㉕ · Decof & Decof · One Smith Hill · Providence, RI 02903 · 401-272-1110

Amato A. DeLuca · DeLuca & Weizenbaum · http://www.delucaandweizenbaum.com · 199 North Main Street · Providence, RI 02903 · 401-453-1500

Phillip M. Weinstein · ⑩ · Philip M. Weinstein · 99 Wayland Avenue, Suite 200 · Providence, RI 02906 · 401-521-3500

MERGERS & ACQUISITIONS LAW

Providence

Stephen J. Carlotti · ⑩ · Hinckley, Allen & Snyder · http://www.haslaw.com · 50 Kennedy Plaza, Suite 1500 · Providence, RI 02903-3293 · 401-274-2000

John F. Corrigan · ⑩ · John F. Corrigan · 90 Elm Street · Providence, RI 02903 · 401-276-8350

Margaret D. Farrell · Hinckley, Allen & Snyder · http://www.haslaw.com · 50 Kennedy Plaza, Suite 1500 Providence, RI 02903-3293 · 401-274-2000

V. Duncan Johnson · ⑩ · Edwards Angell Palmer & Dodge · 2800 Financial Plaza · Providence, RI 02903 · 401-274-9200

NON-WHITE-COLLAR CRIMINAL DEFENSE

Providence

Thomas G. Briody · Law Offices of Thomas G. Briody · 91 Friendship Street, Third Floor · Providence, RI 02903-3819 · 401-751-5151

John F. Cicilline · ⑩ · John F. Cicilline · 381 Atwells Avenue · Providence, RI 02909 · 401-273-5600

Peter A. DiBiase · ㉕ · Peter A. DiBiase · 91 Friendship Street · Providence, RI 02903 · 401-831-5020

Lise J. Gescheidt · MacFadyen, Gescheidt & O'Brien · The Owen Building · 101 Dyer Street · Providence, RI 02903 · 401-751-5090

John E. MacDonald · LaRochelle & MacDonald · http://www.aggressivelegalservices.com · One Turks Head Place, Suite 1440 · Providence, RI 02903 · 401-421-1440

John A. MacFadyen III · ⑳ · MacFadyen, Gescheidt & O'Brien · The Owen Building · 101 Dyer Street · Providence, RI 02903 · 401-751-5090

Robert B. Mann · ⑩ · Mann & Mitchell · One Turks Head Place, Suite 610 · Providence, RI 02903 · 401-351-5770

C. Leonard O'Brien · ⑩ · MacFadyen, Gescheidt & O'Brien · The Owen Building · 101 Dyer Street · Providence, RI 02903 · 401-751-5090

Anthony M. Traini · Law Offices of Anthony M. Traini · 56 Pine Street, Suite Two · Providence, RI 02903 · 401-621-4700

PERSONAL INJURY LITIGATION

Jamestown

A. Lauriston Parks · ⑩ · A. Lauriston Parks · 53 Narragansett Avenue · Jamestown, RI 02835 · 401-423-8900

Providence

Joseph V. Cavanagh, Jr. · ㉕ · Blish & Cavanagh · Commerce Center · 30 Exchange Terrace · Providence, RI 02903 · 401-831-8900

Peter J. Cerilli · Peter J. Cerilli · 56 Pine Street · Providence, RI 02806 · 401-272-7800

Leonard Decof · ㉕ · Decof & Decof · One Smith Hill · Providence, RI 02903 · 401-272-1110

Mark B. Decof · Decof & Decof · One Smith Hill · Providence, RI 02903 · 401-272-1110

Amato A. DeLuca · DeLuca & Weizenbaum · http://www.delucaandweizenbaum.com · 199 North Main Street · Providence, RI 02903 · 401-453-1500

Gerald C. DeMaria, Sr. · Higgins, Cavanaugh & Cooney · The Hay Building, Fourth Floor · 123 Dyer Street · Providence, RI 02903 · 401-272-3500

John F. Dolan · ⑳ · Rice Dolan & Kershaw · 72 Pine Street, Suite Three · Providence, RI 02903 · 401-272-8800

Mark P. Dolan · Rice Dolan & Kershaw · 72 Pine Street, Suite Three · Providence, RI 02903 · 401-272-8800

John S. Foley · Decof & Decof · One Smith Hill · Providence, RI 02903 · 401-272-1110

Lauren E. Jones · Jones Associates · 72 South Main Street · Providence, RI 02903 · 401-274-4446

Joseph A. Kelly · ⑳ · Carroll, Kelly & Murphy · 155 South Main Street · Providence, RI 02903 · 401-331-7272

R. Daniel Prentiss · ⑩ · The Prentiss Law Firm · One Turks Head Place, Suite 380 · Providence, RI 02903 · 401-824-5150

Paul V. Reynolds · ⑩ · Reynolds, DeMarco & Boland · 146 Westminster Street, Suite 400 · Providence, RI 02903 · 401-861-5522

John A. Tarantino · Adler Pollock & Sheehan · One Citizens Plaza, Eighth Floor · Providence, RI 02903-1345 · 401-274-7200

Phillip M. Weinstein · ⑩ · Philip M. Weinstein · 99 Wayland Avenue, Suite 200 · Providence, RI 02906 · 401-521-3500

Max Wistow · ⑳ · Wistow & Barylick · 61 Weybosset Street · Providence, RI 02903 · 401-831-2700

PRODUCT LIABILITY LITIGATION

Providence

Paul V. Curcio · Adler Pollock & Sheehan · One Citizens Plaza, Eighth Floor · Providence, RI 02903-1345 · 401-274-7200

Leonard Decof · ㉕ · Decof & Decof · One Smith Hill · Providence, RI 02903 · 401-272-1110

Gerald C. DeMaria, Sr. · Higgins, Cavanaugh & Cooney · The Hay Building, Fourth Floor · 123 Dyer Street · Providence, RI 02903 · 401-272-3500

John A. Tarantino · Adler Pollock & Sheehan · One Citizens Plaza, Eighth Floor · Providence, RI 02903-1345 · 401-274-7200

David A. Wollin · Adler Pollock & Sheehan · One Citizens Plaza, Eighth Floor · Providence, RI 02903-1345 · 401-274-7200

PUBLIC FINANCE LAW

Providence

Normand G. Benoit · Partridge Snow & Hahn · 180 South Main Street · Providence, RI 02903 · 401-861-8200

Eugene G. Bernardo II · Partridge Snow & Hahn · 180 South Main Street · Providence, RI 02903 · 401-861-8200

Ellen M. Flynn Corneau · Edwards Angell Palmer & Dodge · 2800 Financial Plaza · Providence, RI 02903 · 401-274-9200

Malcolm Farmer III · ⑩ · Hinckley, Allen & Snyder · http://www.haslaw.com · 50 Kennedy Plaza, Suite 1500 · Providence, RI 02903-3293 · 401-274-2000

Karen S. D. Grande · Edwards Angell Palmer & Dodge · 2800 Financial Plaza · Providence, RI 02903 · 401-274-9200

Sandra M. Mack · Hinckley, Allen & Snyder · http://www.haslaw.com · 50 Kennedy Plaza, Suite 1500 · Providence, RI 02903-3293 · 401-274-2000

James R. McGuirk · ⑩ · Edwards Angell Palmer & Dodge · 2800 Financial Plaza · Providence, RI 02903 401-274-9200

James J. Skeffington · Edwards Angell Palmer & Dodge · 2800 Financial Plaza · Providence, RI 02903 · 401-274-9200

REAL ESTATE LAW

Providence

E. Jerome Batty · ⑳ · Hinckley, Allen & Snyder · http://www.haslaw.com · 50 Kennedy Plaza, Suite 1500 Providence, RI 02903-3293 · 401-274-2000

John M. Boehnert · Partridge Snow & Hahn · 180 South Main Street · Providence, RI 02903 · 401-861-8200

David M. Gilden · ⑩ · Partridge Snow & Hahn · 180 South Main Street · Providence, RI 02903 · 401-861-8200

Stanley J. Kanter · Adler Pollock & Sheehan · One Citizens Plaza, Eighth Floor · Providence, RI 02903-1345 · 401-274-7200

Gail E. McCann · ⑩ · Edwards Angell Palmer & Dodge · 2800 Financial Plaza · Providence, RI 02903 · 401-274-9200

David J. Rubin · ⑩ · Hinckley, Allen & Snyder · http://www.haslaw.com · 50 Kennedy Plaza, Suite 1500 · Providence, RI 02903-3293 · 401-274-2000

Robert I. Stolzman · Adler Pollock & Sheehan · One Citizens Plaza, Eighth Floor · Providence, RI 02903-1345 · 401-274-7200

David J. Tracy · ⑳ · Hinckley, Allen & Snyder · http://www.haslaw.com · 50 Kennedy Plaza, Suite 1500 · Providence, RI 02903-3293 · 401-274-2000

Joseph F. Whinery · Cameron & Mittleman · 56 Exchange Terrace · Providence, RI 02903 · 401-331-5700

SECURITIES LAW

Providence

John F. Corrigan · ⑩ · John F. Corrigan · 90 Elm Street · Providence, RI 02903 · 401-276-8350

Margaret D. Farrell · Hinckley, Allen & Snyder · http://www.haslaw.com · 50 Kennedy Plaza, Suite 1500 Providence, RI 02903-3293 · 401-274-2000

TAX LAW

Providence

Justin S. Holden · ⑩ · Holden & O'Brien · 155 South Main Street, Suite 405 · Providence, RI 02903 · 401-421-1300

E. Hans Lundsten · Adler Pollock & Sheehan · One Citizens Plaza, Eighth Floor · Providence, RI 02903-1345 · 401-274-7200

H. Peter Olsen · ㉕ · Hinckley, Allen & Snyder · http://www.haslaw.com · 50 Kennedy Plaza, Suite 1500 · Providence, RI 02903-3293 · 401-274-2000

Charles J. Reilly · Reilly Law Associates · 1040 Turks Head Building · Providence, RI 02903 · 401-861-1120

TRUSTS AND ESTATES

Pawtucket

Nancy Fisher Chudacoff · Hardy Tabor & Chudacoff · 24 Spring Street · Pawtucket, RI 02866 · 401-727-1616

Providence

Leon C. Boghossian III · Hinckley, Allen & Snyder · http://www.haslaw.com · 50 Kennedy Plaza, Suite 1500 · Providence, RI 02903-3293 · 401-274-2000

Nathan W. Chace · ⑩ · Chace Ruttenberg & Freedman · One Park Row, Suite 300 · Providence, RI 02903 · 401-453-6400

Karen G. DelPonte · Cameron & Mittleman · 56 Exchange Terrace · Providence, RI 02903 · 401-331-5700

Kinnaird Howland · ⑩ · Edwards Angell Palmer & Dodge · 2800 Financial Plaza · Providence, RI 02903 401-274-9200

Mary Louise Kennedy · ⑳ · Edwards Angell Palmer & Dodge · 2800 Financial Plaza · Providence, RI 02903 · 401-274-9200

A. Max Kohlenberg · Edwards Angell Palmer & Dodge · 2800 Financial Plaza · Providence, RI 02903 · 401-274-9200

Doris J. Licht · ⑩ · Hinckley, Allen & Snyder · http://www.haslaw.com · 50 Kennedy Plaza, Suite 1500 · Providence, RI 02903-3293 · 401-274-2000

Benjamin G. Paster · ⑳ · Paster & Harpootian · 1000 Chapel View Road, Suite 220 · Providence, RI 02920 · 401-455-9800

David T. Riedel · ⑩ · Tillinghast Licht · 10 Weybosset Street · Providence, RI 02903 · 401-456-1200

Paul A. Silver · Hinckley, Allen & Snyder · http://www.haslaw.com · 50 Kennedy Plaza, Suite 1500 · Providence, RI 02903-3293 · 401-274-2000

WHITE-COLLAR CRIMINAL DEFENSE

Providence

William P. Devereaux · Pannone, Lopes & Devereaux · http://www.pldlaw.com · 317 Iron Horse Way, Suite 301 · Providence, RI 02908 · 401-824-5100

Peter A. DiBiase · ㉕ · Peter A. DiBiase · 91 Friendship Street · Providence, RI 02903 · 401-831-5020

Lise J. Gescheidt · MacFadyen, Gescheidt & O'Brien · The Owen Building · 101 Dyer Street · Providence, RI 02903 · 401-751-5090

John A. MacFadyen III · ⑳ · MacFadyen, Gescheidt & O'Brien · The Owen Building · 101 Dyer Street · Providence, RI 02903 · 401-751-5090

Robert B. Mann · ⑩ · Mann & Mitchell · One Turks Head Place, Suite 610 · Providence, RI 02903 · 401-351-5770

C. Leonard O'Brien · ⑩ · MacFadyen, Gescheidt & O'Brien · The Owen Building · 101 Dyer Street · Providence, RI 02903 · 401-751-5090

Patricia K. Rocha · Adler Pollock & Sheehan · One Citizens Plaza, Eighth Floor · Providence, RI 02903-1345 · 401-274-7200

John A. Tarantino · Adler Pollock & Sheehan · One Citizens Plaza, Eighth Floor · Providence, RI 02903-1345 · 401-274-7200

Anthony M. Traini · Law Offices of Anthony M. Traini · 56 Pine Street, Suite Two · Providence, RI 02903 · 401-621-4700

WORKERS' COMPENSATION LAW

Cranston

Robyn K. Factor · Kirshenbaum & Kirshenbaum · 888 Reservoir Avenue · Cranston, RI 02910 · 401-946-3200

Providence

Gary J. Levine · Homonoff, Levine & Pulner · 369 South Main Street · Providence, RI 02903 · 401-521-3100

Warwick

Michael A. St. Pierre · Revens, Revens & St. Pierre · 946 Centerville Road · Warwick, RI 02886 · 401-822-2900

SOUTH CAROLINA

ADMINISTRATIVE LAW

Charleston

Michael A. Molony · Young Clement Rivers · 28 Broad Street · P.O. Box 993 · Charleston, SC 29402 · 843-577-4000

Columbia

James C. Gray, Jr. · Nelson Mullins Riley & Scarborough · Meridian, 17th Floor · 1320 Main Street · P.O. Box 11070 · Columbia, SC 29211 · 803-799-2000

David B. Summer, Jr. · Parker Poe Adams & Bernstein · http://www.parkerpoe.com · 1201 Main Street, Suite 1450 · P.O. Box 1509 · Columbia, SC 29202 · 803-255-8000

Greenville

Ronald E. Cardwell · McNair Law Firm · http://www.mcnair.net · Bank of America Plaza, Suite 900 · 101 North Main Street · P.O. Box 447 · Greenville, SC 29602 · 864-271-4940

ALTERNATIVE DISPUTE RESOLUTION

Anderson

Michael D. Glenn · Glenn, Haigler, McClain & Stathakis · 121 West Benson Street · Anderson, SC 29624 864-226-1885

Charleston

Capers G. Barr III · Barr, Unger and McIntosh · 11 Broad Street · P.O. Box 1037 · Charleston, SC 29402 · 843-577-5083

William C. Cleveland III · Buist Moore Smythe McGee · http://www.buistmoore.com · Five Exchange Street · P.O. Box 999 · Charleston, SC 29402-0999 · 843-722-3400

M. Dawes Cooke, Jr. · Barnwell Whaley Patterson & Helms · 885 Island Park Drive · P.O. Drawer H · Charleston, SC 29402-0197 · 843-577-7700

Wade H. Logan III · Nelson Mullins Riley & Scarborough · Liberty Center, Suite 600 · 151 Meeting Street · Charleston, SC 29401-2239 · 843-853-5200

Bachman S. Smith III · Haynsworth Sinkler Boyd · http://www.hsblawfirm.com · 134 Meeting Street, Third Floor · P.O. Box 340 · Charleston, SC 29402-0340 · 843-722-3366

G. Trenholm Walker · Pratt-Thomas, Epting & Walker · 16 Charlotte Street · P.O. Drawer 22247 · Charleston, SC 29413-2247 · 843-727-2200

Thomas J. Wills · Wills & Massalon · 134 Meeting Street, Suite 100 · Charleston, SC 29401 · 843-727-1144

Columbia

M. Malissa Burnette · Burnette & Rothstein · 2322 Devine Street · Columbia, SC 29205 · 803-251-0202

Danny C. Crowe · Turner, Padget, Graham & Laney · 1901 Main Street, 17th Floor · P.O. Box 1473 · Columbia, SC 29202 · 803-254-2200

D. Cravens Ravenel · Baker, Ravenel & Bender · http://www.brblegal.com · 3710 Landmark Drive, Suite 400 · P.O. Box 8057 · Columbia, SC 29202 · 803-799-9091

Franklin G. Shuler, Jr. · Turner, Padget, Graham & Laney · 1901 Main Street, 17th Floor · P.O. Box 1473 · Columbia, SC 29202 · 803-254-2200

Walter B. Todd, Jr. · Todd & Ward · 1709 Devonshire Drive · P.O. Box 1549 · Columbia, SC 29204 · 803-779-4383

Florence

Karl A. Folkens · Folkens Law Firm · Six 01 West Evans Street · P.O. Box 6139 · Florence, SC 29502-6139 · 843-665-0100

Richard L. Hinson · Turner, Padget, Graham & Laney · BB&T Building, Fouth Floor · 1831 West Evans Street · P.O. Box 5478 · Florence, SC 29502-5478 · 843-662-9008

Greenville

Mark W. Bakker · Wyche, Burgess, Freeman & Parham · 44 East Camperdown Way · P.O. Box 728 · Greenville, SC 29602-0728 · 864-242-8200

Theron G. Cochran · a · Love, Thornton, Arnold & Thomason · 410 East Washington Street · P.O. Box 10045 · Greenville, SC 29603 · 864-242-6360

Eric K. Englebardt · Turner, Padget, Graham & Laney · 200 East Broad Street, Suite 250 · P.O. Box 1509 Greenville, SC 29602 · 864-552-4600

Jack D. Griffeth · Collins & Lacy · http://www.collinsandlacy.com · 37 Villa Road, Suite 500 · P.O. Box 5819 · Greenville, SC 29606 · 864-282-9100

William M. Hagood III · a · Love, Thornton, Arnold & Thomason · 410 East Washington Street · P.O. Box 10045 · Greenville, SC 29603 · 864-242-6360

Robert W. Hassold, Jr. · Robert W. Hassold, Jr. · P.O. Box 8882 · Greenville, SC 29604-8882 · 864-370-1070

Charles S. Mauney · Gallivan, White & Boyd · One Liberty Square, Suite 1200 · 55 Beattie Place · P.O. Box 10589 · Greenville, SC 29603 · 864-271-9580

James C. Sarratt · The Legal Clinic of Sarratt & Clarke · Six Brookside Circle · Greenville, SC 29609 · 864-271-4100

Thomas L. Stephenson · Nexsen Pruet · http://www.nexsenpruet.com · 201 West McBee Avenue, Suite 400 · P.O. Drawer 10648 · Greenville, SC 29601 · 864-370-2211

Thomas W. Traxler · Carter, Smith, Merriam, Rogers & Traxler · 900 East North Street · P.O. Box 10828 Greenville, SC 29603 · 864-242-3566

Greenwood

Robert M. Erwin, Jr. · Robert M. Erwin, Jr. · 305 Main Street · Greenwood, SC 29646 · 864-229-5010

Mt. Pleasant

Connie C. Harnass III · Connie C. Harnass, III · 505 Belle Hall Parkway, Suite 101 · Mt. Pleasant, SC 29464 · 843-856-2627

ANTITRUST LAW

Columbia

William C. Boyd · a · Haynsworth Sinkler Boyd · http://www.hsblawfirm.com · 1201 Main Street, 22nd Floor · P.O. Box 11889 · Columbia, SC 29211-1889 · 803-779-3080

Manton M. Grier · Haynsworth Sinkler Boyd · http://www.hsblawfirm.com · 1201 Main Street, 22nd Floor · P.O. Box 11889 · Columbia, SC 29211-1889 · 803-779-3080

Greenville

Henry L. Parr, Jr. · Wyche, Burgess, Freeman & Parham · 44 East Camperdown Way · P.O. Box 728 · Greenville, SC 29602-0728 · 864-242-8200

APPELLATE LAW

Charleston

John C. von Lehe, Jr. · 2) · Nelson Mullins Riley & Scarborough · Liberty Center, Suite 600 · 151 Meeting Street · Charleston, SC 29401-2239 · 843-853-5200

Columbia

Charles E. Baker · Baker, Ravenel & Bender · http://www.brblegal.com · 3710 Landmark Drive, Suite 400 · P.O. Box 8057 · Columbia, SC 29202 · 803-799-9091

C. Mitchell Brown · Nelson Mullins Riley & Scarborough · Meridian, 17th Floor · 1320 Main Street · P.O. Box 11070 · Columbia, SC 29211 · 803-799-2000

Charles E. Carpenter, Jr. · Carpenter Appeals & Trial Support · 1201 Main Street, Suite 900 · Columbia, SC 29201 · 803-758-2886

C. Dixon Lee III · McLaren & Lee · 1508 Laurel Street · P.O. Box 11809 · Columbia, SC 29211-1809 · 803-799-3074

James B. Richardson, Jr. · James B. Richardson, Jr. · 1229 Lincoln Street · Columbia, SC 29201-3135 · 803-799-9412

Jack B. Swerling · a · Law Offices of Jack B. Swerling · http://www.jackswerling.com · 1720 Main Street, Suite 301 · Columbia, SC 29201 · 803-765-2626

William T. Toal · Johnson Toal & Battiste · 1615 Barnwell Street · P.O. Box 1431 · Columbia, SC 29201 · 803-252-9700

Florence

J. René Josey · Turner, Padget, Graham & Laney · BB&T Building, Fouth Floor · 1831 West Evans Street · P.O. Box 5478 · Florence, SC 29502-5478 · 843-662-9008

Greenville

David L. Moore, Jr. · Love, Thornton, Arnold & Thomason · 410 East Washington Street · P.O. Box 10045 · Greenville, SC 29603 · 864-242-6360

BANKING LAW

Charleston

Mark S. Sharpe · Warren & Sinkler · 171 Church Street, Suite 340 · P.O. Box 1254 · Charleston, SC 29402 · 843-577-0660

John H. Warren III · a · Warren & Sinkler · 171 Church Street, Suite 340 · P.O. Box 1254 · Charleston, SC 29402 · 843-577-0660

Columbia

John W. Currie · a · McNair Law Firm · http://www.mcnair.net · 1301 Gervais Street, 11th Floor · P.O. Box 11390 · Columbia, SC 29211 · 803-799-9800

M. Craig Garner, Jr. · McNair Law Firm · http://www.mcnair.net · 1301 Gervais Street, 11th Floor · P.O. Box 11390 · Columbia, SC 29211 · 803-799-9800

George S. King, Jr. · a · Haynsworth Sinkler Boyd · http://www.hsblawfirm.com · 1201 Main Street, 22nd Floor · P.O. Box 11889 · Columbia, SC 29211-1889 · 803-779-3080

Lanneau W. Lambert, Jr. · Turner, Padget, Graham & Laney · 1901 Main Street, 17th Floor · P.O. Box 1473 · Columbia, SC 29202 · 803-254-2200

Alan M. Lipsitz · Nexsen Pruet · http://www.nexsenpruet.com · First Citizens Building, Suite 700 · 1230 Main Street · P.O. Drawer 2426 · Columbia, SC 29202-2426 · 803-771-8900

Thomas E. Lydon · McAngus, Goudelock & Courie · 700 Gervais Street, Suite 300 · P.O. Box 12519 · Columbia, SC 29211-2519 · 803-779-2300

John T. Moore · a · Nelson Mullins Riley & Scarborough · Meridian, 17th Floor · 1320 Main Street · P.O. Box 11070 · Columbia, SC 29211 · 803-799-2000

BANKRUPTCY AND CREDITOR-DEBTOR RIGHTS LAW

Charleston

Gerald M. Finkel · 2% · Finkel Law Firm · http://www.finkellaw.com · 3955 Faber Place Drive, Suite 200 · P.O. Box 225 · Charleston, SC 29402 · 843-577-5460

J. Ronald Jones, Jr. · Clawson & Staubes · 126 Seven Farms Drive, Suite 200 · Charleston, SC 29492-7595 · 843-577-2026

Cynthia J. Lowery · Moore & Van Allen · 40 Calhoun Street, Suite 300 · P.O. Box 22828 · Charleston, SC 29401-2828 · 843-579-7000

Ivan N. Nossokoff · Ivan N. Nossokoff · 1470 Tobias Gadson Boulevard, Suite 107 · Charleston, SC 29407-4835 · 843-571-5442

Charles P. Summerall IV · Buist Moore Smythe McGee · http://www.buistmoore.com · Five Exchange Street · P.O. Box 999 · Charleston, SC 29402-0999 · 843-722-3400

David B. Wheeler · Moore & Van Allen · 40 Calhoun Street, Suite 300 · P.O. Box 22828 · Charleston, SC 29401-2828 · 843-579-7000

Columbia

Linda K. Barr · Nelson Mullins Riley & Scarborough · Meridian, 17th Floor · 1320 Main Street · P.O. Box 11070 · Columbia, SC 29211 · 803-799-2000

Barbara G. Barton · Barton Law Firm · 1715 Pickens Street · P.O. Box 12046 · Columbia, SC 29211 · 803-256-6400

Michael M. Beal · McNair Law Firm · http://www.mcnair.net · 1301 Gervais Street, 11th Floor · P.O. Box 11390 · Columbia, SC 29211 · 803-799-9800

John B. Butler III · John B. Butler III · 1217 Anthony Avenue · Columbia, SC 29201 · 803-256-9661

George B. Cauthen · a · Nelson Mullins Riley & Scarborough · Meridian, 17th Floor · 1320 Main Street · P.O. Box 11070 · Columbia, SC 29211 · 803-799-2000

Richard R. Gleissner · Finkel Law Firm · http://www.finkellaw.com · 1201 Main Street, Suite 1800 · P.O. Box 1799 · Columbia, SC 29202 · 803-765-2935

R. Geoffrey Levy · R. Geoffrey Levy · 2300 Wayne Street · Columbia, SC 29201 · 803-256-4693

G. William McCarthy, Jr. · McCarthy Law Firm · 1717 Pickens Street · P.O. Box 11332 · Columbia, SC 29211 · 803-771-8836

Stanley H. McGuffin · Haynsworth Sinkler Boyd · http://www.hsblawfirm.com · 1201 Main Street, 22nd Floor · P.O. Box 11889 · Columbia, SC 29211-1889 · 803-779-3080

Julio E. Mendoza, Jr. · Nexsen Pruet · http://www.nexsenpruet.com · First Citizens Building, Suite 700 · 1230 Main Street · P.O. Drawer 2426 · Columbia, SC 29202-2426 · 803-771-8900

William H. Short, Jr. · Haynsworth Sinkler Boyd · http://www.hsblawfirm.com · 1201 Main Street, 22nd Floor · P.O. Box 11889 · Columbia, SC 29211-1889 · 803-779-3080

Greenville

Weyman C. Carter · McNair Law Firm · http://www.mcnair.net · Bank of America Plaza, Suite 900 · 101 North Main Street · P.O. Box 447 · Greenville, SC 29602 · 864-271-4940

James H. Cassidy · Roe Cassidy Coates & Price · 1052 North Church Street · P.O. Box 10529 · Greenville, SC 29603 · 864-349-2600

D. Allen Grumbine · Womble Carlyle Sandridge & Rice · 550 South Main Street, Suite 400 · P.O. Box 10208 · Greenville, SC 29603-0208 · 864-255-5400

F. Marion Hughes · Smith Moore Leatherwood · http://www.smithmoorelaw.com · The Leatherwood Plaza, Suite 500 · 300 East McBee Avenue · P.O. Box 87 · Greenville, SC 29602 · 864-242-6440

Randy A. Skinner · Skinner & Associates · Two Liberty Square · 75 Beattie Place, Suite 500 · Greenville, SC 29601 · 864-232-2007

Rory D. Whelehan · Womble Carlyle Sandridge & Rice · 550 South Main Street, Suite 400 · P.O. Box 10208 · Greenville, SC 29603-0208 · 864-255-5400

Mount Pleasant

Robert A. Kerr, Jr. · Hagood & Kerr · http://www.hagoodkerr.com · 654 Coleman Boulevard · P.O. Box 220 · Mount Pleasant, SC 29465 · 843-972-1000

Mt. Pleasant

Kevin Campbell · Campbell Law Firm · 890 Johnnie Dodds Boulevard · Mt. Pleasant, SC 29464 · 843-884-6874

North Charleston

R. Michael Drose · Drose Law Firm · 3955 Faber Place · North Charleston, SC 29405 · 843-767-8888

BET-THE-COMPANY LITIGATION

Charleston

Paul A. Dominick · Nexsen Pruet · http://www.nexsenpruet.com · 205 King Street, Suite 400 · P.O. Box 486 · Charleston, SC 29402 · 843-577-9440

Marvin D. Infinger · Haynsworth Sinkler Boyd · http://www.hsblawfirm.com · 134 Meeting Street, Third Floor · P.O. Box 340 · Charleston, SC 29402-0340 · 843-722-3366

John P. Linton · Duffy & Young · 96 Broad Street · Charleston, SC 29401 · 843-720-2044

Morris D. Rosen · 2% · Rosen, Rosen & Hagood · http://www.rrhlawfirm.com · 134 Meeting Street, Suite 200 · P.O. Box 893 · Charleston, SC 29401 · 843-577-6726

J. Rutledge Young, Jr. · 2% · Young Clement Rivers · 28 Broad Street · P.O. Box 993 · Charleston, SC 29402 · 843-577-4000

Columbia

David E. Dukes · Nelson Mullins Riley & Scarborough · Meridian, 17th Floor · 1320 Main Street · P.O. Box 11070 · Columbia, SC 29211 · 803-799-2000

Elizabeth Van Doren Gray · Sowell Gray Stepp & Laffitte · http://www.sowell.com · 1310 Gadsden Street · P.O. Box 11449 · Columbia, SC 29211 · 803-929-1400

Edward W. Mullins, Jr. · 2% · Nelson Mullins Riley & Scarborough · Meridian, 17th Floor · 1320 Main Street · P.O. Box 11070 · Columbia, SC 29211 · 803-799-2000

Joel H. Smith · Nelson Mullins Riley & Scarborough · Meridian, 17th Floor · 1320 Main Street · P.O. Box 11070 · Columbia, SC 29211 · 803-799-2000

Thornwell F. Sowell · Sowell Gray Stepp & Laffitte · http://www.sowell.com · 1310 Gadsden Street · P.O. Box 11449 · Columbia, SC 29211 · 803-929-1400

Greenville

L. Gray Geddie, Jr. · a · Ogletree Deakins · http://www.ogletreedeakins.com · The Ogletree Building · 300 North Main Street · P.O. Box 2757 · Greenville, SC 29602 · 864-271-1300

Frank S. Holleman III · Wyche, Burgess, Freeman & Parham · 44 East Camperdown Way · P.O. Box 728 Greenville, SC 29602-0728 · 864-242-8200

Wallace K. Lightsey · a · Wyche, Burgess, Freeman & Parham · 44 East Camperdown Way · P.O. Box 728 · Greenville, SC 29602-0728 · 864-242-8200

Thomas W. Traxler · Carter, Smith, Merriam, Rogers & Traxler · 900 East North Street · P.O. Box 10828 Greenville, SC 29603 · 864-242-3566

COMMERCIAL LITIGATION

Charleston

Charles J. Baker III · Buist Moore Smythe McGee · http://www.buistmoore.com · Five Exchange Street · P.O. Box 999 · Charleston, SC 29402-0999 · 843-722-3400

William C. Cleveland III · Buist Moore Smythe McGee · http://www.buistmoore.com · Five Exchange Street · P.O. Box 999 · Charleston, SC 29402-0999 · 843-722-3400

M. Dawes Cooke, Jr. · Barnwell Whaley Patterson & Helms · 885 Island Park Drive · P.O. Drawer H · Charleston, SC 29402-0197 · 843-577-7700

Paul A. Dominick · Nexsen Pruet · http://www.nexsenpruet.com · 205 King Street, Suite 400 · P.O. Box 486 · Charleston, SC 29402 · 843-577-9440

Morris A. Ellison · a · Buist Moore Smythe McGee · http://www.buistmoore.com · Five Exchange Street P.O. Box 999 · Charleston, SC 29402-0999 · 843-722-3400

Richard A. Farrier, Jr. · Nelson Mullins Riley & Scarborough · Liberty Center, Suite 600 · 151 Meeting Street · Charleston, SC 29401-2239 · 843-853-5200

Gerald M. Finkel · 2% · Finkel Law Firm · http://www.finkellaw.com · 3955 Faber Place Drive, Suite 200 · P.O. Box 225 · Charleston, SC 29402 · 843-577-5460

Henry E. Grimball · Buist Moore Smythe McGee · http://www.buistmoore.com · Five Exchange Street · P.O. Box 999 · Charleston, SC 29402-0999 · 843-722-3400

Robert H. Hood · 2% · Hood Law Firm · http://www.hoodlaw.com · 172 Meeting Street · P.O. Box 1508 · Charleston, SC 29402 · 843-577-4435

Marvin D. Infinger · Haynsworth Sinkler Boyd · http://www.hsblawfirm.com · 134 Meeting Street, Third Floor · P.O. Box 340 · Charleston, SC 29402-0340 · 843-722-3366

Harold W. Jacobs · a · Nexsen Pruet · http://www.nexsenpruet.com · 205 King Street, Suite 400 · P.O. Box 486 · Charleston, SC 29402 · 843-577-9440

John P. Linton · Duffy & Young · 96 Broad Street · Charleston, SC 29401 · 843-720-2044

Morris D. Rosen · 2% · Rosen, Rosen & Hagood · http://www.rrhlawfirm.com · 134 Meeting Street, Suite 200 · P.O. Box 893 · Charleston, SC 29401 · 843-577-6726

Richard S. Rosen · a · Rosen, Rosen & Hagood · http://www.rrhlawfirm.com · 134 Meeting Street, Suite 200 · P.O. Box 893 · Charleston, SC 29401 · 843-577-6726

G. Dana Sinkler · Warren & Sinkler · 171 Church Street, Suite 340 · P.O. Box 1254 · Charleston, SC 29402 · 843-577-0660

Thomas S. Tisdale, Jr. · a · Nexsen Pruet · http://www.nexsenpruet.com · 205 King Street, Suite 400 · P.O. Box 486 · Charleston, SC 29402 · 843-577-9440

Bradish J. Waring · Nexsen Pruet · http://www.nexsenpruet.com · 205 King Street, Suite 400 · P.O. Box 486 · Charleston, SC 29402 · 843-577-9440

J. Rutledge Young, Jr. · 2% · Young Clement Rivers · 28 Broad Street · P.O. Box 993 · Charleston, SC 29402 · 843-577-4000

Columbia

C. Mitchell Brown · Nelson Mullins Riley & Scarborough · Meridian, 17th Floor · 1320 Main Street · P.O. Box 11070 · Columbia, SC 29211 · 803-799-2000

Russell T. Burke · Nexsen Pruet · http://www.nexsenpruet.com · First Citizens Building, Suite 700 · 1230 Main Street · P.O. Drawer 2426 · Columbia, SC 29202-2426 · 803-771-8900

Charles E. Carpenter, Jr. · Carpenter Appeals & Trial Support · 1201 Main Street, Suite 900 · Columbia, SC 29201 · 803-758-2886

Gray T. Culbreath · Collins & Lacy · http://www.collinsandlacy.com · 1330 Lady Street, Sixth Floor · P.O. Box 12487 · Columbia, SC 29211 · 803-256-2660

Robert W. Dibble, Jr. · McNair Law Firm · http://www.mcnair.net · 1301 Gervais Street, 11th Floor · P.O. Box 11390 · Columbia, SC 29211 · 803-799-9800

David E. Dukes · Nelson Mullins Riley & Scarborough · Meridian, 17th Floor · 1320 Main Street · P.O. Box 11070 · Columbia, SC 29211 · 803-799-2000

Elizabeth Van Doren Gray · Sowell Gray Stepp & Laffitte · http://www.sowell.com · 1310 Gadsden Street · P.O. Box 11449 · Columbia, SC 29211 · 803-929-1400

Manton M. Grier · Haynsworth Sinkler Boyd · http://www.hsblawfirm.com · 1201 Main Street, 22nd Floor · P.O. Box 11889 · Columbia, SC 29211-1889 · 803-779-3080

Kevin A. Hall · Nelson Mullins Riley & Scarborough · Meridian, 17th Floor · 1320 Main Street · P.O. Box 11070 · Columbia, SC 29211 · 803-799-2000

William C. Hubbard · a · Nelson Mullins Riley & Scarborough · Meridian, 17th Floor · 1320 Main Street P.O. Box 11070 · Columbia, SC 29211 · 803-799-2000

S. Keith Hutto · Nelson Mullins Riley & Scarborough · Meridian, 17th Floor · 1320 Main Street · P.O. Box 11070 · Columbia, SC 29211 · 803-799-2000

Celeste T. Jones · McNair Law Firm · http://www.mcnair.net · 1301 Gervais Street, 11th Floor · P.O. Box 11390 · Columbia, SC 29211 · 803-799-9800

D. Larry Kristinik III · Nelson Mullins Riley & Scarborough · Meridian, 17th Floor · 1320 Main Street · P.O. Box 11070 · Columbia, SC 29211 · 803-799-2000

John F. Kuppens · Nelson Mullins Riley & Scarborough · Meridian, 17th Floor · 1320 Main Street · P.O. Box 11070 · Columbia, SC 29211 · 803-799-2000

LeRoy F. Laney · Riley Pope & Laney · 2838 Devine Street · Columbia, SC 29205 · 803-799-9993

John T. Lay, Jr. · Ellis, Lawhorne & Sims · http://www.ellislawhorne.com · 1501 Main Street, Fifth Floor P.O. Box 2285 · Columbia, SC 29202 · 803-254-4190

James K. Lehman · Nelson Mullins Riley & Scarborough · Meridian, 17th Floor · 1320 Main Street · P.O. Box 11070 · Columbia, SC 29211 · 803-799-2000

Francis M. Mack · Richardson, Plowden & Robinson · 1900 Barnwell Street · P.O. Box 7788 · Columbia, SC 29202 · 803-771-4400

Thomas E. McCutchen, Jr. · 2% · McCutchen Blanton Johnson & Barnette · 1414 Lady Street · P.O. Drawer 11209 · Columbia, SC 29211-1209 · 803-799-9791

Stephen G. Morrison · a · Nelson Mullins Riley & Scarborough · Meridian, 17th Floor · 1320 Main Street · P.O. Box 11070 · Columbia, SC 29211 · 803-799-2000

John C. Moylan III · Wyche, Burgess, Freeman & Parham · 1122 Lady Street, Suite 810 · P.O. Box 12247 Columbia, SC 29211-2247 · 803-254-6542

Edward W. Mullins, Jr. · 2% · Nelson Mullins Riley & Scarborough · Meridian, 17th Floor · 1320 Main Street · P.O. Box 11070 · Columbia, SC 29211 · 803-799-2000

Curtis L. Ott · Turner, Padget, Graham & Laney · 1901 Main Street, 17th Floor · P.O. Box 1473 · Columbia, SC 29202 · 803-254-2200

D. Cravens Ravenel · Baker, Ravenel & Bender · http://www.brblegal.com · 3710 Landmark Drive, Suite 400 · P.O. Box 8057 · Columbia, SC 29202 · 803-799-9091

B. Rush Smith III · Nelson Mullins Riley & Scarborough · Meridian, 17th Floor · 1320 Main Street · P.O. Box 11070 · Columbia, SC 29211 · 803-799-2000

Joel H. Smith · Nelson Mullins Riley & Scarborough · Meridian, 17th Floor · 1320 Main Street · P.O. Box 11070 · Columbia, SC 29211 · 803-799-2000

Thornwell F. Sowell · Sowell Gray Stepp & Laffitte · http://www.sowell.com · 1310 Gadsden Street · P.O. Box 11449 · Columbia, SC 29211 · 803-929-1400

W. Duvall Spruill · Turner, Padget, Graham & Laney · 1901 Main Street, 17th Floor · P.O. Box 1473 · Columbia, SC 29202 · 803-254-2200

Robert E. Stepp · Sowell Gray Stepp & Laffitte · http://www.sowell.com · 1310 Gadsden Street · P.O. Box 11449 · Columbia, SC 29211 · 803-929-1400

Ronald J. Tryon · Parker Poe Adams & Bernstein · http://www.parkerpoe.com · 1201 Main Street, Suite 1450 · P.O. Box 1509 · Columbia, SC 29202 · 803-255-8000

J. Calhoun Watson · Sowell Gray Stepp & Laffitte · http://www.sowell.com · 1310 Gadsden Street · P.O. Box 11449 · Columbia, SC 29211 · 803-929-1400

James L. Werner · Parker Poe Adams & Bernstein · http://www.parkerpoe.com · 1201 Main Street, Suite 1450 · P.O. Box 1509 · Columbia, SC 29202 · 803-255-8000

Florence

W. Reynolds Williams · a · Willcox, Buyck & Williams · 248 West Evans Street · P.O. Box 1909 · Florence, SC 29503 · 843-662-3258

Greenville

W. Howard Boyd, Jr. · Gallivan, White & Boyd · One Liberty Square, Suite 1200 · 55 Beattie Place · P.O. Box 10589 · Greenville, SC 29603 · 864-271-9580

James H. Cassidy · Roe Cassidy Coates & Price · 1052 North Church Street · P.O. Box 10529 · Greenville, SC 29603 · 864-349-2600

L. Franklin Elmore · Elmore and Wall · 301 North Main Street, Suite 2000 · P.O. Box 1887 · Greenville, SC 29602 · 864-255-9500

Gregory J. English · Wyche, Burgess, Freeman & Parham · 44 East Camperdown Way · P.O. Box 728 · Greenville, SC 29602-0728 · 864-242-8200

Steven E. Farrar · Smith Moore Leatherwood · http://www.smithmoorelaw.com · The Leatherwood Plaza, Suite 500 · 300 East McBee Avenue · P.O. Box 87 · Greenville, SC 29602 · 864-242-6440

L. Gray Geddie, Jr. · a · Ogletree Deakins · http://www.ogletreedeakins.com · The Ogletree Building · 300 North Main Street · P.O. Box 2757 · Greenville, SC 29602 · 864-271-1300

Michael J. Giese · a · Smith Moore Leatherwood · http://www.smithmoorelaw.com · The Leatherwood Plaza, Suite 500 · 300 East McBee Avenue · P.O. Box 87 · Greenville, SC 29602 · 864-242-6440

Mason A. Goldsmith · a · Love, Thornton, Arnold & Thomason · 410 East Washington Street · P.O. Box 10045 · Greenville, SC 29603 · 864-242-6360

Frank S. Holleman III · Wyche, Burgess, Freeman & Parham · 44 East Camperdown Way · P.O. Box 728 Greenville, SC 29602-0728 · 864-242-8200

Ellis M. Johnston II · a · Haynsworth Sinkler Boyd · http://www.hsblawfirm.com · Two Liberty Square, 11th Floor · 75 Beattie Place · P.O. Box 2048 · Greenville, SC 29602-2048 · 864-240-3200

John E. Johnston · a · Smith Moore Leatherwood · http://www.smithmoorelaw.com · The Leatherwood Plaza, Suite 500 · 300 East McBee Avenue · P.O. Box 87 · Greenville, SC 29602 · 864-242-6440

Wallace K. Lightsey · a · Wyche, Burgess, Freeman & Parham · 44 East Camperdown Way · P.O. Box 728 · Greenville, SC 29602-0728 · 864-242-8200

H. Sam Mabry III · Haynsworth Sinkler Boyd · http://www.hsblawfirm.com · Two Liberty Square, 11th Floor · 75 Beattie Place · P.O. Box 2048 · Greenville, SC 29602-2048 · 864-240-3200

William Francis Marion, Jr. · Haynsworth Sinkler Boyd · http://www.hsblawfirm.com · Two Liberty Square, 11th Floor · 75 Beattie Place · P.O. Box 2048 · Greenville, SC 29602-2048 · 864-240-3200

Samuel W. Outten · Womble Carlyle Sandridge & Rice · 550 South Main Street, Suite 400 · P.O. Box 10208 · Greenville, SC 29603-0208 · 864-255-5400

G. Dewey Oxner, Jr. · 2% · Haynsworth Sinkler Boyd · http://www.hsblawfirm.com · Two Liberty Square, 11th Floor · 75 Beattie Place · P.O. Box 2048 · Greenville, SC 29602-2048 · 864-240-3200

James C. Parham, Jr. · a · Wyche, Burgess, Freeman & Parham · 44 East Camperdown Way · P.O. Box 728 · Greenville, SC 29602-0728 · 864-242-8200

Henry L. Parr, Jr. · Wyche, Burgess, Freeman & Parham · 44 East Camperdown Way · P.O. Box 728 · Greenville, SC 29602-0728 · 864-242-8200

A. Marvin Quattlebaum, Jr. · Nelson Mullins Riley & Scarborough · Poinsett Plaza, Suite 900 · 104 South Main Street · Greenville, SC 29601-2122 · 864-250-2300

T. S. Stern, Jr. · Covington, Patrick, Hagins, Stern & Lewis · 211 Pettigru Street · P.O. Box 2343 · Greenville, SC 29601 · 864-242-9000

Troy A. Tessier · Wyche, Burgess, Freeman & Parham · 44 East Camperdown Way · P.O. Box 728 · Greenville, SC 29602-0728 · 864-242-8200

Thomas W. Traxler · Carter, Smith, Merriam, Rogers & Traxler · 900 East North Street · P.O. Box 10828 Greenville, SC 29603 · 864-242-3566

Daniel B. White · a · Gallivan, White & Boyd · One Liberty Square, Suite 1200 · 55 Beattie Place · P.O. Box 10589 · Greenville, SC 29603 · 864-271-9580

Marshall Winn · Wyche, Burgess, Freeman & Parham · 44 East Camperdown Way · P.O. Box 728 · Greenville, SC 29602-0728 · 864-242-8200

Ronald K. Wray II · Gallivan, White & Boyd · One Liberty Square, Suite 1200 · 55 Beattie Place · P.O. Box 10589 · Greenville, SC 29603 · 864-271-9580

Mount Pleasant

Ben A. Hagood, Jr. · Hagood & Kerr · http://www.hagoodkerr.com · 654 Coleman Boulevard · P.O. Box 220 · Mount Pleasant, SC 29465 · 843-972-1000

Myrtle Beach

R. Wayne Byrd · Turner, Padget, Graham & Laney · Founders Centre, Suite 301 · 2411 North Oak Street Myrtle Beach, SC 29577 · 843-213-5500

Rock Hill

Benjamin A. Johnson · Robinson, Bradshaw & Hinson · http://www.rbh.com · 140 East Main Street, Suite 420 · Rock Hill, SC 29730 · 803-325-2900

Spartanburg

Kevin A. Dunlap · Parker Poe Adams & Bernstein · http://www.parkerpoe.com · 100 Dunbar Street, Suite 206 · Spartanburg, SC 29306 · 864-591-2030

Frank H. Gibbes III · a · Gibbes Burton · 308 East St. John Street · Spartanburg, SC 29302 · 864-327-5000

CONSTRUCTION LAW

Charleston

Charles J. Baker III · Buist Moore Smythe McGee · http://www.buistmoore.com · Five Exchange Street · P.O. Box 999 · Charleston, SC 29402-0999 · 843-722-3400

C. Allen Gibson, Jr. · Buist Moore Smythe McGee · http://www.buistmoore.com · Five Exchange Street P.O. Box 999 · Charleston, SC 29402-0999 · 843-722-3400

H. Brewton Hagood · Rosen, Rosen & Hagood · http://www.rrhlawfirm.com · 134 Meeting Street, Suite 200 · P.O. Box 893 · Charleston, SC 29401 · 843-577-6726

Marvin D. Infinger · Haynsworth Sinkler Boyd · http://www.hsblawfirm.com · 134 Meeting Street, Third Floor · P.O. Box 340 · Charleston, SC 29402-0340 · 843-722-3366

W. Jefferson Leath, Jr. · Leath Bouch & Crawford · 92 Broad Street · P.O. Box 59 · Charleston, SC 29402 · 843-937-8811

Claron A. Robertson III · Robertson & Hollingsworth · Wachovia Center, Suite 300 · 177 Meeting Street Charleston, SC 29401 · 843-723-6470

Columbia

Daniel T. Brailsford · Robinson, McFadden & Moore · Bank of America Plaza, Suite 1200 · 1901 Main Street · P.O. Box 944 · Columbia, SC 29202 · 803-779-8900

Henry W. Brown · Nexsen Pruet · http://www.nexsenpruet.com · First Citizens Building, Suite 700 · 1230 Main Street · P.O. Drawer 2426 · Columbia, SC 29202-2426 · 803-771-8900

James L. Bruner · Bruner, Powell, Robbins, Wall & Mullins · http://www.bprwm.com · 1735 St. Julian Place, Suite 200 · P.O. Box 61110 · Columbia, SC 29260-1110 · 803-252-7693

John E. Cuttino · Turner, Padget, Graham & Laney · 1901 Main Street, 17th Floor · P.O. Box 1473 · Columbia, SC 29202 · 803-254-2200

Thomas B. Jackson III · Tyler, Cassell, Jackson, Peace & Silver · 1331 Elmwood Avenue, Suite 300 · P.O. Box 11656 · Columbia, SC 29211-1656 · 803-779-4997

Francis M. Mack · Richardson, Plowden & Robinson · 1900 Barnwell Street · P.O. Box 7788 · Columbia, SC 29202 · 803-771-4400

Franklin J. Smith, Jr. · Richardson, Plowden & Robinson · 1900 Barnwell Street · P.O. Box 7788 · Columbia, SC 29202 · 803-771-4400

Henry P. Wall · Bruner, Powell, Robbins, Wall & Mullins · http://www.bprwm.com · 1735 St. Julian Place, Suite 200 · P.O. Box 61110 · Columbia, SC 29260-1110 · 803-252-7693

James L. Werner · Parker Poe Adams & Bernstein · http://www.parkerpoe.com · 1201 Main Street, Suite 1450 · P.O. Box 1509 · Columbia, SC 29202 · 803-255-8000

Florence

Lawrence B. Orr · Orr, Elmore & Ervin · 504 Coit Street · P.O. Box 2527 · Florence, SC 29503 · 843-413-0111

Greenville

Thomas J. Coker, Jr. · Haynsworth Sinkler Boyd · http://www.hsblawfirm.com · Two Liberty Square, 11th Floor · 75 Beattie Place · P.O. Box 2048 · Greenville, SC 29602-2048 · 864-240-3200

John R. Devlin · Devlin & Parkinson · 27 Cleveland Street, Suite 201 · P.O. Box 10387 · Greenville, SC 29603-0387 · 864-242-4050

L. Franklin Elmore · Elmore and Wall · 301 North Main Street, Suite 2000 · P.O. Box 1887 · Greenville, SC 29602 · 864-255-9500

Leo H. Hill · a · Nelson Mullins Riley & Scarborough · Poinsett Plaza, Suite 900 · 104 South Main Street Greenville, SC 29601-2122 · 864-250-2300

N. Ward Lambert · Harper Lambert & Brown · 420 East Park Avenue, Suite 220 · Greenville, SC 29601 · 864-235-5535

T. S. Stern, Jr. · Covington, Patrick, Hagins, Stern & Lewis · 211 Pettigru Street · P.O. Box 2343 · Greenville, SC 29601 · 864-242-9000

Mount Pleasant

Walter H. Bundy, Jr. · Smith, Bundy, Bybee & Barnett · Building F, Suite 100 · 1037 Chuck Dawley Boulevard · P.O. Box 1542 · Mount Pleasant, SC 29465-1542 · 843-881-1623

Rock Hill

Herbert W. Hamilton · Hamilton Martens Ballou & Sipe · http://www.hmbslaw.com · 130 East Main Street, Suite 201 · P.O. Box 10940 · Rock Hill, SC 29731 · 803-329-7672

CORPORATE GOVERNANCE AND COMPLIANCE LAW

Columbia

Suzanne H. Clawson · Haynsworth Sinkler Boyd · http://www.hsblawfirm.com · 1201 Main Street, 22nd Floor · P.O. Box 11889 · Columbia, SC 29211-1889 · 803-779-3080

Greenville

Jo Watson Hackl · Wyche, Burgess, Freeman & Parham · 44 East Camperdown Way · P.O. Box 728 · Greenville, SC 29602-0728 · 864-242-8200

CORPORATE LAW

Charleston

W. E. Applegate III · Moore & Van Allen · 40 Calhoun Street, Suite 300 · P.O. Box 22828 · Charleston, SC 29401-2828 · 843-579-7000

Scott Y. Barnes · a · Warren & Sinkler · 171 Church Street, Suite 340 · P.O. Box 1254 · Charleston, SC 29402 · 843-577-0660

J. Sidney Boone, Jr. · a · McNair Law Firm · http://www.mcnair.net · 100 Calhoun Street, Suite 400 · P.O. Box 1431 · Charleston, SC 29402-1431 · 843-723-7831

Robert L. Clement, Jr. · a · Young Clement Rivers · 28 Broad Street · P.O. Box 993 · Charleston, SC 29402 · 843-577-4000

William E. Craver III · Craver & Webb · The Franke Building, Suite 120 · 171 Church Street · Charleston, SC 29401 · 843-577-7557

John B. Hagerty · Nelson Mullins Riley & Scarborough · Liberty Center, Suite 600 · 151 Meeting Street · Charleston, SC 29401-2239 · 843-853-5200

J. David Hawkins · Nexsen Pruet · http://www.nexsenpruet.com · 205 King Street, Suite 400 · P.O. Box 486 · Charleston, SC 29402 · 843-577-9440

Michael D. Jones · Haynsworth Sinkler Boyd · http://www.hsblawfirm.com · 134 Meeting Street, Third Floor · P.O. Box 340 · Charleston, SC 29402-0340 · 843-722-3366

Julie O. Medich · Haynsworth Sinkler Boyd · http://www.hsblawfirm.com · 134 Meeting Street, Third Floor · P.O. Box 340 · Charleston, SC 29402-0340 · 843-722-3366

Mark S. Sharpe · Warren & Sinkler · 171 Church Street, Suite 340 · P.O. Box 1254 · Charleston, SC 29402 · 843-577-0660

Susan M. Smythe · a · Buist Moore Smythe McGee · http://www.buistmoore.com · Five Exchange Street · P.O. Box 999 · Charleston, SC 29402-0999 · 843-722-3400

John H. Warren III · a · Warren & Sinkler · 171 Church Street, Suite 340 · P.O. Box 1254 · Charleston, SC 29402 · 843-577-0660

Columbia

William C. Boyd · a · Haynsworth Sinkler Boyd · http://www.hsblawfirm.com · 1201 Main Street, 22nd Floor · P.O. Box 11889 · Columbia, SC 29211-1889 · 803-779-3080

John W. Currie · a · McNair Law Firm · http://www.mcnair.net · 1301 Gervais Street, 11th Floor · P.O. Box 11390 · Columbia, SC 29211 · 803-799-9800

Gus M. Dixon · Nelson Mullins Riley & Scarborough · Meridian, 17th Floor · 1320 Main Street · P.O. Box 11070 · Columbia, SC 29211 · 803-799-2000

Randolph B. Epting · Haynsworth Sinkler Boyd · http://www.hsblawfirm.com · 1201 Main Street, 22nd Floor · P.O. Box 11889 · Columbia, SC 29211-1889 · 803-779-3080

Daniel J. Fritze · Nelson Mullins Riley & Scarborough · Meridian, 17th Floor · 1320 Main Street · P.O. Box 11070 · Columbia, SC 29211 · 803-799-2000

Julian Hennig III · Nexsen Pruet · http://www.nexsenpruet.com · First Citizens Building, Suite 700 · 1230 Main Street · P.O. Drawer 2426 · Columbia, SC 29202-2426 · 803-771-8900

P. Mason Hogue, Jr. · Nelson Mullins Riley & Scarborough · Meridian, 17th Floor · 1320 Main Street · P.O. Box 11070 · Columbia, SC 29211 · 803-799-2000

George S. King, Jr. · a · Haynsworth Sinkler Boyd · http://www.hsblawfirm.com · 1201 Main Street, 22nd Floor · P.O. Box 11889 · Columbia, SC 29211-1889 · 803-779-3080

G. Marcus Knight · Nexsen Pruet · http://www.nexsenpruet.com · First Citizens Building, Suite 700 · 1230 Main Street · P.O. Drawer 2426 · Columbia, SC 29202-2426 · 803-771-8900

Martin C. McWilliams, Jr. · a · Haynsworth Sinkler Boyd · http://www.hsblawfirm.com · 1201 Main Street, 22nd Floor · P.O. Box 11889 · Columbia, SC 29211-1889 · 803-779-3080

Edward G. Menzie · 2% · Nexsen Pruet · http://www.nexsenpruet.com · First Citizens Building, Suite 700 1230 Main Street · P.O. Drawer 2426 · Columbia, SC 29202-2426 · 803-771-8900

William M. Musser · McNair Law Firm · http://www.mcnair.net · 1301 Gervais Street, 11th Floor · P.O. Box 11390 · Columbia, SC 29211 · 803-799-9800

Greenville

Eric B. Amstutz · Wyche, Burgess, Freeman & Parham · 44 East Camperdown Way · P.O. Box 728 · Greenville, SC 29602-0728 · 864-242-8200

David L. Freeman · 2% · Wyche, Burgess, Freeman & Parham · 44 East Camperdown Way · P.O. Box 728 Greenville, SC 29602-0728 · 864-242-8200

D. Allen Grumbine · Womble Carlyle Sandridge & Rice · 550 South Main Street, Suite 400 · P.O. Box 10208 · Greenville, SC 29603-0208 · 864-255-5400

Jo Watson Hackl · Wyche, Burgess, Freeman & Parham · 44 East Camperdown Way · P.O. Box 728 · Greenville, SC 29602-0728 · 864-242-8200

Cary H. Hall, Jr. · a · Wyche, Burgess, Freeman & Parham · 44 East Camperdown Way · P.O. Box 728 · Greenville, SC 29602-0728 · 864-242-8200

William W. Kehl · Wyche, Burgess, Freeman & Parham · 44 East Camperdown Way · P.O. Box 728 · Greenville, SC 29602-0728 · 864-242-8200

David A. Merline, Jr. · a · Merline & Meacham · http://www.merlineandmeacham.com · 812 East North Street · P.O. Box 10796 · Greenville, SC 29603 · 864-242-4080

John R. Thomas · 2) · Thomas & Fisher · http://www.thomasandfisher.com · The Ogletree Building, Suite 401 · 300 North Main Street · P.O. Box 2248 · Greenville, SC 29602-2248 · 864-232-0041

C. Thomas Wyche · a · Wyche, Burgess, Freeman & Parham · 44 East Camperdown Way · P.O. Box 728 Greenville, SC 29602-0728 · 864-242-8200

DUI/DWI DEFENSE

Charleston

Timothy C. Kulp · Timothy C. Kulp · 116 Church Street · Charleston, SC 29401 · 843-853-3310

Columbia

Leigh J. Leventis · Leigh J. Leventis Law Office · 1913 Bull Street · P.O. Box 11067 · Columbia, SC 29201 · 803-256-0113

Joseph M. McCulloch · Joseph M. McCulloch · 1426 Richland Street, Second Floor · Columbia, SC 29201 · 803-779-0005

Greenville

James W. Bannister · Bannister & Wyatt · 401 Pettigru Street · P.O. Box 10007 · Greenville, SC 29603 · 864-298-0084

O. W. Bannister, Jr. · a · Bannister & Wyatt · 401 Pettigru Street · P.O. Box 10007 · Greenville, SC 29603 · 864-298-0084

Orangeburg

C. Bradley Hutto · Williams & Williams · 370 St. Paull Street N.E. · P.O. Box 1084 · Orangeburg, SC 29115 · 803-534-5218

ELDER LAW

Greenville

Michael B. Bridges · Dobson, Jones, Ball, Phillips & Bridges · 1306 South Church Street · P.O. Box 1923 · Greenville, SC 29602 · 864-271-8171

EMINENT DOMAIN AND CONDEMNATION LAW

Columbia

Keith M. Babcock · Lewis, Babcock & Hawkins · 1513 Hampton Street · P.O. Box 11208 · Columbia, SC 29211 · 803-771-8000

Mount Pleasant

Richard D. Bybee · Smith, Bundy, Bybee & Barnett · Building F, Suite 100 · 1037 Chuck Dawley Boulevard · P.O. Box 1542 · Mount Pleasant, SC 29465-1542 · 843-881-1623

Myrtle Beach

Howell V. Bellamy, Jr. · Bellamy, Rutenberg, Copeland, Epps, Gravely & Bowers · 1000 Twenty-Ninth Avenue North · P.O. Box 357 · Myrtle Beach, SC 29578 · 843-448-2400

EMPLOYEE BENEFITS LAW

Charleston

Amy Y. Jenkins · McAngus, Goudelock & Courie · 78 Wentworth Street, Suite 200 · P.O. Box 877 · Charleston, SC 29402-0877 · 843-576-2900

Columbia

Michael T. Brittingham · Nexsen Pruet · http://www.nexsenpruet.com · First Citizens Building, Suite 700 · 1230 Main Street · P.O. Drawer 2426 · Columbia, SC 29202-2426 · 803-771-8900

Kenneth Allan Janik · Nelson Mullins Riley & Scarborough · Meridian, 17th Floor · 1320 Main Street · P.O. Box 11070 · Columbia, SC 29211 · 803-799-2000

R. Kent Porth · a · Nexsen Pruet · http://www.nexsenpruet.com · First Citizens Building, Suite 700 · 1230 Main Street · P.O. Drawer 2426 · Columbia, SC 29202-2426 · 803-771-8900

Joseph D. Walker · a · McNair Law Firm · http://www.mcnair.net · 1301 Gervais Street, 11th Floor · P.O. Box 11390 · Columbia, SC 29211 · 803-799-9800

Greenville

Thomas M. Christina · a · Ogletree Deakins · http://www.ogletreedeakins.com · The Ogletree Building · 300 North Main Street · P.O. Box 2757 · Greenville, SC 29602 · 864-271-1300

Joel A. Daniel · Ogletree Deakins · http://www.ogletreedeakins.com · The Ogletree Building · 300 North Main Street · P.O. Box 2757 · Greenville, SC 29602 · 864-271-1300

William L. Dennis · a · Smith Moore Leatherwood · http://www.smithmoorelaw.com · The Leatherwood Plaza, Suite 500 · 300 East McBee Avenue · P.O. Box 87 · Greenville, SC 29602 · 864-242-6440

David A. Merline, Jr. · a · Merline & Meacham · http://www.merlineandmeacham.com · 812 East North Street · P.O. Box 10796 · Greenville, SC 29603 · 864-242-4080

Andreas N. Satterfield, Jr. · Jackson Lewis · http://www.jacksonlewis.com · One Liberty Square, Suite 800 · 55 Beattie Place · Greenville, SC 29601 · 864-232-7000

John R. Thomas · 2) · Thomas & Fisher · http://www.thomasandfisher.com · The Ogletree Building, Suite 401 · 300 North Main Street · P.O. Box 2248 · Greenville, SC 29602-2248 · 864-232-0041

ENERGY LAW

Charleston

Lucas C. Padgett, Jr. · a · McNair Law Firm · http://www.mcnair.net · 100 Calhoun Street, Suite 400 · P.O. Box 1431 · Charleston, SC 29402-1431 · 843-723-7831

Columbia

Robert T. Bockman · McNair Law Firm · http://www.mcnair.net · 1301 Gervais Street, 11th Floor · P.O. Box 11390 · Columbia, SC 29211 · 803-799-9800

M. John Bowen, Jr. · McNair Law Firm · http://www.mcnair.net · 1301 Gervais Street, 11th Floor · P.O. Box 11390 · Columbia, SC 29211 · 803-799-9800

Greenville

Leo H. Hill · a · Nelson Mullins Riley & Scarborough · Poinsett Plaza, Suite 900 · 104 South Main Street Greenville, SC 29601-2122 · 864-250-2300

ENVIRONMENTAL LAW

Charleston

Timothy W. Bouch · a · Leath Bouch & Crawford · 92 Broad Street · P.O. Box 59 · Charleston, SC 29402 · 843-937-8811

Sean D. Houseal · Buist Moore Smythe McGee · http://www.buistmoore.com · Five Exchange Street · P.O. Box 999 · Charleston, SC 29402-0999 · 843-722-3400

Eric C. Schweitzer · a · Ogletree Deakins · http://www.ogletreedeakins.com · 211 King Street, Suite 200 Charleston, SC 29401 · 843-853-1300

Mary A. Shahid · McNair Law Firm · http://www.mcnair.net · 100 Calhoun Street, Suite 400 · P.O. Box 1431 · Charleston, SC 29402-1431 · 843-723-7831

Newman Jackson Smith · a · Nelson Mullins Riley & Scarborough · Liberty Center, Suite 600 · 151 Meeting Street · Charleston, SC 29401-2239 · 843-853-5200

William L. Want · 2) · Charleston School of Law · P.O. Box 535 · Charleston, SC 29403 · 843-329-1000

Columbia

Karen A. Crawford · Nelson Mullins Riley & Scarborough · Meridian, 17th Floor · 1320 Main Street · P.O. Box 11070 · Columbia, SC 29211 · 803-799-2000

Bernard F. Hawkins, Jr. · Nelson Mullins Riley & Scarborough · Meridian, 17th Floor · 1320 Main Street P.O. Box 11070 · Columbia, SC 29211 · 803-799-2000

W. Thomas Lavender, Jr. · a · Nexsen Pruet · http://www.nexsenpruet.com · First Citizens Building, Suite 700 · 1230 Main Street · P.O. Drawer 2426 · Columbia, SC 29202-2426 · 803-771-8900

Elizabeth B. Partlow · Ogletree Deakins · http://www.ogletreedeakins.com · 1320 Main Street, Suite 600 Columbia, SC 29201 · 803-252-1300

Sara S. Rogers · McNair Law Firm · http://www.mcnair.net · 1301 Gervais Street, 11th Floor · P.O. Box 11390 · Columbia, SC 29211 · 803-799-9800

Greenville

Ronald E. Cardwell · McNair Law Firm · http://www.mcnair.net · Bank of America Plaza, Suite 900 · 101 North Main Street · P.O. Box 447 · Greenville, SC 29602 · 864-271-4940

Phillip L. Conner · McNair Law Firm · http://www.mcnair.net · Bank of America Plaza, Suite 900 · 101 North Main Street · P.O. Box 447 · Greenville, SC 29602 · 864-271-4940

R. Howard Grubbs · a · Womble Carlyle Sandridge & Rice · 550 South Main Street, Suite 400 · P.O. Box 10208 · Greenville, SC 29603-0208 · 864-255-5400

Leon C. Harmon · Nexsen Pruet · http://www.nexsenpruet.com · 201 West McBee Avenue, Suite 400 · P.O. Drawer 10648 · Greenville, SC 29601 · 864-370-2211

Mount Pleasant

Ben A. Hagood, Jr. · Hagood & Kerr · http://www.hagoodkerr.com · 654 Coleman Boulevard · P.O. Box 220 · Mount Pleasant, SC 29465 · 843-972-1000

Cotton C. Harness III · a · Cotton C. Harness III · 505 Belle Hall Parkway, Suite 101 · Mount Pleasant, SC 29464 · 843-856-2627

Gordon C. Rhea · Richardson, Patrick, Westbrook & Brickman · 1037 Chuck Dawley Boulevard, Building A · P.O. Box 1007 · Mount Pleasant, SC 29465 · 843-727-6500

Ellison D. Smith IV · Smith, Bundy, Bybee & Barnett · Building F, Suite 100 · 1037 Chuck Dawley Boulevard · P.O. Box 1542 · Mount Pleasant, SC 29465-1542 · 843-881-1623

FAMILY LAW

Aiken

Vicki Johnson Snelgrove · Johnson, Johnson, Whittle & Snelgrove · 117 Pendleton Street, NW · P.O. Box 2619 · Aiken, SC 29802-2619 · 803-649-5338

Charleston

Morris D. Rosen · 2% · Rosen, Rosen & Hagood · http://www.rrhlawfirm.com · 134 Meeting Street, Suite 200 · P.O. Box 893 · Charleston, SC 29401 · 843-577-6726

Robert N. Rosen · a · Rosen Law Firm · http://www.rosen-lawfirm.com · 18 Broad Street, Suite 201 · Charleston, SC 29401 · 843-377-1700

Ann M. Stirling · a · Stirling & O'Connell · 145 King Street, Suite 410 · P.O. Box 882 · Charleston, SC 29402 · 843-577-9890

Paul E. Tinkler · Paul E. Tinkler · 154 King Street, Third Floor · P.O. Box 366 · Charleston, SC 29402-0366 · 843-853-5203

Clemson

Pamela A. E. Deal · Deal & Deal · 122 Strode Circle · P.O. Box 1764 · Clemson, SC 29633 · 864-654-1669

Columbia

Victoria L. Eslinger · Nexsen Pruet · http://www.nexsenpruet.com · First Citizens Building, Suite 700 · 1230 Main Street · P.O. Drawer 2426 · Columbia, SC 29202-2426 · 803-771-8900

Kermit S. King · 2) · Law Office of Kermit S. King · 2008 Marion Street, Suite C · P.O. Box 7667 · Columbia, SC 29202 · 803-779-3090

C. Dixon Lee III · McLaren & Lee · 1508 Laurel Street · P.O. Box 11809 · Columbia, SC 29211-1809 · 803-799-3074

Ken H. Lester · Ken H. Lester · 1901 Gadsden Street, Suite A · Columbia, SC 29201 · 803-252-4700

John O. McDougall · a · McDougall & Self · 791 Greenlawn Drive, Suite Four · P.O. Box 90860 · Columbia, SC 29290 · 803-776-3130

James T. McLaren · a · McLaren & Lee · 1508 Laurel Street · P.O. Box 11809 · Columbia, SC 29211-1809 · 803-799-3074

Carol H. Sanders · Carol Sanders · 1819 Marion Street · P.O. Box 8626 · Columbia, SC 29202 · 803-799-7666

Conway

George M. Hearn, Jr. · Hearn, Brittain & Martin · 1206 Third Avenue · Conway, SC 29526 · 843-248-3172

Greenville

Timothy E. Madden · Nelson Mullins Riley & Scarborough · Poinsett Plaza, Suite 900 · 104 South Main Street · Greenville, SC 29601-2122 · 864-250-2300

Kenneth C. Porter · a · Porter & Rosenfeld · 411 Pettigru Street · P.O. Box 4277 · Greenville, SC 29608-4277 · 864-235-9613

Thomas W. Traxler · Carter, Smith, Merriam, Rogers & Traxler · 900 East North Street · P.O. Box 10828 Greenville, SC 29603 · 864-242-3566

Mount Pleasant

Mark O. Andrews · a · Andrews & Shull · 755 Johnnie Dodds Boulevard · Mount Pleasant, SC 29464-3026 · 843-881-8886

Lon H. Shull III · Andrews & Shull · 755 Johnnie Dodds Boulevard · Mount Pleasant, SC 29464-3026 · 843-881-8886

Spartanburg

Robert M. Holland · Holland Law Firm · Palmetto Bank Building, Suite 206 · 101 West Saint John Street Spartanburg, SC 29304 · 864-582-0416

Grace Knie · Grace Knie · 250 Magnolia Street · Spartanburg, SC 29304 · 864-582-3991

Jack W. Lawrence · Lawrence & Rudasill · http://www.lawrencerudasill.com · 111 South Spring Street · P.O. Box 5722 · Spartanburg, SC 29304 · 864-583-5057

John B. White, Jr. · Harrison, White, Smith & Coggins · 178 West Main Street · P.O. Box 3547 · Spartanburg, SC 29304 · 864-585-5100

West Columbia

J. Mark Taylor · Moore, Taylor & Thomas · 1700 Sunset Boulevard · P.O. Box 5709 · West Columbia, SC 29169 · 803-796-9160

FAMILY LAW MEDIATION

Charleston

Robert N. Rosen · a · Rosen Law Firm · http://www.rosen-lawfirm.com · 18 Broad Street, Suite 201 · Charleston, SC 29401 · 843-377-1700

Greenville

Stephen S. Bartlett · Stephen S. Bartlett · 819 East North Street · P.O. Box 757 · Greenville, SC 29601 · 864-331-3067

Bobby H. Mann, Jr. · Temple Mann Briggs & Hill · 819 East North Street · Greenville, SC 29601 · 864-242-4995

James C. Sarratt · The Legal Clinic of Sarratt & Clarke · Six Brookside Circle · Greenville, SC 29609 · 864-271-4100

Mount Pleasant

Mark O. Andrews · a · Andrews & Shull · 755 Johnnie Dodds Boulevard · Mount Pleasant, SC 29464-3026 · 843-881-8886

FIRST AMENDMENT LAW

Charleston

D. A. Brockinton, Jr. · a · Brockinton & Brockinton · P.O. Box 656 · Charleston, SC 29402-0656 · 843-766-0511

John J. Kerr · Buist Moore Smythe McGee · http://www.buistmoore.com · Five Exchange Street · P.O. Box 999 · Charleston, SC 29402-0999 · 843-722-3400

Thomas S. Tisdale, Jr. · a · Nexsen Pruet · http://www.nexsenpruet.com · 205 King Street, Suite 400 · P.O. Box 486 · Charleston, SC 29402 · 843-577-9440

Columbia

Jay Bender · a · Baker, Ravenel & Bender · http://www.brblegal.com · 3710 Landmark Drive, Suite 400 · P.O. Box 8057 · Columbia, SC 29202 · 803-799-9091

Greenville

David L. Freeman · 2% · Wyche, Burgess, Freeman & Parham · 44 East Camperdown Way · P.O. Box 728 Greenville, SC 29602-0728 · 864-242-8200

Wallace K. Lightsey · a · Wyche, Burgess, Freeman & Parham · 44 East Camperdown Way · P.O. Box 728 · Greenville, SC 29602-0728 · 864-242-8200

Carl F. Muller · Wyche, Burgess, Freeman & Parham · 44 East Camperdown Way · P.O. Box 728 · Greenville, SC 29602-0728 · 864-242-8200

FRANCHISE LAW

Columbia

S. Keith Hutto · Nelson Mullins Riley & Scarborough · Meridian, 17th Floor · 1320 Main Street · P.O. Box 11070 · Columbia, SC 29211 · 803-799-2000

Steven A. McKelvey, Jr. · Nelson Mullins Riley & Scarborough · Meridian, 17th Floor · 1320 Main Street P.O. Box 11070 · Columbia, SC 29211 · 803-799-2000

Greenville

Natalma M. McKnew · Smith Moore Leatherwood · http://www.smithmoorelaw.com · The Leatherwood Plaza, Suite 500 · 300 East McBee Avenue · P.O. Box 87 · Greenville, SC 29602 · 864-242-6440

GOVERNMENT RELATIONS LAW

Charleston

Newman Jackson Smith · a · Nelson Mullins Riley & Scarborough · Liberty Center, Suite 600 · 151 Meeting Street · Charleston, SC 29401-2239 · 843-853-5200

Columbia

Stephen K. Benjamin · McAngus, Goudelock & Courie · 700 Gervais Street, Suite 300 · P.O. Box 12519 · Columbia, SC 29211-2519 · 803-779-2300

Dwight F. Drake · Nelson Mullins Riley & Scarborough · Meridian, 17th Floor · 1320 Main Street · P.O. Box 11070 · Columbia, SC 29211 · 803-799-2000

James P. Fields, Jr. · McNair Law Firm · http://www.mcnair.net · 1301 Gervais Street, 11th Floor · P.O. Box 11390 · Columbia, SC 29211 · 803-799-9800

James H. Hodges · Hodges Consulting Group · 1122 Lady Street, Suite 850 · Columbia, SC 29201 · 803-251-2300

John C. Moylan III · Wyche, Burgess, Freeman & Parham · 1122 Lady Street, Suite 810 · P.O. Box 12247 Columbia, SC 29211-2247 · 803-254-6542

James H. Quackenbush, Jr. · Berry, Quackenbush & Stuart · 1122 Lady Street, Fifth Floor · P.O. Box 394 · Columbia, SC 29202 · 803-779-2650

Theodore D. Riley · Riley Pope & Laney · 2838 Devine Street · Columbia, SC 29205 · 803-799-9993

George B. Wolfe · Nelson Mullins Riley & Scarborough · Meridian, 17th Floor · 1320 Main Street · P.O. Box 11070 · Columbia, SC 29211 · 803-799-2000

HEALTH CARE LAW

Anderson

Wm. Douglas Gray · McNair Law Firm · http://www.mcnair.net · 500 South McDuffie Street · Anderson, SC 29622 · 864-226-1688

Charleston

J. Marshall Allen · Buist Moore Smythe McGee · http://www.buistmoore.com · Five Exchange Street · P.O. Box 999 · Charleston, SC 29402-0999 · 843-722-3400

Mary Agnes Hood Craig · Hood Law Firm · http://www.hoodlaw.com · 172 Meeting Street · P.O. Box 1508 · Charleston, SC 29402 · 843-577-4435

Robert H. Hood · 2% · Hood Law Firm · http://www.hoodlaw.com · 172 Meeting Street · P.O. Box 1508 · Charleston, SC 29402 · 843-577-4435

Cynthia B. Hutto · Nelson Mullins Riley & Scarborough · Liberty Center, Suite 600 · 151 Meeting Street Charleston, SC 29401-2239 · 843-853-5200

Columbia

Stuart M. Andrews, Jr. · a · Nelson Mullins Riley & Scarborough · Meridian, 17th Floor · 1320 Main Street · P.O. Box 11070 · Columbia, SC 29211 · 803-799-2000

Charles E. Carpenter, Jr. · Carpenter Appeals & Trial Support · 1201 Main Street, Suite 900 · Columbia, SC 29201 · 803-758-2886

Frederick A. Crawford · Richardson, Plowden & Robinson · 1900 Barnwell Street · P.O. Box 7788 · Columbia, SC 29202 · 803-771-4400

M. Elizabeth Crum · McNair Law Firm · http://www.mcnair.net · 1301 Gervais Street, 11th Floor · P.O. Box 11390 · Columbia, SC 29211 · 803-799-9800

M. Craig Garner, Jr. · McNair Law Firm · http://www.mcnair.net · 1301 Gervais Street, 11th Floor · P.O. Box 11390 · Columbia, SC 29211 · 803-799-9800

Timothy L. Hewson · Nexsen Pruet · http://www.nexsenpruet.com · First Citizens Building, Suite 700 · 1230 Main Street · P.O. Drawer 2426 · Columbia, SC 29202-2426 · 803-771-8900

Celeste T. Jones · McNair Law Firm · http://www.mcnair.net · 1301 Gervais Street, 11th Floor · P.O. Box 11390 · Columbia, SC 29211 · 803-799-9800

Matthew B. Roberts · Nexsen Pruet · http://www.nexsenpruet.com · First Citizens Building, Suite 700 · 1230 Main Street · P.O. Drawer 2426 · Columbia, SC 29202-2426 · 803-771-8900

David B. Summer, Jr. · Parker Poe Adams & Bernstein · http://www.parkerpoe.com · 1201 Main Street, Suite 1450 · P.O. Box 1509 · Columbia, SC 29202 · 803-255-8000

Daniel J. Westbrook · Nelson Mullins Riley & Scarborough · Meridian, 17th Floor · 1320 Main Street · P.O. Box 11070 · Columbia, SC 29211 · 803-799-2000

Greenville

William W. Kehl · Wyche, Burgess, Freeman & Parham · 44 East Camperdown Way · P.O. Box 728 · Greenville, SC 29602-0728 · 864-242-8200

Sandra Louise Weikel Miller · Womble Carlyle Sandridge & Rice · 550 South Main Street, Suite 400 · P.O. Box 10208 · Greenville, SC 29603-0208 · 864-255-5400

G. Dewey Oxner, Jr. · 2% · Haynsworth Sinkler Boyd · http://www.hsblawfirm.com · Two Liberty Square, 11th Floor · 75 Beattie Place · P.O. Box 2048 · Greenville, SC 29602-2048 · 864-240-3200

Donna Kivett Tribble · Nelson Mullins Riley & Scarborough · Poinsett Plaza, Suite 900 · 104 South Main Street · Greenville, SC 29601-2122 · 864-250-2300

Matthew P. Utecht · Haynsworth Sinkler Boyd · http://www.hsblawfirm.com · Two Liberty Square, 11th Floor · 75 Beattie Place · P.O. Box 2048 · Greenville, SC 29602-2048 · 864-240-3200

Stephen P. Williams · Haynsworth Sinkler Boyd · http://www.hsblawfirm.com · Two Liberty Square, 11th Floor · 75 Beattie Place · P.O. Box 2048 · Greenville, SC 29602-2048 · 864-240-3200

IMMIGRATION LAW

Spartanburg

Patrick L. Cont · Sturm & Cont · 159 Hall Street · Spartanburg, SC 29302 · 864-580-2020

INSURANCE LAW

Charleston

Samuel R. Clawson · Clawson & Staubes · 126 Seven Farms Drive, Suite 200 · Charleston, SC 29492-7595 · 843-577-2026

Gerald M. Finkel · 2% · Finkel Law Firm · http://www.finkellaw.com · 3955 Faber Place Drive, Suite 200 · P.O. Box 225 · Charleston, SC 29402 · 843-577-5460

Henry E. Grimball · Buist Moore Smythe McGee · http://www.buistmoore.com · Five Exchange Street · P.O. Box 999 · Charleston, SC 29402-0999 · 843-722-3400

E. Warren Moise · Grimball & Cabaniss · 473 Savannah Highway · P.O. Box 816 · Charleston, SC 29402-0816 · 843-722-0311

Elizabeth Scott Moise · Nelson Mullins Riley & Scarborough · Liberty Center, Suite 600 · 151 Meeting Street · Charleston, SC 29401-2239 · 843-853-5200

Michael A. Molony · Young Clement Rivers · 28 Broad Street · P.O. Box 993 · Charleston, SC 29402 · 843-577-4000

James D. Myrick · Buist Moore Smythe McGee · http://www.buistmoore.com · Five Exchange Street · P.O. Box 999 · Charleston, SC 29402-0999 · 843-722-3400

Columbia

Charles E. Baker · Baker, Ravenel & Bender · http://www.brblegal.com · 3710 Landmark Drive, Suite 400 · P.O. Box 8057 · Columbia, SC 29202 · 803-799-9091

James C. Gray, Jr. · Nelson Mullins Riley & Scarborough · Meridian, 17th Floor · 1320 Main Street · P.O. Box 11070 · Columbia, SC 29211 · 803-799-2000

Thomas C. Salane · Turner, Padget, Graham & Laney · 1901 Main Street, 17th Floor · P.O. Box 1473 · Columbia, SC 29202 · 803-254-2200

Greenville

G. D. Morgan, Jr. · McAngus, Goudelock & Courie · Two Liberty Square, Suite 300 · 75 Beattie Place · P.O. Box 2980 · Greenville, SC 29602-2980 · 864-239-4000

Robert D. Moseley, Jr. · Smith Moore Leatherwood · http://www.smithmoorelaw.com · The Leatherwood Plaza, Suite 500 · 300 East McBee Avenue · P.O. Box 87 · Greenville, SC 29602 · 864-242-6440

A. Marvin Quattlebaum, Jr. · Nelson Mullins Riley & Scarborough · Poinsett Plaza, Suite 900 · 104 South Main Street · Greenville, SC 29601-2122 · 864-250-2300

INTELLECTUAL PROPERTY LAW

Columbia

Mark C. Dukes · Nelson Mullins Riley & Scarborough · Meridian, 17th Floor · 1320 Main Street · P.O. Box 11070 · Columbia, SC 29211 · 803-799-2000

William Y. Klett III · Nexsen Pruet · http://www.nexsenpruet.com · First Citizens Building, Suite 700 · 1230 Main Street · P.O. Drawer 2426 · Columbia, SC 29202-2426 · 803-771-8900

Greenville

Julian W. Dority · a · Dority & Manning · One Liberty Square, Suite 1600 · 55 Beattie Place · P.O. Box 1449 · Greenville, SC 29601 · 864-271-1592

Cort R. Flint · McNair Law Firm · http://www.mcnair.net · Bank of America Plaza, Suite 900 · 101 North Main Street · P.O. Box 447 · Greenville, SC 29602 · 864-271-4940

Wellington M. Manning, Jr. · a · Dority & Manning · One Liberty Square, Suite 1600 · 55 Beattie Place P.O. Box 1449 · Greenville, SC 29601 · 864-271-1592

J. Bennett Mullinax · J. Bennett Mullinax · 3447 Pelham Road, Suite 206 · Greenville, SC 29616-1029 · 864-987-9696

Timothy D. St. Clair · Turner, Padget, Graham & Laney · 200 East Broad Street, Suite 250 · P.O. Box 1509 · Greenville, SC 29602 · 864-552-4600

LABOR AND EMPLOYMENT LAW

Charleston

Cherie W. Blackburn · Nelson Mullins Riley & Scarborough · Liberty Center, Suite 600 · 151 Meeting Street · Charleston, SC 29401-2239 · 843-853-5200

Molly Hughes Cherry · Nexsen Pruet · http://www.nexsenpruet.com · 205 King Street, Suite 400 · P.O. Box 486 · Charleston, SC 29402 · 843-577-9440

J. Walker Coleman IV · Parker Poe Adams & Bernstein · http://www.parkerpoe.com · 200 Meeting Street, Suite 301 · Charleston, SC 29401-3156 · 843-727-2650

Carol B. Ervin · Young Clement Rivers · 28 Broad Street · P.O. Box 993 · Charleston, SC 29402 · 843-577-4000

Allan R. Holmes · Gibbs & Holmes · 171 Church Street, Suite 110 · P.O. Box 938 · Charleston, SC 29402-0938 · 843-722-0033

Amy Y. Jenkins · McAngus, Goudelock & Courie · 78 Wentworth Street, Suite 200 · P.O. Box 877 · Charleston, SC 29402-0877 · 843-576-2900

David B. McCormack · Buist Moore Smythe McGee · http://www.buistmoore.com · Five Exchange Street · P.O. Box 999 · Charleston, SC 29402-0999 · 843-722-3400

A. Christopher Potts · Hitchcock & Potts · 31 Broad Street · P.O. Box 1113 · Charleston, SC 29402 · 843-577-5000

Terry Ann Rickson · Terry Rickson · 102 Wappoo Creek Drive, Suite Eight · Charleston, SC 29412 · 843-722-1500

Eric C. Schweitzer · a · Ogletree Deakins · http://www.ogletreedeakins.com · 211 King Street, Suite 200 Charleston, SC 29401 · 843-853-1300

Catherine Templeton · Ogletree Deakins · http://www.ogletreedeakins.com · 211 King Street, Suite 200 · Charleston, SC 29401 · 843-853-1300

David S. Yandle · Buist Moore Smythe McGee · http://www.buistmoore.com · Five Exchange Street · P.O. Box 999 · Charleston, SC 29402-0999 · 843-722-3400

Vance J. Bettis · Gignilliat, Savitz & Bettis · 900 Elmwood Avenue, Suite 100 · Columbia, SC 29201 · 803-799-9311

M. Malissa Burnette · Burnette & Rothstein · 2322 Devine Street · Columbia, SC 29205 · 803-251-0202

Michael D. Carrouth · Fisher & Phillips · http://www.laborlawyers.com · 1901 Main Street, Suite 1400 · P.O. Box 11612 · Columbia, SC 29211 · 803-255-0000

Carl B. Carruth · McNair Law Firm · http://www.mcnair.net · 1301 Gervais Street, 11th Floor · P.O. Box 11390 · Columbia, SC 29211 · 803-799-9800

J. Lewis Cromer · Cromer & Mabry · 1225 Pickens Street · P.O. Box 11675 · Columbia, SC 29211 · 803-799-9530

David E. Dubberly · Nexsen Pruet · http://www.nexsenpruet.com · First Citizens Building, Suite 700 · 1230 Main Street · P.O. Drawer 2426 · Columbia, SC 29202-2426 · 803-771-8900

G. Daniel Ellzey · Fisher & Phillips · http://www.laborlawyers.com · 1901 Main Street, Suite 1400 · P.O. Box 11612 · Columbia, SC 29211 · 803-255-0000

Victoria L. Eslinger · Nexsen Pruet · http://www.nexsenpruet.com · First Citizens Building, Suite 700 · 1230 Main Street · P.O. Drawer 2426 · Columbia, SC 29202-2426 · 803-771-8900

William H. Floyd III · Nexsen Pruet · http://www.nexsenpruet.com · First Citizens Building, Suite 700 · 1230 Main Street · P.O. Drawer 2426 · Columbia, SC 29202-2426 · 803-771-8900

George A. Harper · Constangy, Brooks & Smith · http://www.constangy.com · 1301 Gervais Street, Suite 810 · Columbia, SC 29201-3326 · 803-256-3200

Sue Erwin Harper · Nelson Mullins Riley & Scarborough · Meridian, 17th Floor · 1320 Main Street · P.O. Box 11070 · Columbia, SC 29211 · 803-799-2000

Katherine Dudley Helms · a · Ogletree Deakins · http://www.ogletreedeakins.com · 1320 Main Street, Suite 600 · Columbia, SC 29201 · 803-252-1300

Henry S. Knight, Jr. · Constangy, Brooks & Smith · http://www.constangy.com · 1301 Gervais Street, Suite 810 · Columbia, SC 29201-3326 · 803-256-3200

Herbert W. Louthian · Louthian Law Firm · The Marlboro Building, Suite 300 · 1116 Blanding Street · Columbia, SC 29201 · 803-256-4274

Susan P. McWilliams · Nexsen Pruet · http://www.nexsenpruet.com · First Citizens Building, Suite 700 · 1230 Main Street · P.O. Drawer 2426 · Columbia, SC 29202-2426 · 803-771-8900

Richard J. Morgan · McNair Law Firm · http://www.mcnair.net · 1301 Gervais Street, 11th Floor · P.O. Box 11390 · Columbia, SC 29211 · 803-799-9800

Leigh Mullikin Nason · a · Ogletree Deakins · http://www.ogletreedeakins.com · 1320 Main Street, Suite 600 · Columbia, SC 29201 · 803-252-1300

Jonathan P. Pearson · Fisher & Phillips · http://www.laborlawyers.com · 1901 Main Street, Suite 1400 · P.O. Box 11612 · Columbia, SC 29211 · 803-255-0000

David E. Rothstein · Burnette & Rothstein · 2322 Devine Street · Columbia, SC 29205 · 803-251-0202

Franklin G. Shuler, Jr. · Turner, Padget, Graham & Laney · 1901 Main Street, 17th Floor · P.O. Box 1473 · Columbia, SC 29202 · 803-254-2200

Charles T. Speth II · a · Ogletree Deakins · http://www.ogletreedeakins.com · 1320 Main Street, Suite 600 · Columbia, SC 29201 · 803-252-1300

Jim O. Stuckey II · Littler Mendelson · 1201 Main Street, Suite 1930 · Columbia, SC 29201 · 803-231-2500

J. Hagood Tighe · Fisher & Phillips · http://www.laborlawyers.com · 1901 Main Street, Suite 1400 · P.O. Box 11612 · Columbia, SC 29211 · 803-255-0000

Florence

Mark W. Buyck III · Willcox, Buyck & Williams · 248 West Evans Street · P.O. Box 1909 · Florence, SC 29503 · 843-662-3258

Greenville

Mark W. Bakker · Wyche, Burgess, Freeman & Parham · 44 East Camperdown Way · P.O. Box 728 · Greenville, SC 29602-0728 · 864-242-8200

E. Grantland Burns · Nexsen Pruet · http://www.nexsenpruet.com · 201 West McBee Avenue, Suite 400 P.O. Drawer 10648 · Greenville, SC 29601 · 864-370-2211

Donald A. Cockrill · Ogletree Deakins · http://www.ogletreedeakins.com · The Ogletree Building · 300 North Main Street · P.O. Box 2757 · Greenville, SC 29602 · 864-271-1300

John G. Creech · a · Ogletree Deakins · http://www.ogletreedeakins.com · The Ogletree Building · 300 North Main Street · P.O. Box 2757 · Greenville, SC 29602 · 864-271-1300

J. Howard Daniel · a · Ogletree Deakins · http://www.ogletreedeakins.com · The Ogletree Building · 300 North Main Street · P.O. Box 2757 · Greenville, SC 29602 · 864-271-1300

Ingrid B. Erwin · Jackson Lewis · http://www.jacksonlewis.com · One Liberty Square, Suite 800 · 55 Beattie Place · Greenville, SC 29601 · 864-232-7000

William H. Foster · Nelson Mullins Riley & Scarborough · Poinsett Plaza, Suite 900 · 104 South Main Street · Greenville, SC 29601-2122 · 864-250-2300

L. Gray Geddie, Jr. · a · Ogletree Deakins · http://www.ogletreedeakins.com · The Ogletree Building · 300 North Main Street · P.O. Box 2757 · Greenville, SC 29602 · 864-271-1300

J. Theodore Gentry · Wyche, Burgess, Freeman & Parham · 44 East Camperdown Way · P.O. Box 728 · Greenville, SC 29602-0728 · 864-242-8200

Thomas G. Greaves III · a · Ogletree Deakins · http://www.ogletreedeakins.com · The Ogletree Building · 300 North Main Street · P.O. Box 2757 · Greenville, SC 29602 · 864-271-1300

Knox L. Haynsworth, Jr. · 2% · Ogletree Deakins · http://www.ogletreedeakins.com · The Ogletree Building · 300 North Main Street · P.O. Box 2757 · Greenville, SC 29602 · 864-271-1300

Stephen J. Henry · Stephen Henry Law Firm · 406 Pettigru Street · Greenville, SC 29601-3115 · 864-232-9700

Phillip A. Kilgore · Ogletree Deakins · http://www.ogletreedeakins.com · The Ogletree Building · 300 North Main Street · P.O. Box 2757 · Greenville, SC 29602 · 864-271-1300

Robert O. King · Ogletree Deakins · http://www.ogletreedeakins.com · The Ogletree Building · 300 North Main Street · P.O. Box 2757 · Greenville, SC 29602 · 864-271-1300

William Ross McKibbon, Jr. · a · Ogletree Deakins · http://www.ogletreedeakins.com · The Ogletree Building · 300 North Main Street · P.O. Box 2757 · Greenville, SC 29602 · 864-271-1300

Rita M. McKinney · McNair Law Firm · http://www.mcnair.net · Bank of America Plaza, Suite 900 · 101 North Main Street · P.O. Box 447 · Greenville, SC 29602 · 864-271-4940

D. Randle Moody II · Roe Cassidy Coates & Price · 1052 North Church Street · P.O. Box 10529 · Greenville, SC 29603 · 864-349-2600

Brian P. Murphy · Brian Murphy Law Firm · 708 East McBee Avenue · Greenville, SC 29601 · 864-370-9400

R. Allison Phinney · Ogletree Deakins · http://www.ogletreedeakins.com · The Ogletree Building · 300 North Main Street · P.O. Box 2757 · Greenville, SC 29602 · 864-271-1300

Michael S. Pitts · Nexsen Pruet · http://www.nexsenpruet.com · 201 West McBee Avenue, Suite 400 · P.O. Drawer 10648 · Greenville, SC 29601 · 864-370-2211

Andreas N. Satterfield, Jr. · Jackson Lewis · http://www.jacksonlewis.com · One Liberty Square, Suite 800 · 55 Beattie Place · Greenville, SC 29601 · 864-232-7000

Lewis T. Smoak · a · Ogletree Deakins · http://www.ogletreedeakins.com · The Ogletree Building · 300 North Main Street · P.O. Box 2757 · Greenville, SC 29602 · 864-271-1300

Thomas L. Stephenson · Nexsen Pruet · http://www.nexsenpruet.com · 201 West McBee Avenue, Suite 400 · P.O. Drawer 10648 · Greenville, SC 29601 · 864-370-2211

J. Hamilton Stewart III · a · Ogletree Deakins · http://www.ogletreedeakins.com · The Ogletree Building · 300 North Main Street · P.O. Box 2757 · Greenville, SC 29602 · 864-271-1300

Kristofer K. Strasser · Ogletree Deakins · http://www.ogletreedeakins.com · The Ogletree Building · 300 North Main Street · P.O. Box 2757 · Greenville, SC 29602 · 864-271-1300

Fred W. Suggs · a · Ogletree Deakins · http://www.ogletreedeakins.com · The Ogletree Building · 300 North Main Street · P.O. Box 2757 · Greenville, SC 29602 · 864-271-1300

M. Baker Wyche III · Ogletree Deakins · http://www.ogletreedeakins.com · The Ogletree Building · 300 North Main Street · P.O. Box 2757 · Greenville, SC 29602 · 864-271-1300

Myrtle Beach

Henrietta U. Golding · McNair Law Firm · http://www.mcnair.net · Founders Center, Suite 206 · 2411 Oak Street · P.O. Box 336 · Myrtle Beach, SC 29578 · 843-444-1107

Spartanburg

Wade E. Ballard · Ford & Harrison · http://www.fordharrison.com · 100 Dunbar Street, Suite 300 · Spartanburg, SC 29306 · 864-699-1100

Michael W. Bishop · Ford & Harrison · http://www.fordharrison.com · 100 Dunbar Street, Suite 300 · Spartanburg, SC 29306 · 864-699-1100

Donald C. Coggins, Jr. · Harrison, White, Smith & Coggins · 178 West Main Street · P.O. Box 3547 · Spartanburg, SC 29304 · 864-585-5100

Patrick L. Cont · Sturm & Cont · 159 Hall Street · Spartanburg, SC 29302 · 864-580-2020

S. Clay Keim · Ford & Harrison · http://www.fordharrison.com · 100 Dunbar Street, Suite 300 · Spartanburg, SC 29306 · 864-699-1100

LEGAL MALPRACTICE LAW

Charleston

Susan Taylor Wall · Parker Poe Adams & Bernstein · http://www.parkerpoe.com · 200 Meeting Street, Suite 301 · Charleston, SC 29401-3156 · 843-727-2650

Columbia

A. Camden Lewis · Lewis, Babcock & Hawkins · 1513 Hampton Street · P.O. Box 11208 · Columbia, SC 29211 · 803-771-8000

Warren C. Powell, Jr. · Bruner, Powell, Robbins, Wall & Mullins · http://www.bprwm.com · 1735 St. Julian Place, Suite 200 · P.O. Box 61110 · Columbia, SC 29260-1110 · 803-252-7693

Greenville

Steven E. Farrar · Smith Moore Leatherwood · http://www.smithmoorelaw.com · The Leatherwood Plaza, Suite 500 · 300 East McBee Avenue · P.O. Box 87 · Greenville, SC 29602 · 864-242-6440

Spartanburg

Donald C. Coggins, Jr. · Harrison, White, Smith & Coggins · 178 West Main Street · P.O. Box 3547 · Spartanburg, SC 29304 · 864-585-5100

MARITIME LAW

Charleston

R. Randall Bridwell · Charleston School of Law · P.O. Box 535 · Charleston, SC 29403 · 843-329-1000

David M. Collins · Buist Moore Smythe McGee · http://www.buistmoore.com · Five Exchange Street · P.O. Box 999 · Charleston, SC 29402-0999 · 843-722-3400

Marvin D. Infinger · Haynsworth Sinkler Boyd · http://www.hsblawfirm.com · 134 Meeting Street, Third Floor · P.O. Box 340 · Charleston, SC 29402-0340 · 843-722-3366

Benjamin Allston Moore, Jr. · 2) · Buist Moore Smythe McGee · http://www.buistmoore.com · Five Exchange Street · P.O. Box 999 · Charleston, SC 29402-0999 · 843-722-3400

Gordon D. Schreck · 2) · Buist Moore Smythe McGee · http://www.buistmoore.com · Five Exchange Street · P.O. Box 999 · Charleston, SC 29402-0999 · 843-722-3400

MASS TORT LITIGATION

Charleston

A. Hoyt Rowell III · Richardson, Patrick, Westbrook & Brickman · 174 East Bay Street · P.O. Box 879 · Charleston, SC 29401-2132 · 843-727-6500

Columbia

Steven W. Ouzts · Turner, Padget, Graham & Laney · 1901 Main Street, 17th Floor · P.O. Box 1473 · Columbia, SC 29202 · 803-254-2200

R. Bruce Shaw · a · Nelson Mullins Riley & Scarborough · Meridian, 17th Floor · 1320 Main Street · P.O. Box 11070 · Columbia, SC 29211 · 803-799-2000

Kenneth M. Suggs · a · Janet Jenner & Suggs · 500 Taylor Street · Columbia, SC 29201 · 803-726-0050

David G. Traylor, Jr. · Nelson Mullins Riley & Scarborough · Meridian, 17th Floor · 1320 Main Street · P.O. Box 11070 · Columbia, SC 29211 · 803-799-2000

Mount Pleasant

Ronald L. Motley · a · Motley Rice · 28 Bridgeside Boulevard · Mount Pleasant, SC 29464 · 843-216-9000

Joseph F. Rice · Motley Rice · 28 Bridgeside Boulevard · Mount Pleasant, SC 29464 · 843-216-9000

MEDICAL MALPRACTICE LAW

Anderson

Wm. Douglas Gray · McNair Law Firm · http://www.mcnair.net · 500 South McDuffie Street · Anderson, SC 29622 · 864-226-1688

Charleston

John K. Blincow · Turner, Padget, Graham & Laney · Gateway Center, Suite 200 · 40 Calhoun Street · P.O. Box 22129 · Charleston, SC 29413 · 843-576-2800

Richard S. Rosen · a · Rosen, Rosen & Hagood · http://www.rrhlawfirm.com · 134 Meeting Street, Suite 200 · P.O. Box 893 · Charleston, SC 29401 · 843-577-6726

Susan C. Rosen · Rosen Law Firm · http://www.rosen-lawfirm.com · 18 Broad Street, Suite 201 · Charleston, SC 29401 · 843-377-1700

Columbia

Charles E. Hill · Turner, Padget, Graham & Laney · 1901 Main Street, 17th Floor · P.O. Box 1473 · Columbia, SC 29202 · 803-254-2200

Kenneth M. Suggs · a · Janet Jenner & Suggs · 500 Taylor Street · Columbia, SC 29201 · 803-726-0050

Greenville

J. Benjamin Alexander · Haynsworth Sinkler Boyd · http://www.hsblawfirm.com · Two Liberty Square, 11th Floor · 75 Beattie Place · P.O. Box 2048 · Greenville, SC 29602-2048 · 864-240-3200

Wallace K. Lightsey · a · Wyche, Burgess, Freeman & Parham · 44 East Camperdown Way · P.O. Box 728 · Greenville, SC 29602-0728 · 864-242-8200

G. Dewey Oxner, Jr. · 2% · Haynsworth Sinkler Boyd · http://www.hsblawfirm.com · Two Liberty Square, 11th Floor · 75 Beattie Place · P.O. Box 2048 · Greenville, SC 29602-2048 · 864-240-3200

James C. Parham, Jr. · a · Wyche, Burgess, Freeman & Parham · 44 East Camperdown Way · P.O. Box 728 · Greenville, SC 29602-0728 · 864-242-8200

Sarah McMillan Purnell · Haynsworth Sinkler Boyd · http://www.hsblawfirm.com · Two Liberty Square, 11th Floor · 75 Beattie Place · P.O. Box 2048 · Greenville, SC 29602-2048 · 864-240-3200

Matthew P. Utecht · Haynsworth Sinkler Boyd · http://www.hsblawfirm.com · Two Liberty Square, 11th Floor · 75 Beattie Place · P.O. Box 2048 · Greenville, SC 29602-2048 · 864-240-3200

Spartanburg

William U. Gunn · 2) · Holcombe Bomar · 100 Dunbar Street, Suite 200 · P.O. Drawer 1897 · Spartanburg, SC 29304-1897 · 864-594-5300

H. Spencer King · The Ward Law Firm · 233 South Pine Street · P.O. Box 3188 · Spartanburg, SC 29304 864-573-8500

MERGERS & ACQUISITIONS LAW

Columbia

William C. Boyd · a · Haynsworth Sinkler Boyd · http://www.hsblawfirm.com · 1201 Main Street, 22nd Floor · P.O. Box 11889 · Columbia, SC 29211-1889 · 803-779-3080

Gus M. Dixon · Nelson Mullins Riley & Scarborough · Meridian, 17th Floor · 1320 Main Street · P.O. Box 11070 · Columbia, SC 29211 · 803-799-2000

Randolph B. Epting · Haynsworth Sinkler Boyd · http://www.hsblawfirm.com · 1201 Main Street, 22nd Floor · P.O. Box 11889 · Columbia, SC 29211-1889 · 803-779-3080

Daniel J. Fritze · Nelson Mullins Riley & Scarborough · Meridian, 17th Floor · 1320 Main Street · P.O. Box 11070 · Columbia, SC 29211 · 803-799-2000

P. Mason Hogue, Jr. · Nelson Mullins Riley & Scarborough · Meridian, 17th Floor · 1320 Main Street · P.O. Box 11070 · Columbia, SC 29211 · 803-799-2000

G. Marcus Knight · Nexsen Pruet · http://www.nexsenpruet.com · First Citizens Building, Suite 700 · 1230 Main Street · P.O. Drawer 2426 · Columbia, SC 29202-2426 · 803-771-8900

Edward G. Menzie · 2% · Nexsen Pruet · http://www.nexsenpruet.com · First Citizens Building, Suite 700 1230 Main Street · P.O. Drawer 2426 · Columbia, SC 29202-2426 · 803-771-8900

William M. Musser · McNair Law Firm · http://www.mcnair.net · 1301 Gervais Street, 11th Floor · P.O. Box 11390 · Columbia, SC 29211 · 803-799-9800

MUNICIPAL LAW

Columbia

Danny C. Crowe · Turner, Padget, Graham & Laney · 1901 Main Street, 17th Floor · P.O. Box 1473 · Columbia, SC 29202 · 803-254-2200

NON-PROFIT/CHARITIES LAW

Greenville

Keith G. Meacham · Merline & Meacham · http://www.merlineandmeacham.com · 812 East North Street P.O. Box 10796 · Greenville, SC 29603 · 864-242-4080

Charleston

Dale T. Cobb, Jr. · a · Belk, Cobb, Infinger & Goldstein · 2344 Cosgrove Avenue · P.O. Box 71121 · Charleston, SC 29415 · 843-554-4291

Francis J. Cornely · Francis J. Cornely · 15 Prioleau Street · P.O. Box 75 · Charleston, SC 29401 · 843-937-4090

Coming B. Gibbs, Jr. · 2% · Gibbs & Holmes · 171 Church Street, Suite 110 · P.O. Box 938 · Charleston, SC 29402-0938 · 843-722-0033

Gedney M. Howe III · 2% · Gedney M. Howe, III · Eight Chalmers Street · P.O. Box 1034 · Charleston, SC 29402 · 843-722-8048

Lionel S. Lofton · a · Lofton & Lofton · 225 Seven Farms Drive, Suite 109 · Charleston, SC 29492 · 843-722-6319

Michael P. O'Connell · a · Stirling & O'Connell · 145 King Street, Suite 410 · P.O. Box 882 · Charleston, SC 29402 · 843-577-9890

Andrew J. Savage III · a · Savage & Savage · 15 Prioleau Street · P.O. Box 1002 · Charleston, SC 29402 · 843-720-7470

Columbia

John D. Delgado · Law Firm of John Delgado · 914 Richland Street, Suite A102 · Columbia, SC 29201 · 803-254-7745

Jonathan S. Gasser · Harris & Gasser · 1529 Laurel Street · Columbia, SC 29201 · 803-779-7080

Gregory P. Harris · Harris & Gasser · 1529 Laurel Street · Columbia, SC 29201 · 803-779-7080

I. S. Leevy Johnson · a · Johnson Toal & Battiste · 1615 Barnwell Street · P.O. Box 1431 · Columbia, SC 29201 · 803-252-9700

Leigh J. Leventis · Leigh J. Leventis Law Office · 1913 Bull Street · P.O. Box 11067 · Columbia, SC 29201 · 803-256-0113

Jack B. Swerling · a · Law Offices of Jack B. Swerling · http://www.jackswerling.com · 1720 Main Street, Suite 301 · Columbia, SC 29201 · 803-765-2626

Florence

J. René Josey · Turner, Padget, Graham & Laney · BB&T Building, Fouth Floor · 1831 West Evans Street · P.O. Box 5478 · Florence, SC 29502-5478 · 843-662-9008

Greenville

James W. Bannister · Bannister & Wyatt · 401 Pettigru Street · P.O. Box 10007 · Greenville, SC 29603 · 864-298-0084

O. W. Bannister, Jr. · a · Bannister & Wyatt · 401 Pettigru Street · P.O. Box 10007 · Greenville, SC 29603 · 864-298-0084

Spartanburg

John B. White, Jr. · Harrison, White, Smith & Coggins · 178 West Main Street · P.O. Box 3547 · Spartanburg, SC 29304 · 864-585-5100

PERSONAL INJURY LITIGATION

Aiken

Robert L. Buchanan, Jr. · Buchanan Law Office · 212 Newberry Street, NW · P.O. Box 463 · Aiken, SC 29802-0463 · 803-649-2586

Todd J. Johnson · Johnson, Johnson, Whittle & Snelgrove · 117 Pendleton Street, NW · P.O. Box 2619 · Aiken, SC 29802-2619 · 803-649-5338

Ronald A. Maxwell · Maxwell Law Firm · 225 Chesterfield Street, NW · P.O. Box 1115 · Aiken, SC 29801 · 803-641-6700

Anderson

William N. Epps, Jr. · Epps & Nelson · 230 West Whitner Street · Anderson, SC 29621 · 864-224-2111

Michael D. Glenn · Glenn, Haigler, McClain & Stathakis · 121 West Benson Street · Anderson, SC 29624 864-226-1885

Steven M. Krause · Krause, Moorhead & Draisen · 207 East Calhoun Street · Anderson, SC 29621 · 864-225-4000

Barnwell

Terry E. Richardson, Jr. · Richardson, Patrick, Westbrook & Brickman · 1730 Jackson Street · P.O. Box 1368 · Barnwell, SC 29812 · 803-259-9900

Charleston

M. Dawes Cooke, Jr. · Barnwell Whaley Patterson & Helms · 885 Island Park Drive · P.O. Drawer H · Charleston, SC 29402-0197 · 843-577-7700

Joseph P. Griffith, Jr. · Joe Griffith Law Firm · Seven State Street · Charleston, SC 29401 · 843-225-5563

Henry E. Grimball · Buist Moore Smythe McGee · http://www.buistmoore.com · Five Exchange Street · P.O. Box 999 · Charleston, SC 29402-0999 · 843-722-3400

William C. Helms · Barnwell Whaley Patterson & Helms · 885 Island Park Drive · P.O. Drawer H · Charleston, SC 29402-0197 · 843-577-7700

Robert H. Hood · 2% · Hood Law Firm · http://www.hoodlaw.com · 172 Meeting Street · P.O. Box 1508 · Charleston, SC 29402 · 843-577-4435

Gedney M. Howe III · 2% · Gedney M. Howe, III · Eight Chalmers Street · P.O. Box 1034 · Charleston, SC 29402 · 843-722-8048

Carl H. Jacobson · Uricchio, Howe, Krell, Jacobson, Toporek, Theos & Keith · 17½ Broad Street · P.O. Box 399 · Charleston, SC 29401 · 843-723-7491

George J. Kefalos · a · George J. Kefalos · Three State Street · Charleston, SC 29401 · 843-722-6612

Lionel S. Lofton · a · Lofton & Lofton · 225 Seven Farms Drive, Suite 109 · Charleston, SC 29492 · 843-722-6319

Wade H. Logan III · Nelson Mullins Riley & Scarborough · Liberty Center, Suite 600 · 151 Meeting Street · Charleston, SC 29401-2239 · 843-853-5200

Francis X. McCann · Law Offices of Frank McCann · P.O. Box 247 · Charleston, SC 29402 · 843-577-4242

James D. Myrick · Buist Moore Smythe McGee · http://www.buistmoore.com · Five Exchange Street · P.O. Box 999 · Charleston, SC 29402-0999 · 843-722-3400

Morris D. Rosen · 2% · Rosen, Rosen & Hagood · http://www.rrhlawfirm.com · 134 Meeting Street, Suite 200 · P.O. Box 893 · Charleston, SC 29401 · 843-577-6726

Richard S. Rosen · a · Rosen, Rosen & Hagood · http://www.rrhlawfirm.com · 134 Meeting Street, Suite 200 · P.O. Box 893 · Charleston, SC 29401 · 843-577-6726

Susan C. Rosen · Rosen Law Firm · http://www.rosen-lawfirm.com · 18 Broad Street, Suite 201 · Charleston, SC 29401 · 843-377-1700

David L. Savage · Savage & Savage · 15 Prioleau Street · P.O. Box 1002 · Charleston, SC 29402 · 843-720-7470

Henry B. Smythe, Jr. · Buist Moore Smythe McGee · http://www.buistmoore.com · Five Exchange Street · P.O. Box 999 · Charleston, SC 29402-0999 · 843-722-3400

Mark C. Tanenbaum · a · Mark C. Tanenbaum · http://www.tanenbaumlaw.com · 241-243 East Bay Street · Charleston, SC 29401 · 843-577-5100

Alan D. Toporek · Uricchio, Howe, Krell, Jacobson, Toporek, Theos & Keith · 17½ Broad Street · P.O. Box 399 · Charleston, SC 29401 · 843-723-7491

Columbia

Luther J. Battiste III · Johnson Toal & Battiste · 1615 Barnwell Street · P.O. Box 1431 · Columbia, SC 29201 · 803-252-9700

Christopher J. Daniels · Nelson Mullins Riley & Scarborough · Meridian, 17th Floor · 1320 Main Street · P.O. Box 11070 · Columbia, SC 29211 · 803-799-2000

David E. Dukes · Nelson Mullins Riley & Scarborough · Meridian, 17th Floor · 1320 Main Street · P.O. Box 11070 · Columbia, SC 29211 · 803-799-2000

Carl B. Epps III · Nelson Mullins Riley & Scarborough · Meridian, 17th Floor · 1320 Main Street · P.O. Box 11070 · Columbia, SC 29211 · 803-799-2000

Robert W. Foster, Jr. · Nelson Mullins Riley & Scarborough · Meridian, 17th Floor · 1320 Main Street · P.O. Box 11070 · Columbia, SC 29211 · 803-799-2000

Richard M. Gergel · a · Gergel, Nickles & Solomon · 1519 Richland Street · P.O. Box 1866 · Columbia, SC 29202-1866 · 803-779-8080

Richard A. Harpootlian · Richard A. Harpootlian · 1410 Laurel Street · P.O. Box 1090 · Columbia, SC 29202 · 803-252-4848

I. S. Leevy Johnson · a · Johnson Toal & Battiste · 1615 Barnwell Street · P.O. Box 1431 · Columbia, SC 29201 · 803-252-9700

Pope D. Johnson III · McCutchen Blanton Johnson & Barnette · 1414 Lady Street · P.O. Drawer 11209 · Columbia, SC 29211-1209 · 803-799-9791

John D. Kassel · a · John D. Kassel · 1703 Richland Street · P.O. Box 1476 · Columbia, SC 29202 · 803-256-4242

Rebecca Laffitte · Sowell Gray Stepp & Laffitte · http://www.sowell.com · 1310 Gadsden Street · P.O. Box 11449 · Columbia, SC 29211 · 803-929-1400

Thomas E. McCutchen, Jr. · 2% · McCutchen Blanton Johnson & Barnette · 1414 Lady Street · P.O. Drawer 11209 · Columbia, SC 29211-1209 · 803-799-9791

Edward W. Mullins, Jr. · 2% · Nelson Mullins Riley & Scarborough · Meridian, 17th Floor · 1320 Main Street · P.O. Box 11070 · Columbia, SC 29211 · 803-799-2000

D. Cravens Ravenel · Baker, Ravenel & Bender · http://www.brblegal.com · 3710 Landmark Drive, Suite 400 · P.O. Box 8057 · Columbia, SC 29202 · 803-799-9091

R. Bruce Shaw · a · Nelson Mullins Riley & Scarborough · Meridian, 17th Floor · 1320 Main Street · P.O. Box 11070 · Columbia, SC 29211 · 803-799-2000

Joel H. Smith · Nelson Mullins Riley & Scarborough · Meridian, 17th Floor · 1320 Main Street · P.O. Box 11070 · Columbia, SC 29211 · 803-799-2000

Carl L. Solomon · Gergel, Nickles & Solomon · 1519 Richland Street · P.O. Box 1866 · Columbia, SC 29202-1866 · 803-779-8080

Kenneth M. Suggs · a · Janet Jenner & Suggs · 500 Taylor Street · Columbia, SC 29201 · 803-726-0050

Monteith P. Todd · Sowell Gray Stepp & Laffitte · http://www.sowell.com · 1310 Gadsden Street · P.O. Box 11449 · Columbia, SC 29211 · 803-929-1400

David G. Traylor, Jr. · Nelson Mullins Riley & Scarborough · Meridian, 17th Floor · 1320 Main Street · P.O. Box 11070 · Columbia, SC 29211 · 803-799-2000

Florence

Mark W. Buyck, Jr. · 2% · Willcox, Buyck & Williams · 248 West Evans Street · P.O. Box 1909 · Florence, SC 29503 · 843-662-3258

Greenville

Eugene C. Covington, Jr. · a · Covington, Patrick, Hagins, Stern & Lewis · 211 Pettigru Street · P.O. Box 2343 · Greenville, SC 29601 · 864-242-9000

Robert P. Foster · Foster Law Firm · 610 East McBee Avenue, Suite 104 · Greenville, SC 29602 · 864-242-6200

Michael J. Giese · a · Smith Moore Leatherwood · http://www.smithmoorelaw.com · The Leatherwood Plaza, Suite 500 · 300 East McBee Avenue · P.O. Box 87 · Greenville, SC 29602 · 864-242-6440

John E. Johnston · a · Smith Moore Leatherwood · http://www.smithmoorelaw.com · The Leatherwood Plaza, Suite 500 · 300 East McBee Avenue · P.O. Box 87 · Greenville, SC 29602 · 864-242-6440

Stephen R. H. Lewis · Covington, Patrick, Hagins, Stern & Lewis · 211 Pettigru Street · P.O. Box 2343 · Greenville, SC 29601 · 864-242-9000

H. Sam Mabry III · Haynsworth Sinkler Boyd · http://www.hsblawfirm.com · Two Liberty Square, 11th Floor · 75 Beattie Place · P.O. Box 2048 · Greenville, SC 29602-2048 · 864-240-3200

William Francis Marion, Jr. · Haynsworth Sinkler Boyd · http://www.hsblawfirm.com · Two Liberty Square, 11th Floor · 75 Beattie Place · P.O. Box 2048 · Greenville, SC 29602-2048 · 864-240-3200

Dana C. Mitchell III · Mitchell Law Firm · Seven Mills Avenue · P.O. Box 10285 · Greenville, SC 29603 864-232-9330

David L. Moore, Jr. · Love, Thornton, Arnold & Thomason · 410 East Washington Street · P.O. Box 10045 · Greenville, SC 29603 · 864-242-6360

G. D. Morgan, Jr. · McAngus, Goudelock & Courie · Two Liberty Square, Suite 300 · 75 Beattie Place · P.O. Box 2980 · Greenville, SC 29602-2980 · 864-239-4000

Robert D. Moseley, Jr. · Smith Moore Leatherwood · http://www.smithmoorelaw.com · The Leatherwood Plaza, Suite 500 · 300 East McBee Avenue · P.O. Box 87 · Greenville, SC 29602 · 864-242-6440

G. Dewey Oxner, Jr. · 2% · Haynsworth Sinkler Boyd · http://www.hsblawfirm.com · Two Liberty Square, 11th Floor · 75 Beattie Place · P.O. Box 2048 · Greenville, SC 29602-2048 · 864-240-3200

D. Michael Parham · a · Parham, Smith & Dodson · Smith Barney Building, Second Floor · 501 River Street · Greenville, SC 29601 · 864-242-9008

Douglas F. Patrick · a · Covington, Patrick, Hagins, Stern & Lewis · 211 Pettigru Street · P.O. Box 2343 Greenville, SC 29601 · 864-242-9000

Sarah McMillan Purnell · Haynsworth Sinkler Boyd · http://www.hsblawfirm.com · Two Liberty Square, 11th Floor · 75 Beattie Place · P.O. Box 2048 · Greenville, SC 29602-2048 · 864-240-3200

Phillip E. Reeves · Gallivan, White & Boyd · One Liberty Square, Suite 1200 · 55 Beattie Place · P.O. Box 10589 · Greenville, SC 29603 · 864-271-9580

T. David Rheney · Gallivan, White & Boyd · One Liberty Square, Suite 1200 · 55 Beattie Place · P.O. Box 10589 · Greenville, SC 29603 · 864-271-9580

Kurt M. Rozelsky · Smith Moore Leatherwood · http://www.smithmoorelaw.com · The Leatherwood Plaza, Suite 500 · 300 East McBee Avenue · P.O. Box 87 · Greenville, SC 29602 · 864-242-6440

Matthew P. Utecht · Haynsworth Sinkler Boyd · http://www.hsblawfirm.com · Two Liberty Square, 11th Floor · 75 Beattie Place · P.O. Box 2048 · Greenville, SC 29602-2048 · 864-240-3200

Daniel B. White · a · Gallivan, White & Boyd · One Liberty Square, Suite 1200 · 55 Beattie Place · P.O. Box 10589 · Greenville, SC 29603 · 864-271-9580

Greenwood

Robert M. Erwin, Jr. · Robert M. Erwin, Jr. · 305 Main Street · Greenwood, SC 29646 · 864-229-5010

Greer

J. Kendall Few · 2) · J. Kendall Few · 95 Stillhouse Ridge · Greer, SC 29650 · 864-334-1400

Mount Pleasant

Ronald L. Motley · a · Motley Rice · 28 Bridgeside Boulevard · Mount Pleasant, SC 29464 · 843-216-9000

Mt. Pleasant

Edward Vernon Ferrell Glenn · Law Offices of E. Vernon F. Glenn · 211 Scott Street · Mt. Pleasant, SC 29464 · 843-971-1999

Geoffrey H. Waggoner · Geoffrey H. Waggoner · 501 Belle Hall Parkway, Suite 202 · P.O. Box 865 · Mt. Pleasant, SC 29465 · 843-972-0426

Spartanburg

Kenneth C. Anthony, Jr. · a · Anthony Law Firm · 250 Magnolia Street · P.O. Box 3565 · Spartanburg, SC 29304-3565 · 864-582-2355

William U. Gunn · 2) · Holcombe Bomar · 100 Dunbar Street, Suite 200 · P.O. Drawer 1897 · Spartanburg, SC 29304-1897 · 864-594-5300

Patrick E. Knie · Patrick E. Knie · 250 Magnolia Street · P.O. Box 5159 · Spartanburg, SC 29304-5159 · 864-582-5118

Gary W. Poliakoff · Poliakoff & Associates · 215 Magnolia Street · Spartanburg, SC 29304 · 864-582-5472

Michael E. Spears · a · Michael E. Spears · 172 East Main Street, Suite 200 · P.O. Box 5806 · Spartanburg, SC 29304-5806 · 864-583-3535

Richard W. Vieth · Henderson Brandt & Vieth · 360 East Henry Street, Suite 101 · Spartanburg, SC 29302 · 864-582-2962

Walhalla

Larry C. Brandt · Larry C. Brandt · 3691 Blue Ridge Boulevard · P.O. Drawer 738 · Walhalla, SC 29691 · 864-638-5406

PRODUCT LIABILITY LITIGATION

Charleston

Michael T. Cole · Nelson Mullins Riley & Scarborough · Liberty Center, Suite 600 · 151 Meeting Street · Charleston, SC 29401-2239 · 843-853-5200

Columbia

Gray T. Culbreath · Collins & Lacy · http://www.collinsandlacy.com · 1330 Lady Street, Sixth Floor · P.O. Box 12487 · Columbia, SC 29211 · 803-256-2660

Christopher J. Daniels · Nelson Mullins Riley & Scarborough · Meridian, 17th Floor · 1320 Main Street · P.O. Box 11070 · Columbia, SC 29211 · 803-799-2000

William S. Davies, Jr. · a · Nelson Mullins Riley & Scarborough · Meridian, 17th Floor · 1320 Main Street · P.O. Box 11070 · Columbia, SC 29211 · 803-799-2000

Elbert S. Dorn · Turner, Padget, Graham & Laney · 1901 Main Street, 17th Floor · P.O. Box 1473 · Columbia, SC 29202 · 803-254-2200

David E. Dukes · Nelson Mullins Riley & Scarborough · Meridian, 17th Floor · 1320 Main Street · P.O. Box 11070 · Columbia, SC 29211 · 803-799-2000

Robert W. Foster, Jr. · Nelson Mullins Riley & Scarborough · Meridian, 17th Floor · 1320 Main Street · P.O. Box 11070 · Columbia, SC 29211 · 803-799-2000

Pope D. Johnson III · McCutchen Blanton Johnson & Barnette · 1414 Lady Street · P.O. Drawer 11209 · Columbia, SC 29211-1209 · 803-799-9791

John D. Kassel · a · John D. Kassel · 1703 Richland Street · P.O. Box 1476 · Columbia, SC 29202 · 803-256-4242

Frank B.B. Knowlton · Nelson Mullins Riley & Scarborough · Meridian, 17th Floor · 1320 Main Street · P.O. Box 11070 · Columbia, SC 29211 · 803-799-2000

John T. Lay, Jr. · Ellis, Lawhorne & Sims · http://www.ellislawhorne.com · 1501 Main Street, Fifth Floor P.O. Box 2285 · Columbia, SC 29202 · 803-254-4190

Stephen G. Morrison · a · Nelson Mullins Riley & Scarborough · Meridian, 17th Floor · 1320 Main Street · P.O. Box 11070 · Columbia, SC 29211 · 803-799-2000

Curtis L. Ott · Turner, Padget, Graham & Laney · 1901 Main Street, 17th Floor · P.O. Box 1473 · Columbia, SC 29202 · 803-254-2200

Steven W. Ouzts · Turner, Padget, Graham & Laney · 1901 Main Street, 17th Floor · P.O. Box 1473 · Columbia, SC 29202 · 803-254-2200

D. Cravens Ravenel · Baker, Ravenel & Bender · http://www.brblegal.com · 3710 Landmark Drive, Suite 400 · P.O. Box 8057 · Columbia, SC 29202 · 803-799-9091

R. Bruce Shaw · a · Nelson Mullins Riley & Scarborough · Meridian, 17th Floor · 1320 Main Street · P.O. Box 11070 · Columbia, SC 29211 · 803-799-2000

Joel H. Smith · Nelson Mullins Riley & Scarborough · Meridian, 17th Floor · 1320 Main Street · P.O. Box 11070 · Columbia, SC 29211 · 803-799-2000

Kenneth M. Suggs · a · Janet Jenner & Suggs · 500 Taylor Street · Columbia, SC 29201 · 803-726-0050

David G. Traylor, Jr. · Nelson Mullins Riley & Scarborough · Meridian, 17th Floor · 1320 Main Street · P.O. Box 11070 · Columbia, SC 29211 · 803-799-2000

Greenville

W. Howard Boyd, Jr. · Gallivan, White & Boyd · One Liberty Square, Suite 1200 · 55 Beattie Place · P.O. Box 10589 · Greenville, SC 29603 · 864-271-9580

James D. Brice · Gallivan, White & Boyd · One Liberty Square, Suite 1200 · 55 Beattie Place · P.O. Box 10589 · Greenville, SC 29603 · 864-271-9580

H. Sam Mabry III · Haynsworth Sinkler Boyd · http://www.hsblawfirm.com · Two Liberty Square, 11th Floor · 75 Beattie Place · P.O. Box 2048 · Greenville, SC 29602-2048 · 864-240-3200

William Francis Marion, Jr. · Haynsworth Sinkler Boyd · http://www.hsblawfirm.com · Two Liberty Square, 11th Floor · 75 Beattie Place · P.O. Box 2048 · Greenville, SC 29602-2048 · 864-240-3200

C. William McGee · Gallivan, White & Boyd · One Liberty Square, Suite 1200 · 55 Beattie Place · P.O. Box 10589 · Greenville, SC 29603 · 864-271-9580

David L. Moore, Jr. · Love, Thornton, Arnold & Thomason · 410 East Washington Street · P.O. Box 10045 · Greenville, SC 29603 · 864-242-6360

Phillip E. Reeves · Gallivan, White & Boyd · One Liberty Square, Suite 1200 · 55 Beattie Place · P.O. Box 10589 · Greenville, SC 29603 · 864-271-9580

Kurt M. Rozelsky · Smith Moore Leatherwood · http://www.smithmoorelaw.com · The Leatherwood Plaza, Suite 500 · 300 East McBee Avenue · P.O. Box 87 · Greenville, SC 29602 · 864-242-6440

Daniel B. White · a · Gallivan, White & Boyd · One Liberty Square, Suite 1200 · 55 Beattie Place · P.O. Box 10589 · Greenville, SC 29603 · 864-271-9580

Mount Pleasant

Ronald L. Motley · a · Motley Rice · 28 Bridgeside Boulevard · Mount Pleasant, SC 29464 · 843-216-9000

Spartanburg

William U. Gunn · 2) · Holcombe Bomar · 100 Dunbar Street, Suite 200 · P.O. Drawer 1897 · Spartanburg, SC 29304-1897 · 864-594-5300

PROFESSIONAL MALPRACTICE LAW

Charleston

Robert H. Hood · 2% · Hood Law Firm · http://www.hoodlaw.com · 172 Meeting Street · P.O. Box 1508 · Charleston, SC 29402 · 843-577-4435

Susan Taylor Wall · Parker Poe Adams & Bernstein · http://www.parkerpoe.com · 200 Meeting Street, Suite 301 · Charleston, SC 29401-3156 · 843-727-2650

John S. Wilkerson III · Turner, Padget, Graham & Laney · Gateway Center, Suite 200 · 40 Calhoun Street · P.O. Box 22129 · Charleston, SC 29413 · 843-576-2800

Columbia

J. Calhoun Watson · Sowell Gray Stepp & Laffitte · http://www.sowell.com · 1310 Gadsden Street · P.O. Box 11449 · Columbia, SC 29211 · 803-929-1400

Greenville

Steven E. Farrar · Smith Moore Leatherwood · http://www.smithmoorelaw.com · The Leatherwood Plaza, Suite 500 · 300 East McBee Avenue · P.O. Box 87 · Greenville, SC 29602 · 864-242-6440

Sarah McMillan Purnell · Haynsworth Sinkler Boyd · http://www.hsblawfirm.com · Two Liberty Square, 11th Floor · 75 Beattie Place · P.O. Box 2048 · Greenville, SC 29602-2048 · 864-240-3200

PUBLIC FINANCE LAW

Charleston

Charlton deSaussure, Jr. · Haynsworth Sinkler Boyd · http://www.hsblawfirm.com · 134 Meeting Street, Third Floor · P.O. Box 340 · Charleston, SC 29402-0340 · 843-722-3366

Rion D. Foley · McNair Law Firm · http://www.mcnair.net · 100 Calhoun Street, Suite 400 · P.O. Box 1431 · Charleston, SC 29402-1431 · 843-723-7831

John Paul Trouche · Haynsworth Sinkler Boyd · http://www.hsblawfirm.com · 134 Meeting Street, Third Floor · P.O. Box 340 · Charleston, SC 29402-0340 · 843-722-3366

M. William Youngblood · McNair Law Firm · http://www.mcnair.net · 100 Calhoun Street, Suite 400 · P.O. Box 1431 · Charleston, SC 29402-1431 · 843-723-7831

Columbia

O. Wayne Corley · McNair Law Firm · http://www.mcnair.net · 1301 Gervais Street, 11th Floor · P.O. Box 11390 · Columbia, SC 29211 · 803-799-9800

Theodore B. DuBose · Haynsworth Sinkler Boyd · http://www.hsblawfirm.com · 1201 Main Street, 22nd Floor · P.O. Box 11889 · Columbia, SC 29211-1889 · 803-779-3080

Alan M. Lipsitz · Nexsen Pruet · http://www.nexsenpruet.com · First Citizens Building, Suite 700 · 1230 Main Street · P.O. Drawer 2426 · Columbia, SC 29202-2426 · 803-771-8900

Margaret Christian Pope · Pope Zeigler · 1411 Gervais St., Suite 300 · P.O. Box 11509 · Columbia, SC 29211-1509 · 803-354-4900

John K. Van Duys · Haynsworth Sinkler Boyd · http://www.hsblawfirm.com · 1201 Main Street, 22nd Floor · P.O. Box 11889 · Columbia, SC 29211-1889 · 803-779-3080

Greenville

Robert S. Galloway III · Haynsworth Sinkler Boyd · http://www.hsblawfirm.com · Two Liberty Square, 11th Floor · 75 Beattie Place · P.O. Box 2048 · Greenville, SC 29602-2048 · 864-240-3200

Kathleen Crum McKinney · Haynsworth Sinkler Boyd · http://www.hsblawfirm.com · Two Liberty Square, 11th Floor · 75 Beattie Place · P.O. Box 2048 · Greenville, SC 29602-2048 · 864-240-3200

E. Tyler Smith · Haynsworth Sinkler Boyd · http://www.hsblawfirm.com · Two Liberty Square, 11th Floor · 75 Beattie Place · P.O. Box 2048 · Greenville, SC 29602-2048 · 864-240-3200

RAILROAD LAW

Barnwell

Terry E. Richardson, Jr. · Richardson, Patrick, Westbrook & Brickman · 1730 Jackson Street · P.O. Box 1368 · Barnwell, SC 29812 · 803-259-9900

Greenville

Daniel B. White · a · Gallivan, White & Boyd · One Liberty Square, Suite 1200 · 55 Beattie Place · P.O. Box 10589 · Greenville, SC 29603 · 864-271-9580

Hampton

John E. Parker · Peters, Murdaugh, Parker, Eltzroth & Detrick · 101 Mulberry · P.O. Box 457 · Hampton, SC 29924 · 803-943-2111

REAL ESTATE LAW

Aiken

R. E. Hanna III · Hull, Towill, Norman, Barrett & Salley · 111 Park Avenue, SW · Aiken, SC 29801 · 803-648-4213

William H. Tucker · Hull, Towill, Norman, Barrett & Salley · 111 Park Avenue, SW · Aiken, SC 29801 · 803-648-4213

Charleston

William J. Bates · a · Young Clement Rivers · 28 Broad Street · P.O. Box 993 · Charleston, SC 29402 · 843-577-4000

J. Sidney Boone, Jr. · a · McNair Law Firm · http://www.mcnair.net · 100 Calhoun Street, Suite 400 · P.O. Box 1431 · Charleston, SC 29402-1431 · 843-723-7831

David H. Crawford · Buist Moore Smythe McGee · http://www.buistmoore.com · Five Exchange Street · P.O. Box 999 · Charleston, SC 29402-0999 · 843-722-3400

Morris A. Ellison · a · Buist Moore Smythe McGee · http://www.buistmoore.com · Five Exchange Street P.O. Box 999 · Charleston, SC 29402-0999 · 843-722-3400

Elaine H. Fowler · Turner, Padget, Graham & Laney · Gateway Center, Suite 200 · 40 Calhoun Street · P.O. Box 22129 · Charleston, SC 29413 · 843-576-2800

W. Foster Gaillard · a · Buist Moore Smythe McGee · http://www.buistmoore.com · Five Exchange Street · P.O. Box 999 · Charleston, SC 29402-0999 · 843-722-3400

Matthew J. Norton · Parker Poe Adams & Bernstein · http://www.parkerpoe.com · 200 Meeting Street, Suite 301 · Charleston, SC 29401-3156 · 843-727-2650

Neil C. Robinson, Jr. · a · Nexsen Pruet · http://www.nexsenpruet.com · 205 King Street, Suite 400 · P.O. Box 486 · Charleston, SC 29402 · 843-577-9440

Mark S. Sharpe · Warren & Sinkler · 171 Church Street, Suite 340 · P.O. Box 1254 · Charleston, SC 29402 · 843-577-0660

Susan M. Smythe · a · Buist Moore Smythe McGee · http://www.buistmoore.com · Five Exchange Street · P.O. Box 999 · Charleston, SC 29402-0999 · 843-722-3400

David M. Swanson · Haynsworth Sinkler Boyd · http://www.hsblawfirm.com · 134 Meeting Street, Third Floor · P.O. Box 340 · Charleston, SC 29402-0340 · 843-722-3366

John H. Warren III · a · Warren & Sinkler · 171 Church Street, Suite 340 · P.O. Box 1254 · Charleston, SC 29402 · 843-577-0660

Columbia

William C. Boyd · a · Haynsworth Sinkler Boyd · http://www.hsblawfirm.com · 1201 Main Street, 22nd Floor · P.O. Box 11889 · Columbia, SC 29211-1889 · 803-779-3080

Joel E. Gottlieb · Gottlieb & Smith · Bank of America Plaza, Suite 600 · 1901 Main Street · P.O. Box 51 · Columbia, SC 29201 · 803-765-9291

William O. Higgins · Ellis, Lawhorne & Sims · http://www.ellislawhorne.com · 1501 Main Street, Fifth Floor · P.O. Box 2285 · Columbia, SC 29202 · 803-254-4190

W. Leighton Lord III · Nexsen Pruet · http://www.nexsenpruet.com · First Citizens Building, Suite 700 · 1230 Main Street · P.O. Drawer 2426 · Columbia, SC 29202-2426 · 803-771-8900

John B. McArthur · Haynsworth Sinkler Boyd · http://www.hsblawfirm.com · 1201 Main Street, 22nd Floor · P.O. Box 11889 · Columbia, SC 29211-1889 · 803-779-3080

William P. McElveen, Jr. · Ellis, Lawhorne & Sims · http://www.ellislawhorne.com · 1501 Main Street, Fifth Floor · P.O. Box 2285 · Columbia, SC 29202 · 803-254-4190

Edward G. Menzie · 2% · Nexsen Pruet · http://www.nexsenpruet.com · First Citizens Building, Suite 700 1230 Main Street · P.O. Drawer 2426 · Columbia, SC 29202-2426 · 803-771-8900

Frank E. Robinson II · a · Richardson, Plowden & Robinson · 1900 Barnwell Street · P.O. Box 7788 · Columbia, SC 29202 · 803-771-4400

Ralph C. Robinson, Jr. · Callison Tighe & Robinson · Palmetto Armory Office Building, Suite 200 · 1812 Lincoln Street · P.O. Box 1390 · Columbia, SC 29202-1390 · 803-256-2371

Ralston B. Vanzant II · 2% · Nelson Mullins Riley & Scarborough · Meridian, 17th Floor · 1320 Main Street · P.O. Box 11070 · Columbia, SC 29211 · 803-799-2000

H. Dave Whitener, Jr. · Whitener & Wharton · 2001 Park Street · Columbia, SC 29201-2006 · 803-779-7830

Georgetown

James B. Moore, Jr. · McNair Law Firm · http://www.mcnair.net · 121 Screven Street · P.O. Box 418 · Georgetown, SC 29442 · 843-546-6102

Greenville

Anne S. Ellefson · Haynsworth Sinkler Boyd · http://www.hsblawfirm.com · Two Liberty Square, 11th Floor · 75 Beattie Place · P.O. Box 2048 · Greenville, SC 29602-2048 · 864-240-3200

Larry D. Estridge · a · Womble Carlyle Sandridge & Rice · 550 South Main Street, Suite 400 · P.O. Box 10208 · Greenville, SC 29603-0208 · 864-255-5400

F. Douglas P. Evans · Brown, Massey, Evans, McLeod & Haynsworth · 106 Williams Street · P.O. Box 2464 · Greenville, SC 29602 · 864-271-7424

Mark R. Holmes · Smith Moore Leatherwood · http://www.smithmoorelaw.com · The Leatherwood Plaza, Suite 500 · 300 East McBee Avenue · P.O. Box 87 · Greenville, SC 29602 · 864-242-6440

Arthur L. Howson, Jr. · Gallivan, White & Boyd · One Liberty Square, Suite 1200 · 55 Beattie Place · P.O. Box 10589 · Greenville, SC 29603 · 864-271-9580

Charles E. McDonald, Jr. · Haynsworth Sinkler Boyd · http://www.hsblawfirm.com · Two Liberty Square, 11th Floor · 75 Beattie Place · P.O. Box 2048 · Greenville, SC 29602-2048 · 864-240-3200

Cecil H. Nelson, Jr. · Nelson Law Firm · 25 East Court Street, Suite 201 · Greenville, SC 29601 · 864-232-3766

A. Marvin Quattlebaum · Smith Moore Leatherwood · http://www.smithmoorelaw.com · The Leatherwood Plaza, Suite 500 · 300 East McBee Avenue · P.O. Box 87 · Greenville, SC 29602 · 864-242-6440

W. Lindsay Smith · Womble Carlyle Sandridge & Rice · 550 South Main Street, Suite 400 · P.O. Box 10208 · Greenville, SC 29603-0208 · 864-255-5400

James I. Warren III · Wyche, Burgess, Freeman & Parham · 44 East Camperdown Way · P.O. Box 728 · Greenville, SC 29602-0728 · 864-242-8200

John F. Wyatt · a · Bannister & Wyatt · 401 Pettigru Street · P.O. Box 10007 · Greenville, SC 29603 · 864-298-0084

Hilton Head Island

Cary S. Griffin · McNair Law Firm · http://www.mcnair.net · Shelter Cove Executive Park, Suite 400 · 23-B Shelter Cove Lane · Hilton Head Island, SC 29928 · 843-785-2171

Mount Pleasant

Elizabeth W. Settle · Hagood & Kerr · http://www.hagoodkerr.com · 654 Coleman Boulevard · P.O. Box 220 · Mount Pleasant, SC 29465 · 843-972-1000

Myrtle Beach

Otis Allen Jeffcoat III · Jeffcoat, Pike & Nappier · 2024 Corporate Centre Drive, Suite 206 · P.O. Box 3678 · Myrtle Beach, SC 29577 · 843-626-9000

Lynn Gatlin Stevens · McNair Law Firm · http://www.mcnair.net · Founders Center, Suite 206 · 2411 Oak Street · P.O. Box 336 · Myrtle Beach, SC 29578 · 843-444-1107

SECURITIES LAW

Charleston

John H. Warren III · a · Warren & Sinkler · 171 Church Street, Suite 340 · P.O. Box 1254 · Charleston, SC 29402 · 843-577-0660

Columbia

Joseph D. Clark · Haynsworth Sinkler Boyd · http://www.hsblawfirm.com · 1201 Main Street, 22nd Floor P.O. Box 11889 · Columbia, SC 29211-1889 · 803-779-3080

Suzanne H. Clawson · Haynsworth Sinkler Boyd · http://www.hsblawfirm.com · 1201 Main Street, 22nd Floor · P.O. Box 11889 · Columbia, SC 29211-1889 · 803-779-3080

John W. Currie · a · McNair Law Firm · http://www.mcnair.net · 1301 Gervais Street, 11th Floor · P.O. Box 11390 · Columbia, SC 29211 · 803-799-9800

Gus M. Dixon · Nelson Mullins Riley & Scarborough · Meridian, 17th Floor · 1320 Main Street · P.O. Box 11070 · Columbia, SC 29211 · 803-799-2000

Daniel J. Fritze · Nelson Mullins Riley & Scarborough · Meridian, 17th Floor · 1320 Main Street · P.O. Box 11070 · Columbia, SC 29211 · 803-799-2000

Julian Hennig III · Nexsen Pruet · http://www.nexsenpruet.com · First Citizens Building, Suite 700 · 1230 Main Street · P.O. Drawer 2426 · Columbia, SC 29202-2426 · 803-771-8900

P. Mason Hogue, Jr. · Nelson Mullins Riley & Scarborough · Meridian, 17th Floor · 1320 Main Street · P.O. Box 11070 · Columbia, SC 29211 · 803-799-2000

George S. King, Jr. · a · Haynsworth Sinkler Boyd · http://www.hsblawfirm.com · 1201 Main Street, 22nd Floor · P.O. Box 11889 · Columbia, SC 29211-1889 · 803-779-3080

G. Marcus Knight · Nexsen Pruet · http://www.nexsenpruet.com · First Citizens Building, Suite 700 · 1230 Main Street · P.O. Drawer 2426 · Columbia, SC 29202-2426 · 803-771-8900

Edward G. Menzie · 2% · Nexsen Pruet · http://www.nexsenpruet.com · First Citizens Building, Suite 700 1230 Main Street · P.O. Drawer 2426 · Columbia, SC 29202-2426 · 803-771-8900

Greenville

Andrew B. Coburn · Wyche, Burgess, Freeman & Parham · 44 East Camperdown Way · P.O. Box 728 · Greenville, SC 29602-0728 · 864-242-8200

Neil E. Grayson · Nelson Mullins Riley & Scarborough · Poinsett Plaza, Suite 900 · 104 South Main Street · Greenville, SC 29601-2122 · 864-250-2300

John M. Jennings · Nelson Mullins Riley & Scarborough · Poinsett Plaza, Suite 900 · 104 South Main Street · Greenville, SC 29601-2122 · 864-250-2300

Elizabeth O. Temple · Womble Carlyle Sandridge & Rice · 550 South Main Street, Suite 400 · P.O. Box 10208 · Greenville, SC 29603-0208 · 864-255-5400

TAX LAW

Charleston

Scott Y. Barnes · a · Warren & Sinkler · 171 Church Street, Suite 340 · P.O. Box 1254 · Charleston, SC 29402 · 843-577-0660

Edward G. R. Bennett · Evans, Carter, Kunes & Bennett · 115 Church Street · P.O. Box 369 · Charleston, SC 29402-0369 · 843-577-2300

T. Heyward Carter, Jr. · a · Evans, Carter, Kunes & Bennett · 115 Church Street · P.O. Box 369 · Charleston, SC 29402-0369 · 843-577-2300

J. Michael Grant · a · Grant & Kuyk · 171 Church Street, Suite 260 · P.O. Box 395 · Charleston, SC 29402 · 843-723-5200

Thomas F. Moran · Nelson Mullins Riley & Scarborough · Liberty Center, Suite 600 · 151 Meeting Street · Charleston, SC 29401-2239 · 843-853-5200

Irvin J. Slotchiver · a · Slotchiver & Slotchiver · 44 State Street · Charleston, SC 29401-2810 · 843-577-6531

John C. von Lehe, Jr. · 2) · Nelson Mullins Riley & Scarborough · Liberty Center, Suite 600 · 151 Meeting Street · Charleston, SC 29401-2239 · 843-853-5200

Columbia

George S. Bailey · Nelson Mullins Riley & Scarborough · Meridian, 17th Floor · 1320 Main Street · P.O. Box 11070 · Columbia, SC 29211 · 803-799-2000

Frank W. Cureton · Haynsworth Sinkler Boyd · http://www.hsblawfirm.com · 1201 Main Street, 22nd Floor · P.O. Box 11889 · Columbia, SC 29211-1889 · 803-779-3080

J. Donald Dial, Jr. · 2% · Haynsworth Sinkler Boyd · http://www.hsblawfirm.com · 1201 Main Street, 22nd Floor · P.O. Box 11889 · Columbia, SC 29211-1889 · 803-779-3080

Erik P. Doerring · McNair Law Firm · http://www.mcnair.net · 1301 Gervais Street, 11th Floor · P.O. Box 11390 · Columbia, SC 29211 · 803-799-9800

Randolph B. Epting · Haynsworth Sinkler Boyd · http://www.hsblawfirm.com · 1201 Main Street, 22nd Floor · P.O. Box 11889 · Columbia, SC 29211-1889 · 803-779-3080

Theodore J. Hopkins, Jr. · Haynsworth Sinkler Boyd · http://www.hsblawfirm.com · 1201 Main Street, 22nd Floor · P.O. Box 11889 · Columbia, SC 29211-1889 · 803-779-3080

Kenneth Allan Janik · Nelson Mullins Riley & Scarborough · Meridian, 17th Floor · 1320 Main Street · P.O. Box 11070 · Columbia, SC 29211 · 803-799-2000

Fred L. Kingsmore, Jr. · Nexsen Pruet · http://www.nexsenpruet.com · First Citizens Building, Suite 700 1230 Main Street · P.O. Drawer 2426 · Columbia, SC 29202-2426 · 803-771-8900

Burnet R. Maybank III · Nexsen Pruet · http://www.nexsenpruet.com · First Citizens Building, Suite 700 1230 Main Street · P.O. Drawer 2426 · Columbia, SC 29202-2426 · 803-771-8900

Jonathan H. Nason · McNair Law Firm · http://www.mcnair.net · 1301 Gervais Street, 11th Floor · P.O. Box 11390 · Columbia, SC 29211 · 803-799-9800

Joseph D. Walker · a · McNair Law Firm · http://www.mcnair.net · 1301 Gervais Street, 11th Floor · P.O. Box 11390 · Columbia, SC 29211 · 803-799-9800

Robert Young · 2) · Law Office of Robert Young · 1901 Main Street, Suite 1590 · P.O. Box 8144 · Columbia, SC 29202 · 803-254-2020

Darlington

John Jay James II · a · Paulling & James · 112 Cashua Street · P.O. Box 507 · Darlington, SC 29540 · 843-393-3881

Florence

John R. Chase · Haynsworth Sinkler Boyd · http://www.hsblawfirm.com · 1831 West Evans Street · P.O. Box 6617 · Florence, SC 29502-6617 · 843-669-6002

Michael G. Roberts · Turner, Padget, Graham & Laney · BB&T Building, Fouth Floor · 1831 West Evans Street · P.O. Box 5478 · Florence, SC 29502-5478 · 843-662-9008

J. Munford Scott, Jr. · a · Turner, Padget, Graham & Laney · BB&T Building, Fouth Floor · 1831 West Evans Street · P.O. Box 5478 · Florence, SC 29502-5478 · 843-662-9008

John M. Scott III · Turner, Padget, Graham & Laney · BB&T Building, Fouth Floor · 1831 West Evans Street · P.O. Box 5478 · Florence, SC 29502-5478 · 843-662-9008

Greenville

Robert E. August · Merline & Meacham · http://www.merlineandmeacham.com · 812 East North Street · P.O. Box 10796 · Greenville, SC 29603 · 864-242-4080

C. Vincent Brown · Brown, Massey, Evans, McLeod & Haynsworth · 106 Williams Street · P.O. Box 2464 Greenville, SC 29602 · 864-271-7424

Randy E. Fisher · Thomas & Fisher · http://www.thomasandfisher.com · The Ogletree Building, Suite 401 · 300 North Main Street · P.O. Box 2248 · Greenville, SC 29602-2248 · 864-232-0041

Cary H. Hall, Jr. · a · Wyche, Burgess, Freeman & Parham · 44 East Camperdown Way · P.O. Box 728 · Greenville, SC 29602-0728 · 864-242-8200

J. Tod Hyche · Smith Moore Leatherwood · http://www.smithmoorelaw.com · The Leatherwood Plaza, Suite 500 · 300 East McBee Avenue · P.O. Box 87 · Greenville, SC 29602 · 864-242-6440

Richard A. Jones, Jr. · Dobson, Jones, Ball, Phillips & Bridges · 1306 South Church Street · P.O. Box 1923 · Greenville, SC 29602 · 864-271-8171

Keith G. Meacham · Merline & Meacham · http://www.merlineandmeacham.com · 812 East North Street P.O. Box 10796 · Greenville, SC 29603 · 864-242-4080

David A. Merline · 2) · Merline & Meacham · http://www.merlineandmeacham.com · 812 East North Street · P.O. Box 10796 · Greenville, SC 29603 · 864-242-4080

David A. Merline, Jr. · a · Merline & Meacham · http://www.merlineandmeacham.com · 812 East North Street · P.O. Box 10796 · Greenville, SC 29603 · 864-242-4080

John R. Thomas · 2) · Thomas & Fisher · http://www.thomasandfisher.com · The Ogletree Building, Suite 401 · 300 North Main Street · P.O. Box 2248 · Greenville, SC 29602-2248 · 864-232-0041

Hilton Head Island

Michael L. M. Jordan · a · McNair Law Firm · http://www.mcnair.net · Shelter Cove Executive Park, Suite 400 · 23-B Shelter Cove Lane · Hilton Head Island, SC 29928 · 843-785-2171

William A. Ruth · 2) · Ruth & MacNeille · 40 Pope Avenue · P.O. Drawer 5706 · Hilton Head Island, SC 29938 · 843-785-4251

Mount Pleasant

Robert B. Pearlman · Pearlman & Pearlman · 751 Johnnie Dodds Boulevard · Mount Pleasant, SC 29464 843-881-7443

Rock Hill

W. Henry Sipe III · Hamilton Martens Ballou & Sipe · http://www.hmbslaw.com · 130 East Main Street, Suite 201 · P.O. Box 10940 · Rock Hill, SC 29731 · 803-329-7672

TECHNOLOGY LAW

Columbia

Mark C. Dukes · Nelson Mullins Riley & Scarborough · Meridian, 17th Floor · 1320 Main Street · P.O. Box 11070 · Columbia, SC 29211 · 803-799-2000

TRUSTS AND ESTATES

Aiken

Paige Weeks Johnson · Johnson, Johnson, Whittle & Snelgrove · 117 Pendleton Street, NW · P.O. Box 2619 · Aiken, SC 29802-2619 · 803-649-5338

Charleston

Edward G. R. Bennett · Evans, Carter, Kunes & Bennett · 115 Church Street · P.O. Box 369 · Charleston, SC 29402-0369 · 843-577-2300

C. Michael Branham · Young Clement Rivers · 28 Broad Street · P.O. Box 993 · Charleston, SC 29402 · 843-577-4000

T. Heyward Carter, Jr. · a · Evans, Carter, Kunes & Bennett · 115 Church Street · P.O. Box 369 · Charleston, SC 29402-0369 · 843-577-2300

Robert M. Kunes · 2) · Evans, Carter, Kunes & Bennett · 115 Church Street · P.O. Box 369 · Charleston, SC 29402-0369 · 843-577-2300

Kenneth F. Smith · Buist Moore Smythe McGee · http://www.buistmoore.com · Five Exchange Street · P.O. Box 999 · Charleston, SC 29402-0999 · 843-722-3400

Columbia

George S. Bailey · Nelson Mullins Riley & Scarborough · Meridian, 17th Floor · 1320 Main Street · P.O. Box 11070 · Columbia, SC 29211 · 803-799-2000

Wm. Bert Brannon · Moses Koon & Brackett · http://www.mkb-law.com · 1441 Main Street, Suite 400 · P.O. Box 100261 · Columbia, SC 29202-3261 · 803-461-2300

Rita Bragg Cullum · Ellis, Lawhorne & Sims · http://www.ellislawhorne.com · 1501 Main Street, Fifth Floor · P.O. Box 2285 · Columbia, SC 29202 · 803-254-4190

Frank W. Cureton · Haynsworth Sinkler Boyd · http://www.hsblawfirm.com · 1201 Main Street, 22nd Floor · P.O. Box 11889 · Columbia, SC 29211-1889 · 803-779-3080

J. Donald Dial, Jr. · 2% · Haynsworth Sinkler Boyd · http://www.hsblawfirm.com · 1201 Main Street, 22nd Floor · P.O. Box 11889 · Columbia, SC 29211-1889 · 803-779-3080

Carole H. Gunter · Mays, Foster & Gunter · 2512 Devine Street · Columbia, SC 29205-2442 · 803-254-7091

W. Steven Johnson · a · Todd & Johnson · 609 Sims Avenue · Columbia, SC 29205 · 803-252-1500

Catherine H. Kennedy · Nelson Mullins Riley & Scarborough · Meridian, 17th Floor · 1320 Main Street · P.O. Box 11070 · Columbia, SC 29211 · 803-799-2000

Fred L. Kingsmore, Jr. · Nexsen Pruet · http://www.nexsenpruet.com · First Citizens Building, Suite 700 1230 Main Street · P.O. Drawer 2426 · Columbia, SC 29202-2426 · 803-771-8900

William G. Newsome III · Nexsen Pruet · http://www.nexsenpruet.com · First Citizens Building, Suite 700 · 1230 Main Street · P.O. Drawer 2426 · Columbia, SC 29202-2426 · 803-771-8900

Julian J. Nexsen · Nexsen Pruet · http://www.nexsenpruet.com · First Citizens Building, Suite 700 · 1230 Main Street · P.O. Drawer 2426 · Columbia, SC 29202-2426 · 803-771-8900

David C. Sojourner · Ellis, Lawhorne & Sims · http://www.ellislawhorne.com · 1501 Main Street, Fifth Floor · P.O. Box 2285 · Columbia, SC 29202 · 803-254-4190

Karen Hudson Thomas · Ellis, Lawhorne & Sims · http://www.ellislawhorne.com · 1501 Main Street, Fifth Floor · P.O. Box 2285 · Columbia, SC 29202 · 803-254-4190

Kenneth B. Wingate · a · Sweeny, Wingate & Barrow · 1515 Lady Street · P.O. Box 12129 · Columbia, SC 29201 · 803-256-2233

Darlington

John Jay James II · a · Paulling & James · 112 Cashua Street · P.O. Box 507 · Darlington, SC 29540 · 843-393-3881

Florence

John R. Chase · Haynsworth Sinkler Boyd · http://www.hsblawfirm.com · 1831 West Evans Street · P.O. Box 6617 · Florence, SC 29502-6617 · 843-669-6002

Robert E. August · Merline & Meacham · http://www.merlineandmeacham.com · 812 East North Street · P.O. Box 10796 · Greenville, SC 29603 · 864-242-4080

C. Vincent Brown · Brown, Massey, Evans, McLeod & Haynsworth · 106 Williams Street · P.O. Box 2464 Greenville, SC 29602 · 864-271-7424

Daniel A. Collins · Collins & Collins · 17 A Caledon Court · Greenville, SC 29615 · 864-370-2277

William L. Dennis · a · Smith Moore Leatherwood · http://www.smithmoorelaw.com · The Leatherwood Plaza, Suite 500 · 300 East McBee Avenue · P.O. Box 87 · Greenville, SC 29602 · 864-242-6440

Randy E. Fisher · Thomas & Fisher · http://www.thomasandfisher.com · The Ogletree Building, Suite 401 · 300 North Main Street · P.O. Box 2248 · Greenville, SC 29602-2248 · 864-232-0041

J. Tod Hyche · Smith Moore Leatherwood · http://www.smithmoorelaw.com · The Leatherwood Plaza, Suite 500 · 300 East McBee Avenue · P.O. Box 87 · Greenville, SC 29602 · 864-242-6440

Richard A. Jones, Jr. · Dobson, Jones, Ball, Phillips & Bridges · 1306 South Church Street · P.O. Box 1923 · Greenville, SC 29602 · 864-271-8171

R. David Massey · Brown, Massey, Evans, McLeod & Haynsworth · 106 Williams Street · P.O. Box 2464 · Greenville, SC 29602 · 864-271-7424

Keith G. Meacham · Merline & Meacham · http://www.merlineandmeacham.com · 812 East North Street P.O. Box 10796 · Greenville, SC 29603 · 864-242-4080

David A. Merline · 2) · Merline & Meacham · http://www.merlineandmeacham.com · 812 East North Street · P.O. Box 10796 · Greenville, SC 29603 · 864-242-4080

David A. Merline, Jr. · a · Merline & Meacham · http://www.merlineandmeacham.com · 812 East North Street · P.O. Box 10796 · Greenville, SC 29603 · 864-242-4080

Lesley R. Moore · Wyche, Burgess, Freeman & Parham · 44 East Camperdown Way · P.O. Box 728 · Greenville, SC 29602-0728 · 864-242-8200

Virginia M. Phillips · Dobson, Jones, Ball, Phillips & Bridges · 1306 South Church Street · P.O. Box 1923 Greenville, SC 29602 · 864-271-8171

J. Kurt Schumacher, Jr. · Schumacher Law · P.O. Box 8399 · Greenville, SC 29604 · 864-430-1791

B. Joel Stoudenmire · Nexsen Pruet · http://www.nexsenpruet.com · 201 West McBee Avenue, Suite 400 P.O. Drawer 10648 · Greenville, SC 29601 · 864-370-2211

Charles M. Stuart, Jr. · a · Charles M. Stuart, Jr. · 862 South Pleasantburg Drive, Suite F · Greenville, SC 29607 · 864-232-5411

John R. Thomas · 2) · Thomas & Fisher · http://www.thomasandfisher.com · The Ogletree Building, Suite 401 · 300 North Main Street · P.O. Box 2248 · Greenville, SC 29602-2248 · 864-232-0041

Hilton Head Island

Michael L. M. Jordan · a · McNair Law Firm · http://www.mcnair.net · Shelter Cove Executive Park, Suite 400 · 23-B Shelter Cove Lane · Hilton Head Island, SC 29928 · 843-785-2171

William A. Ruth · 2) · Ruth & MacNeille · 40 Pope Avenue · P.O. Drawer 5706 · Hilton Head Island, SC 29938 · 843-785-4251

Myrtle Beach

James F. McCrackin · Nelson Mullins Riley & Scarborough · Beach First Center, Third Floor · 3751 Robert M. Grissom Parkway · Myrtle Beach, SC 29577-3165 · 843-448-3500

Hugh T. Rice, Jr. · Rice, MacDonald & Winters · Parkway Center, Suite 200 · 950 Forty-Eighth Avenue North · Myrtle Beach, SC 29577-5434 · 843-449-4493

Rock Hill

James Carlisle Hardin III · 2) · James C. Hardin III · 113 East Main Street, Suite 330 · Rock Hill, SC 29730 · 803-329-7601

W. Henry Sipe III · Hamilton Martens Ballou & Sipe · http://www.hmbslaw.com · 130 East Main Street, Suite 201 · P.O. Box 10940 · Rock Hill, SC 29731 · 803-329-7672

Spartanburg

James B. Drennan III · 2) · Dennis, Shaw & Drennan · 103 LaFayette Street · P.O. Box 891 · Spartanburg, SC 29304-0891 · 864-582-0708

James W. Shaw · Dennis, Shaw & Drennan · 103 LaFayette Street · P.O. Box 891 · Spartanburg, SC 29304-0891 · 864-582-0708

WATER LAW

Charleston

Newman Jackson Smith · a · Nelson Mullins Riley & Scarborough · Liberty Center, Suite 600 · 151 Meeting Street · Charleston, SC 29401-2239 · 843-853-5200

WHITE-COLLAR CRIMINAL DEFENSE

Charleston

Dale T. Cobb, Jr. · a · Belk, Cobb, Infinger & Goldstein · 2344 Cosgrove Avenue · P.O. Box 71121 · Charleston, SC 29415 · 843-554-4291

Coming B. Gibbs, Jr. · 2% · Gibbs & Holmes · 171 Church Street, Suite 110 · P.O. Box 938 · Charleston, SC 29402-0938 · 843-722-0033

Gedney M. Howe III · 2% · Gedney M. Howe, III · Eight Chalmers Street · P.O. Box 1034 · Charleston, SC 29402 · 843-722-8048

Lionel S. Lofton · a · Lofton & Lofton · 225 Seven Farms Drive, Suite 109 · Charleston, SC 29492 · 843-722-6319

Michael P. O'Connell · a · Stirling & O'Connell · 145 King Street, Suite 410 · P.O. Box 882 · Charleston, SC 29402 · 843-577-9890

Andrew J. Savage III · a · Savage & Savage · 15 Prioleau Street · P.O. Box 1002 · Charleston, SC 29402 · 843-720-7470

Columbia

Joel W. Collins, Jr. · Collins & Lacy · http://www.collinsandlacy.com · 1330 Lady Street, Sixth Floor · P.O. Box 12487 · Columbia, SC 29211 · 803-256-2660

John D. Delgado · Law Firm of John Delgado · 914 Richland Street, Suite A102 · Columbia, SC 29201 · 803-254-7745

Jonathan S. Gasser · Harris & Gasser · 1529 Laurel Street · Columbia, SC 29201 · 803-779-7080

Gregory P. Harris · Harris & Gasser · 1529 Laurel Street · Columbia, SC 29201 · 803-779-7080

I. S. Leevy Johnson · a · Johnson Toal & Battiste · 1615 Barnwell Street · P.O. Box 1431 · Columbia, SC 29201 · 803-252-9700

Celeste T. Jones · McNair Law Firm · http://www.mcnair.net · 1301 Gervais Street, 11th Floor · P.O. Box 11390 · Columbia, SC 29211 · 803-799-9800

Jack B. Swerling · a · Law Offices of Jack B. Swerling · http://www.jackswerling.com · 1720 Main Street, Suite 301 · Columbia, SC 29201 · 803-765-2626

Florence

J. René Josey · Turner, Padget, Graham & Laney · BB&T Building, Fouth Floor · 1831 West Evans Street · P.O. Box 5478 · Florence, SC 29502-5478 · 843-662-9008

Greenville

James W. Bannister · Bannister & Wyatt · 401 Pettigru Street · P.O. Box 10007 · Greenville, SC 29603 · 864-298-0084

O. W. Bannister, Jr. · a · Bannister & Wyatt · 401 Pettigru Street · P.O. Box 10007 · Greenville, SC 29603 · 864-298-0084

WORKERS' COMPENSATION LAW

Charleston

Malcolm M. Crosland · Steinberg Law Firm · http://www.steinberglawfirm.com · 61 Broad Street · P.O. Box Nine · Charleston, SC 29402 · 843-720-2800

Mark Davis · McAngus, Goudelock & Courie · 78 Wentworth Street, Suite 200 · P.O. Box 877 · Charleston, SC 29402-0877 · 843-576-2900

Wallace G. Holland · Young Clement Rivers · 28 Broad Street · P.O. Box 993 · Charleston, SC 29402 · 843-577-4000

Carl H. Jacobson · Uricchio, Howe, Krell, Jacobson, Toporek, Theos & Keith · 17½ Broad Street · P.O. Box 399 · Charleston, SC 29401 · 843-723-7491

David T. Pearlman · Steinberg Law Firm · http://www.steinberglawfirm.com · 61 Broad Street · P.O. Box Nine · Charleston, SC 29402 · 843-720-2800

Columbia

Ellen M. Adams · Collins & Lacy · http://www.collinsandlacy.com · 1330 Lady Street, Sixth Floor · P.O. Box 12487 · Columbia, SC 29211 · 803-256-2660

Luther J. Battiste III · Johnson Toal & Battiste · 1615 Barnwell Street · P.O. Box 1431 · Columbia, SC 29201 · 803-252-9700

Grady L. Beard · Sowell Gray Stepp & Laffitte · http://www.sowell.com · 1310 Gadsden Street · P.O. Box 11449 · Columbia, SC 29211 · 803-929-1400

Thomas P. Bellinger · McWhirter, Bellinger & Associates · http://www.mcwhirterlaw.com · 1807 Hampton Street · Columbia, SC 29201 · 803-252-5523

Michael E. Chase · Turner, Padget, Graham & Laney · 1901 Main Street, 17th Floor · P.O. Box 1473 · Columbia, SC 29202 · 803-254-2200

Ajerenal Danley · The Danley Law Firm · http://www.thedanleylawfirm.com · 240 Stone Ridge Drive, Suite 401 · P.O. Box 1454 · Columbia, SC 29202 · 803-254-2269

William S. Davies, Jr. · ⑩ · Nelson Mullins Riley & Scarborough · Meridian, 17th Floor · 1320 Main Street · P.O. Box 11070 · Columbia, SC 29211 · 803-799-2000

Sherod H. Eadon, Jr. · ⑩ · Lee, Eadon, Isgett, Popwell & Reardon · 1314 Lincoln Street · P.O. Box 1505 Columbia, SC 29202 · 803-799-9811

F. Earl Ellis, Jr. · ⑩ · Ellis, Lawhorne & Sims · http://www.ellislawhorne.com · 1501 Main Street, Fifth Floor · P.O. Box 2285 · Columbia, SC 29202 · 803-254-4190

Scott B. Garrett · McAngus, Goudelock & Courie · 700 Gervais Street, Suite 300 · P.O. Box 12519 · Columbia, SC 29211-2519 · 803-779-2300

J. Russell Goudelock III · McAngus, Goudelock & Courie · 700 Gervais Street, Suite 300 · P.O. Box 12519 · Columbia, SC 29211-2519 · 803-779-2300

William L. Harbison · Ellis, Lawhorne & Sims · http://www.ellislawhorne.com · 1501 Main Street, Fifth Floor · P.O. Box 2285 · Columbia, SC 29202 · 803-254-4190

Christopher G. Isgett · Lee, Eadon, Isgett, Popwell & Reardon · 1314 Lincoln Street · P.O. Box 1505 · Columbia, SC 29202 · 803-799-9811

D. Michael Kelly · ⑩ · The Mike Kelly Law Group · 500 Taylor Street, Fourth Floor · Columbia, SC 29201 · 803-726-0123

Stanford E. Lacy · Collins & Lacy · http://www.collinsandlacy.com · 1330 Lady Street, Sixth Floor · P.O. Box 12487 · Columbia, SC 29211 · 803-256-2660

Ernest G. Lawhorne · Ellis, Lawhorne & Sims · http://www.ellislawhorne.com · 1501 Main Street, Fifth Floor · P.O. Box 2285 · Columbia, SC 29202 · 803-254-4190

Mary Sowell League · Ellis, Lawhorne & Sims · http://www.ellislawhorne.com · 1501 Main Street, Fifth Floor · P.O. Box 2285 · Columbia, SC 29202 · 803-254-4190

W. Hugh McAngus · ⑩ · McAngus, Goudelock & Courie · 700 Gervais Street, Suite 300 · P.O. Box 12519 Columbia, SC 29211-2519 · 803-779-2300

H. Patterson McWhirter · McWhirter, Bellinger & Associates · http://www.mcwhirterlaw.com · 1807 Hampton Street · Columbia, SC 29201 · 803-252-5523

James P. Newman, Jr. · Howser, Newman & Besley · 1508 Washington Street · P.O. Box 12009 · Columbia, SC 29211 · 803-758-6000

Samuel F. Painter · Nexsen Pruet · http://www.nexsenpruet.com · First Citizens Building, Suite 700 · 1230 Main Street · P.O. Drawer 2426 · Columbia, SC 29202-2426 · 803-771-8900

Shannon T. Poteat · Willson Jones Carter & Baxley · 4500 Fort Jackson Boulevard · Columbia, SC 29209 803-782-2520

Andrew N. Safran · a · Andrew N. Safran · 1400 Pickens Street, Suite 104 · P.O. Box 12089 · Columbia, SC 29211 · 803-256-6689

Lana H. Sims, Jr. · Ellis, Lawhorne & Sims · http://www.ellislawhorne.com · 1501 Main Street, Fifth Floor · P.O. Box 2285 · Columbia, SC 29202 · 803-254-4190

William Smith II · Chappell, Smith & Arden · 1510 Calhoun St. · Columbia, SC 29201 · 803-929-3600

Goose Creek

Thomas M. White · Steinberg Law Firm · http://www.steinberglawfirm.com · 118 Goose Creek Boulevard P.O. Box 1028 · Goose Creek, SC 29445 · 843-572-0700

Greenville

Alan R. Cochran · Cochran Law Firm · 1617 East North Street · Greenville, SC 29607 · 864-235-8163

Vernon F. Dunbar · Turner, Padget, Graham & Laney · 200 East Broad Street, Suite 250 · P.O. Box 1509 Greenville, SC 29602 · 864-552-4600

Johnnie Dodenhoff Fulton · Fulton & Barr · 1001 East Washington Street · Greenville, SC 29601 · 864-235-3154

Henry Mills Gallivan · a · Gallivan, White & Boyd · One Liberty Square, Suite 1200 · 55 Beattie Place · P.O. Box 10589 · Greenville, SC 29603 · 864-271-9580

Russell T. Infinger · Nexsen Pruet · http://www.nexsenpruet.com · 201 West McBee Avenue, Suite 400 · P.O. Drawer 10648 · Greenville, SC 29601 · 864-370-2211

Jeffrey S. Jones · Willson, Jones, Carter & Baxley · 872 South Pleasantburg Drive · Greenville, SC 29607 864-527-3280

Richard B. Kale · Willson, Jones, Carter & Baxley · 872 South Pleasantburg Drive · Greenville, SC 29607 864-527-3280

Linda B. McKenzie · a · Bowen McKenzie & Bowen · 25 Mills Avenue · P.O. Box 2547 · Greenville, SC 29602 · 864-271-2270

William E. Shaughnessy · a · Turner, Padget, Graham & Laney · 200 East Broad Street, Suite 250 · P.O. Box 1509 · Greenville, SC 29602 · 864-552-4600

Kathryn Williams · Kathryn Williams · 619 North Main Street · P.O. Box 10693 · Greenville, SC 29603 · 864-235-6254

Harold J. Willson · Willson, Jones, Carter & Baxley · 872 South Pleasantburg Drive · Greenville, SC 29607 · 864-527-3280

Mount Pleasant

Johnnie W. Baxley III · Willson, Jones, Carter & Baxley · 421 Wando Park Boulevard, Suite 100 · Mount Pleasant, SC 29464 · 843-284-1082

Mt. Pleasant

Roy A. Howell III · Trask & Howell · http://www.trask-howell.com · 763 Johnnie Dodds Boulevard · P.O. Box 2167 · Mt. Pleasant, SC 29565 · 843-881-4228

Harold E. Trask · a · Trask & Howell · http://www.trask-howell.com · 763 Johnnie Dodds Boulevard · P.O. Box 2167 · Mt. Pleasant, SC 29565 · 843-881-4228

Spartanburg

Ben C. Harrison · Harrison, White, Smith & Coggins · 178 West Main Street · P.O. Box 3547 · Spartanburg, SC 29304 · 864-585-5100

M. Terry Haselden · a · M. Terry Haselden · 389 East Henry Street, Suite 105 · P.O. Box 18182 · Spartanburg, SC 29318 · 864-585-1045

Danny R. Smith · Harrison, White, Smith & Coggins · 178 West Main Street · P.O. Box 3547 · Spartanburg, SC 29304 · 864-585-5100

SOUTH DAKOTA

ADMINISTRATIVE LAW

Pierre

Timothy M. Engel · May, Adam, Gerdes & Thompson · 503 South Pierre Street · P.O. Box 160 · Pierre, SD 57501-0160 · 605-224-8803

David A. Gerdes · ⑩ · May, Adam, Gerdes & Thompson · 503 South Pierre Street · P.O. Box 160 · Pierre, SD 57501-0160 · 605-224-8803

Rapid City

Michael M. Hickey · Bangs, McCullen, Butler, Foye & Simmons · 333 West Boulevard, Suite 400 · P.O. Box 2670 · Rapid City, SD 57709 · 605-343-1040

Sioux Falls

Thomas J. Welk · ⑩ · Boyce, Greenfield, Pashby & Welk · 101 North Phillips Avenue, Suite 600 · P.O. Box 5015 · Sioux Falls, SD 57117-5015 · 605-336-2424

ALTERNATIVE DISPUTE RESOLUTION

Belle Fourche

Robert L. Morris II · Day Morris Law Firm · http://blackhillsportal.com/dbs/daymorris · 117 Fifth Avenue · P.O. Box 370 · Belle Fourche, SD 57717-0370 · 605-723-7777

Rapid City

Steven C. Beardsley · Beardsley, Jensen & Von Wald · 4200 Beach Drive, Suite Three · P.O. Box 9579 · Rapid City, SD 57709-9579 · 605-721-2800

Jeffrey G. Hurd · Bangs, McCullen, Butler, Foye & Simmons · 333 West Boulevard, Suite 400 · P.O. Box 2670 · Rapid City, SD 57709 · 605-343-1040

John K. Nooney · Nooney Solay & Van Norman · 632 Main Street, Second Floor · P.O. Box 8030 · Rapid City, SD 57709-8030 · 605-721-5846

ANTITRUST LAW

Rapid City

Thomas H. Foye · ㉕ · Bangs, McCullen, Butler, Foye & Simmons · 333 West Boulevard, Suite 400 · P.O. Box 2670 · Rapid City, SD 57709 · 605-343-1040

Jeffrey G. Hurd · Bangs, McCullen, Butler, Foye & Simmons · 333 West Boulevard, Suite 400 · P.O. Box 2670 · Rapid City, SD 57709 · 605-343-1040

Sioux Falls

Thomas J. Welk · ⑩ · Boyce, Greenfield, Pashby & Welk · 101 North Phillips Avenue, Suite 600 · P.O. Box 5015 · Sioux Falls, SD 57117-5015 · 605-336-2424

APPELLATE LAW

Rapid City

Craig Pfeifle · Lynn, Jackson, Shultz & Lebrun · http://www.lynnjackson.com · First National Bank Building, Eighth Floor · 909 Saint Joseph Street · P.O. Box 8250 · Rapid City, SD 57709-8250 · 605-342-2592

Sioux Falls

Ronald A. Parsons, Jr. · Johnson, Heidepriem, Janklow, Abdallah & Johnson, · 431 North Phillips Avenue, Suite 400 · Sioux Falls, SD 57104 · 605-338-4304

BANKING LAW

Pierre

Timothy M. Engel · May, Adam, Gerdes & Thompson · 503 South Pierre Street · P.O. Box 160 · Pierre, SD 57501-0160 · 605-224-8803

Rapid City

Curtis Jensen · DeMersseman Jensen Christianson Stanton & Huffman · 516 Fifth Street · P.O. Box 1820 Rapid City, SD 57709-1820 · 605-342-2814

Sioux Falls

Charles D. Gullickson · ⑩ · Davenport, Evans, Hurwitz & Smith · 206 West 14th Street · P.O. Box 1030 · Sioux Falls, SD 57101-1030 · 605-336-2880

Douglas J. Hajek · Davenport, Evans, Hurwitz & Smith · 206 West 14th Street · P.O. Box 1030 · Sioux Falls, SD 57101-1030 · 605-336-2880

David L. Knudson · ⑩ · Davenport, Evans, Hurwitz & Smith · 206 West 14th Street · P.O. Box 1030 · Sioux Falls, SD 57101-1030 · 605-336-2880

BANKRUPTCY AND CREDITOR-DEBTOR RIGHTS LAW

Rapid City

James P. Hurley · ⑩ · Bangs, McCullen, Butler, Foye & Simmons · 333 West Boulevard, Suite 400 · P.O. Box 2670 · Rapid City, SD 57709 · 605-343-1040

John H. Mairose · John H. Mairose · 2640 Jackson Boulevard, Suite Three · Rapid City, SD 57702-3474 · 605-348-7836

Robert Nash · ⑩ · Wilson, Olson & Nash · 2640 Jackson Boulevard · P.O. Box 1552 · Rapid City, SD 57709 · 605-342-7090

J. Crisman Palmer · Gunderson, Palmer, Nelson & Ashmore · http://www.gundersonpalmer.com · Assurant Building · 440 Mount Rushmore Road · P.O. Box 8045 · Rapid City, SD 57709-8045 · 605-342-1078

Sioux Falls

Roger W. Damgaard · ⑳ · Woods, Fuller, Shultz & Smith · 300 South Phillips Avenue, Suite 300 · P.O. Box 5027 · Sioux Falls, SD 57117-5027 · 605-336-3890

Clair R. Gerry · ⑩ · Stuart, Gerry & Schlimgen · 507 West 10th Street · P.O. Box 966 · Sioux Falls, SD 57101-0966 · 605-336-6400

Robert E. Hayes · ⑳ · Davenport, Evans, Hurwitz & Smith · 206 West 14th Street · P.O. Box 1030 · Sioux Falls, SD 57101-1030 · 605-336-2880

Scott Perrenoud · Cadwell, Sanford, Deibert & Garry · River Centre, Suite 200 · 200 East 10th Street · P.O. Box 2498 · Sioux Falls, SD 57101-2498 · 605-336-0828

BET-THE-COMPANY LITIGATION

Rapid City

Thomas G. Fritz · Lynn, Jackson, Shultz & Lebrun · http://www.lynnjackson.com · First National Bank Building, Eighth Floor · 909 Saint Joseph Street · P.O. Box 8250 · Rapid City, SD 57709-8250 · 605-342-2592

Aberdeen

Reed A. Rasmussen · Siegel, Barnett & Schutz · Capitol Building, Suite 400 · 415 South Main Street · P.O. Box 490 · Aberdeen, SD 57402-0490 · 605-225-5420

Belle Fourche

Wesley W. Buckmaster · Buckmaster Law Office · 1501 Fifth Avenue · P.O. Box 726 · Belle Fourche, SD 57717-2083 · 605-892-2623

Michael W. Day · ⑩ · Day Morris Law Firm · http://blackhillsportal.com/dbs/daymorris · 117 Fifth Avenue · P.O. Box 370 · Belle Fourche, SD 57717-0370 · 605-723-7777

Pierre

Robert B. Anderson · ⑩ · May, Adam, Gerdes & Thompson · 503 South Pierre Street · P.O. Box 160 · Pierre, SD 57501-0160 · 605-224-8803

Timothy M. Engel · May, Adam, Gerdes & Thompson · 503 South Pierre Street · P.O. Box 160 · Pierre, SD 57501-0160 · 605-224-8803

Rapid City

Edward C. Carpenter · Costello, Porter, Hill, Heisterkamp, Bushnell & Carpenter · 200 Security Building · 704 St. Joseph Street · P.O. Box 290 · Rapid City, SD 57709-0290 · 605-343-2410

Thomas G. Fritz · Lynn, Jackson, Shultz & Lebrun · http://www.lynnjackson.com · First National Bank Building, Eighth Floor · 909 Saint Joseph Street · P.O. Box 8250 · Rapid City, SD 57709-8250 · 605-342-2592

G. Verne Goodsell · Goodsell Quinn · 246 Founders Park Drive, Suite 201 · P.O. Box 9249 · Rapid City, SD 57709-9249 · 605-343-3000

Gene N. Lebrun · Lynn, Jackson, Shultz & Lebrun · http://www.lynnjackson.com · First National Bank Building, Eighth Floor · 909 Saint Joseph Street · P.O. Box 8250 · Rapid City, SD 57709-8250 · 605-342-2592

Steve Oberg · Lynn, Jackson, Shultz & Lebrun · http://www.lynnjackson.com · First National Bank Building, Eighth Floor · 909 Saint Joseph Street · P.O. Box 8250 · Rapid City, SD 57709-8250 · 605-342-2592

J. Crisman Palmer · Gunderson, Palmer, Nelson & Ashmore · http://www.gundersonpalmer.com · Assurant Building · 440 Mount Rushmore Road · P.O. Box 8045 · Rapid City, SD 57709-8045 · 605-342-1078

Haven L. Stuck · Lynn, Jackson, Shultz & Lebrun · http://www.lynnjackson.com · First National Bank Building, Eighth Floor · 909 Saint Joseph Street · P.O. Box 8250 · Rapid City, SD 57709-8250 · 605-342-2592

Sioux Falls

William P. Fuller · Fuller & Sabers · 7521 South Louise Avenue · Sioux Falls, SD 57108 · 605-333-0003

Mark W. Haigh · Davenport, Evans, Hurwitz & Smith · 206 West 14th Street · P.O. Box 1030 · Sioux Falls, SD 57101-1030 · 605-336-2880

Steven M. Johnson · ⑩ · Johnson, Heidepriem, Janklow, Abdallah & Johnson, · 431 North Phillips Avenue, Suite 400 · Sioux Falls, SD 57104 · 605-338-4304

Michael L. Luce · ⑩ · Davenport, Evans, Hurwitz & Smith · 206 West 14th Street · P.O. Box 1030 · Sioux Falls, SD 57101-1030 · 605-336-2880

Lee A. Magnuson · Lynn, Jackson, Shultz & Lebrun · http://www.lynnjackson.com · U.S. Bank Building, Eighth and Ninth Floors · 141 North Main Avenue · P.O. Box 2700 · Sioux Falls, SD 57101-2700 · 605-332-5999

Gary J. Pashby · ⑳ · Boyce, Greenfield, Pashby & Welk · 101 North Phillips Avenue, Suite 600 · P.O. Box 5015 · Sioux Falls, SD 57117-5015 · 605-336-2424

Steven W. Sanford · ⑩ · Cadwell, Sanford, Deibert & Garry · River Centre, Suite 200 · 200 East 10th Street · P.O. Box 2498 · Sioux Falls, SD 57101-2498 · 605-336-0828

Michael J. Schaffer · Schaffer Law Office · 311 East 14th Street · Sioux Falls, SD 57104-5022 · 605-274-6760

William G. Taylor, Jr. · ⑳ · Woods, Fuller, Shultz & Smith · 300 South Phillips Avenue, Suite 300 · P.O. Box 5027 · Sioux Falls, SD 57117-5027 · 605-336-3890

Gary P. Thimsen · Woods, Fuller, Shultz & Smith · 300 South Phillips Avenue, Suite 300 · P.O. Box 5027 Sioux Falls, SD 57117-5027 · 605-336-3890

Thomas J. Welk · ⑩ · Boyce, Greenfield, Pashby & Welk · 101 North Phillips Avenue, Suite 600 · P.O. Box 5015 · Sioux Falls, SD 57117-5015 · 605-336-2424

Watertown

James C. Roby · Green, Schulz, Roby, Oviatt, Cummings & Linngren · 816 South Broadway · P.O. Box 1600 · Watertown, SD 57201-6600 · 605-886-5812

CONSTRUCTION LAW

Rapid City

Gregory J. Erlandson · Bangs, McCullen, Butler, Foye & Simmons · 333 West Boulevard, Suite 400 · P.O. Box 2670 · Rapid City, SD 57709 · 605-343-1040

Terry L. Hofer · Bangs, McCullen, Butler, Foye & Simmons · 333 West Boulevard, Suite 400 · P.O. Box 2670 · Rapid City, SD 57709 · 605-343-1040

Michael C. Loos · Clayborne, Loos & Strommen · 2834 Jackson Boulevard, Suite 201 · P.O. Box 9129 · Rapid City, SD 57702 · 605-721-1517

Sioux Falls

Michael L. Luce · ⑩ · Davenport, Evans, Hurwitz & Smith · 206 West 14th Street · P.O. Box 1030 · Sioux Falls, SD 57101-1030 · 605-336-2880

Gary J. Pashby · ⑳ · Boyce, Greenfield, Pashby & Welk · 101 North Phillips Avenue, Suite 600 · P.O. Box 5015 · Sioux Falls, SD 57117-5015 · 605-336-2424

Steven W. Sanford · ⑩ · Cadwell, Sanford, Deibert & Garry · River Centre, Suite 200 · 200 East 10th Street · P.O. Box 2498 · Sioux Falls, SD 57101-2498 · 605-336-0828

Rapid City

Thomas H. Foye · ㉕ · Bangs, McCullen, Butler, Foye & Simmons · 333 West Boulevard, Suite 400 · P.O. Box 2670 · Rapid City, SD 57709 · 605-343-1040

Patrick G. Goetzinger · Gunderson, Palmer, Nelson & Ashmore · http://www.gundersonpalmer.com · Assurant Building · 440 Mount Rushmore Road · P.O. Box 8045 · Rapid City, SD 57709-8045 · 605-342-1078

Richard Huffman · ⑩ · DeMersseman Jensen Christianson Stanton & Huffman · 516 Fifth Street · P.O. Box 1820 · Rapid City, SD 57709-1820 · 605-342-2814

Curtis Jensen · DeMersseman Jensen Christianson Stanton & Huffman · 516 Fifth Street · P.O. Box 1820 Rapid City, SD 57709-1820 · 605-342-2814

Gene N. Lebrun · Lynn, Jackson, Shultz & Lebrun · http://www.lynnjackson.com · First National Bank Building, Eighth Floor · 909 Saint Joseph Street · P.O. Box 8250 · Rapid City, SD 57709-8250 · 605-342-2592

Sioux Falls

Scott B. Anderson · Davenport, Evans, Hurwitz & Smith · 206 West 14th Street · P.O. Box 1030 · Sioux Falls, SD 57101-1030 · 605-336-2880

Jonathan P. Brown · Davenport, Evans, Hurwitz & Smith · 206 West 14th Street · P.O. Box 1030 · Sioux Falls, SD 57101-1030 · 605-336-2880

Richard A. Cutler · ⑳ · Cutler & Donahoe · 100 North Phillips Avenue, Ninth Floor · Sioux Falls, SD 57104-6725 · 605-335-4950

Russell R. Greenfield · ⑩ · Boyce, Greenfield, Pashby & Welk · 101 North Phillips Avenue, Suite 600 · P.O. Box 5015 · Sioux Falls, SD 57117-5015 · 605-336-2424

Bradley C. Grossenburg · ⑩ · Woods, Fuller, Shultz & Smith · 300 South Phillips Avenue, Suite 300 · P.O. Box 5027 · Sioux Falls, SD 57117-5027 · 605-336-3890

Douglas J. Hajek · Davenport, Evans, Hurwitz & Smith · 206 West 14th Street · P.O. Box 1030 · Sioux Falls, SD 57101-1030 · 605-336-2880

David L. Knudson · ⑩ · Davenport, Evans, Hurwitz & Smith · 206 West 14th Street · P.O. Box 1030 · Sioux Falls, SD 57101-1030 · 605-336-2880

Lee A. Magnuson · Lynn, Jackson, Shultz & Lebrun · http://www.lynnjackson.com · U.S. Bank Building, Eighth and Ninth Floors · 141 North Main Avenue · P.O. Box 2700 · Sioux Falls, SD 57101-2700 · 605-332-5999

William G. Taylor, Jr. · ⑳ · Woods, Fuller, Shultz & Smith · 300 South Phillips Avenue, Suite 300 · P.O. Box 5027 · Sioux Falls, SD 57117-5027 · 605-336-3890

James M. Wiederrich · Woods, Fuller, Shultz & Smith · 300 South Phillips Avenue, Suite 300 · P.O. Box 5027 · Sioux Falls, SD 57117-5027 · 605-336-3890

EDUCATION LAW

Rapid City

Jane Pfeifle · Lynn, Jackson, Shultz & Lebrun · http://www.lynnjackson.com · First National Bank Building, Eighth Floor · 909 Saint Joseph Street · P.O. Box 8250 · Rapid City, SD 57709-8250 · 605-342-2592

EMPLOYEE BENEFITS LAW

Rapid City

Thomas H. Foye · ㉕ · Bangs, McCullen, Butler, Foye & Simmons · 333 West Boulevard, Suite 400 · P.O. Box 2670 · Rapid City, SD 57709 · 605-343-1040

Sioux Falls

Sarah Richardson Larson · ⑩ · Davenport, Evans, Hurwitz & Smith · 206 West 14th Street · P.O. Box 1030 · Sioux Falls, SD 57101-1030 · 605-336-2880

ENERGY LAW

Belle Fourche

Max Main · ⑳ · Bennett, Main & Gubbrud · http://www.bellelaw.com · 618 State Street · Belle Fourche, SD 57717-1489 · 605-892-2011

Pierre

David A. Gerdes · ⑩ · May, Adam, Gerdes & Thompson · 503 South Pierre Street · P.O. Box 160 · Pierre, SD 57501-0160 · 605-224-8803

Rapid City

Gene N. Lebrun · Lynn, Jackson, Shultz & Lebrun · http://www.lynnjackson.com · First National Bank Building, Eighth Floor · 909 Saint Joseph Street · P.O. Box 8250 · Rapid City, SD 57709-8250 · 605-342-2592

Sioux Falls

Thomas J. Welk · ⑩ · Boyce, Greenfield, Pashby & Welk · 101 North Phillips Avenue, Suite 600 · P.O. Box 5015 · Sioux Falls, SD 57117-5015 · 605-336-2424

ENVIRONMENTAL LAW

Belle Fourche

Max Main · ⑳ · Bennett, Main & Gubbrud · http://www.bellelaw.com · 618 State Street · Belle Fourche, SD 57717-1489 · 605-892-2011

FAMILY LAW

Rapid City

Linda Lea M. Viken · Viken Law Firm · http://www.vikenlaw.com · 4200 Beach Drive, Suite Four · Rapid City, SD 57702 · 605-721-7230

James L. Waggoner · James L. Waggoner · 731 St. Joseph Street · P.O. Box 254 · Rapid City, SD 57709-0254 · 605-342-0540

Sioux Falls

Lee R. Burd · Burd & Wieck · 601 South Cliff Avenue, Suite A · Sioux Falls, SD 57104-5241 · 605-332-4351

Richard A. Johnson · ⑩ · Strange, Farrell & Johnson · 141 North Main Avenue, Suite 200 · Sioux Falls, SD 57104-6429 · 605-339-4500

Scott D. Kading · Moore, Rasmussen, Kading & Kunstle · 2415 West 57th Street · P.O. Box 1477 · Sioux Falls, SD 57108-1477 · 605-336-1730

Catherine V. Piersol · Piersol & Voigt · 101 North Main Avenue, Suite 201 · Sioux Falls, SD 57104 · 605-339-0909

FIRST AMENDMENT LAW

Sioux Falls

Jon E. Arneson · Jon E. Arneson · 123 South Main Avenue, Suite 202 · Sioux Falls, SD 57104-6430 · 605-335-0083

Timothy M. Gebhart · ⑩ · Davenport, Evans, Hurwitz & Smith · 206 West 14th Street · P.O. Box 1030 · Sioux Falls, SD 57101-1030 · 605-336-2880

Ronald A. Parsons, Jr. · Johnson, Heidepriem, Janklow, Abdallah & Johnson, · 431 North Phillips Avenue, Suite 400 · Sioux Falls, SD 57104 · 605-338-4304

HEALTH CARE LAW

Pierre

David A. Gerdes · ⑩ · May, Adam, Gerdes & Thompson · 503 South Pierre Street · P.O. Box 160 · Pierre, SD 57501-0160 · 605-224-8803

Rapid City

Daniel F. Duffy · Bangs, McCullen, Butler, Foye & Simmons · 333 West Boulevard, Suite 400 · P.O. Box 2670 · Rapid City, SD 57709 · 605-343-1040

Jeffrey G. Hurd · Bangs, McCullen, Butler, Foye & Simmons · 333 West Boulevard, Suite 400 · P.O. Box 2670 · Rapid City, SD 57709 · 605-343-1040

Sioux Falls

Heather R. Springer · Boyce, Greenfield, Pashby & Welk · 101 North Phillips Avenue, Suite 600 · P.O. Box 5015 · Sioux Falls, SD 57117-5015 · 605-336-2424

Monte R. Walz · Davenport, Evans, Hurwitz & Smith · 206 West 14th Street · P.O. Box 1030 · Sioux Falls, SD 57101-1030 · 605-336-2880

Thomas J. Welk · ⑩ · Boyce, Greenfield, Pashby & Welk · 101 North Phillips Avenue, Suite 600 · P.O. Box 5015 · Sioux Falls, SD 57117-5015 · 605-336-2424

INSURANCE LAW

Rapid City

Craig Pfeifle · Lynn, Jackson, Shultz & Lebrun · http://www.lynnjackson.com · First National Bank Building, Eighth Floor · 909 Saint Joseph Street · P.O. Box 8250 · Rapid City, SD 57709-8250 · 605-342-2592

Sioux Falls

Daniel R. Fritz · Lynn, Jackson, Shultz & Lebrun · http://www.lynnjackson.com · U.S. Bank Building, Eighth and Ninth Floors · 141 North Main Avenue · P.O. Box 2700 · Sioux Falls, SD 57101-2700 · 605-332-5999

Mark W. Haigh · Davenport, Evans, Hurwitz & Smith · 206 West 14th Street · P.O. Box 1030 · Sioux Falls, SD 57101-1030 · 605-336-2880

James E. Moore · Woods, Fuller, Shultz & Smith · 300 South Phillips Avenue, Suite 300 · P.O. Box 5027 · Sioux Falls, SD 57117-5027 · 605-336-3890

INTELLECTUAL PROPERTY LAW

Rapid City

Gene N. Lebrun · Lynn, Jackson, Shultz & Lebrun · http://www.lynnjackson.com · First National Bank Building, Eighth Floor · 909 Saint Joseph Street · P.O. Box 8250 · Rapid City, SD 57709-8250 · 605-342-2592

LABOR AND EMPLOYMENT LAW

Rapid City

Michael M. Hickey · Bangs, McCullen, Butler, Foye & Simmons · 333 West Boulevard, Suite 400 · P.O. Box 2670 · Rapid City, SD 57709 · 605-343-1040

Craig Pfeifle · Lynn, Jackson, Shultz & Lebrun · http://www.lynnjackson.com · First National Bank Building, Eighth Floor · 909 Saint Joseph Street · P.O. Box 8250 · Rapid City, SD 57709-8250 · 605-342-2592

Jane Pfeifle · Lynn, Jackson, Shultz & Lebrun · http://www.lynnjackson.com · First National Bank Building, Eighth Floor · 909 Saint Joseph Street · P.O. Box 8250 · Rapid City, SD 57709-8250 · 605-342-2592

Sioux Falls

Richard D. Casey · Lynn, Jackson, Shultz & Lebrun · http://www.lynnjackson.com · U.S. Bank Building, Eighth and Ninth Floors · 141 North Main Avenue · P.O. Box 2700 · Sioux Falls, SD 57101-2700 · 605-332-5999

Michael S. McKnight · ⑩ · Boyce, Greenfield, Pashby & Welk · 101 North Phillips Avenue, Suite 600 · P.O. Box 5015 · Sioux Falls, SD 57117-5015 · 605-336-2424

R. Alan Peterson · Lynn, Jackson, Shultz & Lebrun · http://www.lynnjackson.com · U.S. Bank Building, Eighth and Ninth Floors · 141 North Main Avenue · P.O. Box 2700 · Sioux Falls, SD 57101-2700 · 605-332-5999

J. G. Shultz · Woods, Fuller, Shultz & Smith · 300 South Phillips Avenue, Suite 300 · P.O. Box 5027 · Sioux Falls, SD 57117-5027 · 605-336-3890

Susan Brunick Simons · ⑩ · Davenport, Evans, Hurwitz & Smith · 206 West 14th Street · P.O. Box 1030 Sioux Falls, SD 57101-1030 · 605-336-2880

Jon C. Sogn · Lynn, Jackson, Shultz & Lebrun · http://www.lynnjackson.com · U.S. Bank Building, Eighth and Ninth Floors · 141 North Main Avenue · P.O. Box 2700 · Sioux Falls, SD 57101-2700 · 605-332-5999

Gary P. Thimsen · Woods, Fuller, Shultz & Smith · 300 South Phillips Avenue, Suite 300 · P.O. Box 5027 Sioux Falls, SD 57117-5027 · 605-336-3890

LAND USE & ZONING LAW

Rapid City

Thomas H. Foye · ㉕ · Bangs, McCullen, Butler, Foye & Simmons · 333 West Boulevard, Suite 400 · P.O. Box 2670 · Rapid City, SD 57709 · 605-343-1040

Patrick G. Goetzinger · Gunderson, Palmer, Nelson & Ashmore · http://www.gundersonpalmer.com · Assurant Building · 440 Mount Rushmore Road · P.O. Box 8045 · Rapid City, SD 57709-8045 · 605-342-1078

John H. Raforth · ⑩ · Bangs, McCullen, Butler, Foye & Simmons · 333 West Boulevard, Suite 400 · P.O. Box 2670 · Rapid City, SD 57709 · 605-343-1040

MEDICAL MALPRACTICE LAW

Aberdeen

Reed A. Rasmussen · Siegel, Barnett & Schutz · Capitol Building, Suite 400 · 415 South Main Street · P.O. Box 490 · Aberdeen, SD 57402-0490 · 605-225-5420

Rapid City

Lonnie R. Braun · Thomas Braun Bernard Burke · 4200 Beach Drive, Suite One · Rapid City, SD 57702 605-348-7516

Daniel F. Duffy · Bangs, McCullen, Butler, Foye & Simmons · 333 West Boulevard, Suite 400 · P.O. Box 2670 · Rapid City, SD 57709 · 605-343-1040

Sioux Falls

Edwin E. Evans · ⑩ · Davenport, Evans, Hurwitz & Smith · 206 West 14th Street · P.O. Box 1030 · Sioux Falls, SD 57101-1030 · 605-336-2880

Mark W. Haigh · Davenport, Evans, Hurwitz & Smith · 206 West 14th Street · P.O. Box 1030 · Sioux Falls, SD 57101-1030 · 605-336-2880

Roger A. Sudbeck · Boyce, Greenfield, Pashby & Welk · 101 North Phillips Avenue, Suite 600 · P.O. Box 5015 · Sioux Falls, SD 57117-5015 · 605-336-2424

MERGERS & ACQUISITIONS LAW

Rapid City

Thomas H. Foye · ㉕ · Bangs, McCullen, Butler, Foye & Simmons · 333 West Boulevard, Suite 400 · P.O. Box 2670 · Rapid City, SD 57709 · 605-343-1040

Patrick G. Goetzinger · Gunderson, Palmer, Nelson & Ashmore · http://www.gundersonpalmer.com · Assurant Building · 440 Mount Rushmore Road · P.O. Box 8045 · Rapid City, SD 57709-8045 · 605-342-1078

Sioux Falls

Jonathan P. Brown · Davenport, Evans, Hurwitz & Smith · 206 West 14th Street · P.O. Box 1030 · Sioux Falls, SD 57101-1030 · 605-336-2880

Vance R. C. Goldammer · Murphy, Goldammer & Prendergast · Wells Fargo Building, Suite 402 · 101 North Phillips Avenue · P.O. Box 1535 · Sioux Falls, SD 57101-1535 · 605-331-2975

Douglas J. Hajek · Davenport, Evans, Hurwitz & Smith · 206 West 14th Street · P.O. Box 1030 · Sioux Falls, SD 57101-1030 · 605-336-2880

David L. Knudson · ⑩ · Davenport, Evans, Hurwitz & Smith · 206 West 14th Street · P.O. Box 1030 · Sioux Falls, SD 57101-1030 · 605-336-2880

James M. Wiederrich · Woods, Fuller, Shultz & Smith · 300 South Phillips Avenue, Suite 300 · P.O. Box 5027 · Sioux Falls, SD 57117-5027 · 605-336-3890

MINING LAW

Belle Fourche

Max Main · ⑳ · Bennett, Main & Gubbrud · http://www.bellelaw.com · 618 State Street · Belle Fourche, SD 57717-1489 · 605-892-2011

MUNICIPAL LAW

Belle Fourche

Dwight A. Gubbrud · Bennett, Main & Gubbrud · http://www.bellelaw.com · 618 State Street · Belle Fourche, SD 57717-1489 · 605-892-2011

Rapid City

Donald P. Knudsen · Gunderson, Palmer, Nelson & Ashmore · http://www.gundersonpalmer.com · Assurant Building · 440 Mount Rushmore Road · P.O. Box 8045 · Rapid City, SD 57709-8045 · 605-342-1078

NATIVE AMERICAN LAW

Winner

J. Mick Grossenburg · J. M. Grossenburg · 501 South Main Street · Winner, SD 57580 · 605-842-1676

NATURAL RESOURCES LAW

Belle Fourche

Max Main · 20 · Bennett, Main & Gubbrud · http://www.bellelaw.com · 618 State Street · Belle Fourche, SD 57717-1489 · 605-892-2011

NON-PROFIT/CHARITIES LAW

Rapid City

Thomas H. Foye · 25 · Bangs, McCullen, Butler, Foye & Simmons · 333 West Boulevard, Suite 400 · P.O. Box 2670 · Rapid City, SD 57709 · 605-343-1040

Patrick G. Goetzinger · Gunderson, Palmer, Nelson & Ashmore · http://www.gundersonpalmer.com · Assurant Building · 440 Mount Rushmore Road · P.O. Box 8045 · Rapid City, SD 57709-8045 · 605-342-1078

John H. Raforth · 10 · Bangs, McCullen, Butler, Foye & Simmons · 333 West Boulevard, Suite 400 · P.O. Box 2670 · Rapid City, SD 57709 · 605-343-1040

NON-WHITE-COLLAR CRIMINAL DEFENSE

Pierre

Brad A. Schreiber · Schreiber Law Firm · 740 East Sioux Avenue, Suite 109 · Pierre, SD 57501 · 605-494-3004

Rapid City

Randal E. Connelly · 10 · Randal E. Connelly · 703 Fourth Street · Rapid City, SD 57701-3601 · 605-342-7330

Sioux Falls

Sidney B. Strange · 25 · Strange, Farrell & Johnson · 141 North Main Avenue, Suite 200 · Sioux Falls, SD 57104-6429 · 605-339-4500

Winner

Stanley E. Whiting · Stanley E. Whiting · 142 East Third Street · Winner, SD 57580 · 605-842-3373

OIL & GAS LAW

Belle Fourche

Max Main · (20) · Bennett, Main & Gubbrud · http://www.bellelaw.com · 618 State Street · Belle Fourche, SD 57717-1489 · 605-892-2011

PERSONAL INJURY LITIGATION

Aberdeen

Reed A. Rasmussen · Siegel, Barnett & Schutz · Capitol Building, Suite 400 · 415 South Main Street · P.O. Box 490 · Aberdeen, SD 57402-0490 · 605-225-5420

Roy A. Wise · Richardson, Wyly, Wise, Sauck & Hieb · One Court Street · P.O. Box 1030 · Aberdeen, SD 57402-1030 · 605-225-6310

Belle Fourche

Robert L. Morris II · Day Morris Law Firm · http://blackhillsportal.com/dbs/daymorris · 117 Fifth Avenue · P.O. Box 370 · Belle Fourche, SD 57717-0370 · 605-723-7777

Gregory

Wally A. Eklund · Johnson Eklund Law Office · 405 Main Street · P.O. Box 149 · Gregory, SD 57533 · 605-835-8391

Pierre

Charles M. Thompson · (10) · May, Adam, Gerdes & Thompson · 503 South Pierre Street · P.O. Box 160 · Pierre, SD 57501-0160 · 605-224-8803

Rapid City

Michael Abourezk · Abourezk & Garcia · 2020 West Omaha · P.O. Box 9460 · Rapid City, SD 57709 · 605-342-0097

Kenneth E. Barker · (10) · Barker, Wilson, Reynolds & Burke · 4200 Beach Drive · Rapid City, SD 57702 · 605-723-8000

Daniel F. Duffy · Bangs, McCullen, Butler, Foye & Simmons · 333 West Boulevard, Suite 400 · P.O. Box 2670 · Rapid City, SD 57709 · 605-343-1040

Gregory A. Eiesland · (10) · Johnson Eiesland Law Offices · 4020 Jackson Boulevard · P.O. Box 6900 · Rapid City, SD 57709-6900 · 605-348-7300

Gregory J. Erlandson · Bangs, McCullen, Butler, Foye & Simmons · 333 West Boulevard, Suite 400 · P.O. Box 2670 · Rapid City, SD 57709 · 605-343-1040

Thomas G. Fritz · Lynn, Jackson, Shultz & Lebrun · http://www.lynnjackson.com · First National Bank Building, Eighth Floor · 909 Saint Joseph Street · P.O. Box 8250 · Rapid City, SD 57709-8250 · 605-342-2592

Glen H. Johnson · (10) · Johnson Eiesland Law Offices · 4020 Jackson Boulevard · P.O. Box 6900 · Rapid City, SD 57709-6900 · 605-348-7300

Steve Oberg · Lynn, Jackson, Shultz & Lebrun · http://www.lynnjackson.com · First National Bank Building, Eighth Floor · 909 Saint Joseph Street · P.O. Box 8250 · Rapid City, SD 57709-8250 · 605-342-2592

Terence R. Quinn · ⑩ · Goodsell Quinn · 246 Founders Park Drive, Suite 201 · P.O. Box 9249 · Rapid City, SD 57709-9249 · 605-343-3000

Sioux Falls

Douglas M. Deibert · Cadwell, Sanford, Deibert & Garry · River Centre, Suite 200 · 200 East 10th Street P.O. Box 2498 · Sioux Falls, SD 57101-2498 · 605-336-0828

Edwin E. Evans · ⑩ · Davenport, Evans, Hurwitz & Smith · 206 West 14th Street · P.O. Box 1030 · Sioux Falls, SD 57101-1030 · 605-336-2880

Mark W. Haigh · Davenport, Evans, Hurwitz & Smith · 206 West 14th Street · P.O. Box 1030 · Sioux Falls, SD 57101-1030 · 605-336-2880

Scott N. Heidepriem · ⑩ · Johnson, Heidepriem, Janklow, Abdallah & Johnson, · 431 North Phillips Avenue, Suite 400 · Sioux Falls, SD 57104 · 605-338-4304

Carleton R. Hoy · ㉕ · Hoy Trial Lawyers · 1608 West Russell Street · Sioux Falls, SD 57104-1330 · 605-334-8900

Steven M. Johnson · ⑩ · Johnson, Heidepriem, Janklow, Abdallah & Johnson, · 431 North Phillips Avenue, Suite 400 · Sioux Falls, SD 57104 · 605-338-4304

Stephen C. Landon · Cadwell, Sanford, Deibert & Garry · River Centre, Suite 200 · 200 East 10th Street · P.O. Box 2498 · Sioux Falls, SD 57101-2498 · 605-336-0828

Michael L. Luce · ⑩ · Davenport, Evans, Hurwitz & Smith · 206 West 14th Street · P.O. Box 1030 · Sioux Falls, SD 57101-1030 · 605-336-2880

Mark V. Meierhenry · ⑩ · Danfort & Meierhenry · 315 South Phillips Avenue · Sioux Falls, SD 57104 · 605-336-3075

Thomas J. Nicholson · Nicholson & Nicholson · 224 North Phillips Avenue · Sioux Falls, SD 57104 · 605-335-7100

Gary J. Pashby · ⑳ · Boyce, Greenfield, Pashby & Welk · 101 North Phillips Avenue, Suite 600 · P.O. Box 5015 · Sioux Falls, SD 57117-5015 · 605-336-2424

R. Alan Peterson · Lynn, Jackson, Shultz & Lebrun · http://www.lynnjackson.com · U.S. Bank Building, Eighth and Ninth Floors · 141 North Main Avenue · P.O. Box 2700 · Sioux Falls, SD 57101-2700 · 605-332-5999

Michael J. Schaffer · Schaffer Law Office · 311 East 14th Street · Sioux Falls, SD 57104-5022 · 605-274-6760

Jon C. Sogn · Lynn, Jackson, Shultz & Lebrun · http://www.lynnjackson.com · U.S. Bank Building, Eighth and Ninth Floors · 141 North Main Avenue · P.O. Box 2700 · Sioux Falls, SD 57101-2700 · 605-332-5999

Arlo D. Sommervold · ⑩ · Sommervold Law Firm · 1610 South Minnesota Avenue · P.O. Box 1148 · Sioux Falls, SD 57101-1148 · 605-339-7289

Roger A. Sudbeck · Boyce, Greenfield, Pashby & Welk · 101 North Phillips Avenue, Suite 600 · P.O. Box 5015 · Sioux Falls, SD 57117-5015 · 605-336-2424

Gary P. Thimsen · Woods, Fuller, Shultz & Smith · 300 South Phillips Avenue, Suite 300 · P.O. Box 5027 Sioux Falls, SD 57117-5027 · 605-336-3890

Watertown

Nancy J. Turbak · ⑩ · Turbak Law Office · 1301 Fourth Street, NE · Watertown, SD 57201-1206 · 605-886-8361

Winner

J. Mick Grossenburg · J. M. Grossenburg · 501 South Main Street · Winner, SD 57580 · 605-842-1676

PRODUCT LIABILITY LITIGATION

Rapid City

Gregory J. Erlandson · Bangs, McCullen, Butler, Foye & Simmons · 333 West Boulevard, Suite 400 · P.O. Box 2670 · Rapid City, SD 57709 · 605-343-1040

Sioux Falls

Steven M. Johnson · ⑩ · Johnson, Heidepriem, Janklow, Abdallah & Johnson, · 431 North Phillips Avenue, Suite 400 · Sioux Falls, SD 57104 · 605-338-4304

Michael L. Luce · ⑩ · Davenport, Evans, Hurwitz & Smith · 206 West 14th Street · P.O. Box 1030 · Sioux Falls, SD 57101-1030 · 605-336-2880

Gary J. Pashby · ⑳ · Boyce, Greenfield, Pashby & Welk · 101 North Phillips Avenue, Suite 600 · P.O. Box 5015 · Sioux Falls, SD 57117-5015 · 605-336-2424

Arlo D. Sommervold · ⑩ · Sommervold Law Firm · 1610 South Minnesota Avenue · P.O. Box 1148 · Sioux Falls, SD 57101-1148 · 605-339-7289

Yankton

Michael F. Marlow · Johnson, Miner, Marlow, Woodward & Huff · 200 West Third Street · P.O. Box 667 · Yankton, SD 57078 · 605-665-5009

PROFESSIONAL MALPRACTICE LAW

Sioux Falls

Edwin E. Evans · ⑩ · Davenport, Evans, Hurwitz & Smith · 206 West 14th Street · P.O. Box 1030 · Sioux Falls, SD 57101-1030 · 605-336-2880

Mark W. Haigh · Davenport, Evans, Hurwitz & Smith · 206 West 14th Street · P.O. Box 1030 · Sioux Falls, SD 57101-1030 · 605-336-2880

Roger A. Sudbeck · Boyce, Greenfield, Pashby & Welk · 101 North Phillips Avenue, Suite 600 · P.O. Box 5015 · Sioux Falls, SD 57117-5015 · 605-336-2424

RAILROAD LAW

Sioux Falls

Brian J. Donahoe · Cutler & Donahoe · 100 North Phillips Avenue, Ninth Floor · Sioux Falls, SD 57104-6725 · 605-335-4950

REAL ESTATE LAW

Rapid City

Thomas H. Foye · ㉕ · Bangs, McCullen, Butler, Foye & Simmons · 333 West Boulevard, Suite 400 · P.O. Box 2670 · Rapid City, SD 57709 · 605-343-1040

Patrick G. Goetzinger · Gunderson, Palmer, Nelson & Ashmore · http://www.gundersonpalmer.com · Assurant Building · 440 Mount Rushmore Road · P.O. Box 8045 · Rapid City, SD 57709-8045 · 605-342-1078

Richard Huffman · ⑩ · DeMersseman Jensen Christianson Stanton & Huffman · 516 Fifth Street · P.O. Box 1820 · Rapid City, SD 57709-1820 · 605-342-2814

Curtis Jensen · DeMersseman Jensen Christianson Stanton & Huffman · 516 Fifth Street · P.O. Box 1820 Rapid City, SD 57709-1820 · 605-342-2814

James W. Olson · Wilson, Olson & Nash · 2640 Jackson Boulevard · P.O. Box 1552 · Rapid City, SD 57709 · 605-342-7090

Charles L. Riter · ⑳ · Bangs, McCullen, Butler, Foye & Simmons · 333 West Boulevard, Suite 400 · P.O. Box 2670 · Rapid City, SD 57709 · 605-343-1040

Haven L. Stuck · Lynn, Jackson, Shultz & Lebrun · http://www.lynnjackson.com · First National Bank Building, Eighth Floor · 909 Saint Joseph Street · P.O. Box 8250 · Rapid City, SD 57709-8250 · 605-342-2592

Sioux Falls

Jeffrey D. Brekke · May & Johnson · 6805 South Minnesota Avenue, Suite 100 · Sioux Falls, SD 57108 · 605-336-2565

Jonathan P. Brown · Davenport, Evans, Hurwitz & Smith · 206 West 14th Street · P.O. Box 1030 · Sioux Falls, SD 57101-1030 · 605-336-2880

Richard A. Cutler · ⑳ · Cutler & Donahoe · 100 North Phillips Avenue, Ninth Floor · Sioux Falls, SD 57104-6725 · 605-335-4950

P. Daniel Donohue · ⑩ · Davenport, Evans, Hurwitz & Smith · 206 West 14th Street · P.O. Box 1030 · Sioux Falls, SD 57101-1030 · 605-336-2880

Gregg S. Greenfield · Boyce, Greenfield, Pashby & Welk · 101 North Phillips Avenue, Suite 600 · P.O. Box 5015 · Sioux Falls, SD 57117-5015 · 605-336-2424

Russell R. Greenfield · ⑩ · Boyce, Greenfield, Pashby & Welk · 101 North Phillips Avenue, Suite 600 · P.O. Box 5015 · Sioux Falls, SD 57117-5015 · 605-336-2424

William G. Taylor, Jr. · ⑳ · Woods, Fuller, Shultz & Smith · 300 South Phillips Avenue, Suite 300 · P.O. Box 5027 · Sioux Falls, SD 57117-5027 · 605-336-3890

TAX LAW

Rapid City

Thomas H. Foye · 25 · Bangs, McCullen, Butler, Foye & Simmons · 333 West Boulevard, Suite 400 · P.O. Box 2670 · Rapid City, SD 57709 · 605-343-1040

John H. Raforth · 10 · Bangs, McCullen, Butler, Foye & Simmons · 333 West Boulevard, Suite 400 · P.O. Box 2670 · Rapid City, SD 57709 · 605-343-1040

Charles L. Riter · 20 · Bangs, McCullen, Butler, Foye & Simmons · 333 West Boulevard, Suite 400 · P.O. Box 2670 · Rapid City, SD 57709 · 605-343-1040

Sioux Falls

Bradley C. Grossenburg · 10 · Woods, Fuller, Shultz & Smith · 300 South Phillips Avenue, Suite 300 · P.O. Box 5027 · Sioux Falls, SD 57117-5027 · 605-336-3890

Catherine A. Tanck · Davenport, Evans, Hurwitz & Smith · 206 West 14th Street · P.O. Box 1030 · Sioux Falls, SD 57101-1030 · 605-336-2880

TRANSPORTATION LAW

Sioux Falls

Arlo D. Sommervold · 10 · Sommervold Law Firm · 1610 South Minnesota Avenue · P.O. Box 1148 · Sioux Falls, SD 57101-1148 · 605-339-7289

TRUSTS AND ESTATES

Brookings

Lewayne M. Erickson · Lewayne M. Erickson · 517 Sixth Street · Brookings, SD 57006-1436 · 605-692-6158

Rapid City

Thomas H. Foye · 25 · Bangs, McCullen, Butler, Foye & Simmons · 333 West Boulevard, Suite 400 · P.O. Box 2670 · Rapid City, SD 57709 · 605-343-1040

John H. Raforth · 10 · Bangs, McCullen, Butler, Foye & Simmons · 333 West Boulevard, Suite 400 · P.O. Box 2670 · Rapid City, SD 57709 · 605-343-1040

Charles L. Riter · 20 · Bangs, McCullen, Butler, Foye & Simmons · 333 West Boulevard, Suite 400 · P.O. Box 2670 · Rapid City, SD 57709 · 605-343-1040

Sioux Falls

P. Daniel Donohue · 10 · Davenport, Evans, Hurwitz & Smith · 206 West 14th Street · P.O. Box 1030 · Sioux Falls, SD 57101-1030 · 605-336-2880

Bradley C. Grossenburg · 10 · Woods, Fuller, Shultz & Smith · 300 South Phillips Avenue, Suite 300 · P.O. Box 5027 · Sioux Falls, SD 57117-5027 · 605-336-3890

Merle A. Johnson · ⓴ · Woods, Fuller, Shultz & Smith · 300 South Phillips Avenue, Suite 300 · P.O. Box 5027 · Sioux Falls, SD 57117-5027 · 605-336-3890

Sarah Richardson Larson · ❿ · Davenport, Evans, Hurwitz & Smith · 206 West 14th Street · P.O. Box 1030 · Sioux Falls, SD 57101-1030 · 605-336-2880

Richard Moe · ㉕ · May & Johnson · 6805 South Minnesota Avenue, Suite 100 · Sioux Falls, SD 57108 · 605-336-2565

James E. Moore · ㉕ · Moore, Rasmussen, Kading & Kunstle · 2415 West 57th Street · P.O. Box 1477 · Sioux Falls, SD 57108-1477 · 605-336-1730

Watertown

J. Douglas Austin · ❿ · Austin, Hinderaker, Hopper, Strait & Bratland · 25 First Avenue, SW · P.O. Box 966 · Watertown, SD 57201-0966 · 605-886-5823

WATER LAW

Belle Fourche

Max Main · ⓴ · Bennett, Main & Gubbrud · http://www.bellelaw.com · 618 State Street · Belle Fourche, SD 57717-1489 · 605-892-2011

WHITE-COLLAR CRIMINAL DEFENSE

Pierre

Brad A. Schreiber · Schreiber Law Firm · 740 East Sioux Avenue, Suite 109 · Pierre, SD 57501 · 605-494-3004

Rapid City

Randal E. Connelly · ❿ · Randal E. Connelly · 703 Fourth Street · Rapid City, SD 57701-3601 · 605-342-7330

Winner

Stanley E. Whiting · Stanley E. Whiting · 142 East Third Street · Winner, SD 57580 · 605-842-3373

WORKERS' COMPENSATION LAW

Pierre

Robert B. Anderson · ❿ · May, Adam, Gerdes & Thompson · 503 South Pierre Street · P.O. Box 160 · Pierre, SD 57501-0160 · 605-224-8803

Timothy M. Engel · May, Adam, Gerdes & Thompson · 503 South Pierre Street · P.O. Box 160 · Pierre, SD 57501-0160 · 605-224-8803

Rapid City

Dennis W. Finch · Finch Bettman Maks & Hogue · 1506 Mountain View Road, Suite 101 · Rapid City, SD 57702 · 605-348-6547

Michael M. Hickey · Bangs, McCullen, Butler, Foye & Simmons · 333 West Boulevard, Suite 400 · P.O. Box 2670 · Rapid City, SD 57709 · 605-343-1040

Patricia A. Meyers · Costello, Porter, Hill, Heisterkamp, Bushnell & Carpenter · 200 Security Building · 704 St. Joseph Street · P.O. Box 290 · Rapid City, SD 57709-0290 · 605-343-2410

Michael J. Simpson · Julius & Simpson · 801 Mount Rushmore Road, Suite 203 · P.O. Box 8025 · Rapid City, SD 57709-8025 · 605-716-1000

Sioux Falls

Comet H. Haraldson · ⑩ · Woods, Fuller, Shultz & Smith · 300 South Phillips Avenue, Suite 300 · P.O. Box 5027 · Sioux Falls, SD 57117-5027 · 605-336-3890

Michael S. McKnight · ⑩ · Boyce, Greenfield, Pashby & Welk · 101 North Phillips Avenue, Suite 600 · P.O. Box 5015 · Sioux Falls, SD 57117-5015 · 605-336-2424

Rick W. Orr · Davenport, Evans, Hurwitz & Smith · 206 West 14th Street · P.O. Box 1030 · Sioux Falls, SD 57101-1030 · 605-336-2880

J. G. Shultz · Woods, Fuller, Shultz & Smith · 300 South Phillips Avenue, Suite 300 · P.O. Box 5027 · Sioux Falls, SD 57117-5027 · 605-336-3890

Susan Brunick Simons · ⑩ · Davenport, Evans, Hurwitz & Smith · 206 West 14th Street · P.O. Box 1030 Sioux Falls, SD 57101-1030 · 605-336-2880

TENNESSEE

ADMINISTRATIVE LAW

Knoxville

Warren L. Gooch · Kramer Rayson · http://www.kramer-rayson.com · First Tennessee Plaza, Suite 2500 · 800 South Gay Street · P.O. Box 629 · Knoxville, TN 37901-0629 · 865-525-5134

Richard W. Krieg · Lewis, King, Krieg & Waldrop · http://www.lewisking.com · One Centre Square, Fifth Floor · 620 Market Street · P.O. Box 2425 · Knoxville, TN 37901 · 865-546-4646

Charles E. Young, Jr. · Kramer Rayson · http://www.kramer-rayson.com · First Tennessee Plaza, Suite 2500 · 800 South Gay Street · P.O. Box 629 · Knoxville, TN 37901-0629 · 865-525-5134

Memphis

Ronald M. Harkavy · Harkavy Shainberg Kaplan & Dunstan · 6060 Poplar Avenue, Suite 140 · Memphis, TN 38119 · 901-761-1263

Richard R. Spore III · Bass, Berry & Sims · http://www.bassberry.com · The Tower at Peabody Place, Suite 900 · 100 Peabody Place · Memphis, TN 38103-2625 · 901-543-5900

Nashville

Alexander B. Buchanan · Waller Lansden Dortch & Davis · http://www.wallerlaw.com · Nashville City Center, Suite 2700 · 511 Union Street · P.O. Box 198966 · Nashville, TN 37219-8966 · 615-244-6380

J. Andrew Goddard · a · Bass, Berry & Sims · http://www.bassberry.com · 315 Deaderick Street, Suite 2700 · Nashville, TN 37238-3001 · 615-742-6200

G. Brian Jackson · Miller & Martin · http://www.millermartin.com · One Nashville Place, Suite 1200 · 150 Fourth Avenue North · Nashville, TN 37219-2433 · 615-244-9270

William L. Penny · Stites & Harbison · http://www.stites.com · SunTrust Plaza, Suite 800 · 401 Commerce Street · Nashville, TN 37219 · 615-244-5200

W. Brantley Phillips, Jr. · Bass, Berry & Sims · http://www.bassberry.com · 315 Deaderick Street, Suite 2700 · Nashville, TN 37238-3001 · 615-742-6200

Matthew J. Sweeney III · Baker, Donelson, Bearman, Caldwell & Berkowitz · http://www.bakerdonelson.com · Commerce Center, Suite 1000 · 211 Commerce Street · Nashville, TN 37201 · 615-726-5600

ALTERNATIVE DISPUTE RESOLUTION

Chattanooga

William L. Brown · Miller & Martin · http://www.millermartin.com · Volunteer Building, Suite 1000 · 832 Georgia Avenue · Chattanooga, TN 37402-2289 · 423-756-6600

Roger W. Dickson · a · Miller & Martin · http://www.millermartin.com · Volunteer Building, Suite 1000 · 832 Georgia Avenue · Chattanooga, TN 37402-2289 · 423-756-6600

Charles J. Gearhiser · 2% · Gearhiser, Peters, Lockaby, Cavett & Elliott · http://www.gplce.com · 320 McCallie Avenue · Chattanooga, TN 37402 · 423-756-5171

H. Richard Marcus · Franklin, Cooper & Marcus · 837 Fortwood Street · Chattanooga, TN 37403-2358 · 423-756-3596

Columbia

Jerry C. Colley · 2% · Colley and Colley · 710 North Main Street · P.O. Box 1476 · Columbia, TN 38402-1476 · 931-388-8564

Kingsport

William T. Wray, Jr. · The Wray Law Firm · P.O. Box 1303 · Kingsport, TN 37662 · 423-378-0101

Knoxville

Bruce A. Anderson · Anderson Reeves & Herbert · Tyson Place, Suite 130 · 2607 Kingston Pike · Knoxville, TN 37919 · 865-540-1977

Robert R. Campbell · 2) · Hodges, Doughty & Carson · 617 Main Street · P.O. Box 869 · Knoxville, TN 37901-0869 · 865-546-9611

Lewis R. Hagood · 2) · Arnett, Draper & Hagood · First Tennessee Plaza, Suite 2300 · P.O. Box 300 · Knoxville, TN 37929-2300 · 865-546-7000

John K. Harber · Pryor, Flynn, Priest & Harber · Two Centre Square, Suite 600 · 625 Gay Street · P.O. Box 870 · Knoxville, TN 37902 · 865-522-4191

Patrick H. Hardin · Patrick H. Hardin Attorney and Arbitrator · P.O. Box 11427 · Knoxville, TN 37939-1427 · 865-974-6809

James H. London · London & Amburn · BankEast Building, Suite 900 · 607 Market Street · Knoxville, TN 37916 · 865-637-0203

Robert P. Murrian · Reeves, Herbert & Murrian · Tyson Place, Suite 130 · 2607 Kingston Pike · Knoxville, TN 37919 · 865-540-1977

Pamela L. Reeves · Anderson Reeves & Herbert · Tyson Place, Suite 130 · 2607 Kingston Pike · Knoxville, TN 37919 · 865-540-1977

Sarah Y. Sheppeard · a · Sheppeard Swanson & Mynatt · 616 West Hill Avenue · P.O. Box 2149 · Knoxville, TN 37901-2149 · 865-546-3653

Charles W. Swanson · Sheppeard Swanson & Mynatt · 616 West Hill Avenue · P.O. Box 2149 · Knoxville, TN 37901-2149 · 865-546-3653

William D. Vines III · Butler, Vines and Babb · 2701 Kingston Pike · P.O. Box 2649 · Knoxville, TN 37901 · 865-637-3531

Howard H. Vogel · O'Neil, Parker and Williamson · 416 Cumberland Avenue, SW · P.O. Box 217 · Knoxville, TN 37902 · 865-546-7190

William A. Young · O'Neil, Parker and Williamson · 416 Cumberland Avenue, SW · P.O. Box 217 · Knoxville, TN 37902 · 865-546-7190

Memphis

Leo M. Bearman, Jr. · a · Baker, Donelson, Bearman, Caldwell & Berkowitz · http://www.bakerdonelson.com · First Tennessee Building, Suite 2000 · 165 Madison Avenue · Memphis, TN 38103 · 901-526-2000

Allen S. Blair · 2% · Harris Shelton Hanover Walsh · One Commerce Square, Suite 2700 · Memphis, TN 38103 · 901-525-1455

W. J. Michael Cody · Burch, Porter & Johnson · http://www.bpjlaw.com · 130 North Court Avenue · Memphis, TN 38103 · 901-524-5000

Hayden D. Lait · Mediation and Law Office of Hayden Lait · 266 South Front Street, Suite 206 · Memphis, TN 38103 · 901-527-1301

C. Suzanne Landers · Landers & Associates · Cotton Exchange Building, Ninth Floor · 65 Union Avenue Memphis, TN 38103 · 901-522-1010

Christopher G. Lazarini · Bass, Berry & Sims · http://www.bassberry.com · The Tower at Peabody Place, Suite 900 · 100 Peabody Place · Memphis, TN 38103-2625 · 901-543-5900

Allen T. Malone · Burch, Porter & Johnson · http://www.bpjlaw.com · 130 North Court Avenue · Memphis, TN 38103 · 901-524-5000

Dorothy Johnson Pounders · a · Pounders Coleman · 1770 Kirby Parkway, Suite 105 · Memphis, TN 38138 · 901-752-1250

Michael Richards · Baker, Donelson, Bearman, Caldwell & Berkowitz · http://www.bakerdonelson.com · First Tennessee Building, Suite 2000 · 165 Madison Avenue · Memphis, TN 38103 · 901-526-2000

Shepherd D. Tate · a · Bass, Berry & Sims · http://www.bassberry.com · The Tower at Peabody Place, Suite 900 · 100 Peabody Place · Memphis, TN 38103-2625 · 901-543-5900

Murfreesboro

John T. Blankenship · Blankenship and Blankenship · 307 Hickerson Drive · Murfreesboro, TN 37129 · 615-893-4160

Nashville

Robert S. Brandt · Trauger & Tuke · The Southern Turf Building · 222 Fourth Avenue North · Nashville, TN 37219-2117 · 615-256-8585

Gregory L. Cashion · Smith Cashion & Orr · 231 Third Avenue North · Nashville, TN 37201-1603 · 615-742-8555

Lewis H. Conner, Jr. · 2) · Waller Lansden Dortch & Davis · http://www.wallerlaw.com · Nashville City Center, Suite 2700 · 511 Union Street · P.O. Box 198966 · Nashville, TN 37219-8966 · 615-244-6380

Thomas C. Corts · Ortale, Kelly, Herbert & Crawford · Noel Place, Third Floor · 200 Fourth Avenue North · P.O. Box 198985 · Nashville, TN 37219-8985 · 615-256-9999

Stephen E. Cox · Stephen E. Cox · 172 Second Avenue North, Suite 214 · Nashville, TN 37201 · 615-467-3848

Hal D. Hardin · a · Hal D. Hardin · 211 Union Street, Suite 200 · Nashville, TN 37201 · 615-369-3377

L. Wearen Hughes · Bass, Berry & Sims · http://www.bassberry.com · 315 Deaderick Street, Suite 2700 · Nashville, TN 37238-3001 · 615-742-6200

Randal S. Mashburn · a · Baker, Donelson, Bearman, Caldwell & Berkowitz · http://www.bakerdonelson.com · Commerce Center, Suite 1000 · 211 Commerce Street · Nashville, TN 37201 · 615-726-5600

Robert G. McDowell · Baker, Donelson, Bearman, Caldwell & Berkowitz · http://www.bakerdonelson.com · Commerce Center, Suite 1000 · 211 Commerce Street · Nashville, TN 37201 · 615-726-5600

George B. McGugin · a · Geroge B. McGugin · P.O. Box 58384 · Nashville, TN 37205-8384 · 615-292-3964

William P. Ortale · Ortale, Kelly, Herbert & Crawford · Noel Place, Third Floor · 200 Fourth Avenue North · P.O. Box 198985 · Nashville, TN 37219-8985 · 615-256-9999

D. Tracy Shaw · Howell & Fisher · Court Square Building · 300 James Robertson Parkway · Nashville, TN 37201-1107 · 615-244-3370

Matthew J. Sweeney III · Baker, Donelson, Bearman, Caldwell & Berkowitz · http://www.bakerdonelson.com · Commerce Center, Suite 1000 · 211 Commerce Street · Nashville, TN 37201 · 615-726-5600

David K. Taylor · Boult, Cummings, Conners & Berry · http://www.boultcummings.com · Roundabout Plaza, Suite 700 · 1600 Division Street · P.O. Box 340025 · Nashville, TN 37203 · 615-244-2582

Vincent E. Wehby · a · Vincent E. Wehby · 501 Union Street, Suite 500 · Nashville, TN 37219 · 615-255-7534

ANTITRUST LAW

Chattanooga

Carlos C. Smith · a · Miller & Martin · http://www.millermartin.com · Volunteer Building, Suite 1000 · 832 Georgia Avenue · Chattanooga, TN 37402-2289 · 423-756-6600

Memphis

John W. McQuiston II · a · Evans Petree Bogatin · http://www.evanspetree.com · 1000 Ridgeway Loop Road, Suite 200 · Memphis, TN 38120 · 901-525-6781

Nashville

Paul A. Alexis · Boult, Cummings, Conners & Berry · http://www.boultcummings.com · Roundabout Plaza, Suite 700 · 1600 Division Street · P.O. Box 340025 · Nashville, TN 37203 · 615-244-2582

Andrée S. Blumstein · Sherrard & Roe · http://www.sherrardroe.com · 424 Church Street, Suite 2000 · Nashville, TN 37219-3304 · 615-742-4200

Paul S. Davidson · Waller Lansden Dortch & Davis · http://www.wallerlaw.com · Nashville City Center, Suite 2700 · 511 Union Street · P.O. Box 198966 · Nashville, TN 37219-8966 · 615-244-6380

Maclin P. Davis, Jr. · 2% · Waller Lansden Dortch & Davis · http://www.wallerlaw.com · Nashville City Center, Suite 2700 · 511 Union Street · P.O. Box 198966 · Nashville, TN 37219-8966 · 615-244-6380

R. Dale Grimes · a · Bass, Berry & Sims · http://www.bassberry.com · 315 Deaderick Street, Suite 2700 · Nashville, TN 37238-3001 · 615-742-6200

Robert J. Walker · a · Walker, Tipps & Malone · 2300 One Nashville Place · 150 Fourth Avenue North · Nashville, TN 37219 · 615-313-6000

APPELLATE LAW

Knoxville

Howard H. Vogel · O'Neil, Parker and Williamson · 416 Cumberland Avenue, SW · P.O. Box 217 · Knoxville, TN 37902 · 865-546-7190

Memphis

Leo M. Bearman, Jr. · a · Baker, Donelson, Bearman, Caldwell & Berkowitz · http://www.bakerdonelson.com · First Tennessee Building, Suite 2000 · 165 Madison Avenue · Memphis, TN 38103 · 901-526-2000

Brian S. Faughnan · Adams and Reese · http://www.adamsandreese.com · Brinkley Plaza, Suite 700 · 80 Monroe Avenue · Memphis, TN 38103 · 901-525-3234

Robert L. Hutton · Glankler Brown · http://www.glankler.com · One Commerce Square, Suite 1700 · Memphis, TN 38103 · 901-525-1322

George T. Lewis III · Baker, Donelson, Bearman, Caldwell & Berkowitz · http://www.bakerdonelson.com First Tennessee Building, Suite 2000 · 165 Madison Avenue · Memphis, TN 38103 · 901-526-2000

Charles F. Newman · a · Burch, Porter & Johnson · http://www.bpjlaw.com · 130 North Court Avenue · Memphis, TN 38103 · 901-524-5000

Nashville

Andrée S. Blumstein · Sherrard & Roe · http://www.sherrardroe.com · 424 Church Street, Suite 2000 · Nashville, TN 37219-3304 · 615-742-4200

Maclin P. Davis, Jr. · 2% · Waller Lansden Dortch & Davis · http://www.wallerlaw.com · Nashville City Center, Suite 2700 · 511 Union Street · P.O. Box 198966 · Nashville, TN 37219-8966 · 615-244-6380

Mary M. Schaffner · a · Howell & Fisher · Court Square Building · 300 James Robertson Parkway · Nashville, TN 37201-1107 · 615-244-3370

BANKING LAW

Brentwood

J. Franklin McCreary · Gerrish & McCreary · 5214 Maryland Way, Suite 406 · Brentwood, TN 37027 · 615-251-0900

Chattanooga

Kenneth C. Beckman · Baker, Donelson, Bearman, Caldwell & Berkowitz · http://www.bakerdonelson.com · 1800 Republic Centre · 633 Chestnut Street · Chattanooga, TN 37450-1800 · 423-756-2010

Richard B. Gossett · ⑩ · Baker, Donelson, Bearman, Caldwell & Berkowitz · http://www.bakerdonelson.com · 1800 Republic Centre · 633 Chestnut Street · Chattanooga, TN 37450-1800 · 423-756-2010

James M. Haley IV · Miller & Martin · http://www.millermartin.com · Volunteer Building, Suite 1000 · 832 Georgia Avenue · Chattanooga, TN 37402-2289 · 423-756-6600

J. Patrick Murphy · Miller & Martin · http://www.millermartin.com · Volunteer Building, Suite 1000 · 832 Georgia Avenue · Chattanooga, TN 37402-2289 · 423-756-6600

Susan Elliott Rich · Baker, Donelson, Bearman, Caldwell & Berkowitz · http://www.bakerdonelson.com · 1800 Republic Centre · 633 Chestnut Street · Chattanooga, TN 37450-1800 · 423-756-2010

Kingsport

William C. Argabrite · Hunter, Smith & Davis · 1212 North Eastman Road · P.O. Box 3740 · Kingsport, TN 37664 · 423-378-8000

Memphis

Mary L. Aronov · Baker, Donelson, Bearman, Caldwell & Berkowitz · http://www.bakerdonelson.com · First Tennessee Building, Suite 2000 · 165 Madison Avenue · Memphis, TN 38103 · 901-526-2000

Robert Grattan Brown, Jr. · ㉕ · Glankler Brown · http://www.glankler.com · One Commerce Square, Suite 1700 · Memphis, TN 38103 · 901-525-1322

Jeffrey C. Gerrish · Gerrish & McCreary · 700 Colonial Road, Suite 200 · Memphis, TN 38117 · 615-251-0900

John A. Good · ⑩ · Bass, Berry & Sims · http://www.bassberry.com · The Tower at Peabody Place, Suite 900 · 100 Peabody Place · Memphis, TN 38103-2625 · 901-543-5900

Robert C. Liddon, Jr. · Baker, Donelson, Bearman, Caldwell & Berkowitz · http://www.bakerdonelson.com · 6060 Poplar Avenue, Suite 440 · Memphis, TN 38119 · 901-579-3100

Anita I. Lotz · Farris Bobango Branan · http://www.farrismathews.com · 1100 Ridgeway Loop Road, Suite 400 · Memphis, TN 38120 · 901-259-7120

Anne B. Mathes · Baker, Donelson, Bearman, Caldwell & Berkowitz · http://www.bakerdonelson.com · First Tennessee Building, Suite 2000 · 165 Madison Avenue · Memphis, TN 38103 · 901-526-2000

James B. McLaren, Jr. · Adams and Reese · http://www.adamsandreese.com · Brinkley Plaza, Suite 700 · 80 Monroe Avenue · Memphis, TN 38103 · 901-525-3234

Peter R. Pettit · Bass, Berry & Sims · http://www.bassberry.com · The Tower at Peabody Place, Suite 900 100 Peabody Place · Memphis, TN 38103-2625 · 901-543-5900

Jackie G. Prester · Baker, Donelson, Bearman, Caldwell & Berkowitz · http://www.bakerdonelson.com · First Tennessee Building, Suite 2000 · 165 Madison Avenue · Memphis, TN 38103 · 901-526-2000

Glen G. Reid, Jr. · ⑩ · Wyatt, Tarrant & Combs · http://www.wyattfirm.com · The Renaissance Center, Suite 800 · 1715 Aaron Brenner Drive · Memphis, TN 38120 · 901-537-1000

John C. Speer · Bass, Berry & Sims · http://www.bassberry.com · The Tower at Peabody Place, Suite 900 100 Peabody Place · Memphis, TN 38103-2625 · 901-543-5900

Richard R. Spore III · Bass, Berry & Sims · http://www.bassberry.com · The Tower at Peabody Place, Suite 900 · 100 Peabody Place · Memphis, TN 38103-2625 · 901-543-5900

John A. Stemmler · Bass, Berry & Sims · http://www.bassberry.com · The Tower at Peabody Place, Suite 900 · 100 Peabody Place · Memphis, TN 38103-2625 · 901-543-5900

J. Robert Walker · Baker, Donelson, Bearman, Caldwell & Berkowitz · http://www.bakerdonelson.com · First Tennessee Building, Suite 2000 · 165 Madison Avenue · Memphis, TN 38103 · 901-526-2000

E. Woods Weathersby · Evans Petree Bogatin · http://www.evanspetree.com · 1000 Ridgeway Loop Road, Suite 200 · Memphis, TN 38120 · 901-525-6781

Nashville

Katherine Simpson Allen · a · Stites & Harbison · http://www.stites.com · SunTrust Plaza, Suite 800 · 401 Commerce Street · Nashville, TN 37219 · 615-244-5200

Julian L. Bibb · a · Stites & Harbison · http://www.stites.com · SunTrust Plaza, Suite 800 · 401 Commerce Street · Nashville, TN 37219 · 615-244-5200

Robert N. Buchanan III · Stites & Harbison · http://www.stites.com · SunTrust Plaza, Suite 800 · 401 Commerce Street · Nashville, TN 37219 · 615-244-5200

Robert R. Campbell, Jr. · Waller Lansden Dortch & Davis · http://www.wallerlaw.com · Nashville City Center, Suite 2700 · 511 Union Street · P.O. Box 198966 · Nashville, TN 37219-8966 · 615-244-6380

Davis H. Carr · a · Boult, Cummings, Conners & Berry · http://www.boultcummings.com · Roundabout Plaza, Suite 700 · 1600 Division Street · P.O. Box 340025 · Nashville, TN 37203 · 615-244-2582

Charles W. Cook III · Adams and Reese · http://www.adamsandreese.com · Fifth Third Center, Suite 2800 · 424 Church Street · Nashville, TN 37219 · 615-259-1450

Felix R. Dowsley III · Bass, Berry & Sims · http://www.bassberry.com · 315 Deaderick Street, Suite 2700 · Nashville, TN 37238-3001 · 615-742-6200

William W. Earthman III · Boult, Cummings, Conners & Berry · http://www.boultcummings.com · Roundabout Plaza, Suite 700 · 1600 Division Street · P.O. Box 340025 · Nashville, TN 37203 · 615-244-2582

Kathryn Reed Edge · Miller & Martin · http://www.millermartin.com · One Nashville Place, Suite 1200 · 150 Fourth Avenue North · Nashville, TN 37219-2433 · 615-244-9270

Steven J. Eisen · a · Baker, Donelson, Bearman, Caldwell & Berkowitz · http://www.bakerdonelson.com Commerce Center, Suite 1000 · 211 Commerce Street · Nashville, TN 37201 · 615-726-5600

Charles A. Grice · Stites & Harbison · http://www.stites.com · SunTrust Plaza, Suite 800 · 401 Commerce Street · Nashville, TN 37219 · 615-244-5200

Robert L. Harris · Waller Lansden Dortch & Davis · http://www.wallerlaw.com · Nashville City Center, Suite 2700 · 511 Union Street · P.O. Box 198966 · Nashville, TN 37219-8966 · 615-244-6380

Michael J. Hinchion · Stites & Harbison · http://www.stites.com · SunTrust Plaza, Suite 800 · 401 Commerce Street · Nashville, TN 37219 · 615-244-5200

D. Reed Houk · Adams and Reese · http://www.adamsandreese.com · Fifth Third Center, Suite 2800 · 424 Church Street · Nashville, TN 37219 · 615-259-1450

Julie N. Jones · a · Bass, Berry & Sims · http://www.bassberry.com · 315 Deaderick Street, Suite 2700 · Nashville, TN 37238-3001 · 615-742-6200

Roger G. Jones · a · Boult, Cummings, Conners & Berry · http://www.boultcummings.com · Roundabout Plaza, Suite 700 · 1600 Division Street · P.O. Box 340025 · Nashville, TN 37203 · 615-244-2582

Howard H. Lamar III · Bass, Berry & Sims · http://www.bassberry.com · 315 Deaderick Street, Suite 2700 Nashville, TN 37238-3001 · 615-742-6200

Thomas W. Lawless · Lawless & Associates · The Customs House, Suite 403 · 701 Broadway · Nashville, TN 37203 · 615-351-7839

Gerald F. Mace · Waller Lansden Dortch & Davis · http://www.wallerlaw.com · Nashville City Center, Suite 2700 · 511 Union Street · P.O. Box 198966 · Nashville, TN 37219-8966 · 615-244-6380

Bradley A. MacLean · a · Stites & Harbison · http://www.stites.com · SunTrust Plaza, Suite 800 · 401 Commerce Street · Nashville, TN 37219 · 615-244-5200

John E. Murdock III · Boult, Cummings, Conners & Berry · http://www.boultcummings.com · Roundabout Plaza, Suite 700 · 1600 Division Street · P.O. Box 340025 · Nashville, TN 37203 · 615-244-2582

Michael S. Peek · Bass, Berry & Sims · http://www.bassberry.com · 315 Deaderick Street, Suite 2700 · Nashville, TN 37238-3001 · 615-742-6200

Michael D. Roberts · Sherrard & Roe · http://www.sherrardroe.com · 424 Church Street, Suite 2000 · Nashville, TN 37219-3304 · 615-742-4200

Charles S. Sanger · Boult, Cummings, Conners & Berry · http://www.boultcummings.com · Roundabout Plaza, Suite 700 · 1600 Division Street · P.O. Box 340025 · Nashville, TN 37203 · 615-244-2582

Cynthia N. Sellers · Bass, Berry & Sims · http://www.bassberry.com · 315 Deaderick Street, Suite 2700 · Nashville, TN 37238-3001 · 615-742-6200

Daniel W. Small · Stites & Harbison · http://www.stites.com · SunTrust Plaza, Suite 800 · 401 Commerce Street · Nashville, TN 37219 · 615-244-5200

James S. Tate, Jr. · a · Bass, Berry & Sims · http://www.bassberry.com · 315 Deaderick Street, Suite 2700 · Nashville, TN 37238-3001 · 615-742-6200

T. Stephen C. Taylor · Bass, Berry & Sims · http://www.bassberry.com · 315 Deaderick Street, Suite 2700 Nashville, TN 37238-3001 · 615-742-6200

Bob F. Thompson · a · Bass, Berry & Sims · http://www.bassberry.com · 315 Deaderick Street, Suite 2700 · Nashville, TN 37238-3001 · 615-742-6200

F. Mitchell Walker, Jr. · Bass, Berry & Sims · http://www.bassberry.com · 315 Deaderick Street, Suite 2700 · Nashville, TN 37238-3001 · 615-742-6200

David J. White · Baker, Donelson, Bearman, Caldwell & Berkowitz · http://www.bakerdonelson.com · Commerce Center, Suite 1000 · 211 Commerce Street · Nashville, TN 37201 · 615-726-5600

Chattanooga

Bruce C. Bailey · Chambliss, Bahner & Stophel · http://www.cbslawfirm.com · 1000 Tallan Building · Two Union Square · Chattanooga, TN 37402 · 423-756-3000

William Crutchfield, Jr. · Chambliss, Bahner & Stophel · http://www.cbslawfirm.com · 1000 Tallan Building · Two Union Square · Chattanooga, TN 37402 · 423-756-3000

Jerrold D. Farinash · Kennedy, Koontz & Farinash · 320 North Holtzclaw Avenue · Chattanooga, TN 37404 · 423-622-4535

Richard B. Gossett · ⑩ · Baker, Donelson, Bearman, Caldwell & Berkowitz · http://www.bakerdonelson.com · 1800 Republic Centre · 633 Chestnut Street · Chattanooga, TN 37450-1800 · 423-756-2010

Richard C. Kennedy · ⑩ · Kennedy, Koontz & Farinash · 320 North Holtzclaw Avenue · Chattanooga, TN 37404 · 423-622-4535

Thomas E. Ray · ⑳ · Samples, Jennings, Ray & Clem · Shallowford Law Center · 130 Jordan Drive · Chattanooga, TN 37421 · 423-892-2006

Shelley D. Rucker · Miller & Martin · http://www.millermartin.com · Volunteer Building, Suite 1000 · 832 Georgia Avenue · Chattanooga, TN 37402-2289 · 423-756-6600

Kyle R. Weems · ㉕ · Weems & Ronan · 5312 Ringgold Road, Suite 203 · Chattanooga, TN 37412 · 423-624-1000

Knoxville

John A. Walker, Jr. · ⑳ · Walker & Walker · 507 South Gay Street, Suite 1200 · P.O. Box 2774 · Knoxville, TN 37901 · 865-523-0700

Memphis

James E. Bailey III · Farris Bobango Branan · http://www.farrismathews.com · One Commerce Square, Suite 2000 · Memphis, TN 38103 · 901-259-7100

J. David Blaylock · ⑳ · Glankler Brown · http://www.glankler.com · One Commerce Square, Suite 1700 · Memphis, TN 38103 · 901-525-1322

E. Franklin Childress, Jr. · Baker, Donelson, Bearman, Caldwell & Berkowitz · http://www.bakerdonelson.com · First Tennessee Building, Suite 2000 · 165 Madison Avenue · Memphis, TN 38103 · 901-526-2000

David J. Cocke · Evans Petree Bogatin · 1661 International Place Drive, Suite 300 · Memphis, TN 38120 901-767-1234

Michael P. Coury · ⑩ · Farris Bobango Branan · http://www.farrismathews.com · One Commerce Square, Suite 2000 · Memphis, TN 38103 · 901-259-7100

Steven N. Douglass · Harris Shelton Hanover Walsh · One Commerce Square, Suite 2700 · Memphis, TN 38103 · 901-525-1455

John R. Dunlap · ⑳ · Farris Bobango Branan · http://www.farrismathews.com · One Commerce Square, Suite 2000 · Memphis, TN 38103 · 901-259-7100

David J. Harris · Burch, Porter & Johnson · http://www.bpjlaw.com · 130 North Court Avenue · Memphis, TN 38103 · 901-524-5000

Jack S. Magids · Magids Cottam · 1661 International Place Drive · Memphis, TN 38120 · 901-682-6431

Toni C. Parker · a · Law Office of Toni Campbell Parker · 1661 International Place, Suite 400 · P.O. Box 240666 · Memphis, TN 38124 · 901-483-1020

Stephen W. Ragland · Bass, Berry & Sims · http://www.bassberry.com · The Tower at Peabody Place, Suite 900 · 100 Peabody Place · Memphis, TN 38103-2625 · 901-543-5900

John L. Ryder · 2% · Harris Shelton Hanover Walsh · One Commerce Square, Suite 2700 · Memphis, TN 38103 · 901-525-1455

Henry C. Shelton III · a · Adams and Reese · http://www.adamsandreese.com · Brinkley Plaza, Suite 700 80 Monroe Avenue · Memphis, TN 38103 · 901-525-3234

Ellen B. Vergos · Wyatt, Tarrant & Combs · http://www.wyattfirm.com · The Renaissance Center, Suite 800 · 1715 Aaron Brenner Drive · Memphis, TN 38120 · 901-537-1000

Nashville

Lawrence R. Ahern III · 2) · Burr & Forman · http://www.burr.com · 700 Two American Center · 3102 West End Avenue · Nashville, TN 37203 · 615-724-3200

G. Rhea Bucy · 2) · Gullett, Sanford, Robinson & Martin · 315 Deaderick Street, Suite 1100 · P.O. Box 198888 · Nashville, TN 37219-8888 · 615-244-4994

Thomas H. Forrester · Gullett, Sanford, Robinson & Martin · 315 Deaderick Street, Suite 1100 · P.O. Box 198888 · Nashville, TN 37219-8888 · 615-244-4994

Craig V. Gabbert, Jr. · 2) · Harwell Howard Hyne Gabbert & Manner · http://www.h3gm.com · 315 Deaderick Street, Suite 1800 · Nashville, TN 37238-1800 · 615-256-0500

Robert J. Gonzales · MGLAW · http://www.mglaw.net · 2525 West End Avenue, Suite 1475 · Nashville, TN 37203 · 615-846-8000

Robert C. Goodrich, Jr. · a · Stites & Harbison · http://www.stites.com · SunTrust Plaza, Suite 800 · 401 Commerce Street · Nashville, TN 37219 · 615-244-5200

Robert A. Guy · Waller Lansden Dortch & Davis · http://www.wallerlaw.com · Nashville City Center, Suite 2700 · 511 Union Street · P.O. Box 198966 · Nashville, TN 37219-8966 · 615-244-6380

Barbara D. Holmes · Harwell Howard Hyne Gabbert & Manner · http://www.h3gm.com · 315 Deaderick Street, Suite 1800 · Nashville, TN 37238-1800 · 615-256-0500

Gene L. Humphreys · Bass, Berry & Sims · http://www.bassberry.com · 315 Deaderick Street, Suite 2700 Nashville, TN 37238-3001 · 615-742-6200

Paul G. Jennings · Bass, Berry & Sims · http://www.bassberry.com · 315 Deaderick Street, Suite 2700 · Nashville, TN 37238-3001 · 615-742-6200

Roger G. Jones · a · Boult, Cummings, Conners & Berry · http://www.boultcummings.com · Roundabout Plaza, Suite 700 · 1600 Division Street · P.O. Box 340025 · Nashville, TN 37203 · 615-244-2582

James R. Kelley · 2) · Neal & Harwell · One Nashville Place, Suite 2000 · 150 Fourth Avenue North · Nashville, TN 37219-2498 · 615-244-1713

Joseph Allen Kelly · MGLAW · http://www.mglaw.net · 2525 West End Avenue, Suite 1475 · Nashville, TN 37203 · 615-846-8000

David E. Lemke · Waller Lansden Dortch & Davis · http://www.wallerlaw.com · Nashville City Center, Suite 2700 · 511 Union Street · P.O. Box 198966 · Nashville, TN 37219-8966 · 615-244-6380

Bradley A. MacLean · a · Stites & Harbison · http://www.stites.com · SunTrust Plaza, Suite 800 · 401 Commerce Street · Nashville, TN 37219 · 615-244-5200

Randal S. Mashburn · a · Baker, Donelson, Bearman, Caldwell & Berkowitz · http://www.bakerdonelson.com · Commerce Center, Suite 1000 · 211 Commerce Street · Nashville, TN 37201 · 615-726-5600

John C. McLemore · Garfinkle, McLemore & Walker · 2000 Richard Jones Road, Suite 250 · P.O. Box 158249 · Nashville, TN 37215-2885 · 615-383-9495

Marc T. McNamee · a · Neal & Harwell · One Nashville Place, Suite 2000 · 150 Fourth Avenue North · Nashville, TN 37219-2498 · 615-244-1713

Robert J. Mendes · MGLAW · http://www.mglaw.net · 2525 West End Avenue, Suite 1475 · Nashville, TN 37203 · 615-846-8000

William L. Norton III · a · Boult, Cummings, Conners & Berry · http://www.boultcummings.com · Roundabout Plaza, Suite 700 · 1600 Division Street · P.O. Box 340025 · Nashville, TN 37203 · 615-244-2582

William R. O'Bryan, Jr. · a · Miller & Martin · http://www.millermartin.com · One Nashville Place, Suite 1200 · 150 Fourth Avenue North · Nashville, TN 37219-2433 · 615-244-9270

Michael R. Paslay · Waller Lansden Dortch & Davis · http://www.wallerlaw.com · Nashville City Center, Suite 2700 · 511 Union Street · P.O. Box 198966 · Nashville, TN 37219-8966 · 615-244-6380

Wm. Robert Pope, Jr. · White & Reasor · http://www.whitereasor.com · Two American Center, Suite 1150 · 3102 West End Avenue · Nashville, TN 37203-1304 · 615-383-3345

Glenn B. Rose · Harwell Howard Hyne Gabbert & Manner · http://www.h3gm.com · 315 Deaderick Street, Suite 1800 · Nashville, TN 37238-1800 · 615-256-0500

John H. Rowland · Baker, Donelson, Bearman, Caldwell & Berkowitz · http://www.bakerdonelson.com · Commerce Center, Suite 1000 · 211 Commerce Street · Nashville, TN 37201 · 615-726-5600

Ronald G. Steen, Jr. · Stites & Harbison · http://www.stites.com · SunTrust Plaza, Suite 800 · 401 Commerce Street · Nashville, TN 37219 · 615-244-5200

Larry Stewart · Adams and Reese · http://www.adamsandreese.com · Fifth Third Center, Suite 2800 · 424 Church Street · Nashville, TN 37219 · 615-259-1450

John C. Tishler · Waller Lansden Dortch & Davis · http://www.wallerlaw.com · Nashville City Center, Suite 2700 · 511 Union Street · P.O. Box 198966 · Nashville, TN 37219-8966 · 615-244-6380

BET-THE-COMPANY LITIGATION

Brentwood

John A. Day · a · Day & Blair · 5300 Maryland Way, Suite 300 · Brentwood, TN 37027 · 615-742-4880

Chattanooga

T. Maxfield Bahner · 2) · Chambliss, Bahner & Stophel · http://www.cbslawfirm.com · 1000 Tallan Building · Two Union Square · Chattanooga, TN 37402 · 423-756-3000

Roger W. Dickson · a · Miller & Martin · http://www.millermartin.com · Volunteer Building, Suite 1000 · 832 Georgia Avenue · Chattanooga, TN 37402-2289 · 423-756-6600

Charles J. Gearhiser · 2% · Gearhiser, Peters, Lockaby, Cavett & Elliott · http://www.gplce.com · 320 McCallie Avenue · Chattanooga, TN 37402 · 423-756-5171

Hugh J. Moore, Jr. · a · Chambliss, Bahner & Stophel · http://www.cbslawfirm.com · 1000 Tallan Building · Two Union Square · Chattanooga, TN 37402 · 423-756-3000

Knoxville

Bernard E. Bernstein · 2) · Bernstein, Stair & McAdams · 4823 Old Kingston Pike, Suite 300 · Knoxville, TN 37919 · 865-546-8030

Dwight E. Tarwater · Paine, Tarwater, Bickers and Tillman · First Tennessee Plaza, Suite 1100 · 800 South Gay Street · P.O. Box 198 · Knoxville, TN 37929 · 865-525-0880

Memphis

Leo M. Bearman, Jr. · a · Baker, Donelson, Bearman, Caldwell & Berkowitz · http://www.bakerdonelson.com · First Tennessee Building, Suite 2000 · 165 Madison Avenue · Memphis, TN 38103 · 901-526-2000

Jef Feibelman · a · Burch, Porter & Johnson · http://www.bpjlaw.com · 130 North Court Avenue · Memphis, TN 38103 · 901-524-5000

J. Brook Lathram · a · Burch, Porter & Johnson · http://www.bpjlaw.com · 130 North Court Avenue · Memphis, TN 38103 · 901-524-5000

Charles F. Newman · a · Burch, Porter & Johnson · http://www.bpjlaw.com · 130 North Court Avenue · Memphis, TN 38103 · 901-524-5000

Joel Porter · a · Burch, Porter & Johnson · http://www.bpjlaw.com · 130 North Court Avenue · Memphis, TN 38103 · 901-524-5000

Glen G. Reid, Jr. · a · Wyatt, Tarrant & Combs · http://www.wyattfirm.com · The Renaissance Center, Suite 800 · 1715 Aaron Brenner Drive · Memphis, TN 38120 · 901-537-1000

Nashville

H. Lee Barfield II · a · Bass, Berry & Sims · http://www.bassberry.com · 315 Deaderick Street, Suite 2700 Nashville, TN 37238-3001 · 615-742-6200

Robert E. Boston · Waller Lansden Dortch & Davis · http://www.wallerlaw.com · Nashville City Center, Suite 2700 · 511 Union Street · P.O. Box 198966 · Nashville, TN 37219-8966 · 615-244-6380

William L. Harbison · Sherrard & Roe · http://www.sherrardroe.com · 424 Church Street, Suite 2000 · Nashville, TN 37219-3304 · 615-742-4200

Aubrey B. Harwell, Jr. · 2% · Neal & Harwell · One Nashville Place, Suite 2000 · 150 Fourth Avenue North · Nashville, TN 37219-2498 · 615-244-1713

Robert J. Walker · a · Walker, Tipps & Malone · 2300 One Nashville Place · 150 Fourth Avenue North · Nashville, TN 37219 · 615-313-6000

William R. Willis, Jr. · 2) · Willis & Knight · 215 Second Avenue North · Nashville, TN 37201 · 615-259-9600

CIVIL RIGHTS LAW

Nashville

Richard J. Braun · Braun & Crotwell · 501 Union Street, Suite 500 · Nashville, TN 37219 · 615-259-1550

COMMERCIAL LITIGATION

Brentwood

John A. Day · a · Day & Blair · 5300 Maryland Way, Suite 300 · Brentwood, TN 37027 · 615-742-4880

Chattanooga

Donald J. Aho · Miller & Martin · http://www.millermartin.com · Volunteer Building, Suite 1000 · 832 Georgia Avenue · Chattanooga, TN 37402-2289 · 423-756-6600

T. Maxfield Bahner · 2) · Chambliss, Bahner & Stophel · http://www.cbslawfirm.com · 1000 Tallan Building · Two Union Square · Chattanooga, TN 37402 · 423-756-3000

Scott N. Brown, Jr. · Spears, Moore, Rebman & Williams · Pioneer Building, Sixth Floor · 801 Broad Street · P.O. Box 1749 · Chattanooga, TN 37401-1749 · 423-756-7000

Rosemarie L. Bryan · Chambliss, Bahner & Stophel · http://www.cbslawfirm.com · 1000 Tallan Building · Two Union Square · Chattanooga, TN 37402 · 423-756-3000

Douglas M. Campbell · Campbell & Campbell · James Building, Suite 1200 · 735 Broad Street · Chattanooga, TN 37402-1835 · 423-266-1108

Joe A. Conner · Baker, Donelson, Bearman, Caldwell & Berkowitz · http://www.bakerdonelson.com · 1800 Republic Centre · 633 Chestnut Street · Chattanooga, TN 37450-1800 · 423-756-2010

George M. Derryberry · a · George M. Derryberry · 651 East Fourth Street, Suite 401 · Chattanooga, TN 37403 · 423-267-9777

Roger W. Dickson · a · Miller & Martin · http://www.millermartin.com · Volunteer Building, Suite 1000 · 832 Georgia Avenue · Chattanooga, TN 37402-2289 · 423-756-6600

Sam D. Elliott · Gearhiser, Peters, Lockaby, Cavett & Elliott · http://www.gplce.com · 320 McCallie Avenue · Chattanooga, TN 37402 · 423-756-5171

Charles J. Gearhiser · 2% · Gearhiser, Peters, Lockaby, Cavett & Elliott · http://www.gplce.com · 320 McCallie Avenue · Chattanooga, TN 37402 · 423-756-5171

Thomas O. Helton · 2% · Baker, Donelson, Bearman, Caldwell & Berkowitz · http://www.bakerdonelson.com · 1800 Republic Centre · 633 Chestnut Street · Chattanooga, TN 37450-1800 · 423-756-2010

Robert L. Lockaby, Jr. · a · Gearhiser, Peters, Lockaby, Cavett & Elliott · http://www.gplce.com · 320 McCallie Avenue · Chattanooga, TN 37402 · 423-756-5171

Hugh J. Moore, Jr. · a · Chambliss, Bahner & Stophel · http://www.cbslawfirm.com · 1000 Tallan Building · Two Union Square · Chattanooga, TN 37402 · 423-756-3000

W. Randall Wilson · Miller & Martin · http://www.millermartin.com · Volunteer Building, Suite 1000 · 832 Georgia Avenue · Chattanooga, TN 37402-2289 · 423-756-6600

Covington

J. Houston Gordon · 2% · Law Office of J. Houston Gordon · P.O. Box 846 · Covington, TN 38019 · 901-476-7100

Knoxville

Bernard E. Bernstein · 2) · Bernstein, Stair & McAdams · 4823 Old Kingston Pike, Suite 300 · Knoxville, TN 37919 · 865-546-8030

W. Kyle Carpenter · Woolf, McClane, Bright, Allen & Carpenter · 900 Riverview Tower · 900 South Gay Street · P.O. Box 900 · Knoxville, TN 37901-0900 · 865-215-1000

Thomas M. Hale · Kramer Rayson · http://www.kramer-rayson.com · First Tennessee Plaza, Suite 2500 · 800 South Gay Street · P.O. Box 629 · Knoxville, TN 37901-0629 · 865-525-5134

John T. Johnson, Jr. · Kramer Rayson · http://www.kramer-rayson.com · First Tennessee Plaza, Suite 2500 · 800 South Gay Street · P.O. Box 629 · Knoxville, TN 37901-0629 · 865-525-5134

James H. London · London & Amburn · BankEast Building, Suite 900 · 607 Market Street · Knoxville, TN 37916 · 865-637-0203

John A. Lucas · Merchant & Gould · 110 McGhee Tyson Boulevard · Knoxville, TN 37701 · 865-380-5978

Dennis R. McClane · Woolf, McClane, Bright, Allen & Carpenter · 900 Riverview Tower · 900 South Gay Street · P.O. Box 900 · Knoxville, TN 37901-0900 · 865-215-1000

James G. O'Kane · Baker, O'Kane, Atkins & Thompson · 2607 Kingston Pike, Suite 200 · P.O. Box 1708 · Knoxville, TN 37901 · 865-637-5600

Clarence Risin · Baker, Donelson, Bearman, Caldwell & Berkowitz · http://www.bakerdonelson.com · 2200 Riverview Tower · 900 South Gay Street · P.O. Box 1792 · Knoxville, TN 37902 · 865-549-7000

Dwight E. Tarwater · Paine, Tarwater, Bickers and Tillman · First Tennessee Plaza, Suite 1100 · 800 South Gay Street · P.O. Box 198 · Knoxville, TN 37929 · 865-525-0880

Howard H. Vogel · O'Neil, Parker and Williamson · 416 Cumberland Avenue, SW · P.O. Box 217 · Knoxville, TN 37902 · 865-546-7190

Maryville

David T. Black · Kizer & Black · http://www.kizer-black.com · 329 Cates Street · Maryville, TN 37801 · 865-982-7650

Leo M. Bearman, Jr. · a · Baker, Donelson, Bearman, Caldwell & Berkowitz · http://www.bakerdonelson.com · First Tennessee Building, Suite 2000 · 165 Madison Avenue · Memphis, TN 38103 · 901-526-2000

Saul C. Belz · Glankler Brown · http://www.glankler.com · One Commerce Square, Suite 1700 · Memphis, TN 38103 · 901-525-1322

Nathan A. Bicks · Burch, Porter & Johnson · http://www.bpjlaw.com · 130 North Court Avenue · Memphis, TN 38103 · 901-524-5000

Sam B. Blair, Jr. · Baker, Donelson, Bearman, Caldwell & Berkowitz · http://www.bakerdonelson.com · First Tennessee Building, Suite 2000 · 165 Madison Avenue · Memphis, TN 38103 · 901-526-2000

Oscar C. Carr III · 2) · Glankler Brown · http://www.glankler.com · One Commerce Square, Suite 1700 · Memphis, TN 38103 · 901-525-1322

Richard M. Carter · Martin, Tate, Morrow & Marston · International Place Tower II, Suite 1000 · 6410 Poplar Avenue · Memphis, TN 38119-4843 · 901-522-9000

Lee James Chase III · a · Glankler Brown · http://www.glankler.com · One Commerce Square, Suite 1700 · Memphis, TN 38103 · 901-525-1322

Robert E. Craddock, Jr. · Wyatt, Tarrant & Combs · http://www.wyattfirm.com · The Renaissance Center, Suite 800 · 1715 Aaron Brenner Drive · Memphis, TN 38120 · 901-537-1000

Robert L. Crawford · Wyatt, Tarrant & Combs · http://www.wyattfirm.com · The Renaissance Center, Suite 800 · 1715 Aaron Brenner Drive · Memphis, TN 38120 · 901-537-1000

Jef Feibelman · a · Burch, Porter & Johnson · http://www.bpjlaw.com · 130 North Court Avenue · Memphis, TN 38103 · 901-524-5000

Gregory G. Fletcher · Baker, Donelson, Bearman, Caldwell & Berkowitz · http://www.bakerdonelson.com · First Tennessee Building, Suite 2000 · 165 Madison Avenue · Memphis, TN 38103 · 901-526-2000

James R. Garts, Jr. · a · Garts Law Firm · 369 North Main Street · Memphis, TN 38103 · 901-834-8911

R. Mark Glover · Baker, Donelson, Bearman, Caldwell & Berkowitz · http://www.bakerdonelson.com · First Tennessee Building, Suite 2000 · 165 Madison Avenue · Memphis, TN 38103 · 901-526-2000

David J. Harris · Burch, Porter & Johnson · http://www.bpjlaw.com · 130 North Court Avenue · Memphis, TN 38103 · 901-524-5000

Charles W. Hill · Glankler Brown · http://www.glankler.com · One Commerce Square, Suite 1700 · Memphis, TN 38103 · 901-525-1322

Frank M. Holbrook · Butler, Snow, O'Mara, Stevens and Cannada · http://www.butlersnow.com · The Crescent Center, Suite 500 · 6075 Poplar Avenue · P.O. Box 171443 · Memphis, TN 38119 · 901-680-7200

Robert L. Hutton · Glankler Brown · http://www.glankler.com · One Commerce Square, Suite 1700 · Memphis, TN 38103 · 901-525-1322

James L. Kirby · Harris Shelton Hanover Walsh · One Commerce Square, Suite 2700 · Memphis, TN 38103 · 901-525-1455

J. Brook Lathram · a · Burch, Porter & Johnson · http://www.bpjlaw.com · 130 North Court Avenue · Memphis, TN 38103 · 901-524-5000

George T. Lewis III · Baker, Donelson, Bearman, Caldwell & Berkowitz · http://www.bakerdonelson.com First Tennessee Building, Suite 2000 · 165 Madison Avenue · Memphis, TN 38103 · 901-526-2000

Allen T. Malone · Burch, Porter & Johnson · http://www.bpjlaw.com · 130 North Court Avenue · Memphis, TN 38103 · 901-524-5000

John W. McQuiston II · a · Evans Petree Bogatin · http://www.evanspetree.com · 1000 Ridgeway Loop Road, Suite 200 · Memphis, TN 38120 · 901-525-6781

Charles F. Newman · a · Burch, Porter & Johnson · http://www.bpjlaw.com · 130 North Court Avenue · Memphis, TN 38103 · 901-524-5000

Randall D. Noel · Butler, Snow, O'Mara, Stevens and Cannada · http://www.butlersnow.com · The Crescent Center, Suite 500 · 6075 Poplar Avenue · P.O. Box 171443 · Memphis, TN 38119 · 901-680-7200

Lucian T. Pera · Adams and Reese · http://www.adamsandreese.com · Brinkley Plaza, Suite 700 · 80 Monroe Avenue · Memphis, TN 38103 · 901-525-3234

Eugene J. Podesta, Jr. · Baker, Donelson, Bearman, Caldwell & Berkowitz · http://www.bakerdonelson.com · First Tennessee Building, Suite 2000 · 165 Madison Avenue · Memphis, TN 38103 · 901-526-2000

Joel Porter · a · Burch, Porter & Johnson · http://www.bpjlaw.com · 130 North Court Avenue · Memphis, TN 38103 · 901-524-5000

Glen G. Reid, Jr. · a · Wyatt, Tarrant & Combs · http://www.wyattfirm.com · The Renaissance Center, Suite 800 · 1715 Aaron Brenner Drive · Memphis, TN 38120 · 901-537-1000

DeWitt M. Shy, Jr. · Burch, Porter & Johnson · http://www.bpjlaw.com · 130 North Court Avenue · Memphis, TN 38103 · 901-524-5000

Joe D. Spicer · 2% · Spicer, Flynn & Rudstrom · 175 Toyota Plaza, Suite 800 · Memphis, TN 38103 · 901-523-1333

Jerry Stauffer · Baker, Donelson, Bearman, Caldwell & Berkowitz · http://www.bakerdonelson.com · First Tennessee Building, Suite 2000 · 165 Madison Avenue · Memphis, TN 38103 · 901-526-2000

Shepherd D. Tate · a · Bass, Berry & Sims · http://www.bassberry.com · The Tower at Peabody Place, Suite 900 · 100 Peabody Place · Memphis, TN 38103-2625 · 901-543-5900

Mark Vorder-Bruegge, Jr. · Wyatt, Tarrant & Combs · http://www.wyattfirm.com · The Renaissance Center, Suite 800 · 1715 Aaron Brenner Drive · Memphis, TN 38120 · 901-537-1000

David C. Wade · a · Martin, Tate, Morrow & Marston · International Place Tower II, Suite 1000 · 6410 Poplar Avenue · Memphis, TN 38119-4843 · 901-522-9000

C. Barry Ward · a · Glankler Brown · http://www.glankler.com · One Commerce Square, Suite 1700 · Memphis, TN 38103 · 901-525-1322

Buckner P. Wellford · Baker, Donelson, Bearman, Caldwell & Berkowitz · http://www.bakerdonelson.com · First Tennessee Building, Suite 2000 · 165 Madison Avenue · Memphis, TN 38103 · 901-526-2000

Nashville

Paul A. Alexis · Boult, Cummings, Conners & Berry · http://www.boultcummings.com · Roundabout Plaza, Suite 700 · 1600 Division Street · P.O. Box 340025 · Nashville, TN 37203 · 615-244-2582

H. Lee Barfield II · a · Bass, Berry & Sims · http://www.bassberry.com · 315 Deaderick Street, Suite 2700 Nashville, TN 37238-3001 · 615-742-6200

J. Randolph Bibb, Jr. · Waller Lansden Dortch & Davis · http://www.wallerlaw.com · Nashville City Center, Suite 2700 · 511 Union Street · P.O. Box 198966 · Nashville, TN 37219-8966 · 615-244-6380

Robert E. Boston · Waller Lansden Dortch & Davis · http://www.wallerlaw.com · Nashville City Center, Suite 2700 · 511 Union Street · P.O. Box 198966 · Nashville, TN 37219-8966 · 615-244-6380

Eugene N. Bulso, Jr. · Leader, Bulso & Nolan · http://www.leaderbulso.com · 414 Union Street, Suite 1740 · Nashville, TN 37219 · 615-780-4100

Julie Murphy Burnstein · Boult, Cummings, Conners & Berry · http://www.boultcummings.com · Roundabout Plaza, Suite 700 · 1600 Division Street · P.O. Box 340025 · Nashville, TN 37203 · 615-244-2582

L. Webb Campbell II · Sherrard & Roe · http://www.sherrardroe.com · 424 Church Street, Suite 2000 · Nashville, TN 37219-3304 · 615-742-4200

Scott D. Carey · Baker, Donelson, Bearman, Caldwell & Berkowitz · http://www.bakerdonelson.com · Commerce Center, Suite 1000 · 211 Commerce Street · Nashville, TN 37201 · 615-726-5600

Lewis H. Conner, Jr. · 2) · Waller Lansden Dortch & Davis · http://www.wallerlaw.com · Nashville City Center, Suite 2700 · 511 Union Street · P.O. Box 198966 · Nashville, TN 37219-8966 · 615-244-6380

Walter H. Crouch · Waller Lansden Dortch & Davis · http://www.wallerlaw.com · Nashville City Center, Suite 2700 · 511 Union Street · P.O. Box 198966 · Nashville, TN 37219-8966 · 615-244-6380

Michael L. Dagley · Bass, Berry & Sims · http://www.bassberry.com · 315 Deaderick Street, Suite 2700 · Nashville, TN 37238-3001 · 615-742-6200

Paul S. Davidson · Waller Lansden Dortch & Davis · http://www.wallerlaw.com · Nashville City Center, Suite 2700 · 511 Union Street · P.O. Box 198966 · Nashville, TN 37219-8966 · 615-244-6380

Ames Davis · 2) · Waller Lansden Dortch & Davis · http://www.wallerlaw.com · Nashville City Center, Suite 2700 · 511 Union Street · P.O. Box 198966 · Nashville, TN 37219-8966 · 615-244-6380

Maclin P. Davis, Jr. · 2% · Waller Lansden Dortch & Davis · http://www.wallerlaw.com · Nashville City Center, Suite 2700 · 511 Union Street · P.O. Box 198966 · Nashville, TN 37219-8966 · 615-244-6380

Wallace W. Dietz · Bass, Berry & Sims · http://www.bassberry.com · 315 Deaderick Street, Suite 2700 · Nashville, TN 37238-3001 · 615-742-6200

James M. Doran, Jr. · Waller Lansden Dortch & Davis · http://www.wallerlaw.com · Nashville City Center, Suite 2700 · 511 Union Street · P.O. Box 198966 · Nashville, TN 37219-8966 · 615-244-6380

D. Alexander Fardon · Harwell Howard Hyne Gabbert & Manner · http://www.h3gm.com · 315 Deaderick Street, Suite 1800 · Nashville, TN 37238-1800 · 615-256-0500

Samuel Lanier Felker · Bass, Berry & Sims · http://www.bassberry.com · 315 Deaderick Street, Suite 2700 · Nashville, TN 37238-3001 · 615-742-6200

Samuel P. Funk · Sherrard & Roe · http://www.sherrardroe.com · 424 Church Street, Suite 2000 · Nashville, TN 37219-3304 · 615-742-4200

Craig V. Gabbert, Jr. · 2) · Harwell Howard Hyne Gabbert & Manner · http://www.h3gm.com · 315 Deaderick Street, Suite 1800 · Nashville, TN 37238-1800 · 615-256-0500

William W. Gibson · Wyatt, Tarrant & Combs · http://www.wyattfirm.com · 2525 West End Avenue, Suite 1500 · Nashville, TN 37203-1423 · 615-244-0020

R. Dale Grimes · a · Bass, Berry & Sims · http://www.bassberry.com · 315 Deaderick Street, Suite 2700 · Nashville, TN 37238-3001 · 615-742-6200

Garry K. Grooms · Stites & Harbison · http://www.stites.com · SunTrust Plaza, Suite 800 · 401 Commerce Street · Nashville, TN 37219 · 615-244-5200

William L. Harbison · Sherrard & Roe · http://www.sherrardroe.com · 424 Church Street, Suite 2000 · Nashville, TN 37219-3304 · 615-742-4200

Robb S. Harvey · Waller Lansden Dortch & Davis · http://www.wallerlaw.com · Nashville City Center, Suite 2700 · 511 Union Street · P.O. Box 198966 · Nashville, TN 37219-8966 · 615-244-6380

Aubrey B. Harwell, Jr. · 2% · Neal & Harwell · One Nashville Place, Suite 2000 · 150 Fourth Avenue North · Nashville, TN 37219-2498 · 615-244-1713

John S. Hicks · Baker, Donelson, Bearman, Caldwell & Berkowitz · http://www.bakerdonelson.com · Commerce Center, Suite 1000 · 211 Commerce Street · Nashville, TN 37201 · 615-726-5600

John R. Jacobson · Riley Warnock & Jacobson · 1906 West End Avenue · Nashville, TN 37203 · 615-320-3700

Phillip B. Jones · Evans, Jones & Reynolds · Suntrust Plaza, Suite 710 · 401 Commerce Street · P.O. Box 190627 · Nashville, TN 37219-0627 · 615-259-4685

David A. King · Bass, Berry & Sims · http://www.bassberry.com · 315 Deaderick Street, Suite 2700 · Nashville, TN 37238-3001 · 615-742-6200

Philip M. Kirkpatrick · a · Stewart, Estes & Donnell · Fifth Third Center, Suite 1401 · 424 Church Street · Nashville, TN 37219 · 615-244-6538

Thomas W. Lawrence, Jr. · Parker, Lawrence, Cantrell & Dean · 200 Fourth Avenue North, Fifth Floor · Nashville, TN 37219 · 615-255-7500

J. Richard Lodge, Jr. · Bass, Berry & Sims · http://www.bassberry.com · 315 Deaderick Street, Suite 2700 Nashville, TN 37238-3001 · 615-742-6200

Blakeley D. Matthews · Cornelius & Collins · Nashville City Center, Suite 1500 · 511 Union Street · P.O. Box 190695 · Nashville, TN 37219-0695 · 615-244-1440

Malcolm L. McCune · Blackburn & McCune · 101 Lea Avenue · Nashville, TN 37210 · 615-254-7770

Anthony J. McFarland · Bass, Berry & Sims · http://www.bassberry.com · 315 Deaderick Street, Suite 2700 · Nashville, TN 37238-3001 · 615-742-6200

Robert J. Mendes · MGLAW · http://www.mglaw.net · 2525 West End Avenue, Suite 1475 · Nashville, TN 37203 · 615-846-8000

Russell B. Morgan · Boult, Cummings, Conners & Berry · http://www.boultcummings.com · Roundabout Plaza, Suite 700 · 1600 Division Street · P.O. Box 340025 · Nashville, TN 37203 · 615-244-2582

Patricia H. Moskal · Boult, Cummings, Conners & Berry · http://www.boultcummings.com · Roundabout Plaza, Suite 700 · 1600 Division Street · P.O. Box 340025 · Nashville, TN 37203 · 615-244-2582

Barbara J. Moss · Stites & Harbison · http://www.stites.com · SunTrust Plaza, Suite 800 · 401 Commerce Street · Nashville, TN 37219 · 615-244-5200

William L. Norton III · a · Boult, Cummings, Conners & Berry · http://www.boultcummings.com · Roundabout Plaza, Suite 700 · 1600 Division Street · P.O. Box 340025 · Nashville, TN 37203 · 615-244-2582

William R. O'Bryan, Jr. · a · Miller & Martin · http://www.millermartin.com · One Nashville Place, Suite 1200 · 150 Fourth Avenue North · Nashville, TN 37219-2433 · 615-244-9270

W. Travis Parham · Waller Lansden Dortch & Davis · http://www.wallerlaw.com · Nashville City Center, Suite 2700 · 511 Union Street · P.O. Box 198966 · Nashville, TN 37219-8966 · 615-244-6380

Robert S. Patterson · Boult, Cummings, Conners & Berry · http://www.boultcummings.com · Roundabout Plaza, Suite 700 · 1600 Division Street · P.O. Box 340025 · Nashville, TN 37203 · 615-244-2582

C. Mark Pickrell · Waller Lansden Dortch & Davis · http://www.wallerlaw.com · Nashville City Center, Suite 2700 · 511 Union Street · P.O. Box 198966 · Nashville, TN 37219-8966 · 615-244-6380

Thomas K. Potter III · Burr & Forman · http://www.burr.com · 700 Two American Center · 3102 West End Avenue · Nashville, TN 37203 · 615-724-3200

E. Todd Presnell · Miller & Martin · http://www.millermartin.com · One Nashville Place, Suite 1200 · 150 Fourth Avenue North · Nashville, TN 37219-2433 · 615-244-9270

Daniel H. Puryear · Smythe Puryear & Robertson · Pilcher Building, Third Floor · 144 Second Avenue North · Nashville, TN 37201 · 615-255-4849

Gregory S. Reynolds · Riley Warnock & Jacobson · 1906 West End Avenue · Nashville, TN 37203 · 615-320-3700

Steven Riley · Riley Warnock & Jacobson · 1906 West End Avenue · Nashville, TN 37203 · 615-320-3700

Glenn B. Rose · Harwell Howard Hyne Gabbert & Manner · http://www.h3gm.com · 315 Deaderick Street, Suite 1800 · Nashville, TN 37238-1800 · 615-256-0500

Gary C. Shockley · a · Baker, Donelson, Bearman, Caldwell & Berkowitz · http://www.bakerdonelson.com · Commerce Center, Suite 1000 · 211 Commerce Street · Nashville, TN 37201 · 615-726-5600

Paul G. Summers · Waller Lansden Dortch & Davis · http://www.wallerlaw.com · Nashville City Center, Suite 2700 · 511 Union Street · P.O. Box 198966 · Nashville, TN 37219-8966 · 615-244-6380

Matthew J. Sweeney III · Baker, Donelson, Bearman, Caldwell & Berkowitz · http://www.bakerdonelson.com · Commerce Center, Suite 1000 · 211 Commerce Street · Nashville, TN 37201 · 615-726-5600

Overton Thompson III · Bass, Berry & Sims · http://www.bassberry.com · 315 Deaderick Street, Suite 2700 · Nashville, TN 37238-3001 · 615-742-6200

Thor Y. Urness · Boult, Cummings, Conners & Berry · http://www.boultcummings.com · Roundabout Plaza, Suite 700 · 1600 Division Street · P.O. Box 340025 · Nashville, TN 37203 · 615-244-2582

Robert J. Walker · a · Walker, Tipps & Malone · 2300 One Nashville Place · 150 Fourth Avenue North · Nashville, TN 37219 · 615-313-6000

John Knox Walkup · Wyatt, Tarrant & Combs · http://www.wyattfirm.com · 2525 West End Avenue, Suite 1500 · Nashville, TN 37203-1423 · 615-244-0020

Timothy L. Warnock · Riley Warnock & Jacobson · 1906 West End Avenue · Nashville, TN 37203 · 615-320-3700

A. Russell Willis · Willis & Knight · 215 Second Avenue North · Nashville, TN 37201 · 615-259-9600

William R. Willis, Jr. · 2) · Willis & Knight · 215 Second Avenue North · Nashville, TN 37201 · 615-259-9600

John R. Wingo · Frost Brown Todd · http://www.frostbrowntodd.com · 424 Church Street, Suite 1600 · Nashville, TN 37219-2308 · 615-251-5550

Joseph A. Woodruff · Waller Lansden Dortch & Davis · http://www.wallerlaw.com · Nashville City Center, Suite 2700 · 511 Union Street · P.O. Box 198966 · Nashville, TN 37219-8966 · 615-244-6380

CONSTRUCTION LAW

Chattanooga

Joe A. Conner · Baker, Donelson, Bearman, Caldwell & Berkowitz · http://www.bakerdonelson.com · 1800 Republic Centre · 633 Chestnut Street · Chattanooga, TN 37450-1800 · 423-756-2010

Knoxville

Robert H. Green · Kennerly Montgomery & Finley · Bank of America Center, Fourth Floor · 550 Main Avenue · P.O. Box 442 · Knoxville, TN 37901-0442 · 865-546-7311

Albert J. Harb · Hodges, Doughty & Carson · 617 Main Street · P.O. Box 869 · Knoxville, TN 37901-0869 · 865-546-9611

Jack M. Tallent II · Kennerly Montgomery & Finley · Bank of America Center, Fourth Floor · 550 Main Avenue · P.O. Box 442 · Knoxville, TN 37901-0442 · 865-546-7311

R. Loy Waldrop · Lewis, King, Krieg & Waldrop · http://www.lewisking.com · One Centre Square, Fifth Floor · 620 Market Street · P.O. Box 2425 · Knoxville, TN 37901 · 865-546-4646

Memphis

Joseph T. Getz · Less, Getz & Lipman · 100 Peabody Place, Suite 1000 · Memphis, TN 38103 · 901-525-8700

Michael I. Less · Less, Getz & Lipman · 100 Peabody Place, Suite 1000 · Memphis, TN 38103 · 901-525-8700

James B. Summers · Allen, Summers, Simpson, Lillie & Gresham · Brinkley Plaza, Suite 650 · 80 Monroe Avenue · Memphis, TN 38103 · 901-763-4200

Murfreesboro

John T. Blankenship · Blankenship and Blankenship · 307 Hickerson Drive · Murfreesboro, TN 37129 · 615-893-4160

Nashville

Gregory L. Cashion · Smith Cashion & Orr · 231 Third Avenue North · Nashville, TN 37201-1603 · 615-742-8555

Christopher S. Dunn · Waller Lansden Dortch & Davis · http://www.wallerlaw.com · Nashville City Center, Suite 2700 · 511 Union Street · P.O. Box 198966 · Nashville, TN 37219-8966 · 615-244-6380

David N. Garst · Lewis, King, Krieg & Waldrop · http://www.lewisking.com · Suntrust Bank Building, Suite 1500 · 201 Fourth Avenue North · P.O. Box 198615 · Nashville, TN 37219 · 615-259-1366

L. Wearen Hughes · Bass, Berry & Sims · http://www.bassberry.com · 315 Deaderick Street, Suite 2700 · Nashville, TN 37238-3001 · 615-742-6200

Lawrence C. Maxwell · Baker, Donelson, Bearman, Caldwell & Berkowitz · http://www.bakerdonelson.com · Commerce Center, Suite 1000 · 211 Commerce Street · Nashville, TN 37201 · 615-726-5600

Don L. Smith · Smith Cashion & Orr · 231 Third Avenue North · Nashville, TN 37201-1603 · 615-742-8555

David K. Taylor · Boult, Cummings, Conners & Berry · http://www.boultcummings.com · Roundabout Plaza, Suite 700 · 1600 Division Street · P.O. Box 340025 · Nashville, TN 37203 · 615-244-2582

CORPORATE GOVERNANCE AND COMPLIANCE LAW

Johnson City

Linda M. Crouch-McCreadie · Baker, Donelson, Bearman, Caldwell & Berkowitz · http://www.bakerdonelson.com · 100 Med Tech Parkway, Suite 200 · P.O. Box 3038 · Johnson City, TN 37602 · 423-928-0181

Memphis

Samuel D. Chafetz · 2% · Baker, Donelson, Bearman, Caldwell & Berkowitz · http://www.bakerdonelson.com · First Tennessee Building, Suite 2000 · 165 Madison Avenue · Memphis, TN 38103 · 901-526-2000

Robert J. DelPriore · Baker, Donelson, Bearman, Caldwell & Berkowitz · http://www.bakerdonelson.com · First Tennessee Building, Suite 2000 · 165 Madison Avenue · Memphis, TN 38103 · 901-526-2000

John A. Good · a · Bass, Berry & Sims · http://www.bassberry.com · The Tower at Peabody Place, Suite 900 · 100 Peabody Place · Memphis, TN 38103-2625 · 901-543-5900

Matthew S. Heiter · Baker, Donelson, Bearman, Caldwell & Berkowitz · http://www.bakerdonelson.com · First Tennessee Building, Suite 2000 · 165 Madison Avenue · Memphis, TN 38103 · 901-526-2000

Nashville

Gary M. Brown · a · Baker, Donelson, Bearman, Caldwell & Berkowitz · http://www.bakerdonelson.com Commerce Center, Suite 1000 · 211 Commerce Street · Nashville, TN 37201 · 615-726-5600

James H. Cheek III · 2) · Bass, Berry & Sims · http://www.bassberry.com · 315 Deaderick Street, Suite 2700 · Nashville, TN 37238-3001 · 615-742-6200

J. Page Davidson · Bass, Berry & Sims · http://www.bassberry.com · 315 Deaderick Street, Suite 2700 · Nashville, TN 37238-3001 · 615-742-6200

Howard H. Lamar III · Bass, Berry & Sims · http://www.bassberry.com · 315 Deaderick Street, Suite 2700 Nashville, TN 37238-3001 · 615-742-6200

Mark Manner · a · Harwell Howard Hyne Gabbert & Manner · http://www.h3gm.com · 315 Deaderick Street, Suite 1800 · Nashville, TN 37238-1800 · 615-256-0500

J. Allen Overby · Bass, Berry & Sims · http://www.bassberry.com · 315 Deaderick Street, Suite 2700 · Nashville, TN 37238-3001 · 615-742-6200

J. Bradbury Reed · a · Bass, Berry & Sims · http://www.bassberry.com · 315 Deaderick Street, Suite 2700 Nashville, TN 37238-3001 · 615-742-6200

Todd J. Rolapp · Bass, Berry & Sims · http://www.bassberry.com · 315 Deaderick Street, Suite 2700 · Nashville, TN 37238-3001 · 615-742-6200

Glenn B. Rose · Harwell Howard Hyne Gabbert & Manner · http://www.h3gm.com · 315 Deaderick Street, Suite 1800 · Nashville, TN 37238-1800 · 615-256-0500

Samuel E. Stumpf, Jr. · a · Bass, Berry & Sims · http://www.bassberry.com · 315 Deaderick Street, Suite 2700 · Nashville, TN 37238-3001 · 615-742-6200

Bob F. Thompson · a · Bass, Berry & Sims · http://www.bassberry.com · 315 Deaderick Street, Suite 2700 · Nashville, TN 37238-3001 · 615-742-6200

F. Mitchell Walker, Jr. · Bass, Berry & Sims · http://www.bassberry.com · 315 Deaderick Street, Suite 2700 · Nashville, TN 37238-3001 · 615-742-6200

Leigh Walton · a · Bass, Berry & Sims · http://www.bassberry.com · 315 Deaderick Street, Suite 2700 · Nashville, TN 37238-3001 · 615-742-6200

CORPORATE LAW

Chattanooga

William P. Aiken · a · Chambliss, Bahner & Stophel · http://www.cbslawfirm.com · 1000 Tallan Building Two Union Square · Chattanooga, TN 37402 · 423-756-3000

J. Guy Beatty, Jr. · Miller & Martin · http://www.millermartin.com · Volunteer Building, Suite 1000 · 832 Georgia Avenue · Chattanooga, TN 37402-2289 · 423-756-6600

Kenneth C. Beckman · Baker, Donelson, Bearman, Caldwell & Berkowitz · http://www.bakerdonelson.com · 1800 Republic Centre · 633 Chestnut Street · Chattanooga, TN 37450-1800 · 423-756-2010

Thomas A. Caldwell · 2% · Baker, Donelson, Bearman, Caldwell & Berkowitz · http://www.bakerdonelson.com · 1800 Republic Centre · 633 Chestnut Street · Chattanooga, TN 37450-1800 · 423-756-2010

Carl E. Hartley · Baker, Donelson, Bearman, Caldwell & Berkowitz · http://www.bakerdonelson.com · 1800 Republic Centre · 633 Chestnut Street · Chattanooga, TN 37450-1800 · 423-756-2010

J. Nelson Irvine · Chambliss, Bahner & Stophel · http://www.cbslawfirm.com · 1000 Tallan Building · Two Union Square · Chattanooga, TN 37402 · 423-756-3000

E. Stephen Jett · Chambliss, Bahner & Stophel · http://www.cbslawfirm.com · 1000 Tallan Building · Two Union Square · Chattanooga, TN 37402 · 423-756-3000

W. Scott McGinness, Jr. · Miller & Martin · http://www.millermartin.com · Volunteer Building, Suite 1000 · 832 Georgia Avenue · Chattanooga, TN 37402-2289 · 423-756-6600

Hugh F. Sharber · Miller & Martin · http://www.millermartin.com · Volunteer Building, Suite 1000 · 832 Georgia Avenue · Chattanooga, TN 37402-2289 · 423-756-6600

Carlos C. Smith · a · Miller & Martin · http://www.millermartin.com · Volunteer Building, Suite 1000 · 832 Georgia Avenue · Chattanooga, TN 37402-2289 · 423-756-6600

Glenn C. Stophel · ㉕ · Chambliss, Bahner & Stophel · http://www.cbslawfirm.com · 1000 Tallan Building Two Union Square · Chattanooga, TN 37402 · 423-756-3000

Johnson City

Linda M. Crouch-McCreadie · Baker, Donelson, Bearman, Caldwell & Berkowitz · http://www.bakerdonelson.com · 100 Med Tech Parkway, Suite 200 · P.O. Box 3038 · Johnson City, TN 37602 · 423-928-0181

William Gregory Hall · Baker, Donelson, Bearman, Caldwell & Berkowitz · http://www.bakerdonelson.com · 100 Med Tech Parkway, Suite 200 · P.O. Box 3038 · Johnson City, TN 37602 · 423-928-0181

Robert D. Van de Vuurst · Baker, Donelson, Bearman, Caldwell & Berkowitz · http://www.bakerdonelson.com · 100 Med Tech Parkway, Suite 200 · P.O. Box 3038 · Johnson City, TN 37602 · 423-928-0181

Knoxville

E. Bruce Foster, Jr. · ⑳ · Bass, Berry & Sims · http://www.bassberry.com · Riverview Tower, Suite 1700 · 900 South Gay Street · P.O. Box 1509 · Knoxville, TN 37901-1509 · 865-521-6200

Thomas M. Hale · Kramer Rayson · http://www.kramer-rayson.com · First Tennessee Plaza, Suite 2500 · 800 South Gay Street · P.O. Box 629 · Knoxville, TN 37901-0629 · 865-525-5134

Dennis R. McClane · Woolf, McClane, Bright, Allen & Carpenter · 900 Riverview Tower · 900 South Gay Street · P.O. Box 900 · Knoxville, TN 37901-0900 · 865-215-1000

William C. Myers, Jr. · ⑩ · Wagner, Myers & Sanger · 1801 First Tennessee Plaza · Knoxville, TN 37929 · 865-525-4600

Herbert S. Sanger, Jr. · ⑩ · Wagner, Myers & Sanger · 1801 First Tennessee Plaza · Knoxville, TN 37929 · 865-525-4600

Robert F. Worthington, Jr. · ⑩ · Baker, Donelson, Bearman, Caldwell & Berkowitz · http://www.bakerdonelson.com · 2200 Riverview Tower · 900 South Gay Street · P.O. Box 1792 · Knoxville, TN 37902 · 865-549-7000

Memphis

Ben C. Adams, Jr. · Baker, Donelson, Bearman, Caldwell & Berkowitz · http://www.bakerdonelson.com · First Tennessee Building, Suite 2000 · 165 Madison Avenue · Memphis, TN 38103 · 901-526-2000

G. Patrick Arnoult · Evans Petree Bogatin · 1661 International Place Drive, Suite 300 · Memphis, TN 38120 · 901-767-1234

John A. Bobango · Farris Bobango Branan · http://www.farrismathews.com 1100 Ridgeway Loop Road, Suite 400 · Memphis, TN 38120 · 901-259-7120

Robert Grattan Brown, Jr. · ㉕ · Glankler Brown · http://www.glankler.com · One Commerce Square, Suite 1700 · Memphis, TN 38103 · 901-525-1322

L. Don Campbell, Jr. · Butler, Snow, O'Mara, Stevens and Cannada · http://www.butlersnow.com · The Crescent Center, Suite 500 · 6075 Poplar Avenue · P.O. Box 171443 · Memphis, TN 38119 · 901-680-7200

Samuel D. Chafetz · ㉕ · Baker, Donelson, Bearman, Caldwell & Berkowitz · http://www.bakerdonelson.com · First Tennessee Building, Suite 2000 · 165 Madison Avenue · Memphis, TN 38103 · 901-526-2000

Charles R. Crawford · Butler, Snow, O'Mara, Stevens and Cannada · http://www.butlersnow.com · The Crescent Center, Suite 500 · 6075 Poplar Avenue · P.O. Box 171443 · Memphis, TN 38119 · 901-680-7200

Robert J. DelPriore · Baker, Donelson, Bearman, Caldwell & Berkowitz · http://www.bakerdonelson.com · First Tennessee Building, Suite 2000 · 165 Madison Avenue · Memphis, TN 38103 · 901-526-2000

Lewis R. Donelson III · ㉕ · Baker, Donelson, Bearman, Caldwell & Berkowitz · http://www.bakerdonelson.com · First Tennessee Building, Suite 2000 · 165 Madison Avenue · Memphis, TN 38103 · 901-526-2000

Joe M. Duncan · ⑩ · Burch, Porter & Johnson · http://www.bpjlaw.com · 130 North Court Avenue · Memphis, TN 38103 · 901-524-5000

Desiree M. Franklin · Baker, Donelson, Bearman, Caldwell & Berkowitz · http://www.bakerdonelson.com · First Tennessee Building, Suite 2000 · 165 Madison Avenue · Memphis, TN 38103 · 901-526-2000

John A. Good · ⑩ · Bass, Berry & Sims · http://www.bassberry.com · The Tower at Peabody Place, Suite 900 · 100 Peabody Place · Memphis, TN 38103-2625 · 901-543-5900

Lee A. Harkavy · Wyatt, Tarrant & Combs · http://www.wyattfirm.com · The Renaissance Center, Suite 800 · 1715 Aaron Brenner Drive · Memphis, TN 38120 · 901-537-1000

Matthew S. Heiter · Baker, Donelson, Bearman, Caldwell & Berkowitz · http://www.bakerdonelson.com · First Tennessee Building, Suite 2000 · 165 Madison Avenue · Memphis, TN 38103 · 901-526-2000

Russell J. Hensley, Jr. · Evans Petree Bogatin · 1661 International Place Drive, Suite 300 · Memphis, TN 38120 · 901-767-1234

Michael D. Kaplan · Harkavy Shainberg Kaplan & Dunstan · 6060 Poplar Avenue, Suite 140 · Memphis, TN 38119 · 901-761-1263

John E. Kruger · Baker, Donelson, Bearman, Caldwell & Berkowitz · http://www.bakerdonelson.com · First Tennessee Building, Suite 2000 · 165 Madison Avenue · Memphis, TN 38103 · 901-526-2000

Jack S. Magids · Magids Cottam · 1661 International Place Drive · Memphis, TN 38120 · 901-682-6431

William T. Mays, Jr. · Glankler Brown · http://www.glankler.com · One Commerce Square, Suite 1700 · Memphis, TN 38103 · 901-525-1322

G. Robert Morris · Butler, Snow, O'Mara, Stevens and Cannada · http://www.butlersnow.com · The Crescent Center, Suite 500 · 6075 Poplar Avenue · P.O. Box 171443 · Memphis, TN 38119 · 901-680-7200

Marye Helen Owen · Farris Bobango Branan · http://www.farrismathews.com · 1100 Ridgeway Loop Road, Suite 400 · Memphis, TN 38120 · 901-259-7120

Douglas P. Quay · Glankler Brown · http://www.glankler.com · One Commerce Square, Suite 1700 · Memphis, TN 38103 · 901-525-1322

Boyd L. Rhodes, Jr. · Wyatt, Tarrant & Combs · http://www.wyattfirm.com · The Renaissance Center, Suite 800 · 1715 Aaron Brenner Drive · Memphis, TN 38120 · 901-537-1000

Thaddeus S. Rodda, Jr. · Evans Petree Bogatin · 1661 International Place Drive, Suite 300 · Memphis, TN 38120 · 901-767-1234

William S. Solmson · ⑩ · Wyatt, Tarrant & Combs · http://www.wyattfirm.com · The Renaissance Center, Suite 800 · 1715 Aaron Brenner Drive · Memphis, TN 38120 · 901-537-1000

Jerry Stauffer · Baker, Donelson, Bearman, Caldwell & Berkowitz · http://www.bakerdonelson.com · First Tennessee Building, Suite 2000 · 165 Madison Avenue · Memphis, TN 38103 · 901-526-2000

S. Shepherd Tate · a · Martin, Tate, Morrow & Marston · International Place Tower II, Suite 1000 · 6410 Poplar Avenue · Memphis, TN 38119-4843 · 901-522-9000

J. Robert Walker · Baker, Donelson, Bearman, Caldwell & Berkowitz · http://www.bakerdonelson.com · First Tennessee Building, Suite 2000 · 165 Madison Avenue · Memphis, TN 38103 · 901-526-2000

Frank L. Watson, Jr. · a · Baker, Donelson, Bearman, Caldwell & Berkowitz · http://www.bakerdonelson.com · First Tennessee Building, Suite 2000 · 165 Madison Avenue · Memphis, TN 38103 · 901-526-2000

Laurel C. Williams · Burch, Porter & Johnson · http://www.bpjlaw.com · 130 North Court Avenue · Memphis, TN 38103 · 901-524-5000

Nashville

Patrick L. Alexander · Boult, Cummings, Conners & Berry · http://www.boultcummings.com · Roundabout Plaza, Suite 700 · 1600 Division Street · P.O. Box 340025 · Nashville, TN 37203 · 615-244-2582

Lauren W. Anderson · Baker, Donelson, Bearman, Caldwell & Berkowitz · http://www.bakerdonelson.com · Commerce Center, Suite 1000 · 211 Commerce Street · Nashville, TN 37201 · 615-726-5600

Andrea C. Barach · Boult, Cummings, Conners & Berry · http://www.boultcummings.com · Roundabout Plaza, Suite 700 · 1600 Division Street · P.O. Box 340025 · Nashville, TN 37203 · 615-244-2582

Samuel W. Bartholomew, Jr. · Adams and Reese · http://www.adamsandreese.com · Fifth Third Center, Suite 2800 · 424 Church Street · Nashville, TN 37219 · 615-259-1450

Julian L. Bibb · a · Stites & Harbison · http://www.stites.com · SunTrust Plaza, Suite 800 · 401 Commerce Street · Nashville, TN 37219 · 615-244-5200

George W. Bishop III · a · Waller Lansden Dortch & Davis · http://www.wallerlaw.com · Nashville City Center, Suite 2700 · 511 Union Street · P.O. Box 198966 · Nashville, TN 37219-8966 · 615-244-6380

Stephen T. Braun · Boult, Cummings, Conners & Berry · http://www.boultcummings.com · Roundabout Plaza, Suite 700 · 1600 Division Street · P.O. Box 340025 · Nashville, TN 37203 · 615-244-2582

Gary M. Brown · a · Baker, Donelson, Bearman, Caldwell & Berkowitz · http://www.bakerdonelson.com Commerce Center, Suite 1000 · 211 Commerce Street · Nashville, TN 37201 · 615-726-5600

Martin S. Brown, Jr. · Adams and Reese · http://www.adamsandreese.com · Fifth Third Center, Suite 2800 · 424 Church Street · Nashville, TN 37219 · 615-259-1450

Alexander B. Buchanan · Waller Lansden Dortch & Davis · http://www.wallerlaw.com · Nashville City Center, Suite 2700 · 511 Union Street · P.O. Box 198966 · Nashville, TN 37219-8966 · 615-244-6380

Ashby Q. Burks · Baker, Donelson, Bearman, Caldwell & Berkowitz · http://www.bakerdonelson.com · Commerce Center, Suite 1000 · 211 Commerce Street · Nashville, TN 37201 · 615-726-5600

A. Stuart Campbell · Stites & Harbison · http://www.stites.com · SunTrust Plaza, Suite 800 · 401 Commerce Street · Nashville, TN 37219 · 615-244-5200

James H. Cheek III · 2) · Bass, Berry & Sims · http://www.bassberry.com · 315 Deaderick Street, Suite 2700 · Nashville, TN 37238-3001 · 615-742-6200

Glen A. Civitts · Harwell Howard Hyne Gabbert & Manner · http://www.h3gm.com · 315 Deaderick Street, Suite 1800 · Nashville, TN 37238-1800 · 615-256-0500

J. Chase Cole · a · Waller Lansden Dortch & Davis · http://www.wallerlaw.com · Nashville City Center, Suite 2700 · 511 Union Street · P.O. Box 198966 · Nashville, TN 37219-8966 · 615-244-6380

David Cox · Harwell Howard Hyne Gabbert & Manner · http://www.h3gm.com · 315 Deaderick Street, Suite 1800 · Nashville, TN 37238-1800 · 615-256-0500

George V. Crawford, Jr. · Gullett, Sanford, Robinson & Martin · 315 Deaderick Street, Suite 1100 · P.O. Box 198888 · Nashville, TN 37219-8888 · 615-244-4994

J. Page Davidson · Bass, Berry & Sims · http://www.bassberry.com · 315 Deaderick Street, Suite 2700 · Nashville, TN 37238-3001 · 615-742-6200

Bruce C. Doeg · Baker, Donelson, Bearman, Caldwell & Berkowitz · http://www.bakerdonelson.com · Commerce Center, Suite 1000 · 211 Commerce Street · Nashville, TN 37201 · 615-726-5600

B. Riney Green · Bass, Berry & Sims · http://www.bassberry.com · 315 Deaderick Street, Suite 2700 · Nashville, TN 37238-3001 · 615-742-6200

Tonya M. Grindon · Baker, Donelson, Bearman, Caldwell & Berkowitz · http://www.bakerdonelson.com Commerce Center, Suite 1000 · 211 Commerce Street · Nashville, TN 37201 · 615-726-5600

Beth Conner Guest · Waller Lansden Dortch & Davis · http://www.wallerlaw.com · Nashville City Center, Suite 2700 · 511 Union Street · P.O. Box 198966 · Nashville, TN 37219-8966 · 615-244-6380

John B. Hardcastle, Jr. · a · Boult, Cummings, Conners & Berry · http://www.boultcummings.com · Roundabout Plaza, Suite 700 · 1600 Division Street · P.O. Box 340025 · Nashville, TN 37203 · 615-244-2582

J. Reginald Hill · a · Waller Lansden Dortch & Davis · http://www.wallerlaw.com · Nashville City Center, Suite 2700 · 511 Union Street · P.O. Box 198966 · Nashville, TN 37219-8966 · 615-244-6380

E. Berry Holt III · a · Boult, Cummings, Conners & Berry · http://www.boultcummings.com · Roundabout Plaza, Suite 700 · 1600 Division Street · P.O. Box 340025 · Nashville, TN 37203 · 615-244-2582

Ernest E. Hyne II · Harwell Howard Hyne Gabbert & Manner · http://www.h3gm.com · 315 Deaderick Street, Suite 1800 · Nashville, TN 37238-1800 · 615-256-0500

Howard H. Lamar III · Bass, Berry & Sims · http://www.bassberry.com · 315 Deaderick Street, Suite 2700 Nashville, TN 37238-3001 · 615-742-6200

Robins H. Ledyard · Bass, Berry & Sims · http://www.bassberry.com · 315 Deaderick Street, Suite 2700 · Nashville, TN 37238-3001 · 615-742-6200

Mark Manner · a · Harwell Howard Hyne Gabbert & Manner · http://www.h3gm.com · 315 Deaderick Street, Suite 1800 · Nashville, TN 37238-1800 · 615-256-0500

Donald I. N. McKenzie · a · Law Office of Donald I.N. McKenzie · 4015 Hillsboro Pike · Nashville, TN 37215 · 615-297-7001

E. Marlee Mitchell · Waller Lansden Dortch & Davis · http://www.wallerlaw.com · Nashville City Center, Suite 2700 · 511 Union Street · P.O. Box 198966 · Nashville, TN 37219-8966 · 615-244-6380

Elizabeth E. Moore · Sherrard & Roe · http://www.sherrardroe.com · 424 Church Street, Suite 2000 · Nashville, TN 37219-3304 · 615-742-4200

J. Allen Overby · Bass, Berry & Sims · http://www.bassberry.com · 315 Deaderick Street, Suite 2700 · Nashville, TN 37238-3001 · 615-742-6200

Mary Ellen Sullivan Pickrell · Waller Lansden Dortch & Davis · http://www.wallerlaw.com · Nashville City Center, Suite 2700 · 511 Union Street · P.O. Box 198966 · Nashville, TN 37219-8966 · 615-244-6380

John N. Popham IV · Harwell Howard Hyne Gabbert & Manner · http://www.h3gm.com · 315 Deaderick Street, Suite 1800 · Nashville, TN 37238-1800 · 615-256-0500

G. Scott Rayson · Waller Lansden Dortch & Davis · http://www.wallerlaw.com · Nashville City Center, Suite 2700 · 511 Union Street · P.O. Box 198966 · Nashville, TN 37219-8966 · 615-244-6380

J. Bradbury Reed · a · Bass, Berry & Sims · http://www.bassberry.com · 315 Deaderick Street, Suite 2700 Nashville, TN 37238-3001 · 615-742-6200

Cynthia Y. Reisz · Bass, Berry & Sims · http://www.bassberry.com · 315 Deaderick Street, Suite 2700 · Nashville, TN 37238-3001 · 615-742-6200

Todd J. Rolapp · Bass, Berry & Sims · http://www.bassberry.com · 315 Deaderick Street, Suite 2700 · Nashville, TN 37238-3001 · 615-742-6200

Thomas J. Sherrard III · 2) · Sherrard & Roe · http://www.sherrardroe.com · 424 Church Street, Suite 2000 · Nashville, TN 37219-3304 · 615-742-4200

Joseph A. Sowell III · Waller Lansden Dortch & Davis · http://www.wallerlaw.com · Nashville City Center, Suite 2700 · 511 Union Street · P.O. Box 198966 · Nashville, TN 37219-8966 · 615-244-6380

Samuel E. Stumpf, Jr. · a · Bass, Berry & Sims · http://www.bassberry.com · 315 Deaderick Street, Suite 2700 · Nashville, TN 37238-3001 · 615-742-6200

Bob F. Thompson · a · Bass, Berry & Sims · http://www.bassberry.com · 315 Deaderick Street, Suite 2700 · Nashville, TN 37238-3001 · 615-742-6200

John W. Titus · Boult, Cummings, Conners & Berry · http://www.boultcummings.com · Roundabout Plaza, Suite 700 · 1600 Division Street · P.O. Box 340025 · Nashville, TN 37203 · 615-244-2582

John R. Voigt · a · Sherrard & Roe · http://www.sherrardroe.com · 424 Church Street, Suite 2000 · Nashville, TN 37219-3304 · 615-742-4200

F. Mitchell Walker, Jr. · Bass, Berry & Sims · http://www.bassberry.com · 315 Deaderick Street, Suite 2700 · Nashville, TN 37238-3001 · 615-742-6200

Leigh Walton · a · Bass, Berry & Sims · http://www.bassberry.com · 315 Deaderick Street, Suite 2700 · Nashville, TN 37238-3001 · 615-742-6200

Christopher C. Whitson · Sherrard & Roe · http://www.sherrardroe.com · 424 Church Street, Suite 2000 · Nashville, TN 37219-3304 · 615-742-4200

DUI/DWI DEFENSE

Kingsport

R. Wayne Culbertson · R. Wayne Culbertson · 119 West Market Street · Kingsport, TN 37660 · 423-247-6161

Knoxville

Ralph E. Harwell · Ralph E. Harwell · 2131 First Tennessee Plaza · Knoxville, TN 37929 · 865-637-8900

Steve Oberman · The Oberman Law Firm · 550 West Main Street, Suite 730 · Knoxville, TN 37902 · 865-249-7200

Memphis

Leslie I. Ballin · a · Ballin, Ballin & Fishman · 200 Jefferson Avenue, Suite 1250 · Memphis, TN 38103-2396 · 901-525-6278

Robert M. Brannon, Jr. · Brannon Law Firm · 295 Washington Avenue, Suite Three · Memphis, TN 38103-1911 · 901-521-1710

Nashville

Hal D. Hardin · a · Hal D. Hardin · 211 Union Street, Suite 200 · Nashville, TN 37201 · 615-369-3377

Roger T. May · a · May & Ryan · 219 Second Avenue North, Suite 300 · Nashville, TN 37201-1618 · 615-256-7337

Patrick McNally · Hollins, Wagster, Weatherly & Raybin · http://www.hwylaw.com · Fifth Third Center, Suite 2200 · 424 Church Street · Nashville, TN 37219 · 615-256-6666

Edward Stephen Ryan · May & Ryan · 219 Second Avenue North, Suite 300 · Nashville, TN 37201-1618 615-256-7337

Peter J. Strianse · a · Tune, Entrekin & White · AmSouth Center, Suite 1700 · 315 Deaderick Street · Nashville, TN 37238-1700 · 615-244-2770

ELDER LAW

Chattanooga

Dana B. Perry · Chambliss, Bahner & Stophel · http://www.cbslawfirm.com · 1000 Tallan Building · Two Union Square · Chattanooga, TN 37402 · 423-756-3000

Hendersonville

Timothy L. Takacs · Elder Law Practice of Timothy L. Takacs · 201 Walton Ferry Road · Hendersonville, TN 37075-3522 · 615-824-2571

Knoxville

Monica J. Franklin · Hill and Franklin · 402 Northshore Drive · Knoxville, TN 37919 · 865-588-3700

Kelly Guyton Frère · Guyton & Frère · The Offices at Franklin Square, Suite 505 · 9724 Kingston Pike · Knoxville, TN 37922 · 865-694-0373

Matthew B. Frère · Guyton & Frère · The Offices at Franklin Square, Suite 505 · 9724 Kingston Pike · Knoxville, TN 37922 · 865-694-0373

Memphis

William King Self, Jr. · Apperson, Crump & Maxwell · 6000 Poplar Avenue, Suite 400 · Memphis, TN 38119 · 901-756-6300

Nashville

Colleen P. MacLean · Colleen P. MacLean · P.O. Box 121439 · Nashville, TN 37212 · 615-726-1614

EMINENT DOMAIN AND CONDEMNATION LAW

Chattanooga

Joe A. Conner · Baker, Donelson, Bearman, Caldwell & Berkowitz · http://www.bakerdonelson.com · 1800 Republic Centre · 633 Chestnut Street · Chattanooga, TN 37450-1800 · 423-756-2010

Knoxville

John J. Britton · Lewis, King, Krieg & Waldrop · http://www.lewisking.com · One Centre Square, Fifth Floor · 620 Market Street · P.O. Box 2425 · Knoxville, TN 37901 · 865-546-4646

Lebanon

Jere N. McCulloch · Rochelle, McCulloch & Aulds · 109 Castle Heights Avenue North · Lebanon, TN 37087 · 615-444-1433

Memphis

John Kevin Walsh · Harris Shelton Hanover Walsh · One Commerce Square, Suite 2700 · Memphis, TN 38103 · 901-525-1455

Murfreesboro

James C. Cope · Cope Hudson Scarlett Reed and McCreary · 16 Public Square North · P.O. Box 884 · Murfreesboro, TN 37133-0884 · 615-893-5522

Nashville

James W. Fisher, Jr. · Lassiter, Tidwell, Davis, Keller & Hogan · 1850 One Nashville Place · 150 Fourth Avenue North · Nashville, TN 37219-2408 · 615-259-9344

Jonathan Harwell · Harwell Howard Hyne Gabbert & Manner · http://www.h3gm.com · 315 Deaderick Street, Suite 1800 · Nashville, TN 37238-1800 · 615-256-0500

Clark H. Tidwell · Lassiter, Tidwell, Davis, Keller & Hogan · 1850 One Nashville Place · 150 Fourth Avenue North · Nashville, TN 37219-2408 · 615-259-9344

EMPLOYEE BENEFITS LAW

Chattanooga

Thomas A. Caldwell · 2% · Baker, Donelson, Bearman, Caldwell & Berkowitz · http://www.bakerdonelson.com · 1800 Republic Centre · 633 Chestnut Street · Chattanooga, TN 37450-1800 · 423-756-2010

Christopher A. Crevasse · Miller & Martin · http://www.millermartin.com · Volunteer Building, Suite 1000 · 832 Georgia Avenue · Chattanooga, TN 37402-2289 · 423-756-6600

Roy C. Maddox, Jr. · Horton, Maddox & Anderson · One Central Plaza, Suite 600 · 835 Georgia Avenue · Chattanooga, TN 37402 · 423-265-2560

Donald E. Morton · a · Miller & Martin · http://www.millermartin.com · Volunteer Building, Suite 1000 · 832 Georgia Avenue · Chattanooga, TN 37402-2289 · 423-756-6600

William E. Robinson · Baker, Donelson, Bearman, Caldwell & Berkowitz · http://www.bakerdonelson.com · 1800 Republic Centre · 633 Chestnut Street · Chattanooga, TN 37450-1800 · 423-756-2010

Knoxville

S. Russell Headrick · a · Baker, Donelson, Bearman, Caldwell & Berkowitz · http://www.bakerdonelson.com · 2200 Riverview Tower · 900 South Gay Street · P.O. Box 1792 · Knoxville, TN 37902 · 865-549-7000

Robert S. Marquis · 2) · Woolf, McClane, Bright, Allen & Carpenter · 900 Riverview Tower · 900 South Gay Street · P.O. Box 900 · Knoxville, TN 37901-0900 · 865-215-1000

William E. Mason · William E. Mason · 313 North Forest Park Boulevard · Knoxville, TN 37939 · 865-584-5603

Memphis

David A. Thornton · Bass, Berry & Sims · http://www.bassberry.com · The Tower at Peabody Place, Suite 900 · 100 Peabody Place · Memphis, TN 38103-2625 · 901-543-5900

Nashville

James W. Berry, Jr. · a · Frost Brown Todd · http://www.frostbrowntodd.com · 424 Church Street, Suite 1600 · Nashville, TN 37219-2308 · 615-251-5550

James B. Bristol · Waller Lansden Dortch & Davis · http://www.wallerlaw.com · Nashville City Center, Suite 2700 · 511 Union Street · P.O. Box 198966 · Nashville, TN 37219-8966 · 615-244-6380

Gordon Earle Nichols · a · Boult, Cummings, Conners & Berry · http://www.boultcummings.com · Roundabout Plaza, Suite 700 · 1600 Division Street · P.O. Box 340025 · Nashville, TN 37203 · 615-244-2582

Fritz Richter III · Bass, Berry & Sims · http://www.bassberry.com · 315 Deaderick Street, Suite 2700 · Nashville, TN 37238-3001 · 615-742-6200

Bynum E. Tudor III · a · Tudor Law Firm · 116 Wilson Pike Circle, Suite 207 · Nashville, TN 37027 · 615-726-1000

Signal Mountain

Wallace M. Davies · 2) · Wallace M. Davies · James Building, Suite 203-B · P.O. Box 245 · Signal Mountain, TN 37377 · 423-756-7533

ENERGY LAW

Chattanooga

Joe A. Conner · Baker, Donelson, Bearman, Caldwell & Berkowitz · http://www.bakerdonelson.com · 1800 Republic Centre · 633 Chestnut Street · Chattanooga, TN 37450-1800 · 423-756-2010

Frederick L. Hitchcock · a · Chambliss, Bahner & Stophel · http://www.cbslawfirm.com · 1000 Tallan Building · Two Union Square · Chattanooga, TN 37402 · 423-756-3000

Carlos C. Smith · a · Miller & Martin · http://www.millermartin.com · Volunteer Building, Suite 1000 · 832 Georgia Avenue · Chattanooga, TN 37402-2289 · 423-756-6600

Knoxville

Herbert S. Sanger, Jr. · a · Wagner, Myers & Sanger · 1801 First Tennessee Plaza · Knoxville, TN 37929 · 865-525-4600

Nashville

J. Andrew Goddard · a · Bass, Berry & Sims · http://www.bassberry.com · 315 Deaderick Street, Suite 2700 · Nashville, TN 37238-3001 · 615-742-6200

T. G. Pappas · 2% · Bass, Berry & Sims · http://www.bassberry.com · 315 Deaderick Street, Suite 2700 · Nashville, TN 37238-3001 · 615-742-6200

Henry M. Walker · Boult, Cummings, Conners & Berry · http://www.boultcummings.com · Roundabout Plaza, Suite 700 · 1600 Division Street · P.O. Box 340025 · Nashville, TN 37203 · 615-244-2582

ENTERTAINMENT LAW

Nashville

Orville Almon, Jr. · Zumwalt, Almon & Hayes · 1014 Sixteenth Avenue South · Nashville, TN 37212 · 615-256-7200

Casey Del Casino · Adams and Reese · http://www.adamsandreese.com · Music Row · 901 Eighteenth Avenue South · Nashville, TN 37212 · 615-341-0068

Linda Edell Howard · Adams and Reese · http://www.adamsandreese.com · Fifth Third Center, Suite 2800 · 424 Church Street · Nashville, TN 37219 · 615-259-1450

Robin Mitchell Joyce · Milom Joyce Horsnell Crow · 3310 West End Avenue, Suite 610 · Nashville, TN 37203 · 615-255-6161

Philip M. Kirkpatrick · a · Stewart, Estes & Donnell · Fifth Third Center, Suite 1401 · 424 Church Street · Nashville, TN 37219 · 615-244-6538

Kenneth L. Kraus · a · Loeb & Loeb · 1906 Acklen Avenue · Nashville, TN 37212-3700 · 615-749-8300

Samuel D. Lipshie · a · Boult, Cummings, Conners & Berry · http://www.boultcummings.com · Roundabout Plaza, Suite 700 · 1600 Division Street · P.O. Box 340025 · Nashville, TN 37203 · 615-244-2582

W. Michael Milom · a · Milom Joyce Horsnell Crow · 3310 West End Avenue, Suite 610 · Nashville, TN 37203 · 615-255-6161

Robert L. Sullivan · a · Loeb & Loeb · 1906 Acklen Avenue · Nashville, TN 37212-3700 · 615-749-8300

ENVIRONMENTAL LAW

Chattanooga

James W. Gentry, Jr. · 2) · Spears, Moore, Rebman & Williams · Pioneer Building, Sixth Floor · 801 Broad Street · P.O. Box 1749 · Chattanooga, TN 37401-1749 · 423-756-7000

Knoxville

Mary LeAnn Mynatt · Baker, Donelson, Bearman, Caldwell & Berkowitz · http://www.bakerdonelson.com · 2200 Riverview Tower · 900 South Gay Street · P.O. Box 1792 · Knoxville, TN 37902 · 865-549-7000

Memphis

Oscar C. Carr III · 2) · Glankler Brown · http://www.glankler.com · One Commerce Square, Suite 1700 · Memphis, TN 38103 · 901-525-1322

Allen T. Malone · Burch, Porter & Johnson · http://www.bpjlaw.com · 130 North Court Avenue · Memphis, TN 38103 · 901-524-5000

Charles F. Newman · a · Burch, Porter & Johnson · http://www.bpjlaw.com · 130 North Court Avenue · Memphis, TN 38103 · 901-524-5000

Nashville

J. Andrew Goddard · a · Bass, Berry & Sims · http://www.bassberry.com · 315 Deaderick Street, Suite 2700 · Nashville, TN 37238-3001 · 615-742-6200

Robert J. Martineau · Waller Lansden Dortch & Davis · http://www.wallerlaw.com · Nashville City Center, Suite 2700 · 511 Union Street · P.O. Box 198966 · Nashville, TN 37219-8966 · 615-244-6380

Michael D. Pearigen · Farmer and Luna · 333 Union Street, Suite 300 · Nashville, TN 37201 · 615-254-9146

William L. Penny · Stites & Harbison · http://www.stites.com · SunTrust Plaza, Suite 800 · 401 Commerce Street · Nashville, TN 37219 · 615-244-5200

Gary C. Shockley · a · Baker, Donelson, Bearman, Caldwell & Berkowitz · http://www.bakerdonelson.com · Commerce Center, Suite 1000 · 211 Commerce Street · Nashville, TN 37201 · 615-726-5600

Robert M. Steele · Baker, Donelson, Bearman, Caldwell & Berkowitz · http://www.bakerdonelson.com · Commerce Center, Suite 1000 · 211 Commerce Street · Nashville, TN 37201 · 615-726-5600

G. Scott Thomas · Bass, Berry & Sims · http://www.bassberry.com · 315 Deaderick Street, Suite 2700 · Nashville, TN 37238-3001 · 615-742-6200

Jessalyn H. Zeigler · Bass, Berry & Sims · http://www.bassberry.com · 315 Deaderick Street, Suite 2700 · Nashville, TN 37238-3001 · 615-742-6200

EQUIPMENT FINANCE LAW

Nashville

Katherine Simpson Allen · a · Stites & Harbison · http://www.stites.com · SunTrust Plaza, Suite 800 · 401 Commerce Street · Nashville, TN 37219 · 615-244-5200

Julie N. Jones · a · Bass, Berry & Sims · http://www.bassberry.com · 315 Deaderick Street, Suite 2700 · Nashville, TN 37238-3001 · 615-742-6200

John E. Murdock III · Boult, Cummings, Conners & Berry · http://www.boultcummings.com · Roundabout Plaza, Suite 700 · 1600 Division Street · P.O. Box 340025 · Nashville, TN 37203 · 615-244-2582

ETHICS AND PROFESSIONAL RESPONSIBILITY LAW

Memphis

Jef Feibelman · a · Burch, Porter & Johnson · http://www.bpjlaw.com · 130 North Court Avenue · Memphis, TN 38103 · 901-524-5000

Albert C. Harvey · a · Thomason, Hendrix, Harvey, Johnson & Mitchell · One Commerce Square, 29th Floor · 40 South Main Street · Memphis, TN 38103 · 901-525-8721

Lucian T. Pera · Adams and Reese · http://www.adamsandreese.com · Brinkley Plaza, Suite 700 · 80 Monroe Avenue · Memphis, TN 38103 · 901-525-3234

Nashville

Coburn Dewees Berry IV · Bass, Berry & Sims · http://www.bassberry.com · 315 Deaderick Street, Suite 2700 · Nashville, TN 37238-3001 · 615-742-6200

FAMILY LAW

Brentwood

Grant C. Glassford · Grant C. Glassford · 5115 Maryland Way, Suite 301 · Brentwood, TN 37027 · 615-376-9800

Centerville

Douglas T. Bates III · Douglas T. Bates, III · 406 West Public Square · P.O. Box One · Centerville, TN 37033 · 931-729-4085

Chattanooga

William H. Horton · 2) · Horton, Maddox & Anderson · One Central Plaza, Suite 600 · 835 Georgia Avenue · Chattanooga, TN 37402 · 423-265-2560

Jennifer H. Lawrence · Lawrence, Lawrence & Richardson · 200 East Eighth Street · Chattanooga, TN 37402 · 423-756-5031

Phillip C. Lawrence · a · Lawrence, Lawrence & Richardson · 200 East Eighth Street · Chattanooga, TN 37402 · 423-756-5031

Glenna M. Ramer · a · Ramer & Hedrick · 2305 Hickory Valley Road, Suite A · Chattanooga, TN 37421 423-855-4444

Franklin

Edward P. Silva · Hartzog & Silva · McEwen-German Building · 123 Fifth Avenue North · P.O. Box 664 · Franklin, TN 37065 · 615-790-1500

Virginia Lee Story · Story & Abernathy · 136 Fourth Avenue South · P.O. Box 1608 · Franklin, TN 37605-1608 · 615-790-1778

Knoxville

Sarah Y. Sheppeard · a · Sheppeard Swanson & Mynatt · 616 West Hill Avenue · P.O. Box 2149 · Knoxville, TN 37901-2149 · 865-546-3653

L. Caesar Stair III · Bernstein, Stair & McAdams · 4823 Old Kingston Pike, Suite 300 · Knoxville, TN 37919 · 865-546-8030

Memphis

Stevan L. Black · a · Black McLaren Jones Ryland & Griffee · http://www.blackmclaw.com · 530 Oak Court Drive, Suite 360 · Memphis, TN 38117 · 901-762-0535

Joe M. Duncan · a · Burch, Porter & Johnson · http://www.bpjlaw.com · 130 North Court Avenue · Memphis, TN 38103 · 901-524-5000

Dorothy Johnson Pounders · a · Pounders Coleman · 1770 Kirby Parkway, Suite 105 · Memphis, TN 38138 · 901-752-1250

Daniel Loyd Taylor · a · Law Offices of Daniel Loyd Taylor · 6263 Poplar Avenue, Suite 601 · Memphis, TN 38119 · 901-682-1206

Kay Farese Turner · a · Turner Putnam · 530 Oak Court Drive, Suite 155 · Memphis, TN 38117 · 901-529-4040

Nashville

Michael W. Binkley · Michael W. Binkley · 150 Second Avenue North, Suite 300 · Nashville, TN 37201 · 615-244-8630

Lewis H. Conner, Jr. · 2) · Waller Lansden Dortch & Davis · http://www.wallerlaw.com · Nashville City Center, Suite 2700 · 511 Union Street · P.O. Box 198966 · Nashville, TN 37219-8966 · 615-244-6380

Maclin P. Davis, Jr. · 2% · Waller Lansden Dortch & Davis · http://www.wallerlaw.com · Nashville City Center, Suite 2700 · 511 Union Street · P.O. Box 198966 · Nashville, TN 37219-8966 · 615-244-6380

Larry G. Hayes, Jr. · Jackson, Kweller, McKinney, Warden & Hayes · 214 Second Avenue North, Suite 103 · Nashville, TN 37201 · 615-256-2602

John J. Hollins, Jr. · Hollins, Wagster, Weatherly & Raybin · http://www.hwylaw.com · Fifth Third Center, Suite 2200 · 424 Church Street · Nashville, TN 37219 · 615-256-6666

John J. Hollins, Sr. · 2) · Hollins, Wagster, Weatherly & Raybin · http://www.hwylaw.com · Fifth Third Center, Suite 2200 · 424 Church Street · Nashville, TN 37219 · 615-256-6666

Robert L. Jackson · a · Jackson, Kweller, McKinney, Warden & Hayes · 214 Second Avenue North, Suite 103 · Nashville, TN 37201 · 615-256-2602

Mary Frances Lyle · a · Corley, Henard, Lyle, Levy & Langford · 424 Church Street, Suite 2925 · Nashville, TN 37219 · 615-627-4677

James G. Martin III · 2) · Stites & Harbison · http://www.stites.com · SunTrust Plaza, Suite 800 · 401 Commerce Street · Nashville, TN 37219 · 615-244-5200

Marlene Eskind Moses · Moses and Townsend · One Church Street Building, Suite 500 · Nashville, TN 37201-1607 · 615-242-2521

Rose T. Palermo · a · Cheatham Palermo & Garrett · 43 Music Square West · P.O. Box 121857 · Nashville, TN 37212 · 615-244-4270

Phillip R. Robinson · Robinson Phillip · L & C Tower, Suite 2400 · 401 Church Street · Nashville, TN 37219 · 615-467-1801

Gregory D. Smith · Stites & Harbison · http://www.stites.com · SunTrust Plaza, Suite 800 · 401 Commerce Street · Nashville, TN 37219 · 615-244-5200

Philip E. Smith · Robinson Phillip · L & C Tower, Suite 2400 · 401 Church Street · Nashville, TN 37219 615-467-1801

Pamela A. Taylor · Stites & Harbison · http://www.stites.com · SunTrust Plaza, Suite 800 · 401 Commerce Street · Nashville, TN 37219 · 615-244-5200

Robert D. Tuke · a · Trauger & Tuke · The Southern Turf Building · 222 Fourth Avenue North · Nashville, TN 37219-2117 · 615-256-8585

FAMILY LAW MEDIATION

Knoxville

Sarah Y. Sheppeard · a · Sheppeard Swanson & Mynatt · 616 West Hill Avenue · P.O. Box 2149 · Knoxville, TN 37901-2149 · 865-546-3653

Memphis

Dorothy Johnson Pounders · a · Pounders Coleman · 1770 Kirby Parkway, Suite 105 · Memphis, TN 38138 · 901-752-1250

Nashville

Lewis H. Conner, Jr. · 2) · Waller Lansden Dortch & Davis · http://www.wallerlaw.com · Nashville City Center, Suite 2700 · 511 Union Street · P.O. Box 198966 · Nashville, TN 37219-8966 · 615-244-6380

FIRST AMENDMENT LAW

Chattanooga

Anthony A. Jackson · Chambliss, Bahner & Stophel · http://www.cbslawfirm.com · 1000 Tallan Building Two Union Square · Chattanooga, TN 37402 · 423-756-3000

Knoxville

S. Russell Headrick · a · Baker, Donelson, Bearman, Caldwell & Berkowitz · http://www.bakerdonelson.com · 2200 Riverview Tower · 900 South Gay Street · P.O. Box 1792 · Knoxville, TN 37902 · 865-549-7000

Richard L. Hollow · a · Hollow & Hollow · 410 Montbrook Lane, Suite 200 · P.O. Box 11166 · Knoxville, TN 37939-1166 · 865-769-1715

Memphis

Jerry E. Mitchell · a · Thomason, Hendrix, Harvey, Johnson & Mitchell · One Commerce Square, 29th Floor · 40 South Main Street · Memphis, TN 38103 · 901-525-8721

Charles F. Newman · a · Burch, Porter & Johnson · http://www.bpjlaw.com · 130 North Court Avenue · Memphis, TN 38103 · 901-524-5000

Lucian T. Pera · Adams and Reese · http://www.adamsandreese.com · Brinkley Plaza, Suite 700 · 80 Monroe Avenue · Memphis, TN 38103 · 901-525-3234

Nashville

Robb S. Harvey · Waller Lansden Dortch & Davis · http://www.wallerlaw.com · Nashville City Center, Suite 2700 · 511 Union Street · P.O. Box 198966 · Nashville, TN 37219-8966 · 615-244-6380

Alan D. Johnson · Willis & Knight · 215 Second Avenue North · Nashville, TN 37201 · 615-259-9600

Douglas R. Pierce · King & Ballow · 1100 Union Street Plaza · 315 Union Street · Nashville, TN 37201 · 615-259-3456

William R. Willis, Jr. · ⑳ · Willis & Knight · 215 Second Avenue North · Nashville, TN 37201 · 615-259-9600

FRANCHISE LAW

Knoxville

Kelli L. Thompson · Baker, Donelson, Bearman, Caldwell & Berkowitz · http://www.bakerdonelson.com 2200 Riverview Tower · 900 South Gay Street · P.O. Box 1792 · Knoxville, TN 37902 · 865-549-7000

Memphis

Henry Stephen Brown · Brown Law Firm · 850 Ridge Lake Boulevard, Suite 300 · Memphis, TN 38120 901-213-2355

Grady M. Garrison · ⑩ · Baker, Donelson, Bearman, Caldwell & Berkowitz · http://www.bakerdonelson.com · 6060 Poplar Avenue, Suite 440 · Memphis, TN 38119 · 901-579-3100

Nashville

Gary M. Brown · ⑩ · Baker, Donelson, Bearman, Caldwell & Berkowitz · http://www.bakerdonelson.com Commerce Center, Suite 1000 · 211 Commerce Street · Nashville, TN 37201 · 615-726-5600

Joel R. Buckberg · Baker, Donelson, Bearman, Caldwell & Berkowitz · http://www.bakerdonelson.com · Commerce Center, Suite 1000 · 211 Commerce Street · Nashville, TN 37201 · 615-726-5600

Matthew J. Sweeney III · Baker, Donelson, Bearman, Caldwell & Berkowitz · http://www.bakerdonelson.com · Commerce Center, Suite 1000 · 211 Commerce Street · Nashville, TN 37201 · 615-726-5600

GOVERNMENT RELATIONS LAW

Knoxville

Warren L. Gooch · Kramer Rayson · http://www.kramer-rayson.com · First Tennessee Plaza, Suite 2500 · 800 South Gay Street · P.O. Box 629 · Knoxville, TN 37901-0629 · 865-525-5134

Memphis

John M. Farris · Farris Bobango Branan · http://www.farrismathews.com · One Commerce Square, Suite 2000 · Memphis, TN 38103 · 901-259-7100

Nashville

Betty Anderson · Baker, Donelson, Bearman, Caldwell & Berkowitz · http://www.bakerdonelson.com · Commerce Center, Suite 1000 · 211 Commerce Street · Nashville, TN 37201 · 615-726-5600

William R. Bruce · Adams and Reese · http://www.adamsandreese.com · Fifth Third Center, Suite 2800 · 424 Church Street · Nashville, TN 37219 · 615-259-1450

Dan H. Elrod · ⑩ · Miller & Martin · http://www.millermartin.com · One Nashville Place, Suite 1200 · 150 Fourth Avenue North · Nashville, TN 37219-2433 · 615-244-9270

J. Leigh Griffith · ⑩ · Waller Lansden Dortch & Davis · http://www.wallerlaw.com · Nashville City Center, Suite 2700 · 511 Union Street · P.O. Box 198966 · Nashville, TN 37219-8966 · 615-244-6380

Dan Haskell · Gullett, Sanford, Robinson & Martin · 315 Deaderick Street, Suite 1100 · P.O. Box 198888 · Nashville, TN 37219-8888 · 615-244-4994

J. Richard Lodge, Jr. · Bass, Berry & Sims · http://www.bassberry.com · 315 Deaderick Street, Suite 2700 Nashville, TN 37238-3001 · 615-742-6200

Jones Wilson Luna · Farmer and Luna · 333 Union Street, Suite 300 · Nashville, TN 37201 · 615-254-9146

John C. Lyell · Lyell Law Firm · 211 Seventh Avenue North, Suite 300 · Nashville, TN 37219 · 615-255-0033

Harlan Mathews · Farris Bobango Branan · http://www.farrismathews.com · 618 Church Street, Suite 300 · Nashville, TN 37219 · 615-726-1200

Nathan H. Ridley · Boult, Cummings, Conners & Berry · http://www.boultcummings.com · Roundabout Plaza, Suite 700 · 1600 Division Street · P.O. Box 340025 · Nashville, TN 37203 · 615-244-2582

Guilford F. Thornton, Jr. · Adams and Reese · http://www.adamsandreese.com · Fifth Third Center, Suite 2800 · 424 Church Street · Nashville, TN 37219 · 615-259-1450

James M. Weaver · Waller Lansden Dortch & Davis · http://www.wallerlaw.com · Nashville City Center, Suite 2700 · 511 Union Street · P.O. Box 198966 · Nashville, TN 37219-8966 · 615-244-6380

Justin P. Wilson · Waller Lansden Dortch & Davis · http://www.wallerlaw.com · Nashville City Center, Suite 2700 · 511 Union Street · P.O. Box 198966 · Nashville, TN 37219-8966 · 615-244-6380

HEALTH CARE LAW

Chattanooga

William P. Aiken · ⑩ · Chambliss, Bahner & Stophel · http://www.cbslawfirm.com · 1000 Tallan Building Two Union Square · Chattanooga, TN 37402 · 423-756-3000

E. Stephen Jett · Chambliss, Bahner & Stophel · http://www.cbslawfirm.com · 1000 Tallan Building · Two Union Square · Chattanooga, TN 37402 · 423-756-3000

Howard I. Levine · ⑩ · Miller & Martin · http://www.millermartin.com · Volunteer Building, Suite 1000 · 832 Georgia Avenue · Chattanooga, TN 37402-2289 · 423-756-6600

Fred H. Moore · ⑩ · Spears, Moore, Rebman & Williams · Pioneer Building, Sixth Floor · 801 Broad Street · P.O. Box 1749 · Chattanooga, TN 37401-1749 · 423-756-7000

Ward W. Nelson · Miller & Martin · http://www.millermartin.com · Volunteer Building, Suite 1000 · 832 Georgia Avenue · Chattanooga, TN 37402-2289 · 423-756-6600

Jackson

Angela C. Youngberg · Rainey, Kizer, Reviere & Bell · 105 South Highland Avenue · P.O. Box 1147 · Jackson, TN 38302 · 731-423-2414

Kingsport

William T. Gamble · a · Wilson, Worley, Moore, Gamble & Stout · Eastman Credit Union Building, Second Floor · 2021 Meadowview Lane · P.O. Box 88 · Kingsport, TN 37662-0088 · 423-723-0400

Knoxville

Rick L. Powers · a · Arnett, Draper & Hagood · First Tennessee Plaza, Suite 2300 · P.O. Box 300 · Knoxville, TN 37929-2300 · 865-546-7000

Memphis

Robert K. Alvarez · a · Bourland, Heflin, Alvarez & Minor · http://www.bhammlaw.com · 5400 Poplar Avenue, Suite 100 · Memphis, TN 38119 · 901-683-3526

Lee James Chase III · a · Glankler Brown · http://www.glankler.com · One Commerce Square, Suite 1700 · Memphis, TN 38103 · 901-525-1322

Charles R. Crawford · Butler, Snow, O'Mara, Stevens and Cannada · http://www.butlersnow.com · The Crescent Center, Suite 500 · 6075 Poplar Avenue · P.O. Box 171443 · Memphis, TN 38119 · 901-680-7200

A. Neal Graham · a · Harris Shelton Hanover Walsh · 6060 Poplar Avenue, Suite 450 · Memphis, TN 38119 · 901-682-1455

Charles M. Key · Wyatt, Tarrant & Combs · http://www.wyattfirm.com · The Renaissance Center, Suite 800 · 1715 Aaron Brenner Drive · Memphis, TN 38120 · 901-537-1000

David H. Lillard, Jr. · Burch, Porter & Johnson · http://www.bpjlaw.com · 130 North Court Avenue · Memphis, TN 38103 · 901-524-5000

Thomas R. Prewitt, Jr. · a · Adams and Reese · http://www.adamsandreese.com · Brinkley Plaza, Suite 700 · 80 Monroe Avenue · Memphis, TN 38103 · 901-525-3234

Scott B. Shanker · Bass, Berry & Sims · http://www.bassberry.com · The Tower at Peabody Place, Suite 900 · 100 Peabody Place · Memphis, TN 38103-2625 · 901-543-5900

J. Max Shelton · a · Harris Shelton Hanover Walsh · One Commerce Square, Suite 2700 · Memphis, TN 38103 · 901-525-1455

George T. Wheeler, Jr. · a · Harris Shelton Hanover Walsh · 6060 Poplar Avenue, Suite 450 · Memphis, TN 38119 · 901-682-1455

Nashville

H. Lee Barfield II · a · Bass, Berry & Sims · http://www.bassberry.com · 315 Deaderick Street, Suite 2700 Nashville, TN 37238-3001 · 615-742-6200

Thomas E. Bartrum · Baker, Donelson, Bearman, Caldwell & Berkowitz · http://www.bakerdonelson.com · Commerce Center, Suite 1000 · 211 Commerce Street · Nashville, TN 37201 · 615-726-5600

George W. Bishop III · a · Waller Lansden Dortch & Davis · http://www.wallerlaw.com · Nashville City Center, Suite 2700 · 511 Union Street · P.O. Box 198966 · Nashville, TN 37219-8966 · 615-244-6380

Stephen T. Braun · Boult, Cummings, Conners & Berry · http://www.boultcummings.com · Roundabout Plaza, Suite 700 · 1600 Division Street · P.O. Box 340025 · Nashville, TN 37203 · 615-244-2582

Michael D. Brent · Boult, Cummings, Conners & Berry · http://www.boultcummings.com · Roundabout Plaza, Suite 700 · 1600 Division Street · P.O. Box 340025 · Nashville, TN 37203 · 615-244-2582

Ashby Q. Burks · Baker, Donelson, Bearman, Caldwell & Berkowitz · http://www.bakerdonelson.com · Commerce Center, Suite 1000 · 211 Commerce Street · Nashville, TN 37201 · 615-726-5600

Kevin B. Campbell · Boult, Cummings, Conners & Berry · http://www.boultcummings.com · Roundabout Plaza, Suite 700 · 1600 Division Street · P.O. Box 340025 · Nashville, TN 37203 · 615-244-2582

Richard G. Cowart · a · Baker, Donelson, Bearman, Caldwell & Berkowitz · http://www.bakerdonelson.com · Commerce Center, Suite 1000 · 211 Commerce Street · Nashville, TN 37201 · 615-726-5600

Dan H. Elrod · a · Miller & Martin · http://www.millermartin.com · One Nashville Place, Suite 1200 · 150 Fourth Avenue North · Nashville, TN 37219-2433 · 615-244-9270

John E. Gillmor · a · Boult, Cummings, Conners & Berry · http://www.boultcummings.com · Roundabout Plaza, Suite 700 · 1600 Division Street · P.O. Box 340025 · Nashville, TN 37203 · 615-244-2582

Frank Grace, Jr. · a · Waller Lansden Dortch & Davis · http://www.wallerlaw.com · Nashville City Center, Suite 2700 · 511 Union Street · P.O. Box 198966 · Nashville, TN 37219-8966 · 615-244-6380

John B. Hardcastle, Jr. · a · Boult, Cummings, Conners & Berry · http://www.boultcummings.com · Roundabout Plaza, Suite 700 · 1600 Division Street · P.O. Box 340025 · Nashville, TN 37203 · 615-244-2582

J. Reginald Hill · a · Waller Lansden Dortch & Davis · http://www.wallerlaw.com · Nashville City Center, Suite 2700 · 511 Union Street · P.O. Box 198966 · Nashville, TN 37219-8966 · 615-244-6380

Michael R. Hill · Harwell Howard Hyne Gabbert & Manner · http://www.h3gm.com · 315 Deaderick Street, Suite 1800 · Nashville, TN 37238-1800 · 615-256-0500

E. Berry Holt III · a · Boult, Cummings, Conners & Berry · http://www.boultcummings.com · Roundabout Plaza, Suite 700 · 1600 Division Street · P.O. Box 340025 · Nashville, TN 37203 · 615-244-2582

Howard H. Lamar III · Bass, Berry & Sims · http://www.bassberry.com · 315 Deaderick Street, Suite 2700 Nashville, TN 37238-3001 · 615-742-6200

Nora L. Liggett · Waller Lansden Dortch & Davis · http://www.wallerlaw.com · Nashville City Center, Suite 2700 · 511 Union Street · P.O. Box 198966 · Nashville, TN 37219-8966 · 615-244-6380

Kim Harvey Looney · Waller Lansden Dortch & Davis · http://www.wallerlaw.com · Nashville City Center, Suite 2700 · 511 Union Street · P.O. Box 198966 · Nashville, TN 37219-8966 · 615-244-6380

Mark Manner · a · Harwell Howard Hyne Gabbert & Manner · http://www.h3gm.com · 315 Deaderick Street, Suite 1800 · Nashville, TN 37238-1800 · 615-256-0500

Claire F. Miley · Bass, Berry & Sims · http://www.bassberry.com · 315 Deaderick Street, Suite 2700 · Nashville, TN 37238-3001 · 615-742-6200

T. Scott Noonan · Bass, Berry & Sims · http://www.bassberry.com · 315 Deaderick Street, Suite 2700 · Nashville, TN 37238-3001 · 615-742-6200

Tracy A. Powell · Sherrard & Roe · http://www.sherrardroe.com · 424 Church Street, Suite 2000 · Nashville, TN 37219-3304 · 615-742-4200

Patricia Owen Powers · Waller Lansden Dortch & Davis · http://www.wallerlaw.com · Nashville City Center, Suite 2700 · 511 Union Street · P.O. Box 198966 · Nashville, TN 37219-8966 · 615-244-6380

G. Scott Rayson · Waller Lansden Dortch & Davis · http://www.wallerlaw.com · Nashville City Center, Suite 2700 · 511 Union Street · P.O. Box 198966 · Nashville, TN 37219-8966 · 615-244-6380

Cynthia Y. Reisz · Bass, Berry & Sims · http://www.bassberry.com · 315 Deaderick Street, Suite 2700 · Nashville, TN 37238-3001 · 615-742-6200

Mary M. Schaffner · a · Howell & Fisher · Court Square Building · 300 James Robertson Parkway · Nashville, TN 37201-1107 · 615-244-3370

Joseph A. Sowell III · Waller Lansden Dortch & Davis · http://www.wallerlaw.com · Nashville City Center, Suite 2700 · 511 Union Street · P.O. Box 198966 · Nashville, TN 37219-8966 · 615-244-6380

John R. Voigt · a · Sherrard & Roe · http://www.sherrardroe.com · 424 Church Street, Suite 2000 · Nashville, TN 37219-3304 · 615-742-4200

Leigh Walton · a · Bass, Berry & Sims · http://www.bassberry.com · 315 Deaderick Street, Suite 2700 · Nashville, TN 37238-3001 · 615-742-6200

William H. West · Baker, Donelson, Bearman, Caldwell & Berkowitz · http://www.bakerdonelson.com · Commerce Center, Suite 1000 · 211 Commerce Street · Nashville, TN 37201 · 615-726-5600

William R. Willis, Jr. · 2) · Willis & Knight · 215 Second Avenue North · Nashville, TN 37201 · 615-259-9600

IMMIGRATION LAW

Chattanooga

Robert C. Divine · a · Baker, Donelson, Bearman, Caldwell & Berkowitz · http://www.bakerdonelson.com · 1800 Republic Centre · 633 Chestnut Street · Chattanooga, TN 37450-1800 · 423-756-2010

Memphis

Rehim Babaoglu · a · Thomason, Hendrix, Harvey, Johnson & Mitchell · One Commerce Square, 29th Floor · 40 South Main Street · Memphis, TN 38103 · 901-525-8721

Kemper B. Durand · a · Thomason, Hendrix, Harvey, Johnson & Mitchell · One Commerce Square, 29th Floor · 40 South Main Street · Memphis, TN 38103 · 901-525-8721

Gregory Siskind · Siskind Susser · 1028 Oakhaven Road · Memphis, TN 38119 · 901-682-6455

Lynn Susser · Siskind Susser · 1028 Oakhaven Road · Memphis, TN 38119 · 901-682-6455

Nashville

L. Mabel Arroyo · Baker, Donelson, Bearman, Caldwell & Berkowitz · http://www.bakerdonelson.com · Commerce Center, Suite 1000 · 211 Commerce Street · Nashville, TN 37201 · 615-726-5600

Marilyn J. Devine · Haas and Devine · 1808 West End Avenue, Suite 1500 · Nashville, TN 37203 · 615-321-0010

Michael S. Mizell · Waller Lansden Dortch & Davis · http://www.wallerlaw.com · Nashville City Center, Suite 2700 · 511 Union Street · P.O. Box 198966 · Nashville, TN 37219-8966 · 615-244-6380

Linda Rose · Rose Immigration Law Firm · Loews Vanderbilt Plaza, Suite 935 · 2100 West End Avenue · Nashville, TN 37203 · 615-321-2256

INFORMATION TECHNOLOGY LAW

Nashville

Robert L. Brewer · Bass, Berry & Sims · http://www.bassberry.com · 315 Deaderick Street, Suite 2700 · Nashville, TN 37238-3001 · 615-742-6200

Bruce C. Doeg · Baker, Donelson, Bearman, Caldwell & Berkowitz · http://www.bakerdonelson.com · Commerce Center, Suite 1000 · 211 Commerce Street · Nashville, TN 37201 · 615-726-5600

Jason I. Epstein · Baker, Donelson, Bearman, Caldwell & Berkowitz · http://www.bakerdonelson.com · Commerce Center, Suite 1000 · 211 Commerce Street · Nashville, TN 37201 · 615-726-5600

Kelly L. Frey · Baker, Donelson, Bearman, Caldwell & Berkowitz · http://www.bakerdonelson.com · Commerce Center, Suite 1000 · 211 Commerce Street · Nashville, TN 37201 · 615-726-5600

Lydia A. Jones · Adams and Reese · http://www.adamsandreese.com · Fifth Third Center, Suite 2800 · 424 Church Street · Nashville, TN 37219 · 615-259-1450

E. Andrew Norwood · Waller Lansden Dortch & Davis · http://www.wallerlaw.com · Nashville City Center, Suite 2700 · 511 Union Street · P.O. Box 198966 · Nashville, TN 37219-8966 · 615-244-6380

Christopher A. Sloan · Boult, Cummings, Conners & Berry · http://www.boultcummings.com · Roundabout Plaza, Suite 700 · 1600 Division Street · P.O. Box 340025 · Nashville, TN 37203 · 615-244-2582

INSURANCE LAW

Jackson

Russell E. Reviere · Rainey, Kizer, Reviere & Bell · 105 South Highland Avenue · P.O. Box 1147 · Jackson, TN 38302 · 731-423-2414

Knoxville

S. Russell Headrick · a · Baker, Donelson, Bearman, Caldwell & Berkowitz · http://www.bakerdonelson.com · 2200 Riverview Tower · 900 South Gay Street · P.O. Box 1792 · Knoxville, TN 37902 · 865-549-7000

Memphis

Robert E. Craddock, Jr. · Wyatt, Tarrant & Combs · http://www.wyattfirm.com · The Renaissance Center, Suite 800 · 1715 Aaron Brenner Drive · Memphis, TN 38120 · 901-537-1000

Nashville

H. Lee Barfield II · a · Bass, Berry & Sims · http://www.bassberry.com · 315 Deaderick Street, Suite 2700 Nashville, TN 37238-3001 · 615-742-6200

W. Davidson Broemel · Burr & Forman · http://www.burr.com · 700 Two American Center · 3102 West End Avenue · Nashville, TN 37203 · 615-724-3200

Kevin M. Doherty · Burr & Forman · http://www.burr.com · 700 Two American Center · 3102 West End Avenue · Nashville, TN 37203 · 615-724-3200

Dan H. Elrod · a · Miller & Martin · http://www.millermartin.com · One Nashville Place, Suite 1200 · 150 Fourth Avenue North · Nashville, TN 37219-2433 · 615-244-9270

Paula A. Flowers · Farmer and Luna · 333 Union Street, Suite 300 · Nashville, TN 37201 · 615-254-9146

H. Frederick Humbracht, Jr. · Boult, Cummings, Conners & Berry · http://www.boultcummings.com · Roundabout Plaza, Suite 700 · 1600 Division Street · P.O. Box 340025 · Nashville, TN 37203 · 615-244-2582

Robins H. Ledyard · Bass, Berry & Sims · http://www.bassberry.com · 315 Deaderick Street, Suite 2700 · Nashville, TN 37238-3001 · 615-742-6200

J. Richard Lodge, Jr. · Bass, Berry & Sims · http://www.bassberry.com · 315 Deaderick Street, Suite 2700 Nashville, TN 37238-3001 · 615-742-6200

T. Stephen C. Taylor · Bass, Berry & Sims · http://www.bassberry.com · 315 Deaderick Street, Suite 2700 Nashville, TN 37238-3001 · 615-742-6200

Guilford F. Thornton, Jr. · Adams and Reese · http://www.adamsandreese.com · Fifth Third Center, Suite 2800 · 424 Church Street · Nashville, TN 37219 · 615-259-1450

John Knox Walkup · Wyatt, Tarrant & Combs · http://www.wyattfirm.com · 2525 West End Avenue, Suite 1500 · Nashville, TN 37203-1423 · 615-244-0020

Amanda Haynes Young · Miller & Martin · http://www.millermartin.com · One Nashville Place, Suite 1200 · 150 Fourth Avenue North · Nashville, TN 37219-2433 · 615-244-9270

INTELLECTUAL PROPERTY LAW

Knoxville

Peter L. Brewer · Baker, Donelson, Bearman, Caldwell & Berkowitz · http://www.bakerdonelson.com · 2200 Riverview Tower · 900 South Gay Street · P.O. Box 1792 · Knoxville, TN 37902 · 865-549-7000

Memphis

Kemper B. Durand · a · Thomason, Hendrix, Harvey, Johnson & Mitchell · One Commerce Square, 29th Floor · 40 South Main Street · Memphis, TN 38103 · 901-525-8721

Grady M. Garrison · a · Baker, Donelson, Bearman, Caldwell & Berkowitz · http://www.bakerdonelson.com · 6060 Poplar Avenue, Suite 440 · Memphis, TN 38119 · 901-579-3100

Scott K. Haight · Baker, Donelson, Bearman, Caldwell & Berkowitz · http://www.bakerdonelson.com · First Tennessee Building, Suite 2000 · 165 Madison Avenue · Memphis, TN 38103 · 901-526-2000

Valerie Walsh Johnson · Baker, Donelson, Bearman, Caldwell & Berkowitz · http://www.bakerdonelson.com · First Tennessee Building, Suite 2000 · 165 Madison Avenue · Memphis, TN 38103 · 901-526-2000

Nashville

Reber M. Boult · Adams and Reese · http://www.adamsandreese.com · Fifth Third Center, Suite 2800 · 424 Church Street · Nashville, TN 37219 · 615-259-1450

Robert P. Felber, Jr. · Waller Lansden Dortch & Davis · http://www.wallerlaw.com · Nashville City Center, Suite 2700 · 511 Union Street · P.O. Box 198966 · Nashville, TN 37219-8966 · 615-244-6380

Robb S. Harvey · Waller Lansden Dortch & Davis · http://www.wallerlaw.com · Nashville City Center, Suite 2700 · 511 Union Street · P.O. Box 198966 · Nashville, TN 37219-8966 · 615-244-6380

Christian A. Horsnell · Milom Joyce Horsnell Crow · 3310 West End Avenue, Suite 610 · Nashville, TN 37203 · 615-255-6161

Linda Edell Howard · Adams and Reese · http://www.adamsandreese.com · Fifth Third Center, Suite 2800 · 424 Church Street · Nashville, TN 37219 · 615-259-1450

Paul W. Kruse · Bone McAllester Norton · Nashville City Center, Suite 1600 · 511 Union Street · Nashville, TN 37219 · 615-238-6300

W. Michael Milom · a · Milom Joyce Horsnell Crow · 3310 West End Avenue, Suite 610 · Nashville, TN 37203 · 615-255-6161

Lynn Morrow · Adams and Reese · http://www.adamsandreese.com · Music Row · 901 Eighteenth Avenue South · Nashville, TN 37212 · 615-341-0068

E. Andrew Norwood · Waller Lansden Dortch & Davis · http://www.wallerlaw.com · Nashville City Center, Suite 2700 · 511 Union Street · P.O. Box 198966 · Nashville, TN 37219-8966 · 615-244-6380

Christopher A. Sloan · Boult, Cummings, Conners & Berry · http://www.boultcummings.com · Roundabout Plaza, Suite 700 · 1600 Division Street · P.O. Box 340025 · Nashville, TN 37203 · 615-244-2582

Thor Y. Urness · Boult, Cummings, Conners & Berry · http://www.boultcummings.com · Roundabout Plaza, Suite 700 · 1600 Division Street · P.O. Box 340025 · Nashville, TN 37203 · 615-244-2582

LABOR AND EMPLOYMENT LAW

Brentwood

Stafford F. McNamee · a · Hooper, Zinn & McNamee · 109 Westpark Drive, Suite 300 · Brentwood, TN 37027 · 615-661-5472

Chattanooga

John R. Bode · Miller & Martin · http://www.millermartin.com · Volunteer Building, Suite 1000 · 832 Georgia Avenue · Chattanooga, TN 37402-2289 · 423-756-6600

Harry F. Burnette · a · Burnette, Dobson & Pinchak · 713 Cherry Street, Second Floor · Chattanooga, TN 37402 · 423-266-2121

Hal F. S. Clements · 2) · Miller & Martin · http://www.millermartin.com · Volunteer Building, Suite 1000 832 Georgia Avenue · Chattanooga, TN 37402-2289 · 423-756-6600

Steven F. Dobson · Burnette, Dobson & Pinchak · 713 Cherry Street, Second Floor · Chattanooga, TN 37402 · 423-266-2121

John C. Harrison · Baker, Donelson, Bearman, Caldwell & Berkowitz · http://www.bakerdonelson.com · 1800 Republic Centre · 633 Chestnut Street · Chattanooga, TN 37450-1800 · 423-756-2010

John B. Phillips, Jr. · a · Miller & Martin · http://www.millermartin.com · Volunteer Building, Suite 1000 · 832 Georgia Avenue · Chattanooga, TN 37402-2289 · 423-756-6600

William H. Pickering · Chambliss, Bahner & Stophel · http://www.cbslawfirm.com · 1000 Tallan Building Two Union Square · Chattanooga, TN 37402 · 423-756-3000

Frank P. Pinchak · 2) · Burnette, Dobson & Pinchak · 713 Cherry Street, Second Floor · Chattanooga, TN 37402 · 423-266-2121

Christopher H. Steger · Miller & Martin · http://www.millermartin.com · Volunteer Building, Suite 1000 832 Georgia Avenue · Chattanooga, TN 37402-2289 · 423-756-6600

W. Ferber Tracy · Spears, Moore, Rebman & Williams · Pioneer Building, Sixth Floor · 801 Broad Street · P.O. Box 1749 · Chattanooga, TN 37401-1749 · 423-756-7000

William G. Trumpeter · a · Miller & Martin · http://www.millermartin.com · Volunteer Building, Suite 1000 · 832 Georgia Avenue · Chattanooga, TN 37402-2289 · 423-756-6600

Johnson City

Steven H. Trent · Baker, Donelson, Bearman, Caldwell & Berkowitz · http://www.bakerdonelson.com · 100 Med Tech Parkway, Suite 200 · P.O. Box 3038 · Johnson City, TN 37602 · 423-928-0181

Knoxville

David A. Burkhalter II · a · Burkhalter, Rayson & Associates · 111 South Central Street · P.O. Box 2777 · Knoxville, TN 37901 · 865-524-4974

Lewis R. Hagood · 2) · Arnett, Draper & Hagood · First Tennessee Plaza, Suite 2300 · P.O. Box 300 · Knoxville, TN 37929-2300 · 865-546-7000

Fletcher L. Hudson · 2% · Baker, Donelson, Bearman, Caldwell & Berkowitz · http://www.bakerdonelson.com · 2200 Riverview Tower · 900 South Gay Street · P.O. Box 1792 · Knoxville, TN 37902 · 865-549-7000

Steven E. Kramer · Kramer Rayson · http://www.kramer-rayson.com · First Tennessee Plaza, Suite 2500 · 800 South Gay Street · P.O. Box 629 · Knoxville, TN 37901-0629 · 865-525-5134

Edward G. Phillips · a · Kramer Rayson · http://www.kramer-rayson.com · First Tennessee Plaza, Suite 2500 · 800 South Gay Street · P.O. Box 629 · Knoxville, TN 37901-0629 · 865-525-5134

Edwin H. Rayson · 2% · Kramer Rayson · http://www.kramer-rayson.com · First Tennessee Plaza, Suite 2500 · 800 South Gay Street · P.O. Box 629 · Knoxville, TN 37901-0629 · 865-525-5134

John B. Rayson · 2% · Kramer Rayson · http://www.kramer-rayson.com · First Tennessee Plaza, Suite 2500 800 South Gay Street · P.O. Box 629 · Knoxville, TN 37901-0629 · 865-525-5134

Ronald A. Rayson · Burkhalter, Rayson & Associates · 111 South Central Street · P.O. Box 2777 · Knoxville, TN 37901 · 865-524-4974

William A. Young · O'Neil, Parker and Williamson · 416 Cumberland Avenue, SW · P.O. Box 217 · Knoxville, TN 37902 · 865-546-7190

Mark A. Allen · a · Provost & Umphrey Law Firm · White Station Tower, Suite 700 · 5050 Poplar Avenue · Memphis, TN 38157 · 901-680-0292

Stephen H. Biller · Luckett Pinstein Ridder · 1669 Kirby Parkway, Suite 106 · Memphis, TN 38120 · 901-763-1800

Allen S. Blair · 2% · Harris Shelton Hanover Walsh · One Commerce Square, Suite 2700 · Memphis, TN 38103 · 901-525-1455

Louis P. Britt · Ford & Harrison · http://www.fordharrison.com · 795 Ridge Lake Boulevard, Suite 300 · Memphis, TN 38120 · 901-291-1500

Donald A. Donati · 2) · Donati Law Firm · 1545 Union Avenue · Memphis, TN 38104 · 901-278-1004

Donna K. Fisher · a · Ogletree Deakins · http://www.ogletreedeakins.com · International Place Tower Two, Suite 300 · 6410 Poplar Avenue · Memphis, TN 38119 · 901-767-6160

Herbert E. Gerson · a · Ford & Harrison · http://www.fordharrison.com · 795 Ridge Lake Boulevard, Suite 300 · Memphis, TN 38120 · 901-291-1500

Deborah G. Godwin · a · Godwin, Morris, Laurenzi & Bloomfield · 50 North Front Street, Suite 800 · P.O. Box 3290 · Memphis, TN 38173-0290 · 901-528-1702

Thomas L. Henderson · Ogletree Deakins · http://www.ogletreedeakins.com · International Place Tower Two, Suite 300 · 6410 Poplar Avenue · Memphis, TN 38119 · 901-767-6160

Charles W. Hill · Glankler Brown · http://www.glankler.com · One Commerce Square, Suite 1700 · Memphis, TN 38103 · 901-525-1322

N. Victoria Holladay · Ford & Harrison · http://www.fordharrison.com · 795 Ridge Lake Boulevard, Suite 300 · Memphis, TN 38120 · 901-291-1500

Charles V. Holmes · Ogletree Deakins · http://www.ogletreedeakins.com · International Place Tower Two, Suite 300 · 6410 Poplar Avenue · Memphis, TN 38119 · 901-767-6160

Steven Hymowitz · 2) · Kiesewetter Wise Kaplan Prather · 3725 Champion Hills Drive, Suite 3000 · Memphis, TN 38125 · 901-795-6695

David P. Jaqua · Butler, Snow, O'Mara, Stevens and Cannada · http://www.butlersnow.com · The Crescent Center, Suite 500 · 6075 Poplar Avenue · P.O. Box 171443 · Memphis, TN 38119 · 901-680-7200

Jonathan E. Kaplan · Kiesewetter Wise Kaplan Prather · 3725 Champion Hills Drive, Suite 3000 · Memphis, TN 38125 · 901-795-6695

Jay W. Kiesewetter · Kiesewetter Wise Kaplan Prather · 3725 Champion Hills Drive, Suite 3000 · Memphis, TN 38125 · 901-795-6695

Frederick J. Lewis · 2% · Ogletree Deakins · http://www.ogletreedeakins.com · International Place Tower Two, Suite 300 · 6410 Poplar Avenue · Memphis, TN 38119 · 901-767-6160

Edward J. McKenney, Jr. · Harris Shelton Hanover Walsh · One Commerce Square, Suite 2700 · Memphis, TN 38103 · 901-525-1455

Samuel Morris · Godwin, Morris, Laurenzi & Bloomfield · 50 North Front Street, Suite 800 · P.O. Box 3290 · Memphis, TN 38173-0290 · 901-528-1702

James R. Mulroy · Jackson Lewis · http://www.jacksonlewis.com · Memphis Clark Tower, Suite 2700 · 5100 Poplar Avenue · Memphis, TN 38137 · 901-881-2650

Dan M. Norwood · 2) · Norwood, Howard & Atchley · 266 South Front Street, Suite 206 · Memphis, TN 38104 · 901-276-7676

Arnold E. Perl · 2% · Ford & Harrison · http://www.fordharrison.com · 795 Ridge Lake Boulevard, Suite 300 · Memphis, TN 38120 · 901-291-1500

Paul E. Prather · Kiesewetter Wise Kaplan Prather · 3725 Champion Hills Drive, Suite 3000 · Memphis, TN 38125 · 901-795-6695

William Ryan · Donati Law Firm · 1545 Union Avenue · Memphis, TN 38104 · 901-278-1004

Stephen L. Shields · a · Jackson, Shields, Yeiser & Holt · 262 German Oak Drive · Memphis, TN 38018 901-754-8001

Delaine R. Smith · Ford & Harrison · http://www.fordharrison.com · 795 Ridge Lake Boulevard, Suite 300 Memphis, TN 38120 · 901-291-1500

James H. Stock, Jr. · Weintraub, Stock & Grisham · The Renaissance Center, Suite 512 · 1715 Aaron Brenner Drive · Memphis, TN 38120 · 901-526-0431

Thomas J. Walsh, Jr. · Ford & Harrison · http://www.fordharrison.com · 795 Ridge Lake Boulevard, Suite 300 · Memphis, TN 38120 · 901-291-1500

Keith A. Warren · Ford & Harrison · http://www.fordharrison.com · 795 Ridge Lake Boulevard, Suite 300 Memphis, TN 38120 · 901-291-1500

Jeff Weintraub · a · Weintraub, Stock & Grisham · The Renaissance Center, Suite 512 · 1715 Aaron Brenner Drive · Memphis, TN 38120 · 901-526-0431

Maurice Wexler · Baker, Donelson, Bearman, Caldwell & Berkowitz · http://www.bakerdonelson.com · First Tennessee Building, Suite 2000 · 165 Madison Avenue · Memphis, TN 38103 · 901-526-2000

Edward R. Young · Baker, Donelson, Bearman, Caldwell & Berkowitz · http://www.bakerdonelson.com · First Tennessee Building, Suite 2000 · 165 Madison Avenue · Memphis, TN 38103 · 901-526-2000

Morristown

William R. Seale · Wimberly Lawson Seale Wright & Daves · 929 West First North Street · P.O. Box 1066 · Morristown, TN 37816-1066 · 423-587-6870

Nashville

Robert L. Ballow · 2% · King & Ballow · 1100 Union Street Plaza · 315 Union Street · Nashville, TN 37201 · 615-259-3456

George E. Barrett · 2) · Barrett, Johnston & Parsley · 217 Second Avenue North · Nashville, TN 37201-1697 · 615-244-2202

Margaret L. Behm · Dodson, Parker & Behm · 306 Gay Street, Suite 400 · Nashville, TN 37201 · 615-254-2291

William A. Blue, Jr. · Constangy, Brooks & Smith · http://www.constangy.com · SunTrust Plaza, Suite 700 · 401 Commerce Street · Nashville, TN 37219 · 615-320-5200

Robert E. Boston · Waller Lansden Dortch & Davis · http://www.wallerlaw.com · Nashville City Center, Suite 2700 · 511 Union Street · P.O. Box 198966 · Nashville, TN 37219-8966 · 615-244-6380

C. Dewey Branstetter, Jr. · a · Branstetter Stranch & Jennings · 227 Second Avenue North, Fourth Floor · Nashville, TN 37201-1631 · 615-254-8801

Larry W. Bridgesmith · Waller Lansden Dortch & Davis · http://www.wallerlaw.com · Nashville City Center, Suite 2700 · 511 Union Street · P.O. Box 198966 · Nashville, TN 37219-8966 · 615-244-6380

Karen L.C. Ellis · a · Bass, Berry & Sims · http://www.bassberry.com · 315 Deaderick Street, Suite 2700 · Nashville, TN 37238-3001 · 615-742-6200

Keith D. Frazier · Ogletree Deakins · http://www.ogletreedeakins.com · Financial Center, Suite 800 · 424 Church Street · Nashville, TN 37219 · 615-254-1900

Tim K. Garrett · Bass, Berry & Sims · http://www.bassberry.com · 315 Deaderick Street, Suite 2700 · Nashville, TN 37238-3001 · 615-742-6200

R. Jan Jennings · a · Branstetter Stranch & Jennings · 227 Second Avenue North, Fourth Floor · Nashville, TN 37201-1631 · 615-254-8801

Douglas S. Johnston, Jr. · Barrett, Johnston & Parsley · 217 Second Avenue North · Nashville, TN 37201-1697 · 615-244-2202

Matthew C. Lonergan · Boult, Cummings, Conners & Berry · http://www.boultcummings.com · Roundabout Plaza, Suite 700 · 1600 Division Street · P.O. Box 340025 · Nashville, TN 37203 · 615-244-2582

Richard C. Lowe · King & Ballow · 1100 Union Street Plaza · 315 Union Street · Nashville, TN 37201 · 615-259-3456

Anne C. Martin · Bone McAllester Norton · Nashville City Center, Suite 1600 · 511 Union Street · Nashville, TN 37219 · 615-238-6300

Joseph O. Martin, Jr. · 2% · Gullett, Sanford, Robinson & Martin · 315 Deaderick Street, Suite 1100 · P.O. Box 198888 · Nashville, TN 37219-8888 · 615-244-4994

John J. Matchulat · Baker, Donelson, Bearman, Caldwell & Berkowitz · http://www.bakerdonelson.com · Commerce Center, Suite 1000 · 211 Commerce Street · Nashville, TN 37201 · 615-726-5600

Barbara J. Moss · Stites & Harbison · http://www.stites.com · SunTrust Plaza, Suite 800 · 401 Commerce Street · Nashville, TN 37219 · 615-244-5200

William N. Ozier · 2% · Bass, Berry & Sims · http://www.bassberry.com · 315 Deaderick Street, Suite 2700 Nashville, TN 37238-3001 · 615-742-6200

Richard R. Parker · Ogletree Deakins · http://www.ogletreedeakins.com · Financial Center, Suite 800 · 424 Church Street · Nashville, TN 37219 · 615-254-1900

Kevin H. Sharp · Drescher & Sharp · 1720 West End Avenue, Suite 300 · Nashville, TN 37203 · 615-425-7111

C. Eric Stevens · Miller & Martin · http://www.millermartin.com · One Nashville Place, Suite 1200 · 150 Fourth Avenue North · Nashville, TN 37219-2433 · 615-244-9270

James G. Stranch III · 2) · Branstetter Stranch & Jennings · 227 Second Avenue North, Fourth Floor · Nashville, TN 37201-1631 · 615-254-8801

Jane Branstetter Stranch · a · Branstetter Stranch & Jennings · 227 Second Avenue North, Fourth Floor Nashville, TN 37201-1631 · 615-254-8801

Irwin B. Venick · Dobbins & Venick · Parkview Towers, Suite 1010 · 210 Twenty-Fifth Avenue North · Nashville, TN 37203-5253 · 615-321-5659

R. Eddie Wayland · ⑩ · King & Ballow · 1100 Union Street Plaza · 315 Union Street · Nashville, TN 37201 · 615-259-3456

LAND USE & ZONING LAW

Memphis

Nathan A. Bicks · Burch, Porter & Johnson · http://www.bpjlaw.com · 130 North Court Avenue · Memphis, TN 38103 · 901-524-5000

Homer B. Branan III · Farris Bobango Branan · http://www.farrismathews.com · One Commerce Square, Suite 2000 · Memphis, TN 38103 · 901-259-7100

Ronald M. Harkavy · Harkavy Shainberg Kaplan & Dunstan · 6060 Poplar Avenue, Suite 140 · Memphis, TN 38119 · 901-761-1263

Robert S. Kirk, Jr. · Farris Bobango Branan · http://www.farrismathews.com · 1100 Ridgeway Loop Road, Suite 400 · Memphis, TN 38120 · 901-259-7120

Nashville

Coburn Dewees Berry IV · Bass, Berry & Sims · http://www.bassberry.com · 315 Deaderick Street, Suite 2700 · Nashville, TN 37238-3001 · 615-742-6200

Douglas Berry · Hubbard, Berry and Harris · SunTrust Bank Building, Suite 1420 · 201 Fourth Avenue North · Nashville, TN 37219 · 615-251-5444

Julian L. Bibb · ⑩ · Stites & Harbison · http://www.stites.com · SunTrust Plaza, Suite 800 · 401 Commerce Street · Nashville, TN 37219 · 615-244-5200

Robert N. Buchanan III · Stites & Harbison · http://www.stites.com · SunTrust Plaza, Suite 800 · 401 Commerce Street · Nashville, TN 37219 · 615-244-5200

George A. Dean · Parker, Lawrence, Cantrell & Dean · 200 Fourth Avenue North, Fifth Floor · Nashville, TN 37219 · 615-255-7500

J. Bryan Echols · Stites & Harbison · http://www.stites.com · SunTrust Plaza, Suite 800 · 401 Commerce Street · Nashville, TN 37219 · 615-244-5200

Kenneth P. Ezell · Baker, Donelson, Bearman, Caldwell & Berkowitz · http://www.bakerdonelson.com · Commerce Center, Suite 1000 · 211 Commerce Street · Nashville, TN 37201 · 615-726-5600

John A. Gupton III · Baker, Donelson, Bearman, Caldwell & Berkowitz · http://www.bakerdonelson.com Commerce Center, Suite 1000 · 211 Commerce Street · Nashville, TN 37201 · 615-726-5600

Jonathan Harwell · Harwell Howard Hyne Gabbert & Manner · http://www.h3gm.com · 315 Deaderick Street, Suite 1800 · Nashville, TN 37238-1800 · 615-256-0500

Shawn R. Henry · Tune, Entrekin & White · AmSouth Center, Suite 1700 · 315 Deaderick Street · Nashville, TN 37238-1700 · 615-244-2770

Jeffrey R. King · Stites & Harbison · http://www.stites.com · SunTrust Plaza, Suite 800 · 401 Commerce Street · Nashville, TN 37219 · 615-244-5200

James L. Murphy III · Boult, Cummings, Conners & Berry · http://www.boultcummings.com · Roundabout Plaza, Suite 700 · 1600 Division Street · P.O. Box 340025 · Nashville, TN 37203 · 615-244-2582

Laurence M. Papel · Baker, Donelson, Bearman, Caldwell & Berkowitz · http://www.bakerdonelson.com Commerce Center, Suite 1000 · 211 Commerce Street · Nashville, TN 37201 · 615-726-5600

Wesley D. Turner · Gullett, Sanford, Robinson & Martin · 315 Deaderick Street, Suite 1100 · P.O. Box 198888 · Nashville, TN 37219-8888 · 615-244-4994

Thomas V. White · Tune, Entrekin & White · AmSouth Center, Suite 1700 · 315 Deaderick Street · Nashville, TN 37238-1700 · 615-244-2770

LEGAL MALPRACTICE LAW

Knoxville

Darryl G. Lowe · a · Lowe & Yeager · Riverview Tower, Suite 1950 · 900 South Gay Street · Knoxville, TN 37902 · 865-521-6527

Memphis

Leo M. Bearman, Jr. · a · Baker, Donelson, Bearman, Caldwell & Berkowitz · http://www.bakerdonelson.com · First Tennessee Building, Suite 2000 · 165 Madison Avenue · Memphis, TN 38103 · 901-526-2000

N. Richard Glassman · a · Glassman, Edwards, Wade & Wyatt · 26 North Second Street · Memphis, TN 38103 · 901-527-4673

Nashville

Winston Evans · Evans, Jones & Reynolds · Suntrust Plaza, Suite 710 · 401 Commerce Street · P.O. Box 190627 · Nashville, TN 37219-0627 · 615-259-4685

Douglas M. Fisher · a · Howell & Fisher · Court Square Building · 300 James Robertson Parkway · Nashville, TN 37201-1107 · 615-244-3370

Darrell G. Townsend · a · Howell & Fisher · Court Square Building · 300 James Robertson Parkway · Nashville, TN 37201-1107 · 615-244-3370

LEVERAGED BUYOUTS AND PRIVATE EQUITY LAW

Memphis

Samuel D. Chafetz · 2% · Baker, Donelson, Bearman, Caldwell & Berkowitz · http://www.bakerdonelson.com · First Tennessee Building, Suite 2000 · 165 Madison Avenue · Memphis, TN 38103 · 901-526-2000

Matthew S. Heiter · Baker, Donelson, Bearman, Caldwell & Berkowitz · http://www.bakerdonelson.com · First Tennessee Building, Suite 2000 · 165 Madison Avenue · Memphis, TN 38103 · 901-526-2000

Nashville

James H. Cheek III · 2) · Bass, Berry & Sims · http://www.bassberry.com · 315 Deaderick Street, Suite 2700 · Nashville, TN 37238-3001 · 615-742-6200

J. Page Davidson · Bass, Berry & Sims · http://www.bassberry.com · 315 Deaderick Street, Suite 2700 · Nashville, TN 37238-3001 · 615-742-6200

Todd J. Rolapp · Bass, Berry & Sims · http://www.bassberry.com · 315 Deaderick Street, Suite 2700 · Nashville, TN 37238-3001 · 615-742-6200

MARITIME LAW

Memphis

Lee Jeff Bloomfield · a · Godwin, Morris, Laurenzi & Bloomfield · 50 North Front Street, Suite 800 · P.O. Box 3290 · Memphis, TN 38173-0290 · 901-528-1702

G. Ray Bratton · Bratton, O'Neal & Thorp · 675 Oakleaf Office Lane, Suite 200 · Memphis, TN 38117 · 901-684-6100

MASS TORT LITIGATION

Knoxville

Thomas Alan Bickers · Paine, Tarwater, Bickers and Tillman · First Tennessee Plaza, Suite 1100 · 800 South Gay Street · P.O. Box 198 · Knoxville, TN 37929 · 865-525-0880

Hugh B. Bright, Jr. · Woolf, McClane, Bright, Allen & Carpenter · 900 Riverview Tower · 900 South Gay Street · P.O. Box 900 · Knoxville, TN 37901-0900 · 865-215-1000

Dwight E. Tarwater · Paine, Tarwater, Bickers and Tillman · First Tennessee Plaza, Suite 1100 · 800 South Gay Street · P.O. Box 198 · Knoxville, TN 37929 · 865-525-0880

Memphis

Cannon F. Allen · Adams and Reese · http://www.adamsandreese.com · Brinkley Plaza, Suite 700 · 80 Monroe Avenue · Memphis, TN 38103 · 901-525-3234

Sam B. Blair, Jr. · Baker, Donelson, Bearman, Caldwell & Berkowitz · http://www.bakerdonelson.com · First Tennessee Building, Suite 2000 · 165 Madison Avenue · Memphis, TN 38103 · 901-526-2000

Charles C. Harrell · Butler, Snow, O'Mara, Stevens and Cannada · http://www.butlersnow.com · The Crescent Center, Suite 500 · 6075 Poplar Avenue · P.O. Box 171443 · Memphis, TN 38119 · 901-680-7200

J. Brook Lathram · a · Burch, Porter & Johnson · http://www.bpjlaw.com · 130 North Court Avenue · Memphis, TN 38103 · 901-524-5000

DeWitt M. Shy, Jr. · Burch, Porter & Johnson · http://www.bpjlaw.com · 130 North Court Avenue · Memphis, TN 38103 · 901-524-5000

Nashville

J. Randolph Bibb, Jr. · Waller Lansden Dortch & Davis · http://www.wallerlaw.com · Nashville City Center, Suite 2700 · 511 Union Street · P.O. Box 198966 · Nashville, TN 37219-8966 · 615-244-6380

Thomas M. Donnell, Jr. · Stewart, Estes & Donnell · Fifth Third Center, Suite 1401 · 424 Church Street Nashville, TN 37219 · 615-244-6538

James M. Doran, Jr. · Waller Lansden Dortch & Davis · http://www.wallerlaw.com · Nashville City Center, Suite 2700 · 511 Union Street · P.O. Box 198966 · Nashville, TN 37219-8966 · 615-244-6380

Samuel Lanier Felker · Bass, Berry & Sims · http://www.bassberry.com · 315 Deaderick Street, Suite 2700 · Nashville, TN 37238-3001 · 615-742-6200

Anthony J. McFarland · Bass, Berry & Sims · http://www.bassberry.com · 315 Deaderick Street, Suite 2700 · Nashville, TN 37238-3001 · 615-742-6200

Gary C. Shockley · a · Baker, Donelson, Bearman, Caldwell & Berkowitz · http://www.bakerdonelson.com · Commerce Center, Suite 1000 · 211 Commerce Street · Nashville, TN 37201 · 615-726-5600

MEDICAL MALPRACTICE LAW

Brentwood

John A. Day · a · Day & Blair · 5300 Maryland Way, Suite 300 · Brentwood, TN 37027 · 615-742-4880

Chattanooga

William E. Godbold III · Leitner, Williams, Dooley & Napolitan · Pioneer Building, Third Floor · 801 Broad Street · Chattanooga, TN 37402-2621 · 423-265-0214

Thomas O. Helton · 2% · Baker, Donelson, Bearman, Caldwell & Berkowitz · http://www.bakerdonelson.com · 1800 Republic Centre · 633 Chestnut Street · Chattanooga, TN 37450-1800 · 423-756-2010

Covington

J. Houston Gordon · 2% · Law Office of J. Houston Gordon · P.O. Box 846 · Covington, TN 38019 · 901-476-7100

Hendersonville

F. Dulin Kelly · Kelly, Kelly and Allman · 629 East Main Street · Hendersonville, TN 37075 · 615-824-3703

Jackson

Jerry D. Kizer, Jr. · Rainey, Kizer, Reviere & Bell · 105 South Highland Avenue · P.O. Box 1147 · Jackson, TN 38302 · 731-423-2414

Marty R. Phillips · Rainey, Kizer, Reviere & Bell · 105 South Highland Avenue · P.O. Box 1147 · Jackson, TN 38302 · 731-423-2414

Johnson City

Olen Haynes, Sr. · Arnold, Haynes & Sanders · 207 East Main Street · Johnson City, TN 37605 · 423-928-0165

Knoxville

Sidney W. Gilreath · 2% · Gilreath & Associates · Bank Of America Center, Suite 600 · 550 Main Avenue · P.O. Box 1270 · Knoxville, TN 37901-1270 · 865-637-2442

Harry P. Ogden · Baker, Donelson, Bearman, Caldwell & Berkowitz · http://www.bakerdonelson.com · 2200 Riverview Tower · 900 South Gay Street · P.O. Box 1792 · Knoxville, TN 37902 · 865-549-7000

Robert E. Pryor, Sr. · a · Pryor, Flynn, Priest & Harber · Two Centre Square, Suite 600 · 625 Gay Street P.O. Box 870 · Knoxville, TN 37902 · 865-522-4191

Memphis

Darrell E. Baker · Baker and Whitt · 6800 Poplar Pike, Suite 205 · Memphis, TN 38138-7439 · 901-737-5656

Leo M. Bearman, Jr. · a · Baker, Donelson, Bearman, Caldwell & Berkowitz · http://www.bakerdonelson.com · First Tennessee Building, Suite 2000 · 165 Madison Avenue · Memphis, TN 38103 · 901-526-2000

William L. Bomar · Glankler Brown · http://www.glankler.com · One Commerce Square, Suite 1700 · Memphis, TN 38103 · 901-525-1322

David M. Cook · a · The Hardison Law Firm · 119 South Main Street, Suite 800 · Memphis, TN 38103 · 901-525-8776

William W. Dunlap, Jr. · Harris Shelton Hanover Walsh · One Commerce Square, Suite 2700 · Memphis, TN 38103 · 901-525-1455

William H. Haltom, Jr. · Thomason, Hendrix, Harvey, Johnson & Mitchell · One Commerce Square, 29th Floor · 40 South Main Street · Memphis, TN 38103 · 901-525-8721

Albert C. Harvey · a · Thomason, Hendrix, Harvey, Johnson & Mitchell · One Commerce Square, 29th Floor · 40 South Main Street · Memphis, TN 38103 · 901-525-8721

J. Kimbrough Johnson · a · Thomason, Hendrix, Harvey, Johnson & Mitchell · One Commerce Square, 29th Floor · 40 South Main Street · Memphis, TN 38103 · 901-525-8721

Les Jones · Burch, Porter & Johnson · http://www.bpjlaw.com · 130 North Court Avenue · Memphis, TN 38103 · 901-524-5000

Michael E. Keeney · Thomason, Hendrix, Harvey, Johnson & Mitchell · One Commerce Square, 29th Floor · 40 South Main Street · Memphis, TN 38103 · 901-525-8721

James L. Kirby · Harris Shelton Hanover Walsh · One Commerce Square, Suite 2700 · Memphis, TN 38103 · 901-525-1455

Jerry E. Mitchell · a · Thomason, Hendrix, Harvey, Johnson & Mitchell · One Commerce Square, 29th Floor · 40 South Main Street · Memphis, TN 38103 · 901-525-8721

Robert L. Moore · Heaton and Moore · 100 North Main Building, Suite 3400 · Memphis, TN 38103-0534 · 901-526-5975

Gary K. Morrell · a · Boswell Law Firm · 45 North Third Street, Second Floor · P.O. Box 798 · Memphis, TN 38103 · 901-522-0050

Jerry O. Potter · The Hardison Law Firm · 119 South Main Street, Suite 800 · Memphis, TN 38103 · 901-525-8776

Gary K. Smith · a · Gary K. Smith & Associates · 100 Peabody Place, Suite 1300 · Memphis, TN 38103 · 901-544-6399

Jill M. Steinberg · Baker, Donelson, Bearman, Caldwell & Berkowitz · http://www.bakerdonelson.com · First Tennessee Building, Suite 2000 · 165 Madison Avenue · Memphis, TN 38103 · 901-526-2000

Buckner P. Wellford · Baker, Donelson, Bearman, Caldwell & Berkowitz · http://www.bakerdonelson.com · First Tennessee Building, Suite 2000 · 165 Madison Avenue · Memphis, TN 38103 · 901-526-2000

James D. Wilson · Harris Shelton Hanover Walsh · One Commerce Square, Suite 2700 · Memphis, TN 38103 · 901-525-1455

Nashville

Steven E. Anderson · Walker, Tipps & Malone · 2300 One Nashville Place · 150 Fourth Avenue North · Nashville, TN 37219 · 615-313-6000

H. Lee Barfield II · a · Bass, Berry & Sims · http://www.bassberry.com · 315 Deaderick Street, Suite 2700 Nashville, TN 37238-3001 · 615-742-6200

Dixie W. Cooper · Gideon & Wiseman · 1100 Noel Place · 200 Fourth Avenue North · Nashville, TN 37219-2144 · 615-254-0400

Clarence J. Gideon, Jr. · a · Gideon & Wiseman · 1100 Noel Place · 200 Fourth Avenue North · Nashville, TN 37219-2144 · 615-254-0400

David A. King · Bass, Berry & Sims · http://www.bassberry.com · 315 Deaderick Street, Suite 2700 · Nashville, TN 37238-3001 · 615-742-6200

Randall L. Kinnard · a · Kinnard, Clayton & Beveridge · http://www.kinnardclaytonandbeveridge.com · 127 Woodmont Boulevard · Nashville, TN 37205 · 615-297-1007

Noel F. Stahl · a · Miller & Martin · http://www.millermartin.com · One Nashville Place, Suite 1200 · 150 Fourth Avenue North · Nashville, TN 37219-2433 · 615-244-9270

Darrell G. Townsend · a · Howell & Fisher · Court Square Building · 300 James Robertson Parkway · Nashville, TN 37201-1107 · 615-244-3370

Robert L. Trentham · Miller & Martin · http://www.millermartin.com · One Nashville Place, Suite 1200 · 150 Fourth Avenue North · Nashville, TN 37219-2433 · 615-244-9270

Daniel D. Warlick · Daniel D. Warlick · 611 Commerce Street, Suite 2712 · Nashville, TN 37203 · 615-254-6117

Thomas A. Wiseman III · a · Gideon & Wiseman · 1100 Noel Place · 200 Fourth Avenue North · Nashville, TN 37219-2144 · 615-254-0400

MERGERS & ACQUISITIONS LAW

Chattanooga

E. Stephen Jett · Chambliss, Bahner & Stophel · http://www.cbslawfirm.com · 1000 Tallan Building · Two Union Square · Chattanooga, TN 37402 · 423-756-3000

Johnson City

Linda M. Crouch-McCreadie · Baker, Donelson, Bearman, Caldwell & Berkowitz · http://www.bakerdonelson.com · 100 Med Tech Parkway, Suite 200 · P.O. Box 3038 · Johnson City, TN 37602 · 423-928-0181

Memphis

John A. Bobango · Farris Bobango Branan · http://www.farrismathews.com 1100 Ridgeway Loop Road, Suite 400 · Memphis, TN 38120 · 901-259-7120

Samuel D. Chafetz · ㉕ · Baker, Donelson, Bearman, Caldwell & Berkowitz · http://www.bakerdonelson.com · First Tennessee Building, Suite 2000 · 165 Madison Avenue · Memphis, TN 38103 · 901-526-2000

Robert J. DelPriore · Baker, Donelson, Bearman, Caldwell & Berkowitz · http://www.bakerdonelson.com · First Tennessee Building, Suite 2000 · 165 Madison Avenue · Memphis, TN 38103 · 901-526-2000

John A. Good · ⑩ · Bass, Berry & Sims · http://www.bassberry.com · The Tower at Peabody Place, Suite 900 · 100 Peabody Place · Memphis, TN 38103-2625 · 901-543-5900

Nashville

George W. Bishop III · ⑩ · Waller Lansden Dortch & Davis · http://www.wallerlaw.com · Nashville City Center, Suite 2700 · 511 Union Street · P.O. Box 198966 · Nashville, TN 37219-8966 · 615-244-6380

Stephen T. Braun · Boult, Cummings, Conners & Berry · http://www.boultcummings.com · Roundabout Plaza, Suite 700 · 1600 Division Street · P.O. Box 340025 · Nashville, TN 37203 · 615-244-2582

Ashby Q. Burks · Baker, Donelson, Bearman, Caldwell & Berkowitz · http://www.bakerdonelson.com · Commerce Center, Suite 1000 · 211 Commerce Street · Nashville, TN 37201 · 615-726-5600

James H. Cheek III · ⑳ · Bass, Berry & Sims · http://www.bassberry.com · 315 Deaderick Street, Suite 2700 · Nashville, TN 37238-3001 · 615-742-6200

Glen A. Civitts · Harwell Howard Hyne Gabbert & Manner · http://www.h3gm.com · 315 Deaderick Street, Suite 1800 · Nashville, TN 37238-1800 · 615-256-0500

J. Chase Cole · ⑩ · Waller Lansden Dortch & Davis · http://www.wallerlaw.com · Nashville City Center, Suite 2700 · 511 Union Street · P.O. Box 198966 · Nashville, TN 37219-8966 · 615-244-6380

Richard G. Cowart · ⑩ · Baker, Donelson, Bearman, Caldwell & Berkowitz · http://www.bakerdonelson.com · Commerce Center, Suite 1000 · 211 Commerce Street · Nashville, TN 37201 · 615-726-5600

David Cox · Harwell Howard Hyne Gabbert & Manner · http://www.h3gm.com · 315 Deaderick Street, Suite 1800 · Nashville, TN 37238-1800 · 615-256-0500

J. Page Davidson · Bass, Berry & Sims · http://www.bassberry.com · 315 Deaderick Street, Suite 2700 · Nashville, TN 37238-3001 · 615-742-6200

B. Riney Green · Bass, Berry & Sims · http://www.bassberry.com · 315 Deaderick Street, Suite 2700 · Nashville, TN 37238-3001 · 615-742-6200

Tonya M. Grindon · Baker, Donelson, Bearman, Caldwell & Berkowitz · http://www.bakerdonelson.com Commerce Center, Suite 1000 · 211 Commerce Street · Nashville, TN 37201 · 615-726-5600

John B. Hardcastle, Jr. · ⑩ · Boult, Cummings, Conners & Berry · http://www.boultcummings.com · Roundabout Plaza, Suite 700 · 1600 Division Street · P.O. Box 340025 · Nashville, TN 37203 · 615-244-2582

J. Reginald Hill · ⑩ · Waller Lansden Dortch & Davis · http://www.wallerlaw.com · Nashville City Center, Suite 2700 · 511 Union Street · P.O. Box 198966 · Nashville, TN 37219-8966 · 615-244-6380

E. Berry Holt III · a · Boult, Cummings, Conners & Berry · http://www.boultcummings.com · Roundabout Plaza, Suite 700 · 1600 Division Street · P.O. Box 340025 · Nashville, TN 37203 · 615-244-2582

Ernest E. Hyne II · Harwell Howard Hyne Gabbert & Manner · http://www.h3gm.com · 315 Deaderick Street, Suite 1800 · Nashville, TN 37238-1800 · 615-256-0500

J. James Jenkins, Jr. · Bass, Berry & Sims · http://www.bassberry.com · 315 Deaderick Street, Suite 2700 Nashville, TN 37238-3001 · 615-742-6200

Howard H. Lamar III · Bass, Berry & Sims · http://www.bassberry.com · 315 Deaderick Street, Suite 2700 Nashville, TN 37238-3001 · 615-742-6200

Mark Manner · a · Harwell Howard Hyne Gabbert & Manner · http://www.h3gm.com · 315 Deaderick Street, Suite 1800 · Nashville, TN 37238-1800 · 615-256-0500

J. Allen Overby · Bass, Berry & Sims · http://www.bassberry.com · 315 Deaderick Street, Suite 2700 · Nashville, TN 37238-3001 · 615-742-6200

G. Scott Rayson · Waller Lansden Dortch & Davis · http://www.wallerlaw.com · Nashville City Center, Suite 2700 · 511 Union Street · P.O. Box 198966 · Nashville, TN 37219-8966 · 615-244-6380

J. Bradbury Reed · a · Bass, Berry & Sims · http://www.bassberry.com · 315 Deaderick Street, Suite 2700 Nashville, TN 37238-3001 · 615-742-6200

Todd J. Rolapp · Bass, Berry & Sims · http://www.bassberry.com · 315 Deaderick Street, Suite 2700 · Nashville, TN 37238-3001 · 615-742-6200

Thomas J. Sherrard III · 2) · Sherrard & Roe · http://www.sherrardroe.com · 424 Church Street, Suite 2000 · Nashville, TN 37219-3304 · 615-742-4200

Samuel E. Stumpf, Jr. · a · Bass, Berry & Sims · http://www.bassberry.com · 315 Deaderick Street, Suite 2700 · Nashville, TN 37238-3001 · 615-742-6200

Bob F. Thompson · a · Bass, Berry & Sims · http://www.bassberry.com · 315 Deaderick Street, Suite 2700 · Nashville, TN 37238-3001 · 615-742-6200

F. Mitchell Walker, Jr. · Bass, Berry & Sims · http://www.bassberry.com · 315 Deaderick Street, Suite 2700 · Nashville, TN 37238-3001 · 615-742-6200

Leigh Walton · a · Bass, Berry & Sims · http://www.bassberry.com · 315 Deaderick Street, Suite 2700 · Nashville, TN 37238-3001 · 615-742-6200

MUNICIPAL LAW

Chattanooga

Sam D. Elliott · Gearhiser, Peters, Lockaby, Cavett & Elliott · http://www.gplce.com · 320 McCallie Avenue · Chattanooga, TN 37402 · 423-756-5171

Memphis

C. Thomas Cates · 2) · Burch, Porter & Johnson · http://www.bpjlaw.com · 130 North Court Avenue · Memphis, TN 38103 · 901-524-5000

Henry L. Klein · a · Apperson, Crump & Maxwell · 6000 Poplar Avenue, Suite 400 · Memphis, TN 38119 · 901-756-6300

Edward J. McKenney, Jr. · Harris Shelton Hanover Walsh · One Commerce Square, Suite 2700 · Memphis, TN 38103 · 901-525-1455

Robert D. Meyers · Kiesewetter Wise Kaplan Prather · 3725 Champion Hills Drive, Suite 3000 · Memphis, TN 38125 · 901-795-6695

J. Martin Regan · Thomason, Hendrix, Harvey, Johnson & Mitchell · One Commerce Square, 29th Floor 40 South Main Street · Memphis, TN 38103 · 901-525-8721

Nashville

George A. Dean · Parker, Lawrence, Cantrell & Dean · 200 Fourth Avenue North, Fifth Floor · Nashville, TN 37219 · 615-255-7500

Jonathan Harwell · Harwell Howard Hyne Gabbert & Manner · http://www.h3gm.com · 315 Deaderick Street, Suite 1800 · Nashville, TN 37238-1800 · 615-256-0500

James L. Murphy III · Boult, Cummings, Conners & Berry · http://www.boultcummings.com · Roundabout Plaza, Suite 700 · 1600 Division Street · P.O. Box 340025 · Nashville, TN 37203 · 615-244-2582

Thomas V. White · Tune, Entrekin & White · AmSouth Center, Suite 1700 · 315 Deaderick Street · Nashville, TN 37238-1700 · 615-244-2770

MUTUAL FUNDS LAW

Nashville

James H. Cheek III · 2) · Bass, Berry & Sims · http://www.bassberry.com · 315 Deaderick Street, Suite 2700 · Nashville, TN 37238-3001 · 615-742-6200

Bob F. Thompson · a · Bass, Berry & Sims · http://www.bassberry.com · 315 Deaderick Street, Suite 2700 · Nashville, TN 37238-3001 · 615-742-6200

F. Mitchell Walker, Jr. · Bass, Berry & Sims · http://www.bassberry.com · 315 Deaderick Street, Suite 2700 · Nashville, TN 37238-3001 · 615-742-6200

NATURAL RESOURCES LAW

Nashville

J. Andrew Goddard · a · Bass, Berry & Sims · http://www.bassberry.com · 315 Deaderick Street, Suite 2700 · Nashville, TN 37238-3001 · 615-742-6200

G. Scott Thomas · Bass, Berry & Sims · http://www.bassberry.com · 315 Deaderick Street, Suite 2700 · Nashville, TN 37238-3001 · 615-742-6200

Jessalyn H. Zeigler · Bass, Berry & Sims · http://www.bassberry.com · 315 Deaderick Street, Suite 2700 · Nashville, TN 37238-3001 · 615-742-6200

NON-PROFIT/CHARITIES LAW

Brentwood

Steven K. Wood · Thrailkill, Harris, Wood & Boswell · 5141 Virginia Way, Suite 240 · P.O. Box 2408 · Brentwood, TN 37024-2408 · 615-376-3555

Chattanooga

Alan L. Cates · Husch Blackwell Sanders · http://www.huschblackwell.com · Dome Building, Suite 300 · 736 Georgia Avenue · Chattanooga, TN 37402 · 423-266-5500

Knoxville

Dan W. Holbrook · 2) · Holbrook, Peterson & Smith · Tyson Place, Suite 150 · 2607 Kingston Pike · Knoxville, TN 37919 · 865-523-2900

Nashville

Richard D. Holton · 2% · Holton Blackstone & Mayberry · SunTrust Center, Suite 2800 · 424 Church Street · Nashville, TN 37205 · 615-823-7642

Michel G. Kaplan · 2% · Sherrard & Roe · http://www.sherrardroe.com · 424 Church Street, Suite 2000 · Nashville, TN 37219-3304 · 615-742-4200

James McCarten · White & Reasor · http://www.whitereasor.com · Two American Center, Suite 1150 · 3102 West End Avenue · Nashville, TN 37203-1304 · 615-383-3345

NON-WHITE-COLLAR CRIMINAL DEFENSE

Chattanooga

Gary D. Gerbitz · Miller & Martin · http://www.millermartin.com · Volunteer Building, Suite 1000 · 832 Georgia Avenue · Chattanooga, TN 37402-2289 · 423-756-6600

Jerry H. Summers · 2% · Summers & Wyatt · http://www.summersandwyatt.com · The James Building, Suite 800 · 735 Broad Street · Chattanooga, TN 37402-3496 · 423-265-2385

Cleveland

James F. Logan, Jr. · a · Logan, Thompson, Miller, Bilbo & Thompson · 30 Second Street, NW · P.O. Box 191 · Cleveland, TN 37364-0191 · 423-476-2251

Greeneville

Jerry W. Laughlin · Rogers, Laughlin, Nunnally, Hood & Crum · 100 South Main Street · Greeneville, TN 37743-4922 · 423-639-5183

John T. Milburn Rogers · a · Rogers, Laughlin, Nunnally, Hood & Crum · 100 South Main Street · Greeneville, TN 37743-4922 · 423-639-5183

Kingsport

R. Wayne Culbertson · R. Wayne Culbertson · 119 West Market Street · Kingsport, TN 37660 · 423-247-6161

Knoxville

Donald A. Bosch · Bosch Law Firm · http://www.boschlawfirm.com · 712 South Gay Street · Knoxville, TN 37902 · 865-637-2142

Wade V. Davies · Ritchie, Dillard & Davies · Main Place, Suite 300 · 606 West Main Street · P.O. Box 1126 · Knoxville, TN 37901-1126 · 865-637-0661

William Thomas Dillard III · a · Ritchie, Dillard & Davies · Main Place, Suite 300 · 606 West Main Street · P.O. Box 1126 · Knoxville, TN 37901-1126 · 865-637-0661

David M. Eldridge · Eldridge & Blakney · http://www.eldridge-blakney.com · The Cherokee Building, Suite 101 · 400 West Church Avenue · P.O. Box 398 · Knoxville, TN 37901-0398 · 865-544-2010

Ralph E. Harwell · Ralph E. Harwell · 2131 First Tennessee Plaza · Knoxville, TN 37929 · 865-637-8900

Gregory P. Isaacs · The Isaacs Ramsey Law Firm · 618 South Gay Street, Suite 300 · Knoxville, TN 37929-2448 · 865-673-6735

Herbert S. Moncier · a · Law Office of Herbert S. Moncier · Bank of America Center, Suite 775 · 550 West Main Street · Knoxville, TN 37902 · 865-546-7746

Steve Oberman · The Oberman Law Firm · 550 West Main Street, Suite 730 · Knoxville, TN 37902 · 865-249-7200

Douglas A. Trant · a · Douglas A. Trant · Riverview Tower, Suite 1502 · 900 South Gay Street · Knoxville, TN 37902-1810 · 865-525-7980

Memphis

Leslie I. Ballin · a · Ballin, Ballin & Fishman · 200 Jefferson Avenue, Suite 1250 · Memphis, TN 38103-2396 · 901-525-6278

Robert M. Brannon, Jr. · Brannon Law Firm · 295 Washington Avenue, Suite Three · Memphis, TN 38103-1911 · 901-521-1710

Robert L. Hutton · Glankler Brown · http://www.glankler.com · One Commerce Square, Suite 1700 · Memphis, TN 38103 · 901-525-1322

William D. Massey · Law Office of Massey McClusky · 3074 East Street · Memphis, TN 38128 · 901-384-4004

Nashville

Paul J. Bruno · Bell, Tennent & Frogge · Bank of America Plaza, Suite 904 · 414 Union Street · Nashville, TN 37219 · 615-244-1110

Hal D. Hardin · a · Hal D. Hardin · 211 Union Street, Suite 200 · Nashville, TN 37201 · 615-369-3377

Roger T. May · a · May & Ryan · 219 Second Avenue North, Suite 300 · Nashville, TN 37201-1618 · 615-256-7337

Richard McGee · Richard McGee · 1308 Rosa L. Parks Boulevard North · Nashville, TN 37208 · 615-254-0202

James W. Price, Jr. · Price, Hill & Kolarich · 201 Fourth Avenue North, Suite 1800 · Nashville, TN 37219 · 615-244-5772

David L. Raybin · Hollins, Wagster, Weatherly & Raybin · http://www.hwylaw.com · Fifth Third Center, Suite 2200 · 424 Church Street · Nashville, TN 37219 · 615-256-6666

Peter J. Strianse · a · Tune, Entrekin & White · AmSouth Center, Suite 1700 · 315 Deaderick Street · Nashville, TN 37238-1700 · 615-244-2770

James L. Weatherly, Jr. · Hollins, Wagster, Weatherly & Raybin · http://www.hwylaw.com · Fifth Third Center, Suite 2200 · 424 Church Street · Nashville, TN 37219 · 615-256-6666

Vincent E. Wehby · a · Vincent E. Wehby · 501 Union Street, Suite 500 · Nashville, TN 37219 · 615-255-7534

Springfield

Larry D. Wilks · Law Offices of Larry D. Wilks · 509 West Court Square · Springfield, TN 37172 · 615-384-8444

PERSONAL INJURY LITIGATION

Brentwood

John A. Day · a · Day & Blair · 5300 Maryland Way, Suite 300 · Brentwood, TN 37027 · 615-742-4880

Chattanooga

Michael A. Anderson · Horton, Maddox & Anderson · One Central Plaza, Suite 600 · 835 Georgia Avenue · Chattanooga, TN 37402 · 423-265-2560

William L. Brown · Miller & Martin · http://www.millermartin.com · Volunteer Building, Suite 1000 · 832 Georgia Avenue · Chattanooga, TN 37402-2289 · 423-756-6600

Michael R. Campbell · a · Campbell & Campbell · James Building, Suite 1200 · 735 Broad Street · Chattanooga, TN 37402-1835 · 423-266-1108

Charles J. Gearhiser · 2% · Gearhiser, Peters, Lockaby, Cavett & Elliott · http://www.gplce.com · 320 McCallie Avenue · Chattanooga, TN 37402 · 423-756-5171

Paul R. Leitner · 2) · Leitner, Williams, Dooley & Napolitan · Pioneer Building, Third Floor · 801 Broad Street · Chattanooga, TN 37402-2621 · 423-265-0214

Thomas H. O'Neal · 2) · O'Neal, Walker & Boehm · 1600 First Tennessee Building · 701 Market Street · Chattanooga, TN 37402 · 423-756-5111

Jerry H. Summers · 2% · Summers & Wyatt · http://www.summersandwyatt.com · The James Building, Suite 800 · 735 Broad Street · Chattanooga, TN 37402-3496 · 423-265-2385

Thomas A. Williams · Leitner, Williams, Dooley & Napolitan · Pioneer Building, Third Floor · 801 Broad Street · Chattanooga, TN 37402-2621 · 423-265-0214

W. Randall Wilson · Miller & Martin · http://www.millermartin.com · Volunteer Building, Suite 1000 · 832 Georgia Avenue · Chattanooga, TN 37402-2289 · 423-756-6600

Covington

J. Houston Gordon · 2% · Law Office of J. Houston Gordon · P.O. Box 846 · Covington, TN 38019 · 901-476-7100

Greeneville

John T. Milburn Rogers · a · Rogers, Laughlin, Nunnally, Hood & Crum · 100 South Main Street · Greeneville, TN 37743-4922 · 423-639-5183

Hendersonville

F. Dulin Kelly · Kelly, Kelly and Allman · 629 East Main Street · Hendersonville, TN 37075 · 615-824-3703

Johnson City

Olen Haynes, Sr. · Arnold, Haynes & Sanders · 207 East Main Street · Johnson City, TN 37605 · 423-928-0165

Kingsport

R. Wayne Culbertson · R. Wayne Culbertson · 119 West Market Street · Kingsport, TN 37660 · 423-247-6161

Jimmie C. Miller · Hunter, Smith & Davis · 1212 North Eastman Road · P.O. Box 3740 · Kingsport, TN 37664 · 423-378-8000

Knoxville

John W. Baker, Jr. · Baker, O'Kane, Atkins & Thompson · 2607 Kingston Pike, Suite 200 · P.O. Box 1708 · Knoxville, TN 37901 · 865-637-5600

Sidney W. Gilreath · 2% · Gilreath & Associates · Bank Of America Center, Suite 600 · 550 Main Avenue · P.O. Box 1270 · Knoxville, TN 37901-1270 · 865-637-2442

John T. Johnson, Jr. · Kramer Rayson · http://www.kramer-rayson.com · First Tennessee Plaza, Suite 2500 · 800 South Gay Street · P.O. Box 629 · Knoxville, TN 37901-0629 · 865-525-5134

Richard W. Krieg · Lewis, King, Krieg & Waldrop · http://www.lewisking.com · One Centre Square, Fifth Floor · 620 Market Street · P.O. Box 2425 · Knoxville, TN 37901 · 865-546-4646

James G. O'Kane · Baker, O'Kane, Atkins & Thompson · 2607 Kingston Pike, Suite 200 · P.O. Box 1708 · Knoxville, TN 37901 · 865-637-5600

Harry P. Ogden · Baker, Donelson, Bearman, Caldwell & Berkowitz · http://www.bakerdonelson.com · 2200 Riverview Tower · 900 South Gay Street · P.O. Box 1792 · Knoxville, TN 37902 · 865-549-7000

P. Edward Pratt · Baker, Donelson, Bearman, Caldwell & Berkowitz · http://www.bakerdonelson.com · 2200 Riverview Tower · 900 South Gay Street · P.O. Box 1792 · Knoxville, TN 37902 · 865-549-7000

Timothy A. Priest · Pryor, Flynn, Priest & Harber · Two Centre Square, Suite 600 · 625 Gay Street · P.O. Box 870 · Knoxville, TN 37902 · 865-522-4191

Robert E. Pryor, Sr. · a · Pryor, Flynn, Priest & Harber · Two Centre Square, Suite 600 · 625 Gay Street P.O. Box 870 · Knoxville, TN 37902 · 865-522-4191

Thomas S. Scott, Jr. · Ball & Scott · http://www.ballandscott.com · 550 West Main Avenue, Suite 750 · Knoxville, TN 37902 · 865-525-7028

Arthur G. Seymour, Jr. · a · Frantz, McConnell & Seymour · 550 West Main Avenue, Suite 500 · P.O. Box 39 · Knoxville, TN 37901 · 865-546-9321

William A. Simms · Arnett, Draper & Hagood · First Tennessee Plaza, Suite 2300 · P.O. Box 300 · Knoxville, TN 37929-2300 · 865-546-7000

Dwight E. Tarwater · Paine, Tarwater, Bickers and Tillman · First Tennessee Plaza, Suite 1100 · 800 South Gay Street · P.O. Box 198 · Knoxville, TN 37929 · 865-525-0880

Dalton L. Townsend · a · Hodges, Doughty & Carson · 617 Main Street · P.O. Box 869 · Knoxville, TN 37901-0869 · 865-546-9611

William D. Vines III · Butler, Vines and Babb · 2701 Kingston Pike · P.O. Box 2649 · Knoxville, TN 37901 · 865-637-3531

Louis C. Woolf · 2) · Woolf, McClane, Bright, Allen & Carpenter · 900 Riverview Tower · 900 South Gay Street · P.O. Box 900 · Knoxville, TN 37901-0900 · 865-215-1000

William A. Young · O'Neil, Parker and Williamson · 416 Cumberland Avenue, SW · P.O. Box 217 · Knoxville, TN 37902 · 865-546-7190

Memphis

Louis F. Allen · Glankler Brown · http://www.glankler.com · One Commerce Square, Suite 1700 · Memphis, TN 38103 · 901-525-1322

Leo M. Bearman, Jr. · a · Baker, Donelson, Bearman, Caldwell & Berkowitz · http://www.bakerdonelson.com · First Tennessee Building, Suite 2000 · 165 Madison Avenue · Memphis, TN 38103 · 901-526-2000

Sam B. Blair, Jr. · Baker, Donelson, Bearman, Caldwell & Berkowitz · http://www.bakerdonelson.com · First Tennessee Building, Suite 2000 · 165 Madison Avenue · Memphis, TN 38103 · 901-526-2000

William L. Bomar · Glankler Brown · http://www.glankler.com · One Commerce Square, Suite 1700 · Memphis, TN 38103 · 901-525-1322

Oscar C. Carr III · 2) · Glankler Brown · http://www.glankler.com · One Commerce Square, Suite 1700 · Memphis, TN 38103 · 901-525-1322

James D. Causey · 2% · Causey & Caywood · 5100 Poplar Avenue, Suite 3125 · Memphis, TN 38137 · 901-526-0206

Lee James Chase III · a · Glankler Brown · http://www.glankler.com · One Commerce Square, Suite 1700 · Memphis, TN 38103 · 901-525-1322

M. Anderson Cobb, Jr. · a · Harris Shelton Hanover Walsh · 6060 Poplar Avenue, Suite 450 · Memphis, TN 38119 · 901-682-1455

David M. Cook · a · The Hardison Law Firm · 119 South Main Street, Suite 800 · Memphis, TN 38103 · 901-525-8776

William W. Dunlap, Jr. · Harris Shelton Hanover Walsh · One Commerce Square, Suite 2700 · Memphis, TN 38103 · 901-525-1455

Robert M. Fargarson · Fargarson & Brooke · Cotton Exchange Building, Ninth Floor · 65 Union Avenue P.O. Drawer 3543 · Memphis, TN 38173-0543 · 901-523-2500

Robert D. Flynn · Spicer, Flynn & Rudstrom · 175 Toyota Plaza, Suite 800 · Memphis, TN 38103 · 901-523-1333

Robert L. Green · a · Allen, Summers, Simpson, Lillie & Gresham · Brinkley Plaza, Suite 650 · 80 Monroe Avenue · Memphis, TN 38103 · 901-763-4200

William H. Haltom, Jr. · Thomason, Hendrix, Harvey, Johnson & Mitchell · One Commerce Square, 29th Floor · 40 South Main Street · Memphis, TN 38103 · 901-525-8721

Albert C. Harvey · a · Thomason, Hendrix, Harvey, Johnson & Mitchell · One Commerce Square, 29th Floor · 40 South Main Street · Memphis, TN 38103 · 901-525-8721

William M. Jeter · a · Jeter & Nahmias · 35 Union Avenue, Suite 300 · Memphis, TN 38103 · 901-544-1556

J. Kimbrough Johnson · a · Thomason, Hendrix, Harvey, Johnson & Mitchell · One Commerce Square, 29th Floor · 40 South Main Street · Memphis, TN 38103 · 901-525-8721

Les Jones · Burch, Porter & Johnson · http://www.bpjlaw.com · 130 North Court Avenue · Memphis, TN 38103 · 901-524-5000

Michael E. Keeney · Thomason, Hendrix, Harvey, Johnson & Mitchell · One Commerce Square, 29th Floor · 40 South Main Street · Memphis, TN 38103 · 901-525-8721

George T. Lewis III · Baker, Donelson, Bearman, Caldwell & Berkowitz · http://www.bakerdonelson.com First Tennessee Building, Suite 2000 · 165 Madison Avenue · Memphis, TN 38103 · 901-526-2000

Bruce A. McMullen · Baker, Donelson, Bearman, Caldwell & Berkowitz · http://www.bakerdonelson.com First Tennessee Building, Suite 2000 · 165 Madison Avenue · Memphis, TN 38103 · 901-526-2000

Jerry E. Mitchell · a · Thomason, Hendrix, Harvey, Johnson & Mitchell · One Commerce Square, 29th Floor · 40 South Main Street · Memphis, TN 38103 · 901-525-8721

Robert L. Moore · Heaton and Moore · 100 North Main Building, Suite 3400 · Memphis, TN 38103-0534 · 901-526-5975

Gary K. Morrell · a · Boswell Law Firm · 45 North Third Street, Second Floor · P.O. Box 798 · Memphis, TN 38103 · 901-522-0050

Eugene J. Podesta, Jr. · Baker, Donelson, Bearman, Caldwell & Berkowitz · http://www.bakerdonelson.com · First Tennessee Building, Suite 2000 · 165 Madison Avenue · Memphis, TN 38103 · 901-526-2000

Jerry O. Potter · The Hardison Law Firm · 119 South Main Street, Suite 800 · Memphis, TN 38103 · 901-525-8776

Glen G. Reid, Jr. · a · Wyatt, Tarrant & Combs · http://www.wyattfirm.com · The Renaissance Center, Suite 800 · 1715 Aaron Brenner Drive · Memphis, TN 38120 · 901-537-1000

Kenneth R. Rudstrom · Spicer, Flynn & Rudstrom · 175 Toyota Plaza, Suite 800 · Memphis, TN 38103 · 901-523-1333

Gary K. Smith · a · Gary K. Smith & Associates · 100 Peabody Place, Suite 1300 · Memphis, TN 38103 · 901-544-6399

Joe D. Spicer · 2% · Spicer, Flynn & Rudstrom · 175 Toyota Plaza, Suite 800 · Memphis, TN 38103 · 901-523-1333

Jill M. Steinberg · Baker, Donelson, Bearman, Caldwell & Berkowitz · http://www.bakerdonelson.com · First Tennessee Building, Suite 2000 · 165 Madison Avenue · Memphis, TN 38103 · 901-526-2000

Buckner P. Wellford · Baker, Donelson, Bearman, Caldwell & Berkowitz · http://www.bakerdonelson.com · First Tennessee Building, Suite 2000 · 165 Madison Avenue · Memphis, TN 38103 · 901-526-2000

Nashville

Gail Vaughn Ashworth · a · Gideon & Wiseman · 1100 Noel Place · 200 Fourth Avenue North · Nashville, TN 37219-2144 · 615-254-0400

H. Lee Barfield II · a · Bass, Berry & Sims · http://www.bassberry.com · 315 Deaderick Street, Suite 2700 Nashville, TN 37238-3001 · 615-742-6200

J. Randolph Bibb, Jr. · Waller Lansden Dortch & Davis · http://www.wallerlaw.com · Nashville City Center, Suite 2700 · 511 Union Street · P.O. Box 198966 · Nashville, TN 37219-8966 · 615-244-6380

W. Gary Blackburn · Blackburn & McCune · 101 Lea Avenue · Nashville, TN 37210 · 615-254-7770

John P. Branham · a · Bone McAllester Norton · Nashville City Center, Suite 1600 · 511 Union Street · Nashville, TN 37219 · 615-238-6300

Jack A. Butler · 2% · Butler Elkin & Associates · 417 Washington Square Building · 222 Second Avenue North · Nashville, TN 37201 · 615-244-3300

Scott D. Carey · Baker, Donelson, Bearman, Caldwell & Berkowitz · http://www.bakerdonelson.com · Commerce Center, Suite 1000 · 211 Commerce Street · Nashville, TN 37201 · 615-726-5600

Thomas I. Carlton, Jr. · Cornelius & Collins · Nashville City Center, Suite 1500 · 511 Union Street · P.O. Box 190695 · Nashville, TN 37219-0695 · 615-244-1440

Thomas C. Corts · Ortale, Kelly, Herbert & Crawford · Noel Place, Third Floor · 200 Fourth Avenue North · P.O. Box 198985 · Nashville, TN 37219-8985 · 615-256-9999

Samuel Lanier Felker · Bass, Berry & Sims · http://www.bassberry.com · 315 Deaderick Street, Suite 2700 · Nashville, TN 37238-3001 · 615-742-6200

Douglas M. Fisher · a · Howell & Fisher · Court Square Building · 300 James Robertson Parkway · Nashville, TN 37201-1107 · 615-244-3370

Clarence J. Gideon, Jr. · a · Gideon & Wiseman · 1100 Noel Place · 200 Fourth Avenue North · Nashville, TN 37219-2144 · 615-254-0400

Hal D. Hardin · a · Hal D. Hardin · 211 Union Street, Suite 200 · Nashville, TN 37201 · 615-369-3377

David A. King · Bass, Berry & Sims · http://www.bassberry.com · 315 Deaderick Street, Suite 2700 · Nashville, TN 37238-3001 · 615-742-6200

Randall L. Kinnard · a · Kinnard, Clayton & Beveridge · http://www.kinnardclaytonandbeveridge.com · 127 Woodmont Boulevard · Nashville, TN 37205 · 615-297-1007

Thomas W. Lawrence, Jr. · Parker, Lawrence, Cantrell & Dean · 200 Fourth Avenue North, Fifth Floor · Nashville, TN 37219 · 615-255-7500

William D. Leader, Jr. · Leader, Bulso & Nolan · http://www.leaderbulso.com · 414 Union Street, Suite 1740 · Nashville, TN 37219 · 615-780-4100

Gayle Malone, Jr. · a · Walker, Tipps & Malone · 2300 One Nashville Place · 150 Fourth Avenue North Nashville, TN 37219 · 615-313-6000

Malcolm L. McCune · Blackburn & McCune · 101 Lea Avenue · Nashville, TN 37210 · 615-254-7770

George B. McGugin · a · Geroge B. McGugin · P.O. Box 58384 · Nashville, TN 37205-8384 · 615-292-3964

James F. Neal · 2% · Neal & Harwell · One Nashville Place, Suite 2000 · 150 Fourth Avenue North · Nashville, TN 37219-2498 · 615-244-1713

George H. Nolan · Leader, Bulso & Nolan · http://www.leaderbulso.com · 414 Union Street, Suite 1740 · Nashville, TN 37219 · 615-780-4100

John Norris · Norris & Norris · 424 Church Street, Suite 1300 · Nashville, TN 37219 · 615-627-3959

David Randolph Smith · Law Office of David Randolph Smith & Edward J. Schmidt III · Hillsboro Village · 1913 Twenty-First Avenue South · Nashville, TN 37212 · 615-742-1775

Noel F. Stahl · a · Miller & Martin · http://www.millermartin.com · One Nashville Place, Suite 1200 · 150 Fourth Avenue North · Nashville, TN 37219-2433 · 615-244-9270

John R. Tarpley · Lewis, King, Krieg & Waldrop · http://www.lewisking.com · Suntrust Bank Building, Suite 1500 · 201 Fourth Avenue North · P.O. Box 198615 · Nashville, TN 37219 · 615-259-1366

Darrell G. Townsend · a · Howell & Fisher · Court Square Building · 300 James Robertson Parkway · Nashville, TN 37201-1107 · 615-244-3370

Robert L. Trentham · Miller & Martin · http://www.millermartin.com · One Nashville Place, Suite 1200 · 150 Fourth Avenue North · Nashville, TN 37219-2433 · 615-244-9270

Robert J. Walker · a · Walker, Tipps & Malone · 2300 One Nashville Place · 150 Fourth Avenue North · Nashville, TN 37219 · 615-313-6000

William S. Walton · Miller & Martin · http://www.millermartin.com · One Nashville Place, Suite 1200 · 150 Fourth Avenue North · Nashville, TN 37219-2433 · 615-244-9270

Daniel D. Warlick · Daniel D. Warlick · 611 Commerce Street, Suite 2712 · Nashville, TN 37203 · 615-254-6117

William R. Willis, Jr. · 2) · Willis & Knight · 215 Second Avenue North · Nashville, TN 37201 · 615-259-9600

Thomas A. Wiseman III · a · Gideon & Wiseman · 1100 Noel Place · 200 Fourth Avenue North · Nashville, TN 37219-2144 · 615-254-0400

Springfield

Larry D. Wilks · Law Offices of Larry D. Wilks · 509 West Court Square · Springfield, TN 37172 · 615-384-8444

PRIVATE FUNDS LAW

Memphis

Samuel D. Chafetz · 2% · Baker, Donelson, Bearman, Caldwell & Berkowitz · http://www.bakerdonelson.com · First Tennessee Building, Suite 2000 · 165 Madison Avenue · Memphis, TN 38103 · 901-526-2000

Matthew S. Heiter · Baker, Donelson, Bearman, Caldwell & Berkowitz · http://www.bakerdonelson.com · First Tennessee Building, Suite 2000 · 165 Madison Avenue · Memphis, TN 38103 · 901-526-2000

Nashville

Samuel E. Stumpf, Jr. · a · Bass, Berry & Sims · http://www.bassberry.com · 315 Deaderick Street, Suite 2700 · Nashville, TN 37238-3001 · 615-742-6200

PRODUCT LIABILITY LITIGATION

Brentwood

John A. Day · a · Day & Blair · 5300 Maryland Way, Suite 300 · Brentwood, TN 37027 · 615-742-4880

Knoxville

W. Kyle Carpenter · Woolf, McClane, Bright, Allen & Carpenter · 900 Riverview Tower · 900 South Gay Street · P.O. Box 900 · Knoxville, TN 37901-0900 · 865-215-1000

Sidney W. Gilreath · 2% · Gilreath & Associates · Bank Of America Center, Suite 600 · 550 Main Avenue · P.O. Box 1270 · Knoxville, TN 37901-1270 · 865-637-2442

Howard E. Jarvis · Woolf, McClane, Bright, Allen & Carpenter · 900 Riverview Tower · 900 South Gay Street · P.O. Box 900 · Knoxville, TN 37901-0900 · 865-215-1000

Harry P. Ogden · Baker, Donelson, Bearman, Caldwell & Berkowitz · http://www.bakerdonelson.com · 2200 Riverview Tower · 900 South Gay Street · P.O. Box 1792 · Knoxville, TN 37902 · 865-549-7000

Robert E. Pryor, Sr. · a · Pryor, Flynn, Priest & Harber · Two Centre Square, Suite 600 · 625 Gay Street P.O. Box 870 · Knoxville, TN 37902 · 865-522-4191

William A. Simms · Arnett, Draper & Hagood · First Tennessee Plaza, Suite 2300 · P.O. Box 300 · Knoxville, TN 37929-2300 · 865-546-7000

Deborah C. Stevens · Lewis, King, Krieg & Waldrop · http://www.lewisking.com · One Centre Square, Fifth Floor · 620 Market Street · P.O. Box 2425 · Knoxville, TN 37901 · 865-546-4646

Dalton L. Townsend · a · Hodges, Doughty & Carson · 617 Main Street · P.O. Box 869 · Knoxville, TN 37901-0869 · 865-546-9611

Louis C. Woolf · 2) · Woolf, McClane, Bright, Allen & Carpenter · 900 Riverview Tower · 900 South Gay Street · P.O. Box 900 · Knoxville, TN 37901-0900 · 865-215-1000

Memphis

Leo M. Bearman, Jr. · a · Baker, Donelson, Bearman, Caldwell & Berkowitz · http://www.bakerdonelson.com · First Tennessee Building, Suite 2000 · 165 Madison Avenue · Memphis, TN 38103 · 901-526-2000

Sam B. Blair, Jr. · Baker, Donelson, Bearman, Caldwell & Berkowitz · http://www.bakerdonelson.com · First Tennessee Building, Suite 2000 · 165 Madison Avenue · Memphis, TN 38103 · 901-526-2000

Charles C. Harrell · Butler, Snow, O'Mara, Stevens and Cannada · http://www.butlersnow.com · The Crescent Center, Suite 500 · 6075 Poplar Avenue · P.O. Box 171443 · Memphis, TN 38119 · 901-680-7200

J. Brook Lathram · a · Burch, Porter & Johnson · http://www.bpjlaw.com · 130 North Court Avenue · Memphis, TN 38103 · 901-524-5000

Philip E. Mischke · Wyatt, Tarrant & Combs · http://www.wyattfirm.com · The Renaissance Center, Suite 800 · 1715 Aaron Brenner Drive · Memphis, TN 38120 · 901-537-1000

Glen G. Reid, Jr. · a · Wyatt, Tarrant & Combs · http://www.wyattfirm.com · The Renaissance Center, Suite 800 · 1715 Aaron Brenner Drive · Memphis, TN 38120 · 901-537-1000

DeWitt M. Shy, Jr. · Burch, Porter & Johnson · http://www.bpjlaw.com · 130 North Court Avenue · Memphis, TN 38103 · 901-524-5000

Jill M. Steinberg · Baker, Donelson, Bearman, Caldwell & Berkowitz · http://www.bakerdonelson.com · First Tennessee Building, Suite 2000 · 165 Madison Avenue · Memphis, TN 38103 · 901-526-2000

Buckner P. Wellford · Baker, Donelson, Bearman, Caldwell & Berkowitz · http://www.bakerdonelson.com · First Tennessee Building, Suite 2000 · 165 Madison Avenue · Memphis, TN 38103 · 901-526-2000

Nashville

J. Randolph Bibb, Jr. · Waller Lansden Dortch & Davis · http://www.wallerlaw.com · Nashville City Center, Suite 2700 · 511 Union Street · P.O. Box 198966 · Nashville, TN 37219-8966 · 615-244-6380

Thomas I. Carlton, Jr. · Cornelius & Collins · Nashville City Center, Suite 1500 · 511 Union Street · P.O. Box 190695 · Nashville, TN 37219-0695 · 615-244-1440

James M. Doran, Jr. · Waller Lansden Dortch & Davis · http://www.wallerlaw.com · Nashville City Center, Suite 2700 · 511 Union Street · P.O. Box 198966 · Nashville, TN 37219-8966 · 615-244-6380

Samuel Lanier Felker · Bass, Berry & Sims · http://www.bassberry.com · 315 Deaderick Street, Suite 2700 · Nashville, TN 37238-3001 · 615-742-6200

John R. Tarpley · Lewis, King, Krieg & Waldrop · http://www.lewisking.com · Suntrust Bank Building, Suite 1500 · 201 Fourth Avenue North · P.O. Box 198615 · Nashville, TN 37219 · 615-259-1366

Robert J. Walker · a · Walker, Tipps & Malone · 2300 One Nashville Place · 150 Fourth Avenue North · Nashville, TN 37219 · 615-313-6000

Joseph R. Wheeler · Cornelius & Collins · Nashville City Center, Suite 1500 · 511 Union Street · P.O. Box 190695 · Nashville, TN 37219-0695 · 615-244-1440

PROFESSIONAL MALPRACTICE LAW

Memphis

Leo M. Bearman, Jr. · a · Baker, Donelson, Bearman, Caldwell & Berkowitz · http://www.bakerdonelson.com · First Tennessee Building, Suite 2000 · 165 Madison Avenue · Memphis, TN 38103 · 901-526-2000

Oscar C. Carr III · 2) · Glankler Brown · http://www.glankler.com · One Commerce Square, Suite 1700 · Memphis, TN 38103 · 901-525-1322

Les Jones · Burch, Porter & Johnson · http://www.bpjlaw.com · 130 North Court Avenue · Memphis, TN 38103 · 901-524-5000

Eugene J. Podesta, Jr. · Baker, Donelson, Bearman, Caldwell & Berkowitz · http://www.bakerdonelson.com · First Tennessee Building, Suite 2000 · 165 Madison Avenue · Memphis, TN 38103 · 901-526-2000

Nashville

John S. Hicks · Baker, Donelson, Bearman, Caldwell & Berkowitz · http://www.bakerdonelson.com · Commerce Center, Suite 1000 · 211 Commerce Street · Nashville, TN 37201 · 615-726-5600

Malcolm L. McCune · Blackburn & McCune · 101 Lea Avenue · Nashville, TN 37210 · 615-254-7770

PROJECT FINANCE LAW

Chattanooga

Jay A. Young · Chambliss, Bahner & Stophel · http://www.cbslawfirm.com · 1000 Tallan Building · Two Union Square · Chattanooga, TN 37402 · 423-756-3000

Knoxville

Dennis B. Ragsdale · Long, Ragsdale & Waters · 1111 Northshore Drive, Suite S-700 · Knoxville, TN 37919 · 865-584-4040

Memphis

James B. McLaren, Jr. · Adams and Reese · http://www.adamsandreese.com · Brinkley Plaza, Suite 700 · 80 Monroe Avenue · Memphis, TN 38103 · 901-525-3234

John A. Stemmler · Bass, Berry & Sims · http://www.bassberry.com · The Tower at Peabody Place, Suite 900 · 100 Peabody Place · Memphis, TN 38103-2625 · 901-543-5900

PUBLIC FINANCE LAW

Chattanooga

Alfred E. Smith, Jr. · Miller & Martin · http://www.millermartin.com · Volunteer Building, Suite 1000 · 832 Georgia Avenue · Chattanooga, TN 37402-2289 · 423-756-6600

Knoxville

G. Mark Mamantov · Bass, Berry & Sims · http://www.bassberry.com · Riverview Tower, Suite 1700 · 900 South Gay Street · P.O. Box 1509 · Knoxville, TN 37901-1509 · 865-521-6200

Memphis

Cheryl W. Patterson · Wyatt, Tarrant & Combs · http://www.wyattfirm.com · The Renaissance Center, Suite 800 · 1715 Aaron Brenner Drive · Memphis, TN 38120 · 901-537-1000

Nashville

Patrick L. Alexander · Boult, Cummings, Conners & Berry · http://www.boultcummings.com · Roundabout Plaza, Suite 700 · 1600 Division Street · P.O. Box 340025 · Nashville, TN 37203 · 615-244-2582

Cynthia M. Barnett · Adams and Reese · http://www.adamsandreese.com · Fifth Third Center, Suite 2800 · 424 Church Street · Nashville, TN 37219 · 615-259-1450

George H. Masterson · Bass, Berry & Sims · http://www.bassberry.com · 315 Deaderick Street, Suite 2700 · Nashville, TN 37238-3001 · 615-742-6200

Karen S. Neal · Bass, Berry & Sims · http://www.bassberry.com · 315 Deaderick Street, Suite 2700 · Nashville, TN 37238-3001 · 615-742-6200

Keith B. Simmons · Bass, Berry & Sims · http://www.bassberry.com · 315 Deaderick Street, Suite 2700 · Nashville, TN 37238-3001 · 615-742-6200

Charles K. Wray · Bass, Berry & Sims · http://www.bassberry.com · 315 Deaderick Street, Suite 2700 · Nashville, TN 37238-3001 · 615-742-6200

RAILROAD LAW

Chattanooga

Pamela Rymer O'Dwyer · a · Paty, Rymer & Ulin · 19 Patten Parkway · Chattanooga, TN 37402-2297 · 423-756-6770

Knoxville

John W. Baker, Jr. · Baker, O'Kane, Atkins & Thompson · 2607 Kingston Pike, Suite 200 · P.O. Box 1708 · Knoxville, TN 37901 · 865-637-5600

Memphis

Everett B. Gibson · Bateman - Gibson · Cotton Exchange Building, Suite 1010 · 65 Union Avenue · P.O. Box 3351 · Memphis, TN 38173-0351 · 901-526-0412

Nashville

Gareth S. Aden · Gullett, Sanford, Robinson & Martin · 315 Deaderick Street, Suite 1100 · P.O. Box 198888 · Nashville, TN 37219-8888 · 615-244-4994

REAL ESTATE LAW

Chattanooga

Kenneth C. Beckman · Baker, Donelson, Bearman, Caldwell & Berkowitz · http://www.bakerdonelson.com · 1800 Republic Centre · 633 Chestnut Street · Chattanooga, TN 37450-1800 · 423-756-2010

Steve A. Bovell · a · Landstone · 3804 Saint Elmo Avenue, Suite 103 · Chattanooga, TN 37409 · 423-821-7558

Richard D. Crotteau · 2) · Miller & Martin · http://www.millermartin.com · Volunteer Building, Suite 1000 · 832 Georgia Avenue · Chattanooga, TN 37402-2289 · 423-756-6600

Richard D. Faulkner, Jr. · Baker, Donelson, Bearman, Caldwell & Berkowitz · http://www.bakerdonelson.com · 1800 Republic Centre · 633 Chestnut Street · Chattanooga, TN 37450-1800 · 423-756-2010

James M. Haley IV · Miller & Martin · http://www.millermartin.com · Volunteer Building, Suite 1000 · 832 Georgia Avenue · Chattanooga, TN 37402-2289 · 423-756-6600

Richard T. Hudson · Chambliss, Bahner & Stophel · http://www.cbslawfirm.com · 1000 Tallan Building · Two Union Square · Chattanooga, TN 37402 · 423-756-3000

Susan Elliott Rich · Baker, Donelson, Bearman, Caldwell & Berkowitz · http://www.bakerdonelson.com · 1800 Republic Centre · 633 Chestnut Street · Chattanooga, TN 37450-1800 · 423-756-2010

Ross I. Schram III · Baker, Donelson, Bearman, Caldwell & Berkowitz · http://www.bakerdonelson.com · 1800 Republic Centre · 633 Chestnut Street · Chattanooga, TN 37450-1800 · 423-756-2010

Michael N. St. Charles · Chambliss, Bahner & Stophel · http://www.cbslawfirm.com · 1000 Tallan Building · Two Union Square · Chattanooga, TN 37402 · 423-756-3000

Knoxville

David E. Fielder · Baker, Donelson, Bearman, Caldwell & Berkowitz · http://www.bakerdonelson.com · 2200 Riverview Tower · 900 South Gay Street · P.O. Box 1792 · Knoxville, TN 37902 · 865-549-7000

David W. Long · a · Long, Ragsdale & Waters · 1111 Northshore Drive, Suite S-700 · Knoxville, TN 37919 · 865-584-4040

G. Mark Mamantov · Bass, Berry & Sims · http://www.bassberry.com · Riverview Tower, Suite 1700 · 900 South Gay Street · P.O. Box 1509 · Knoxville, TN 37901-1509 · 865-521-6200

Dennis R. McClane · Woolf, McClane, Bright, Allen & Carpenter · 900 Riverview Tower · 900 South Gay Street · P.O. Box 900 · Knoxville, TN 37901-0900 · 865-215-1000

Dennis B. Ragsdale · Long, Ragsdale & Waters · 1111 Northshore Drive, Suite S-700 · Knoxville, TN 37919 · 865-584-4040

Memphis

Mary L. Aronov · Baker, Donelson, Bearman, Caldwell & Berkowitz · http://www.bakerdonelson.com · First Tennessee Building, Suite 2000 · 165 Madison Avenue · Memphis, TN 38103 · 901-526-2000

C. Thomas Cates · 2) · Burch, Porter & Johnson · http://www.bpjlaw.com · 130 North Court Avenue · Memphis, TN 38103 · 901-524-5000

Michael B. Chance · Baker, Donelson, Bearman, Caldwell & Berkowitz · http://www.bakerdonelson.com First Tennessee Building, Suite 2000 · 165 Madison Avenue · Memphis, TN 38103 · 901-526-2000

M. Anderson Cobb, Jr. · a · Harris Shelton Hanover Walsh · 6060 Poplar Avenue, Suite 450 · Memphis, TN 38119 · 901-682-1455

Charles C. Cottam · Magids Cottam · 1661 International Place Drive · Memphis, TN 38120 · 901-682-6431

LeeAnne Marshall Cox · Burch, Porter & Johnson · http://www.bpjlaw.com · 130 North Court Avenue · Memphis, TN 38103 · 901-524-5000

Allen C. Dunstan · Harkavy Shainberg Kaplan & Dunstan · 6060 Poplar Avenue, Suite 140 · Memphis, TN 38119 · 901-761-1263

B. Douglas Earthman · Glankler Brown · http://www.glankler.com · 6000 Poplar Avenue, Suite 100 · Memphis, TN 38119 · 901-685-1322

Neil Harkavy · Harkavy Shainberg Kaplan & Dunstan · 6060 Poplar Avenue, Suite 140 · Memphis, TN 38119 · 901-761-1263

Ronald M. Harkavy · Harkavy Shainberg Kaplan & Dunstan · 6060 Poplar Avenue, Suite 140 · Memphis, TN 38119 · 901-761-1263

R. Hunter Humphreys · Glankler Brown · http://www.glankler.com · One Commerce Square, Suite 1700 · Memphis, TN 38103 · 901-525-1322

James B. Jalenak · Harris Shelton Hanover Walsh · 6060 Poplar Avenue, Suite 450 · Memphis, TN 38119 · 901-682-1455

Phillip G. Kaminsky · Harris Shelton Hanover Walsh · 6060 Poplar Avenue, Suite 450 · Memphis, TN 38119 · 901-682-1455

Michael D. Kaplan · Harkavy Shainberg Kaplan & Dunstan · 6060 Poplar Avenue, Suite 140 · Memphis, TN 38119 · 901-761-1263

Robert C. Liddon, Jr. · Baker, Donelson, Bearman, Caldwell & Berkowitz · http://www.bakerdonelson.com · 6060 Poplar Avenue, Suite 440 · Memphis, TN 38119 · 901-579-3100

John B. Maxwell, Jr. · a · Apperson, Crump & Maxwell · 6000 Poplar Avenue, Suite 400 · Memphis, TN 38119 · 901-756-6300

Carla Peacher-Ryan · Baker, Donelson, Bearman, Caldwell & Berkowitz · http://www.bakerdonelson.com · First Tennessee Building, Suite 2000 · 165 Madison Avenue · Memphis, TN 38103 · 901-526-2000

J. William Pierce, Jr. · Glankler Brown · http://www.glankler.com · 6000 Poplar Avenue, Suite 100 · Memphis, TN 38119 · 901-685-1322

Richard C. Raines · Wyatt, Tarrant & Combs · http://www.wyattfirm.com · The Renaissance Center, Suite 800 · 1715 Aaron Brenner Drive · Memphis, TN 38120 · 901-537-1000

W. Rowlett Scott · 2) · Burch, Porter & Johnson · http://www.bpjlaw.com · 130 North Court Avenue · Memphis, TN 38103 · 901-524-5000

Raymond M. Shainberg · Harkavy Shainberg Kaplan & Dunstan · 6060 Poplar Avenue, Suite 140 · Memphis, TN 38119 · 901-761-1263

Richard R. Spore III · Bass, Berry & Sims · http://www.bassberry.com · The Tower at Peabody Place, Suite 900 · 100 Peabody Place · Memphis, TN 38103-2625 · 901-543-5900

John A. Stemmler · Bass, Berry & Sims · http://www.bassberry.com · The Tower at Peabody Place, Suite 900 · 100 Peabody Place · Memphis, TN 38103-2625 · 901-543-5900

James C. Warner · a · Martin, Tate, Morrow & Marston · International Place Tower II, Suite 1000 · 6410 Poplar Avenue · Memphis, TN 38119-4843 · 901-522-9000

E. Woods Weathersby · Evans Petree Bogatin · http://www.evanspetree.com · 1000 Ridgeway Loop Road, Suite 200 · Memphis, TN 38120 · 901-525-6781

Michael C. Williams · Evans Petree Bogatin · http://www.evanspetree.com · 1000 Ridgeway Loop Road, Suite 200 · Memphis, TN 38120 · 901-525-6781

Nashville

Alfred E. Abbey · 2) · Miller & Martin · http://www.millermartin.com · One Nashville Place, Suite 1200 · 150 Fourth Avenue North · Nashville, TN 37219-2433 · 615-244-9270

Stephen C. Baker · Waller Lansden Dortch & Davis · http://www.wallerlaw.com · Nashville City Center, Suite 2700 · 511 Union Street · P.O. Box 198966 · Nashville, TN 37219-8966 · 615-244-6380

Coburn Dewees Berry IV · Bass, Berry & Sims · http://www.bassberry.com · 315 Deaderick Street, Suite 2700 · Nashville, TN 37238-3001 · 615-742-6200

Douglas Berry · Hubbard, Berry and Harris · SunTrust Bank Building, Suite 1420 · 201 Fourth Avenue North · Nashville, TN 37219 · 615-251-5444

Kim A. Brown · Sherrard & Roe · http://www.sherrardroe.com · 424 Church Street, Suite 2000 · Nashville, TN 37219-3304 · 615-742-4200

Robert N. Buchanan III · Stites & Harbison · http://www.stites.com · SunTrust Plaza, Suite 800 · 401 Commerce Street · Nashville, TN 37219 · 615-244-5200

Robert R. Campbell, Jr. · Waller Lansden Dortch & Davis · http://www.wallerlaw.com · Nashville City Center, Suite 2700 · 511 Union Street · P.O. Box 198966 · Nashville, TN 37219-8966 · 615-244-6380

Ann Peldo Cargile · Boult, Cummings, Conners & Berry · http://www.boultcummings.com · Roundabout Plaza, Suite 700 · 1600 Division Street · P.O. Box 340025 · Nashville, TN 37203 · 615-244-2582

C. Mark Carver · Sherrard & Roe · http://www.sherrardroe.com · 424 Church Street, Suite 2000 · Nashville, TN 37219-3304 · 615-742-4200

James R. Cheshire III · Waller Lansden Dortch & Davis · http://www.wallerlaw.com · Nashville City Center, Suite 2700 · 511 Union Street · P.O. Box 198966 · Nashville, TN 37219-8966 · 615-244-6380

George V. Crawford, Jr. · Gullett, Sanford, Robinson & Martin · 315 Deaderick Street, Suite 1100 · P.O. Box 198888 · Nashville, TN 37219-8888 · 615-244-4994

J. Greer Cummings · Boult, Cummings, Conners & Berry · http://www.boultcummings.com · Roundabout Plaza, Suite 700 · 1600 Division Street · P.O. Box 340025 · Nashville, TN 37203 · 615-244-2582

George A. Dean · Parker, Lawrence, Cantrell & Dean · 200 Fourth Avenue North, Fifth Floor · Nashville, TN 37219 · 615-255-7500

Felix R. Dowsley III · Bass, Berry & Sims · http://www.bassberry.com · 315 Deaderick Street, Suite 2700 · Nashville, TN 37238-3001 · 615-742-6200

Kenneth P. Ezell · Baker, Donelson, Bearman, Caldwell & Berkowitz · http://www.bakerdonelson.com · Commerce Center, Suite 1000 · 211 Commerce Street · Nashville, TN 37201 · 615-726-5600

John A. Gupton III · Baker, Donelson, Bearman, Caldwell & Berkowitz · http://www.bakerdonelson.com Commerce Center, Suite 1000 · 211 Commerce Street · Nashville, TN 37201 · 615-726-5600

Matthew T. Harris · Waller Lansden Dortch & Davis · http://www.wallerlaw.com · Nashville City Center, Suite 2700 · 511 Union Street · P.O. Box 198966 · Nashville, TN 37219-8966 · 615-244-6380

John R. Haynes · Boult, Cummings, Conners & Berry · http://www.boultcummings.com · Roundabout Plaza, Suite 700 · 1600 Division Street · P.O. Box 340025 · Nashville, TN 37203 · 615-244-2582

Sam D. Hodges III · Grissim & Hodges · 323 Union Street · Nashville, TN 37201 · 615-255-7496

Robert M. Holland, Jr. · Miller & Martin · http://www.millermartin.com · One Nashville Place, Suite 1200 · 150 Fourth Avenue North · Nashville, TN 37219-2433 · 615-244-9270

D. Reed Houk · Adams and Reese · http://www.adamsandreese.com · Fifth Third Center, Suite 2800 · 424 Church Street · Nashville, TN 37219 · 615-259-1450

Jack F. King, Jr. · Miller & Martin · http://www.millermartin.com · One Nashville Place, Suite 1200 · 150 Fourth Avenue North · Nashville, TN 37219-2433 · 615-244-9270

Jeffrey R. King · Stites & Harbison · http://www.stites.com · SunTrust Plaza, Suite 800 · 401 Commerce Street · Nashville, TN 37219 · 615-244-5200

Michael S. Peek · Bass, Berry & Sims · http://www.bassberry.com · 315 Deaderick Street, Suite 2700 · Nashville, TN 37238-3001 · 615-742-6200

Charles B. Reasor, Jr. · White & Reasor · http://www.whitereasor.com · Two American Center, Suite 1150 · 3102 West End Avenue · Nashville, TN 37203-1304 · 615-383-3345

Cynthia N. Sellers · Bass, Berry & Sims · http://www.bassberry.com · 315 Deaderick Street, Suite 2700 · Nashville, TN 37238-3001 · 615-742-6200

D. Mark Sheets · Bass, Berry & Sims · http://www.bassberry.com · 315 Deaderick Street, Suite 2700 · Nashville, TN 37238-3001 · 615-742-6200

Barrett B. Sutton · Waller Lansden Dortch & Davis · http://www.wallerlaw.com · Nashville City Center, Suite 2700 · 511 Union Street · P.O. Box 198966 · Nashville, TN 37219-8966 · 615-244-6380

James S. Tate, Jr. · ⑩ · Bass, Berry & Sims · http://www.bassberry.com · 315 Deaderick Street, Suite 2700 · Nashville, TN 37238-3001 · 615-742-6200

J. Thomas Trent, Jr. · Boult, Cummings, Conners & Berry · http://www.boultcummings.com · Roundabout Plaza, Suite 700 · 1600 Division Street · P.O. Box 340025 · Nashville, TN 37203 · 615-244-2582

Wesley D. Turner · Gullett, Sanford, Robinson & Martin · 315 Deaderick Street, Suite 1100 · P.O. Box 198888 · Nashville, TN 37219-8888 · 615-244-4994

Richard F. Warren, Jr. · Boult, Cummings, Conners & Berry · http://www.boultcummings.com · Roundabout Plaza, Suite 700 · 1600 Division Street · P.O. Box 340025 · Nashville, TN 37203 · 615-244-2582

Warren H. Wild, Jr. · Stites & Harbison · http://www.stites.com · SunTrust Plaza, Suite 800 · 401 Commerce Street · Nashville, TN 37219 · 615-244-5200

Robert E. Wood · Boult, Cummings, Conners & Berry · http://www.boultcummings.com · Roundabout Plaza, Suite 700 · 1600 Division Street · P.O. Box 340025 · Nashville, TN 37203 · 615-244-2582

SECURITIES LAW

Johnson City

Linda M. Crouch-McCreadie · Baker, Donelson, Bearman, Caldwell & Berkowitz · http://www.bakerdonelson.com · 100 Med Tech Parkway, Suite 200 · P.O. Box 3038 · Johnson City, TN 37602 · 423-928-0181

Memphis

Scott T. Beall · Law Offices of Scott T. Beall · Atrium I, Suite 215 · 6800 Poplar · Memphis, TN 38138 · 901-681-0500

John A. Bobango · Farris Bobango Branan · http://www.farrismathews.com 1100 Ridgeway Loop Road, Suite 400 · Memphis, TN 38120 · 901-259-7120

Robert J. DelPriore · Baker, Donelson, Bearman, Caldwell & Berkowitz · http://www.bakerdonelson.com · First Tennessee Building, Suite 2000 · 165 Madison Avenue · Memphis, TN 38103 · 901-526-2000

John A. Good · ⑩ · Bass, Berry & Sims · http://www.bassberry.com · The Tower at Peabody Place, Suite 900 · 100 Peabody Place · Memphis, TN 38103-2625 · 901-543-5900

Shepherd D. Tate · a · Bass, Berry & Sims · http://www.bassberry.com · The Tower at Peabody Place, Suite 900 · 100 Peabody Place · Memphis, TN 38103-2625 · 901-543-5900

Nashville

Gary M. Brown · a · Baker, Donelson, Bearman, Caldwell & Berkowitz · http://www.bakerdonelson.com Commerce Center, Suite 1000 · 211 Commerce Street · Nashville, TN 37201 · 615-726-5600

James H. Cheek III · 2) · Bass, Berry & Sims · http://www.bassberry.com · 315 Deaderick Street, Suite 2700 · Nashville, TN 37238-3001 · 615-742-6200

David Cox · Harwell Howard Hyne Gabbert & Manner · http://www.h3gm.com · 315 Deaderick Street, Suite 1800 · Nashville, TN 37238-1800 · 615-256-0500

J. Page Davidson · Bass, Berry & Sims · http://www.bassberry.com · 315 Deaderick Street, Suite 2700 · Nashville, TN 37238-3001 · 615-742-6200

J. James Jenkins, Jr. · Bass, Berry & Sims · http://www.bassberry.com · 315 Deaderick Street, Suite 2700 Nashville, TN 37238-3001 · 615-742-6200

Howard H. Lamar III · Bass, Berry & Sims · http://www.bassberry.com · 315 Deaderick Street, Suite 2700 Nashville, TN 37238-3001 · 615-742-6200

Mark Manner · a · Harwell Howard Hyne Gabbert & Manner · http://www.h3gm.com · 315 Deaderick Street, Suite 1800 · Nashville, TN 37238-1800 · 615-256-0500

J. Allen Overby · Bass, Berry & Sims · http://www.bassberry.com · 315 Deaderick Street, Suite 2700 · Nashville, TN 37238-3001 · 615-742-6200

Todd J. Rolapp · Bass, Berry & Sims · http://www.bassberry.com · 315 Deaderick Street, Suite 2700 · Nashville, TN 37238-3001 · 615-742-6200

Bob F. Thompson · a · Bass, Berry & Sims · http://www.bassberry.com · 315 Deaderick Street, Suite 2700 · Nashville, TN 37238-3001 · 615-742-6200

F. Mitchell Walker, Jr. · Bass, Berry & Sims · http://www.bassberry.com · 315 Deaderick Street, Suite 2700 · Nashville, TN 37238-3001 · 615-742-6200

Leigh Walton · a · Bass, Berry & Sims · http://www.bassberry.com · 315 Deaderick Street, Suite 2700 · Nashville, TN 37238-3001 · 615-742-6200

STRUCTURED FINANCE LAW

Chattanooga

Kenneth C. Beckman · Baker, Donelson, Bearman, Caldwell & Berkowitz · http://www.bakerdonelson.com · 1800 Republic Centre · 633 Chestnut Street · Chattanooga, TN 37450-1800 · 423-756-2010

James M. Haley IV · Miller & Martin · http://www.millermartin.com · Volunteer Building, Suite 1000 · 832 Georgia Avenue · Chattanooga, TN 37402-2289 · 423-756-6600

Susan Elliott Rich · Baker, Donelson, Bearman, Caldwell & Berkowitz · http://www.bakerdonelson.com · 1800 Republic Centre · 633 Chestnut Street · Chattanooga, TN 37450-1800 · 423-756-2010

Louann P. Smith · Baker, Donelson, Bearman, Caldwell & Berkowitz · http://www.bakerdonelson.com · 1800 Republic Centre · 633 Chestnut Street · Chattanooga, TN 37450-1800 · 423-756-2010

Memphis

C. Thomas Cates · 2) · Burch, Porter & Johnson · http://www.bpjlaw.com · 130 North Court Avenue · Memphis, TN 38103 · 901-524-5000

Desiree M. Franklin · Baker, Donelson, Bearman, Caldwell & Berkowitz · http://www.bakerdonelson.com · First Tennessee Building, Suite 2000 · 165 Madison Avenue · Memphis, TN 38103 · 901-526-2000

Neil Harkavy · Harkavy Shainberg Kaplan & Dunstan · 6060 Poplar Avenue, Suite 140 · Memphis, TN 38119 · 901-761-1263

Carla Peacher-Ryan · Baker, Donelson, Bearman, Caldwell & Berkowitz · http://www.bakerdonelson.com · First Tennessee Building, Suite 2000 · 165 Madison Avenue · Memphis, TN 38103 · 901-526-2000

J. William Pierce, Jr. · Glankler Brown · http://www.glankler.com · 6000 Poplar Avenue, Suite 100 · Memphis, TN 38119 · 901-685-1322

Richard C. Raines · Wyatt, Tarrant & Combs · http://www.wyattfirm.com · The Renaissance Center, Suite 800 · 1715 Aaron Brenner Drive · Memphis, TN 38120 · 901-537-1000

TAX LAW

Brentwood

H. Stennis Little, Jr. · 2% · Little, House & Griffith · Building Two, Suite 150 · 750 Old Hickory Boulevard · Brentwood, TN 37027 · 615-256-5150

Larry T. Thrailkill · 2) · Thrailkill, Harris, Wood & Boswell · 5141 Virginia Way, Suite 240 · P.O. Box 2408 · Brentwood, TN 37024-2408 · 615-376-3555

Steven K. Wood · Thrailkill, Harris, Wood & Boswell · 5141 Virginia Way, Suite 240 · P.O. Box 2408 · Brentwood, TN 37024-2408 · 615-376-3555

Chattanooga

Thomas A. Caldwell · 2% · Baker, Donelson, Bearman, Caldwell & Berkowitz · http://www.bakerdonelson.com · 1800 Republic Centre · 633 Chestnut Street · Chattanooga, TN 37450-1800 · 423-756-2010

Carl E. Hartley · Baker, Donelson, Bearman, Caldwell & Berkowitz · http://www.bakerdonelson.com · 1800 Republic Centre · 633 Chestnut Street · Chattanooga, TN 37450-1800 · 423-756-2010

Ansley T. Moses · Miller & Martin · http://www.millermartin.com · Volunteer Building, Suite 1000 · 832 Georgia Avenue · Chattanooga, TN 37402-2289 · 423-756-6600

R. Wayne Peters · a · Gearhiser, Peters, Lockaby, Cavett & Elliott · http://www.gplce.com · 320 McCallie Avenue · Chattanooga, TN 37402 · 423-756-5171

Glenn C. Stophel · 2% · Chambliss, Bahner & Stophel · http://www.cbslawfirm.com · 1000 Tallan Building Two Union Square · Chattanooga, TN 37402 · 423-756-3000

Knoxville

Dale C. Allen · a · Woolf, McClane, Bright, Allen & Carpenter · 900 Riverview Tower · 900 South Gay Street · P.O. Box 900 · Knoxville, TN 37901-0900 · 865-215-1000

Mack A. Gentry · ㉕ · Gentry, Tipton & McLemore · 900 South Gay Street, Suite 2300 · P.O. Box 1990 · Knoxville, TN 37901 · 865-525-5300

Robert S. Marquis · ⑳ · Woolf, McClane, Bright, Allen & Carpenter · 900 Riverview Tower · 900 South Gay Street · P.O. Box 900 · Knoxville, TN 37901-0900 · 865-215-1000

Memphis

John A. Bobango · Farris Bobango Branan · http://www.farrismathews.com 1100 Ridgeway Loop Road, Suite 400 · Memphis, TN 38120 · 901-259-7120

G. Rice Byars, Jr. · Harris Shelton Hanover Walsh · 6060 Poplar Avenue, Suite 450 · Memphis, TN 38119 · 901-682-1455

Lewis R. Donelson III · ㉕ · Baker, Donelson, Bearman, Caldwell & Berkowitz · http://www.bakerdonelson.com · First Tennessee Building, Suite 2000 · 165 Madison Avenue · Memphis, TN 38103 · 901-526-2000

William H. D. Fones, Jr. · Baker, Donelson, Bearman, Caldwell & Berkowitz · http://www.bakerdonelson.com · First Tennessee Building, Suite 2000 · 165 Madison Avenue · Memphis, TN 38103 · 901-526-2000

William T. Mays, Jr. · Glankler Brown · http://www.glankler.com · One Commerce Square, Suite 1700 · Memphis, TN 38103 · 901-525-1322

George J. Nassar, Jr. · Glankler Brown · http://www.glankler.com · One Commerce Square, Suite 1700 · Memphis, TN 38103 · 901-525-1322

Herbert B. Wolf, Jr. · Husch Blackwell Sanders · http://www.huschblackwell.com · One Memphis Place, Suite 1501 · 200 Jefferson Avenue · Memphis, TN 38103 · 901-523-1123

Nashville

Joseph W. Gibbs · ⑩ · Boult, Cummings, Conners & Berry · http://www.boultcummings.com · Roundabout Plaza, Suite 700 · 1600 Division Street · P.O. Box 340025 · Nashville, TN 37203 · 615-244-2582

James C. Gooch · ㉕ · Bass, Berry & Sims · http://www.bassberry.com · 315 Deaderick Street, Suite 2700 · Nashville, TN 37238-3001 · 615-742-6200

Joe M. Goodman · Adams and Reese · http://www.adamsandreese.com · Fifth Third Center, Suite 2800 · 424 Church Street · Nashville, TN 37219 · 615-259-1450

J. Leigh Griffith · ⑩ · Waller Lansden Dortch & Davis · http://www.wallerlaw.com · Nashville City Center, Suite 2700 · 511 Union Street · P.O. Box 198966 · Nashville, TN 37219-8966 · 615-244-6380

Richard D. Holton · ㉕ · Holton Blackstone & Mayberry · SunTrust Center, Suite 2800 · 424 Church Street · Nashville, TN 37205 · 615-823-7642

Laurence O'Bryan Howard · Howard & Mobley · 200 Thirty-First Avenue North, Suite 100 · Nashville, TN 37203 · 615-627-4444

H. Wynne James III · ㉕ · Waller Lansden Dortch & Davis · http://www.wallerlaw.com · Nashville City Center, Suite 2700 · 511 Union Street · P.O. Box 198966 · Nashville, TN 37219-8966 · 615-244-6380

Richard A. Johnson · Waller Lansden Dortch & Davis · http://www.wallerlaw.com · Nashville City Center, Suite 2700 · 511 Union Street · P.O. Box 198966 · Nashville, TN 37219-8966 · 615-244-6380

Michel G. Kaplan · 2% · Sherrard & Roe · http://www.sherrardroe.com · 424 Church Street, Suite 2000 · Nashville, TN 37219-3304 · 615-742-4200

James McCarten · White & Reasor · http://www.whitereasor.com · Two American Center, Suite 1150 · 3102 West End Avenue · Nashville, TN 37203-1304 · 615-383-3345

Bryan W. Metcalf · Bass, Berry & Sims · http://www.bassberry.com · 315 Deaderick Street, Suite 2700 · Nashville, TN 37238-3001 · 615-742-6200

Jeffrey Mobley · a · Howard & Mobley · 200 Thirty-First Avenue North, Suite 100 · Nashville, TN 37203 · 615-627-4444

Patricia H. Moskal · Boult, Cummings, Conners & Berry · http://www.boultcummings.com · Roundabout Plaza, Suite 700 · 1600 Division Street · P.O. Box 340025 · Nashville, TN 37203 · 615-244-2582

Wm. Robert Pope, Jr. · White & Reasor · http://www.whitereasor.com · Two American Center, Suite 1150 · 3102 West End Avenue · Nashville, TN 37203-1304 · 615-383-3345

Edwin S. Pyle · Wyatt, Tarrant & Combs · http://www.wyattfirm.com · 2525 West End Avenue, Suite 1500 · Nashville, TN 37203-1423 · 615-244-0020

J. Allen Reynolds III · Evans, Jones & Reynolds · Suntrust Plaza, Suite 710 · 401 Commerce Street · P.O. Box 190627 · Nashville, TN 37219-0627 · 615-259-4685

Michael D. Sontag · a · Bass, Berry & Sims · http://www.bassberry.com · 315 Deaderick Street, Suite 2700 · Nashville, TN 37238-3001 · 615-742-6200

Michael Stewart · Waller Lansden Dortch & Davis · http://www.wallerlaw.com · Nashville City Center, Suite 2700 · 511 Union Street · P.O. Box 198966 · Nashville, TN 37219-8966 · 615-244-6380

Charles A. Trost · 2) · Waller Lansden Dortch & Davis · http://www.wallerlaw.com · Nashville City Center, Suite 2700 · 511 Union Street · P.O. Box 198966 · Nashville, TN 37219-8966 · 615-244-6380

G. Michael Yopp · a · Waller Lansden Dortch & Davis · http://www.wallerlaw.com · Nashville City Center, Suite 2700 · 511 Union Street · P.O. Box 198966 · Nashville, TN 37219-8966 · 615-244-6380

TECHNOLOGY LAW

Nashville

Bruce C. Doeg · Baker, Donelson, Bearman, Caldwell & Berkowitz · http://www.bakerdonelson.com · Commerce Center, Suite 1000 · 211 Commerce Street · Nashville, TN 37201 · 615-726-5600

Jason I. Epstein · Baker, Donelson, Bearman, Caldwell & Berkowitz · http://www.bakerdonelson.com · Commerce Center, Suite 1000 · 211 Commerce Street · Nashville, TN 37201 · 615-726-5600

Kelly L. Frey · Baker, Donelson, Bearman, Caldwell & Berkowitz · http://www.bakerdonelson.com · Commerce Center, Suite 1000 · 211 Commerce Street · Nashville, TN 37201 · 615-726-5600

G. Scott Thomas · Bass, Berry & Sims · http://www.bassberry.com · 315 Deaderick Street, Suite 2700 · Nashville, TN 37238-3001 · 615-742-6200

TIMBER LAW

Memphis

Marye Helen Owen · Farris Bobango Branan · http://www.farrismathews.com · 1100 Ridgeway Loop Road, Suite 400 · Memphis, TN 38120 · 901-259-7120

TRANSPORTATION LAW

Chattanooga

Kenneth Stephen Powers · Baker, Donelson, Bearman, Caldwell & Berkowitz · http://www.bakerdonelson.com · 1800 Republic Centre · 633 Chestnut Street · Chattanooga, TN 37450-1800 · 423-756-2010

Nashville

Kenneth M. Bryant · Miller & Martin · http://www.millermartin.com · One Nashville Place, Suite 1200 · 150 Fourth Avenue North · Nashville, TN 37219-2433 · 615-244-9270

Scott D. Carey · Baker, Donelson, Bearman, Caldwell & Berkowitz · http://www.bakerdonelson.com · Commerce Center, Suite 1000 · 211 Commerce Street · Nashville, TN 37201 · 615-726-5600

R. Eddie Wayland · ⑩ · King & Ballow · 1100 Union Street Plaza · 315 Union Street · Nashville, TN 37201 · 615-259-3456

TRUSTS AND ESTATES

Bristol

Erin Sheehey Downs · Jones, King & Downs · http://www.jkdlaw.com · 105 Landmark Lane · Bristol, TN 37620 · 423-764-5535

Chattanooga

Thomas A. Caldwell · ㉕ · Baker, Donelson, Bearman, Caldwell & Berkowitz · http://www.bakerdonelson.com · 1800 Republic Centre · 633 Chestnut Street · Chattanooga, TN 37450-1800 · 423-756-2010

Alan L. Cates · Husch Blackwell Sanders · http://www.huschblackwell.com · Dome Building, Suite 300 · 736 Georgia Avenue · Chattanooga, TN 37402 · 423-266-5500

Terry A. Cavett · Gearhiser, Peters, Lockaby, Cavett & Elliott · http://www.gplce.com · 320 McCallie Avenue · Chattanooga, TN 37402 · 423-756-5171

Hugh F. Kendall · ⑩ · Kendall Van Dolson · 1208 Pointe Center Drive, Suite 220 · Chattanooga, TN 37421 · 423-499-9863

Virginia C. Love · ⑩ · Baker, Donelson, Bearman, Caldwell & Berkowitz · http://www.bakerdonelson.com · 1800 Republic Centre · 633 Chestnut Street · Chattanooga, TN 37450-1800 · 423-756-2010

Donald E. Morton · ⑩ · Miller & Martin · http://www.millermartin.com · Volunteer Building, Suite 1000 · 832 Georgia Avenue · Chattanooga, TN 37402-2289 · 423-756-6600

R. Wayne Peters · a · Gearhiser, Peters, Lockaby, Cavett & Elliott · http://www.gplce.com · 320 McCallie Avenue · Chattanooga, TN 37402 · 423-756-5171

Randall D. Van Dolson · a · Kendall Van Dolson · 1208 Pointe Center Drive, Suite 220 · Chattanooga, TN 37421 · 423-499-9863

Knoxville

Dan W. Holbrook · 2) · Holbrook, Peterson & Smith · Tyson Place, Suite 150 · 2607 Kingston Pike · Knoxville, TN 37919 · 865-523-2900

Wayne R. Kramer · a · Kramer Rayson · http://www.kramer-rayson.com · First Tennessee Plaza, Suite 2500 · 800 South Gay Street · P.O. Box 629 · Knoxville, TN 37901-0629 · 865-525-5134

Robert S. Marquis · 2) · Woolf, McClane, Bright, Allen & Carpenter · 900 Riverview Tower · 900 South Gay Street · P.O. Box 900 · Knoxville, TN 37901-0900 · 865-215-1000

Anne M. McKinney · a · Anne M. McKinney · 1019 Orchid Avenue · Knoxville, TN 37912 · 865-525-8700

Marshall H. Peterson · a · Holbrook, Peterson & Smith · Tyson Place, Suite 150 · 2607 Kingston Pike · Knoxville, TN 37919 · 865-523-2900

Jonathan Reed · Egerton, McAfee, Armistead & Davis · Riverview Tower, Suite 1400 · 900 South Gay Street · Knoxville, TN 37902 · 865-546-0500

Maryville

Martha S. L. Black · Kizer & Black · http://www.kizer-black.com · 329 Cates Street · Maryville, TN 37801 · 865-982-7650

Memphis

Ben C. Adams, Jr. · Baker, Donelson, Bearman, Caldwell & Berkowitz · http://www.bakerdonelson.com · First Tennessee Building, Suite 2000 · 165 Madison Avenue · Memphis, TN 38103 · 901-526-2000

Thomas R. Buckner · a · Apperson, Crump & Maxwell · 6000 Poplar Avenue, Suite 400 · Memphis, TN 38119 · 901-756-6300

G. Rice Byars, Jr. · Harris Shelton Hanover Walsh · 6060 Poplar Avenue, Suite 450 · Memphis, TN 38119 · 901-682-1455

Joe M. Duncan · a · Burch, Porter & Johnson · http://www.bpjlaw.com · 130 North Court Avenue · Memphis, TN 38103 · 901-524-5000

James R. Hall, Jr. · Baker, Donelson, Bearman, Caldwell & Berkowitz · http://www.bakerdonelson.com · First Tennessee Building, Suite 2000 · 165 Madison Avenue · Memphis, TN 38103 · 901-526-2000

W. Thomas Hutton · 2) · Martin, Tate, Morrow & Marston · International Place Tower II, Suite 1000 · 6410 Poplar Avenue · Memphis, TN 38119-4843 · 901-522-9000

A. Stephen McDaniel · Williams, McDaniel, Wolfe & Womack · 5521 Murray Road · P.O. Box 172247 · Memphis, TN 38119 · 901-767-8200

James J. McMahon · a · Law Offices of James J. McMahon · 6800 Poplar Avenue Atrium One, Suite 215 Memphis, TN 38138 · 901-681-0500

John F. Murrah · Evans Petree Bogatin · 1661 International Place Drive, Suite 300 · Memphis, TN 38120 · 901-767-1234

George J. Nassar, Jr. · Glankler Brown · http://www.glankler.com · One Commerce Square, Suite 1700 · Memphis, TN 38103 · 901-525-1322

W. L. Nichol IV · Evans Petree Bogatin · http://www.evanspetree.com · 1000 Ridgeway Loop Road, Suite 200 · Memphis, TN 38120 · 901-525-6781

R. Michael Potter · a · Burch, Porter & Johnson · http://www.bpjlaw.com · 130 North Court Avenue · Memphis, TN 38103 · 901-524-5000

Raymond M. Shainberg · Harkavy Shainberg Kaplan & Dunstan · 6060 Poplar Avenue, Suite 140 · Memphis, TN 38119 · 901-761-1263

S. Shepherd Tate · a · Martin, Tate, Morrow & Marston · International Place Tower II, Suite 1000 · 6410 Poplar Avenue · Memphis, TN 38119-4843 · 901-522-9000

Jeffrey E. Thompson · Martin, Tate, Morrow & Marston · International Place Tower II, Suite 1000 · 6410 Poplar Avenue · Memphis, TN 38119-4843 · 901-522-9000

Blanchard E. Tual · Tual Graves · 1000 Brookfield Road, Suite 120 · Memphis, TN 38119 · 901-474-1222

Joseph B. Walker · 2% · Adams and Reese · http://www.adamsandreese.com · Brinkley Plaza, Suite 700 · 80 Monroe Avenue · Memphis, TN 38103 · 901-525-3234

Nashville

Stephanie Edwards · Howard & Mobley · 200 Thirty-First Avenue North, Suite 100 · Nashville, TN 37203 · 615-627-4444

Tommy C. Estes · Manier & Herod · One Nashville Place, Suite 2200 · 150 Fourth Avenue North · Nashville, TN 37219-2494 · 615-244-0030

James C. Gooch · 2% · Bass, Berry & Sims · http://www.bassberry.com · 315 Deaderick Street, Suite 2700 · Nashville, TN 37238-3001 · 615-742-6200

Joe M. Goodman · Adams and Reese · http://www.adamsandreese.com · Fifth Third Center, Suite 2800 · 424 Church Street · Nashville, TN 37219 · 615-259-1450

William L. Harbison · Sherrard & Roe · http://www.sherrardroe.com · 424 Church Street, Suite 2000 · Nashville, TN 37219-3304 · 615-742-4200

Richard D. Holton · 2% · Holton Blackstone & Mayberry · SunTrust Center, Suite 2800 · 424 Church Street · Nashville, TN 37205 · 615-823-7642

Laurence O'Bryan Howard · Howard & Mobley · 200 Thirty-First Avenue North, Suite 100 · Nashville, TN 37203 · 615-627-4444

Richard A. Johnson · Waller Lansden Dortch & Davis · http://www.wallerlaw.com · Nashville City Center, Suite 2700 · 511 Union Street · P.O. Box 198966 · Nashville, TN 37219-8966 · 615-244-6380

Michel G. Kaplan · 2% · Sherrard & Roe · http://www.sherrardroe.com · 424 Church Street, Suite 2000 · Nashville, TN 37219-3304 · 615-742-4200

James McCarten · White & Reasor · http://www.whitereasor.com · Two American Center, Suite 1150 · 3102 West End Avenue · Nashville, TN 37203-1304 · 615-383-3345

Jeffrey Mobley · ⑩ · Howard & Mobley · 200 Thirty-First Avenue North, Suite 100 · Nashville, TN 37203 · 615-627-4444

Edwin S. Pyle · Wyatt, Tarrant & Combs · http://www.wyattfirm.com · 2525 West End Avenue, Suite 1500 · Nashville, TN 37203-1423 · 615-244-0020

J. Allen Reynolds III · Evans, Jones & Reynolds · Suntrust Plaza, Suite 710 · 401 Commerce Street · P.O. Box 190627 · Nashville, TN 37219-0627 · 615-259-4685

Jack Wright Robinson, Sr. · ㉕ · Gullett, Sanford, Robinson & Martin · 315 Deaderick Street, Suite 1100 P.O. Box 198888 · Nashville, TN 37219-8888 · 615-244-4994

Michael D. Sontag · ⑩ · Bass, Berry & Sims · http://www.bassberry.com · 315 Deaderick Street, Suite 2700 · Nashville, TN 37238-3001 · 615-742-6200

Charles A. Trost · ⑳ · Waller Lansden Dortch & Davis · http://www.wallerlaw.com · Nashville City Center, Suite 2700 · 511 Union Street · P.O. Box 198966 · Nashville, TN 37219-8966 · 615-244-6380

VENTURE CAPITAL LAW

Memphis

John A. Bobango · Farris Bobango Branan · http://www.farrismathews.com 1100 Ridgeway Loop Road, Suite 400 · Memphis, TN 38120 · 901-259-7120

Matthew S. Heiter · Baker, Donelson, Bearman, Caldwell & Berkowitz · http://www.bakerdonelson.com · First Tennessee Building, Suite 2000 · 165 Madison Avenue · Memphis, TN 38103 · 901-526-2000

Nashville

Bruce C. Doeg · Baker, Donelson, Bearman, Caldwell & Berkowitz · http://www.bakerdonelson.com · Commerce Center, Suite 1000 · 211 Commerce Street · Nashville, TN 37201 · 615-726-5600

Howard H. Lamar III · Bass, Berry & Sims · http://www.bassberry.com · 315 Deaderick Street, Suite 2700 Nashville, TN 37238-3001 · 615-742-6200

WATER LAW

Chattanooga

James W. Gentry, Jr. · ⑳ · Spears, Moore, Rebman & Williams · Pioneer Building, Sixth Floor · 801 Broad Street · P.O. Box 1749 · Chattanooga, TN 37401-1749 · 423-756-7000

Nashville

J. Andrew Goddard · ⑩ · Bass, Berry & Sims · http://www.bassberry.com · 315 Deaderick Street, Suite 2700 · Nashville, TN 37238-3001 · 615-742-6200

William L. Penny · Stites & Harbison · http://www.stites.com · SunTrust Plaza, Suite 800 · 401 Commerce Street · Nashville, TN 37219 · 615-244-5200

Chattanooga

Gary D. Gerbitz · Miller & Martin · http://www.millermartin.com · Volunteer Building, Suite 1000 · 832 Georgia Avenue · Chattanooga, TN 37402-2289 · 423-756-6600

Jerry H. Summers · 2% · Summers & Wyatt · http://www.summersandwyatt.com · The James Building, Suite 800 · 735 Broad Street · Chattanooga, TN 37402-3496 · 423-265-2385

Cleveland

James F. Logan, Jr. · a · Logan, Thompson, Miller, Bilbo & Thompson · 30 Second Street, NW · P.O. Box 191 · Cleveland, TN 37364-0191 · 423-476-2251

Greeneville

Jerry W. Laughlin · Rogers, Laughlin, Nunnally, Hood & Crum · 100 South Main Street · Greeneville, TN 37743-4922 · 423-639-5183

John T. Milburn Rogers · a · Rogers, Laughlin, Nunnally, Hood & Crum · 100 South Main Street · Greeneville, TN 37743-4922 · 423-639-5183

Kingsport

R. Wayne Culbertson · R. Wayne Culbertson · 119 West Market Street · Kingsport, TN 37660 · 423-247-6161

Knoxville

Wade V. Davies · Ritchie, Dillard & Davies · Main Place, Suite 300 · 606 West Main Street · P.O. Box 1126 · Knoxville, TN 37901-1126 · 865-637-0661

William Thomas Dillard III · a · Ritchie, Dillard & Davies · Main Place, Suite 300 · 606 West Main Street · P.O. Box 1126 · Knoxville, TN 37901-1126 · 865-637-0661

David M. Eldridge · Eldridge & Blakney · http://www.eldridge-blakney.com · The Cherokee Building, Suite 101 · 400 West Church Avenue · P.O. Box 398 · Knoxville, TN 37901-0398 · 865-544-2010

Herbert S. Moncier · a · Law Office of Herbert S. Moncier · Bank of America Center, Suite 775 · 550 West Main Street · Knoxville, TN 37902 · 865-546-7746

Douglas A. Trant · a · Douglas A. Trant · Riverview Tower, Suite 1502 · 900 South Gay Street · Knoxville, TN 37902-1810 · 865-525-7980

Memphis

Leslie I. Ballin · a · Ballin, Ballin & Fishman · 200 Jefferson Avenue, Suite 1250 · Memphis, TN 38103-2396 · 901-525-6278

Robert M. Brannon, Jr. · Brannon Law Firm · 295 Washington Avenue, Suite Three · Memphis, TN 38103-1911 · 901-521-1710

James D. Causey · 2% · Causey & Caywood · 5100 Poplar Avenue, Suite 3125 · Memphis, TN 38137 · 901-526-0206

Kemper B. Durand · a · Thomason, Hendrix, Harvey, Johnson & Mitchell · One Commerce Square, 29th Floor · 40 South Main Street · Memphis, TN 38103 · 901-525-8721

James R. Garts, Jr. · a · Garts Law Firm · 369 North Main Street · Memphis, TN 38103 · 901-834-8911

Robert L. Hutton · Glankler Brown · http://www.glankler.com · One Commerce Square, Suite 1700 · Memphis, TN 38103 · 901-525-1322

William D. Massey · Law Office of Massey McClusky · 3074 East Street · Memphis, TN 38128 · 901-384-4004

Nashville

Paul J. Bruno · Bell, Tennent & Frogge · Bank of America Plaza, Suite 904 · 414 Union Street · Nashville, TN 37219 · 615-244-1110

William H. Farmer · Farmer and Luna · 333 Union Street, Suite 300 · Nashville, TN 37201 · 615-254-9146

Hal D. Hardin · a · Hal D. Hardin · 211 Union Street, Suite 200 · Nashville, TN 37201 · 615-369-3377

Aubrey B. Harwell, Jr. · 2% · Neal & Harwell · One Nashville Place, Suite 2000 · 150 Fourth Avenue North · Nashville, TN 37219-2498 · 615-244-1713

Roger T. May · a · May & Ryan · 219 Second Avenue North, Suite 300 · Nashville, TN 37201-1618 · 615-256-7337

Richard McGee · Richard McGee · 1308 Rosa L. Parks Boulevard North · Nashville, TN 37208 · 615-254-0202

James F. Neal · 2% · Neal & Harwell · One Nashville Place, Suite 2000 · 150 Fourth Avenue North · Nashville, TN 37219-2498 · 615-244-1713

James W. Price, Jr. · Price, Hill & Kolarich · 201 Fourth Avenue North, Suite 1800 · Nashville, TN 37219 · 615-244-5772

David L. Raybin · Hollins, Wagster, Weatherly & Raybin · http://www.hwylaw.com · Fifth Third Center, Suite 2200 · 424 Church Street · Nashville, TN 37219 · 615-256-6666

James F. Sanders · 2) · Neal & Harwell · One Nashville Place, Suite 2000 · 150 Fourth Avenue North · Nashville, TN 37219-2498 · 615-244-1713

Peter J. Strianse · a · Tune, Entrekin & White · AmSouth Center, Suite 1700 · 315 Deaderick Street · Nashville, TN 37238-1700 · 615-244-2770

James L. Weatherly, Jr. · Hollins, Wagster, Weatherly & Raybin · http://www.hwylaw.com · Fifth Third Center, Suite 2200 · 424 Church Street · Nashville, TN 37219 · 615-256-6666

Vincent E. Wehby · a · Vincent E. Wehby · 501 Union Street, Suite 500 · Nashville, TN 37219 · 615-255-7534

Springfield

Larry D. Wilks · Law Offices of Larry D. Wilks · 509 West Court Square · Springfield, TN 37172 · 615-384-8444

Bristol

Michael F. Blair · PennStuart · 804 Anderson Street · Bristol, TN 37620 · 423-793-4800

Chattanooga

Paul Campbell III · a · Campbell & Campbell · James Building, Suite 1200 · 735 Broad Street · Chattanooga, TN 37402-1835 · 423-266-1108

W. Randall Wilson · Miller & Martin · http://www.millermartin.com · Volunteer Building, Suite 1000 · 832 Georgia Avenue · Chattanooga, TN 37402-2289 · 423-756-6600

Jackson

Robert O. Binkley, Jr. · Rainey, Kizer, Reviere & Bell · 105 South Highland Avenue · P.O. Box 1147 · Jackson, TN 38302 · 731-423-2414

John D. Burleson · Rainey, Kizer, Reviere & Bell · 105 South Highland Avenue · P.O. Box 1147 · Jackson, TN 38302 · 731-423-2414

Johnson City

Jennifer P. Keller · Baker, Donelson, Bearman, Caldwell & Berkowitz · http://www.bakerdonelson.com · 100 Med Tech Parkway, Suite 200 · P.O. Box 3038 · Johnson City, TN 37602 · 423-928-0181

Knoxville

Robert W. Knolton · a · Kramer Rayson · http://www.kramer-rayson.com · First Tennessee Plaza, Suite 2500 · 800 South Gay Street · P.O. Box 629 · Knoxville, TN 37901-0629 · 865-525-5134

David N. Wedekind · Hodges, Doughty & Carson · 617 Main Street · P.O. Box 869 · Knoxville, TN 37901-0869 · 865-546-9611

Herbert B. Williams · Stokes & Rutherford · 920 Volunteer Landing, Suite 100 · Knoxville, TN 37915 · 865-544-3833

Madison

William L. Underhill · Underhill, Neewald, Hager & Underhill · 509 Lentz Drive · Madison, TN 37115-5101 · 615-865-5533

Memphis

Henry T. V. Miller · a · McDonald Kuhn · 119 South Main, Suite 400 · P.O. Box 3160 · Memphis, TN 38173-0160 · 901-526-0606

Stephen P. Miller · McDonald Kuhn · 119 South Main, Suite 400 · P.O. Box 3160 · Memphis, TN 38173-0160 · 901-526-0606

Nashville

Jack A. Butler · 2% · Butler Elkin & Associates · 417 Washington Square Building · 222 Second Avenue North · Nashville, TN 37201 · 615-244-3300

David J. Deming · Manier & Herod · One Nashville Place, Suite 2200 · 150 Fourth Avenue North · Nashville, TN 37219-2494 · 615-244-0030

David E. High · David High · Court Square Building, Second Floor · 300 James Robertson Parkway · Nashville, TN 37201 · 615-256-1000

Terry L. Hill · a · Manier & Herod · One Nashville Place, Suite 2200 · 150 Fourth Avenue North · Nashville, TN 37219-2494 · 615-244-0030

TEXAS

ADMINISTRATIVE LAW

Austin

Albert R. Axe, Jr. · Winstead · http://www.winstead.com · 401 Congress Avenue, Suite 2100 · Austin, TX 78701 · 512-370-2800

Molly J. Cagle · ⑩ · Vinson & Elkins · http://www.velaw.com · 2801 Via Fortuna, Suite 100 · Austin, TX 78746-7568 · 512-542-8400

Walter E. Demond · ⑩ · Clark, Thomas & Winters · 300 West Sixth Street, 15th Floor · P.O. Box 1148 · Austin, TX 78767 · 512-472-8800

David C. Duggins · ⑩ · Clark, Thomas & Winters · 300 West Sixth Street, 15th Floor · P.O. Box 1148 · Austin, TX 78767 · 512-472-8800

Robert J. Hearon, Jr. · ㉕ · Graves, Dougherty, Hearon & Moody · http://www.gdhm.com · 401 Congress Avenue, Suite 2200 · P.O. Box 98 · Austin, TX 78767-0098 · 512-480-5600

Nancy R. Hudson · Graves, Dougherty, Hearon & Moody · http://www.gdhm.com · 401 Congress Avenue, Suite 2200 · P.O. Box 98 · Austin, TX 78767-0098 · 512-480-5600

Mary A. Keeney · Graves, Dougherty, Hearon & Moody · http://www.gdhm.com · 401 Congress Avenue, Suite 2200 · P.O. Box 98 · Austin, TX 78767-0098 · 512-480-5600

Andrew Kever · Winstead · http://www.winstead.com · 401 Congress Avenue, Suite 2100 · Austin, TX 78701 · 512-370-2800

Lloyd P. Lochridge · ㉕ · McGinnis, Lochridge & Kilgore · http://www.mcginnislaw.com · 600 Congress Avenue, Suite 2100 · Austin, TX 78701 · 512-495-6000

Dudley D. McCalla · Heath, Davis & McCalla · 720 Brazos Street, Suite 200 · Austin, TX 78701 · 512-478-5671

Pike Powers · Fulbright & Jaworski · http://www.fulbright.com · 600 Congress Avenue, Suite 2400 · Austin, TX 78701-2978 · 512-474-5201

Philip F. Ricketts · ⑩ · Bracewell & Giuliani · http://www.bgllp.com · 111 Congress Avenue, Suite 2300 · Austin, TX 78701 · 512-472-7800

John A. Riley · Vinson & Elkins · http://www.velaw.com · 2801 Via Fortuna, Suite 100 · Austin, TX 78746-7568 · 512-542-8400

Celina Romero · Clark, Thomas & Winters · 300 West Sixth Street, 15th Floor · P.O. Box 1148 · Austin, TX 78767 · 512-472-8800

Pete Schenkkan · ⑩ · Graves, Dougherty, Hearon & Moody · http://www.gdhm.com · 401 Congress Avenue, Suite 2200 · P.O. Box 98 · Austin, TX 78767-0098 · 512-480-5600

Larry E. Temple · ⑩ · Larry E. Temple · 400 West 15th Street, Suite 1510 · Austin, TX 78701 · 512-477-4467

Michael J. Tomsu · Vinson & Elkins · http://www.velaw.com · 2801 Via Fortuna, Suite 100 · Austin, TX 78746-7568 · 512-542-8400

Rex D. VanMiddlesworth · ⑩ · Andrews Kurth · http://www.andrewskurth.com · 111 Congress Avenue, Suite 1700 · Austin, TX 78701-4069 · 512-320-9200

Dallas

Richard L. Adams · Vinson & Elkins · http://www.velaw.com · Trammell Crow Center, Suite 3700 · 2001 Ross Avenue · Dallas, TX 75201-2975 · 214-220-7700

Fort Worth

Dee J. Kelly, Jr. · Kelly, Hart & Hallman · Wells Fargo Tower, Suite 2500 · 201 Main Street · Fort Worth, TX 76102 · 817-332-2500

Dee J. Kelly, Sr. · ⑩ · Kelly, Hart & Hallman · Wells Fargo Tower, Suite 2500 · 201 Main Street · Fort Worth, TX 76102 · 817-332-2500

Richard W. Wiseman · Brown, Dean, Wiseman, Liser, Proctor & Hart · Fort Worth Club Building, Suite 200 · 306 West Seventh Street · Fort Worth, TX 76102-4905 · 817-332-1391

Houston

Jonathan S. Day · ⑩ · Andrews Kurth · http://www.andrewskurth.com · 600 Travis Street, Suite 4200 · Houston, TX 77002 · 713-220-4200

Charles A. Moore · Dewey & LeBoeuf · Reliant Energy Plaza, Suite 2550 · 1000 Main Street · Houston, TX 77002 · 713-287-2000

Aledo

John W. Hughes · John W. Hughes · 4524 Knoll Ridge · Aledo, TX 76008 · 817-377-4800

Arlington

Donald O. Pratt · Pratt & Yungblut · 2221 East Lamar Boulevard, Suite 150 · Arlington, TX 76006 · 817-633-2200

Beaumont

Robert A. Black · MehaffyWeber · http://www.mehaffyweber.com · 2615 Calder Avenue · P.O. Box 16 · Beaumont, TX 77702 · 409-835-5011

Carrollton

Sherrie R. Abney · Law Offices of Sherrie R. Abney · 2840 Keller Springs Road, Suite 204 · Carrollton, TX 75006-4829 · 972-417-7198

Corpus Christi

Marvin L. Nebrat · Marvin L. Nebrat · 615 North Upper Broadway, Suite 1200 · Corpus Christi, TX 78477-0301 · 361-882-4254

Dallas

Ted M. Akin · Ted M. Akin · 3023 Hester Avenue · Dallas, TX 75205-3525 · 214-821-6370

J. Michael Amis · Burdin Mediations · 4514 Cole Avenue, Suite 1450 · Dallas, TX 75205-5412 · 214-528-1411

Courtenay L. Bass · Gilbert Mediation Group · 3131 McKinney Avenue, Suite 125 · Dallas, TX 75204 · 214-303-4500

Mary M. Burdin · Burdin Mediations · 4514 Cole Avenue, Suite 1450 · Dallas, TX 75205-5412 · 214-528-1411

William Frank Carroll · Cox Smith Matthews · http://www.coxsmith.com · 1201 Elm Street, Suite 3300 · Dallas, TX 75270 · 214-698-7800

Gay G. Cox · Gay G. Cox · http://www.mediate.com/ggcox · 2213 Boll Street · Dallas, TX 75204 · 214-522-0150

Suzanne Duvall · Burdin Mediations · 4514 Cole Avenue, Suite 1450 · Dallas, TX 75205-5412 · 214-528-1411

John L. Estes · Locke Lord Bissell & Liddell · 2200 Ross Avenue, Suite 2200 · Dallas, TX 75201-6776 · 214-740-8000

Jeffrey A. Ford · Ford Nassen & Baldwin · 8080 North Central Expressway, Suite 1600 · Dallas, TX 75206-1819 · 214-523-5100

Kathy Fragnoli · Burdin Mediations · 4514 Cole Avenue, Suite 1450 · Dallas, TX 75205-5412 · 214-528-1411

Mark W. Gilbert · Lyon, Gorsky, Haring & Gilbert · 3131 McKinney Avenue, Suite 100 · Dallas, TX 75204-2430 · 214-965-0090

Hugh E. Hackney · Greenberg Traurig · http://www.gtlaw.com · JP Morgan Chase Tower, Suite 5200 · 2200 Ross Avenue · Dallas, TX 75201 · 972-419-9100

Earl F. Hale, Jr. · Earl F. Hale, Jr. · 4144 North Central Expressway, Suite 225 · Dallas, TX 75204-3140 · 214-515-0199

Robert W. Jordan · Baker Botts · http://www.bakerbotts.com · Trammell Crow Center, Suite 600 · 2001 Ross Avenue · Dallas, TX 75201-2980 · 214-953-6500

Jerome S. Levy · Jerome S. Levy · 100 Crescent Court, Suite 700 · Dallas, TX 75201 · 214-459-6440

Jay J. Madrid · Winstead · http://www.winstead.com · Renaissance Tower, Suite 5400 · 1201 Elm Street · Dallas, TX 75270-2199 · 214-745-5400

Robert J. Matlock · Robert J. Matlock · 12221 Merit Drive, Suite 1660 · Dallas, TX 75251 · 972-387-9955

Lawrence R. Maxwell, Jr. · Lawrence R. Maxwell, Jr. · 8226 Douglas Avenue, Suite 550 · Dallas, TX 75225 · 214-265-9668

Gaynell C. Methvin · ⑩ · Gaynell C. Methvin · 300 Crescent Court, Suite 1500 · Dallas, TX 75201 · 214-978-4999

Cecilia H. Morgan · JAMS · 8401 North Central Expressway, Suite 610 · Dallas, TX 75225 · 214-744-5267

Christopher Marc Nolland · Christopher Marc Nolland · 1717 Main Street, Suite 5550 · Dallas, TX 75201 · 214-653-4360

Walter E. Parker, Jr. · Gilbert Mediation Group · 3131 McKinney Avenue, Suite 125 · Dallas, TX 75204 214-303-4500

Will Pryor · Will Pryor · Two Lincoln Centre, Suite 626 · 5420 LBJ Freeway · Dallas, TX 75240-0000 · 469-374-0222

Kenneth Jay Rubenstein · Kenneth Jay Rubenstein · 6608 Avalon Avenue · Dallas, TX 75214 · 214-244-1105

Paul Salzberger · Paul Louis Salzberger · 10840 Sanden Drive, Suite A · Dallas, TX 75238 · 214-696-0631

William B. Short, Jr. · Coats, Rose, Yale, Ryman & Lee · 5420 Lyndon B. Johnson Freeway, Suite 1300 · Dallas, TX 75240 · 972-982-8450

Maxel B. Silverberg · Maxel B. Silverberg · Millennium I, Suite 600 · 15455 Dallas Parkway · Dallas, TX 75001 · 972-764-4300

Sidney Stahl · Sidney Stahl · 12119 Elysian Court · Dallas, TX 75230 · 214-720-4070

Melvin H. Wolovits · Wolovits Dispute Resolution · 9400 North Central Expressway, Suite 250 · Dallas, TX 75231 · 214-373-3777

Fort Worth

Edwin G. Bell · ⑩ · Edwin G. Bell · 749 North Main Street · P.O. Box 64369 · Fort Worth, TX 76106-9418 · 817-335-2246

Kay Elkins Elliott · The Law Offices of Kay Elkins Elliot · 1609 Sunset Terrace · Fort Worth, TX 76102 214-546-3338

Wade H. McMullen · Wade H. McMullen · 6300 Ridglea Place, Suite 509 · Fort Worth, TX 76116-5731 · 817-731-4163

Houston

Edward Bergman III · Bergman ADR Group · Nine Greenway Plaza, Suite 3130 · Houston, TX 77046 · 713-977-1717

John P. Bowman · Fulbright & Jaworski · http://www.fulbright.com · Fulbright Tower, Suite 5100 · 1301 McKinney Street · Houston, TX 77010-3095 · 713-651-5151

Patrick M. Flynn · ⑳ · Patrick M. Flynn · 1225 North Loop West, Suite 1000 · Houston, TX 77008 · 713-861-6163

Jack C. Goldstein · Law Office of Jack C Goldstein · 16 Sugarberry Circle · Houston, TX 77024-7251 · 713-782-7821

Jeff Joyce · Winstead · http://www.winstead.com · JPMorgan Chase Tower, Suite 1100 · 600 Travis Street Houston, TX 77002 · 713-650-8400

Alan F. Levin · Levin & Kasner · Summit Tower, Suite 500 · 11 Greenway Plaza · Houston, TX 77046 · 713-877-1600

David G. Matthiesen · Matthiesen & Associates · 511 Lovett Boulevard · Houston, TX 77006 · 713-877-8522

William T. Miller · ⑳ · Andrews Kurth · http://www.andrewskurth.com · 600 Travis Street, Suite 4200 · Houston, TX 77002 · 713-220-4200

Barbara A. Radnofsky · ⑩ · Barbara Radnofsky · 303 Timber Terrace Road · Houston, TX 77024 · 713-858-8509

Martin R. Sadler · Martin, Disiere, Jefferson & Wisdom · http://www.mdjwlaw.com · Niels Esperson Building, Suite 1800 · 808 Travis Street · Houston, TX 77002 · 713-632-1700

Richard A. Schwartz · Schwartz, Junell, Greenberg & Oathout · 909 Fannin Street, Suite 2700 · Houston, TX 77010 · 713-752-0017

Karl S. Stern · Vinson & Elkins · http://www.velaw.com · First City Tower, Suite 2500 · 1001 Fannin Street · Houston, TX 77002-6760 · 713-758-2222

Irving

Priscilla Kim Park · The Law & ADR Offices of Priscilla Kim Park · The Urban Towers, Suite 1650 · 222 West Las Colinas Boulevard · Irving, TX 75039 · 817-481-2739

Ross W. Stoddard III · Ross W. Stoddard III, Attorney Mediator · Williams Square in Las Colinas, Suite 1795 · 5215 North O'Connor Boulevard · Irving, TX 75039-3743 · 972-869-2300

Rockwall

Susan Z. Wright · Susan Z. Wright · 603 North Goliad Street · Rockwall, TX 75087 · 972-772-0285

San Angelo

Donald W. Griffis · Jackson Walker · 301 West Beauregard Avenue, Suite 200 · San Angelo, TX 76903 · 325-481-2550

San Antonio

Solomon J. Casseb III · Casseb & Pearl · 127 East Travis Street · San Antonio, TX 78205 · 210-223-4381

Gary Javore · Johnson, Christopher, Javore & Cochran · 5802 Northwest Expressway · San Antonio, TX 78201 · 210-733-6235

Daniel O. Kustoff · Lang & Kustoff · 4103 Parkdale Street · San Antonio, TX 78229-2520 · 210-614-9444

Donald R. Philbin, Jr. · Donald R. Philbin, Jr. · http://www.adrtoolbox.com · P.O. Box 12286 · San Antonio, TX 78212 · 210-212-7100

Thomas J. Smith · ⑩ · Law Office of Thomas J. Smith · 112 East Pecan Street, Suite 3050 · San Antonio, TX 78205-3501 · 210-227-7565

Tyler

James W. Knowles · Wilson Law Firm · P.O. Box 7339 · Tyler, TX 75711-7339 · 903-509-5000

ANTITRUST LAW

Dallas

Mark W. Bayer · Gardere Wynne Sewell · http://www.gardere.com · 1601 Elm Street, Suite 3000 · Dallas, TX 75201 · 214-999-3000

Jerry L. Beane · Andrews Kurth · http://www.andrewskurth.com · 1717 Main Street, Suite 3700 · Dallas, TX 75201 · 214-659-4400

Stacy L. Brainin · Haynes and Boone · 901 Main Street, Suite 3100 · Dallas, TX 75202 · 214-651-5000

Ronald W. Breaux · Haynes and Boone · 901 Main Street, Suite 3100 · Dallas, TX 75202 · 214-651-5000

Craig Lewis Caesar · McGlinchey Stafford · http://www.mcglinchey.com · 2711 North Haskell Avenue, Suite 2700 · Dallas, TX 75204 · 214-257-1700

Robert M. Cohan · Jackson Walker · Bank of America Plaza, Suite 6000 · 901 Main Street · Dallas, TX 75202 · 214-953-6000

Curtis L. Frisbie, Jr. · Gardere Wynne Sewell · http://www.gardere.com · 1601 Elm Street, Suite 3000 · Dallas, TX 75201 · 214-999-3000

Alan W. Harris · Law Offices of Alan W. Harris · 325 North Saint Paul Street, Suite 2700 · Dallas, TX 75201 · 214-965-8200

Robin P. Hartmann · ⑩ · Haynes and Boone · 901 Main Street, Suite 3100 · Dallas, TX 75202 · 214-651-5000

Gregory S.C. Huffman · Thompson & Knight · http://www.tklaw.com · One Arts Plaza, Suite 1500 · 1722 Routh Street · Dallas, TX 75201-2533 · 214-969-1700

Thomas R. Jackson · Jones Day · 2727 North Harwood Street · Dallas, TX 75201-1515 · 214-220-3939

William M. Katz, Jr. · Thompson & Knight · http://www.tklaw.com · One Arts Plaza, Suite 1500 · 1722 Routh Street · Dallas, TX 75201-2533 · 214-969-1700

David R. McAtee II · Haynes and Boone · 901 Main Street, Suite 3100 · Dallas, TX 75202 · 214-651-5000

Timothy R. McCormick · ⑩ · Thompson & Knight · http://www.tklaw.com · One Arts Plaza, Suite 1500 · 1722 Routh Street · Dallas, TX 75201-2533 · 214-969-1700

John H. McElhaney · ㉕ · Locke Lord Bissell & Liddell · 2200 Ross Avenue, Suite 2200 · Dallas, TX 75201-6776 · 214-740-8000

Barry F. McNeil · Haynes and Boone · 901 Main Street, Suite 3100 · Dallas, TX 75202 · 214-651-5000

M. Sean Royall · Gibson, Dunn & Crutcher · 2100 McKinney Avenue, Suite 1100 · Dallas, TX 75201-7390 · 214-698-3100

Russell Yager · Vinson & Elkins · http://www.velaw.com · Trammell Crow Center, Suite 3700 · 2001 Ross Avenue · Dallas, TX 75201-2975 · 214-220-7700

Houston

Richard N. Carrell · Fulbright & Jaworski · http://www.fulbright.com · Fulbright Tower, Suite 5100 · 1301 McKinney Street · Houston, TX 77010-3095 · 713-651-5151

Robin C. Gibbs · ⑩ · Gibbs & Bruns · http://www.gibbs-bruns.com · 1100 Louisiana Street, Suite 5300 · Houston, TX 77002 · 713-650-8805

Lauren J. Harrison · Vinson & Elkins · http://www.velaw.com · First City Tower, Suite 2500 · 1001 Fannin Street · Houston, TX 77002-6760 · 713-758-2222

David T. Harvin · ㉕ · Vinson & Elkins · http://www.velaw.com · First City Tower, Suite 2500 · 1001 Fannin Street · Houston, TX 77002-6760 · 713-758-2222

Layne E. Kruse · Fulbright & Jaworski · http://www.fulbright.com · Fulbright Tower, Suite 5100 · 1301 McKinney Street · Houston, TX 77010-3095 · 713-651-5151

Daniel M. McClure · Fulbright & Jaworski · http://www.fulbright.com · Fulbright Tower, Suite 5100 · 1301 McKinney Street · Houston, TX 77010-3095 · 713-651-5151

Rufus W. Oliver III · Baker Botts · http://www.bakerbotts.com · One Shell Plaza · 910 Louisiana Street · Houston, TX 77002-1210 · 713-229-1234

William R. Pakalka · Fulbright & Jaworski · http://www.fulbright.com · Fulbright Tower, Suite 5100 · 1301 McKinney Street · Houston, TX 77010-3095 · 713-651-5151

Harry M. Reasoner · ㉕ · Vinson & Elkins · http://www.velaw.com · First City Tower, Suite 2500 · 1001 Fannin Street · Houston, TX 77002-6760 · 713-758-2222

James A. Reeder, Jr. · Vinson & Elkins · http://www.velaw.com · First City Tower, Suite 2500 · 1001 Fannin Street · Houston, TX 77002-6760 · 713-758-2222

Alison L. Smith · Haynes and Boone · One Houston Center, Suite 2100 · 1221 McKinney Street · Houston, TX 77010 · 713-547-2000

Karl S. Stern · Vinson & Elkins · http://www.velaw.com · First City Tower, Suite 2500 · 1001 Fannin Street · Houston, TX 77002-6760 · 713-758-2222

Stephen D. Susman · ㉕ · Susman Godfrey · 1000 Louisiana, Suite 5100 · Houston, TX 77002-5096 · 713-651-9366

G. Allan Van Fleet · Greenberg Traurig · http://www.gtlaw.com · 1000 Louisiana Street, Suite 1800 · Houston, TX 77002 · 713-374-3500

APPELLATE LAW

Austin

Douglas W. Alexander · Alexander Dubose Jones & Townsend · http://www.adjtlaw.com · 515 Congress Avenue, Suite 2350 · Austin, TX 78701 · 512-482-9300

Debora B. Alsup · Thompson & Knight · http://www.tklaw.com · 98 San Jacinto Boulevard, Suite 1900 · Austin, TX 78701 · 512-469-6100

Pamela S. Baron · Pamela Stanton Baron · P.O. Box 5573 · Austin, TX 78763 · 512-479-8480

Leslie A. Benitez · Clark, Thomas & Winters · 300 West Sixth Street, 15th Floor · P.O. Box 1148 · Austin, TX 78767 · 512-472-8800

David L. Botsford · ⑩ · Law Office of David L. Botsford · http://www.davidbotsfordlaw.com · 1307 West Avenue · Austin, TX 78701 · 512-479-8030

Dana Livingston Cobb · Alexander Dubose Jones & Townsend · http://www.adjtlaw.com · 515 Congress Avenue, Suite 2350 · Austin, TX 78701 · 512-482-9300

Gregory S. Coleman · Yetter Warden & Coleman · http://www.yetterwarden.com · Chase Tower, Suite 750 · 221 West Sixth Street · Austin, TX 78701 · 512-533-0150

Craig T. Enoch · Winstead · http://www.winstead.com · 401 Congress Avenue, Suite 2100 · Austin, TX 78701 · 512-370-2800

Marcy H. Greer · Fulbright & Jaworski · http://www.fulbright.com · 600 Congress Avenue, Suite 2400 · Austin, TX 78701-2978 · 512-474-5201

Keith S. Hampton · Keith Hampton, Attorney at Law · 1103 Nueces Street · Austin, TX 78701 · 512-476-8484

Michael A. Hatchell · Locke Lord Bissell & Liddell · 100 Congress Avenue, Suite 300 · Austin, TX 78701-4042 · 512-305-4785

Terrence W. Kirk · Terrence W. Kirk · 502 West 13th Street · Austin, TX 78701 · 512-236-8511

Marc Knisely · McGinnis, Lochridge & Kilgore · http://www.mcginnislaw.com · 600 Congress Avenue, Suite 2100 · Austin, TX 78701 · 512-495-6000

Thomas R. Phillips · Baker Botts · http://www.bakerbotts.com · 1500 San Jacinto Center · 98 San Jacinto Boulevard · Austin, TX 78701-4039 · 512-322-2500

Pete Schenkkan · ⑩ · Graves, Dougherty, Hearon & Moody · http://www.gdhm.com · 401 Congress Avenue, Suite 2200 · P.O. Box 98 · Austin, TX 78767-0098 · 512-480-5600

David A. Schulman · David A. Schulman · P.O. Box 783 · Austin, TX 78767-0783 · 512-474-4747

Charles Watson · Locke Lord Bissell & Liddell · 100 Congress Avenue, Suite 300 · Austin, TX 78701-4042 · 512-305-4785

Jane M. N. Webre · Scott, Douglass & McConnico · 600 Congress Avenue, Suite 1500 · Austin, TX 78701-3234 · 512-495-6300

Brownsville

Neil E. Norquest · Rodriguez Colvin Chaney & Saenz · 1201 East Van Buren · P.O. Box 2155 · Brownsville, TX 78522 · 956-542-7441

Corpus Christi

Russell H. McMains · ⑩ · Law Offices of Russell H. McMains · 500 North Shoreline Boulevard, Suite 1100 · P.O. Box 2846 · Corpus Christi, TX 78403 · 361-887-4455

Dallas

G. Luke Ashley · Thompson & Knight · http://www.tklaw.com · One Arts Plaza, Suite 1500 · 1722 Routh Street · Dallas, TX 75201-2533 · 214-969-1700

Royal H. Brin, Jr. · Strasburger & Price · http://www.strasburger.com · 901 Main Street, Suite 4400 · Dallas, TX 75202-3794 · 214-651-4300

Nina Cortell · Haynes and Boone · 901 Main Street, Suite 3100 · Dallas, TX 75202 · 214-651-5000

William V. Dorsaneo III · William V. Dorsaneo, III · Southern Methodist University Dedman School Of Law · 3315 Daniel Avenue · Dallas, TX 75205 · 214-768-8999

Charles T. Frazier, Jr. · Alexander Dubose Jones & Townsend · http://www.adjtlaw.com · One Energy Square, Suite 717 · 4925 Greenville Avenue · Dallas, TX 75206 · 214-369-2358

Sharon N. Freytag · Haynes and Boone · 901 Main Street, Suite 3100 · Dallas, TX 75202 · 214-651-5000

Deborah G. Hankinson · Hankinson Levinger · 2305 Cedar Springs Road, Suite 230 · Dallas, TX 75201-6955 · 215-754-9190

P. Michael Jung · Strasburger & Price · http://www.strasburger.com · 901 Main Street, Suite 4400 · Dallas, TX 75202-3794 · 214-651-4300

Samara L. Kline · Baker Botts · http://www.bakerbotts.com · Trammell Crow Center, Suite 600 · 2001 Ross Avenue · Dallas, TX 75201-2980 · 214-953-6500

Thomas S. Leatherbury · ⑩ · Vinson & Elkins · http://www.velaw.com · Trammell Crow Center, Suite 3700 · 2001 Ross Avenue · Dallas, TX 75201-2975 · 214-220-7700

Jeffrey S. Levinger · Hankinson Levinger · 2305 Cedar Springs Road, Suite 230 · Dallas, TX 75201-6955 215-754-9190

Richard R. Orsinger · ⑳ · McCurley Orsinger McCurley Nelson & Downing · http://www.momnd.com · 5950 Sherry Lane, Eighth Floor · Dallas, TX 75225 · 214-273-2400

Sidney K. Powell · Powell & Pearce · 1920 Abrams Parkway, Suite 369 · Dallas, TX 75214 · 214-653-3933

Marvin S. Sloman · ㉕ · Carrington, Coleman, Sloman & Blumenthal · 901 Main Street, Suite 5500 · Dallas, TX 75202 · 214-855-3000

Scott P. Stolley · Thompson & Knight · http://www.tklaw.com · One Arts Plaza, Suite 1500 · 1722 Routh Street · Dallas, TX 75201-2533 · 214-969-1700

Ben Taylor · Fulbright & Jaworski · http://www.fulbright.com · 2200 Ross Avenue, Suite 2800 · Dallas, TX 75201 · 214-855-8000

Gary A. Udashen · Sorrels, Udashen & Anton · 2301 Cedar Springs Road, Suite 400 · Dallas, TX 75201 · 214-468-8100

Robert Udashen · Sorrels, Udashen & Anton · 2301 Cedar Springs Road, Suite 400 · Dallas, TX 75201 · 214-468-8100

Fort Worth

David Keltner · Kelly, Hart & Hallman · Wells Fargo Tower, Suite 2500 · 201 Main Street · Fort Worth, TX 76102 · 817-332-2500

Karen S. Precella · Haynes and Boone · 201 Main Street, Suite 2200 · Fort Worth, TX 76102 · 817-347-6600

Stephen Lyle Tatum · Cantey & Hanger · 300 Cantey Hanger Plaza · 600 West Sixth Street · Fort Worth, TX 76102-3685 · 817-877-2800

Harlingen

Roger W. Hughes · Adams & Graham · 222 East Van Buren Avenue, West Tower · Harlingen, TX 78550 956-428-7495

Houston

Murry B. Cohen · Akin Gump Strauss Hauer & Feld · 1111 Louisiana Street, 44th Floor · Houston, TX 77002-5200 · 713-220-5800

Kevin Dubose · Alexander Dubose Jones & Townsend · http://www.adjtlaw.com · 1844 Harvard Street · Houston, TX 77008-4342 · 713-523-2358

Claudia Wilson Frost · Pillsbury Winthrop Shaw Pittman · http://www.pillsburylaw.com · Two Houston Center, Suite 2000 · 909 Fannin Street · Houston, TX 77010-1018 · 713-276-7600

David M. Gunn · Beck, Redden & Secrest · http://www.brsfirm.com · One Houston Center, Suite 4500 · 1221 McKinney Street · Houston, TX 77010-2010 · 713-951-3700

Warren W. Harris · Bracewell & Giuliani · http://www.bgllp.com · 711 Louisiana Street, Suite 2300 · Houston, TX 77002-2770 · 713-223-2300

Jennifer Bruch Hogan · Hogan & Hogan · Two Houston Center, Suite 2700 · 909 Fannin Street · Houston, TX 77010 · 713-222-8800

Richard P. Hogan, Jr. · Hogan & Hogan · Two Houston Center, Suite 2700 · 909 Fannin Street · Houston, TX 77010 · 713-222-8800

Alene Ross Levy · Haynes and Boone · One Houston Center, Suite 2100 · 1221 McKinney Street · Houston, TX 77010 · 713-547-2000

Lynne Liberato · Haynes and Boone · One Houston Center, Suite 2100 · 1221 McKinney Street · Houston, TX 77010 · 713-547-2000

Katherine MacKillop · Fulbright & Jaworski · http://www.fulbright.com · Fulbright Tower, Suite 5100 · 1301 McKinney Street · Houston, TX 77010-3095 · 713-651-5151

Alice Oliver-Parrott · ⑩ · Alice Oliver-Parrott · 5009 Caroline, Suite 100 · Houston, TX 77004 · 713-222-6338

Russell S. Post · Beck, Redden & Secrest · http://www.brsfirm.com · One Houston Center, Suite 4500 · 1221 McKinney Street · Houston, TX 77010-2010 · 713-951-3700

Robert M. Roach · Cook & Roach · Heritage Plaza, Suite 2650 · 1111 Bagby Street · Houston, TX 77002 713-652-2800

Gwendolyn J. Samora · Vinson & Elkins · http://www.velaw.com · First City Tower, Suite 2500 · 1001 Fannin Street · Houston, TX 77002-6760 · 713-758-2222

Reagan W. Simpson · King & Spalding · 1100 Louisiana Street, Suite 4000 · Houston, TX 77002-5213 · 713-751-3200

Joy M. Soloway · Fulbright & Jaworski · http://www.fulbright.com · Fulbright Tower, Suite 5100 · 1301 McKinney Street · Houston, TX 77010-3095 · 713-651-5151

Richard L. Stanley · ⑩ · Howrey · 1111 Louisiana, 25th Floor · Houston, TX 77002-5242 · 713-787-1400

Macey R. Stokes · Baker Botts · http://www.bakerbotts.com · One Shell Plaza · 910 Louisiana Street · Houston, TX 77002-1210 · 713-229-1234

Stephen G. Tipps · Baker Botts · http://www.bakerbotts.com · One Shell Plaza · 910 Louisiana Street · Houston, TX 77002-1210 · 713-229-1234

Roger D. Townsend · Alexander Dubose Jones & Townsend · http://www.adjtlaw.com · 1844 Harvard Street · Houston, TX 77008-4342 · 713-523-2358

Thomas C. Wright · Wright Brown & Close · Three Riverway, Suite 600 · Houston, TX 77056 · 713-572-4321

Marie R. Yeates · Vinson & Elkins · http://www.velaw.com · First City Tower, Suite 2500 · 1001 Fannin Street · Houston, TX 77002-6760 · 713-758-2222

Lubbock

Donald M. Hunt · Mullin Hoard & Brown · Wells Fargo Center, Suite 700 · 1500 Broadway · P.O. Box 2585 · Lubbock, TX 79408-2585 · 806-765-7491

San Antonio

Samuel H. Bayless · The Law Offices of Samuel Bayless · 441 Burr Road · San Antonio, TX 78205 · 210-253-7110

Sharon E. Callaway · Crofts & Callaway · 4040 Broadway Street, Suite 525 · San Antonio, TX 78209-6300 · 210-225-5551

Thomas H. Crofts, Jr. · Crofts & Callaway · 4040 Broadway Street, Suite 525 · San Antonio, TX 78209-6300 · 210-225-5551

W. Wendell Hall · Fulbright & Jaworski · http://www.fulbright.com · 300 Convent Street, Suite 2200 · San Antonio, TX 78205-3792 · 210-224-5575

Andrew L. Kerr · Strasburger & Price · http://www.strasburger.com · 300 Convent Street, Suite 900 · San Antonio, TX 78205-3715 · 210-250-6000

Cynthia H. Orr · Goldstein, Goldstein & Hilley · Tower Life Building, 29th Floor · 310 South St. Mary's Street · San Antonio, TX 78205-3106 · 210-226-1463

Luther H. Soules III · Soules & Wallace · P.O. Box 15588 · San Antonio, TX 78212 · 210-224-9144

BANKING LAW

Austin

William H. Daniel · ⑩ · McGinnis, Lochridge & Kilgore · http://www.mcginnislaw.com · 600 Congress Avenue, Suite 2100 · Austin, TX 78701 · 512-495-6000

Joseph M. Ford · DLA Piper · 1221 South MoPac Expressway, Suite 400 · Austin, TX 78746-7650 · 512-457-7000

Royce Jay Hailey, Jr. · ⑩ · DLA Piper · 1221 South MoPac Expressway, Suite 400 · Austin, TX 78746-7650 · 512-457-7000

Robert Clarke Heidrick, Jr. · ⑩ · Graves, Dougherty, Hearon & Moody · http://www.gdhm.com · 401 Congress Avenue, Suite 2200 · P.O. Box 98 · Austin, TX 78767-0098 · 512-480-5600

George E. Henderson · ⑩ · Fulbright & Jaworski · http://www.fulbright.com · 600 Congress Avenue, Suite 2400 · Austin, TX 78701-2978 · 512-474-5201

Karen Neeley · Cox Smith Matthews · http://www.coxsmith.com · 111 Congress, Suite 2800 · Austin, TX 78701-4084 · 512-703-6300

James L. Pledger · Jackson Walker · 100 Congress Avenue, Suite 1100 · Austin, TX 78701 · 512-236-2000

Roy C. Snodgrass · ⑩ · Graves, Dougherty, Hearon & Moody · http://www.gdhm.com · 401 Congress Avenue, Suite 2200 · P.O. Box 98 · Austin, TX 78767-0098 · 512-480-5600

William F. Stutts · ⑩ · Baker Botts · http://www.bakerbotts.com · 1500 San Jacinto Center · 98 San Jacinto Boulevard · Austin, TX 78701-4039 · 512-322-2500

Larry E. Temple · ⑩ · Larry E. Temple · 400 West 15th Street, Suite 1510 · Austin, TX 78701 · 512-477-4467

Michael A. Wren · ⑩ · McGinnis, Lochridge & Kilgore · http://www.mcginnislaw.com · 600 Congress Avenue, Suite 2100 · Austin, TX 78701 · 512-495-6000

Beaumont

Phil Dunlap · ⑩ · Wells, Peyton, Greenberg & Hunt · 550 Fannin Street, Suite 600 · P.O. Box 3708 · Beaumont, TX 77701 · 409-838-2644

Gary Neale Reger · ⑩ · Orgain, Bell & Tucker · 470 Orleans Street · P.O. Box 1751 · Beaumont, TX 77704-1751 · 409-838-6412

Walter D. Snider · ⑩ · Snider & Byrd · 3560 Delaware Street, Suite 308 · Beaumont, TX 77706 · 409-924-9595

Boerne

Rhonda Graff Jolley · ⑩ · Nunley Davis Jolley Cluck Aelvoet · 1580 South Main Street, Suite 200 · Boerne, TX 78006 · 830-816-3333

Edward G. Vaughan · ⑩ · Edward G. Vaughan · 1580 South Main Street, Suite 200 · Boerne, TX 78006 · 830-816-2456

Dallas

Linton Elzie Barbee · ⑩ · Law Office of Linton Barbee · 4541 Northaven Road · Dallas, TX 75229-4127 214-534-7405

David Barbour · Andrews Kurth · http://www.andrewskurth.com · 1717 Main Street, Suite 3700 · Dallas, TX 75201 · 214-659-4400

Dorothy H. Bjorck · ⑩ · Thompson & Knight · http://www.tklaw.com · One Arts Plaza, Suite 1500 · 1722 Routh Street · Dallas, TX 75201-2533 · 214-969-1700

Sanford M. Brown · Bracewell & Giuliani · http://www.bgllp.com · 1445 Ross Avenue, Suite 3800 · Dallas, TX 75202-2711 · 214-468-3800

Terry W. Conner · ⑩ · Haynes and Boone · 901 Main Street, Suite 3100 · Dallas, TX 75202 · 214-651-5000

O. Paul Corley, Jr. · ⑩ · Thompson & Knight · http://www.tklaw.com · One Arts Plaza, Suite 1500 · 1722 Routh Street · Dallas, TX 75201-2533 · 214-969-1700

James A. Donohoe · ⑩ · Thompson & Knight · http://www.tklaw.com · One Arts Plaza, Suite 1500 · 1722 Routh Street · Dallas, TX 75201-2533 · 214-969-1700

Jeffrey D. Dunn · Munsch Hardt Kopf & Harr · 3800 Lincoln Plaza · 500 North Akard Street · Dallas, TX 75201-6659 · 214-855-7500

Ira D. Einsohn · ⑩ · Winstead · http://www.winstead.com · Renaissance Tower, Suite 5400 · 1201 Elm Street · Dallas, TX 75270-2199 · 214-745-5400

Daniel C. Garner · ⑩ · Hunton & Williams · 1445 Ross Avenue, Suite 3700 · Dallas, TX 75202-2799 · 214-979-3000

Thomas E. Gillespie · Jones Day · 2727 North Harwood Street · Dallas, TX 75201-1515 · 214-220-3939

Roderick A. Goyne · Baker Botts · http://www.bakerbotts.com · Trammell Crow Center, Suite 600 · 2001 Ross Avenue · Dallas, TX 75201-2980 · 214-953-6500

M. Lawrence Hicks, Jr. · ⑩ · Thompson & Knight · http://www.tklaw.com · One Arts Plaza, Suite 1500 · 1722 Routh Street · Dallas, TX 75201-2533 · 214-969-1700

Michael W. Hilliard · ⑩ · Winstead · http://www.winstead.com · Renaissance Tower, Suite 5400 · 1201 Elm Street · Dallas, TX 75270-2199 · 214-745-5400

Joe T. Hyde · Winstead · http://www.winstead.com · Renaissance Tower, Suite 5400 · 1201 Elm Street · Dallas, TX 75270-2199 · 214-745-5400

Robert B. Jackson · Thompson & Knight · http://www.tklaw.com · One Arts Plaza, Suite 1500 · 1722 Routh Street · Dallas, TX 75201-2533 · 214-969-1700

Gene L. Jameson · ⑩ · Jameson & Powers · http://www.jamesonpowerslaw.com · 17480 Dallas Parkway, Suite 211 · Dallas, TX 75287 · 972-732-8083

Mark B. Knowles · DLA Piper · 1717 Main Street, Suite 4600 · Dallas, TX 75201-4629 · 214-743-4500

James R. Littlejohn · ⑩ · Winstead · http://www.winstead.com · Renaissance Tower, Suite 5400 · 1201 Elm Street · Dallas, TX 75270-2199 · 214-745-5400

James A. Markus · Vinson & Elkins · http://www.velaw.com · Trammell Crow Center, Suite 3700 · 2001 Ross Avenue · Dallas, TX 75201-2975 · 214-220-7700

Joseph Clark Mathews · Hunton & Williams · 1445 Ross Avenue, Suite 3700 · Dallas, TX 75202-2799 · 214-979-3000

James Stanley Matthews · Vinson & Elkins · http://www.velaw.com · Trammell Crow Center, Suite 3700 2001 Ross Avenue · Dallas, TX 75201-2975 · 214-220-7700

T. Randall Matthews · Winstead · http://www.winstead.com · Renaissance Tower, Suite 5400 · 1201 Elm Street · Dallas, TX 75270-2199 · 214-745-5400

James W. McKellar · ⑩ · Thompson & Knight · http://www.tklaw.com · One Arts Plaza, Suite 1500 · 1722 Routh Street · Dallas, TX 75201-2533 · 214-969-1700

Gary G. Null · ⑩ · K&L Gates · 1717 Main Street, Suite 2800 · Dallas, TX 75201 · 214-939-5500

Michael K. O'Neal · Winstead · http://www.winstead.com · Renaissance Tower, Suite 5400 · 1201 Elm Street · Dallas, TX 75270-2199 · 214-745-5400

Rod Phelan · ⑩ · Baker Botts · http://www.bakerbotts.com · Trammell Crow Center, Suite 600 · 2001 Ross Avenue · Dallas, TX 75201-2980 · 214-953-6500

John W. Rain · ⑩ · Thompson & Knight · http://www.tklaw.com · One Arts Plaza, Suite 1500 · 1722 Routh Street · Dallas, TX 75201-2533 · 214-969-1700

Harry M. Roberts, Jr. · ㉕ · Thompson & Knight · http://www.tklaw.com · One Arts Plaza, Suite 1500 · 1722 Routh Street · Dallas, TX 75201-2533 · 214-969-1700

Kenneth A. Rogers · Haynes and Boone · 901 Main Street, Suite 3100 · Dallas, TX 75202 · 214-651-5000

Robert F. See, Jr. · ㉕ · Robert F. See, Jr. & Associates · http://www.rseelawfirm.com · 901 Main Street, Suite 3601 · Dallas, TX 75202 · 214-761-3001

Larry Van Smith · ⑩ · McGlinchey Stafford · http://www.mcglinchey.com · 2711 North Haskell Avenue, Suite 2700 · Dallas, TX 75204 · 214-257-1700

Melissa Ruman Stewart · Winstead · http://www.winstead.com · Renaissance Tower, Suite 5400 · 1201 Elm Street · Dallas, TX 75270-2199 · 214-745-5400

Daniel F. Susie · Winstead · http://www.winstead.com · Renaissance Tower, Suite 5400 · 1201 Elm Street Dallas, TX 75270-2199 · 214-745-5400

Ben B. West · ㉕ · Thompson & Knight · http://www.tklaw.com · One Arts Plaza, Suite 1500 · 1722 Routh Street · Dallas, TX 75201-2533 · 214-969-1700

Glenn D. West · Weil Gotshal & Manges · 200 Crescent Court, Suite 300 · Dallas, TX 75201 · 214-746-7700

Robert E. Wilson · ㉕ · Haynes and Boone · 901 Main Street, Suite 3100 · Dallas, TX 75202 · 214-651-5000

Valinda B. Wolfert · Vinson & Elkins · http://www.velaw.com · Trammell Crow Center, Suite 3700 · 2001 Ross Avenue · Dallas, TX 75201-2975 · 214-220-7700

William D. Young · Vinson & Elkins · http://www.velaw.com · Trammell Crow Center, Suite 3700 · 2001 Ross Avenue · Dallas, TX 75201-2975 · 214-220-7700

El Paso

Taffy D. Bagley · ⑩ · Taffy Bagley · 201 East Main Drive, Suite 601 · El Paso, TX 79901 · 915-543-6700

Marc P. Bernat · ⑩ · Gordon & Mott · 4695 North Mesa Street, Suite 100 · El Paso, TX 79912 · 915-545-1133

Bernard D. Felsen · Scott, Hulse, Marshall, Feuille, Finger & Thurmond · 1100 Chase Tower · 201 East Main Street · El Paso, TX 79901 · 915-533-2493

Guy N. Fields III · ⑩ · The Fields Law Firm · 501 Executive Center Boulevard, Suite 101 · El Paso, TX 79902 · 915-351-4000

C. Michael Ginnings · ⑩ · Gordon & Mott · 4695 North Mesa Street, Suite 100 · El Paso, TX 79912 · 915-545-1133

G. Russell Hill · ⑩ · Scott, Hulse, Marshall, Feuille, Finger & Thurmond · 1100 Chase Tower · 201 East Main Street · El Paso, TX 79901 · 915-533-2493

Graford

Robert Edward Wood, Jr. · ⑩ · Robert E. Wood Jr. · 20 Shoal Creek Court · Graford, TX 76449 · 214-549-2242

Houston

Kenneth M. Anderson · Vinson & Elkins · http://www.velaw.com · First City Tower, Suite 2500 · 1001 Fannin Street · Houston, TX 77002-6760 · 713-758-2222

Larry G. Barbour · Vinson & Elkins · http://www.velaw.com · First City Tower, Suite 2500 · 1001 Fannin Street · Houston, TX 77002-6760 · 713-758-2222

Nelson R. Block · Winstead · http://www.winstead.com · JPMorgan Chase Tower, Suite 1100 · 600 Travis Street · Houston, TX 77002 · 713-650-8400

Jeff J. Brashier · Winstead · http://www.winstead.com · JPMorgan Chase Tower, Suite 1100 · 600 Travis Street · Houston, TX 77002 · 713-650-8400

Timothy R. Brown · Thompson & Knight · http://www.tklaw.com · 333 Clay Street, Suite 3300 · Houston, TX 77002 · 713-654-8111

Theresa Einhorn · Haynes and Boone · One Houston Center, Suite 2100 · 1221 McKinney Street · Houston, TX 77010 · 713-547-2000

Mark C. Evans · Bracewell & Giuliani · http://www.bgllp.com · 711 Louisiana Street, Suite 2300 · Houston, TX 77002-2770 · 713-223-2300

Dewey J. Gonsoulin, Jr. · Bracewell & Giuliani · http://www.bgllp.com · 711 Louisiana Street, Suite 2300 Houston, TX 77002-2770 · 713-223-2300

William J. Hayes · Bracewell & Giuliani · http://www.bgllp.com · 711 Louisiana Street, Suite 2300 · Houston, TX 77002-2770 · 713-223-2300

Ann C. Jacobs · Nathan Sommers Jacobs · 2800 Post Oak Boulevard, 61st Floor · Houston, TX 77056 · 713-960-0303

David R. Keyes · ⑳ · Winstead · http://www.winstead.com · JPMorgan Chase Tower, Suite 1100 · 600 Travis Street · Houston, TX 77002 · 713-650-8400

R. Bruce LaBoon · ⑩ · Locke Lord Bissell & Liddell · JP Morgan Chase Tower, Suite 3400 · 600 Travis Street · Houston, TX 77002 · 713-226-1200

Marilyn C. Maloney · ⑩ · Liskow & Lewis · http://www.liskow.com · First City Tower, Suite 1800 · 1001 Fannin Street · Houston, TX 77002-4102 · 713-651-2900

Gail Merel · Andrews Kurth · http://www.andrewskurth.com · 600 Travis Street, Suite 4200 · Houston, TX 77002 · 713-220-4200

Craig W. Murray · Vinson & Elkins · http://www.velaw.com · First City Tower, Suite 2500 · 1001 Fannin Street · Houston, TX 77002-6760 · 713-758-2222

Michael E. Niebruegge · Mayer Brown · Bank of America Center, Suite 3400 · 700 Louisiana Street · Houston, TX 77002-2730 · 713-238-3000

Thomas J. Perich · Andrews Kurth · http://www.andrewskurth.com · 600 Travis Street, Suite 4200 · Houston, TX 77002 · 713-220-4200

Robert R. Rabalais · Vinson & Elkins · http://www.velaw.com · First City Tower, Suite 2500 · 1001 Fannin Street · Houston, TX 77002-6760 · 713-758-2222

J. Scott Sheehan · ⑩ · Greenberg Traurig · http://www.gtlaw.com · 1000 Louisiana Street, Suite 1800 · Houston, TX 77002 · 713-374-3500

Nick H. Sorensen · Porter & Hedges · 1000 Main Street, 36th Floor · Houston, TX 77002 · 713-226-0600

Douglas E. Stewart · ⑩ · Sutherland · http://www.sutherland.com · Two Houston Center, Suite 2200 · 909 Fannin · Houston, TX 77010-1043 · 713-470-6100

Stephen C. Tarry · Vinson & Elkins · http://www.velaw.com · First City Tower, Suite 2500 · 1001 Fannin Street · Houston, TX 77002-6760 · 713-758-2222

Sanford A. Weiner · ㉕ · Vinson & Elkins · http://www.velaw.com · First City Tower, Suite 2500 · 1001 Fannin Street · Houston, TX 77002-6760 · 713-758-2222

Donald E. Wood · Sutherland · http://www.sutherland.com · Two Houston Center, Suite 2200 · 909 Fannin · Houston, TX 77010-1043 · 713-470-6100

San Antonio

Kerry T. Benedict · Cox Smith Matthews · http://www.coxsmith.com · 112 East Pecan Street, Suite 1800 · San Antonio, TX 78205-1521 · 210-554-5500

T. Drew Cauthorn · ⑩ · Hornberger Sheehan Fuller & Beiter · Quarry Heights, Suite 300 · 7373 Broadway · San Antonio, TX 78209 · 210-271-1700

Cary Plotkin Kavy · ⑩ · Cox Smith Matthews · http://www.coxsmith.com · 112 East Pecan Street, Suite 1800 · San Antonio, TX 78205-1521 · 210-554-5500

James C. Norman · ⑩ · Norman & Oliver · 7373 Broadway, Suite 504 · San Antonio, TX 78209 · 210-822-8972

J. David Oppenheimer · ⑩ · Oppenheimer, Blend, Harrison & Tate · 711 Navarro Street, Suite 600 · San Antonio, TX 78205-1796 · 210-224-2000

Nancy H. Stumberg · ⑩ · Nancy H. Stumberg · 227 West Olmos Drive · San Antonio, TX 78212 · 210-271-0448

BANKRUPTCY AND CREDITOR-DEBTOR RIGHTS LAW

Amarillo

John Huffaker · Sprouse Shrader Smith · 701 South Taylor, Suite 500 · P.O. Box 15008 · Amarillo, TX 79105-5008 · 806-468-3300

Austin

C. Wade Cooper · Jackson Walker · 100 Congress Avenue, Suite 1100 · Austin, TX 78701 · 512-236-2000

Sarah B. Foster · Haynes and Boone · 600 Congress Avenue, Suite 1300 · Austin, TX 78701-3285 · 512-867-8400

George E. Henderson · ⑩ · Fulbright & Jaworski · http://www.fulbright.com · 600 Congress Avenue, Suite 2400 · Austin, TX 78701-2978 · 512-474-5201

Joseph D. Martinec · ⑳ · Martinec, Winn, Vickers & McElroy · One American Center, Suite 500 · 600 Congress Avenue · Austin, TX 78701 · 512-476-0750

Rebecca S. McElroy · Martinec, Winn, Vickers & McElroy · One American Center, Suite 500 · 600 Congress Avenue · Austin, TX 78701 · 512-476-0750

Stephen A. Roberts · ⑩ · Strasburger & Price · http://www.strasburger.com · 600 Congress Avenue, Suite 1600 · Austin, TX 78701-2974 · 512-499-3600

Berry D. Spears · Fulbright & Jaworski · http://www.fulbright.com · 600 Congress Avenue, Suite 2400 · Austin, TX 78701-2978 · 512-474-5201

William F. Stutts · ⑩ · Baker Botts · http://www.bakerbotts.com · 1500 San Jacinto Center · 98 San Jacinto Boulevard · Austin, TX 78701-4039 · 512-322-2500

Eric J. Taube · ⑩ · Hohmann Taube & Summers · 100 Congress Avenue, 18th Floor · Austin, TX 78701-4042 · 512-472-5997

Steve P. Turner · Barrett Daffin Frappier Turner & Engel · 610 West Fifth Street, Suite 602 · Austin, TX 78701 · 972-386-5040

Beaumont

Gary Neale Reger · ⑩ · Orgain, Bell & Tucker · 470 Orleans Street · P.O. Box 1751 · Beaumont, TX 77704-1751 · 409-838-6412

Corpus Christi

Harrell Z. Browning · Law Office of Harrell Browning · 600 Leopard Street, Suite 103 · Corpus Christi, TX 78473-1601 · 361-883-1940

Shelby A. Jordan · ⑳ · Jordan, Hyden, Womble, Culbreth & Holzer · Bank of America, Suite 900 · 500 North Shoreline Boulevard · Corpus Christi, TX 78471-0000 · 361-884-5678

Dallas

Robert D. Albergotti · ⑩ · Haynes and Boone · 901 Main Street, Suite 3100 · Dallas, TX 75202 · 214-651-5000

Michael W. Anglin · Fulbright & Jaworski · http://www.fulbright.com · 2200 Ross Avenue, Suite 2800 · Dallas, TX 75201 · 214-855-8000

Keith Miles Aurzada · Powell Goldstein · http://www.pogolaw.com · JP Morgan Chase Tower, Suite 3300 2200 Ross Avenue · Dallas, TX 75201 · 214-721-8000

David M. Bennett · Thompson & Knight · http://www.tklaw.com · One Arts Plaza, Suite 1500 · 1722 Routh Street · Dallas, TX 75201-2533 · 214-969-1700

Joseph M. Coleman · ⑩ · Kane, Russell, Coleman & Logan · Thanksgiving Tower, Suite 3700 · 1601 Elm Street · Dallas, TX 75201 · 214-777-4200

Josiah M. Daniel III · Vinson & Elkins · http://www.velaw.com · Trammell Crow Center, Suite 3700 · 2001 Ross Avenue · Dallas, TX 75201-2975 · 214-220-7700

James A. Donohoe · ⑩ · Thompson & Knight · http://www.tklaw.com · One Arts Plaza, Suite 1500 · 1722 Routh Street · Dallas, TX 75201-2533 · 214-969-1700

R. Michael Farquhar · Winstead · http://www.winstead.com · Renaissance Tower, Suite 5400 · 1201 Elm Street · Dallas, TX 75270-2199 · 214-745-5400

Toby L. Gerber · Fulbright & Jaworski · http://www.fulbright.com · 2200 Ross Avenue, Suite 2800 · Dallas, TX 75201 · 214-855-8000

Charles R. Gibbs · Akin Gump Strauss Hauer & Feld · 1700 Pacific Avenue, Suite 4100 · Dallas, TX 75201-4675 · 214-969-2800

Stephen A. Goodwin · Carrington, Coleman, Sloman & Blumenthal · 901 Main Street, Suite 5500 · Dallas, TX 75202 · 214-855-3000

Paul E. Heath · Vinson & Elkins · http://www.velaw.com · Trammell Crow Center, Suite 3700 · 2001 Ross Avenue · Dallas, TX 75201-2975 · 214-220-7700

Michael S. Held · Hunton & Williams · 1445 Ross Avenue, Suite 3700 · Dallas, TX 75202-2799 · 214-979-3000

Clifton R. Jessup, Jr. · ⑩ · Greenberg Traurig · http://www.gtlaw.com · JP Morgan Chase Tower, Suite 5200 · 2200 Ross Avenue · Dallas, TX 75201 · 972-419-9100

E. Paul Keiffer · Wright Ginsberg Brusilow · 1401 Elm Place, Suite 4750 · Dallas, TX 75202 · 214-651-6500

Jack L. Kinzie · Baker Botts · http://www.bakerbotts.com · Trammell Crow Center, Suite 600 · 2001 Ross Avenue · Dallas, TX 75201-2980 · 214-953-6500

James J. Lee · Vinson & Elkins · http://www.velaw.com · Trammell Crow Center, Suite 3700 · 2001 Ross Avenue · Dallas, TX 75201-2975 · 214-220-7700

Mark E. MacDonald · ⑳ · MacDonald + MacDonald · http://www.macdonaldlaw.com · 9938 Ontario · Dallas, TX 75220 · 214-237-4220

James A. Markus · Vinson & Elkins · http://www.velaw.com · Trammell Crow Center, Suite 3700 · 2001 Ross Avenue · Dallas, TX 75201-2975 · 214-220-7700

Stephen A. McCartin · Gardere Wynne Sewell · http://www.gardere.com · 1601 Elm Street, Suite 3000 · Dallas, TX 75201 · 214-999-3000

E. Lee Morris · Munsch Hardt Kopf & Harr · 3800 Lincoln Plaza · 500 North Akard Street · Dallas, TX 75201-6659 · 214-855-7500

Russell L. Munsch · Munsch Hardt Kopf & Harr · 3800 Lincoln Plaza · 500 North Akard Street · Dallas, TX 75201-6659 · 214-855-7500

Patrick J. Neligan, Jr. · Neligan Foley · 1700 Pacific Avenue, Suite 2600 · Dallas, TX 75201 · 214-840-5300

Holland N. O'Neil · Gardere Wynne Sewell · http://www.gardere.com · 1601 Elm Street, Suite 3000 · Dallas, TX 75201 · 214-999-3000

Robin E. Phelan · ⑳ · Haynes and Boone · 901 Main Street, Suite 3100 · Dallas, TX 75202 · 214-651-5000

James Prince II · Baker Botts · http://www.bakerbotts.com · Trammell Crow Center, Suite 600 · 2001 Ross Avenue · Dallas, TX 75201-2980 · 214-953-6500

Peter J. Riley · Thompson & Knight · http://www.tklaw.com · One Arts Plaza, Suite 1500 · 1722 Routh Street · Dallas, TX 75201-2533 · 214-969-1700

Richard M. Roberson · Gardere Wynne Sewell · http://www.gardere.com · 1601 Elm Street, Suite 3000 · Dallas, TX 75201 · 214-999-3000

Michael R. Rochelle · Rochelle, Hutcheson & McCullough · 325 North St. Paul Street, Suite 4500 · Dallas, TX 75201 · 214-953-0182

Michael A. Rosenthal · Gibson, Dunn & Crutcher · 2100 McKinney Avenue, Suite 1100 · Dallas, TX 75201-7390 · 214-698-3100

Judith W. Ross · Baker Botts · http://www.bakerbotts.com · Trammell Crow Center, Suite 600 · 2001 Ross Avenue · Dallas, TX 75201-2980 · 214-953-6500

Deirdre B. Ruckman · Gardere Wynne Sewell · http://www.gardere.com · 1601 Elm Street, Suite 3000 · Dallas, TX 75201 · 214-999-3000

Martin A. Sosland · Weil Gotshal & Manges · 200 Crescent Court, Suite 300 · Dallas, TX 75201 · 214-746-7700

Daniel C. Stewart · ㉕ · Vinson & Elkins · http://www.velaw.com · Trammell Crow Center, Suite 3700 · 2001 Ross Avenue · Dallas, TX 75201-2975 · 214-220-7700

Samuel M. Stricklin · Bracewell & Giuliani · http://www.bgllp.com · 1445 Ross Avenue, Suite 3800 · Dallas, TX 75202-2711 · 214-468-3800

Louis R. Strubeck, Jr. · Fulbright & Jaworski · http://www.fulbright.com · 2200 Ross Avenue, Suite 2800 Dallas, TX 75201 · 214-855-8000

William L. Wallander · Vinson & Elkins · http://www.velaw.com · Trammell Crow Center, Suite 3700 · 2001 Ross Avenue · Dallas, TX 75201-2975 · 214-220-7700

Bruce H. White · Greenberg Traurig · http://www.gtlaw.com · JP Morgan Chase Tower, Suite 5200 · 2200 Ross Avenue · Dallas, TX 75201 · 972-419-9100

Joseph J. Wielebinski · Munsch Hardt Kopf & Harr · 3800 Lincoln Plaza · 500 North Akard Street · Dallas, TX 75201-6659 · 214-855-7500

Frank J. Wright · Wright Ginsberg Brusilow · 1401 Elm Place, Suite 4750 · Dallas, TX 75202 · 214-651-6500

El Paso

Bernard D. Felsen · Scott, Hulse, Marshall, Feuille, Finger & Thurmond · 1100 Chase Tower · 201 East Main Street · El Paso, TX 79901 · 915-533-2493

H. Christopher Mott · ⑩ · Gordon & Mott · 4695 North Mesa Street, Suite 100 · El Paso, TX 79912 · 915-545-1133

Fort Worth

John Y. Bonds III · Shannon, Gracey, Ratliff & Miller · http://www.shannongracey.com · 777 Main Street, Suite 3800 · Fort Worth, TX 76102 · 817-336-9333

Michael A. McConnell · 20 · Kelly, Hart & Hallman · Wells Fargo Tower, Suite 2500 · 201 Main Street · Fort Worth, TX 76102 · 817-332-2500

John D. Penn · Haynes and Boone · 201 Main Street, Suite 2200 · Fort Worth, TX 76102 · 817-347-6600

Stephen M. Pezanosky · Haynes and Boone · 201 Main Street, Suite 2200 · Fort Worth, TX 76102 · 817-347-6600

Houston

David J. Askanase · Hughes, Watters & Askanase · Three Allen Center, 29th Floor · 333 Clay Street · Houston, TX 77002 · 713-759-0818

Sharon Marie Beausoleil-Mayer · Fulbright & Jaworski · http://www.fulbright.com · Fulbright Tower, Suite 5100 · 1301 McKinney Street · Houston, TX 77010-3095 · 713-651-5151

Charles A. Beckham, Jr. · 10 · Haynes and Boone · One Houston Center, Suite 2100 · 1221 McKinney Street · Houston, TX 77010 · 713-547-2000

Evelyn H. Biery · 25 · Fulbright & Jaworski · http://www.fulbright.com · Fulbright Tower, Suite 5100 · 1301 McKinney Street · Houston, TX 77010-3095 · 713-651-5151

Jonathan Christiaan Bolton · Fulbright & Jaworski · http://www.fulbright.com · Fulbright Tower, Suite 5100 · 1301 McKinney Street · Houston, TX 77010-3095 · 713-651-5151

Rhett G. Campbell · Thompson & Knight · http://www.tklaw.com · 333 Clay Street, Suite 3300 · Houston, TX 77002 · 713-654-8111

Zack A. Clement · 10 · Fulbright & Jaworski · http://www.fulbright.com · Fulbright Tower, Suite 5100 · 1301 McKinney Street · Houston, TX 77010-3095 · 713-651-5151

Tony Davis · Baker Botts · http://www.bakerbotts.com · One Shell Plaza · 910 Louisiana Street · Houston, TX 77002-1210 · 713-229-1234

Joseph G. Epstein · Winstead · http://www.winstead.com · JPMorgan Chase Tower, Suite 1100 · 600 Travis Street · Houston, TX 77002 · 713-650-8400

Elizabeth Freeman · Locke Lord Bissell & Liddell · JP Morgan Chase Tower, Suite 3400 · 600 Travis Street · Houston, TX 77002 · 713-226-1200

Thomas H. Grace · Locke Lord Bissell & Liddell · JP Morgan Chase Tower, Suite 3400 · 600 Travis Street · Houston, TX 77002 · 713-226-1200

William R. Greendyke · Fulbright & Jaworski · http://www.fulbright.com · Fulbright Tower, Suite 5100 · 1301 McKinney Street · Houston, TX 77010-3095 · 713-651-5151

Thomas S. Henderson · Thomas S. Henderson · South Tower, Pennzoil Place, Suite 3100 · 711 Louisiana Street · Houston, TX 77002 · 713-227-9500

John F. Higgins · Porter & Hedges · 1000 Main Street, 36th Floor · Houston, TX 77002 · 713-226-0600

Patrick L. Hughes · Haynes and Boone · One Houston Center, Suite 2100 · 1221 McKinney Street · Houston, TX 77010 · 713-547-2000

David R. Jones · Porter & Hedges · 1000 Main Street, 36th Floor · Houston, TX 77002 · 713-226-0600

Henry J. Kaim · King & Spalding · 1100 Louisiana Street, Suite 4000 · Houston, TX 77002-5213 · 713-751-3200

Kenric D. Kattner · Haynes and Boone · One Houston Center, Suite 2100 · 1221 McKinney Street · Houston, TX 77010 · 713-547-2000

Joel P. Kay · (10) · Hughes, Watters & Askanase · Three Allen Center, 29th Floor · 333 Clay Street · Houston, TX 77002 · 713-759-0818

Wayne Kitchens · Hughes, Watters & Askanase · Three Allen Center, 29th Floor · 333 Clay Street · Houston, TX 77002 · 713-759-0818

Marcy E. Kurtz · Bracewell & Giuliani · http://www.bgllp.com · 711 Louisiana Street, Suite 2300 · Houston, TX 77002-2770 · 713-223-2300

John A. Lee · Andrews Kurth · http://www.andrewskurth.com · 600 Travis Street, Suite 4200 · Houston, TX 77002 · 713-220-4200

Jarrel D. McDaniel · (20) · King & Spalding · 1100 Louisiana Street, Suite 4000 · Houston, TX 77002-5213 713-751-3200

John P. Melko · Gardere Wynne Sewell · http://www.gardere.com · 1000 Louisiana, Suite 3400 · Houston, TX 77002-5011 · 713-276-5500

Alfredo R. Perez · (10) · Weil Gotshal & Manges · Bank of America Building, Suite 1600 · 700 Louisiana Street · Houston, TX 77002 · 713-546-5000

Thomas J. Perich · Andrews Kurth · http://www.andrewskurth.com · 600 Travis Street, Suite 4200 · Houston, TX 77002 · 713-220-4200

Hugh M. Ray · (20) · Andrews Kurth · http://www.andrewskurth.com · 600 Travis Street, Suite 4200 · Houston, TX 77002 · 713-220-4200

Edward L. Ripley · King & Spalding · 1100 Louisiana Street, Suite 4000 · Houston, TX 77002-5213 · 713-751-3200

Edward L. Rothberg · Weycer, Kaplan, Pulaski & Zuber · http://www.wkpz.com · 11 Greenway Plaza, Suite 1400 · Houston, TX 77046 · 713-961-9045

Bruce J. Ruzinsky · Jackson Walker · 1401 McKinney Street, Suite 1900 · Houston, TX 77010-4008 · 713-752-4200

Myron M. Sheinfeld · (25) · King & Spalding · 1100 Louisiana Street, Suite 4000 · Houston, TX 77002-5213 · 713-751-3200

S. Margie Venus · Akin Gump Strauss Hauer & Feld · 1111 Louisiana Street, 44th Floor · Houston, TX 77002-5200 · 713-220-5800

Mark W. Wege · King & Spalding · 1100 Louisiana Street, Suite 4000 · Houston, TX 77002-5213 · 713-751-3200

John E. West · Vinson & Elkins · http://www.velaw.com · First City Tower, Suite 2500 · 1001 Fannin Street · Houston, TX 77002-6760 · 713-758-2222

William A. Wood · Bracewell & Giuliani · http://www.bgllp.com · 711 Louisiana Street, Suite 2300 · Houston, TX 77002-2770 · 713-223-2300

Nederland

John J. Durkay · John J. Durkay · 324 Highway 69 · Nederland, TX 77627 · 409-527-3349

San Antonio

Mark E. Andrews · Cox Smith Matthews · http://www.coxsmith.com · 112 East Pecan Street, Suite 1800 · San Antonio, TX 78205-1521 · 210-554-5500

R. Glen Ayers · ⑩ · Langley & Banack · Trinity Plaza II, Suite 900 · 745 East Mulberry Avenue · San Antonio, TX 78212-3166 · 210-736-6600

Diann M. Bartek · Cox Smith Matthews · http://www.coxsmith.com · 112 East Pecan Street, Suite 1800 · San Antonio, TX 78205-1521 · 210-554-5500

Raymond W. Battaglia · ⑩ · Oppenheimer, Blend, Harrison & Tate · 711 Navarro Street, Suite 600 · San Antonio, TX 78205-1796 · 210-224-2000

David S. Gragg · Langley & Banack · Trinity Plaza II, Suite 900 · 745 East Mulberry Avenue · San Antonio, TX 78212-3166 · 210-736-6600

Claiborne B. Gregory, Jr. · ⑳ · Jackson Walker · Weston Centre, Suite 2400 · 112 East Pecan Street · San Antonio, TX 78205 · 210-978-7700

James A. Hoffman · Clemens & Spencer · http://www.clemens-spencer.com · 1300 Weston Centre · 112 East Pecan Street · San Antonio, TX 78205-1517 · 210-227-7121

Ronald Hornberger · ⑳ · Plunkett & Gibson · http://www.plunkett-gibson.com · 70 Northeast Loop 410, Suite 1100 · San Antonio, TX 78216 · 210-734-7092

Carol E. Jendrzey · Cox Smith Matthews · http://www.coxsmith.com · 112 East Pecan Street, Suite 1800 · San Antonio, TX 78205-1521 · 210-554-5500

Michael M. Parker · Fulbright & Jaworski · http://www.fulbright.com · 300 Convent Street, Suite 2200 · San Antonio, TX 78205-3792 · 210-224-5575

Jack M. Partain, Jr. · ⑩ · Fulbright & Jaworski · http://www.fulbright.com · 300 Convent Street, Suite 2200 · San Antonio, TX 78205-3792 · 210-224-5575

John H. Tate II · ㉕ · Oppenheimer, Blend, Harrison & Tate · 711 Navarro Street, Suite 600 · San Antonio, TX 78205-1796 · 210-224-2000

Eric Terry · Haynes and Boone · 112 East Pecan Street, Suite 900 · San Antonio, TX 78205-1540 · 210-978-7000

Deborah D. Williamson · ⑩ · Cox Smith Matthews · http://www.coxsmith.com · 112 East Pecan Street, Suite 1800 · San Antonio, TX 78205-1521 · 210-554-5500

Waxahachie

David W. Elmquist · Reed & Elmquist · 604 Water Street · Waxahachie, TX 75165 · 972-938-7334

BET-THE-COMPANY LITIGATION

Austin

Martha S. Dickie · Akin & Almanza · 2301 South Capitol of Texas Highway, Building H · Austin, TX 78746 · 512-474-9486

Casey L. Dobson · Scott, Douglass & McConnico · 600 Congress Avenue, Suite 1500 · Austin, TX 78701-3234 · 512-495-6300

Richard Edwin Gray III · ⑩ · Gray & Becker · 900 West Avenue · Austin, TX 78701 · 512-482-0061

Timothy J. Herman · Segal McCambridge Singer & Mahoney · 100 Congress Avenue, Suite 800 · Austin, TX 78701 · 512-476-7834

Randy R. Howry · Herman Howry & Breen · http://www.hermanhowry.com · 1900 Pearl Street · Austin, TX 78705 · 512-474-7300

Patton G. Lochridge · ⑩ · McGinnis, Lochridge & Kilgore · http://www.mcginnislaw.com · 600 Congress Avenue, Suite 2100 · Austin, TX 78701 · 512-495-6000

Stephen E. McConnico · ⑩ · Scott, Douglass & McConnico · 600 Congress Avenue, Suite 1500 · Austin, TX 78701-3234 · 512-495-6300

John J. McKetta III · ⑳ · Graves, Dougherty, Hearon & Moody · http://www.gdhm.com · 401 Congress Avenue, Suite 2200 · P.O. Box 98 · Austin, TX 78767-0098 · 512-480-5600

Roy Q. Minton · ㉕ · Minton, Burton, Foster & Collins · 1100 Guadalupe Street · Austin, TX 78701-2198 512-476-4873

Shannon H. Ratliff · ⑩ · Ratliff Law Firm · 600 Congress Avenue, Suite 3100 · Austin, TX 78701-2984 · 512-493-9600

Thomas H. Watkins · ⑳ · Brown McCarroll · 111 Congress Avenue, Suite 1400 · Austin, TX 78701-4093 · 512-472-5456

Dallas

George W. Bramblett, Jr. · ⑩ · Haynes and Boone · 901 Main Street, Suite 3100 · Dallas, TX 75202 · 214-651-5000

George C. Chapman · ㉕ · Thompson & Knight · http://www.tklaw.com · One Arts Plaza, Suite 1500 · 1722 Routh Street · Dallas, TX 75201-2533 · 214-969-1700

James E. Coleman, Jr. · ㉕ · Carrington, Coleman, Sloman & Blumenthal · 901 Main Street, Suite 5500 · Dallas, TX 75202 · 214-855-3000

Nina Cortell · Haynes and Boone · 901 Main Street, Suite 3100 · Dallas, TX 75202 · 214-651-5000

William B. Dawson · Vinson & Elkins · http://www.velaw.com · Trammell Crow Center, Suite 3700 · 2001 Ross Avenue · Dallas, TX 75201-2975 · 214-220-7700

Thomas S. Leatherbury · ⑩ · Vinson & Elkins · http://www.velaw.com · Trammell Crow Center, Suite 3700 · 2001 Ross Avenue · Dallas, TX 75201-2975 · 214-220-7700

John H. Martin · ⑩ · Thompson & Knight · http://www.tklaw.com · One Arts Plaza, Suite 1500 · 1722 Routh Street · Dallas, TX 75201-2533 · 214-969-1700

Mike McKool, Jr. · ⑩ · McKool Smith · http://www.mckoolsmith.com · 300 Crescent Court, Suite 1500 · Dallas, TX 75201 · 214-978-4000

Robert H. Mow, Jr. · ㉕ · K&L Gates · 1717 Main Street, Suite 2800 · Dallas, TX 75201 · 214-939-5500

Terrell W. Oxford · ⑩ · Susman Godfrey · 901 Main Street, Suite 5100 · Dallas, TX 75202-3775 · 214-754-1900

Rod Phelan · ⑩ · Baker Botts · http://www.bakerbotts.com · Trammell Crow Center, Suite 600 · 2001 Ross Avenue · Dallas, TX 75201-2980 · 214-953-6500

Richard A. Sayles · Sayles/Werbner · http://www.swtriallaw.com · 1201 Elm Street, 44th Floor · Dallas, TX 75270 · 214-939-8700

Mark S. Werbner · ⑩ · Sayles/Werbner · http://www.swtriallaw.com · 1201 Elm Street, 44th Floor · Dallas, TX 75270 · 214-939-8700

Fletcher L. Yarbrough · ㉕ · Carrington, Coleman, Sloman & Blumenthal · 901 Main Street, Suite 5500 · Dallas, TX 75202 · 214-855-3000

Fort Worth

Rowland David Broiles · ⑳ · Cagle Broiles · 100 North Forest Park Boulevard, Suite 220 · Fort Worth, TX 76102 · 817-335-3311

Donald E. Herrmann · ⑩ · Kelly, Hart & Hallman · Wells Fargo Tower, Suite 2500 · 201 Main Street · Fort Worth, TX 76102 · 817-332-2500

Kleber C. Miller · ㉕ · Shannon, Gracey, Ratliff & Miller · http://www.shannongracey.com · 777 Main Street, Suite 3800 · Fort Worth, TX 76102 · 817-336-9333

Marshall M. Searcy, Jr. · ⑩ · Kelly, Hart & Hallman · Wells Fargo Tower, Suite 2500 · 201 Main Street · Fort Worth, TX 76102 · 817-332-2500

Houston

David J. Beck · ㉕ · Beck, Redden & Secrest · http://www.brsfirm.com · One Houston Center, Suite 4500 1221 McKinney Street · Houston, TX 77010-2010 · 713-951-3700

David Howard Berg · ⑩ · Berg & Androphy · http://www.bafirm.com · 3704 Travis Street · Houston, TX 77002 · 713-529-5622

B. Daryl Bristow · ⑩ · Baker Botts · http://www.bakerbotts.com · One Shell Plaza · 910 Louisiana Street · Houston, TX 77002-1210 · 713-229-1234

Wayne Fisher · ㉕ · Fisher, Boyd, Brown, Boudreaux & Huguenard · Riviana Building, 14th Floor · 2777 Allen Parkway · Houston, TX 77019 · 713-400-4000

Murray J. Fogler · Beck, Redden & Secrest · http://www.brsfirm.com · One Houston Center, Suite 4500 · 1221 McKinney Street · Houston, TX 77010-2010 · 713-951-3700

Robin C. Gibbs · ⑩ · Gibbs & Bruns · http://www.gibbs-bruns.com · 1100 Louisiana Street, Suite 5300 · Houston, TX 77002 · 713-650-8805

H. Lee Godfrey · ⑩ · Susman Godfrey · 1000 Louisiana, Suite 5100 · Houston, TX 77002-5096 · 713-651-9366

J. Clifford Gunter III · Bracewell & Giuliani · http://www.bgllp.com · 711 Louisiana Street, Suite 2300 · Houston, TX 77002-2770 · 713-223-2300

Joseph D. Jamail · ㉕ · Jamail & Kolius · 500 Dallas Street, Suite 3434 · Houston, TX 77002 · 713-651-3000

Richard L. Josephson · Baker Botts · http://www.bakerbotts.com · One Shell Plaza · 910 Louisiana Street Houston, TX 77002-1210 · 713-229-1234

Neal S. Manne · Susman Godfrey · 1000 Louisiana, Suite 5100 · Houston, TX 77002-5096 · 713-651-9366

Harry M. Reasoner · ㉕ · Vinson & Elkins · http://www.velaw.com · First City Tower, Suite 2500 · 1001 Fannin Street · Houston, TX 77002-6760 · 713-758-2222

William C. Slusser · ⑩ · Slusser Wilson & Partridge · 4720 Three Allen Center · 333 Clay Street · Houston, TX 77002 · 713-860-3300

Stephen D. Susman · ㉕ · Susman Godfrey · 1000 Louisiana, Suite 5100 · Houston, TX 77002-5096 · 713-651-9366

San Antonio

Stephen P. Allison · Haynes and Boone · 112 East Pecan Street, Suite 900 · San Antonio, TX 78205-1540 210-978-7000

Emerson Banack, Jr. · ⑩ · Langley & Banack · Trinity Plaza II, Suite 900 · 745 East Mulberry Avenue · San Antonio, TX 78212-3166 · 210-736-6600

Ricardo G. Cedillo · Davis, Cedillo & Mendoza · McCombs Plaza, Suite 500 · 755 East Mulberry Avenue San Antonio, TX 78212 · 210-822-6666

Barry A. Chasnoff · Akin Gump Strauss Hauer & Feld · 300 Convent Street, Suite 1500 · San Antonio, TX 78205-3732 · 210-281-7000

R. Laurence Macon · Akin Gump Strauss Hauer & Feld · 300 Convent Street, Suite 1500 · San Antonio, TX 78205-3732 · 210-281-7000

Howard P. Newton · Cox Smith Matthews · http://www.coxsmith.com · 112 East Pecan Street, Suite 1800 San Antonio, TX 78205-1521 · 210-554-5500

Allen Lewin Plunkett · ⑩ · Plunkett & Gibson · http://www.plunkett-gibson.com · 70 Northeast Loop 410, Suite 1100 · San Antonio, TX 78216 · 210-734-7092

Luther H. Soules III · Soules & Wallace · P.O. Box 15588 · San Antonio, TX 78212 · 210-224-9144

George H. Spencer, Jr. · ⑩ · Clemens & Spencer · http://www.clemens-spencer.com · 1300 Weston Centre · 112 East Pecan Street · San Antonio, TX 78205-1517 · 210-227-7121

John W. Weber, Jr. · Fulbright & Jaworski · http://www.fulbright.com · 300 Convent Street, Suite 2200 · San Antonio, TX 78205-3792 · 210-224-5575

Wichita Falls

Lonny D. Morrison · Morrison & Shelton · City National Building, Suite 400 · 807 Eighth Street · Wichita Falls, TX 76301 · 940-322-2929

BIOTECHNOLOGY LAW

Austin

Tracey B. Davies · Vinson & Elkins · http://www.velaw.com · 2801 Via Fortuna, Suite 100 · Austin, TX 78746-7568 · 512-542-8400

Steven Lee Highlander · Fulbright & Jaworski · http://www.fulbright.com · 600 Congress Avenue, Suite 2400 · Austin, TX 78701-2978 · 512-474-5201

David L. Parker · Fulbright & Jaworski · http://www.fulbright.com · 600 Congress Avenue, Suite 2400 · Austin, TX 78701-2978 · 512-474-5201

Gina N. Shishima · Fulbright & Jaworski · http://www.fulbright.com · 600 Congress Avenue, Suite 2400 · Austin, TX 78701-2978 · 512-474-5201

Dallas

Robert Eldon Hanson · Sonnenschein Nath & Rosenthal · 1717 Main Street, Suite 3400 · Dallas, TX 75201-4612 · 214-259-0900

COLLABORATIVE LAW: FAMILY LAW

Austin

Kristen A. Algert · Ausley, Algert, Robertson & Flores · http://www.ausley-algert.com · 3307 Northland Drive, Suite 420 · Austin, TX 78731 · 512-454-8791

Janice Loy Green · Farris & Green · 6407 Sumac Drive · P.O. Box 29198 · Austin, TX 78731-4114 · 512-473-8591

Dallas

Janet P. Brumley · Verner & Brumley · http://www.vernerbrumley.com · 3131 TurtleCreek Boulevard, Penthouse Suite · Dallas, TX 75219 · 214-526-5234

Carla M. Calabrese · Calabrese Huff · http://www.calabreselaw.com · 5944 Luther Lane, Suite 875 · Dallas, TX 75225 · 214-939-3000

Gay G. Cox · Gay G. Cox · http://www.mediate.com/ggcox · 2213 Boll Street · Dallas, TX 75204 · 214-522-0150

Paula Larsen · ⑩ · Goranson, Bain, Larsen & Greenwald · 8150 North Central Expressway, Suite 1850 · Dallas, TX 75206 · 214-373-7676

Robert J. Matlock · Robert J. Matlock · 12221 Merit Drive, Suite 1660 · Dallas, TX 75251 · 972-387-9955

Houston

Norma L. Trusch · Norma Levine Trusch Law Firm · 4550 Post Oak Place, Suite 341 · Houston, TX 77027 · 713-961-0256

Plano

Jody L. Johnson · Allison and Johnson · 5000 Legacy Drive, Suite 160 · Plano, TX 75024-3112 · 972-608-4300

COMMERCIAL LITIGATION

Abilene

Stephen H. Suttle · ⑩ · McMahon Surovik Suttle · http://www.mcmahonlawtx.com · 400 Pine Street, Suite 800 · P.O. Box 3679 · Abilene, TX 79604 · 325-676-9183

Amarillo

Maston C. Courtney · Courtney, Countiss, Brian & Bailey · Chase Tower, Suite 1700 · 600 South Tyler Street · P.O. Box 9238 · Amarillo, TX 79105 · 806-372-5569

Marvin W. Jones · Sprouse Shrader Smith · 701 South Taylor, Suite 500 · P.O. Box 15008 · Amarillo, TX 79105-5008 · 806-468-3300

Tom Morris · Underwood, Wilson, Berry, Stein & Johnson · 500 South Taylor, Suite 1200, Lock Box 233 · P.O. Box 9158 · Amarillo, TX 79105 · 806-376-5613

Harlow Sprouse · ⑩ · Sprouse Shrader Smith · 701 South Taylor, Suite 500 · P.O. Box 15008 · Amarillo, TX 79105-5008 · 806-468-3300

Austin

Thomas A. Albright II · Albright & Albright · 14916 Crosscreek Drive · Austin, TX 78737 · 512-716-8400

William J. Albright · Albright & Albright · 14916 Crosscreek Drive · Austin, TX 78737 · 512-716-8400

Robert C. Alden · Byrd, Davis & Furman · 707 West 34th Street · Austin, TX 78705 · 512-454-3751

Debora B. Alsup · Thompson & Knight · http://www.tklaw.com · 98 San Jacinto Boulevard, Suite 1900 · Austin, TX 78701 · 512-469-6100

W. Stephen Benesh · Bracewell & Giuliani · http://www.bgllp.com · 111 Congress Avenue, Suite 2300 · Austin, TX 78701 · 512-472-7800

Wayne W. Bost · Winstead · http://www.winstead.com · 401 Congress Avenue, Suite 2100 · Austin, TX 78701 · 512-370-2800

Sean E. Breen · Herman Howry & Breen · http://www.hermanhowry.com · 1900 Pearl Street · Austin, TX 78705 · 512-474-7300

Doug Brothers · George & Brothers · Norwood Tower, Suite 1100 · 114 West Seventh Street · Austin, TX 78701 · 512-495-1400

Donna Brown · Donna Brown · 1705 South Capital of Texas Highway, Suite 160 · Austin, TX 78746 · 512-732-2376

James W. Cannon, Jr. · Baker Botts · http://www.bakerbotts.com · 1500 San Jacinto Center · 98 San Jacinto Boulevard · Austin, TX 78701-4039 · 512-322-2500

Martha S. Dickie · Akin & Almanza · 2301 South Capitol of Texas Highway, Building H · Austin, TX 78746 · 512-474-9486

Mary Schaerdel Dietz · Fulbright & Jaworski · http://www.fulbright.com · 600 Congress Avenue, Suite 2400 · Austin, TX 78701-2978 · 512-474-5201

Casey L. Dobson · Scott, Douglass & McConnico · 600 Congress Avenue, Suite 1500 · Austin, TX 78701-3234 · 512-495-6300

John L. Foster · Minton, Burton, Foster & Collins · 1100 Guadalupe Street · Austin, TX 78701-2198 · 512-476-4873

R. James George, Jr. · ⑳ · George & Brothers · Norwood Tower, Suite 1100 · 114 West Seventh Street · Austin, TX 78701 · 512-495-1400

Richard Edwin Gray III · ⑩ · Gray & Becker · 900 West Avenue · Austin, TX 78701 · 512-482-0061

Marcy H. Greer · Fulbright & Jaworski · http://www.fulbright.com · 600 Congress Avenue, Suite 2400 · Austin, TX 78701-2978 · 512-474-5201

Brian S. Greig · ⓴ · Fulbright & Jaworski · http://www.fulbright.com · 600 Congress Avenue, Suite 2400 · Austin, TX 78701-2978 · 512-474-5201

John M. Harmon · Graves, Dougherty, Hearon & Moody · http://www.gdhm.com · 401 Congress Avenue, Suite 2200 · P.O. Box 98 · Austin, TX 78767-0098 · 512-480-5600

Richard W. Harrison · Fritz, Byrne, Head & Harrison · San Jacinto Center, Suite 2000 · 98 San Jacinto Boulevard · Austin, TX 78701-4286 · 512-476-2020

Robert J. Hearon, Jr. · ㉕ · Graves, Dougherty, Hearon & Moody · http://www.gdhm.com · 401 Congress Avenue, Suite 2200 · P.O. Box 98 · Austin, TX 78767-0098 · 512-480-5600

Timothy J. Herman · Segal McCambridge Singer & Mahoney · 100 Congress Avenue, Suite 800 · Austin, TX 78701 · 512-476-7834

Randy R. Howry · Herman Howry & Breen · http://www.hermanhowry.com · 1900 Pearl Street · Austin, TX 78705 · 512-474-7300

Peter D. Kennedy · Graves, Dougherty, Hearon & Moody · http://www.gdhm.com · 401 Congress Avenue, Suite 2200 · P.O. Box 98 · Austin, TX 78767-0098 · 512-480-5600

Lloyd P. Lochridge · ㉕ · McGinnis, Lochridge & Kilgore · http://www.mcginnislaw.com · 600 Congress Avenue, Suite 2100 · Austin, TX 78701 · 512-495-6000

Patton G. Lochridge · ⓾ · McGinnis, Lochridge & Kilgore · http://www.mcginnislaw.com · 600 Congress Avenue, Suite 2100 · Austin, TX 78701 · 512-495-6000

Michael D. Marin · Vinson & Elkins · http://www.velaw.com · 2801 Via Fortuna, Suite 100 · Austin, TX 78746-7568 · 512-542-8400

Stephen E. McConnico · ⓾ · Scott, Douglass & McConnico · 600 Congress Avenue, Suite 1500 · Austin, TX 78701-3234 · 512-495-6300

John B. McFarland · Graves, Dougherty, Hearon & Moody · http://www.gdhm.com · 401 Congress Avenue, Suite 2200 · P.O. Box 98 · Austin, TX 78767-0098 · 512-480-5600

John J. McKetta III · ⓴ · Graves, Dougherty, Hearon & Moody · http://www.gdhm.com · 401 Congress Avenue, Suite 2200 · P.O. Box 98 · Austin, TX 78767-0098 · 512-480-5600

Roy Q. Minton · ㉕ · Minton, Burton, Foster & Collins · 1100 Guadalupe Street · Austin, TX 78701-2198 512-476-4873

Robert B. Neblett III · Jackson Walker · 100 Congress Avenue, Suite 1100 · Austin, TX 78701 · 512-236-2000

William M. Parrish · Winstead · http://www.winstead.com · 401 Congress Avenue, Suite 2100 · Austin, TX 78701 · 512-370-2800

Pike Powers · Fulbright & Jaworski · http://www.fulbright.com · 600 Congress Avenue, Suite 2400 · Austin, TX 78701-2978 · 512-474-5201

Shannon H. Ratliff · ⓾ · Ratliff Law Firm · 600 Congress Avenue, Suite 3100 · Austin, TX 78701-2984 · 512-493-9600

Thomas T. Rogers · Jackson Walker · 100 Congress Avenue, Suite 1100 · Austin, TX 78701 · 512-236-2000

Terry L. Scarborough · Hance Scarborough · 111 Congress Avenue, Suite 500 · Austin, TX 78701 · 512-479-8888

John Schwartz · Locke Lord Bissell & Liddell · 100 Congress Avenue, Suite 300 · Austin, TX 78701-4042 · 512-305-4785

Matthew J. Sullivan · DuBois, Bryant & Campbell · http://www.dbcllp.com · 700 Lavaca Street, Suite 1300 · Austin, TX 78701 · 512-457-8000

Eric J. Taube · ⑩ · Hohmann Taube & Summers · 100 Congress Avenue, 18th Floor · Austin, TX 78701-4042 · 512-472-5997

Terry O. Tottenham · ⑩ · Fulbright & Jaworski · http://www.fulbright.com · 600 Congress Avenue, Suite 2400 · Austin, TX 78701-2978 · 512-474-5201

Thomas H. Watkins · ⑳ · Brown McCarroll · 111 Congress Avenue, Suite 1400 · Austin, TX 78701-4093 · 512-472-5456

T. B. Wright · ⑩ · Wright & Greenhill · 221 West Sixth Street, Suite 1800 · Austin, TX 78701 · 512-476-4600

Richard D. Yeomans · Graves, Dougherty, Hearon & Moody · http://www.gdhm.com · 401 Congress Avenue, Suite 2200 · P.O. Box 98 · Austin, TX 78767-0098 · 512-480-5600

Beaumont

Paul F. Ferguson, Jr. · Provost & Umphrey Law Firm · Stedman Building · 490 Park Street · P.O. Box 4905 · Beaumont, TX 77704 · 409-835-6000

Gilbert I. Low · ⑳ · Orgain, Bell & Tucker · 470 Orleans Street · P.O. Box 1751 · Beaumont, TX 77704-1751 · 409-838-6412

Bruce Partain · Wells, Peyton, Greenberg & Hunt · 550 Fannin Street, Suite 600 · P.O. Box 3708 · Beaumont, TX 77701 · 409-838-2644

J. Hoke Peacock II · ⑩ · Orgain, Bell & Tucker · 470 Orleans Street · P.O. Box 1751 · Beaumont, TX 77704-1751 · 409-838-6412

Wayne A. Reaud · ⑩ · Reaud, Morgan & Quinn · 801 Laurel Street · P.O. Box 26005 · Beaumont, TX 77720-6005 · 409-838-1000

Corpus Christi

Jose A. Canales · ⑳ · Canales & Simonson · 2601 Morgan Avenue · P.O. Box 5624 · Corpus Christi, TX 78465 · 361-883-0601

Andrew M. Greenwell · Harris & Greenwell · 615 North Upper Broadway, Suite 1700 · Corpus Christi, TX 78477 · 361-883-1946

James R. Harris · ⑳ · Harris & Greenwell · 615 North Upper Broadway, Suite 1700 · Corpus Christi, TX 78477 · 361-883-1946

Van Huseman · ⑩ · Huseman, Dodson & Hummell · 600 Leopard Street, Suite 2100 · Corpus Christi, TX 78473-2707 · 361-883-3563

Russell H. McMains · ⑩ · Law Offices of Russell H. McMains · 500 North Shoreline Boulevard, Suite 1100 · P.O. Box 2846 · Corpus Christi, TX 78403 · 361-887-4455

Jorge C. Rangel · The Rangel Law Firm · 615 Upper North Broadway, Suite 2020 · P.O. Box 2683 · Corpus Christi, TX 78403-2683 · 361-883-8500

James H. Robichaux · Branscomb · 802 North Carancahua Street, Suite 1900 · Corpus Christi, TX 78470-0700 · 361-888-9261

Dallas

Rodney Acker · ⑩ · Fulbright & Jaworski · http://www.fulbright.com · 2200 Ross Avenue, Suite 2800 · Dallas, TX 75201 · 214-855-8000

Robert D. Allen · Meckler Bulger Tilson Marick & Pearson · 10,000 North Central Expressway, Suite 1450 · Dallas, TX 75231 · 214-265-6200

Kim J. Askew · K&L Gates · 1717 Main Street, Suite 2800 · Dallas, TX 75201 · 214-939-5500

W. Mike Baggett · Winstead · http://www.winstead.com · Renaissance Tower, Suite 5400 · 1201 Elm Street · Dallas, TX 75270-2199 · 214-745-5400

William L. Banowsky · Thompson & Knight · http://www.tklaw.com · One Arts Plaza, Suite 1500 · 1722 Routh Street · Dallas, TX 75201-2533 · 214-969-1700

Barry C. Barnett · Susman Godfrey · 901 Main Street, Suite 5100 · Dallas, TX 75202-3775 · 214-754-1900

Samuel F. Baxter · McKool Smith · http://www.mckoolsmith.com · 300 Crescent Court, Suite 1500 · Dallas, TX 75201 · 214-978-4000

Jerry L. Beane · Andrews Kurth · http://www.andrewskurth.com · 1717 Main Street, Suite 3700 · Dallas, TX 75201 · 214-659-4400

Bryant C. Boren, Jr. · Baker Botts · http://www.bakerbotts.com · Trammell Crow Center, Suite 600 · 2001 Ross Avenue · Dallas, TX 75201-2980 · 214-953-6500

George E. Bowles · Locke Lord Bissell & Liddell · 2200 Ross Avenue, Suite 2200 · Dallas, TX 75201-6776 · 214-740-8000

George W. Bramblett, Jr. · ⑩ · Haynes and Boone · 901 Main Street, Suite 3100 · Dallas, TX 75202 · 214-651-5000

William A. Brewer III · Bickel & Brewer · 4800 Bank One Center · 1717 Main Street · Dallas, TX 75201 214-653-4000

James David Brown · Winstead · http://www.winstead.com · Renaissance Tower, Suite 5400 · 1201 Elm Street · Dallas, TX 75270-2199 · 214-745-5400

Ophelia F. Camiña · Susman Godfrey · 901 Main Street, Suite 5100 · Dallas, TX 75202-3775 · 214-754-1900

Larry D. Carlson · Baker Botts · http://www.bakerbotts.com · Trammell Crow Center, Suite 600 · 2001 Ross Avenue · Dallas, TX 75201-2980 · 214-953-6500

George C. Chapman · ㉕ · Thompson & Knight · http://www.tklaw.com · One Arts Plaza, Suite 1500 · 1722 Routh Street · Dallas, TX 75201-2533 · 214-969-1700

Jerry K. Clements · Locke Lord Bissell & Liddell · 2200 Ross Avenue, Suite 2200 · Dallas, TX 75201-6776 · 214-740-8000

William D. Cobb, Jr. · Cobb Martinez Woodward · 1700 Pacific Avenue, Suite 4545 · Dallas, TX 75201 · 214-220-5200

Paul E. Coggins · Fish & Richardson · 1717 Main Street, Suite 5000 · Dallas, TX 75201 · 214-747-5070

Robert M. Cohan · Jackson Walker · Bank of America Plaza, Suite 6000 · 901 Main Street · Dallas, TX 75202 · 214-953-6000

James E. Coleman, Jr. · 25 · Carrington, Coleman, Sloman & Blumenthal · 901 Main Street, Suite 5500 · Dallas, TX 75202 · 214-855-3000

Donald Colleluori · Figari & Davenport · http://www.figdav.com · 3400 Bank of America Plaza · 901 Main Street · Dallas, TX 75202-3796 · 214-939-2000

Nina Cortell · Haynes and Boone · 901 Main Street, Suite 3100 · Dallas, TX 75202 · 214-651-5000

Gary C. Crapster · Strasburger & Price · http://www.strasburger.com · 901 Main Street, Suite 4400 · Dallas, TX 75202-3794 · 214-651-4300

Gary J. Cruciani · Diamond McCarthy · Renaissance Tower, 34th Floor · 1201 Elm Street · Dallas, TX 75270 · 214-389-5300

Charles W. Cunningham · McKool Smith · http://www.mckoolsmith.com · 300 Crescent Court, Suite 1500 · Dallas, TX 75201 · 214-978-4000

Greg W. Curry · Thompson & Knight · http://www.tklaw.com · One Arts Plaza, Suite 1500 · 1722 Routh Street · Dallas, TX 75201-2533 · 214-969-1700

Theodore W. Daniel · Fulbright & Jaworski · http://www.fulbright.com · 2200 Ross Avenue, Suite 2800 · Dallas, TX 75201 · 214-855-8000

Mark Talbot Davenport · 10 · Figari & Davenport · http://www.figdav.com · 3400 Bank of America Plaza · 901 Main Street · Dallas, TX 75202-3796 · 214-939-2000

Robert E. Davis · 20 · K&L Gates · 1717 Main Street, Suite 2800 · Dallas, TX 75201 · 214-939-5500

Dan D. Davison · Fulbright & Jaworski · http://www.fulbright.com · 2200 Ross Avenue, Suite 2800 · Dallas, TX 75201 · 214-855-8000

William B. Dawson · Vinson & Elkins · http://www.velaw.com · Trammell Crow Center, Suite 3700 · 2001 Ross Avenue · Dallas, TX 75201-2975 · 214-220-7700

David R. Deary · Loewinsohn Flegle Deary · 12377 Merit Drive, Suite 900 · Dallas, TX 75251-2224 · 214-572-1700

Karl G. Dial · Fulbright & Jaworski · http://www.fulbright.com · 2200 Ross Avenue, Suite 2800 · Dallas, TX 75201 · 214-855-8000

Timothy S. Durst · Baker Botts · http://www.bakerbotts.com · Trammell Crow Center, Suite 600 · 2001 Ross Avenue · Dallas, TX 75201-2980 · 214-953-6500

A. Erin Dwyer · 10 · Figari & Davenport · http://www.figdav.com · 3400 Bank of America Plaza · 901 Main Street · Dallas, TX 75202-3796 · 214-939-2000

Robert Elkin · McKool Smith · http://www.mckoolsmith.com · 300 Crescent Court, Suite 1500 · Dallas, TX 75201 · 214-978-4000

Ernest E. Figari, Jr. · 25 · Figari & Davenport · http://www.figdav.com · 3400 Bank of America Plaza · 901 Main Street · Dallas, TX 75202-3796 · 214-939-2000

Jim L. Flegle, Jr. · Loewinsohn Flegle Deary · 12377 Merit Drive, Suite 900 · Dallas, TX 75251-2224 · 214-572-1700

Sharon N. Freytag · Haynes and Boone · 901 Main Street, Suite 3100 · Dallas, TX 75202 · 214-651-5000

Curtis L. Frisbie, Jr. · Gardere Wynne Sewell · http://www.gardere.com · 1601 Elm Street, Suite 3000 · Dallas, TX 75201 · 214-999-3000

Paul R. Genender · K&L Gates · 1717 Main Street, Suite 2800 · Dallas, TX 75201 · 214-939-5500

John Anderson Gilliam · ⑳ · Jenkens & Gilchrist · 500 North Akard Street, Suite 200 · Dallas, TX 75201 214-855-4500

Brett C. Govett · Fulbright & Jaworski · http://www.fulbright.com · 2200 Ross Avenue, Suite 2800 · Dallas, TX 75201 · 214-855-8000

Thomas A. Graves · ⑩ · McKool Smith · http://www.mckoolsmith.com · 300 Crescent Court, Suite 1500 · Dallas, TX 75201 · 214-978-4000

T. Ray Guy · Weil Gotshal & Manges · 200 Crescent Court, Suite 300 · Dallas, TX 75201 · 214-746-7700

Alan W. Harris · Law Offices of Alan W. Harris · 325 North Saint Paul Street, Suite 2700 · Dallas, TX 75201 · 214-965-8200

Joe B. Harrison · Gardere Wynne Sewell · http://www.gardere.com · 1601 Elm Street, Suite 3000 · Dallas, TX 75201 · 214-999-3000

Robin P. Hartmann · ⑩ · Haynes and Boone · 901 Main Street, Suite 3100 · Dallas, TX 75202 · 214-651-5000

Craig A. Haynes · Thompson & Knight · http://www.tklaw.com · One Arts Plaza, Suite 1500 · 1722 Routh Street · Dallas, TX 75201-2533 · 214-969-1700

Noel M. B. Hensley · Haynes and Boone · 901 Main Street, Suite 3100 · Dallas, TX 75202 · 214-651-5000

Karen L. Hirschman · Vinson & Elkins · http://www.velaw.com · Trammell Crow Center, Suite 3700 · 2001 Ross Avenue · Dallas, TX 75201-2975 · 214-220-7700

James Holmes · The Schmidt Firm · 2911 Turtle Creek Boulevard, Suite 1400 · Dallas, TX 75219 · 214-521-4898

Gregory S.C. Huffman · Thompson & Knight · http://www.tklaw.com · One Arts Plaza, Suite 1500 · 1722 Routh Street · Dallas, TX 75201-2533 · 214-969-1700

Brian J. Hurst · Baker & McKenzie · 2300 Trammell Crow Center · 2001 Ross Avenue · Dallas, TX 75201 · 214-978-3000

Sim Israeloff · Cowles & Thompson · http://www.cowlesthompson.com · Bank of America Plaza, Suite 4000 · 901 Main Street · Dallas, TX 75202 · 214-672-2000

James D. Jordan · Munsch Hardt Kopf & Harr · 3800 Lincoln Plaza · 500 North Akard Street · Dallas, TX 75201-6659 · 214-855-7500

Mark T. Josephs · Jackson Walker · Bank of America Plaza, Suite 6000 · 901 Main Street · Dallas, TX 75202 · 214-953-6000

P. Michael Jung · Strasburger & Price · http://www.strasburger.com · 901 Main Street, Suite 4400 · Dallas, TX 75202-3794 · 214-651-4300

Gary S. Kessler · ⑩ · Kessler & Collins · 2100 Ross Avenue, Suite 750 · Dallas, TX 75201 · 214-379-0722

Samara L. Kline · Baker Botts · http://www.bakerbotts.com · Trammell Crow Center, Suite 600 · 2001 Ross Avenue · Dallas, TX 75201-2980 · 214-953-6500

Paul M. Koning · K&L Gates · 1717 Main Street, Suite 2800 · Dallas, TX 75201 · 214-939-5500

George M. Kryder · ⑩ · Vinson & Elkins · http://www.velaw.com · Trammell Crow Center, Suite 3700 · 2001 Ross Avenue · Dallas, TX 75201-2975 · 214-220-7700

Thomas E. Kurth · Haynes and Boone · 901 Main Street, Suite 3100 · Dallas, TX 75202 · 214-651-5000

George C. Lamb III · Baker Botts · http://www.bakerbotts.com · Trammell Crow Center, Suite 600 · 2001 Ross Avenue · Dallas, TX 75201-2980 · 214-953-6500

Kathleen M. LaValle · Jackson Walker · Bank of America Plaza, Suite 6000 · 901 Main Street · Dallas, TX 75202 · 214-953-6000

Thomas S. Leatherbury · ⑩ · Vinson & Elkins · http://www.velaw.com · Trammell Crow Center, Suite 3700 · 2001 Ross Avenue · Dallas, TX 75201-2975 · 214-220-7700

Lewis T. LeClair · McKool Smith · http://www.mckoolsmith.com · 300 Crescent Court, Suite 1500 · Dallas, TX 75201 · 214-978-4000

Jeffrey S. Levinger · Hankinson Levinger · 2305 Cedar Springs Road, Suite 230 · Dallas, TX 75201-6955 215-754-9190

Alan S. Loewinsohn · Loewinsohn Flegle Deary · 12377 Merit Drive, Suite 900 · Dallas, TX 75251-2224 214-572-1700

John A. Mackintosh · ⑩ · Thompson & Knight · http://www.tklaw.com · One Arts Plaza, Suite 1500 · 1722 Routh Street · Dallas, TX 75201-2533 · 214-969-1700

Jay J. Madrid · Winstead · http://www.winstead.com · Renaissance Tower, Suite 5400 · 1201 Elm Street · Dallas, TX 75270-2199 · 214-745-5400

John H. Martin · ⑩ · Thompson & Knight · http://www.tklaw.com · One Arts Plaza, Suite 1500 · 1722 Routh Street · Dallas, TX 75201-2533 · 214-969-1700

Timothy R. McCormick · ⑩ · Thompson & Knight · http://www.tklaw.com · One Arts Plaza, Suite 1500 · 1722 Routh Street · Dallas, TX 75201-2533 · 214-969-1700

John H. McElhaney · ㉕ · Locke Lord Bissell & Liddell · 2200 Ross Avenue, Suite 2200 · Dallas, TX 75201-6776 · 214-740-8000

Scott M. McElhaney · Jackson Walker · Bank of America Plaza, Suite 6000 · 901 Main Street · Dallas, TX 75202 · 214-953-6000

Mike McKool, Jr. · ⑩ · McKool Smith · http://www.mckoolsmith.com · 300 Crescent Court, Suite 1500 · Dallas, TX 75201 · 214-978-4000

Barry F. McNeil · Haynes and Boone · 901 Main Street, Suite 3100 · Dallas, TX 75202 · 214-651-5000

Thomas M. Melsheimer · Fish & Richardson · 1717 Main Street, Suite 5000 · Dallas, TX 75201 · 214-747-5070

Brian D. Melton · Shackelford, Melton & McKinley · 3333 Lee Parkway, 10th Floor · Dallas, TX 75219 · 214-780-1400

Ralph I. Miller · Weil Gotshal & Manges · 200 Crescent Court, Suite 300 · Dallas, TX 75201 · 214-746-7700

Bruce Monning · Monning & Wynne · Cumberland Hill School Building · 1901 North Akard Street · Dallas, TX 75201 · 214-871-7171

Timothy W. Mountz · Baker Botts · http://www.bakerbotts.com · Trammell Crow Center, Suite 600 · 2001 Ross Avenue · Dallas, TX 75201-2980 · 214-953-6500

Robert H. Mow, Jr. · ㉕ · K&L Gates · 1717 Main Street, Suite 2800 · Dallas, TX 75201 · 214-939-5500

Terence M. Murphy · Jones Day · 2727 North Harwood Street · Dallas, TX 75201-1515 · 214-220-3939

David R. Noteware · ⑳ · Thompson & Knight · http://www.tklaw.com · One Arts Plaza, Suite 1500 · 1722 Routh Street · Dallas, TX 75201-2533 · 214-969-1700

Terrell W. Oxford · ⑩ · Susman Godfrey · 901 Main Street, Suite 5100 · Dallas, TX 75202-3775 · 214-754-1900

Carol C. Payne · Vinson & Elkins · http://www.velaw.com · Trammell Crow Center, Suite 3700 · 2001 Ross Avenue · Dallas, TX 75201-2975 · 214-220-7700

Rod Phelan · ⑩ · Baker Botts · http://www.bakerbotts.com · Trammell Crow Center, Suite 600 · 2001 Ross Avenue · Dallas, TX 75201-2980 · 214-953-6500

Eric Pinker · Lynn Tillotson Pinker & Cox · http://www.lynnllp.com · 750 North Paul Street, Suite 1400 · Dallas, TX 75201 · 214-981-3800

Richard D. Pullman · Collins Basinger & Pullman · http://cblegal.lawoffice.com · One Lincoln Center, Suite 525 · 5400 LBJ Freeway · Dallas, TX 75240 · 972-661-2622

Stephen C. Rasch · Thompson & Knight · http://www.tklaw.com · One Arts Plaza, Suite 1500 · 1722 Routh Street · Dallas, TX 75201-2533 · 214-969-1700

Charles W. Sartain · Looper Reed & McGraw · 4100 Thanksgiving Tower · 1601 Elm Street · Dallas, TX 75201 · 214-954-4135

Richard A. Sayles · Sayles/Werbner · http://www.swtriallaw.com · 1201 Elm Street, 44th Floor · Dallas, TX 75270 · 214-939-8700

Paul D. Schoonover · ⑩ · Kleiman Lawrence Baskind Fitzgerald · 8750 North Central Expressway, Suite 777 · Dallas, TX 75231 · 214-265-7400

Mark A. Shank · ⑩ · K&L Gates · 1717 Main Street, Suite 2800 · Dallas, TX 75201 · 214-939-5500

Gordon M. Shapiro · Jackson Walker · Bank of America Plaza, Suite 6000 · 901 Main Street · Dallas, TX 75202 · 214-953-6000

N. Henry Simpson · Simpson Woolley · 700 The Quadrangle · 2828 Routh Street · Dallas, TX 75201 · 214-871-5080

William D. Sims · ⑩ · Vinson & Elkins · http://www.velaw.com · Trammell Crow Center, Suite 3700 · 2001 Ross Avenue · Dallas, TX 75201-2975 · 214-220-7700

Jonathan B. Skidmore · Fulbright & Jaworski · http://www.fulbright.com · 2200 Ross Avenue, Suite 2800 Dallas, TX 75201 · 214-855-8000

Marvin S. Sloman · ㉕ · Carrington, Coleman, Sloman & Blumenthal · 901 Main Street, Suite 5500 · Dallas, TX 75202 · 214-855-3000

Michael C. Steindorf · Fulbright & Jaworski · http://www.fulbright.com · 2200 Ross Avenue, Suite 2800 · Dallas, TX 75201 · 214-855-8000

Theodore Stevenson III · McKool Smith · http://www.mckoolsmith.com · 300 Crescent Court, Suite 1500 Dallas, TX 75201 · 214-978-4000

Donald Curtis Templin · Haynes and Boone · 901 Main Street, Suite 3100 · Dallas, TX 75202 · 214-651-5000

Robb L. Voyles · Baker Botts · http://www.bakerbotts.com · Trammell Crow Center, Suite 600 · 2001 Ross Avenue · Dallas, TX 75201-2980 · 214-953-6500

Paul C. Watler · 10 · Jackson Walker · Bank of America Plaza, Suite 6000 · 901 Main Street · Dallas, TX 75202 · 214-953-6000

Mark S. Werbner · 10 · Sayles/Werbner · http://www.swtriallaw.com · 1201 Elm Street, 44th Floor · Dallas, TX 75270 · 214-939-8700

Elizabeth B. Whitaker · Whitaker · 5930 Royal Lane · Dallas, TX 75230 · 214-732-9130

Russell Yager · Vinson & Elkins · http://www.velaw.com · Trammell Crow Center, Suite 3700 · 2001 Ross Avenue · Dallas, TX 75201-2975 · 214-220-7700

Fletcher L. Yarbrough · 25 · Carrington, Coleman, Sloman & Blumenthal · 901 Main Street, Suite 5500 · Dallas, TX 75202 · 214-855-3000

El Paso

Jeffrey S. Alley · Windle, Hood, Alley, Norton, Brittain & Jay · Chase Tower, Suite 1350 · 201 East Main Street · El Paso, TX 79901 · 915-545-4900

E. Link Beck · 10 · Beck & Given · 5915 Silver Springs Drive, Building Four · El Paso, TX 79912 · 915-544-5545

Eric M. Brittain · Windle, Hood, Alley, Norton, Brittain & Jay · Chase Tower, Suite 1350 · 201 East Main Street · El Paso, TX 79901 · 915-545-4900

Milton C. Colia · Kemp Smith · http://www.kempsmith.com · 221 North Kansas, Suite 1700 · El Paso, TX 79901-1441 · 915-533-4424

Harrel L. Davis III · Gordon & Mott · 4695 North Mesa Street, Suite 100 · El Paso, TX 79912 · 915-545-1133

Bryan H. Hall · Beck & Given · 5915 Silver Springs Drive, Building Four · El Paso, TX 79912 · 915-544-5545

Richard G. Munzinger · 20 · Scott, Hulse, Marshall, Feuille, Finger & Thurmond · 1100 Chase Tower · 201 East Main Street · El Paso, TX 79901 · 915-533-2493

David R. Pierce · Law Office of David Pierce · 221 North Kansas, Suite 504 · El Paso, TX 79901 · 915-351-9772

Clyde A. Pine, Jr. · Mounce, Green, Myers, Safi & Galatzan · Kayser Building, 17th Floor · 100 North Stanton Street · P.O. Box 1977 · El Paso, TX 79950-1977 · 915-532-2000

Robert E. Valdez · Ray, Valdez, McChristian & Jeans · 5822 Cromo Drive · El Paso, TX 79912 · 915-832-7200

Fort Worth

Victor Anderson, Jr. · Shannon, Gracey, Ratliff & Miller · http://www.shannongracey.com · 777 Main Street, Suite 3800 · Fort Worth, TX 76102 · 817-336-9333

James B. Barlow · 10 · Barlow Garsek & Simon · Landers Point Office Building, Suite 100 · 3815 Lisbon Street · Fort Worth, TX 76107 · 817-731-4500

Lars L. Berg · Kelly, Hart & Hallman · Wells Fargo Tower, Suite 2500 · 201 Main Street · Fort Worth, TX 76102 · 817-332-2500

Rowland David Broiles · ⑳ · Cagle Broiles · 100 North Forest Park Boulevard, Suite 220 · Fort Worth, TX 76102 · 817-335-3311

Hugh G. Connor II · Kelly, Hart & Hallman · Wells Fargo Tower, Suite 2500 · 201 Main Street · Fort Worth, TX 76102 · 817-332-2500

Beale Dean · ⑳ · Brown, Dean, Wiseman, Liser, Proctor & Hart · Fort Worth Club Building, Suite 200 · 306 West Seventh Street · Fort Worth, TX 76102-4905 · 817-332-1391

Albon O. Head, Jr. · Jackson Walker · 301 Commerce Street, Suite 2400 · Fort Worth, TX 76102 · 817-334-7200

Donald E. Herrmann · ⑩ · Kelly, Hart & Hallman · Wells Fargo Tower, Suite 2500 · 201 Main Street · Fort Worth, TX 76102 · 817-332-2500

E. Glen Johnson · Kelly, Hart & Hallman · Wells Fargo Tower, Suite 2500 · 201 Main Street · Fort Worth, TX 76102 · 817-332-2500

Dee J. Kelly, Jr. · Kelly, Hart & Hallman · Wells Fargo Tower, Suite 2500 · 201 Main Street · Fort Worth, TX 76102 · 817-332-2500

Dee J. Kelly, Sr. · ⑩ · Kelly, Hart & Hallman · Wells Fargo Tower, Suite 2500 · 201 Main Street · Fort Worth, TX 76102 · 817-332-2500

Kleber C. Miller · ㉕ · Shannon, Gracey, Ratliff & Miller · http://www.shannongracey.com · 777 Main Street, Suite 3800 · Fort Worth, TX 76102 · 817-336-9333

Marshall M. Searcy, Jr. · ⑩ · Kelly, Hart & Hallman · Wells Fargo Tower, Suite 2500 · 201 Main Street · Fort Worth, TX 76102 · 817-332-2500

E. Michael Sheehan · Thompson & Knight · http://www.tklaw.com · 1600 Burnett Plaza, Unit One, Suite 1600 · 801 Cherry Street · Fort Worth, TX 76102-6881 · 817-347-1700

Stephen Lyle Tatum · Cantey & Hanger · 300 Cantey Hanger Plaza · 600 West Sixth Street · Fort Worth, TX 76102-3685 · 817-877-2800

R. H. Wallace, Jr. · ⑩ · Shannon, Gracey, Ratliff & Miller · http://www.shannongracey.com · 777 Main Street, Suite 3800 · Fort Worth, TX 76102 · 817-336-9333

Thomas J. Williams · ⑩ · Haynes and Boone · 201 Main Street, Suite 2200 · Fort Worth, TX 76102 · 817-347-6600

Galveston

Stephen R. Lewis, Jr. · ⑩ · Lewis & Williams · 2200 Market Street, Suite 750 · Galveston, TX 77550-1551 · 409-762-1900

Houston

Linda L. Addison · ⑩ · Fulbright & Jaworski · http://www.fulbright.com · Fulbright Tower, Suite 5100 · 1301 McKinney Street · Houston, TX 77010-3095 · 713-651-5151

Scott J. Atlas · Weil Gotshal & Manges · Bank of America Building, Suite 1600 · 700 Louisiana Street · Houston, TX 77002 · 713-546-5000

Charles Lynde Babcock · ⑩ · Jackson Walker · 1401 McKinney Street, Suite 1900 · Houston, TX 77010-4008 · 713-752-4200

David J. Beck · ㉕ · Beck, Redden & Secrest · http://www.brsfirm.com · One Houston Center, Suite 4500 1221 McKinney Street · Houston, TX 77010-2010 · 713-951-3700

John B. Beckworth · Watt, Beckworth, Thompson & Henneman · 1800 Pennzoil Place, South Tower · 711 Louisiana Street · Houston, TX 77002 · 713-650-8100

David Howard Berg · ⑩ · Berg & Androphy · http://www.bafirm.com · 3704 Travis Street · Houston, TX 77002 · 713-529-5622

R. Doak Bishop · King & Spalding · 1100 Louisiana Street, Suite 4000 · Houston, TX 77002-5213 · 713-751-3200

Maria Wyckoff Boyce · Baker Botts · http://www.bakerbotts.com · One Shell Plaza · 910 Louisiana Street Houston, TX 77002-1210 · 713-229-1234

B. Daryl Bristow · ⑩ · Baker Botts · http://www.bakerbotts.com · One Shell Plaza · 910 Louisiana Street · Houston, TX 77002-1210 · 713-229-1234

Reagan M. Brown · Fulbright & Jaworski · http://www.fulbright.com · Fulbright Tower, Suite 5100 · 1301 McKinney Street · Houston, TX 77010-3095 · 713-651-5151

Phillip T. Bruns · Gibbs & Bruns · http://www.gibbs-bruns.com · 1100 Louisiana Street, Suite 5300 · Houston, TX 77002 · 713-650-8805

Richard H. Caldwell · ⑩ · Andrews Kurth · http://www.andrewskurth.com · 600 Travis Street, Suite 4200 Houston, TX 77002 · 713-220-4200

Richard N. Carrell · Fulbright & Jaworski · http://www.fulbright.com · Fulbright Tower, Suite 5100 · 1301 McKinney Street · Houston, TX 77010-3095 · 713-651-5151

John L. Carter · Vinson & Elkins · http://www.velaw.com · First City Tower, Suite 2500 · 1001 Fannin Street · Houston, TX 77002-6760 · 713-758-2222

Winstol D. Carter · Morgan Lewis & Bockius · 1000 Louisiana St., Suite 4200 · Houston, TX 77002-5006 713-890-5000

Murry B. Cohen · Akin Gump Strauss Hauer & Feld · 1111 Louisiana Street, 44th Floor · Houston, TX 77002-5200 · 713-220-5800

Grant Cook · The Cook Law Firm · http://www.grantcooklaw.com · 5005 Riverway, Suite 210 · Houston, TX 77056 · 713-552-0700

Morgan Lee Copeland, Jr. · Vinson & Elkins · http://www.velaw.com · First City Tower, Suite 2500 · 1001 Fannin Street · Houston, TX 77002-6760 · 713-758-2222

Stephen C. Dillard · ⑩ · Fulbright & Jaworski · http://www.fulbright.com · Fulbright Tower, Suite 5100 · 1301 McKinney Street · Houston, TX 77010-3095 · 713-651-5151

Jeff Dyches · Fulbright & Jaworski · http://www.fulbright.com · Fulbright Tower, Suite 5100 · 1301 McKinney Street · Houston, TX 77010-3095 · 713-651-5151

Phillip Bruce Dye, Jr. · Vinson & Elkins · http://www.velaw.com · First City Tower, Suite 2500 · 1001 Fannin Street · Houston, TX 77002-6760 · 713-758-2222

Wayne Fisher · ㉕ · Fisher, Boyd, Brown, Boudreaux & Huguenard · Riviana Building, 14th Floor · 2777 Allen Parkway · Houston, TX 77019 · 713-400-4000

N. Scott Fletcher · Vinson & Elkins · http://www.velaw.com · First City Tower, Suite 2500 · 1001 Fannin Street · Houston, TX 77002-6760 · 713-758-2222

Murray J. Fogler · Beck, Redden & Secrest · http://www.brsfirm.com · One Houston Center, Suite 4500 · 1221 McKinney Street · Houston, TX 77010-2010 · 713-951-3700

Ronald G. Franklin · Franklin, Cardwell & Jones · 1001 McKinney Street, 18th Floor · Houston, TX 77002-6417 · 713-222-6025

Jean C. Frizzell · Gibbs & Bruns · http://www.gibbs-bruns.com · 1100 Louisiana Street, Suite 5300 · Houston, TX 77002 · 713-650-8805

Claudia Wilson Frost · Pillsbury Winthrop Shaw Pittman · http://www.pillsburylaw.com · Two Houston Center, Suite 2000 · 909 Fannin Street · Houston, TX 77010-1018 · 713-276-7600

Robin C. Gibbs · ⑩ · Gibbs & Bruns · http://www.gibbs-bruns.com · 1100 Louisiana Street, Suite 5300 · Houston, TX 77002 · 713-650-8805

Mark K. Glasser · Baker Botts · http://www.bakerbotts.com · One Shell Plaza · 910 Louisiana Street · Houston, TX 77002-1210 · 713-229-1234

Thomas C. Godbold · Fulbright & Jaworski · http://www.fulbright.com · Fulbright Tower, Suite 5100 · 1301 McKinney Street · Houston, TX 77010-3095 · 713-651-5151

H. Lee Godfrey · ⑩ · Susman Godfrey · 1000 Louisiana, Suite 5100 · Houston, TX 77002-5096 · 713-651-9366

Richard E. Griffin · Jackson Walker · 1401 McKinney Street, Suite 1900 · Houston, TX 77010-4008 · 713-752-4200

David M. Gunn · Beck, Redden & Secrest · http://www.brsfirm.com · One Houston Center, Suite 4500 · 1221 McKinney Street · Houston, TX 77010-2010 · 713-951-3700

J. Clifford Gunter III · Bracewell & Giuliani · http://www.bgllp.com · 711 Louisiana Street, Suite 2300 · Houston, TX 77002-2770 · 713-223-2300

David T. Harvin · ㉕ · Vinson & Elkins · http://www.velaw.com · First City Tower, Suite 2500 · 1001 Fannin Street · Houston, TX 77002-6760 · 713-758-2222

Daniel K. Hedges · Porter & Hedges · 1000 Main Street, 36th Floor · Houston, TX 77002 · 713-226-0600

Joseph D. Jamail · ㉕ · Jamail & Kolius · 500 Dallas Street, Suite 3434 · Houston, TX 77002 · 713-651-3000

Philip J. John, Jr. · Baker Botts · http://www.bakerbotts.com · One Shell Plaza · 910 Louisiana Street · Houston, TX 77002-1210 · 713-229-1234

Frank G. Jones · ⑩ · Fulbright & Jaworski · http://www.fulbright.com · Fulbright Tower, Suite 5100 · 1301 McKinney Street · Houston, TX 77010-3095 · 713-651-5151

Richard L. Josephson · Baker Botts · http://www.bakerbotts.com · One Shell Plaza · 910 Louisiana Street Houston, TX 77002-1210 · 713-229-1234

William Edward Junell, Jr. · ⑩ · Schwartz, Junell, Greenberg & Oathout · 909 Fannin Street, Suite 2700 Houston, TX 77010 · 713-752-0017

Richard P. Keeton · ㉕ · Nickens Keeton Lawless Farrell Flack · 600 Travis Street, Suite 7500 · Houston, TX 77002 · 713-571-9191

Dana G. Kirk · The Kirk Law Firm · 4600 Post Oak Place, Suite 100 · Houston, TX 77027 · 713-651-0050

Layne E. Kruse · Fulbright & Jaworski · http://www.fulbright.com · Fulbright Tower, Suite 5100 · 1301 McKinney Street · Houston, TX 77010-3095 · 713-651-5151

Lynne Liberato · Haynes and Boone · One Houston Center, Suite 2100 · 1221 McKinney Street · Houston, TX 77010 · 713-547-2000

William P. Maines · Fulbright & Jaworski · http://www.fulbright.com · Fulbright Tower, Suite 5100 · 1301 McKinney Street · Houston, TX 77010-3095 · 713-651-5151

James E. Maloney · Baker Botts · http://www.bakerbotts.com · One Shell Plaza · 910 Louisiana Street · Houston, TX 77002-1210 · 713-229-1234

Neal S. Manne · Susman Godfrey · 1000 Louisiana, Suite 5100 · Houston, TX 77002-5096 · 713-651-9366

William E. Matthews · ⑩ · Gardere Wynne Sewell · http://www.gardere.com · 1000 Louisiana, Suite 3400 Houston, TX 77002-5011 · 713-276-5500

Daniel M. McClure · Fulbright & Jaworski · http://www.fulbright.com · Fulbright Tower, Suite 5100 · 1301 McKinney Street · Houston, TX 77010-3095 · 713-651-5151

Andrew McCollam III · Andrew McCollam · 2777 Allen Parkway, Suite 977 · Houston, TX 77019 · 713-640-5020

D. Ferguson McNiel III · Vinson & Elkins · http://www.velaw.com · First City Tower, Suite 2500 · 1001 Fannin Street · Houston, TX 77002-6760 · 713-758-2222

Patrick W. Mizell · Vinson & Elkins · http://www.velaw.com · First City Tower, Suite 2500 · 1001 Fannin Street · Houston, TX 77002-6760 · 713-758-2222

H. Dixon Montague · Vinson & Elkins · http://www.velaw.com · First City Tower, Suite 2500 · 1001 Fannin Street · Houston, TX 77002-6760 · 713-758-2222

Dudley Oldham · Fulbright & Jaworski · http://www.fulbright.com · Fulbright Tower, Suite 5100 · 1301 McKinney Street · Houston, TX 77010-3095 · 713-651-5151

William R. Pakalka · Fulbright & Jaworski · http://www.fulbright.com · Fulbright Tower, Suite 5100 · 1301 McKinney Street · Houston, TX 77010-3095 · 713-651-5151

Kathy D. Patrick · Gibbs & Bruns · http://www.gibbs-bruns.com · 1100 Louisiana Street, Suite 5300 · Houston, TX 77002 · 713-650-8805

Gerard G. Pecht · Fulbright & Jaworski · http://www.fulbright.com · Fulbright Tower, Suite 5100 · 1301 McKinney Street · Houston, TX 77010-3095 · 713-651-5151

Michael W. Perrin · Bailey Perrin Bailey · The Lyric Centre, Suite 2100 · 440 Louisiana Street · Houston, TX 77002 · 713-425-7100

Barrett H. Reasoner · Gibbs & Bruns · http://www.gibbs-bruns.com · 1100 Louisiana Street, Suite 5300 · Houston, TX 77002 · 713-650-8805

Harry M. Reasoner · ㉕ · Vinson & Elkins · http://www.velaw.com · First City Tower, Suite 2500 · 1001 Fannin Street · Houston, TX 77002-6760 · 713-758-2222

James A. Reeder, Jr. · Vinson & Elkins · http://www.velaw.com · First City Tower, Suite 2500 · 1001 Fannin Street · Houston, TX 77002-6760 · 713-758-2222

Chris Reynolds · Gibbs & Bruns · http://www.gibbs-bruns.com · 1100 Louisiana Street, Suite 5300 · Houston, TX 77002 · 713-650-8805

Charles W. Schwartz · Skadden, Arps, Slate, Meagher & Flom · 1000 Louisiana, Suite 6800 · Houston, TX 77002 · 713-655-5100

Richard A. Schwartz · Schwartz, Junell, Greenberg & Oathout · 909 Fannin Street, Suite 2700 · Houston, TX 77010 · 713-752-0017

George W. Shepherd · Cruse, Scott, Henderson & Allen · 2777 Allen Parkway, Seventh Floor · Houston, TX 77019-2141 · 713-650-6600

J. Todd Shields · Fulbright & Jaworski · http://www.fulbright.com · Fulbright Tower, Suite 5100 · 1301 McKinney Street · Houston, TX 77010-3095 · 713-651-5151

Jonathan B. Shoebotham · Thompson & Knight · http://www.tklaw.com · 333 Clay Street, Suite 3300 · Houston, TX 77002 · 713-654-8111

William C. Slusser · ⑩ · Slusser Wilson & Partridge · 4720 Three Allen Center · 333 Clay Street · Houston, TX 77002 · 713-860-3300

Karl S. Stern · Vinson & Elkins · http://www.velaw.com · First City Tower, Suite 2500 · 1001 Fannin Street · Houston, TX 77002-6760 · 713-758-2222

Macey R. Stokes · Baker Botts · http://www.bakerbotts.com · One Shell Plaza · 910 Louisiana Street · Houston, TX 77002-1210 · 713-229-1234

Samuel E. Stubbs · Pillsbury Winthrop Shaw Pittman · http://www.pillsburylaw.com · Two Houston Center, Suite 2000 · 909 Fannin Street · Houston, TX 77010-1018 · 713-276-7600

Harry P. Susman · Susman Godfrey · 1000 Louisiana, Suite 5100 · Houston, TX 77002-5096 · 713-651-9366

Stephen D. Susman · ㉕ · Susman Godfrey · 1000 Louisiana, Suite 5100 · Houston, TX 77002-5096 · 713-651-9366

George Irvin Terrell · ⑳ · Baker Botts · http://www.bakerbotts.com · One Shell Plaza · 910 Louisiana Street · Houston, TX 77002-1210 · 713-229-1234

Mark L. D. Wawro · ⑩ · Susman Godfrey · 1000 Louisiana, Suite 5100 · Houston, TX 77002-5096 · 713-651-9366

Marie R. Yeates · Vinson & Elkins · http://www.velaw.com · First City Tower, Suite 2500 · 1001 Fannin Street · Houston, TX 77002-6760 · 713-758-2222

R. Paul Yetter · Yetter Warden & Coleman · http://www.yetterwarden.com · Two Houston Center, Suite 3600 · 909 Fannin Street · Houston, TX 77010 · 713-632-8000

Steven M. Zager · Akin Gump Strauss Hauer & Feld · 1111 Louisiana Street, 44th Floor · Houston, TX 77002-5200 · 713-220-5800

Johnson City

Robert Q. Keith · ⑩ · Keith & Weber · 112 North Nugent · P.O. Box 155 · Johnson City, TX 78636 · 830-825-2111

Kerrville

Richard C. Mosty · Law Offices of Richard C. Mosty · 222 Sidney Baker, Suite 400 · Kerrville, TX 78028-5983 · 830-792-7711

League City

Scott C. Krist · Krist Law Firm · http://www.kristlaw.com · Marina View Building, Suite 120 · 2600 South Shore Boulevard · League City, TX 77573 · 281-283-8500

Longview

S. Calvin Capshaw · Capshaw DeRieux · The Energy Centre, Suite 220 · Longview, TX 75601-5157 · 903-236-9800

Midland

Barry N. Beck · Cotton, Bledsoe, Tighe & Dawson · 500 West Illinois Street, Suite 300 · P.O. Box 2776 · Midland, TX 79702-5782 · 432-684-5782

Harold L. Hensley, Jr. · (20) · Hinkle, Hensley, Shanor & Martin · 550 West Texas Avenue, Suite 1200 · P.O. Box 3580 · Midland, TX 79702 · 432-683-4691

San Angelo

Donald W. Griffis · Jackson Walker · 301 West Beauregard Avenue, Suite 200 · San Angelo, TX 76903 · 325-481-2550

San Antonio

Stephen P. Allison · Haynes and Boone · 112 East Pecan Street, Suite 900 · San Antonio, TX 78205-1540 210-978-7000

Emerson Banack, Jr. · (10) · Langley & Banack · Trinity Plaza II, Suite 900 · 745 East Mulberry Avenue · San Antonio, TX 78212-3166 · 210-736-6600

Kevin Michael Beiter · (10) · Hornberger Sheehan Fuller & Beiter · Quarry Heights, Suite 300 · 7373 Broadway · San Antonio, TX 78209 · 210-271-1700

Richard M. Butler · Langley & Banack · Trinity Plaza II, Suite 900 · 745 East Mulberry Avenue · San Antonio, TX 78212-3166 · 210-736-6600

Ricardo G. Cedillo · Davis, Cedillo & Mendoza · McCombs Plaza, Suite 500 · 755 East Mulberry Avenue San Antonio, TX 78212 · 210-822-6666

Barry A. Chasnoff · Akin Gump Strauss Hauer & Feld · 300 Convent Street, Suite 1500 · San Antonio, TX 78205-3732 · 210-281-7000

Richard C. Danysh · Bracewell & Giuliani · http://www.bgllp.com · One Alamo Center, Suite 800 · 106 South St. Mary's Street · San Antonio, TX 78205-3603 · 210-226-1166

Dean V. Fleming · Fulbright & Jaworski · http://www.fulbright.com · 300 Convent Street, Suite 2200 · San Antonio, TX 78205-3792 · 210-224-5575

W. Wendell Hall · Fulbright & Jaworski · http://www.fulbright.com · 300 Convent Street, Suite 2200 · San Antonio, TX 78205-3792 · 210-224-5575

John Alex Huddleston · Strasburger & Price · http://www.strasburger.com · 300 Convent Street, Suite 900 · San Antonio, TX 78205-3715 · 210-250-6000

Lamont A. Jefferson · Haynes and Boone · 112 East Pecan Street, Suite 900 · San Antonio, TX 78205-1540 · 210-978-7000

Andrew L. Kerr · Strasburger & Price · http://www.strasburger.com · 300 Convent Street, Suite 900 · San Antonio, TX 78205-3715 · 210-250-6000

Daniel McNeel Lane, Jr. · Akin Gump Strauss Hauer & Feld · 300 Convent Street, Suite 1500 · San Antonio, TX 78205-3732 · 210-281-7000

R. Laurence Macon · Akin Gump Strauss Hauer & Feld · 300 Convent Street, Suite 1500 · San Antonio, TX 78205-3732 · 210-281-7000

Linda S. McDonald · Langley & Banack · Trinity Plaza II, Suite 900 · 745 East Mulberry Avenue · San Antonio, TX 78212-3166 · 210-736-6600

Joyce W. Moore · Langley & Banack · Trinity Plaza II, Suite 900 · 745 East Mulberry Avenue · San Antonio, TX 78212-3166 · 210-736-6600

Robert G. Newman · Fulbright & Jaworski · http://www.fulbright.com · 300 Convent Street, Suite 2200 · San Antonio, TX 78205-3792 · 210-224-5575

Howard P. Newton · Cox Smith Matthews · http://www.coxsmith.com · 112 East Pecan Street, Suite 1800 San Antonio, TX 78205-1521 · 210-554-5500

John M. Pinckney III · Strasburger & Price · http://www.strasburger.com · 300 Convent Street, Suite 900 San Antonio, TX 78205-3715 · 210-250-6000

Marvin G. Pipkin · Pipkin, Oliver & Bradley · 1020 Northeast Loop 410, Suite 810 · San Antonio, TX 78209 · 210-820-0082

Allen Lewin Plunkett · ⑩ · Plunkett & Gibson · http://www.plunkett-gibson.com · 70 Northeast Loop 410, Suite 1100 · San Antonio, TX 78216 · 210-734-7092

David M. Prichard · Prichard, Hawkins, McFarland and Young · http://www.phmy.com · Union Square, Suite 600 · 10101 Reunion Place · San Antonio, TX 78216 · 210-477-7400

Ricardo R. Reyna · Brock Person Guerra Reyna · 1506 Bexar Crossing · San Antonio, TX 78232-1587 · 210-979-0100

Brett W. Schouest · Cox Smith Matthews · http://www.coxsmith.com · 112 East Pecan Street, Suite 1800 San Antonio, TX 78205-1521 · 210-554-5500

Barry Snell · Bayne, Snell & Krause · 8626 Tesoro Drive, Suite 500 · San Antonio, TX 78217 · 210-824-3278

Luther H. Soules III · Soules & Wallace · P.O. Box 15588 · San Antonio, TX 78212 · 210-224-9144

George H. Spencer, Jr. · ⑩ · Clemens & Spencer · http://www.clemens-spencer.com · 1300 Weston Centre · 112 East Pecan Street · San Antonio, TX 78205-1517 · 210-227-7121

John W. Weber, Jr. · Fulbright & Jaworski · http://www.fulbright.com · 300 Convent Street, Suite 2200 · San Antonio, TX 78205-3792 · 210-224-5575

Texarkana

Jennifer Haltom Doan · Haltom & Doan · Crown Executive Plaza, Suite 1-A · 6500 North Summerhill Road · Texarkana, TX 75505-6227 · 903-255-1000

James N. Haltom · Haltom & Doan · Crown Executive Plaza, Suite 1-A · 6500 North Summerhill Road · Texarkana, TX 75505-6227 · 903-255-1000

Nicholas H. Patton · ⑩ · Patton, Tidwell & Schroeder · 4605 Texas Boulevard · P.O. Box 5398 · Texarkana, TX 75505-5398 · 903-792-7080

Damon Young · ⑩ · Young, Pickett & Lee · 4122 Texas Boulevard · P.O. Box 1897 · Texarkana, TX 75504 · 903-794-1303

Tyler

Otis W. Carroll · Ireland Carroll & Kelley · 6101 South Broadway, Suite 500 · Tyler, TX 75703 · 903-561-1600

Wichita Falls

Lonny D. Morrison · Morrison & Shelton · City National Building, Suite 400 · 807 Eighth Street · Wichita Falls, TX 76301 · 940-322-2929

COMMUNICATIONS LAW

Austin

James W. Checkley, Jr. · Locke Lord Bissell & Liddell · 100 Congress Avenue, Suite 300 · Austin, TX 78701-4042 · 512-305-4785

Joseph Alan Holman · ⑩ · Locke Lord Bissell & Liddell · 100 Congress Avenue, Suite 300 · Austin, TX 78701-4042 · 512-305-4785

Philip F. Ricketts · ⑩ · Bracewell & Giuliani · http://www.bgllp.com · 111 Congress Avenue, Suite 2300 · Austin, TX 78701 · 512-472-7800

Dallas

Van H. Beckwith · Baker Botts · http://www.bakerbotts.com · Trammell Crow Center, Suite 600 · 2001 Ross Avenue · Dallas, TX 75201-2980 · 214-953-6500

Bryant C. Boren, Jr. · Baker Botts · http://www.bakerbotts.com · Trammell Crow Center, Suite 600 · 2001 Ross Avenue · Dallas, TX 75201-2980 · 214-953-6500

Don J. McDermett, Jr. · Baker Botts · http://www.bakerbotts.com · Trammell Crow Center, Suite 600 · 2001 Ross Avenue · Dallas, TX 75201-2980 · 214-953-6500

Peter Vogel · Gardere Wynne Sewell · http://www.gardere.com · 1601 Elm Street, Suite 3000 · Dallas, TX 75201 · 214-999-3000

CONSTRUCTION LAW

Arlington

Donald O. Pratt · Pratt & Yungblut · 2221 East Lamar Boulevard, Suite 150 · Arlington, TX 76006 · 817-633-2200

Patrick J. Wielinski · Cokinos, Bosien & Young · 2221 East Lamar, Suite 750 · Arlington, TX 76006 · 817-635-3600

Stephen K. Yungblut · Pratt & Yungblut · 2221 East Lamar Boulevard, Suite 150 · Arlington, TX 76006 · 817-633-2200

Austin

William R. Allensworth · ⑩ · Allensworth & Porter · 620 Congress Avenue, Suite 100 · Austin, TX 78701 512-708-1250

George C. Baldwin · Ford Nassen & Baldwin · 98 San Jacinto Boulevard, Suite 1450 · Austin, TX 78701 · 512-236-0009

Robert C. Bass, Jr. · Winstead · http://www.winstead.com · 401 Congress Avenue, Suite 2100 · Austin, TX 78701 · 512-370-2800

Ann Y. Riddel · Ann Y. Riddel · 703 Spofford Street · P.O. Box 1912 · Austin, TX 78767-1912 · 512-478-2588

Lee H. Shidlofsky · Visser Shidlofsky · Greystone Plaza, Suite 430 · 7200 North Mopac Expressway · Austin, TX 78731 · 512-795-0600

Dallas

Michael F. Albers · Hunton & Williams · 1445 Ross Avenue, Suite 3700 · Dallas, TX 75202-2799 · 214-979-3000

Joseph F. Canterbury, Jr. · Canterbury, Stuber, Elder, Gooch & Surratt · Occidental Tower, Suite 1000 · 5005 LBJ Freeway · Dallas, TX 75244 · 972-239-7493

Hollye C. Fisk · Fisk & Fielder · 400 Tower North · 2710 North Stemmons Freeway · Dallas, TX 75207 · 214-638-3744

Jeffrey A. Ford · Ford Nassen & Baldwin · 8080 North Central Expressway, Suite 1600 · Dallas, TX 75206-1819 · 214-523-5100

W. Kyle Gooch · Canterbury, Stuber, Elder, Gooch & Surratt · Occidental Tower, Suite 1000 · 5005 LBJ Freeway · Dallas, TX 75244 · 972-239-7493

Robert L. Meyers III · Ford Nassen & Baldwin · 8080 North Central Expressway, Suite 1600 · Dallas, TX 75206-1819 · 214-523-5100

Michelle I. Rieger · Winstead · http://www.winstead.com · Renaissance Tower, Suite 5400 · 1201 Elm Street · Dallas, TX 75270-2199 · 214-745-5400

Thomas Alan Shiels · Matthews, Stein, Shiels, Pearce, Knott, Eden & Davis · 8131 LBJ Freeway, Suite 700 · Dallas, TX 75251 · 972-234-3400

William B. Short, Jr. · Coats, Rose, Yale, Ryman & Lee · 5420 Lyndon B. Johnson Freeway, Suite 1300 · Dallas, TX 75240 · 972-982-8450

Paul B. Underkofler · Goins, Underkofler, Crawford & Langdon · Renaissance Tower, Suite 4800 · 1201 Elm Street · Dallas, TX 75270 · 214-969-5454

Fred D. Wilshusen · Thomas, Feldman & Wilshusen · 9400 NCX Tower, Suite 900 · 9400 North Central Expressway · Dallas, TX 75231-5027 · 214-369-3008

Fort Worth

Richard W. Wiseman · Brown, Dean, Wiseman, Liser, Proctor & Hart · Fort Worth Club Building, Suite 200 · 306 West Seventh Street · Fort Worth, TX 76102-4905 · 817-332-1391

William K. Andrews · Andrews Myers Coulter & Cohen · 3900 Essex Lane, Suite 800 · Houston, TX 77027 · 713-850-4200

John P. Cahill, Jr. · Hays, McConn, Rice & Pickering · http://www.haysmcconn.com · 1233 West Loop South, Suite 1000 · Houston, TX 77027 · 713-752-8300

William M. Coats · Coats, Rose, Yale, Ryman & Lee · Three Greenway Plaza, Suite 2000 · Houston, TX 77046 · 713-651-0111

Eric M. Cohen · Andrews Myers Coulter & Cohen · 3900 Essex Lane, Suite 800 · Houston, TX 77027 · 713-850-4200

Gregory M. Cokinos · Cokinos, Bosien & Young · Four Houston Center, 16th Floor · 1221 Lamar · Houston, TX 77010 · 713-535-5500

Keith E. Coulter · Andrews Myers Coulter & Cohen · 3900 Essex Lane, Suite 800 · Houston, TX 77027 · 713-850-4200

William W. Davidson · Andrews Myers Coulter & Cohen · 3900 Essex Lane, Suite 800 · Houston, TX 77027 · 713-850-4200

Linda Dieken Emery · Andrews Myers Coulter & Cohen · 3900 Essex Lane, Suite 800 · Houston, TX 77027 · 713-850-4200

Richard P. Flake · Cokinos, Bosien & Young · Four Houston Center, 16th Floor · 1221 Lamar · Houston, TX 77010 · 713-535-5500

Mark Guthrie · Winstead · http://www.winstead.com · JPMorgan Chase Tower, Suite 1100 · 600 Travis Street · Houston, TX 77002 · 713-650-8400

Charles S. Kelley · Mayer Brown · Bank of America Center, Suite 3400 · 700 Louisiana Street · Houston, TX 77002-2730 · 713-238-3000

William K. Luyties · Lorance & Thompson · http://www.lorancethompson.com · 2900 North Loop West, Suite 500 · Houston, TX 77092 · 713-868-5560

D. Ferguson McNiel III · Vinson & Elkins · http://www.velaw.com · First City Tower, Suite 2500 · 1001 Fannin Street · Houston, TX 77002-6760 · 713-758-2222

Bruce W. Merwin · ⑩ · Haynes and Boone · One Houston Center, Suite 2100 · 1221 McKinney Street · Houston, TX 77010 · 713-547-2000

Thomas W. Myers · Andrews Myers Coulter & Cohen · 3900 Essex Lane, Suite 800 · Houston, TX 77027 · 713-850-4200

David D. Peden · Porter & Hedges · 1000 Main Street, 36th Floor · Houston, TX 77002 · 713-226-0600

Michael T. Powell · Haynes and Boone · One Houston Center, Suite 2100 · 1221 McKinney Street · Houston, TX 77010 · 713-547-2000

Allison J. Snyder · Porter & Hedges · 1000 Main Street, 36th Floor · Houston, TX 77002 · 713-226-0600

William Jason Walker · Andrews Myers Coulter & Cohen · 3900 Essex Lane, Suite 800 · Houston, TX 77027 · 713-850-4200

D. Gibson Walton · Vinson & Elkins · http://www.velaw.com · First City Tower, Suite 2500 · 1001 Fannin Street · Houston, TX 77002-6760 · 713-758-2222

William B. Westcott · Andrews Myers Coulter & Cohen · 3900 Essex Lane, Suite 800 · Houston, TX 77027 · 713-850-4200

League City

Thomas R. Barber · Coats, Rose, Yale, Ryman & Lee · 2600 South Shore Boulevard, Suite 200 · League City, TX 77573 · 713-651-0111

Barry S. Rabon · Coats, Rose, Yale, Ryman & Lee · 2600 South Shore Boulevard, Suite 200 · League City, TX 77573 · 713-651-0111

McAllen

Robert L. Guerra · Thornton, Biechlin, Segrato, Reynolds & Guerra · 418 East Dove Avenue · McAllen, TX 78504 · 956-630-3080

San Antonio

John Alex Huddleston · Strasburger & Price · http://www.strasburger.com · 300 Convent Street, Suite 900 · San Antonio, TX 78205-3715 · 210-250-6000

Allen Lewin Plunkett · ⑩ · Plunkett & Gibson · http://www.plunkett-gibson.com · 70 Northeast Loop 410, Suite 1100 · San Antonio, TX 78216 · 210-734-7092

William W. Sommers · The Gardiner Law Firm · 745 East Mulberry Avenue, Suite 500 · San Antonio, TX 78212-3154 · 210-733-8191

Edward F. Valdespino · Strasburger & Price · http://www.strasburger.com · 300 Convent Street, Suite 900 · San Antonio, TX 78205-3715 · 210-250-6000

John W. Weber, Jr. · Fulbright & Jaworski · http://www.fulbright.com · 300 Convent Street, Suite 2200 · San Antonio, TX 78205-3792 · 210-224-5575

CORPORATE GOVERNANCE AND COMPLIANCE LAW

Dallas

Michael M. Boone · ⑳ · Haynes and Boone · 901 Main Street, Suite 3100 · Dallas, TX 75202 · 214-651-5000

Bruce A. Cheatham · Bracewell & Giuliani · http://www.bgllp.com · 1445 Ross Avenue, Suite 3800 · Dallas, TX 75202-2711 · 214-468-3800

Steven K. Cochran · ㉕ · Thompson & Knight · http://www.tklaw.com · One Arts Plaza, Suite 1500 · 1722 Routh Street · Dallas, TX 75201-2533 · 214-969-1700

Byron F. Egan · ⑩ · Jackson Walker · Bank of America Plaza, Suite 6000 · 901 Main Street · Dallas, TX 75202 · 214-953-6000

James R. Griffin · Fulbright & Jaworski · http://www.fulbright.com · 2200 Ross Avenue, Suite 2800 · Dallas, TX 75201 · 214-855-8000

Michael A. Saslaw · Weil Gotshal & Manges · 200 Crescent Court, Suite 300 · Dallas, TX 75201 · 214-746-7700

Larry L. Schoenbrun · ㉕ · Gardere Wynne Sewell · http://www.gardere.com · 1601 Elm Street, Suite 3000 · Dallas, TX 75201 · 214-999-3000

Jim A. Watson · ⑳ · Carrington, Coleman, Sloman & Blumenthal · 901 Main Street, Suite 5500 · Dallas, TX 75202 · 214-855-3000

Michael D. Wortley · ⑩ · Vinson & Elkins · http://www.velaw.com · Trammell Crow Center, Suite 3700 · 2001 Ross Avenue · Dallas, TX 75201-2975 · 214-220-7700

Fletcher L. Yarbrough · ㉕ · Carrington, Coleman, Sloman & Blumenthal · 901 Main Street, Suite 5500 · Dallas, TX 75202 · 214-855-3000

Houston

James A. Baker III · Baker Botts · http://www.bakerbotts.com · One Shell Plaza · 910 Louisiana Street · Houston, TX 77002-1210 · 713-229-1234

Joseph A. Cialone II · ⑳ · Baker Botts · http://www.bakerbotts.com · One Shell Plaza · 910 Louisiana Street · Houston, TX 77002-1210 · 713-229-1234

Michael W. Conlon · Fulbright & Jaworski · http://www.fulbright.com · Fulbright Tower, Suite 5100 · 1301 McKinney Street · Houston, TX 77010-3095 · 713-651-5151

Tull R. Florey · Baker Botts · http://www.bakerbotts.com · One Shell Plaza · 910 Louisiana Street · Houston, TX 77002-1210 · 713-229-1234

Marc H. Folladori · Mayer Brown · Bank of America Center, Suite 3400 · 700 Louisiana Street · Houston, TX 77002-2730 · 713-238-3000

Ricardo Garcia-Moreno · Haynes and Boone · One Houston Center, Suite 2100 · 1221 McKinney Street · Houston, TX 77010 · 713-547-2000

Charles E. Harrell · Duane Morris · 3200 Southwest Freeway, Suite 3150 · Houston, TX 77027-7534 · 713-402-3916

Robert S. Harrell · ⑩ · Fulbright & Jaworski · http://www.fulbright.com · Fulbright Tower, Suite 5100 · 1301 McKinney Street · Houston, TX 77010-3095 · 713-651-5151

C. Michael Harrington · ⑩ · Vinson & Elkins · http://www.velaw.com · First City Tower, Suite 2500 · 1001 Fannin Street · Houston, TX 77002-6760 · 713-758-2222

Peggy A. Heeg · Fulbright & Jaworski · http://www.fulbright.com · Fulbright Tower, Suite 5100 · 1301 McKinney Street · Houston, TX 77010-3095 · 713-651-5151

T. Mark Kelly · ⑩ · Vinson & Elkins · http://www.velaw.com · First City Tower, Suite 2500 · 1001 Fannin Street · Houston, TX 77002-6760 · 713-758-2222

J. David Kirkland, Jr. · Baker Botts · http://www.bakerbotts.com · One Shell Plaza · 910 Louisiana Street Houston, TX 77002-1210 · 713-229-1234

Geoffrey A. Long · Bracewell & Giuliani · http://www.bgllp.com · 711 Louisiana Street, Suite 2300 · Houston, TX 77002-2770 · 713-223-2300

Edgar J. Marston III · ⑩ · Bracewell & Giuliani · http://www.bgllp.com · 711 Louisiana Street, Suite 2300 Houston, TX 77002-2770 · 713-223-2300

Stephen A. Massad · ⑳ · Baker Botts · http://www.bakerbotts.com · One Shell Plaza · 910 Louisiana Street · Houston, TX 77002-1210 · 713-229-1234

Gene J. Oshman · Baker Botts · http://www.bakerbotts.com · One Shell Plaza · 910 Louisiana Street · Houston, TX 77002-1210 · 713-229-1234

Theodore W. Paris · Baker Botts · http://www.bakerbotts.com · One Shell Plaza · 910 Louisiana Street · Houston, TX 77002-1210 · 713-229-1234

Dallas Robert Parker · ㉕ · Thompson & Knight · http://www.tklaw.com · 333 Clay Street, Suite 3300 · Houston, TX 77002 · 713-654-8111

Gerard G. Pecht · Fulbright & Jaworski · http://www.fulbright.com · Fulbright Tower, Suite 5100 · 1301 McKinney Street · Houston, TX 77010-3095 · 713-651-5151

T. William Porter III · ㉕ · Porter & Hedges · 1000 Main Street, 36th Floor · Houston, TX 77002 · 713-226-0600

Arthur H. Rogers III · ㉕ · Fulbright & Jaworski · http://www.fulbright.com · Fulbright Tower, Suite 5100 · 1301 McKinney Street · Houston, TX 77010-3095 · 713-651-5151

Walter J. Smith · ⑩ · Baker Botts · http://www.bakerbotts.com · One Shell Plaza · 910 Louisiana Street · Houston, TX 77002-1210 · 713-229-1234

Charles H. Still, Jr. · Bracewell & Giuliani · http://www.bgllp.com · 711 Louisiana Street, Suite 2300 · Houston, TX 77002-2770 · 713-223-2300

Charles H. Still, Sr. · ㉕ · Kelly, Hart & Hallman · Wells Fargo Plaza, Suite 4700 · 1000 Louisiana Street · Houston, TX 77002 · 713-654-4600

R. Joel Swanson · ㉕ · Baker Botts · http://www.bakerbotts.com · One Shell Plaza · 910 Louisiana Street · Houston, TX 77002-1210 · 713-229-1234

Charles C. Szalkowski · ⑩ · Baker Botts · http://www.bakerbotts.com · One Shell Plaza · 910 Louisiana Street · Houston, TX 77002-1210 · 713-229-1234

The Woodlands

Jeffrey R. Harder · Winstead · http://www.winstead.com · 24 Waterway Avenue, Suite 500 · The Woodlands, TX 77380 · 281-681-5900

R. Clyde Parker, Jr. · Winstead · http://www.winstead.com · 24 Waterway Avenue, Suite 500 · The Woodlands, TX 77380 · 281-681-5900

CORPORATE LAW

Austin

Karen J. Bartoletti · ⑳ · Graves, Dougherty, Hearon & Moody · http://www.gdhm.com · 401 Congress Avenue, Suite 2200 · P.O. Box 98 · Austin, TX 78767-0098 · 512-480-5600

Mike Bengston · Baker Botts · http://www.bakerbotts.com · 1500 San Jacinto Center · 98 San Jacinto Boulevard · Austin, TX 78701-4039 · 512-322-2500

Diana K. Borden · Graves, Dougherty, Hearon & Moody · http://www.gdhm.com · 401 Congress Avenue, Suite 2200 · P.O. Box 98 · Austin, TX 78767-0098 · 512-480-5600

W. Amon Burton, Jr. · ㉕ · W. Amon Burton, Jr. · 1306 Guadalupe Street · Austin, TX 78701-1629 · 512-473-8903

C. Joseph Cain · ⑩ · Clark, Thomas & Winters · 300 West Sixth Street, 15th Floor · P.O. Box 1148 · Austin, TX 78767 · 512-472-8800

J. Rowland Cook · ⑳ · Winstead · http://www.winstead.com · 401 Congress Avenue, Suite 2100 · Austin, TX 78701 · 512-370-2800

Michael L. Cook · ㉕ · Winstead · http://www.winstead.com · 401 Congress Avenue, Suite 2100 · Austin, TX 78701 · 512-370-2800

Rod Edens, Jr. · ㉕ · Graves, Dougherty, Hearon & Moody · http://www.gdhm.com · 401 Congress Avenue, Suite 2200 · P.O. Box 98 · Austin, TX 78767-0098 · 512-480-5600

Brian P. Fenske · Fulbright & Jaworski · http://www.fulbright.com · 600 Congress Avenue, Suite 2400 · Austin, TX 78701-2978 · 512-474-5201

J. Nixon Fox III · Vinson & Elkins · http://www.velaw.com · 2801 Via Fortuna, Suite 100 · Austin, TX 78746-7568 · 512-542-8400

John E. Gangstad · ⑳ · Bickerstaff, Heath, Delgado & Acosta · 816 Congress Avenue, Suite 1700 · Austin, TX 78701-2443 · 512-472-8021

John J. Gilluly III · DLA Piper · 1221 South MoPac Expressway, Suite 400 · Austin, TX 78746-7650 · 512-457-7000

Paul Michael Hebert · ⑳ · Paul Michael Hebert · 1301 West 25th Street, Suite 545 · Austin, TX 78705-4236 · 512-476-2884

Robert Clarke Heidrick, Jr. · ⑩ · Graves, Dougherty, Hearon & Moody · http://www.gdhm.com · 401 Congress Avenue, Suite 2200 · P.O. Box 98 · Austin, TX 78767-0098 · 512-480-5600

James M. Laughead · Graves, Dougherty, Hearon & Moody · http://www.gdhm.com · 401 Congress Avenue, Suite 2200 · P.O. Box 98 · Austin, TX 78767-0098 · 512-480-5600

J. Kathryn Lindauer · ⑩ · Winstead · http://www.winstead.com · 401 Congress Avenue, Suite 2100 · Austin, TX 78701 · 512-370-2800

L. Frank Oliver · ⑳ · Oliver & Oliver · 100 Congress Avenue, Suite 2100 · P.O. Box 489 · Austin, TX 78767-0489 · 512-370-4050

William Pollard · William Pollard · 800 Rio Grande Street · Austin, TX 78701 · 512-474-1554

Phillip M. Slinkard · K&L Gates · 111 Congress Avenue, Suite 900 · Austin, TX 78701 · 512-482-6800

Paul R. Tobias · Wilson Sonsini Goodrich & Rosati · Las Cimas IV, Fifth Floor · 900 South Capital of Texas Highway · Austin, TX 78746-5546 · 512-338-5400

William R. Volk · ㉕ · Vinson & Elkins · http://www.velaw.com · 2801 Via Fortuna, Suite 100 · Austin, TX 78746-7568 · 512-542-8400

Darrell R. Windham · ⑩ · Fulbright & Jaworski · http://www.fulbright.com · 600 Congress Avenue, Suite 2400 · Austin, TX 78701-2978 · 512-474-5201

Beaumont

Benny H. Hughes, Jr. · ⑩ · Orgain, Bell & Tucker · 470 Orleans Street · P.O. Box 1751 · Beaumont, TX 77704-1751 · 409-838-6412

Corpus Christi

Charles W. Thomasson · ⑳ · Gary, Thomasson, Hall & Marks · 615 North Upper Broadway, Suite 800 · P.O. Box 2888 · Corpus Christi, TX 78403-0033 · 361-884-1961

Craig Adams · Baker Botts · http://www.bakerbotts.com · Trammell Crow Center, Suite 600 · 2001 Ross Avenue · Dallas, TX 75201-2980 · 214-953-6500

Thomas G. Adler · Fulbright & Jaworski · http://www.fulbright.com · 2200 Ross Avenue, Suite 2800 · Dallas, TX 75201 · 214-855-8000

Andrew M. Baker · Baker Botts · http://www.bakerbotts.com · Trammell Crow Center, Suite 600 · 2001 Ross Avenue · Dallas, TX 75201-2980 · 214-953-6500

Bryan E. Bishop · Locke Lord Bissell & Liddell · 2200 Ross Avenue, Suite 2200 · Dallas, TX 75201-6776 · 214-740-8000

Alan J. Bogdanow · ⑩ · Vinson & Elkins · http://www.velaw.com · Trammell Crow Center, Suite 3700 · 2001 Ross Avenue · Dallas, TX 75201-2975 · 214-220-7700

Michael M. Boone · ⑳ · Haynes and Boone · 901 Main Street, Suite 3100 · Dallas, TX 75202 · 214-651-5000

Sam P. Burford, Jr. · ⑳ · Thompson & Knight · http://www.tklaw.com · One Arts Plaza, Suite 1500 · 1722 Routh Street · Dallas, TX 75201-2533 · 214-969-1700

Jeffrey A. Chapman · ⑩ · Vinson & Elkins · http://www.velaw.com · Trammell Crow Center, Suite 3700 · 2001 Ross Avenue · Dallas, TX 75201-2975 · 214-220-7700

Bruce A. Cheatham · Bracewell & Giuliani · http://www.bgllp.com · 1445 Ross Avenue, Suite 3800 · Dallas, TX 75202-2711 · 214-468-3800

Wilson Chu · Haynes and Boone · 901 Main Street, Suite 3100 · Dallas, TX 75202 · 214-651-5000

Steven K. Cochran · ㉕ · Thompson & Knight · http://www.tklaw.com · One Arts Plaza, Suite 1500 · 1722 Routh Street · Dallas, TX 75201-2533 · 214-969-1700

Harlan P. Cohen · Gibson, Dunn & Crutcher · 2100 McKinney Avenue, Suite 1100 · Dallas, TX 75201-7390 · 214-698-3100

R. Scott Cohen · Weil Gotshal & Manges · 200 Crescent Court, Suite 300 · Dallas, TX 75201 · 214-746-7700

George W. Coleman · ㉕ · George W. Coleman · 2626 Cole Avenue, Suite 400 · Dallas, TX 75204 · 214-668-5690

Ann Marie Cowdrey · Thompson & Knight · http://www.tklaw.com · One Arts Plaza, Suite 1500 · 1722 Routh Street · Dallas, TX 75201-2533 · 214-969-1700

Joseph Dannenmaier · Thompson & Knight · http://www.tklaw.com · One Arts Plaza, Suite 1500 · 1722 Routh Street · Dallas, TX 75201-2533 · 214-969-1700

Mark Early · Vinson & Elkins · http://www.velaw.com · Trammell Crow Center, Suite 3700 · 2001 Ross Avenue · Dallas, TX 75201-2975 · 214-220-7700

Byron F. Egan · ⑩ · Jackson Walker · Bank of America Plaza, Suite 6000 · 901 Main Street · Dallas, TX 75202 · 214-953-6000

Angela Fontana · Weil Gotshal & Manges · 200 Crescent Court, Suite 300 · Dallas, TX 75201 · 214-746-7700

D. Gilbert Friedlander · Weil Gotshal & Manges · 200 Crescent Court, Suite 300 · Dallas, TX 75201 · 214-746-7700

Henry Gilchrist · ㉕ · Hunton & Williams · 1445 Ross Avenue, Suite 3700 · Dallas, TX 75202-2799 · 214-979-3000

Lawrence E. Glasgow · Gardere Wynne Sewell · http://www.gardere.com · 1601 Elm Street, Suite 3000 · Dallas, TX 75201 · 214-999-3000

Carol Glendenning · Strasburger & Price · http://www.strasburger.com · 901 Main Street, Suite 4400 · Dallas, TX 75202-3794 · 214-651-4300

Don M. Glendenning · Locke Lord Bissell & Liddell · 2200 Ross Avenue, Suite 2200 · Dallas, TX 75201-6776 · 214-740-8000

Lawrence B. Goldstein · Gardere Wynne Sewell · http://www.gardere.com · 1601 Elm Street, Suite 3000 · Dallas, TX 75201 · 214-999-3000

Alan G. Harvey · Baker & McKenzie · 2300 Trammell Crow Center · 2001 Ross Avenue · Dallas, TX 75201 · 214-978-3000

William R. Hays III · Haynes and Boone · 901 Main Street, Suite 3100 · Dallas, TX 75202 · 214-651-5000

Glen James Hettinger · Fulbright & Jaworski · http://www.fulbright.com · 2200 Ross Avenue, Suite 2800 Dallas, TX 75201 · 214-855-8000

Jeffrey B. Hitt · Weil Gotshal & Manges · 200 Crescent Court, Suite 300 · Dallas, TX 75201 · 214-746-7700

Thomas William Hughes · Fulbright & Jaworski · http://www.fulbright.com · 2200 Ross Avenue, Suite 2800 · Dallas, TX 75201 · 214-855-8000

James L. Irish III · ⑳ · Thompson & Knight · http://www.tklaw.com · One Arts Plaza, Suite 1500 · 1722 Routh Street · Dallas, TX 75201-2533 · 214-969-1700

Robert L. Kimball · Vinson & Elkins · http://www.velaw.com · Trammell Crow Center, Suite 3700 · 2001 Ross Avenue · Dallas, TX 75201-2975 · 214-220-7700

Mary R. Korby · Weil Gotshal & Manges · 200 Crescent Court, Suite 300 · Dallas, TX 75201 · 214-746-7700

Neel Lemon · Baker Botts · http://www.bakerbotts.com · Trammell Crow Center, Suite 600 · 2001 Ross Avenue · Dallas, TX 75201-2980 · 214-953-6500

Larry Steven Leshin · ⑩ · Hunton & Williams · 1445 Ross Avenue, Suite 3700 · Dallas, TX 75202-2799 · 214-979-3000

Brian M. Lidji · Lidji & Dorey · 500 North Akard, Suite 3500 · Dallas, TX 75201 · 214-774-1200

Jack M. Little · ㉕ · Thompson & Knight · http://www.tklaw.com · One Arts Plaza, Suite 1500 · 1722 Routh Street · Dallas, TX 75201-2533 · 214-969-1700

Peter Alan Lodwick · Thompson & Knight · http://www.tklaw.com · One Arts Plaza, Suite 1500 · 1722 Routh Street · Dallas, TX 75201-2533 · 214-969-1700

David G. Luther, Jr. · K&L Gates · 1717 Main Street, Suite 2800 · Dallas, TX 75201 · 214-939-5500

Don J. McDermett, Jr. · Baker Botts · http://www.bakerbotts.com · Trammell Crow Center, Suite 600 · 2001 Ross Avenue · Dallas, TX 75201-2980 · 214-953-6500

John B. McKnight · Locke Lord Bissell & Liddell · 2200 Ross Avenue, Suite 2200 · Dallas, TX 75201-6776 · 214-740-8000

Rodney L. Moore · Vinson & Elkins · http://www.velaw.com · Trammell Crow Center, Suite 3700 · 2001 Ross Avenue · Dallas, TX 75201-2975 · 214-220-7700

Geoffrey L. Newton · Baker Botts · http://www.bakerbotts.com · Trammell Crow Center, Suite 600 · 2001 Ross Avenue · Dallas, TX 75201-2980 · 214-953-6500

A. Winston Oxley · Vinson & Elkins · http://www.velaw.com · Trammell Crow Center, Suite 3700 · 2001 Ross Avenue · Dallas, TX 75201-2975 · 214-220-7700

Alan J. Perkins · Gardere Wynne Sewell · http://www.gardere.com · 1601 Elm Street, Suite 3000 · Dallas, TX 75201 · 214-999-3000

Douglass M. Rayburn · Baker Botts · http://www.bakerbotts.com · Trammell Crow Center, Suite 600 · 2001 Ross Avenue · Dallas, TX 75201-2980 · 214-953-6500

Darrel A. Rice · ⑩ · Haynes and Boone · 901 Main Street, Suite 3100 · Dallas, TX 75202 · 214-651-5000

Daryl Bruce Robertson · Hunton & Williams · 1445 Ross Avenue, Suite 3700 · Dallas, TX 75202-2799 · 214-979-3000

James S. Ryan III · Jackson Walker · Bank of America Plaza, Suite 6000 · 901 Main Street · Dallas, TX 75202 · 214-953-6000

Gregory R. Samuel · Haynes and Boone · 901 Main Street, Suite 3100 · Dallas, TX 75202 · 214-651-5000

Robert Sarfatis · Gardere Wynne Sewell · http://www.gardere.com · 1601 Elm Street, Suite 3000 · Dallas, TX 75201 · 214-999-3000

Michael A. Saslaw · Weil Gotshal & Manges · 200 Crescent Court, Suite 300 · Dallas, TX 75201 · 214-746-7700

Larry L. Schoenbrun · ㉕ · Gardere Wynne Sewell · http://www.gardere.com · 1601 Elm Street, Suite 3000 · Dallas, TX 75201 · 214-999-3000

Sally A. Schreiber · Munsch Hardt Kopf & Harr · 3800 Lincoln Plaza · 500 North Akard Street · Dallas, TX 75201-6659 · 214-855-7500

Irwin F. Sentilles III · Gibson, Dunn & Crutcher · 2100 McKinney Avenue, Suite 1100 · Dallas, TX 75201-7390 · 214-698-3100

Janice V. Sharry · Haynes and Boone · 901 Main Street, Suite 3100 · Dallas, TX 75202 · 214-651-5000

Kenneth L. Stewart · Fulbright & Jaworski · http://www.fulbright.com · 2200 Ross Avenue, Suite 2800 · Dallas, TX 75201 · 214-855-8000

R. Jay Tabor · Weil Gotshal & Manges · 200 Crescent Court, Suite 300 · Dallas, TX 75201 · 214-746-7700

Richard A. Tulli · Gardere Wynne Sewell · http://www.gardere.com · 1601 Elm Street, Suite 3000 · Dallas, TX 75201 · 214-999-3000

Jim A. Watson · ⑳ · Carrington, Coleman, Sloman & Blumenthal · 901 Main Street, Suite 5500 · Dallas, TX 75202 · 214-855-3000

Glenn D. West · Weil Gotshal & Manges · 200 Crescent Court, Suite 300 · Dallas, TX 75201 · 214-746-7700

Michael D. Wortley · (10) · Vinson & Elkins · http://www.velaw.com · Trammell Crow Center, Suite 3700 · 2001 Ross Avenue · Dallas, TX 75201-2975 · 214-220-7700

Fletcher L. Yarbrough · (25) · Carrington, Coleman, Sloman & Blumenthal · 901 Main Street, Suite 5500 · Dallas, TX 75202 · 214-855-3000

Jeffrey A. Zlotky · Thompson & Knight · http://www.tklaw.com · One Arts Plaza, Suite 1500 · 1722 Routh Street · Dallas, TX 75201-2533 · 214-969-1700

El Paso

Marc P. Bernat · (10) · Gordon & Mott · 4695 North Mesa Street, Suite 100 · El Paso, TX 79912 · 915-545-1133

Bernard D. Felsen · Scott, Hulse, Marshall, Feuille, Finger & Thurmond · 1100 Chase Tower · 201 East Main Street · El Paso, TX 79901 · 915-533-2493

C. Michael Ginnings · (10) · Gordon & Mott · 4695 North Mesa Street, Suite 100 · El Paso, TX 79912 · 915-545-1133

Allan M. Goldfarb · Kemp Smith · http://www.kempsmith.com · 221 North Kansas, Suite 1700 · El Paso, TX 79901-1441 · 915-533-4424

Patrick R. Gordon · Gordon & Mott · 4695 North Mesa Street, Suite 100 · El Paso, TX 79912 · 915-545-1133

W. Dean Hester · (10) · Ainsa Hutson · 5809 Acacia Circle · El Paso, TX 79912 · 915-845-5300

G. Russell Hill · (10) · Scott, Hulse, Marshall, Feuille, Finger & Thurmond · 1100 Chase Tower · 201 East Main Street · El Paso, TX 79901 · 915-533-2493

Fort Worth

Brian D. Barnard · Haynes and Boone · 201 Main Street, Suite 2200 · Fort Worth, TX 76102 · 817-347-6600

F. Richard Bernasek · Kelly, Hart & Hallman · Wells Fargo Tower, Suite 2500 · 201 Main Street · Fort Worth, TX 76102 · 817-332-2500

William P. Hallman, Jr. · (10) · Kelly, Hart & Hallman · Wells Fargo Tower, Suite 2500 · 201 Main Street · Fort Worth, TX 76102 · 817-332-2500

Mark L. Hart, Jr. · (20) · Kelly, Hart & Hallman · Wells Fargo Tower, Suite 2500 · 201 Main Street · Fort Worth, TX 76102 · 817-332-2500

Dee J. Kelly, Sr. · (10) · Kelly, Hart & Hallman · Wells Fargo Tower, Suite 2500 · 201 Main Street · Fort Worth, TX 76102 · 817-332-2500

Sam Rosen · Shannon, Gracey, Ratliff & Miller · http://www.shannongracey.com · 777 Main Street, Suite 3800 · Fort Worth, TX 76102 · 817-336-9333

Highlands

M. Ann Newton · Newton Tech Law · P.O. Drawer E · Highlands, TX 77526 · 281-772-4907

John C. Ale · Skadden, Arps, Slate, Meagher & Flom · 1000 Louisiana, Suite 6800 · Houston, TX 77002 · 713-655-5100

Eric S. Anderson · 25 · Fulbright & Jaworski · http://www.fulbright.com · Fulbright Tower, Suite 5100 · 1301 McKinney Street · Houston, TX 77010-3095 · 713-651-5151

Kenneth M. Anderson · Vinson & Elkins · http://www.velaw.com · First City Tower, Suite 2500 · 1001 Fannin Street · Houston, TX 77002-6760 · 713-758-2222

Chris J. Arntzen · Baker Botts · http://www.bakerbotts.com · One Shell Plaza · 910 Louisiana Street · Houston, TX 77002-1210 · 713-229-1234

Marcia E. Backus · Vinson & Elkins · http://www.velaw.com · First City Tower, Suite 2500 · 1001 Fannin Street · Houston, TX 77002-6760 · 713-758-2222

Frank E. Bayouth · Skadden, Arps, Slate, Meagher & Flom · 1000 Louisiana, Suite 6800 · Houston, TX 77002 · 713-655-5100

A. T. Blackshear, Jr. · 25 · Fulbright & Jaworski · http://www.fulbright.com · Fulbright Tower, Suite 5100 · 1301 McKinney Street · Houston, TX 77010-3095 · 713-651-5151

Douglas S. Bland · 10 · Vinson & Elkins · http://www.velaw.com · First City Tower, Suite 2500 · 1001 Fannin Street · Houston, TX 77002-6760 · 713-758-2222

John L. Bland · 25 · Bracewell & Giuliani · http://www.bgllp.com · 711 Louisiana Street, Suite 2300 · Houston, TX 77002-2770 · 713-223-2300

John R. Brantley · Bracewell & Giuliani · http://www.bgllp.com · 711 Louisiana Street, Suite 2300 · Houston, TX 77002-2770 · 713-223-2300

Donald White Brodsky · Baker Hostetler · http://www.bakerlaw.com · 1000 Louisiana, Suite 2000 · Houston, TX 77002-5009 · 713-751-1600

David C. Buck · Andrews Kurth · http://www.andrewskurth.com · 600 Travis Street, Suite 4200 · Houston, TX 77002 · 713-220-4200

John T. Cabaniss · 25 · Andrews Kurth · http://www.andrewskurth.com · 600 Travis Street, Suite 4200 · Houston, TX 77002 · 713-220-4200

Richard H. Caldwell · 10 · Andrews Kurth · http://www.andrewskurth.com · 600 Travis Street, Suite 4200 Houston, TX 77002 · 713-220-4200

Joseph A. Cialone II · 20 · Baker Botts · http://www.bakerbotts.com · One Shell Plaza · 910 Louisiana Street · Houston, TX 77002-1210 · 713-229-1234

Nicole E. Clark · Vinson & Elkins · http://www.velaw.com · First City Tower, Suite 2500 · 1001 Fannin Street · Houston, TX 77002-6760 · 713-758-2222

Fielding B. Cochran III · Vinson & Elkins · http://www.velaw.com · First City Tower, Suite 2500 · 1001 Fannin Street · Houston, TX 77002-6760 · 713-758-2222

Randolph C. Coley · King & Spalding · 1100 Louisiana Street, Suite 4000 · Houston, TX 77002-5213 · 713-751-3200

Christopher S. Collins · Vinson & Elkins · http://www.velaw.com · First City Tower, Suite 2500 · 1001 Fannin Street · Houston, TX 77002-6760 · 713-758-2222

Michael W. Conlon · Fulbright & Jaworski · http://www.fulbright.com · Fulbright Tower, Suite 5100 · 1301 McKinney Street · Houston, TX 77010-3095 · 713-651-5151

John B. Connally IV · Vinson & Elkins · http://www.velaw.com · First City Tower, Suite 2500 · 1001 Fannin Street · Houston, TX 77002-6760 · 713-758-2222

Rufus P. Cormier, Jr. · ㉕ · Baker Botts · http://www.bakerbotts.com · One Shell Plaza · 910 Louisiana Street · Houston, TX 77002-1210 · 713-229-1234

Allen B. Craig III · Gardere Wynne Sewell · http://www.gardere.com · 1000 Louisiana, Suite 3400 · Houston, TX 77002-5011 · 713-276-5500

Joshua Davidson · Baker Botts · http://www.bakerbotts.com · One Shell Plaza · 910 Louisiana Street · Houston, TX 77002-1210 · 713-229-1234

Joseph C. Dilg · ⑩ · Vinson & Elkins · http://www.velaw.com · First City Tower, Suite 2500 · 1001 Fannin Street · Houston, TX 77002-6760 · 713-758-2222

Jeff C. Dodd · ⑩ · Andrews Kurth · http://www.andrewskurth.com · 600 Travis Street, Suite 4200 · Houston, TX 77002 · 713-220-4200

William N. Finnegan IV · Vinson & Elkins · http://www.velaw.com · First City Tower, Suite 2500 · 1001 Fannin Street · Houston, TX 77002-6760 · 713-758-2222

Tull R. Florey · Baker Botts · http://www.bakerbotts.com · One Shell Plaza · 910 Louisiana Street · Houston, TX 77002-1210 · 713-229-1234

Jeffery Burton Floyd · ⑩ · Vinson & Elkins · http://www.velaw.com · First City Tower, Suite 2500 · 1001 Fannin Street · Houston, TX 77002-6760 · 713-758-2222

Marc H. Folladori · Mayer Brown · Bank of America Center, Suite 3400 · 700 Louisiana Street · Houston, TX 77002-2730 · 713-238-3000

Frank T. Garcia · ⑳ · Fulbright & Jaworski · http://www.fulbright.com · Fulbright Tower, Suite 5100 · 1301 McKinney Street · Houston, TX 77010-3095 · 713-651-5151

Robert F. Gray, Jr. · ⑩ · Mayer Brown · Bank of America Center, Suite 3400 · 700 Louisiana Street · Houston, TX 77002-2730 · 713-238-3000

W. Garney Griggs · Strasburger & Price · http://www.strasburger.com · 1401 McKinney Street, Suite 2200 Houston, TX 77010-4035 · 713-951-5600

William D. Gutermuth · ⑩ · Bracewell & Giuliani · http://www.bgllp.com · 711 Louisiana Street, Suite 2300 · Houston, TX 77002-2770 · 713-223-2300

Charles E. Harrell · Duane Morris · 3200 Southwest Freeway, Suite 3150 · Houston, TX 77027-7534 · 713-402-3916

C. Michael Harrington · ⑩ · Vinson & Elkins · http://www.velaw.com · First City Tower, Suite 2500 · 1001 Fannin Street · Houston, TX 77002-6760 · 713-758-2222

William T. Heller IV · Thompson & Knight · http://www.tklaw.com · 333 Clay Street, Suite 3300 · Houston, TX 77002 · 713-654-8111

Rennae Henry · Baker Botts · http://www.bakerbotts.com · One Shell Plaza · 910 Louisiana Street · Houston, TX 77002-1210 · 713-229-1234

Michael P. Irvin · Fulbright & Jaworski · http://www.fulbright.com · Fulbright Tower, Suite 5100 · 1301 McKinney Street · Houston, TX 77010-3095 · 713-651-5151

Robert V. Jewell · Andrews Kurth · http://www.andrewskurth.com · 600 Travis Street, Suite 4200 · Houston, TX 77002 · 713-220-4200

Jay D. Kelley · Vinson & Elkins · http://www.velaw.com · First City Tower, Suite 2500 · 1001 Fannin Street · Houston, TX 77002-6760 · 713-758-2222

T. Mark Kelly · ⑩ · Vinson & Elkins · http://www.velaw.com · First City Tower, Suite 2500 · 1001 Fannin Street · Houston, TX 77002-6760 · 713-758-2222

David R. Keyes · ⑳ · Winstead · http://www.winstead.com · JPMorgan Chase Tower, Suite 1100 · 600 Travis Street · Houston, TX 77002 · 713-650-8400

J. David Kirkland, Jr. · Baker Botts · http://www.bakerbotts.com · One Shell Plaza · 910 Louisiana Street Houston, TX 77002-1210 · 713-229-1234

Jay T. Kolb · Baker Botts · http://www.bakerbotts.com · One Shell Plaza · 910 Louisiana Street · Houston, TX 77002-1210 · 713-229-1234

Christine B. LaFollette · Akin Gump Strauss Hauer & Feld · 1111 Louisiana Street, 44th Floor · Houston, TX 77002-5200 · 713-220-5800

Kevin Paul Lewis · Vinson & Elkins · http://www.velaw.com · First City Tower, Suite 2500 · 1001 Fannin Street · Houston, TX 77002-6760 · 713-758-2222

Edgar J. Marston III · ⑩ · Bracewell & Giuliani · http://www.bgllp.com · 711 Louisiana Street, Suite 2300 Houston, TX 77002-2770 · 713-223-2300

Stephen A. Massad · ⑳ · Baker Botts · http://www.bakerbotts.com · One Shell Plaza · 910 Louisiana Street · Houston, TX 77002-1210 · 713-229-1234

Douglas E. McWilliams · Vinson & Elkins · http://www.velaw.com · First City Tower, Suite 2500 · 1001 Fannin Street · Houston, TX 77002-6760 · 713-758-2222

Jeffrey S. Munoz · Vinson & Elkins · http://www.velaw.com · First City Tower, Suite 2500 · 1001 Fannin Street · Houston, TX 77002-6760 · 713-758-2222

Craig W. Murray · Vinson & Elkins · http://www.velaw.com · First City Tower, Suite 2500 · 1001 Fannin Street · Houston, TX 77002-6760 · 713-758-2222

Michael E. Niebruegge · Mayer Brown · Bank of America Center, Suite 3400 · 700 Louisiana Street · Houston, TX 77002-2730 · 713-238-3000

G. Michael O'Leary · Andrews Kurth · http://www.andrewskurth.com · 600 Travis Street, Suite 4200 · Houston, TX 77002 · 713-220-4200

David P. Oelman · Vinson & Elkins · http://www.velaw.com · First City Tower, Suite 2500 · 1001 Fannin Street · Houston, TX 77002-6760 · 713-758-2222

Gary W. Orloff · ⑩ · Bracewell & Giuliani · http://www.bgllp.com · 711 Louisiana Street, Suite 2300 · Houston, TX 77002-2770 · 713-223-2300

Gene J. Oshman · Baker Botts · http://www.bakerbotts.com · One Shell Plaza · 910 Louisiana Street · Houston, TX 77002-1210 · 713-229-1234

Theodore W. Paris · Baker Botts · http://www.bakerbotts.com · One Shell Plaza · 910 Louisiana Street · Houston, TX 77002-1210 · 713-229-1234

Dallas Robert Parker · ㉕ · Thompson & Knight · http://www.tklaw.com · 333 Clay Street, Suite 3300 · Houston, TX 77002 · 713-654-8111

Philip D. Peacock · ㉕ · Andrews Kurth · http://www.andrewskurth.com · 600 Travis Street, Suite 4200 · Houston, TX 77002 · 713-220-4200

David Stanley Peterman · Fulbright & Jaworski · http://www.fulbright.com · Fulbright Tower, Suite 5100 · 1301 McKinney Street · Houston, TX 77010-3095 · 713-651-5151

Felix P. Phillips, Jr. · Baker Botts · http://www.bakerbotts.com · One Shell Plaza · 910 Louisiana Street · Houston, TX 77002-1210 · 713-229-1234

Michael K. Pierce · Thompson & Knight · http://www.tklaw.com · 333 Clay Street, Suite 3300 · Houston, TX 77002 · 713-654-8111

Joe S. Poff · Baker Botts · http://www.bakerbotts.com · One Shell Plaza · 910 Louisiana Street · Houston, TX 77002-1210 · 713-229-1234

T. William Porter III · ㉕ · Porter & Hedges · 1000 Main Street, 36th Floor · Houston, TX 77002 · 713-226-0600

Charles D. Powell · Fulbright & Jaworski · http://www.fulbright.com · Fulbright Tower, Suite 5100 · 1301 McKinney Street · Houston, TX 77010-3095 · 713-651-5151

James M. Prince · Vinson & Elkins · http://www.velaw.com · First City Tower, Suite 2500 · 1001 Fannin Street · Houston, TX 77002-6760 · 713-758-2222

Frank M. Putman · ⑩ · Gardere Wynne Sewell · http://www.gardere.com · 1000 Louisiana, Suite 3400 · Houston, TX 77002-5011 · 713-276-5500

Robert R. Rabalais · Vinson & Elkins · http://www.velaw.com · First City Tower, Suite 2500 · 1001 Fannin Street · Houston, TX 77002-6760 · 713-758-2222

Robert G. Reedy · Porter & Hedges · 1000 Main Street, 36th Floor · Houston, TX 77002 · 713-226-0600

Bradley J. Richards · Haynes and Boone · One Houston Center, Suite 2100 · 1221 McKinney Street · Houston, TX 77010 · 713-547-2000

Arthur H. Rogers III · ㉕ · Fulbright & Jaworski · http://www.fulbright.com · Fulbright Tower, Suite 5100 · 1301 McKinney Street · Houston, TX 77010-3095 · 713-651-5151

Eddy J. Rogers, Jr. · ⑩ · Andrews Kurth · http://www.andrewskurth.com · 600 Travis Street, Suite 4200 · Houston, TX 77002 · 713-220-4200

David L. Ronn · Greenberg Traurig · http://www.gtlaw.com · 1000 Louisiana Street, Suite 1800 · Houston, TX 77002 · 713-374-3500

Kelly Brunetti Rose · Baker Botts · http://www.bakerbotts.com · One Shell Plaza · 910 Louisiana Street · Houston, TX 77002-1210 · 713-229-1234

Margo Sneller Scholin · Baker Botts · http://www.bakerbotts.com · One Shell Plaza · 910 Louisiana Street · Houston, TX 77002-1210 · 713-229-1234

Walter J. Smith · ⑩ · Baker Botts · http://www.bakerbotts.com · One Shell Plaza · 910 Louisiana Street · Houston, TX 77002-1210 · 713-229-1234

N. L. Stevens III · Gardere Wynne Sewell · http://www.gardere.com · 1000 Louisiana, Suite 3400 · Houston, TX 77002-5011 · 713-276-5500

Charles H. Still, Jr. · Bracewell & Giuliani · http://www.bgllp.com · 711 Louisiana Street, Suite 2300 · Houston, TX 77002-2770 · 713-223-2300

Charles H. Still, Sr. · ㉕ · Kelly, Hart & Hallman · Wells Fargo Plaza, Suite 4700 · 1000 Louisiana Street · Houston, TX 77002 · 713-654-4600

David Harry Stone · Vinson & Elkins · http://www.velaw.com · First City Tower, Suite 2500 · 1001 Fannin Street · Houston, TX 77002-6760 · 713-758-2222

Charles L. Strauss · Fulbright & Jaworski · http://www.fulbright.com · Fulbright Tower, Suite 5100 · 1301 McKinney Street · Houston, TX 77010-3095 · 713-651-5151

R. Joel Swanson · ㉕ · Baker Botts · http://www.bakerbotts.com · One Shell Plaza · 910 Louisiana Street · Houston, TX 77002-1210 · 713-229-1234

Charles C. Szalkowski · ⑩ · Baker Botts · http://www.bakerbotts.com · One Shell Plaza · 910 Louisiana Street · Houston, TX 77002-1210 · 713-229-1234

Darrell W. Taylor · Baker Botts · http://www.bakerbotts.com · One Shell Plaza · 910 Louisiana Street · Houston, TX 77002-1210 · 713-229-1234

Timothy S. Taylor · Baker Botts · http://www.bakerbotts.com · One Shell Plaza · 910 Louisiana Street · Houston, TX 77002-1210 · 713-229-1234

Michael S. Telle · Bracewell & Giuliani · http://www.bgllp.com · 711 Louisiana Street, Suite 2300 · Houston, TX 77002-2770 · 713-223-2300

Timothy J. Unger · Andrews Kurth · http://www.andrewskurth.com · 600 Travis Street, Suite 4200 · Houston, TX 77002 · 713-220-4200

John A. Watson · ㉕ · Fulbright & Jaworski · http://www.fulbright.com · Fulbright Tower, Suite 5100 · 1301 McKinney Street · Houston, TX 77010-3095 · 713-651-5151

Marcus A. Watts · Locke Lord Bissell & Liddell · JP Morgan Chase Tower, Suite 3400 · 600 Travis Street · Houston, TX 77002 · 713-226-1200

Fredric A. Weber · ⑩ · Fulbright & Jaworski · http://www.fulbright.com · Fulbright Tower, Suite 5100 · 1301 McKinney Street · Houston, TX 77010-3095 · 713-651-5151

Sanford A. Weiner · ㉕ · Vinson & Elkins · http://www.velaw.com · First City Tower, Suite 2500 · 1001 Fannin Street · Houston, TX 77002-6760 · 713-758-2222

Sean T. Wheeler · Baker Botts · http://www.bakerbotts.com · One Shell Plaza · 910 Louisiana Street · Houston, TX 77002-1210 · 713-229-1234

William W. Wiggins · Porter & Hedges · 1000 Main Street, 36th Floor · Houston, TX 77002 · 713-226-0600

R. Daniel Witschey, Jr. · ⑳ · Bracewell & Giuliani · http://www.bgllp.com · 711 Louisiana Street, Suite 2300 · Houston, TX 77002-2770 · 713-223-2300

Michael W. Wood · Akin Gump Strauss Hauer & Feld · 1111 Louisiana Street, 44th Floor · Houston, TX 77002-5200 · 713-220-5800

Scott Neal Wulfe · ⑩ · Vinson & Elkins · http://www.velaw.com · First City Tower, Suite 2500 · 1001 Fannin Street · Houston, TX 77002-6760 · 713-758-2222

Midland

James M. Alsup · Lynch, Chappell & Alsup · The Summit, Suite 700 · 300 North Marienfeld · Midland, TX 79701 · 432-683-3351

Dan G. LeRoy · Cotton, Bledsoe, Tighe & Dawson · 500 West Illinois Street, Suite 300 · P.O. Box 2776 · Midland, TX 79702-5782 · 432-684-5782

Russel W. Neisig · Bullock, Scott, Neisig, Morgan, Leeton & Strauss · 500 West Texas Avenue, Suite 700 Midland, TX 79701-4200 · 432-683-5501

San Antonio

T. Drew Cauthorn · ⑩ · Hornberger Sheehan Fuller & Beiter · Quarry Heights, Suite 300 · 7373 Broadway · San Antonio, TX 78209 · 210-271-1700

James M. Doyle, Jr. · Law Offices of James M. Doyle, Jr. · 111 West Olmos Drive · San Antonio, TX 78212 · 210-829-7183

John D. Fisch · Cox Smith Matthews · http://www.coxsmith.com · 112 East Pecan Street, Suite 1800 · San Antonio, TX 78205-1521 · 210-554-5500

Richard E. Goldsmith · ㉕ · Cox Smith Matthews · http://www.coxsmith.com · 112 East Pecan Street, Suite 1800 · San Antonio, TX 78205-1521 · 210-554-5500

Steven R. Jacobs · Jackson Walker · Weston Centre, Suite 2400 · 112 East Pecan Street · San Antonio, TX 78205 · 210-978-7700

Daryl L. Lansdale, Jr. · Fulbright & Jaworski · http://www.fulbright.com · 300 Convent Street, Suite 2200 · San Antonio, TX 78205-3792 · 210-224-5575

Bruce M. Mitchell · Oppenheimer, Blend, Harrison & Tate · 711 Navarro Street, Suite 600 · San Antonio, TX 78205-1796 · 210-224-2000

J. David Oppenheimer · ⑩ · Oppenheimer, Blend, Harrison & Tate · 711 Navarro Street, Suite 600 · San Antonio, TX 78205-1796 · 210-224-2000

Cecil Schenker · Cox Smith Matthews · http://www.coxsmith.com · 112 East Pecan Street, Suite 1800 · San Antonio, TX 78205-1521 · 210-554-5500

James B. Smith, Jr. · Cox Smith Matthews · http://www.coxsmith.com · 112 East Pecan Street, Suite 1800 · San Antonio, TX 78205-1521 · 210-554-5500

Patrick B. Tobin · Jackson Walker · Weston Centre, Suite 2400 · 112 East Pecan Street · San Antonio, TX 78205 · 210-978-7700

Dan G. Webster III · ⑳ · Cox Smith Matthews · http://www.coxsmith.com · 112 East Pecan Street, Suite 1800 · San Antonio, TX 78205-1521 · 210-554-5500

The Woodlands

R. Clyde Parker, Jr. · Winstead · http://www.winstead.com · 24 Waterway Avenue, Suite 500 · The Woodlands, TX 77380 · 281-681-5900

DERIVATIVES LAW

Austin

William F. Stutts · ⑩ · Baker Botts · http://www.bakerbotts.com · 1500 San Jacinto Center · 98 San Jacinto Boulevard · Austin, TX 78701-4039 · 512-322-2500

Dallas

Gayle A. Boone · Bracewell & Giuliani · http://www.bgllp.com · 1445 Ross Avenue, Suite 3800 · Dallas, TX 75202-2711 · 214-468-3800

George C. Lamb III · Baker Botts · http://www.bakerbotts.com · Trammell Crow Center, Suite 600 · 2001 Ross Avenue · Dallas, TX 75201-2980 · 214-953-6500

Timothy W. Mountz · Baker Botts · http://www.bakerbotts.com · Trammell Crow Center, Suite 600 · 2001 Ross Avenue · Dallas, TX 75201-2980 · 214-953-6500

Patricia J. Villareal · Jones Day · 2727 North Harwood Street · Dallas, TX 75201-1515 · 214-220-3939

Houston

Rhett G. Campbell · Thompson & Knight · http://www.tklaw.com · 333 Clay Street, Suite 3300 · Houston, TX 77002 · 713-654-8111

Craig R. Enochs · Jackson Walker · 1401 McKinney Street, Suite 1900 · Houston, TX 77010-4008 · 713-752-4200

Bill Hart, Jr. · Baker Botts · http://www.bakerbotts.com · One Shell Plaza · 910 Louisiana Street · Houston, TX 77002-1210 · 713-229-1234

Brandon Lobb · Locke Lord Bissell & Liddell · JP Morgan Chase Tower, Suite 3400 · 600 Travis Street · Houston, TX 77002 · 713-226-1200

Mark W. Miller · Locke Lord Bissell & Liddell · JP Morgan Chase Tower, Suite 3400 · 600 Travis Street Houston, TX 77002 · 713-226-1200

Chad E. Mills · Sutherland · http://www.sutherland.com · Two Houston Center, Suite 2200 · 909 Fannin · Houston, TX 77010-1043 · 713-470-6100

Robert R. Rabalais · Vinson & Elkins · http://www.velaw.com · First City Tower, Suite 2500 · 1001 Fannin Street · Houston, TX 77002-6760 · 713-758-2222

John S. Rainey · Greenberg Traurig · http://www.gtlaw.com · 1000 Louisiana Street, Suite 1800 · Houston, TX 77002 · 713-374-3500

Paris A. Theofanidis · Vinson & Elkins · http://www.velaw.com · First City Tower, Suite 2500 · 1001 Fannin Street · Houston, TX 77002-6760 · 713-758-2222

Paul B. Turner · Sutherland · http://www.sutherland.com · Two Houston Center, Suite 2200 · 909 Fannin Houston, TX 77010-1043 · 713-470-6100

Paul E. Vrana · Jackson Walker · 1401 McKinney Street, Suite 1900 · Houston, TX 77010-4008 · 713-752-4200

DUI/DWI DEFENSE

Houston

W. Troy McKinney · Schneider & McKinney · The Lyric Center, Suite 800 · 440 Louisiana · Houston, TX 77002 · 713-951-9994

J. Gary Trichter · Trichter & Murphy · The Historic Kirby Mansion · 2000 Smith Street · Houston, TX 77002 · 713-654-7007

San Antonio

Samuel H. Bayless · The Law Offices of Samuel Bayless · 441 Burr Road · San Antonio, TX 78205 · 210-253-7110

John F. Carroll · ⑩ · John F. Carroll · 111 West Olmos Drive · San Antonio, TX 78212 · 210-829-7183

George Scharmen · Law Offices of George A. Scharmen · 315 Dwyer Avenue · San Antonio, TX 78204 · 210-226-8021

Mark Stevens · ⑩ · Mark Stevens · Tower Life Building, Suite 1505 · 310 South St. Mary's Street · San Antonio, TX 78205 · 210-226-1433

EDUCATION LAW

Austin

Jefferson K. Brim · Brim, Arnett, Robinett, Hanner, Conners & McCormick · 2525 Wallingwood Drive, Building 14 · Austin, TX 78746 · 512-328-0048

Karl Tiger Hanner · Brim, Arnett, Robinett, Hanner, Conners & McCormick · 2525 Wallingwood Drive, Building 14 · Austin, TX 78746 · 512-328-0048

Jim Walsh · Walsh, Anderson, Brown, Schulze & Aldridge · Centennial Towers, Suite 500 · 505 East Huntland Drive · P.O. Box 2156 · Austin, TX 78768-2156 · 512-454-6864

Beaumont

Tanner T. Hunt, Jr. · Wells, Peyton, Greenberg & Hunt · 550 Fannin Street, Suite 600 · P.O. Box 3708 · Beaumont, TX 77701 · 409-838-2644

El Paso

S. Anthony Safi · Mounce, Green, Myers, Safi & Galatzan · Kayser Building, 17th Floor · 100 North Stanton Street · P.O. Box 1977 · El Paso, TX 79950-1977 · 915-532-2000

Fort Worth

Lynn Rossi Scott · Brackett & Ellis · 100 Main Street · Fort Worth, TX 76102 · 817-338-1700

Grapevine

Neal W. Adams · Adams, Lynch & Loftin · 3950 Highway 360 · Grapevine, TX 76051-6741 · 817-552-7742

Houston

David M. Feldman · Feldman & Rogers · 5718 Westheimer, Suite 1200 · Houston, TX 77057 · 713-960-6000

Kelly Frels · Bracewell & Giuliani · http://www.bgllp.com · 711 Louisiana Street, Suite 2300 · Houston, TX 77002-2770 · 713-223-2300

Jeffrey J. Horner · Bracewell & Giuliani · http://www.bgllp.com · 711 Louisiana Street, Suite 2300 · Houston, TX 77002-2770 · 713-223-2300

J. David Thompson III · Bracewell & Giuliani · http://www.bgllp.com · 711 Louisiana Street, Suite 2300 · Houston, TX 77002-2770 · 713-223-2300

Arlington

Charles Kennedy · Law Office of Charles Kennedy · 2405 Cales Drive, Suite A · Arlington, TX 76013 · 817-795-8843

Austin

Harry Clyde Farrell III · Harry Clyde Farrell III · 1411 West Avenue, Suite 100 · Austin, TX 78701-1537 512-323-2977

Deborah A. Green · Law Offices of Deborah Green · 7200 North Mopac Expressway · Austin, TX 78731 512-349-9595

G. Gaye Thompson · Thompson & Tiemann · P.O. Box 201988 · Austin, TX 78720-1988 · 512-335-6800

Baytown

Pi-Yi G. Mayo · Pi-Yi G. Mayo · 5223 Garth Road · Baytown, TX 77521-9665 · 281-421-5774

Bellaire

Molly Dear Abshire · Wright Abshire Attorneys · 4949 Bissonett Street · Bellaire, TX 77401 · 713-660-9595

Wesley E. Wright · Wright Abshire Attorneys · 4949 Bissonett Street · Bellaire, TX 77401 · 713-660-9595

Corpus Christi

Carol Bailey · Carol Bailey · 700 Everhart Road, Suite B-2 · Corpus Christi, TX 78411 · 361-814-9200

Dripping Springs

Renée Colwill Lovelace · The Lovelace Law Firm · 151 Loop 64, Suite E · P.O. Box 1268 · Dripping Springs, TX 78620 · 512-858-0707

Marilyn G. Miller · Marilyn G. Miller · 151 Loop 64 East, Suite D · P.O. Box 917 · Dripping Springs, TX 78620-0917 · 512-894-0319

El Paso

Stancy Stribling · Hobson, Stribling & Carson · 4110 Rio Bravo, Suite 220 · El Paso, TX 79902 · 915-351-9886

Houston

Sharon Brand Gardner · Crain, Caton & James · Five Houston Center, 17th Floor · 1401 McKinney Street · Houston, TX 77010-1079 · 713-658-2323

Christina Lesher · Law Office of Christina Lesher · 2719 Colquitt Street · Houston, TX 77098 · 713-529-5900

San Antonio

Patricia F. Sitchler · Schoenbaum, Curphy & Scanlan · 112 East Pecan Street, 30th Floor · San Antonio, TX 78205-1516 · 210-224-4491

Kathleen T. Whitehead · K.T. Whitehead · 3004 Nacogdoches Road · San Antonio, TX 78217 · 210-930-4300

EMINENT DOMAIN AND CONDEMNATION LAW

Angleton

Joseph Patterson · Patterson & Edquist · 120 West Myrtle Street · Angleton, TX 77515 · 979-848-3433

Austin

Stephen I. Adler · Barron, Adler & Anderson · 808 Nueces Street · Austin, TX 78701 · 512-478-4995

Michael M. Barron · Barron, Adler & Anderson · 808 Nueces Street · Austin, TX 78701 · 512-478-4995

Dallas

Joseph H. Staley, Jr. · Law Office Joseph H. Staley · 5949 Sherry Lane, Suite 501 · Dallas, TX 75225 · 214-739-3700

Kenneth A. Wright · Kenneth A. Wright · http://www.wrightatty.com · 2711 LBJ Freeway, Suite 360 · Dallas, TX 75234 · 972-484-1800

Fort Worth

Richard W. Wiseman · Brown, Dean, Wiseman, Liser, Proctor & Hart · Fort Worth Club Building, Suite 200 · 306 West Seventh Street · Fort Worth, TX 76102-4905 · 817-332-1391

Houston

J. Mark Breeding · Andrews Kurth · http://www.andrewskurth.com · 600 Travis Street, Suite 4200 · Houston, TX 77002 · 713-220-4200

Stephen K. Carroll · Fulbright & Jaworski · http://www.fulbright.com · Fulbright Tower, Suite 5100 · 1301 McKinney Street · Houston, TX 77010-3095 · 713-651-5151

H. Dixon Montague · Vinson & Elkins · http://www.velaw.com · First City Tower, Suite 2500 · 1001 Fannin Street · Houston, TX 77002-6760 · 713-758-2222

Thomas E. Sheffield · Barron, Adler & Anderson · 1001 McKinney Street, Suite 400 · Houston, TX 77002-6417 · 713-526-1500

EMPLOYEE BENEFITS LAW

Austin

Lydia Wommack Barton · ⑩ · Barton Law Office · 2905 San Gabriel, Suite 216 · Austin, TX 78705 · 512-494-1314

Ronald Bradshaw · Vinson & Elkins · http://www.velaw.com · 2801 Via Fortuna, Suite 100 · Austin, TX 78746-7568 · 512-542-8400

Miriam M. Burke · Vinson & Elkins · http://www.velaw.com · 2801 Via Fortuna, Suite 100 · Austin, TX 78746-7568 · 512-542-8400

C. Joseph Cain · ⑩ · Clark, Thomas & Winters · 300 West Sixth Street, 15th Floor · P.O. Box 1148 · Austin, TX 78767 · 512-472-8800

Charles H. Campbell · Jackson Walker · 100 Congress Avenue, Suite 1100 · Austin, TX 78701 · 512-236-2000

David I. Kuperman · ㉕ · Kuperman, Orr & Albers · 2801 Via Fortuna, Suite 530 · Austin, TX 78746 · 512-473-4100

Beaumont

John Creighton III · ⑩ · Orgain, Bell & Tucker · 470 Orleans Street · P.O. Box 1751 · Beaumont, TX 77704-1751 · 409-838-6412

Corpus Christi

Gerald W. Ostarch · ⑳ · Gary, Thomasson, Hall & Marks · 615 North Upper Broadway, Suite 800 · P.O. Box 2888 · Corpus Christi, TX 78403-0033 · 361-884-1961

Dallas

L. Scott Austin · Hunton & Williams · 1445 Ross Avenue, Suite 3700 · Dallas, TX 75202-2799 · 214-979-3000

Stuart M. Bumpas · ⑳ · Locke Lord Bissell & Liddell · 2200 Ross Avenue, Suite 2200 · Dallas, TX 75201-6776 · 214-740-8000

Edward Philip Bush · ⑩ · Locke Lord Bissell & Liddell · 2200 Ross Avenue, Suite 2200 · Dallas, TX 75201-6776 · 214-740-8000

James F. Carey · Jones Day · 2727 North Harwood Street · Dallas, TX 75201-1515 · 214-220-3939

John M. Collins · Haynes and Boone · 901 Main Street, Suite 3100 · Dallas, TX 75202 · 214-651-5000

Barry W. Cowan · Fulbright & Jaworski · http://www.fulbright.com · 2200 Ross Avenue, Suite 2800 · Dallas, TX 75201 · 214-855-8000

Greta E. Cowart · Haynes and Boone · 901 Main Street, Suite 3100 · Dallas, TX 75202 · 214-651-5000

T. David Cowart · ⑩ · Sonnenschein Nath & Rosenthal · 1717 Main Street, Suite 3400 · Dallas, TX 75201-4612 · 214-259-0900

David C. D'Alessandro · Vinson & Elkins · http://www.velaw.com · Trammell Crow Center, Suite 3700 · 2001 Ross Avenue · Dallas, TX 75201-2975 · 214-220-7700

Felicia A. Finston · Baker Botts · http://www.bakerbotts.com · Trammell Crow Center, Suite 600 · 2001 Ross Avenue · Dallas, TX 75201-2980 · 214-953-6500

Sharon M. Fountain · ⑩ · Thompson & Knight · http://www.tklaw.com · One Arts Plaza, Suite 1500 · 1722 Routh Street · Dallas, TX 75201-2533 · 214-969-1700

James Robert Griffin · Jackson Walker · Bank of America Plaza, Suite 6000 · 901 Main Street · Dallas, TX 75202 · 214-953-6000

Robert M. Herman · ⑩ · Robert M. Herman · 8117 Preston Road, Suite 300 · Dallas, TX 75225 · 214-692-5858

Thomas M. Hoffman · Gardere Wynne Sewell · http://www.gardere.com · 1601 Elm Street, Suite 3000 · Dallas, TX 75201 · 214-999-3000

J. Mike Holt · ⑳ · Thompson & Knight · http://www.tklaw.com · One Arts Plaza, Suite 1500 · 1722 Routh Street · Dallas, TX 75201-2533 · 214-969-1700

Riva T. Johnson · Morgan Lewis & Bockius · 1717 Main Street, Suite 3200 · Dallas, TX 75201 · 214-466-4000

James M. Klancnik · ⑩ · James M. Klancnik · 5956 Sherry Lane, Suite 1000 · Dallas, TX 75225-8021 · 214-739-2004

Bruce Douglas Pingree · ⑳ · Baker Botts · http://www.bakerbotts.com · Trammell Crow Center, Suite 600 · 2001 Ross Avenue · Dallas, TX 75201-2980 · 214-953-6500

Charles F. Plenge · ⑩ · Haynes and Boone · 901 Main Street, Suite 3100 · Dallas, TX 75202 · 214-651-5000

Cecil A. Ray, Jr. · ⑳ · Cecil A. Ray, Jr. · 9400 North Central Expressway, Suite 306 · Dallas, TX 75231-5039 · 214-739-1713

John S. Rice · ⑩ · Hunton & Williams · 1445 Ross Avenue, Suite 3700 · Dallas, TX 75202-2799 · 214-979-3000

Gary G. Short · ⑩ · Jones Day · 2727 North Harwood Street · Dallas, TX 75201-1515 · 214-220-3939

Robert J. Stokes · ⑩ · Baker Botts · http://www.bakerbotts.com · Trammell Crow Center, Suite 600 · 2001 Ross Avenue · Dallas, TX 75201-2980 · 214-953-6500

Karen K. Suhre · ⑩ · Karen K. Suhre · 3109 Knox Street, Suite 322 · Dallas, TX 75205 · 214-821-1115

Henry Talavera · Hunton & Williams · 1445 Ross Avenue, Suite 3700 · Dallas, TX 75202-2799 · 214-979-3000

Erin Turley · Morgan Lewis & Bockius · 1717 Main Street, Suite 3200 · Dallas, TX 75201 · 214-466-4000

Jim A. Watson · ⑳ · Carrington, Coleman, Sloman & Blumenthal · 901 Main Street, Suite 5500 · Dallas, TX 75202 · 214-855-3000

Susan A. Wetzel · Haynes and Boone · 901 Main Street, Suite 3100 · Dallas, TX 75202 · 214-651-5000

Linda A. Wilkins · Locke Lord Bissell & Liddell · 2200 Ross Avenue, Suite 2200 · Dallas, TX 75201-6776 · 214-740-8000

Shelly A. Youree · Thompson & Knight · http://www.tklaw.com · One Arts Plaza, Suite 1500 · 1722 Routh Street · Dallas, TX 75201-2533 · 214-969-1700

El Paso

Robert B. Zaboroski · ⑩ · Zaboroski & Zaboroski · 4110 Rio Bravo, Suite 220 · El Paso, TX 79902-1032 · 915-541-1221

Fort Worth

R. Gordon Appleman · ㉕ · Thompson & Knight · http://www.tklaw.com · 1600 Burnett Plaza, Unit One, Suite 1600 · 801 Cherry Street · Fort Worth, TX 76102-6881 · 817-347-1700

Harry Edward Bartel · ⑩ · Cantey & Hanger · 300 Cantey Hanger Plaza · 600 West Sixth Street · Fort Worth, TX 76102-3685 · 817-877-2800

Noel C. Ice · ⑩ · Cantey & Hanger · 300 Cantey Hanger Plaza · 600 West Sixth Street · Fort Worth, TX 76102-3685 · 817-877-2800

J. David Tracy · ⑩ · Cantey & Hanger · 300 Cantey Hanger Plaza · 600 West Sixth Street · Fort Worth, TX 76102-3685 · 817-877-2800

Houston

Michael A. Abbott · Gardere Wynne Sewell · http://www.gardere.com · 1000 Louisiana, Suite 3400 · Houston, TX 77002-5011 · 713-276-5500

Brian R. Bloom · Vinson & Elkins · http://www.velaw.com · First City Tower, Suite 2500 · 1001 Fannin Street · Houston, TX 77002-6760 · 713-758-2222

Mark A. Bodron · Baker Botts · http://www.bakerbotts.com · One Shell Plaza · 910 Louisiana Street · Houston, TX 77002-1210 · 713-229-1234

J. Cal Courtney, Jr. · ⑳ · Courtney & Associates · 2016 State Street · Houston, TX 77057-3011 · 713-706-4100

Christopher R. Fenelon · Andrews Kurth · http://www.andrewskurth.com · 600 Travis Street, Suite 4200 Houston, TX 77002 · 713-220-4200

Jesse J. Gelsomini · Haynes and Boone · One Houston Center, Suite 2100 · 1221 McKinney Street · Houston, TX 77010 · 713-547-2000

Carol H. Jewett · ⑳ · Vinson & Elkins · http://www.velaw.com · First City Tower, Suite 2500 · 1001 Fannin Street · Houston, TX 77002-6760 · 713-758-2222

Mark S. Miller · ⑩ · Fulbright & Jaworski · http://www.fulbright.com · Fulbright Tower, Suite 5100 · 1301 McKinney Street · Houston, TX 77010-3095 · 713-651-5151

John E. Neslage · ⑳ · Baker Botts · http://www.bakerbotts.com · One Shell Plaza · 910 Louisiana Street · Houston, TX 77002-1210 · 713-229-1234

James R. Raborn · ⑳ · Baker Botts · http://www.bakerbotts.com · One Shell Plaza · 910 Louisiana Street · Houston, TX 77002-1210 · 713-229-1234

Edward A. Razim III · Locke Lord Bissell & Liddell · JP Morgan Chase Tower, Suite 3400 · 600 Travis Street · Houston, TX 77002 · 713-226-1200

Alan J. Robin · Vinson & Elkins · http://www.velaw.com · First City Tower, Suite 2500 · 1001 Fannin Street · Houston, TX 77002-6760 · 713-758-2222

Stephanie Schroepfer · ⑩ · Fulbright & Jaworski · http://www.fulbright.com · Fulbright Tower, Suite 5100 · 1301 McKinney Street · Houston, TX 77010-3095 · 713-651-5151

Gail W. Stewart · Baker Botts · http://www.bakerbotts.com · One Shell Plaza · 910 Louisiana Street · Houston, TX 77002-1210 · 713-229-1234

San Antonio

William M. Fisher · Cox Smith Matthews · http://www.coxsmith.com · 112 East Pecan Street, Suite 1800 · San Antonio, TX 78205-1521 · 210-554-5500

Joseph B. Friedman, Jr. · ⑩ · Fulbright & Jaworski · http://www.fulbright.com · 300 Convent Street, Suite 2200 · San Antonio, TX 78205-3792 · 210-224-5575

Sylvan S. Lang, Jr. · Lang & Kustoff · 4103 Parkdale Street · San Antonio, TX 78229-2520 · 210-614-9444

R. Bradley Oxford · Cox Smith Matthews · http://www.coxsmith.com · 112 East Pecan Street, Suite 1800 San Antonio, TX 78205-1521 · 210-554-5500

Mary M. Potter · ⑩ · Cox Smith Matthews · http://www.coxsmith.com · 112 East Pecan Street, Suite 1800 San Antonio, TX 78205-1521 · 210-554-5500

Joshua A. Sutin · Cox Smith Matthews · http://www.coxsmith.com · 112 East Pecan Street, Suite 1800 · San Antonio, TX 78205-1521 · 210-554-5500

Robert B. Werner · ⑩ · Langley & Banack · Trinity Plaza II, Suite 900 · 745 East Mulberry Avenue · San Antonio, TX 78212-3166 · 210-736-6600

ENERGY LAW

Austin

James G. Boyle · Herrera & Boyle · 816 Congress Avenue, Suite 1120 · Austin, TX 78701 · 512-474-1492

Marianne Carroll · Brown McCarroll · 111 Congress Avenue, Suite 1400 · Austin, TX 78701-4093 · 512-472-5456

James W. Checkley, Jr. · Locke Lord Bissell & Liddell · 100 Congress Avenue, Suite 300 · Austin, TX 78701-4042 · 512-305-4785

Walter E. Demond · ⑩ · Clark, Thomas & Winters · 300 West Sixth Street, 15th Floor · P.O. Box 1148 · Austin, TX 78767 · 512-472-8800

David C. Duggins · ⑩ · Clark, Thomas & Winters · 300 West Sixth Street, 15th Floor · P.O. Box 1148 · Austin, TX 78767 · 512-472-8800

Geoffrey M. Gay · ⑩ · Lloyd, Gosselink, Blevins, Rochelle & Townsend · http://www.lglawfirm.com · 816 Congress Avenue, Suite 1900 · Austin, TX 78701 · 512-322-5800

Robert J. Hearon, Jr. · ㉕ · Graves, Dougherty, Hearon & Moody · http://www.gdhm.com · 401 Congress Avenue, Suite 2200 · P.O. Box 98 · Austin, TX 78767-0098 · 512-480-5600

Joseph Alan Holman · ⑩ · Locke Lord Bissell & Liddell · 100 Congress Avenue, Suite 300 · Austin, TX 78701-4042 · 512-305-4785

Thomas B. Hudson, Jr. · ⑩ · Graves, Dougherty, Hearon & Moody · http://www.gdhm.com · 401 Congress Avenue, Suite 2200 · P.O. Box 98 · Austin, TX 78767-0098 · 512-480-5600

Patton G. Lochridge · ⑩ · McGinnis, Lochridge & Kilgore · http://www.mcginnislaw.com · 600 Congress Avenue, Suite 2100 · Austin, TX 78701 · 512-495-6000

Campbell McGinnis · McGinnis, Lochridge & Kilgore · http://www.mcginnislaw.com · 600 Congress Avenue, Suite 2100 · Austin, TX 78701 · 512-495-6000

Lino Mendiola III · Andrews Kurth · http://www.andrewskurth.com · 111 Congress Avenue, Suite 1700 · Austin, TX 78701-4069 · 512-320-9200

Ron H. Moss · Graves, Dougherty, Hearon & Moody · http://www.gdhm.com · 401 Congress Avenue, Suite 2200 · P.O. Box 98 · Austin, TX 78767-0098 · 512-480-5600

Roger P. Nevola · ⑩ · Roger P. Nevola · 1723 Palma Plaza · P.O. Box 2103 · Austin, TX 78703 · 512-499-0500

Richard P. Noland · Sutherland · http://www.sutherland.com · Austin Centre, Suite 970 · 701 Brazos Street · Austin, TX 78701-3232 · 512-721-2700

Phillip G. Oldham · Andrews Kurth · http://www.andrewskurth.com · 111 Congress Avenue, Suite 1700 · Austin, TX 78701-4069 · 512-320-9200

Philip F. Ricketts · ⑩ · Bracewell & Giuliani · http://www.bgllp.com · 111 Congress Avenue, Suite 2300 · Austin, TX 78701 · 512-472-7800

Pete Schenkkan · ⑩ · Graves, Dougherty, Hearon & Moody · http://www.gdhm.com · 401 Congress Avenue, Suite 2200 · P.O. Box 98 · Austin, TX 78767-0098 · 512-480-5600

Edward C. Small · Jackson Walker · 100 Congress Avenue, Suite 1100 · Austin, TX 78701 · 512-236-2000

Rex D. VanMiddlesworth · ⑩ · Andrews Kurth · http://www.andrewskurth.com · 111 Congress Avenue, Suite 1700 · Austin, TX 78701-4069 · 512-320-9200

Dallas

Richard L. Adams · Vinson & Elkins · http://www.velaw.com · Trammell Crow Center, Suite 3700 · 2001 Ross Avenue · Dallas, TX 75201-2975 · 214-220-7700

Jo Ann Biggs · Vinson & Elkins · http://www.velaw.com · Trammell Crow Center, Suite 3700 · 2001 Ross Avenue · Dallas, TX 75201-2975 · 214-220-7700

Terry I. Cross · Haynes and Boone · 901 Main Street, Suite 3100 · Dallas, TX 75202 · 214-651-5000

Andrew B. Derman · Thompson & Knight · http://www.tklaw.com · One Arts Plaza, Suite 1500 · 1722 Routh Street · Dallas, TX 75201-2533 · 214-969-1700

Robert M. Fillmore · Hunton & Williams · 1445 Ross Avenue, Suite 3700 · Dallas, TX 75202-2799 · 214-979-3000

Stanley G. Harvey · Winstead · http://www.winstead.com · Renaissance Tower, Suite 5400 · 1201 Elm Street · Dallas, TX 75270-2199 · 214-745-5400

John B. Holden, Jr. · Jackson Walker · Bank of America Plaza, Suite 6000 · 901 Main Street · Dallas, TX 75202 · 214-953-6000

Frank P. McEachern · Jackson Walker · Bank of America Plaza, Suite 6000 · 901 Main Street · Dallas, TX 75202 · 214-953-6000

David S. Peck · Vinson & Elkins · http://www.velaw.com · Trammell Crow Center, Suite 3700 · 2001 Ross Avenue · Dallas, TX 75201-2975 · 214-220-7700

Rod Phelan · ⑩ · Baker Botts · http://www.bakerbotts.com · Trammell Crow Center, Suite 600 · 2001 Ross Avenue · Dallas, TX 75201-2980 · 214-953-6500

John W. Rain · ⑩ · Thompson & Knight · http://www.tklaw.com · One Arts Plaza, Suite 1500 · 1722 Routh Street · Dallas, TX 75201-2533 · 214-969-1700

Charles W. Sartain · Looper Reed & McGraw · 4100 Thanksgiving Tower · 1601 Elm Street · Dallas, TX 75201 · 214-954-4135

El Paso

Norman J. Gordon · ⑩ · Mounce, Green, Myers, Safi & Galatzan · Kayser Building, 17th Floor · 100 North Stanton Street · P.O. Box 1977 · El Paso, TX 79950-1977 · 915-532-2000

Fort Worth

Kleber C. Miller · ㉕ · Shannon, Gracey, Ratliff & Miller · http://www.shannongracey.com · 777 Main Street, Suite 3800 · Fort Worth, TX 76102 · 817-336-9333

Houston

David F. Asmus · Baker Botts · http://www.bakerbotts.com · One Shell Plaza · 910 Louisiana Street · Houston, TX 77002-1210 · 713-229-1234

Marcia E. Backus · Vinson & Elkins · http://www.velaw.com · First City Tower, Suite 2500 · 1001 Fannin Street · Houston, TX 77002-6760 · 713-758-2222

R. Doak Bishop · King & Spalding · 1100 Louisiana Street, Suite 4000 · Houston, TX 77002-5213 · 713-751-3200

Douglas S. Bland · ⑩ · Vinson & Elkins · http://www.velaw.com · First City Tower, Suite 2500 · 1001 Fannin Street · Houston, TX 77002-6760 · 713-758-2222

John P. Bowman · Fulbright & Jaworski · http://www.fulbright.com · Fulbright Tower, Suite 5100 · 1301 McKinney Street · Houston, TX 77010-3095 · 713-651-5151

Charles F. Caldwell · Vinson & Elkins · http://www.velaw.com · First City Tower, Suite 2500 · 1001 Fannin Street · Houston, TX 77002-6760 · 713-758-2222

Fielding B. Cochran III · Vinson & Elkins · http://www.velaw.com · First City Tower, Suite 2500 · 1001 Fannin Street · Houston, TX 77002-6760 · 713-758-2222

John P. Cogan, Jr. · McDermott Will & Emery · 1000 Louisiana, Suite 1300 · Houston, TX 77002 · 713-653-1700

John B. Connally IV · Vinson & Elkins · http://www.velaw.com · First City Tower, Suite 2500 · 1001 Fannin Street · Houston, TX 77002-6760 · 713-758-2222

J. Gregory Copeland · Baker Botts · http://www.bakerbotts.com · One Shell Plaza · 910 Louisiana Street · Houston, TX 77002-1210 · 713-229-1234

Kenneth S. Culotta · King & Spalding · 1100 Louisiana Street, Suite 4000 · Houston, TX 77002-5213 · 713-751-3200

J.Todd Culwell · Pillsbury Winthrop Shaw Pittman · http://www.pillsburylaw.com · Two Houston Center, Suite 2000 · 909 Fannin Street · Houston, TX 77010-1018 · 713-276-7600

Allen D. Cummings · Law Offices of Allen D. Cummings · Wortham Tower, Suite 1675 · 2727 Allen Parkway · Houston, TX 77019 · 888-832-1115

Thad Thano Dameris · Hogan & Hartson · Pennzoil Place, Suite 2100 · 711 Louisiana Street · Houston, TX 77002 · 713-632-1400

Stephen D. Davis · Vinson & Elkins · http://www.velaw.com · First City Tower, Suite 2500 · 1001 Fannin Street · Houston, TX 77002-6760 · 713-758-2222

Jonathan S. Day · ⑩ · Andrews Kurth · http://www.andrewskurth.com · 600 Travis Street, Suite 4200 · Houston, TX 77002 · 713-220-4200

Joseph C. Dilg · ⑩ · Vinson & Elkins · http://www.velaw.com · First City Tower, Suite 2500 · 1001 Fannin Street · Houston, TX 77002-6760 · 713-758-2222

George F. Goolsby · Baker Botts · http://www.bakerbotts.com · One Shell Plaza · 910 Louisiana Street · Houston, TX 77002-1210 · 713-229-1234

J. Clifford Gunter III · Bracewell & Giuliani · http://www.bgllp.com · 711 Louisiana Street, Suite 2300 · Houston, TX 77002-2770 · 713-223-2300

Peggy A. Heeg · Fulbright & Jaworski · http://www.fulbright.com · Fulbright Tower, Suite 5100 · 1301 McKinney Street · Houston, TX 77010-3095 · 713-651-5151

Michael P. Irvin · Fulbright & Jaworski · http://www.fulbright.com · Fulbright Tower, Suite 5100 · 1301 McKinney Street · Houston, TX 77010-3095 · 713-651-5151

Robert V. Jewell · Andrews Kurth · http://www.andrewskurth.com · 600 Travis Street, Suite 4200 · Houston, TX 77002 · 713-220-4200

Jay D. Kelley · Vinson & Elkins · http://www.velaw.com · First City Tower, Suite 2500 · 1001 Fannin Street · Houston, TX 77002-6760 · 713-758-2222

George F. Kutzschbach · Fulbright & Jaworski · http://www.fulbright.com · Fulbright Tower, Suite 5100 1301 McKinney Street · Houston, TX 77010-3095 · 713-651-5151

John G. Mauel · Pillsbury Winthrop Shaw Pittman · http://www.pillsburylaw.com · Two Houston Center, Suite 2000 · 909 Fannin Street · Houston, TX 77010-1018 · 713-276-7600

Henry S. May, Jr. · Vinson & Elkins · http://www.velaw.com · First City Tower, Suite 2500 · 1001 Fannin Street · Houston, TX 77002-6760 · 713-758-2222

Charles A. Moore · Dewey & LeBoeuf · Reliant Energy Plaza, Suite 2550 · 1000 Main Street · Houston, TX 77002 · 713-287-2000

Jeffrey S. Munoz · Vinson & Elkins · http://www.velaw.com · First City Tower, Suite 2500 · 1001 Fannin Street · Houston, TX 77002-6760 · 713-758-2222

Michael E. Niebruegge · Mayer Brown · Bank of America Center, Suite 3400 · 700 Louisiana Street · Houston, TX 77002-2730 · 713-238-3000

Glenn L. Pinkerton · Vinson & Elkins · http://www.velaw.com · First City Tower, Suite 2500 · 1001 Fannin Street · Houston, TX 77002-6760 · 713-758-2222

G. Alan Rafte · Bracewell & Giuliani · http://www.bgllp.com · 711 Louisiana Street, Suite 2300 · Houston, TX 77002-2770 · 713-223-2300

Albert S. Tabor, Jr. · Vinson & Elkins · http://www.velaw.com · First City Tower, Suite 2500 · 1001 Fannin Street · Houston, TX 77002-6760 · 713-758-2222

Robert H. Thomas · Porter & Hedges · 1000 Main Street, 36th Floor · Houston, TX 77002 · 713-226-0600

Mark J. Thurber · Andrews Kurth · http://www.andrewskurth.com · 600 Travis Street, Suite 4200 · Houston, TX 77002 · 713-220-4200

Timothy J. Unger · Andrews Kurth · http://www.andrewskurth.com · 600 Travis Street, Suite 4200 · Houston, TX 77002 · 713-220-4200

Jose' L. Valera · King & Spalding · 1100 Louisiana Street, Suite 4000 · Houston, TX 77002-5213 · 713-751-3200

J. Lanier Yeates · Gordon, Arata, McCollam, Duplantis & Eagan · http://www.gordonarata.com · One Riverway, Suite 1300 · 777 South Post Oak Lane · Houston, TX 77027-3533 · 713-333-5500

San Antonio

Diana Liebmann · Haynes and Boone · 112 East Pecan Street, Suite 900 · San Antonio, TX 78205-1540 · 210-978-7000

W. Roger Wilson · ⑩ · Cox Smith Matthews · http://www.coxsmith.com · 112 East Pecan Street, Suite 1800 · San Antonio, TX 78205-1521 · 210-554-5500

Jon Clair Wood · ⑩ · Cox Smith Matthews · http://www.coxsmith.com · 112 East Pecan Street, Suite 1800 · San Antonio, TX 78205-1521 · 210-554-5500

ENTERTAINMENT LAW

Austin

Lawrence A. Waks · Jackson Walker · 100 Congress Avenue, Suite 1100 · Austin, TX 78701 · 512-236-2000

Dallas

D'Lesli M. Davis · Fulbright & Jaworski · http://www.fulbright.com · 2200 Ross Avenue, Suite 2800 · Dallas, TX 75201 · 214-855-8000

ENVIRONMENTAL LAW

Austin

Albert R. Axe, Jr. · Winstead · http://www.winstead.com · 401 Congress Avenue, Suite 2100 · Austin, TX 78701 · 512-370-2800

James D. Braddock · Haynes and Boone · 600 Congress Avenue, Suite 1300 · Austin, TX 78701-3285 · 512-867-8400

Patricia Finn Braddock · ⑩ · Fulbright & Jaworski · http://www.fulbright.com · 600 Congress Avenue, Suite 2400 · Austin, TX 78701-2978 · 512-474-5201

Carrick Brooke-Davidson · Guida, Slavich & Flores · 106 East Sixth Street, Suite 900 · Austin, TX 78701 · 512-476-6300

Sara Marquis Burgin · ⑩ · Baker Botts · http://www.bakerbotts.com · 1500 San Jacinto Center · 98 San Jacinto Boulevard · Austin, TX 78701-4039 · 512-322-2500

Molly J. Cagle · ⑩ · Vinson & Elkins · http://www.velaw.com · 2801 Via Fortuna, Suite 100 · Austin, TX 78746-7568 · 512-542-8400

Jeff Civins · ⑳ · Haynes and Boone · 600 Congress Avenue, Suite 1300 · Austin, TX 78701-3285 · 512-867-8400

Leonard H. Dougal · Jackson Walker · 100 Congress Avenue, Suite 1100 · Austin, TX 78701 · 512-236-2000

Pamela M. Giblin · ⑳ · Baker Botts · http://www.bakerbotts.com · 1500 San Jacinto Center · 98 San Jacinto Boulevard · Austin, TX 78701-4039 · 512-322-2500

Alan M. Glen · Smith, Robertson, Elliott, Glen, Klein & Bell · http://www.sreglaw.com · 221 West Sixth Street, Suite 1100 · Austin, TX 78701 · 512-225-5800

R. Kinnan Golemon · ⑳ · KG Strategies · 111 Congress Avenue, Suite 1500 · Austin, TX 78701-4043 · 512-479-9707

Peter Gregg · Beveridge & Diamond · 98 San Jacinto Boulevard, Suite 1420 · Austin, TX 78701-4039 · 512-391-8000

Eric Groten · Boulette & Golden · Three Barton Skyway, Suite 300 · 1221 South MoPac Expressway · Austin, TX 78746 · 512-732-8900

Philip S. Haag · Winstead · http://www.winstead.com · 401 Congress Avenue, Suite 2100 · Austin, TX 78701 · 512-370-2800

John D. Head · Fritz, Byrne, Head & Harrison · San Jacinto Center, Suite 2000 · 98 San Jacinto Boulevard Austin, TX 78701-4286 · 512-476-2020

Aileen M. Hooks · Baker Botts · http://www.bakerbotts.com · 1500 San Jacinto Center · 98 San Jacinto Boulevard · Austin, TX 78701-4039 · 512-322-2500

Robert Keith Hopson · ⑩ · Brown McCarroll · 111 Congress Avenue, Suite 1400 · Austin, TX 78701-4093 · 512-472-5456

John L. Howard, Jr. · Vinson & Elkins · http://www.velaw.com · 2801 Via Fortuna, Suite 100 · Austin, TX 78746-7568 · 512-542-8400

Rodman C. Johnson · Brown McCarroll · 111 Congress Avenue, Suite 1400 · Austin, TX 78701-4093 · 512-472-5456

Jennifer Keane · Baker Botts · http://www.bakerbotts.com · 1500 San Jacinto Center · 98 San Jacinto Boulevard · Austin, TX 78701-4039 · 512-322-2500

Derek R. McDonald · Baker Botts · http://www.bakerbotts.com · 1500 San Jacinto Center · 98 San Jacinto Boulevard · Austin, TX 78701-4039 · 512-322-2500

Mary S. Mendoza · Haynes and Boone · 600 Congress Avenue, Suite 1300 · Austin, TX 78701-3285 · 512-867-8400

James C. Morriss III · ⑳ · Thompson & Knight · http://www.tklaw.com · 98 San Jacinto Boulevard, Suite 1900 · Austin, TX 78701 · 512-469-6100

Michael J. Nasi · Jackson Walker · 100 Congress Avenue, Suite 1100 · Austin, TX 78701 · 512-236-2000

Roger P. Nevola · ⑩ · Roger P. Nevola · 1723 Palma Plaza · P.O. Box 2103 · Austin, TX 78703 · 512-499-0500

P. Bane Phillippi · Haynes and Boone · 600 Congress Avenue, Suite 1300 · Austin, TX 78701-3285 · 512-867-8400

Kenneth R. Ramirez · Brown McCarroll · 111 Congress Avenue, Suite 1400 · Austin, TX 78701-4093 · 512-472-5456

Mary B. Reagan · McGinnis, Lochridge & Kilgore · http://www.mcginnislaw.com · 600 Congress Avenue, Suite 2100 · Austin, TX 78701 · 512-495-6000

Robert Renbarger · Fritz, Byrne, Head & Harrison · San Jacinto Center, Suite 2000 · 98 San Jacinto Boulevard · Austin, TX 78701-4286 · 512-476-2020

John A. Riley · Vinson & Elkins · http://www.velaw.com · 2801 Via Fortuna, Suite 100 · Austin, TX 78746-7568 · 512-542-8400

Celina Romero · Clark, Thomas & Winters · 300 West Sixth Street, 15th Floor · P.O. Box 1148 · Austin, TX 78767 · 512-472-8800

Pete Schenkkan · ⑩ · Graves, Dougherty, Hearon & Moody · http://www.gdhm.com · 401 Congress Avenue, Suite 2200 · P.O. Box 98 · Austin, TX 78767-0098 · 512-480-5600

Paul Seals · Akin Gump Strauss Hauer & Feld · 300 West Sixth Street, Suite 2100 · Austin, TX 78701-3911 · 512-499-6200

Robert Walton Shelton · ⑩ · Robert Walton Shelton · 4131 Spicewood Springs Road, Building I, Suite One · P.O. Box 27367 · Austin, TX 78755-2367 · 512-338-0191

Keith A. Shuley · K&L Gates · 111 Congress Avenue, Suite 900 · Austin, TX 78701 · 512-482-6800

Edward C. Small · Jackson Walker · 100 Congress Avenue, Suite 1100 · Austin, TX 78701 · 512-236-2000

Cynthia C. Smiley · Kelly, Hart & Hallman · 301 Congress Avenue, Suite 2000 · Austin, TX 78701 · 512-495-6400

Robert T. Stewart · Kelly, Hart & Hallman · 301 Congress Avenue, Suite 2000 · Austin, TX 78701 · 512-495-6400

John J. Vay · Law Office of John J. Vay · Building Three, Suite 400 · 1250 South Capital Of Texas Highway · Austin, TX 78746 · 512-329-2010

Timothy A. Wilkins · Bracewell & Giuliani · http://www.bgllp.com · 111 Congress Avenue, Suite 2300 · Austin, TX 78701 · 512-472-7800

Danny Worrell · Brown McCarroll · 111 Congress Avenue, Suite 1400 · Austin, TX 78701-4093 · 512-472-5456

Susan G. Zachos · ⑩ · Law Offices of Susan G. Zachos · Barton Oaks Plaza One, Suite 300 · 901 South Mopac Expressway · Austin, TX 78746 · 512-329-1930

Beaumont

David E. Grove · David E. Grove · San Jacinto Building, Suite 1007 · 595 Orleans Street · Beaumont, TX 77701 · 409-835-5500

Dallas

Frederick W. Addison III · Munsch Hardt Kopf & Harr · 3800 Lincoln Plaza · 500 North Akard Street · Dallas, TX 75201-6659 · 214-855-7500

Thomas B. Alleman · Winstead · http://www.winstead.com · Renaissance Tower, Suite 5400 · 1201 Elm Street · Dallas, TX 75270-2199 · 214-745-5400

Cynthia J. Bishop · Gardere Wynne Sewell · http://www.gardere.com · 1601 Elm Street, Suite 3000 · Dallas, TX 75201 · 214-999-3000

Patrick R. Cowlishaw · Jackson Walker · Bank of America Plaza, Suite 6000 · 901 Main Street · Dallas, TX 75202 · 214-953-6000

Scott D. Deatherage · Thompson & Knight · http://www.tklaw.com · One Arts Plaza, Suite 1500 · 1722 Routh Street · Dallas, TX 75201-2533 · 214-969-1700

Diana C. Dutton · ⑩ · Akin Gump Strauss Hauer & Feld · 1700 Pacific Avenue, Suite 4100 · Dallas, TX 75201-4675 · 214-969-2800

Allison K. Exall · Curran Tomko Tarski · 2001 Bryan Street, Suite 2050 · Dallas, TX 75201 · 214-270-1400

Laurence K. Gustafson · Haynes and Boone · 901 Main Street, Suite 3100 · Dallas, TX 75202 · 214-651-5000

James B. Harris · ⑳ · Thompson & Knight · http://www.tklaw.com · One Arts Plaza, Suite 1500 · 1722 Routh Street · Dallas, TX 75201-2533 · 214-969-1700

Charles C. Jordan · Carrington, Coleman, Sloman & Blumenthal · 901 Main Street, Suite 5500 · Dallas, TX 75202 · 214-855-3000

Patrick Larkin · Strasburger & Price · http://www.strasburger.com · 901 Main Street, Suite 4400 · Dallas, TX 75202-3794 · 214-651-4300

Sally A. Longroy · Carrington, Coleman, Sloman & Blumenthal · 901 Main Street, Suite 5500 · Dallas, TX 75202 · 214-855-3000

Frances E. Phillips · ⑩ · Gardere Wynne Sewell · http://www.gardere.com · 1601 Elm Street, Suite 3000 · Dallas, TX 75201 · 214-999-3000

Greg Rogers · Guida, Slavich & Flores · 750 North St. Paul Street, Suite 200 · Dallas, TX 75201 · 214-692-0009

A. Kay Roska · Thompson & Knight · http://www.tklaw.com · One Arts Plaza, Suite 1500 · 1722 Routh Street · Dallas, TX 75201-2533 · 214-969-1700

John Slavich · Guida, Slavich & Flores · 750 North St. Paul Street, Suite 200 · Dallas, TX 75201 · 214-692-0009

Fort Worth

Sarah Walls · Cantey & Hanger · 300 Cantey Hanger Plaza · 600 West Sixth Street · Fort Worth, TX 76102-3685 · 817-877-2800

Houston

Christopher B. Amandes · ⑩ · Vinson & Elkins · http://www.velaw.com · First City Tower, Suite 2500 · 1001 Fannin Street · Houston, TX 77002-6760 · 713-758-2222

Debra L. Baker · Connelly, Baker, Wotring & Jackson · 700 JPMorgan Chase Tower · 600 Travis Street · Houston, TX 77002 · 713-980-1700

David J. Beck · ㉕ · Beck, Redden & Secrest · http://www.brsfirm.com · One Houston Center, Suite 4500 1221 McKinney Street · Houston, TX 77010-2010 · 713-951-3700

Kelly D. Brown · Crain, Caton & James · Five Houston Center, 17th Floor · 1401 McKinney Street · Houston, TX 77010-1079 · 713-658-2323

Heather M. Corken · Fulbright & Jaworski · http://www.fulbright.com · Fulbright Tower, Suite 5100 · 1301 McKinney Street · Houston, TX 77010-3095 · 713-651-5151

Carol E. Dinkins · ⑳ · Vinson & Elkins · http://www.velaw.com · First City Tower, Suite 2500 · 1001 Fannin Street · Houston, TX 77002-6760 · 713-758-2222

Richard O. Faulk · Gardere Wynne Sewell · http://www.gardere.com · 1000 Louisiana, Suite 3400 · Houston, TX 77002-5011 · 713-276-5500

Ragna O. Henrichs · ⑩ · Porter & Hedges · 1000 Main Street, 36th Floor · Houston, TX 77002 · 713-226-0600

Tracy D. Hester · Bracewell & Giuliani · http://www.bgllp.com · 711 Louisiana Street, Suite 2300 · Houston, TX 77002-2770 · 713-223-2300

Gerald Higdon · Sutherland · http://www.sutherland.com · Two Houston Center, Suite 2200 · 909 Fannin Houston, TX 77010-1043 · 713-470-6100

Mary W. Koks · Munsch Hardt Kopf & Harr · Bank of America Center, Suite 4600 · 700 Louisiana Street · Houston, TX 77002-2732 · 713-222-1470

Matthew L. Kuryla · Baker Botts · http://www.bakerbotts.com · One Shell Plaza · 910 Louisiana Street · Houston, TX 77002-1210 · 713-229-1234

Edward Clark Lewis · Fulbright & Jaworski · http://www.fulbright.com · Fulbright Tower, Suite 5100 · 1301 McKinney Street · Houston, TX 77010-3095 · 713-651-5151

Sharon M. Mattox · Vinson & Elkins · http://www.velaw.com · First City Tower, Suite 2500 · 1001 Fannin Street · Houston, TX 77002-6760 · 713-758-2222

Robert Emmett Morse III · ⑩ · Crain, Caton & James · Five Houston Center, 17th Floor · 1401 McKinney Street · Houston, TX 77010-1079 · 713-658-2323

Larry W. Nettles · Vinson & Elkins · http://www.velaw.com · First City Tower, Suite 2500 · 1001 Fannin Street · Houston, TX 77002-6760 · 713-758-2222

Eva Fromm O'Brien · Fulbright & Jaworski · http://www.fulbright.com · Fulbright Tower, Suite 5100 · 1301 McKinney Street · Houston, TX 77010-3095 · 713-651-5151

Gerald J. Pels · Sutherland · http://www.sutherland.com · Two Houston Center, Suite 2200 · 909 Fannin · Houston, TX 77010-1043 · 713-470-6100

Tracie J. Renfroe · King & Spalding · 1100 Louisiana Street, Suite 4000 · Houston, TX 77002-5213 · 713-751-3200

James E. Smith · ⑩ · Beirne, Maynard & Parsons · 1300 Post Oak Boulevard, Suite 2500 · Houston, TX 77056-3000 · 713-623-0887

Andrew Strong · Pillsbury Winthrop Shaw Pittman · http://www.pillsburylaw.com · Two Houston Center, Suite 2000 · 909 Fannin Street · Houston, TX 77010-1018 · 713-276-7600

Mark J. White · ⑩ · Baker Botts · http://www.bakerbotts.com · One Shell Plaza · 910 Louisiana Street · Houston, TX 77002-1210 · 713-229-1234

EQUIPMENT FINANCE LAW

Austin

William F. Stutts · ⑩ · Baker Botts · http://www.bakerbotts.com · 1500 San Jacinto Center · 98 San Jacinto Boulevard · Austin, TX 78701-4039 · 512-322-2500

Dallas

Larry A. Makel · Patton Boggs · 2001 Ross Avenue, Suite 3000 · Dallas, TX 75201 · 214-758-1500

Fort Worth

Stephen C. Howell · Brown Dean Wiseman Proctor Hart & Howell · 307 West Seventh Street, Suite 1918 Fort Worth, TX 76102 · 817-332-1391

Houston

Nelson R. Block · Winstead · http://www.winstead.com · JPMorgan Chase Tower, Suite 1100 · 600 Travis Street · Houston, TX 77002 · 713-650-8400

FAMILY LAW

Addison

Michael P. Geary · Geary Porter & Donovan · http://www.gpd.com · One Bent Tree Tower, Suite 400 · 16475 Dallas Parkway · Addison, TX 75001-6837 · 972-349-2225

Larry L. Martin · Geary Porter & Donovan · http://www.gpd.com · One Bent Tree Tower, Suite 400 · 16475 Dallas Parkway · Addison, TX 75001-6837 · 972-349-2225

Amarillo

Sally Holt Emerson · Underwood, Wilson, Berry, Stein & Johnson · 500 South Taylor, Suite 1200, Lock Box 233 · P.O. Box 9158 · Amarillo, TX 79105 · 806-376-5613

Douglas R. Woodburn · Woodburn, Watkins & Jackson · 500 South Taylor, Suite 510 · Amarillo, TX 79101 · 806-374-9584

Austin

Kristen A. Algert · Ausley, Algert, Robertson & Flores · http://www.ausley-algert.com · 3307 Northland Drive, Suite 420 · Austin, TX 78731 · 512-454-8791

Thomas L. Ausley · ⑳ · Ausley, Algert, Robertson & Flores · http://www.ausley-algert.com · 3307 Northland Drive, Suite 420 · Austin, TX 78731 · 512-454-8791

Patricia A. English · ⑳ · Noelke English & Prescott · 700 Lavaca, Suite 930 · Austin, TX 78701 · 512-480-9777

James E. Farris · ⑩ · Farris & Green · 6407 Sumac Drive · P.O. Box 29198 · Austin, TX 78731-4114 · 512-473-8591

Janice L. Green · Farris & Green · 6407 Sumac Drive · P.O. Box 29198 · Austin, TX 78731-4114 · 512-473-8591

Keith D. Maples · Noelke English Maples St. Leger · Barton Oaks Plaza II, Suite 200 · 901 South Mopac Expressway · Austin, TX 78746 · 512-480-9777

David F. Minton · Minton, Burton, Foster & Collins · 1100 Guadalupe Street · Austin, TX 78701-2198 · 512-476-4873

Lea C. Noelke · Noelke English & Prescott · 700 Lavaca, Suite 930 · Austin, TX 78701 · 512-480-9777

Eric Robertson · Ausley, Algert, Robertson & Flores · http://www.ausley-algert.com · 3307 Northland Drive, Suite 420 · Austin, TX 78731 · 512-454-8791

Jennifer Tull · Law Offices of Jennifer Tull · 506 West Seventh Street · Austin, TX 78701 · 512-472-1919

Beaumont

David E. Grove · David E. Grove · San Jacinto Building, Suite 1007 · 595 Orleans Street · Beaumont, TX 77701 · 409-835-5500

Corpus Christi

Ann E. Coover · Coover & Coover · 921 North Chaparral Street, Suite 102 · Corpus Christi, TX 78401-2028 · 361-882-2100

William A. Dudley · ⑩ · Law Office of William A. Dudley · 1126 Third Street · Corpus Christi, TX 78404-2312 · 361-884-3488

Dallas

Leota H. Alexander · Leota H. Alexander · 8350 North Central Expressway, Suite 1111 · Dallas, TX 75206-1838 · 214-242-6444

Jeffrey O. Anderson · The Andersons, Attorneys and Counselors at Law · 15301 Dallas Parkway, Suite 250 · Dallas, TX 75001 · 972-248-8383

Angeline L. Bain · ⑩ · Goranson, Bain, Larsen & Greenwald · 8150 North Central Expressway, Suite 1850 · Dallas, TX 75206 · 214-373-7676

Janet P. Brumley · Verner & Brumley · http://www.vernerbrumley.com · 3131 TurtleCreek Boulevard, Penthouse Suite · Dallas, TX 75219 · 214-526-5234

Carla M. Calabrese · Calabrese Huff · http://www.calabreselaw.com · 5944 Luther Lane, Suite 875 · Dallas, TX 75225 · 214-939-3000

Edwin W. Davis · McShane & Davis · Campbell Centre I, Suite 1200 · 8350 North Central Expressway · Dallas, TX 75206 · 214-365-9007

Michael R. DeBruin · Koons, Fuller, Vanden, Eykel & Robertson · http://www.koonsfuller.com · 2311 Cedar Springs Road, Suite 300 · Dallas, TX 75201 · 214-871-2727

Scott Downing · McCurley Orsinger McCurley Nelson & Downing · http://www.momnd.com · 5950 Sherry Lane, Eighth Floor · Dallas, TX 75225 · 214-273-2400

Kevin R. Fuller · ⑩ · Koons, Fuller, Vanden, Eykel & Robertson · http://www.koonsfuller.com · 2311 Cedar Springs Road, Suite 300 · Dallas, TX 75201 · 214-871-2727

Thomas P. Goranson · ⑳ · Goranson, Bain, Larsen & Greenwald · 8150 North Central Expressway, Suite 1850 · Dallas, TX 75206 · 214-373-7676

Thomas A. Greenwald · Goranson, Bain, Larsen & Greenwald · 8150 North Central Expressway, Suite 1850 · Dallas, TX 75206 · 214-373-7676

Larry Hance · Hance & Wickham · Two Lincoln Center, Suite 626 · 5420 LBJ Freeway · Dallas, TX 75420 · 469-374-9600

Douglas A. Harrison · Gardere Wynne Sewell · http://www.gardere.com · 1601 Elm Street, Suite 3000 · Dallas, TX 75201 · 214-999-3000

Paula Larsen · ⑩ · Goranson, Bain, Larsen & Greenwald · 8150 North Central Expressway, Suite 1850 · Dallas, TX 75206 · 214-373-7676

Ronald E. Massingill · Ron Massingill · Two Turtle Creek Village, 18th Floor · 3838 Oak Lawn Avenue · Dallas, TX 75219 · 214-528-5000

Beth E. Maultsby · Goranson, Bain, Larsen & Greenwald · 8150 North Central Expressway, Suite 1850 · Dallas, TX 75206 · 214-373-7676

Mary Johanna McCurley · McCurley Orsinger McCurley Nelson & Downing · http://www.momnd.com · 5950 Sherry Lane, Eighth Floor · Dallas, TX 75225 · 214-273-2400

Mike McCurley · ⑳ · McCurley Orsinger McCurley Nelson & Downing · http://www.momnd.com · 5950 Sherry Lane, Eighth Floor · Dallas, TX 75225 · 214-273-2400

John V. McShane, Jr. · John V. McShane · Campbell Centre, Tower I, Suite 1200 · 8350 North Central Expressway · Dallas, TX 75206-1624 · 214-365-9007

Keith M. Nelson · McCurley Orsinger McCurley Nelson & Downing · http://www.momnd.com · 5950 Sherry Lane, Eighth Floor · Dallas, TX 75225 · 214-273-2400

Richard R. Orsinger · ⑳ · McCurley Orsinger McCurley Nelson & Downing · http://www.momnd.com · 5950 Sherry Lane, Eighth Floor · Dallas, TX 75225 · 214-273-2400

Kenneth G. Raggio · Raggio & Raggio · 3316 Oak Grove Avenue, Suite 100 · Dallas, TX 75204 · 214-880-7500

Thomas Louis Raggio · Raggio & Raggio · 3316 Oak Grove Avenue, Suite 100 · Dallas, TX 75204 · 214-880-7500

Ike Vanden Eykel · ⑩ · Koons, Fuller, Vanden, Eykel & Robertson · http://www.koonsfuller.com · 2311 Cedar Springs Road, Suite 300 · Dallas, TX 75201 · 214-871-2727

Brian L. Webb · ⑳ · Webb & Associates · 2730 KPMG Centre · 717 North Harwood Street · Dallas, TX 75201 · 214-871-2730

Denton

Robert N. Eames · Holmes, Woods, Diggs & Eames · 1517 Centre Place Drive, Suite 300 · Denton, TX 76205 · 940-484-8200

Curtis M. Loveless · ⑳ · Loveless & Loveless · 218 North Elm Street · Denton, TX 76201 · 940-387-3776

El Paso

David R. McClure · ⑳ · David R. McClure · 218 West Franklin Avenue · El Paso, TX 79901-1120 · 915-544-8181

Larry H. Schwartz · ㉕ · Schwartz & Earp · 609 Laurel Street · El Paso, TX 79903-3401 · 915-542-1533

Fort Worth

James B. Barlow · ⑩ · Barlow Garsek & Simon · Landers Point Office Building, Suite 100 · 3815 Lisbon Street · Fort Worth, TX 76107 · 817-731-4500

J. Steven King · ⑩ · The King Law Firm · 2900 Airport Freeway · Fort Worth, TX 76111 · 817-838-3338

James M. Loveless · Loveless & Naylor · 2900 Airport Freeway · Fort Worth, TX 76111 · 817-831-6800

Stephen J. Naylor · Law Office of Stephen J. Naylor · 101 Summit Avenue, Suite 906 · Fort Worth, TX 76102 · 817-332-7703

Gary Lyndon Nickelson · ⑩ · Law Office of Gary Nickelson · 5201 West Freeway, Suite 100 · Fort Worth, TX 76107-5200 · 817-735-4000

Houston

J. D. Bucky Allshouse · ⑩ · J. D. Bucky Allshouse · Three River Way, Suite 1420 · Houston, TX 77056 · 713-951-0002

Steve A. Bavousett · Steve A. Bavousett · 1820 One Riverway · Houston, TX 77056 · 713-871-9587

Wendy S. Burgower · Burgower & Rainwater · 3355 West Alabama, Suite 825 · Houston, TX 77098 · 713-529-3982

Warren Cole · Warren Cole · 3355 West Alabama, Suite 825 · Houston, TX 77098 · 713-275-4444

Thomas R. Conner · Conner & Lindamood · http://www.lawcl.com · 1221 Lamar Street, Suite 1010 · Houston, TX 77010 · 713-654-2112

Donn C. Fullenweider · ㉕ · The Fullenweider Firm · http://www.fullenweider.com · 4265 San Felipe, Suite 1400 · Houston, TX 77027 · 713-624-4100

Stewart W. Gagnon · ⑩ · Fulbright & Jaworski · http://www.fulbright.com · Fulbright Tower, Suite 5100 1301 McKinney Street · Houston, TX 77010-3095 · 713-651-5151

Robert S. Hoffman · Fulbright & Jaworski · http://www.fulbright.com · Fulbright Tower, Suite 5100 · 1301 McKinney Street · Houston, TX 77010-3095 · 713-651-5151

Joan Foote Jenkins · ⑩ · Jenkins & Kamin · Two Greenway Plaza, Suite 600 · Houston, TX 77046 · 713-600-5500

Lynn Kamin · Jenkins & Kamin · Two Greenway Plaza, Suite 600 · Houston, TX 77046 · 713-600-5500

Brenda D. Keen · ⑩ · Brenda D. Keen · http://www.brendakeen.com · 1800 Bering Drive, Suite 690 · Houston, TX 77057 · 713-972-1320

John F. Nichols, Jr. · Jenkins & Kamin · Two Greenway Plaza, Suite 600 · Houston, TX 77046 · 713-600-5500

John F. Nichols, Sr. · ㉕ · Nichols Law · http://www.nicholslaw.com · 1301 McKinney Street, Suite 2900 · Houston, TX 77010 · 713-654-0708

Donald R. Royall · ㉕ · The Royalls · 4550 Post Oak Place, Suite 341 · Houston, TX 77027 · 713-462-6500

Steven H. Schweitzer · The Fullenweider Firm · http://www.fullenweider.com · 4265 San Felipe, Suite 1400 · Houston, TX 77027 · 713-624-4100

J. Lindsey Short, Jr. · ⑳ · Short Carter Morris · http://www.shortcartermorris.com · 1177 West Loop South, Suite 700 · Houston, TX 77027 · 713-626-3345

Harry Lee Tindall · ㉕ · Tindall & Foster · 1300 Post Oak Boulevard, Suite 1550 · Houston, TX 77056-3081 · 713-622-8733

Patricia A. Wicoff · Schlanger, Silver, Barg & Paine · 109 North Post Oak Lane, Suite 300 · Houston, TX 77024 · 713-785-1700

Randall B. Wilhite · The Fullenweider Firm · http://www.fullenweider.com · 4265 San Felipe, Suite 1400 Houston, TX 77027 · 713-624-4100

Alvin L. Zimmerman · Zimmerman, Axelrad, Meyer, Stern & Wise · 3040 Post Oak Boulevard, Suite 1300 · Houston, TX 77056-6560 · 713-552-1234

Longview

R. Laughton Whitehead, Jr. · ⑩ · R. L. Whitehead, Jr. · 505 North Green Street · P.O. Box 688 · Longview, TX 75606-0688 · 903-758-0561

McKinney

William M. Boyd · ㉕ · Boyd Veigel · 218 East Louisiana Street · P.O. Box 1179 · McKinney, TX 75070 · 972-542-0191

George Parker · Parker and Montgomery · 121 South Tennessee Street · McKinney, TX 75069 · 972-562-2212

Plano

Julie Crawford · Koons, Fuller, Vanden, Eykel & Robertson · http://www.koonsfuller.com · 5700 West Plano Parkway, Suite 2200 · Plano, TX 75093-2411 · 972-769-2727

Jody L. Johnson · Allison and Johnson · 5000 Legacy Drive, Suite 160 · Plano, TX 75024-3112 · 972-608-4300

Kathryn J. Murphy · Goranson, Bain, Larsen & Greenwald · Two Legacy Town Center, Suite 400 · 6900 North Dallas Parkway · Plano, TX 75024 · 214-473-9696

Richard L. Robertson · ⑩ · Koons, Fuller, Vanden, Eykel & Robertson · http://www.koonsfuller.com · 5700 West Plano Parkway, Suite 2200 · Plano, TX 75093-2411 · 972-769-2727

San Antonio

Sam C. Bashara · ⑳ · Sam C. Bashara · 111 Soledad Street, Suite 1800 · San Antonio, TX 78205-2229 · 210-227-1496

Jo Chris Lopez · Langley & Banack · Trinity Plaza II, Suite 900 · 745 East Mulberry Avenue · San Antonio, TX 78212-3166 · 210-736-6600

James E. Monnig · ⑩ · Law Offices of James E. Monnig · 310 South Saint Mary's, Suite 1470 · San Antonio, TX 78232 · 210-224-5400

B. F. Pennypacker III · Wilson & Pennypacker · 8620 North New Braunfels, Suite 101 · San Antonio, TX 78217-6361 · 210-826-4001

Cheryl L. Wilson · ⑩ · Wilson & Pennypacker · 8620 North New Braunfels, Suite 101 · San Antonio, TX 78217-6361 · 210-826-4001

Southlake

Heather L. King · Koons, Fuller, Vanden, Eykel & Robertson · http://www.koonsfuller.com · 181 Grand Avenue, Suite 225 · Southlake, TX 76092 · 817-481-2710

Tyler

Bruce D. Bain · Bain, Files, Jarrett and Bain · 109 West Ferguson Street · P.O. Box 2013 · Tyler, TX 75710 · 903-595-3573

Jerry E. Bain · ⑳ · Bain, Files, Jarrett and Bain · 109 West Ferguson Street · P.O. Box 2013 · Tyler, TX 75710 · 903-595-3573

Michael E. Jarrett · Bain, Files, Jarrett and Bain · 109 West Ferguson Street · P.O. Box 2013 · Tyler, TX 75710 · 903-595-3573

Victoria

Jackie W. Marr · ⑩ · Marr, Meier & Bradicich · First Victoria Bank Building, Suite 200 · P.O. Box 550 · Victoria, TX 77902-0550 · 361-573-4344

Weatherford

G. Thomas Vick, Jr. · ⑩ · Vick, Carney & Smith · 111 York Avenue · Weatherford, TX 76086-3295 · 817-596-5533

Westlake Village

Coye Conner, Jr. · ⑳ · Coye Conner, Jr. · 4101 Aspen Lane · Westlake Village, TX 76262 · 903-533-0661

FAMILY LAW MEDIATION

Austin

Kristen A. Algert · Ausley, Algert, Robertson & Flores · http://www.ausley-algert.com · 3307 Northland Drive, Suite 420 · Austin, TX 78731 · 512-454-8791

Janice Loy Green · Farris & Green · 6407 Sumac Drive · P.O. Box 29198 · Austin, TX 78731-4114 · 512-473-8591

Dallas

Gay G. Cox · Gay G. Cox · http://www.mediate.com/ggcox · 2213 Boll Street · Dallas, TX 75204 · 214-522-0150

Robert J. Matlock · Robert J. Matlock · 12221 Merit Drive, Suite 1660 · Dallas, TX 75251 · 972-387-9955

Beth E. Maultsby · Goranson, Bain, Larsen & Greenwald · 8150 North Central Expressway, Suite 1850 · Dallas, TX 75206 · 214-373-7676

Houston

Steve A. Bavousett · Steve A. Bavousett · 1820 One Riverway · Houston, TX 77056 · 713-871-9587

Warren Cole · Warren Cole · 3355 West Alabama, Suite 825 · Houston, TX 77098 · 713-275-4444

Donald R. Royall · ㉕ · The Royalls · 4550 Post Oak Place, Suite 341 · Houston, TX 77027 · 713-462-6500

Norma L. Trusch · Norma Levine Trusch Law Firm · 4550 Post Oak Place, Suite 341 · Houston, TX 77027 · 713-961-0256

Randall B. Wilhite · The Fullenweider Firm · http://www.fullenweider.com · 4265 San Felipe, Suite 1400 Houston, TX 77027 · 713-624-4100

San Antonio

Solomon J. Casseb III · Casseb & Pearl · 127 East Travis Street · San Antonio, TX 78205 · 210-223-4381

Benjamin R. Chappell · Bray & Chappell · 315 North Frost Center · 1250 Northeast Loop 410 · San Antonio, TX 78209-1525 · 210-828-2058

Terrell

Rothwell Pool · Law Office of Rothwell B. Pool · 408 West Nash · P.O. Box 517 · Terrell, TX 75160 · 972-524-7585

FIRST AMENDMENT LAW

Austin

David H. Donaldson, Jr. · ⑩ · Graves, Dougherty, Hearon & Moody · http://www.gdhm.com · 401 Congress Avenue, Suite 2200 · P.O. Box 98 · Austin, TX 78767-0098 · 512-480-5600

Julie Ford · George & Brothers · Norwood Tower, Suite 1100 · 114 West Seventh Street · Austin, TX 78701 · 512-495-1400

R. James George, Jr. · ⑳ · George & Brothers · Norwood Tower, Suite 1100 · 114 West Seventh Street · Austin, TX 78701 · 512-495-1400

James A. Hemphill · Graves, Dougherty, Hearon & Moody · http://www.gdhm.com · 401 Congress Avenue, Suite 2200 · P.O. Box 98 · Austin, TX 78767-0098 · 512-480-5600

Peter D. Kennedy · Graves, Dougherty, Hearon & Moody · http://www.gdhm.com · 401 Congress Avenue, Suite 2200 · P.O. Box 98 · Austin, TX 78767-0098 · 512-480-5600

Dallas

Robert P. Latham · Jackson Walker · Bank of America Plaza, Suite 6000 · 901 Main Street · Dallas, TX 75202 · 214-953-6000

Thomas S. Leatherbury · ⑩ · Vinson & Elkins · http://www.velaw.com · Trammell Crow Center, Suite 3700 · 2001 Ross Avenue · Dallas, TX 75201-2975 · 214-220-7700

Michael L. Raiff · Vinson & Elkins · http://www.velaw.com · Trammell Crow Center, Suite 3700 · 2001 Ross Avenue · Dallas, TX 75201-2975 · 214-220-7700

Paul C. Watler · ⑩ · Jackson Walker · Bank of America Plaza, Suite 6000 · 901 Main Street · Dallas, TX 75202 · 214-953-6000

El Paso

Richard G. Munzinger · ⑳ · Scott, Hulse, Marshall, Feuille, Finger & Thurmond · 1100 Chase Tower · 201 East Main Street · El Paso, TX 79901 · 915-533-2493

Fort Worth

Thomas J. Williams · ⑩ · Haynes and Boone · 201 Main Street, Suite 2200 · Fort Worth, TX 76102 · 817-347-6600

Houston

Charles Lynde Babcock · ⑩ · Jackson Walker · 1401 McKinney Street, Suite 1900 · Houston, TX 77010-4008 · 713-752-4200

Nancy W. Hamilton · Jackson Walker · 1401 McKinney Street, Suite 1900 · Houston, TX 77010-4008 · 713-752-4200

William W. Ogden · ⑩ · Ogden, Gibson, Broocks & Longoria · 1900 Pennzoil South Tower · 711 Louisiana Street · Houston, TX 77002 · 713-844-3000

San Antonio

Mark J. Cannan · Clemens & Spencer · http://www.clemens-spencer.com · 1300 Weston Centre · 112 East Pecan Street · San Antonio, TX 78205-1517 · 210-227-7121

FRANCHISE LAW

Austin

Charles B. Cannon · Charles B. Cannon · 701 Brazos Street, Suite 500 · Austin, TX 78701-3232 · 512-334-6544

Gayle Cannon · ⑩ · Haynes and Boone · 600 Congress Avenue, Suite 1300 · Austin, TX 78701-3285 · 512-867-8400

Lloyd E. Ferguson · Strasburger & Price · http://www.strasburger.com · 600 Congress Avenue, Suite 1600 Austin, TX 78701-2974 · 512-499-3600

Robert A. Lauer · Haynes and Boone · 600 Congress Avenue, Suite 1300 · Austin, TX 78701-3285 · 512-867-8400

Dallas

Deborah S. Coldwell · Haynes and Boone · 901 Main Street, Suite 3100 · Dallas, TX 75202 · 214-651-5000

Ann Hurwitz · ⑩ · DLA Piper · 1717 Main Street, Suite 4600 · Dallas, TX 75201-4629 · 214-743-4500

Earsa Jackson · Strasburger & Price · http://www.strasburger.com · 901 Main Street, Suite 4400 · Dallas, TX 75202-3794 · 214-651-4300

Joyce G. Mazero · ⑩ · Haynes and Boone · 901 Main Street, Suite 3100 · Dallas, TX 75202 · 214-651-5000

Michael E. Santa Maria · Baker & McKenzie · 2300 Trammell Crow Center · 2001 Ross Avenue · Dallas, TX 75201 · 214-978-3000

Richardson

Cheryl L. Mullin · Mullin Law · http://www.mullinlawpc.com · 2425 North Central Expressway, Suite 200 · Richardson, TX 75080 · 972-931-0022

GAMING LAW

Dallas

Charles W. Blau · Meadows, Collier, Reed, Cousins & Blau · 901 Main Street, Suite 3700 · Dallas, TX 75202 · 214-744-3700

GOVERNMENT RELATIONS LAW

Austin

Lisa K. Anderson · Brown McCarroll · 111 Congress Avenue, Suite 1400 · Austin, TX 78701-4093 · 512-472-5456

J. Gaylord Armstrong · McGinnis, Lochridge & Kilgore · http://www.mcginnislaw.com · 600 Congress Avenue, Suite 2100 · Austin, TX 78701 · 512-495-6000

Thomas J. Bond · Greenberg Traurig · http://www.gtlaw.com · One American Center, Suite 300 · 600 Congress Avenue · Austin, TX 78701 · 512-320-7200

James E. Brown · James E. Brown · P.O. Box 426 · Austin, TX 78767 · 512-457-0600

Randy C. Cain · Entwhistle & Cappucci · 1122 Colorado Street, Suite 106 · Austin, TX 78701 · 512-637-4994

Kent Allen Caperton · Ben Barnes Group · 98 San Jacinto Boulevard, Suite 250 · Austin, TX 78701-4299 512-322-0128

Randall H. Erben · Law Offices of Randall H. Erben · 807 Brazos Street, Suite 402 · Austin, TX 78701-2508 · 512-472-1682

Thomas A. Forbes · Kemp Smith · http://www.kempsmith.com · 816 Congress Avenue, Suite 1150 · Austin, TX 78701 · 512-320-5466

Pamela M. Giblin · ⑳ · Baker Botts · http://www.bakerbotts.com · 1500 San Jacinto Center · 98 San Jacinto Boulevard · Austin, TX 78701-4039 · 512-322-2500

R. Kinnan Golemon · ⑳ · KG Strategies · 111 Congress Avenue, Suite 1500 · Austin, TX 78701-4043 · 512-479-9707

Galt Graydon · The Graydon Group · 1001 Congress Avenue, Suite 400 · Austin, TX 78701 · 512-225-1001

Jack Wallace Gullahorn · Jack Wallace Gullahorn · P.O. Box 140045 · Austin, TX 78714 · 512-751-7074

Dowe D. Gullatt · Clark, Thomas & Winters · 300 West Sixth Street, 15th Floor · P.O. Box 1148 · Austin, TX 78767 · 512-472-8800

Clinton P. Hackney · Clinton P. Hackney · P.O. Box 163164 · Austin, TX 78716-3164 · 512-472-9022

John L. Howard, Jr. · Vinson & Elkins · http://www.velaw.com · 2801 Via Fortuna, Suite 100 · Austin, TX 78746-7568 · 512-542-8400

Gordon R. Johnson · Johnson and Johnson · Westgate Building, Suite 208 · 1122 Colorado Street · Austin, TX 78701-2100 · 512-478-7777

Robert E. Johnson, Jr. · Johnson and Johnson · Westgate Building, Suite 208 · 1122 Colorado Street · Austin, TX 78701-2100 · 512-478-7777

Bill Jones · Vinson & Elkins · http://www.velaw.com · 2801 Via Fortuna, Suite 100 · Austin, TX 78746-7568 · 512-542-8400

John M. Joseph · Clark, Thomas & Winters · 300 West Sixth Street, 15th Floor · P.O. Box 1148 · Austin, TX 78767 · 512-472-8800

Demetrius G. McDaniel · Greenberg Traurig · http://www.gtlaw.com · One American Center, Suite 300 · 600 Congress Avenue · Austin, TX 78701 · 512-320-7200

W. A. Messer III · W.A. Messer III · 604 West 14th Street · Austin, TX 78701-1726 · 512-472-0798

Deborah Goodell Polan · Deborah Goodell Polan Attorney at Law · 823 Congress Avenue, Suite 1305 · Austin, TX 78701 · 512-708-9896

Pike Powers · Fulbright & Jaworski · http://www.fulbright.com · 600 Congress Avenue, Suite 2400 · Austin, TX 78701-2978 · 512-474-5201

Carl S. Richie, Jr. · Carl S. Richie Jr. Attorney at Law · 1122 Colorado Street, Suite 210 · Austin, TX 78701 · 512-478-3802

Edward C. Small · Jackson Walker · 100 Congress Avenue, Suite 1100 · Austin, TX 78701 · 512-236-2000

Terral J. Smith · Sessions Lambert Selwyn · 3305 Northland Drive, Suite 301 · Austin, TX 78731 · 512-600-1012

Robert Strauser · Baker Botts · http://www.bakerbotts.com · 1500 San Jacinto Center · 98 San Jacinto Boulevard · Austin, TX 78701-4039 · 512-322-2500

Mark Vane · Gardere Wynne Sewell · http://www.gardere.com · One American Center, Suite 3000 · 600 Congress Avenue · Austin, TX 78701-2978 · 512-542-7000

Jill Warren · The Patriot Group · 919 Congress Avenue, Suite 1140 · Austin, TX 78701 · 512-477-6700

John Bill Watkins · Vinson & Elkins · http://www.velaw.com · 2801 Via Fortuna, Suite 100 · Austin, TX 78746-7568 · 512-542-8400

Ellen C. Williams · Law Offices of Ellen C. Williams · 1122 Colorado Street, Suite 1803 · Austin, TX 78701-0000 · 512-970-9597

Dallas

Robert W. Jordan · Baker Botts · http://www.bakerbotts.com · Trammell Crow Center, Suite 600 · 2001 Ross Avenue · Dallas, TX 75201-2980 · 214-953-6500

Ronald Kirk · Vinson & Elkins · http://www.velaw.com · Trammell Crow Center, Suite 3700 · 2001 Ross Avenue · Dallas, TX 75201-2975 · 214-220-7700

Houston

Robert D. Miller · Locke Lord Bissell & Liddell · JP Morgan Chase Tower, Suite 3400 · 600 Travis Street · Houston, TX 77002 · 713-226-1200

HEALTH CARE LAW

Amarillo

Mary Margaret Bearden · ⑩ · Brown & Fortunato · http://www.bf-law.com · 905 South Fillmore, Suite 400 · P.O. Box 9418 · Amarillo, TX 79105 · 806-345-6300

Austin

Kathryn M. Darling · Strasburger & Price · http://www.strasburger.com · 600 Congress Avenue, Suite 1600 · Austin, TX 78701-2974 · 512-499-3600

William D. Darling · ⑩ · Strasburger & Price · http://www.strasburger.com · 600 Congress Avenue, Suite 1600 · Austin, TX 78701-2974 · 512-499-3600

Catherine M. Greaves · Thompson & Knight · http://www.tklaw.com · 98 San Jacinto Boulevard, Suite 1900 · Austin, TX 78701 · 512-469-6100

David W. Hilgers · ⑩ · Brown McCarroll · 111 Congress Avenue, Suite 1400 · Austin, TX 78701-4093 · 512-472-5456

Penny Hobbs · McGinnis, Lochridge & Kilgore · http://www.mcginnislaw.com · 600 Congress Avenue, Suite 2100 · Austin, TX 78701 · 512-495-6000

Hal Katz · Brown McCarroll · 111 Congress Avenue, Suite 1400 · Austin, TX 78701-4093 · 512-472-5456

Edward S. McHorse · Graves, Dougherty, Hearon & Moody · http://www.gdhm.com · 401 Congress Avenue, Suite 2200 · P.O. Box 98 · Austin, TX 78767-0098 · 512-480-5600

Ace Pickens · ⑩ · Brown McCarroll · 111 Congress Avenue, Suite 1400 · Austin, TX 78701-4093 · 512-472-5456

Kathy L. Poppitt · Thompson & Knight · http://www.tklaw.com · 98 San Jacinto Boulevard, Suite 1900 · Austin, TX 78701 · 512-469-6100

Yvonne K. Puig · ⑩ · Fulbright & Jaworski · http://www.fulbright.com · 600 Congress Avenue, Suite 2400 Austin, TX 78701-2978 · 512-474-5201

Kevin A. Reed · Davis and Wilkerson · 1801 South MoPac, Suite 300 · Austin, TX 78746 · 512-482-0614

Elizabeth N. Rogers · Vinson & Elkins · http://www.velaw.com · 2801 Via Fortuna, Suite 100 · Austin, TX 78746-7568 · 512-542-8400

Michael R. Sharp · ⑩ · Sharp & Cobos · 4705 Spicewood Springs Road, Suite 100 · Austin, TX 78759 · 512-473-2265

Sharron Swann · Swann & Waddill · Building One, Suite 110 · 7004 Bee Cave Road · Austin, TX 78746 · 512-681-3720

Terry O. Tottenham · ⑩ · Fulbright & Jaworski · http://www.fulbright.com · 600 Congress Avenue, Suite 2400 · Austin, TX 78701-2978 · 512-474-5201

Beaumont

Patricia D. Chamblin · ⑩ · MehaffyWeber · http://www.mehaffyweber.com · 2615 Calder Avenue · P.O. Box 16 · Beaumont, TX 77702 · 409-835-5011

Jo Ben Whittenburg · Orgain, Bell & Tucker · 470 Orleans Street · P.O. Box 1751 · Beaumont, TX 77704-1751 · 409-838-6412

Dallas

David A. Berry · Greenberg Traurig · http://www.gtlaw.com · 600 Three Galleria Tower · 13155 Noel Road · Dallas, TX 75240 · 972-419-1250

Denise Webb Glass · Fulbright & Jaworski · http://www.fulbright.com · 2200 Ross Avenue, Suite 2800 · Dallas, TX 75201 · 214-855-8000

Jonathan Henderson · K&L Gates · 1717 Main Street, Suite 2800 · Dallas, TX 75201 · 214-939-5500

Bruce F. Howell · Powell Goldstein · http://www.pogolaw.com · JP Morgan Chase Tower, Suite 3300 · 2200 Ross Avenue · Dallas, TX 75201 · 214-721-8000

Todd P. Kelly · ⑩ · Fulbright & Jaworski · http://www.fulbright.com · 2200 Ross Avenue, Suite 2800 · Dallas, TX 75201 · 214-855-8000

Michael L. Malone · ⑩ · Greenberg Traurig · http://www.gtlaw.com · JP Morgan Chase Tower, Suite 5200 · 2200 Ross Avenue · Dallas, TX 75201 · 972-419-9100

Andrew N. Meyercord · Looper Reed & McGraw · 4100 Thanksgiving Tower · 1601 Elm Street · Dallas, TX 75201 · 214-954-4135

J. Anthony Patterson, Jr. · ⑩ · Fulbright & Jaworski · http://www.fulbright.com · 2200 Ross Avenue, Suite 2800 · Dallas, TX 75201 · 214-855-8000

Frank E. Sheeder III · Jones Day · 2727 North Harwood Street · Dallas, TX 75201-1515 · 214-220-3939

El Paso

Joseph L. Hood, Jr. · Windle, Hood, Alley, Norton, Brittain & Jay · Chase Tower, Suite 1350 · 201 East Main Street · El Paso, TX 79901 · 915-545-4900

Richard G. Munzinger · ⑳ · Scott, Hulse, Marshall, Feuille, Finger & Thurmond · 1100 Chase Tower · 201 East Main Street · El Paso, TX 79901 · 915-533-2493

Fort Worth

Richard L. Griffith · ⑳ · Cantey & Hanger · 300 Cantey Hanger Plaza · 600 West Sixth Street · Fort Worth, TX 76102-3685 · 817-877-2800

Darrell L. Keith · ⑩ · Keith Law Firm · The Keith Building · 1705 West Seventh Street · Fort Worth, TX 76102 · 817-338-1400

Galveston

Jon David Epstein · ⑩ · Greer, Herz & Adams · One Moody Plaza, 18th Floor · Galveston, TX 77550 · 409-797-3200

Houston

Jerry A. Bell, Jr. · ⑩ · Fulbright & Jaworski · http://www.fulbright.com · Fulbright Tower, Suite 5100 · 1301 McKinney Street · Houston, TX 77010-3095 · 713-651-5151

Barron P. Bogatto · Jackson Walker · 1401 McKinney Street, Suite 1900 · Houston, TX 77010-4008 · 713-752-4200

Donna S. Clark · Baker Hostetler · http://www.bakerlaw.com · 1000 Louisiana, Suite 2000 · Houston, TX 77002-5009 · 713-751-1600

Mark W. Coffin · Seyfarth Shaw · 700 Louisiana Street, Suite 3700 · Houston, TX 77002-2797 · 713-225-2300

Robert F. Corrigan, Jr. · Fulbright & Jaworski · http://www.fulbright.com · Fulbright Tower, Suite 5100 1301 McKinney Street · Houston, TX 77010-3095 · 713-651-5151

Dennis C. Dunn · King & Spalding · 1100 Louisiana Street, Suite 4000 · Houston, TX 77002-5213 · 713-751-3200

Gary W. Eiland · ⑩ · King & Spalding · 1100 Louisiana Street, Suite 4000 · Houston, TX 77002-5213 · 713-751-3200

Gregory N. Etzel · Baker Hostetler · http://www.bakerlaw.com · 1000 Louisiana, Suite 2000 · Houston, TX 77002-5009 · 713-751-1600

Susan Feigin Harris · Baker Hostetler · http://www.bakerlaw.com · 1000 Louisiana, Suite 2000 · Houston, TX 77002-5009 · 713-751-1600

Debbi M. Johnstone · ⑩ · Fulbright & Jaworski · http://www.fulbright.com · Fulbright Tower, Suite 5100 1301 McKinney Street · Houston, TX 77010-3095 · 713-651-5151

Nancy C. LeGros · King & Spalding · 1100 Louisiana Street, Suite 4000 · Houston, TX 77002-5213 · 713-751-3200

B. Scott McBride · Baker Hostetler · http://www.bakerlaw.com · 1000 Louisiana, Suite 2000 · Houston, TX 77002-5009 · 713-751-1600

Barbara A. Radnofsky · ⑩ · Barbara Radnofsky · 303 Timber Terrace Road · Houston, TX 77024 · 713-858-8509

Lisa Lepow Turboff · McGlinchey Stafford · http://www.mcglinchey.com · 1001 McKinney Street, Suite 1500 · Houston, TX 77002 · 713-520-1900

Ivan Wood, Jr. · Strasburger & Price · http://www.strasburger.com · 1401 McKinney Street, Suite 2200 · Houston, TX 77010-4035 · 713-951-5600

San Antonio

David L. Butler · Brin & Brin · 10999 IH10 West, Suite 800 · San Antonio, TX 78230-3878 · 210-341-9711

Cynthia Day Grimes · ⑩ · Ball & Weed · 10001 Reunion Place, Suite 600 · San Antonio, TX 78216 · 210-731-6300

Michael L. Kreager · The Kreager Law Firm · 7373 Broadway, Suite 500 · San Antonio, TX 78209-3262 · 210-829-7722

Bruce M. Mitchell · Oppenheimer, Blend, Harrison & Tate · 711 Navarro Street, Suite 600 · San Antonio, TX 78205-1796 · 210-224-2000

Edgar C. Morrison, Jr. · Jackson Walker · Weston Centre, Suite 2400 · 112 East Pecan Street · San Antonio, TX 78205 · 210-978-7700

Kathleen Quiroz · Oppenheimer, Blend, Harrison & Tate · 711 Navarro Street, Suite 600 · San Antonio, TX 78205-1796 · 210-224-2000

IMMIGRATION LAW

Austin

Daniel M. Kowalski · ⑩ · Law Office of Daniel M. Kowalski · 111 Congress Avenue, Fourth Floor · Austin, TX 78701 · 512-370-3155

Robert F. Loughran · Tindall & Foster · 100 Congress Avenue, Suite 1500 · Austin, TX 78701 · 512-478-9475

Mark G. Murov · ⑩ · Murov & Ward · 8808 Westminster Glen Avenue · Austin, TX 78730-3000 · 512-372-4167

Paul Parsons · ⑩ · Paul Parsons, Attorney at Law · 704 Rio Grande Street · Austin, TX 78701 · 512-477-7887

G. Wellington Smith · G. Wellington Smith · 1600 Nueces Street · Austin, TX 78701 · 512-476-7163

Dallas

Sarah Z. Brown · Miley & Brown · 705 Ross Avenue · Dallas, TX 75202-2007 · 214-692-8800

Richard Fernandez · Fernandez & Fernandez · 3010 Lyndon B. Johnson Freeway, Suite 732 · Dallas, TX 75234-7770 · 972-247-2272

Eugene J. Flynn · ⑩ · Eugene J. Flynn · 1511 Villars Street · Dallas, TX 75204-5439 · 214-821-1661

Richard A. Gump, Jr. · ⑩ · Law Offices of Richard A. Gump, Jr. · One Galleria Tower, Suite 1940 · 13355 Noel Road · Lock Box 39 · Dallas, TX 75240-6834 · 972-386-9544

Elise A. Healy · Spencer Crain Cubbage Healy & McNamara · Renaissance Tower, Suite 4100 · 1201 Elm Street · Dallas, TX 75270 · 214-290-0002

Harry J. Joe · ⑩ · Winstead · http://www.winstead.com · Renaissance Tower, Suite 5400 · 1201 Elm Street · Dallas, TX 75270-2199 · 214-745-5400

Steven Michael Ladik · ⑩ · Berry, Appleman & Leiden · 3232 McKinney Avenue, Suite 500 · Dallas, TX 75204-2429 · 214-442-7300

Craig E. Miley · ⑩ · Miley & Brown · 705 Ross Avenue · Dallas, TX 75202-2007 · 214-692-8800

Shawn A. Orme · Berry, Appleman & Leiden · 3232 McKinney Avenue, Suite 500 · Dallas, TX 75204-2429 · 214-442-7300

J. Joseph Reina · Reina & Bates · http://www.reinalaw.com · 1120 Empire Central Place · Dallas, TX 75247 · 214-905-9100

Michelle L. Saenz-Rodriguez · Saenz-Rodriguez & Associates · 2720 North Stemmons Freeway, Suite 1200 · Dallas, TX 75207-2212 · 214-637-5700

Paige L. Taylor · Berry, Appleman & Leiden · 3232 McKinney Avenue, Suite 500 · Dallas, TX 75204-2429 · 214-442-7300

Charla Truett · Law Offices of Richard A. Gump, Jr. · One Galleria Tower, Suite 1940 · 13355 Noel Road Lock Box 39 · Dallas, TX 75240-6834 · 972-386-9544

El Paso

Kathleen C. Walker · ⑩ · Brown McCarroll · 221 North Kansas Street, Suite 2000 · El Paso, TX 79901 · 915-545-4716

Harlingen

Jodilyn Marie Goodwin · Law Office of Jodi Goodwin · 1322 East Tyler Avenue · Harlingen, TX 78550-7142 · 956-428-7212

Houston

Brian K. Bates · ⑩ · Reina & Bates · http://www.reinalaw.com · 123 Northpoint Drive, Suite 190 · Houston, TX 77060 · 281-448-9500

Rebecca Burdette · ⑩ · Quan, Burdette & Perez · 5177 Richmond Avenue, Suite 800 · Houston, TX 77056 · 713-625-9200

Magali S. Candler · Tindall & Foster · 600 Travis Street, Suite 2800 · Houston, TX 77002-3094 · 713-229-8733

Nancy A. Falgout · Nancy Falgout · 3303 Louisiana, Suite 230 · P.O. Box 7873 · Houston, TX 77270-0000 · 713-520-1618

Charles C. Foster · ⑩ · Tindall & Foster · 600 Travis Street, Suite 2800 · Houston, TX 77002-3094 · 713-229-8733

Harry Gee, Jr. · ⑩ · Law Office of Harry Gee, Jr. and Associates · 5847 San Felipe Street, Suite 2950 · Houston, TX 77057-3010 · 713-781-0071

Judy J. Lee · Quan, Burdette & Perez · 5177 Richmond Avenue, Suite 800 · Houston, TX 77056 · 713-625-9200

Imran B. Mirza · Law Office of Imran Beg Mirza · 2425 West Loop South, Suite 200 · Houston, TX 77027 · 713-297-8860

José R. Pérez, Jr. · Quan, Burdette & Perez · 5177 Richmond Avenue, Suite 800 · Houston, TX 77056 · 713-625-9200

Richard L. Prinz · ⑩ · Richard Prinz · 500 Jefferson Street, Suite 2040 · Houston, TX 77002-7339 · 713-651-9111

Gordon J. Quan · ⑩ · Quan, Burdette & Perez · 5177 Richmond Avenue, Suite 800 · Houston, TX 77056 · 713-625-9200

H. Richard Sindelar III · Tindall & Foster · 600 Travis Street, Suite 2800 · Houston, TX 77002-3094 · 713-229-8733

Peter D. Williamson · ⑩ · Chamberlain, Hrdlicka, White, Williams & Martin · 1200 Smith Street, Suite 1400 · Houston, TX 77002 · 713-658-1818

McKinney

Garry L. Davis · The Law Offices of Garry L. Davis · 1700 Redbud Lane, Suite 180 · P.O. Box 332 · McKinney, TX 75070 · 972-548-5690

Nacogdoches

Richard S. Fischer · ⑩ · The Law Offices of Richard S. Fischer · 114 South Pecan Street · Nacogdoches, TX 75961 · 936-564-2222

San Antonio

Simon M. Azar-Farr · Simon M. Azar- Farr · 2313 North Flores Street · San Antonio, TX 78212 · 210-736-4122

Nancy Taylor Shivers · ⑩ · Shivers & Shivers · 1146 South Alamo Street · San Antonio, TX 78210-1178 · 210-226-9725

Robert Arley Shivers · ⑩ · Shivers & Shivers · 1146 South Alamo Street · San Antonio, TX 78210-1178 · 210-226-9725

San Benito

Elisabeth S. Brodyaga · Elisabeth S. Brodyaga · 17891 Landrum Park Road · San Benito, TX 78586 · 956-421-3226

INFORMATION TECHNOLOGY LAW

Austin

Jerry M. Keys · Matheson/Keys · Building One, Suite 110 · 7004 Bee Cave · Austin, TX 78746 · 512-681-3730

Dallas

Todd A. Fisher · K&L Gates · 1717 Main Street, Suite 2800 · Dallas, TX 75201 · 214-939-5500

John A. Funk · Morgan Lewis & Bockius · 1717 Main Street, Suite 3200 · Dallas, TX 75201 · 214-466-4000

David N. Guedry · Jones Day · 2727 North Harwood Street · Dallas, TX 75201-1515 · 214-220-3939

Dean William Harvey · Vinson & Elkins · http://www.velaw.com · Trammell Crow Center, Suite 3700 · 2001 Ross Avenue · Dallas, TX 75201-2975 · 214-220-7700

John E. Howell · K&L Gates · 1717 Main Street, Suite 2800 · Dallas, TX 75201 · 214-939-5500

Chad W. King · K&L Gates · 1717 Main Street, Suite 2800 · Dallas, TX 75201 · 214-939-5500

John W. Martin · Baker Botts · http://www.bakerbotts.com · Trammell Crow Center, Suite 600 · 2001 Ross Avenue · Dallas, TX 75201-2980 · 214-953-6500

Don J. McDermett, Jr. · Baker Botts · http://www.bakerbotts.com · Trammell Crow Center, Suite 600 · 2001 Ross Avenue · Dallas, TX 75201-2980 · 214-953-6500

David Monk · Baker Botts · http://www.bakerbotts.com · Trammell Crow Center, Suite 600 · 2001 Ross Avenue · Dallas, TX 75201-2980 · 214-953-6500

Stacey Smotherman · Fulbright & Jaworski · http://www.fulbright.com · 2200 Ross Avenue, Suite 2800 · Dallas, TX 75201 · 214-855-8000

Peter Vogel · Gardere Wynne Sewell · http://www.gardere.com · 1601 Elm Street, Suite 3000 · Dallas, TX 75201 · 214-999-3000

Houston

Jeff C. Dodd · ⑩ · Andrews Kurth · http://www.andrewskurth.com · 600 Travis Street, Suite 4200 · Houston, TX 77002 · 713-220-4200

Robert S. Harrell · ⑩ · Fulbright & Jaworski · http://www.fulbright.com · Fulbright Tower, Suite 5100 · 1301 McKinney Street · Houston, TX 77010-3095 · 713-651-5151

Raymond Nimmer · University of Houston Law Center · 100 Law Center · Houston, TX 77204-6060 · 713-743-2113

INSURANCE LAW

Arlington

Patrick J. Wielinski · Cokinos, Bosien & Young · 2221 East Lamar, Suite 750 · Arlington, TX 76006 · 817-635-3600

Austin

Jeff W. Autrey · Winstead · http://www.winstead.com · 401 Congress Avenue, Suite 2100 · Austin, TX 78701 · 512-370-2800

Thomas J. Bond · Greenberg Traurig · http://www.gtlaw.com · One American Center, Suite 300 · 600 Congress Avenue · Austin, TX 78701 · 512-320-7200

Linda J. Burgess · Winstead · http://www.winstead.com · 401 Congress Avenue, Suite 2100 · Austin, TX 78701 · 512-370-2800

Burnie Burner · Long, Burner, Parks & DeLargy · 106 East Sixth Street, Suite 300 · P.O. Box 2212 · Austin, TX 78768-2212 · 512-474-1587

Susan G. Conway · Graves, Dougherty, Hearon & Moody · http://www.gdhm.com · 401 Congress Avenue, Suite 2200 · P.O. Box 98 · Austin, TX 78767-0098 · 512-480-5600

Will D. Davis · Heath, Davis & McCalla · 720 Brazos Street, Suite 200 · Austin, TX 78701 · 512-478-5671

Hector De Leon · De Leon, Boggins & Icenogle · Chase Tower, Suite 1050 · 221 West Sixth Street · Austin, TX 78701 · 512-478-5308

Elisabeth DeLargy · Long, Burner, Parks & DeLargy · 106 East Sixth Street, Suite 300 · P.O. Box 2212 · Austin, TX 78768-2212 · 512-474-1587

Alex Gonzales · Winstead · http://www.winstead.com · 401 Congress Avenue, Suite 2100 · Austin, TX 78701 · 512-370-2800

Guy M. Hohmann · Hohmann Taube & Summers · 100 Congress Avenue, 18th Floor · Austin, TX 78701-4042 · 512-472-5997

Mary F. Keller · York, Keller & Field · 816 Congress Avenue, Suite 1670 · Austin, TX 78701 · 512-867-1616

David D. Knoll · Thompson, Coe, Cousins & Irons · http://www.thompsoncoe.com · Austin Centre, Suite 1500 · 701 Brazos · Austin, TX 78701 · 512-708-8200

J. Mark Lawless · Nickens Keeton Lawless Farrell Flack · 327 Congress Avenue, Suite 490 · Austin, TX 78701 · 512-472-3067

Dudley D. McCalla · Heath, Davis & McCalla · 720 Brazos Street, Suite 200 · Austin, TX 78701 · 512-478-5671

Michael Quinn · Quinn Seelig & Hayes · 5511 Parkcrest, Suite 107 · Austin, TX 78731 · 512-542-9243

Michael Sean Quinn · Quinn Hayes & Quinn · 5511 Parkcrest, Suite 107 · Austin, TX 78703 · 512-542-9243

Forrest C. Roan · Winstead · http://www.winstead.com · 401 Congress Avenue, Suite 2100 · Austin, TX 78701 · 512-370-2800

Barry Senterfitt · Greenberg Traurig · http://www.gtlaw.com · One American Center, Suite 300 · 600 Congress Avenue · Austin, TX 78701 · 512-320-7200

Larry F. York · McGinnis, Lochridge & Kilgore · http://www.mcginnislaw.com · 600 Congress Avenue, Suite 2100 · Austin, TX 78701 · 512-495-6000

Corpus Christi

Russell H. McMains · ⑩ · Law Offices of Russell H. McMains · 500 North Shoreline Boulevard, Suite 1100 · P.O. Box 2846 · Corpus Christi, TX 78403 · 361-887-4455

Dallas

Thomas B. Alleman · Winstead · http://www.winstead.com · Renaissance Tower, Suite 5400 · 1201 Elm Street · Dallas, TX 75270-2199 · 214-745-5400

Veronica M. Bates · Hermes Sargent Bates · 901 Main Street, Suite 5200 · Dallas, TX 75202 · 214-749-6000

Beth D. Bradley · Tollefson Bradley Ball and Mitchell · 2811 McKinney Avenue, Suite 250 · Dallas, TX 75204 · 214-665-0100

R. Brent Cooper · Cooper & Scully · 900 Jackson Street, Suite 100 · Dallas, TX 75202 · 214-712-9500

Sidney H. Davis, Jr. · Touchstone Bernays · http://www.touchstonelaw.com · 4040 Renaissance Tower · 1201 Elm Street · Dallas, TX 75270-2196 · 214-741-1166

Jeffrey A. Ford · Ford Nassen & Baldwin · 8080 North Central Expressway, Suite 1600 · Dallas, TX 75206-1819 · 214-523-5100

Michael W. Huddleston · Shannon, Gracey, Ratliff & Miller · http://www.shannongracey.com · 500 North Akard Street, Suite 2500 · Dallas, TX 75201 · 214-245-3090

Andrew G. Jubinsky · Figari & Davenport · http://www.figdav.com · 3400 Bank of America Plaza · 901 Main Street · Dallas, TX 75202-3796 · 214-939-2000

Michael Keeley · Strasburger & Price · http://www.strasburger.com · 901 Main Street, Suite 4400 · Dallas, TX 75202-3794 · 214-651-4300

David N. Kitner · Strasburger & Price · http://www.strasburger.com · 901 Main Street, Suite 4400 · Dallas, TX 75202-3794 · 214-651-4300

George Lankford · Fanning Harper and Martinson · Two Energy Square, Suite 1300 · 4849 Greenville Avenue · Dallas, TX 75206 · 214-369-1300

John J. Little · Little Pedersen Fankhauser · http://www.lpf-law.com · 901 Main Street, Suite 4110 · Dallas, TX 75202 · 214-573-2300

Ernest Martin, Jr. · Haynes and Boone · 901 Main Street, Suite 3100 · Dallas, TX 75202 · 214-651-5000

James H. Moody III · Quilling, Selander, Cummiskey & Lownds · Bryan Tower, Suite 1800 · 2001 Bryan Street · Dallas, TX 75201 · 214-871-2100

Werner A. Powers · Haynes and Boone · 901 Main Street, Suite 3100 · Dallas, TX 75202 · 214-651-5000

Paul D. Schoonover · ⑩ · Kleiman Lawrence Baskind Fitzgerald · 8750 North Central Expressway, Suite 777 · Dallas, TX 75231 · 214-265-7400

John C. Tollefson · Tollefson Bradley Ball and Mitchell · 2811 McKinney Avenue, Suite 250 · Dallas, TX 75204 · 214-665-0100

Thomas L. Woodman · Winstead · http://www.winstead.com · Renaissance Tower, Suite 5400 · 1201 Elm Street · Dallas, TX 75270-2199 · 214-745-5400

El Paso

Richard A. Bonner · Kemp Smith · http://www.kempsmith.com · 221 North Kansas, Suite 1700 · El Paso, TX 79901-1441 · 915-533-4424

Houston

David H. Brown · Brown & Kornegay · 2777 Allen Parkway, Suite 977 · Houston, TX 77019 · 713-528-3700

Reagan M. Brown · Fulbright & Jaworski · http://www.fulbright.com · Fulbright Tower, Suite 5100 · 1301 McKinney Street · Houston, TX 77010-3095 · 713-651-5151

Robert J. Cunningham · Cook & Roach · Heritage Plaza, Suite 2650 · 1111 Bagby Street · Houston, TX 77002 · 713-652-2800

David D. Disiere · Martin, Disiere, Jefferson & Wisdom · http://www.mdjwlaw.com · Niels Esperson Building, Suite 1800 · 808 Travis Street · Houston, TX 77002 · 713-632-1700

Brian S. Martin · Thompson, Coe, Cousins & Irons · http://www.thompsoncoe.com · One Riverway, Suite 1600 · Houston, TX 77056 · 713-403-8210

Christopher W. Martin · Martin, Disiere, Jefferson & Wisdom · http://www.mdjwlaw.com · Niels Esperson Building, Suite 1800 · 808 Travis Street · Houston, TX 77002 · 713-632-1700

Vincent E. Morgan · Pillsbury Winthrop Shaw Pittman · http://www.pillsburylaw.com · Two Houston Center, Suite 2000 · 909 Fannin Street · Houston, TX 77010-1018 · 713-276-7600

Stephen P. Pate · Fulbright & Jaworski · http://www.fulbright.com · Fulbright Tower, Suite 5100 · 1301 McKinney Street · Houston, TX 77010-3095 · 713-651-5151

Robert M. Roach · Cook & Roach · Heritage Plaza, Suite 2650 · 1111 Bagby Street · Houston, TX 77002 713-652-2800

Martin R. Sadler · Martin, Disiere, Jefferson & Wisdom · http://www.mdjwlaw.com · Niels Esperson Building, Suite 1800 · 808 Travis Street · Houston, TX 77002 · 713-632-1700

San Antonio

Sylvan S. Lang, Jr. · Lang & Kustoff · 4103 Parkdale Street · San Antonio, TX 78229-2520 · 210-614-9444

Thomas H. Veitch · Langley & Banack · Trinity Plaza II, Suite 900 · 745 East Mulberry Avenue · San Antonio, TX 78212-3166 · 210-736-6600

Austin

Alan D. Albright · Fish & Richardson · One Congress Plaza, Suite 810 · 111 Congress Avenue · Austin, TX 78701 · 512-472-5070

William G. Barber · Pirkey Barber · 600 Congress Avenue, Suite 2120 · Austin, TX 78701 · 512-322-5200

Michael C. Barrett · Fulbright & Jaworski · http://www.fulbright.com · 600 Congress Avenue, Suite 2400 Austin, TX 78701-2978 · 512-474-5201

Christopher R. Benson · Fulbright & Jaworski · http://www.fulbright.com · 600 Congress Avenue, Suite 2400 · Austin, TX 78701-2978 · 512-474-5201

Tracey B. Davies · Vinson & Elkins · http://www.velaw.com · 2801 Via Fortuna, Suite 100 · Austin, TX 78746-7568 · 512-542-8400

Andrew J. Dillon · Dillon & Yudell · 8911 North Capital of Texas Highway, Suite 2110 · Austin, TX 78759 · 512-343-6116

Bryan Farney · Dechert · 300 West Sixth Street, Suite 1850 · Austin, TX 78701 · 512-394-3000

Thomas R. Felger · Baker Botts · http://www.bakerbotts.com · 1500 San Jacinto Center · 98 San Jacinto Boulevard · Austin, TX 78701-4039 · 512-322-2500

Mark T. Garrett · Fulbright & Jaworski · http://www.fulbright.com · 600 Congress Avenue, Suite 2400 · Austin, TX 78701-2978 · 512-474-5201

Richard J. Groos · Fulbright & Jaworski · http://www.fulbright.com · 600 Congress Avenue, Suite 2400 · Austin, TX 78701-2978 · 512-474-5201

Wayne Harding · Dewey & LeBoeuf · 401 Congress Avenue, Suite 3200 · Austin, TX 78701-3788 · 512-226-0300

Jerry M. Keys · Matheson/Keys · Building One, Suite 110 · 7004 Bee Cave · Austin, TX 78746 · 512-681-3730

Kevin Kudlac · Weil Gotshal & Manges · 8911 Capital of Texas Highway, Suite 1350 · Austin, TX 78759 512-349-1930

David L. Parker · Fulbright & Jaworski · http://www.fulbright.com · 600 Congress Avenue, Suite 2400 · Austin, TX 78701-2978 · 512-474-5201

William M. Parrish · Winstead · http://www.winstead.com · 401 Congress Avenue, Suite 2100 · Austin, TX 78701 · 512-370-2800

Louis T. Pirkey · ⑩ · Pirkey Barber · 600 Congress Avenue, Suite 2120 · Austin, TX 78701 · 512-322-5200

Amber Hatfield Rovner · Weil Gotshal & Manges · 8911 Capital of Texas Highway, Suite 1350 · Austin, TX 78759 · 512-349-1930

Willem G. Schuurman · Vinson & Elkins · http://www.velaw.com · 2801 Via Fortuna, Suite 100 · Austin, TX 78746-7568 · 512-542-8400

Gina N. Shishima · Fulbright & Jaworski · http://www.fulbright.com · 600 Congress Avenue, Suite 2400 · Austin, TX 78701-2978 · 512-474-5201

Travis Gordon White · McKool Smith · http://www.mckoolsmith.com · 300 West Sixth Street, Suite 1700 Austin, TX 78701 · 512-692-8700

Corpus Christi

Craig A. Ansel · Davis Hutchinson & Wilkerson · 802 North Carancahua Street, Suite 1270 · Corpus Christi, TX 78470-0400 · 361-882-2272

Martin C. Davis · Davis Hutchinson & Wilkerson · 802 North Carancahua Street, Suite 1270 · Corpus Christi, TX 78470-0400 · 361-882-2272

Susan E. Hutchinson · Davis Hutchinson & Wilkerson · 802 North Carancahua Street, Suite 1270 · Corpus Christi, TX 78470-0400 · 361-882-2272

Dallas

Samuel F. Baxter · McKool Smith · http://www.mckoolsmith.com · 300 Crescent Court, Suite 1500 · Dallas, TX 75201 · 214-978-4000

James P. Bradley · Sidley Austin · 717 North Harwood Street, Suite 3400 · Dallas, TX 75201 · 214-981-3300

Eric W. Buether · Greenberg Traurig · http://www.gtlaw.com · 600 Three Galleria Tower · 13155 Noel Road · Dallas, TX 75240 · 972-419-1250

Larry D. Carlson · Baker Botts · http://www.bakerbotts.com · Trammell Crow Center, Suite 600 · 2001 Ross Avenue · Dallas, TX 75201-2980 · 214-953-6500

Jeffrey A. Carter · McKool Smith · http://www.mckoolsmith.com · 300 Crescent Court, Suite 1500 · Dallas, TX 75201 · 214-978-4000

Douglas Cawley · McKool Smith · http://www.mckoolsmith.com · 300 Crescent Court, Suite 1500 · Dallas, TX 75201 · 214-978-4000

Robert M. Chiaviello, Jr. · Fulbright & Jaworski · http://www.fulbright.com · 2200 Ross Avenue, Suite 2800 · Dallas, TX 75201 · 214-855-8000

Max Ciccarelli · Thompson & Knight · http://www.tklaw.com · One Arts Plaza, Suite 1500 · 1722 Routh Street · Dallas, TX 75201-2533 · 214-969-1700

Dan D. Davison · Fulbright & Jaworski · http://www.fulbright.com · 2200 Ross Avenue, Suite 2800 · Dallas, TX 75201 · 214-855-8000

Timothy S. Durst · Baker Botts · http://www.bakerbotts.com · Trammell Crow Center, Suite 600 · 2001 Ross Avenue · Dallas, TX 75201-2980 · 214-953-6500

Elisabeth A. Evert · Hitchcock Evert · http://www.hitchcockevert.com · 750 North St. Paul Street, Suite 1110 · Dallas, TX 75201 · 214-953-1111

Hilda C. Galvan · Jones Day · 2727 North Harwood Street · Dallas, TX 75201-1515 · 214-220-3939

Kenneth R. Glaser · Gardere Wynne Sewell · http://www.gardere.com · 1601 Elm Street, Suite 3000 · Dallas, TX 75201 · 214-999-3000

Brett C. Govett · Fulbright & Jaworski · http://www.fulbright.com · 2200 Ross Avenue, Suite 2800 · Dallas, TX 75201 · 214-855-8000

Herbert J. Hammond · Thompson & Knight · http://www.tklaw.com · One Arts Plaza, Suite 1500 · 1722 Routh Street · Dallas, TX 75201-2533 · 214-969-1700

J. Pat Heptig · Heptig Law Group · One Lincoln Center, Suite 1200 · 5400 LBJ Freeway · Dallas, TX 75240 · 214-451-2154

Robert P. Latham · Jackson Walker · Bank of America Plaza, Suite 6000 · 901 Main Street · Dallas, TX 75202 · 214-953-6000

Steven C. Malin · Sidley Austin · 717 North Harwood Street, Suite 3400 · Dallas, TX 75201 · 214-981-3300

David L. McCombs · Haynes and Boone · 901 Main Street, Suite 3100 · Dallas, TX 75202 · 214-651-5000

V. Bryan Medlock, Jr. · ⑩ · Sidley Austin · 717 North Harwood Street, Suite 3400 · Dallas, TX 75201 · 214-981-3300

Kevin J. Meek · Baker Botts · http://www.bakerbotts.com · Trammell Crow Center, Suite 600 · 2001 Ross Avenue · Dallas, TX 75201-2980 · 214-953-6500

Gaynell C. Methvin · ⑩ · Gaynell C. Methvin · 300 Crescent Court, Suite 1500 · Dallas, TX 75201 · 214-978-4999

Rod Phelan · ⑩ · Baker Botts · http://www.bakerbotts.com · Trammell Crow Center, Suite 600 · 2001 Ross Avenue · Dallas, TX 75201-2980 · 214-953-6500

Phillip B. Philbin · Haynes and Boone · 901 Main Street, Suite 3100 · Dallas, TX 75202 · 214-651-5000

Mark Reiter · Gibson, Dunn & Crutcher · 2100 McKinney Avenue, Suite 1100 · Dallas, TX 75201-7390 · 214-698-3100

Molly Buck Richard · ⑩ · Richard Law Group · 8411 Preston Road, Suite 890 · Dallas, TX 75225 · 214-206-4300

Jerry R. Selinger · ⑩ · Morgan Lewis & Bockius · 1717 Main Street, Suite 3200 · Dallas, TX 75201 · 214-466-4000

Barton E. Showalter · Baker Botts · http://www.bakerbotts.com · Trammell Crow Center, Suite 600 · 2001 Ross Avenue · Dallas, TX 75201-2980 · 214-953-6500

Bruce S. Sostek · Thompson & Knight · http://www.tklaw.com · One Arts Plaza, Suite 1500 · 1722 Routh Street · Dallas, TX 75201-2533 · 214-969-1700

Theodore Stevenson III · McKool Smith · http://www.mckoolsmith.com · 300 Crescent Court, Suite 1500 Dallas, TX 75201 · 214-978-4000

Donald Curtis Templin · Haynes and Boone · 901 Main Street, Suite 3100 · Dallas, TX 75202 · 214-651-5000

Robert W. Turner · ⑩ · Jones Day · 2727 North Harwood Street · Dallas, TX 75201-1515 · 214-220-3939

David G. Wille · Baker Botts · http://www.bakerbotts.com · Trammell Crow Center, Suite 600 · 2001 Ross Avenue · Dallas, TX 75201-2980 · 214-953-6500

Houston

Charles S. Baker · Porter & Hedges · 1000 Main Street, 36th Floor · Houston, TX 77002 · 713-226-0600

Nicolas G. Barzoukas · Weil Gotshal & Manges · Bank of America Building, Suite 1600 · 700 Louisiana Street · Houston, TX 77002 · 713-546-5000

Margaret Anne Boulware · ⑩ · Baker & McKenzie · 711 Louisiana Street, Suite 3400 · Houston, TX 77002-2716 · 713-427-5000

Louis Brucculeri · Wong, Cabello, Lutsch, Rutherford & Brucculeri · http://www.counselip.com · Chasewood Bank Building, Suite 600 · 20333 SH 249 · Houston, TX 77070 · 832-446-2400

Rodney K. Caldwell · ⑩ · Howrey · 1111 Louisiana, 25th Floor · Houston, TX 77002-5242 · 713-787-1400

Jack C. Goldstein · Law Office of Jack C Goldstein · 16 Sugarberry Circle · Houston, TX 77024-7251 · 713-782-7821

David J. Healey · Weil Gotshal & Manges · Bank of America Building, Suite 1600 · 700 Louisiana Street · Houston, TX 77002 · 713-546-5000

Michael F. Heim · Heim, Payne & Chorush · http://www.hpcllp.com · JP Morgan Chase Tower, Suite 6710 · 600 Travis Street · Houston, TX 77002 · 713-221-2000

Lester L. Hewitt · ⑩ · Akin Gump Strauss Hauer & Feld · 1111 Louisiana Street, 44th Floor · Houston, TX 77002-5200 · 713-220-5800

Sharon A. Israel · Mayer Brown · Bank of America Center, Suite 3400 · 700 Louisiana Street · Houston, TX 77002-2730 · 713-238-3000

John R. Keville · Howrey · 1111 Louisiana, 25th Floor · Houston, TX 77002-5242 · 713-787-1400

Albert B. Kimball, Jr. · Bracewell & Giuliani · http://www.bgllp.com · 711 Louisiana Street, Suite 2300 · Houston, TX 77002-2770 · 713-223-2300

Paul E. Krieger · Morgan Lewis & Bockius · 1000 Louisiana St., Suite 4200 · Houston, TX 77002-5006 · 713-890-5000

William L. LaFuze · ⑩ · Vinson & Elkins · http://www.velaw.com · First City Tower, Suite 2500 · 1001 Fannin Street · Houston, TX 77002-6760 · 713-758-2222

John F. Lynch · ⑩ · Howrey · 1111 Louisiana, 25th Floor · Houston, TX 77002-5242 · 713-787-1400

Marilyn C. Maloney · ⑩ · Liskow & Lewis · http://www.liskow.com · First City Tower, Suite 1800 · 1001 Fannin Street · Houston, TX 77002-4102 · 713-651-2900

J. Clark Martin · ⑩ · Kelly, Hart & Hallman · Wells Fargo Plaza, Suite 4700 · 1000 Louisiana Street · Houston, TX 77002 · 713-654-4600

Robert McAughan · Locke Lord Bissell & Liddell · JP Morgan Chase Tower, Suite 3400 · 600 Travis Street · Houston, TX 77002 · 713-226-1200

Floyd R. Nation · ⑩ · Howrey · 1111 Louisiana, 25th Floor · Houston, TX 77002-5242 · 713-787-1400

Raymond Nimmer · University of Houston Law Center · 100 Law Center · Houston, TX 77204-6060 · 713-743-2113

John D. Norris · ⑩ · Howrey · 1111 Louisiana, 25th Floor · Houston, TX 77002-5242 · 713-787-1400

Jayme Partridge · Slusser Wilson & Partridge · 4720 Three Allen Center · 333 Clay Street · Houston, TX 77002 · 713-860-3300

Scott F. Partridge · ⑩ · Baker Botts · http://www.bakerbotts.com · One Shell Plaza · 910 Louisiana Street Houston, TX 77002-1210 · 713-229-1234

William D. Raman · Wong, Cabello, Lutsch, Rutherford & Brucculeri · http://www.counselip.com · Chasewood Bank Building, Suite 600 · 20333 SH 249 · Houston, TX 77070 · 832-446-2400

John C. Rawls · Fulbright & Jaworski · http://www.fulbright.com · Fulbright Tower, Suite 5100 · 1301 McKinney Street · Houston, TX 77010-3095 · 713-651-5151

James W. Repass · Fulbright & Jaworski · http://www.fulbright.com · Fulbright Tower, Suite 5100 · 1301 McKinney Street · Houston, TX 77010-3095 · 713-651-5151

Keith A. Rutherford · Wong, Cabello, Lutsch, Rutherford & Brucculeri · http://www.counselip.com · Chasewood Bank Building, Suite 600 · 20333 SH 249 · Houston, TX 77070 · 832-446-2400

William C. Slusser · ⑩ · Slusser Wilson & Partridge · 4720 Three Allen Center · 333 Clay Street · Houston, TX 77002 · 713-860-3300

Gene L. Spears · Baker Botts · http://www.bakerbotts.com · One Shell Plaza · 910 Louisiana Street · Houston, TX 77002-1210 · 713-229-1234

Richard L. Stanley · ⑩ · Howrey · 1111 Louisiana, 25th Floor · Houston, TX 77002-5242 · 713-787-1400

Michael O. Sutton · ⑩ · Locke Lord Bissell & Liddell · JP Morgan Chase Tower, Suite 3400 · 600 Travis Street · Houston, TX 77002 · 713-226-1200

Ben D. Tobor · Greenberg Traurig · http://www.gtlaw.com · 1000 Louisiana Street, Suite 1800 · Houston, TX 77002 · 713-374-3500

Max L. Tribble, Jr. · Susman Godfrey · 1000 Louisiana, Suite 5100 · Houston, TX 77002-5096 · 713-651-9366

Danny L. Williams · Williams, Morgan & Amerson · 10333 Richmond Avenue, Suite 1100 · Houston, TX 77042 · 713-934-7000

Russell T. Wong · Wong, Cabello, Lutsch, Rutherford & Brucculeri · http://www.counselip.com · Chasewood Bank Building, Suite 600 · 20333 SH 249 · Houston, TX 77070 · 832-446-2400

Longview

S. Calvin Capshaw · Capshaw DeRieux · The Energy Centre, Suite 220 · Longview, TX 75601-5157 · 903-236-9800

Marshall

Franklin Jones, Jr. · ㉕ · Jones & Jones · 201 West Houston Street · P.O. Drawer 1249 · Marshall, TX 75671-1249 · 903-938-4395

Carl R. Roth · The Roth Law Firm · 115 North Wellington Street, Suite 200 · P.O. Box 876 · Marshall, TX 75671 · 903-935-1665

San Antonio

J. Daniel Harkins · Cox Smith Matthews · http://www.coxsmith.com · 112 East Pecan Street, Suite 1800 · San Antonio, TX 78205-1521 · 210-554-5500

Gale Roy Peterson · ⑩ · Cox Smith Matthews · http://www.coxsmith.com · 112 East Pecan Street, Suite 1800 · San Antonio, TX 78205-1521 · 210-554-5500

Tyler

Otis W. Carroll · Ireland Carroll & Kelley · 6101 South Broadway, Suite 500 · Tyler, TX 75703 · 903-561-1600

INTERNATIONAL ARBITRATION

Dallas

Mark A. Calhoun · Greenberg Traurig · http://www.gtlaw.com · JP Morgan Chase Tower, Suite 5200 · 2200 Ross Avenue · Dallas, TX 75201 · 972-419-9100

Robert W. Jordan · Baker Botts · http://www.bakerbotts.com · Trammell Crow Center, Suite 600 · 2001 Ross Avenue · Dallas, TX 75201-2980 · 214-953-6500

Jay J. Madrid · Winstead · http://www.winstead.com · Renaissance Tower, Suite 5400 · 1201 Elm Street · Dallas, TX 75270-2199 · 214-745-5400

Houston

C. Mark Baker · Fulbright & Jaworski · http://www.fulbright.com · Fulbright Tower, Suite 5100 · 1301 McKinney Street · Houston, TX 77010-3095 · 713-651-5151

R. Doak Bishop · King & Spalding · 1100 Louisiana Street, Suite 4000 · Houston, TX 77002-5213 · 713-751-3200

John P. Bowman · Fulbright & Jaworski · http://www.fulbright.com · Fulbright Tower, Suite 5100 · 1301 McKinney Street · Houston, TX 77010-3095 · 713-651-5151

Platt W. Davis III · Platt W. Davis · 7500 San Felipe, Suite 600 · Houston, TX 77063 · 713-914-8030

Phillip Bruce Dye, Jr. · Vinson & Elkins · http://www.velaw.com · First City Tower, Suite 2500 · 1001 Fannin Street · Houston, TX 77002-6760 · 713-758-2222

William H. Knull III · Mayer Brown · Bank of America Center, Suite 3400 · 700 Louisiana Street · Houston, TX 77002-2730 · 713-238-3000

Guy Stanford Lipe · Vinson & Elkins · http://www.velaw.com · First City Tower, Suite 2500 · 1001 Fannin Street · Houston, TX 77002-6760 · 713-758-2222

James Lloyd Loftis · Vinson & Elkins · http://www.velaw.com · First City Tower, Suite 2500 · 1001 Fannin Street · Houston, TX 77002-6760 · 713-758-2222

Kevin O'Gorman · Fulbright & Jaworski · http://www.fulbright.com · Fulbright Tower, Suite 5100 · 1301 McKinney Street · Houston, TX 77010-3095 · 713-651-5151

Adam P. Schiffer · Schiffer Odom Hicks · Phoenix Tower, Suite 2390 · 3200 Southwest Freeway · Houston, TX 77027 · 713-357-5150

Ben H. Sheppard, Jr. · University of Houston Law Center · 100 Law Center · Houston, TX 77204-6060 · 713-743-2113

Timothy J. Tyler · Mayer Brown · Bank of America Center, Suite 3400 · 700 Louisiana Street · Houston, TX 77002-2730 · 713-238-3000

INTERNATIONAL TRADE AND FINANCE LAW

Dallas

Larry B. Pascal · Haynes and Boone · 901 Main Street, Suite 3100 · Dallas, TX 75202 · 214-651-5000

Fred C. Pedersen · Little Pedersen Fankhauser · http://www.lpf-law.com · 901 Main Street, Suite 4110 · Dallas, TX 75202 · 214-573-2300

Timothy E. Powers · Haynes and Boone · 901 Main Street, Suite 3100 · Dallas, TX 75202 · 214-651-5000

William D. Young · Vinson & Elkins · http://www.velaw.com · Trammell Crow Center, Suite 3700 · 2001 Ross Avenue · Dallas, TX 75201-2975 · 214-220-7700

Houston

David F. Asmus · Baker Botts · http://www.bakerbotts.com · One Shell Plaza · 910 Louisiana Street · Houston, TX 77002-1210 · 713-229-1234

Marcia E. Backus · Vinson & Elkins · http://www.velaw.com · First City Tower, Suite 2500 · 1001 Fannin Street · Houston, TX 77002-6760 · 713-758-2222

Larry G. Barbour · Vinson & Elkins · http://www.velaw.com · First City Tower, Suite 2500 · 1001 Fannin Street · Houston, TX 77002-6760 · 713-758-2222

J. Mark Brazzil · Vinson & Elkins · http://www.velaw.com · First City Tower, Suite 2500 · 1001 Fannin Street · Houston, TX 77002-6760 · 713-758-2222

John P. Cogan, Jr. · McDermott Will & Emery · 1000 Louisiana, Suite 1300 · Houston, TX 77002 · 713-653-1700

Stephen D. Davis · Vinson & Elkins · http://www.velaw.com · First City Tower, Suite 2500 · 1001 Fannin Street · Houston, TX 77002-6760 · 713-758-2222

Joseph C. Dilg · ⑩ · Vinson & Elkins · http://www.velaw.com · First City Tower, Suite 2500 · 1001 Fannin Street · Houston, TX 77002-6760 · 713-758-2222

Phillip Bruce Dye, Jr. · Vinson & Elkins · http://www.velaw.com · First City Tower, Suite 2500 · 1001 Fannin Street · Houston, TX 77002-6760 · 713-758-2222

Mark C. Evans · Bracewell & Giuliani · http://www.bgllp.com · 711 Louisiana Street, Suite 2300 · Houston, TX 77002-2770 · 713-223-2300

Michael S. Goldberg · Baker Botts · http://www.bakerbotts.com · One Shell Plaza · 910 Louisiana Street · Houston, TX 77002-1210 · 713-229-1234

George F. Goolsby · Baker Botts · http://www.bakerbotts.com · One Shell Plaza · 910 Louisiana Street · Houston, TX 77002-1210 · 713-229-1234

Jay D. Kelley · Vinson & Elkins · http://www.velaw.com · First City Tower, Suite 2500 · 1001 Fannin Street · Houston, TX 77002-6760 · 713-758-2222

Jay T. Kolb · Baker Botts · http://www.bakerbotts.com · One Shell Plaza · 910 Louisiana Street · Houston, TX 77002-1210 · 713-229-1234

Kevin Paul Lewis · Vinson & Elkins · http://www.velaw.com · First City Tower, Suite 2500 · 1001 Fannin Street · Houston, TX 77002-6760 · 713-758-2222

Glenn L. Pinkerton · Vinson & Elkins · http://www.velaw.com · First City Tower, Suite 2500 · 1001 Fannin Street · Houston, TX 77002-6760 · 713-758-2222

Ben H. Sheppard, Jr. · University of Houston Law Center · 100 Law Center · Houston, TX 77204-6060 · 713-743-2113

Mark R. Spradling · Vinson & Elkins · http://www.velaw.com · First City Tower, Suite 2500 · 1001 Fannin Street · Houston, TX 77002-6760 · 713-758-2222

Clark G. Thompson, Jr. · Bracewell & Giuliani · http://www.bgllp.com · 711 Louisiana Street, Suite 2300 Houston, TX 77002-2770 · 713-223-2300

William H. Weiland · Winstead · http://www.winstead.com · JPMorgan Chase Tower, Suite 1100 · 600 Travis Street · Houston, TX 77002 · 713-650-8400

Blake H. Winburne · Baker Botts · http://www.bakerbotts.com · One Shell Plaza · 910 Louisiana Street · Houston, TX 77002-1210 · 713-229-1234

LABOR AND EMPLOYMENT LAW

Austin

Jason S. Boulette · Boulette & Golden · Three Barton Skyway, Suite 300 · 1221 South MoPac Expressway · Austin, TX 78746 · 512-732-8900

Scott Brutocao · Ogletree Deakins · http://www.ogletreedeakins.com · 301 Congress Avenue, Suite 1250 · Austin, TX 78701 · 512-344-4700

B. Craig Deats · 10 · Deats, Durst, Owen & Levy · 1204 San Antonio Street, Suite 203 · Austin, TX 78701 · 512-474-6200

Philip Durst · Deats, Durst, Owen & Levy · 1204 San Antonio Street, Suite 203 · Austin, TX 78701 · 512-474-6200

Mark R. Flora · 10 · Constangy, Brooks & Smith · http://www.constangy.com · 98 San Jacinto Boulevard, Suite 615 · Austin, TX 78701 · 512-382-8800

Michael W. Fox · 10 · Ogletree Deakins · http://www.ogletreedeakins.com · 301 Congress Avenue, Suite 1250 · Austin, TX 78701 · 512-344-4700

Brian S. Greig · 20 · Fulbright & Jaworski · http://www.fulbright.com · 600 Congress Avenue, Suite 2400 · Austin, TX 78701-2978 · 512-474-5201

Christopher H. Hahn · Boulette & Golden · Three Barton Skyway, Suite 300 · 1221 South MoPac Expressway · Austin, TX 78746 · 512-732-8900

Sherrard L. Hayes II · Fulbright & Jaworski · http://www.fulbright.com · 600 Congress Avenue, Suite 2400 · Austin, TX 78701-2978 · 512-474-5201

Gregg R. Kronenberger · 10 · Boulette & Golden · Three Barton Skyway, Suite 300 · 1221 South MoPac Expressway · Austin, TX 78746 · 512-732-8900

Thomas A. Nesbitt · DeShazo & Nesbitt · http://www.deshazonesbitt.com · 816 Congress Avenue, Suite 1280 · Austin, TX 78701 · 512-617-5562

Martha P. Owen · 10 · Deats, Durst, Owen & Levy · 1204 San Antonio Street, Suite 203 · Austin, TX 78701 · 512-474-6200

Glenda L. Pittman · 10 · Pittman & Fink · 8000 Anderson Square, Suite 101 · Austin, TX 78757 · 512-499-0902

Kevin M. Sadler · Baker Botts · http://www.bakerbotts.com · 1500 San Jacinto Center · 98 San Jacinto Boulevard · Austin, TX 78701-4039 · 512-322-2500

Beaumont

Robert J. Hambright · ㉕ · Orgain, Bell & Tucker · 470 Orleans Street · P.O. Box 1751 · Beaumont, TX 77704-1751 · 409-838-6412

Dallas

Jennifer B. Altabef · Carrington, Coleman, Sloman & Blumenthal · 901 Main Street, Suite 5500 · Dallas, TX 75202 · 214-855-3000

G. William Baab · ㉕ · Baab & Denison · 2777 North Stemmons Freeway, Suite 1100 · Dallas, TX 75207 214-637-0750

Hershell L. Barnes, Jr. · ⑳ · Barnes & Harrington · 3710 Rawlins Street, Suite 950 · Dallas, TX 75219 · 214-615-7925

J. Derek Braziel · Lee & Braziel · 1801 North Lamar Street, Suite 325 · Dallas, TX 75202 · 214-749-1400

Michael R. Buchanan · Ogletree Deakins · http://www.ogletreedeakins.com · 700 Preston Commons · 8117 Preston Road · Dallas, TX 75225 · 214-987-3800

G. Allen Butler · ㉕ · Hunton & Williams · 1445 Ross Avenue, Suite 3700 · Dallas, TX 75202-2799 · 214-979-3000

Bennett W. Cervin · ㉕ · Thompson & Knight · http://www.tklaw.com · One Arts Plaza, Suite 1500 · 1722 Routh Street · Dallas, TX 75201-2533 · 214-969-1700

Edward B. Cloutman III · ⑳ · Edward B. Cloutman III · 3301 Elm Street · Dallas, TX 75226-1637 · 214-939-9222

Dan Dargene · Winstead · http://www.winstead.com · Renaissance Tower, Suite 5400 · 1201 Elm Street · Dallas, TX 75270-2199 · 214-745-5400

Sanford R. Denison · ⑩ · Baab & Denison · 2777 North Stemmons Freeway, Suite 1100 · Dallas, TX 75207 · 214-637-0750

Gary D. Eisenstat · Figari & Davenport · http://www.figdav.com · 3400 Bank of America Plaza · 901 Main Street · Dallas, TX 75202-3796 · 214-939-2000

David M. Ellis · ⑩ · K&L Gates · 1717 Main Street, Suite 2800 · Dallas, TX 75201 · 214-939-5500

Stephen F. Fink · ⑳ · Thompson & Knight · http://www.tklaw.com · One Arts Plaza, Suite 1500 · 1722 Routh Street · Dallas, TX 75201-2533 · 214-969-1700

W. Gary Fowler · Jackson Walker · Bank of America Plaza, Suite 6000 · 901 Main Street · Dallas, TX 75202 · 214-953-6000

Stephen E. Fox · Fish & Richardson · 1717 Main Street, Suite 5000 · Dallas, TX 75201 · 214-747-5070

Laura M. Franze · ⑩ · Hunton & Williams · 1445 Ross Avenue, Suite 3700 · Dallas, TX 75202-2799 · 214-979-3000

Hal K. Gillespie · ⑩ · Gillespie, Rozen, Watsky & Motley · 3402 Oak Grove Avenue, Suite 200 · Dallas, TX 75204 · 214-720-2009

Dan Hartsfield · Baker Botts · http://www.bakerbotts.com · Trammell Crow Center, Suite 600 · 2001 Ross Avenue · Dallas, TX 75201-2980 · 214-953-6500

John V. Jansonius · ⑩ · Akin Gump Strauss Hauer & Feld · 1700 Pacific Avenue, Suite 4100 · Dallas, TX 75201-4675 · 214-969-2800

Stuart B. Johnston, Jr. · Vinson & Elkins · http://www.velaw.com · Trammell Crow Center, Suite 3700 · 2001 Ross Avenue · Dallas, TX 75201-2975 · 214-220-7700

Phillip R. Jones · ㉕ · Locke Lord Bissell & Liddell · 2200 Ross Avenue, Suite 2200 · Dallas, TX 75201-6776 · 214-740-8000

William L. Keller · ㉕ · Hunton & Williams · 1445 Ross Avenue, Suite 3700 · Dallas, TX 75202-2799 · 214-979-3000

Allan G. King · Littler Mendelson · 2001 Ross Avenue, Suite 2600 · Lock Box 116 · Dallas, TX 75201-2931 · 214-880-8100

Richard M. Kobdish · Fulbright & Jaworski · http://www.fulbright.com · 2200 Ross Avenue, Suite 2800 · Dallas, TX 75201 · 214-855-8000

David C. Lonergan · Hunton & Williams · 1445 Ross Avenue, Suite 3700 · Dallas, TX 75202-2799 · 214-979-3000

Robert E. Luxen · Hallett & Perrin · 2001 Bryan Street, Suite 3900 · Dallas, TX 75201 · 214-953-0053

Jane Makela · ⑩ · Carrington, Coleman, Sloman & Blumenthal · 901 Main Street, Suite 5500 · Dallas, TX 75202 · 214-855-3000

Ronald E. Manthey · Morgan Lewis & Bockius · 1717 Main Street, Suite 3200 · Dallas, TX 75201 · 214-466-4000

Michael P. Maslanka · ⑩ · Ford & Harrison · http://www.fordharrison.com · 1601 Elm Street, Suite 4450 · Dallas, TX 75201 · 214-256-4700

John Francis McCarthy, Jr. · ⑩ · Littler Mendelson · 2001 Ross Avenue, Suite 2600 · Lock Box 116 · Dallas, TX 75201-2931 · 214-880-8100

Steven R. McCown · ⑩ · Littler Mendelson · 2001 Ross Avenue, Suite 2600 · Lock Box 116 · Dallas, TX 75201-2931 · 214-880-8100

M. Scott McDonald · Littler Mendelson · 2001 Ross Avenue, Suite 2600 · Lock Box 116 · Dallas, TX 75201-2931 · 214-880-8100

Scott M. McElhaney · Jackson Walker · Bank of America Plaza, Suite 6000 · 901 Main Street · Dallas, TX 75202 · 214-953-6000

Bryant S. McFall · Ogletree Deakins · http://www.ogletreedeakins.com · 700 Preston Commons · 8117 Preston Road · Dallas, TX 75225 · 214-987-3800

John Edward McFall · Ogletree Deakins · http://www.ogletreedeakins.com · 700 Preston Commons · 8117 Preston Road · Dallas, TX 75225 · 214-987-3800

Lawrence J. McNamara · Spencer Crain Cubbage Healy & McNamara · Renaissance Tower, Suite 4100 · 1201 Elm Street · Dallas, TX 75270 · 214-290-0002

Kenneth H. Molberg · ⑳ · Wilson, Williams & Molberg · 2214 Main Street · Dallas, TX 75201-4324 · 214-748-5276

Susan D. Motley · Advocacy · 1420 West Mockingbird Lane, Suite 450 · Dallas, TX 75247-4932 · 214-630-0916

Christie A. Newkirk · K&L Gates · 1717 Main Street, Suite 2800 · Dallas, TX 75201 · 214-939-5500

Genice A. G. Rabe · Genice A. G. Rabe · 3301 Elm Street · Dallas, TX 75226-1637 · 214-939-9228

Yona Rozen · ⑩ · Gillespie, Rozen, Watsky & Motley · 3402 Oak Grove Avenue, Suite 200 · Dallas, TX 75204 · 214-720-2009

Elizabeth A. Schartz · Thompson & Knight · http://www.tklaw.com · One Arts Plaza, Suite 1500 · 1722 Routh Street · Dallas, TX 75201-2533 · 214-969-1700

Mark A. Shank · ⑩ · K&L Gates · 1717 Main Street, Suite 2800 · Dallas, TX 75201 · 214-939-5500

Robert Elwood Sheeder · ⑩ · Bracewell & Giuliani · http://www.bgllp.com · 1445 Ross Avenue, Suite 3800 · Dallas, TX 75202-2711 · 214-468-3800

Steven W. Sloan · Thompson & Knight · http://www.tklaw.com · One Arts Plaza, Suite 1500 · 1722 Routh Street · Dallas, TX 75201-2533 · 214-969-1700

Arlene Switzer Steinfield · K&L Gates · 1717 Main Street, Suite 2800 · Dallas, TX 75201 · 214-939-5500

William C. Strock · ⑳ · Haynes and Boone · 901 Main Street, Suite 3100 · Dallas, TX 75202 · 214-651-5000

David K. Watsky · Gillespie, Rozen, Watsky & Motley · 3402 Oak Grove Avenue, Suite 200 · Dallas, TX 75204 · 214-720-2009

Lon R. Williams, Jr. · Bracewell & Giuliani · http://www.bgllp.com · 1445 Ross Avenue, Suite 3800 · Dallas, TX 75202-2711 · 214-468-3800

Jonathan C. Wilson · ⑩ · Haynes and Boone · 901 Main Street, Suite 3100 · Dallas, TX 75202 · 214-651-5000

El Paso

Clara Burns · Kemp Smith · http://www.kempsmith.com · 221 North Kansas, Suite 1700 · El Paso, TX 79901-1441 · 915-533-4424

Charles C. High, Jr. · ⑳ · Kemp Smith · http://www.kempsmith.com · 221 North Kansas, Suite 1700 · El Paso, TX 79901-1441 · 915-533-4424

David L. Kern · Kern Law Firm · 1300 North El Paso Street · El Paso, TX 79902 · 915-542-1900

Rosemary Morales Marin · Scott, Hulse, Marshall, Feuille, Finger & Thurmond · 1100 Chase Tower · 201 East Main Street · El Paso, TX 79901 · 915-533-2493

Michael D. McQueen · Kemp Smith · http://www.kempsmith.com · 221 North Kansas, Suite 1700 · El Paso, TX 79901-1441 · 915-533-4424

Enrique Moreno · ⑩ · Law Offices of Enrique Moreno · 701 Magoffin Avenue · El Paso, TX 79901-2507 915-533-9977

John A. Wenke · Law Office of John A Wenke · 501 East California Avenue · El Paso, TX 79902 · 915-351-8877

Fort Worth

Lars L. Berg · Kelly, Hart & Hallman · Wells Fargo Tower, Suite 2500 · 201 Main Street · Fort Worth, TX 76102 · 817-332-2500

Terry S. Boone · Haynes and Boone · 201 Main Street, Suite 2200 · Fort Worth, TX 76102 · 817-347-6600

Beale Dean · ⑳ · Brown, Dean, Wiseman, Liser, Proctor & Hart · Fort Worth Club Building, Suite 200 · 306 West Seventh Street · Fort Worth, TX 76102-4905 · 817-332-1391

Gary L. Ingram · Jackson Walker · 301 Commerce Street, Suite 2400 · Fort Worth, TX 76102 · 817-334-7200

Patrick J. Maher · Shannon, Gracey, Ratliff & Miller · http://www.shannongracey.com · 777 Main Street, Suite 3800 · Fort Worth, TX 76102 · 817-336-9333

Henry H. Robinson · Kelly, Hart & Hallman · Wells Fargo Tower, Suite 2500 · 201 Main Street · Fort Worth, TX 76102 · 817-332-2500

James R. Tanner · ⑩ · Tanner & Associates · Plains Capital Bank Towers, Suite 100 · 6000 Western Place Fort Worth, TX 76107-4654 · 817-377-8833

Friendswood

Jay Thomas Youngdahl · ⑳ · The Youngdahl Law Firm · 1414 South Friendswood Drive · Friendswood, TX 77546 · 281-996-0750

Houston

Joseph Y. Ahmad · Ahmad, Zavitsanos & Anaipakos · 1221 McKinney Street, Suite 3460 · Houston, TX 77010 · 713-655-1101

Jay R. Aldis · Bracewell & Giuliani · http://www.bgllp.com · 711 Louisiana Street, Suite 2300 · Houston, TX 77002-2770 · 713-223-2300

William H. Bruckner · Bruckner Burch · 1415 Louisiana Street, Suite 2125 · Houston, TX 77002-5006 · 713-877-8788

Richard J. Burch · Bruckner Burch · 1415 Louisiana Street, Suite 2125 · Houston, TX 77002-5006 · 713-877-8788

Katherine L. Butler · Butler & Harris · 1007 Heights Boulevard · Houston, TX 77008 · 713-526-5677

William John Bux · Locke Lord Bissell & Liddell · JP Morgan Chase Tower, Suite 3400 · 600 Travis Street · Houston, TX 77002 · 713-226-1200

James V. Carroll III · ⑩ · Littler Mendelson · The Chevron Tower, Suite 1900 · 1301 McKinney Street · Houston, TX 77010 · 713-951-9400

Darryl K. Carter · Glickman Law Firm · 3800 Two Houston Center · 909 Fannin Street · Houston, TX 77010 · 713-658-1122

Shauna Johnson Clark · Fulbright & Jaworski · http://www.fulbright.com · Fulbright Tower, Suite 5100 · 1301 McKinney Street · Houston, TX 77010-3095 · 713-651-5151

Lawrence H. Clore · ⑩ · Fulbright & Jaworski · http://www.fulbright.com · Fulbright Tower, Suite 5100 · 1301 McKinney Street · Houston, TX 77010-3095 · 713-651-5151

M. Carter Crow · Fulbright & Jaworski · http://www.fulbright.com · Fulbright Tower, Suite 5100 · 1301 McKinney Street · Houston, TX 77010-3095 · 713-651-5151

A. L. Dent III · ⑩ · Law Office of A.L. Dent · 7941 Katy Freeway, Suite 295 · Houston, TX 77024-1924 · 713-465-4611

Dennis P. Duffy · Baker Botts · http://www.bakerbotts.com · One Shell Plaza · 910 Louisiana Street · Houston, TX 77002-1210 · 713-229-1234

Patrick M. Flynn · ⑳ · Patrick M. Flynn · 1225 North Loop West, Suite 1000 · Houston, TX 77008 · 713-861-6163

Ed Friedman · Locke Lord Bissell & Liddell · JP Morgan Chase Tower, Suite 3400 · 600 Travis Street · Houston, TX 77002 · 713-226-1200

Barbara J. Gardner · Tucker, Vaughan, Gardner & Barnes · http://www.tuckervaughan.com · JP Morgan Chase Building, Suite 1600 · 712 Main Steeet · Houston, TX 77002-3297 · 713-228-7425

Laura Gibson · Ogden, Gibson, Broocks & Longoria · 1900 Pennzoil South Tower · 711 Louisiana Street · Houston, TX 77002 · 713-844-3000

Julius Glickman · ⑩ · Glickman Law Firm · 3800 Two Houston Center · 909 Fannin Street · Houston, TX 77010 · 713-658-1122

Rebecca G. Gottsegen · Jones Walker · http://www.joneswalker.com · JP Morgan Chase Tower, Suite 6601 · 600 Travis Street · Houston, TX 77002 · 713-437-1800

Amy Karff Halevy · Bracewell & Giuliani · http://www.bgllp.com · 711 Louisiana Street, Suite 2300 · Houston, TX 77002-2770 · 713-223-2300

Douglas E. Hamel · ⑩ · Vinson & Elkins · http://www.velaw.com · First City Tower, Suite 2500 · 1001 Fannin Street · Houston, TX 77002-6760 · 713-758-2222

Alfred J. Harper II · ⑳ · Morgan Lewis & Bockius · 1000 Louisiana St., Suite 4200 · Houston, TX 77002-5006 · 713-890-5000

Margaret A. Harris · ⑩ · Butler & Harris · 1007 Heights Boulevard · Houston, TX 77008 · 713-526-5677

Linda Ottinger Headley · Littler Mendelson · The Chevron Tower, Suite 1900 · 1301 McKinney Street · Houston, TX 77010 · 713-951-9400

Dennis G. Herlong · Law Office of Dennis Herlong · http://www.dennisherlong.com · 440 Louisiana, Suite 900 · Houston, TX 77002-6708 · 713-228-9222

Samuel E. Hooper · Neel, Hooper & Banes · 1700 West Loop South, Suite 1400 · Houston, TX 77027-3008 · 713-629-1800

Kenneth D. Hughes · The Hughes Law Firm · First City Tower, 19th Floor, Suite 1925 · 1001 Fannin Street · Houston, TX 77002 · 832-419-2088

W. Carl Jordan · ⑳ · Vinson & Elkins · http://www.velaw.com · First City Tower, Suite 2500 · 1001 Fannin Street · Houston, TX 77002-6760 · 713-758-2222

V. Scott Kneese · ㉕ · Bracewell & Giuliani · http://www.bgllp.com · 711 Louisiana Street, Suite 2300 · Houston, TX 77002-2770 · 713-223-2300

Elizabeth Kroger · Martin, Disiere, Jefferson & Wisdom · http://www.mdjwlaw.com · Niels Esperson Building, Suite 1800 · 808 Travis Street · Houston, TX 77002 · 713-632-1700

Jeffrey C. Londa · ⑩ · Ogletree Deakins · http://www.ogletreedeakins.com · One Allen Center, Suite 3000 · 500 Dallas Street · Houston, TX 77002-4709 · 713-655-0855

Scott R. Mclaughlin · Shook, Hardy & Bacon · JPMorgan Chase Tower, Suite 1600 · 600 Travis Street · Houston, TX 77002-2992 · 713-227-8008

Ted D. Meyer · Jones Day · 717 Texas, Suite 300 · Houston, TX 77002-2712 · 832-239-3939

Michael D. Mitchell · Ogletree Deakins · http://www.ogletreedeakins.com · One Allen Center, Suite 3000 500 Dallas Street · Houston, TX 77002-4709 · 713-655-0855

R. Michael Moore · ⑩ · R. Michael Moore · 4400 Post Oak Parkway, Suite 1980 · Houston, TX 77027 · 713-621-8185

James M. Neel · Neel, Hooper & Banes · 1700 West Loop South, Suite 1400 · Houston, TX 77027-3008 · 713-629-1800

Eric H. Nelson · ⑩ · Eric H. Nelson · 3303 Main Street, Suite 300 · Houston, TX 77002-9321 · 713-526-1998

Kerry E. Notestine · Littler Mendelson · The Chevron Tower, Suite 1900 · 1301 McKinney Street · Houston, TX 77010 · 713-951-9400

Nancy L. Patterson · Morgan Lewis & Bockius · 1000 Louisiana St., Suite 4200 · Houston, TX 77002-5006 · 713-890-5000

Lisa H. Pennington · Baker Hostetler · http://www.bakerlaw.com · 1000 Louisiana, Suite 2000 · Houston, TX 77002-5009 · 713-751-1600

Gregg M. Rosenberg · ⑩ · Rosenberg & Sprovach · 11 Greenway Plaza, Suite 2810 · Houston, TX 77046 713-960-8300

Anthony P. Rosenstein · ⑩ · Baker Botts · http://www.bakerbotts.com · One Shell Plaza · 910 Louisiana Street · Houston, TX 77002-1210 · 713-229-1234

Shadow Sloan · Vinson & Elkins · http://www.velaw.com · First City Tower, Suite 2500 · 1001 Fannin Street · Houston, TX 77002-6760 · 713-758-2222

L. Chapman Smith · ㉕ · Baker Botts · http://www.bakerbotts.com · One Shell Plaza · 910 Louisiana Street · Houston, TX 77002-1210 · 713-229-1234

Eliot P. Tucker · ㉕ · Tucker, Vaughan, Gardner & Barnes · http://www.tuckervaughan.com · JP Morgan Chase Building, Suite 1600 · 712 Main Steeet · Houston, TX 77002-3297 · 713-228-7425

Teresa S. Valderrama · ⑩ · Jackson Lewis · http://www.jacksonlewis.com · Wedge International Tower, Suite 3325 · 1415 Louisiana · Houston, TX 77002-7360 · 713-650-0404

Holly H. Williamson · Hunton & Williams · Bank of America Center, Suite 4200 · 700 Louisiana Street · Houston, TX 77002 · 713-229-5700

Thomas H. Wilson · Vinson & Elkins · http://www.velaw.com · First City Tower, Suite 2500 · 1001 Fannin Street · Houston, TX 77002-6760 · 713-758-2222

W. Jackson Wisdom · Martin, Disiere, Jefferson & Wisdom · http://www.mdjwlaw.com · Niels Esperson Building, Suite 1800 · 808 Travis Street · Houston, TX 77002 · 713-632-1700

T. J. Wray · ⑩ · Fulbright & Jaworski · http://www.fulbright.com · Fulbright Tower, Suite 5100 · 1301 McKinney Street · Houston, TX 77010-3095 · 713-651-5151

John Zavitsanos · Ahmad, Zavitsanos & Anaipakos · 1221 McKinney Street, Suite 3460 · Houston, TX 77010 · 713-655-1101

Lockport

Paul A. Schorn · Paul Schorn · 505 South Main Street · Lockport, TX 78644 · 512-376-3200

San Antonio

Mario A. Barrera · Bracewell & Giuliani · http://www.bgllp.com · One Alamo Center, Suite 800 · 106 South St. Mary's Street · San Antonio, TX 78205-3603 · 210-226-1166

Cynthia M. Benedict · Fulbright & Jaworski · http://www.fulbright.com · 300 Convent Street, Suite 2200 · San Antonio, TX 78205-3792 · 210-224-5575

Robert E. Bettac · Ogletree Deakins · http://www.ogletreedeakins.com · 2700 Weston Centre · 112 East Pecan Street · San Antonio, TX 78205 · 210-354-1300

Ramon D. Bissmeyer · Cox Smith Matthews · http://www.coxsmith.com · 112 East Pecan Street, Suite 1800 · San Antonio, TX 78205-1521 · 210-554-5500

Leslie Selig Byrd · Bracewell & Giuliani · http://www.bgllp.com · One Alamo Center, Suite 800 · 106 South St. Mary's Street · San Antonio, TX 78205-3603 · 210-226-1166

Kala Scott Dumont · Gaul and Dumont · 924 Camaron · San Antonio, TX 78212 · 210-225-0685

John A. Ferguson, Jr. · Bracewell & Giuliani · http://www.bgllp.com · One Alamo Center, Suite 800 · 106 South St. Mary's Street · San Antonio, TX 78205-3603 · 210-226-1166

Dawn B. Finlayson · The Gardiner Law Firm · 745 East Mulberry Avenue, Suite 500 · San Antonio, TX 78212-3154 · 210-733-8191

Ben F. Foster, Jr. · ⑩ · Cox Smith Matthews · http://www.coxsmith.com · 112 East Pecan Street, Suite 1800 · San Antonio, TX 78205-1521 · 210-554-5500

Malinda A. Gaul · Gaul and Dumont · 924 Camaron · San Antonio, TX 78212 · 210-225-0685

Jeffrey A. Goldberg · The Law Office of Jeffrey A. Goldberg · 9901 IH-10 West, Suite 690 · San Antonio, TX 78230-2252 · 210-690-2200

Thad Harkins · Harkins, Latimer and Dahl · Travis Building, Suite 242 · 405 North St. Mary's Street · San Antonio, TX 78205-1722 · 210-527-0900

Alex L. Katzman · Katzman & Katzman · 12451 Starcrest Drive, Suite 106 · San Antonio, TX 78216 · 210-979-7300

James H. Kizziar · Bracewell & Giuliani · http://www.bgllp.com · One Alamo Center, Suite 800 · 106 South St. Mary's Street · San Antonio, TX 78205-3603 · 210-226-1166

Sylvan S. Lang, Jr. · Lang & Kustoff · 4103 Parkdale Street · San Antonio, TX 78229-2520 · 210-614-9444

Glen D. Mangum · Glen D. Mangum · 924 Camaron Street · San Antonio, TX 78212-5111 · 210-227-3666

Donna K. McElroy · Cox Smith Matthews · http://www.coxsmith.com · 112 East Pecan Street, Suite 1800 San Antonio, TX 78205-1521 · 210-554-5500

George P. Parker, Jr. · Bracewell & Giuliani · http://www.bgllp.com · One Alamo Center, Suite 800 · 106 South St. Mary's Street · San Antonio, TX 78205-3603 · 210-226-1166

Philip J. Pfeiffer · ⑳ · Fulbright & Jaworski · http://www.fulbright.com · 300 Convent Street, Suite 2200 · San Antonio, TX 78205-3792 · 210-224-5575

Robert A. Rapp, Jr. · The Law Office of Robert Rapp · 201 East Commerce, Suite 370 · San Antonio, TX 78205 · 210-224-4664

Lawrence D. Smith · Ogletree Deakins · http://www.ogletreedeakins.com · 2700 Weston Centre · 112 East Pecan Street · San Antonio, TX 78205 · 210-354-1300

Randolph P. Tower · Clemens & Spencer · http://www.clemens-spencer.com · 1300 Weston Centre · 112 East Pecan Street · San Antonio, TX 78205-1517 · 210-227-7121

David Van Os · ⑳ · David Van Os & Associates · 115 East Travis Street, Suite 618 · San Antonio, TX 78205 · 210-299-1800

J. Tullos Wells · Bracewell & Giuliani · http://www.bgllp.com · One Alamo Center, Suite 800 · 106 South St. Mary's Street · San Antonio, TX 78205-3603 · 210-226-1166

LAND USE & ZONING LAW

Austin

David B. Armbrust · ㉕ · Armbrust & Brown · http://www.abaustin.com · 100 Congress Avenue, Suite 1300 · Austin, TX 78701 · 512-435-2300

Dallas

Arthur J. Anderson · Winstead · http://www.winstead.com · Renaissance Tower, Suite 5400 · 1201 Elm Street · Dallas, TX 75270-2199 · 214-745-5400

William S. Dahlstrom · Jackson Walker · Bank of America Plaza, Suite 6000 · 901 Main Street · Dallas, TX 75202 · 214-953-6000

Susan Mead · Jackson Walker · Bank of America Plaza, Suite 6000 · 901 Main Street · Dallas, TX 75202 · 214-953-6000

Kirk R. Williams · Winstead · http://www.winstead.com · Renaissance Tower, Suite 5400 · 1201 Elm Street · Dallas, TX 75270-2199 · 214-745-5400

LEGAL MALPRACTICE LAW

Amarillo

Thomas C. Riney · Riney & Mayfield · http://www.rineymayfield.com · 600 Maxor Building · 320 South Polk Street · Amarillo, TX 79101-1426 · 806-468-3200

Austin

Doug Brothers · George & Brothers · Norwood Tower, Suite 1100 · 114 West Seventh Street · Austin, TX 78701 · 512-495-1400

Don L. Davis · ⑩ · Byrd, Davis & Furman · 707 West 34th Street · Austin, TX 78705 · 512-454-3751

Tommy Jacks · ⑩ · Jacks Law Firm · 1205 Rio Grande Street · Austin, TX 78701-1709 · 512-478-4422

Stephen E. McConnico · ⑩ · Scott, Douglass & McConnico · 600 Congress Avenue, Suite 1500 · Austin, TX 78701-3234 · 512-495-6300

Broadus A. Spivey · ㉕ · Law Offices of Dicky Grigg · 48 East Avenue, Suite 100 · Austin, TX 78701 · 512-474-6061

T. B. Wright · ⑩ · Wright & Greenhill · 221 West Sixth Street, Suite 1800 · Austin, TX 78701 · 512-476-4600

Corpus Christi

Tom Hermansen · ⑩ · Hermansen, McKibben, Woolsey & Villarreal · 1100 Tower II · 555 North Carancahua · Corpus Christi, TX 78478 · 361-882-6611

Dallas

Robert F. Begert · Burford & Ryburn · 3100 Lincoln Plaza · 500 North Akard · Dallas, TX 75201 · 214-740-3100

George W. Bramblett, Jr. · ⑩ · Haynes and Boone · 901 Main Street, Suite 3100 · Dallas, TX 75202 · 214-651-5000

James E. Coleman, Jr. · ㉕ · Carrington, Coleman, Sloman & Blumenthal · 901 Main Street, Suite 5500 · Dallas, TX 75202 · 214-855-3000

James E. Cowles · ⑩ · Cowles & Thompson · http://www.cowlesthompson.com · Bank of America Plaza, Suite 4000 · 901 Main Street · Dallas, TX 75202 · 214-672-2000

Mark T. Josephs · Jackson Walker · Bank of America Plaza, Suite 6000 · 901 Main Street · Dallas, TX 75202 · 214-953-6000

Paul M. Koning · K&L Gates · 1717 Main Street, Suite 2800 · Dallas, TX 75201 · 214-939-5500

George M. Kryder · ⑩ · Vinson & Elkins · http://www.velaw.com · Trammell Crow Center, Suite 3700 · 2001 Ross Avenue · Dallas, TX 75201-2975 · 214-220-7700

Timothy W. Mountz · Baker Botts · http://www.bakerbotts.com · Trammell Crow Center, Suite 600 · 2001 Ross Avenue · Dallas, TX 75201-2980 · 214-953-6500

Robert H. Mow, Jr. · ㉕ · K&L Gates · 1717 Main Street, Suite 2800 · Dallas, TX 75201 · 214-939-5500

Rod Phelan · ⑩ · Baker Botts · http://www.bakerbotts.com · Trammell Crow Center, Suite 600 · 2001 Ross Avenue · Dallas, TX 75201-2980 · 214-953-6500

David W. Shuford · Shuford & Associates · 2902 Carlisle Street, Suite 100 · Dallas, TX 75204 · 214-742-1701

Robb L. Voyles · Baker Botts · http://www.bakerbotts.com · Trammell Crow Center, Suite 600 · 2001 Ross Avenue · Dallas, TX 75201-2980 · 214-953-6500

Fletcher L. Yarbrough · ㉕ · Carrington, Coleman, Sloman & Blumenthal · 901 Main Street, Suite 5500 · Dallas, TX 75202 · 214-855-3000

Fort Worth

Darrell L. Keith · ⑩ · Keith Law Firm · The Keith Building · 1705 West Seventh Street · Fort Worth, TX 76102 · 817-338-1400

Kleber C. Miller · ㉕ · Shannon, Gracey, Ratliff & Miller · http://www.shannongracey.com · 777 Main Street, Suite 3800 · Fort Worth, TX 76102 · 817-336-9333

R. H. Wallace, Jr. · ⑩ · Shannon, Gracey, Ratliff & Miller · http://www.shannongracey.com · 777 Main Street, Suite 3800 · Fort Worth, TX 76102 · 817-336-9333

Houston

David J. Beck · ㉕ · Beck, Redden & Secrest · http://www.brsfirm.com · One Houston Center, Suite 4500 1221 McKinney Street · Houston, TX 77010-2010 · 713-951-3700

Reagan M. Brown · Fulbright & Jaworski · http://www.fulbright.com · Fulbright Tower, Suite 5100 · 1301 McKinney Street · Houston, TX 77010-3095 · 713-651-5151

Richard H. Caldwell · ⑩ · Andrews Kurth · http://www.andrewskurth.com · 600 Travis Street, Suite 4200 Houston, TX 77002 · 713-220-4200

Robin C. Gibbs · ⑩ · Gibbs & Bruns · http://www.gibbs-bruns.com · 1100 Louisiana Street, Suite 5300 · Houston, TX 77002 · 713-650-8805

Robert S. Harrell · ⑩ · Fulbright & Jaworski · http://www.fulbright.com · Fulbright Tower, Suite 5100 · 1301 McKinney Street · Houston, TX 77010-3095 · 713-651-5151

Frank G. Jones · ⑩ · Fulbright & Jaworski · http://www.fulbright.com · Fulbright Tower, Suite 5100 · 1301 McKinney Street · Houston, TX 77010-3095 · 713-651-5151

Arno W. Krebs, Jr. · ⑩ · Fulbright & Jaworski · http://www.fulbright.com · Fulbright Tower, Suite 5100 · 1301 McKinney Street · Houston, TX 77010-3095 · 713-651-5151

William E. Matthews · ⑩ · Gardere Wynne Sewell · http://www.gardere.com · 1000 Louisiana, Suite 3400 Houston, TX 77002-5011 · 713-276-5500

Kenneth Tekell · ⑩ · Tekell, Book, Matthews & Limmer · 4300 One Houston Center · 1221 McKinney Street · Houston, TX 77010-2015 · 713-222-9542

San Antonio

Robert R. Biechlin, Jr. · Thornton, Biechlin, Segrato, Reynolds & Guerra · One International Centre, Suite 500 · 100 Northeast Loop 410 · San Antonio, TX 78216 · 210-342-5555

Mark L. Greenwald · Law Office of Mark L. Greenwald · 9901 IH 10 West, Suite 800 · San Antonio, TX 78230 · 210-696-2550

Allen Lewin Plunkett · ⑩ · Plunkett & Gibson · http://www.plunkett-gibson.com · 70 Northeast Loop 410, Suite 1100 · San Antonio, TX 78216 · 210-734-7092

Richard J. Reynolds III · Thornton, Biechlin, Segrato, Reynolds & Guerra · One International Centre, Suite 500 · 100 Northeast Loop 410 · San Antonio, TX 78216 · 210-342-5555

George H. Spencer, Jr. · ⑩ · Clemens & Spencer · http://www.clemens-spencer.com · 1300 Weston Centre · 112 East Pecan Street · San Antonio, TX 78205-1517 · 210-227-7121

Austin

J. Rowland Cook · ⑳ · Winstead · http://www.winstead.com · 401 Congress Avenue, Suite 2100 · Austin, TX 78701 · 512-370-2800

Dallas

Andrew M. Baker · Baker Botts · http://www.bakerbotts.com · Trammell Crow Center, Suite 600 · 2001 Ross Avenue · Dallas, TX 75201-2980 · 214-953-6500

Geoffrey L. Newton · Baker Botts · http://www.bakerbotts.com · Trammell Crow Center, Suite 600 · 2001 Ross Avenue · Dallas, TX 75201-2980 · 214-953-6500

Larry L. Schoenbrun · ㉕ · Gardere Wynne Sewell · http://www.gardere.com · 1601 Elm Street, Suite 3000 · Dallas, TX 75201 · 214-999-3000

Ted Schweinfurth · Baker & McKenzie · 2300 Trammell Crow Center · 2001 Ross Avenue · Dallas, TX 75201 · 214-978-3000

R. Jay Tabor · Weil Gotshal & Manges · 200 Crescent Court, Suite 300 · Dallas, TX 75201 · 214-746-7700

Glenn D. West · Weil Gotshal & Manges · 200 Crescent Court, Suite 300 · Dallas, TX 75201 · 214-746-7700

Houston

Randolph C. Coley · King & Spalding · 1100 Louisiana Street, Suite 4000 · Houston, TX 77002-5213 · 713-751-3200

Ricardo Garcia-Moreno · Haynes and Boone · One Houston Center, Suite 2100 · 1221 McKinney Street · Houston, TX 77010 · 713-547-2000

Robert F. Gray, Jr. · ⑩ · Mayer Brown · Bank of America Center, Suite 3400 · 700 Louisiana Street · Houston, TX 77002-2730 · 713-238-3000

Thomas D. Manford III · Bracewell & Giuliani · http://www.bgllp.com · 711 Louisiana Street, Suite 2300 Houston, TX 77002-2770 · 713-223-2300

Theodore W. Paris · Baker Botts · http://www.bakerbotts.com · One Shell Plaza · 910 Louisiana Street · Houston, TX 77002-1210 · 713-229-1234

Felix P. Phillips, Jr. · Baker Botts · http://www.bakerbotts.com · One Shell Plaza · 910 Louisiana Street · Houston, TX 77002-1210 · 713-229-1234

Charles D. Powell · Fulbright & Jaworski · http://www.fulbright.com · Fulbright Tower, Suite 5100 · 1301 McKinney Street · Houston, TX 77010-3095 · 713-651-5151

Edward E. Rhyne, Jr. · Fulbright & Jaworski · http://www.fulbright.com · Fulbright Tower, Suite 5100 · 1301 McKinney Street · Houston, TX 77010-3095 · 713-651-5151

Charles C. Szalkowski · ⑩ · Baker Botts · http://www.bakerbotts.com · One Shell Plaza · 910 Louisiana Street · Houston, TX 77002-1210 · 713-229-1234

The Woodlands

Jeffrey R. Harder · Winstead · http://www.winstead.com · 24 Waterway Avenue, Suite 500 · The Woodlands, TX 77380 · 281-681-5900

R. Clyde Parker, Jr. · Winstead · http://www.winstead.com · 24 Waterway Avenue, Suite 500 · The Woodlands, TX 77380 · 281-681-5900

MARITIME LAW

Beaumont

Hubert Oxford III · ⑩ · Benckenstein & Oxford · 3535 Calder Avenue, Suite 300 · P.O. Drawer 150 · Beaumont, TX 77704 · 409-833-9182

Alan G. Sampson · Benckenstein & Oxford · 3535 Calder Avenue, Suite 300 · P.O. Drawer 150 · Beaumont, TX 77704 · 409-833-9182

Corpus Christi

Ralph F. Meyer · Royston, Rayzor, Vickery & Williams · http://www.roystonlaw.com · Frost Bank Plaza, Suite 1300 · 802 North Carancahua Street · Corpus Christi, TX 78470 · 361-884-8808

Galveston

James R. Watkins · Royston, Rayzor, Vickery & Williams · http://www.roystonlaw.com · 2102 Mechanic Street, Suite 205 · Galveston, TX 77550-1692 · 409-763-1623

Houston

George F. Chandler III · Hill Rivkins & Hayden · JP Morgan Chase Bank Building, Suite 1515 · 712 Main Street · Houston, TX 77002-3209 · 713-222-1515

James P. Cooney · ⑩ · Royston, Rayzor, Vickery & Williams · http://www.roystonlaw.com · 1001 McKinney, Suite 1100 · Houston, TX 77002-6418 · 713-224-8380

William A. Durham · Eastham, Watson, Dale & Forney · The Niels Esperson Building, 20th Floor · 808 Travis Street · Houston, TX 77002-5769 · 713-225-0905

John M. Elsley · Royston, Rayzor, Vickery & Williams · http://www.roystonlaw.com · 1001 McKinney, Suite 1100 · Houston, TX 77002-6418 · 713-224-8380

Bradley A. Jackson · Royston, Rayzor, Vickery & Williams · http://www.roystonlaw.com · 1001 McKinney, Suite 1100 · Houston, TX 77002-6418 · 713-224-8380

Robert L. Klawetter · Eastham, Watson, Dale & Forney · The Niels Esperson Building, 20th Floor · 808 Travis Street · Houston, TX 77002-5769 · 713-225-0905

Marion E. McDaniel, Jr. · Locke Lord Bissell & Liddell · JP Morgan Chase Tower, Suite 3400 · 600 Travis Street · Houston, TX 77002 · 713-226-1200

Edward J. Patterson III · Fulbright & Jaworski · http://www.fulbright.com · Fulbright Tower, Suite 5100 1301 McKinney Street · Houston, TX 77010-3095 · 713-651-5151

John R. Pearson · Gardere Wynne Sewell · http://www.gardere.com · 1000 Louisiana, Suite 3400 · Houston, TX 77002-5011 · 713-276-5500

William W. Pugh · Liskow & Lewis · http://www.liskow.com · First City Tower, Suite 1800 · 1001 Fannin Street · Houston, TX 77002-4102 · 713-651-2900

Steven L. Roberts · ⑩ · Sutherland · http://www.sutherland.com · Two Houston Center, Suite 2200 · 909 Fannin · Houston, TX 77010-1043 · 713-470-6100

John L. Schouest · Wilson Elser Moskowitz Edelman & Dicker · 5847 San Felipe, Suite 2300 · Houston, TX 77057-4033 · 713-353-2000

Eugene J. Silva, Sr. · ⑩ · Eugene J. Silva Sr. · 1001 Fannin Street, Suite 2300 · Houston, TX 77002-6760 713-758-2014

John F. Unger · Royston, Rayzor, Vickery & Williams · http://www.roystonlaw.com · 1001 McKinney, Suite 1100 · Houston, TX 77002-6418 · 713-224-8380

David R. Walker · Royston, Rayzor, Vickery & Williams · http://www.roystonlaw.com · 1001 McKinney, Suite 1100 · Houston, TX 77002-6418 · 713-224-8380

Hal Watson · Locke Lord Bissell & Liddell · JP Morgan Chase Tower, Suite 3400 · 600 Travis Street · Houston, TX 77002 · 713-226-1200

Ronald L. White · White Mackillop & Baham · 2200 West Loop South, Suite 1000 · Houston, TX 77027 · 713-599-0211

James C. Winton · Baker Hostetler · http://www.bakerlaw.com · 1000 Louisiana, Suite 2000 · Houston, TX 77002-5009 · 713-751-1600

MASS TORT LITIGATION

Corpus Christi

James H. Robichaux · Branscomb · 802 North Carancahua Street, Suite 1900 · Corpus Christi, TX 78470-0700 · 361-888-9261

Dallas

Frederick M. Baron · Baron & Blue · 5956 Sherry Lane, Suite 1616 · Dallas, TX 75225 · 214-265-4400

Lisa Blue · Baron & Blue · 5956 Sherry Lane, Suite 1616 · Dallas, TX 75225 · 214-265-4400

Gary D. Elliston · Dehay & Elliston · Bank of America Plaza Building, Suite 3500 · 901 Main Street · Dallas, TX 75202-3736 · 214-210-2400

Terence M. Murphy · Jones Day · 2727 North Harwood Street · Dallas, TX 75201-1515 · 214-220-3939

C. L. Mike Schmidt · ⑳ · The Schmidt Firm · 2911 Turtle Creek Boulevard, Suite 1400 · Dallas, TX 75219 · 214-521-4898

Michael E. Schmidt · The Schmidt Firm · 2911 Turtle Creek Boulevard, Suite 1400 · Dallas, TX 75219 · 214-521-4898

Scott Summy · Baron & Budd · 3102 Oak Lawn Avenue, Suite 1100 · Dallas, TX 75219 · 214-521-3605

Houston

Morgan Lee Copeland, Jr. · Vinson & Elkins · http://www.velaw.com · First City Tower, Suite 2500 · 1001 Fannin Street · Houston, TX 77002-6760 · 713-758-2222

Otway B. Denny, Jr. · ⑩ · Fulbright & Jaworski · http://www.fulbright.com · Fulbright Tower, Suite 5100 1301 McKinney Street · Houston, TX 77010-3095 · 713-651-5151

Stephen C. Dillard · ⑩ · Fulbright & Jaworski · http://www.fulbright.com · Fulbright Tower, Suite 5100 · 1301 McKinney Street · Houston, TX 77010-3095 · 713-651-5151

Stephen M. Fernelius · Fulbright & Jaworski · http://www.fulbright.com · Fulbright Tower, Suite 5100 · 1301 McKinney Street · Houston, TX 77010-3095 · 713-651-5151

Paula W. Hinton · Vinson & Elkins · http://www.velaw.com · First City Tower, Suite 2500 · 1001 Fannin Street · Houston, TX 77002-6760 · 713-758-2222

Don Jackson · Ware, Jackson, Lee & Chambers · America Tower, 42nd Floor · 2929 Allen Parkway · Houston, TX 77019 · 713-659-6400

Richard L. Josephson · Baker Botts · http://www.bakerbotts.com · One Shell Plaza · 910 Louisiana Street Houston, TX 77002-1210 · 713-229-1234

W. Mark Lanier · The Lanier Law Firm · 6810 FM 1960 West · Houston, TX 77069 · 713-659-5200

Gerry Lowry · Fulbright & Jaworski · http://www.fulbright.com · Fulbright Tower, Suite 5100 · 1301 McKinney Street · Houston, TX 77010-3095 · 713-651-5151

Robert E. Meadows · King & Spalding · 1100 Louisiana Street, Suite 4000 · Houston, TX 77002-5213 · 713-751-3200

Ricky A. Raven · Thompson & Knight · http://www.tklaw.com · 333 Clay Street, Suite 3300 · Houston, TX 77002 · 713-654-8111

Robert M. Schick · Vinson & Elkins · http://www.velaw.com · First City Tower, Suite 2500 · 1001 Fannin Street · Houston, TX 77002-6760 · 713-758-2222

Kenneth Tekell · ⑩ · Tekell, Book, Matthews & Limmer · 4300 One Houston Center · 1221 McKinney Street · Houston, TX 77010-2015 · 713-222-9542

John Eddie Williams, Jr. · Williams Kherkher Hart Boundas · 8441 Gulf Freeway, Suite 600 · Houston, TX 77017-5051 · 713-230-2200

William D. Wood · Fulbright & Jaworski · http://www.fulbright.com · Fulbright Tower, Suite 5100 · 1301 McKinney Street · Houston, TX 77010-3095 · 713-651-5151

San Antonio

Robert G. Newman · Fulbright & Jaworski · http://www.fulbright.com · 300 Convent Street, Suite 2200 · San Antonio, TX 78205-3792 · 210-224-5575

MEDIA LAW

Austin

Lawrence A. Waks · Jackson Walker · 100 Congress Avenue, Suite 1100 · Austin, TX 78701 · 512-236-2000

Amarillo

Thomas C. Riney · Riney & Mayfield · http://www.rineymayfield.com · 600 Maxor Building · 320 South Polk Street · Amarillo, TX 79101-1426 · 806-468-3200

Austin

Mark T. Beaman · Germer Gertz · 301 Congress Avenue, Suite 1700 · Austin, TX 78701 · 512-472-0288

Tommy Jacks · (10) · Jacks Law Firm · 1205 Rio Grande Street · Austin, TX 78701-1709 · 512-478-4422

Yvonne K. Puig · (10) · Fulbright & Jaworski · http://www.fulbright.com · 600 Congress Avenue, Suite 2400 Austin, TX 78701-2978 · 512-474-5201

Terry O. Tottenham · (10) · Fulbright & Jaworski · http://www.fulbright.com · 600 Congress Avenue, Suite 2400 · Austin, TX 78701-2978 · 512-474-5201

William O. Whitehurst · (10) · Whitehurst, Harkness, Ozmun & Brees · Westgate Building, 24th Floor · 1122 Colorado Street · P.O. Box 1802 · Austin, TX 78767 · 866-594-8630

Corpus Christi

William R. Edwards · (25) · The Edwards Law Firm · http://www.edwardsfirm.com · 802 North Carancahua Street, Suite 1400 · P.O. Box 480 · Corpus Christi, TX 78403-0480 · 361-698-7600

Dallas

Charla Aldous · Aldous Law Firm · 2305 Cedar Springs Road, Suite 200 · Dallas, TX 75201 · 214-526-5595

Frank L. Branson · (20) · Law Offices of Frank L. Branson · http://www.flbranson.com · Highland Park Place, Suite 1800 · 4514 Cole Avenue · Dallas, TX 75205 · 214-522-0200

Michael E. Schmidt · The Schmidt Firm · 2911 Turtle Creek Boulevard, Suite 1400 · Dallas, TX 75219 · 214-521-4898

Paula Fisette Sweeney · (10) · Howie & Sweeney · 3811 Turtle Creek Boulevard, Suite 1900 · Dallas, TX 75219 · 214-523-8800

Les Weisbrod · Miller, Curtis & Weisbrod · P.O. Box 821329 · Dallas, TX 75382 · 214-373-3761

El Paso

Walter L. Boyaki · Miranda & Boyaki · 4621 Pershing Drive · El Paso, TX 79903-1017 · 915-566-8688

Jim Curtis · (10) · Kemp Smith · http://www.kempsmith.com · 221 North Kansas, Suite 1700 · El Paso, TX 79901-1441 · 915-533-4424

David S. Jeans · (10) · Ray, Valdez, McChristian & Jeans · 5822 Cromo Drive · El Paso, TX 79912 · 915-832-7200

H. Keith Myers · (10) · Mounce, Green, Myers, Safi & Galatzan · Kayser Building, 17th Floor · 100 North Stanton Street · P.O. Box 1977 · El Paso, TX 79950-1977 · 915-532-2000

Evelina Ortega · Evelina Ortega · 521 Texas Avenue · El Paso, TX 79901-1417 · 915-544-4222

Michael D. Volk · Volk Poulos & Coates · Building One · 5915 Silver Springs · El Paso, TX 79912 · 915-760-5151

Fort Worth

Richard L. Griffith · ⑳ · Cantey & Hanger · 300 Cantey Hanger Plaza · 600 West Sixth Street · Fort Worth, TX 76102-3685 · 817-877-2800

Darrell L. Keith · ⑩ · Keith Law Firm · The Keith Building · 1705 West Seventh Street · Fort Worth, TX 76102 · 817-338-1400

Houston

James R. Boston, Jr. · Boston & Hughes · http://www.bostonhughes.com · 1616 South Voss Road, Suite 550 · Houston, TX 77057 · 713-961-1122

Olan J. Boudreaux · Fisher, Boyd, Brown, Boudreaux & Huguenard · Riviana Building, 14th Floor · 2777 Allen Parkway · Houston, TX 77019 · 713-400-4000

Larry P. Boyd · ⑩ · Fisher, Boyd, Brown, Boudreaux & Huguenard · Riviana Building, 14th Floor · 2777 Allen Parkway · Houston, TX 77019 · 713-400-4000

Thomas K. Brown · Fisher, Boyd, Brown, Boudreaux & Huguenard · Riviana Building, 14th Floor · 2777 Allen Parkway · Houston, TX 77019 · 713-400-4000

Suzan K. Cardwell · Franklin, Cardwell & Jones · 1001 McKinney Street, 18th Floor · Houston, TX 77002-6417 · 713-222-6025

Michael C. Feehan · Kacal, Adams & Law · One Riverway, Suite 1200 · Houston, TX 77056 · 713-529-3992

Wayne Fisher · ㉕ · Fisher, Boyd, Brown, Boudreaux & Huguenard · Riviana Building, 14th Floor · 2777 Allen Parkway · Houston, TX 77019 · 713-400-4000

Hartley Hampton · Fibich, Hampton & Leebron · http://www.fibichhampton.com · Five Houston Center, Suite 1800 · 1401 McKinney · Houston, TX 77010 · 713-751-0025

Charles W. Hurd · Fulbright & Jaworski · http://www.fulbright.com · Fulbright Tower, Suite 5100 · 1301 McKinney Street · Houston, TX 77010-3095 · 713-651-5151

David R. Iler · Fulbright & Jaworski · http://www.fulbright.com · Fulbright Tower, Suite 5100 · 1301 McKinney Street · Houston, TX 77010-3095 · 713-651-5151

Brian P. Johnson · Johnson, Spalding, Doyle, West and Trent · 919 Milam Street, Suite 1700 · Houston, TX 77002 · 713-222-2323

Marion Kruse · The Kruse Law Firm · 3355 West Alabama Street, Suite 1050 · Houston, TX 77098 · 713-624-1234

Richard M. Law · Kacal, Adams & Law · One Riverway, Suite 1200 · Houston, TX 77056 · 713-529-3992

Jack McGehee · McGehee Wachsman · 1225 North Loop West, Suite 810 · Houston, TX 77008 · 713-864-4000

Richard Warren Mithoff · ⑳ · Mithoff Law Firm · One Allen Center, Penthouse · 500 Dallas Street · Houston, TX 77002 · 713-654-1122

Jim M. Perdue, Jr. · Perdue & Kidd · 2727 Allen Parkway, Suite 800 · Houston, TX 77019 · 713-520-2500

Jim M. Perdue, Sr. · ㉕ · Perdue & Kidd · 2727 Allen Parkway, Suite 800 · Houston, TX 77019 · 713-520-2500

Barbara A. Radnofsky · ⑩ · Barbara Radnofsky · 303 Timber Terrace Road · Houston, TX 77024 · 713-858-8509

Michael Y. Saunders · ⑩ · Helm, Pletcher, Bowen & Saunders · America Tower, Suite 2700 · 2929 Allen Parkway · Houston, TX 77019-2157 · 713-522-4550

Craig Smyser · Smyser Kaplan and Veselka · Bank of America Center, Suite 2300 · 700 Louisiana · Houston, TX 77002 · 713-221-2300

Robert J. Swift · Fulbright & Jaworski · http://www.fulbright.com · Fulbright Tower, Suite 5100 · 1301 McKinney Street · Houston, TX 77010-3095 · 713-651-5151

Jeffrey Uzick · Uzick & Oncken · 238 Westcott · Houston, TX 77007 · 713-869-2900

Paul Waldner · Vickery, Waldner & Mallia · One Riverway, Suite 1150 · Houston, TX 77056 · 713-526-1100

San Antonio

Charles A. Deacon · Fulbright & Jaworski · http://www.fulbright.com · 300 Convent Street, Suite 2200 · San Antonio, TX 78205-3792 · 210-224-5575

Jerry A. Gibson · ⑩ · Plunkett & Gibson · http://www.plunkett-gibson.com · 70 Northeast Loop 410, Suite 1100 · San Antonio, TX 78216 · 210-734-7092

Cynthia Day Grimes · ⑩ · Ball & Weed · 10001 Reunion Place, Suite 600 · San Antonio, TX 78216 · 210-731-6300

Clarence V. Lyons · ⑳ · Lyons & Rhodes · 126 Villita Street · San Antonio, TX 78205-2735 · 210-225-5251

MERGERS & ACQUISITIONS LAW

Austin

J. Rowland Cook · ⑳ · Winstead · http://www.winstead.com · 401 Congress Avenue, Suite 2100 · Austin, TX 78701 · 512-370-2800

Brian P. Fenske · Fulbright & Jaworski · http://www.fulbright.com · 600 Congress Avenue, Suite 2400 · Austin, TX 78701-2978 · 512-474-5201

Paul Michael Hebert · ⑳ · Paul Michael Hebert · 1301 West 25th Street, Suite 545 · Austin, TX 78705-4236 · 512-476-2884

Robert Clarke Heidrick, Jr. · ⑩ · Graves, Dougherty, Hearon & Moody · http://www.gdhm.com · 401 Congress Avenue, Suite 2200 · P.O. Box 98 · Austin, TX 78767-0098 · 512-480-5600

Paul E. Hurdlow · DLA Piper · 1221 South MoPac Expressway, Suite 400 · Austin, TX 78746-7650 · 512-457-7000

Paul R. Tobias · Wilson Sonsini Goodrich & Rosati · Las Cimas IV, Fifth Floor · 900 South Capital of Texas Highway · Austin, TX 78746-5546 · 512-338-5400

William R. Volk · 25 · Vinson & Elkins · http://www.velaw.com · 2801 Via Fortuna, Suite 100 · Austin, TX 78746-7568 · 512-542-8400

Dallas

Andrew M. Baker · Baker Botts · http://www.bakerbotts.com · Trammell Crow Center, Suite 600 · 2001 Ross Avenue · Dallas, TX 75201-2980 · 214-953-6500

Alan J. Bogdanow · 10 · Vinson & Elkins · http://www.velaw.com · Trammell Crow Center, Suite 3700 · 2001 Ross Avenue · Dallas, TX 75201-2975 · 214-220-7700

Jeffrey A. Chapman · 10 · Vinson & Elkins · http://www.velaw.com · Trammell Crow Center, Suite 3700 · 2001 Ross Avenue · Dallas, TX 75201-2975 · 214-220-7700

Wilson Chu · Haynes and Boone · 901 Main Street, Suite 3100 · Dallas, TX 75202 · 214-651-5000

R. Scott Cohen · Weil Gotshal & Manges · 200 Crescent Court, Suite 300 · Dallas, TX 75201 · 214-746-7700

Mark Early · Vinson & Elkins · http://www.velaw.com · Trammell Crow Center, Suite 3700 · 2001 Ross Avenue · Dallas, TX 75201-2975 · 214-220-7700

Lawrence E. Glasgow · Gardere Wynne Sewell · http://www.gardere.com · 1601 Elm Street, Suite 3000 · Dallas, TX 75201 · 214-999-3000

Robert B. Hale · Fulbright & Jaworski · http://www.fulbright.com · 2200 Ross Avenue, Suite 2800 · Dallas, TX 75201 · 214-855-8000

Alan G. Harvey · Baker & McKenzie · 2300 Trammell Crow Center · 2001 Ross Avenue · Dallas, TX 75201 · 214-978-3000

Glen James Hettinger · Fulbright & Jaworski · http://www.fulbright.com · 2200 Ross Avenue, Suite 2800 Dallas, TX 75201 · 214-855-8000

Jeffrey B. Hitt · Weil Gotshal & Manges · 200 Crescent Court, Suite 300 · Dallas, TX 75201 · 214-746-7700

Thomas William Hughes · Fulbright & Jaworski · http://www.fulbright.com · 2200 Ross Avenue, Suite 2800 · Dallas, TX 75201 · 214-855-8000

Robert L. Kimball · Vinson & Elkins · http://www.velaw.com · Trammell Crow Center, Suite 3700 · 2001 Ross Avenue · Dallas, TX 75201-2975 · 214-220-7700

Mary R. Korby · Weil Gotshal & Manges · 200 Crescent Court, Suite 300 · Dallas, TX 75201 · 214-746-7700

Neel Lemon · Baker Botts · http://www.bakerbotts.com · Trammell Crow Center, Suite 600 · 2001 Ross Avenue · Dallas, TX 75201-2980 · 214-953-6500

Larry Steven Leshin · 10 · Hunton & Williams · 1445 Ross Avenue, Suite 3700 · Dallas, TX 75202-2799 · 214-979-3000

Rodney L. Moore · Vinson & Elkins · http://www.velaw.com · Trammell Crow Center, Suite 3700 · 2001 Ross Avenue · Dallas, TX 75201-2975 · 214-220-7700

Geoffrey L. Newton · Baker Botts · http://www.bakerbotts.com · Trammell Crow Center, Suite 600 · 2001 Ross Avenue · Dallas, TX 75201-2980 · 214-953-6500

A. Winston Oxley · Vinson & Elkins · http://www.velaw.com · Trammell Crow Center, Suite 3700 · 2001 Ross Avenue · Dallas, TX 75201-2975 · 214-220-7700

Douglass M. Rayburn · Baker Botts · http://www.bakerbotts.com · Trammell Crow Center, Suite 600 · 2001 Ross Avenue · Dallas, TX 75201-2980 · 214-953-6500

James S. Ryan III · Jackson Walker · Bank of America Plaza, Suite 6000 · 901 Main Street · Dallas, TX 75202 · 214-953-6000

Michael A. Saslaw · Weil Gotshal & Manges · 200 Crescent Court, Suite 300 · Dallas, TX 75201 · 214-746-7700

Larry L. Schoenbrun · ㉕ · Gardere Wynne Sewell · http://www.gardere.com · 1601 Elm Street, Suite 3000 · Dallas, TX 75201 · 214-999-3000

Kenneth L. Stewart · Fulbright & Jaworski · http://www.fulbright.com · 2200 Ross Avenue, Suite 2800 · Dallas, TX 75201 · 214-855-8000

R. Jay Tabor · Weil Gotshal & Manges · 200 Crescent Court, Suite 300 · Dallas, TX 75201 · 214-746-7700

Glenn D. West · Weil Gotshal & Manges · 200 Crescent Court, Suite 300 · Dallas, TX 75201 · 214-746-7700

Michael D. Wortley · ⑩ · Vinson & Elkins · http://www.velaw.com · Trammell Crow Center, Suite 3700 · 2001 Ross Avenue · Dallas, TX 75201-2975 · 214-220-7700

El Paso

Bernard D. Felsen · Scott, Hulse, Marshall, Feuille, Finger & Thurmond · 1100 Chase Tower · 201 East Main Street · El Paso, TX 79901 · 915-533-2493

Fort Worth

F. Richard Bernasek · Kelly, Hart & Hallman · Wells Fargo Tower, Suite 2500 · 201 Main Street · Fort Worth, TX 76102 · 817-332-2500

Houston

John C. Ale · Skadden, Arps, Slate, Meagher & Flom · 1000 Louisiana, Suite 6800 · Houston, TX 77002 · 713-655-5100

Marcia E. Backus · Vinson & Elkins · http://www.velaw.com · First City Tower, Suite 2500 · 1001 Fannin Street · Houston, TX 77002-6760 · 713-758-2222

Douglas S. Bland · ⑩ · Vinson & Elkins · http://www.velaw.com · First City Tower, Suite 2500 · 1001 Fannin Street · Houston, TX 77002-6760 · 713-758-2222

Joseph A. Cialone II · ⑳ · Baker Botts · http://www.bakerbotts.com · One Shell Plaza · 910 Louisiana Street · Houston, TX 77002-1210 · 713-229-1234

Christopher S. Collins · Vinson & Elkins · http://www.velaw.com · First City Tower, Suite 2500 · 1001 Fannin Street · Houston, TX 77002-6760 · 713-758-2222

John B. Connally IV · Vinson & Elkins · http://www.velaw.com · First City Tower, Suite 2500 · 1001 Fannin Street · Houston, TX 77002-6760 · 713-758-2222

Joshua Davidson · Baker Botts · http://www.bakerbotts.com · One Shell Plaza · 910 Louisiana Street · Houston, TX 77002-1210 · 713-229-1234

William N. Finnegan IV · Vinson & Elkins · http://www.velaw.com · First City Tower, Suite 2500 · 1001 Fannin Street · Houston, TX 77002-6760 · 713-758-2222

Marc H. Folladori · Mayer Brown · Bank of America Center, Suite 3400 · 700 Louisiana Street · Houston, TX 77002-2730 · 713-238-3000

Keith R. Fullenweider · Vinson & Elkins · http://www.velaw.com · First City Tower, Suite 2500 · 1001 Fannin Street · Houston, TX 77002-6760 · 713-758-2222

Robert V. Jewell · Andrews Kurth · http://www.andrewskurth.com · 600 Travis Street, Suite 4200 · Houston, TX 77002 · 713-220-4200

T. Mark Kelly · ⑩ · Vinson & Elkins · http://www.velaw.com · First City Tower, Suite 2500 · 1001 Fannin Street · Houston, TX 77002-6760 · 713-758-2222

J. David Kirkland, Jr. · Baker Botts · http://www.bakerbotts.com · One Shell Plaza · 910 Louisiana Street Houston, TX 77002-1210 · 713-229-1234

Stephen A. Massad · ⑳ · Baker Botts · http://www.bakerbotts.com · One Shell Plaza · 910 Louisiana Street · Houston, TX 77002-1210 · 713-229-1234

G. Michael O'Leary · Andrews Kurth · http://www.andrewskurth.com · 600 Travis Street, Suite 4200 · Houston, TX 77002 · 713-220-4200

David P. Oelman · Vinson & Elkins · http://www.velaw.com · First City Tower, Suite 2500 · 1001 Fannin Street · Houston, TX 77002-6760 · 713-758-2222

Gene J. Oshman · Baker Botts · http://www.bakerbotts.com · One Shell Plaza · 910 Louisiana Street · Houston, TX 77002-1210 · 713-229-1234

Theodore W. Paris · Baker Botts · http://www.bakerbotts.com · One Shell Plaza · 910 Louisiana Street · Houston, TX 77002-1210 · 713-229-1234

David Stanley Peterman · Fulbright & Jaworski · http://www.fulbright.com · Fulbright Tower, Suite 5100 · 1301 McKinney Street · Houston, TX 77010-3095 · 713-651-5151

Joe S. Poff · Baker Botts · http://www.bakerbotts.com · One Shell Plaza · 910 Louisiana Street · Houston, TX 77002-1210 · 713-229-1234

Kelly Brunetti Rose · Baker Botts · http://www.bakerbotts.com · One Shell Plaza · 910 Louisiana Street · Houston, TX 77002-1210 · 713-229-1234

Walter J. Smith · ⑩ · Baker Botts · http://www.bakerbotts.com · One Shell Plaza · 910 Louisiana Street · Houston, TX 77002-1210 · 713-229-1234

Charles H. Still, Sr. · ㉕ · Kelly, Hart & Hallman · Wells Fargo Plaza, Suite 4700 · 1000 Louisiana Street · Houston, TX 77002 · 713-654-4600

R. Joel Swanson · ㉕ · Baker Botts · http://www.bakerbotts.com · One Shell Plaza · 910 Louisiana Street · Houston, TX 77002-1210 · 713-229-1234

John A. Watson · ㉕ · Fulbright & Jaworski · http://www.fulbright.com · Fulbright Tower, Suite 5100 · 1301 McKinney Street · Houston, TX 77010-3095 · 713-651-5151

Marcus A. Watts · Locke Lord Bissell & Liddell · JP Morgan Chase Tower, Suite 3400 · 600 Travis Street · Houston, TX 77002 · 713-226-1200

Scott Neal Wulfe · ⑩ · Vinson & Elkins · http://www.velaw.com · First City Tower, Suite 2500 · 1001 Fannin Street · Houston, TX 77002-6760 · 713-758-2222

San Antonio

T. Drew Cauthorn · ⑩ · Hornberger Sheehan Fuller & Beiter · Quarry Heights, Suite 300 · 7373 Broadway · San Antonio, TX 78209 · 210-271-1700

The Woodlands

Jeffrey R. Harder · Winstead · http://www.winstead.com · 24 Waterway Avenue, Suite 500 · The Woodlands, TX 77380 · 281-681-5900

MINING LAW

Austin

Roger P. Nevola · ⑩ · Roger P. Nevola · 1723 Palma Plaza · P.O. Box 2103 · Austin, TX 78703 · 512-499-0500

MUNICIPAL LAW

Arlington

James Thomas Jeffrey, Jr. · Law Offices of Jim Jeffrey · 2214 Park Springs Boulevard · Arlington, TX 76103 · 817-261-4640

Austin

John M. Joseph · Clark, Thomas & Winters · 300 West Sixth Street, 15th Floor · P.O. Box 1148 · Austin, TX 78767 · 512-472-8800

Dallas

David J. LaBrec · Strasburger & Price · http://www.strasburger.com · 901 Main Street, Suite 4400 · Dallas, TX 75202-3794 · 214-651-4300

D. Randall Montgomery · D. Randall Montgomery & Associates · 12400 Coit Road, Suite 560 · Dallas, TX 75251 · 214-292-2600

El Paso

Norman J. Gordon · ⑩ · Mounce, Green, Myers, Safi & Galatzan · Kayser Building, 17th Floor · 100 North Stanton Street · P.O. Box 1977 · El Paso, TX 79950-1977 · 915-532-2000

Frisco

William Andrew Messer · The Messer Law Firm · 6351 Preston Road, Suite 350 · Frisco, TX 75034 · 469-633-1133

Houston

Francis J. Coleman, Jr. · ⑩ · Vinson & Elkins · http://www.velaw.com · First City Tower, Suite 2500 · 1001 Fannin Street · Houston, TX 77002-6760 · 713-758-2222

John J. Hightower · Olson & Olson · Wortham Tower, Suite 600 · 2727 Allen Parkway · Houston, TX 77019-2133 · 713-533-3800

San Antonio

William M. McKamie · Law Offices of William M. McKamie · 13750 San Pedro, Suite 640 · San Antonio, TX 78232 · 210-546-2122

NATIVE AMERICAN LAW

Houston

John Robert Pitts · John R. Pitts · P.O. Box 27130 · Houston, TX 77227 · 713-552-1854

NATURAL RESOURCES LAW

Addison

Bruce W. Claycombe · Geary Porter & Donovan · http://www.gpd.com · One Bent Tree Tower, Suite 400 · 16475 Dallas Parkway · Addison, TX 75001-6837 · 972-349-2225

Amarillo

Harlow Sprouse · ⑩ · Sprouse Shrader Smith · 701 South Taylor, Suite 500 · P.O. Box 15008 · Amarillo, TX 79105-5008 · 806-468-3300

Austin

Glenn E. Johnson · ⑩ · Kelly, Hart & Hallman · 301 Congress Avenue, Suite 2000 · Austin, TX 78701 · 512-495-6400

Patton G. Lochridge · ⑩ · McGinnis, Lochridge & Kilgore · http://www.mcginnislaw.com · 600 Congress Avenue, Suite 2100 · Austin, TX 78701 · 512-495-6000

John B. McFarland · Graves, Dougherty, Hearon & Moody · http://www.gdhm.com · 401 Congress Avenue, Suite 2200 · P.O. Box 98 · Austin, TX 78767-0098 · 512-480-5600

Roger P. Nevola · ⑩ · Roger P. Nevola · 1723 Palma Plaza · P.O. Box 2103 · Austin, TX 78703 · 512-499-0500

Shannon H. Ratliff · ⑩ · Ratliff Law Firm · 600 Congress Avenue, Suite 3100 · Austin, TX 78701-2984 · 512-493-9600

Pete Schenkkan · ⑩ · Graves, Dougherty, Hearon & Moody · http://www.gdhm.com · 401 Congress Avenue, Suite 2200 · P.O. Box 98 · Austin, TX 78767-0098 · 512-480-5600

H. Philip Whitworth, Jr. · ⑩ · Scott, Douglass & McConnico · 600 Congress Avenue, Suite 1500 · Austin, TX 78701-3234 · 512-495-6300

Susan G. Zachos · ⑩ · Law Offices of Susan G. Zachos · Barton Oaks Plaza One, Suite 300 · 901 South Mopac Expressway · Austin, TX 78746 · 512-329-1930

Dallas

Terry I. Cross · Haynes and Boone · 901 Main Street, Suite 3100 · Dallas, TX 75202 · 214-651-5000

Andrew B. Derman · Thompson & Knight · http://www.tklaw.com · One Arts Plaza, Suite 1500 · 1722 Routh Street · Dallas, TX 75201-2533 · 214-969-1700

Arthur J. Wright · Thompson & Knight · http://www.tklaw.com · One Arts Plaza, Suite 1500 · 1722 Routh Street · Dallas, TX 75201-2533 · 214-969-1700

Fort Worth

Robert C. Grable · ⑩ · Kelly, Hart & Hallman · Wells Fargo Tower, Suite 2500 · 201 Main Street · Fort Worth, TX 76102 · 817-332-2500

Dee J. Kelly, Sr. · ⑩ · Kelly, Hart & Hallman · Wells Fargo Tower, Suite 2500 · 201 Main Street · Fort Worth, TX 76102 · 817-332-2500

Houston

David F. Asmus · Baker Botts · http://www.bakerbotts.com · One Shell Plaza · 910 Louisiana Street · Houston, TX 77002-1210 · 713-229-1234

Douglas C. Atnipp · Greenberg Traurig · http://www.gtlaw.com · 1000 Louisiana Street, Suite 1800 · Houston, TX 77002 · 713-374-3500

David J. Beck · ㉕ · Beck, Redden & Secrest · http://www.brsfirm.com · One Houston Center, Suite 4500 1221 McKinney Street · Houston, TX 77010-2010 · 713-951-3700

Theodore R. Borrego · ⑳ · Law Offices of Theodore R. Borrego · 19 Briar Hollow Lane, Suite 235 · Houston, TX 77027 · 713-840-8250

Fielding B. Cochran III · Vinson & Elkins · http://www.velaw.com · First City Tower, Suite 2500 · 1001 Fannin Street · Houston, TX 77002-6760 · 713-758-2222

J. Gregory Copeland · Baker Botts · http://www.bakerbotts.com · One Shell Plaza · 910 Louisiana Street · Houston, TX 77002-1210 · 713-229-1234

Michael P. Darden · Baker Botts · http://www.bakerbotts.com · One Shell Plaza · 910 Louisiana Street · Houston, TX 77002-1210 · 713-229-1234

David G. Dunlap · Jackson Walker · 1401 McKinney Street, Suite 1900 · Houston, TX 77010-4008 · 713-752-4200

Uriel E. Dutton · ㉕ · Fulbright & Jaworski · http://www.fulbright.com · Fulbright Tower, Suite 5100 · 1301 McKinney Street · Houston, TX 77010-3095 · 713-651-5151

George F. Goolsby · Baker Botts · http://www.bakerbotts.com · One Shell Plaza · 910 Louisiana Street · Houston, TX 77002-1210 · 713-229-1234

Michael P. Irvin · Fulbright & Jaworski · http://www.fulbright.com · Fulbright Tower, Suite 5100 · 1301 McKinney Street · Houston, TX 77010-3095 · 713-651-5151

George F. Kutzschbach · Fulbright & Jaworski · http://www.fulbright.com · Fulbright Tower, Suite 5100 1301 McKinney Street · Houston, TX 77010-3095 · 713-651-5151

Henry S. May, Jr. · Vinson & Elkins · http://www.velaw.com · First City Tower, Suite 2500 · 1001 Fannin Street · Houston, TX 77002-6760 · 713-758-2222

Andrew McCollam III · Andrew McCollam · 2777 Allen Parkway, Suite 977 · Houston, TX 77019 · 713-640-5020

Michael P. Pearson · Jackson Walker · 1401 McKinney Street, Suite 1900 · Houston, TX 77010-4008 · 713-752-4200

Michael K. Pierce · Thompson & Knight · http://www.tklaw.com · 333 Clay Street, Suite 3300 · Houston, TX 77002 · 713-654-8111

G. Alan Rafte · Bracewell & Giuliani · http://www.bgllp.com · 711 Louisiana Street, Suite 2300 · Houston, TX 77002-2770 · 713-223-2300

Donald G. Sinex · Zukowski, Bresennan & Sinex · 1177 West Loop South, Suite 1100 · Houston, TX 77027 · 713-965-9969

Craig G. Townsend · Adams and Reese · http://www.adamsandreese.com · One Houston Center, Suite 4400 · 1221 McKinney Street · Houston, TX 77010 · 713-652-5151

Hugh Tucker · Baker Botts · http://www.bakerbotts.com · One Shell Plaza · 910 Louisiana Street · Houston, TX 77002-1210 · 713-229-1234

Dick Watt · Watt, Beckworth, Thompson & Henneman · 1800 Pennzoil Place, South Tower · 711 Louisiana Street · Houston, TX 77002 · 713-650-8100

Midland

Robert C. Bledsoe · Cotton, Bledsoe, Tighe & Dawson · 500 West Illinois Street, Suite 300 · P.O. Box 2776 · Midland, TX 79702-5782 · 432-684-5782

Harold L. Hensley, Jr. · 20 · Hinkle, Hensley, Shanor & Martin · 550 West Texas Avenue, Suite 1200 · P.O. Box 3580 · Midland, TX 79702 · 432-683-4691

Russel W. Neisig · Bullock, Scott, Neisig, Morgan, Leeton & Strauss · 500 West Texas Avenue, Suite 700 Midland, TX 79701-4200 · 432-683-5501

Susan R. Richardson · Cotton, Bledsoe, Tighe & Dawson · 500 West Illinois Street, Suite 300 · P.O. Box 2776 · Midland, TX 79702-5782 · 432-684-5782

Thomas R. Scott · 10 · Bullock, Scott, Neisig, Morgan, Leeton & Strauss · 500 West Texas Avenue, Suite 700 · Midland, TX 79701-4200 · 432-683-5501

Charles L. Tighe · 10 · Cotton, Bledsoe, Tighe & Dawson · 500 West Illinois Street, Suite 300 · P.O. Box 2776 · Midland, TX 79702-5782 · 432-684-5782

Palmer

Lawrence B. Mentzer · Miller & Mentzer · 100 North Main Street · P.O. Box 130 · Palmer, TX 75152 · 214-720-2222

San Antonio

Kevin Michael Beiter · 10 · Hornberger Sheehan Fuller & Beiter · Quarry Heights, Suite 300 · 7373 Broadway · San Antonio, TX 78209 · 210-271-1700

Richard T. Brady · 20 · Cox Smith Matthews · http://www.coxsmith.com · 112 East Pecan Street, Suite 1800 · San Antonio, TX 78205-1521 · 210-554-5500

Laura H. Burney · Law Offices of Laura H. Burney · 4040 Broadway, Suite 602 · San Antonio, TX 78209 210-821-5757

J. Randall Patterson · J. Randall Patterson · 14800 San Pedro Avenue, Suite 120 · San Antonio, TX 78232-3733 · 210-377-3111

Jon R. Ray · ⑩ · Cox Smith Matthews · http://www.coxsmith.com · 112 East Pecan Street, Suite 1800 · San Antonio, TX 78205-1521 · 210-554-5500

David H.O. Roth · Cox Smith Matthews · http://www.coxsmith.com · 112 East Pecan Street, Suite 1800 · San Antonio, TX 78205-1521 · 210-554-5500

Paul H. Smith · ⑳ · Cox Smith Matthews · http://www.coxsmith.com · 112 East Pecan Street, Suite 1800 · San Antonio, TX 78205-1521 · 210-554-5500

NON-PROFIT/CHARITIES LAW

Austin

Thomas J. Brorby · ⑳ · Brorby, Crozier & Dobie · 111 Congress Avenue, Suite 2250 · Austin, TX 78701 · 512-320-7040

Brian W. Crozier · Brorby, Crozier & Dobie · 111 Congress Avenue, Suite 2250 · Austin, TX 78701 · 512-320-7040

Dallas

Stuart M. Bumpas · ⑳ · Locke Lord Bissell & Liddell · 2200 Ross Avenue, Suite 2200 · Dallas, TX 75201-6776 · 214-740-8000

Ronald Roy Cresswell · ⑳ · Locke Lord Bissell & Liddell · 2200 Ross Avenue, Suite 2200 · Dallas, TX 75201-6776 · 214-740-8000

David M. Rosenberg · Thompson & Knight · http://www.tklaw.com · One Arts Plaza, Suite 1500 · 1722 Routh Street · Dallas, TX 75201-2533 · 214-969-1700

El Paso

Carl E. Ryan · ⑩ · Ryan Sanders & Gluth · 310 North Mesa Street, Suite 300 · El Paso, TX 79901 · 915-351-1100

Fort Worth

Dulaney G. Steer · Kelly, Hart & Hallman · Wells Fargo Tower, Suite 2500 · 201 Main Street · Fort Worth, TX 76102 · 817-332-2500

Rice M. Tilley, Jr. · ㉕ · Haynes and Boone · 201 Main Street, Suite 2200 · Fort Worth, TX 76102 · 817-347-6600

Houston

G. Edward Deery · Fulbright & Jaworski · http://www.fulbright.com · Fulbright Tower, Suite 5100 · 1301 McKinney Street · Houston, TX 77010-3095 · 713-651-5151

Ronald S. Webster · Fizer, Beck, Webster, Bentley & Scroggins · 1330 Post Oak Boulevard, Suite 2900 · Houston, TX 77056 · 713-840-7710

Alan V. Ytterberg · Fulbright & Jaworski · http://www.fulbright.com · Fulbright Tower, Suite 5100 · 1301 McKinney Street · Houston, TX 77010-3095 · 713-651-5151

Walter P. Zivley · ㉕ · Locke Lord Bissell & Liddell · JP Morgan Chase Tower, Suite 3400 · 600 Travis Street · Houston, TX 77002 · 713-226-1200

Austin

David L. Botsford · ⑩ · Law Office of David L. Botsford · http://www.davidbotsfordlaw.com · 1307 West Avenue · Austin, TX 78701 · 512-479-8030

Warren L. Collins, Jr. · Minton, Burton, Foster & Collins · 1100 Guadalupe Street · Austin, TX 78701-2198 · 512-476-4873

Bill Fitzgerald · ㉕ · Fitzgerald & Meissner · 812 San Antonio Street, Suite 400 · Austin, TX 78701 · 512-474-4700

Christopher M. Gunter · Christopher M. Gunter · 600 West Ninth Street · Austin, TX 78701-2212 · 512-476-2494

Wayne D. Meissner · Fitzgerald & Meissner · 812 San Antonio Street, Suite 400 · Austin, TX 78701 · 512-474-4700

Roy Q. Minton · ㉕ · Minton, Burton, Foster & Collins · 1100 Guadalupe Street · Austin, TX 78701-2198 512-476-4873

E. G. Morris · ⑩ · The Law Office of E.G. Morris · http://www.egmlaw.com · 608 West 12th Street, Suite B · Austin, TX 78701 · 512-478-0758

David A. Sheppard · ⑩ · David A. Sheppard · Chase Bank Building, Suite 1550 · 700 Lavaca Street · Austin, TX 78701 · 512-478-9483

Joseph A. Turner · Joseph A. Turner · 1504 West Avenue · Austin, TX 78701 · 512-474-4892

William A. White · ⑩ · The Law Office of Bill White · 1307 West Avenue · Austin, TX 78701 · 512-476-1494

Beaumont

Joseph C. Hawthorn · ⑳ · Joseph C. Hawthorn · 485 Milam Street · Beaumont, TX 77701-3518 · 409-838-3969

Corpus Christi

Jose A. Canales · ⑳ · Canales & Simonson · 2601 Morgan Avenue · P.O. Box 5624 · Corpus Christi, TX 78465 · 361-883-0601

J. Douglas Tinker · ⑳ · Law Office of J. Douglas Tinker · 622 South Tancahua Street · P.O. Box 276 · Corpus Christi, TX 78403 · 361-882-4378

Dallas

Bruce Anton · Sorrels, Udashen & Anton · 2301 Cedar Springs Road, Suite 400 · Dallas, TX 75201 · 214-468-8100

William A. Bratton III · William A. Bratton · 2828 Routh Street, Suite 850 · Lock Box 10 · Dallas, TX 75201-7666 · 214-871-1133

James D. Burnham · ⑩ · Law Office of James D. Burnham · Expressway Tower, Suite 515 · 6116 North Central Expressway · Dallas, TX 75206-5133 · 214-750-6616

Michael Paul Gibson · ㉕ · Burleson, Pate & Gibson · 2414 North Akard Street, Suite 700 · Dallas, TX 75201 · 214-871-4900

Ronald L. Goranson · Ronald L. Goranson · One Quadrangle Tower, Suite 850 · 2828 Routh Street · Lock Box 10 · Dallas, TX 75201-1424 · 214-651-1122

Robert C. Hinton · ⑩ · Robert Hinton & Associates · 4040 North Central Expressway, Suite 810 · Dallas, TX 75204 · 214-219-9300

Thomas W. Mills, Jr. · Mills & Williams · 5910 North Central Expressway, Suite 900 · Dallas, TX 75206-5141 · 214-265-9265

George R. Milner, Jr. · ⑳ · Milner & Finn · 2828 North Harwood Street, Suite 1950 · Dallas, TX 75201 · 214-651-1121

Tom Pappas · Burleson, Pate & Gibson · 2414 North Akard Street, Suite 700 · Dallas, TX 75201 · 214-871-4900

William M. Ravkind · Ravkind & Associates · One Meadows Building, Suite 200 · 5005 Greenville Avenue · Dallas, TX 75206 · 214-365-4426

Barry Sorrels · ⑩ · Sorrels, Udashen & Anton · 2301 Cedar Springs Road, Suite 400 · Dallas, TX 75201 · 214-468-8100

Gary A. Udashen · Sorrels, Udashen & Anton · 2301 Cedar Springs Road, Suite 400 · Dallas, TX 75201 · 214-468-8100

Robert Udashen · Sorrels, Udashen & Anton · 2301 Cedar Springs Road, Suite 400 · Dallas, TX 75201 · 214-468-8100

Denton

Jerry W. Cobb · Jerry Cobb · 525 North Locust Street · P.O. Box 1399 · Denton, TX 76202-2027 · 940-566-7010

Rick Hagen · Jackson & Hagen · The Texas Building, Suite 302 · 100 West Oak Street · Denton, TX 76201 · 940-566-1001

El Paso

Joseph Abraham, Jr. · ⑳ · The Law Firm of Carlos Eduardo Cárdenas · Toltec Building, Third Floor · 717 East San Antonio Street · P.O. Box 512312 · El Paso, TX 79951-0004 · 915-532-1601

James O. Darnell · ⑩ · Jim Darnell · http://www.jdarnell.com · 310 North Mesa Street, Suite 212 · El Paso, TX 79901 · 915-532-2442

Michael R. Gibson · Michael R. Gibson · http://www.mrgibsonlaw.com · 521 Texas Avenue · El Paso, TX 79901-1417 · 915-532-2977

Luis E. Islas · Luis E. Islas · 1216 Montana Avenue · El Paso, TX 79903-4001 · 915-562-7111

Dolph Quijano, Jr. · Adolph Quijano, Jr. · 707 Myrtle Avenue · El Paso, TX 79901 · 915-542-1051

Gary B. Weiser · ⑩ · Gary B. Weiser · 521 Texas Avenue · El Paso, TX 79901 · 915-544-0880

Fort Worth

Tim Evans · ⑳ · Evans, Gandy, Daniel & Moore · http://www.egdmlaw.com · 115 West Second Street, Suite 202 · Fort Worth, TX 76102 · 817-332-3822

Jeffrey A. Kearney · ⑩ · Kearney | Wynn · 505 Main Street, Suite 220 · Fort Worth, TX 76102 · 817-336-5600

Jack Vernon Strickland, Jr. · ⑩ · Law Offices of Jack V. Strickland · 909 Throckmorton Street · Fort Worth, TX 76102 · 817-338-1000

William Reagan Wynn · Kearney | Wynn · 505 Main Street, Suite 220 · Fort Worth, TX 76102 · 817-336-5600

Houston

Joel M. Androphy · Berg & Androphy · http://www.bafirm.com · 3704 Travis Street · Houston, TX 77002 · 713-529-5622

R. Todd Bennett · R. Todd Bennett · http://www.rtoddbennettpc.com · The Niels Esperson Building, 24th Floor · 808 Travis Street · Houston, TX 77002 · 713-752-2728

Michael DeGeurin · ⑳ · Foreman DeGeurin Nugent · 300 Main Street · Houston, TX 77002 · 713-655-9000

Dick DeGuerin · ㉕ · DeGuerin & Dickson · The Republic Building, Seventh Floor · 1018 Preston Avenue · Houston, TX 77002 · 713-223-5959

Richard Haynes · ㉕ · Richard Haynes & Associates · 314 North Post Oak Lane, Second Floor · Houston, TX 77024 · 713-868-1111

Edward A. Mallett · Mallett Guiberson Saper · JP Morgan Chase Tower, Suite 1900 · 600 Travis Street · Houston, TX 77002 · 713-236-1900

W. Troy McKinney · Schneider & McKinney · The Lyric Center, Suite 800 · 440 Louisiana · Houston, TX 77002 · 713-951-9994

Michael W. Ramsey · ⑳ · Michael W. Ramsey · 2120 Welch Street · Houston, TX 77019-5616 · 713-523-7878

Randolph Lee Schaffer, Jr. · ⑳ · The Schaffer Firm · Fulbright Tower, Suite 3100 · 1301 McKinney Street · Houston, TX 77010 · 713-951-9555

George McCall Secrest, Jr. · ⑩ · Bennett & Secrest · The Neils Esperson Building, 24th Floor · 808 Travis Street · Houston, TX 77002 · 713-757-0679

San Antonio

Roy R. Barrera, Sr. · ㉕ · Nicholas & Barrera · 424 East Nueva Street · San Antonio, TX 78205 · 210-224-5811

Charles D. Butts · ⑳ · Charles D. Butts · Petroleum Tower II, Suite 510 · 8626 Tesoro Drive · San Antonio, TX 78217 · 210-240-8239

John F. Carroll · ⑩ · John F. Carroll · 111 West Olmos Drive · San Antonio, TX 78212 · 210-829-7183

John A. Convery · Hasdorff & Convery · 1005 South Alamo Street · San Antonio, TX 78210 · 210-738-9060

John M. Economidy · John M. Economidy · 111 Soledad Street, Suite 348 · San Antonio, TX 78205 · 210-299-7685

Gerald Harris Goldstein · (20) · Goldstein, Goldstein & Hilley · Tower Life Building, 29th Floor · 310 South St. Mary's Street · San Antonio, TX 78205-3106 · 210-226-1463

Michael Clark Gross · Michael Clark Gross · 106 South St. Marys Street, Suite 260 · San Antonio, TX 78205 · 210-354-1919

Patrick L. Hancock · Patrick L. Hancock · 310 South St. Marys Street, Suite 1500 · San Antonio, TX 78205 · 210-223-8844

Van G. Hilley · Goldstein, Goldstein & Hilley · Tower Life Building, 29th Floor · 310 South St. Mary's Street · San Antonio, TX 78205-3106 · 210-226-1463

Michael W. McCrum · Thompson & Knight · http://www.tklaw.com · 4040 Broadway, Suite 615 · San Antonio, TX 78209 · 210-225-2285

James B. Parks · James B. Parks · 214 Dwyer Avenue, Suite 210 · San Antonio, TX 78204 · 210-229-1322

John M. Pinckney III · Strasburger & Price · http://www.strasburger.com · 300 Convent Street, Suite 900 San Antonio, TX 78205-3715 · 210-250-6000

Mark Stevens · (10) · Mark Stevens · Tower Life Building, Suite 1505 · 310 South St. Mary's Street · San Antonio, TX 78205 · 210-226-1433

Stephanie L. Stevens · Saint Mary's School of Law · 2507 Northwest 36th Street · San Antonio, TX 78228 · 210-431-5710

Texarkana

Damon Young · (10) · Young, Pickett & Lee · 4122 Texas Boulevard · P.O. Box 1897 · Texarkana, TX 75504 · 903-794-1303

Tyler

F. R. Files, Jr. · (20) · Bain, Files, Jarrett and Bain · 109 West Ferguson Street · P.O. Box 2013 · Tyler, TX 75710 · 903-595-3573

OIL & GAS LAW

Amarillo

Maston C. Courtney · Courtney, Countiss, Brian & Bailey · Chase Tower, Suite 1700 · 600 South Tyler Street · P.O. Box 9238 · Amarillo, TX 79105 · 806-372-5569

Harlow Sprouse · (10) · Sprouse Shrader Smith · 701 South Taylor, Suite 500 · P.O. Box 15008 · Amarillo, TX 79105-5008 · 806-468-3300

Austin

James N. Cowden · Scott, Douglass & McConnico · 600 Congress Avenue, Suite 1500 · Austin, TX 78701-3234 · 512-495-6300

Walter E. Demond · (10) · Clark, Thomas & Winters · 300 West Sixth Street, 15th Floor · P.O. Box 1148 · Austin, TX 78767 · 512-472-8800

Glenn E. Johnson · ⑩ · Kelly, Hart & Hallman · 301 Congress Avenue, Suite 2000 · Austin, TX 78701 · 512-495-6400

Patton G. Lochridge · ⑩ · McGinnis, Lochridge & Kilgore · http://www.mcginnislaw.com · 600 Congress Avenue, Suite 2100 · Austin, TX 78701 · 512-495-6000

Carroll G. Martin · Scott, Douglass & McConnico · 600 Congress Avenue, Suite 1500 · Austin, TX 78701-3234 · 512-495-6300

John B. McFarland · Graves, Dougherty, Hearon & Moody · http://www.gdhm.com · 401 Congress Avenue, Suite 2200 · P.O. Box 98 · Austin, TX 78767-0098 · 512-480-5600

Elizabeth N. Miller · Scott, Douglass & McConnico · 600 Congress Avenue, Suite 1500 · Austin, TX 78701-3234 · 512-495-6300

Shannon H. Ratliff · ⑩ · Ratliff Law Firm · 600 Congress Avenue, Suite 3100 · Austin, TX 78701-2984 · 512-493-9600

John G. Soule · Scott, Douglass & McConnico · 600 Congress Avenue, Suite 1500 · Austin, TX 78701-3234 · 512-495-6300

Andrew M. Taylor · Bracewell & Giuliani · http://www.bgllp.com · 111 Congress Avenue, Suite 2300 · Austin, TX 78701 · 512-472-7800

H. Philip Whitworth, Jr. · ⑩ · Scott, Douglass & McConnico · 600 Congress Avenue, Suite 1500 · Austin, TX 78701-3234 · 512-495-6300

Dallas

Greg W. Curry · Thompson & Knight · http://www.tklaw.com · One Arts Plaza, Suite 1500 · 1722 Routh Street · Dallas, TX 75201-2533 · 214-969-1700

Craig A. Haynes · Thompson & Knight · http://www.tklaw.com · One Arts Plaza, Suite 1500 · 1722 Routh Street · Dallas, TX 75201-2533 · 214-969-1700

Thomas E. Kurth · Haynes and Boone · 901 Main Street, Suite 3100 · Dallas, TX 75202 · 214-651-5000

Arthur J. Wright · Thompson & Knight · http://www.tklaw.com · One Arts Plaza, Suite 1500 · 1722 Routh Street · Dallas, TX 75201-2533 · 214-969-1700

Fort Worth

Robert C. Grable · ⑩ · Kelly, Hart & Hallman · Wells Fargo Tower, Suite 2500 · 201 Main Street · Fort Worth, TX 76102 · 817-332-2500

Dee J. Kelly, Sr. · ⑩ · Kelly, Hart & Hallman · Wells Fargo Tower, Suite 2500 · 201 Main Street · Fort Worth, TX 76102 · 817-332-2500

Jeffrey C. King · K&L Gates · D.R. Horton Tower, Suite 3000 · 301 Commerce · Fort Worth, TX 76102 · 817-347-5270

Kleber C. Miller · ㉕ · Shannon, Gracey, Ratliff & Miller · http://www.shannongracey.com · 777 Main Street, Suite 3800 · Fort Worth, TX 76102 · 817-336-9333

Todd W. Spake · Kelly, Hart & Hallman · Wells Fargo Tower, Suite 2500 · 201 Main Street · Fort Worth, TX 76102 · 817-332-2500

David F. Asmus · Baker Botts · http://www.bakerbotts.com · One Shell Plaza · 910 Louisiana Street · Houston, TX 77002-1210 · 713-229-1234

Douglas C. Atnipp · Greenberg Traurig · http://www.gtlaw.com · 1000 Louisiana Street, Suite 1800 · Houston, TX 77002 · 713-374-3500

Marcia E. Backus · Vinson & Elkins · http://www.velaw.com · First City Tower, Suite 2500 · 1001 Fannin Street · Houston, TX 77002-6760 · 713-758-2222

Geoffrey H. Bracken · Gardere Wynne Sewell · http://www.gardere.com · 1000 Louisiana, Suite 3400 · Houston, TX 77002-5011 · 713-276-5500

Phillip T. Bruns · Gibbs & Bruns · http://www.gibbs-bruns.com · 1100 Louisiana Street, Suite 5300 · Houston, TX 77002 · 713-650-8805

Rhett G. Campbell · Thompson & Knight · http://www.tklaw.com · 333 Clay Street, Suite 3300 · Houston, TX 77002 · 713-654-8111

John P. Cogan, Jr. · McDermott Will & Emery · 1000 Louisiana, Suite 1300 · Houston, TX 77002 · 713-653-1700

Michael P. Darden · Baker Botts · http://www.bakerbotts.com · One Shell Plaza · 910 Louisiana Street · Houston, TX 77002-1210 · 713-229-1234

David G. Dunlap · Jackson Walker · 1401 McKinney Street, Suite 1900 · Houston, TX 77010-4008 · 713-752-4200

Uriel E. Dutton · ㉕ · Fulbright & Jaworski · http://www.fulbright.com · Fulbright Tower, Suite 5100 · 1301 McKinney Street · Houston, TX 77010-3095 · 713-651-5151

George F. Goolsby · Baker Botts · http://www.bakerbotts.com · One Shell Plaza · 910 Louisiana Street · Houston, TX 77002-1210 · 713-229-1234

Thomas Hutcheson · Winstead · http://www.winstead.com · JPMorgan Chase Tower, Suite 1100 · 600 Travis Street · Houston, TX 77002 · 713-650-8400

Michael P. Irvin · Fulbright & Jaworski · http://www.fulbright.com · Fulbright Tower, Suite 5100 · 1301 McKinney Street · Houston, TX 77010-3095 · 713-651-5151

Jay D. Kelley · Vinson & Elkins · http://www.velaw.com · First City Tower, Suite 2500 · 1001 Fannin Street · Houston, TX 77002-6760 · 713-758-2222

Jay T. Kolb · Baker Botts · http://www.bakerbotts.com · One Shell Plaza · 910 Louisiana Street · Houston, TX 77002-1210 · 713-229-1234

George F. Kutzschbach · Fulbright & Jaworski · http://www.fulbright.com · Fulbright Tower, Suite 5100 1301 McKinney Street · Houston, TX 77010-3095 · 713-651-5151

Andrew McCollam III · Andrew McCollam · 2777 Allen Parkway, Suite 977 · Houston, TX 77019 · 713-640-5020

Eugene M. Nettles · Porter & Hedges · 1000 Main Street, 36th Floor · Houston, TX 77002 · 713-226-0600

Jesse Pierce · King & Spalding · 1100 Louisiana Street, Suite 4000 · Houston, TX 77002-5213 · 713-751-3200

G. Alan Rafte · Bracewell & Giuliani · http://www.bgllp.com · 711 Louisiana Street, Suite 2300 · Houston, TX 77002-2770 · 713-223-2300

Robert H. Thomas · Porter & Hedges · 1000 Main Street, 36th Floor · Houston, TX 77002 · 713-226-0600

Joseph Thompson III · Watt, Beckworth, Thompson & Henneman · 1800 Pennzoil Place, South Tower · 711 Louisiana Street · Houston, TX 77002 · 713-650-8100

Hugh Tucker · Baker Botts · http://www.bakerbotts.com · One Shell Plaza · 910 Louisiana Street · Houston, TX 77002-1210 · 713-229-1234

Dick Watt · Watt, Beckworth, Thompson & Henneman · 1800 Pennzoil Place, South Tower · 711 Louisiana Street · Houston, TX 77002 · 713-650-8100

Midland

Harold L. Hensley, Jr. · ⑳ · Hinkle, Hensley, Shanor & Martin · 550 West Texas Avenue, Suite 1200 · P.O. Box 3580 · Midland, TX 79702 · 432-683-4691

Susan R. Richardson · Cotton, Bledsoe, Tighe & Dawson · 500 West Illinois Street, Suite 300 · P.O. Box 2776 · Midland, TX 79702-5782 · 432-684-5782

Thomas R. Scott · ⑩ · Bullock, Scott, Neisig, Morgan, Leeton & Strauss · 500 West Texas Avenue, Suite 700 · Midland, TX 79701-4200 · 432-683-5501

Charles L. Tighe · ⑩ · Cotton, Bledsoe, Tighe & Dawson · 500 West Illinois Street, Suite 300 · P.O. Box 2776 · Midland, TX 79702-5782 · 432-684-5782

San Antonio

Kevin Michael Beiter · ⑩ · Hornberger Sheehan Fuller & Beiter · Quarry Heights, Suite 300 · 7373 Broadway · San Antonio, TX 78209 · 210-271-1700

Richard T. Brady · ⑳ · Cox Smith Matthews · http://www.coxsmith.com · 112 East Pecan Street, Suite 1800 · San Antonio, TX 78205-1521 · 210-554-5500

Jon R. Ray · ⑩ · Cox Smith Matthews · http://www.coxsmith.com · 112 East Pecan Street, Suite 1800 · San Antonio, TX 78205-1521 · 210-554-5500

David H.O. Roth · Cox Smith Matthews · http://www.coxsmith.com · 112 East Pecan Street, Suite 1800 · San Antonio, TX 78205-1521 · 210-554-5500

Paul H. Smith · ⑳ · Cox Smith Matthews · http://www.coxsmith.com · 112 East Pecan Street, Suite 1800 · San Antonio, TX 78205-1521 · 210-554-5500

PERSONAL INJURY LITIGATION

Abilene

Stephen H. Suttle · ⑩ · McMahon Surovik Suttle · http://www.mcmahonlawtx.com · 400 Pine Street, Suite 800 · P.O. Box 3679 · Abilene, TX 79604 · 325-676-9183

Amarillo

Marvin W. Jones · Sprouse Shrader Smith · 701 South Taylor, Suite 500 · P.O. Box 15008 · Amarillo, TX 79105-5008 · 806-468-3300

Thomas C. Riney · Riney & Mayfield · http://www.rineymayfield.com · 600 Maxor Building · 320 South Polk Street · Amarillo, TX 79101-1426 · 806-468-3200

Austin

Craig Douglas Ball · Craig Douglas Ball · 1101 Ridgecrest Drive · Austin, TX 78746 · 512-514-0182

Mark T. Beaman · Germer Gertz · 301 Congress Avenue, Suite 1700 · Austin, TX 78701 · 512-472-0288

David P. Boyce · Wright & Greenhill · 221 West Sixth Street, Suite 1800 · Austin, TX 78701 · 512-476-4600

Sean E. Breen · Herman Howry & Breen · http://www.hermanhowry.com · 1900 Pearl Street · Austin, TX 78705 · 512-474-7300

Eugene W. Brees III · Whitehurst, Harkness, Ozmun & Brees · Westgate Building, 24th Floor · 1122 Colorado Street · P.O. Box 1802 · Austin, TX 78767 · 866-594-8630

Thomas M. Bullion III · Germer Gertz · 301 Congress Avenue, Suite 1700 · Austin, TX 78701 · 512-472-0288

George B. Butts · ⑩ · DLA Piper · 1221 South MoPac Expressway, Suite 400 · Austin, TX 78746-7650 · 512-457-7000

Don L. Davis · ⑩ · Byrd, Davis & Furman · 707 West 34th Street · Austin, TX 78705 · 512-454-3751

Mike Davis · Slack & Davis · http://www.slackdavis.com · 2705 Bee Cave Road, Suite 220 · Austin, TX 78746 · 512-795-8686

Kenneth J. Ferguson · Clark, Thomas & Winters · 300 West Sixth Street, 15th Floor · P.O. Box 1148 · Austin, TX 78767 · 512-472-8800

Rick Freeman · ⑩ · Rick Freeman · 811 Barton Springs Road, Suite 740 · Austin, TX 78704 · 512-477-6111

James H. Furman · Byrd, Davis & Furman · 707 West 34th Street · Austin, TX 78705 · 512-454-3751

Richard H. Grafton · Germer Gertz · 301 Congress Avenue, Suite 1700 · Austin, TX 78701 · 512-472-0288

Richard Alan Grigg · ⑩ · Law Offices of Dicky Grigg · 48 East Avenue, Suite 100 · Austin, TX 78701 · 512-474-6061

Thomas R. Harkness · ⑩ · Whitehurst, Harkness, Ozmun & Brees · Westgate Building, 24th Floor · 1122 Colorado Street · P.O. Box 1802 · Austin, TX 78767 · 866-594-8630

Jay Harvey · Winckler & Harvey · Building Two, Suite 222 · 4407 Bee Cave Road · Austin, TX 78746 · 512-306-1800

Richard C. Hile · ⑩ · Dies & Hile · 1601 Rio Grande Street, Suite 330 · Austin, TX 78701-1149 · 512-476-4394

Randy R. Howry · Herman Howry & Breen · http://www.hermanhowry.com · 1900 Pearl Street · Austin, TX 78705 · 512-474-7300

Michael S. Hull · ⑩ · Hull Henricks & MacRae · Chase Bank Tower, Suite 2000 · 221 West Sixth Street · Austin, TX 78701 · 512-472-4554

Tommy Jacks · ⑩ · Jacks Law Firm · 1205 Rio Grande Street · Austin, TX 78701-1709 · 512-478-4422

Stephen E. McConnico · ⑩ · Scott, Douglass & McConnico · 600 Congress Avenue, Suite 1500 · Austin, TX 78701-3234 · 512-495-6300

Mark R. Mueller · Mueller Law Offices · http://www.muellerlaw.com · 404 West Seventh Street · Austin, TX 78701 · 512-478-1236

Jeff D. Otto · Thompson, Coe, Cousins & Irons · http://www.thompsoncoe.com · Austin Centre, Suite 1500 · 701 Brazos · Austin, TX 78701 · 512-708-8200

A. Carl Pierce · Wright & Greenhill · 221 West Sixth Street, Suite 1800 · Austin, TX 78701 · 512-476-4600

Michael L. Slack · ⑩ · Slack & Davis · http://www.slackdavis.com · 2705 Bee Cave Road, Suite 220 · Austin, TX 78746 · 512-795-8686

Broadus A. Spivey · ㉕ · Law Offices of Dicky Grigg · 48 East Avenue, Suite 100 · Austin, TX 78701 · 512-474-6061

Tom A. Stribling · CLEAT · 400 West 14th Street, Suite 200 · Austin, TX 78701-3161 · 512-495-9111

Terry O. Tottenham · ⑩ · Fulbright & Jaworski · http://www.fulbright.com · 600 Congress Avenue, Suite 2400 · Austin, TX 78701-2978 · 512-474-5201

Ronald D. Wamsted · Thompson, Coe, Cousins & Irons · http://www.thompsoncoe.com · Austin Centre, Suite 1500 · 701 Brazos · Austin, TX 78701 · 512-708-8200

Kirk Preston Watson · ⑩ · K&L Gates · 111 Congress Avenue, Suite 900 · Austin, TX 78701 · 512-482-6800

Mikal C. Watts · Watts Law Firm · 111 Congress Avenue, Suite 1010 · Austin, TX 78701 · 512-479-0500

William O. Whitehurst · ⑩ · Whitehurst, Harkness, Ozmun & Brees · Westgate Building, 24th Floor · 1122 Colorado Street · P.O. Box 1802 · Austin, TX 78767 · 866-594-8630

Jay Winckler · Winckler & Harvey · Building Two, Suite 222 · 4407 Bee Cave Road · Austin, TX 78746 · 512-306-1800

T. B. Wright · ⑩ · Wright & Greenhill · 221 West Sixth Street, Suite 1800 · Austin, TX 78701 · 512-476-4600

Beaumont

Robert A. Black · MehaffyWeber · http://www.mehaffyweber.com · 2615 Calder Avenue · P.O. Box 16 · Beaumont, TX 77702 · 409-835-5011

Morris C. Carrington · MehaffyWeber · http://www.mehaffyweber.com · 2615 Calder Avenue · P.O. Box 16 · Beaumont, TX 77702 · 409-835-5011

Jack P. Carroll · Orgain, Bell & Tucker · 470 Orleans Street · P.O. Box 1751 · Beaumont, TX 77704-1751 409-838-6412

Patricia D. Chamblin · ⑩ · MehaffyWeber · http://www.mehaffyweber.com · 2615 Calder Avenue · P.O. Box 16 · Beaumont, TX 77702 · 409-835-5011

Sandra F. Clark · MehaffyWeber · http://www.mehaffyweber.com · 2615 Calder Avenue · P.O. Box 16 · Beaumont, TX 77702 · 409-835-5011

Brent W. Coon · Brent Coon & Associates · 3550 Fannin · Beaumont, TX 77701 · 409-835-2666

Paul F. Ferguson, Jr. · Provost & Umphrey Law Firm · Stedman Building · 490 Park Street · P.O. Box 4905 · Beaumont, TX 77704 · 409-835-6000

Gerald R. Flatten · ⑩ · Rienstra, Dowell & Flatten · San Jacinto Building, Suite 1007 · 595 Orleans Street Beaumont, TX 77701 · 409-833-6317

Lawrence L. Germer · ⑩ · Germer Gertz · 550 Fannin Street, Suite 400 · P.O. Box 4915 · Beaumont, TX 77701 · 409-654-6700

Gilbert I. Low · ⑳ · Orgain, Bell & Tucker · 470 Orleans Street · P.O. Box 1751 · Beaumont, TX 77704-1751 · 409-838-6412

Glen W. Morgan · Reaud, Morgan & Quinn · 801 Laurel Street · P.O. Box 26005 · Beaumont, TX 77720-6005 · 409-838-1000

Hubert Oxford III · ⑩ · Benckenstein & Oxford · 3535 Calder Avenue, Suite 300 · P.O. Drawer 150 · Beaumont, TX 77704 · 409-833-9182

James E. Payne · Provost & Umphrey Law Firm · Stedman Building · 490 Park Street · P.O. Box 4905 · Beaumont, TX 77704 · 409-835-6000

Wayne A. Reaud · ⑩ · Reaud, Morgan & Quinn · 801 Laurel Street · P.O. Box 26005 · Beaumont, TX 77720-6005 · 409-838-1000

Thomas Walter Umphrey · ⑩ · Provost & Umphrey Law Firm · Stedman Building · 490 Park Street · P.O. Box 4905 · Beaumont, TX 77704 · 409-835-6000

Jo Ben Whittenburg · Orgain, Bell & Tucker · 470 Orleans Street · P.O. Box 1751 · Beaumont, TX 77704-1751 · 409-838-6412

Brownsville

Mitchell C. Chaney · Rodriguez Colvin Chaney & Saenz · 1201 East Van Buren · P.O. Box 2155 · Brownsville, TX 78522 · 956-542-7441

Corpus Christi

William A. Abernethy · ⑩ · Donnell, Abernethy & Kieschnick · Tower II, Suite 400 · 555 North Carancahua · P.O. Box 2624 · Corpus Christi, TX 78478 · 361-888-5551

Guy H. Allison · ⑳ · Guy H. Allison · 500 North Water Street, Suite 1200 · Corpus Christi, TX 78471 · 361-884-8900

Darrell L. Barger · ⑩ · Hartline, Dacus, Barger, Dreyer & Kern · One Shoreline Plaza, North Tower, Suite 2000 · 800 North Shoreline Boulevard · Corpus Christi, TX 78401 · 361-866-8000

Jose A. Canales · ⑳ · Canales & Simonson · 2601 Morgan Avenue · P.O. Box 5624 · Corpus Christi, TX 78465 · 361-883-0601

Anthony F. Constant · ⑩ · Constant Law Firm · South Tower, Suite 2700 · 800 North Shoreline Boulevard · Corpus Christi, TX 78401 · 361-887-8800

Richard W. Crews · Hartline, Dacus, Barger, Dreyer & Kern · One Shoreline Plaza, North Tower, Suite 2000 · 800 North Shoreline Boulevard · Corpus Christi, TX 78401 · 361-866-8000

William R. Edwards · ㉕ · The Edwards Law Firm · http://www.edwardsfirm.com · 802 North Carancahua Street, Suite 1400 · P.O. Box 480 · Corpus Christi, TX 78403-0480 · 361-698-7600

Rene M. Haas · ⑩ · Perry & Haas · http://www.perryhaas.com · Frost Bank Plaza, Suite 2300 · 802 North Carancahua Street · P.O. Box 1500 · Corpus Christi, TX 78403-1500 · 361-880-7500

Tom Hermansen · ⑩ · Hermansen, McKibben, Woolsey & Villarreal · 1100 Tower II · 555 North Carancahua · Corpus Christi, TX 78478 · 361-882-6611

Van Huseman · ⑩ · Huseman, Dodson & Hummell · 600 Leopard Street, Suite 2100 · Corpus Christi, TX 78473-2707 · 361-883-3563

James F. McKibben, Jr. · Hermansen, McKibben, Woolsey & Villarreal · 1100 Tower II · 555 North Carancahua · Corpus Christi, TX 78478 · 361-882-6611

Russell H. McMains · ⑩ · Law Offices of Russell H. McMains · 500 North Shoreline Boulevard, Suite 1100 · P.O. Box 2846 · Corpus Christi, TX 78403 · 361-887-4455

David L. Perry · ⑳ · Perry & Haas · http://www.perryhaas.com · Frost Bank Plaza, Suite 2300 · 802 North Carancahua Street · P.O. Box 1500 · Corpus Christi, TX 78403-1500 · 361-880-7500

Anthony E. Pletcher · Watts Law Firm · Tower II Building, 14th Floor · 555 North Carancahua Street · Corpus Christi, TX 78478-0801 · 361-887-0500

Jorge C. Rangel · The Rangel Law Firm · 615 Upper North Broadway, Suite 2020 · P.O. Box 2683 · Corpus Christi, TX 78403-2683 · 361-883-8500

Michael G. Terry · ⑩ · Hartline, Dacus, Barger, Dreyer & Kern · One Shoreline Plaza, North Tower, Suite 2000 · 800 North Shoreline Boulevard · Corpus Christi, TX 78401 · 361-866-8000

Dallas

Charla Aldous · Aldous Law Firm · 2305 Cedar Springs Road, Suite 200 · Dallas, TX 75201 · 214-526-5595

G. Luke Ashley · Thompson & Knight · http://www.tklaw.com · One Arts Plaza, Suite 1500 · 1722 Routh Street · Dallas, TX 75201-2533 · 214-969-1700

Michael R. Berry · Thompson & Knight · http://www.tklaw.com · One Arts Plaza, Suite 1500 · 1722 Routh Street · Dallas, TX 75201-2533 · 214-969-1700

Frank L. Branson · ⑳ · Law Offices of Frank L. Branson · http://www.flbranson.com · Highland Park Place, Suite 1800 · 4514 Cole Avenue · Dallas, TX 75205 · 214-522-0200

Arlen D. Bynum · ㉕ · Law Offices of Arlen Dean Bynum · 4144 North Central Expressway, Suite 1030 · Dallas, TX 75204-3140 · 214-559-0500

James E. Coleman, Jr. · ㉕ · Carrington, Coleman, Sloman & Blumenthal · 901 Main Street, Suite 5500 · Dallas, TX 75202 · 214-855-3000

James E. Cowles · ⑩ · Cowles & Thompson · http://www.cowlesthompson.com · Bank of America Plaza, Suite 4000 · 901 Main Street · Dallas, TX 75202 · 214-672-2000

Robert D. Crain · Crain Lewis · 3400 Carlisle, Suite 300 · Dallas, TX 75204 · 214-522-9404

W. Richard Davis · ㉕ · Strasburger & Price · http://www.strasburger.com · 901 Main Street, Suite 4400 · Dallas, TX 75202-3794 · 214-651-4300

Alfred W. Ellis · Sommerman & Quesada · Turtle Creek Center, Suite 1400 · 3811 Turtle Creek Boulevard · Dallas, TX 75219-4461 · 214-720-0720

Frank Finn · ⑩ · Thompson & Knight · http://www.tklaw.com · One Arts Plaza, Suite 1500 · 1722 Routh Street · Dallas, TX 75201-2533 · 214-969-1700

Joe B. Harrison · Gardere Wynne Sewell · http://www.gardere.com · 1601 Elm Street, Suite 3000 · Dallas, TX 75201 · 214-999-3000

Ralph C. Jones · Jones Geisler · 3400 Carlisle Street, Suite 300 · Dallas, TX 75204 · 214-276-6000

John H. Martin · ⑩ · Thompson & Knight · http://www.tklaw.com · One Arts Plaza, Suite 1500 · 1722 Routh Street · Dallas, TX 75201-2533 · 214-969-1700

George A. Quesada · Sommerman & Quesada · Turtle Creek Center, Suite 1400 · 3811 Turtle Creek Boulevard · Dallas, TX 75219-4461 · 214-720-0720

Robert R. Roby · Curran Tomko Tarski · 2001 Bryan Street, Suite 2050 · Dallas, TX 75201 · 214-270-1400

Robert F. Ruckman · Jackson Walker · Bank of America Plaza, Suite 6000 · 901 Main Street · Dallas, TX 75202 · 214-953-6000

Ladd C. Sanger · Slack & Davis · http://www.slackdavis.com · 2911 Turtle Creek Boulevard, Suite 1400 · Dallas, TX 75219 · 214-528-8686

C. L. Mike Schmidt · ⑳ · The Schmidt Firm · 2911 Turtle Creek Boulevard, Suite 1400 · Dallas, TX 75219 · 214-521-4898

Paula Fisette Sweeney · ⑩ · Howie & Sweeney · 3811 Turtle Creek Boulevard, Suite 1900 · Dallas, TX 75219 · 214-523-8800

Windle Turley · ㉕ · Turley Law Firm · 1000 Turley Law Center · 6440 North Central Expressway · Dallas, TX 75206 · 214-691-4025

Roger G. Williams · Wilson, Williams & Molberg · 2214 Main Street · Dallas, TX 75201-4324 · 214-748-5276

Edwin E. Wright III · ⑳ · Stradley & Wright · 9330 LBJ Freeway, Suite 1400 · Dallas, TX 75243 · 972-231-6001

Denton

Rick Hagen · Jackson & Hagen · The Texas Building, Suite 302 · 100 West Oak Street · Denton, TX 76201 · 940-566-1001

Michael J. Whitten · The Whitten Law Firm · 218 North Elm Street · Denton, TX 76201 · 940-383-1618

El Paso

Jeffrey S. Alley · Windle, Hood, Alley, Norton, Brittain & Jay · Chase Tower, Suite 1350 · 201 East Main Street · El Paso, TX 79901 · 915-545-4900

Eric M. Brittain · Windle, Hood, Alley, Norton, Brittain & Jay · Chase Tower, Suite 1350 · 201 East Main Street · El Paso, TX 79901 · 915-545-4900

Milton C. Colia · Kemp Smith · http://www.kempsmith.com · 221 North Kansas, Suite 1700 · El Paso, TX 79901-1441 · 915-533-4424

Jim Curtis · ⑩ · Kemp Smith · http://www.kempsmith.com · 221 North Kansas, Suite 1700 · El Paso, TX 79901-1441 · 915-533-4424

David S. Jeans · ⑩ · Ray, Valdez, McChristian & Jeans · 5822 Cromo Drive · El Paso, TX 79912 · 915-832-7200

Enrique Moreno · ⑩ · Law Offices of Enrique Moreno · 701 Magoffin Avenue · El Paso, TX 79901-2507 915-533-9977

H. Keith Myers · ⑩ · Mounce, Green, Myers, Safi & Galatzan · Kayser Building, 17th Floor · 100 North Stanton Street · P.O. Box 1977 · El Paso, TX 79950-1977 · 915-532-2000

J. Roberto Oaxaca · ⑩ · Oaxaca Bernal & Associates · 1515 Montana Avenue · El Paso, TX 79902-5619 · 915-544-0406

Mark C. Walker · Brown McCarroll · 221 North Kansas Street, Suite 2000 · El Paso, TX 79901 · 915-545-4716

Fort Worth

Edwin G. Bell · ⑩ · Edwin G. Bell · 749 North Main Street · P.O. Box 64369 · Fort Worth, TX 76106-9418 · 817-335-2246

Randall E. Betty · Shannon, Gracey, Ratliff & Miller · http://www.shannongracey.com · 777 Main Street, Suite 3800 · Fort Worth, TX 76102 · 817-336-9333

Kae L. Brockermeyer · ⑩ · Kae L. Brockermeyer · P.O. Box 789 · Fort Worth, TX 83014 · 817-377-8585

John P. Camp · ⑩ · Law Office of John P Camp · P.O. Box 101251 · Fort Worth, TX 76185 · 817-732-1519

Beale Dean · ⑳ · Brown, Dean, Wiseman, Liser, Proctor & Hart · Fort Worth Club Building, Suite 200 · 306 West Seventh Street · Fort Worth, TX 76102-4905 · 817-332-1391

Michael F. Felber · Michael F. Felber · The Mallick Tower, Suite 101 · 101 Summit Avenue · Fort Worth, TX 76102 · 817-877-5900

Richard L. Griffith · ⑳ · Cantey & Hanger · 300 Cantey Hanger Plaza · 600 West Sixth Street · Fort Worth, TX 76102-3685 · 817-877-2800

Stephen C. Howell · Brown Dean Wiseman Proctor Hart & Howell · 307 West Seventh Street, Suite 1918 Fort Worth, TX 76102 · 817-332-1391

John S. Jose · Jose, Henry, Brantley, MacLean & Alvarado · 675 North Henderson · Fort Worth, TX 76107 · 817-877-3303

Darrell L. Keith · ⑩ · Keith Law Firm · The Keith Building · 1705 West Seventh Street · Fort Worth, TX 76102 · 817-338-1400

George Grant Liser · ⑩ · Brown, Dean, Wiseman, Liser, Proctor & Hart · Fort Worth Club Building, Suite 200 · 306 West Seventh Street · Fort Worth, TX 76102-4905 · 817-332-1391

Kleber C. Miller · ㉕ · Shannon, Gracey, Ratliff & Miller · http://www.shannongracey.com · 777 Main Street, Suite 3800 · Fort Worth, TX 76102 · 817-336-9333

Jonathan D. F. Nelson · Watson, Caraway, Nelson, Midkiff & Luningham · 1000 Commerce Building · 307 West Seventh Street · Fort Worth, TX 76102 · 817-870-1717

John W. Proctor · Brown, Dean, Wiseman, Liser, Proctor & Hart · Fort Worth Club Building, Suite 200 · 306 West Seventh Street · Fort Worth, TX 76102-4905 · 817-332-1391

Richard U. Simon · ⑩ · Brackett & Ellis · 100 Main Street · Fort Worth, TX 76102 · 817-338-1700

Houston

Robert L. Adams · Kacal, Adams & Law · One Riverway, Suite 1200 · Houston, TX 77056 · 713-529-3992

Brock C. Akers · ⑩ · Phillips & Akers · 3200 Southwest Freeway, Suite 3200 · Houston, TX 77027 · 713-552-9595

Fields Alexander · Beck, Redden & Secrest · http://www.brsfirm.com · One Houston Center, Suite 4500 · 1221 McKinney Street · Houston, TX 77010-2010 · 713-951-3700

Joel M. Androphy · Berg & Androphy · http://www.bafirm.com · 3704 Travis Street · Houston, TX 77002 · 713-529-5622

John B. Beckworth · Watt, Beckworth, Thompson & Henneman · 1800 Pennzoil Place, South Tower · 711 Louisiana Street · Houston, TX 77002 · 713-650-8100

J. Michael Bell · Thompson & Knight · http://www.tklaw.com · 333 Clay Street, Suite 3300 · Houston, TX 77002 · 713-654-8111

David Howard Berg · ⑩ · Berg & Androphy · http://www.bafirm.com · 3704 Travis Street · Houston, TX 77002 · 713-529-5622

Edward F. Blizzard · Blizzard, McCarthy & Nabers · http://www.blizzardlaw.com · Lyric Centre, Suite 1710 · 440 Louisiana Street · Houston, TX 77002-1636 · 713-844-3750

William C. Book, Jr. · Tekell, Book, Matthews & Limmer · 4300 One Houston Center · 1221 McKinney Street · Houston, TX 77010-2015 · 713-222-9542

Olan J. Boudreaux · Fisher, Boyd, Brown, Boudreaux & Huguenard · Riviana Building, 14th Floor · 2777 Allen Parkway · Houston, TX 77019 · 713-400-4000

Larry P. Boyd · ⑩ · Fisher, Boyd, Brown, Boudreaux & Huguenard · Riviana Building, 14th Floor · 2777 Allen Parkway · Houston, TX 77019 · 713-400-4000

David H. Brown · Brown & Kornegay · 2777 Allen Parkway, Suite 977 · Houston, TX 77019 · 713-528-3700

Thomas K. Brown · Fisher, Boyd, Brown, Boudreaux & Huguenard · Riviana Building, 14th Floor · 2777 Allen Parkway · Houston, TX 77019 · 713-400-4000

David H. Burrow · ⑩ · Law Office of David H. Burrow · One Allen Center, Suite 3450 · 500 Dallas Street Houston, TX 77002 · 713-222-6333

Richard H. Caldwell · ⑩ · Andrews Kurth · http://www.andrewskurth.com · 600 Travis Street, Suite 4200 Houston, TX 77002 · 713-220-4200

Richard N. Carrell · Fulbright & Jaworski · http://www.fulbright.com · Fulbright Tower, Suite 5100 · 1301 McKinney Street · Houston, TX 77010-3095 · 713-651-5151

Howard L. Close · Wright Brown & Close · Three Riverway, Suite 600 · Houston, TX 77056 · 713-572-4321

Morgan Lee Copeland, Jr. · Vinson & Elkins · http://www.velaw.com · First City Tower, Suite 2500 · 1001 Fannin Street · Houston, TX 77002-6760 · 713-758-2222

Otway B. Denny, Jr. · ⑩ · Fulbright & Jaworski · http://www.fulbright.com · Fulbright Tower, Suite 5100 1301 McKinney Street · Houston, TX 77010-3095 · 713-651-5151

Stephen C. Dillard · ⑩ · Fulbright & Jaworski · http://www.fulbright.com · Fulbright Tower, Suite 5100 · 1301 McKinney Street · Houston, TX 77010-3095 · 713-651-5151

Michael P. Doyle · Doyle Raizner · One Houston Center, Suite 4100 · 1221 McKinney · Houston, TX 77010 · 713-571-1146

Daryl G. Dursum · Adams and Reese · http://www.adamsandreese.com · One Houston Center, Suite 4400 1221 McKinney Street · Houston, TX 77010 · 713-652-5151

Wayne Fisher · ㉕ · Fisher, Boyd, Brown, Boudreaux & Huguenard · Riviana Building, 14th Floor · 2777 Allen Parkway · Houston, TX 77019 · 713-400-4000

Daniel V. Flatten · ⑩ · Porter & Hedges · 1000 Main Street, 36th Floor · Houston, TX 77002 · 713-226-0600

Ronald G. Franklin · Franklin, Cardwell & Jones · 1001 McKinney Street, 18th Floor · Houston, TX 77002-6417 · 713-222-6025

Kathleen A. Gallagher · Vinson & Elkins · http://www.velaw.com · First City Tower, Suite 2500 · 1001 Fannin Street · Houston, TX 77002-6760 · 713-758-2222

Michael T. Gallagher · ㉕ · The Gallagher Law Firm · 2905 Sackett Street · Houston, TX 77098 · 713-222-8080

H. Lee Godfrey · ⑩ · Susman Godfrey · 1000 Louisiana, Suite 5100 · Houston, TX 77002-5096 · 713-651-9366

Barbara L. Hachenburg · Germer Gertz · Three Allen Center, Suite 4950 · 333 Clay Street · Houston, TX 77002 · 713-650-1313

Michael S. Hays · Hays, McConn, Rice & Pickering · http://www.haysmcconn.com · 1233 West Loop South, Suite 1000 · Houston, TX 77027 · 713-752-8300

J. Graham Hill · Locke Lord Bissell & Liddell · JP Morgan Chase Tower, Suite 3400 · 600 Travis Street · Houston, TX 77002 · 713-226-1200

Charles W. Hurd · Fulbright & Jaworski · http://www.fulbright.com · Fulbright Tower, Suite 5100 · 1301 McKinney Street · Houston, TX 77010-3095 · 713-651-5151

Joseph D. Jamail · ㉕ · Jamail & Kolius · 500 Dallas Street, Suite 3434 · Houston, TX 77002 · 713-651-3000

Frank G. Jones · ⑩ · Fulbright & Jaworski · http://www.fulbright.com · Fulbright Tower, Suite 5100 · 1301 McKinney Street · Houston, TX 77010-3095 · 713-651-5151

Richard L. Josephson · Baker Botts · http://www.bakerbotts.com · One Shell Plaza · 910 Louisiana Street Houston, TX 77002-1210 · 713-229-1234

Kevin D. Krist · Law Office of Kevin Krist · http://www.kevinkristlaw.com · Clock Tower Building, Suite 102 · 3401 Allen Parkway · Houston, TX 77019 · 713-284-1660

Scott D. Lassetter · The Lassetter Law Firm · 708 Main Street, Suite 200 · Houston, TX 77002 · 713-523-0325

James Russell Leahy · Locke Lord Bissell & Liddell · JP Morgan Chase Tower, Suite 3400 · 600 Travis Street · Houston, TX 77002 · 713-226-1200

Gerry Lowry · Fulbright & Jaworski · http://www.fulbright.com · Fulbright Tower, Suite 5100 · 1301 McKinney Street · Houston, TX 77010-3095 · 713-651-5151

Michael P. Mallia · ⑩ · The Mallia Law Firm · One Riverway, Suite 610 · Houston, TX 77056 · 713-224-1100

Barclay A. Manley · Fulbright & Jaworski · http://www.fulbright.com · Fulbright Tower, Suite 5100 · 1301 McKinney Street · Houston, TX 77010-3095 · 713-651-5151

Neal S. Manne · Susman Godfrey · 1000 Louisiana, Suite 5100 · Houston, TX 77002-5096 · 713-651-9366

Robert E. Meadows · King & Spalding · 1100 Louisiana Street, Suite 4000 · Houston, TX 77002-5213 · 713-751-3200

Richard Warren Mithoff · ⑳ · Mithoff Law Firm · One Allen Center, Penthouse · 500 Dallas Street · Houston, TX 77002 · 713-654-1122

Nick C. Nichols · ⑳ · Abraham, Watkins, Nichols, Sorrels, Matthews & Friend · 800 Commerce Street · Houston, TX 77002-1776 · 713-222-7211

Knox D. Nunnally · Vinson & Elkins · http://www.velaw.com · First City Tower, Suite 2500 · 1001 Fannin Street · Houston, TX 77002-6760 · 713-758-2222

Dudley Oldham · Fulbright & Jaworski · http://www.fulbright.com · Fulbright Tower, Suite 5100 · 1301 McKinney Street · Houston, TX 77010-3095 · 713-651-5151

Alice Oliver-Parrott · ⑩ · Alice Oliver-Parrott · 5009 Caroline, Suite 100 · Houston, TX 77004 · 713-222-6338

Jim M. Perdue, Sr. · ㉕ · Perdue & Kidd · 2727 Allen Parkway, Suite 800 · Houston, TX 77019 · 713-520-2500

Michael W. Perrin · Bailey Perrin Bailey · The Lyric Centre, Suite 2100 · 440 Louisiana Street · Houston, TX 77002 · 713-425-7100

Barbara A. Radnofsky · ⑩ · Barbara Radnofsky · 303 Timber Terrace Road · Houston, TX 77024 · 713-858-8509

Joe Winston Redden, Jr. · ⑩ · Beck, Redden & Secrest · http://www.brsfirm.com · One Houston Center, Suite 4500 · 1221 McKinney Street · Houston, TX 77010-2010 · 713-951-3700

Don R. Riddle · ⑩ · Riddle & Baumgartner · 9400 FM 1960 West, Suite 210 · Houston, TX 77070 · 281-890-4488

Steven L. Roberts · ⑩ · Sutherland · http://www.sutherland.com · Two Houston Center, Suite 2200 · 909 Fannin · Houston, TX 77010-1043 · 713-470-6100

Michael Y. Saunders · ⑩ · Helm, Pletcher, Bowen & Saunders · America Tower, Suite 2700 · 2929 Allen Parkway · Houston, TX 77019-2157 · 713-522-4550

Robert M. Schick · Vinson & Elkins · http://www.velaw.com · First City Tower, Suite 2500 · 1001 Fannin Street · Houston, TX 77002-6760 · 713-758-2222

Reagan W. Simpson · King & Spalding · 1100 Louisiana Street, Suite 4000 · Houston, TX 77002-5213 · 713-751-3200

Samuel E. Stubbs · Pillsbury Winthrop Shaw Pittman · http://www.pillsburylaw.com · Two Houston Center, Suite 2000 · 909 Fannin Street · Houston, TX 77010-1018 · 713-276-7600

Kenneth Tekell · ⑩ · Tekell, Book, Matthews & Limmer · 4300 One Houston Center · 1221 McKinney Street · Houston, TX 77010-2015 · 713-222-9542

Paul Waldner · Vickery, Waldner & Mallia · One Riverway Suite 1150 · Houston, TX 77056 · 713-526-1100

David B. Weinstein · Weinstein Tippetts & Little · 7660 Woodway, Suite 500 · Houston, TX 77063 · 713-244-0600

Gene M. Williams · Shook, Hardy & Bacon · JPMorgan Chase Tower, Suite 1600 · 600 Travis Street · Houston, TX 77002-2992 · 713-227-8008

Johnson City

Robert Q. Keith · ⑩ · Keith & Weber · 112 North Nugent · P.O. Box 155 · Johnson City, TX 78636 · 830-825-2111

League City

Ronald D. Krist · ⑳ · Krist Law Firm · http://www.kristlaw.com · Marina View Building, Suite 120 · 2600 South Shore Boulevard · League City, TX 77573 · 281-283-8500

Scott C. Krist · Krist Law Firm · http://www.kristlaw.com · Marina View Building, Suite 120 · 2600 South Shore Boulevard · League City, TX 77573 · 281-283-8500

Longview

Glenn A. Perry · ⑩ · Sloan, Bagley & Perry Law Firm · 101 East Whaley Street · P.O. Drawer 2909 · Longview, TX 75606 · 903-757-7000

Lubbock

Forrest B. Bowers · ⑩ · Bowers Law Office · 1401 Texas Avenue · P.O. Box 327 · Lubbock, TX 79408 · 806-762-0863

Marshall

Franklin Jones, Jr. · ㉕ · Jones & Jones · 201 West Houston Street · P.O. Drawer 1249 · Marshall, TX 75671-1249 · 903-938-4395

Carl R. Roth · The Roth Law Firm · 115 North Wellington Street, Suite 200 · P.O. Box 876 · Marshall, TX 75671 · 903-935-1665

McAllen

Robert L. Guerra · Thornton, Biechlin, Segrato, Reynolds & Guerra · 418 East Dove Avenue · McAllen, TX 78504 · 956-630-3080

Joseph L. Segrato · Thornton, Biechlin, Segrato, Reynolds & Guerra · 418 East Dove Avenue · McAllen, TX 78504 · 956-630-3080

Midland

Harold L. Hensley, Jr. · ⑳ · Hinkle, Hensley, Shanor & Martin · 550 West Texas Avenue, Suite 1200 · P.O. Box 3580 · Midland, TX 79702 · 432-683-4691

Robert R. Biechlin, Jr. · Thornton, Biechlin, Segrato, Reynolds & Guerra · One International Centre, Suite 500 · 100 Northeast Loop 410 · San Antonio, TX 78216 · 210-342-5555

James L. Branton · ⑳ · Branton & Hall · One Riverwalk Place, Suite 1700 · 700 North St. Mary's Street · San Antonio, TX 78205 · 210-224-4474

George G. Brin · ⑩ · Brin & Brin · 10999 IH10 West, Suite 800 · San Antonio, TX 78230-3878 · 210-341-9711

Charles A. Deacon · Fulbright & Jaworski · http://www.fulbright.com · 300 Convent Street, Suite 2200 · San Antonio, TX 78205-3792 · 210-224-5575

Leo Figueroa · Law Offices of Frank Herrera · Riverview Towers, Suite 1900 · 111 Soledad Street · San Antonio, TX 78205 · 210-224-1054

Jerry A. Gibson · ⑩ · Plunkett & Gibson · http://www.plunkett-gibson.com · 70 Northeast Loop 410, Suite 1100 · San Antonio, TX 78216 · 210-734-7092

Cynthia Day Grimes · ⑩ · Ball & Weed · 10001 Reunion Place, Suite 600 · San Antonio, TX 78216 · 210-731-6300

Fred Riley Jones · Goode Casseb Jones · 2122 North Main Avenue · P.O. Box 120480 · San Antonio, TX 78212 · 210-733-6030

Andrew L. Kerr · Strasburger & Price · http://www.strasburger.com · 300 Convent Street, Suite 900 · San Antonio, TX 78205-3715 · 210-250-6000

Douglas D. Ketterman · Ketterman Rowland & Westlund · 16500 San Pedro Avenue, Suite 302 · San Antonio, TX 78232-2252 · 210-490-7402

Sylvan S. Lang, Jr. · Lang & Kustoff · 4103 Parkdale Street · San Antonio, TX 78229-2520 · 210-614-9444

Clarence V. Lyons · ⑳ · Lyons & Rhodes · 126 Villita Street · San Antonio, TX 78205-2735 · 210-225-5251

J. Michael Myers · Ball & Weed · 10001 Reunion Place, Suite 600 · San Antonio, TX 78216 · 210-731-6300

Allen Lewin Plunkett · ⑩ · Plunkett & Gibson · http://www.plunkett-gibson.com · 70 Northeast Loop 410, Suite 1100 · San Antonio, TX 78216 · 210-734-7092

David M. Prichard · Prichard, Hawkins, McFarland and Young · http://www.phmy.com · Union Square, Suite 600 · 10101 Reunion Place · San Antonio, TX 78216 · 210-477-7400

Richard J. Reynolds III · Thornton, Biechlin, Segrato, Reynolds & Guerra · One International Centre, Suite 500 · 100 Northeast Loop 410 · San Antonio, TX 78216 · 210-342-5555

Jesse Thomas Rhodes III · Lyons & Rhodes · 126 Villita Street · San Antonio, TX 78205-2735 · 210-225-5251

Fidel Rodriguez, Jr. · Law Offices of Fidel Rodriguez Jr. · 111 Soledad, Suite 1300 · San Antonio, TX 78205 · 210-224-1057

Brett B. Rowe · Evans & Rowe · http://www.evansrowe.com · Union Square, Suite 900 · 10101 Reunion Place · San Antonio, TX 78216-4175 · 210-340-6555

Daniel J. T. Sciano · ⑩ · Tinsman & Sciano · http://www.tsslawyers.com · 10107 McAllister Freeway · San Antonio, TX 78216 · 210-225-3121

David Stephenson · Clemens & Spencer · http://www.clemens-spencer.com · 1300 Weston Centre · 112 East Pecan Street · San Antonio, TX 78205-1517 · 210-227-7121

Edward F. Valdespino · Strasburger & Price · http://www.strasburger.com · 300 Convent Street, Suite 900 · San Antonio, TX 78205-3715 · 210-250-6000

Kyle C. Watson · Goode Casseb Jones · 2122 North Main Avenue · P.O. Box 120480 · San Antonio, TX 78212 · 210-733-6030

John W. Weber, Jr. · Fulbright & Jaworski · http://www.fulbright.com · 300 Convent Street, Suite 2200 · San Antonio, TX 78205-3792 · 210-224-5575

Mary I. Wilson · Lyons & Rhodes · 126 Villita Street · San Antonio, TX 78205-2735 · 210-225-5251

Stevensville

Ernest H. Cannon · ⑩ · Ernest H. Cannon · 505 North Graham Street · P.O. Box 1193 · Stevensville, TX 76401 · 254-918-1006

Sugarland

Randy L. Fairless · Johanson & Fairless · 1456 First Colony Boulevard · Sugarland, TX 77479 · 281-313-5000

Texarkana

Nicholas H. Patton · ⑩ · Patton, Tidwell & Schroeder · 4605 Texas Boulevard · P.O. Box 5398 · Texarkana, TX 75505-5398 · 903-792-7080

Victoria

Kevin D. Cullen · Cullen, Carsner, Seerden & Cullen · 119 South Main Street · P.O. Box 2938 · Victoria, TX 77902 · 361-573-6318

PRIVATE FUNDS LAW

Dallas

D. Forrest Brumbaugh · Fulbright & Jaworski · http://www.fulbright.com · 2200 Ross Avenue, Suite 2800 · Dallas, TX 75201 · 214-855-8000

Jeffrey B. Hitt · Weil Gotshal & Manges · 200 Crescent Court, Suite 300 · Dallas, TX 75201 · 214-746-7700

Don J. McDermett, Jr. · Baker Botts · http://www.bakerbotts.com · Trammell Crow Center, Suite 600 · 2001 Ross Avenue · Dallas, TX 75201-2980 · 214-953-6500

Geoffrey L. Newton · Baker Botts · http://www.bakerbotts.com · Trammell Crow Center, Suite 600 · 2001 Ross Avenue · Dallas, TX 75201-2980 · 214-953-6500

The Woodlands

R. Clyde Parker, Jr. · Winstead · http://www.winstead.com · 24 Waterway Avenue, Suite 500 · The Woodlands, TX 77380 · 281-681-5900

Austin

Thomas M. Bullion III · Germer Gertz · 301 Congress Avenue, Suite 1700 · Austin, TX 78701 · 512-472-0288

Kenneth J. Ferguson · Clark, Thomas & Winters · 300 West Sixth Street, 15th Floor · P.O. Box 1148 · Austin, TX 78767 · 512-472-8800

Richard H. Grafton · Germer Gertz · 301 Congress Avenue, Suite 1700 · Austin, TX 78701 · 512-472-0288

Michael R. Klatt · Clark, Thomas & Winters · 300 West Sixth Street, 15th Floor · P.O. Box 1148 · Austin, TX 78767 · 512-472-8800

Broadus A. Spivey · 25 · Law Offices of Dicky Grigg · 48 East Avenue, Suite 100 · Austin, TX 78701 · 512-474-6061

Terry O. Tottenham · 10 · Fulbright & Jaworski · http://www.fulbright.com · 600 Congress Avenue, Suite 2400 · Austin, TX 78701-2978 · 512-474-5201

Lana K. Varney · Fulbright & Jaworski · http://www.fulbright.com · 600 Congress Avenue, Suite 2400 · Austin, TX 78701-2978 · 512-474-5201

Ronald D. Wamsted · Thompson, Coe, Cousins & Irons · http://www.thompsoncoe.com · Austin Centre, Suite 1500 · 701 Brazos · Austin, TX 78701 · 512-708-8200

T. B. Wright · 10 · Wright & Greenhill · 221 West Sixth Street, Suite 1800 · Austin, TX 78701 · 512-476-4600

Beaumont

Robert A. Black · MehaffyWeber · http://www.mehaffyweber.com · 2615 Calder Avenue · P.O. Box 16 · Beaumont, TX 77702 · 409-835-5011

Dallas

Earl B. Austin · Baker Botts · http://www.bakerbotts.com · Trammell Crow Center, Suite 600 · 2001 Ross Avenue · Dallas, TX 75201-2980 · 214-953-6500

Michael R. Berry · Thompson & Knight · http://www.tklaw.com · One Arts Plaza, Suite 1500 · 1722 Routh Street · Dallas, TX 75201-2533 · 214-969-1700

Frank L. Branson · 20 · Law Offices of Frank L. Branson · http://www.flbranson.com · Highland Park Place, Suite 1800 · 4514 Cole Avenue · Dallas, TX 75205 · 214-522-0200

William D. Cobb, Jr. · Cobb Martinez Woodward · 1700 Pacific Avenue, Suite 4545 · Dallas, TX 75201 · 214-220-5200

Kyle Dryer · Hartline, Dacus, Barger, Dreyer & Kern · 6688 North Central Expressway · Dallas, TX 75206 · 214-954-4010

Thomas E. Fennell · Jones Day · 2727 North Harwood Street · Dallas, TX 75201-1515 · 214-220-3939

R. Chris Harvey · Curran Tomko Tarski · 2001 Bryan Street, Suite 2050 · Dallas, TX 75201 · 214-270-1400

Sydney B. McDole · Jones Day · 2727 North Harwood Street · Dallas, TX 75201-1515 · 214-220-3939

Joseph S. Pevsner · Thompson & Knight · http://www.tklaw.com · One Arts Plaza, Suite 1500 · 1722 Routh Street · Dallas, TX 75201-2533 · 214-969-1700

Michael E. Schmidt · The Schmidt Firm · 2911 Turtle Creek Boulevard, Suite 1400 · Dallas, TX 75219 · 214-521-4898

Vincent S. Walkowiak · Fulbright & Jaworski · http://www.fulbright.com · 2200 Ross Avenue, Suite 2800 Dallas, TX 75201 · 214-855-8000

Houston

Fields Alexander · Beck, Redden & Secrest · http://www.brsfirm.com · One Houston Center, Suite 4500 · 1221 McKinney Street · Houston, TX 77010-2010 · 713-951-3700

Larry P. Boyd · 10 · Fisher, Boyd, Brown, Boudreaux & Huguenard · Riviana Building, 14th Floor · 2777 Allen Parkway · Houston, TX 77019 · 713-400-4000

Reagan M. Brown · Fulbright & Jaworski · http://www.fulbright.com · Fulbright Tower, Suite 5100 · 1301 McKinney Street · Houston, TX 77010-3095 · 713-651-5151

Thomas K. Brown · Fisher, Boyd, Brown, Boudreaux & Huguenard · Riviana Building, 14th Floor · 2777 Allen Parkway · Houston, TX 77019 · 713-400-4000

Richard H. Caldwell · 10 · Andrews Kurth · http://www.andrewskurth.com · 600 Travis Street, Suite 4200 Houston, TX 77002 · 713-220-4200

Winstol D. Carter · Morgan Lewis & Bockius · 1000 Louisiana St., Suite 4200 · Houston, TX 77002-5006 713-890-5000

Otway B. Denny, Jr. · 10 · Fulbright & Jaworski · http://www.fulbright.com · Fulbright Tower, Suite 5100 1301 McKinney Street · Houston, TX 77010-3095 · 713-651-5151

Stephen C. Dillard · 10 · Fulbright & Jaworski · http://www.fulbright.com · Fulbright Tower, Suite 5100 · 1301 McKinney Street · Houston, TX 77010-3095 · 713-651-5151

Wayne Fisher · 25 · Fisher, Boyd, Brown, Boudreaux & Huguenard · Riviana Building, 14th Floor · 2777 Allen Parkway · Houston, TX 77019 · 713-400-4000

Kathleen A. Gallagher · Vinson & Elkins · http://www.velaw.com · First City Tower, Suite 2500 · 1001 Fannin Street · Houston, TX 77002-6760 · 713-758-2222

Michael T. Gallagher · 25 · The Gallagher Law Firm · 2905 Sackett Street · Houston, TX 77098 · 713-222-8080

Frank G. Jones · 10 · Fulbright & Jaworski · http://www.fulbright.com · Fulbright Tower, Suite 5100 · 1301 McKinney Street · Houston, TX 77010-3095 · 713-651-5151

Richard L. Josephson · Baker Botts · http://www.bakerbotts.com · One Shell Plaza · 910 Louisiana Street Houston, TX 77002-1210 · 713-229-1234

Gerry Lowry · Fulbright & Jaworski · http://www.fulbright.com · Fulbright Tower, Suite 5100 · 1301 McKinney Street · Houston, TX 77010-3095 · 713-651-5151

Richard Warren Mithoff · 20 · Mithoff Law Firm · One Allen Center, Penthouse · 500 Dallas Street · Houston, TX 77002 · 713-654-1122

Knox D. Nunnally · Vinson & Elkins · http://www.velaw.com · First City Tower, Suite 2500 · 1001 Fannin Street · Houston, TX 77002-6760 · 713-758-2222

Robert M. Schick · Vinson & Elkins · http://www.velaw.com · First City Tower, Suite 2500 · 1001 Fannin Street · Houston, TX 77002-6760 · 713-758-2222

Samuel E. Stubbs · Pillsbury Winthrop Shaw Pittman · http://www.pillsburylaw.com · Two Houston Center, Suite 2000 · 909 Fannin Street · Houston, TX 77010-1018 · 713-276-7600

David B. Weinstein · Weinstein Tippetts & Little · 7660 Woodway, Suite 500 · Houston, TX 77063 · 713-244-0600

Gene M. Williams · Shook, Hardy & Bacon · JPMorgan Chase Tower, Suite 1600 · 600 Travis Street · Houston, TX 77002-2992 · 713-227-8008

San Antonio

Allen Lewin Plunkett · ⑩ · Plunkett & Gibson · http://www.plunkett-gibson.com · 70 Northeast Loop 410, Suite 1100 · San Antonio, TX 78216 · 210-734-7092

David M. Prichard · Prichard, Hawkins, McFarland and Young · http://www.phmy.com · Union Square, Suite 600 · 10101 Reunion Place · San Antonio, TX 78216 · 210-477-7400

John W. Weber, Jr. · Fulbright & Jaworski · http://www.fulbright.com · 300 Convent Street, Suite 2200 · San Antonio, TX 78205-3792 · 210-224-5575

PROFESSIONAL MALPRACTICE LAW

Austin

Sam Johnson · Scott, Douglass & McConnico · 600 Congress Avenue, Suite 1500 · Austin, TX 78701-3234 · 512-495-6300

Paul Emil Knisely · Knisely and Prehoditch · 48 East Avenue · Austin, TX 78701 · 512-474-6061

Stephen E. McConnico · ⑩ · Scott, Douglass & McConnico · 600 Congress Avenue, Suite 1500 · Austin, TX 78701-3234 · 512-495-6300

Broadus A. Spivey · ㉕ · Law Offices of Dicky Grigg · 48 East Avenue, Suite 100 · Austin, TX 78701 · 512-474-6061

T. B. Wright · ⑩ · Wright & Greenhill · 221 West Sixth Street, Suite 1800 · Austin, TX 78701 · 512-476-4600

Dallas

Frank L. Branson · ⑳ · Law Offices of Frank L. Branson · http://www.flbranson.com · Highland Park Place, Suite 1800 · 4514 Cole Avenue · Dallas, TX 75205 · 214-522-0200

Karen L. Hirschman · Vinson & Elkins · http://www.velaw.com · Trammell Crow Center, Suite 3700 · 2001 Ross Avenue · Dallas, TX 75201-2975 · 214-220-7700

Timothy W. Mountz · Baker Botts · http://www.bakerbotts.com · Trammell Crow Center, Suite 600 · 2001 Ross Avenue · Dallas, TX 75201-2980 · 214-953-6500

Rod Phelan · ⑩ · Baker Botts · http://www.bakerbotts.com · Trammell Crow Center, Suite 600 · 2001 Ross Avenue · Dallas, TX 75201-2980 · 214-953-6500

Fort Worth

Darrell L. Keith · ⑩ · Keith Law Firm · The Keith Building · 1705 West Seventh Street · Fort Worth, TX 76102 · 817-338-1400

Kleber C. Miller · ㉕ · Shannon, Gracey, Ratliff & Miller · http://www.shannongracey.com · 777 Main Street, Suite 3800 · Fort Worth, TX 76102 · 817-336-9333

PROJECT FINANCE LAW

Dallas

Robert D. Albergotti · ⑩ · Haynes and Boone · 901 Main Street, Suite 3100 · Dallas, TX 75202 · 214-651-5000

Robert L. Kimball · Vinson & Elkins · http://www.velaw.com · Trammell Crow Center, Suite 3700 · 2001 Ross Avenue · Dallas, TX 75201-2975 · 214-220-7700

Keith H. Mullen · Winstead · http://www.winstead.com · Renaissance Tower, Suite 5400 · 1201 Elm Street · Dallas, TX 75270-2199 · 214-745-5400

Luke A. Weedon · Baker Botts · http://www.bakerbotts.com · Trammell Crow Center, Suite 600 · 2001 Ross Avenue · Dallas, TX 75201-2980 · 214-953-6500

Houston

Marcia E. Backus · Vinson & Elkins · http://www.velaw.com · First City Tower, Suite 2500 · 1001 Fannin Street · Houston, TX 77002-6760 · 713-758-2222

Larry G. Barbour · Vinson & Elkins · http://www.velaw.com · First City Tower, Suite 2500 · 1001 Fannin Street · Houston, TX 77002-6760 · 713-758-2222

Douglas S. Bland · ⑩ · Vinson & Elkins · http://www.velaw.com · First City Tower, Suite 2500 · 1001 Fannin Street · Houston, TX 77002-6760 · 713-758-2222

Bernard F. Clark · Haynes and Boone · One Houston Center, Suite 2100 · 1221 McKinney Street · Houston, TX 77010 · 713-547-2000

Fielding B. Cochran III · Vinson & Elkins · http://www.velaw.com · First City Tower, Suite 2500 · 1001 Fannin Street · Houston, TX 77002-6760 · 713-758-2222

John P. Cogan, Jr. · McDermott Will & Emery · 1000 Louisiana, Suite 1300 · Houston, TX 77002 · 713-653-1700

Kenneth S. Culotta · King & Spalding · 1100 Louisiana Street, Suite 4000 · Houston, TX 77002-5213 · 713-751-3200

Mark C. Evans · Bracewell & Giuliani · http://www.bgllp.com · 711 Louisiana Street, Suite 2300 · Houston, TX 77002-2770 · 713-223-2300

Jay D. Kelley · Vinson & Elkins · http://www.velaw.com · First City Tower, Suite 2500 · 1001 Fannin Street · Houston, TX 77002-6760 · 713-758-2222

Stephen Krebs · Baker Botts · http://www.bakerbotts.com · One Shell Plaza · 910 Louisiana Street · Houston, TX 77002-1210 · 713-229-1234

John G. Mauel · Pillsbury Winthrop Shaw Pittman · http://www.pillsburylaw.com · Two Houston Center, Suite 2000 · 909 Fannin Street · Houston, TX 77010-1018 · 713-276-7600

G. Alan Rafte · Bracewell & Giuliani · http://www.bgllp.com · 711 Louisiana Street, Suite 2300 · Houston, TX 77002-2770 · 713-223-2300

Bradley J. Richards · Haynes and Boone · One Houston Center, Suite 2100 · 1221 McKinney Street · Houston, TX 77010 · 713-547-2000

Mark R. Spradling · Vinson & Elkins · http://www.velaw.com · First City Tower, Suite 2500 · 1001 Fannin Street · Houston, TX 77002-6760 · 713-758-2222

Dahl C. Thompson · Andrews Kurth · http://www.andrewskurth.com · 600 Travis Street, Suite 4200 · Houston, TX 77002 · 713-220-4200

Mark J. Thurber · Andrews Kurth · http://www.andrewskurth.com · 600 Travis Street, Suite 4200 · Houston, TX 77002 · 713-220-4200

Timothy J. Unger · Andrews Kurth · http://www.andrewskurth.com · 600 Travis Street, Suite 4200 · Houston, TX 77002 · 713-220-4200

Randel R. Young · Fulbright & Jaworski · http://www.fulbright.com · Fulbright Tower, Suite 5100 · 1301 McKinney Street · Houston, TX 77010-3095 · 713-651-5151

PUBLIC FINANCE LAW

Austin

Nancy M. Hagquist · Winstead · http://www.winstead.com · 401 Congress Avenue, Suite 2100 · Austin, TX 78701 · 512-370-2800

W. Glenn Opel · Vinson & Elkins · http://www.velaw.com · 2801 Via Fortuna, Suite 100 · Austin, TX 78746-7568 · 512-542-8400

Elizabeth Peake Rippy · Vinson & Elkins · http://www.velaw.com · 2801 Via Fortuna, Suite 100 · Austin, TX 78746-7568 · 512-542-8400

Jerry E. Turner · Vinson & Elkins · http://www.velaw.com · 2801 Via Fortuna, Suite 100 · Austin, TX 78746-7568 · 512-542-8400

Dallas

Ben A. Brooks III · Vinson & Elkins · http://www.velaw.com · Trammell Crow Center, Suite 3700 · 2001 Ross Avenue · Dallas, TX 75201-2975 · 214-220-7700

Harlan P. Cohen · Gibson, Dunn & Crutcher · 2100 McKinney Avenue, Suite 1100 · Dallas, TX 75201-7390 · 214-698-3100

Robert R. Collins III · Vinson & Elkins · http://www.velaw.com · Trammell Crow Center, Suite 3700 · 2001 Ross Avenue · Dallas, TX 75201-2975 · 214-220-7700

Robert D. Dransfield · Fulbright & Jaworski · http://www.fulbright.com · 2200 Ross Avenue, Suite 2800 · Dallas, TX 75201 · 214-855-8000

Joseph E. Eckert · McCall, Parkhurst & Horton · 717 North Harwood, Ninth Floor · Dallas, TX 75201-6587 · 214-754-9200

Bob C. Griffo · Andrews Kurth · http://www.andrewskurth.com · 1717 Main Street, Suite 3700 · Dallas, TX 75201 · 214-659-4400

Elton R. Hutchison · Vinson & Elkins · http://www.velaw.com · Trammell Crow Center, Suite 3700 · 2001 Ross Avenue · Dallas, TX 75201-2975 · 214-220-7700

Richard M. Kobdish · Fulbright & Jaworski · http://www.fulbright.com · 2200 Ross Avenue, Suite 2800 · Dallas, TX 75201 · 214-855-8000

Jeffrey A. Leuschel · McCall, Parkhurst & Horton · 717 North Harwood, Ninth Floor · Dallas, TX 75201-6587 · 214-754-9200

Richard C. Porter · McCall, Parkhurst & Horton · 717 North Harwood, Ninth Floor · Dallas, TX 75201-6587 · 214-754-9200

Alan H. Raynor · McCall, Parkhurst & Horton · 717 North Harwood, Ninth Floor · Dallas, TX 75201-6587 · 214-754-9200

George G. Rodriguez · Vinson & Elkins · http://www.velaw.com · Trammell Crow Center, Suite 3700 · 2001 Ross Avenue · Dallas, TX 75201-2975 · 214-220-7700

Fort Worth

R. Daniel Settle, Jr. · Kelly, Hart & Hallman · Wells Fargo Tower, Suite 2500 · 201 Main Street · Fort Worth, TX 76102 · 817-332-2500

Houston

Joe B. Allen · Allen Boone Humphries Robinson · Phoenix Tower, Suite 2600 · 3200 Southwest Freeway Houston, TX 77027 · 713-860-6400

Eric S. Anderson · ㉕ · Fulbright & Jaworski · http://www.fulbright.com · Fulbright Tower, Suite 5100 · 1301 McKinney Street · Houston, TX 77010-3095 · 713-651-5151

Todd B. Brewer · Andrews Kurth · http://www.andrewskurth.com · 600 Travis Street, Suite 4200 · Houston, TX 77002 · 713-220-4200

Francis J. Coleman, Jr. · ⑩ · Vinson & Elkins · http://www.velaw.com · First City Tower, Suite 2500 · 1001 Fannin Street · Houston, TX 77002-6760 · 713-758-2222

Robert M. Collie, Jr. · ⑩ · Andrews Kurth · http://www.andrewskurth.com · 600 Travis Street, Suite 4200 Houston, TX 77002 · 713-220-4200

Jonathan S. Day · ⑩ · Andrews Kurth · http://www.andrewskurth.com · 600 Travis Street, Suite 4200 · Houston, TX 77002 · 713-220-4200

Kathleen R. Ellison · Fulbright & Jaworski · http://www.fulbright.com · Fulbright Tower, Suite 5100 · 1301 McKinney Street · Houston, TX 77010-3095 · 713-651-5151

Steven H. Gerdes · Vinson & Elkins · http://www.velaw.com · First City Tower, Suite 2500 · 1001 Fannin Street · Houston, TX 77002-6760 · 713-758-2222

R. Todd Greenwalt · Vinson & Elkins · http://www.velaw.com · First City Tower, Suite 2500 · 1001 Fannin Street · Houston, TX 77002-6760 · 713-758-2222

Patricia Hunt Holmes · Vinson & Elkins · http://www.velaw.com · First City Tower, Suite 2500 · 1001 Fannin Street · Houston, TX 77002-6760 · 713-758-2222

Richard D. Huff · Fulbright & Jaworski · http://www.fulbright.com · Fulbright Tower, Suite 5100 · 1301 McKinney Street · Houston, TX 77010-3095 · 713-651-5151

Ann C. Jacobs · Nathan Sommers Jacobs · 2800 Post Oak Boulevard, 61st Floor · Houston, TX 77056 · 713-960-0303

Gregg H. Jones · Andrews Kurth · http://www.andrewskurth.com · 600 Travis Street, Suite 4200 · Houston, TX 77002 · 713-220-4200

Thomas A. Sage · Vinson & Elkins · http://www.velaw.com · First City Tower, Suite 2500 · 1001 Fannin Street · Houston, TX 77002-6760 · 713-758-2222

T. Neil Thomas · Fulbright & Jaworski · http://www.fulbright.com · Fulbright Tower, Suite 5100 · 1301 McKinney Street · Houston, TX 77010-3095 · 713-651-5151

Barron F. Wallace · Vinson & Elkins · http://www.velaw.com · First City Tower, Suite 2500 · 1001 Fannin Street · Houston, TX 77002-6760 · 713-758-2222

Fredric A. Weber · ⑩ · Fulbright & Jaworski · http://www.fulbright.com · Fulbright Tower, Suite 5100 · 1301 McKinney Street · Houston, TX 77010-3095 · 713-651-5151

Rick A. Witte · Andrews Kurth · http://www.andrewskurth.com · 600 Travis Street, Suite 4200 · Houston, TX 77002 · 713-220-4200

San Antonio

Lisa G. Adelman · Fulbright & Jaworski · http://www.fulbright.com · 300 Convent Street, Suite 2200 · San Antonio, TX 78205-3792 · 210-224-5575

Clayton Binford · Fulbright & Jaworski · http://www.fulbright.com · 300 Convent Street, Suite 2200 · San Antonio, TX 78205-3792 · 210-224-5575

W. Jeffrey Kuhn · Fulbright & Jaworski · http://www.fulbright.com · 300 Convent Street, Suite 2200 · San Antonio, TX 78205-3792 · 210-224-5575

M. Paul Martin · Winstead · http://www.winstead.com · 700 North St. Mary's Street, Suite 1900 · San Antonio, TX 78205 · 210-277-6800

Michael L. Spain · Fulbright & Jaworski · http://www.fulbright.com · 300 Convent Street, Suite 2200 · San Antonio, TX 78205-3792 · 210-224-5575

RAILROAD LAW

Austin

Robert B. Burns, Jr. · Burns Anderson Jury & Brennan · 7804 Bell Mountain Drive · P.O. Box 26300 · Austin, TX 78755-6300 · 512-338-5322

Dallas

Mark A. Calhoun · Greenberg Traurig · http://www.gtlaw.com · JP Morgan Chase Tower, Suite 5200 · 2200 Ross Avenue · Dallas, TX 75201 · 972-419-9100

Fort Worth

Albon O. Head, Jr. · Jackson Walker · 301 Commerce Street, Suite 2400 · Fort Worth, TX 76102 · 817-334-7200

John W. Proctor · Brown, Dean, Wiseman, Liser, Proctor & Hart · Fort Worth Club Building, Suite 200 · 306 West Seventh Street · Fort Worth, TX 76102-4905 · 817-332-1391

Galveston

Douglas W. Poole · McLeod, Alexander, Powell and Apffel · 802 Rosenberg · P.O. Box 629 · Galveston, TX 77553 · 409-763-2481

Houston

Daniel V. Flatten · ⑩ · Porter & Hedges · 1000 Main Street, 36th Floor · Houston, TX 77002 · 713-226-0600

Mainess Gibson · Connelly, Baker, Wotring & Jackson · 700 JPMorgan Chase Tower · 600 Travis Street · Houston, TX 77002 · 713-980-1700

H. Daniel Spain · ⑩ · Spain Hastings & Ward · 909 Fannin Street, Suite 3900 · Houston, TX 77010 · 713-650-9700

Robert M. Tramuto · Jones & Granger · 10000 Memorial Drive, Suite 888 · Houston, TX 77024 · 713-668-0230

Lubbock

D. Thomas Johnson · McWhorter Cobb and Johnson · 1722 Broadway · P.O. Box 2547 · Lubbock, TX 79408 · 806-762-0214

San Antonio

James L. Walker · Jackson Walker · Weston Centre, Suite 2400 · 112 East Pecan Street · San Antonio, TX 78205 · 210-978-7700

REAL ESTATE LAW

Arlington

Robert L. Russell Bush · The Bush Firm · 4025 Woodland Park Boulevard, Suite 190 · Arlington, TX 76013 · 817-274-5992

Austin

Rick M. Albers · Kuperman, Orr & Albers · 2801 Via Fortuna, Suite 530 · Austin, TX 78746 · 512-473-4100

Jim Alsup · Jackson Walker · 100 Congress Avenue, Suite 1100 · Austin, TX 78701 · 512-236-2000

David B. Armbrust · ㉕ · Armbrust & Brown · http://www.abaustin.com · 100 Congress Avenue, Suite 1300 · Austin, TX 78701 · 512-435-2300

Kimberly S. Beckham · Armbrust & Brown · http://www.abaustin.com · 100 Congress Avenue, Suite 1300 Austin, TX 78701 · 512-435-2300

William Terry Bray · ㉕ · Graves, Dougherty, Hearon & Moody · http://www.gdhm.com · 401 Congress Avenue, Suite 2200 · P.O. Box 98 · Austin, TX 78767-0098 · 512-480-5600

Frank B. Brown · Armbrust & Brown · http://www.abaustin.com · 100 Congress Avenue, Suite 1300 · Austin, TX 78701 · 512-435-2300

William D. Brown · Sneed, Vine & Perry · 901 Congress Avenue · P.O. Box 1409 · Austin, TX 78767 · 512-476-6955

William Charles Bryant · DuBois, Bryant & Campbell · http://www.dbcllp.com · 700 Lavaca Street, Suite 1300 · Austin, TX 78701 · 512-457-8000

Samuel D. Byars · ⑩ · Armbrust & Brown · http://www.abaustin.com · 100 Congress Avenue, Suite 1300 · Austin, TX 78701 · 512-435-2300

James T. Cameron · Strasburger & Price · http://www.strasburger.com · 600 Congress Avenue, Suite 1600 Austin, TX 78701-2974 · 512-499-3600

Robert G. Converse · ⑩ · Fulbright & Jaworski · http://www.fulbright.com · 600 Congress Avenue, Suite 2400 · Austin, TX 78701-2978 · 512-474-5201

Michael L. Cook · ㉕ · Winstead · http://www.winstead.com · 401 Congress Avenue, Suite 2100 · Austin, TX 78701 · 512-370-2800

Thomas I. Davies · Stahl Bernal & Davies · 7320 North MoPac, Suite 211 · Austin, TX 78731 · 512-346-5558

Robert L. Davis · ⑩ · Brown McCarroll · 111 Congress Avenue, Suite 1400 · Austin, TX 78701-4093 · 512-472-5456

Royce Jay Hailey, Jr. · ⑩ · DLA Piper · 1221 South MoPac Expressway, Suite 400 · Austin, TX 78746-7650 · 512-457-7000

Brad B. Hawley · Locke Lord Bissell & Liddell · 100 Congress Avenue, Suite 300 · Austin, TX 78701-4042 · 512-305-4785

R. Alan Haywood · ⑩ · Graves, Dougherty, Hearon & Moody · http://www.gdhm.com · 401 Congress Avenue, Suite 2200 · P.O. Box 98 · Austin, TX 78767-0098 · 512-480-5600

Wayne Hollingsworth · Armbrust & Brown · http://www.abaustin.com · 100 Congress Avenue, Suite 1300 Austin, TX 78701 · 512-435-2300

L. Jeffery Hubenak · Locke Lord Bissell & Liddell · 100 Congress Avenue, Suite 300 · Austin, TX 78701-4042 · 512-305-4785

Gregg C. Krumme · Armbrust & Brown · http://www.abaustin.com · 100 Congress Avenue, Suite 1300 · Austin, TX 78701 · 512-435-2300

Sue Brooks Littlefield · Armbrust & Brown · http://www.abaustin.com · 100 Congress Avenue, Suite 1300 · Austin, TX 78701 · 512-435-2300

William H. Locke, Jr. · ⑩ · Graves, Dougherty, Hearon & Moody · http://www.gdhm.com · 401 Congress Avenue, Suite 2200 · P.O. Box 98 · Austin, TX 78767-0098 · 512-480-5600

Steve R. Martens · Jackson Walker · 100 Congress Avenue, Suite 1100 · Austin, TX 78701 · 512-236-2000

Amy M. Mitchell · Fulbright & Jaworski · http://www.fulbright.com · 600 Congress Avenue, Suite 2400 · Austin, TX 78701-2978 · 512-474-5201

Daniel W. Nelson · Daniel W. Nelson · 1301 West 25th Street, Suite 570 · Austin, TX 78705 · 512-457-8003

Richard C. Reed III · DuBois, Bryant & Campbell · http://www.dbcllp.com · 700 Lavaca Street, Suite 1300 · Austin, TX 78701 · 512-457-8000

Susan J. Savage · Hurst Savage & Vanderburg · 814 West 10th Street · Austin, TX 78701 · 512-474-8400

Jane S. Smith · Fulbright & Jaworski · http://www.fulbright.com · 600 Congress Avenue, Suite 2400 · Austin, TX 78701-2978 · 512-474-5201

Timothy C. Taylor · Jackson Walker · 100 Congress Avenue, Suite 1100 · Austin, TX 78701 · 512-236-2000

Rick Triplett · ⑩ · Graves, Dougherty, Hearon & Moody · http://www.gdhm.com · 401 Congress Avenue, Suite 2200 · P.O. Box 98 · Austin, TX 78767-0098 · 512-480-5600

Ann E. Vanderburg · ⑩ · Hurst Savage & Vanderburg · 814 West 10th Street · Austin, TX 78701 · 512-474-8400

Beaumont

C. Cohron Crutchfield, Jr. · Germer Gertz · 550 Fannin Street, Suite 400 · P.O. Box 4915 · Beaumont, TX 77701 · 409-654-6700

Phil Dunlap · ⑩ · Wells, Peyton, Greenberg & Hunt · 550 Fannin Street, Suite 600 · P.O. Box 3708 · Beaumont, TX 77701 · 409-838-2644

Gary Neale Reger · ⑩ · Orgain, Bell & Tucker · 470 Orleans Street · P.O. Box 1751 · Beaumont, TX 77704-1751 · 409-838-6412

Thomas J. Sibley · Thomas J. Sibley · 3450-B North Dowlen Road · P.O. Box 3945 · Beaumont, TX 77706 · 409-835-9944

Bellaire

Charles J. Jacobus · ⑩ · Charles J. Jacobus · 6750 West Loop South, Suite 615 · Bellaire, TX 77401 · 713-839-8800

Richard Melamed · Richard Melamed · 6750 West Loop South, Suite 615 · Bellaire, TX 77401 · 713-839-8800

Brenham

Steve Haley · Moorman, Tate, Moorman, Urquhart & Haley · http://www.moormantate.com · 207 East Main Street · P.O. Box 1808 · Brenham, TX 77834-1808 · 979-836-5664

Corpus Christi

David Z. Conoly · ⑩ · David Z. Conoly · 1930 Glenoak · P.O. Box 181115 · Corpus Christi, TX 78480 · 361-937-6400

J. E. Rehler · Gary, Thomasson, Hall & Marks · 615 North Upper Broadway, Suite 800 · P.O. Box 2888 · Corpus Christi, TX 78403-0033 · 361-884-1961

Stewart N. Rice · Wood, Boykin & Wolter · 615 North Upper Broadway, Suite 1100 · Corpus Christi, TX 78477-0397 · 361-888-9201

Craig L. Williams · Branscomb · 802 North Carancahua Street, Suite 1900 · Corpus Christi, TX 78470-0700 · 361-888-9261

Arthur J. Anderson · Winstead · http://www.winstead.com · Renaissance Tower, Suite 5400 · 1201 Elm Street · Dallas, TX 75270-2199 · 214-745-5400

Patrick M. Arnold · Powell Coleman & Arnold · 8080 North Central Expressway, Suite 1380 · Dallas, TX 75206 · 214-373-8767

Robert J. Banta · Locke Lord Bissell & Liddell · 2200 Ross Avenue, Suite 2200 · Dallas, TX 75201-6776 214-740-8000

Lester V. Baum · Powell Coleman & Arnold · 8080 North Central Expressway, Suite 1380 · Dallas, TX 75206 · 214-373-8767

Bryan C. Birkeland · Jackson Walker · Bank of America Plaza, Suite 6000 · 901 Main Street · Dallas, TX 75202 · 214-953-6000

Michael R. Boulden · Vinson & Elkins · http://www.velaw.com · Trammell Crow Center, Suite 3700 · 2001 Ross Avenue · Dallas, TX 75201-2975 · 214-220-7700

Lawrence J. Brannian · (20) · Lawrence J. Brannian · 8150 North Central Expressway, Suite 1800 · Dallas, TX 75206 · 214-691-2500

Andrew L. Campbell · Andrews Kurth · http://www.andrewskurth.com · 1717 Main Street, Suite 3700 · Dallas, TX 75201 · 214-659-4400

William T. Cavanaugh, Jr. · Munsch Hardt Kopf & Harr · 3800 Lincoln Plaza · 500 North Akard Street · Dallas, TX 75201-6659 · 214-855-7500

Bruce R. Coleman · Powell Coleman & Arnold · 8080 North Central Expressway, Suite 1380 · Dallas, TX 75206 · 214-373-8767

Paul E. Comeaux · Thompson & Knight · http://www.tklaw.com · One Arts Plaza, Suite 1500 · 1722 Routh Street · Dallas, TX 75201-2533 · 214-969-1700

William S. Dahlstrom · Jackson Walker · Bank of America Plaza, Suite 6000 · 901 Main Street · Dallas, TX 75202 · 214-953-6000

Michael A. Deahl · Powell Coleman & Arnold · 8080 North Central Expressway, Suite 1380 · Dallas, TX 75206 · 214-373-8767

T. Andrew Dow · Winstead · http://www.winstead.com · Renaissance Tower, Suite 5400 · 1201 Elm Street · Dallas, TX 75270-2199 · 214-745-5400

Jonathan W. Dunlay · Baker Botts · http://www.bakerbotts.com · Trammell Crow Center, Suite 600 · 2001 Ross Avenue · Dallas, TX 75201-2980 · 214-953-6500

Robert W. Dupuy · Brown McCarroll · 2001 Ross Avenue, Suite 2000 · Dallas, TX 75201 · 214-999-6100

Robert C. Feldman · Weil Gotshal & Manges · 200 Crescent Court, Suite 300 · Dallas, TX 75201 · 214-746-7700

Michael P. Haggerty · Jackson Walker · Bank of America Plaza, Suite 6000 · 901 Main Street · Dallas, TX 75202 · 214-953-6000

Martha Harris · Thompson & Knight · http://www.tklaw.com · One Arts Plaza, Suite 1500 · 1722 Routh Street · Dallas, TX 75201-2533 · 214-969-1700

M. Lawrence Hicks, Jr. · (10) · Thompson & Knight · http://www.tklaw.com · One Arts Plaza, Suite 1500 · 1722 Routh Street · Dallas, TX 75201-2533 · 214-969-1700

Steven R. Jenkins · Haynes and Boone · 901 Main Street, Suite 3100 · Dallas, TX 75202 · 214-651-5000

Randy R. Jurgensmeyer · Vinson & Elkins · http://www.velaw.com · Trammell Crow Center, Suite 3700 2001 Ross Avenue · Dallas, TX 75201-2975 · 214-220-7700

Ray T. Khirallah · Thompson & Knight · http://www.tklaw.com · One Arts Plaza, Suite 1500 · 1722 Routh Street · Dallas, TX 75201-2533 · 214-969-1700

J. Kenneth Kopf · Winstead · http://www.winstead.com · Renaissance Tower, Suite 5400 · 1201 Elm Street · Dallas, TX 75270-2199 · 214-745-5400

Alfred G. Kyle · Bracewell & Giuliani · http://www.bgllp.com · 1445 Ross Avenue, Suite 3800 · Dallas, TX 75202-2711 · 214-468-3800

Carl Bennett Lee · ⑩ · Akin Gump Strauss Hauer & Feld · 1700 Pacific Avenue, Suite 4100 · Dallas, TX 75201-4675 · 214-969-2800

Mark G. Magilow · ⑩ · Locke Lord Bissell & Liddell · 2200 Ross Avenue, Suite 2200 · Dallas, TX 75201-6776 · 214-740-8000

Paul A. Martin · Vinson & Elkins · http://www.velaw.com · Trammell Crow Center, Suite 3700 · 2001 Ross Avenue · Dallas, TX 75201-2975 · 214-220-7700

Susan Mead · Jackson Walker · Bank of America Plaza, Suite 6000 · 901 Main Street · Dallas, TX 75202 · 214-953-6000

Charles W. Morris · Brown McCarroll · 2001 Ross Avenue, Suite 2000 · Dallas, TX 75201 · 214-999-6100

Mark V. Murray · ㉕ · Glast, Phillips & Murray · 2200 One Galleria Tower · 13355 Noel Road, LB 48 · Dallas, TX 75240-1518 · 972-419-8300

John M. Nolan · ⑩ · Winstead · http://www.winstead.com · Renaissance Tower, Suite 5400 · 1201 Elm Street · Dallas, TX 75270-2199 · 214-745-5400

Edward A. Peterson · ㉕ · Winstead · http://www.winstead.com · Renaissance Tower, Suite 5400 · 1201 Elm Street · Dallas, TX 75270-2199 · 214-745-5400

William D. Powell · ㉕ · Powell Coleman & Arnold · 8080 North Central Expressway, Suite 1380 · Dallas, TX 75206 · 214-373-8767

Randall M. Ratner · ⑩ · Akin Gump Strauss Hauer & Feld · 1700 Pacific Avenue, Suite 4100 · Dallas, TX 75201-4675 · 214-969-2800

Harry M. Roberts, Jr. · ㉕ · Thompson & Knight · http://www.tklaw.com · One Arts Plaza, Suite 1500 · 1722 Routh Street · Dallas, TX 75201-2533 · 214-969-1700

Joel L. Ross · Vinson & Elkins · http://www.velaw.com · Trammell Crow Center, Suite 3700 · 2001 Ross Avenue · Dallas, TX 75201-2975 · 214-220-7700

Tina M. Ross · Greenberg Traurig · http://www.gtlaw.com · JP Morgan Chase Tower, Suite 5200 · 2200 Ross Avenue · Dallas, TX 75201 · 972-419-9100

Ralph G. Santos · Greenberg Traurig · http://www.gtlaw.com · 600 Three Galleria Tower · 13155 Noel Road · Dallas, TX 75240 · 972-419-1250

Robert F. See, Jr. · ㉕ · Robert F. See, Jr. & Associates · http://www.rseelawfirm.com · 901 Main Street, Suite 3601 · Dallas, TX 75202 · 214-761-3001

Clinton B. Shouse · Law Office of Clinton Shouse · 10056 Surrey Oaks · Dallas, TX 75229 · 214-361-2598

Mark M. Sloan · Thompson & Knight · http://www.tklaw.com · One Arts Plaza, Suite 1500 · 1722 Routh Street · Dallas, TX 75201-2533 · 214-969-1700

Larry Van Smith · ⑩ · McGlinchey Stafford · http://www.mcglinchey.com · 2711 North Haskell Avenue, Suite 2700 · Dallas, TX 75204 · 214-257-1700

Charles W. Spencer · ㉕ · Law Office of Charles W. Spencer · 8111 LBJ Freeway, Suite 920 · Dallas, TX 75251-0000 · 972-680-8386

Robb P. Stewart · Locke Lord Bissell & Liddell · 2200 Ross Avenue, Suite 2200 · Dallas, TX 75201-6776 · 214-740-8000

Kevin A. Sullivan · Winstead · http://www.winstead.com · Renaissance Tower, Suite 5400 · 1201 Elm Street · Dallas, TX 75270-2199 · 214-745-5400

James A. Taylor · Baker Botts · http://www.bakerbotts.com · Trammell Crow Center, Suite 600 · 2001 Ross Avenue · Dallas, TX 75201-2980 · 214-953-6500

James H. Wallenstein · ㉕ · Hunton & Williams · 1445 Ross Avenue, Suite 3700 · Dallas, TX 75202-2799 214-979-3000

Winston Willard Walp II · Fulbright & Jaworski · http://www.fulbright.com · 2200 Ross Avenue, Suite 2800 · Dallas, TX 75201 · 214-855-8000

David A. Weatherbie · Carrie, Cramer & Weatherbie · 5956 Sherry Lane, Suite 1204 · Dallas, TX 75225-8023 · 214-369-2250

Mark A. Weibel · Fulbright & Jaworski · http://www.fulbright.com · 2200 Ross Avenue, Suite 2800 · Dallas, TX 75201 · 214-855-8000

Philip D. Weller · ⑳ · DLA Piper · 1717 Main Street, Suite 4600 · Dallas, TX 75201-4629 · 214-743-4500

Ben B. West · ㉕ · Thompson & Knight · http://www.tklaw.com · One Arts Plaza, Suite 1500 · 1722 Routh Street · Dallas, TX 75201-2533 · 214-969-1700

James Richard White · ⑩ · Winstead · http://www.winstead.com · Renaissance Tower, Suite 5400 · 1201 Elm Street · Dallas, TX 75270-2199 · 214-745-5400

Richard W. Wilhelm · Munsch Hardt Kopf & Harr · 3800 Lincoln Plaza · 500 North Akard Street · Dallas, TX 75201-6659 · 214-855-7500

Kirk R. Williams · Winstead · http://www.winstead.com · Renaissance Tower, Suite 5400 · 1201 Elm Street · Dallas, TX 75270-2199 · 214-745-5400

Robert E. Wilson · ㉕ · Haynes and Boone · 901 Main Street, Suite 3100 · Dallas, TX 75202 · 214-651-5000

Eldon Lee Youngblood · ㉕ · McGlinchey Stafford · http://www.mcglinchey.com · 2711 North Haskell Avenue, Suite 2700 · Dallas, TX 75204 · 214-257-1700

El Paso

Michael F. Ainsa · ⑩ · Ainsa Hutson · 5809 Acacia Circle · El Paso, TX 79912 · 915-845-5300

Taffy D. Bagley · ⑩ · Taffy Bagley · 201 East Main Drive, Suite 601 · El Paso, TX 79901 · 915-543-6700

W. David Bernard · ⑩ · Scott, Hulse, Marshall, Feuille, Finger & Thurmond · 1100 Chase Tower · 201 East Main Street · El Paso, TX 79901 · 915-533-2493

Marc P. Bernat · ⑩ · Gordon & Mott · 4695 North Mesa Street, Suite 100 · El Paso, TX 79912 · 915-545-1133

John S. Birkelbach · ⑩ · Mounce, Green, Myers, Safi & Galatzan · Kayser Building, 17th Floor · 100 North Stanton Street · P.O. Box 1977 · El Paso, TX 79950-1977 · 915-532-2000

Bernard D. Felsen · Scott, Hulse, Marshall, Feuille, Finger & Thurmond · 1100 Chase Tower · 201 East Main Street · El Paso, TX 79901 · 915-533-2493

Risher Smith Gilbert · ⑩ · The Gilbert Law Firm · Chase Tower, Suite 601 · 201 East Main · P.O. Box 472 · El Paso, TX 79943-0472 · 915-532-6622

Michael J. Hutson · Ainsa Hutson · 5809 Acacia Circle · El Paso, TX 79912 · 915-845-5300

Terry L. Johnson · Ryan Sanders & Gluth · 310 North Mesa Street, Suite 300 · El Paso, TX 79901 · 915-351-1100

Tim Johnson · Gordon & Mott · 4695 North Mesa Street, Suite 100 · El Paso, TX 79912 · 915-545-1133

Christopher A. Paul · ⑩ · Kemp Smith · http://www.kempsmith.com · 221 North Kansas, Suite 1700 · El Paso, TX 79901-1441 · 915-533-4424

Fort Worth

Jay S. Garrett · Law, Snakard & Gambill · 1600 West Seventh Street, Suite 500 · Fort Worth, TX 76102-2598 · 817-335-7373

Patricia Meadows · Kelly, Hart & Hallman · Wells Fargo Tower, Suite 2500 · 201 Main Street · Fort Worth, TX 76102 · 817-332-2500

Sharon S. Millians · ⑩ · Kelly, Hart & Hallman · Wells Fargo Tower, Suite 2500 · 201 Main Street · Fort Worth, TX 76102 · 817-332-2500

William D. Ratliff · Haynes and Boone · 201 Main Street, Suite 2200 · Fort Worth, TX 76102 · 817-347-6600

Houston

Mark B. Arnold · Andrews Kurth · http://www.andrewskurth.com · 600 Travis Street, Suite 4200 · Houston, TX 77002 · 713-220-4200

Howard T. Ayers, Jr. · ⑩ · Andrews Kurth · http://www.andrewskurth.com · 600 Travis Street, Suite 4200 Houston, TX 77002 · 713-220-4200

Barton R. Bentley · ⑩ · Fizer, Beck, Webster, Bentley & Scroggins · 1330 Post Oak Boulevard, Suite 2900 · Houston, TX 77056 · 713-840-7710

Nelson R. Block · Winstead · http://www.winstead.com · JPMorgan Chase Tower, Suite 1100 · 600 Travis Street · Houston, TX 77002 · 713-650-8400

Stephen M. Block · Thompson & Knight · http://www.tklaw.com · 333 Clay Street, Suite 3300 · Houston, TX 77002 · 713-654-8111

Denis Clive Braham · Winstead · http://www.winstead.com · JPMorgan Chase Tower, Suite 1100 · 600 Travis Street · Houston, TX 77002 · 713-650-8400

Timothy R. Brown · Thompson & Knight · http://www.tklaw.com · 333 Clay Street, Suite 3300 · Houston, TX 77002 · 713-654-8111

George S. Craft · Porter & Hedges · 1000 Main Street, 36th Floor · Houston, TX 77002 · 713-226-0600

E. Scot Dixon · Vinson & Elkins · http://www.velaw.com · First City Tower, Suite 2500 · 1001 Fannin Street · Houston, TX 77002-6760 · 713-758-2222

Melvin A. Dow · ㉕ · Winstead · http://www.winstead.com · JPMorgan Chase Tower, Suite 1100 · 600 Travis Street · Houston, TX 77002 · 713-650-8400

Fred H. Dunlop · ㉕ · Baker Botts · http://www.bakerbotts.com · One Shell Plaza · 910 Louisiana Street · Houston, TX 77002-1210 · 713-229-1234

Uriel E. Dutton · ㉕ · Fulbright & Jaworski · http://www.fulbright.com · Fulbright Tower, Suite 5100 · 1301 McKinney Street · Houston, TX 77010-3095 · 713-651-5151

Gregory Erwin · ⑩ · Winstead · http://www.winstead.com · JPMorgan Chase Tower, Suite 1100 · 600 Travis Street · Houston, TX 77002 · 713-650-8400

Jack E. Fields · ㉕ · Andrews Kurth · http://www.andrewskurth.com · 600 Travis Street, Suite 4200 · Houston, TX 77002 · 713-220-4200

Mark C. Hodges · Andrews Kurth · http://www.andrewskurth.com · 600 Travis Street, Suite 4200 · Houston, TX 77002 · 713-220-4200

John S. Hollyfield · ㉕ · Fulbright & Jaworski · http://www.fulbright.com · Fulbright Tower, Suite 5100 · 1301 McKinney Street · Houston, TX 77010-3095 · 713-651-5151

Randall K. Howard · ⑳ · Akin Gump Strauss Hauer & Feld · 1111 Louisiana Street, 44th Floor · Houston, TX 77002-5200 · 713-220-5800

Stephen C. Jacobs · Locke Lord Bissell & Liddell · JP Morgan Chase Tower, Suite 3400 · 600 Travis Street · Houston, TX 77002 · 713-226-1200

M. Marvin Katz · ㉕ · Mayer Brown · Bank of America Center, Suite 3400 · 700 Louisiana Street · Houston, TX 77002-2730 · 713-238-3000

Michael K. Kuhn · Jackson Walker · 1401 McKinney Street, Suite 1900 · Houston, TX 77010-4008 · 713-752-4200

Robert S. Ladd · Haynes and Boone · One Houston Center, Suite 2100 · 1221 McKinney Street · Houston, TX 77010 · 713-547-2000

Barbara J. LeBarron · LeBarron Law · 4105 A Blossom Street · Houston, TX 77007 · 832-369-0116

Marley Lott · Baker Botts · http://www.bakerbotts.com · One Shell Plaza · 910 Louisiana Street · Houston, TX 77002-1210 · 713-229-1234

Marilyn C. Maloney · ⑩ · Liskow & Lewis · http://www.liskow.com · First City Tower, Suite 1800 · 1001 Fannin Street · Houston, TX 77002-4102 · 713-651-2900

Vincent L. Marino · Winstead · http://www.winstead.com · JPMorgan Chase Tower, Suite 1100 · 600 Travis Street · Houston, TX 77002 · 713-650-8400

Thomas J. McCaffrey · Haynes and Boone · One Houston Center, Suite 2100 · 1221 McKinney Street · Houston, TX 77010 · 713-547-2000

Daniel E. McCormick · ⑩ · Andrews Kurth · http://www.andrewskurth.com · 600 Travis Street, Suite 4200 · Houston, TX 77002 · 713-220-4200

Bruce W. Merwin · ⑩ · Haynes and Boone · One Houston Center, Suite 2100 · 1221 McKinney Street · Houston, TX 77010 · 713-547-2000

Alfred M. Meyerson · Thompson & Knight · http://www.tklaw.com · 333 Clay Street, Suite 3300 · Houston, TX 77002 · 713-654-8111

H. Dixon Montague · Vinson & Elkins · http://www.velaw.com · First City Tower, Suite 2500 · 1001 Fannin Street · Houston, TX 77002-6760 · 713-758-2222

Thomas O. Moore III · ⑩ · Bracewell & Giuliani · http://www.bgllp.com · 711 Louisiana Street, Suite 2300 · Houston, TX 77002-2770 · 713-223-2300

Marvin D. Nathan · Nathan Sommers Jacobs · 2800 Post Oak Boulevard, 61st Floor · Houston, TX 77056 713-960-0303

Kent Newsome · Greenberg Traurig · http://www.gtlaw.com · 1000 Louisiana Street, Suite 1800 · Houston, TX 77002 · 713-374-3500

Kurt D. Nondorf · Jackson Walker · 1401 McKinney Street, Suite 1900 · Houston, TX 77010-4008 · 713-752-4200

Jonathan A. Peckham · Adams and Reese · http://www.adamsandreese.com · One Houston Center, Suite 4400 · 1221 McKinney Street · Houston, TX 77010 · 713-652-5151

Barry E. Putterman · Winstead · http://www.winstead.com · JPMorgan Chase Tower, Suite 1100 · 600 Travis Street · Houston, TX 77002 · 713-650-8400

Gary Rachlin · Liskow & Lewis · http://www.liskow.com · First City Tower, Suite 1800 · 1001 Fannin Street · Houston, TX 77002-4102 · 713-651-2900

James W. Robertson · ⑩ · Locke Lord Bissell & Liddell · JP Morgan Chase Tower, Suite 3400 · 600 Travis Street · Houston, TX 77002 · 713-226-1200

David M. Robins · Thompson & Knight · http://www.tklaw.com · 333 Clay Street, Suite 3300 · Houston, TX 77002 · 713-654-8111

Lee D. Schlanger · ㉕ · Schlanger, Silver, Barg & Paine · 109 North Post Oak Lane, Suite 300 · Houston, TX 77024 · 713-785-1700

Ronald M. Shoss · Mayer Brown · Bank of America Center, Suite 3400 · 700 Louisiana Street · Houston, TX 77002-2730 · 713-238-3000

Louis E. Silver · Schlanger, Silver, Barg & Paine · 109 North Post Oak Lane, Suite 300 · Houston, TX 77024 · 713-785-1700

Consuella D. Simmons · Baker Botts · http://www.bakerbotts.com · One Shell Plaza · 910 Louisiana Street · Houston, TX 77002-1210 · 713-229-1234

William B. Sing · Fulbright & Jaworski · http://www.fulbright.com · Fulbright Tower, Suite 5100 · 1301 McKinney Street · Houston, TX 77010-3095 · 713-651-5151

Joseph O. Slovacek · Hoover Slovacek · 5847 San Felipe, Suite 2200 · P.O. Box 4547 · Houston, TX 77210-4547 · 713-977-8686

Clark G. Thompson, Jr. · Bracewell & Giuliani · http://www.bgllp.com · 711 Louisiana Street, Suite 2300 Houston, TX 77002-2770 · 713-223-2300

W. David Tidholm · Porter & Hedges · 1000 Main Street, 36th Floor · Houston, TX 77002 · 713-226-0600

Robert C. Walker · Campbell & Riggs · 1980 Post Oak Boulevard, Suite 2300 · Houston, TX 77056 · 713-621-6721

Neil A. Wasserstrom · Mayer Brown · Bank of America Center, Suite 3400 · 700 Louisiana Street · Houston, TX 77002-2730 · 713-238-3000

Sanford A. Weiner · ㉕ · Vinson & Elkins · http://www.velaw.com · First City Tower, Suite 2500 · 1001 Fannin Street · Houston, TX 77002-6760 · 713-758-2222

Reid C. Wilson · Wilson, Cribbs & Goren · 2500 Fannin Street · Houston, TX 77002 · 713-222-9000

Jack G. Wise · Porter & Hedges · 1000 Main Street, 36th Floor · Houston, TX 77002 · 713-226-0600

Robert Payton Wright · Baker Botts · http://www.bakerbotts.com · One Shell Plaza · 910 Louisiana Street Houston, TX 77002-1210 · 713-229-1234

Richardson

Richard K. Martin · Haynes and Boone · 2505 North Plano Road, Suite 4000 · Richardson, TX 75802 · 972-739-6900

Ann M. Saegert · Haynes and Boone · 2505 North Plano Road, Suite 4000 · Richardson, TX 75802 · 972-739-6900

San Antonio

James H. Barrow · James H. Barrow · 1280 Frost Bank Tower · 100 West Houston Street · San Antonio, TX 78205 · 210-226-5400

J. Cary Barton · ⑩ · Barton, East & Caldwell · 700 North St. Mary's Street, Suite 1825 · San Antonio, TX 78205-3501 · 210-225-1655

Kerry T. Benedict · Cox Smith Matthews · http://www.coxsmith.com · 112 East Pecan Street, Suite 1800 · San Antonio, TX 78205-1521 · 210-554-5500

Peter Broderick · Cox Smith Matthews · http://www.coxsmith.com · 112 East Pecan Street, Suite 1800 · San Antonio, TX 78205-1521 · 210-554-5500

J. Russell Davis · Davis, Cedillo & Mendoza · McCombs Plaza, Suite 500 · 755 East Mulberry Avenue · San Antonio, TX 78212 · 210-822-6666

Kenneth M. Gindy · ⑳ · Kenneth M. Gindy · P.O. Box 37343 · San Antonio, TX 78237 · 210-434-5577

Stephen Lloyd Golden · Drenner & Golden Stuart Wolff · 300 Convent Street, Suite 2650 · San Antonio, TX 78205 · 210-745-3700

Richard F. Halter · ⑩ · Bobbitt, Halter & Watson · 8700 Crownhill Boulevard, Suite 300 · San Antonio, TX 78209-1128 · 210-824-1555

Richard L. Kerr · Kerr Negron · 750 East Mulberry Avenue, Suite 510 · San Antonio, TX 78212 · 210-738-8750

James M. McDonough · Cox Smith Matthews · http://www.coxsmith.com · 112 East Pecan Street, Suite 1800 · San Antonio, TX 78205-1521 · 210-554-5500

Michael A. Morell · Michael A. Morell · 5150 Broadway, Number 618 · San Antonio, TX 78209 · 210-829-8895

James C. Norman · ⑩ · Norman & Oliver · 7373 Broadway, Suite 504 · San Antonio, TX 78209 · 210-822-8972

Frank Z. Ruttenberg · Bracewell & Giuliani · http://www.bgllp.com · One Alamo Center, Suite 800 · 106 South St. Mary's Street · San Antonio, TX 78205-3603 · 210-226-1166

Banks M. Smith · Schoenbaum, Curphy & Scanlan · 112 East Pecan Street, 30th Floor · San Antonio, TX 78205-1516 · 210-224-4491

Thomas J. Smith · ⑩ · Law Office of Thomas J. Smith · 112 East Pecan Street, Suite 3050 · San Antonio, TX 78205-3501 · 210-227-7565

John B. Stewart · Cox Smith Matthews · http://www.coxsmith.com · 112 East Pecan Street, Suite 1800 · San Antonio, TX 78205-1521 · 210-554-5500

James M. Summers · ⑩ · Fulbright & Jaworski · http://www.fulbright.com · 300 Convent Street, Suite 2200 · San Antonio, TX 78205-3792 · 210-224-5575

Lewis T. Tarver, Jr. · ⑳ · Cox Smith Matthews · http://www.coxsmith.com · 112 East Pecan Street, Suite 1800 · San Antonio, TX 78205-1521 · 210-554-5500

Steven A. Waters · ⑩ · Haynes and Boone · 112 East Pecan Street, Suite 900 · San Antonio, TX 78205-1540 · 210-978-7000

Jamie M. Wilson · Wilson & Wilson Law · 3303 Oakwell Court, Suite 110 · San Antonio, TX 78218 · 210-804-0800

John D. Wittenberg, Jr. · Hornberger Sheehan Fuller & Beiter · Quarry Heights, Suite 300 · 7373 Broadway · San Antonio, TX 78209 · 210-271-1700

SECURITIES LAW

Austin

J. Rowland Cook · ⑳ · Winstead · http://www.winstead.com · 401 Congress Avenue, Suite 2100 · Austin, TX 78701 · 512-370-2800

Brian P. Fenske · Fulbright & Jaworski · http://www.fulbright.com · 600 Congress Avenue, Suite 2400 · Austin, TX 78701-2978 · 512-474-5201

John J. Gilluly III · DLA Piper · 1221 South MoPac Expressway, Suite 400 · Austin, TX 78746-7650 · 512-457-7000

Paul E. Hurdlow · DLA Piper · 1221 South MoPac Expressway, Suite 400 · Austin, TX 78746-7650 · 512-457-7000

J. Kathryn Lindauer · ⑩ · Winstead · http://www.winstead.com · 401 Congress Avenue, Suite 2100 · Austin, TX 78701 · 512-370-2800

Phillip M. Slinkard · K&L Gates · 111 Congress Avenue, Suite 900 · Austin, TX 78701 · 512-482-6800

Paul R. Tobias · Wilson Sonsini Goodrich & Rosati · Las Cimas IV, Fifth Floor · 900 South Capital of Texas Highway · Austin, TX 78746-5546 · 512-338-5400

William R. Volk · ㉕ · Vinson & Elkins · http://www.velaw.com · 2801 Via Fortuna, Suite 100 · Austin, TX 78746-7568 · 512-542-8400

Dallas

Craig Adams · Baker Botts · http://www.bakerbotts.com · Trammell Crow Center, Suite 600 · 2001 Ross Avenue · Dallas, TX 75201-2980 · 214-953-6500

Andrew M. Baker · Baker Botts · http://www.bakerbotts.com · Trammell Crow Center, Suite 600 · 2001 Ross Avenue · Dallas, TX 75201-2980 · 214-953-6500

George W. Bramblett, Jr. · ⑩ · Haynes and Boone · 901 Main Street, Suite 3100 · Dallas, TX 75202 · 214-651-5000

Jeffrey A. Chapman · ⑩ · Vinson & Elkins · http://www.velaw.com · Trammell Crow Center, Suite 3700 · 2001 Ross Avenue · Dallas, TX 75201-2975 · 214-220-7700

William B. Dawson · Vinson & Elkins · http://www.velaw.com · Trammell Crow Center, Suite 3700 · 2001 Ross Avenue · Dallas, TX 75201-2975 · 214-220-7700

Timothy S. Durst · Baker Botts · http://www.bakerbotts.com · Trammell Crow Center, Suite 600 · 2001 Ross Avenue · Dallas, TX 75201-2980 · 214-953-6500

Ernest E. Figari, Jr. · ㉕ · Figari & Davenport · http://www.figdav.com · 3400 Bank of America Plaza · 901 Main Street · Dallas, TX 75202-3796 · 214-939-2000

Noel M. B. Hensley · Haynes and Boone · 901 Main Street, Suite 3100 · Dallas, TX 75202 · 214-651-5000

Glen James Hettinger · Fulbright & Jaworski · http://www.fulbright.com · 2200 Ross Avenue, Suite 2800 Dallas, TX 75201 · 214-855-8000

Thomas William Hughes · Fulbright & Jaworski · http://www.fulbright.com · 2200 Ross Avenue, Suite 2800 · Dallas, TX 75201 · 214-855-8000

Mary R. Korby · Weil Gotshal & Manges · 200 Crescent Court, Suite 300 · Dallas, TX 75201 · 214-746-7700

George C. Lamb III · Baker Botts · http://www.bakerbotts.com · Trammell Crow Center, Suite 600 · 2001 Ross Avenue · Dallas, TX 75201-2980 · 214-953-6500

Larry Steven Leshin · ⑩ · Hunton & Williams · 1445 Ross Avenue, Suite 3700 · Dallas, TX 75202-2799 · 214-979-3000

Peter Alan Lodwick · Thompson & Knight · http://www.tklaw.com · One Arts Plaza, Suite 1500 · 1722 Routh Street · Dallas, TX 75201-2533 · 214-969-1700

Timothy R. McCormick · ⑩ · Thompson & Knight · http://www.tklaw.com · One Arts Plaza, Suite 1500 · 1722 Routh Street · Dallas, TX 75201-2533 · 214-969-1700

Don J. McDermett, Jr. · Baker Botts · http://www.bakerbotts.com · Trammell Crow Center, Suite 600 · 2001 Ross Avenue · Dallas, TX 75201-2980 · 214-953-6500

Timothy W. Mountz · Baker Botts · http://www.bakerbotts.com · Trammell Crow Center, Suite 600 · 2001 Ross Avenue · Dallas, TX 75201-2980 · 214-953-6500

Geoffrey L. Newton · Baker Botts · http://www.bakerbotts.com · Trammell Crow Center, Suite 600 · 2001 Ross Avenue · Dallas, TX 75201-2980 · 214-953-6500

Douglass M. Rayburn · Baker Botts · http://www.bakerbotts.com · Trammell Crow Center, Suite 600 · 2001 Ross Avenue · Dallas, TX 75201-2980 · 214-953-6500

Larry L. Schoenbrun · ㉕ · Gardere Wynne Sewell · http://www.gardere.com · 1601 Elm Street, Suite 3000 · Dallas, TX 75201 · 214-999-3000

Patricia J. Villareal · Jones Day · 2727 North Harwood Street · Dallas, TX 75201-1515 · 214-220-3939

Robb L. Voyles · Baker Botts · http://www.bakerbotts.com · Trammell Crow Center, Suite 600 · 2001 Ross Avenue · Dallas, TX 75201-2980 · 214-953-6500

Taylor H. Wilson · Haynes and Boone · 901 Main Street, Suite 3100 · Dallas, TX 75202 · 214-651-5000

Fort Worth

F. Richard Bernasek · Kelly, Hart & Hallman · Wells Fargo Tower, Suite 2500 · 201 Main Street · Fort Worth, TX 76102 · 817-332-2500

Kleber C. Miller · ㉕ · Shannon, Gracey, Ratliff & Miller · http://www.shannongracey.com · 777 Main Street, Suite 3800 · Fort Worth, TX 76102 · 817-336-9333

Houston

John C. Ale · Skadden, Arps, Slate, Meagher & Flom · 1000 Louisiana, Suite 6800 · Houston, TX 77002 · 713-655-5100

James A. Baker III · Baker Botts · http://www.bakerbotts.com · One Shell Plaza · 910 Louisiana Street · Houston, TX 77002-1210 · 713-229-1234

Donald White Brodsky · Baker Hostetler · http://www.bakerlaw.com · 1000 Louisiana, Suite 2000 · Houston, TX 77002-5009 · 713-751-1600

Michael W. Conlon · Fulbright & Jaworski · http://www.fulbright.com · Fulbright Tower, Suite 5100 · 1301 McKinney Street · Houston, TX 77010-3095 · 713-651-5151

Samuel W. Cooper · Baker Botts · http://www.bakerbotts.com · One Shell Plaza · 910 Louisiana Street · Houston, TX 77002-1210 · 713-229-1234

Jeffery Burton Floyd · ⑩ · Vinson & Elkins · http://www.velaw.com · First City Tower, Suite 2500 · 1001 Fannin Street · Houston, TX 77002-6760 · 713-758-2222

Marc H. Folladori · Mayer Brown · Bank of America Center, Suite 3400 · 700 Louisiana Street · Houston, TX 77002-2730 · 713-238-3000

Jean C. Frizzell · Gibbs & Bruns · http://www.gibbs-bruns.com · 1100 Louisiana Street, Suite 5300 · Houston, TX 77002 · 713-650-8805

Robin C. Gibbs · ⑩ · Gibbs & Bruns · http://www.gibbs-bruns.com · 1100 Louisiana Street, Suite 5300 · Houston, TX 77002 · 713-650-8805

Mark K. Glasser · Baker Botts · http://www.bakerbotts.com · One Shell Plaza · 910 Louisiana Street · Houston, TX 77002-1210 · 713-229-1234

David T. Harvin · ㉕ · Vinson & Elkins · http://www.velaw.com · First City Tower, Suite 2500 · 1001 Fannin Street · Houston, TX 77002-6760 · 713-758-2222

J. David Kirkland, Jr. · Baker Botts · http://www.bakerbotts.com · One Shell Plaza · 910 Louisiana Street Houston, TX 77002-1210 · 713-229-1234

Stephen A. Massad · ⑳ · Baker Botts · http://www.bakerbotts.com · One Shell Plaza · 910 Louisiana Street · Houston, TX 77002-1210 · 713-229-1234

Jacks C. Nickens · Nickens Keeton Lawless Farrell Flack · 600 Travis Street, Suite 7500 · Houston, TX 77002 · 713-571-9191

Gene J. Oshman · Baker Botts · http://www.bakerbotts.com · One Shell Plaza · 910 Louisiana Street · Houston, TX 77002-1210 · 713-229-1234

Gerard G. Pecht · Fulbright & Jaworski · http://www.fulbright.com · Fulbright Tower, Suite 5100 · 1301 McKinney Street · Houston, TX 77010-3095 · 713-651-5151

Joe S. Poff · Baker Botts · http://www.bakerbotts.com · One Shell Plaza · 910 Louisiana Street · Houston, TX 77002-1210 · 713-229-1234

T. William Porter III · ㉕ · Porter & Hedges · 1000 Main Street, 36th Floor · Houston, TX 77002 · 713-226-0600

Barrett H. Reasoner · Gibbs & Bruns · http://www.gibbs-bruns.com · 1100 Louisiana Street, Suite 5300 · Houston, TX 77002 · 713-650-8805

Walter J. Smith · ⑩ · Baker Botts · http://www.bakerbotts.com · One Shell Plaza · 910 Louisiana Street · Houston, TX 77002-1210 · 713-229-1234

David D. Sterling · Baker Botts · http://www.bakerbotts.com · One Shell Plaza · 910 Louisiana Street · Houston, TX 77002-1210 · 713-229-1234

Charles H. Still, Sr. · ㉕ · Kelly, Hart & Hallman · Wells Fargo Plaza, Suite 4700 · 1000 Louisiana Street · Houston, TX 77002 · 713-654-4600

Charles L. Strauss · Fulbright & Jaworski · http://www.fulbright.com · Fulbright Tower, Suite 5100 · 1301 McKinney Street · Houston, TX 77010-3095 · 713-651-5151

R. Joel Swanson · ㉕ · Baker Botts · http://www.bakerbotts.com · One Shell Plaza · 910 Louisiana Street · Houston, TX 77002-1210 · 713-229-1234

Charles C. Szalkowski · ⑩ · Baker Botts · http://www.bakerbotts.com · One Shell Plaza · 910 Louisiana Street · Houston, TX 77002-1210 · 713-229-1234

Fredric A. Weber · ⑩ · Fulbright & Jaworski · http://www.fulbright.com · Fulbright Tower, Suite 5100 · 1301 McKinney Street · Houston, TX 77010-3095 · 713-651-5151

San Antonio

T. Drew Cauthorn · ⑩ · Hornberger Sheehan Fuller & Beiter · Quarry Heights, Suite 300 · 7373 Broadway · San Antonio, TX 78209 · 210-271-1700

James M. Doyle, Jr. · Law Offices of James M. Doyle, Jr. · 111 West Olmos Drive · San Antonio, TX 78212 · 210-829-7183

SPORTS LAW

Dallas

Robert P. Latham · Jackson Walker · Bank of America Plaza, Suite 6000 · 901 Main Street · Dallas, TX 75202 · 214-953-6000

Paul D. Schoonover · ⑩ · Kleiman Lawrence Baskind Fitzgerald · 8750 North Central Expressway, Suite 777 · Dallas, TX 75231 · 214-265-7400

Houston

Denis Clive Braham · Winstead · http://www.winstead.com · JPMorgan Chase Tower, Suite 1100 · 600 Travis Street · Houston, TX 77002 · 713-650-8400

Ricardo Garcia-Moreno · Haynes and Boone · One Houston Center, Suite 2100 · 1221 McKinney Street · Houston, TX 77010 · 713-547-2000

STRUCTURED FINANCE LAW

Dallas

David Barbour · Andrews Kurth · http://www.andrewskurth.com · 1717 Main Street, Suite 3700 · Dallas, TX 75201 · 214-659-4400

Patrick C. Sargent · Andrews Kurth · http://www.andrewskurth.com · 1717 Main Street, Suite 3700 · Dallas, TX 75201 · 214-659-4400

Kevin A. Sullivan · Winstead · http://www.winstead.com · Renaissance Tower, Suite 5400 · 1201 Elm Street · Dallas, TX 75270-2199 · 214-745-5400

Mark A. Weibel · Fulbright & Jaworski · http://www.fulbright.com · 2200 Ross Avenue, Suite 2800 · Dallas, TX 75201 · 214-855-8000

TAX LAW

Austin

Carolyn M. Beckett · Giordani, Schurig, Beckett & Tackett · http://www.gsbtlaw.com · 100 Congress Avenue, 22nd Floor · Austin, TX 78701 · 512-370-2720

Joyce R. Bode · Fulbright & Jaworski · http://www.fulbright.com · 600 Congress Avenue, Suite 2400 · Austin, TX 78701-2978 · 512-474-5201

Thomas J. Brorby · ⑳ · Brorby, Crozier & Dobie · 111 Congress Avenue, Suite 2250 · Austin, TX 78701 · 512-320-7040

Frank B. Brown · Armbrust & Brown · http://www.abaustin.com · 100 Congress Avenue, Suite 1300 · Austin, TX 78701 · 512-435-2300

C. Joseph Cain · ⑩ · Clark, Thomas & Winters · 300 West Sixth Street, 15th Floor · P.O. Box 1148 · Austin, TX 78767 · 512-472-8800

Michael L. Cook · ㉕ · Winstead · http://www.winstead.com · 401 Congress Avenue, Suite 2100 · Austin, TX 78701 · 512-370-2800

Brian W. Crozier · Brorby, Crozier & Dobie · 111 Congress Avenue, Suite 2250 · Austin, TX 78701 · 512-320-7040

Mark W. Eidman · Scott, Douglass & McConnico · 600 Congress Avenue, Suite 1500 · Austin, TX 78701-3234 · 512-495-6300

David I. Kuperman · ㉕ · Kuperman, Orr & Albers · 2801 Via Fortuna, Suite 530 · Austin, TX 78746 · 512-473-4100

Bryan W. Lee · DuBois, Bryant & Campbell · http://www.dbcllp.com · 700 Lavaca Street, Suite 1300 · Austin, TX 78701 · 512-457-8000

Ira A. Lipstet · DuBois, Bryant & Campbell · http://www.dbcllp.com · 700 Lavaca Street, Suite 1300 · Austin, TX 78701 · 512-457-8000

James F. Martens · Martens and Associates · 301 Congress Avenue, Suite 1950 · Austin, TX 78701 · 512-542-9898

Christina A. Mondrik · Mondrik and Associates · Bank of America Tower, Suite 1850 · 515 Congress Avenue · Austin, TX 78701 · 512-542-9300

J. Andrew Norval · Saunders & Norval · 2630 Exposition Boulevard, Suite 203 · Austin, TX 78703-1757 · 512-472-7111

Patrick L. O'Daniel · Fulbright & Jaworski · http://www.fulbright.com · 600 Congress Avenue, Suite 2400 Austin, TX 78701-2978 · 512-474-5201

William Pollard · William Pollard · 800 Rio Grande Street · Austin, TX 78701 · 512-474-1554

Robert E. Reetz, Jr. · Brown McCarroll · 111 Congress Avenue, Suite 1400 · Austin, TX 78701-4093 · 512-472-5456

Donald F. Wood · ⑳ · Vinson & Elkins · http://www.velaw.com · 2801 Via Fortuna, Suite 100 · Austin, TX 78746-7568 · 512-542-8400

Beaumont

John Creighton III · ⑩ · Orgain, Bell & Tucker · 470 Orleans Street · P.O. Box 1751 · Beaumont, TX 77704-1751 · 409-838-6412

S. L. Greenberg · ⑩ · Wells, Peyton, Greenberg & Hunt · 550 Fannin Street, Suite 600 · P.O. Box 3708 · Beaumont, TX 77701 · 409-838-2644

Corpus Christi

Kenton E. McDonald · ⑩ · Branscomb · 802 North Carancahua Street, Suite 1900 · Corpus Christi, TX 78470-0700 · 361-888-9261

Gerald W. Ostarch · ⑳ · Gary, Thomasson, Hall & Marks · 615 North Upper Broadway, Suite 800 · P.O. Box 2888 · Corpus Christi, TX 78403-0033 · 361-884-1961

Paul O. Price · Paul O. Price · 337 University · Corpus Christi, TX 78412 · 361-980-8543

Dallas

Robert H. Albaral · Baker & McKenzie · 2300 Trammell Crow Center · 2001 Ross Avenue · Dallas, TX 75201 · 214-978-3000

Val J. Albright · Gardere Wynne Sewell · http://www.gardere.com · 1601 Elm Street, Suite 3000 · Dallas, TX 75201 · 214-999-3000

Christopher F. Allison · Locke Lord Bissell & Liddell · 2200 Ross Avenue, Suite 2200 · Dallas, TX 75201-6776 · 214-740-8000

Buford P. Berry · 20 · Thompson & Knight · http://www.tklaw.com · One Arts Plaza, Suite 1500 · 1722 Routh Street · Dallas, TX 75201-2533 · 214-969-1700

John Brusniak, Jr. · Brusniak Blackwell · 17400 Dallas Parkway, Suite 112 · Dallas, TX 75287 · 972-250-6363

Daniel L. Butcher · Strasburger & Price · http://www.strasburger.com · 901 Main Street, Suite 4400 · Dallas, TX 75202-3794 · 214-651-4300

R. Brent Clifton · 10 · Locke Lord Bissell & Liddell · 2200 Ross Avenue, Suite 2200 · Dallas, TX 75201-6776 · 214-740-8000

John R. Cohn · Thompson & Knight · http://www.tklaw.com · One Arts Plaza, Suite 1500 · 1722 Routh Street · Dallas, TX 75201-2533 · 214-969-1700

Robert D. Collier · Meadows, Collier, Reed, Cousins & Blau · 901 Main Street, Suite 3700 · Dallas, TX 75202 · 214-744-3700

Trey Cousins · Meadows, Collier, Reed, Cousins & Blau · 901 Main Street, Suite 3700 · Dallas, TX 75202 · 214-744-3700

David E. Cowling · Jones Day · 2727 North Harwood Street · Dallas, TX 75201-1515 · 214-220-3939

Thomas Crichton IV · Vinson & Elkins · http://www.velaw.com · Trammell Crow Center, Suite 3700 · 2001 Ross Avenue · Dallas, TX 75201-2975 · 214-220-7700

Robert E. Davis · 20 · K&L Gates · 1717 Main Street, Suite 2800 · Dallas, TX 75201 · 214-939-5500

Dennis B. Drapkin · 10 · Jones Day · 2727 North Harwood Street · Dallas, TX 75201-1515 · 214-220-3939

Jack R. Dugan · 10 · Strasburger & Price · http://www.strasburger.com · 901 Main Street, Suite 4400 · Dallas, TX 75202-3794 · 214-651-4300

William D. Elliott · Law Offices of William D. Elliott · 2626 Cole Avenue, Suite 600 · Dallas, TX 75204 · 214-922-9393

Herschell Gene Emery · 25 · Locke Lord Bissell & Liddell · 2200 Ross Avenue, Suite 2200 · Dallas, TX 75201-6776 · 214-740-8000

Richard M. Fijolek · Haynes and Boone · 901 Main Street, Suite 3100 · Dallas, TX 75202 · 214-651-5000

Michael G. Frankel · 10 · Ernst & Young · 2100 Ross Avenue, Suite 1500 · Dallas, TX 75201 · 214-969-8000

Richard A. Freling · 25 · Jones Day · 2727 North Harwood Street · Dallas, TX 75201-1515 · 214-220-3939

David G. Glickman · 20 · Baker & McKenzie · 2300 Trammell Crow Center · 2001 Ross Avenue · Dallas, TX 75201 · 214-978-3000

Thomas R. Helfand · Winstead · http://www.winstead.com · Renaissance Tower, Suite 5400 · 1201 Elm Street · Dallas, TX 75270-2199 · 214-745-5400

Kathryn G. Henkel · 10 · K&L Gates · 1717 Main Street, Suite 2800 · Dallas, TX 75201 · 214-939-5500

William H. Hornberger · Jackson Walker · Bank of America Plaza, Suite 6000 · 901 Main Street · Dallas, TX 75202 · 214-953-6000

Vester T. Hughes, Jr. · 25 · K&L Gates · 1717 Main Street, Suite 2800 · Dallas, TX 75201 · 214-939-5500

William D. Jordan · (10) · Johnson, Jordan, Nipper & Monk · Three Galleria Tower, Suite 1050, LB Three 13155 Noel Road · Dallas, TX 75240-1531 · 972-392-1123

Ronald D. Kerridge · K&L Gates · 1717 Main Street, Suite 2800 · Dallas, TX 75201 · 214-939-5500

Donald Paul Lan, Jr. · Kroney Morse Lan · 12221 Merit Drive, Suite 1210 · Dallas, TX 75251 · 972-386-8500

Cym H. Lowell · (20) · Gardere Wynne Sewell · http://www.gardere.com · 1601 Elm Street, Suite 3000 · Dallas, TX 75201 · 214-999-3000

Stephen D. Marcus · Baker Botts · http://www.bakerbotts.com · Trammell Crow Center, Suite 600 · 2001 Ross Avenue · Dallas, TX 75201-2980 · 214-953-6500

P. Mike McCullough · (20) · Thompson & Knight · http://www.tklaw.com · One Arts Plaza, Suite 1500 · 1722 Routh Street · Dallas, TX 75201-2533 · 214-969-1700

Mary A. McNulty · Thompson & Knight · http://www.tklaw.com · One Arts Plaza, Suite 1500 · 1722 Routh Street · Dallas, TX 75201-2533 · 214-969-1700

James S. Meyer · Vinson & Elkins · http://www.velaw.com · Trammell Crow Center, Suite 3700 · 2001 Ross Avenue · Dallas, TX 75201-2975 · 214-220-7700

Daniel J. Micciche · Akin Gump Strauss Hauer & Feld · 1700 Pacific Avenue, Suite 4100 · Dallas, TX 75201-4675 · 214-969-2800

Daniel P. Novakov · Greenberg Traurig · http://www.gtlaw.com · JP Morgan Chase Tower, Suite 5200 · 2200 Ross Avenue · Dallas, TX 75201 · 972-419-9100

Cynthia Morgan Ohlenforst · K&L Gates · 1717 Main Street, Suite 2800 · Dallas, TX 75201 · 214-939-5500

Emily A. Parker · (25) · Thompson & Knight · http://www.tklaw.com · One Arts Plaza, Suite 1500 · 1722 Routh Street · Dallas, TX 75201-2533 · 214-969-1700

David L. Sinak · (10) · Gibson, Dunn & Crutcher · 2100 McKinney Avenue, Suite 1100 · Dallas, TX 75201-7390 · 214-698-3100

Kevin Thomason · Thompson & Knight · http://www.tklaw.com · One Arts Plaza, Suite 1500 · 1722 Routh Street · Dallas, TX 75201-2533 · 214-969-1700

Todd Wallace · Jones Day · 2727 North Harwood Street · Dallas, TX 75201-1515 · 214-220-3939

Ronald G. Weitz · Jones Day · 2727 North Harwood Street · Dallas, TX 75201-1515 · 214-220-3939

R. David Wheat · Thompson & Knight · http://www.tklaw.com · One Arts Plaza, Suite 1500 · 1722 Routh Street · Dallas, TX 75201-2533 · 214-969-1700

El Paso

Jeffrey C. Brown · Scott, Hulse, Marshall, Feuille, Finger & Thurmond · 1100 Chase Tower · 201 East Main Street · El Paso, TX 79901 · 915-533-2493

Guy N. Fields III · (10) · The Fields Law Firm · 501 Executive Center Boulevard, Suite 101 · El Paso, TX 79902 · 915-351-4000

Patrick R. Gordon · Gordon & Mott · 4695 North Mesa Street, Suite 100 · El Paso, TX 79912 · 915-545-1133

Clinton E. Wolf, Jr. · Kemp Smith · http://www.kempsmith.com · 221 North Kansas, Suite 1700 · El Paso, TX 79901-1441 · 915-533-4424

Fort Worth

R. Gordon Appleman · ㉕ · Thompson & Knight · http://www.tklaw.com · 1600 Burnett Plaza, Unit One, Suite 1600 · 801 Cherry Street · Fort Worth, TX 76102-6881 · 817-347-1700

William W. Bell · Winstead · http://www.winstead.com · Carter Burgess Plaza, Suite 1100 · 777 Main Street · Fort Worth, TX 76102 · 817-420-8200

Noel C. Ice · ⑩ · Cantey & Hanger · 300 Cantey Hanger Plaza · 600 West Sixth Street · Fort Worth, TX 76102-3685 · 817-877-2800

J. David Tracy · ⑩ · Cantey & Hanger · 300 Cantey Hanger Plaza · 600 West Sixth Street · Fort Worth, TX 76102-3685 · 817-877-2800

Galveston

Steven C. Salch · ㉕ · Law Office of Steven C. Salch · 2228 Mechanic, Suite 100 · Galveston, TX 77550-1591 · 409-763-5551

Houston

Roger D. Aksamit · Thompson & Knight · http://www.tklaw.com · 333 Clay Street, Suite 3300 · Houston, TX 77002 · 713-654-8111

John R. Allender · ⑩ · Fulbright & Jaworski · http://www.fulbright.com · Fulbright Tower, Suite 5100 · 1301 McKinney Street · Houston, TX 77010-3095 · 713-651-5151

Charles L. Almond · Vinson & Elkins · http://www.velaw.com · First City Tower, Suite 2500 · 1001 Fannin Street · Houston, TX 77002-6760 · 713-758-2222

Paul H. Asofsky · ⑩ · Weil Gotshal & Manges · Bank of America Building, Suite 1600 · 700 Louisiana Street · Houston, TX 77002 · 713-546-5000

A. T. Blackshear, Jr. · ㉕ · Fulbright & Jaworski · http://www.fulbright.com · Fulbright Tower, Suite 5100 · 1301 McKinney Street · Houston, TX 77010-3095 · 713-651-5151

Judith M. Blissard · Vinson & Elkins · http://www.velaw.com · First City Tower, Suite 2500 · 1001 Fannin Street · Houston, TX 77002-6760 · 713-758-2222

Nancy T. Bowen · Fulbright & Jaworski · http://www.fulbright.com · Fulbright Tower, Suite 5100 · 1301 McKinney Street · Houston, TX 77010-3095 · 713-651-5151

William H. Caudill · ⑩ · Fulbright & Jaworski · http://www.fulbright.com · Fulbright Tower, Suite 5100 · 1301 McKinney Street · Houston, TX 77010-3095 · 713-651-5151

Allen B. Craig III · Gardere Wynne Sewell · http://www.gardere.com · 1000 Louisiana, Suite 3400 · Houston, TX 77002-5011 · 713-276-5500

Timothy J. Devetski · Vinson & Elkins · http://www.velaw.com · First City Tower, Suite 2500 · 1001 Fannin Street · Houston, TX 77002-6760 · 713-758-2222

Thomas W. Ford, Jr. · Andrews Kurth · http://www.andrewskurth.com · 600 Travis Street, Suite 4200 · Houston, TX 77002 · 713-220-4200

George Matthew Gerachis · Vinson & Elkins · http://www.velaw.com · First City Tower, Suite 2500 · 1001 Fannin Street · Houston, TX 77002-6760 · 713-758-2222

Steven H. Gerdes · Vinson & Elkins · http://www.velaw.com · First City Tower, Suite 2500 · 1001 Fannin Street · Houston, TX 77002-6760 · 713-758-2222

R. Todd Greenwalt · Vinson & Elkins · http://www.velaw.com · First City Tower, Suite 2500 · 1001 Fannin Street · Houston, TX 77002-6760 · 713-758-2222

Marc E. Grossberg · (10) · Thompson & Knight · http://www.tklaw.com · 333 Clay Street, Suite 3300 · Houston, TX 77002 · 713-654-8111

Charles W. Hall · (25) · Fulbright & Jaworski · http://www.fulbright.com · Fulbright Tower, Suite 5100 · 1301 McKinney Street · Houston, TX 77010-3095 · 713-651-5151

George A. Hrdlicka · Chamberlain, Hrdlicka, White, Williams & Martin · 1200 Smith Street, Suite 1400 · Houston, TX 77002 · 713-658-1818

R. Joe Hull · Bracewell & Giuliani · http://www.bgllp.com · 711 Louisiana Street, Suite 2300 · Houston, TX 77002-2770 · 713-223-2300

Richard A. Husseini · Baker Botts · http://www.bakerbotts.com · One Shell Plaza · 910 Louisiana Street · Houston, TX 77002-1210 · 713-229-1234

Gray Jennings · (10) · Baker Botts · http://www.bakerbotts.com · One Shell Plaza · 910 Louisiana Street · Houston, TX 77002-1210 · 713-229-1234

Gregg H. Jones · Andrews Kurth · http://www.andrewskurth.com · 600 Travis Street, Suite 4200 · Houston, TX 77002 · 713-220-4200

Andrius R. Kontrimas · Fulbright & Jaworski · http://www.fulbright.com · Fulbright Tower, Suite 5100 · 1301 McKinney Street · Houston, TX 77010-3095 · 713-651-5151

Stephen A. Kuntz · Fulbright & Jaworski · http://www.fulbright.com · Fulbright Tower, Suite 5100 · 1301 McKinney Street · Houston, TX 77010-3095 · 713-651-5151

William S. Lee · Fulbright & Jaworski · http://www.fulbright.com · Fulbright Tower, Suite 5100 · 1301 McKinney Street · Houston, TX 77010-3095 · 713-651-5151

John Edward Lynch · Vinson & Elkins · http://www.velaw.com · First City Tower, Suite 2500 · 1001 Fannin Street · Houston, TX 77002-6760 · 713-758-2222

L. Price Manford · Vinson & Elkins · http://www.velaw.com · First City Tower, Suite 2500 · 1001 Fannin Street · Houston, TX 77002-6760 · 713-758-2222

Thomas P. Marinis, Jr. · (10) · Vinson & Elkins · http://www.velaw.com · First City Tower, Suite 2500 · 1001 Fannin Street · Houston, TX 77002-6760 · 713-758-2222

Mark R. Martin · Gardere Wynne Sewell · http://www.gardere.com · 1000 Louisiana, Suite 3400 · Houston, TX 77002-5011 · 713-276-5500

Barry R. Miller · (10) · Vinson & Elkins · http://www.velaw.com · First City Tower, Suite 2500 · 1001 Fannin Street · Houston, TX 77002-6760 · 713-758-2222

Arthur M. Nathan · Haynes and Boone · One Houston Center, Suite 2100 · 1221 McKinney Street · Houston, TX 77010 · 713-547-2000

Gregory V. Nelson · Baker Botts · http://www.bakerbotts.com · One Shell Plaza · 910 Louisiana Street · Houston, TX 77002-1210 · 713-229-1234

Edward C. Osterberg, Jr. · ⓴ · Vinson & Elkins · http://www.velaw.com · First City Tower, Suite 2500 · 1001 Fannin Street · Houston, TX 77002-6760 · 713-758-2222

Melinda R. Phelan · Baker & McKenzie · 711 Louisiana Street, Suite 3400 · Houston, TX 77002-2716 · 713-427-5000

John W. Porter · Baker Botts · http://www.bakerbotts.com · One Shell Plaza · 910 Louisiana Street · Houston, TX 77002-1210 · 713-229-1234

John Ransom · Porter & Hedges · 1000 Main Street, 36th Floor · Houston, TX 77002 · 713-226-0600

Glen A. Rosenbaum · Vinson & Elkins · http://www.velaw.com · First City Tower, Suite 2500 · 1001 Fannin Street · Houston, TX 77002-6760 · 713-758-2222

Stuart F. Schaffer · Baker Botts · http://www.bakerbotts.com · One Shell Plaza · 910 Louisiana Street · Houston, TX 77002-1210 · 713-229-1234

N. Susan Stone · ❿ · Baker & McKenzie · 711 Louisiana Street, Suite 3400 · Houston, TX 77002-2716 · 713-427-5000

Jasper G. Taylor III · Fulbright & Jaworski · http://www.fulbright.com · Fulbright Tower, Suite 5100 · 1301 McKinney Street · Houston, TX 77010-3095 · 713-651-5151

Mitch Tiras · Locke Lord Bissell & Liddell · JP Morgan Chase Tower, Suite 3400 · 600 Travis Street · Houston, TX 77002 · 713-226-1200

John A. Townsend · ❿ · Townsend & Jones · http://www.tjtaxlaw.com · 5615 Kirby Drive, Suite 830 · Houston, TX 77005 · 713-521-9977

Frederick Tuthill · Winstead · http://www.winstead.com · JPMorgan Chase Tower, Suite 1100 · 600 Travis Street · Houston, TX 77002 · 713-650-8400

Edward D. Urquhart · Edward D. Urquhart · 8811 Westheimer, Suite 206 · Houston, TX 77063 · 713-426-3300

Benjamin G. Wells · ❿ · Baker Botts · http://www.bakerbotts.com · One Shell Plaza · 910 Louisiana Street · Houston, TX 77002-1210 · 713-229-1234

Walter P. Zivley · ㉕ · Locke Lord Bissell & Liddell · JP Morgan Chase Tower, Suite 3400 · 600 Travis Street · Houston, TX 77002 · 713-226-1200

San Antonio

Stanley L. Blend · ㉕ · Oppenheimer, Blend, Harrison & Tate · 711 Navarro Street, Suite 600 · San Antonio, TX 78205-1796 · 210-224-2000

Elizabeth A. Copeland · Oppenheimer, Blend, Harrison & Tate · 711 Navarro Street, Suite 600 · San Antonio, TX 78205-1796 · 210-224-2000

R. James Curphy · ⓴ · Schoenbaum, Curphy & Scanlan · 112 East Pecan Street, 30th Floor · San Antonio, TX 78205-1516 · 210-224-4491

Barbara Spudis De Marigny · Oppenheimer, Blend, Harrison & Tate · 711 Navarro Street, Suite 600 · San Antonio, TX 78205-1796 · 210-224-2000

Darin N. Digby · Schoenbaum, Curphy & Scanlan · 112 East Pecan Street, 30th Floor · San Antonio, TX 78205-1516 · 210-224-4491

Richard E. Goldsmith · ㉕ · Cox Smith Matthews · http://www.coxsmith.com · 112 East Pecan Street, Suite 1800 · San Antonio, TX 78205-1521 · 210-554-5500

Charles M. Hornberger · ⑩ · Hornberger Sheehan Fuller & Beiter · Quarry Heights, Suite 300 · 7373 Broadway · San Antonio, TX 78209 · 210-271-1700

Farley P. Katz · ⑳ · Strasburger & Price · http://www.strasburger.com · 300 Convent Street, Suite 900 · San Antonio, TX 78205-3715 · 210-250-6000

William H. Lester, Jr. · Cox Smith Matthews · http://www.coxsmith.com · 112 East Pecan Street, Suite 1800 · San Antonio, TX 78205-1521 · 210-554-5500

Charles J. Muller · ⑩ · Strasburger & Price · http://www.strasburger.com · 300 Convent Street, Suite 900 · San Antonio, TX 78205-3715 · 210-250-6000

Stanley Schoenbaum · ㉕ · Schoenbaum, Curphy & Scanlan · 112 East Pecan Street, 30th Floor · San Antonio, TX 78205-1516 · 210-224-4491

George William Scofield · ⑩ · Fulbright & Jaworski · http://www.fulbright.com · 300 Convent Street, Suite 2200 · San Antonio, TX 78205-3792 · 210-224-5575

TECHNOLOGY LAW

Amarillo

James Wester · Underwood, Wilson, Berry, Stein & Johnson · 500 South Taylor, Suite 1200, Lock Box 233 · P.O. Box 9158 · Amarillo, TX 79105 · 806-376-5613

Austin

William A. Broussard, Sr. · William A. Broussard · P.O. Box 162926 · Austin, TX 78716-2926 · 512-263-7794

Dallas

Dean William Harvey · Vinson & Elkins · http://www.velaw.com · Trammell Crow Center, Suite 3700 · 2001 Ross Avenue · Dallas, TX 75201-2975 · 214-220-7700

John W. Martin · Baker Botts · http://www.bakerbotts.com · Trammell Crow Center, Suite 600 · 2001 Ross Avenue · Dallas, TX 75201-2980 · 214-953-6500

David L. McCombs · Haynes and Boone · 901 Main Street, Suite 3100 · Dallas, TX 75202 · 214-651-5000

Bruce S. Sostek · Thompson & Knight · http://www.tklaw.com · One Arts Plaza, Suite 1500 · 1722 Routh Street · Dallas, TX 75201-2533 · 214-969-1700

Highlands

M. Ann Newton · Newton Tech Law · P.O. Drawer E · Highlands, TX 77526 · 281-772-4907

Houston

Charles D. Powell · Fulbright & Jaworski · http://www.fulbright.com · Fulbright Tower, Suite 5100 · 1301 McKinney Street · Houston, TX 77010-3095 · 713-651-5151

Bradley J. Richards · Haynes and Boone · One Houston Center, Suite 2100 · 1221 McKinney Street · Houston, TX 77010 · 713-547-2000

TRANSPORTATION LAW

Dallas

John H. Martin · ⑩ · Thompson & Knight · http://www.tklaw.com · One Arts Plaza, Suite 1500 · 1722 Routh Street · Dallas, TX 75201-2533 · 214-969-1700

Robert F. Ruckman · Jackson Walker · Bank of America Plaza, Suite 6000 · 901 Main Street · Dallas, TX 75202 · 214-953-6000

Charles H. Smith · Smith & Moore · 3030 Lincoln Plaza · 500 North Akard Street · Dallas, TX 75201-6606 · 214-740-4200

Fort Worth

Stephen C. Howell · Brown Dean Wiseman Proctor Hart & Howell · 307 West Seventh Street, Suite 1918 Fort Worth, TX 76102 · 817-332-1391

Houston

Richard H. Caldwell · ⑩ · Andrews Kurth · http://www.andrewskurth.com · 600 Travis Street, Suite 4200 Houston, TX 77002 · 713-220-4200

Winstol D. Carter · Morgan Lewis & Bockius · 1000 Louisiana St., Suite 4200 · Houston, TX 77002-5006 713-890-5000

Rachel Giesber Clingman · Sutherland · http://www.sutherland.com · Two Houston Center, Suite 2200 · 909 Fannin · Houston, TX 77010-1043 · 713-470-6100

Thad Thano Dameris · Hogan & Hartson · Pennzoil Place, Suite 2100 · 711 Louisiana Street · Houston, TX 77002 · 713-632-1400

Dudley Oldham · Fulbright & Jaworski · http://www.fulbright.com · Fulbright Tower, Suite 5100 · 1301 McKinney Street · Houston, TX 77010-3095 · 713-651-5151

TRUSTS AND ESTATES

Addison

Lawrence M. Wolfish · Wolfish & Newman · 16475 Dallas Parkway, Suite 395 · Addison, TX 75001 · 972-248-4656

Austin

Thomas Orr Barton · ⑩ · McGinnis, Lochridge & Kilgore · http://www.mcginnislaw.com · 600 Congress Avenue, Suite 2100 · Austin, TX 78701 · 512-495-6000

Kathleen Ford Bay · Blazier, Christensen, Bigelow & Virr · 1500 Chase Tower · 221 West Sixth Street · Austin, TX 78701 · 512-476-2622

Rhonda H. Brink · ⑩ · Law Offices of Rhonda H. Brink · 5247 Burnet Road, Suite 52 · Austin, TX 78757 512-454-8400

Patricia A. Campbell · Graves, Dougherty, Hearon & Moody · http://www.gdhm.com · 401 Congress Avenue, Suite 2200 · P.O. Box 98 · Austin, TX 78767-0098 · 512-480-5600

Donald F. Carnes · Hopper & Associates · 400 West 15th Street, Suite 808 · Austin, TX 78701 · 512-615-6195

Elizabeth G. Deleery · Osborne, Helman, Knebel & Deleery · 301 Congress Avenue, Suite 1910 · Austin, TX 78701-4041 · 512-542-2000

Beth Ann Eccles · Eccles Law Office · Wells Fargo Tower, Suite 900 · 400 West 15th Street · Austin, TX 78701 · 512-617-1974

Leslie C. Giordani · Giordani, Schurig, Beckett & Tackett · http://www.gsbtlaw.com · 100 Congress Avenue, 22nd Floor · Austin, TX 78701 · 512-370-2720

Alvin J. Golden · ⑳ · Ikard & Golden · 400 West 15th Street, Suite 975 · Austin, TX 78701 · 512-472-6695

David H. Goodman · David H. Goodman · 114 West Seventh Street, Suite 900 · Austin, TX 78701 · 512-457-5009

Deborah A. Green · Law Offices of Deborah Green · 7200 North Mopac Expressway · Austin, TX 78731 512-349-9595

Stephen Jody Helman · ⑩ · Osborne, Helman, Knebel & Deleery · 301 Congress Avenue, Suite 1910 · Austin, TX 78701-4041 · 512-542-2000

Samuel K. Hildebrand · Clark, Thomas & Winters · 300 West Sixth Street, 15th Floor · P.O. Box 1148 · Austin, TX 78767 · 512-472-8800

Kevin Holcomb · ⑩ · Graves, Dougherty, Hearon & Moody · http://www.gdhm.com · 401 Congress Avenue, Suite 2200 · P.O. Box 98 · Austin, TX 78767-0098 · 512-480-5600

J. Craig Hopper · Hopper & Associates · 400 West 15th Street, Suite 808 · Austin, TX 78701 · 512-615-6195

H. David Hughes · ㉕ · Brown McCarroll · 111 Congress Avenue, Suite 1400 · Austin, TX 78701-4093 · 512-472-5456

Frank N. Ikard, Jr. · ㉕ · Ikard & Golden · 400 West 15th Street, Suite 975 · Austin, TX 78701 · 512-472-6695

Jerry Frank Jones · Ikard & Golden · 400 West 15th Street, Suite 975 · Austin, TX 78701 · 512-472-6695

Glenn M. Karisch · Barnes & Karisch · 2901-D Bee Caves Road · Austin, TX 78746 · 512-328-8355

D'Ana Mikeska · McGinnis, Lochridge & Kilgore · http://www.mcginnislaw.com · 600 Congress Avenue, Suite 2100 · Austin, TX 78701 · 512-495-6000

Michele A. Mobley · DuBois, Bryant & Campbell · http://www.dbcllp.com · 700 Lavaca Street, Suite 1300 · Austin, TX 78701 · 512-457-8000

Duncan E. Osborne · ⑳ · Osborne, Helman, Knebel & Deleery · 301 Congress Avenue, Suite 1910 · Austin, TX 78701-4041 · 512-542-2000

William D. Pargaman · Brown McCarroll · 111 Congress Avenue, Suite 1400 · Austin, TX 78701-4093 · 512-472-5456

Michael H. Ripp, Jr. · Giordani, Schurig, Beckett & Tackett · http://www.gsbtlaw.com · 100 Congress Avenue, 22nd Floor · Austin, TX 78701 · 512-370-2720

C. Stephen Saunders · ⑩ · Saunders & Norval · 2630 Exposition Boulevard, Suite 203 · Austin, TX 78703-1757 · 512-472-7111

Elizabeth M. Schurig · Giordani, Schurig, Beckett & Tackett · http://www.gsbtlaw.com · 100 Congress Avenue, 22nd Floor · Austin, TX 78701 · 512-370-2720

Derry W. Swanger · ⑩ · Giordani, Schurig, Beckett & Tackett · http://www.gsbtlaw.com · 100 Congress Avenue, 22nd Floor · Austin, TX 78701 · 512-370-2720

Steven J. Tackett · Giordani, Schurig, Beckett & Tackett · http://www.gsbtlaw.com · 100 Congress Avenue, 22nd Floor · Austin, TX 78701 · 512-370-2720

Terry Lee Vanderburg · The Office of Lee Vanderburg · 814 West 10th Street · Austin, TX 78701 · 512-474-4252

Thomas F. Virr · Blazier, Christensen, Bigelow & Virr · 1500 Chase Tower · 221 West Sixth Street · Austin, TX 78701 · 512-476-2622

James A. Williams · ⑳ · Graves, Dougherty, Hearon & Moody · http://www.gdhm.com · 401 Congress Avenue, Suite 2200 · P.O. Box 98 · Austin, TX 78767-0098 · 512-480-5600

Beaumont

John Creighton III · ⑩ · Orgain, Bell & Tucker · 470 Orleans Street · P.O. Box 1751 · Beaumont, TX 77704-1751 · 409-838-6412

S. L. Greenberg · ⑩ · Wells, Peyton, Greenberg & Hunt · 550 Fannin Street, Suite 600 · P.O. Box 3708 · Beaumont, TX 77701 · 409-838-2644

H. Banker Phares · H. Banker Phares · 8141 Gladys Avenue, Suite 102 · Beaumont, TX 77706 · 409-866-2626

John B. Quigley · Wells, Peyton, Greenberg & Hunt · 550 Fannin Street, Suite 600 · P.O. Box 3708 · Beaumont, TX 77701 · 409-838-2644

William H. Yoes · The Yoes Law Firm · Texas State Bank Building, Suite 235 · 3535 Calder Avenue · P.O. Box 7584 · Beaumont, TX 77726-7584 · 409-833-2352

Brenham

R. Hal Moorman · Moorman, Tate, Moorman, Urquhart & Haley · http://www.moormantate.com · 207 East Main Street · P.O. Box 1808 · Brenham, TX 77834-1808 · 979-836-5664

Corpus Christi

Martin C. Davis · Davis Hutchinson & Wilkerson · 802 North Carancahua Street, Suite 1270 · Corpus Christi, TX 78470-0400 · 361-882-2272

Richard L. Leshin · ⑩ · Welder, Leshin & Mahaffey · One Shoreline Plaza, North Tower, Suite 300 · 800 North Shoreline Boulevard · Corpus Christi, TX 78401 · 361-561-8000

Scott L. Sherman · Branscomb · 802 North Carancahua Street, Suite 1900 · Corpus Christi, TX 78470-0700 · 361-888-9261

Michael W. Stukenberg · ⑩ · Branscomb · 802 North Carancahua Street, Suite 1900 · Corpus Christi, TX 78470-0700 · 361-888-9261

Barbara McComas Anderson · ⑳ · Law Office of Barbara McComas Anderson · P.O. Box 181147 · Dallas, TX 75218 · 214-367-8090

John F. Bergner · Winstead · http://www.winstead.com · Renaissance Tower, Suite 5400 · 1201 Elm Street · Dallas, TX 75270-2199 · 214-745-5400

Santo Bisignano, Jr. · ⑩ · Bisignano & Harrison · Sterling Plaza, Suite 770 · 5949 Sherry Lane · Dallas, TX 75225-8003 · 214-360-9777

Stuart M. Bumpas · ⑳ · Locke Lord Bissell & Liddell · 2200 Ross Avenue, Suite 2200 · Dallas, TX 75201-6776 · 214-740-8000

Mary Clariday Burdette · Calloway, Norris, Burdette & Weber · http://www.cnbwlaw.com · 400 Turtle Creek Centre · 3811 Turtle Creek Boulevard · Dallas, TX 75219 · 214-521-1520

R. W. Calloway · ㉕ · Calloway, Norris, Burdette & Weber · http://www.cnbwlaw.com · 400 Turtle Creek Centre · 3811 Turtle Creek Boulevard · Dallas, TX 75219 · 214-521-1520

Thomas H. Cantrill · ⑳ · Hunton & Williams · 1445 Ross Avenue, Suite 3700 · Dallas, TX 75202-2799 · 214-979-3000

I. Scott Carter · Mincey-Carter · Three Forest Plaza, Suite 200 · 12221 Merit Drive · Dallas, TX 75251 · 469-916-1980

John M. Collins · Haynes and Boone · 901 Main Street, Suite 3100 · Dallas, TX 75202 · 214-651-5000

Ronald Roy Cresswell · ⑳ · Locke Lord Bissell & Liddell · 2200 Ross Avenue, Suite 2200 · Dallas, TX 75201-6776 · 214-740-8000

William D. Elliott · Law Offices of William D. Elliott · 2626 Cole Avenue, Suite 600 · Dallas, TX 75204 · 214-922-9393

Herschell Gene Emery · ㉕ · Locke Lord Bissell & Liddell · 2200 Ross Avenue, Suite 2200 · Dallas, TX 75201-6776 · 214-740-8000

Mark A. Fankhauser · ⑩ · Little Pedersen Fankhauser · http://www.lpf-law.com · 901 Main Street, Suite 4110 · Dallas, TX 75202 · 214-573-2300

Barbara B. Ferguson · Thompson & Knight · http://www.tklaw.com · One Arts Plaza, Suite 1500 · 1722 Routh Street · Dallas, TX 75201-2533 · 214-969-1700

Derek L. Fletcher · Winstead · http://www.winstead.com · Renaissance Tower, Suite 5400 · 1201 Elm Street · Dallas, TX 75270-2199 · 214-745-5400

Michael L. Graham · ⑩ · The Graham Law Firm · 100 Highland Park Village, Suite 200 · Dallas, TX 75205 · 214-599-7000

Nathan K. Griffin · D. Woodward Glenn · 2626 Cole Avenue, Suite 510 · Dallas, TX 75204 · 214-871-9333

Bob D. Harrison · ⑩ · Bisignano & Harrison · Sterling Plaza, Suite 770 · 5949 Sherry Lane · Dallas, TX 75225-8003 · 214-360-9777

James J. Hartnett, Jr. · The Hartnett Law Firm · The Hartnett Building · 2920 North Pearl Street · Dallas, TX 75201-7315 · 214-742-4655

James J. Hartnett, Sr. · (25) · The Hartnett Law Firm · The Hartnett Building · 2920 North Pearl Street · Dallas, TX 75201-7315 · 214-742-4655

Will Ford Hartnett · The Hartnett Law Firm · The Hartnett Building · 2920 North Pearl Street · Dallas, TX 75201-7315 · 214-742-4655

Jack W. Hawkins · (20) · Gardere Wynne Sewell · http://www.gardere.com · 1601 Elm Street, Suite 3000 · Dallas, TX 75201 · 214-999-3000

Kathryn G. Henkel · (10) · K&L Gates · 1717 Main Street, Suite 2800 · Dallas, TX 75201 · 214-939-5500

T. Wesley Holmes · Fisher & Holmes · 2800 Lincoln Plaza · 500 North Akard Street · Dallas, TX 75201 · 214-661-9400

Charles R. Johnson · (10) · Johnson, Jordan, Nipper & Monk · Three Galleria Tower, Suite 1050, LB Three · 13155 Noel Road · Dallas, TX 75240-1531 · 972-392-1123

William D. Jordan · (10) · Johnson, Jordan, Nipper & Monk · Three Galleria Tower, Suite 1050, LB Three 13155 Noel Road · Dallas, TX 75240-1531 · 972-392-1123

Jack M. Kinnebrew · (25) · Strasburger & Price · http://www.strasburger.com · 901 Main Street, Suite 4400 · Dallas, TX 75202-3794 · 214-651-4300

Robert H. Kroney · (10) · Kroney Morse Lan · 12221 Merit Drive, Suite 1210 · Dallas, TX 75251 · 972-386-8500

Donald Paul Lan, Jr. · Kroney Morse Lan · 12221 Merit Drive, Suite 1210 · Dallas, TX 75251 · 972-386-8500

P. Mike McCullough · (20) · Thompson & Knight · http://www.tklaw.com · One Arts Plaza, Suite 1500 · 1722 Routh Street · Dallas, TX 75201-2533 · 214-969-1700

Barkley T. Miller · Law Office of Barkley T. Miller · 12900 Preston Road, Suite 325 · Dallas, TX 75230-1364 · 972-934-0178

James M. Mincey, Jr. · Mincey-Carter · Three Forest Plaza, Suite 200 · 12221 Merit Drive · Dallas, TX 75251 · 469-916-1980

Roy J. Monk · Johnson, Jordan, Nipper & Monk · Three Galleria Tower, Suite 1050, LB Three · 13155 Noel Road · Dallas, TX 75240-1531 · 972-392-1123

William R. Mureiko · Thompson & Knight · http://www.tklaw.com · One Arts Plaza, Suite 1500 · 1722 Routh Street · Dallas, TX 75201-2533 · 214-969-1700

Alex E. Nakos · Malouf Lynch Jackson & Swinson · 12222 Merit Drive, Suite 1000 · Dallas, TX 75251 · 214-273-0600

Paul T. Nipper · Johnson, Jordan, Nipper & Monk · Three Galleria Tower, Suite 1050, LB Three · 13155 Noel Road · Dallas, TX 75240-1531 · 972-392-1123

John R. Norris III · (10) · Calloway, Norris, Burdette & Weber · http://www.cnbwlaw.com · 400 Turtle Creek Centre · 3811 Turtle Creek Boulevard · Dallas, TX 75219 · 214-521-1520

Keith V. Novick · Gardere Wynne Sewell · http://www.gardere.com · 1601 Elm Street, Suite 3000 · Dallas, TX 75201 · 214-999-3000

Rust E. Reid · (25) · Thompson & Knight · http://www.tklaw.com · One Arts Plaza, Suite 1500 · 1722 Routh Street · Dallas, TX 75201-2533 · 214-969-1700

Terry L. Simmons · Thompson & Knight · http://www.tklaw.com · One Arts Plaza, Suite 1500 · 1722 Routh Street · Dallas, TX 75201-2533 · 214-969-1700

Edward V. Smith III · ⑳ · Edward V. Smith · 2911 Turtle Creek Boulevard, Suite 1010 · Dallas, TX 75219 · 214-528-1590

Marjorie J. Stephens · Law Office of Marjorie J. Stephens · 8330 Meadow Road, Suite 216 · Dallas, TX 75231 · 214-373-7195

Donald A. Swanson, Jr. · ㉕ · Johnson, Jordan, Nipper & Monk · Three Galleria Tower, Suite 1050, LB Three · 13155 Noel Road · Dallas, TX 75240-1531 · 972-392-1123

Robert Hyer Thomas · ㉕ · Strasburger & Price · http://www.strasburger.com · 901 Main Street, Suite 4400 · Dallas, TX 75202-3794 · 214-651-4300

Scott D. Weber · Calloway, Norris, Burdette & Weber · http://www.cnbwlaw.com · 400 Turtle Creek Centre · 3811 Turtle Creek Boulevard · Dallas, TX 75219 · 214-521-1520

El Paso

Marc P. Bernat · ⑩ · Gordon & Mott · 4695 North Mesa Street, Suite 100 · El Paso, TX 79912 · 915-545-1133

Karin Armen Carson · Hobson, Stribling & Carson · 4110 Rio Bravo, Suite 220 · El Paso, TX 79902 · 915-351-9886

Alan D. Gluth · Ryan Sanders & Gluth · 310 North Mesa Street, Suite 300 · El Paso, TX 79901 · 915-351-1100

Allan M. Goldfarb · Kemp Smith · http://www.kempsmith.com · 221 North Kansas, Suite 1700 · El Paso, TX 79901-1441 · 915-533-4424

David P. Hassler · ⑩ · Scott, Hulse, Marshall, Feuille, Finger & Thurmond · 1100 Chase Tower · 201 East Main Street · El Paso, TX 79901 · 915-533-2493

Leila Safi Hobson · ⑩ · Hobson, Stribling & Carson · 4110 Rio Bravo, Suite 220 · El Paso, TX 79902 · 915-351-9886

Sandra S. Moore-Duarte · Neill, Strelitz, Moore-Duarte · 501 Executive Center, Suite 200 · El Paso, TX 79902 · 915-533-2739

Carl E. Ryan · ⑩ · Ryan Sanders & Gluth · 310 North Mesa Street, Suite 300 · El Paso, TX 79901 · 915-351-1100

Amy S. Sanders · Ryan Sanders & Gluth · 310 North Mesa Street, Suite 300 · El Paso, TX 79901 · 915-351-1100

Stancy Stribling · Hobson, Stribling & Carson · 4110 Rio Bravo, Suite 220 · El Paso, TX 79902 · 915-351-9886

Clinton E. Wolf, Jr. · Kemp Smith · http://www.kempsmith.com · 221 North Kansas, Suite 1700 · El Paso, TX 79901-1441 · 915-533-4424

Fort Worth

Michael G. Appleman · Cantey & Hanger · 300 Cantey Hanger Plaza · 600 West Sixth Street · Fort Worth, TX 76102-3685 · 817-877-2800

R. Gordon Appleman · ㉕ · Thompson & Knight · http://www.tklaw.com · 1600 Burnett Plaza, Unit One, Suite 1600 · 801 Cherry Street · Fort Worth, TX 76102-6881 · 817-347-1700

David C. Bakutis · Bakutis, McCully & Sawyer · 500 West Seventh Street, Suite 725 · Fort Worth, TX 76102 · 817-335-2208

Harry Edward Bartel · ⑩ · Cantey & Hanger · 300 Cantey Hanger Plaza · 600 West Sixth Street · Fort Worth, TX 76102-3685 · 817-877-2800

Michael V. Bourland · Bourland, Wall & Wenzel · City Center Tower II, Suite 1500 · 301 Commerce Street · Fort Worth, TX 76102 · 817-877-1088

Thomas Allan Howeth · ㉕ · Cantey & Hanger · 300 Cantey Hanger Plaza · 600 West Sixth Street · Fort Worth, TX 76102-3685 · 817-877-2800

Noel C. Ice · ⑩ · Cantey & Hanger · 300 Cantey Hanger Plaza · 600 West Sixth Street · Fort Worth, TX 76102-3685 · 817-877-2800

Lisa H. Jamieson · Shannon, Gracey, Ratliff & Miller · http://www.shannongracey.com · 777 Main Street, Suite 3800 · Fort Worth, TX 76102 · 817-336-9333

Rice M. Tilley, Jr. · ㉕ · Haynes and Boone · 201 Main Street, Suite 2200 · Fort Worth, TX 76102 · 817-347-6600

J. David Tracy · ⑩ · Cantey & Hanger · 300 Cantey Hanger Plaza · 600 West Sixth Street · Fort Worth, TX 76102-3685 · 817-877-2800

Houston

Stefnee D. Ashlock · Fizer, Beck, Webster, Bentley & Scroggins · 1330 Post Oak Boulevard, Suite 2900 · Houston, TX 77056 · 713-840-7710

Roger Q. Beck · Fizer, Beck, Webster, Bentley & Scroggins · 1330 Post Oak Boulevard, Suite 2900 · Houston, TX 77056 · 713-840-7710

James E. Brill · James E. Brill · P.O. Box 22870 · Houston, TX 77227-2870 · 713-626-7272

Michael J. Cenatiempo · ⑩ · Cenatiempo & Ditta · 1400 Post Oak Boulevard, Suite 1150 · Houston, TX 77056-3005 · 713-655-1550

Richard R. Cruse · ⑩ · Chamberlain, Hrdlicka, White, Williams & Martin · 1200 Smith Street, Suite 1400 Houston, TX 77002 · 713-658-1818

Mickey R. Davis · Bracewell & Giuliani · http://www.bgllp.com · 711 Louisiana Street, Suite 2300 · Houston, TX 77002-2770 · 713-223-2300

G. Edward Deery · Fulbright & Jaworski · http://www.fulbright.com · Fulbright Tower, Suite 5100 · 1301 McKinney Street · Houston, TX 77010-3095 · 713-651-5151

Louis M. Ditta · Cenatiempo & Ditta · 1400 Post Oak Boulevard, Suite 1150 · Houston, TX 77056-3005 · 713-655-1550

Stephanie Donaho · ⑩ · Locke Lord Bissell & Liddell · JP Morgan Chase Tower, Suite 3400 · 600 Travis Street · Houston, TX 77002 · 713-226-1200

Stephen T. Dyer · Baker Botts · http://www.bakerbotts.com · One Shell Plaza · 910 Louisiana Street · Houston, TX 77002-1210 · 713-229-1234

W. Alvin Early · W. Alvin Early · 5718 Westheimer Road, Suite 763 · Houston, TX 77057-5732 · 713-266-2373

Don E. Fizer · ⑩ · Fizer, Beck, Webster, Bentley & Scroggins · 1330 Post Oak Boulevard, Suite 2900 · Houston, TX 77056 · 713-840-7710

Sharon Brand Gardner · Crain, Caton & James · Five Houston Center, 17th Floor · 1401 McKinney Street · Houston, TX 77010-1079 · 713-658-2323

Charles W. Giraud III · ㉕ · Bracewell & Giuliani · http://www.bgllp.com · 711 Louisiana Street, Suite 2300 · Houston, TX 77002-2770 · 713-223-2300

L. Henry Gissel, Jr. · ㉕ · Fulbright & Jaworski · http://www.fulbright.com · Fulbright Tower, Suite 5100 1301 McKinney Street · Houston, TX 77010-3095 · 713-651-5151

Anne Hardiman · Anne Hardiman · 3749 Robinhood · Houston, TX 77005 · 713-416-2406

John L. Hopwood · ⑩ · Locke Lord Bissell & Liddell · JP Morgan Chase Tower, Suite 3400 · 600 Travis Street · Houston, TX 77002 · 713-226-1200

Mark A. Jacob · Locke Lord Bissell & Liddell · JP Morgan Chase Tower, Suite 3400 · 600 Travis Street · Houston, TX 77002 · 713-226-1200

Richard L. Jukes · ⑩ · Richard Lee Jukes · 1770 St. James Place, Suite 607 · Houston, TX 77056-3500 · 713-877-9998

Linda Kelly · Dinkins Kelly Lenox Lamb · 815 Walker, Suite 240 · Houston, TX 77002-5762 · 713-759-0900

Ronald W. Kesterson · Baker Botts · http://www.bakerbotts.com · One Shell Plaza · 910 Louisiana Street Houston, TX 77002-1210 · 713-229-1234

Yolanda Chavez Knull · Vinson & Elkins · http://www.velaw.com · First City Tower, Suite 2500 · 1001 Fannin Street · Houston, TX 77002-6760 · 713-758-2222

Rodney C. Koenig · ⑳ · Fulbright & Jaworski · http://www.fulbright.com · Fulbright Tower, Suite 5100 · 1301 McKinney Street · Houston, TX 77010-3095 · 713-651-5151

Terri Lacy · Andrews Kurth · http://www.andrewskurth.com · 600 Travis Street, Suite 4200 · Houston, TX 77002 · 713-220-4200

Jack W. Lawter, Jr. · ⑩ · Lawter & Lawter · 5615 Kirby Drive, Suite 930 · Houston, TX 77005 · 713-522-9400

Robert S. MacIntyre, Jr. · MacIntyre & McCulloch · 3900 Essex Lane · Houston, TX 77027 · 713-572-2900

Kent H. McMahan · ⑳ · Fulbright & Jaworski · http://www.fulbright.com · Fulbright Tower, Suite 5100 · 1301 McKinney Street · Houston, TX 77010-3095 · 713-651-5151

William T. Miller · ⑳ · Andrews Kurth · http://www.andrewskurth.com · 600 Travis Street, Suite 4200 · Houston, TX 77002 · 713-220-4200

Sarah Patel Pacheco · Crain, Caton & James · Five Houston Center, 17th Floor · 1401 McKinney Street · Houston, TX 77010-1079 · 713-658-2323

Lawrence J. Pirtle · ⑩ · Gardere Wynne Sewell · http://www.gardere.com · 1000 Louisiana, Suite 3400 · Houston, TX 77002-5011 · 713-276-5500

John W. Porter · Baker Botts · http://www.bakerbotts.com · One Shell Plaza · 910 Louisiana Street · Houston, TX 77002-1210 · 713-229-1234

Joseph W. Royce · Looper Reed & McGraw · 1300 Post Oak Boulevard, Suite 2000 · Houston, TX 77056 713-986-7000

Marjorie S. Schultz · Marjorie S.Schultz & Associates · 3401 Louisiana Street, Suite 380 · Houston, TX 77002 · 713-521-3434

C. Boone Schwartzel · C. Boone Schwartzel · 1010 Lamar Street, Suite 1520 · Houston, TX 77002 · 713-654-1133

Jerry M. Scroggins · Fizer, Beck, Webster, Bentley & Scroggins · 1330 Post Oak Boulevard, Suite 2900 · Houston, TX 77056 · 713-840-7710

Robert A. Seale, Jr. · Liskow & Lewis · http://www.liskow.com · First City Tower, Suite 1800 · 1001 Fannin Street · Houston, TX 77002-4102 · 713-651-2900

Joseph C. Sleeth, Jr. · Fulbright & Jaworski · http://www.fulbright.com · Fulbright Tower, Suite 5100 · 1301 McKinney Street · Houston, TX 77010-3095 · 713-651-5151

R. Eric Viehman · Vinson & Elkins · http://www.velaw.com · First City Tower, Suite 2500 · 1001 Fannin Street · Houston, TX 77002-6760 · 713-758-2222

Alan V. Ytterberg · Fulbright & Jaworski · http://www.fulbright.com · Fulbright Tower, Suite 5100 · 1301 McKinney Street · Houston, TX 77010-3095 · 713-651-5151

Walter P. Zivley · 25 · Locke Lord Bissell & Liddell · JP Morgan Chase Tower, Suite 3400 · 600 Travis Street · Houston, TX 77002 · 713-226-1200

Katy

Betty B. Moser · Betty B. Moser · 565 South Mason Road, Suite 412 · Katy, TX 77450 · 281-398-1792

San Antonio

James J. Aycock · 10 · Bayern & Aycock · 745 East Mulberry Avenue, Suite 300 · San Antonio, TX 78212 210-731-8300

Arthur H. Bayern · 25 · Bayern & Aycock · 745 East Mulberry Avenue, Suite 300 · San Antonio, TX 78212 · 210-731-8300

Taylor S. Boone · 10 · Oppenheimer, Blend, Harrison & Tate · 711 Navarro Street, Suite 600 · San Antonio, TX 78205-1796 · 210-224-2000

Darin N. Digby · Schoenbaum, Curphy & Scanlan · 112 East Pecan Street, 30th Floor · San Antonio, TX 78205-1516 · 210-224-4491

Edgar M. Duncan · Duncan, Weakley & Bressler · 1020 Northeast Loop 410, Suite 500 · San Antonio, TX 78209 · 210-224-0781

Richard E. Goldsmith · 25 · Cox Smith Matthews · http://www.coxsmith.com · 112 East Pecan Street, Suite 1800 · San Antonio, TX 78205-1521 · 210-554-5500

Charles M. Hornberger · 10 · Hornberger Sheehan Fuller & Beiter · Quarry Heights, Suite 300 · 7373 Broadway · San Antonio, TX 78209 · 210-271-1700

Kevin Philip Kennedy · Kevin Philip Kennedy · 1920 Nacogdoches Road, Suite 100 · San Antonio, TX 78209 · 210-824-0771

Nancy Nowlin Kerr · Fulbright & Jaworski · http://www.fulbright.com · 300 Convent Street, Suite 2200 · San Antonio, TX 78205-3792 · 210-224-5575

Joyce W. Moore · Langley & Banack · Trinity Plaza II, Suite 900 · 745 East Mulberry Avenue · San Antonio, TX 78212-3166 · 210-736-6600

Allan G. Paterson, Jr. · 20 · Cox Smith Matthews · http://www.coxsmith.com · 112 East Pecan Street, Suite 1800 · San Antonio, TX 78205-1521 · 210-554-5500

William Scanlan, Jr. · 20 · Schoenbaum, Curphy & Scanlan · 112 East Pecan Street, 30th Floor · San Antonio, TX 78205-1516 · 210-224-4491

Stanley Schoenbaum · 25 · Schoenbaum, Curphy & Scanlan · 112 East Pecan Street, 30th Floor · San Antonio, TX 78205-1516 · 210-224-4491

Patricia F. Sitchler · Schoenbaum, Curphy & Scanlan · 112 East Pecan Street, 30th Floor · San Antonio, TX 78205-1516 · 210-224-4491

Banks M. Smith · Schoenbaum, Curphy & Scanlan · 112 East Pecan Street, 30th Floor · San Antonio, TX 78205-1516 · 210-224-4491

David P. Stanush · Oppenheimer, Blend, Harrison & Tate · 711 Navarro Street, Suite 600 · San Antonio, TX 78205-1796 · 210-224-2000

Harry W. Wolff, Jr. · Cox Smith Matthews · http://www.coxsmith.com · 112 East Pecan Street, Suite 1800 · San Antonio, TX 78205-1521 · 210-554-5500

James C. Woo · James C. Woo · Northwest Center, Suite 800 · 7550 West IH 10 · San Antonio, TX 78229-5815 · 210-349-6484

Glen A. Yale · 10 · Stumpf Farrimond · 112 East Pecan Street, Suite 700 · San Antonio, TX 78205 · 210-231-0919

Sugarland

Kurt M. Andreason · 10 · Andreason Law Firm · 4840 B Sweetwater Boulevard · P.O. Box 19429 · Sugarland, TX 77479 · 281-265-1561

Temple

Thomas C. Baird · Baird, Crews, Schiller and Whitaker · 15 North Main Street · Temple, TX 76501 · 254-774-8333

Texarkana

William B. Roberts · Patton, Roberts, McWilliams & Capshaw · Century Bank Plaza, Suite 400 · 2900 St. Michael Drive · P.O. Box 6128 · Texarkana, TX 75505-6128 · 903-334-7000

Tyler

Michael D. Allen · Allen - Lottmann · 3805 Old Bullard Road · Tyler, TX 75701 · 903-534-0006

VENTURE CAPITAL LAW

Austin

Paul R. Tobias · Wilson Sonsini Goodrich & Rosati · Las Cimas IV, Fifth Floor · 900 South Capital of Texas Highway · Austin, TX 78746-5546 · 512-338-5400

William R. Volk · ㉕ · Vinson & Elkins · http://www.velaw.com · 2801 Via Fortuna, Suite 100 · Austin, TX 78746-7568 · 512-542-8400

Dallas

Darrel A. Rice · ⑩ · Haynes and Boone · 901 Main Street, Suite 3100 · Dallas, TX 75202 · 214-651-5000

Houston

Robert F. Gray, Jr. · ⑩ · Mayer Brown · Bank of America Center, Suite 3400 · 700 Louisiana Street · Houston, TX 77002-2730 · 713-238-3000

Dallas Robert Parker · ㉕ · Thompson & Knight · http://www.tklaw.com · 333 Clay Street, Suite 3300 · Houston, TX 77002 · 713-654-8111

David Stanley Peterman · Fulbright & Jaworski · http://www.fulbright.com · Fulbright Tower, Suite 5100 · 1301 McKinney Street · Houston, TX 77010-3095 · 713-651-5151

Felix P. Phillips, Jr. · Baker Botts · http://www.bakerbotts.com · One Shell Plaza · 910 Louisiana Street · Houston, TX 77002-1210 · 713-229-1234

Charles D. Powell · Fulbright & Jaworski · http://www.fulbright.com · Fulbright Tower, Suite 5100 · 1301 McKinney Street · Houston, TX 77010-3095 · 713-651-5151

Charles C. Szalkowski · ⑩ · Baker Botts · http://www.bakerbotts.com · One Shell Plaza · 910 Louisiana Street · Houston, TX 77002-1210 · 713-229-1234

Scott Neal Wulfe · ⑩ · Vinson & Elkins · http://www.velaw.com · First City Tower, Suite 2500 · 1001 Fannin Street · Houston, TX 77002-6760 · 713-758-2222

The Woodlands

Jeffrey R. Harder · Winstead · http://www.winstead.com · 24 Waterway Avenue, Suite 500 · The Woodlands, TX 77380 · 281-681-5900

WATER LAW

Austin

David Blanke · Vinson & Elkins · http://www.velaw.com · 2801 Via Fortuna, Suite 100 · Austin, TX 78746-7568 · 512-542-8400

Sara Marquis Burgin · ⑩ · Baker Botts · http://www.bakerbotts.com · 1500 San Jacinto Center · 98 San Jacinto Boulevard · Austin, TX 78701-4039 · 512-322-2500

Molly J. Cagle · ⑩ · Vinson & Elkins · http://www.velaw.com · 2801 Via Fortuna, Suite 100 · Austin, TX 78746-7568 · 512-542-8400

Douglas G. Caroom · Bickerstaff, Heath, Delgado & Acosta · 816 Congress Avenue, Suite 1700 · Austin, TX 78701-2443 · 512-472-8021

Jeff Civins · ⓴ · Haynes and Boone · 600 Congress Avenue, Suite 1300 · Austin, TX 78701-3285 · 512-867-8400

Leonard H. Dougal · Jackson Walker · 100 Congress Avenue, Suite 1100 · Austin, TX 78701 · 512-236-2000

Darcy A. Frownfelter · Kemp Smith · http://www.kempsmith.com · 816 Congress Avenue, Suite 1150 · Austin, TX 78701 · 512-320-5466

R. Kinnan Golemon · ⓴ · KG Strategies · 111 Congress Avenue, Suite 1500 · Austin, TX 78701-4043 · 512-479-9707

Robin A. Melvin · Graves, Dougherty, Hearon & Moody · http://www.gdhm.com · 401 Congress Avenue, Suite 2200 · P.O. Box 98 · Austin, TX 78767-0098 · 512-480-5600

Andrew S. Miller · Kemp Smith · http://www.kempsmith.com · 816 Congress Avenue, Suite 1150 · Austin, TX 78701 · 512-320-5466

Roger P. Nevola · ❿ · Roger P. Nevola · 1723 Palma Plaza · P.O. Box 2103 · Austin, TX 78703 · 512-499-0500

P. Bane Phillippi · Haynes and Boone · 600 Congress Avenue, Suite 1300 · Austin, TX 78701-3285 · 512-867-8400

Kenneth R. Ramirez · Brown McCarroll · 111 Congress Avenue, Suite 1400 · Austin, TX 78701-4093 · 512-472-5456

Mary K. Sahs · Carls, McDonald & Dalrymple · Barton Oaks Plaza, Building Two, Suite 500 · 901 South Mopac Expressway · Austin, TX 78746 · 512-623-5443

Robert Walton Shelton · ❿ · Robert Walton Shelton · 4131 Spicewood Springs Road, Building I, Suite One · P.O. Box 27367 · Austin, TX 78755-2367 · 512-338-0191

Cynthia C. Smiley · Kelly, Hart & Hallman · 301 Congress Avenue, Suite 2000 · Austin, TX 78701 · 512-495-6400

Bruce Wasinger · Bickerstaff, Heath, Delgado & Acosta · 816 Congress Avenue, Suite 1700 · Austin, TX 78701-2443 · 512-472-8021

WHITE-COLLAR CRIMINAL DEFENSE

Austin

David L. Botsford · ❿ · Law Office of David L. Botsford · http://www.davidbotsfordlaw.com · 1307 West Avenue · Austin, TX 78701 · 512-479-8030

Warren L. Collins, Jr. · Minton, Burton, Foster & Collins · 1100 Guadalupe Street · Austin, TX 78701-2198 · 512-476-4873

Bill Fitzgerald · ㉕ · Fitzgerald & Meissner · 812 San Antonio Street, Suite 400 · Austin, TX 78701 · 512-474-4700

Christopher M. Gunter · Christopher M. Gunter · 600 West Ninth Street · Austin, TX 78701-2212 · 512-476-2494

Wayne D. Meissner · Fitzgerald & Meissner · 812 San Antonio Street, Suite 400 · Austin, TX 78701 · 512-474-4700

Roy Q. Minton · ㉕ · Minton, Burton, Foster & Collins · 1100 Guadalupe Street · Austin, TX 78701-2198 512-476-4873

E. G. Morris · ⑩ · The Law Office of E.G. Morris · http://www.egmlaw.com · 608 West 12th Street, Suite B · Austin, TX 78701 · 512-478-0758

David A. Sheppard · ⑩ · David A. Sheppard · Chase Bank Building, Suite 1550 · 700 Lavaca Street · Austin, TX 78701 · 512-478-9483

Joseph A. Turner · Joseph A. Turner · 1504 West Avenue · Austin, TX 78701 · 512-474-4892

William A. White · ⑩ · The Law Office of Bill White · 1307 West Avenue · Austin, TX 78701 · 512-476-1494

Beaumont

Joseph C. Hawthorn · ⑳ · Joseph C. Hawthorn · 485 Milam Street · Beaumont, TX 77701-3518 · 409-838-3969

Gilbert I. Low · ⑳ · Orgain, Bell & Tucker · 470 Orleans Street · P.O. Box 1751 · Beaumont, TX 77704-1751 · 409-838-6412

Corpus Christi

Russell H. McMains · ⑩ · Law Offices of Russell H. McMains · 500 North Shoreline Boulevard, Suite 1100 · P.O. Box 2846 · Corpus Christi, TX 78403 · 361-887-4455

J. Douglas Tinker · ⑳ · Law Office of J. Douglas Tinker · 622 South Tancahua Street · P.O. Box 276 · Corpus Christi, TX 78403 · 361-882-4378

Dallas

Shirley Baccus-Lobel · Law Offices of Shirley Baccus-Lobel · http://www.lobellaw.com · The Oaks, Suite 250 · 2929 Carlisle · Dallas, TX 75204 · 214-220-8460

Charles W. Blau · Meadows, Collier, Reed, Cousins & Blau · 901 Main Street, Suite 3700 · Dallas, TX 75202 · 214-744-3700

Paul E. Coggins · Fish & Richardson · 1717 Main Street, Suite 5000 · Dallas, TX 75201 · 214-747-5070

Michael Paul Gibson · ㉕ · Burleson, Pate & Gibson · 2414 North Akard Street, Suite 700 · Dallas, TX 75201 · 214-871-4900

Robert C. Hinton · ⑩ · Robert Hinton & Associates · 4040 North Central Expressway, Suite 810 · Dallas, TX 75204 · 214-219-9300

Barry F. McNeil · Haynes and Boone · 901 Main Street, Suite 3100 · Dallas, TX 75202 · 214-651-5000

Charles M. Meadows, Jr. · Meadows, Collier, Reed, Cousins & Blau · 901 Main Street, Suite 3700 · Dallas, TX 75202 · 214-744-3700

Thomas M. Melsheimer · Fish & Richardson · 1717 Main Street, Suite 5000 · Dallas, TX 75201 · 214-747-5070

Thomas W. Mills, Jr. · Mills & Williams · 5910 North Central Expressway, Suite 900 · Dallas, TX 75206-5141 · 214-265-9265

George R. Milner, Jr. · ⑳ · Milner & Finn · 2828 North Harwood Street, Suite 1950 · Dallas, TX 75201 · 214-651-1121

William M. Ravkind · Ravkind & Associates · One Meadows Building, Suite 200 · 5005 Greenville Avenue · Dallas, TX 75206 · 214-365-4426

Barry Sorrels · ⑩ · Sorrels, Udashen & Anton · 2301 Cedar Springs Road, Suite 400 · Dallas, TX 75201 · 214-468-8100

Gary A. Udashen · Sorrels, Udashen & Anton · 2301 Cedar Springs Road, Suite 400 · Dallas, TX 75201 · 214-468-8100

Robert Udashen · Sorrels, Udashen & Anton · 2301 Cedar Springs Road, Suite 400 · Dallas, TX 75201 · 214-468-8100

Mark S. Werbner · ⑩ · Sayles/Werbner · http://www.swtriallaw.com · 1201 Elm Street, 44th Floor · Dallas, TX 75270 · 214-939-8700

Denton

Rick Hagen · Jackson & Hagen · The Texas Building, Suite 302 · 100 West Oak Street · Denton, TX 76201 · 940-566-1001

El Paso

Joseph Abraham, Jr. · ⑳ · The Law Firm of Carlos Eduardo Cárdenas · Toltec Building, Third Floor · 717 East San Antonio Street · P.O. Box 512312 · El Paso, TX 79951-0004 · 915-532-1601

E. Link Beck · ⑩ · Beck & Given · 5915 Silver Springs Drive, Building Four · El Paso, TX 79912 · 915-544-5545

James O. Darnell · ⑩ · Jim Darnell · http://www.jdarnell.com · 310 North Mesa Street, Suite 212 · El Paso, TX 79901 · 915-532-2442

Luis E. Islas · Luis E. Islas · 1216 Montana Avenue · El Paso, TX 79903-4001 · 915-562-7111

Dolph Quijano, Jr. · Adolph Quijano, Jr. · 707 Myrtle Avenue · El Paso, TX 79901 · 915-542-1051

Gary B. Weiser · ⑩ · Gary B. Weiser · 521 Texas Avenue · El Paso, TX 79901 · 915-544-0880

Fort Worth

Tim Evans · ⑳ · Evans, Gandy, Daniel & Moore · http://www.egdmlaw.com · 115 West Second Street, Suite 202 · Fort Worth, TX 76102 · 817-332-3822

Jeffrey A. Kearney · ⑩ · Kearney | Wynn · 505 Main Street, Suite 220 · Fort Worth, TX 76102 · 817-336-5600

Jack Vernon Strickland, Jr. · ⑩ · Law Offices of Jack V. Strickland · 909 Throckmorton Street · Fort Worth, TX 76102 · 817-338-1000

R. H. Wallace, Jr. · ⑩ · Shannon, Gracey, Ratliff & Miller · http://www.shannongracey.com · 777 Main Street, Suite 3800 · Fort Worth, TX 76102 · 817-336-9333

William Reagan Wynn · Kearney | Wynn · 505 Main Street, Suite 220 · Fort Worth, TX 76102 · 817-336-5600

Houston

Joel M. Androphy · Berg & Androphy · http://www.bafirm.com · 3704 Travis Street · Houston, TX 77002 · 713-529-5622

R. Todd Bennett · R. Todd Bennett · http://www.rtoddbennettpc.com · The Niels Esperson Building, 24th Floor · 808 Travis Street · Houston, TX 77002 · 713-752-2728

David Howard Berg · ⑩ · Berg & Androphy · http://www.bafirm.com · 3704 Travis Street · Houston, TX 77002 · 713-529-5622

Shaun G. Clarke · Gerger & Clarke · First City Tower, Suite 1950 · 1001 Fannin · Houston, TX 77002 · 713-224-4400

Dan L. Cogdell · ⑩ · Cogdell Law Group · 402 Main Street, Second Floor · Houston, TX 77002 · 713-426-2244

Michael DeGeurin · ⑳ · Foreman DeGeurin Nugent · 300 Main Street · Houston, TX 77002 · 713-655-9000

Dick DeGuerin · ㉕ · DeGuerin & Dickson · The Republic Building, Seventh Floor · 1018 Preston Avenue · Houston, TX 77002 · 713-223-5959

Lawrence D. Finder · Haynes and Boone · One Houston Center, Suite 2100 · 1221 McKinney Street · Houston, TX 77010 · 713-547-2000

David Gerger · ⑩ · Gerger & Associates · First City Tower, Suite 1950 · Houston, TX 77002 · 713-224-4400

Thomas A. Hagemann · Gardere Wynne Sewell · http://www.gardere.com · 1000 Louisiana, Suite 3400 · Houston, TX 77002-5011 · 713-276-5500

Richard Haynes · ㉕ · Richard Haynes & Associates · 314 North Post Oak Lane, Second Floor · Houston, TX 77024 · 713-868-1111

Edward A. Mallett · Mallett Guiberson Saper · JP Morgan Chase Tower, Suite 1900 · 600 Travis Street · Houston, TX 77002 · 713-236-1900

Michael W. Ramsey · ⑳ · Michael W. Ramsey · 2120 Welch Street · Houston, TX 77019-5616 · 713-523-7878

Kent Schaffer · Bires & Schaffer · http://www.biresandschaffer.com · JP Morgan/Chase Building, 31st Floor · 712 Main Street · Houston, TX 77002 · 713-228-8500

Randolph Lee Schaffer, Jr. · ⑳ · The Schaffer Firm · Fulbright Tower, Suite 3100 · 1301 McKinney Street · Houston, TX 77010 · 713-951-9555

Stanley G. Schneider · Schneider & McKinney · The Lyric Center, Suite 800 · 440 Louisiana · Houston, TX 77002 · 713-951-9994

George McCall Secrest, Jr. · ⑩ · Bennett & Secrest · The Neils Esperson Building, 24th Floor · 808 Travis Street · Houston, TX 77002 · 713-757-0679

Ronald G. Woods · Ronald G. Woods · http://www.ronwoodslaw.com · 5300 Memorial, Suite 1000 · Houston, TX 77007 · 713-862-9600

San Antonio

Roy R. Barrera, Sr. · ㉕ · Nicholas & Barrera · 424 East Nueva Street · San Antonio, TX 78205 · 210-224-5811

Samuel H. Bayless · The Law Offices of Samuel Bayless · 441 Burr Road · San Antonio, TX 78205 · 210-253-7110

Charles D. Butts · ⑳ · Charles D. Butts · Petroleum Tower II, Suite 510 · 8626 Tesoro Drive · San Antonio, TX 78217 · 210-240-8239

John F. Carroll · ⑩ · John F. Carroll · 111 West Olmos Drive · San Antonio, TX 78212 · 210-829-7183

John A. Convery · Hasdorff & Convery · 1005 South Alamo Street · San Antonio, TX 78210 · 210-738-9060

Gerald Harris Goldstein · ⑳ · Goldstein, Goldstein & Hilley · Tower Life Building, 29th Floor · 310 South St. Mary's Street · San Antonio, TX 78205-3106 · 210-226-1463

Reese L. Harrison, Jr. · ⑳ · Oppenheimer, Blend, Harrison & Tate · 711 Navarro Street, Suite 600 · San Antonio, TX 78205-1796 · 210-224-2000

Van G. Hilley · Goldstein, Goldstein & Hilley · Tower Life Building, 29th Floor · 310 South St. Mary's Street · San Antonio, TX 78205-3106 · 210-226-1463

Jack Paul Leon · ⑩ · Law Offices of Jack Paul Leon · 500 Lexington Avenue · San Antonio, TX 78215-1930 · 210-223-4254

Michael W. McCrum · Thompson & Knight · http://www.tklaw.com · 4040 Broadway, Suite 615 · San Antonio, TX 78209 · 210-225-2285

Cynthia H. Orr · Goldstein, Goldstein & Hilley · Tower Life Building, 29th Floor · 310 South St. Mary's Street · San Antonio, TX 78205-3106 · 210-226-1463

James B. Parks · James B. Parks · 214 Dwyer Avenue, Suite 210 · San Antonio, TX 78204 · 210-229-1322

Mark Stevens · ⑩ · Mark Stevens · Tower Life Building, Suite 1505 · 310 South St. Mary's Street · San Antonio, TX 78205 · 210-226-1433

Texarkana

Damon Young · ⑩ · Young, Pickett & Lee · 4122 Texas Boulevard · P.O. Box 1897 · Texarkana, TX 75504 · 903-794-1303

Tyler

F. R. Files, Jr. · ⑳ · Bain, Files, Jarrett and Bain · 109 West Ferguson Street · P.O. Box 2013 · Tyler, TX 75710 · 903-595-3573

UTAH

ADMINISTRATIVE LAW

Salt Lake City

Jerold G. Oldroyd · Ballard Spahr Andrews & Ingersoll · One Utah Center, Suite 800 · 201 South Main Street · Salt Lake City, UT 84111-2221 · 801-531-3000

Lawrence E. Stevens · Parsons Behle & Latimer · http://www.parsonsbehlelaw.com · 201 South Main Street, Suite 1800 · P.O. Box 45898 · Salt Lake City, UT 84145-0898 · 801-532-1234

St. George

M. Kent Christopherson · M. Kent Christopherson · 2281 South Wedgewood Drive · P.O. Box 2350 · St. George, UT 84771-2350 · 435-688-1342

ALTERNATIVE DISPUTE RESOLUTION

Ogden

Brian R. Florence · a · Mediation Services · 1943 East 6200 South · Ogden, UT 84403 · 801-476-3200

Salt Lake City

William B. Bohling · Bohling Hobbs Professional Mediation · 466 East 500 South, Suite 200 · Salt Lake City, UT 84111 · 801-983-1300

Francis J. Carney · a · Anderson & Karrenberg · Chase Tower, Suite 700 · 50 West Broadway · Salt Lake City, UT 84101-2006 · 801-534-1700

Paul S. Felt · a · Paul S. Felt · 1410 Wilton Avenue · P.O. Box 581227 · Salt Lake City, UT 84158-1227 · 801-487-0214

Robert H. Henderson · Robert Henderson · 266 Eleventh Avenue · Salt Lake City, UT 84103 · 801-647-2420

Karin S. Hobbs · Karin Stone Hobbs · 466 East 500 South, Suite 200 · Salt Lake City, UT 84111 · 801-983-1300

James R. Holbrook · University of Utah · S. J. Quinney College Of Law · 332 South 1400 East · Salt Lake City, UT 84112-0730 · 801-585-9693

Stephen B. Nebeker · Ray Quinney & Nebeker · 36 South State Street, Suite 1400 · P.O. Box 45385 · Salt Lake City, UT 84145-0385 · 801-532-1500

David E. Roth · David E. Roth · 48 West 300 South, Suite 1601 North · Salt Lake City, UT 84101 · 801-359-1438

Alan L. Sullivan · a · Snell & Wilmer · Beneficial Tower, Suite 1200 · 15 West South Temple · Salt Lake City, UT 84101-1547 · 801-257-1900

Michael D. Zimmerman · Snell & Wilmer · Beneficial Tower, Suite 1200 · 15 West South Temple · Salt Lake City, UT 84101-1547 · 801-257-1900

ANTITRUST LAW

Salt Lake City

Daniel L. Berman · 2% · Berman & Savage · 170 South Main Street, Suite 500 · Salt Lake City, UT 84101 801-328-2200

Richard D. Burbidge · a · Burbidge, Mitchell & Gross · Parkside Tower, Suite 920 · 215 South State Street · Salt Lake City, UT 84111 · 801-355-6677

Richard W. Casey · Howrey · 170 South Main Street, Suite 400 · Salt Lake City, UT 84101 · 801-533-8383

Jonathan A. Dibble · Ray Quinney & Nebeker · 36 South State Street, Suite 1400 · P.O. Box 45385 · Salt Lake City, UT 84145-0385 · 801-532-1500

Raymond J. Etcheverry · a · Parsons Behle & Latimer · http://www.parsonsbehlelaw.com · 201 South Main Street, Suite 1800 · P.O. Box 45898 · Salt Lake City, UT 84145-0898 · 801-532-1234

James S. Jardine · a · Ray Quinney & Nebeker · 36 South State Street, Suite 1400 · P.O. Box 45385 · Salt Lake City, UT 84145-0385 · 801-532-1500

John W. Mackay · Ray Quinney & Nebeker · 36 South State Street, Suite 1400 · P.O. Box 45385 · Salt Lake City, UT 84145-0385 · 801-532-1500

Andrew H. Stone · Jones Waldo · 170 South Main Street, Suite 1500 · Salt Lake City, UT 84101-1644 · 801-521-3200

Clark Waddoups · Parr, Waddoups, Brown, Gee & Loveless · 185 South State Street, Suite 1300 · P.O. Box 11019 · Salt Lake City, UT 84147-1537 · 801-532-7840

APPELLATE LAW

Salt Lake City

Michael D. Zimmerman · Snell & Wilmer · Beneficial Tower, Suite 1200 · 15 West South Temple · Salt Lake City, UT 84101-1547 · 801-257-1900

BANKING LAW

Salt Lake City

John A. Beckstead · Holland & Hart · 60 East South Temple, Suite 2000 · Salt Lake City, UT 84111-1031 · 801-595-7800

Peter W. Billings, Jr. · a · Fabian & Clendenin · 215 South State Street, Suite 1200 · P.O. Box 510210 · Salt Lake City, UT 84151 · 801-531-8900

Thomas T. Billings · VanCott, Bagley, Cornwall & McCarthy · 36 South State Street, Suite 1900 · Salt Lake City, UT 84102 · 801-532-3333

Louis H. Callister · a · Callister, Nebeker & McCullough · Zions Bank Building, Suite 900 · 10 East South Temple · Salt Lake City, UT 84133 · 801-530-7300

Scott Hancock Clark · a · Ray Quinney & Nebeker · 36 South State Street, Suite 1400 · P.O. Box 45385 Salt Lake City, UT 84145-0385 · 801-532-1500

Brian D. Cunningham · Snell & Wilmer · Beneficial Tower, Suite 1200 · 15 West South Temple · Salt Lake City, UT 84101-1547 · 801-257-1900

Gary E. Doctorman · Parsons Behle & Latimer · http://www.parsonsbehlelaw.com · 201 South Main Street, Suite 1800 · P.O. Box 45898 · Salt Lake City, UT 84145-0898 · 801-532-1234

W. Jeffrey Fillmore · Callister, Nebeker & McCullough · Zions Bank Building, Suite 900 · 10 East South Temple · Salt Lake City, UT 84133 · 801-530-7300

Kevin G. Glade · Ray Quinney & Nebeker · 36 South State Street, Suite 1400 · P.O. Box 45385 · Salt Lake City, UT 84145-0385 · 801-532-1500

Douglas M. Monson · Ray Quinney & Nebeker · 36 South State Street, Suite 1400 · P.O. Box 45385 · Salt Lake City, UT 84145-0385 · 801-532-1500

Jerold G. Oldroyd · Ballard Spahr Andrews & Ingersoll · One Utah Center, Suite 800 · 201 South Main Street · Salt Lake City, UT 84111-2221 · 801-531-3000

George R. Sutton · a · Jones Waldo · 170 South Main Street, Suite 1500 · Salt Lake City, UT 84101-1644 · 801-521-3200

BANKRUPTCY AND CREDITOR-DEBTOR RIGHTS LAW

Salt Lake City

J. Thomas Beckett · Parsons Behle & Latimer · http://www.parsonsbehlelaw.com · 201 South Main Street, Suite 1800 · P.O. Box 45898 · Salt Lake City, UT 84145-0898 · 801-532-1234

Peter W. Billings, Jr. · a · Fabian & Clendenin · 215 South State Street, Suite 1200 · P.O. Box 510210 · Salt Lake City, UT 84151 · 801-531-8900

Mona Lyman Burton · Holland & Hart · 60 East South Temple, Suite 2000 · Salt Lake City, UT 84111-1031 · 801-595-7800

Kenneth L. Cannon II · a · Durham Jones & Pinegar · 111 East Broadway, Suite 900 · P.O. Box 4050 · Salt Lake City, UT 84110 · 801-415-3000

Duane H. Gillman · Durham Jones & Pinegar · 111 East Broadway, Suite 900 · P.O. Box 4050 · Salt Lake City, UT 84110 · 801-415-3000

George Hofmann · Parsons Kinghorn Harris · 111 East Broadway Street, 11th Floor · Salt Lake City, UT 84111 · 801-363-4300

Peggy Hunt · Ray Quinney & Nebeker · 36 South State Street, Suite 1400 · P.O. Box 45385 · Salt Lake City, UT 84145-0385 · 801-532-1500

Annette W. Jarvis · Ray Quinney & Nebeker · 36 South State Street, Suite 1400 · P.O. Box 45385 · Salt Lake City, UT 84145-0385 · 801-532-1500

Lon A. Jenkins · Jones Waldo · 170 South Main Street, Suite 1500 · Salt Lake City, UT 84101-1644 · 801-521-3200

Michael R. Johnson · Snell & Wilmer · Beneficial Tower, Suite 1200 · 15 West South Temple · Salt Lake City, UT 84101-1547 · 801-257-1900

Gary E. Jubber · Fabian & Clendenin · 215 South State Street, Suite 1200 · P.O. Box 510210 · Salt Lake City, UT 84151 · 801-531-8900

Penrod W. Keith · Durham Jones & Pinegar · 111 East Broadway, Suite 900 · P.O. Box 4050 · Salt Lake City, UT 84110 · 801-415-3000

Danny C. Kelly · a · Stoel Rives · http://www.stoel.com · 201 South Main Street, Suite 1100 · Salt Lake City, UT 84111-4904 · 801-328-3131

David E. Leta · a · Snell & Wilmer · Beneficial Tower, Suite 1200 · 15 West South Temple · Salt Lake City, UT 84101-1547 · 801-257-1900

Robert B. Lochhead · Parr, Waddoups, Brown, Gee & Loveless · 185 South State Street, Suite 1300 · P.O. Box 11019 · Salt Lake City, UT 84147-1537 · 801-532-7840

Joel T. Marker · Mckay Burton & Thurman · 170 South Main Street, Suite 800 · Salt Lake City, UT 84101 · 801-521-4135

Adelaide Maudsley · Chapman & Cutler · 201 South Main Street · Salt Lake City, UT 84111 · 801-533-0066

Steven Jack McCardell · a · Durham Jones & Pinegar · 111 East Broadway, Suite 900 · P.O. Box 4050 · Salt Lake City, UT 84110 · 801-415-3000

R. Kimball Mosier · Parsons Kinghorn Harris · 111 East Broadway Street, 11th Floor · Salt Lake City, UT 84111 · 801-363-4300

J. Robert Nelson · VanCott, Bagley, Cornwall & McCarthy · 36 South State Street, Suite 1900 · Salt Lake City, UT 84102 · 801-532-3333

Herschel J. Saperstein · 2% · Ray Quinney & Nebeker · 36 South State Street, Suite 1400 · P.O. Box 45385 · Salt Lake City, UT 84145-0385 · 801-532-1500

Roger G. Segal · a · Cohne, Rappaport & Segal · 257 East 200 South, Suite 700 · P.O. Box 11008 · Salt Lake City, UT 84147-0008 · 801-532-2666

Jeffrey L. Shields · Callister, Nebeker & McCullough · Zions Bank Building, Suite 900 · 10 East South Temple · Salt Lake City, UT 84133 · 801-530-7300

Jeffrey Weston Shields · Jones Waldo · 170 South Main Street, Suite 1500 · Salt Lake City, UT 84101-1644 · 801-521-3200

Gerald H. Suniville · VanCott, Bagley, Cornwall & McCarthy · 36 South State Street, Suite 1900 · Salt Lake City, UT 84102 · 801-532-3333

Steven T. Waterman · Ray Quinney & Nebeker · 36 South State Street, Suite 1400 · P.O. Box 45385 · Salt Lake City, UT 84145-0385 · 801-532-1500

Kim R. Wilson · Snow, Christensen & Martineau · http://www.scmlaw.com · 10 Exchange Place, 11th Floor · P.O. Box 45000 · Salt Lake City, UT 84145 · 801-521-9000

BET-THE-COMPANY LITIGATION

Salt Lake City

Richard D. Burbidge · a · Burbidge, Mitchell & Gross · Parkside Tower, Suite 920 · 215 South State Street · Salt Lake City, UT 84111 · 801-355-6677

James S. Jardine · a · Ray Quinney & Nebeker · 36 South State Street, Suite 1400 · P.O. Box 45385 · Salt Lake City, UT 84145-0385 · 801-532-1500

Alan L. Sullivan · a · Snell & Wilmer · Beneficial Tower, Suite 1200 · 15 West South Temple · Salt Lake City, UT 84101-1547 · 801-257-1900

Elliott J. Williams · a · Williams & Hunt · 257 East 200 South, Suite 500 · P.O. Box 45678 · Salt Lake City, UT 84145-5678 · 801-521-5678

Salt Lake City

John A. Adams · Ray Quinney & Nebeker · 36 South State Street, Suite 1400 · P.O. Box 45385 · Salt Lake City, UT 84145-0385 · 801-532-1500

John A. Anderson · Stoel Rives · http://www.stoel.com · 201 South Main Street, Suite 1100 · Salt Lake City, UT 84111-4904 · 801-328-3131

Robert M. Anderson · 2) · VanCott, Bagley, Cornwall & McCarthy · 36 South State Street, Suite 1900 · Salt Lake City, UT 84102 · 801-532-3333

John P. Ashton · VanCott, Bagley, Cornwall & McCarthy · 36 Scuth State Street, Suite 1900 · Salt Lake City, UT 84102 · 801-532-3333

Gary F. Bendinger · a · Howrey · 170 South Main Street, Suite 400 · Salt Lake City, UT 84101 · 801-533-8383

Arthur B. Berger · Ray Quinney & Nebeker · 36 South State Street, Suite 1400 · P.O. Box 45385 · Salt Lake City, UT 84145-0385 · 801-532-1500

Daniel L. Berman · 2% · Berman & Savage · 170 South Main Street, Suite 500 · Salt Lake City, UT 84101 801-328-2200

Kenneth B. Black · Stoel Rives · http://www.stoel.com · 201 Scuth Main Street, Suite 1100 · Salt Lake City, UT 84111-4904 · 801-328-3131

Alan C. Bradshaw · Manning Curtis Bradshaw & Bednar · New House Building, Third Floor · 10 Exchange Place · Salt Lake City, UT 84111 · 801-363-5678

Richard D. Burbidge · a · Burbidge, Mitchell & Gross · Parkside Tower, Suite 920 · 215 South State Street · Salt Lake City, UT 84111 · 801-355-6677

H. Dickson Burton · TraskBritt · http://www.traskbritt.com · 230 South 500 East, Suite 300 · P.O. Box 2550 · Salt Lake City, UT 84110-2550 · 801-532-1922

Robert S. Campbell, Jr. · 2% · VanCott, Bagley, Cornwall & McCarthy · 36 South State Street, Suite 1900 Salt Lake City, UT 84102 · 801-532-3333

Richard W. Casey · Howrey · 170 South Main Street, Suite 400 · Salt Lake City, UT 84101 · 801-533-8383

Robert S. Clark · Parr, Waddoups, Brown, Gee & Loveless · 185 South State Street, Suite 1300 · P.O. Box 11019 · Salt Lake City, UT 84147-1537 · 801-532-7840

Curtis J. Drake · Snell & Wilmer · Beneficial Tower, Suite 1200 · 15 West South Temple · Salt Lake City, UT 84101-1547 · 801-257-1900

Raymond J. Etcheverry · a · Parsons Behle & Latimer · http://www.parsonsbehlelaw.com · 201 South Main Street, Suite 1800 · P.O. Box 45898 · Salt Lake City, UT 84145-0898 · 801-532-1234

David A. Greenwood · Howrey · 170 South Main Street, Suite 400 · Salt Lake City, UT 84101 · 801-533-8383

Jay D. Gurmankin · Holme Roberts & Owen · http://www.hro.com · 299 South Main Street, Suite 1800 · Salt Lake City, UT 84111-2263 · 801-521-5800

Stephen E. W. Hale · Parr, Waddoups, Brown, Gee & Loveless · 185 South State Street, Suite 1300 · P.O. Box 11019 · Salt Lake City, UT 84147-1537 · 801-532-7840

George M. Haley · Holme Roberts & Owen · http://www.hro.com · 299 South Main Street, Suite 1800 · Salt Lake City, UT 84111-2263 · 801-521-5800

Glenn C. Hanni · a · Strong & Hanni · Three Triad Center, Suite 500 · Salt Lake City, UT 84180 · 801-532-7080

Rich L. Humpherys · a · Christensen & Jensen · Beneficial Tower, Suite 800 · 15 West South Temple · Salt Lake City, UT 84101 · 801-323-5000

George A. Hunt · Williams & Hunt · 257 East 200 South, Suite 500 · P.O. Box 45678 · Salt Lake City, UT 84145-5678 · 801-521-5678

James S. Jardine · a · Ray Quinney & Nebeker · 36 South State Street, Suite 1400 · P.O. Box 45385 · Salt Lake City, UT 84145-0385 · 801-532-1500

David J. Jordan · a · Stoel Rives · http://www.stoel.com · 201 South Main Street, Suite 1100 · Salt Lake City, UT 84111-4904 · 801-328-3131

Thomas R. Karrenberg · a · Anderson & Karrenberg · Chase Tower, Suite 700 · 50 West Broadway · Salt Lake City, UT 84101-2006 · 801-534-1700

Colin P. King · a · Dewsnup, King & Olsen · http://www.dkolaw.com · Beneficial Financial Group, Suite 2400 · 36 South State Street · Salt Lake City, UT 84111-0024 · 801-533-0400

Michael L. Larsen · Parsons Behle & Latimer · http://www.parsonsbehlelaw.com · 201 South Main Street, Suite 1800 · P.O. Box 45898 · Salt Lake City, UT 84145-0898 · 801-532-1234

Perrin R. Love · Clyde Snow Sessions & Swenson · One Utah Center, Suite 1300 · 201 South Main Street Salt Lake City, UT 84111-2216 · 801-322-2516

Brent V. Manning · Manning Curtis Bradshaw & Bednar · New House Building, Third Floor · 10 Exchange Place · Salt Lake City, UT 84111 · 801-363-5678

Mark Morris · Snell & Wilmer · Beneficial Tower, Suite 1200 · 15 West South Temple · Salt Lake City, UT 84101-1547 · 801-257-1900

E. Scott Savage · Berman & Savage · 170 South Main Street, Suite 500 · Salt Lake City, UT 84101 · 801-328-2200

John A. Snow · VanCott, Bagley, Cornwall & McCarthy · 36 South State Street, Suite 1900 · Salt Lake City, UT 84102 · 801-532-3333

Lawrence E. Stevens · Parsons Behle & Latimer · http://www.parsonsbehlelaw.com · 201 South Main Street, Suite 1800 · P.O. Box 45898 · Salt Lake City, UT 84145-0898 · 801-532-1234

Alan L. Sullivan · a · Snell & Wilmer · Beneficial Tower, Suite 1200 · 15 West South Temple · Salt Lake City, UT 84101-1547 · 801-257-1900

Clark Waddoups · Parr, Waddoups, Brown, Gee & Loveless · 185 South State Street, Suite 1300 · P.O. Box 11019 · Salt Lake City, UT 84147-1537 · 801-532-7840

Max D. Wheeler · Snow, Christensen & Martineau · http://www.scmlaw.com · 10 Exchange Place, 11th Floor · P.O. Box 45000 · Salt Lake City, UT 84145 · 801-521-9000

Francis M. Wikstrom · a · Parsons Behle & Latimer · http://www.parsonsbehlelaw.com · 201 South Main Street, Suite 1800 · P.O. Box 45898 · Salt Lake City, UT 84145-0898 · 801-532-1234

Elliott J. Williams · a · Williams & Hunt · 257 East 200 South, Suite 500 · P.O. Box 45678 · Salt Lake City, UT 84145-5678 · 801-521-5678

Donald J. Winder · Winder & Haslam · 175 West 200 South, Suite 4000 · P.O. Box 2668 · Salt Lake City, UT 84110-2668 · 801-322-2222

Michael D. Zimmerman · Snell & Wilmer · Beneficial Tower, Suite 1200 · 15 West South Temple · Salt Lake City, UT 84101-1547 · 801-257-1900

COMMUNICATIONS LAW

Salt Lake City

Jeffrey J. Hunt · Parr, Waddoups, Brown, Gee & Loveless · 185 South State Street, Suite 1300 · P.O. Box 11019 · Salt Lake City, UT 84147-1537 · 801-532-7840

Gregory B. Monson · a · Stoel Rives · http://www.stoel.com · 201 South Main Street, Suite 1100 · Salt Lake City, UT 84111-4904 · 801-328-3131

David C. Reymann · Parr, Waddoups, Brown, Gee & Loveless · 185 South State Street, Suite 1300 · P.O. Box 11019 · Salt Lake City, UT 84147-1537 · 801-532-7840

Ted D. Smith · Stoel Rives · http://www.stoel.com · 201 South Main Street, Suite 1100 · Salt Lake City, UT 84111-4904 · 801-328-3131

CONSTRUCTION LAW

Salt Lake City

Stephen E. W. Hale · Parr, Waddoups, Brown, Gee & Loveless · 185 South State Street, Suite 1300 · P.O. Box 11019 · Salt Lake City, UT 84147-1537 · 801-532-7840

Roger D. Henriksen · Parr, Waddoups, Brown, Gee & Loveless · 185 South State Street, Suite 1300 · P.O. Box 11019 · Salt Lake City, UT 84147-1537 · 801-532-7840

David W. Slaughter · Snow, Christensen & Martineau · http://www.scmlaw.com · 10 Exchange Place, 11th Floor · P.O. Box 45000 · Salt Lake City, UT 84145 · 801-521-9000

John A. Snow · VanCott, Bagley, Cornwall & McCarthy · 36 South State Street, Suite 1900 · Salt Lake City, UT 84102 · 801-532-3333

CORPORATE GOVERNANCE AND COMPLIANCE LAW

Salt Lake City

P. Christian Anderson · Ballard Spahr Andrews & Ingersoll · One Utah Center, Suite 800 · 201 South Main Street · Salt Lake City, UT 84111-2221 · 801-531-3000

David E. Gee · Parr, Waddoups, Brown, Gee & Loveless · 185 South State Street, Suite 1300 · P.O. Box 11019 · Salt Lake City, UT 84147-1537 · 801-532-7840

Brian G. Lloyd · Parr, Waddoups, Brown, Gee & Loveless · 185 South State Street, Suite 1300 · P.O. Box 11019 · Salt Lake City, UT 84147-1537 · 801-532-7840

Scott W. Loveless · Parr, Waddoups, Brown, Gee & Loveless · 185 South State Street, Suite 1300 · P.O. Box 11019 · Salt Lake City, UT 84147-1537 · 801-532-7840

John Gary Weston · Snell & Wilmer · Beneficial Tower, Suite 1200 · 15 West South Temple · Salt Lake City, UT 84101-1547 · 801-257-1900

CORPORATE LAW

Salt Lake City

P. Christian Anderson · Ballard Spahr Andrews & Ingersoll · One Utah Center, Suite 800 201 South Main Street · Salt Lake City, UT 84111-2221 · 801-531-3000

Robert M. Anderson · 2) · VanCott, Bagley, Cornwall & McCarthy · 36 South State Street, Suite 1900 · Salt Lake City, UT 84102 · 801-532-3333

David G. Angerbauer · Holland & Hart · 60 East South Temple, Suite 2000 · Salt Lake City, UT 84111-1031 · 801-595-7800

Peter W. Billings, Jr. · a · Fabian & Clendenin · 215 South State Street, Suite 1200 · P.O. Box 510210 · Salt Lake City, UT 84151 · 801-531-8900

Mark E. Bonham · Ray Quinney & Nebeker · 36 South State Street, Suite 1400 · P.O. Box 45385 · Salt Lake City, UT 84145-0385 · 801-532-1500

Kent H. Collins · Parr, Waddoups, Brown, Gee & Loveless · 185 South State Street, Suite 1300 · P.O. Box 11019 · Salt Lake City, UT 84147-1537 · 801-532-7840

Brent J. Giauque · Stoel Rives · http://www.stoel.com · 201 South Main Street, Suite 1100 · Salt Lake City, UT 84111-4904 · 801-328-3131

Jeffrey M. Jones · Durham Jones & Pinegar · 111 East Broadway, Suite 900 · P.O. Box 4050 · Salt Lake City, UT 84110 · 801-415-3000

Nathan W. Jones · Stoel Rives · http://www.stoel.com · 201 South Main Street, Suite 1100 · Salt Lake City, UT 84111-4904 · 801-328-3131

James B. Lee · 2) · Parsons Behle & Latimer · http://www.parsonsbehlelaw.com · 201 Scuth Main Street, Suite 1800 · P.O. Box 45898 · Salt Lake City, UT 84145-0898 · 801-532-1234

Gregory E. Lindley · Holland & Hart · 60 East South Temple, Suite 2000 · Salt Lake City, UT 84111-1031 · 801-595-7800

David H. Little · Holme Roberts & Owen · http://www.hro.com · 299 South Main Street, Suite 1800 · Salt Lake City, UT 84111-2263 · 801-521-5800

Brian G. Lloyd · Parr, Waddoups, Brown, Gee & Loveless · 185 South State Street, Suite 1300 · P.O. Box 11019 · Salt Lake City, UT 84147-1537 · 801-532-7840

Scott W. Loveless · Parr, Waddoups, Brown, Gee & Loveless · 185 South State Street, Suite 1300 · P.O. Box 11019 · Salt Lake City, UT 84147-1537 · 801-532-7840

Geoffrey W. Mangum · Parsons Behle & Latimer · http://www.parsonsbehlelaw.com · 201 South Main Street, Suite 1800 · P.O. Box 45898 · Salt Lake City, UT 84145-0898 · 801-532-1234

Ronald G. Moffitt · Stoel Rives · http://www.stoel.com · 201 South Main Street, Suite 1100 · Salt Lake City, UT 84111-4904 · 801-328-3131

John Parsons · Parsons Kinghorn Harris · 111 East Broadway Street, 11th Floor · Salt Lake City, UT 84111 · 801-363-4300

Ronald S. Poelman · Jones Waldo · 170 South Main Street, Suite 1500 · Salt Lake City, UT 84101-1644 · 801-521-3200

David R. Rudd · Ballard Spahr Andrews & Ingersoll · One Utah Center, Suite 800 · 201 South Main Street · Salt Lake City, UT 84111-2221 · 801-531-3000

Michael W. Spence · Ray Quinney & Nebeker · 36 South State Street, Suite 1400 · P.O. Box 45385 · Salt Lake City, UT 84145-0385 · 801-532-1500

Stephen D. Swindle · a · VanCott, Bagley, Cornwall & McCarthy · 36 South State Street, Suite 1900 · Salt Lake City, UT 84102 · 801-532-3333

Nolan S. Taylor · Dorsey & Whitney · 170 South Main Street, Suite 900 · Salt Lake City, UT 84101-1655 801-933-7360

Thomas R. Taylor · Holme Roberts & Owen · http://www.hro.com · 299 South Main Street, Suite 1800 · Salt Lake City, UT 84111-2263 · 801-521-5800

Reed W. Topham · Stoel Rives · http://www.stoel.com · 201 South Main Street, Suite 1100 · Salt Lake City, UT 84111-4904 · 801-328-3131

John Gary Weston · Snell & Wilmer · Beneficial Tower, Suite 1200 · 15 West South Temple · Salt Lake City, UT 84101-1547 · 801-257-1900

Randon W. Wilson · Jones Waldo · 170 South Main Street, Suite 1500 · Salt Lake City, UT 84101-1644 · 801-521-3200

R. Gary Winger · Ray Quinney & Nebeker · 36 South State Street, Suite 1400 · P.O. Box 45385 · Salt Lake City, UT 84145-0385 · 801-532-1500

EDUCATION LAW

Salt Lake City

John E. S. Robson · Fabian & Clendenin · 215 South State Street, Suite 1200 · P.O. Box 510210 · Salt Lake City, UT 84151 · 801-531-8900

ELDER LAW

Salt Lake City

Calvin Curtis · Calvin C. Curtis · 299 South Main Street, Suite 1300 · Salt Lake City, UT 84111 · 801-534-4430

EMINENT DOMAIN AND CONDEMNATION LAW

Salt Lake City

Paul C. Drecksel · Parr, Waddoups, Brown, Gee & Loveless · 185 South State Street, Suite 1300 · P.O. Box 11019 · Salt Lake City, UT 84147-1537 · 801-532-7840

Perrin R. Love · Clyde Snow Sessions & Swenson · One Utah Center, Suite 1300 · 201 South Main Street Salt Lake City, UT 84111-2216 · 801-322-2516

Robert E. Mansfield · Snell & Wilmer · Beneficial Tower, Suite 1200 · 15 West South Temple · Salt Lake City, UT 84101-1547 · 801-257-1900

EMPLOYEE BENEFITS LAW

Salt Lake City

David A. Anderson · ⑩ · Parsons Behle & Latimer · http://www.parsonsbehlelaw.com · 201 South Main Street, Suite 1800 · P.O. Box 45898 · Salt Lake City, UT 84145-0898 · 801-532-1234

Bruce E. Babcock · Jones Waldo · 170 South Main Street, Suite 1500 · Salt Lake City, UT 84101-1644 · 801-521-3200

Lorin C. Barker · Kirton & McConkie · Eagle Gate Tower, Suite 1800 · 60 East South Temple · P.O. Box 45120 · Salt Lake City, UT 84145-0120 · 801-328-3600

John S. Chindlund · ⑩ · Prince, Yeates & Geldzahler · City Centre I, Suite 900 · 175 East 400 South · Salt Lake City, UT 84111 · 801-524-1000

John E. Gates · Snow, Christensen & Martineau · http://www.scmlaw.com · 10 Exchange Place, 11th Floor · P.O. Box 45000 · Salt Lake City, UT 84145 · 801-521-9000

Narrvel E. Hall · Ray Quinney & Nebeker · 36 South State Street, Suite 1400 · P.O. Box 45385 · Salt Lake City, UT 84145-0385 · 801-532-1500

W. Waldan Lloyd · Callister, Nebeker & McCullough · Zions Bank Building, Suite 900 · 10 East South Temple · Salt Lake City, UT 84133 · 801-530-7300

John R. Madsen · Ray Quinney & Nebeker · 36 South State Street, Suite 1400 · P.O. Box 45385 · Salt Lake City, UT 84145-0385 · 801-532-1500

Kenneth B. Tillou · Parr, Waddoups, Brown, Gee & Loveless · 185 South State Street, Suite 1300 · P.O. Box 11019 · Salt Lake City, UT 84147-1537 · 801-532-7840

Steven D. Woodland · Stoel Rives · http://www.stoel.com · 201 South Main Street, Suite 1100 · Salt Lake City, UT 84111-4904 · 801-328-3131

ENERGY LAW

Salt Lake City

Brian W. Burnett · Callister, Nebeker & McCullough · Zions Bank Building, Suite 900 · 10 East South Temple · Salt Lake City, UT 84133 · 801-530-7300

A. John Davis III · Holme Roberts & Owen · http://www.hro.com · 299 South Main Street, Suite 1800 · Salt Lake City, UT 84111-2263 · 801-521-5800

Gary A. Dodge · Hatch, James & Dodge · 10 West Broadway, Suite 400 · Salt Lake City, UT 84101 · 801-363-6363

Denise A. Dragoo · Snell & Wilmer · Beneficial Tower, Suite 1200 · 15 West South Temple · Salt Lake City, UT 84101-1547 · 801-257-1900

Oliver W. Gushee, Jr. · a · Holme Roberts & Owen · http://www.hro.com · 299 South Main Street, Suite 1800 · Salt Lake City, UT 84111-2263 · 801-521-5800

James A. Holtkamp · 2) · Holland & Hart · 60 East South Temple, Suite 2000 · Salt Lake City, UT 84111-1031 · 801-595-7800

Stephen J. Hull · a · Parsons Behle & Latimer · http://www.parsonsbehlelaw.com · 201 South Main Street, Suite 1800 · P.O. Box 45898 · Salt Lake City, UT 84145-0898 · 801-532-1234

Dallin W. Jensen · a · Parsons Behle & Latimer · http://www.parsonsbehlelaw.com · 201 South Main Street, Suite 1800 · P.O. Box 45898 · Salt Lake City, UT 84145-0898 · 801-532-1234

Daniel A. Jensen · Parr, Waddoups, Brown, Gee & Loveless · 185 South State Street, Suite 1300 · P.O. Box 11019 · Salt Lake City, UT 84147-1537 · 801-532-7840

John S. Kirkham · a · Stoel Rives · http://www.stoel.com · 201 South Main Street, Suite 1100 · Salt Lake City, UT 84111-4904 · 801-328-3131

James B. Lee · 2) · Parsons Behle & Latimer · http://www.parsonsbehlelaw.com · 201 South Main Street, Suite 1800 · P.O. Box 45898 · Salt Lake City, UT 84145-0898 · 801-532-1234

Michael J. Malmquist · Parsons Behle & Latimer · http://www.parsonsbehlelaw.com · 201 South Main Street, Suite 1800 · P.O. Box 45898 · Salt Lake City, UT 84145-0898 · 801-532-1234

Matthew McNulty III · VanCott, Bagley, Cornwall & McCarthy · 36 South State Street, Suite 1900 · Salt Lake City, UT 84102 · 801-532-3333

Gregory B. Monson · a · Stoel Rives · http://www.stoel.com · 201 South Main Street, Suite 1100 · Salt Lake City, UT 84111-4904 · 801-328-3131

Clayton J. Parr · 2) · Parr, Waddoups, Brown, Gee & Loveless · 185 South State Street, Suite 1300 · P.O. Box 11019 · Salt Lake City, UT 84147-1537 · 801-532-7840

F. Robert Reeder · a · Parsons Behle & Latimer · http://www.parsonsbehlelaw.com · 201 South Main Street, Suite 1800 · P.O. Box 45898 · Salt Lake City, UT 84145-0898 · 801-532-1234

Gregory P. Williams · a · VanCott, Bagley, Cornwall & McCarthy · 36 South State Street, Suite 1900 · Salt Lake City, UT 84102 · 801-532-3333

ENVIRONMENTAL LAW

Salt Lake City

Martin K. Banks · Stoel Rives · http://www.stoel.com · 201 South Main Street, Suite 1100 · Salt Lake City, UT 84111-4904 · 801-328-3131

Bradley R. Cahoon · Snell & Wilmer · Beneficial Tower, Suite 1200 · 15 West South Temple · Salt Lake City, UT 84101-1547 · 801-257-1900

Steven J. Christiansen · Parr, Waddoups, Brown, Gee & Loveless · 185 South State Street, Suite 1300 · P.O. Box 11019 · Salt Lake City, UT 84147-1537 · 801-532-7840

Steven E. Clyde · a · Clyde Snow Sessions & Swenson · One Utah Center, Suite 1300 · 201 South Main Street · Salt Lake City, UT 84111-2216 · 801-322-2516

Denise A. Dragoo · Snell & Wilmer · Beneficial Tower, Suite 1200 · 15 West South Temple · Salt Lake City, UT 84101-1547 · 801-257-1900

Craig D. Galli · Holland & Hart · 60 East South Temple, Suite 2000 · Salt Lake City, UT 84111-1031 · 801-595-7800

James A. Holtkamp · 2) · Holland & Hart · 60 East South Temple, Suite 2000 · Salt Lake City, UT 84111-1031 · 801-595-7800

Dallin W. Jensen · a · Parsons Behle & Latimer · http://www.parsonsbehlelaw.com · 201 South Main Street, Suite 1800 · P.O. Box 45898 · Salt Lake City, UT 84145-0898 · 801-532-1234

Daniel A. Jensen · Parr, Waddoups, Brown, Gee & Loveless · 185 South State Street, Suite 1300 · P.O. Box 11019 · Salt Lake City, UT 84147-1537 · 801-532-7840

Lee E. Kapaloski · 2) · Parsons Behle & Latimer · http://www.parsonsbehlelaw.com · 201 South Main Street, Suite 1800 · P.O. Box 45898 · Salt Lake City, UT 84145-0898 · 801-532-1234

H. Michael Keller · a · VanCott, Bagley, Cornwall & McCarthy · 36 South State Street, Suite 1900 · Salt Lake City, UT 84102 · 801-532-3333

Lisa A. Kirschner · Parsons Behle & Latimer · http://www.parsonsbehlelaw.com · 201 South Main Street, Suite 1800 · P.O. Box 45898 · Salt Lake City, UT 84145-0898 · 801-532-1234

James B. Lee · 2) · Parsons Behle & Latimer · http://www.parsonsbehlelaw.com · 201 South Main Street, Suite 1800 · P.O. Box 45898 · Salt Lake City, UT 84145-0898 · 801-532-1234

Michael J. Malmquist · Parsons Behle & Latimer · http://www.parsonsbehlelaw.com · 201 South Main Street, Suite 1800 · P.O. Box 45898 · Salt Lake City, UT 84145-0898 · 801-532-1234

Kevin Reid Murray · a · Chapman & Cutler · 201 South Main Street · Salt Lake City, UT 84111 · 801-533-0066

Hal J. Pos · Parsons Behle & Latimer · http://www.parsonsbehlelaw.com · 201 South Main Street, Suite 1800 · P.O. Box 45898 · Salt Lake City, UT 84145-0898 · 801-532-1234

Michael J. Tomko · Parsons Behle & Latimer · http://www.parsonsbehlelaw.com · 201 South Main Street, Suite 1800 · P.O. Box 45898 · Salt Lake City, UT 84145-0898 · 801-532-1234

David W. Tundermann · a · Parsons Behle & Latimer · http://www.parsonsbehlelaw.com · 201 South Main Street, Suite 1800 · P.O. Box 45898 · Salt Lake City, UT 84145-0898 · 801-532-1234

Jody L. Williams · Holme Roberts & Owen · http://www.hro.com · 299 South Main Street, Suite 1800 · Salt Lake City, UT 84111-2263 · 801-521-5800

FAMILY LAW

North Salt Lake City

Neil Crist · Neil B. Crist · 230 North Cutler Road, Suite Five · North Salt Lake City, UT 84054 · 801-298-7200

Ogden

Martin W. Custen · a · Martin W. Custen · 1004 Twenty-Fourth Street · Ogden, UT 84401 · 801-621-3662

Provo

Don R. Petersen · a · Howard, Lewis & Petersen · 120 East 300 North Street · P.O. Box 1248 · Provo, UT 84603 · 801-373-6345

Brent D. Young · Ivie & Young · 226 West 2230 North, Suite 210 · P.O. Box 657 · Provo, UT 84603 · 801-375-3000

Salt Lake City

Dean C. Andreasen · Clyde Snow Sessions & Swenson · One Utah Center, Suite 1300 · 201 South Main Street · Salt Lake City, UT 84111-2216 · 801-322-2516

Helen E. Christian · a · Dart, Adamson & Donovan · 370 East South Temple, Suite 400 · Salt Lake City, UT 84111 · 801-521-6383

Mary C. Corporon · Corporon & Williams · 405 South Main Street, Suite 700 · Salt Lake City, UT 84102 801-328-1162

David S. Dolowitz · 2) · Cohne, Rappaport & Segal · 257 East 200 South, Suite 700 · P.O. Box 11008 · Salt Lake City, UT 84147-0008 · 801-532-2666

Sharon A. Donovan · a · Dart, Adamson & Donovan · 370 East South Temple, Suite 400 · Salt Lake City, UT 84111 · 801-521-6383

A. Howard Lundgren · Durham Jones & Pinegar · 111 East Broadway, Suite 900 · P.O. Box 4050 · Salt Lake City, UT 84110 · 801-415-3000

Ellen M. Maycock · a · Kruse, Landa, Maycock & Ricks · 136 East South Temple, 21st Floor · P.O. Box 45561 · Salt Lake City, UT 84145-0561 · 801-531-7090

Clark W. Sessions · 2) · Clyde Snow Sessions & Swenson · One Utah Center, Suite 1300 · 201 South Main Street · Salt Lake City, UT 84111-2216 · 801-322-2516

Sandy

Frederick N. Green · a · Law Office of Frederick N. Green · 7390 South Creek Road, Suite 104 · Sandy, UT 84093 · 801-401-0185

FAMILY LAW MEDIATION

North Salt Lake City

Neil Crist · Neil B. Crist · 230 North Cutler Road, Suite Five · North Salt Lake City, UT 84054 · 801-298-7200

Ogden

Martin W. Custen · a · Martin W. Custen · 1004 Twenty-Fourth Street · Ogden, UT 84401 · 801-621-3662

Brian R. Florence · a · Mediation Services · 1943 East 6200 South · Ogden, UT 84403 · 801-476-3200

Provo

Don R. Petersen · a · Howard, Lewis & Petersen · 120 East 300 North Street · P.O. Box 1248 · Provo, UT 84603 · 801-373-6345

Salt Lake City

Dean C. Andreasen · Clyde Snow Sessions & Swenson · One Utah Center, Suite 1300 · 201 South Main Street · Salt Lake City, UT 84111-2216 · 801-322-2516

Helen E. Christian · a · Dart, Adamson & Donovan · 370 East South Temple, Suite 400 · Salt Lake City, UT 84111 · 801-521-6383

Mary C. Corporon · Corporon & Williams · 405 South Main Street, Suite 700 · Salt Lake City, UT 84102 801-328-1162

David S. Dolowitz · 2) · Cohne, Rappaport & Segal · 257 East 200 South, Suite 700 · P.O. Box 11008 · Salt Lake City, UT 84147-0008 · 801-532-2666

Sharon A. Donovan · a · Dart, Adamson & Donovan · 370 East South Temple, Suite 400 · Salt Lake City, UT 84111 · 801-521-6383

William W. Downes · William Downes · 1945 South 1100 East, Suite 200 · Salt Lake City, UT 84106-4092 · 801-531-7400

A. Howard Lundgren · Durham Jones & Pinegar · 111 East Broadway, Suite 900 · P.O. Box 4050 · Salt Lake City, UT 84110 · 801-415-3000

Ellen M. Maycock · a · Kruse, Landa, Maycock & Ricks · 136 East South Temple, 21st Floor · P.O. Box 45561 · Salt Lake City, UT 84145-0561 · 801-531-7090

Clark W. Sessions · 2) · Clyde Snow Sessions & Swenson · One Utah Center, Suite 1300 · 201 South Main Street · Salt Lake City, UT 84111-2216 · 801-322-2516

Sandy

Frederick N. Green · a · Law Office of Frederick N. Green · 7390 South Creek Road, Suite 104 · Sandy, UT 84093 · 801-401-0185

FIRST AMENDMENT LAW

Salt Lake City

Randy L. Dryer · a · Parsons Behle & Latimer · http://www.parsonsbehlelaw.com · 201 South Main Street, Suite 1800 · P.O. Box 45898 · Salt Lake City, UT 84145-0898 · 801-532-1234

Jeffrey J. Hunt · Parr, Waddoups, Brown, Gee & Loveless · 185 South State Street, Suite 1300 · P.O. Box 11019 · Salt Lake City, UT 84147-1537 · 801-532-7840

Von G. Keetch · Kirton & McConkie · Eagle Gate Tower, Suite 1800 · 60 East South Temple · P.O. Box 45120 · Salt Lake City, UT 84145-0120 · 801-328-3600

Michael Patrick O'Brien · Jones Waldo · 170 South Main Street, Suite 1500 · Salt Lake City, UT 84101-1644 · 801-521-3200

David C. Reymann · Parr, Waddoups, Brown, Gee & Loveless · 185 South State Street, Suite 1300 · P.O. Box 11019 · Salt Lake City, UT 84147-1537 · 801-532-7840

Richard A. Van Wagoner · Snow, Christensen & Martineau · http://www.scmlaw.com · 10 Exchange Place, 11th Floor · P.O. Box 45000 · Salt Lake City, UT 84145 · 801-521-9000

Sandy

D. Miles Holman · a · Holman & Walker · 9533 South 700 East, Suite 100 · Sandy, UT 84070 · 801-990-4990

FRANCHISE LAW

Salt Lake City

David W. Slaughter · Snow, Christensen & Martineau · http://www.scmlaw.com · 10 Exchange Place, 11th Floor · P.O. Box 45000 · Salt Lake City, UT 84145 · 801-521-9000

GOVERNMENT RELATIONS LAW

Salt Lake City

David R. Bird · Parsons Behle & Latimer · http://www.parsonsbehlelaw.com · 201 South Main Street, Suite 1800 · P.O. Box 45898 · Salt Lake City, UT 84145-0898 · 801-532-1234

Bradley R. Cahoon · Snell & Wilmer · Beneficial Tower, Suite 1200 · 15 West South Temple · Salt Lake City, UT 84101-1547 · 801-257-1900

Denise A. Dragoo · Snell & Wilmer · Beneficial Tower, Suite 1200 · 15 West South Temple · Salt Lake City, UT 84101-1547 · 801-257-1900

Gerald H. Kinghorn · Parsons Kinghorn Harris · 111 East Broadway Street, 11th Floor · Salt Lake City, UT 84111 · 801-363-4300

HEALTH CARE LAW

Salt Lake City

Curtis J. Drake · Snell & Wilmer · Beneficial Tower, Suite 1200 · 15 West South Temple · Salt Lake City, UT 84101-1547 · 801-257-1900

Philip R. Fishler · Strong & Hanni · Three Triad Center, Suite 500 · Salt Lake City, UT 84180 · 801-532-7080

Elliott J. Williams · a · Williams & Hunt · 257 East 200 South, Suite 500 · P.O. Box 45678 · Salt Lake City, UT 84145-5678 · 801-521-5678

IMMIGRATION LAW

Ogden

Timothy M. Wheelwright · Durham Jones & Pinegar · 1104 East Country Hills Drive, Suite 710 · Ogden, UT 84403 · 801-395-2424

Salt Lake City

Lorna Rogers Burgess · a · Parsons Behle & Latimer · http://www.parsonsbehlelaw.com · 201 South Main Street, Suite 1800 · P.O. Box 45898 · Salt Lake City, UT 84145-0898 · 801-532-1234

David E. Littlefield · a · Littlefield & Peterson · 426 South 500 East · Salt Lake City, UT 84102 · 801-531-0435

Barbara V. Melendez · Kirton & McConkie · Eagle Gate Tower, Suite 1800 · 60 East South Temple · P.O. Box 45120 · Salt Lake City, UT 84145-0120 · 801-328-3600

Janice Radler Olson · a · Gardner and Olson · 2257 South 1100 East, Suite 201 · Salt Lake City, UT 84106 · 801-468-1400

West Jordan

Leonor E. Perretta · Perretta Law Office · 8831 South Redwood, Suite A · West Jordan, UT 84088 · 801-263-1213

INFORMATION TECHNOLOGY LAW

Salt Lake City

Randall B. Bateman · Bateman IP Law Group · Judge Building, Suite 550 · Eight East Broadway · P.O. Box 1319 · Salt Lake City, UT 84110 · 801-533-0320

H. Dickson Burton · TraskBritt · http://www.traskbritt.com · 230 South 500 East, Suite 300 · P.O. Box 2550 · Salt Lake City, UT 84110-2550 · 801-532-1922

John H. Rees · Callister, Nebeker & McCullough · Zions Bank Building, Suite 900 · 10 East South Temple · Salt Lake City, UT 84133 · 801-530-7300

Terry E. Welch · Parr, Waddoups, Brown, Gee & Loveless · 185 South State Street, Suite 1300 · P.O. Box 11019 · Salt Lake City, UT 84147-1537 · 801-532-7840

INSURANCE LAW

Salt Lake City

Alan C. Bradshaw · Manning Curtis Bradshaw & Bednar · New House Building, Third Floor · 10 Exchange Place · Salt Lake City, UT 84111 · 801-363-5678

Rich L. Humpherys · a · Christensen & Jensen · Beneficial Tower, Suite 800 · 15 West South Temple · Salt Lake City, UT 84101 · 801-323-5000

INTELLECTUAL PROPERTY LAW

Lindon

Jon C. Christiansen · Tech Law Ventures · Canopy Data Center Building, Suite 220 · 333 South 520 West · Lindon, UT 84042 · 801-805-3684

Salt Lake City

John P. Ashton · VanCott, Bagley, Cornwall & McCarthy · 36 South State Street, Suite 1900 · Salt Lake City, UT 84102 · 801-532-3333

Arthur B. Berger · Ray Quinney & Nebeker · 36 South State Street, Suite 1400 · P.O. Box 45385 · Salt Lake City, UT 84145-0385 · 801-532-1500

Mark M. Bettilyon · Ray Quinney & Nebeker · 36 South State Street, Suite 1400 · P.O. Box 45385 · Salt Lake City, UT 84145-0385 · 801-532-1500

Laurence Bond · TraskBritt · http://www.traskbritt.com · 230 South 500 East, Suite 300 · P.O. Box 2550 · Salt Lake City, UT 84110-2550 · 801-532-1922

William S. Britt · a · TraskBritt · http://www.traskbritt.com · 230 South 500 East, Suite 300 · P.O. Box 2550 · Salt Lake City, UT 84110-2550 · 801-532-1922

H. Dickson Burton · TraskBritt · http://www.traskbritt.com · 230 South 500 East, Suite 300 · P.O. Box 2550 · Salt Lake City, UT 84110-2550 · 801-532-1922

Edgar R. Cataxinos · TraskBritt · http://www.traskbritt.com · 230 South 500 East, Suite 300 · P.O. Box 2550 · Salt Lake City, UT 84110-2550 · 801-532-1922

Barton W. Giddings · Stoel Rives · http://www.stoel.com · 201 South Main Street, Suite 1100 · Salt Lake City, UT 84111-4904 · 801-328-3131

Rick B. Hoggard · Ray Quinney & Nebeker · 36 South State Street, Suite 1400 · P.O. Box 45385 · Salt Lake City, UT 84145-0385 · 801-532-1500

Kevin B. Laurence · Stoel Rives · http://www.stoel.com · 201 South Main Street, Suite 1100 · Salt Lake City, UT 84111-4904 · 801-328-3131

Brent P. Lorimer · Workman Nydegger · 1000 Eagle Gate Tower · 60 East South Temple · Salt Lake City, UT 84111 · 801-533-9800

Michael E. Mangelson · Stoel Rives · http://www.stoel.com · 201 South Main Street, Suite 1100 · Salt Lake City, UT 84111-4904 · 801-328-3131

David G. Mangum · Parsons Behle & Latimer · http://www.parsonsbehlelaw.com · 201 South Main Street, Suite 1800 · P.O. Box 45898 · Salt Lake City, UT 84145-0898 · 801-532-1234

Eric L. Maschoff · Workman Nydegger · 1000 Eagle Gate Tower · 60 East South Temple · Salt Lake City, UT 84111 · 801-533-9800

Rick D. Nydegger · a · Workman Nydegger · 1000 Eagle Gate Tower · 60 East South Temple · Salt Lake City, UT 84111 · 801-533-9800

C. Kevin Speirs · Parsons Behle & Latimer · http://www.parsonsbehlelaw.com · 201 South Main Street, Suite 1800 · P.O. Box 45898 · Salt Lake City, UT 84145-0898 · 801-532-1234

David V. Trask · a · TraskBritt · http://www.traskbritt.com · 230 South 500 East, Suite 300 · P.O. Box 2550 · Salt Lake City, UT 84110-2550 · 801-532-1922

Allen C. Turner · TraskBritt · http://www.traskbritt.com · 230 South 500 East, Suite 300 · P.O. Box 2550 · Salt Lake City, UT 84110-2550 · 801-532-1922

Thomas Vuksinick · Workman Nydegger · 1000 Eagle Gate Tower · 60 East South Temple · Salt Lake City, UT 84111 · 801-533-9800

Joseph A. Walkowski · TraskBritt · http://www.traskbritt.com · 230 South 500 East, Suite 300 · P.O. Box 2550 · Salt Lake City, UT 84110-2550 · 801-532-1922

Terry E. Welch · Parr, Waddoups, Brown, Gee & Loveless · 185 South State Street, Suite 1300 · P.O. Box 11019 · Salt Lake City, UT 84147-1537 · 801-532-7840

Salt Lake City

David A. Anderson · a · Parsons Behle & Latimer · http://www.parsonsbehlelaw.com · 201 South Main Street, Suite 1800 · P.O. Box 45898 · Salt Lake City, UT 84145-0898 · 801-532-1234

Lois A. Baar · a · Holland & Hart · 60 East South Temple, Suite 2000 · Salt Lake City, UT 84111-1031 · 801-595-7800

Steven C. Bednar · Manning Curtis Bradshaw & Bednar · New House Building, Third Floor · 10 Exchange Place · Salt Lake City, UT 84111 · 801-363-5678

Bryan K. Benard · Holland & Hart · 60 East South Temple, Suite 2000 · Salt Lake City, UT 84111-1031 801-595-7800

Elisabeth R. Blattner-Thompson · Parsons Behle & Latimer · http://www.parsonsbehlelaw.com · 201 South Main Street, Suite 1800 · P.O. Box 45898 · Salt Lake City, UT 84145-0898 · 801-532-1234

Michael E. Blue · Ray Quinney & Nebeker · 36 South State Street, Suite 1400 · P.O. Box 45385 · Salt Lake City, UT 84145-0385 · 801-532-1500

John S. Chindlund · a · Prince, Yeates & Geldzahler · City Centre I, Suite 900 · 175 East 400 South · Salt Lake City, UT 84111 · 801-524-1000

Stephen W. Cook · 2) · Cook & Associates · 323 South 600 East, Suite 200 · Salt Lake City, UT 84102 · 801-595-8600

Elizabeth T. Dunning · 2) · Holme Roberts & Owen · http://www.hro.com · 299 South Main Street, Suite 1800 · Salt Lake City, UT 84111-2263 · 801-521-5800

Matthew M. Durham · Stoel Rives · http://www.stoel.com · 201 South Main Street, Suite 1100 · Salt Lake City, UT 84111-4904 · 801-328-3131

W. Mark Gavre · Parsons Behle & Latimer · http://www.parsonsbehlelaw.com · 201 South Main Street, Suite 1800 · P.O. Box 45898 · Salt Lake City, UT 84145-0898 · 801-532-1234

Scott A. Hagen · Ray Quinney & Nebeker · 36 South State Street, Suite 1400 · P.O. Box 45385 · Salt Lake City, UT 84145-0385 · 801-532-1500

Heidi E. C. Leithead · Parr, Waddoups, Brown, Gee & Loveless · 185 South State Street, Suite 1300 · P.O. Box 11019 · Salt Lake City, UT 84147-1537 · 801-532-7840

James S. Lowrie · a · Jones Waldo · 170 South Main Street, Suite 1500 · Salt Lake City, UT 84101-1644 801-521-3200

Michael Patrick O'Brien · Jones Waldo · 170 South Main Street, Suite 1500 · Salt Lake City, UT 84101-1644 · 801-521-3200

Stanley J. Preston · Snow, Christensen & Martineau · http://www.scmlaw.com · 10 Exchange Place, 11th Floor · P.O. Box 45000 · Salt Lake City, UT 84145 · 801-521-9000

Robert O. Rice · Ray Quinney & Nebeker · 36 South State Street, Suite 1400 · P.O. Box 45385 · Salt Lake City, UT 84145-0385 · 801-532-1500

Arthur F. Sandack · 2% · Arthur F. Sandack · Judge Building, Suite 510 · Eight East Broadway · Salt Lake City, UT 84111 · 801-532-7858

Lauren I. Scholnick · Strindberg, Scholnick & Chamness · 426 North, 300 West · Salt Lake City, UT 84103 · 801-359-4169

Janet Hugie Smith · 2) · Ray Quinney & Nebeker · 36 South State Street, Suite 1400 · P.O. Box 45385 · Salt Lake City, UT 84145-0385 · 801-532-1500

Erik Strindberg · Strindberg, Scholnick & Chamness · 426 North, 300 West · Salt Lake City, UT 84103 · 801-359-4169

Frederick R. Thaler, Jr. · Ray Quinney & Nebeker · 36 South State Street, Suite 1400 · P.O. Box 45385 · Salt Lake City, UT 84145-0385 · 801-532-1500

Robert H. Wilde · a · Robert H. Wilde · 935 East South Union Avenue, Suite D-102 · P.O. Box 71922 · Salt Lake City, UT 84171 · 801-255-4774

Michael A. Zody · Parsons Behle & Latimer · http://www.parsonsbehlelaw.com · 201 South Main Street, Suite 1800 · P.O. Box 45898 · Salt Lake City, UT 84145-0898 · 801-532-1234

LAND USE & ZONING LAW

Salt Lake City

Jeffrey W. Appel · Ray Quinney & Nebeker · 36 South State Street, Suite 1400 · P.O. Box 45385 · Salt Lake City, UT 84145-0385 · 801-532-1500

Jody K. Burnett · Williams & Hunt · 257 East 200 South, Suite 500 · P.O. Box 45678 · Salt Lake City, UT 84145-5678 · 801-521-5678

Robert A. McConnell · Parr, Waddoups, Brown, Gee & Loveless · 185 South State Street, Suite 1300 · P.O. Box 11019 · Salt Lake City, UT 84147-1537 · 801-532-7840

Andrew M. Morse · Snow, Christensen & Martineau · http://www.scmlaw.com · 10 Exchange Place, 11th Floor · P.O. Box 45000 · Salt Lake City, UT 84145 · 801-521-9000

LEGAL MALPRACTICE LAW

Salt Lake City

M. David Eckersley · a · Prince, Yeates & Geldzahler · City Centre I, Suite 900 · 175 East 400 South · Salt Lake City, UT 84111 · 801-524-1000

Matthew L. Lalli · Snell & Wilmer · Beneficial Tower, Suite 1200 · 15 West South Temple · Salt Lake City, UT 84101-1547 · 801-257-1900

Michael F. Skolnick · Kipp & Christian · http://www.kippandchristian.com · 10 Exchange Place, Fourth Floor · Salt Lake City, UT 84111 · 801-521-3773

John A. Snow · VanCott, Bagley, Cornwall & McCarthy · 36 South State Street, Suite 1900 · Salt Lake City, UT 84102 · 801-532-3333

MEDICAL MALPRACTICE LAW

Salt Lake City

Ralph L. Dewsnup · a · Dewsnup, King & Olsen · http://www.dkolaw.com · Beneficial Financial Group, Suite 2400 · 36 South State Street · Salt Lake City, UT 84111-0024 · 801-533-0400

Tim D. Dunn · Dunn & Dunn · 505 East 200 South, Second Floor · Salt Lake City, UT 84102 · 801-521-6677

J. Anthony Eyre · a · Kipp & Christian · http://www.kippandchristian.com · 10 Exchange Place, Fourth Floor · Salt Lake City, UT 84111 · 801-521-3773

Dennis C. Ferguson · Williams & Hunt · 257 East 200 South, Suite 500 · P.O. Box 45678 · Salt Lake City, UT 84145-5678 · 801-521-5678

Colin P. King · a · Dewsnup, King & Olsen · http://www.dkolaw.com · Beneficial Financial Group, Suite 2400 · 36 South State Street · Salt Lake City, UT 84111-0024 · 801-533-0400

Roger T. Sharp · a · Roger T. Sharp · 2825 East Cottonwood Parkway, Suite 500 · Salt Lake City, UT 84121 · 801-990-3405

Charles H. Thronson · a · Parsons Behle & Latimer · http://www.parsonsbehlelaw.com · 201 South Main Street, Suite 1800 · P.O. Box 45898 · Salt Lake City, UT 84145-0898 · 801-532-1234

David G. Williams · Snow, Christensen & Martineau · http://www.scmlaw.com · 10 Exchange Place, 11th Floor · P.O. Box 45000 · Salt Lake City, UT 84145 · 801-521-9000

Elliott J. Williams · a · Williams & Hunt · 257 East 200 South, Suite 500 · P.O. Box 45678 · Salt Lake City, UT 84145-5678 · 801-521-5678

MERGERS & ACQUISITIONS LAW

Salt Lake City

P. Christian Anderson · Ballard Spahr Andrews & Ingersoll · One Utah Center, Suite 800 · 201 South Main Street · Salt Lake City, UT 84111-2221 · 801-531-3000

David G. Angerbauer · Holland & Hart · 60 East South Temple, Suite 2000 · Salt Lake City, UT 84111-1031 · 801-595-7800

Mark E. Bonham · Ray Quinney & Nebeker · 36 South State Street, Suite 1400 · P.O. Box 45385 · Salt Lake City, UT 84145-0385 · 801-532-1500

Jeffrey M. Jones · Durham Jones & Pinegar · 111 East Broadway, Suite 900 · P.O. Box 4050 · Salt Lake City, UT 84110 · 801-415-3000

N. Todd Leishman · Durham Jones & Pinegar · 111 East Broadway, Suite 900 · P.O. Box 4050 · Salt Lake City, UT 84110 · 801-415-3000

Gregory E. Lindley · Holland & Hart · 60 East South Temple, Suite 2000 · Salt Lake City, UT 84111-1031 · 801-595-7800

David H. Little · Holme Roberts & Owen · http://www.hro.com · 299 South Main Street, Suite 1800 · Salt Lake City, UT 84111-2263 · 801-521-5800

Brian G. Lloyd · Parr, Waddoups, Brown, Gee & Loveless · 185 South State Street, Suite 1300 · P.O. Box 11019 · Salt Lake City, UT 84147-1537 · 801-532-7840

Scott W. Loveless · Parr, Waddoups, Brown, Gee & Loveless · 185 South State Street, Suite 1300 · P.O. Box 11019 · Salt Lake City, UT 84147-1537 · 801-532-7840

Ronald G. Moffitt · Stoel Rives · http://www.stoel.com · 201 South Main Street, Suite 1100 · Salt Lake City, UT 84111-4904 · 801-328-3131

Ronald S. Poelman · Jones Waldo · 170 South Main Street, Suite 1500 · Salt Lake City, UT 84101-1644 · 801-521-3200

David R. Rudd · Ballard Spahr Andrews & Ingersoll · One Utah Center, Suite 800 · 201 South Main Street · Salt Lake City, UT 84111-2221 · 801-531-3000

Brent M. Stevenson · Parr, Waddoups, Brown, Gee & Loveless · 185 South State Street, Suite 1300 · P.O. Box 11019 · Salt Lake City, UT 84147-1537 · 801-532-7840

Nolan S. Taylor · Dorsey & Whitney · 170 South Main Street, Suite 900 · Salt Lake City, UT 84101-1655 801-933-7360

Thomas R. Taylor · Holme Roberts & Owen · http://www.hro.com · 299 South Main Street, Suite 1800 · Salt Lake City, UT 84111-2263 · 801-521-5800

Reed W. Topham · Stoel Rives · http://www.stoel.com · 201 South Main Street, Suite 1100 · Salt Lake City, UT 84111-4904 · 801-328-3131

Randon W. Wilson · Jones Waldo · 170 South Main Street, Suite 1500 · Salt Lake City, UT 84101-1644 · 801-521-3200

R. Gary Winger · Ray Quinney & Nebeker · 36 South State Street, Suite 1400 · P.O. Box 45385 · Salt Lake City, UT 84145-0385 · 801-532-1500

South Jordan

Brian A. Lebrecht · The Lebrecht Group · 406 West South Jordan Parkway, Suite 160 · South Jordan, UT 84095 · 801-983-4948

MINING LAW

Salt Lake City

Denise A. Dragoo · Snell & Wilmer · Beneficial Tower, Suite 1200 · 15 West South Temple · Salt Lake City, UT 84101-1547 · 801-257-1900

Stephen J. Hull · a · Parsons Behle & Latimer · http://www.parsonsbehlelaw.com · 201 South Main Street, Suite 1800 · P.O. Box 45898 · Salt Lake City, UT 84145-0898 · 801-532-1234

Daniel A. Jensen · Parr, Waddoups, Brown, Gee & Loveless · 185 South State Street, Suite 1300 · P.O. Box 11019 · Salt Lake City, UT 84147-1537 · 801-532-7840

John S. Kirkham · a · Stoel Rives · http://www.stoel.com · 201 South Main Street, Suite 1100 · Salt Lake City, UT 84111-4904 · 801-328-3131

James B. Lee · 2) · Parsons Behle & Latimer · http://www.parsonsbehlelaw.com · 201 South Main Street, Suite 1800 · P.O. Box 45898 · Salt Lake City, UT 84145-0898 · 801-532-1234

Michael J. Malmquist · Parsons Behle & Latimer · http://www.parsonsbehlelaw.com · 201 South Main Street, Suite 1800 · P.O. Box 45898 · Salt Lake City, UT 84145-0898 · 801-532-1234

Clayton J. Parr · 2) · Parr, Waddoups, Brown, Gee & Loveless · 185 South State Street, Suite 1300 · P.O. Box 11019 · Salt Lake City, UT 84147-1537 · 801-532-7840

Gregory P. Williams · a · VanCott, Bagley, Cornwall & McCarthy · 36 South State Street, Suite 1900 · Salt Lake City, UT 84102 · 801-532-3333

NATURAL RESOURCES LAW

Salt Lake City

Brian W. Burnett · Callister, Nebeker & McCullough · Zions Bank Building, Suite 900 · 10 East South Temple · Salt Lake City, UT 84133 · 801-530-7300

Thomas W. Clawson · VanCott, Bagley, Cornwall & McCarthy · 36 South State Street, Suite 1900 · Salt Lake City, UT 84102 · 801-532-3333

Steven E. Clyde · a · Clyde Snow Sessions & Swenson · One Utah Center, Suite 1300 · 201 South Main Street · Salt Lake City, UT 84111-2216 · 801-322-2516

Denise A. Dragoo · Snell & Wilmer · Beneficial Tower, Suite 1200 · 15 West South Temple · Salt Lake City, UT 84101-1547 · 801-257-1900

Oliver W. Gushee, Jr. · a · Holme Roberts & Owen · http://www.hro.com · 299 South Main Street, Suite 1800 · Salt Lake City, UT 84111-2263 · 801-521-5800

James A. Holtkamp · 2) · Holland & Hart · 60 East South Temple, Suite 2000 · Salt Lake City, UT 84111-1031 · 801-595-7800

Stephen J. Hull · a · Parsons Behle & Latimer · http://www.parsonsbehlelaw.com · 201 South Main Street, Suite 1800 · P.O. Box 45898 · Salt Lake City, UT 84145-0898 · 801-532-1234

Dallin W. Jensen · a · Parsons Behle & Latimer · http://www.parsonsbehlelaw.com · 201 South Main Street, Suite 1800 · P.O. Box 45898 · Salt Lake City, UT 84145-0898 · 801-532-1234

Daniel A. Jensen · Parr, Waddoups, Brown, Gee & Loveless · 185 South State Street, Suite 1300 · P.O. Box 11019 · Salt Lake City, UT 84147-1537 · 801-532-7840

Lee E. Kapaloski · 2) · Parsons Behle & Latimer · http://www.parsonsbehlelaw.com · 201 South Main Street, Suite 1800 · P.O. Box 45898 · Salt Lake City, UT 84145-0898 · 801-532-1234

H. Michael Keller · a · VanCott, Bagley, Cornwall & McCarthy · 36 South State Street, Suite 1900 · Salt Lake City, UT 84102 · 801-532-3333

Gerald H. Kinghorn · Parsons Kinghorn Harris · 111 East Broadway Street, 11th Floor · Salt Lake City, UT 84111 · 801-363-4300

John S. Kirkham · a · Stoel Rives · http://www.stoel.com · 201 South Main Street, Suite 1100 · Salt Lake City, UT 84111-4904 · 801-328-3131

James B. Lee · 2) · Parsons Behle & Latimer · http://www.parsonsbehlelaw.com · 201 South Main Street, Suite 1800 · P.O. Box 45898 · Salt Lake City, UT 84145-0898 · 801-532-1234

Michael J. Malmquist · Parsons Behle & Latimer · http://www.parsonsbehlelaw.com · 201 South Main Street, Suite 1800 · P.O. Box 45898 · Salt Lake City, UT 84145-0898 · 801-532-1234

Clayton J. Parr · 2) · Parr, Waddoups, Brown, Gee & Loveless · 185 South State Street, Suite 1300 · P.O. Box 11019 · Salt Lake City, UT 84147-1537 · 801-532-7840

William B. Prince · Dorsey & Whitney · 170 South Main Street, Suite 900 · Salt Lake City, UT 84101-1655 · 801-933-7360

Gregory P. Williams · a · VanCott, Bagley, Cornwall & McCarthy · 36 South State Street, Suite 1900 · Salt Lake City, UT 84102 · 801-532-3333

Jody L. Williams · Holme Roberts & Owen · http://www.hro.com · 299 South Main Street, Suite 1800 · Salt Lake City, UT 84111-2263 · 801-521-5800

NON-PROFIT/CHARITIES LAW

Salt Lake City

Bruce L. Olson · Ray Quinney & Nebeker · 36 South State Street, Suite 1400 · P.O. Box 45385 · Salt Lake City, UT 84145-0385 · 801-532-1500

NON-WHITE-COLLAR CRIMINAL DEFENSE

Salt Lake City

D. Gilbert Athay · 2) · D. Gilbert Athay · 43 East 400 South · Salt Lake City, UT 84111 · 801-363-7074

Walter F. Bugden, Jr. · a · Bugden & Isaacson · 445 East 200 South, Suite 150 · Salt Lake City, UT 84111 · 801-467-1700

Loni F. DeLand · a · Loni F. DeLand · 43 East 400 South · Salt Lake City, UT 84111 · 801-364-1333

David V. Finlayson · David V. Finlayson · 43 East 400 South · Salt Lake City, UT 84111 · 801-220-0700

Richard Mauro · Law Office of Richard Mauro · 43 East 400 South · Salt Lake City, UT 84111 · 801-363-9500

Stephen R. McCaughey · 2) · McCaughey & Metos · 10 West Broadway, Suite 650 · Salt Lake City, UT 84101-2002 · 801-364-6474

G. Fred Metos · 2) · McCaughey & Metos · 10 West Broadway, Suite 650 · Salt Lake City, UT 84101-2002 · 801-364-6474

Bradley P. Rich · a · Yengich, Rich & Xaiz · 175 East 400 South, Suite 400 · Salt Lake City, UT 84111 · 801-355-0320

Scott C. Williams · Scott C. Williams · 43 East 400 South · Salt Lake City, UT 84111 · 801-220-0700

Ronald J. Yengich · 2) · Yengich, Rich & Xaiz · 175 East 400 South, Suite 400 · Salt Lake City, UT 84111 · 801-355-0320

OIL & GAS LAW

Cottonwood Heights

Frederick M. MacDonald · Beatty & Wozniak · 6925 Union Park Center, Suite 525 · Cottonwood Heights, UT 84047 · 801-566-8446

Salt Lake City

Thomas W. Clawson · VanCott, Bagley, Cornwall & McCarthy · 36 South State Street, Suite 1900 · Salt Lake City, UT 84102 · 801-532-3333

A. John Davis III · Holme Roberts & Owen · http://www.hro.com · 299 South Main Street, Suite 1800 · Salt Lake City, UT 84111-2263 · 801-521-5800

Angela L. Franklin · Holme Roberts & Owen · http://www.hro.com · 299 South Main Street, Suite 1800 · Salt Lake City, UT 84111-2263 · 801-521-5800

Oliver W. Gushee, Jr. · a · Holme Roberts & Owen · http://www.hro.com · 299 South Main Street, Suite 1800 · Salt Lake City, UT 84111-2263 · 801-521-5800

James A. Holtkamp · 2) · Holland & Hart · 60 East South Temple, Suite 2000 · Salt Lake City, UT 84111-1031 · 801-595-7800

John S. Kirkham · a · Stoel Rives · http://www.stoel.com · 201 South Main Street, Suite 1100 · Salt Lake City, UT 84111-4904 · 801-328-3131

Phillip William Lear · Lear & Lear · The Downey Mansion · 808 East South Temple Street · Salt Lake City, UT 84111 · 801-538-5000

William B. Prince · Dorsey & Whitney · 170 South Main Street, Suite 900 · Salt Lake City, UT 84101-1655 · 801-933-7360

PERSONAL INJURY LITIGATION

Provo

Jackson B. Howard · 2) · Howard, Lewis & Petersen · 120 East 300 North Street · P.O. Box 1248 · Provo, UT 84603 · 801-373-6345

D. David Lambert · Howard, Lewis & Petersen · 120 East 300 North Street · P.O. Box 1248 · Provo, UT 84603 · 801-373-6345

Salt Lake City

John A. Anderson · Stoel Rives · http://www.stoel.com · 201 South Main Street, Suite 1100 · Salt Lake City, UT 84111-4904 · 801-328-3131

Bryon J. Benevento · Snell & Wilmer · Beneficial Tower, Suite 1200 · 15 West South Temple · Salt Lake City, UT 84101-1547 · 801-257-1900

Richard D. Burbidge · a · Burbidge, Mitchell & Gross · Parkside Tower, Suite 920 · 215 South State Street · Salt Lake City, UT 84111 · 801-355-6677

Robert S. Campbell, Jr. · 2% · VanCott, Bagley, Cornwall & McCarthy · 36 South State Street, Suite 1900 Salt Lake City, UT 84102 · 801-532-3333

Francis J. Carney · a · Anderson & Karrenberg · Chase Tower, Suite 700 · 50 West Broadway · Salt Lake City, UT 84101-2006 · 801-534-1700

Harold G. Christensen · a · Snow, Christensen & Martineau · http://www.scmlaw.com · 10 Exchange Place, 11th Floor · P.O. Box 45000 · Salt Lake City, UT 84145 · 801-521-9000

Roger P. Christensen · Christensen & Jensen · Beneficial Tower, Suite 800 · 15 West South Temple · Salt Lake City, UT 84101 · 801-323-5000

Ralph L. Dewsnup · a · Dewsnup, King & Olsen · http://www.dkolaw.com · Beneficial Financial Group, Suite 2400 · 36 South State Street · Salt Lake City, UT 84111-0024 · 801-533-0400

M. David Eckersley · a · Prince, Yeates & Geldzahler · City Centre I, Suite 900 · 175 East 400 South · Salt Lake City, UT 84111 · 801-524-1000

Jeffrey D. Eisenberg · Eisenberg & Gilchrist · 215 South State Street, Suite 900 · Salt Lake City, UT 84111 · 801-366-9100

J. Anthony Eyre · a · Kipp & Christian · http://www.kippandchristian.com · 10 Exchange Place, Fourth Floor · Salt Lake City, UT 84111 · 801-521-3773

Dennis C. Ferguson · Williams & Hunt · 257 East 200 South, Suite 500 · P.O. Box 45678 · Salt Lake City, UT 84145-5678 · 801-521-5678

Phillip S. Ferguson · Christensen & Jensen · Beneficial Tower, Suite 800 · 15 West South Temple · Salt Lake City, UT 84101 · 801-323-5000

Philip R. Fishler · Strong & Hanni · Three Triad Center, Suite 500 · Salt Lake City, UT 84180 · 801-532-7080

Tracy H. Fowler · Snell & Wilmer · Beneficial Tower, Suite 1200 · 15 West South Temple · Salt Lake City, UT 84101-1547 · 801-257-1900

Robert G. Gilchrist · Eisenberg & Gilchrist · 215 South State Street, Suite 900 · Salt Lake City, UT 84111 · 801-366-9100

Glenn C. Hanni · a · Strong & Hanni · Three Triad Center, Suite 500 · Salt Lake City, UT 84180 · 801-532-7080

Timothy C. Houpt · a · Jones Waldo · 170 South Main Street, Suite 1500 · Salt Lake City, UT 84101-1644 · 801-521-3200

Rich L. Humpherys · a · Christensen & Jensen · Beneficial Tower, Suite 800 · 15 West South Temple · Salt Lake City, UT 84101 · 801-323-5000

Colin P. King · a · Dewsnup, King & Olsen · http://www.dkolaw.com · Beneficial Financial Group, Suite 2400 · 36 South State Street · Salt Lake City, UT 84111-0024 · 801-533-0400

Dale J. Lambert · Christensen & Jensen · Beneficial Tower, Suite 800 · 15 West South Temple · Salt Lake City, UT 84101 · 801-323-5000

Shawn McGarry · Kipp & Christian · http://www.kippandchristian.com · 10 Exchange Place, Fourth Floor · Salt Lake City, UT 84111 · 801-521-3773

Edward P. Moriarity · 2% · Moriarity, Badaruddin & Booke · Eight East Broadway, Suite 312 · Salt Lake City, UT 84111 · 866-879-5145

David R. Olsen · Dewsnup, King & Olsen · http://www.dkolaw.com · Beneficial Financial Group, Suite 2400 · 36 South State Street · Salt Lake City, UT 84111-0024 · 801-533-0400

Rick L. Rose · Ray Quinney & Nebeker · 36 South State Street, Suite 1400 · P.O. Box 45385 · Salt Lake City, UT 84145-0385 · 801-532-1500

E. Scott Savage · Berman & Savage · 170 South Main Street, Suite 500 · Salt Lake City, UT 84101 · 801-328-2200

Roger T. Sharp · a · Roger T. Sharp · 2825 East Cottonwood Parkway, Suite 500 · Salt Lake City, UT 84121 · 801-990-3405

Charles H. Thronson · a · Parsons Behle & Latimer · http://www.parsonsbehlelaw.com · 201 South Main Street, Suite 1800 · P.O. Box 45898 · Salt Lake City, UT 84145-0898 · 801-532-1234

Elliott J. Williams · a · Williams & Hunt · 257 East 200 South, Suite 500 · P.O. Box 45678 · Salt Lake City, UT 84145-5678 · 801-521-5678

PRIVATE FUNDS LAW

Salt Lake City

P. Christian Anderson · Ballard Spahr Andrews & Ingersoll · One Utah Center, Suite 800 · 201 South Main Street · Salt Lake City, UT 84111-2221 · 801-531-3000

Mark E. Bonham · Ray Quinney & Nebeker · 36 South State Street, Suite 1400 · P.O. Box 45385 · Salt Lake City, UT 84145-0385 · 801-532-1500

Brian G. Lloyd · Parr, Waddoups, Brown, Gee & Loveless · 185 South State Street, Suite 1300 · P.O. Box 11019 · Salt Lake City, UT 84147-1537 · 801-532-7840

PRODUCT LIABILITY LITIGATION

Salt Lake City

John A. Anderson · Stoel Rives · http://www.stoel.com · 201 South Main Street, Suite 1100 · Salt Lake City, UT 84111-4904 · 801-328-3131

Bryon J. Benevento · Snell & Wilmer · Beneficial Tower, Suite 1200 · 15 West South Temple · Salt Lake City, UT 84101-1547 · 801-257-1900

Robert S. Campbell, Jr. · 2% · VanCott, Bagley, Cornwall & McCarthy · 36 South State Street, Suite 1900 Salt Lake City, UT 84102 · 801-532-3333

Patricia W. Christensen · Parr, Waddoups, Brown, Gee & Loveless · 185 South State Street, Suite 1300 · P.O. Box 11019 · Salt Lake City, UT 84147-1537 · 801-532-7840

Tracy H. Fowler · Snell & Wilmer · Beneficial Tower, Suite 1200 · 15 West South Temple · Salt Lake City, UT 84101-1547 · 801-257-1900

Colin P. King · a · Dewsnup, King & Olsen · http://www.dkolaw.com · Beneficial Financial Group, Suite 2400 · 36 South State Street · Salt Lake City, UT 84111-0024 · 801-533-0400

John R. Lund · Snow, Christensen & Martineau · http://www.scmlaw.com · 10 Exchange Place, 11th Floor · P.O. Box 45000 · Salt Lake City, UT 84145 · 801-521-9000

Rick L. Rose · Ray Quinney & Nebeker · 36 South State Street, Suite 1400 · P.O. Box 45385 · Salt Lake City, UT 84145-0385 · 801-532-1500

PROFESSIONAL MALPRACTICE LAW

Salt Lake City

Gary F. Bendinger · a · Howrey · 170 South Main Street, Suite 400 · Salt Lake City, UT 84101 · 801-533-8383

REAL ESTATE LAW

Salt Lake City

Thomas G. Bennett · Ballard Spahr Andrews & Ingersoll · One Utah Center, Suite 800 · 201 South Main Street · Salt Lake City, UT 84111-2221 · 801-531-3000

Thomas G. Berggren · Jones Waldo · 170 South Main Street, Suite 1500 · Salt Lake City, UT 84101-1644 · 801-521-3200

David K. Broadbent · Holland & Hart · 60 East South Temple, Suite 2000 · Salt Lake City, UT 84111-1031 · 801-595-7800

Stephen K. Christensen · Nelson, Christensen, Helsten, Hollingworth & Williams · 68 South Main Street, Sixth Floor · Salt Lake City, UT 84101-2300 · 801-531-8400

Rand L. Cook · VanCott, Bagley, Cornwall & McCarthy · 36 South State Street, Suite 1900 · Salt Lake City, UT 84102 · 801-532-3333

Thomas A. Ellison · a · Stoel Rives · http://www.stoel.com · 201 South Main Street, Suite 1100 · Salt Lake City, UT 84111-4904 · 801-328-3131

Shawn C. Ferrin · Parsons Behle & Latimer · http://www.parsonsbehlelaw.com · 201 South Main Street, Suite 1800 · P.O. Box 45898 · Salt Lake City, UT 84145-0898 · 801-532-1234

David E. Gee · Parr, Waddoups, Brown, Gee & Loveless · 185 South State Street, Suite 1300 · P.O. Box 11019 · Salt Lake City, UT 84147-1537 · 801-532-7840

Ervin R. Holmes · Stoel Rives · http://www.stoel.com · 201 South Main Street, Suite 1100 · Salt Lake City, UT 84111-4904 · 801-328-3131

Cary D. Jones · Snell & Wilmer · Beneficial Tower, Suite 1200 · 15 West South Temple · Salt Lake City, UT 84101-1547 · 801-257-1900

Guy P. Kroesche · Stoel Rives · http://www.stoel.com · 201 South Main Street, Suite 1100 · Salt Lake City, UT 84111-4904 · 801-328-3131

Bruce A. Maak · a · Parr, Waddoups, Brown, Gee & Loveless · 185 South State Street, Suite 1300 · P.O. Box 11019 · Salt Lake City, UT 84147-1537 · 801-532-7840

Charles L. Maak · 2) · Parr, Waddoups, Brown, Gee & Loveless · 185 South State Street, Suite 1300 · P.O. Box 11019 · Salt Lake City, UT 84147-1537 · 801-532-7840

Douglas Matsumori · Ray Quinney & Nebeker · 36 South State Street, Suite 1400 · P.O. Box 45385 · Salt Lake City, UT 84145-0385 · 801-532-1500

Robert A. McConnell · Parr, Waddoups, Brown, Gee & Loveless · 185 South State Street, Suite 1300 · P.O. Box 11019 · Salt Lake City, UT 84147-1537 · 801-532-7840

Larry G. Moore · Ray Quinney & Nebeker · 36 South State Street, Suite 1400 · P.O. Box 45385 · Salt Lake City, UT 84145-0385 · 801-532-1500

Keven M. Rowe · Jones Waldo · 170 South Main Street, Suite 1500 · Salt Lake City, UT 84101-1644 · 801-521-3200

Ira B. Rubinfeld · Ray Quinney & Nebeker · 36 South State Street, Suite 1400 · P.O. Box 45385 · Salt Lake City, UT 84145-0385 · 801-532-1500

Ronald G. Russell · Parr, Waddoups, Brown, Gee & Loveless · 185 South State Street, Suite 1300 · P.O. Box 11019 · Salt Lake City, UT 84147-1537 · 801-532-7840

Steven E. Tyler · Holland & Hart · 60 East South Temple, Suite 2000 · Salt Lake City, UT 84111-1031 · 801-595-7800

Glen D. Watkins · Jones Waldo · 170 South Main Street, Suite 1500 · Salt Lake City, UT 84101-1644 · 801-521-3200

Gregory P. Williams · a · VanCott, Bagley, Cornwall & McCarthy · 36 South State Street, Suite 1900 · Salt Lake City, UT 84102 · 801-532-3333

SECURITIES LAW

Salt Lake City

Richard W. Casey · Howrey · 170 South Main Street, Suite 400 · Salt Lake City, UT 84101 · 801-533-8383

Nathan W. Jones · Stoel Rives · http://www.stoel.com · 201 South Main Street, Suite 1100 · Salt Lake City, UT 84111-4904 · 801-328-3131

N. Todd Leishman · Durham Jones & Pinegar · 111 East Broadway, Suite 900 · P.O. Box 4050 · Salt Lake City, UT 84110 · 801-415-3000

Brian G. Lloyd · Parr, Waddoups, Brown, Gee & Loveless · 185 South State Street, Suite 1300 · P.O. Box 11019 · Salt Lake City, UT 84147-1537 · 801-532-7840

Scott W. Loveless · Parr, Waddoups, Brown, Gee & Loveless · 185 South State Street, Suite 1300 · P.O. Box 11019 · Salt Lake City, UT 84147-1537 · 801-532-7840

Keith L. Pope · Parr, Waddoups, Brown, Gee & Loveless · 185 South State Street, Suite 1300 · P.O. Box 11019 · Salt Lake City, UT 84147-1537 · 801-532-7840

Mark W. Pugsley · Ray Quinney & Nebeker · 36 South State Street, Suite 1400 · P.O. Box 45385 · Salt Lake City, UT 84145-0385 · 801-532-1500

Reed W. Topham · Stoel Rives · http://www.stoel.com · 201 South Main Street, Suite 1100 · Salt Lake City, UT 84111-4904 · 801-328-3131

Jeffery S. Williams · Nelson, Christensen, Helsten, Hollingworth & Williams · 68 South Main Street, Sixth Floor · Salt Lake City, UT 84101-2300 · 801-531-8400

TAX LAW

Salt Lake City

Lawrence R. Barusch · Parsons Behle & Latimer · http://www.parsonsbehlelaw.com · 201 South Main Street, Suite 1800 · P.O. Box 45898 · Salt Lake City, UT 84145-0898 · 801-532-1234

Charles R. Brown · a · Clyde Snow Sessions & Swenson · One Utah Center, Suite 1300 · 201 South Main Street · Salt Lake City, UT 84111-2216 · 801-322-2516

Kent H. Collins · Parr, Waddoups, Brown, Gee & Loveless · 185 South State Street, Suite 1300 · P.O. Box 11019 · Salt Lake City, UT 84147-1537 · 801-532-7840

Randy M. Grimshaw · Parsons Behle & Latimer · http://www.parsonsbehlelaw.com · 201 South Main Street, Suite 1800 · P.O. Box 45898 · Salt Lake City, UT 84145-0898 · 801-532-1234

Herbert C. Livsey · Ray Quinney & Nebeker · 36 South State Street, Suite 1400 · P.O. Box 45385 · Salt Lake City, UT 84145-0385 · 801-532-1500

Stanley D. Neeleman · Parr, Waddoups, Brown, Gee & Loveless · 185 South State Street, Suite 1300 · P.O. Box 11019 · Salt Lake City, UT 84147-1537 · 801-532-7840

Bruce L. Olson · Ray Quinney & Nebeker · 36 South State Street, Suite 1400 · P.O. Box 45385 · Salt Lake City, UT 84145-0385 · 801-532-1500

Stephen D. Swindle · a · VanCott, Bagley, Cornwall & McCarthy · 36 South State Street, Suite 1900 · Salt Lake City, UT 84102 · 801-532-3333

TRUSTS AND ESTATES

Salt Lake City

J. Keith Adams · a · Stoel Rives · http://www.stoel.com · 201 South Main Street, Suite 1100 · Salt Lake City, UT 84111-4904 · 801-328-3131

Gregory Barrick · Durham Jones & Pinegar · 111 East Broadway, Suite 900 · P.O. Box 4050 · Salt Lake City, UT 84110 · 801-415-3000

Michael D. Blackburn · Blackburn & Stoll · 257 East 200 South, Suite 800 · Salt Lake City, UT 84111-2124 · 801-521-7900

Thomas Christensen, Jr. · a · Blackburn & Stoll · 257 East 200 South, Suite 800 · Salt Lake City, UT 84111-2124 · 801-521-7900

Kent H. Collins · Parr, Waddoups, Brown, Gee & Loveless · 185 South State Street, Suite 1300 · P.O. Box 11019 · Salt Lake City, UT 84147-1537 · 801-532-7840

D. Jay Curtis · Ray Quinney & Nebeker · 36 South State Street, Suite 1400 · P.O. Box 45385 · Salt Lake City, UT 84145-0385 · 801-532-1500

Clark P. Giles · 2) · Ray Quinney & Nebeker · 36 South State Street, Suite 1400 · P.O. Box 45385 · Salt Lake City, UT 84145-0385 · 801-532-1500

Narrvel E. Hall · Ray Quinney & Nebeker · 36 South State Street, Suite 1400 · P.O. Box 45385 · Salt Lake City, UT 84145-0385 · 801-532-1500

Richard H. Johnson II · ⑩ · Stoel Rives · http://www.stoel.com · 201 South Main Street, Suite 1100 · Salt Lake City, UT 84111-4904 · 801-328-3131

Herbert C. Livsey · Ray Quinney & Nebeker · 36 South State Street, Suite 1400 · P.O. Box 45385 · Salt Lake City, UT 84145-0385 · 801-532-1500

Leland S. McCullough II · Callister, Nebeker & McCullough · Parkview Plaza One, Suite 600 · 2180 South 1300 East · Salt Lake City, UT 84106 · 801-530-7359

Stanley D. Neeleman · Parr, Waddoups, Brown, Gee & Loveless · 185 South State Street, Suite 1300 · P.O. Box 11019 · Salt Lake City, UT 84147-1537 · 801-532-7840

David E. Sloan · VanCott, Bagley, Cornwall & McCarthy · 36 South State Street, Suite 1900 · Salt Lake City, UT 84102 · 801-532-3333

Gerald T. Snow · Ray Quinney & Nebeker · 36 South State Street, Suite 1400 · P.O. Box 45385 · Salt Lake City, UT 84145-0385 · 801-532-1500

Stephen D. Swindle · ⑩ · VanCott, Bagley, Cornwall & McCarthy · 36 South State Street, Suite 1900 · Salt Lake City, UT 84102 · 801-532-3333

James F. Wood · Stoel Rives · http://www.stoel.com · 201 South Main Street, Suite 1100 · Salt Lake City, UT 84111-4904 · 801-328-3131

VENTURE CAPITAL LAW

Salt Lake City

P. Christian Anderson · Ballard Spahr Andrews & Ingersoll · One Utah Center, Suite 800 · 201 South Main Street · Salt Lake City, UT 84111-2221 · 801-531-3000

Mark E. Bonham · Ray Quinney & Nebeker · 36 South State Street, Suite 1400 · P.O. Box 45385 · Salt Lake City, UT 84145-0385 · 801-532-1500

Brian G. Lloyd · Parr, Waddoups, Brown, Gee & Loveless · 185 South State Street, Suite 1300 · P.O. Box 11019 · Salt Lake City, UT 84147-1537 · 801-532-7840

Nolan S. Taylor · Dorsey & Whitney · 170 South Main Street, Suite 900 · Salt Lake City, UT 84101-1655 801-933-7360

Matthew G. Wells · Ray Quinney & Nebeker · 36 South State Street, Suite 1400 · P.O. Box 45385 · Salt Lake City, UT 84145-0385 · 801-532-1500

WATER LAW

Salt Lake City

Steven E. Clyde · ⑩ · Clyde Snow Sessions & Swenson · One Utah Center, Suite 1300 · 201 South Main Street · Salt Lake City, UT 84111-2216 · 801-322-2516

Shawn E. Draney · Snow, Christensen & Martineau · http://www.scmlaw.com · 10 Exchange Place, 11th Floor · P.O. Box 45000 · Salt Lake City, UT 84145 · 801-521-9000

Dallin W. Jensen · ⑩ · Parsons Behle & Latimer · http://www.parsonsbehlelaw.com · 201 South Main Street, Suite 1800 · P.O. Box 45898 · Salt Lake City, UT 84145-0898 · 801-532-1234

Daniel A. Jensen · Parr, Waddoups, Brown, Gee & Loveless · 185 South State Street, Suite 1300 · P.O. Box 11019 · Salt Lake City, UT 84147-1537 · 801-532-7840

Lee E. Kapaloski · 2) · Parsons Behle & Latimer · http://www.parsonsbehlelaw.com · 201 South Main Street, Suite 1800 · P.O. Box 45898 · Salt Lake City, UT 84145-0898 · 801-532-1234

James B. Lee · 2) · Parsons Behle & Latimer · http://www.parsonsbehlelaw.com · 201 South Main Street, Suite 1800 · P.O. Box 45898 · Salt Lake City, UT 84145-0898 · 801-532-1234

John H. Mabey, Jr. · Mabey Wright & James · 175 South Main, Suite 1330 · Salt Lake City, UT 84111 · 801-359-3663

Jody L. Williams · Holme Roberts & Owen · http://www.hro.com · 299 South Main Street, Suite 1800 · Salt Lake City, UT 84111-2263 · 801-521-5800

WHITE-COLLAR CRIMINAL DEFENSE

Salt Lake City

D. Gilbert Athay · 2) · D. Gilbert Athay · 43 East 400 South · Salt Lake City, UT 84111 · 801-363-7074

James C. Bradshaw · Brown, Bradshaw & Moffett · 10 West Broadway, Suite 210 · Salt Lake City, UT 84101-1525 · 801-532-5297

Kenneth R. Brown · Brown Bradshaw & Moffat · 10 West Broadway, Suite 210 · Salt Lake City, UT 84101 · 801-532-5297

Walter F. Bugden, Jr. · a · Bugden & Isaacson · 445 East 200 South, Suite 150 · Salt Lake City, UT 84111 · 801-467-1700

Loni F. DeLand · a · Loni F. DeLand · 43 East 400 South · Salt Lake City, UT 84111 · 801-364-1333

Richard Mauro · Law Office of Richard Mauro · 43 East 400 South · Salt Lake City, UT 84111 · 801-363-9500

Stephen R. McCaughey · 2) · McCaughey & Metos · 10 West Broadway, Suite 650 · Salt Lake City, UT 84101-2002 · 801-364-6474

G. Fred Metos · 2) · McCaughey & Metos · 10 West Broadway, Suite 650 · Salt Lake City, UT 84101-2002 · 801-364-6474

Bradley P. Rich · a · Yengich, Rich & Xaiz · 175 East 400 South, Suite 400 · Salt Lake City, UT 84111 · 801-355-0320

Max D. Wheeler · Snow, Christensen & Martineau · http://www.scmlaw.com · 10 Exchange Place, 11th Floor · P.O. Box 45000 · Salt Lake City, UT 84145 · 801-521-9000

Scott C. Williams · Scott C. Williams · 43 East 400 South · Salt Lake City, UT 84111 · 801-220-0700

Ronald J. Yengich · 2) · Yengich, Rich & Xaiz · 175 East 400 South, Suite 400 · Salt Lake City, UT 84111 · 801-355-0320

VERMONT

ADMINISTRATIVE LAW

Burlington

Thomas F. Heilmann · ⑩ · Heilmann Ekman & Associates · 231 South Union Street · P.O. Box 216 · Burlington, VT 05402-0216 · 802-864-4555

ALTERNATIVE DISPUTE RESOLUTION

Arlington

Arthur J. O'Dea · Vermont Dispute Resolution Services · 1013 Old Depot Road · Arlington, VT 05250 · 802-375-0037

Burlington

William A. Fead · Fead Construction Law · 1037-A Hinesburg Road · P.O. Box 673 · Burlington, VT 05402-0673 · 802-863-5808

Thomas E. McCormick · McCormick, Fitzpatrick, Kasper & Burchard · 40 George Street · P.O. Box 638 · Burlington, VT 05402 · 802-863-3494

James W. Spink · Spink & Miller · One Lawson Lane · Burlington, VT 05401 · 802-864-1100

Montpelier

Peter B. Joslin · ⑩ · Theriault & Joslin · 141 Main Street, Suite Four · Montpelier, VT 05602 · 802-223-2381

Rutland

David L. Cleary · ㉕ · Cleary Shahi & Aicher · 110 Merchants Row, Third Floor · P.O. Box 6740 · Rutland, VT 05702-6740 · 802-775-8800

South Burlington

Robert A. Mello · ⑩ · Robert A. Mello & Associates · 1795 Williston Road · South Burlington, VT 05403 802-862-3200

BANKING LAW

Burlington

Thomas R. Melloni · Burak Anderson & Melloni · 30 Main Street · P.O. Box 787 · Burlington, VT 05402-0787 · 802-862-0500

Gail E. Westgate · Primmer Piper Eggleston & Cramer · 150 South Champlain Street · P.O. Box 1489 · Burlington, VT 05402-1489 · 802-864-0880

Middlebury

Kathleen M. Boe · ⑩ · English, Carroll & Boe · 64 Court Street · Middlebury, VT 05753 · 802-388-6711

Rutland

Elizabeth A. Glynn · Ryan Smith & Carbine · Mead Building · 98 Merchants Row · P.O. Box 310 · Rutland, VT 05702-0310 · 802-786-1000

St. Johnsbury

Denise J. Deschenes · Primmer Piper Eggleston & Cramer · 421 Summer Street · P.O. Box 159 · St. Johnsbury, VT 05819 · 802-748-5061

BANKRUPTCY AND CREDITOR-DEBTOR RIGHTS LAW

Bethel

Raymond Obuchowski · Obuchowski & Emens · 1542 Route 107 · P.O. Box 60 · Bethel, VT 05032 · 802-234-6244

Burlington

Douglas J. Wolinsky · ⑳ · Primmer Piper Eggleston & Cramer · 150 South Champlain Street · P.O. Box 1489 · Burlington, VT 05402-1489 · 802-864-0880

BET-THE-COMPANY LITIGATION

Burlington

Robert B. Hemley · ⑳ · Gravel and Shea · http://www.gravelshea.com · 76 St. Paul Street, Seventh Floor · P.O. Box 369 · Burlington, VT 05402-0369 · 802-658-0220

Bethel

Raymond Obuchowski · Obuchowski & Emens · 1542 Route 107 · P.O. Box 60 · Bethel, VT 05032 · 802-234-6244

Burlington

R. Jeffrey Behm · Sheehey Furlong & Behm · 30 Main Street · P.O. Box 66 · Burlington, VT 05402-0066 802-864-9891

S. Crocker Bennett II · ⑩ · Paul Frank + Collins · http://www.pfclaw.com · One Church Street · P.O. Box 1307 · Burlington, VT 05402-1307 · 802-658-2311

Ritchie E. Berger · ⑩ · Dinse, Knapp & McAndrew · 209 Battery Street · P.O. Box 988 · Burlington, VT 05402-0988 · 802-864-5751

Thomas Z. Carlson · Langrock Sperry & Wool · http://www.langrock.com · 210 College Street · P.O. Box 721 · Burlington, VT 05402-0721 · 802-864-0217

Thomas F. Heilmann · ⑩ · Heilmann Ekman & Associates · 231 South Union Street · P.O. Box 216 · Burlington, VT 05402-0216 · 802-864-4555

Robert B. Hemley · ⑳ · Gravel and Shea · http://www.gravelshea.com · 76 St. Paul Street, Seventh Floor · P.O. Box 369 · Burlington, VT 05402-0369 · 802-658-0220

Karen McAndrew · ⑩ · Dinse, Knapp & McAndrew · 209 Battery Street · P.O. Box 988 · Burlington, VT 05402-0988 · 802-864-5751

Jerome F. O'Neill · ⑩ · O'Neill Kellner & Green · 159 Bank Street · P.O. Box 5359 · Burlington, VT 05402-5359 · 802-865-4700

Robert D. Rachlin · ㉕ · Downs Rachlin Martin · 199 Main Street · P.O. Box 190 · Burlington, VT 05402-0190 · 802-863-2375

John T. Sartore · ㉕ · Paul Frank + Collins · http://www.pfclaw.com · One Church Street · P.O. Box 1307 · Burlington, VT 05402-1307 · 802-658-2311

Middlebury

William B. Miller, Jr. · Langrock Sperry & Wool · http://www.langrock.com · 111 South Pleasant Street · P.O. Drawer 351 · Middlebury, VT 05753-0351 · 802-388-6356

Montpelier

Peter B. Joslin · ⑩ · Theriault & Joslin · 141 Main Street, Suite Four · Montpelier, VT 05602 · 802-223-2381

Rutland

David L. Cleary · ㉕ · Cleary Shahi & Aicher · 110 Merchants Row, Third Floor · P.O. Box 6740 · Rutland, VT 05702-6740 · 802-775-8800

South Burlington

Robert A. Mello · ⑩ · Robert A. Mello & Associates · 1795 Williston Road · South Burlington, VT 05403 802-862-3200

CONSTRUCTION LAW

Burlington

William A. Fead · Fead Construction Law · 1037-A Hinesburg Road · P.O. Box 673 · Burlington, VT 05402-0673 · 802-863-5808

CORPORATE LAW

Burlington

Peter S. Erly · Gravel and Shea · http://www.gravelshea.com · 76 St. Paul Street, Seventh Floor · P.O. Box 369 · Burlington, VT 05402-0369 · 802-658-0220

Michael Furlong · Sheehey Furlong & Behm · 30 Main Street · P.O. Box 66 · Burlington, VT 05402-0066 · 802-864-9891

Gail E. Haefner · Paul Frank + Collins · http://www.pfclaw.com · One Church Street · P.O. Box 1307 · Burlington, VT 05402-1307 · 802-658-2311

Stewart H. McConaughy · ⑳ · Gravel and Shea · http://www.gravelshea.com · 76 St. Paul Street, Seventh Floor · P.O. Box 369 · Burlington, VT 05402-0369 · 802-658-0220

Margaret L. Montgomery · Gravel and Shea · http://www.gravelshea.com · 76 St. Paul Street, Seventh Floor · P.O. Box 369 · Burlington, VT 05402-0369 · 802-658-0220

Thomas H. Moody · Downs Rachlin Martin · 199 Main Street · P.O. Box 190 · Burlington, VT 05402-0190 · 802-863-2375

Paul H. Ode, Jr. · Downs Rachlin Martin · 199 Main Street · P.O. Box 190 · Burlington, VT 05402-0190 · 802-863-2375

Middlebury

Kathleen M. Boe · ⑩ · English, Carroll & Boe · 64 Court Street · Middlebury, VT 05753 · 802-388-6711

Rutland

Thomas M. Dowling · ㉕ · Ryan Smith & Carbine · Mead Building · 98 Merchants Row · P.O. Box 310 · Rutland, VT 05702-0310 · 802-786-1000

ELDER LAW

Middlebury

William B. Miller, Jr. · Langrock Sperry & Wool · http://www.langrock.com · 111 South Pleasant Street · P.O. Drawer 351 · Middlebury, VT 05753-0351 · 802-388-6356

Springfield

Mark L. Tapper · Tapper Law Offices · 59 Main Street, Suite 103 · P.O. Box 517 · Springfield, VT 05156 802-885-9666

ENERGY LAW

Burlington

Victoria J. Brown · Primmer Piper Eggleston & Cramer · 150 South Champlain Street · P.O. Box 1489 · Burlington, VT 05402-1489 · 802-864-0880

Kimberly K. Hayden · Downs Rachlin Martin · 199 Main Street · P.O. Box 190 · Burlington, VT 05402-0190 · 802-863-2375

Peter H. Zamore · Sheehey Furlong & Behm · 30 Main Street · P.O. Box 66 · Burlington, VT 05402-0066 · 802-864-9891

Rutland

Edward V. Schwiebert · Kenlan Schwiebert Facey & Goss · http://www.kenlanlaw.com · 71 Allen Street, Suite 401 · P.O. Box 578 · Rutland, VT 05702-0578 · 802-773-3300

St. Johnsbury

John H. Marshall · ⑩ · Downs Rachlin Martin · 90 Prospect Street · P.O. Box 99 · St. Johnsbury, VT 05819-0099 · 802-748-8324

William B. Piper · ⑩ · Primmer Piper Eggleston & Cramer · 421 Summer Street · P.O. Box 159 · St. Johnsbury, VT 05819 · 802-748-5061

ENVIRONMENTAL LAW

Brattleboro

Raymond P. Perra · ⑳ · Weber, Perra & Munzing · 86 Linden Street · P.O. Box 558 · Brattleboro, VT 05302-0558 · 802-257-7161

Peter D. Van Oot · Downs Rachlin Martin · 28 Vernon Street, Suite 501 · P.O. Box Nine · Brattleboro, VT 05302 · 802-258-3070

Burlington

Jon T. Anderson · Burak Anderson & Melloni · 30 Main Street · P.O. Box 787 · Burlington, VT 05402-0787 · 802-862-0500

John R. Ponsetto · ⑳ · Gravel and Shea · http://www.gravelshea.com · 76 St. Paul Street, Seventh Floor · P.O. Box 369 · Burlington, VT 05402-0369 · 802-658-0220

William W. Schroeder · ⑩ · Downs Rachlin Martin · 199 Main Street · P.O. Box 190 · Burlington, VT 05402-0190 · 802-863-2375

Montpelier

David L. Grayck · Cheney, Brock & Saudek · 159 State Street · Montpelier, VT 05602 · 802-223-4000

Stephen A. Reynes · Primmer Piper Eggleston & Cramer · 100 East State Street · P.O. Box 1309 · Montpelier, VT 05601-1309 · 802-223-2102

Barbara G. Ripley · Downs Rachlin Martin · 52 State Street · P.O. Box 1072 · Montpelier, VT 05602-1072 · 802-225-5500

Norwich

C. Daniel Hershenson · ⑩ · Hershenson, Carter, Scott & McGee · 2776 Christian Street · P.O. Box 909 · Norwich, VT 05055 · 802-295-2800

Rutland

James P. W. Goss · Kenlan Schwiebert Facey & Goss · http://www.kenlanlaw.com · 71 Allen Street, Suite 401 · P.O. Box 578 · Rutland, VT 05702-0578 · 802-773-3300

A. Jay Kenlan · ⑩ · Kenlan Schwiebert Facey & Goss · http://www.kenlanlaw.com · 71 Allen Street, Suite 401 · P.O. Box 578 · Rutland, VT 05702-0578 · 802-773-3300

St. Johnsbury

John H. Marshall · ⑩ · Downs Rachlin Martin · 90 Prospect Street · P.O. Box 99 · St. Johnsbury, VT 05819-0099 · 802-748-8324

FAMILY LAW

Burlington

Christopher L. Davis · Langrock Sperry & Wool · http://www.langrock.com · 210 College Street · P.O. Box 721 · Burlington, VT 05402-0721 · 802-864-0217

James W. Murdoch · ⑩ · Murdoch, Hughes & Twarog · 131 Main Street · P.O. Box 363 · Burlington, VT 05402-0363 · 802-864-9811

Susan M. Murray · ⑩ · Langrock Sperry & Wool · http://www.langrock.com · 210 College Street · P.O. Box 721 · Burlington, VT 05402-0721 · 802-864-0217

Middlebury

Beth Robinson · Langrock Sperry & Wool · http://www.langrock.com · 111 South Pleasant Street · P.O. Drawer 351 · Middlebury, VT 05753-0351 · 802-388-6356

Rutland

Stephen A. Dardeck · ⑩ · Tepper Dardeck Levins & Gatos · 73 Center Street · Rutland, VT 05701 · 802-775-7525

Eugene Rakow · Eugene Rakow · 24 Wales Street · P. O. Box Nine · Rutland, VT 05701 · 802-775-0242

FIRST AMENDMENT LAW

Burlington

Thomas F. Heilmann · ⑩ · Heilmann Ekman & Associates · 231 South Union Street · P.O. Box 216 · Burlington, VT 05402-0216 · 802-864-4555

Robert B. Hemley · 20 · Gravel and Shea · http://www.gravelshea.com · 76 St. Paul Street, Seventh Floor · P.O. Box 369 · Burlington, VT 05402-0369 · 802-658-0220

Middlebury

Peter F. Langrock · 25 · Langrock Sperry & Wool · http://www.langrock.com · 111 South Pleasant Street · P.O. Drawer 351 · Middlebury, VT 05753-0351 · 802-388-6356

Mitchell L. Pearl · Langrock Sperry & Wool · http://www.langrock.com · 111 South Pleasant Street · P.O. Drawer 351 · Middlebury, VT 05753-0351 · 802-388-6356

GOVERNMENT RELATIONS LAW

Montpelier

John H. Hollar · Downs Rachlin Martin · 52 State Street · P.O. Box 1072 · Montpelier, VT 05602-1072 · 802-225-5500

HEALTH CARE LAW

Bennington

Thomas H. Jacobs · Jacobs McClintock & Scanlon · 207 West Main Street · P.O. Box 289 · Bennington, VT 05201-0289 · 802-442-8503

Burlington

Anne E. Cramer · 10 · Primmer Piper Eggleston & Cramer · 150 South Champlain Street · P.O. Box 1489 Burlington, VT 05402-1489 · 802-864-0880

Spencer R. Knapp · 10 · Dinse, Knapp & McAndrew · 209 Battery Street · P.O. Box 988 · Burlington, VT 05402-0988 · 802-864-5751

Rutland

Thomas M. Dowling · 25 · Ryan Smith & Carbine · Mead Building · 98 Merchants Row · P.O. Box 310 · Rutland, VT 05702-0310 · 802-786-1000

IMMIGRATION LAW

Burlington

Edward J. Carroll · Carroll & Scribner · 84 Pine Street, Suite 300 · P.O. Box 932 · Burlington, VT 05402-0932 · 802-862-2855

INTELLECTUAL PROPERTY LAW

Burlington

Andrew Manitsky · Gravel and Shea · http://www.gravelshea.com · 76 St. Paul Street, Seventh Floor · P.O. Box 369 · Burlington, VT 05402-0369 · 802-658-0220

Lawrence H. Meier · Downs Rachlin Martin · 199 Main Street · P.O. Box 190 · Burlington, VT 05402-0190 · 802-863-2375

LABOR AND EMPLOYMENT LAW

Brattleboro

Peter B. Robb · Downs Rachlin Martin · 28 Vernon Street, Suite 501 · P.O. Box Nine · Brattleboro, VT 05302 · 802-258-3070

Burlington

Alison J. Bell · Langrock Sperry & Wool · http://www.langrock.com · 210 College Street · P.O. Box 721 · Burlington, VT 05402-0721 · 802-864-0217

Heather Briggs · Gravel and Shea · http://www.gravelshea.com · 76 St. Paul Street, Seventh Floor · P.O. Box 369 · Burlington, VT 05402-0369 · 802-658-0220

Richard T. Cassidy · Hoff Curtis · 100 Main Street · P.O. Box 1124 · Burlington, VT 05402-1124 · 802-864-4531

Robert R. McKearin · Dinse, Knapp & McAndrew · 209 Battery Street · P.O. Box 988 · Burlington, VT 05402-0988 · 802-864-5751

Jeffrey J. Nolan · Dinse, Knapp & McAndrew · 209 Battery Street · P.O. Box 988 · Burlington, VT 05402-0988 · 802-864-5751

Patrica M. Sabalis · Downs Rachlin Martin · 199 Main Street · P.O. Box 190 · Burlington, VT 05402-0190 802-863-2375

Middlebury

Ellen Mercer Fallon · Langrock Sperry & Wool · http://www.langrock.com · 111 South Pleasant Street · P.O. Drawer 351 · Middlebury, VT 05753-0351 · 802-388-6356

LAND USE & ZONING LAW

Brattleboro

Peter D. Van Oot · Downs Rachlin Martin · 28 Vernon Street, Suite 501 · P.O. Box Nine · Brattleboro, VT 05302 · 802-258-3070

Norwich

C. Daniel Hershenson · ⑩ · Hershenson, Carter, Scott & McGee · 2776 Christian Street · P.O. Box 909 · Norwich, VT 05055 · 802-295-2800

Rutland

James P. W. Goss · Kenlan Schwiebert Facey & Goss · http://www.kenlanlaw.com · 71 Allen Street, Suite 401 · P.O. Box 578 · Rutland, VT 05702-0578 · 802-773-3300

A. Jay Kenlan · ⑩ · Kenlan Schwiebert Facey & Goss · http://www.kenlanlaw.com · 71 Allen Street, Suite 401 · P.O. Box 578 · Rutland, VT 05702-0578 · 802-773-3300

LEGAL MALPRACTICE LAW

Rutland

Kaveh S. Shahi · Cleary Shahi & Aicher · 110 Merchants Row, Third Floor · P.O. Box 6740 · Rutland, VT 05702-6740 · 802-775-8800

MASS TORT LITIGATION

Burlington

Robert B. Hemley · 20 · Gravel and Shea · http://www.gravelshea.com · 76 St. Paul Street, Seventh Floor · P.O. Box 369 · Burlington, VT 05402-0369 · 802-658-0220

Norman Williams · Gravel and Shea · http://www.gravelshea.com · 76 St. Paul Street, Seventh Floor · P.O. Box 369 · Burlington, VT 05402-0369 · 802-658-0220

MEDICAL MALPRACTICE LAW

Bennington

D. Patrick Winburn · Winburn Law Offices · http://www.winburnlaw.com · 409 Main Street · Bennington, VT 05201 · 802-447-0100

Burlington

S. Crocker Bennett II · 10 · Paul Frank + Collins · http://www.pfclaw.com · One Church Street · P.O. Box 1307 · Burlington, VT 05402-1307 · 802-658-2311

Ritchie E. Berger · 10 · Dinse, Knapp & McAndrew · 209 Battery Street · P.O. Box 988 · Burlington, VT 05402-0988 · 802-864-5751

Robert B. Hemley · 20 · Gravel and Shea · http://www.gravelshea.com · 76 St. Paul Street, Seventh Floor · P.O. Box 369 · Burlington, VT 05402-0369 · 802-658-0220

John L. Kellner · 10 · O'Neill Kellner & Green · 159 Bank Street · P.O. Box 5359 · Burlington, VT 05402-5359 · 802-865-4700

Christopher J. Maley · Sylvester & Maley · 78 Pine Street · P.O. Box 1053 · Burlington, VT 05402-1053 · 802-864-5722

John P. Maley · 10 · Sylvester & Maley · 78 Pine Street · P.O. Box 1053 · Burlington, VT 05402-1053 · 802-864-5722

Robert D. Rachlin · 25 · Downs Rachlin Martin · 199 Main Street · P.O. Box 190 · Burlington, VT 05402-0190 · 802-863-2375

John T. Sartore · 25 · Paul Frank + Collins · http://www.pfclaw.com · One Church Street · P.O. Box 1307 · Burlington, VT 05402-1307 · 802-658-2311

Alan F. Sylvester · 25 · Sylvester & Maley · 78 Pine Street · P.O. Box 1053 · Burlington, VT 05402-1053 · 802-864-5722

Montpelier

Peter B. Joslin · ⑩ · Theriault & Joslin · 141 Main Street, Suite Four · Montpelier, VT 05602 · 802-223-2381

Rutland

David L. Cleary · ㉕ · Cleary Shahi & Aicher · 110 Merchants Row, Third Floor · P.O. Box 6740 · Rutland, VT 05702-6740 · 802-775-8800

MERGERS & ACQUISITIONS LAW

Burlington

Peter S. Erly · Gravel and Shea · http://www.gravelshea.com · 76 St. Paul Street, Seventh Floor · P.O. Box 369 · Burlington, VT 05402-0369 · 802-658-0220

Michael Furlong · Sheehey Furlong & Behm · 30 Main Street · P.O. Box 66 · Burlington, VT 05402-0066 · 802-864-9891

Gail E. Haefner · Paul Frank + Collins · http://www.pfclaw.com · One Church Street · P.O. Box 1307 · Burlington, VT 05402-1307 · 802-658-2311

Spencer R. Knapp · ⑩ · Dinse, Knapp & McAndrew · 209 Battery Street · P.O. Box 988 · Burlington, VT 05402-0988 · 802-864-5751

Stewart H. McConaughy · ⑳ · Gravel and Shea · http://www.gravelshea.com · 76 St. Paul Street, Seventh Floor · P.O. Box 369 · Burlington, VT 05402-0369 · 802-658-0220

Margaret L. Montgomery · Gravel and Shea · http://www.gravelshea.com · 76 St. Paul Street, Seventh Floor · P.O. Box 369 · Burlington, VT 05402-0369 · 802-658-0220

Thomas H. Moody · Downs Rachlin Martin · 199 Main Street · P.O. Box 190 · Burlington, VT 05402-0190 · 802-863-2375

Paul H. Ode, Jr. · Downs Rachlin Martin · 199 Main Street · P.O. Box 190 · Burlington, VT 05402-0190 · 802-863-2375

MINING LAW

Rutland

James P. W. Goss · Kenlan Schwiebert Facey & Goss · http://www.kenlanlaw.com · 71 Allen Street, Suite 401 · P.O. Box 578 · Rutland, VT 05702-0578 · 802-773-3300

A. Jay Kenlan · ⑩ · Kenlan Schwiebert Facey & Goss · http://www.kenlanlaw.com · 71 Allen Street, Suite 401 · P.O. Box 578 · Rutland, VT 05702-0578 · 802-773-3300

NON-WHITE-COLLAR CRIMINAL DEFENSE

Barre

Kerry B. DeWolfe · Rubin, Kidney, Myer & DeWolfe · 237 North Main Street · Barre, VT 05641-4125 · 802-479-2514

Richard I. Rubin · ⑩ · Rubin, Kidney, Myer & DeWolfe · 237 North Main Street · Barre, VT 05641-4125 802-479-2514

Oreste V. Valsangiacomo, Jr. · ⑳ · Valsangiacomo, Detora & McQuesten · 172 North Main Street · P.O. Box 625 · Barre, VT 05641-0625 · 802-476-4181

Brattleboro

William E. Kraham · Weber, Perra & Munzing · 86 Linden Street · P.O. Box 558 · Brattleboro, VT 05302-0558 · 802-257-7161

Burlington

R. Jeffrey Behm · Sheehey Furlong & Behm · 30 Main Street · P.O. Box 66 · Burlington, VT 05402-0066 802-864-9891

Robert B. Hemley · ⑳ · Gravel and Shea · http://www.gravelshea.com · 76 St. Paul Street, Seventh Floor · P.O. Box 369 · Burlington, VT 05402-0369 · 802-658-0220

James W. Murdoch · ⑩ · Murdoch, Hughes & Twarog · 131 Main Street · P.O. Box 363 · Burlington, VT 05402-0363 · 802-864-9811

Jerome F. O'Neill · ⑩ · O'Neill Kellner & Green · 159 Bank Street · P.O. Box 5359 · Burlington, VT 05402-5359 · 802-865-4700

Robert F. O'Neill · Gravel and Shea · http://www.gravelshea.com · 76 St. Paul Street, Seventh Floor · P.O. Box 369 · Burlington, VT 05402-0369 · 802-658-0220

John L. Pacht · Hoff Curtis · 100 Main Street · P.O. Box 1124 · Burlington, VT 05402-1124 · 802-864-4531

Lisa B. Shelkrot · Langrock Sperry & Wool · http://www.langrock.com · 210 College Street · P.O. Box 721 Burlington, VT 05402-0721 · 802-864-0217

Paul S. Volk · Blodgett, Watts, Volk & Sawyer · 72 Hungerford Terrace · P.O. Box Eight · Burlington, VT 05402 · 802-862-8919

Manchester

Bradley D. Myerson · Myerson Law Offices · http://www.mylwyr.com · 5261 Main Street, Route 7-A · P.O. Box 915 · Manchester, VT 05255-0915 · 802-362-1505

Rutland

Barry E. Griffith · ⑩ · Griffith & Lundeen · 98 Merchants Row, Second Floor · Rutland, VT 05701 · 802-773-7638

White River Junction

Kevin W. Griffin · Griffin Law Office · 34 Gates Street · P.O. Box 799 · White River Junction, VT 05001-0799 · 802-296-6200

Bennington

D. Patrick Winburn · Winburn Law Offices · http://www.winburnlaw.com · 409 Main Street · Bennington, VT 05201 · 802-447-0100

Burlington

S. Crocker Bennett II · ⑩ · Paul Frank + Collins · http://www.pfclaw.com · One Church Street · P.O. Box 1307 · Burlington, VT 05402-1307 · 802-658-2311

Ritchie E. Berger · ⑩ · Dinse, Knapp & McAndrew · 209 Battery Street · P.O. Box 988 · Burlington, VT 05402-0988 · 802-864-5751

Michael S. Brow · Sylvester & Maley · 78 Pine Street · P.O. Box 1053 · Burlington, VT 05402-1053 · 802-864-5722

John F. Evers · O'Neill Kellner & Green · 159 Bank Street · P.O. Box 5359 · Burlington, VT 05402-5359 · 802-865-4700

Michael Green · O'Neill Kellner & Green · 159 Bank Street · P.O. Box 5359 · Burlington, VT 05402-5359 802-865-4700

Robert B. Hemley · ⑳ · Gravel and Shea · http://www.gravelshea.com · 76 St. Paul Street, Seventh Floor · P.O. Box 369 · Burlington, VT 05402-0369 · 802-658-0220

John L. Kellner · ⑩ · O'Neill Kellner & Green · 159 Bank Street · P.O. Box 5359 · Burlington, VT 05402-5359 · 802-865-4700

Robert B. Luce · Downs Rachlin Martin · 199 Main Street · P.O. Box 190 · Burlington, VT 05402-0190 · 802-863-2375

Christopher J. Maley · Sylvester & Maley · 78 Pine Street · P.O. Box 1053 · Burlington, VT 05402-1053 · 802-864-5722

John P. Maley · ⑩ · Sylvester & Maley · 78 Pine Street · P.O. Box 1053 · Burlington, VT 05402-1053 · 802-864-5722

Robert E. Manchester · ⑳ · Manchester Law Office · 87 College Street · P.O. Box 1459 · Burlington, VT 05402-1459 · 802-658-7444

Karen McAndrew · ⑩ · Dinse, Knapp & McAndrew · 209 Battery Street · P.O. Box 988 · Burlington, VT 05402-0988 · 802-864-5751

Thomas E. McCormick · McCormick, Fitzpatrick, Kasper & Burchard · 40 George Street · P.O. Box 638 · Burlington, VT 05402 · 802-863-3494

John D. Monahan, Jr. · Dinse, Knapp & McAndrew · 209 Battery Street · P.O. Box 988 · Burlington, VT 05402-0988 · 802-864-5751

Jerome F. O'Neill · ⑩ · O'Neill Kellner & Green · 159 Bank Street · P.O. Box 5359 · Burlington, VT 05402-5359 · 802-865-4700

Robert D. Rachlin · ㉕ · Downs Rachlin Martin · 199 Main Street · P.O. Box 190 · Burlington, VT 05402-0190 · 802-863-2375

John T. Sartore · ㉕ · Paul Frank + Collins · http://www.pfclaw.com · One Church Street · P.O. Box 1307 · Burlington, VT 05402-1307 · 802-658-2311

Thomas J. Sherrer · Langrock Sperry & Wool · http://www.langrock.com · 210 College Street · P.O. Box 721 · Burlington, VT 05402-0721 · 802-864-0217

James W. Spink · Spink & Miller · One Lawson Lane · Burlington, VT 05401 · 802-864-1100

Alan F. Sylvester · ㉕ · Sylvester & Maley · 78 Pine Street · P.O. Box 1053 · Burlington, VT 05402-1053 · 802-864-5722

Middlebury

Peter F. Langrock · ㉕ · Langrock Sperry & Wool · http://www.langrock.com · 111 South Pleasant Street · P.O. Drawer 351 · Middlebury, VT 05753-0351 · 802-388-6356

Beth Robinson · Langrock Sperry & Wool · http://www.langrock.com · 111 South Pleasant Street · P.O. Drawer 351 · Middlebury, VT 05753-0351 · 802-388-6356

Montpelier

Peter B. Joslin · ⑩ · Theriault & Joslin · 141 Main Street, Suite Four · Montpelier, VT 05602 · 802-223-2381

Newport

Gregory P. Howe · Law Office of Gregory Howe · 5346 U.S. Route Five · Newport, VT 05855-9472 · 802-334-6718

Rutland

David L. Cleary · ㉕ · Cleary Shahi & Aicher · 110 Merchants Row, Third Floor · P.O. Box 6740 · Rutland, VT 05702-6740 · 802-775-8800

R. Joseph O'Rourke · Ryan Smith & Carbine · Mead Building · 98 Merchants Row · P.O. Box 310 · Rutland, VT 05702-0310 · 802-786-1000

John J. Zawistoski · ⑩ · Ryan Smith & Carbine · Mead Building · 98 Merchants Row · P.O. Box 310 · Rutland, VT 05702-0310 · 802-786-1000

St. Johnsbury

James C. Gallagher · Downs Rachlin Martin · 90 Prospect Street · P.O. Box 99 · St. Johnsbury, VT 05819-0099 · 802-748-8324

White River Junction

Michael F. Hanley · Plante & Hanley · 82 Fogg Farm Road · P.O. Box 368 · White River Junction, VT 05001-0368 · 802-295-3151

PRODUCT LIABILITY LITIGATION

Burlington

Robert D. Rachlin · ㉕ · Downs Rachlin Martin · 199 Main Street · P.O. Box 190 · Burlington, VT 05402-0190 · 802-863-2375

John T. Sartore · ㉕ · Paul Frank + Collins · http://www.pfclaw.com · One Church Street · P.O. Box 1307 · Burlington, VT 05402-1307 · 802-658-2311

PROFESSIONAL MALPRACTICE LAW

Burlington

John T. Sartore · ㉕ · Paul Frank + Collins · http://www.pfclaw.com · One Church Street · P.O. Box 1307 · Burlington, VT 05402-1307 · 802-658-2311

Rutland

Kaveh S. Shahi · Cleary Shahi & Aicher · 110 Merchants Row, Third Floor · P.O. Box 6740 · Rutland, VT 05702-6740 · 802-775-8800

PUBLIC FINANCE LAW

Montpelier

J. Paul Giuliani · ⑩ · McKee, Giuliani & Cleveland · TD Banknorth Building, Second Floor · 94 Main Street · P.O. Box 1455 · Montpelier, VT 05601-1455 · 802-223-3479

REAL ESTATE LAW

Burlington

Peter M. Collins · ㉕ · Paul Frank + Collins · http://www.pfclaw.com · One Church Street · P.O. Box 1307 Burlington, VT 05402-1307 · 802-658-2311

David W. M. Conard · Langrock Sperry & Wool · http://www.langrock.com · 210 College Street · P.O. Box 721 · Burlington, VT 05402-0721 · 802-864-0217

Jeremy I. Farkas · Murphy Sullivan Kronk · http://www.mskvt.com · 275 College Street · P.O. Box 4485 · Burlington, VT 05406-4485 · 802-861-7000

Michelle N. Farkas · Gravel and Shea · http://www.gravelshea.com · 76 St. Paul Street, Seventh Floor · P.O. Box 369 · Burlington, VT 05402-0369 · 802-658-0220

Austin D. Hart · Dinse, Knapp & McAndrew · 209 Battery Street · P.O. Box 988 · Burlington, VT 05402-0988 · 802-864-5751

Eric M. Knudsen · Langrock Sperry & Wool · http://www.langrock.com · 210 College Street · P.O. Box 721 · Burlington, VT 05402-0721 · 802-864-0217

Molly K. Lebowitz · Dinse, Knapp & McAndrew · 209 Battery Street · P.O. Box 988 · Burlington, VT 05402-0988 · 802-864-5751

Carl H. Lisman · ⑳ · Lisman, Webster & Leckerling · 84 Pine Street, Fifth Floor · P.O. Box 728 · Burlington, VT 05402 · 802-864-5756

Liam L. Murphy · ⑩ · Murphy Sullivan Kronk · http://www.mskvt.com · 275 College Street · P.O. Box 4485 · Burlington, VT 05406-4485 · 802-861-7000

Robert H. Rushford · Gravel and Shea · http://www.gravelshea.com · 76 St. Paul Street, Seventh Floor · P.O. Box 369 · Burlington, VT 05402-0369 · 802-658-0220

William W. Schroeder · ⑩ · Downs Rachlin Martin · 199 Main Street · P.O. Box 190 · Burlington, VT 05402-0190 · 802-863-2375

Mark L. Sperry III · ⑳ · Langrock Sperry & Wool · http://www.langrock.com · 210 College Street · P.O. Box 721 · Burlington, VT 05402-0721 · 802-864-0217

Lewis K. Sussman · Pierson Wadhams Quinn Yates & Coffrin · 253 South Union Street · Burlington, VT 05401 · 802-863-2888

Neil Wheelwright · Primmer Piper Eggleston & Cramer · 150 South Champlain Street · P.O. Box 1489 · Burlington, VT 05402-1489 · 802-864-0880

Middlebury

F. Rendol Barlow · Langrock Sperry & Wool · http://www.langrock.com · 111 South Pleasant Street · P.O. Drawer 351 · Middlebury, VT 05753-0351 · 802-388-6356

Kathleen M. Boe · ⑩ · English, Carroll & Boe · 64 Court Street · Middlebury, VT 05753 · 802-388-6711

Rutland

John A. Facey III · Kenlan Schwiebert Facey & Goss · http://www.kenlanlaw.com · 71 Allen Street, Suite 401 · P.O. Box 578 · Rutland, VT 05702-0578 · 802-773-3300

A. Jay Kenlan · ⑩ · Kenlan Schwiebert Facey & Goss · http://www.kenlanlaw.com · 71 Allen Street, Suite 401 · P.O. Box 578 · Rutland, VT 05702-0578 · 802-773-3300

St. Johnsbury

James G. Wheeler, Jr. · ⑩ · Downs Rachlin Martin · 90 Prospect Street · P.O. Box 99 · St. Johnsbury, VT 05819-0099 · 802-748-8324

SECURITIES LAW

Burlington

John T. Sartore · ㉕ · Paul Frank + Collins · http://www.pfclaw.com · One Church Street · P.O. Box 1307 · Burlington, VT 05402-1307 · 802-658-2311

TAX LAW

Burlington

Jon R. Eggleston · ㉕ · Primmer Piper Eggleston & Cramer · 150 South Champlain Street · P.O. Box 1489 Burlington, VT 05402-1489 · 802-864-0880

William Roger Prescott · ⑩ · Downs Rachlin Martin · 199 Main Street · P.O. Box 190 · Burlington, VT 05402-0190 · 802-863-2375

Montpelier

Paul P. Hanlon · Paul P. Hanlon · 25 Court Street · Montpelier, VT 05602-2812 · 802-229-9114

Rutland

Thomas M. Dowling · ㉕ · Ryan Smith & Carbine · Mead Building · 98 Merchants Row · P.O. Box 310 · Rutland, VT 05702-0310 · 802-786-1000

John Newman · Kenlan Schwiebert Facey & Goss · http://www.kenlanlaw.com · 71 Allen Street, Suite 401 · P.O. Box 578 · Rutland, VT 05702-0578 · 802-773-3300

TRUSTS AND ESTATES

Barre

David A. Otterman · ⑩ · Otterman and Allen · 188 Washington Street · P.O. Box 473 · Barre, VT 05641-0473 · 802-479-2552

Burlington

C. Kirk Clarke · Clarke, Demas & Baker · 346 Shelburne Road, Second Floor · P.O. Box 4484 · Burlington, VT 05406 · 802-652-1400

Jon R. Eggleston · ㉕ · Primmer Piper Eggleston & Cramer · 150 South Champlain Street · P.O. Box 1489 Burlington, VT 05402-1489 · 802-864-0880

Mark A. Langan · Dinse, Knapp & McAndrew · 209 Battery Street · P.O. Box 988 · Burlington, VT 05402-0988 · 802-864-5751

R. Allan Paul · ⑩ · Paul Frank + Collins · http://www.pfclaw.com · One Church Street · P.O. Box 1307 · Burlington, VT 05402-1307 · 802-658-2311

Alan D. Port · Paul Frank + Collins · http://www.pfclaw.com · One Church Street · P.O. Box 1307 · Burlington, VT 05402-1307 · 802-658-2311

William G. Post, Jr. · ㉕ · Gravel and Shea · http://www.gravelshea.com · 76 St. Paul Street, Seventh Floor · P.O. Box 369 · Burlington, VT 05402-0369 · 802-658-0220

Allen D. Webster · Lisman, Webster & Leckerling · 84 Pine Street, Fifth Floor · P.O. Box 728 · Burlington, VT 05402 · 802-864-5756

Rutland

Thomas M. Dowling · ㉕ · Ryan Smith & Carbine · Mead Building · 98 Merchants Row · P.O. Box 310 · Rutland, VT 05702-0310 · 802-786-1000

Wallingford

Christopher A. Webber, Jr. · ⑩ · Christopher A. Webber, Jr. · 74 North Main Street · P.O. Box 576 · Wallingford, VT 05773-0576 · 802-747-4401

WHITE-COLLAR CRIMINAL DEFENSE

Barre

Kerry B. DeWolfe · Rubin, Kidney, Myer & DeWolfe · 237 North Main Street · Barre, VT 05641-4125 · 802-479-2514

Richard I. Rubin · ⑩ · Rubin, Kidney, Myer & DeWolfe · 237 North Main Street · Barre, VT 05641-4125 802-479-2514

Oreste V. Valsangiacomo, Jr. · ⑳ · Valsangiacomo, Detora & McQuesten · 172 North Main Street · P.O. Box 625 · Barre, VT 05641-0625 · 802-476-4181

Brattleboro

William E. Kraham · Weber, Perra & Munzing · 86 Linden Street · P.O. Box 558 · Brattleboro, VT 05302-0558 · 802-257-7161

Burlington

R. Jeffrey Behm · Sheehey Furlong & Behm · 30 Main Street · P.O. Box 66 · Burlington, VT 05402-0066 802-864-9891

Robert B. Hemley · ⑳ · Gravel and Shea · http://www.gravelshea.com · 76 St. Paul Street, Seventh Floor · P.O. Box 369 · Burlington, VT 05402-0369 · 802-658-0220

James W. Murdoch · ⑩ · Murdoch, Hughes & Twarog · 131 Main Street · P.O. Box 363 · Burlington, VT 05402-0363 · 802-864-9811

Jerome F. O'Neill · ⑩ · O'Neill Kellner & Green · 159 Bank Street · P.O. Box 5359 · Burlington, VT 05402-5359 · 802-865-4700

Robert F. O'Neill · Gravel and Shea · http://www.gravelshea.com · 76 St. Paul Street, Seventh Floor · P.O. Box 369 · Burlington, VT 05402-0369 · 802-658-0220

John L. Pacht · Hoff Curtis · 100 Main Street · P.O. Box 1124 · Burlington, VT 05402-1124 · 802-864-4531

Lisa B. Shelkrot · Langrock Sperry & Wool · http://www.langrock.com · 210 College Street · P.O. Box 721 Burlington, VT 05402-0721 · 802-864-0217

Paul S. Volk · Blodgett, Watts, Volk & Sawyer · 72 Hungerford Terrace · P.O. Box Eight · Burlington, VT 05402 · 802-862-8919

Manchester

Bradley D. Myerson · Myerson Law Offices · http://www.mylwyr.com · 5261 Main Street, Route 7-A · P.O. Box 915 · Manchester, VT 05255-0915 · 802-362-1505

Rutland

Barry E. Griffith · ⑩ · Griffith & Lundeen · 98 Merchants Row, Second Floor · Rutland, VT 05701 · 802-773-7638

White River Junction

Kevin W. Griffin · Griffin Law Office · 34 Gates Street · P.O. Box 799 · White River Junction, VT 05001-0799 · 802-296-6200

Burlington

Robert G. Caine · Paul Frank + Collins · http://www.pfclaw.com · One Church Street · P.O. Box 1307 · Burlington, VT 05402-1307 · 802-658-2311

Michael Green · O'Neill Kellner & Green · 159 Bank Street · P.O. Box 5359 · Burlington, VT 05402-5359 802-865-4700

Keith J. Kasper · McCormick, Fitzpatrick, Kasper & Burchard · 40 George Street · P.O. Box 638 · Burlington, VT 05402 · 802-863-3494

Middlebury

Beth Robinson · Langrock Sperry & Wool · http://www.langrock.com · 111 South Pleasant Street · P.O. Drawer 351 · Middlebury, VT 05753-0351 · 802-388-6356

Rutland

Todd H. Kalter · Kalter & Kalter · Seven Commons Street · Rutland, VT 05701-4652 · 802-775-7459

Glenn S. Morgan · Ryan Smith & Carbine · Mead Building · 98 Merchants Row · P.O. Box 310 · Rutland, VT 05702-0310 · 802-786-1000

Springfield

Andrew C. Boxer · Ellis, Boxer & Blake · 24 Summer Hill Street · P.O. Box 948 · Springfield, VT 05156 · 802-885-2141

VIRGINIA

ADMINISTRATIVE LAW

Charlottesville

Steven W. Blaine · LeClair Ryan · 123 East Main Street, Suite 800 · Charlottesville, VA 22902 · 434-245-3444

Glen Allen

James Patrick Guy II · LeClair Ryan · 4201 Dominion Boulevard, Suite 200 · Glen Allen, VA 23060 · 804-270-0070

Thomas Francis Hancock III · Hancock, Daniel, Johnson & Nagle · 4701 Cox Road, Suite 400 · P.O. Box 72050 · Glen Allen, VA 23255 · 804-967-9604

John A. Pirko · LeClair Ryan · 4201 Dominion Boulevard, Suite 200 · Glen Allen, VA 23060 · 804-270-0070

Richmond

John M. Barr · LeClair Ryan · 951 East Byrd Street, Eighth Floor · P.O. Box 2499 · Richmond, VA 23218-2499 · 804-783-2003

David W. Clarke · LeClair Ryan · 951 East Byrd Street, Eighth Floor · P.O. Box 2499 · Richmond, VA 23218-2499 · 804-783-2003

Anthony J. Gambardella, Jr. · Woods Rogers · http://www.woodsrogers.com · 823 East Main Street, Suite 1200 · Richmond, VA 23219 · 804-343-5020

Carter Glass IV · Troutman Sanders · Troutman Sanders Building · 1001 Haxall Point · P.O. Box 1122 · Richmond, VA 23218-1122 · 804-697-1200

Thomas A. Lisk · LeClair Ryan · 951 East Byrd Street, Eighth Floor · P.O. Box 2499 · Richmond, VA 23218-2499 · 804-783-2003

Eric M. Page · LeClair Ryan · 951 East Byrd Street, Eighth Floor · P.O. Box 2499 · Richmond, VA 23218-2499 · 804-783-2003

Anthony F. Troy · ⑩ · Troutman Sanders · Troutman Sanders Building · 1001 Haxall Point · P.O. Box 1122 · Richmond, VA 23218-1122 · 804-697-1200

Roanoke

George J. A. Clemo · Woods Rogers · http://www.woodsrogers.com · Wachovia Tower, Suite 1400 · 10 South Jefferson Street · P.O. Box 14125 · Roanoke, VA 24038-4125 · 540-983-7600

H. Allen Glover, Jr. · ⑩ · Woods Rogers · http://www.woodsrogers.com · Wachovia Tower, Suite 1400 · 10 South Jefferson Street · P.O. Box 14125 · Roanoke, VA 24038-4125 · 540-983-7600

ALTERNATIVE DISPUTE RESOLUTION

Harrisonburg

M. Bruce Wallinger · ⑩ · Hoover Penrod · 342 South Main Street · Harrisonburg, VA 22801 · 540-433-2444

McLean

Lewis J. Baker · Watt, Tieder, Hoffar & Fitzgerald · http://www.wthf.com · 8405 Greensboro Drive, Suite 100 · McLean, VA 22102 · 703-749-1000

Julian F. Hoffar · Watt, Tieder, Hoffar & Fitzgerald · http://www.wthf.com · 8405 Greensboro Drive, Suite 100 · McLean, VA 22102 · 703-749-1000

David G. Lane · Law Office of David G. Lane · 1420 Spring Hill Road, Suite 600 · McLean, VA 22102 · 703-749-1296

Norfolk

William E. Franczek · Vandeventer Black · 500 World Trade Center, Suite 500 · 101 West Main Street · Norfolk, VA 23510 · 757-446-8600

Daniel R. Warman · Ventker & Warman · 101 West Main Street, Suite 810 · Norfolk, VA 23510 · 757-625-1192

Richmond

John S. Barr · McGuireWoods · http://www.mcguirewoods.com · One James Center · 901 East Cary Street · Richmond, VA 23219-4030 · 804-775-1000

Philip C. Baxa · MercerTrigiani · 16 South Second Street · Richmond, VA 23219 · 804-344-1504

Bradfute W. Davenport, Jr. · Troutman Sanders · Troutman Sanders Building · 1001 Haxall Point · P.O. Box 1122 · Richmond, VA 23218-1122 · 804-697-1200

Robert J. Grey, Jr. · Hunton & Williams · Riverfront Plaza, East Tower · 951 East Byrd Street · Richmond, VA 23219-4074 · 804-788-8200

Roderick B. Mathews · Law Office of Roderick Mathews · 1001 Haxall Point, 12th Floor · Richmond, VA 23219 · 804-697-1232

John B. McCammon · The McCammon Group · Bank of America Center, Suite 1700 · 1111 East Main Street · Richmond, VA 23219 · 804-343-0922

John H. OBrion, Jr. · ⑳ · The McCammon Group · Bank of America Center, Suite 1700 · 1111 East Main Street · Richmond, VA 23219 · 804-343-0922

D. Alan Rudlin · Hunton & Williams · Riverfront Plaza, East Tower · 951 East Byrd Street · Richmond, VA 23219-4074 · 804-788-8200

Jay T. Swett · The McCammon Group · Bank of America Center, Suite 1700 · 1111 East Main Street · Richmond, VA 23219 · 804-343-0922

Roanoke

Frank W. Rogers III · Mundy, Rogers & Associates · 1328 Third Street, SW · P.O. Box 2240 · Roanoke, VA 24009 · 540-982-2900

Salem

Leisa K. Ciaffone · Leisa K. Ciaffone · 30 East Clay Street · P.O. Box 1204 · Salem, VA 24153 · 540-444-0001

Charles B. Phillips · Phillips & Phillips · 111 East Clay Street · Salem, VA 24153 · 540-389-5439

Vienna

Donald G. Gavin · Akerman Senterfitt · http://www.akerman.com · 8100 Boone Boulevard, Suite 700 · Vienna, VA 22182-2683 · 703-790-8750

Mark E. Hanson · Smith Pachter McWhorter · http://www.smithpachter.com · 8000 Towers Crescent Drive, Suite 900 · Vienna, VA 22182-2700 · 703-847-6300

Val S. McWhorter · Smith Pachter McWhorter · http://www.smithpachter.com · 8000 Towers Crescent Drive, Suite 900 · Vienna, VA 22182-2700 · 703-847-6300

Richard F. Smith · Smith Pachter McWhorter · http://www.smithpachter.com · 8000 Towers Crescent Drive, Suite 900 · Vienna, VA 22182-2700 · 703-847-6300

Brian J. Vella · Smith Pachter McWhorter · http://www.smithpachter.com · 8000 Towers Crescent Drive, Suite 900 · Vienna, VA 22182-2700 · 703-847-6300

ANTITRUST LAW

Harrisonburg

Gregory T. St. Ours · Wharton, Aldhizer & Weaver · 100 South Mason Street · P.O. Box 20028 · Harrisonburg, VA 22801-7528 · 540-434-0316

Norfolk

Stephen E. Noona · Kaufman & Canoles · 150 West Main Street, Suite 2100 · P.O. Box 3037 · Norfolk, VA 23514-3037 · 757-624-3000

Conrad M. Shumadine · ⑩ · Willcox & Savage · One Commercial Place, Suite 1800 · Norfolk, VA 23510 757-628-5500

Hunter W. Sims, Jr. · ⑩ · Kaufman & Canoles · 150 West Main Street, Suite 2100 · P.O. Box 3037 · Norfolk, VA 23514-3037 · 757-624-3000

Gregory N. Stillman · ⑩ · Hunton & Williams · 500 East Main Street, Suite 1000 · P.O. Box 3889 · Norfolk, VA 23514 · 757-640-5300

Richmond

J. Edward Betts · Christian & Barton · Mutual Building, Suite 1200 · 909 East Main Street · Richmond, VA 23219-3095 · 804-697-4100

Howard Feller · McGuireWoods · http://www.mcguirewoods.com · One James Center · 901 East Cary Street · Richmond, VA 23219-4030 · 804-775-1000

Thomas G. Slater, Jr. · ⑩ · Hunton & Williams · Riverfront Plaza, East Tower · 951 East Byrd Street · Richmond, VA 23219-4074 · 804-788-8200

Anthony F. Troy · ⑩ · Troutman Sanders · Troutman Sanders Building · 1001 Haxall Point · P.O. Box 1122 · Richmond, VA 23218-1122 · 804-697-1200

James H. Walsh · McGuireWoods · http://www.mcguirewoods.com · One James Center · 901 East Cary Street · Richmond, VA 23219-4030 · 804-775-1000

Roanoke

Heman A. Marshall III · ⑩ · Woods Rogers · http://www.woodsrogers.com · Wachovia Tower, Suite 1400 10 South Jefferson Street · P.O. Box 14125 · Roanoke, VA 24038-4125 · 540-983-7600

William R. Rakes · ⑩ · Gentry Locke Rakes & Moore · http://www.gentrylocke.com · 10 Franklin Road, SE · P.O. Box 40013 · Roanoke, VA 24022-0013 · 540-983-9300

APPELLATE LAW

Norfolk

Conrad M. Shumadine · ⑩ · Willcox & Savage · One Commercial Place, Suite 1800 · Norfolk, VA 23510 757-628-5500

Gregory N. Stillman · ⑩ · Hunton & Williams · 500 East Main Street, Suite 1000 · P.O. Box 3889 · Norfolk, VA 23514 · 757-640-5300

Jerrold G. Weinberg · ㉕ · Weinberg & Stein · 999 Waterside Drive, Suite 1825 · P.O. Box 3789 · Norfolk, VA 23514-3789 · 757-627-1066

Rapidan

Gail S. Marshall · Law Office of Gail S. Marshall · 7393 Shooters Hill Road · Rapidan, VA 22733 · 540-672-3506

Richmond

William G. Broaddus · McGuireWoods · http://www.mcguirewoods.com · One James Center · 901 East Cary Street · Richmond, VA 23219-4030 · 804-775-1000

E. Duncan Getchell, Jr. · McGuireWoods · http://www.mcguirewoods.com · One James Center · 901 East Cary Street · Richmond, VA 23219-4030 · 804-775-1000

David E. Nagle · Jackson Lewis · http://www.jacksonlewis.com · 321 Weest Franklin Street · Richmond, VA 23220 · 804-649-0404

S. Vernon Priddy III · Sands, Anderson, Marks & Miller · http://www.sandsanderson.com · 801 East Main Street, Suite 1800 · P.O. Box 1998 · Richmond, VA 23218-1998 · 804-648-1636

John Charles Thomas · Hunton & Williams · Riverfront Plaza, East Tower · 951 East Byrd Street · Richmond, VA 23219-4074 · 804-788-8200

Roanoke

John D. Eure · Johnson, Ayers & Matthews · First Campbell Square, Suite 300 · 210 First Street, SW · P.O. Box 2200 · Roanoke, VA 24009-2200 · 540-767-2000

Frank K. Friedman · Woods Rogers · http://www.woodsrogers.com · Wachovia Tower, Suite 1400 · 10 South Jefferson Street · P.O. Box 14125 · Roanoke, VA 24038-4125 · 540-983-7600

Monica T. Monday · Gentry Locke Rakes & Moore · http://www.gentrylocke.com · 10 Franklin Road, SE P.O. Box 40013 · Roanoke, VA 24022-0013 · 540-983-9300

William R. Rakes · ⑩ · Gentry Locke Rakes & Moore · http://www.gentrylocke.com · 10 Franklin Road, SE · P.O. Box 40013 · Roanoke, VA 24022-0013 · 540-983-9300

Virginia Beach

L. Steven Emmert · Sykes, Bourdon, Ahern & Levy · Pembroke Office Park, Fifth Floor · 281 Independence Boulevard · Virginia Beach, VA 23462-2989 · 757-499-8971

BANKING LAW

McLean

Stanley M. Franklin · McGuireWoods · http://www.mcguirewoods.com · 1750 Tysons Boulevard, Suite 1800 · McLean, VA 22102-4215 · 703-712-5000

C. Christopher Giragosian · ⑩ · Hunton & Williams · 1751 Pinnacle Drive, Suite 1700 · McLean, VA 22102 · 703-714-7400

Norfolk

Thomas G. Johnson, Jr. · ⑩ · Willcox & Savage · One Commercial Place, Suite 1800 · Norfolk, VA 23510 · 757-628-5500

Alfred M. Randolph, Jr. · Kaufman & Canoles · 150 West Main Street, Suite 2100 · P.O. Box 3037 · Norfolk, VA 23514-3037 · 757-624-3000

Conrad M. Shumadine · ⑩ · Willcox & Savage · One Commercial Place, Suite 1800 · Norfolk, VA 23510 757-628-5500

Richmond

Howard W. Dobbins · ⑩ · Williams Mullen · http://www.williamsmullen.com · Two James Center · 1021 East Cary Street · P.O. Box 1320 · Richmond, VA 23218-1320 · 804-643-1991

Thomas E. duB. Fauls · Troutman Sanders · Troutman Sanders Building · 1001 Haxall Point · P.O. Box 1122 · Richmond, VA 23218-1122 · 804-697-1200

Jeffrey M. Gill · ⑩ · Troutman Sanders · Troutman Sanders Building · 1001 Haxall Point · P.O. Box 1122 Richmond, VA 23218-1122 · 804-697-1200

F. Claiborne Johnston, Jr. · ⑩ · Troutman Sanders · Troutman Sanders Building · 1001 Haxall Point · P.O. Box 1122 · Richmond, VA 23218-1122 · 804-697-1200

Jacob A. Lutz III · ⑩ · Troutman Sanders · Troutman Sanders Building · 1001 Haxall Point · P.O. Box 1122 · Richmond, VA 23218-1122 · 804-697-1200

Dewey B. Morris · ⑩ · Thompson & McMullan · 100 Shockoe Slip, Third Floor · Richmond, VA 23219 · 804-649-7545

Fred W. Palmore III · ⑩ · Troutman Sanders · Troutman Sanders Building · 1001 Haxall Point · P.O. Box 1122 · Richmond, VA 23218-1122 · 804-697-1200

Robert D. Perrow · Williams Mullen · http://www.williamsmullen.com · Two James Center · 1021 East Cary Street · P.O. Box 1320 · Richmond, VA 23218-1320 · 804-643-1991

C. Cotesworth Pinckney · ⑩ · Troutman Sanders · Troutman Sanders Building · 1001 Haxall Point · P.O. Box 1122 · Richmond, VA 23218-1122 · 804-697-1200

J. Waverly Pulley III · ⑩ · Hunton & Williams · Riverfront Plaza, East Tower · 951 East Byrd Street · Richmond, VA 23219-4074 · 804-788-8200

William H. Schwarzschild III · ⑩ · Williams Mullen · http://www.williamsmullen.com · Two James Center · 1021 East Cary Street · P.O. Box 1320 · Richmond, VA 23218-1320 · 804-643-1991

Wayne A. Whitham, Jr. · Williams Mullen · http://www.williamsmullen.com · Two James Center · 1021 East Cary Street · P.O. Box 1320 · Richmond, VA 23218-1320 · 804-643-1991

George P. Whitley · LeClair Ryan · 951 East Byrd Street, Eighth Floor · P.O. Box 2499 · Richmond, VA 23218-2499 · 804-783-2003

Roanoke

Douglas W. Densmore · ⑩ · Gentry Locke Rakes & Moore · http://www.gentrylocke.com · 10 Franklin Road, SE · P.O. Box 40013 · Roanoke, VA 24022-0013 · 540-983-9300

G. Franklin Flippin · ⑩ · Gentry Locke Rakes & Moore · http://www.gentrylocke.com · 10 Franklin Road, SE · P.O. Box 40013 · Roanoke, VA 24022-0013 · 540-983-9300

James C. Hale · LeClair Ryan · 1800 Wachovia Tower · P.O. Drawer 1200 · Roanoke, VA 24006 · 540-510-3000

G. Michael Pace, Jr. · Gentry Locke Rakes & Moore · http://www.gentrylocke.com · 10 Franklin Road, SE · P.O. Box 40013 · Roanoke, VA 24022-0013 · 540-983-9300

William R. Rakes · ⑩ · Gentry Locke Rakes & Moore · http://www.gentrylocke.com · 10 Franklin Road, SE · P.O. Box 40013 · Roanoke, VA 24022-0013 · 540-983-9300

Virginia Beach

Richard C. Beale · Troutman Sanders · 222 Central Park Avenue, Suite 2000 · Virginia Beach, VA 23462 · 757-687-7500

Monroe Kelly III · Williams Mullen · http://www.williamsmullen.com · 222 Central Park Avenue, Suite 1700 · Virginia Beach, VA 23462-3035 · 757-499-8800

C. Grigsby Scifres · Williams Mullen · http://www.williamsmullen.com · 222 Central Park Avenue, Suite 1700 · Virginia Beach, VA 23462-3035 · 757-499-8800

BANKRUPTCY AND CREDITOR-DEBTOR RIGHTS LAW

Alexandria

Richard A. Bartl · ㉕ · Tyler, Bartl, Gorman & Ramsdell · 700 South Washington Street, Suite 216 · Alexandria, VA 22314 · 703-549-5000

Thomas P. Gorman · ⑩ · Tyler, Bartl, Gorman & Ramsdell · 700 South Washington Street, Suite 216 · Alexandria, VA 22314 · 703-549-5000

Robert O. Tyler · ⑳ · Tyler, Bartl, Gorman & Ramsdell · 700 South Washington Street, Suite 216 · Alexandria, VA 22314 · 703-549-5000

Arlington

James R. Schroll · Bean, Kinney & Korman · http://www.beankinney.com · 2300 Wilson Boulevard, Suite 700 · Arlington, VA 22201 · 703-525-4000

Charlottesville

Douglas E. Little · Robert M. Musselman & Associates · 413 Seventh Street, NE · P.O. Box 254 · Charlottesville, VA 22902 · 434-977-4500

W. Stephen Scott · ⑩ · Scott Kroner · 418 East Water Street · P.O. Box 2737 · Charlottesville, VA 22902 · 434-296-2161

Chesapeake

Karen M. Crowley · Marcus, Crowley & Liberatore · http://mskmlaw.com · 1435 Crossways Boulevard, Suite 300 · Chesapeake, VA 23320-2896 · 757-333-4500

Fairfax

Bruce W. Henry · ⑩ · Henry, O'Donnell, Dahnke & Walther · 4103 Chain Bridge Road, Suite 100 · Fairfax, VA 22030 · 703-273-1900

Donald F. King · Odin, Feldman & Pittleman · http://www.ofplaw.com · 9302 Lee Highway, Suite 1100 · Fairfax, VA 22031 · 703-218-2100

Harrisonburg

Dale A. Davenport · Hoover Penrod · 342 South Main Street · Harrisonburg, VA 22801 · 540-433-2444

Stephan W. Milo · Wharton, Aldhizer & Weaver · 100 South Mason Street · P.O. Box 20028 · Harrisonburg, VA 22801-7528 · 540-434-0316

William E. Shmidheiser III · Lenhart Obenshain · http://www.lenhartobenshain.com · 90 North Main Street, Suite 201 · P.O. Box 1287 · Harrisonburg, VA 22803 · 540-437-3100

Leesburg

Christopher L. Rogan · Campbell Miller Zimmerman · 19 East Market Street · Leesburg, VA 20176 · 703-771-8344

Lynchburg

H. David Cox · Cox Law Group · http://www.coxlawgroup.com · 900 Lakeside Drive · Lynchburg, VA 24501 · 434-845-2600

McLean

H. Jason Gold · Wiley Rein · 7925 Jones Branch Drive, Suite 6200 · McLean, VA 22102 · 703-905-2800

Stephen E. Leach · Leach Travell Britt · 8270 Greensboro Drive, Suite 1050 · McLean, VA 22102 · 703-584-8900

Valerie P. Morrison · Wiley Rein · 7925 Jones Branch Drive, Suite 6200 · McLean, VA 22102 · 703-905-2800

Lawrence E. Rifken · McGuireWoods · http://www.mcguirewoods.com · 1750 Tysons Boulevard, Suite 1800 · McLean, VA 22102-4215 · 703-712-5000

Norfolk

Paul K. Campsen · ⑩ · Kaufman & Canoles · 150 West Main Street, Suite 2100 · P.O. Box 3037 · Norfolk, VA 23514-3037 · 757-624-3000

Michael P. Cotter · ⑩ · Vandeventer Black · 500 World Trade Center, Suite 500 · 101 West Main Street · Norfolk, VA 23510 · 757-446-8600

Douglas M. Foley · McGuireWoods · http://www.mcguirewoods.com · World Trade Center, Suite 9000 · 101 West Main Street · Norfolk, VA 23510-1655 · 757-640-3700

Dennis T. Lewandowski · Kaufman & Canoles · 150 West Main Street, Suite 2100 · P.O. Box 3037 · Norfolk, VA 23514-3037 · 757-624-3000

John D. McIntyre · Willcox & Savage · One Commercial Place, Suite 1800 · Norfolk, VA 23510 · 757-628-5500

Ross C. Reeves · ⑩ · Willcox & Savage · One Commercial Place, Suite 1800 · Norfolk, VA 23510 · 757-628-5500

Jerrold G. Weinberg · ㉕ · Weinberg & Stein · 999 Waterside Drive, Suite 1825 · P.O. Box 3789 · Norfolk, VA 23514-3789 · 757-627-1066

Peter G. Zemanian · ⑩ · Zemanian Law Group · 600 Town Point Center · 150 Boush Street · Norfolk, VA 23510 · 757-622-0090

Richmond

Benjamin C. Ackerly · ⑳ · Hunton & Williams · Riverfront Plaza, East Tower · 951 East Byrd Street · Richmond, VA 23219-4074 · 804-788-8200

Paula Steinhilber Beran · Tavenner & Beran · 20 North Eighth Street, Second Floor · Richmond, VA 23219 · 804-783-8300

Tyler P. Brown · Hunton & Williams · Riverfront Plaza, East Tower · 951 East Byrd Street · Richmond, VA 23219-4074 · 804-788-8200

Michael A. Condyles · Kutak Rock · Bank of America Center, Suite 800 · 1111 East Main Street · Richmond, VA 23219-3500 · 804-644-1700

Dion W. Hayes · McGuireWoods · http://www.mcguirewoods.com · One James Center · 901 East Cary Street · Richmond, VA 23219-4030 · 804-775-1000

Bruce H. Matson · LeClair Ryan · 951 East Byrd Street, Eighth Floor · P.O. Box 2499 · Richmond, VA 23218-2499 · 804-783-2003

Fred W. Palmore III · ⑩ · Troutman Sanders · Troutman Sanders Building · 1001 Haxall Point · P.O. Box 1122 · Richmond, VA 23218-1122 · 804-697-1200

William H. Schwarzschild III · ⑩ · Williams Mullen · http://www.williamsmullen.com · Two James Center · 1021 East Cary Street · P.O. Box 1320 · Richmond, VA 23218-1320 · 804-643-1991

Harry Shaia, Jr. · ㉕ · Spinella, Owings & Shaia · 8550 Mayland Drive · Richmond, VA 23294 · 804-747-0920

Lynn Lewis Tavenner · Tavenner & Beran · 20 North Eighth Street, Second Floor · Richmond, VA 23219 · 804-783-8300

Roy M. Terry, Jr. · DurretteBradshaw · http://www.durrettebradshaw.com · Main Street Centre, 20th Floor · 600 East Main Street · Richmond, VA 23219 · 804-775-6900

Roanoke

Howard J. Beck, Jr. · ⑩ · Howard Beck, Jr. · 4648 Brambleton Avenue · Roanoke, VA 24018-3437 · 540-983-9324

Paul M. Black · Spilman Thomas & Battle · http://www.spilmanlaw.com · 310 First Street, Suite 1100 · Roanoke, VA 24002 · 540-512-1800

Roy V. Creasy · Roy V. Creasy · 213 South Jefferson Street, Suite 915 · Roanoke, VA 24011-1735 · 540-342-0729

Tracy Allen Giles · Giles & Lambert · 129 East Campbell Avenue, Suite 300 · Roanoke, VA 24011 · 540-981-9000

Andrew S. Goldstein · Magee, Foster, Goldstein & Sayers · BB&T Bank Building, Suite 1200 · 310 First Street, SW · P.O. Box 404 · Roanoke, VA 24003 · 540-343-9800

Michael E. Hastings · LeClair Ryan · 1800 Wachovia Tower · P.O. Drawer 1200 · Roanoke, VA 24006 · 540-510-3000

Malissa Lambert-Giles · Giles & Lambert · 129 East Campbell Avenue, Suite 300 · Roanoke, VA 24011 · 540-981-9000

Daniel F. Layman, Jr. · ⑩ · Woods Rogers · http://www.woodsrogers.com · Wachovia Tower, Suite 1400 · 10 South Jefferson Street · P.O. Box 14125 · Roanoke, VA 24038-4125 · 540-983-7600

A. Carter Magee, Jr. · Magee, Foster, Goldstein & Sayers · BB&T Bank Building, Suite 1200 · 310 First Street, SW · P.O. Box 404 · Roanoke, VA 24003 · 540-343-9800

Richard C. Maxwell · Woods Rogers · http://www.woodsrogers.com · Wachovia Tower, Suite 1400 · 10 South Jefferson Street · P.O. Box 14125 · Roanoke, VA 24038-4125 · 540-983-7600

Kevin P. Oddo · LeClair Ryan · 1800 Wachovia Tower · P.O. Drawer 1200 · Roanoke, VA 24006 · 540-510-3000

John R. Patterson · John R. Patterson · 213 South Jefferson Street, Suite 910 · Roanoke, VA 24011-1713 · 540-342-5157

Lori D. Thompson · LeClair Ryan · 1800 Wachovia Tower · P.O. Drawer 1200 · Roanoke, VA 24006 · 540-510-3000

Vienna

Stephen K. Gallagher · Venable · http://www.venable.com · 8010 Towers Crescent Drive, Suite 300 · Vienna, VA 22182 · 703-760-1600

Lawrence A. Katz · Venable · http://www.venable.com · 8010 Towers Crescent Drive, Suite 300 · Vienna, VA 22182 · 703-760-1600

Stanley M. Salus · Akerman Senterfitt · http://www.akerman.com · 8100 Boone Boulevard, Suite 700 · Vienna, VA 22182-2683 · 703-790-8750

Virginia Beach

Jonathan L. Hauser · Troutman Sanders · 222 Central Park Avenue, Suite 2000 · Virginia Beach, VA 23462 · 757-687-7500

BET-THE-COMPANY LITIGATION

McLean

Richard O. Duvall · ⑳ · Holland & Knight · http://www.hklaw.com · 1600 Tysons Boulevard, Suite 700 · McLean, VA 22102 · 703-720-8600

Norfolk

Hunter W. Sims, Jr. · ⑩ · Kaufman & Canoles · 150 West Main Street, Suite 2100 · P.O. Box 3037 · Norfolk, VA 23514-3037 · 757-624-3000

Gregory N. Stillman · ⑩ · Hunton & Williams · 500 East Main Street, Suite 1000 · P.O. Box 3889 · Norfolk, VA 23514 · 757-640-5300

Richmond

Everette G. Allen, Jr. · ㉕ · LeClair Ryan · 701 East Byrd Street, 16th Floor · Richmond, VA 23219 · 804-545-1500

James E. Farnham · ㉕ · Hunton & Williams · Riverfront Plaza, East Tower · 951 East Byrd Street · Richmond, VA 23219-4074 · 804-788-8200

Thomas G. Slater, Jr. · ⑩ · Hunton & Williams · Riverfront Plaza, East Tower · 951 East Byrd Street · Richmond, VA 23219-4074 · 804-788-8200

Anne Marie Whittemore · ⑳ · McGuireWoods · http://www.mcguirewoods.com · One James Center · 901 East Cary Street · Richmond, VA 23219-4030 · 804-775-1000

Roanoke

William B. Poff · 25 · Woods Rogers · http://www.woodsrogers.com · Wachovia Tower, Suite 1400 · 10 South Jefferson Street · P.O. Box 14125 · Roanoke, VA 24038-4125 · 540-983-7600

Vienna

William D. Dolan III · Venable · http://www.venable.com · 8010 Towers Crescent Drive, Suite 300 · Vienna, VA 22182 · 703-760-1600

BIOTECHNOLOGY LAW

Charlottesville

Michael P. Drzal · LeClair Ryan · 123 East Main Street, Suite 800 · Charlottesville, VA 22902 · 434-245-3444

Richmond

J. Benjamin English · Hirschler Fleischer · http://www.hirschlerfleischer.com · The Edgeworth Building · 2100 East Cary Street · Richmond, VA 23223-7078 · 804-771-9500

Gary D. LeClair · LeClair Ryan · 951 East Byrd Street, Eighth Floor · P.O. Box 2499 · Richmond, VA 23218-2499 · 804-783-2003

Roanoke

Hugh B. Wellons · LeClair Ryan · 1800 Wachovia Tower · P.O. Drawer 1200 · Roanoke, VA 24006 · 540-510-3000

COLLABORATIVE LAW: FAMILY LAW

Charlottesville

Annie Lee Jacobs · 20 · Parker, McElwain & Jacobs · 2340 Commonwealth Drive · P.O. Box 6186 · Charlottesville, VA 22906 · 434-973-3331

John K. Taggart III · 10 · Tremblay & Smith · http://www.tremblaysmith.com · 105-109 East High Street P.O. Box 1585 · Charlottesville, VA 22902 · 434-977-4455

Susan Davis White · 10 · Susan Davis White · 103 East Water Street, Suite 301 · Charlottesville, VA 22902 · 434-977-0563

Harrisonburg

Lawrence H. Hoover, Jr. · Hoover Penrod · 342 South Main Street · Harrisonburg, VA 22801 · 540-433-2444

Lynchburg

Frank West Morrison · Phillips, Morrison, Johnson & Ferrell · Bank of the James Building, Suite 1403 · 828 Main Street · Lynchburg, VA 24504 · 434-384-0946

Vienna

Frances Fite · Fite & O'Brien · 8027 Leesburg Pike, Suite 304 · Vienna, VA 22182 · 703-821-8575

Alexandria

Robert E. Scully, Jr. · Stites & Harbison · http://www.stites.com · 1199 North Fairfax Street, Suite 900 · Alexandria, VA 22314 · 703-739-4900

Charlottesville

Jonathan T. Blank · McGuireWoods · http://www.mcguirewoods.com · Court Square Building, Suite 300 · 310 Fourth Street, NE · P.O. Box 1288 · Charlottesville, VA 22902-1288 · 434-977-2500

Michael E. Derdeyn · Feil, Pettit and Williams · 530 East Main Street · P.O. Box 2057 · Charlottesville, VA 22902-2057 · 434-979-1400

John V. Little · ⑩ · Michie Hamlett Lowry Rasmussen & Tweel · 500 Court Square, Suite 300 · P.O. Box 298 · Charlottesville, VA 22902-0298 · 434-951-7200

Edward B. Lowry · ⑳ · Michie Hamlett Lowry Rasmussen & Tweel · 500 Court Square, Suite 300 · P.O. Box 298 · Charlottesville, VA 22902-0298 · 434-951-7200

Leigh B. Middleditch, Jr. · ⑳ · McGuireWoods · http://www.mcguirewoods.com · Court Square Building, Suite 300 · 310 Fourth Street, NE · P.O. Box 1288 · Charlottesville, VA 22902-1288 · 434-977-2500

Fairfax

John A. C. Keith · Blankingship & Keith · http://www.blankingship-keith-law.com · 4020 University Drive, Suite 300 · Fairfax, VA 22030 · 703-691-1235

Harrisonburg

J. Jay Litten · Litten & Sipe · 410 Neff Avenue · Harrisonburg, VA 22801 · 540-434-5353

Mark D. Obenshain · Lenhart Obenshain · http://www.lenhartobenshain.com · 90 North Main Street, Suite 201 · P.O. Box 1287 · Harrisonburg, VA 22803 · 540-437-3100

M. Bruce Wallinger · ⑩ · Hoover Penrod · 342 South Main Street · Harrisonburg, VA 22801 · 540-433-2444

Leesburg

Aaron S. Book · Webster Book · One North King Street · Leesburg, VA 20176 · 703-779-8229

Steven T. Webster · Webster Book · One North King Street · Leesburg, VA 20176 · 703-779-8229

Lynchburg

Bernard C. Baldwin III · Edmunds & Williams · 828 Main Street, 19th Floor · P.O. Box 958 · Lynchburg, VA 24505 · 434-846-9000

Robert C. Wood III · ㉕ · Edmunds & Williams · 828 Main Street, 19th Floor · P.O. Box 958 · Lynchburg, VA 24505 · 434-846-9000

McLean

Thomas J. Cawley · ⑩ · Hunton & Williams · 1751 Pinnacle Drive, Suite 1700 · McLean, VA 22102 · 703-714-7400

Richard O. Duvall · ⑳ · Holland & Knight · http://www.hklaw.com · 1600 Tysons Boulevard, Suite 700 · McLean, VA 22102 · 703-720-8600

Stephen M. Sayers · Hunton & Williams · 1751 Pinnacle Drive, Suite 1700 · McLean, VA 22102 · 703-714-7400

Thomas E. Spahn · McGuireWoods · http://www.mcguirewoods.com · 1750 Tysons Boulevard, Suite 1800 · McLean, VA 22102-4215 · 703-712-5000

Warren E. Zirkle · McGuireWoods · http://www.mcguirewoods.com · 1750 Tysons Boulevard, Suite 1800 McLean, VA 22102-4215 · 703-712-5000

Newport News

William L. Stauffer, Jr. · Williams Mullen · http://www.williamsmullen.com · Fountain Plaza Three, Suite 200 · 721 Lakefront Commons · Newport News, VA 23606-3324 · 757-249-5100

Norfolk

Alan D. Albert · ⑩ · LeClair Ryan · 999 Waterside Drive, Suite 2525 · Norfolk, VA 23510 · 757-624-1454

Stanley G. Barr, Jr. · ⑳ · Kaufman & Canoles · 150 West Main Street, Suite 2100 · P.O. Box 3037 · Norfolk, VA 23514-3037 · 757-624-3000

Robert W. McFarland · McGuireWoods · http://www.mcguirewoods.com · World Trade Center, Suite 9000 · 101 West Main Street · Norfolk, VA 23510-1655 · 757-640-3700

John Y. Pearson, Jr. · ⑩ · Willcox & Savage · One Commercial Place, Suite 1800 · Norfolk, VA 23510 · 757-628-5500

John M. Ryan · ⑳ · Vandeventer Black · 500 World Trade Center, Suite 500 · 101 West Main Street · Norfolk, VA 23510 · 757-446-8600

Conrad M. Shumadine · ⑩ · Willcox & Savage · One Commercial Place, Suite 1800 · Norfolk, VA 23510 757-628-5500

Hunter W. Sims, Jr. · ⑩ · Kaufman & Canoles · 150 West Main Street, Suite 2100 · P.O. Box 3037 · Norfolk, VA 23514-3037 · 757-624-3000

Gregory N. Stillman · ⑩ · Hunton & Williams · 500 East Main Street, Suite 1000 · P.O. Box 3889 · Norfolk, VA 23514 · 757-640-5300

Jerrold G. Weinberg · ㉕ · Weinberg & Stein · 999 Waterside Drive, Suite 1825 · P.O. Box 3789 · Norfolk, VA 23514-3789 · 757-627-1066

Richmond

Everette G. Allen, Jr. · ㉕ · LeClair Ryan · 701 East Byrd Street, 16th Floor · Richmond, VA 23219 · 804-545-1500

Susan C. Armstrong · Troutman Sanders · Troutman Sanders Building · 1001 Haxall Point · P.O. Box 1122 · Richmond, VA 23218-1122 · 804-697-1200

Stephen E. Baril · Williams Mullen · http://www.williamsmullen.com · Two James Center · 1021 East Cary Street · P.O. Box 1320 · Richmond, VA 23218-1320 · 804-643-1991

William D. Bayliss · Williams Mullen · http://www.williamsmullen.com · Two James Center · 1021 East Cary Street · P.O. Box 1320 · Richmond, VA 23218-1320 · 804-643-1991

J. William Boland · McGuireWoods · http://www.mcguirewoods.com · One James Center · 901 East Cary Street · Richmond, VA 23219-4030 · 804-775-1000

William G. Broaddus · McGuireWoods · http://www.mcguirewoods.com · One James Center · 901 East Cary Street · Richmond, VA 23219-4030 · 804-775-1000

John K. Burke, Jr. · 10 · Troutman Sanders · Troutman Sanders Building · 1001 Haxall Point · P.O. Box 1122 · Richmond, VA 23218-1122 · 804-697-1200

R. Harvey Chappell, Jr. · 25 · Christian & Barton · Mutual Building, Suite 1200 · 909 East Main Street · Richmond, VA 23219-3095 · 804-697-4100

Richard Cullen · McGuireWoods · http://www.mcguirewoods.com · One James Center · 901 East Cary Street · Richmond, VA 23219-4030 · 804-775-1000

Wyatt B. Durrette, Jr. · DurretteBradshaw · http://www.durrettebradshaw.com · Main Street Centre, 20th Floor · 600 East Main Street · Richmond, VA 23219 · 804-775-6900

John D. Epps · Hunton & Williams · Riverfront Plaza, East Tower · 951 East Byrd Street · Richmond, VA 23219-4074 · 804-788-8200

Hugh M. Fain III · Spotts Fain · http://www.spottsfain.com · 411 East Franklin Street, Suite 600 · Richmond, VA 23219 · 804-697-2000

James E. Farnham · 25 · Hunton & Williams · Riverfront Plaza, East Tower · 951 East Byrd Street · Richmond, VA 23219-4074 · 804-788-8200

Calvin W. Fowler, Jr. · Williams Mullen · http://www.williamsmullen.com · Two James Center · 1021 East Cary Street · P.O. Box 1320 · Richmond, VA 23218-1320 · 804-643-1991

Edward J. Fuhr · 10 · Hunton & Williams · Riverfront Plaza, East Tower · 951 East Byrd Street · Richmond, VA 23219-4074 · 804-788-8200

Warren David Harless · 10 · Christian & Barton · Mutual Building, Suite 1200 · 909 East Main Street · Richmond, VA 23219-3095 · 804-697-4100

Joseph C. Kearfott · Hunton & Williams · Riverfront Plaza, East Tower · 951 East Byrd Street · Richmond, VA 23219-4074 · 804-788-8200

William H. King, Jr. · 25 · McGuireWoods · http://www.mcguirewoods.com · One James Center · 901 East Cary Street · Richmond, VA 23219-4030 · 804-775-1000

Craig Thomas Merritt · Christian & Barton · Mutual Building, Suite 1200 · 909 East Main Street · Richmond, VA 23219-3095 · 804-697-4100

James W. Morris III · 25 · Morris & Morris · Wytestone Plaza, 12th Floor · 801 East Main Street · P.O. Box 30 · Richmond, VA 23218 · 804-344-8300

Stephen A. Northup · 10 · Troutman Sanders · Troutman Sanders Building · 1001 Haxall Point · P.O. Box 1122 · Richmond, VA 23218-1122 · 804-697-1200

John H. OBrion, Jr. · 20 · The McCammon Group · Bank of America Center, Suite 1700 · 1111 East Main Street · Richmond, VA 23219 · 804-343-0922

Scott C. Oostdyk · McGuireWoods · http://www.mcguirewoods.com · One James Center · 901 East Cary Street · Richmond, VA 23219-4030 · 804-775-1000

Rosewell Page III · ㉕ · McGuireWoods · http://www.mcguirewoods.com · One James Center · 901 East Cary Street · Richmond, VA 23219-4030 · 804-775-1000

Russell V. Palmore · Troutman Sanders · Troutman Sanders Building · 1001 Haxall Point · P.O. Box 1122 Richmond, VA 23218-1122 · 804-697-1200

James C. Roberts · ㉕ · Troutman Sanders · Troutman Sanders Building · 1001 Haxall Point · P.O. Box 1122 · Richmond, VA 23218-1122 · 804-697-1200

Robert M. Rolfe · Hunton & Williams · Riverfront Plaza, East Tower · 951 East Byrd Street · Richmond, VA 23219-4074 · 804-788-8200

Gilbert E. Schill, Jr. · McGuireWoods · http://www.mcguirewoods.com · One James Center · 901 East Cary Street · Richmond, VA 23219-4030 · 804-775-1000

Robert D. Seabolt · Troutman Sanders · Troutman Sanders Building · 1001 Haxall Point · P.O. Box 1122 Richmond, VA 23218-1122 · 804-697-1200

Charles M. Sims · LeClair Ryan · 951 East Byrd Street, Eighth Floor · P.O. Box 2499 · Richmond, VA 23218-2499 · 804-783-2003

Thomas G. Slater, Jr. · ⑩ · Hunton & Williams · Riverfront Plaza, East Tower · 951 East Byrd Street · Richmond, VA 23219-4074 · 804-788-8200

Michael W. Smith · ⑳ · Christian & Barton · Mutual Building, Suite 1200 · 909 East Main Street · Richmond, VA 23219-3095 · 804-697-4100

Anthony F. Troy · ⑩ · Troutman Sanders · Troutman Sanders Building · 1001 Haxall Point · P.O. Box 1122 · Richmond, VA 23218-1122 · 804-697-1200

John L. Walker III · Williams Mullen · http://www.williamsmullen.com · Two James Center · 1021 East Cary Street · P.O. Box 1320 · Richmond, VA 23218-1320 · 804-643-1991

Anne Marie Whittemore · ⑳ · McGuireWoods · http://www.mcguirewoods.com · One James Center · 901 East Cary Street · Richmond, VA 23219-4030 · 804-775-1000

Charles Frederick Witthoefft · ⑩ · Hirschler Fleischer · http://www.hirschlerfleischer.com · The Edgeworth Building · 2100 East Cary Street · Richmond, VA 23223-7078 · 804-771-9500

Roanoke

D. Stan Barnhill · ⑩ · Woods Rogers · http://www.woodsrogers.com · Wachovia Tower, Suite 1400 · 10 South Jefferson Street · P.O. Box 14125 · Roanoke, VA 24038-4125 · 540-983-7600

Daniel S. Brown · Woods Rogers · http://www.woodsrogers.com · Wachovia Tower, Suite 1400 · 10 South Jefferson Street · P.O. Box 14125 · Roanoke, VA 24038-4125 · 540-983-7600

Gregory J. Haley · Gentry Locke Rakes & Moore · http://www.gentrylocke.com · 10 Franklin Road, SE · P.O. Box 40013 · Roanoke, VA 24022-0013 · 540-983-9300

James W. Jennings, Jr. · ⑩ · Woods Rogers · http://www.woodsrogers.com · Wachovia Tower, Suite 1400 10 South Jefferson Street · P.O. Box 14125 · Roanoke, VA 24038-4125 · 540-983-7600

Mark D. Loftis · Woods Rogers · http://www.woodsrogers.com · Wachovia Tower, Suite 1400 · 10 South Jefferson Street · P.O. Box 14125 · Roanoke, VA 24038-4125 · 540-983-7600

Kevin P. Oddo · LeClair Ryan · 1800 Wachovia Tower · P.O. Drawer 1200 · Roanoke, VA 24006 · 540-510-3000

William B. Poff · ㉕ · Woods Rogers · http://www.woodsrogers.com · Wachovia Tower, Suite 1400 · 10 South Jefferson Street · P.O. Box 14125 · Roanoke, VA 24038-4125 · 540-983-7600

William R. Rakes · ⑩ · Gentry Locke Rakes & Moore · http://www.gentrylocke.com · 10 Franklin Road, SE · P.O. Box 40013 · Roanoke, VA 24022-0013 · 540-983-9300

Scott J. Sexton · Gentry Locke Rakes & Moore · http://www.gentrylocke.com · 10 Franklin Road, SE · P.O. Box 40013 · Roanoke, VA 24022-0013 · 540-983-9300

Staunton

Colin J. S. Thomas, Jr. · ⑳ · Timberlake, Smith, Thomas & Moses · The Virginia Building · 25 North Central Avenue · P.O. Box 108 · Staunton, VA 24402-0108 · 540-885-1517

Vienna

William D. Dolan III · Venable · http://www.venable.com · 8010 Towers Crescent Drive, Suite 300 · Vienna, VA 22182 · 703-760-1600

Virginia Beach

Donald H. Clark · ⑩ · Williams Mullen · http://www.williamsmullen.com · 222 Central Park Avenue, Suite 1700 · Virginia Beach, VA 23462-3035 · 757-499-8800

L. Steven Emmert · Sykes, Bourdon, Ahern & Levy · Pembroke Office Park, Fifth Floor · 281 Independence Boulevard · Virginia Beach, VA 23462-2989 · 757-499-8971

Jeffrey H. Gray · Troutman Sanders · 222 Central Park Avenue, Suite 2000 · Virginia Beach, VA 23462 · 757-687-7500

Stephen G. Test · Williams Mullen · http://www.williamsmullen.com · 222 Central Park Avenue, Suite 1700 · Virginia Beach, VA 23462-3035 · 757-499-8800

COMMUNICATIONS LAW

Glen Allen

James Patrick Guy II · LeClair Ryan · 4201 Dominion Boulevard, Suite 200 · Glen Allen, VA 23060 · 804-270-0070

Richmond

Louis Richardson Monacell · Christian & Barton · Mutual Building, Suite 1200 · 909 East Main Street · Richmond, VA 23219-3095 · 804-697-4100

JoAnne Lewis Nolte · The Conrad Firm · 1520 West Main Street, Suite 204 · Richmond, VA 23220 · 804-359-6062

Eric M. Page · LeClair Ryan · 951 East Byrd Street, Eighth Floor · P.O. Box 2499 · Richmond, VA 23218-2499 · 804-783-2003

Chesapeake

David A. Hearne · Outland, Gray, O'Keefe & Hubbard · 112 Coastal Way · P.O. Box 2250 · Chesapeake, VA 23327-2250 · 757-547-0171

Benjamin A. Hubbard III · Outland, Gray, O'Keefe & Hubbard · 112 Coastal Way · P.O. Box 2250 · Chesapeake, VA 23327-2250 · 757-547-0171

Falls Church

Joseph H. Kasimer · Kasimer & Annino · http://www.kasimerannino.com · Tysons Office Park · 7653 Leesburg Pike · Falls Church, VA 22043-2520 · 703-893-3914

Leesburg

Randall C. Allen · Randall C. Allen · 105 Loudoun Street, SE · Leesburg, VA 20175 · 703-737-6710

McLean

Lewis J. Baker · Watt, Tieder, Hoffar & Fitzgerald · http://www.wthf.com · 8405 Greensboro Drive, Suite 100 · McLean, VA 22102 · 703-749-1000

Kathleen O. Barnes · Watt, Tieder, Hoffar & Fitzgerald · http://www.wthf.com · 8405 Greensboro Drive, Suite 100 · McLean, VA 22102 · 703-749-1000

Christopher J. Brasco · Watt, Tieder, Hoffar & Fitzgerald · http://www.wthf.com · 8405 Greensboro Drive, Suite 100 · McLean, VA 22102 · 703-749-1000

Thomas M. Brownell · Holland & Knight · http://www.hklaw.com · 1600 Tysons Boulevard, Suite 700 · McLean, VA 22102 · 703-720-8600

Robert K. Cox · Watt, Tieder, Hoffar & Fitzgerald · http://www.wthf.com · 8405 Greensboro Drive, Suite 100 · McLean, VA 22102 · 703-749-1000

Shelly L. Ewald · Watt, Tieder, Hoffar & Fitzgerald · http://www.wthf.com · 8405 Greensboro Drive, Suite 100 · McLean, VA 22102 · 703-749-1000

Robert M. Fitzgerald · Watt, Tieder, Hoffar & Fitzgerald · http://www.wthf.com · 8405 Greensboro Drive, Suite 100 · McLean, VA 22102 · 703-749-1000

Julian F. Hoffar · Watt, Tieder, Hoffar & Fitzgerald · http://www.wthf.com · 8405 Greensboro Drive, Suite 100 · McLean, VA 22102 · 703-749-1000

Vivian Katsantonis · Watt, Tieder, Hoffar & Fitzgerald · http://www.wthf.com · 8405 Greensboro Drive, Suite 100 · McLean, VA 22102 · 703-749-1000

Daniel J. Kraftson · Kraftson Caudle · 1600 Tysons Boulevard, Suite 250 · McLean, VA 22102 · 703-873-5500

David G. Lane · Law Office of David G. Lane · 1420 Spring Hill Road, Suite 600 · McLean, VA 22102 · 703-749-1296

Charlie C.H. Lee · Moore & Lee · http://www.mooreandlee.com · 1650 Tysons Boulevard, Suite 1150 · McLean, VA 22102-4225 · 703-506-2050

Robert M. Moore · Moore & Lee · http://www.mooreandlee.com · 1650 Tysons Boulevard, Suite 1150 · McLean, VA 22102-4225 · 703-506-2050

Carter B. Reid · Watt, Tieder, Hoffar & Fitzgerald · http://www.wthf.com · 8405 Greensboro Drive, Suite 100 · McLean, VA 22102 · 703-749-1000

John B. Tieder, Jr. · Watt, Tieder, Hoffar & Fitzgerald · http://www.wthf.com · 8405 Greensboro Drive, Suite 100 · McLean, VA 22102 · 703-749-1000

Paul A. Varela · Watt, Tieder, Hoffar & Fitzgerald · http://www.wthf.com · 8405 Greensboro Drive, Suite 100 · McLean, VA 22102 · 703-749-1000

Robert G. Watt · Watt, Tieder, Hoffar & Fitzgerald · http://www.wthf.com · 8405 Greensboro Drive, Suite 100 · McLean, VA 22102 · 703-749-1000

Norfolk

William E. Franczek · Vandeventer Black · 500 World Trade Center, Suite 500 · 101 West Main Street · Norfolk, VA 23510 · 757-446-8600

Terence Murphy · Kaufman & Canoles · 150 West Main Street, Suite 2100 · P.O. Box 3037 · Norfolk, VA 23514-3037 · 757-624-3000

Richmond

Stephan F. Andrews · Vandeventer Black · Eighth & Main Building, Suite 1700 · 707 East Main Street · P.O. Box 1558 · Richmond, VA 23218-1558 · 804-237-8800

Philip C. Baxa · MercerTrigiani · 16 South Second Street · Richmond, VA 23219 · 804-344-1504

L. Brad Cann III · LeClair Ryan · 951 East Byrd Street, Eighth Floor · P.O. Box 2499 · Richmond, VA 23218-2499 · 804-783-2003

Bradfute W. Davenport, Jr. · Troutman Sanders · Troutman Sanders Building · 1001 Haxall Point · P.O. Box 1122 · Richmond, VA 23218-1122 · 804-697-1200

Barry A. Hackney · Hirschler Fleischer · http://www.hirschlerfleischer.com · The Edgeworth Building · 2100 East Cary Street · Richmond, VA 23223-7078 · 804-771-9500

Bruce M. Marshall · DurretteBradshaw · http://www.durrettebradshaw.com · Main Street Centre, 20th Floor · 600 East Main Street · Richmond, VA 23219 · 804-775-6900

George Keith Martin · McGuireWoods · http://www.mcguirewoods.com · One James Center · 901 East Cary Street · Richmond, VA 23219-4030 · 804-775-1000

William R. Mauck, Jr. · Williams Mullen · http://www.williamsmullen.com · Two James Center · 1021 East Cary Street · P.O. Box 1320 · Richmond, VA 23218-1320 · 804-643-1991

R. Webb Moore · Hirschler Fleischer · http://www.hirschlerfleischer.com · The Edgeworth Building · 2100 East Cary Street · Richmond, VA 23223-7078 · 804-771-9500

Thomas M. Wolf · LeClair Ryan · 951 East Byrd Street, Eighth Floor · P.O. Box 2499 · Richmond, VA 23218-2499 · 804-783-2003

Roanoke

Robert S. Ballou · Johnson, Ayers & Matthews · First Campbell Square, Suite 300 · 210 First Street, SW · P.O. Box 2200 · Roanoke, VA 24009-2200 · 540-767-2000

D. Stan Barnhill · ⑩ · Woods Rogers · http://www.woodsrogers.com · Wachovia Tower, Suite 1400 · 10 South Jefferson Street · P.O. Box 14125 · Roanoke, VA 24038-4125 · 540-983-7600

K. Brett Marston · Gentry Locke Rakes & Moore · http://www.gentrylocke.com · 10 Franklin Road, SE · P.O. Box 40013 · Roanoke, VA 24022-0013 · 540-983-9300

Charles H. Osterhoudt · Osterhoudt, Prillaman, Natt, Helscher, Yost, Maxwell & Ferguson · 3140 Chaparral Drive, Suite 200-C · P.O. Box 20487 · Roanoke, VA 24018 · 540-989-0000

Vienna

Donald G. Gavin · Akerman Senterfitt · http://www.akerman.com · 8100 Boone Boulevard, Suite 700 · Vienna, VA 22182-2683 · 703-790-8750

Jeffrey G. Gilmore · Akerman Senterfitt · http://www.akerman.com · 8100 Boone Boulevard, Suite 700 · Vienna, VA 22182-2683 · 703-790-8750

Mark E. Hanson · Smith Pachter McWhorter · http://www.smithpachter.com · 8000 Towers Crescent Drive, Suite 900 · Vienna, VA 22182-2700 · 703-847-6300

A. Wayne Lalle, Jr. · Venable · http://www.venable.com · 8010 Towers Crescent Drive, Suite 300 · Vienna, VA 22182 · 703-760-1600

Val S. McWhorter · Smith Pachter McWhorter · http://www.smithpachter.com · 8000 Towers Crescent Drive, Suite 900 · Vienna, VA 22182-2700 · 703-847-6300

Richard F. Smith · Smith Pachter McWhorter · http://www.smithpachter.com · 8000 Towers Crescent Drive, Suite 900 · Vienna, VA 22182-2700 · 703-847-6300

Brian J. Vella · Smith Pachter McWhorter · http://www.smithpachter.com · 8000 Towers Crescent Drive, Suite 900 · Vienna, VA 22182-2700 · 703-847-6300

Virginia Beach

Stephen G. Test · Williams Mullen · http://www.williamsmullen.com · 222 Central Park Avenue, Suite 1700 · Virginia Beach, VA 23462-3035 · 757-499-8800

CORPORATE GOVERNANCE AND COMPLIANCE LAW

Norfolk

William R. Van Buren III · 10 · Kaufman & Canoles · 150 West Main Street, Suite 2100 · P.O. Box 3037 · Norfolk, VA 23514-3037 · 757-624-3000

Richmond

Robert L. Burrus, Jr. · 25 · McGuireWoods · http://www.mcguirewoods.com · One James Center · 901 East Cary Street · Richmond, VA 23219-4030 · 804-775-1000

Clifford A. Cutchins IV · McGuireWoods · http://www.mcguirewoods.com · One James Center · 901 East Cary Street · Richmond, VA 23219-4030 · 804-775-1000

J. Benjamin English · Hirschler Fleischer · http://www.hirschlerfleischer.com · The Edgeworth Building · 2100 East Cary Street · Richmond, VA 23223-7078 · 804-771-9500

Allen C. Goolsby III · 20 · Hunton & Williams · Riverfront Plaza, East Tower · 951 East Byrd Street · Richmond, VA 23219-4074 · 804-788-8200

Louanna O. Heuhsen · Hunton & Williams · Riverfront Plaza, East Tower · 951 East Byrd Street · Richmond, VA 23219-4074 · 804-788-8200

F. Claiborne Johnston, Jr. · ⑩ · Troutman Sanders · Troutman Sanders Building · 1001 Haxall Point · P.O. Box 1122 · Richmond, VA 23218-1122 · 804-697-1200

George P. Whitley · LeClair Ryan · 951 East Byrd Street, Eighth Floor · P.O. Box 2499 · Richmond, VA 23218-2499 · 804-783-2003

CORPORATE LAW

Charlottesville

David L. Dallas, Jr. · Williams Mullen · http://www.williamsmullen.com · 321 East Main Street, Suite 400 Charlottesville, VA 22902-3200 · 434-951-5700

Michael P. Drzal · LeClair Ryan · 123 East Main Street, Suite 800 · Charlottesville, VA 22902 · 434-245-3444

Kurt J. Krueger · McGuireWoods · http://www.mcguirewoods.com · Court Square Building, Suite 300 · 310 Fourth Street, NE · P.O. Box 1288 · Charlottesville, VA 22902-1288 · 434-977-2500

John V. Little · ⑩ · Michie Hamlett Lowry Rasmussen & Tweel · 500 Court Square, Suite 300 · P.O. Box 298 · Charlottesville, VA 22902-0298 · 434-951-7200

Danville

R. Lee Yancey · Clement & Wheatley · 549 Main Street · P.O. Box 8200 · Danville, VA 24543-8200 · 434-793-8200

Harrisonburg

Jeffrey G. Lenhart · Lenhart Obenshain · http://www.lenhartobenshain.com · 90 North Main Street, Suite 201 · P.O. Box 1287 · Harrisonburg, VA 22803 · 540-437-3100

George H. Roberts, Jr. · Wharton, Aldhizer & Weaver · 100 South Mason Street · P.O. Box 20028 · Harrisonburg, VA 22801-7528 · 540-434-0316

Donald E. Showalter · Wharton, Aldhizer & Weaver · 100 South Mason Street · P.O. Box 20028 · Harrisonburg, VA 22801-7528 · 540-434-0316

Lynchburg

John R. Alford, Jr. · ⑩ · Caskie & Frost · 2306 Atherholt Road · P.O. Box 6360 · Lynchburg, VA 24505 · 434-846-2731

Bernard C. Baldwin III · Edmunds & Williams · 828 Main Street, 19th Floor · P.O. Box 958 · Lynchburg, VA 24505 · 434-846-9000

Theodore J. Craddock · ⑩ · Caskie & Frost · 2306 Atherholt Road · P.O. Box 6360 · Lynchburg, VA 24505 · 434-846-2731

McLean

Jocelyn West Brittin · Holland & Knight · http://www.hklaw.com · 1600 Tysons Boulevard, Suite 700 · McLean, VA 22102 · 703-720-8600

Thomas C. Brown, Jr. · ⑳ · McGuireWoods · http://www.mcguirewoods.com · 1750 Tysons Boulevard, Suite 1800 · McLean, VA 22102-4215 · 703-712-5000

Lee R. Marks · Greenberg Traurig · http://www.gtlaw.com · 1750 Tysons Boulevard, Suite 1200 · McLean, VA 22102 · 703-749-1300

William J. Mutryn · Holland & Knight · http://www.hklaw.com · 1600 Tysons Boulevard, Suite 700 · McLean, VA 22102 · 703-720-8600

Norfolk

Charles W. Best, Jr. · (20) · Charles W. Best, Jr. · 999 Waterside Drive, Suite 1835 · Norfolk, VA 23510 · 757-623-0482

George L. Consolvo · Kaufman & Canoles · 150 West Main Street, Suite 2100 · P.O. Box 3037 · Norfolk, VA 23514-3037 · 757-624-3000

David M. Delpierre · Kaufman & Canoles · 150 West Main Street, Suite 2100 · P.O. Box 3037 · Norfolk, VA 23514-3037 · 757-624-3000

Patrick C. Devine, Jr. · (10) · Williams Mullen · http://www.williamsmullen.com · Dominion Tower, Suite 1700 · 999 Waterside Drive · Norfolk, VA 23510-3303 · 757-622-3366

Robert C. Goodman, Jr. · (10) · Kaufman & Canoles · 150 West Main Street, Suite 2100 · P.O. Box 3037 · Norfolk, VA 23514-3037 · 757-624-3000

Thomas C. Inglima · Willcox & Savage · One Commercial Place, Suite 1800 · Norfolk, VA 23510 · 757-628-5500

Gus J. James II · Kaufman & Canoles · 150 West Main Street, Suite 2100 · P.O. Box 3037 · Norfolk, VA 23514-3037 · 757-624-3000

Thomas G. Johnson, Jr. · (10) · Willcox & Savage · One Commercial Place, Suite 1800 · Norfolk, VA 23510 · 757-628-5500

Ray W. King · LeClair Ryan · 999 Waterside Drive, Suite 2525 · Norfolk, VA 23510 · 757-624-1454

Vincent J. Mastracco, Jr. · (20) · Kaufman & Canoles · 150 West Main Street, Suite 2100 · P.O. Box 3037 · Norfolk, VA 23514-3037 · 757-624-3000

Charles V. McPhillips · Kaufman & Canoles · 150 West Main Street, Suite 2100 · P.O. Box 3037 · Norfolk, VA 23514-3037 · 757-624-3000

Robert C. Nusbaum · (25) · Williams Mullen · http://www.williamsmullen.com · Dominion Tower, Suite 1700 · 999 Waterside Drive · Norfolk, VA 23510-3303 · 757-622-3366

William A. Old, Jr. · (10) · Williams Mullen · http://www.williamsmullen.com · Dominion Tower, Suite 1700 · 999 Waterside Drive · Norfolk, VA 23510-3303 · 757-622-3366

Hugh L. Patterson · (10) · Willcox & Savage · One Commercial Place, Suite 1800 · Norfolk, VA 23510 · 757-628-5500

Anita O. Poston · (10) · Vandeventer Black · 500 World Trade Center, Suite 500 · 101 West Main Street · Norfolk, VA 23510 · 757-446-8600

Alfred M. Randolph, Jr. · Kaufman & Canoles · 150 West Main Street, Suite 2100 · P.O. Box 3037 · Norfolk, VA 23514-3037 · 757-624-3000

Toy D. Savage, Jr. · (25) · Willcox & Savage · One Commercial Place, Suite 1800 · Norfolk, VA 23510 · 757-628-5500

William R. Van Buren III · ⑩ · Kaufman & Canoles · 150 West Main Street, Suite 2100 · P.O. Box 3037 · Norfolk, VA 23514-3037 · 757-624-3000

Portsmouth

Albert J. Taylor, Jr. · ⑳ · Williams Mullen · http://www.williamsmullen.com · 355 Crawford Street, Suite 600 · Portsmouth, VA 23704-2823 · 757-391-3366

Richmond

R. Brian Ball · Williams Mullen · http://www.williamsmullen.com · Two James Center · 1021 East Cary Street · P.O. Box 1320 · Richmond, VA 23218-1320 · 804-643-1991

John J. Beardsworth, Jr. · ⑩ · Hunton & Williams · Riverfront Plaza, East Tower · 951 East Byrd Street Richmond, VA 23219-4074 · 804-788-8200

Robert L. Burrus, Jr. · ㉕ · McGuireWoods · http://www.mcguirewoods.com · One James Center · 901 East Cary Street · Richmond, VA 23219-4030 · 804-775-1000

Joseph C. Carter III · McGuireWoods · http://www.mcguirewoods.com · One James Center · 901 East Cary Street · Richmond, VA 23219-4030 · 804-775-1000

Clifford A. Cutchins IV · McGuireWoods · http://www.mcguirewoods.com · One James Center · 901 East Cary Street · Richmond, VA 23219-4030 · 804-775-1000

Howard W. Dobbins · ⑩ · Williams Mullen · http://www.williamsmullen.com · Two James Center · 1021 East Cary Street · P.O. Box 1320 · Richmond, VA 23218-1320 · 804-643-1991

Allen C. Goolsby III · ⑳ · Hunton & Williams · Riverfront Plaza, East Tower · 951 East Byrd Street · Richmond, VA 23219-4074 · 804-788-8200

Leslie A. Grandis · ⑳ · McGuireWoods · http://www.mcguirewoods.com · One James Center · 901 East Cary Street · Richmond, VA 23219-4030 · 804-775-1000

Thomas A. Grant · Troutman Sanders · Troutman Sanders Building · 1001 Haxall Point · P.O. Box 1122 · Richmond, VA 23218-1122 · 804-697-1200

Grant S. Grayson · Cantor Arkema · Bank of America Center · 1111 East Main Street · P.O. Box 561 · Richmond, VA 23218-0561 · 804-644-1400

Elizabeth G. Hester · Troutman Sanders · Troutman Sanders Building · 1001 Haxall Point · P.O. Box 1122 · Richmond, VA 23218-1122 · 804-697-1200

Louanna O. Heuhsen · Hunton & Williams · Riverfront Plaza, East Tower · 951 East Byrd Street · Richmond, VA 23219-4074 · 804-788-8200

F. Claiborne Johnston, Jr. · ⑩ · Troutman Sanders · Troutman Sanders Building · 1001 Haxall Point · P.O. Box 1122 · Richmond, VA 23218-1122 · 804-697-1200

Gary D. LeClair · LeClair Ryan · 951 East Byrd Street, Eighth Floor · P.O. Box 2499 · Richmond, VA 23218-2499 · 804-783-2003

T. Justin Moore III · Hunton & Williams · Riverfront Plaza, East Tower · 951 East Byrd Street · Richmond, VA 23219-4074 · 804-788-8200

Thurston R. Moore · ⑩ · Hunton & Williams · Riverfront Plaza, East Tower · 951 East Byrd Street · Richmond, VA 23219-4074 · 804-788-8200

C. Cotesworth Pinckney · ⑩ · Troutman Sanders · Troutman Sanders Building · 1001 Haxall Point · P.O. Box 1122 · Richmond, VA 23218-1122 · 804-697-1200

Gordon F. Rainey, Jr. · ⑩ · Hunton & Williams · Riverfront Plaza, East Tower · 951 East Byrd Street · Richmond, VA 23219-4074 · 804-788-8200

James C. Roberts · ㉕ · Troutman Sanders · Troutman Sanders Building · 1001 Haxall Point · P.O. Box 1122 · Richmond, VA 23218-1122 · 804-697-1200

Thomas G. Slater, Jr. · ⑩ · Hunton & Williams · Riverfront Plaza, East Tower · 951 East Byrd Street · Richmond, VA 23219-4074 · 804-788-8200

Julious P. Smith, Jr. · ⑩ · Williams Mullen · http://www.williamsmullen.com · Two James Center · 1021 East Cary Street · P.O. Box 1320 · Richmond, VA 23218-1320 · 804-643-1991

R. Gordon Smith · ㉕ · McGuireWoods · http://www.mcguirewoods.com · One James Center · 901 East Cary Street · Richmond, VA 23219-4030 · 804-775-1000

Gary E. Thompson · Hunton & Williams · Riverfront Plaza, East Tower · 951 East Byrd Street · Richmond, VA 23219-4074 · 804-788-8200

Randolph F. Totten · ⑩ · Hunton & Williams · Riverfront Plaza, East Tower · 951 East Byrd Street · Richmond, VA 23219-4074 · 804-788-8200

C. Porter Vaughan III · ⑳ · Hunton & Williams · Riverfront Plaza, East Tower · 951 East Byrd Street · Richmond, VA 23219-4074 · 804-788-8200

George P. Whitley · LeClair Ryan · 951 East Byrd Street, Eighth Floor · P.O. Box 2499 · Richmond, VA 23218-2499 · 804-783-2003

Roanoke

Nicholas C. Conte · Woods Rogers · http://www.woodsrogers.com · Wachovia Tower, Suite 1400 · 10 South Jefferson Street · P.O. Box 14125 · Roanoke, VA 24038-4125 · 540-983-7600

Harwell M. Darby, Jr. · ⑩ · Glenn, Feldmann, Darby & Goodlatte · 210 First Street, SW, Suite 200 · P.O. Box 2887 · Roanoke, VA 24001-2887 · 540-224-8000

F. B. Webster Day · Spilman Thomas & Battle · http://www.spilmanlaw.com · 310 First Street, Suite 1100 Roanoke, VA 24002 · 540-512-1800

Douglas W. Densmore · ⑩ · Gentry Locke Rakes & Moore · http://www.gentrylocke.com · 10 Franklin Road, SE · P.O. Box 40013 · Roanoke, VA 24022-0013 · 540-983-9300

G. Franklin Flippin · ⑩ · Gentry Locke Rakes & Moore · http://www.gentrylocke.com · 10 Franklin Road, SE · P.O. Box 40013 · Roanoke, VA 24022-0013 · 540-983-9300

R. Neal Keesee, Jr. · Woods Rogers · http://www.woodsrogers.com · Wachovia Tower, Suite 1400 · 10 South Jefferson Street · P.O. Box 14125 · Roanoke, VA 24038-4125 · 540-983-7600

Talfourd H. Kemper, Sr. · ⑳ · Woods Rogers · http://www.woodsrogers.com · Wachovia Tower, Suite 1400 · 10 South Jefferson Street · P.O. Box 14125 · Roanoke, VA 24038-4125 · 540-983-7600

G. Michael Pace, Jr. · Gentry Locke Rakes & Moore · http://www.gentrylocke.com · 10 Franklin Road, SE · P.O. Box 40013 · Roanoke, VA 24022-0013 · 540-983-9300

William R. Rakes · ⑩ · Gentry Locke Rakes & Moore · http://www.gentrylocke.com · 10 Franklin Road, SE · P.O. Box 40013 · Roanoke, VA 24022-0013 · 540-983-9300

Alexander I. Saunders · Woods Rogers · http://www.woodsrogers.com · Wachovia Tower, Suite 1400 · 10 South Jefferson Street · P.O. Box 14125 · Roanoke, VA 24038-4125 · 540-983-7600

Tysons Corner

Robert B. Webb III · ⑩ · Squire Sanders · http://www.ssd.com · 8000 Towers Crescent Drive, 14th Floor Tysons Corner, VA 22182-2700 · 703-720-7800

Vienna

Joel M. Birken · ⑳ · Rees Broome · http://www.rbdlaw.com · 8133 Leesburg Pike, Ninth Floor · Vienna, VA 22182 · 703-790-1911

Elizabeth R. Hughes · Venable · http://www.venable.com · 8010 Towers Crescent Drive, Suite 300 · Vienna, VA 22182 · 703-760-1600

Virginia Beach

Thomas R. Frantz · ㉕ · Williams Mullen · http://www.williamsmullen.com · 222 Central Park Avenue, Suite 1700 · Virginia Beach, VA 23462-3035 · 757-499-8800

Thomas A. Rucker · ⑩ · Willcox & Savage · 222 Central Park Avenue, Suite 1500 · Virginia Beach, VA 23462 · 757-628-5600

Jeffrey T. Talbert · Shuttleworth, Ruloff, Swain, Haddad & Morecock · http://www.srgslaw.com · Southport Centre, Suite 300 · 4525 South Boulevard · Virginia Beach, VA 23452-1137 · 757-671-6000

James J. Wheaton · Troutman Sanders · 222 Central Park Avenue, Suite 2000 · Virginia Beach, VA 23462 · 757-687-7500

DERIVATIVES LAW

Norfolk

Robert C. Goodman, Jr. · ⑩ · Kaufman & Canoles · 150 West Main Street, Suite 2100 · P.O. Box 3037 · Norfolk, VA 23514-3037 · 757-624-3000

EDUCATION LAW

Charlottesville

R. Craig Wood · ⑩ · McGuireWoods · http://www.mcguirewoods.com · Court Square Building, Suite 300 310 Fourth Street, NE · P.O. Box 1288 · Charlottesville, VA 22902-1288 · 434-977-2500

Fairfax

John F. Cafferky · Blankingship & Keith · http://www.blankingship-keith-law.com · 4020 University Drive, Suite 300 · Fairfax, VA 22030 · 703-691-1235

Mary E. McGowan · Blankingship & Keith · http://www.blankingship-keith-law.com · 4020 University Drive, Suite 300 · Fairfax, VA 22030 · 703-691-1235

Richmond

Siran S. Faulders · Troutman Sanders · Troutman Sanders Building · 1001 Haxall Point · P.O. Box 1122 · Richmond, VA 23218-1122 · 804-697-1200

William H. Hurd · Troutman Sanders · Troutman Sanders Building · 1001 Haxall Point · P.O. Box 1122 · Richmond, VA 23218-1122 · 804-697-1200

D. Patrick Lacy, Jr. · Reed Smith · Riverfront Plaza - West Tower, Suite 1700 · 901 East Byrd Street · Richmond, VA 23219-4068 · 804-344-3400

Kathleen S. Mehfoud · Reed Smith · Riverfront Plaza - West Tower, Suite 1700 · 901 East Byrd Street · Richmond, VA 23219-4068 · 804-344-3400

Kirk T. Schroder · Schroder Fidlow · http://www.schroderfidlow.com · 1901 East Franklin Street, Suite 107 · Richmond, VA 23223 · 804-225-0505

Roanoke

Jonnie L. Speight · Johnson, Ayers & Matthews · First Campbell Square, Suite 300 · 210 First Street, SW P.O. Box 2200 · Roanoke, VA 24009-2200 · 540-767-2000

Staunton

Douglas L. Guynn · Timberlake, Smith, Thomas & Moses · The Virginia Building · 25 North Central Avenue · P.O. Box 108 · Staunton, VA 24402-0108 · 540-885-1517

G. Rodney Young II · Timberlake, Smith, Thomas & Moses · The Virginia Building · 25 North Central Avenue · P.O. Box 108 · Staunton, VA 24402-0108 · 540-885-1517

ELDER LAW

Arlington

Kelly A. Thompson · Kelly A. Thompson · 46 South Glebe Road, Suite 200 · Arlington, VA 22204-1655 · 703-486-2666

Falls Church

John L. Laster · John L. Laster · Old Brickhouse Square · 103 Rowell Court · Falls Church, VA 22046 · 703-538-3600

Richmond

R. Shawn Majette · Thompson & McMullan · 100 Shockoe Slip, Third Floor · Richmond, VA 23219 · 804-649-7545

Anita G. Vaughn · Hirschler Fleischer · http://www.hirschlerfleischer.com · The Edgeworth Building · 2100 East Cary Street · Richmond, VA 23223-7078 · 804-771-9500

EMINENT DOMAIN AND CONDEMNATION LAW

Arlington

Dana Berliner · Institute for Justice · 900 North Glebe Road, Suite 900 · Arlington, VA 22203 · 703-682-9320

Fairfax

A. Hugo Blankingship, Jr. · ㉕ · Blankingship & Keith · http://www.blankingship-keith-law.com · 4020 University Drive, Suite 300 · Fairfax, VA 22030 · 703-691-1235

Dexter S. Odin · Odin, Feldman & Pittleman · http://www.ofplaw.com · 9302 Lee Highway, Suite 1100 · Fairfax, VA 22031 · 703-218-2100

Paul B. Terpak · Blankingship & Keith · http://www.blankingship-keith-law.com · 4020 University Drive, Suite 300 · Fairfax, VA 22030 · 703-691-1235

Falls Church

Grayson P. Hanes · ⑳ · Reed Smith · 3110 Fairview Park Drive, Suite 1400 · P.O. Box 12001 · Falls Church, VA 22042 · 703-641-4200

Norfolk

Joseph T. Waldo · Waldo & Lyle · http://www.emdomain.com · 301 West Freemason Street · Norfolk, VA 23510 · 757-622-5812

Richmond

William G. Broaddus · McGuireWoods · http://www.mcguirewoods.com · One James Center · 901 East Cary Street · Richmond, VA 23219-4030 · 804-775-1000

John K. Burke, Jr. · ⑩ · Troutman Sanders · Troutman Sanders Building · 1001 Haxall Point · P.O. Box 1122 · Richmond, VA 23218-1122 · 804-697-1200

Francis A. Cherry, Jr. · Randolph, Boyd, Cherry and Vaughan · W.E. Dibrell House · 14 East Main Street · Richmond, VA 23219 · 804-643-6611

John S. Morris III · Beale, Davidson, Etherington & Morris · 701 East Franklin Street, Suite 1200 · Richmond, VA 23219-2503 · 804-788-1500

John R. Walk · Hirschler Fleischer · http://www.hirschlerfleischer.com · The Edgeworth Building · 2100 East Cary Street · Richmond, VA 23223-7078 · 804-771-9500

Roanoke

Ronald M. Ayers · ⑩ · Johnson, Ayers & Matthews · First Campbell Square, Suite 300 · 210 First Street, SW · P.O. Box 2200 · Roanoke, VA 24009-2200 · 540-767-2000

EMPLOYEE BENEFITS LAW

McLean

Martha L. Hutzelman · Kruchko & Fries · 1750 Tysons Boulevard, Suite 560 · McLean, VA 22102-4224 · 703-734-0554

David Albert Mustone · Hunton & Williams · 1751 Pinnacle Drive, Suite 1700 · McLean, VA 22102 · 703-714-7400

Norfolk

Richard C. Mapp III · ⑩ · Kaufman & Canoles · 150 West Main Street, Suite 2100 · P.O. Box 3037 · Norfolk, VA 23514-3037 · 757-624-3000

James R. Warner, Jr. · ⑩ · Willcox & Savage · One Commercial Place, Suite 1800 · Norfolk, VA 23510 · 757-628-5500

Richmond

Robert M. Cipolla · McGuireWoods · http://www.mcguirewoods.com · One James Center · 901 East Cary Street · Richmond, VA 23219-4030 · 804-775-1000

Mark S. Dray · ⑩ · Hunton & Williams · Riverfront Plaza, East Tower · 951 East Byrd Street · Richmond, VA 23219-4074 · 804-788-8200

Thomas C. Foster · McCandlish Holton · 1111 East Main Street, Suite 1500 · Richmond, VA 23219 · 804-775-3100

Catherine M. Marriott · ⑩ · Williams Mullen · http://www.williamsmullen.com · Two James Center · 1021 East Cary Street · P.O. Box 1320 · Richmond, VA 23218-1320 · 804-643-1991

James P. McElligott · ⑩ · McGuireWoods · http://www.mcguirewoods.com · One James Center · 901 East Cary Street · Richmond, VA 23219-4030 · 804-775-1000

J. G. Ritter II · ⑩ · Hunton & Williams · Riverfront Plaza, East Tower · 951 East Byrd Street · Richmond, VA 23219-4074 · 804-788-8200

Wallace M. Starke · ⑩ · Troutman Sanders · Troutman Sanders Building · 1001 Haxall Point · P.O. Box 1122 · Richmond, VA 23218-1122 · 804-697-1200

Evelyn Small Traub · Troutman Sanders · Troutman Sanders Building · 1001 Haxall Point · P.O. Box 1122 · Richmond, VA 23218-1122 · 804-697-1200

Roanoke

N. A. Ammar, Jr. · Spilman Thomas & Battle · http://www.spilmanlaw.com · 310 First Street, Suite 1100 · Roanoke, VA 24002 · 540-512-1800

W. William Gust · Gentry Locke Rakes & Moore · http://www.gentrylocke.com · 10 Franklin Road, SE · P.O. Box 40013 · Roanoke, VA 24022-0013 · 540-983-9300

Alton L. Knighton, Jr. · ⑩ · Woods Rogers · http://www.woodsrogers.com · Wachovia Tower, Suite 1400 · 10 South Jefferson Street · P.O. Box 14125 · Roanoke, VA 24038-4125 · 540-983-7600

David E. Perry · LeClair Ryan · 1800 Wachovia Tower · P.O. Drawer 1200 · Roanoke, VA 24006 · 540-510-3000

ENERGY LAW

Glen Allen

James Patrick Guy II · LeClair Ryan · 4201 Dominion Boulevard, Suite 200 · Glen Allen, VA 23060 · 804-270-0070

Michael L. Hern · LeClair Ryan · 4201 Dominion Boulevard, Suite 200 · Glen Allen, VA 23060 · 804-270-0070

John A. Pirko · LeClair Ryan · 4201 Dominion Boulevard, Suite 200 · Glen Allen, VA 23060 · 804-270-0070

John J. Beardsworth, Jr. · ⑩ · Hunton & Williams · Riverfront Plaza, East Tower · 951 East Byrd Street Richmond, VA 23219-4074 · 804-788-8200

James C. Dimitri · McGuireWoods · http://www.mcguirewoods.com · One James Center · 901 East Cary Street · Richmond, VA 23219-4030 · 804-775-1000

Edward L. Flippen · ⑩ · McGuireWoods · http://www.mcguirewoods.com · One James Center · 901 East Cary Street · Richmond, VA 23219-4030 · 804-775-1000

Anthony J. Gambardella, Jr. · Woods Rogers · http://www.woodsrogers.com · 823 East Main Street, Suite 1200 · Richmond, VA 23219 · 804-343-5020

Richard D. Gary · ⑩ · Hunton & Williams · Riverfront Plaza, East Tower · 951 East Byrd Street · Richmond, VA 23219-4074 · 804-788-8200

Brian R. Greene · Seltzer Greene · 707 East Main Street, Suite 1025 · Richmond, VA 23219 · 804-864-1100

Louis Richardson Monacell · Christian & Barton · Mutual Building, Suite 1200 · 909 East Main Street · Richmond, VA 23219-3095 · 804-697-4100

JoAnne Lewis Nolte · The Conrad Firm · 1520 West Main Street, Suite 204 · Richmond, VA 23220 · 804-359-6062

Donald G. Owens · Troutman Sanders · Troutman Sanders Building · 1001 Haxall Point · P.O. Box 1122 · Richmond, VA 23218-1122 · 804-697-1200

Eric M. Page · LeClair Ryan · 951 East Byrd Street, Eighth Floor · P.O. Box 2499 · Richmond, VA 23218-2499 · 804-783-2003

Edward L. Petrini · Christian & Barton · Mutual Building, Suite 1200 · 909 East Main Street · Richmond, VA 23219-3095 · 804-697-4100

Michael J. Quinan · Christian & Barton · Mutual Building, Suite 1200 · 909 East Main Street · Richmond, VA 23219-3095 · 804-697-4100

Cliona M. Robb · Christian & Barton · Mutual Building, Suite 1200 · 909 East Main Street · Richmond, VA 23219-3095 · 804-697-4100

Guy T. Tripp III · ⑩ · Hunton & Williams · Riverfront Plaza, East Tower · 951 East Byrd Street · Richmond, VA 23219-4074 · 804-788-8200

Stephen H. Watts II · ⑩ · McGuireWoods · http://www.mcguirewoods.com · One James Center · 901 East Cary Street · Richmond, VA 23219-4030 · 804-775-1000

Roanoke

H. Allen Glover, Jr. · ⑩ · Woods Rogers · http://www.woodsrogers.com · Wachovia Tower, Suite 1400 · 10 South Jefferson Street · P.O. Box 14125 · Roanoke, VA 24038-4125 · 540-983-7600

ENTERTAINMENT LAW

Richmond

Philip H. Goodpasture · Williams Mullen · http://www.williamsmullen.com · Two James Center · 1021 East Cary Street · P.O. Box 1320 · Richmond, VA 23218-1320 · 804-643-1991

Kirk T. Schroder · Schroder Fidlow · http://www.schroderfidlow.com · 1901 East Franklin Street, Suite 107 · Richmond, VA 23223 · 804-225-0505

ENVIRONMENTAL LAW

Abingdon

Timothy W. Gresham · PennStuart · Virginia House · 208 East Main Street · P.O. Box 2288 · Abingdon, VA 24212-2288 · 276-628-5151

Norfolk

Patrick A. Genzler · Vandeventer Black · 500 World Trade Center, Suite 500 · 101 West Main Street · Norfolk, VA 23510 · 757-446-8600

Marina Liacouras Phillips · Kaufman & Canoles · 150 West Main Street, Suite 2100 · P.O. Box 3037 · Norfolk, VA 23514-3037 · 757-624-3000

Portsmouth

Susan Taylor Hansen · Cooper, Spong & Davis · The Towne Bank Building, Suite 500 · 200 High Street P.O. Box 1475 · Portsmouth, VA 23704-3721 · 757-397-3481

Richmond

Brian L. Buniva · LeClair Ryan · 951 East Byrd Street, Eighth Floor · P.O. Box 2499 · Richmond, VA 23218-2499 · 804-783-2003

David E. Evans · 20 · McGuireWoods · http://www.mcguirewoods.com · One James Center · 901 East Cary Street · Richmond, VA 23219-4030 · 804-775-1000

Kevin J. Finto · Hunton & Williams · Riverfront Plaza, East Tower · 951 East Byrd Street · Richmond, VA 23219-4074 · 804-788-8200

Manning Gasch, Jr. · 10 · Hunton & Williams · Riverfront Plaza, East Tower · 951 East Byrd Street · Richmond, VA 23219-4074 · 804-788-8200

Timothy G. Hayes · 10 · Hunton & Williams · Riverfront Plaza, East Tower · 951 East Byrd Street · Richmond, VA 23219-4074 · 804-788-8200

Thomas E. Knauer · Williams Mullen · http://www.williamsmullen.com · Two James Center · 1021 East Cary Street · P.O. Box 1320 · Richmond, VA 23218-1320 · 804-643-1991

Channing J. Martin · Williams Mullen · http://www.williamsmullen.com · Two James Center · 1021 East Cary Street · P.O. Box 1320 · Richmond, VA 23218-1320 · 804-643-1991

James E. Ryan, Jr. · Troutman Sanders · Troutman Sanders Building · 1001 Haxall Point · P.O. Box 1122 Richmond, VA 23218-1122 · 804-697-1200

Daniel K. Slone · McGuireWoods · http://www.mcguirewoods.com · One James Center · 901 East Cary Street · Richmond, VA 23219-4030 · 804-775-1000

James A. Thornhill · McGuireWoods · http://www.mcguirewoods.com · One James Center · 901 East Cary Street · Richmond, VA 23219-4030 · 804-775-1000

Roanoke

Paul R. Thomson, Jr. · Woods Rogers · http://www.woodsrogers.com · Wachovia Tower, Suite 1400 · 10 South Jefferson Street · P.O. Box 14125 · Roanoke, VA 24038-4125 · 540-983-7600

Charles L. Williams, Jr. · Gentry Locke Rakes & Moore · http://www.gentrylocke.com · 10 Franklin Road, SE · P.O. Box 40013 · Roanoke, VA 24022-0013 · 540-983-9300

ETHICS AND PROFESSIONAL RESPONSIBILITY LAW

Arlington

Ronald D. Rotunda · George Mason University School of Law · 3301 North Fairfax Drive · Arlington, VA 22201-4426 · 703-993-8041

FAMILY LAW

Alexandria

James Ray Cottrell · 20 · Cottrell Fletcher Schinstock Bartol & Cottrell · http://www.cottrellaw.com · 801 North Fairfax Street, Suite 404 · Alexandria, VA 22314 · 703-836-2770

Karen C. Davis · Law Offices of Karen C. Davis · 6182 Grovedale Court, Suite 200 · Alexandria, VA 22310 · 703-921-5540

Ilona Ely Grenadier · 10 · Grenadier, Anderson, Simpson, Starace & Duffett · 649 South Washington Street · Alexandria, VA 22314 · 703-683-9000

Sharon K. Lieblich · Lieblich & Grimes · 3135 Mount Vernon Avenue · Alexandria, VA 22305 · 703-683-6300

Arlington

James W. Korman · 10 · Bean, Kinney & Korman · http://www.beankinney.com · 2300 Wilson Boulevard, Suite 700 · Arlington, VA 22201 · 703-525-4000

Carol Schrier-Polak · 10 · Bean, Kinney & Korman · http://www.beankinney.com · 2300 Wilson Boulevard, Suite 700 · Arlington, VA 22201 · 703-525-4000

Betty A. Thompson · 25 · Betty A. Thompson · 1800 North Kent Street, Suite 1001 · P.O. Box 12807 · Arlington, VA 22219-2807 · 703-522-8100

Charlottesville

Annie Lee Jacobs · 20 · Parker, McElwain & Jacobs · 2340 Commonwealth Drive · P.O. Box 6186 · Charlottesville, VA 22906 · 434-973-3331

John K. Taggart III · 10 · Tremblay & Smith · http://www.tremblaysmith.com · 105-109 East High Street P.O. Box 1585 · Charlottesville, VA 22902 · 434-977-4455

Ronald R. Tweel · 20 · Michie Hamlett Lowry Rasmussen & Tweel · 500 Court Square, Suite 300 · P.O. Box 298 · Charlottesville, VA 22902-0298 · 434-951-7200

Susan Davis White · 10 · Susan Davis White · 103 East Water Street, Suite 301 · Charlottesville, VA 22902 · 434-977-0563

Chesterfield

Edward D. Barnes · ⑩ · Barnes & Diehl · http://www.thebarneslawfirm.com · Centre Court, Suite A · 9401 Courthouse Road · Chesterfield, VA 23832-6666 · 804-796-1000

Lawrence D. Diehl · ⑩ · Barnes & Diehl · http://www.thebarneslawfirm.com · Centre Court, Suite A · 9401 Courthouse Road · Chesterfield, VA 23832-6666 · 804-796-1000

Colonial Heights

Robert C. Elliott II · ⑩ · Robert C. Elliott II · 105 Valley Road · P.O. Box 428 · Colonial Heights, VA 23834-0428 · 804-520-1240

Fairfax

Marc A. Astore · Marc A. Astore · 10511 Judicial Drive · Fairfax, VA 22030-5114 · 703-273-5100

Beth A. Bittel · Law Offices of Beth Bittel · 10680 Main Street, Suite 250 · Fairfax, VA 22030 · 703-591-1320

Albert M. Bonin · ⑩ · Shoun, Bach, Walinsky & Curran · http://www.shoun.com · 12700 Fair Lakes Circle, Suite 300 · Fairfax, VA 22033 · 703-222-3333

Richard J. Colten · ⑳ · Colten Cummins Watson & Vincent · 3959 Pender Drive, Suite 200 · Fairfax, VA 22030 · 703-277-9700

Gerald R. Curran · Shoun, Bach, Walinsky & Curran · http://www.shoun.com · 12700 Fair Lakes Circle, Suite 300 · Fairfax, VA 22033 · 703-222-3333

Susan M. Hicks · The Susan Hicks Group · http://www.susanhicksgroup.com · 9302 Lee Highway, Suite 700 · Fairfax, VA 22031 · 703-691-4848

Dorothy M. Isaacs · Surovell, Markle, Isaacs and Levy · http://www.smillaw.com · 4010 University Drive, Second Floor · Fairfax, VA 22030 · 703-251-5400

Glenn C. Lewis · Lewis Law Firm · 10306 Eaton Place, Suite 200 · Fairfax, VA 22030 · 703-691-8686

J. Patrick McConnell · Odin, Feldman & Pittleman · http://www.ofplaw.com · 9302 Lee Highway, Suite 1100 · Fairfax, VA 22031 · 703-218-2100

Ann W. Mische · Joseph and Mische · 10521 Judicial Drive, Suite 120 · Fairfax, VA 22030 · 703-273-0500

Philip Schwartz · Schwartz & Associates · 8221 Old Courthouse Road, Suite 101 · Fairfax, VA 22182-3839 · 703-883-8035

Robert E. Shoun · ⑳ · Shoun, Bach, Walinsky & Curran · http://www.shoun.com · 12700 Fair Lakes Circle, Suite 300 · Fairfax, VA 22033 · 703-222-3333

Robert J. Surovell · ⑳ · Surovell, Markle, Isaacs and Levy · http://www.smillaw.com · 4010 University Drive, Second Floor · Fairfax, VA 22030 · 703-251-5400

Edward J. Walinsky · Shoun, Bach, Walinsky & Curran · http://www.shoun.com · 12700 Fair Lakes Circle, Suite 300 · Fairfax, VA 22033 · 703-222-3333

Falls Church

Richard C. Shadyac, Jr. · Feldesman Tucker Leifer Fidell · 5661 Columbia Pike, Suite 200 · Falls Church, VA 22041 · 703-671-5800

Glen Allen

Terrence R. Batzli · Batzli Wood & Stiles · http://www.batzliwood.com · 10900 Nuckols Road, Suite 200 · Glen Allen, VA 23060 · 804-545-9800

Andrea R. Stiles · Batzli Wood & Stiles · http://www.batzliwood.com · 10900 Nuckols Road, Suite 200 · Glen Allen, VA 23060 · 804-545-9800

William C. Wood · Batzli Wood & Stiles · http://www.batzliwood.com · 10900 Nuckols Road, Suite 200 · Glen Allen, VA 23060 · 804-545-9800

Halifax

Carol B. Gravitt · ⑩ · Gravitt & Gravitt · 75 Maple Avenue · P.O. Box 999 · Halifax, VA 24558 · 434-476-6518

Harrisonburg

Franklin R. Blatt · Law Offices of Franklin R. Blatt · http://www.blattlaw.net · 71 East Market Street · Harrisonburg, VA 22801-4126 · 540-433-0202

David A. Penrod · Hoover Penrod · 342 South Main Street · Harrisonburg, VA 22801 · 540-433-2444

McLean

Joseph A. Condo · ㉕ · Condo Roop Kelly & Byrnes · 8444 Westpark Drive, Suite 500 · McLean, VA 22102 · 703-442-0888

David D. Masterman · ⑩ · Masterman & Graham · 8280 Greensboro Drive, Suite 620 · McLean, VA 22102 · 703-827-5500

David E. Roop, Jr. · Condo Roop Kelly & Byrnes · 8444 Westpark Drive, Suite 500 · McLean, VA 22102 703-442-0888

Norfolk

Jerrold G. Weinberg · ㉕ · Weinberg & Stein · 999 Waterside Drive, Suite 1825 · P.O. Box 3789 · Norfolk, VA 23514-3789 · 757-627-1066

Reston

Brian M. Hirsch · Hirsch & Ehlenberger · http://www.novafamilylaw.com · 12110 Sunset Hills Road, Suite 401 · Reston, VA 20190 · 703-481-6063

Arlene T. Starace · Grenadier, Anderson, Simpson, Starace & Duffett · 12359 Sunrise Valley Drive, Suite 230 · Reston, VA 20191 · 703-683-9000

Richmond

Donald K. Butler · ㉕ · ButlerCook · 526 North Boulevard · Richmond, VA 23220 · 804-353-4931

Deanna D. Cook · Law Offices of Deanna D. Cook · 3801 B Westerre Parkway · Richmond, VA 23233 · 804-273-6415

Ronald S. Evans · ⑩ · Brenner, Evans & Millman · 411 East Franklin Street, Suite 200 · P.O. Box 470 · Richmond, VA 23218-0470 · 804-644-1300

Mahlon G. Funk, Jr. · Hirschler Fleischer · http://www.hirschlerfleischer.com · The Edgeworth Building 2100 East Cary Street · Richmond, VA 23223-7078 · 804-771-9500

Murray J. Janus · 25 · Bremner, Janus & Stone · 701 East Franklin Street, Suite 1500 · P.O. Box 826 · Richmond, VA 23219 · 804-643-1400

Rodney M. Poole · Poole and Poole · 4901 Dickens Road, Suite 108 · Richmond, VA 23230 · 804-358-6669

Roanoke

Gary L. Lumsden · 10 · Gary L. Lumsden · 1220 Franklin Road · Roanoke, VA 24016 · 540-982-0566

G. Marshall Mundy · 20 · Mundy, Rogers & Associates · 1328 Third Street, SW · P.O. Box 2240 · Roanoke, VA 24009 · 540-982-2900

Frank W. Rogers III · Mundy, Rogers & Associates · 1328 Third Street, SW · P.O. Box 2240 · Roanoke, VA 24009 · 540-982-2900

David G. Weaver · Weaver Law Firm · 303 Washington Avenue, SW · P.O. Box 780 · Roanoke, VA 24004 540-767-7611

Vienna

Jeff Evan Lowinger · Sandground New & Lowinger · 8000 Towers Crescent Drive, Suite 600 · Vienna, VA 22182 · 703-761-4200

Marcia M. Maddox · Maddox, Cole & Miller · 8221 Old Courthouse Road, Suite 101 · Vienna, VA 22182-3839 · 703-883-8035

Cheryl M. New · Sandground New & Lowinger · 8000 Towers Crescent Drive, Suite 600 · Vienna, VA 22182 · 703-761-4200

Virginia Beach

Barry Kantor · 20 · Christie, Kantor, Griffin & Smith · 477 Viking Drive, Suite 150 · Virginia Beach, VA 23452 · 757-499-9222

Reeves W. Mahoney · Huff, Poole & Mahoney · 4705 Columbus Street · Virginia Beach, VA 23462-6749 · 757-499-1841

Woodbridge

Paul F. Nichols · Nichols, Zauzig & Sandler · 12660 Lake Ridge Drive · Woodbridge, VA 22192 · 703-492-4200

Betty Moore Sandler · Nichols, Zauzig & Sandler · 12660 Lake Ridge Drive · Woodbridge, VA 22192 · 703-492-4200

FAMILY LAW MEDIATION

Arlington

Karen L. Keyes · Law Office of Karen L. Keyes · http://www.keyeslaw.com · 2300 Wilson Boulevard, Suite 240 · Arlington, VA 22201 · 703-528-1991

Carol Schrier-Polak · 10 · Bean, Kinney & Korman · http://www.beankinney.com · 2300 Wilson Boulevard, Suite 700 · Arlington, VA 22201 · 703-525-4000

Lynchburg

Frank West Morrison · Phillips, Morrison, Johnson & Ferrell · Bank of the James Building, Suite 1403 · 828 Main Street · Lynchburg, VA 24504 · 434-384-0946

Roanoke

Cheryl Watson Smith · Cheryl Watson Smith · 5440 Peters Creek Road, Suite 104 · Roanoke, VA 24019-3863 · 540-265-9022

Vienna

Frances Fite · Fite & O'Brien · 8027 Leesburg Pike, Suite 304 · Vienna, VA 22182 · 703-821-8575

FIRST AMENDMENT LAW

Norfolk

Conrad M. Shumadine · ⑩ · Willcox & Savage · One Commercial Place, Suite 1800 · Norfolk, VA 23510 757-628-5500

Richmond

Craig Thomas Merritt · Christian & Barton · Mutual Building, Suite 1200 · 909 East Main Street · Richmond, VA 23219-3095 · 804-697-4100

James B. Thorsen · James B. Thorsen & Associates · 3810 Augusta Avenue · Richmond, VA 23230 · 804-359-3000

Roanoke

D. Stan Barnhill · ⑩ · Woods Rogers · http://www.woodsrogers.com · Wachovia Tower, Suite 1400 · 10 South Jefferson Street · P.O. Box 14125 · Roanoke, VA 24038-4125 · 540-983-7600

FRANCHISE LAW

McLean

Warren L. Lewis · Williams Mullen · http://www.williamsmullen.com · 8270 Greensboro Drive, Suite 700 McLean, VA 22102 · 703-760-5200

Norfolk

Stephen E. Story · Kaufman & Canoles · 150 West Main Street, Suite 2100 · P.O. Box 3037 · Norfolk, VA 23514-3037 · 757-624-3000

Reston

Barry M. Heller · DLA Piper · 1775 Wiehle Avenue, Suite 400 · Reston, VA 20190-5159 · 703-773-4000

Mark A. Kirsch · Plave Koch · 12355 Sunrise Valley Drive, Suite 230 · Reston, VA 20191-3492 · 703-774-1200

H. Bret Lowell · ⑩ · DLA Piper · 1775 Wiehle Avenue, Suite 400 · Reston, VA 20190-5159 · 703-773-4000

Lee J. Plave · Plave Koch · 12355 Sunrise Valley Drive, Suite 230 · Reston, VA 20191-3492 · 703-774-1200

John M. Tifford · Plave Koch · 12355 Sunrise Valley Drive, Suite 230 · Reston, VA 20191-3492 · 703-774-1200

GAMING LAW

Richmond

Mary D. Baril · McGuireWoods · http://www.mcguirewoods.com · One James Center · 901 East Cary Street · Richmond, VA 23219-4030 · 804-775-1000

Thomas A. Lisk · LeClair Ryan · 951 East Byrd Street, Eighth Floor · P.O. Box 2499 · Richmond, VA 23218-2499 · 804-783-2003

James L. Weinberg · Hirschler Fleischer · http://www.hirschlerfleischer.com · The Edgeworth Building · 2100 East Cary Street · Richmond, VA 23223-7078 · 804-771-9500

GOVERNMENT RELATIONS LAW

Glen Allen

W. Scott Johnson · Hancock, Daniel, Johnson & Nagle · 4701 Cox Road, Suite 400 · P.O. Box 72050 · Glen Allen, VA 23255 · 804-967-9604

Norfok

John-Garrett Kemper · Kemper Consulting · 112 Granby Street, Suite 400 · Norfok, VA 23510 · 757-627-1988

Norfolk

Alan D. Albert · ⑩ · LeClair Ryan · 999 Waterside Drive, Suite 2525 · Norfolk, VA 23510 · 757-624-1454

Richmond

Ralph L. Axselle, Jr. · Williams Mullen · http://www.williamsmullen.com · Two James Center · 1021 East Cary Street · P.O. Box 1320 · Richmond, VA 23218-1320 · 804-643-1991

David W. Clarke · LeClair Ryan · 951 East Byrd Street, Eighth Floor · P.O. Box 2499 · Richmond, VA 23218-2499 · 804-783-2003

Robert J. Grey, Jr. · Hunton & Williams · Riverfront Plaza, East Tower · 951 East Byrd Street · Richmond, VA 23219-4074 · 804-788-8200

Reginald N. Jones · Williams Mullen · http://www.williamsmullen.com · Two James Center · 1021 East Cary Street · P.O. Box 1320 · Richmond, VA 23218-1320 · 804-643-1991

Ben R. Lacy IV · Sands, Anderson, Marks & Miller · http://www.sandsanderson.com · 801 East Main Street, Suite 1800 · P.O. Box 1998 · Richmond, VA 23218-1998 · 804-648-1636

Thomas A. Lisk · LeClair Ryan · 951 East Byrd Street, Eighth Floor · P.O. Box 2499 · Richmond, VA 23218-2499 · 804-783-2003

Virginia Beach

Glenn R. Croshaw · Willcox & Savage · 222 Central Park Avenue, Suite 1500 · Virginia Beach, VA 23462 757-628-5600

HEALTH CARE LAW

Charlottesville

Leigh B. Middleditch, Jr. · ⑳ · McGuireWoods · http://www.mcguirewoods.com · Court Square Building, Suite 300 · 310 Fourth Street, NE · P.O. Box 1288 · Charlottesville, VA 22902-1288 · 434-977-2500

Fairfax Station

Barent L. Fake · ⑩ · Barent L. Fake · 6914 Winners Circle · Fairfax Station, VA 22039-1844 · 703-926-5457

Falls Church

Julia Krebs-Markrich · ⑩ · Reed Smith · 3110 Fairview Park Drive, Suite 1400 · P.O. Box 12001 · Falls Church, VA 22042 · 703-641-4200

Glen Allen

M. Bruce Stokes · Goodman, Allen & Filetti · http://www.goodmanallen.com · 4501 Highwoods Parkway, Suite 210 · Glen Allen, VA 23060 · 804-346-0600

Harrisonburg

Glenn M. Hodge · Wharton, Aldhizer & Weaver · 100 South Mason Street · P.O. Box 20028 · Harrisonburg, VA 22801-7528 · 540-434-0316

McLean

Thomas C. Brown, Jr. · ⑳ · McGuireWoods · http://www.mcguirewoods.com · 1750 Tysons Boulevard, Suite 1800 · McLean, VA 22102-4215 · 703-712-5000

Norfolk

Patrick C. Devine, Jr. · ⑩ · Williams Mullen · http://www.williamsmullen.com · Dominion Tower, Suite 1700 · 999 Waterside Drive · Norfolk, VA 23510-3303 · 757-622-3366

T. Braxton McKee · ⑩ · Kaufman & Canoles · 150 West Main Street, Suite 2100 · P.O. Box 3037 · Norfolk, VA 23514-3037 · 757-624-3000

Anita O. Poston · ⑩ · Vandeventer Black · 500 World Trade Center, Suite 500 · 101 West Main Street · Norfolk, VA 23510 · 757-446-8600

Richmond

Virginia H. Hackney · ⑩ · Hunton & Williams · Riverfront Plaza, East Tower · 951 East Byrd Street · Richmond, VA 23219-4074 · 804-788-8200

Mark S. Hedberg · Hunton & Williams · Riverfront Plaza, East Tower · 951 East Byrd Street · Richmond, VA 23219-4074 · 804-788-8200

Matthew D. Jenkins · ⑩ · Hunton & Williams · Riverfront Plaza, East Tower · 951 East Byrd Street · Richmond, VA 23219-4074 · 804-788-8200

Jamie B. Martin · McCandlish Holton · 1111 East Main Street, Suite 1500 · Richmond, VA 23219 · 804-775-3100

Thomas W. McCandlish · ⑩ · McCandlish Holton · 1111 East Main Street, Suite 1500 · Richmond, VA 23219 · 804-775-3100

Malcolm E. Ritsch, Jr. · Williams Mullen · http://www.williamsmullen.com · Two James Center · 1021 East Cary Street · P.O. Box 1320 · Richmond, VA 23218-1320 · 804-643-1991

Stephen D. Rosenthal · Troutman Sanders · Troutman Sanders Building · 1001 Haxall Point · P.O. Box 1122 · Richmond, VA 23218-1122 · 804-697-1200

R. Gordon Smith · ㉕ · McGuireWoods · http://www.mcguirewoods.com · One James Center · 901 East Cary Street · Richmond, VA 23219-4030 · 804-775-1000

Thomas J. Stallings · McGuireWoods · http://www.mcguirewoods.com · One James Center · 901 East Cary Street · Richmond, VA 23219-4030 · 804-775-1000

Roanoke

Heman A. Marshall III · ⑩ · Woods Rogers · http://www.woodsrogers.com · Wachovia Tower, Suite 1400 10 South Jefferson Street · P.O. Box 14125 · Roanoke, VA 24038-4125 · 540-983-7600

Thomas T. Palmer · Woods Rogers · http://www.woodsrogers.com · Wachovia Tower, Suite 1400 · 10 South Jefferson Street · P.O. Box 14125 · Roanoke, VA 24038-4125 · 540-983-7600

IMMIGRATION LAW

Charlottesville

David Z. Izakowitz · McGuireWoods · http://www.mcguirewoods.com · Court Square Building, Suite 300 310 Fourth Street, NE · P.O. Box 1288 · Charlottesville, VA 22902-1288 · 434-977-2500

Fairfax

Jonathan Ginsburg · Fettman, Tolchin & Majors · 10509 Judicial Drive, Suite 300 · Fairfax, VA 22030 · 703-385-9500

Nancy M. Lawrence · Odin, Feldman & Pittleman · http://www.ofplaw.com · 9302 Lee Highway, Suite 1100 · Fairfax, VA 22031 · 703-218-2100

McLean

Laura F. Reiff · Greenberg Traurig · http://www.gtlaw.com · 1750 Tysons Boulevard, Suite 1200 · McLean, VA 22102 · 703-749-1300

Richmond

Eliot Norman · Williams Mullen · http://www.williamsmullen.com · Two James Center · 1021 East Cary Street · P.O. Box 1320 · Richmond, VA 23218-1320 · 804-643-1991

Roanoke

Kenneth J. Lasky · Magee, Foster, Goldstein & Sayers · BB&T Bank Building, Suite 1200 · 310 First Street, SW · P.O. Box 404 · Roanoke, VA 24003 · 540-343-9800

Jeffrey A. Van Doren · LeClair Ryan · 1800 Wachovia Tower · P.O. Drawer 1200 · Roanoke, VA 24006 · 540-510-3000

Virginia Beach

Susan Roussel Blackman · Willcox & Savage · 222 Central Park Avenue, Suite 1500 · Virginia Beach, VA 23462 · 757-628-5600

INFORMATION TECHNOLOGY LAW

Charlottesville

Michael P. Drzal · LeClair Ryan · 123 East Main Street, Suite 800 · Charlottesville, VA 22902 · 434-245-3444

McLean

Jocelyn West Brittin · Holland & Knight · http://www.hklaw.com · 1600 Tysons Boulevard, Suite 700 · McLean, VA 22102 · 703-720-8600

Reston

John T. Westermeier, Jr. · DLA Piper · 1775 Wiehle Avenue, Suite 400 · Reston, VA 20190-5159 · 703-773-4000

Richmond

S. Brian Farmer · Hirschler Fleischer · http://www.hirschlerfleischer.com · The Edgeworth Building · 2100 East Cary Street · Richmond, VA 23223-7078 · 804-771-9500

Rodney A. Satterwhite · McGuireWoods · http://www.mcguirewoods.com · One James Center · 901 East Cary Street · Richmond, VA 23219-4030 · 804-775-1000

INSURANCE LAW

Abingdon

Howard C. McElroy · McElroy, Hodges & Caldwell · 330 Cummings Street · P.O. Box 429 · Abingdon, VA 24212-0429 · 276-628-9515

Charlottesville

James W. Barkley · Morin & Barkley · 123 East Main Street, Seventh Floor · Charlottesville, VA 22902 · 434-293-1200

Danville

Anthony H. Monioudis · Woods Rogers · http://www.woodsrogers.com · 530 Main Street, Suite 201 · Danville, VA 24541 · 434-797-8200

Harrisonburg

J. Jay Litten · Litten & Sipe · 410 Neff Avenue · Harrisonburg, VA 22801 · 540-434-5353

Richmond

John M. Claytor · Harmon Claytor Corrigan & Wellman · Innsbrook Corporate Center, Suite 100 · 4951 Lake Brook Drive · P.O. Box 70280 · Richmond, VA 23255 · 804-747-5200

Robert B. Delano, Jr. · Sands, Anderson, Marks & Miller · http://www.sandsanderson.com · 801 East Main Street, Suite 1800 · P.O. Box 1998 · Richmond, VA 23218-1998 · 804-648-1636

James W. Morris III · ㉕ · Morris & Morris · Wytestone Plaza, 12th Floor · 801 East Main Street · P.O. Box 30 · Richmond, VA 23218 · 804-344-8300

Albert M. Orgain IV · Sands, Anderson, Marks & Miller · http://www.sandsanderson.com · 801 East Main Street, Suite 1800 · P.O. Box 1998 · Richmond, VA 23218-1998 · 804-648-1636

Douglas M. Palais · LeClair Ryan · 951 East Byrd Street, Eighth Floor · P.O. Box 2499 · Richmond, VA 23218-2499 · 804-783-2003

Alexander H. Slaughter · McGuireWoods · http://www.mcguirewoods.com · One James Center · 901 East Cary Street · Richmond, VA 23219-4030 · 804-775-1000

Roanoke

Phillip V. Anderson · Frith, Anderson & Peake · http://www.faplawfirm.com · 29 Franklin Road, SW · P.O. Box 1240 · Roanoke, VA 24006-1240 · 540-772-4600

John D. Eure · Johnson, Ayers & Matthews · First Campbell Square, Suite 300 · 210 First Street, SW · P.O. Box 2200 · Roanoke, VA 24009-2200 · 540-767-2000

Mark D. Loftis · Woods Rogers · http://www.woodsrogers.com · Wachovia Tower, Suite 1400 · 10 South Jefferson Street · P.O. Box 14125 · Roanoke, VA 24038-4125 · 540-983-7600

Staunton

Thomas G. Bell, Jr. · ⑩ · Timberlake, Smith, Thomas & Moses · The Virginia Building · 25 North Central Avenue · P.O. Box 108 · Staunton, VA 24402-0108 · 540-885-1517

Colin J. S. Thomas, Jr. · ⑳ · Timberlake, Smith, Thomas & Moses · The Virginia Building · 25 North Central Avenue · P.O. Box 108 · Staunton, VA 24402-0108 · 540-885-1517

INTELLECTUAL PROPERTY LAW

Alexandria

Arthur I. Neustadt · Oblon, Spivak, McClelland, Maier & Neustadt · 1940 Duke Street · Alexandria, VA 22314 · 703-413-3000

Marvin Petry · Stites & Harbison · http://www.stites.com · 1199 North Fairfax Street, Suite 900 · Alexandria, VA 22314 · 703-739-4900

Arlington

Alan E. J. Branigan · ⑩ · Millen, White, Zelano & Branigan · Arlington Courthouse Plaza I, Suite 1400 · 2200 Clarendon Boulevard · Arlington, VA 22201 · 703-243-6333

Robert W. Faris · Nixon & Vanderhye · 901 North Glebe Road, 11th Floor · Arlington, VA 22203 · 703-816-4000

Larry S. Nixon · ⑩ · Nixon & Vanderhye · 901 North Glebe Road, 11th Floor · Arlington, VA 22203 · 703-816-4000

Mark E. Nusbaum · Nixon & Vanderhye · 901 North Glebe Road, 11th Floor · Arlington, VA 22203 · 703-816-4000

Frank P. Presta · Nixon & Vanderhye · 901 North Glebe Road, 11th Floor · Arlington, VA 22203 · 703-816-4000

Fairfax

James F. Davis · ⑩ · Greenspun Shapiro Davis & Leary · 3955 Chain Bridge Road · Fairfax, VA 22030-3322 · 703-352-0100

Falls Church

James M. Slattery · Birch, Stewart, Kolasch & Birch · 8110 Gatehouse Road, Suite 100 East · P.O. Box 747 · Falls Church, VA 22040 · 703-205-8000

Glen Allen

Charles M. Allen · Goodman, Allen & Filetti · http://www.goodmanallen.com · 4501 Highwoods Parkway, Suite 210 · Glen Allen, VA 23060 · 804-346-0600

Ian D. Titley · The Law Office of Ian D. Titley · http://www.iplawpc.com · 11357 Nucklos Road, Suite 173 · Glen Allen, VA 23059 · 804-364-0405

McLean

Adam R. Hess · Pillsbury Winthrop Shaw Pittman · http://www.pillsburylaw.com · 1650 Tysons Boulevard, 14th Floor · McLean, VA 22102-4859 · 703-905-2000

George M. Sirilla · ⑩ · Pillsbury Winthrop Shaw Pittman · http://www.pillsburylaw.com · 1650 Tysons Boulevard, 14th Floor · McLean, VA 22102-4859 · 703-905-2000

Norfolk

Stephen E. Noona · Kaufman & Canoles · 150 West Main Street, Suite 2100 · P.O. Box 3037 · Norfolk, VA 23514-3037 · 757-624-3000

Gregory N. Stillman · ⑩ · Hunton & Williams · 500 East Main Street, Suite 1000 · P.O. Box 3889 · Norfolk, VA 23514 · 757-640-5300

Stephen E. Story · Kaufman & Canoles · 150 West Main Street, Suite 2100 · P.O. Box 3037 · Norfolk, VA 23514-3037 · 757-624-3000

Robert M. Tata · Hunton & Williams · 500 East Main Street, Suite 1000 · P.O. Box 3889 · Norfolk, VA 23514 · 757-640-5300

Reston

Charles E. Lipsey · Finnegan, Henderson, Farabow, Garrett & Dunner · http://www.finnegan.com · Two Freedom Square · 11955 Freedom Drive · Reston, VA 20190-5675 · 571-203-2700

Richmond

Robert L. Brooke · Troutman Sanders · Troutman Sanders Building · 1001 Haxall Point · P.O. Box 1122 · Richmond, VA 23218-1122 · 804-697-1200

John W. Burke III · McGuireWoods · http://www.mcguirewoods.com · One James Center · 901 East Cary Street · Richmond, VA 23219-4030 · 804-775-1000

Stephen P. Demm · Hunton & Williams · Riverfront Plaza, East Tower · 951 East Byrd Street · Richmond, VA 23219-4074 · 804-788-8200

Maya M. Eckstein · Hunton & Williams · Riverfront Plaza, East Tower · 951 East Byrd Street · Richmond, VA 23219-4074 · 804-788-8200

John B. Farmer · Leading-Edge Law Group · Three James Center, Suite 1130 · 1051 East Cary Street · P.O. Box 1996 · Richmond, VA 23218 · 804-343-3220

Dana J. Finberg · LeClair Ryan · 951 East Byrd Street, Eighth Floor · P.O. Box 2499 · Richmond, VA 23218-2499 · 804-783-2003

Patrick R. Hanes · Williams Mullen · http://www.williamsmullen.com · Two James Center · 1021 East Cary Street · P.O. Box 1320 · Richmond, VA 23218-1320 · 804-643-1991

J. Michael Martinez de Andino · Hunton & Williams · Riverfront Plaza, East Tower · 951 East Byrd Street · Richmond, VA 23219-4074 · 804-788-8200

Dana D. McDaniel · Spotts Fain · http://www.spottsfain.com · 411 East Franklin Street, Suite 600 · Richmond, VA 23219 · 804-697-2000

Christopher J. Mugel · Kaufman & Canoles · Three James Center, 12th Floor · 1051 East Cary Street · Richmond, VA 23219 · 804-771-5700

Brian C. Riopelle · McGuireWoods · http://www.mcguirewoods.com · One James Center · 901 East Cary Street · Richmond, VA 23219-4030 · 804-775-1000

Robert M. Tyler · McGuireWoods · http://www.mcguirewoods.com · One James Center · 901 East Cary Street · Richmond, VA 23219-4030 · 804-775-1000

Roanoke

Tara A. Branscom · LeClair Ryan · 1800 Wachovia Tower · P.O. Drawer 1200 · Roanoke, VA 24006 · 540-510-3000

Virginia Beach

Craig L. Mytelka · Williams Mullen · http://www.williamsmullen.com · 222 Central Park Avenue, Suite 1700 · Virginia Beach, VA 23462-3035 · 757-499-8800

INTERNATIONAL TRADE AND FINANCE LAW

Richmond

John J. Beardsworth, Jr. · ⑩ · Hunton & Williams · Riverfront Plaza, East Tower · 951 East Byrd Street Richmond, VA 23219-4074 · 804-788-8200

Randolph F. Totten · ⑩ · Hunton & Williams · Riverfront Plaza, East Tower · 951 East Byrd Street · Richmond, VA 23219-4074 · 804-788-8200

King F. Tower · Williams Mullen · http://www.williamsmullen.com · Two James Center · 1021 East Cary Street · P.O. Box 1320 · Richmond, VA 23218-1320 · 804-643-1991

LABOR AND EMPLOYMENT LAW

Alexandria

Victor M. Glasberg · Victor M. Glasberg & Associates · 121 South Columbus Street · Alexandria, VA 22314 · 703-684-1100

James S. Ray · ⑩ · Law Offices of James S. Ray · 706 Duke Street · Alexandria, VA 22314 · 703-836-8111

Blacksburg

James K. Cowan, Jr. · LeClair Ryan · 2000 Kraft Drive, Suite 1000 · Blacksburg, VA 24060 · 540-961-2600

Charlottesville

David Z. Izakowitz · McGuireWoods · http://www.mcguirewoods.com · Court Square Building, Suite 300 310 Fourth Street, NE · P.O. Box 1288 · Charlottesville, VA 22902-1288 · 434-977-2500

R. Craig Wood · ⑩ · McGuireWoods · http://www.mcguirewoods.com · Court Square Building, Suite 300 310 Fourth Street, NE · P.O. Box 1288 · Charlottesville, VA 22902-1288 · 434-977-2500

Fairfax

James M. Coleman · Constangy, Brooks & Smith · http://www.constangy.com · 4100 Monument Corner Drive, Suite 520 · Fairfax, VA 22030 · 571-522-6100

Glen Allen

Jay J. Levit · ⑩ · Jay J. Levit Law Office · http://www.jaylevit.com · 10132 West Broad Street · Glen Allen, VA 23060-3303 · 804-270-4600

Harrisonburg

M. Bruce Wallinger · ⑩ · Hoover Penrod · 342 South Main Street · Harrisonburg, VA 22801 · 540-433-2444

Cathleen P. Welsh · Lenhart Obenshain · http://www.lenhartobenshain.com · 90 North Main Street, Suite 201 · P.O. Box 1287 · Harrisonburg, VA 22803 · 540-437-3100

Hopewell

James J. Vergara, Jr. · ⑳ · Vergara & Associates · 100 Main Street Plaza · Hopewell, VA 23860 · 804-458-6394

McLean

Thomas J. Cawley · ⑩ · Hunton & Williams · 1751 Pinnacle Drive, Suite 1700 · McLean, VA 22102 · 703-714-7400

Thomas J. Flaherty · Littler Mendelson · 1650 Tysons Boulevard, Suite 700 · McLean, VA 22102 · 703-442-8425

Michael F. Marino III · ⑳ · Hunton & Williams · 1751 Pinnacle Drive, Suite 1700 · McLean, VA 22102 · 703-714-7400

Thomas P. Murphy · ⑩ · Hunton & Williams · 1751 Pinnacle Drive, Suite 1700 · McLean, VA 22102 · 703-714-7400

Stephen W. Robinson · McGuireWoods · http://www.mcguirewoods.com · 1750 Tysons Boulevard, Suite 1800 · McLean, VA 22102-4215 · 703-712-5000

Daniel P. Westman · Morrison & Foerster · http://www.mofo.com · 1650 Tysons Boulevard, Suite 400 · McLean, VA 22102-4840 · 703-760-7700

Newport News

James H. Shoemaker, Jr. · Patten, Wornom, Hatten & Diamonstein · 12350 Jefferson Avenue, Suite 300 Newport News, VA 23602 · 757-223-4500

Norfolk

Stanley G. Barr, Jr. · ⑳ · Kaufman & Canoles · 150 West Main Street, Suite 2100 · P.O. Box 3037 · Norfolk, VA 23514-3037 · 757-624-3000

Robert J. Barry · Kaufman & Canoles · 150 West Main Street, Suite 2100 · P.O. Box 3037 · Norfolk, VA 23514-3037 · 757-624-3000

John M. Bredehoft · Kaufman & Canoles · 150 West Main Street, Suite 2100 · P.O. Box 3037 · Norfolk, VA 23514-3037 · 757-624-3000

Dean T. Buckius · Vandeventer Black · 500 World Trade Center, Suite 500 · 101 West Main Street · Norfolk, VA 23510 · 757-446-8600

William M. Furr · Willcox & Savage · One Commercial Place, Suite 1800 · Norfolk, VA 23510 · 757-628-5500

Sharon S. Goodwyn · Hunton & Williams · 500 East Main Street, Suite 1000 · P.O. Box 3889 · Norfolk, VA 23514 · 757-640-5300

Scott W. Kezman · Kaufman & Canoles · 150 West Main Street, Suite 2100 · P.O. Box 3037 · Norfolk, VA 23514-3037 · 757-624-3000

Arlene F. Klinedinst · Vandeventer Black · 500 World Trade Center, Suite 500 · 101 West Main Street · Norfolk, VA 23510 · 757-446-8600

Thomas M. Lucas · ⑩ · Willcox & Savage · One Commercial Place, Suite 1800 · Norfolk, VA 23510 · 757-628-5500

James P. Naughton · Hunton & Williams · 500 East Main Street, Suite 1000 · P.O. Box 3889 · Norfolk, VA 23514 · 757-640-5300

William E. Rachels, Jr. · ⑳ · Willcox & Savage · One Commercial Place, Suite 1800 · Norfolk, VA 23510 757-628-5500

John M. Ryan · ⑳ · Vandeventer Black · 500 World Trade Center, Suite 500 · 101 West Main Street · Norfolk, VA 23510 · 757-446-8600

Ann K. Sullivan · Crenshaw, Ware & Martin · 1200 Bank of America Center · One Commercial Place · Norfolk, VA 23510-2111 · 757-623-3000

Burt H. Whitt · ⑳ · Kaufman & Canoles · 150 West Main Street, Suite 2100 · P.O. Box 3037 · Norfolk, VA 23514-3037 · 757-624-3000

Reston

Elaine Charlson Bredehoft · ⑩ · Charlson Bredehoft & Cohen · 11260 Roger Bacon Drive, Suite 201 · Reston, VA 20190 · 703-318-6800

Elizabeth Lewis · Cooley Godward Kronish · One Freedom Square · Reston Town Center · 11951 Freedom Drive · Reston, VA 20190-5656 · 703-456-8000

Richmond

John M. Barr · LeClair Ryan · 951 East Byrd Street, Eighth Floor · P.O. Box 2499 · Richmond, VA 23218-2499 · 804-783-2003

Jack W. Burtch, Jr. · ⑳ · Macaulay & Burtch · http://www.macbur.com · 1015 East Main Street, Third Floor · P.O. Box 8088 · Richmond, VA 23223-0088 · 804-649-4009

Harris D. Butler III · Butler Williams & Skilling · 100 Shockoe Slip, Fourth Floor · Richmond, VA 23219 804-648-4848

David E. Constine III · Troutman Sanders · Troutman Sanders Building · 1001 Haxall Point · P.O. Box 1122 · Richmond, VA 23218-1122 · 804-697-1200

C. Michael DeCamps · Sands, Anderson, Marks & Miller · http://www.sandsanderson.com · 801 East Main Street, Suite 1800 · P.O. Box 1998 · Richmond, VA 23218-1998 · 804-648-1636

Patricia K. Epps · ⑩ · Hunton & Williams · Riverfront Plaza, East Tower · 951 East Byrd Street · Richmond, VA 23219-4074 · 804-788-8200

H. Aubrey Ford III · ⑩ · Cantor Arkema · Bank of America Center · 1111 East Main Street · P.O. Box 561 Richmond, VA 23218-0561 · 804-644-1400

Warren David Harless · ⑩ · Christian & Barton · Mutual Building, Suite 1200 · 909 East Main Street · Richmond, VA 23219-3095 · 804-697-4100

Jonathan P. Harmon · McGuireWoods · http://www.mcguirewoods.com · One James Center · 901 East Cary Street · Richmond, VA 23219-4030 · 804-775-1000

Kevin D. Holden · Kaufman & Canoles · Three James Center, 12th Floor · 1051 East Cary Street · Richmond, VA 23219 · 804-771-5700

Lynn F. Jacob · Williams Mullen · http://www.williamsmullen.com · Two James Center · 1021 East Cary Street · P.O. Box 1320 · Richmond, VA 23218-1320 · 804-643-1991

Gary S. Marshall · McGuireWoods · http://www.mcguirewoods.com · One James Center · 901 East Cary Street · Richmond, VA 23219-4030 · 804-775-1000

James P. McElligott · ⑩ · McGuireWoods · http://www.mcguirewoods.com · One James Center · 901 East Cary Street · Richmond, VA 23219-4030 · 804-775-1000

James V. Meath · ⑩ · Williams Mullen · http://www.williamsmullen.com · Two James Center · 1021 East Cary Street · P.O. Box 1320 · Richmond, VA 23218-1320 · 804-643-1991

David E. Nagle · Jackson Lewis · http://www.jacksonlewis.com · 321 Weest Franklin Street · Richmond, VA 23220 · 804-649-0404

Gregory B. Robertson · ⑩ · Hunton & Williams · Riverfront Plaza, East Tower · 951 East Byrd Street · Richmond, VA 23219-4074 · 804-788-8200

Dana Rust · McGuireWoods · http://www.mcguirewoods.com · One James Center · 901 East Cary Street · Richmond, VA 23219-4030 · 804-775-1000

Rodney A. Satterwhite · McGuireWoods · http://www.mcguirewoods.com · One James Center · 901 East Cary Street · Richmond, VA 23219-4030 · 804-775-1000

David R. Simonsen, Jr. · David R. Simonsen, Jr. · 8003 Franklin Farms Drive, Suite 131 · Richmond, VA 23229-5107 · 804-285-1337

James B. Thorsen · James B. Thorsen & Associates · 3810 Augusta Avenue · Richmond, VA 23230 · 804-359-3000

King F. Tower · Williams Mullen · http://www.williamsmullen.com · Two James Center · 1021 East Cary Street · P.O. Box 1320 · Richmond, VA 23218-1320 · 804-643-1991

D. Eugene Webb, Jr. · ⑳ · Troutman Sanders · Troutman Sanders Building · 1001 Haxall Point · P.O. Box 1122 · Richmond, VA 23218-1122 · 804-697-1200

Hill B. Wellford, Jr. · ㉕ · Hunton & Williams · Riverfront Plaza, East Tower · 951 East Byrd Street · Richmond, VA 23219-4074 · 804-788-8200

W. Carter Younger · ㉕ · McGuireWoods · http://www.mcguirewoods.com · One James Center · 901 East Cary Street · Richmond, VA 23219-4030 · 804-775-1000

Roanoke

Thomas R. Bagby · Woods Rogers · http://www.woodsrogers.com · Wachovia Tower, Suite 1400 · 10 South Jefferson Street · P.O. Box 14125 · Roanoke, VA 24038-4125 · 540-983-7600

Victor O. Cardwell · Woods Rogers · http://www.woodsrogers.com · Wachovia Tower, Suite 1400 · 10 South Jefferson Street · P.O. Box 14125 · Roanoke, VA 24038-4125 · 540-983-7600

Agnis C. Chakravorty · Woods Rogers · http://www.woodsrogers.com · Wachovia Tower, Suite 1400 · 10 South Jefferson Street · P.O. Box 14125 · Roanoke, VA 24038-4125 · 540-983-7600

Terry N. Grimes · Terry N. Grimes · 320 Elm Avenue, SW · Roanoke, VA 24011 · 540-982-3711

Bayard E. Harris · ㉕ · Woods Rogers · http://www.woodsrogers.com · Wachovia Tower, Suite 1400 · 10 South Jefferson Street · P.O. Box 14125 · Roanoke, VA 24038-4125 · 540-983-7600

Paul G. Klockenbrink · Gentry Locke Rakes & Moore · http://www.gentrylocke.com · 10 Franklin Road, SE · P.O. Box 40013 · Roanoke, VA 24022-0013 · 540-983-9300

Clinton S. Morse · ⑳ · LeClair Ryan · 1800 Wachovia Tower · P.O. Drawer 1200 · Roanoke, VA 24006 · 540-510-3000

W. David Paxton · ⑩ · Gentry Locke Rakes & Moore · http://www.gentrylocke.com · 10 Franklin Road, SE · P.O. Box 40013 · Roanoke, VA 24022-0013 · 540-983-9300

Thomas M. Winn III · Woods Rogers · http://www.woodsrogers.com · Wachovia Tower, Suite 1400 · 10 South Jefferson Street · P.O. Box 14125 · Roanoke, VA 24038-4125 · 540-983-7600

Vienna

Edward L. Isler · Isler Dare Ray & Radcliffe · 1919 Gallows Road, Suite 320 · Vienna, VA 22182-3964 · 703-748-2690

Steven W. Ray · Isler Dare Ray & Radcliffe · 1919 Gallows Road, Suite 320 · Vienna, VA 22182-3964 · 703-748-2690

Virginia Beach

Susan Roussel Blackman · Willcox & Savage · 222 Central Park Avenue, Suite 1500 · Virginia Beach, VA 23462 · 757-628-5600

David C. Burton · Williams Mullen · http://www.williamsmullen.com · 222 Central Park Avenue, Suite 1700 · Virginia Beach, VA 23462-3035 · 757-499-8800

Gregory A. Giordano · ⑩ · Troutman Sanders · 222 Central Park Avenue, Suite 2000 · Virginia Beach, VA 23462 · 757-687-7500

Kevin E. Martingayle · Stallings & Bischoff · 2101 Parks Avenue, Suite 801 · Virginia Beach, VA 23451 · 757-422-4700

LAND USE & ZONING LAW

Arlington

Martin D. Walsh · ⑩ · Walsh, Colucci, Lubeley, Emrich & Terpak · Courthouse Plaza, Thirteenth Floor · 2200 Clarendon Boulevard · Arlington, VA 22201-3359 · 703-528-4700

Nan E. Walsh · Walsh, Colucci, Lubeley, Emrich & Terpak · Courthouse Plaza, Thirteenth Floor · 2200 Clarendon Boulevard · Arlington, VA 22201-3359 · 703-528-4700

Charlottesville

Valerie Wagner Long · Williams Mullen · http://www.williamsmullen.com · 321 East Main Street, Suite 400 · Charlottesville, VA 22902-3200 · 434-951-5700

Falls Church

Grayson P. Hanes · ⑳ · Reed Smith · 3110 Fairview Park Drive, Suite 1400 · P.O. Box 12001 · Falls Church, VA 22042 · 703-641-4200

McLean

Carson Lee Fifer, Jr. · ⑩ · McGuireWoods · http://www.mcguirewoods.com · 1750 Tysons Boulevard, Suite 1800 · McLean, VA 22102-4215 · 703-712-5000

Francis A. McDermott · ⑩ · Hunton & Williams · 1751 Pinnacle Drive, Suite 1700 · McLean, VA 22102 · 703-714-7400

Jonathan P. Rak · McGuireWoods · http://www.mcguirewoods.com · 1750 Tysons Boulevard, Suite 1800 McLean, VA 22102-4215 · 703-712-5000

Norfolk

Stephen R. Romine · LeClair Ryan · 999 Waterside Drive, Suite 2525 · Norfolk, VA 23510 · 757-624-1454

Prince William

John H. Foote · ⑩ · Walsh, Colucci, Lubeley, Emrich & Terpak · 4310 Prince William Parkway, Suite 300 · Prince William, VA 22192 · 703-680-4664

Michael D. Lubeley · Walsh, Colucci, Lubeley, Emrich & Terpak · 4310 Prince William Parkway, Suite 300 · Prince William, VA 22192 · 703-680-4664

Reston

Antonio J. Calabrese · Cooley Godward Kronish · One Freedom Square · Reston Town Center · 11951 Freedom Drive · Reston, VA 20190-5656 · 703-456-8000

Richmond

Ralph L. Axselle, Jr. · Williams Mullen · http://www.williamsmullen.com · Two James Center · 1021 East Cary Street · P.O. Box 1320 · Richmond, VA 23218-1320 · 804-643-1991

John V. Cogbill III · ⑩ · McGuireWoods · http://www.mcguirewoods.com · One James Center · 901 East Cary Street · Richmond, VA 23219-4030 · 804-775-1000

Andrew M. Condlin · Williams Mullen · http://www.williamsmullen.com · Two James Center · 1021 East Cary Street · P.O. Box 1320 · Richmond, VA 23218-1320 · 804-643-1991

John R. Easter · Williams Mullen · http://www.williamsmullen.com · Two James Center · 1021 East Cary Street · P.O. Box 1320 · Richmond, VA 23218-1320 · 804-643-1991

Gloria L. Freye · McGuireWoods · http://www.mcguirewoods.com · One James Center · 901 East Cary Street · Richmond, VA 23219-4030 · 804-775-1000

James W. Theobald · ⑩ · Hirschler Fleischer · http://www.hirschlerfleischer.com · The Edgeworth Building · 2100 East Cary Street · Richmond, VA 23223-7078 · 804-771-9500

Jay M. Weinberg · ㉕ · Hirschler Fleischer · http://www.hirschlerfleischer.com · The Edgeworth Building 2100 East Cary Street · Richmond, VA 23223-7078 · 804-771-9500

Roanoke

James F. Douthat · Woods Rogers · http://www.woodsrogers.com · Wachovia Tower, Suite 1400 · 10 South Jefferson Street · P.O. Box 14125 · Roanoke, VA 24038-4125 · 540-983-7600

Daniel F. Layman, Jr. · ⑩ · Woods Rogers · http://www.woodsrogers.com · Wachovia Tower, Suite 1400 · 10 South Jefferson Street · P.O. Box 14125 · Roanoke, VA 24038-4125 · 540-983-7600

Edward A. Natt · Osterhoudt, Prillaman, Natt, Helscher, Yost, Maxwell & Ferguson · 3140 Chaparral Drive, Suite 200-C · P.O. Box 20487 · Roanoke, VA 24018 · 540-989-0000

G. Michael Pace, Jr. · Gentry Locke Rakes & Moore · http://www.gentrylocke.com · 10 Franklin Road, SE · P.O. Box 40013 · Roanoke, VA 24022-0013 · 540-983-9300

Virginia Beach

R. Edward Bourdon, Jr. · Sykes, Bourdon, Ahern & Levy · Pembroke Office Park, Fifth Floor · 281 Independence Boulevard · Virginia Beach, VA 23462-2989 · 757-499-8971

R. J. Nutter · Troutman Sanders · 222 Central Park Avenue, Suite 2000 · Virginia Beach, VA 23462 · 757-687-7500

Williamsburg

Alvin P. Anderson · Kaufman & Canoles · 4801 Courthouse Street, Suite 300 · P.O. Box 6000 · Williamsburg, VA 23188 · 757-259-3800

LEGAL MALPRACTICE LAW

Charlottesville

Thomas E. Albro · ⑩ · Tremblay & Smith · http://www.tremblaysmith.com · 105-109 East High Street · P.O. Box 1585 · Charlottesville, VA 22902 · 434-977-4455

Fairfax

David L. Duff · The Duff Law Firm · 11320 Random Hills Road, Suite 525 · Fairfax, VA 22030 · 703-591-7475

Benjamin W. Glass III · Benjamin W. Glass III · 3915 Old Lee Highway, Suite 22-B · Fairfax, VA 22030 · 703-591-9829

David J. Gogal · Blankingship & Keith · http://www.blankingship-keith-law.com · 4020 University Drive, Suite 300 · Fairfax, VA 22030 · 703-691-1235

John A. C. Keith · Blankingship & Keith · http://www.blankingship-keith-law.com · 4020 University Drive, Suite 300 · Fairfax, VA 22030 · 703-691-1235

Carol T. Stone · Jordan Coyne & Savits · 10509 Judicial Drive, Suite 200 · Fairfax, VA 22030 · 703-246-0900

McLean

Thomas L. Appler · ⑩ · Wilson Elser Moskowitz Edelman & Dicker · 8444 Westpark Drive, Suite 510 · McLean, VA 22102-5102 · 703-245-9300

John J. Brandt · ⑳ · Wilson Elser Moskowitz Edelman & Dicker · 8444 Westpark Drive, Suite 510 · McLean, VA 22102-5102 · 703-245-9300

Paul D. Krause · Wilson Elser Moskowitz Edelman & Dicker · 8444 Westpark Drive, Suite 510 · McLean, VA 22102-5102 · 703-245-9300

Richmond

Matthew B. Murray · ⑩ · Allen, Allen, Allen & Allen · http://www.allenandallen.com · 1809 Staples Mill Road · P.O. Box 6855 · Richmond, VA 23230 · 804-353-1200

Russell V. Palmore · Troutman Sanders · Troutman Sanders Building · 1001 Haxall Point · P.O. Box 1122 Richmond, VA 23218-1122 · 804-697-1200

Gary J. Spahn · Troutman Sanders · Troutman Sanders Building · 1001 Haxall Point · P.O. Box 1122 · Richmond, VA 23218-1122 · 804-697-1200

LEVERAGED BUYOUTS AND PRIVATE EQUITY LAW

McLean

William J. Mutryn · Holland & Knight · http://www.hklaw.com · 1600 Tysons Boulevard, Suite 700 · McLean, VA 22102 · 703-720-8600

Reston

Michael Lincoln · Cooley Godward Kronish · One Freedom Square · Reston Town Center · 11951 Freedom Drive · Reston, VA 20190-5656 · 703-456-8000

Richmond

S. Brian Farmer · Hirschler Fleischer · http://www.hirschlerfleischer.com · The Edgeworth Building · 2100 East Cary Street · Richmond, VA 23223-7078 · 804-771-9500

Gary D. LeClair · LeClair Ryan · 951 East Byrd Street, Eighth Floor · P.O. Box 2499 · Richmond, VA 23218-2499 · 804-783-2003

T. Justin Moore III · Hunton & Williams · Riverfront Plaza, East Tower · 951 East Byrd Street · Richmond, VA 23219-4074 · 804-788-8200

Thurston R. Moore · ⑩ · Hunton & Williams · Riverfront Flaza, East Tower · 951 East Byrd Street · Richmond, VA 23219-4074 · 804-788-8200

Roanoke

Bruce C. Stockburger · ⑩ · Gentry Locke Rakes & Moore · http://www.gentrylocke.com · 10 Franklin Road, SE · P.O. Box 40013 · Roanoke, VA 24022-0013 · 540-983-9300

MARITIME LAW

Norfolk

Patrick M. Brogan · Davey & Brogan · 101 Granby Street. Suite 300 · P.O. Box 3188 · Norfolk, VA 23514-3188 · 757-622-0100

James L. Chapman IV · Crenshaw, Ware & Martin · 1200 Bank of America Center · One Commercial Place · Norfolk, VA 23510-2111 · 757-623-3000

Mark T. Coberly · Vandeventer Black · 500 World Trade Center, Suite 500 · 101 West Main Street · Norfolk, VA 23510 · 757-446-8600

Philip N. Davey · ⑩ · Davey & Brogan · 101 Granby Street, Suite 300 · P.O. Box 3188 · Norfolk, VA 23514-3188 · 757-622-0100

Michael J. Gardner · Troutman Sanders · 150 West Main Street, Suite 1600 · Norfolk, VA 23510 · 757-687-7700

John E. Holloway · Hunton & Williams · 500 East Main Street, Suite 1000 · P.O. Box 3889 · Norfolk, VA 23514 · 757-640-5300

R. Arthur Jett, Jr. · ⑩ · Davey & Brogan · 101 Granby Street, Suite 300 · P.O. Box 3188 · Norfolk, VA 23514-3188 · 757-622-0100

Walter B. Martin, Jr. · ⑳ · Vandeventer Black · 500 World Trade Center, Suite 500 · 101 West Main Street · Norfolk, VA 23510 · 757-446-8600

Edward J. Powers · Vandeventer Black · 500 World Trade Center, Suite 500 · 101 West Main Street · Norfolk, VA 23510 · 757-446-8600

John M. Ryan · ⑳ · Vandeventer Black · 500 World Trade Center, Suite 500 · 101 West Main Street · Norfolk, VA 23510 · 757-446-8600

David H. Sump · Troutman Sanders · 150 West Main Street, Suite 1600 · Norfolk, VA 23510 · 757-687-7700

Guilford D. Ware · ⑩ · Crenshaw, Ware & Martin · 1200 Bank of America Center · One Commercial Place · Norfolk, VA 23510-2111 · 757-623-3000

MASS TORT LITIGATION

Newport News

Robert R. Hatten · ⑩ · Patten, Wornom, Hatten & Diamonstein · 12350 Jefferson Avenue, Suite 300 · Newport News, VA 23602 · 757-223-4500

Norfolk

Bruce T. Bishop · ⑩ · Willcox & Savage · One Commercial Place, Suite 1800 · Norfolk, VA 23510 · 757-628-5500

Richmond

Brickford Y. Brown · Moran Kiker Brown · 4110 East Parham Road · Richmond, VA 23228 · 804-421-6250

John D. Epps · Hunton & Williams · Riverfront Plaza, East Tower · 951 East Byrd Street · Richmond, VA 23219-4074 · 804-788-8200

Michael H. Gladstone · McCandlish Holton · 1111 East Main Street, Suite 1500 · Richmond, VA 23219 · 804-775-3100

David Craig Landin · ㉕ · Hunton & Williams · Riverfront Plaza, East Tower · 951 East Byrd Street · Richmond, VA 23219-4074 · 804-788-8200

Charles G. Meyer III · LeClair Ryan · 951 East Byrd Street, Eighth Floor · P.O. Box 2499 · Richmond, VA 23218-2499 · 804-783-2003

Michael G. Phelan · Butler Williams & Skilling · 100 Shockoe Slip, Fourth Floor · Richmond, VA 23219 · 804-648-4848

Robert F. Redmond, Jr. · Williams Mullen · http://www.williamsmullen.com · Two James Center · 1021 East Cary Street · P.O. Box 1320 · Richmond, VA 23218-1320 · 804-643-1991

Deborah M. Russell · McGuireWoods · http://www.mcguirewoods.com · One James Center · 901 East Cary Street · Richmond, VA 23219-4030 · 804-775-1000

Edward H. Starr, Jr. · Troutman Sanders · Troutman Sanders Building · 1001 Haxall Point · P.O. Box 1122 · Richmond, VA 23218-1122 · 804-697-1200

Samuel L. Tarry, Jr. · McGuireWoods · http://www.mcguirewoods.com · One James Center · 901 East Cary Street · Richmond, VA 23219-4030 · 804-775-1000

Steven R. Williams · McGuireWoods · http://www.mcguirewoods.com · One James Center · 901 East Cary Street · Richmond, VA 23219-4030 · 804-775-1000

MEDIA LAW

Charlottesville

Thomas E. Albro · ⑩ · Tremblay & Smith · http://www.tremblaysmith.com · 105-109 East High Street · P.O. Box 1585 · Charlottesville, VA 22902 · 434-977-4455

Richmond

Philip H. Goodpasture · Williams Mullen · http://www.williamsmullen.com · Two James Center · 1021 East Cary Street · P.O. Box 1320 · Richmond, VA 23218-1320 · 804-643-1991

Craig Thomas Merritt · Christian & Barton · Mutual Building, Suite 1200 · 909 East Main Street · Richmond, VA 23219-3095 · 804-697-4100

MEDICAL MALPRACTICE LAW

Abingdon

Mary Lynn Tate · The Tate Law Firm · Abingdon Professional Centre · 110 Abingdon Place · Abingdon, VA 24211 · 276-628-5185

Alexandria

Gary A. Godard · Miller & Associates · 105 North Alfred Street · Alexandria, VA 22314 · 703-519-8080

Annandale

Robert H. Hovis III · ⑩ · Robert H. Hovis, III · 4544 John Marr Drive · Annandale, VA 22003 · 703-642-5800

Arlington

William E. Artz · ⑩ · William E. Artz · 1700 North Moore Street, Suite 1010 · Arlington, VA 22209 · 703-243-3500

Charlottesville

Thomas E. Albro · ⑩ · Tremblay & Smith · http://www.tremblaysmith.com · 105-109 East High Street · P.O. Box 1585 · Charlottesville, VA 22902 · 434-977-4455

Christine Thomson · Michie Hamlett Lowry Rasmussen & Tweel · 500 Court Square, Suite 300 · P.O. Box 298 · Charlottesville, VA 22902-0298 · 434-951-7200

Fairfax

Stephen L. Altman · Hamilton Altman Canale & Dillon · 10306 Eaton Place, Suite 200 · Fairfax, VA 22030 · 703-591-9700

Gary W. Brown · McCandlish & Lillard · 11350 Random Hills Road, Suite 500 · Fairfax, VA 22030-7429 · 703-273-2288

Benjamin W. Glass III · Benjamin W. Glass III · 3915 Old Lee Highway, Suite 22-B · Fairfax, VA 22030 · 703-591-9829

Richard L. Nagle · Hancock, Daniel, Johnson & Nagle · 3975 Fair Ridge Drive, Suite 475 South · Fairfax, VA 22033 · 703-591-3440

Donna Miller Rostant · Jones & Rostant · 12011 Lee Jackson Memorial Highway, Suite 310 · Fairfax, VA 22033 · 703-352-0522

Michael J. Shevlin · Shevlin & Smith · 3975 University Drive, Suite 405 · Fairfax, VA 22030 · 703-591-0067

Glen Allen

Michael L. Goodman · Goodman, Allen & Filetti · http://www.goodmanallen.com · 4501 Highwoods Parkway, Suite 210 · Glen Allen, VA 23060 · 804-346-0600

Mary M.H. Priddy · Goodman, Allen & Filetti · http://www.goodmanallen.com · 4501 Highwoods Parkway, Suite 210 · Glen Allen, VA 23060 · 804-346-0600

Harrisonburg

Charles F. Hilton · Wharton, Aldhizer & Weaver · 100 South Mason Street · P.O. Box 20028 · Harrisonburg, VA 22801-7528 · 540-434-0316

Marshall H. Ross · Wharton, Aldhizer & Weaver · 100 South Mason Street · P.O. Box 20028 · Harrisonburg, VA 22801-7528 · 540-434-0316

Lorton

James K. Fitzpatrick · Fitzpatrick Law Offices · 8709 Bitterroot Court · Lorton, VA 22079 · 703-690-7557

McLean

Thomas L. Appler · ⑩ · Wilson Elser Moskowitz Edelman & Dicker · 8444 Westpark Drive, Suite 510 · McLean, VA 22102-5102 · 703-245-9300

Cynthia L. Santoni · Wilson Elser Moskowitz Edelman & Dicker · 8444 Westpark Drive, Suite 510 · McLean, VA 22102-5102 · 703-245-9300

Newport News

Avery T. Waterman, Jr. · Patten, Wornom, Hatten & Diamonstein · 12350 Jefferson Avenue, Suite 300 · Newport News, VA 23602 · 757-223-4500

Norfolk

R. Barrow Blackwell · Kaufman & Canoles · 150 West Main Street, Suite 2100 · P.O. Box 3037 · Norfolk, VA 23514-3037 · 757-624-3000

Lisa P. O'Donnell · Bertini O'Donnell & Hammer · http://www.bohlaw.net · 999 Waterside Drive, Suite 1010 · Norfolk, VA 23510 · 757-670-3868

Reston

Robert T. Hall · ㉕ · Hall, Sickels, Frei & Mims · http://www.hallandsickels.com · 12120 Sunset Hills Road, Suite 150 · Reston, VA 20190 · 703-925-0500

Richmond

Irvin V. Cantor · Cantor Arkema · Bank of America Center · 1111 East Main Street · P.O. Box 561 · Richmond, VA 23218-0561 · 804-644-1400

Stephanie E. Grana · Cantor Arkema · Bank of America Center · 1111 East Main Street · P.O. Box 561 · Richmond, VA 23218-0561 · 804-644-1400

Ronald P. Herbert · LeClair Ryan · 951 East Byrd Street, Eighth Floor · P.O. Box 2499 · Richmond, VA 23218-2499 · 804-783-2003

Jason W. Konvicka · Allen, Allen, Allen & Allen · http://www.allenandallen.com · 1809 Staples Mill Road P.O. Box 6855 · Richmond, VA 23230 · 804-353-1200

Malcolm P. McConnell · Allen, Allen, Allen & Allen · http://www.allenandallen.com · 1809 Staples Mill Road · P.O. Box 6855 · Richmond, VA 23230 · 804-353-1200

Matthew B. Murray · ⑩ · Allen, Allen, Allen & Allen · http://www.allenandallen.com · 1809 Staples Mill Road · P.O. Box 6855 · Richmond, VA 23230 · 804-353-1200

M. Pierce Rucker · Sands, Anderson, Marks & Miller · http://www.sandsanderson.com · 801 East Main Street, Suite 1800 · P.O. Box 1998 · Richmond, VA 23218-1998 · 804-648-1636

Lewis T. Stoneburner · Cantor Arkema · Bank of America Center · 1111 East Main Street · P.O. Box 561 Richmond, VA 23218-0561 · 804-644-1400

Thomas W. Williamson, Jr. · ⑳ · Williamson & Lavecchia · http://www.wllc.com · 6800 Paragon Place, Suite 233 · Richmond, VA 23230-1652 · 804-288-1661

Roanoke

T. Daniel Frith III · Frith Law Firm · 303 Washington Avenue, SW · Roanoke, VA 24016 · 540-985-0098

John T. Jessee · LeClair Ryan · 1800 Wachovia Tower · P.O. Drawer 1200 · Roanoke, VA 24006 · 540-510-3000

Jeffrey H. Krasnow · The Krasnow Law Firm · 301 West Campbell Avenue · Roanoke, VA 24016 · 540-982-7654

John E. Lichtenstein · Lichtenstein Fishwick & Johnson · Liberty Trust Building, Suite 400 · 101 South Jefferson Street · P.O. Box 601 · Roanoke, VA 24004-0601 · 540-343-9711

Walter H. Peake III · Frith, Anderson & Peake · http://www.faplawfirm.com · 29 Franklin Road, SW · P.O. Box 1240 · Roanoke, VA 24006-1240 · 540-772-4600

Staunton

C. J. Steuart Thomas III · Timberlake, Smith, Thomas & Moses · The Virginia Building · 25 North Central Avenue · P.O. Box 108 · Staunton, VA 24402-0108 · 540-885-1517

Virginia Beach

Robert J. Haddad · ⑩ · Shuttleworth, Ruloff, Swain, Haddad & Morecock · http://www.srgslaw.com · Southport Centre, Suite 300 · 4525 South Boulevard · Virginia Beach, VA 23452-1137 · 757-671-6000

Edwin Jay Rafal · ⑩ · Shuttleworth, Ruloff, Swain, Haddad & Morecock · http://www.srgslaw.com · Southport Centre, Suite 300 · 4525 South Boulevard · Virginia Beach, VA 23452-1137 · 757-671-6000

Thomas B. Shuttleworth II · ⑩ · Shuttleworth, Ruloff, Swain, Haddad & Morecock · http://www.srgslaw.com · Southport Centre, Suite 300 · 4525 South Boulevard · Virginia Beach, VA 23452-1137 · 757-671-6000

Stephen C. Swain · ⑩ · Shuttleworth, Ruloff, Swain, Haddad & Morecock · http://www.srgslaw.com · Southport Centre, Suite 300 · 4525 South Boulevard · Virginia Beach, VA 23452-1137 · 757-671-6000

Lawrence H. Woodward, Jr. · Shuttleworth, Ruloff, Swain, Haddad & Morecock · http://www.srgslaw.com · Southport Centre, Suite 300 · 4525 South Boulevard · Virginia Beach, VA 23452-1137 · 757-671-6000

Woodbridge

Charles J. Zauzig III · Nichols, Zauzig & Sandler · 12660 Lake Ridge Drive · Woodbridge, VA 22192 · 703-492-4200

MERGERS & ACQUISITIONS LAW

McLean

Kevin J. Lavin · Arnold & Porter · 1600 Tysons Boulevard, Suite 900 · McLean, VA 22102-4865 · 703-720-7000

William J. Mutryn · Holland & Knight · http://www.hklaw.com · 1600 Tysons Boulevard, Suite 700 · McLean, VA 22102 · 703-720-8600

Lawreance T. Yanowitch · Morrison & Foerster · http://www.mofo.com · 1650 Tysons Boulevard, Suite 400 · McLean, VA 22102-4840 · 703-760-7700

Norfolk

Thomas C. Inglima · Willcox & Savage · One Commercial Place, Suite 1800 · Norfolk, VA 23510 · 757-628-5500

Reston

Michael Lincoln · Cooley Godward Kronish · One Freedom Square · Reston Town Center · 11951 Freedom Drive · Reston, VA 20190-5656 · 703-456-8000

Richmond

Clifford A. Cutchins IV · McGuireWoods · http://www.mcguirewoods.com · One James Center · 901 East Cary Street · Richmond, VA 23219-4030 · 804-775-1000

Robert C. Dewar · Williams Mullen · http://www.williamsmullen.com · Two James Center · 1021 East Cary Street · P.O. Box 1320 · Richmond, VA 23218-1320 · 804-643-1991

Matthew D. Jenkins · ⑩ · Hunton & Williams · Riverfront Plaza, East Tower · 951 East Byrd Street · Richmond, VA 23219-4074 · 804-788-8200

F. Claiborne Johnston, Jr. · ⑩ · Troutman Sanders · Troutman Sanders Building · 1001 Haxall Point · P.O. Box 1122 · Richmond, VA 23218-1122 · 804-697-1200

Donald E. King · McGuireWoods · http://www.mcguirewoods.com · One James Center · 901 East Cary Street · Richmond, VA 23219-4030 · 804-775-1000

Gary D. LeClair · LeClair Ryan · 951 East Byrd Street, Eighth Floor · P.O. Box 2499 · Richmond, VA 23218-2499 · 804-783-2003

T. Justin Moore III · Hunton & Williams · Riverfront Plaza, East Tower · 951 East Byrd Street · Richmond, VA 23219-4074 · 804-788-8200

Gary E. Thompson · Hunton & Williams · Riverfront Plaza, East Tower · 951 East Byrd Street · Richmond, VA 23219-4074 · 804-788-8200

Roanoke

Douglas W. Densmore · ⑩ · Gentry Locke Rakes & Moore · http://www.gentrylocke.com · 10 Franklin Road, SE · P.O. Box 40013 · Roanoke, VA 24022-0013 · 540-983-9300

G. Franklin Flippin · ⑩ · Gentry Locke Rakes & Moore · http://www.gentrylocke.com · 10 Franklin Road, SE · P.O. Box 40013 · Roanoke, VA 24022-0013 · 540-983-9300

James C. Hale · LeClair Ryan · 1800 Wachovia Tower · P.O. Drawer 1200 · Roanoke, VA 24006 · 540-510-3000

Vienna

Thomas W. France · Venable · http://www.venable.com · 8010 Towers Crescent Drive, Suite 300 · Vienna, VA 22182 · 703-760-1600

Virginia Beach

James J. Wheaton · Troutman Sanders · 222 Central Park Avenue, Suite 2000 · Virginia Beach, VA 23462 · 757-687-7500

MINING LAW

Abingdon

Timothy W. Gresham · PennStuart · Virginia House · 208 East Main Street · P.O. Box 2288 · Abingdon, VA 24212-2288 · 276-628-5151

Wade Massie · PennStuart · Virginia House · 208 East Main Street · P.O. Box 2288 · Abingdon, VA 24212-2288 · 276-628-5151

MUNICIPAL LAW

Fairfax

Dexter S. Odin · Odin, Feldman & Pittleman · http://www.ofplaw.com · 9302 Lee Highway, Suite 1100 · Fairfax, VA 22031 · 703-218-2100

Norfolk

Stanley G. Barr, Jr. · ⑳ · Kaufman & Canoles · 150 West Main Street, Suite 2100 · P.O. Box 3037 · Norfolk, VA 23514-3037 · 757-624-3000

Timothy A. Coyle · Crenshaw, Ware & Martin · 1200 Bank of America Center · One Commercial Place · Norfolk, VA 23510-2111 · 757-623-3000

Richmond

Benjamin W. Emerson · Sands, Anderson, Marks & Miller · http://www.sandsanderson.com · 801 East Main Street, Suite 1800 · P.O. Box 1998 · Richmond, VA 23218-1998 · 804-648-1636

John A. Gibney, Jr. · Thompson & McMullan · 100 Shockoe Slip, Third Floor · Richmond, VA 23219 · 804-649-7545

Carter Glass IV · Troutman Sanders · Troutman Sanders Building · 1001 Haxall Point · P.O. Box 1122 · Richmond, VA 23218-1122 · 804-697-1200

William H. Hefty · Hefty & Wiley · 1001 East Broad Street · Richmond, VA 23219 · 804-780-3143

George Keith Martin · McGuireWoods · http://www.mcguirewoods.com · One James Center · 901 East Cary Street · Richmond, VA 23219-4030 · 804-775-1000

Patrick M. McSweeney · McSweeney, Crump, Childress & Gould · 11 South 12th Street · P.O. Box 1463 Richmond, VA 23218 · 804-783-6800

Eric M. Page · LeClair Ryan · 951 East Byrd Street, Eighth Floor · P.O. Box 2499 · Richmond, VA 23218-2499 · 804-783-2003

Roger Wiley · Hefty & Wiley · 1001 East Broad Street · Richmond, VA 23219 · 804-780-3143

Roanoke

Gregory J. Haley · Gentry Locke Rakes & Moore · http://www.gentrylocke.com · 10 Franklin Road, SE · P.O. Box 40013 · Roanoke, VA 24022-0013 · 540-983-9300

MUTUAL FUNDS LAW

Norfolk

Robert C. Goodman, Jr. · ⑩ · Kaufman & Canoles · 150 West Main Street, Suite 2100 · P.O. Box 3037 · Norfolk, VA 23514-3037 · 757-624-3000

NATURAL RESOURCES LAW

Richmond

Brian L. Buniva · LeClair Ryan · 951 East Byrd Street, Eighth Floor · P.O. Box 2499 · Richmond, VA 23218-2499 · 804-783-2003

NON-PROFIT/CHARITIES LAW

Richmond

J. William Gray, Jr. · ⑩ · Hunton & Williams · Riverfront Plaza, East Tower · 951 East Byrd Street · Richmond, VA 23219-4074 · 804-788-8200

Michele A. W. McKinnon · McGuireWoods · http://www.mcguirewoods.com · One James Center · 901 East Cary Street · Richmond, VA 23219-4030 · 804-775-1000

Alexandria

James C. Clark · ⑩ · Land, Clark, Carroll, Mendelson & Blair · 524 King Street · P.O. Box 19888 · Alexandria, VA 22320-0888 · 703-836-1000

William B. Cummings · Law Offices of William B. Cummings · P.O. Box 1177 · Alexandria, VA 22313 · 703-836-7997

Marvin D. Miller · ⑩ · Law Offices of Marvin D. Miller · 1203 Duke Street · Alexandria, VA 22314 · 703-548-5000

William B. Moffitt · Moffitt & Brodnax · 108 North Alfred Street · Alexandria, VA 22314 · 703-684-9400

John Kenneth Zwerling · ⑩ · Zwerling, Leibig & Moseley · 108 North Alfred Street · Alexandria, VA 22314 · 703-684-8000

Charlottesville

Francis McQ. Lawrence · St. John, Bowling & Lawrence · 416 Park Street · Charlottesville, VA 22902 · 434-296-7138

Dublin

Michael L. Barbour · Barbour & Simpkins · 500 Newbern Road · P.O. Box 1055 · Dublin, VA 24084 · 540-674-8556

Fairfax

Peter D. Greenspun · ⑩ · Greenspun, Davis & Leary · 3955 Chain Bridge Road, Second Floor · Fairfax, VA 22030 · 703-352-0100

Rodney G. Leffler · Leffler & Hyland · http://www.lefflerhyland.com · 4163 Chain Bridge Road · Fairfax, VA 22030-4102 · 703-293-9300

Jonathan Shapiro · ⑩ · Greenspun, Davis & Leary · 3955 Chain Bridge Road, Second Floor · Fairfax, VA 22030 · 703-352-0100

Harrisonburg

A. Gene Hart, Jr. · A. Gene Hart, Jr. · 71 Court Square, Suite B · Harrisonburg, VA 22801-3720 · 540-434-9595

Norfolk

James O. Broccoletti · Zoby & Broccoletti · http://www.zobybroccoletti.com · 6663 Stoney Point South · Norfolk, VA 23502 · 757-466-0750

Andrew M. Sacks · ⑩ · Sacks & Sacks · Town Point Center, Suite 501 · 150 Boush Street · Norfolk, VA 23510-1615 · 757-623-2753

Stanley E. Sacks · ㉕ · Sacks & Sacks · Town Point Center, Suite 501 · 150 Boush Street · Norfolk, VA 23510-1615 · 757-623-2753

Richmond

Craig S. Cooley · Craig S. Cooley · 3000 Idlewood Avenue · Richmond, VA 23221 · 804-358-2328

Murray J. Janus · ㉕ · Bremner, Janus & Stone · 701 East Franklin Street, Suite 1500 · P.O. Box 826 · Richmond, VA 23219 · 804-643-1400

Roanoke

William H. Cleaveland · William H. Cleaveland · 40 British Woods Drive, Suite 101 · Roanoke, VA 24019 · 540-591-5959

David J. Damico · David J. Damico · 313 Campbell Avenue, SW · P.O. Box 1578 · Roanoke, VA 24007 · 540-343-0888

Raphael E. Ferris · Ferris, Eakin & Thomas · 22 Luck Avenue · P.O. Box 1791 · Roanoke, VA 24008-1791 · 540-344-3233

Robert F. Rider · ⑳ · Robert F. Rider · 24 East Church Avenue, Suite 204 · P.O. Box 773 · Roanoke, VA 24004 · 540-767-1717

Virginia Beach

Robert G. Morecock · ⑩ · Shuttleworth, Ruloff, Swain, Haddad & Morecock · http://www.srgslaw.com · Southport Centre, Suite 300 · 4525 South Boulevard · Virginia Beach, VA 23452-1137 · 757-671-6000

Thomas B. Shuttleworth II · ⑩ · Shuttleworth, Ruloff, Swain, Haddad & Morecock · http://www.srgslaw.com · Southport Centre, Suite 300 · 4525 South Boulevard · Virginia Beach, VA 23452-1137 · 757-671-6000

Stephen C. Swain · ⑩ · Shuttleworth, Ruloff, Swain, Haddad & Morecock · http://www.srgslaw.com · Southport Centre, Suite 300 · 4525 South Boulevard · Virginia Beach, VA 23452-1137 · 757-671-6000

Lawrence H. Woodward, Jr. · Shuttleworth, Ruloff, Swain, Haddad & Morecock · http://www.srgslaw.com · Southport Centre, Suite 300 · 4525 South Boulevard · Virginia Beach, VA 23452-1137 · 757-671-6000

Warrenton

Blair D. Howard · ⑩ · Howard, Morrison, Howard & Whelan · 31 Garrett Street · Warrenton, VA 20186 · 540-349-1155

OIL & GAS LAW

Roanoke

Scott J. Sexton · Gentry Locke Rakes & Moore · http://www.gentrylocke.com · 10 Franklin Road, SE · P.O. Box 40013 · Roanoke, VA 24022-0013 · 540-983-9300

PERSONAL INJURY LITIGATION

Alexandria

Michele Bartoli Cain · Bartoli Cain Law · Firehouse Square, Suite 350 · 908 King Street · Alexandria, VA 22314 · 703-548-3577

Thomas J. Curcio · Law Office of Thomas J. Curcio · http://www.curciolaw.com · 707 Prince Street · Alexandria, VA 22314 · 703-751-4222

Gary A. Godard · Miller & Associates · 105 North Alfred Street · Alexandria, VA 22314 · 703-519-8080

Brian H. Rhatigan · LeClair Ryan · 225 Reinekers Lane, Suite 700 · Alexandria, VA 22314 · 703-684-8007

Annandale

Robert H. Hovis III · ⑩ · Robert H. Hovis, III · 4544 John Marr Drive · Annandale, VA 22003 · 703-642-5800

Arlington

William E. Artz · ⑩ · William E. Artz · 1700 North Moore Street, Suite 1010 · Arlington, VA 22209 · 703-243-3500

Charlottesville

Thomas E. Albro · ⑩ · Tremblay & Smith · http://www.tremblaysmith.com · 105-109 East High Street · P.O. Box 1585 · Charlottesville, VA 22902 · 434-977-4455

L. B. Chandler, Jr. · ㉕ · The Chandler Law Group · http://www.chandlerlawgroup.com · Ednam Professional Center, Suite 100 · 1010 Ednam Center · P.O. Box 6747 · Charlottesville, VA 22903 · 434-971-7273

J. Brian Jackson · McGuireWoods · http://www.mcguirewoods.com · Court Square Building, Suite 300 · 310 Fourth Street, NE · P.O. Box 1288 · Charlottesville, VA 22902-1288 · 434-977-2500

Edward R. Slaughter, Jr. · ⑩ · Michie Hamlett Lowry Rasmussen & Tweel · 500 Court Square, Suite 300 · P.O. Box 298 · Charlottesville, VA 22902-0298 · 434-951-7200

M. Bryan Slaughter · Michie Hamlett Lowry Rasmussen & Tweel · 500 Court Square, Suite 300 · P.O. Box 298 · Charlottesville, VA 22902-0298 · 434-951-7200

Christine Thomson · Michie Hamlett Lowry Rasmussen & Tweel · 500 Court Square, Suite 300 · P.O. Box 298 · Charlottesville, VA 22902-0298 · 434-951-7200

R. Craig Wood · ⑩ · McGuireWoods · http://www.mcguirewoods.com · Court Square Building, Suite 300 310 Fourth Street, NE · P.O. Box 1288 · Charlottesville, VA 22902-1288 · 434-977-2500

H. Robert Yates III · LeClair Ryan · 123 East Main Street, Suite 800 · Charlottesville, VA 22902 · 434-245-3444

John W. Zunka · ⑳ · Zunka, Milnor, Carter & Inigo · 414 Park Street · P.O. Box 1567 · Charlottesville, VA 22902 · 434-977-0191

Christiansburg

Edwin C. Stone · ⑩ · Stone & Kellerman · 304 Roanoke Street · P.O. Box 6123 · Christiansburg, VA 24068 · 540-381-9082

Danville

James A. L. Daniel · ⑩ · Daniel, Medley & Kirby · 110 North Union Street · P.O. Box 720 · Danville, VA 24543 · 434-792-3911

Glen W. Pulley · Clement & Wheatley · 549 Main Street · P.O. Box 8200 · Danville, VA 24543-8200 · 434-793-8200

Fairfax

Stephen L. Altman · Hamilton Altman Canale & Dillon · 10306 Eaton Place, Suite 200 · Fairfax, VA 22030 · 703-591-9700

Gary W. Brown · McCandlish & Lillard · 11350 Random Hills Road, Suite 500 · Fairfax, VA 22030-7429 · 703-273-2288

Peter S. Everett · ⑩ · Blankingship & Keith · http://www.blankingship-keith-law.com · 4020 University Drive, Suite 300 · Fairfax, VA 22030 · 703-691-1235

Benjamin W. Glass III · Benjamin W. Glass III · 3915 Old Lee Highway, Suite 22-B · Fairfax, VA 22030 · 703-591-9829

Edward H. Grove III · Brault, Palmer, Grove, White & Steinhilber · 3554 Chain Bridge Road, Suite 400 · Fairfax, VA 22030 · 703-273-6400

R. Craig Jennings · ⑩ · Jennings & Porter · 3915 Old Lee Highway, Suite 22-B · Fairfax, VA 22030 · 703-359-8620

Rodney G. Leffler · Leffler & Hyland · http://www.lefflerhyland.com · 4163 Chain Bridge Road · Fairfax, VA 22030-4102 · 703-293-9300

Thomas C. Palmer, Jr. · ⑳ · Brault, Palmer, Grove, White & Steinhilber · 3554 Chain Bridge Road, Suite 400 · Fairfax, VA 22030 · 703-273-6400

Thomas G. Smith · Shevlin & Smith · 3975 University Drive, Suite 405 · Fairfax, VA 22030 · 703-591-0067

Tina L. Snee · Tina L. Snee & Associates · 9401 Lee Highway, Suite 206 · Fairfax, VA 22031 · 703-352-8833

Robert J. Stoney · Blankingship & Keith · http://www.blankingship-keith-law.com · 4020 University Drive, Suite 300 · Fairfax, VA 22030 · 703-691-1235

Mark A. Towery · Blankingship & Keith · http://www.blankingship-keith-law.com · 4020 University Drive, Suite 300 · Fairfax, VA 22030 · 703-691-1235

Fredericksburg

John P. Harris III · ⑩ · Harris and Harris · 1619 Jefferson Davis Highway · Fredericksburg, VA 22401 · 540-371-4941

Glen Allen

Michael L. Goodman · Goodman, Allen & Filetti · http://www.goodmanallen.com · 4501 Highwoods Parkway, Suite 210 · Glen Allen, VA 23060 · 804-346-0600

Mary M.H. Priddy · Goodman, Allen & Filetti · http://www.goodmanallen.com · 4501 Highwoods Parkway, Suite 210 · Glen Allen, VA 23060 · 804-346-0600

Great Falls

Thomas P. Mains, Jr. · ㉕ · The Law Offices of Thomas P. Mains, Jr. · P.O. Box 1241 · Great Falls, VA 22066 · 703-757-2900

Hampton

Stephen H. Pitler · Joseph Smith · 2100 Kecoughtan Road · Hampton, VA 23661-0437 · 757-244-7000

Howard P. Smith · Joseph Smith · 2100 Kecoughtan Road · Hampton, VA 23661-0437 · 757-244-7000

Stephen M. Smith · ⑩ · The Brain Injury Law Center · http://www.brain-injury-law-center.com · Smith Building · 2100 Kecoughtan Road · P.O. Box 1437 · Hampton, VA 23661-0437 · 757-244-7000

Harrisonburg

Daniel L. Fitch · Wharton, Aldhizer & Weaver · 100 South Mason Street · P.O. Box 20028 · Harrisonburg, VA 22801-7528 · 540-434-0316

Charles F. Hilton · Wharton, Aldhizer & Weaver · 100 South Mason Street · P.O. Box 20028 · Harrisonburg, VA 22801-7528 · 540-434-0316

David A. Penrod · Hoover Penrod · 342 South Main Street · Harrisonburg, VA 22801 · 540-433-2444

Lorton

James K. Fitzpatrick · Fitzpatrick Law Offices · 8709 Bitterroot Court · Lorton, VA 22079 · 703-690-7557

Louisa

Charles F. Purcell · ⑩ · Purcell & Purcell · Purcell Building · 103 Elm Avenue · P.O. Box 126 · Louisa, VA 23093 · 540-967-2225

Lynchburg

John R. Alford, Jr. · ⑩ · Caskie & Frost · 2306 Atherholt Road · P.O. Box 6360 · Lynchburg, VA 24505 · 434-846-2731

Martinsville

Robert W. Mann · ⑩ · Young, Haskins, Mann, Gregory, McGarry & Wall · 400 Starling Avenue · P.O. Box 72 · Martinsville, VA 24114 · 276-638-2367

McLean

John J. Brandt · ⑳ · Wilson Elser Moskowitz Edelman & Dicker · 8444 Westpark Drive, Suite 510 · McLean, VA 22102-5102 · 703-245-9300

Harvey B. Cohen · ⑩ · Miles & Stockbridge · http://www.milesstockbridge.com · 1751 Pinnacle Drive, Suite 500 · McLean, VA 22102 · 703-903-9000

Newport News

H. Duncan Garnett, Jr. · ⑩ · Patten, Wornom, Hatten & Diamonstein · 12350 Jefferson Avenue, Suite 300 · Newport News, VA 23602 · 757-223-4500

Robert R. Hatten · ⑩ · Patten, Wornom, Hatten & Diamonstein · 12350 Jefferson Avenue, Suite 300 · Newport News, VA 23602 · 757-223-4500

Donald N. Patten · Patten, Wornom, Hatten & Diamonstein · 12350 Jefferson Avenue, Suite 300 · Newport News, VA 23602 · 757-223-4500

Avery T. Waterman, Jr. · Patten, Wornom, Hatten & Diamonstein · 12350 Jefferson Avenue, Suite 300 · Newport News, VA 23602 · 757-223-4500

Norfok

Richard J. Serpe · Richard J. Serpe · 580 East Main Street, Suite 310 · Norfok, VA 23510 · 757-233-0009

Norfolk

Stanley G. Barr, Jr. · ⑳ · Kaufman & Canoles · 150 West Main Street, Suite 2100 · P.O. Box 3037 · Norfolk, VA 23514-3037 · 757-624-3000

Allen W. Beasley · Breeden Salb Beasley & DuVall · 555 East Main Street, Suite 1210 · Norfolk, VA 23510 · 757-622-1111

Bruce T. Bishop · ⑩ · Willcox & Savage · One Commercial Place, Suite 1800 · Norfolk, VA 23510 · 757-628-5500

R. Barrow Blackwell · Kaufman & Canoles · 150 West Main Street, Suite 2100 · P.O. Box 3037 · Norfolk, VA 23514-3037 · 757-624-3000

Jeffrey A. Breit · ⑩ · Breit, Drescher & Imprevento · 1000 Dominion Tower · 999 Waterside Drive · Norfolk, VA 23510-3320 · 757-622-6000

James E. Brydges, Jr. · ⑩ · Taylor and Walker · 555 Main Street, Suite 1300 · P.O. Box 3490 · Norfolk, VA 23510 · 757-625-7300

Richard J. Cromwell · McGuireWoods · http://www.mcguirewoods.com · World Trade Center, Suite 9000 · 101 West Main Street · Norfolk, VA 23510-1655 · 757-640-3700

Guy E. Daugherty · ㉕ · Howell, Daugherty & Brown · One East Plume Street, Fourth Floor · P.O. Box 3929 · Norfolk, VA 23514-3929 · 757-623-7334

John W. Drescher · ⑩ · Breit, Drescher & Imprevento · 1000 Dominion Tower · 999 Waterside Drive · Norfolk, VA 23510-3320 · 757-622-6000

Randolph C. DuVall · Breeden Salb Beasley & DuVall · 555 East Main Street, Suite 1210 · Norfolk, VA 23510 · 757-622-1111

Oscar L. Gilbert · ⑩ · Gilbert & Albiston · Crown Centre, Suite 330 · 580 East Main Street · Norfolk, VA 23510 · 757-625-1188

Richard S. Glasser · ⑳ · Glasser and Glasser · Crown Center, Suite 600 · 580 East Main Street · Norfolk, VA 23510 · 757-625-6787

John A. Heilig · ⑳ · The Heilig Firm · Halifax Building, Suite 325 · 6161 Kempsville Circle · Norfolk, VA 23503 · 757-461-1300

Lisa P. O'Donnell · Bertini O'Donnell & Hammer · http://www.bohlaw.net · 999 Waterside Drive, Suite 1010 · Norfolk, VA 23510 · 757-670-3868

Anita O. Poston · ⑩ · Vandeventer Black · 500 World Trade Center, Suite 500 · 101 West Main Street · Norfolk, VA 23510 · 757-446-8600

Alan B. Rashkind · ⑩ · Furniss, Davis, Rashkind and Saunders · Smithfield Building, Suite 341-B · 6160 Kempsville Circle · P.O. Box 12525 · Norfolk, VA 23541-0525 · 757-461-7100

Andrew M. Sacks · ⑩ · Sacks & Sacks · Town Point Center, Suite 501 · 150 Boush Street · Norfolk, VA 23510-1615 · 757-623-2753

Stanley E. Sacks · 25 · Sacks & Sacks · Town Point Center, Suite 501 · 150 Boush Street · Norfolk, VA 23510-1615 · 757-623-2753

T. Jeffrey Salb · Breeden Salb Beasley & DuVall · 555 East Main Street, Suite 1210 · Norfolk, VA 23510 · 757-622-1111

Richard A. Saunders · 10 · Furniss, Davis, Rashkind and Saunders · Smithfield Building, Suite 341-B · 6160 Kempsville Circle · P.O. Box 12525 · Norfolk, VA 23541-0525 · 757-461-7100

Gregory N. Stillman · 10 · Hunton & Williams · 500 East Main Street, Suite 1000 · P.O. Box 3889 · Norfolk, VA 23514 · 757-640-5300

Portsmouth

Keith H. Bangel · Bangel, Bangel & Bangel · 505 Court Street · P.O. Box 760 · Portsmouth, VA 23705 · 757-397-3471

Willard J. Moody, Sr. · Moody, Strople, Kloeppel, Basilone & Higginbotham · 500 Crawford Street, Suite 300 · P.O. Box 1138 · Portsmouth, VA 23705 · 757-393-4093

Pulaski

Gary C. Hancock · Gilmer, Sadler, Ingram, Sutherland & Hutton · Midtown Professional Office Building 65 East Main Street · P.O. Box 878 · Pulaski, VA 24301-0878 · 540-980-1360

Robert J. Ingram, Sr. · 20 · Gilmer, Sadler, Ingram, Sutherland & Hutton · Midtown Professional Office Building · 65 East Main Street · P.O. Box 878 · Pulaski, VA 24301-0878 · 540-980-1360

Reston

Robert T. Hall · 25 · Hall, Sickels, Frei & Mims · http://www.hallandsickels.com · 12120 Sunset Hills Road, Suite 150 · Reston, VA 20190 · 703-925-0500

Gary B. Mims · Hall, Sickels, Frei & Mims · http://www.hallandsickels.com · 12120 Sunset Hills Road, Suite 150 · Reston, VA 20190 · 703-925-0500

Richmond

George E. Allen III · 20 · Allen, Allen, Allen & Allen · http://www.allenandallen.com · 1809 Staples Mill Road · P.O. Box 6855 · Richmond, VA 23230 · 804-353-1200

W. Coleman Allen, Jr. · 10 · Allen, Allen, Allen & Allen · http://www.allenandallen.com · 1809 Staples Mill Road · P.O. Box 6855 · Richmond, VA 23230 · 804-353-1200

Stephen D. Busch · McGuireWoods · http://www.mcguirewoods.com · One James Center · 901 East Cary Street · Richmond, VA 23219-4030 · 804-775-1000

Irvin V. Cantor · Cantor Arkema · Bank of America Center · 1111 East Main Street · P.O. Box 561 · Richmond, VA 23218-0561 · 804-644-1400

Frank N. Cowan · 20 · CowanGates · 1930 Huguenot Road · P.O. Box 35655 · Richmond, VA 23235-0655 804-320-9100

John D. Epps · Hunton & Williams · Riverfront Plaza, East Tower · 951 East Byrd Street · Richmond, VA 23219-4074 · 804-788-8200

P. Christopher Guedri · 10 · Allen, Allen, Allen & Allen · http://www.allenandallen.com · 1809 Staples Mill Road · P.O. Box 6855 · Richmond, VA 23230 · 804-353-1200

Warren David Harless · ⑩ · Christian & Barton · Mutual Building, Suite 1200 · 909 East Main Street · Richmond, VA 23219-3095 · 804-697-4100

Michael E. Harman · Harman, Claytor, Corrigan & Wellman · 4951 Lake Brook Drive, Suite 100 · P.O. Box 70280 · Richmond, VA 23255 · 804-747-5200

Edward F. Johnson, Jr. · Hundley & Johnson · 5501 Staples Mill Road · P.O. Box 28057 · Richmond, VA 23228-0057 · 804-262-9000

William H. King, Jr. · ㉕ · McGuireWoods · http://www.mcguirewoods.com · One James Center · 901 East Cary Street · Richmond, VA 23219-4030 · 804-775-1000

David Craig Landin · ㉕ · Hunton & Williams · Riverfront Plaza, East Tower · 951 East Byrd Street · Richmond, VA 23219-4074 · 804-788-8200

Charles G. Meyer III · LeClair Ryan · 951 East Byrd Street, Eighth Floor · P.O. Box 2499 · Richmond, VA 23218-2499 · 804-783-2003

James W. Morris III · ㉕ · Morris & Morris · Wytestone Plaza, 12th Floor · 801 East Main Street · P.O. Box 30 · Richmond, VA 23218 · 804-344-8300

Philip B. Morris · ⑩ · Morris & Morris · Wytestone Plaza, 12th Floor · 801 East Main Street · P.O. Box 30 Richmond, VA 23218 · 804-344-8300

Matthew B. Murray · ⑩ · Allen, Allen, Allen & Allen · http://www.allenandallen.com · 1809 Staples Mill Road · P.O. Box 6855 · Richmond, VA 23230 · 804-353-1200

John H. OBrion, Jr. · ⑳ · The McCammon Group · Bank of America Center, Suite 1700 · 1111 East Main Street · Richmond, VA 23219 · 804-343-0922

Rosewell Page III · ㉕ · McGuireWoods · http://www.mcguirewoods.com · One James Center · 901 East Cary Street · Richmond, VA 23219-4030 · 804-775-1000

Russell V. Palmore · Troutman Sanders · Troutman Sanders Building · 1001 Haxall Point · P.O. Box 1122 Richmond, VA 23218-1122 · 804-697-1200

James C. Roberts · ㉕ · Troutman Sanders · Troutman Sanders Building · 1001 Haxall Point · P.O. Box 1122 · Richmond, VA 23218-1122 · 804-697-1200

Deborah M. Russell · McGuireWoods · http://www.mcguirewoods.com · One James Center · 901 East Cary Street · Richmond, VA 23219-4030 · 804-775-1000

Edward E. Scher · Law Office of Edward Scher · http://www.severeinjurylaw.com · 3810 Augusta Avenue Richmond, VA 23230 · 804-421-6000

James C. Shannon · Midkiff, Muncie & Ross · 9030 Stony Point Parkway, Suite 160 · Richmond, VA 23235 · 804-560-9600

John C. Shea · Marks & Harrison · 1500 Forest Avenue · P.O. Box 72020 · Richmond, VA 23255-2020 · 804-282-0999

Thomas G. Slater, Jr. · ⑩ · Hunton & Williams · Riverfront Plaza, East Tower · 951 East Byrd Street · Richmond, VA 23219-4074 · 804-788-8200

Samuel L. Tarry, Jr. · McGuireWoods · http://www.mcguirewoods.com · One James Center · 901 East Cary Street · Richmond, VA 23219-4030 · 804-775-1000

William N. Watkins · Sands, Anderson, Marks & Miller · http://www.sandsanderson.com · 801 East Main Street, Suite 1800 · P.O. Box 1998 · Richmond, VA 23218-1998 · 804-648-1636

Thomas W. Williamson, Jr. · (20) · Williamson & Lavecchia · http://www.wllc.com · 6800 Paragon Place, Suite 233 · Richmond, VA 23230-1652 · 804-288-1661

Roanoke

Phillip V. Anderson · Frith, Anderson & Peake · http://www.faplawfirm.com · 29 Franklin Road, SW · P.O. Box 1240 · Roanoke, VA 24006-1240 · 540-772-4600

J. Rudy Austin · (10) · Gentry Locke Rakes & Moore · http://www.gentrylocke.com · 10 Franklin Road, SE P.O. Box 40013 · Roanoke, VA 24022-0013 · 540-983-9300

Ronald M. Ayers · (10) · Johnson, Ayers & Matthews · First Campbell Square, Suite 300 · 210 First Street, SW · P.O. Box 2200 · Roanoke, VA 24009-2200 · 540-767-2000

David B. Carson · Johnson, Ayers & Matthews · First Campbell Square, Suite 300 · 210 First Street, SW · P.O. Box 2200 · Roanoke, VA 24009-2200 · 540-767-2000

C. Richard Cranwell · (10) · Cranwell, Moore & Emick · P.O. Box 11804 · Roanoke, VA 24022 · 540-344-1000

T. Daniel Frith III · Frith Law Firm · 303 Washington Avenue, SW · Roanoke, VA 24016 · 540-985-0098

David B. Hart · (20) · Wooten Hart · 707 South Jefferson Street, Suite 300 · P.O. Box 12247 · Roanoke, VA 24024 · 540-343-2451

James W. Jennings, Jr. · (10) · Woods Rogers · http://www.woodsrogers.com · Wachovia Tower, Suite 1400 10 South Jefferson Street · P.O. Box 14125 · Roanoke, VA 24038-4125 · 540-983-7600

John T. Jessee · LeClair Ryan · 1800 Wachovia Tower · P.O. Drawer 1200 · Roanoke, VA 24006 · 540-510-3000

John E. Lichtenstein · Lichtenstein Fishwick & Johnson · Liberty Trust Building, Suite 400 · 101 South Jefferson Street · P.O. Box 601 · Roanoke, VA 24004-0601 · 540-343-9711

Joseph A. Matthews, Jr. · (10) · Johnson, Ayers & Matthews · First Campbell Square, Suite 300 · 210 First Street, SW · P.O. Box 2200 · Roanoke, VA 24009-2200 · 540-767-2000

S. D. Roberts Moore · (20) · Gentry Locke Rakes & Moore · http://www.gentrylocke.com · 10 Franklin Road, SE · P.O. Box 40013 · Roanoke, VA 24022-0013 · 540-983-9300

G. Marshall Mundy · (20) · Mundy, Rogers & Associates · 1328 Third Street, SW · P.O. Box 2240 · Roanoke, VA 24009 · 540-982-2900

Walter H. Peake III · Frith, Anderson & Peake · http://www.faplawfirm.com · 29 Franklin Road, SW · P.O. Box 1240 · Roanoke, VA 24006-1240 · 540-772-4600

William B. Poff · (25) · Woods Rogers · http://www.woodsrogers.com · Wachovia Tower, Suite 1400 · 10 South Jefferson Street · P.O. Box 14125 · Roanoke, VA 24038-4125 · 540-983-7600

Frank W. Rogers III · Mundy, Rogers & Associates · 1328 Third Street, SW · P.O. Box 2240 · Roanoke, VA 24009 · 540-982-2900

William P. Wallace, Jr. · Johnson, Ayers & Matthews · First Campbell Square, Suite 300 · 210 First Street, SW · P.O. Box 2200 · Roanoke, VA 24009-2200 · 540-767-2000

Rustburg

Thomas L. Phillips, Jr. · Phillips, Morrison, Johnson & Ferrell · 12576 Wards Road · Rustburg, VA 24588 434-821-5022

Salem

P. Brent Brown · ⑩ · Brown & Jennings · 223 East Main Street · Salem, VA 24153-3841 · 540-444-4010

Staunton

Thomas G. Bell, Jr. · ⑩ · Timberlake, Smith, Thomas & Moses · The Virginia Building · 25 North Central Avenue · P.O. Box 108 · Staunton, VA 24402-0108 · 540-885-1517

P. Donald Moses · ⑩ · Timberlake, Smith, Thomas & Moses · The Virginia Building · 25 North Central Avenue · P.O. Box 108 · Staunton, VA 24402-0108 · 540-885-1517

J. Ross Newell III · Timberlake, Smith, Thomas & Moses · The Virginia Building · 25 North Central Avenue · P.O. Box 108 · Staunton, VA 24402-0108 · 540-885-1517

C. J. Steuart Thomas III · Timberlake, Smith, Thomas & Moses · The Virginia Building · 25 North Central Avenue · P.O. Box 108 · Staunton, VA 24402-0108 · 540-885-1517

Colin J. S. Thomas, Jr. · ⑳ · Timberlake, Smith, Thomas & Moses · The Virginia Building · 25 North Central Avenue · P.O. Box 108 · Staunton, VA 24402-0108 · 540-885-1517

Virginia Beach

Robert J. Haddad · ⑩ · Shuttleworth, Ruloff, Swain, Haddad & Morecock · http://www.srgslaw.com · Southport Centre, Suite 300 · 4525 South Boulevard · Virginia Beach, VA 23452-1137 · 757-671-6000

Glen A. Huff · Huff, Poole & Mahoney · 4705 Columbus Street · Virginia Beach, VA 23462-6749 · 757-499-1841

Edwin Jay Rafal · ⑩ · Shuttleworth, Ruloff, Swain, Haddad & Morecock · http://www.srgslaw.com · Southport Centre, Suite 300 · 4525 South Boulevard · Virginia Beach, VA 23452-1137 · 757-671-6000

Robert L. Samuel, Jr. · Williams Mullen · http://www.williamsmullen.com · 222 Central Park Avenue, Suite 1700 · Virginia Beach, VA 23462-3035 · 757-499-8800

Thomas B. Shuttleworth II · ⑩ · Shuttleworth, Ruloff, Swain, Haddad & Morecock · http://www.srgslaw.com · Southport Centre, Suite 300 · 4525 South Boulevard · Virginia Beach, VA 23452-1137 · 757-671-6000

Stephen C. Swain · ⑩ · Shuttleworth, Ruloff, Swain, Haddad & Morecock · http://www.srgslaw.com · Southport Centre, Suite 300 · 4525 South Boulevard · Virginia Beach, VA 23452-1137 · 757-671-6000

Lawrence H. Woodward, Jr. · Shuttleworth, Ruloff, Swain, Haddad & Morecock · http://www.srgslaw.com · Southport Centre, Suite 300 · 4525 South Boulevard · Virginia Beach, VA 23452-1137 · 757-671-6000

Warrenton

Blair D. Howard · ⑩ · Howard, Morrison, Howard & Whelan · 31 Garrett Street · Warrenton, VA 20186 · 540-349-1155

Woodbridge

Charles J. Zauzig III · Nichols, Zauzig & Sandler · 12660 Lake Ridge Drive · Woodbridge, VA 22192 · 703-492-4200

PRIVATE FUNDS LAW

Richmond

Gary D. LeClair · LeClair Ryan · 951 East Byrd Street, Eighth Floor · P.O. Box 2499 · Richmond, VA 23218-2499 · 804-783-2003

PRODUCT LIABILITY LITIGATION

Abingdon

Wade Massie · PennStuart · Virginia House · 208 East Main Street · P.O. Box 2288 · Abingdon, VA 24212-2288 · 276-628-5151

Charlottesville

L. B. Chandler, Jr. · 25 · The Chandler Law Group · http://www.chandlerlawgroup.com · Ednam Professional Center, Suite 100 · 1010 Ednam Center · P.O. Box 6747 · Charlottesville, VA 22903 · 434-971-7273

J. Brian Jackson · McGuireWoods · http://www.mcguirewoods.com · Court Square Building, Suite 300 · 310 Fourth Street, NE · P.O. Box 1288 · Charlottesville, VA 22902-1288 · 434-977-2500

Fairfax

Thomas C. Palmer, Jr. · 20 · Brault, Palmer, Grove, White & Steinhilber · 3554 Chain Bridge Road, Suite 400 · Fairfax, VA 22030 · 703-273-6400

Lorton

James K. Fitzpatrick · Fitzpatrick Law Offices · 8709 Bitterroot Court · Lorton, VA 22079 · 703-690-7557

Norfolk

Gregory N. Stillman · 10 · Hunton & Williams · 500 East Main Street, Suite 1000 · P.O. Box 3889 · Norfolk, VA 23514 · 757-640-5300

Pulaski

Robert J. Ingram, Sr. · 20 · Gilmer, Sadler, Ingram, Sutherland & Hutton · Midtown Professional Office Building · 65 East Main Street · P.O. Box 878 · Pulaski, VA 24301-0878 · 540-980-1360

Richmond

Terrence M. Bagley · McGuireWoods · http://www.mcguirewoods.com · One James Center · 901 East Cary Street · Richmond, VA 23219-4030 · 804-775-1000

Dabney J. Carr IV · Troutman Sanders · Troutman Sanders Building · 1001 Haxall Point · P.O. Box 1122 Richmond, VA 23218-1122 · 804-697-1200

John D. Epps · Hunton & Williams · Riverfront Plaza, East Tower · 951 East Byrd Street · Richmond, VA 23219-4074 · 804-788-8200

Thomas C. Junker · Junker, Taddeo & Sturm PLC · 17 West Cary Street Road · Richmond, VA 23220 · 804-344-8540

William H. King, Jr. · ㉕ · McGuireWoods · http://www.mcguirewoods.com · One James Center · 901 East Cary Street · Richmond, VA 23219-4030 · 804-775-1000

David Craig Landin · ㉕ · Hunton & Williams · Riverfront Plaza, East Tower · 951 East Byrd Street · Richmond, VA 23219-4074 · 804-788-8200

James W. Morris III · ㉕ · Morris & Morris · Wytestone Plaza, 12th Floor · 801 East Main Street · P.O. Box 30 · Richmond, VA 23218 · 804-344-8300

Lonnie D. Nunley III · ⑩ · Hunton & Williams · Riverfront Plaza, East Tower · 951 East Byrd Street · Richmond, VA 23219-4074 · 804-788-8200

John H. OBrion, Jr. · ⑳ · The McCammon Group · Bank of America Center, Suite 1700 · 1111 East Main Street · Richmond, VA 23219 · 804-343-0922

Stephen D. Otero · Troutman Sanders · Troutman Sanders Building · 1001 Haxall Point · P.O. Box 1122 · Richmond, VA 23218-1122 · 804-697-1200

Rosewell Page III · ㉕ · McGuireWoods · http://www.mcguirewoods.com · One James Center · 901 East Cary Street · Richmond, VA 23219-4030 · 804-775-1000

Michael G. Phelan · Butler Williams & Skilling · 100 Shockoe Slip, Fourth Floor · Richmond, VA 23219 · 804-648-4848

Gary J. Spahn · Troutman Sanders · Troutman Sanders Building · 1001 Haxall Point · P.O. Box 1122 · Richmond, VA 23218-1122 · 804-697-1200

Samuel L. Tarry, Jr. · McGuireWoods · http://www.mcguirewoods.com · One James Center · 901 East Cary Street · Richmond, VA 23219-4030 · 804-775-1000

J. Tracy Walker IV · McGuireWoods · http://www.mcguirewoods.com · One James Center · 901 East Cary Street · Richmond, VA 23219-4030 · 804-775-1000

Steven R. Williams · McGuireWoods · http://www.mcguirewoods.com · One James Center · 901 East Cary Street · Richmond, VA 23219-4030 · 804-775-1000

Roanoke

James W. Jennings, Jr. · ⑩ · Woods Rogers · http://www.woodsrogers.com · Wachovia Tower, Suite 1400 10 South Jefferson Street · P.O. Box 14125 · Roanoke, VA 24038-4125 · 540-983-7600

Mark D. Loftis · Woods Rogers · http://www.woodsrogers.com · Wachovia Tower, Suite 1400 · 10 South Jefferson Street · P.O. Box 14125 · Roanoke, VA 24038-4125 · 540-983-7600

William B. Poff · ㉕ · Woods Rogers · http://www.woodsrogers.com · Wachovia Tower, Suite 1400 · 10 South Jefferson Street · P.O. Box 14125 · Roanoke, VA 24038-4125 · 540-983-7600

Salem

P. Brent Brown · ⑩ · Brown & Jennings · 223 East Main Street · Salem, VA 24153-3841 · 540-444-4010

Staunton

Colin J. S. Thomas, Jr. · ⑳ · Timberlake, Smith, Thomas & Moses · The Virginia Building · 25 North Central Avenue · P.O. Box 108 · Staunton, VA 24402-0108 · 540-885-1517

Virginia Beach

Robert J. Haddad · ⑩ · Shuttleworth, Ruloff, Swain, Haddad & Morecock · http://www.srgslaw.com · Southport Centre, Suite 300 · 4525 South Boulevard · Virginia Beach, VA 23452-1137 · 757-671-6000

Glen A. Huff · Huff, Poole & Mahoney · 4705 Columbus Street · Virginia Beach, VA 23462-6749 · 757-499-1841

Thomas B. Shuttleworth II · ⑩ · Shuttleworth, Ruloff, Swain, Haddad & Morecock · http://www.srgslaw.com · Southport Centre, Suite 300 · 4525 South Boulevard · Virginia Beach, VA 23452-1137 · 757-671-6000

Stephen C. Swain · ⑩ · Shuttleworth, Ruloff, Swain, Haddad & Morecock · http://www.srgslaw.com · Southport Centre, Suite 300 · 4525 South Boulevard · Virginia Beach, VA 23452-1137 · 757-671-6000

PROFESSIONAL MALPRACTICE LAW

Fairfax

John O. Easton · Jordan Coyne & Savits · 10509 Judicial Drive, Suite 200 · Fairfax, VA 22030 · 703-246-0900

Thomas C. Palmer, Jr. · ⑳ · Brault, Palmer, Grove, White & Steinhilber · 3554 Chain Bridge Road, Suite 400 · Fairfax, VA 22030 · 703-273-6400

Harrisonburg

Charles F. Hilton · Wharton, Aldhizer & Weaver · 100 South Mason Street · P.O. Box 20028 · Harrisonburg, VA 22801-7528 · 540-434-0316

Marshall H. Ross · Wharton, Aldhizer & Weaver · 100 South Mason Street · P.O. Box 20028 · Harrisonburg, VA 22801-7528 · 540-434-0316

McLean

Thomas L. Appler · ⑩ · Wilson Elser Moskowitz Edelman & Dicker · 8444 Westpark Drive, Suite 510 · McLean, VA 22102-5102 · 703-245-9300

J. Jonathan Schraub · Sands, Anderson, Marks & Miller · http://www.sandsanderson.com · 1497 Chain Bridge Road, Suite 202 · McLean, VA 22101-5728 · 703-893-3600

Richmond

R. Paul Childress, Jr. · McSweeney, Crump, Childress & Gould · 11 South 12th Street · P.O. Box 1463 · Richmond, VA 23218 · 804-783-6800

Douglas P. Rucker, Jr. · Sands, Anderson, Marks & Miller · http://www.sandsanderson.com · 801 East Main Street, Suite 1800 · P.O. Box 1998 · Richmond, VA 23218-1998 · 804-648-1636

Roanoke

D. Stan Barnhill · ⑩ · Woods Rogers · http://www.woodsrogers.com · Wachovia Tower, Suite 1400 · 10 South Jefferson Street · P.O. Box 14125 · Roanoke, VA 24038-4125 · 540-983-7600

David B. Hart · ⑳ · Wooten Hart · 707 South Jefferson Street, Suite 300 · P.O. Box 12247 · Roanoke, VA 24024 · 540-343-2451

Vienna

Bruce E. Titus · Rees Broome · http://www.rbdlaw.com · 8133 Leesburg Pike, Ninth Floor · Vienna, VA 22182 · 703-790-1911

Virginia Beach

Jeffrey H. Gray · Troutman Sanders · 222 Central Park Avenue, Suite 2000 · Virginia Beach, VA 23462 · 757-687-7500

PROJECT FINANCE LAW

Richmond

John J. Beardsworth, Jr. · ⑩ · Hunton & Williams · Riverfront Plaza, East Tower · 951 East Byrd Street Richmond, VA 23219-4074 · 804-788-8200

J. Benjamin English · Hirschler Fleischer · http://www.hirschlerfleischer.com · The Edgeworth Building · 2100 East Cary Street · Richmond, VA 23223-7078 · 804-771-9500

Roanoke

Alton L. Knighton, Jr. · ⑩ · Woods Rogers · http://www.woodsrogers.com · Wachovia Tower, Suite 1400 · 10 South Jefferson Street · P.O. Box 14125 · Roanoke, VA 24038-4125 · 540-983-7600

PUBLIC FINANCE LAW

Harrisonburg

Carolyn Madden Perry · BotkinRose · 3210 Peoples Drive · Harrisonburg, VA 22801 · 540-437-0019

Lynchburg

Theodore J. Craddock · ⑩ · Caskie & Frost · 2306 Atherholt Road · P.O. Box 6360 · Lynchburg, VA 24505 · 434-846-2731

McLean

Lloyd Richardson · McGuireWoods · http://www.mcguirewoods.com · 1750 Tysons Boulevard, Suite 1800 · McLean, VA 22102-4215 · 703-712-5000

Norfolk

George L. Consolvo · Kaufman & Canoles · 150 West Main Street, Suite 2100 · P.O. Box 3037 · Norfolk, VA 23514-3037 · 757-624-3000

Barry W. Hunter · Kaufman & Canoles · 150 West Main Street, Suite 2100 · P.O. Box 3037 · Norfolk, VA 23514-3037 · 757-624-3000

William L. Nusbaum · Williams Mullen · http://www.williamsmullen.com · Dominion Tower, Suite 1700 999 Waterside Drive · Norfolk, VA 23510-3303 · 757-622-3366

Richmond

Arthur E. Anderson II · McGuireWoods · http://www.mcguirewoods.com · One James Center · 901 East Cary Street · Richmond, VA 23219-4030 · 804-775-1000

Eric E. Ballou · Christian & Barton · Mutual Building, Suite 1200 · 909 East Main Street · Richmond, VA 23219-3095 · 804-697-4100

William R. Derry, Jr. · Troutman Sanders · Troutman Sanders Building · 1001 Haxall Point · P.O. Box 1122 · Richmond, VA 23218-1122 · 804-697-1200

Renee B. Fain · McGuireWoods · http://www.mcguirewoods.com · One James Center · 901 East Cary Street · Richmond, VA 23219-4030 · 804-775-1000

Bonnie M. France · McGuireWoods · http://www.mcguirewoods.com · One James Center · 901 East Cary Street · Richmond, VA 23219-4030 · 804-775-1000

Stephen L. Johnson · Troutman Sanders · Troutman Sanders Building · 1001 Haxall Point · P.O. Box 1122 · Richmond, VA 23218-1122 · 804-697-1200

Christopher G. Kulp · Hunton & Williams · Riverfront Plaza, East Tower · 951 East Byrd Street · Richmond, VA 23219-4074 · 804-788-8200

R. Hart Lee · Williams Mullen · http://www.williamsmullen.com · Two James Center · 1021 East Cary Street · P.O. Box 1320 · Richmond, VA 23218-1320 · 804-643-1991

Bryar C. Nettles · Hunton & Williams · Riverfront Plaza, East Tower · 951 East Byrd Street · Richmond, VA 23219-4074 · 804-788-8200

John D. O'Neill, Jr. · Hunton & Williams · Riverfront Plaza, East Tower · 951 East Byrd Street · Richmond, VA 23219-4074 · 804-788-8200

Robert Dean Pope · Hunton & Williams · Riverfront Plaza, East Tower · 951 East Byrd Street · Richmond, VA 23219-4074 · 804-788-8200

David L. Richardson · McGuireWoods · http://www.mcguirewoods.com · One James Center · 901 East Cary Street · Richmond, VA 23219-4030 · 804-775-1000

Charles P. Shimer · Troutman Sanders · Troutman Sanders Building · 1001 Haxall Point · P.O. Box 1122 Richmond, VA 23218-1122 · 804-697-1200

William J. Strickland · McGuireWoods · http://www.mcguirewoods.com · One James Center · 901 East Cary Street · Richmond, VA 23219-4030 · 804-775-1000

Roanoke

George J. A. Clemo · Woods Rogers · http://www.woodsrogers.com · Wachovia Tower, Suite 1400 · 10 South Jefferson Street · P.O. Box 14125 · Roanoke, VA 24038-4125 · 540-983-7600

Harwell M. Darby, Jr. · ⑩ · Glenn, Feldmann, Darby & Goodlatte · 210 First Street, SW, Suite 200 · P.O. Box 2887 · Roanoke, VA 24001-2887 · 540-224-8000

F. B. Webster Day · Spilman Thomas & Battle · http://www.spilmanlaw.com · 310 First Street, Suite 1100 Roanoke, VA 24002 · 540-512-1800

Alton L. Knighton, Jr. · ⑩ · Woods Rogers · http://www.woodsrogers.com · Wachovia Tower, Suite 1400 · 10 South Jefferson Street · P.O. Box 14125 · Roanoke, VA 24038-4125 · 540-983-7600

RAILROAD LAW

Norfolk

Wiley F. Mitchell, Jr. · Willcox & Savage · One Commercial Place, Suite 1800 · Norfolk, VA 23510 · 757-628-5500

Samuel J. Webster · Willcox & Savage · One Commercial Place, Suite 1800 · Norfolk, VA 23510 · 757-628-5500

Portsmouth

Walton Bondurant · Bondurant Law · 706 London Street · Portsmouth, VA 23704 · 757-397-4677

Willard J. Moody, Sr. · Moody, Strople, Kloeppel, Basilone & Higginbotham · 500 Crawford Street, Suite 300 · P.O. Box 1138 · Portsmouth, VA 23705 · 757-393-4093

Richmond

Susan C. Armstrong · Troutman Sanders · Troutman Sanders Building · 1001 Haxall Point · P.O. Box 1122 · Richmond, VA 23218-1122 · 804-697-1200

Roanoke

Bryan Grimes Creasy · Johnson, Ayers & Matthews · First Campbell Square, Suite 300 · 210 First Street, SW · P.O. Box 2200 · Roanoke, VA 24009-2200 · 540-767-2000

James W. Jennings, Jr. · ⑩ · Woods Rogers · http://www.woodsrogers.com · Wachovia Tower, Suite 1400 10 South Jefferson Street · P.O. Box 14125 · Roanoke, VA 24038-4125 · 540-983-7600

Virginia Beach

Francis P. Hajek · Shapiro, Cooper, Lewis & Appleton · 1294 Diamond Springs Road · Virginia Beach, VA 23455 · 757-460-7776

REAL ESTATE LAW

Alexandria

David S. Mercer · MercerTrigiani · 112 South Alfred Street · Alexandria, VA 22314 · 703-837-5000

Anne K. Planning · Spartin Planning · 1421 Prince Street, Suite 400 · Alexandria, VA 22314 · 703-740-4572

Debbie B. Spartin · Spartin Planning · 1421 Prince Street, Suite 400 · Alexandria, VA 22314 · 703-740-4572

Lucia Anna Trigiani · MercerTrigiani · 112 South Alfred Street · Alexandria, VA 22314 · 703-837-5000

Arlington

Jonathan C. Kinney · Bean, Kinney & Korman · http://www.beankinney.com · 2300 Wilson Boulevard, Suite 700 · Arlington, VA 22201 · 703-525-4000

Martin D. Walsh · 10 · Walsh, Colucci, Lubeley, Emrich & Terpak · Courthouse Plaza, Thirteenth Floor · 2200 Clarendon Boulevard · Arlington, VA 22201-3359 · 703-528-4700

Charlottesville

Steven W. Blaine · LeClair Ryan · 123 East Main Street, Suite 800 · Charlottesville, VA 22902 · 434-245-3444

Richard E. Carter · 10 · Zunka, Milnor, Carter & Inigo · 414 Park Street · P.O. Box 1567 · Charlottesville, VA 22902 · 434-977-0191

James P. Cox III · Michie Hamlett Lowry Rasmussen & Tweel · 500 Court Square, Suite 300 · P.O. Box 298 · Charlottesville, VA 22902-0298 · 434-951-7200

Ralph L. Feil · 10 · Feil, Pettit and Williams · 530 East Main Street · P.O. Box 2057 · Charlottesville, VA 22902-2057 · 434-979-1400

Robert J. Kroner · 10 · Scott Kroner · 418 East Water Street · P.O. Box 2737 · Charlottesville, VA 22902 · 434-296-2161

John V. Little · 10 · Michie Hamlett Lowry Rasmussen & Tweel · 500 Court Square, Suite 300 · P.O. Box 298 · Charlottesville, VA 22902-0298 · 434-951-7200

George B. McCallum III · 10 · McCallum & Kudravetz · 250 East High Street · Charlottesville, VA 22902 434-293-8191

Joseph W. Richmond, Jr. · 10 · Richmond & Fishburne · Queen Charlotte Square · 214 East High Street Charlottesville, VA 22902 · 434-977-8590

Fairfax

A. Hugo Blankingship, Jr. · 25 · Blankingship & Keith · http://www.blankingship-keith-law.com · 4020 University Drive, Suite 300 · Fairfax, VA 22030 · 703-691-1235

John H. Rust III · 10 · Rust & Rust · 10370 Main Street · P.O. Box 460 · Fairfax, VA 22038 · 703-273-0583

Falls Church

Bruce L. Christman · 10 · Reed Smith · 3110 Fairview Park Drive, Suite 1400 · P.O. Box 12001 · Falls Church, VA 22042 · 703-641-4200

Raymond J. Diaz · Whiteford, Taylor & Preston · http://www.wtplaw.com · 3190 Fairview Park Drive, Suite 300 · Falls Church, VA 22042 · 703-573-0351

Grayson P. Hanes · 20 · Reed Smith · 3110 Fairview Park Drive, Suite 1400 · P.O. Box 12001 · Falls Church, VA 22042 · 703-641-4200

Harrisonburg

Glenn M. Hodge · Wharton, Aldhizer & Weaver · 100 South Mason Street · P.O. Box 20028 · Harrisonburg, VA 22801-7528 · 540-434-0316

McLean

Francis A. McDermott · 10 · Hunton & Williams · 1751 Pinnacle Drive, Suite 1700 · McLean, VA 22102 · 703-714-7400

Stuart Mendelsohn · Holland & Knight · http://www.hklaw.com · 1600 Tysons Boulevard, Suite 700 · McLean, VA 22102 · 703-720-8600

David L. Miller · Pillsbury Winthrop Shaw Pittman · http://www.pillsburylaw.com · 1650 Tysons Boulevard, 14th Floor · McLean, VA 22102-4859 · 703-905-2000

Jonathan P. Rak · McGuireWoods · http://www.mcguirewoods.com · 1750 Tysons Boulevard, Suite 1800 McLean, VA 22102-4215 · 703-712-5000

Newport News

Joseph H. Latchum, Jr. · Williams Mullen · http://www.williamsmullen.com · Fountain Plaza Three, Suite 200 · 721 Lakefront Commons · Newport News, VA 23606-3324 · 757-249-5100

Norfolk

Robert L. Dewey · ⑩ · Willcox & Savage · One Commercial Place, Suite 1800 · Norfolk, VA 23510 · 757-628-5500

H. David Embree · Williams Mullen · http://www.williamsmullen.com · Dominion Tower, Suite 1700 · 999 Waterside Drive · Norfolk, VA 23510-3303 · 757-622-3366

Howard E. Gordon · ⑩ · Williams Mullen · http://www.williamsmullen.com · Dominion Tower, Suite 1700 · 999 Waterside Drive · Norfolk, VA 23510-3303 · 757-622-3366

Thomas G. Johnson, Jr. · ⑩ · Willcox & Savage · One Commercial Place, Suite 1800 · Norfolk, VA 23510 · 757-628-5500

Howard W. Martin, Jr. · Crenshaw, Ware & Martin · 1200 Bank of America Center · One Commercial Place · Norfolk, VA 23510-2111 · 757-623-3000

Stephen R. Romine · LeClair Ryan · 999 Waterside Drive, Suite 2525 · Norfolk, VA 23510 · 757-624-1454

Anthony M. Thiel · Willcox & Savage · One Commercial Place, Suite 1800 · Norfolk, VA 23510 · 757-628-5500

Jay F. Wilks · ㉕ · Wilks, Alper & Harwood · Town Point Center, Suite 700 · 150 Boush Street · Norfolk, VA 23510-1637 · 757-623-6500

Mark D. Williamson · McGuireWoods · http://www.mcguirewoods.com · World Trade Center, Suite 9000 101 West Main Street · Norfolk, VA 23510-1655 · 757-640-3700

Prince William

John H. Foote · ⑩ · Walsh, Colucci, Lubeley, Emrich & Terpak · 4310 Prince William Parkway, Suite 300 · Prince William, VA 22192 · 703-680-4664

Michael D. Lubeley · Walsh, Colucci, Lubeley, Emrich & Terpak · 4310 Prince William Parkway, Suite 300 · Prince William, VA 22192 · 703-680-4664

Reston

Antonio J. Calabrese · Cooley Godward Kronish · One Freedom Square · Reston Town Center · 11951 Freedom Drive · Reston, VA 20190-5656 · 703-456-8000

Michael Horwatt · ⑩ · The Law Office of Michael Horwatt · 11710 Plaza America Drive, Suite 2000 · Reston, VA 20190 · 703-689-3800

John G. Lavoie · Cooley Godward Kronish · One Freedom Square · Reston Town Center · 11951 Freedom Drive · Reston, VA 20190-5656 · 703-456-8000

John H. Toole · Cooley Godward Kronish · One Freedom Square · Reston Town Center · 11951 Freedom Drive · Reston, VA 20190-5656 · 703-456-8000

Richmond

David F. Belkowitz · Hirschler Fleischer · http://www.hirschlerfleischer.com · The Edgeworth Building · 2100 East Cary Street · Richmond, VA 23223-7078 · 804-771-9500

Michael C. Buseck · Williams Mullen · http://www.williamsmullen.com · Two James Center · 1021 East Cary Street · P.O. Box 1320 · Richmond, VA 23218-1320 · 804-643-1991

John V. Cogbill III · ⑩ · McGuireWoods · http://www.mcguirewoods.com · One James Center · 901 East Cary Street · Richmond, VA 23219-4030 · 804-775-1000

David S. Cohn · ⑩ · Troutman Sanders · Troutman Sanders Building · 1001 Haxall Point · P.O. Box 1122 Richmond, VA 23218-1122 · 804-697-1200

Andrew M. Condlin · Williams Mullen · http://www.williamsmullen.com · Two James Center · 1021 East Cary Street · P.O. Box 1320 · Richmond, VA 23218-1320 · 804-643-1991

Paul H. Davenport · Hirschler Fleischer · http://www.hirschlerfleischer.com · The Edgeworth Building · 2100 East Cary Street · Richmond, VA 23223-7078 · 804-771-9500

Steven D. Delaney · Williams Mullen · http://www.williamsmullen.com · Two James Center · 1021 East Cary Street · P.O. Box 1320 · Richmond, VA 23218-1320 · 804-643-1991

Gloria L. Freye · McGuireWoods · http://www.mcguirewoods.com · One James Center · 901 East Cary Street · Richmond, VA 23219-4030 · 804-775-1000

T. Craig Harmon · McGuireWoods · http://www.mcguirewoods.com · One James Center · 901 East Cary Street · Richmond, VA 23219-4030 · 804-775-1000

A. Brooks Hock · Williams Mullen · http://www.williamsmullen.com · Two James Center · 1021 East Cary Street · P.O. Box 1320 · Richmond, VA 23218-1320 · 804-643-1991

Neil S. Kessler · Troutman Sanders · Troutman Sanders Building · 1001 Haxall Point · P.O. Box 1122 · Richmond, VA 23218-1122 · 804-697-1200

Edward B. Kidd · ⑩ · Troutman Sanders · Troutman Sanders Building · 1001 Haxall Point · P.O. Box 1122 · Richmond, VA 23218-1122 · 804-697-1200

Nancy R. Little · McGuireWoods · http://www.mcguirewoods.com · One James Center · 901 East Cary Street · Richmond, VA 23219-4030 · 804-775-1000

L. Charles Long, Jr. · ㉕ · Hirschler Fleischer · http://www.hirschlerfleischer.com · The Edgeworth Building · 2100 East Cary Street · Richmond, VA 23223-7078 · 804-771-9500

George Keith Martin · McGuireWoods · http://www.mcguirewoods.com · One James Center · 901 East Cary Street · Richmond, VA 23219-4030 · 804-775-1000

John M. Mercer · Williams Mullen · http://www.williamsmullen.com · Two James Center · 1021 East Cary Street · P.O. Box 1320 · Richmond, VA 23218-1320 · 804-643-1991

Mark S. Shiembob · Troutman Sanders · Troutman Sanders Building · 1001 Haxall Point · P.O. Box 1122 Richmond, VA 23218-1122 · 804-697-1200

John W. Steele · Hirschler Fleischer · http://www.hirschlerfleischer.com · The Edgeworth Building · 2100 East Cary Street · Richmond, VA 23223-7078 · 804-771-9500

Charles R. Swartz · ⑩ · McGuireWoods · http://www.mcguirewoods.com · One James Center · 901 East Cary Street · Richmond, VA 23219-4030 · 804-775-1000

Andrew J. Tapscott · Hunton & Williams · Riverfront Plaza, East Tower · 951 East Byrd Street · Richmond, VA 23219-4074 · 804-788-8200

Michael H. Terry · ⑩ · Hirschler Fleischer · http://www.hirschlerfleischer.com · The Edgeworth Building 2100 East Cary Street · Richmond, VA 23223-7078 · 804-771-9500

James W. Theobald · ⑩ · Hirschler Fleischer · http://www.hirschlerfleischer.com · The Edgeworth Building · 2100 East Cary Street · Richmond, VA 23223-7078 · 804-771-9500

William A. Walsh, Jr. · ⑩ · Hunton & Williams · Riverfront Plaza, East Tower · 951 East Byrd Street · Richmond, VA 23219-4074 · 804-788-8200

Jay M. Weinberg · ㉕ · Hirschler Fleischer · http://www.hirschlerfleischer.com · The Edgeworth Building 2100 East Cary Street · Richmond, VA 23223-7078 · 804-771-9500

Roanoke

Claude D. Carter · Carter, Osborne & Miller · 1401 Franklin Road, SW · P.O. Box 13206 · Roanoke, VA 24032-3206 · 540-982-0234

Robert E. Glenn IV · Glenn, Feldmann, Darby & Goodlatte · 210 First Street, SW, Suite 200 · P.O. Box 2887 · Roanoke, VA 24001-2887 · 540-224-8000

Maryellen F. Goodlatte · Glenn, Feldmann, Darby & Goodlatte · 210 First Street, SW, Suite 200 · P.O. Box 2887 · Roanoke, VA 24001-2887 · 540-224-8000

David C. Helscher · ⑩ · Osterhoudt, Prillaman, Natt, Helscher, Yost, Maxwell & Ferguson · 3140 Chaparral Drive, Suite 200-C · P.O. Box 20487 · Roanoke, VA 24018 · 540-989-0000

Talfourd H. Kemper, Sr. · ⑳ · Woods Rogers · http://www.woodsrogers.com · Wachovia Tower, Suite 1400 · 10 South Jefferson Street · P.O. Box 14125 · Roanoke, VA 24038-4125 · 540-983-7600

Daniel F. Layman, Jr. · ⑩ · Woods Rogers · http://www.woodsrogers.com · Wachovia Tower, Suite 1400 · 10 South Jefferson Street · P.O. Box 14125 · Roanoke, VA 24038-4125 · 540-983-7600

Stephen W. Lemon · Martin, Hopkins & Lemon · First Union Tower, Suite 1000 · 10 South Jefferson Street · P.O. Box 13366 · Roanoke, VA 24033 · 540-982-1000

Edward A. Natt · Osterhoudt, Prillaman, Natt, Helscher, Yost, Maxwell & Ferguson · 3140 Chaparral Drive, Suite 200-C · P.O. Box 20487 · Roanoke, VA 24018 · 540-989-0000

G. Michael Pace, Jr. · Gentry Locke Rakes & Moore · http://www.gentrylocke.com · 10 Franklin Road, SE · P.O. Box 40013 · Roanoke, VA 24022-0013 · 540-983-9300

Michael K. Smeltzer · ⑳ · Woods Rogers · http://www.woodsrogers.com · Wachovia Tower, Suite 1400 · 10 South Jefferson Street · P.O. Box 14125 · Roanoke, VA 24038-4125 · 540-983-7600

Staunton

John W. Sills III · ⑩ · Timberlake, Smith, Thomas & Moses · The Virginia Building · 25 North Central Avenue · P.O. Box 108 · Staunton, VA 24402-0108 · 540-885-1517

Virginia Beach

Michael E. Barney · ⑩ · Kaufman & Canoles · 2101 Parks Avenue, Suite 700 · P.O. Box 626 · Virginia Beach, VA 23451 · 757-491-4000

Thomas F. Betz, Jr. · ⑩ · Troutman Sanders · 222 Central Park Avenue, Suite 2000 · Virginia Beach, VA 23462 · 757-687-7500

Stephen R. Davis · Willcox & Savage · 222 Central Park Avenue, Suite 1500 · Virginia Beach, VA 23462 · 757-628-5600

David Y. Faggert · Faggert & Frieden · 222 Central Park Avenue, Suite 1300 · Virginia Beach, VA 23462 · 757-424-3232

Robert E. Farmer III · ⑩ · Kaufman & Canoles · 2101 Parks Avenue, Suite 700 · P.O. Box 626 · Virginia Beach, VA 23451 · 757-491-4000

Robert E. Ruloff · Shuttleworth, Ruloff, Swain, Haddad & Morecock · http://www.srgslaw.com · Southport Centre, Suite 300 · 4525 South Boulevard · Virginia Beach, VA 23452-1137 · 757-671-6000

Williamsburg

Alvin P. Anderson · Kaufman & Canoles · 4801 Courthouse Street, Suite 300 · P.O. Box 6000 · Williamsburg, VA 23188 · 757-259-3800

Woodstock

Paul J. Neal, Jr. · Paul J. Neal, Jr. · 122 West High Street · P.O. Box 474 · Woodstock, VA 22664-1444 · 540-459-4041

SECURITIES LAW

McLean

Jack L. Lewis · Morrison & Foerster · http://www.mofo.com · 1650 Tysons Boulevard, Suite 400 · McLean, VA 22102-4840 · 703-760-7700

Steven L. Meltzer · Pillsbury Winthrop Shaw Pittman · http://www.pillsburylaw.com · 1650 Tysons Boulevard, 14th Floor · McLean, VA 22102-4859 · 703-905-2000

Reston

Edwin M. Martin, Jr. · DLA Piper · 1775 Wiehle Avenue, Suite 400 · Reston, VA 20190-5159 · 703-773-4000

Nancy A. Spangler · DLA Piper · 1775 Wiehle Avenue, Suite 400 · Reston, VA 20190-5159 · 703-773-4000

Richmond

Edward J. Fuhr · ⑩ · Hunton & Williams · Riverfront Plaza, East Tower · 951 East Byrd Street · Richmond, VA 23219-4074 · 804-788-8200

F. Claiborne Johnston, Jr. · ⑩ · Troutman Sanders · Troutman Sanders Building · 1001 Haxall Point · P.O. Box 1122 · Richmond, VA 23218-1122 · 804-697-1200

William J. Strickland · McGuireWoods · http://www.mcguirewoods.com · One James Center · 901 East Cary Street · Richmond, VA 23219-4030 · 804-775-1000

C. Porter Vaughan III · ⓴ · Hunton & Williams · Riverfront Plaza, East Tower · 951 East Byrd Street · Richmond, VA 23219-4074 · 804-788-8200

George P. Whitley · LeClair Ryan · 951 East Byrd Street, Eighth Floor · P.O. Box 2499 · Richmond, VA 23218-2499 · 804-783-2003

Virginia Beach

Jeffrey H. Gray · Troutman Sanders · 222 Central Park Avenue, Suite 2000 · Virginia Beach, VA 23462 · 757-687-7500

James J. Wheaton · Troutman Sanders · 222 Central Park Avenue, Suite 2000 · Virginia Beach, VA 23462 · 757-687-7500

SPORTS LAW

Norfolk

Lisa P. O'Donnell · Bertini O'Donnell & Hammer · http://www.bohlaw.net · 999 Waterside Drive, Suite 1010 · Norfolk, VA 23510 · 757-670-3868

Virginia Beach

Thomas B. Shuttleworth II · ❿ · Shuttleworth, Ruloff, Swain, Haddad & Morecock · http://www.srgslaw.com · Southport Centre, Suite 300 · 4525 South Boulevard · Virginia Beach, VA 23452-1137 · 757-671-6000

Lawrence H. Woodward, Jr. · Shuttleworth, Ruloff, Swain, Haddad & Morecock · http://www.srgslaw.com · Southport Centre, Suite 300 · 4525 South Boulevard · Virginia Beach, VA 23452-1137 · 757-671-6000

STRUCTURED FINANCE LAW

Richmond

Kevin J. Buckley · Hunton & Williams · Riverfront Plaza, East Tower · 951 East Byrd Street · Richmond, VA 23219-4074 · 804-788-8200

Thomas E. duB. Fauls · Troutman Sanders · Troutman Sanders Building · 1001 Haxall Point · P.O. Box 1122 · Richmond, VA 23218-1122 · 804-697-1200

Randolph F. Totten · ❿ · Hunton & Williams · Riverfront Plaza, East Tower · 951 East Byrd Street · Richmond, VA 23219-4074 · 804-788-8200

Roanoke

George J. A. Clemo · Woods Rogers · http://www.woodsrogers.com · Wachovia Tower, Suite 1400 · 10 South Jefferson Street · P.O. Box 14125 · Roanoke, VA 24038-4125 · 540-983-7600

Charlottesville

Charles D. Fox IV · McGuireWoods · http://www.mcguirewoods.com · Court Square Building, Suite 300 · 310 Fourth Street, NE · P.O. Box 1288 · Charlottesville, VA 22902-1288 · 434-977-2500

David W. Kudravetz · ⑩ · McCallum & Kudravetz · 250 East High Street · Charlottesville, VA 22902 · 434-293-8191

Leigh B. Middleditch, Jr. · ⑳ · McGuireWoods · http://www.mcguirewoods.com · Court Square Building, Suite 300 · 310 Fourth Street, NE · P.O. Box 1288 · Charlottesville, VA 22902-1288 · 434-977-2500

Fairfax

J. Carlton Howard, Jr. · ⑩ · Ritzert & Leyton · 11350 Random Hills Road, Suite 400 · Fairfax, VA 22030 703-934-2660

David A. Lawrence · Odin, Feldman & Pittleman · http://www.ofplaw.com · 9302 Lee Highway, Suite 1100 · Fairfax, VA 22031 · 703-218-2100

James B. Pittleman · Odin, Feldman & Pittleman · http://www.ofplaw.com · 9302 Lee Highway, Suite 1100 · Fairfax, VA 22031 · 703-218-2100

Hampton

James S. McNider III · James S. McNider, III · 32 East Queens Way, Suite B · P.O. Box I · Hampton, VA 23669-0256 · 757-722-8000

McLean

Ronald D. Aucutt · ⑩ · McGuireWoods · http://www.mcguirewoods.com · 1750 Tysons Boulevard, Suite 1800 · McLean, VA 22102-4215 · 703-712-5000

John S. Harper · Morrison & Foerster · http://www.mofo.com · 1650 Tysons Boulevard, Suite 400 · McLean, VA 22102-4840 · 703-760-7700

Norfolk

Allan G. Donn · ㉕ · Willcox & Savage · One Commercial Place, Suite 1800 · Norfolk, VA 23510 · 757-628-5500

Patrick W. Herman · Vandeventer Black · 500 World Trade Center, Suite 500 · 101 West Main Street · Norfolk, VA 23510 · 757-446-8600

Robert C. Nusbaum · ㉕ · Williams Mullen · http://www.williamsmullen.com · Dominion Tower, Suite 1700 · 999 Waterside Drive · Norfolk, VA 23510-3303 · 757-622-3366

William A. Old, Jr. · ⑩ · Williams Mullen · http://www.williamsmullen.com · Dominion Tower, Suite 1700 · 999 Waterside Drive · Norfolk, VA 23510-3303 · 757-622-3366

Toy D. Savage, Jr. · ㉕ · Willcox & Savage · One Commercial Place, Suite 1800 · Norfolk, VA 23510 · 757-628-5500

J. Douglas Sorensen · ⑩ · Kaufman & Canoles · 150 West Main Street, Suite 2100 · P.O. Box 3037 · Norfolk, VA 23514-3037 · 757-624-3000

Maria S. Stefanis · Williams Mullen · http://www.williamsmullen.com · Dominion Tower, Suite 1700 · 999 Waterside Drive · Norfolk, VA 23510-3303 · 757-622-3366

Portsmouth

Albert J. Taylor, Jr. · ⑳ · Williams Mullen · http://www.williamsmullen.com · 355 Crawford Street, Suite 600 · Portsmouth, VA 23704-2823 · 757-391-3366

Richmond

Farhad Aghdami · Williams Mullen · http://www.williamsmullen.com · Two James Center · 1021 East Cary Street · P.O. Box 1320 · Richmond, VA 23218-1320 · 804-643-1991

Craig D. Bell · McGuireWoods · http://www.mcguirewoods.com · One James Center · 901 East Cary Street · Richmond, VA 23219-4030 · 804-775-1000

Cameron N. Cosby · Hunton & Williams · Riverfront Plaza, East Tower · 951 East Byrd Street · Richmond, VA 23219-4074 · 804-788-8200

W. Birch Douglass III · ⑩ · McGuireWoods · http://www.mcguirewoods.com · One James Center · 901 East Cary Street · Richmond, VA 23219-4030 · 804-775-1000

J. Conrad Garcia · Williams Mullen · http://www.williamsmullen.com · Two James Center · 1021 East Cary Street · P.O. Box 1320 · Richmond, VA 23218-1320 · 804-643-1991

J. William Gray, Jr. · ⑩ · Hunton & Williams · Riverfront Plaza, East Tower · 951 East Byrd Street · Richmond, VA 23219-4074 · 804-788-8200

George C. Howell III · ⑩ · Hunton & Williams · Riverfront Plaza, East Tower · 951 East Byrd Street · Richmond, VA 23219-4074 · 804-788-8200

Robert E. Lee · ㉕ · Cook, Heyward, Lee, Hopper & Feehan · 4551 Cox Road, Suite 210 · P.O. Box 29629 Richmond, VA 23242 · 804-747-4500

Robert G. McElroy · McGuireWoods · http://www.mcguirewoods.com · One James Center · 901 East Cary Street · Richmond, VA 23219-4030 · 804-775-1000

Thomas McNally Millhiser · ⑩ · Hunton & Williams · Riverfront Plaza, East Tower · 951 East Byrd Street · Richmond, VA 23219-4074 · 804-788-8200

John B. O'Grady · ⑩ · McGuireWoods · http://www.mcguirewoods.com · One James Center · 901 East Cary Street · Richmond, VA 23219-4030 · 804-775-1000

Craig L. Rascoe · Williams Mullen · http://www.williamsmullen.com · Two James Center · 1021 East Cary Street · P.O. Box 1320 · Richmond, VA 23218-1320 · 804-643-1991

N. Pendleton Rogers · LeClair Ryan · 951 East Byrd Street, Eighth Floor · P.O. Box 2499 · Richmond, VA 23218-2499 · 804-783-2003

Thomas P. Rohman · McGuireWoods · http://www.mcguirewoods.com · One James Center · 901 East Cary Street · Richmond, VA 23219-4030 · 804-775-1000

William L. S. Rowe · ⑩ · Hunton & Williams · Riverfront Plaza, East Tower · 951 East Byrd Street · Richmond, VA 23219-4074 · 804-788-8200

Harold E. Starke, Jr. · ⑩ · Troutman Sanders · Troutman Sanders Building · 1001 Haxall Point · P.O. Box 1122 · Richmond, VA 23218-1122 · 804-697-1200

Roanoke

Neil V. Birkhoff · Woods Rogers · http://www.woodsrogers.com · Wachovia Tower, Suite 1400 · 10 South Jefferson Street · P.O. Box 14125 · Roanoke, VA 24038-4125 · 540-983-7600

W. William Gust · Gentry Locke Rakes & Moore · http://www.gentrylocke.com · 10 Franklin Road, SE · P.O. Box 40013 · Roanoke, VA 24022-0013 · 540-983-9300

Alexander I. Saunders · Woods Rogers · http://www.woodsrogers.com · Wachovia Tower, Suite 1400 · 10 South Jefferson Street · P.O. Box 14125 · Roanoke, VA 24038-4125 · 540-983-7600

Bruce C. Stockburger · ⑩ · Gentry Locke Rakes & Moore · http://www.gentrylocke.com · 10 Franklin Road, SE · P.O. Box 40013 · Roanoke, VA 24022-0013 · 540-983-9300

Virginia Beach

Elizabeth J. Atkinson · LeClair Ryan · One Columbus Center, Suite 525 · 283 Constitution Drive · Virginia Beach, VA 23462 · 757-217-4530

Thomas R. Frantz · ㉕ · Williams Mullen · http://www.williamsmullen.com · 222 Central Park Avenue, Suite 1700 · Virginia Beach, VA 23462-3035 · 757-499-8800

R. Braxton Hill III · ⑳ · Kaufman & Canoles · 2101 Parks Avenue, Suite 700 · P.O. Box 626 · Virginia Beach, VA 23451 · 757-491-4000

TECHNOLOGY LAW

Charlottesville

Michael P. Drzal · LeClair Ryan · 123 East Main Street, Suite 800 · Charlottesville, VA 22902 · 434-245-3444

Reston

Adam Ruttenberg · Cooley Godward Kronish · One Freedom Square · Reston Town Center · 11951 Freedom Drive · Reston, VA 20190-5656 · 703-456-8000

TIMBER LAW

Roanoke

Paul R. Thomson, Jr. · Woods Rogers · http://www.woodsrogers.com · Wachovia Tower, Suite 1400 · 10 South Jefferson Street · P.O. Box 14125 · Roanoke, VA 24038-4125 · 540-983-7600

TRANSPORTATION LAW

Norfolk

Mark T. Coberly · Vandeventer Black · 500 World Trade Center, Suite 500 · 101 West Main Street · Norfolk, VA 23510 · 757-446-8600

John D. Padgett · McGuireWoods · http://www.mcguirewoods.com · World Trade Center, Suite 9000 · 101 West Main Street · Norfolk, VA 23510-1655 · 757-640-3700

Samuel J. Webster · Willcox & Savage · One Commercial Place, Suite 1800 · Norfolk, VA 23510 · 757-628-5500

Richmond

Michael A. Montgomery · Bowman and Brooke · 1111 East Main Street, Suite 2100 · Richmond, VA 23219 · 804-819-1132

Albert M. Orgain IV · Sands, Anderson, Marks & Miller · http://www.sandsanderson.com · 801 East Main Street, Suite 1800 · P.O. Box 1998 · Richmond, VA 23218-1998 · 804-648-1636

C. Stephen Setliff · Setliff & Holland · 500 Libbie Avenue, Second Floor · Richmond, VA 23226 · 804-377-1260

Roanoke

Bradley W. Fitzgerald · Woods Rogers · http://www.woodsrogers.com · Wachovia Tower, Suite 1400 · 10 South Jefferson Street · P.O. Box 14125 · Roanoke, VA 24038-4125 · 540-983-7600

Matthew P. Pritts · Woods Rogers · http://www.woodsrogers.com · Wachovia Tower, Suite 1400 · 10 South Jefferson Street · P.O. Box 14125 · Roanoke, VA 24038-4125 · 540-983-7600

TRUSTS AND ESTATES

Alexandria

William L. Babcock, Jr. · William L. Babcock, Jr. · 526 King Street, Suite 518 · Alexandria, VA 22314-3143 · 703-518-8400

Arlington

A. Paul Lanzillotta · Manning & Murray · 6045 Wilson Boulevard, Suite 300 · Arlington, VA 22205 · 703-532-5400

Donald O. Manning · ⑩ · Manning & Murray · 6045 Wilson Boulevard, Suite 300 · Arlington, VA 22205 · 703-532-5400

William G. Murray · ⑩ · Manning & Murray · 6045 Wilson Boulevard, Suite 300 · Arlington, VA 22205 · 703-532-5400

Kelly A. Thompson · Kelly A. Thompson · 46 South Glebe Road, Suite 200 · Arlington, VA 22204-1655 · 703-486-2666

Bristol

Nell King Bieger · Jones, King & Downs · http://www.jkdlaw.com · 105 Landmark Lane · P.O. Box 1689 · Bristol, VA 24203 · 423-764-5535

Charlottesville

Lucius H. Bracey, Jr. · ⑳ · McGuireWoods · http://www.mcguirewoods.com · Court Square Building, Suite 300 · 310 Fourth Street, NE · P.O. Box 1288 · Charlottesville, VA 22902-1288 · 434-977-2500

Jane C. Clarke · McCallum & Kudravetz · 250 East High Street · Charlottesville, VA 22902 · 434-293-8191

James P. Cox III · Michie Hamlett Lowry Rasmussen & Tweel · 500 Court Square, Suite 300 · P.O. Box 298 · Charlottesville, VA 22902-0298 · 434-951-7200

Charles D. Fox IV · McGuireWoods · http://www.mcguirewoods.com · Court Square Building, Suite 300 · 310 Fourth Street, NE · P.O. Box 1288 · Charlottesville, VA 22902-1288 · 434-977-2500

Julie A. King · McGuireWoods · http://www.mcguirewoods.com · Court Square Building, Suite 300 · 310 Fourth Street, NE · P.O. Box 1288 · Charlottesville, VA 22902-1288 · 434-977-2500

David W. Kudravetz · ⑩ · McCallum & Kudravetz · 250 East High Street · Charlottesville, VA 22902 · 434-293-8191

Edward R. Slaughter, Jr. · ⑩ · Michie Hamlett Lowry Rasmussen & Tweel · 500 Court Square, Suite 300 · P.O. Box 298 · Charlottesville, VA 22902-0298 · 434-951-7200

Fairfax

Peter A. Arntson · ⑩ · McCandlish & Lillard · 11350 Random Hills Road, Suite 500 · Fairfax, VA 22030-7429 · 703-273-2288

David J. Brewer · ⑩ · Odin, Feldman & Pittleman · http://www.ofplaw.com · 9302 Lee Highway, Suite 1100 · Fairfax, VA 22031 · 703-218-2100

Thomas Campbell · Yates, Campbell, Christopher & Yates · 4155 Chain Bridge Road · Fairfax, VA 22030 703-273-4230

John C. Hale · Hale Carlson & Penn · 10511 Judicial Drive · Fairfax, VA 22030 · 703-591-4900

J. Carlton Howard, Jr. · ⑩ · Ritzert & Leyton · 11350 Random Hills Road, Suite 400 · Fairfax, VA 22030 703-934-2660

John A. C. Keith · Blankingship & Keith · http://www.blankingship-keith-law.com · 4020 University Drive, Suite 300 · Fairfax, VA 22030 · 703-691-1235

Munford Yates, Jr. · Yates, Campbell, Christopher & Yates · 4155 Chain Bridge Road · Fairfax, VA 22030 · 703-273-4230

Thomas Yates · Yates, Campbell, Christopher & Yates · 4155 Chain Bridge Road · Fairfax, VA 22030 · 703-273-4230

Falls Church

John G. Jackson · ⑩ · Baskin, Jackson, Hansbarger & Duffett · 301 Park Avenue · Falls Church, VA 22046 · 703-534-3610

John L. Laster · John L. Laster · Old Brickhouse Square · 103 Rowell Court · Falls Church, VA 22046 · 703-538-3600

Lynchburg

Joseph C. Knakal, Jr. · ⑩ · Caskie & Frost · 2306 Atherholt Road · P.O. Box 6360 · Lynchburg, VA 24505 · 434-846-2731

McLean

Ronald D. Aucutt · ⑩ · McGuireWoods · http://www.mcguirewoods.com · 1750 Tysons Boulevard, Suite 1800 · McLean, VA 22102-4215 · 703-712-5000

Richard S. Franklin · Pillsbury Winthrop Shaw Pittman · http://www.pillsburylaw.com · 1650 Tysons Boulevard, 14th Floor · McLean, VA 22102-4859 · 703-905-2000

James E. McNair · Patton Boggs · 8484 Westpark Drive, Suite 900 · McLean, VA 22102 · 783-744-8000

Frederick J. Tansill · ⑩ · Frederick J. Tansill & Associates · 1355 Beverly Road, Suite 215 · McLean, VA 22101-3654 · 703-847-1359

Gino Zaccardelli · McGuireWoods · http://www.mcguirewoods.com · 1750 Tysons Boulevard, Suite 1800 McLean, VA 22102-4215 · 703-712-5000

Middleburg

Constantine L. Dimos · ⑳ · Constantine L. Dimos · 102 West Marshall Street · P.O. Box 2221 · Middleburg, VA 20118 · 540-687-3392

Newport News

Philip L. Hatchett · Kaufman & Canoles · 11817 Canon Boulevard, Suite 408 · Newport News, VA 23606 757-873-6300

Norfolk

Susan C. Alper · Wilks, Alper & Harwood · Town Point Center, Suite 700 · 150 Boush Street · Norfolk, VA 23510-1637 · 757-623-6500

Neal P. Brodsky · LeClair Ryan · 999 Waterside Drive, Suite 2525 · Norfolk, VA 23510 · 757-624-1454

Ann S. Dodson · Kaufman & Canoles · 150 West Main Street, Suite 2100 · P.O. Box 3037 · Norfolk, VA 23514-3037 · 757-624-3000

Allan G. Donn · ㉕ · Willcox & Savage · One Commercial Place, Suite 1800 · Norfolk, VA 23510 · 757-628-5500

Peter M. Huber · ⑩ · Willcox & Savage · One Commercial Place, Suite 1800 · Norfolk, VA 23510 · 757-628-5500

Kirkland M. Kelley · ⑩ · Kaufman & Canoles · 150 West Main Street, Suite 2100 · P.O. Box 3037 · Norfolk, VA 23514-3037 · 757-624-3000

Montgomery Knight, Jr. · ⑩ · Williams Mullen · http://www.williamsmullen.com · Dominion Tower, Suite 1700 · 999 Waterside Drive · Norfolk, VA 23510-3303 · 757-622-3366

Robert C. Nusbaum · ㉕ · Williams Mullen · http://www.williamsmullen.com · Dominion Tower, Suite 1700 · 999 Waterside Drive · Norfolk, VA 23510-3303 · 757-622-3366

Stanley L. Samuels · Williams Mullen · http://www.williamsmullen.com · Dominion Tower, Suite 1700 · 999 Waterside Drive · Norfolk, VA 23510-3303 · 757-622-3366

Toy D. Savage, Jr. · ㉕ · Willcox & Savage · One Commercial Place, Suite 1800 · Norfolk, VA 23510 · 757-628-5500

Lewis W. Webb III · Kaufman & Canoles · 150 West Main Street, Suite 2100 · P.O. Box 3037 · Norfolk, VA 23514-3037 · 757-624-3000

Orange

Frank A. Thomas III · ⑩ · Shackelford, Thomas & Gregg · 149 West Main Street · P.O. Box 871 · Orange, VA 22960 · 540-672-2711

Richmond

Maureen C. Ackerly · McGuireWoods · http://www.mcguirewoods.com · One James Center · 901 East Cary Street · Richmond, VA 23219-4030 · 804-775-1000

David D. Addison · ⑩ · Williams Mullen · http://www.williamsmullen.com · Two James Center · 1021 East Cary Street · P.O. Box 1320 · Richmond, VA 23218-1320 · 804-643-1991

Farhad Aghdami · Williams Mullen · http://www.williamsmullen.com · Two James Center · 1021 East Cary Street · P.O. Box 1320 · Richmond, VA 23218-1320 · 804-643-1991

Michael Armstrong · ⑳ · Armstrong, Bristow, Farley & Schwarzschild · 1807 Libbie Avenue, Suite 200 · Richmond, VA 23226 · 804-282-6170

Dennis I. Belcher · ⑳ · McGuireWoods · http://www.mcguirewoods.com · One James Center · 901 East Cary Street · Richmond, VA 23219-4030 · 804-775-1000

John D. Bristow · Armstrong, Bristow, Farley & Schwarzschild · 1807 Libbie Avenue, Suite 200 · Richmond, VA 23226 · 804-282-6170

W. Birch Douglass III · ⑩ · McGuireWoods · http://www.mcguirewoods.com · One James Center · 901 East Cary Street · Richmond, VA 23219-4030 · 804-775-1000

Matthew M. Farley · Armstrong, Bristow, Farley & Schwarzschild · 1807 Libbie Avenue, Suite 200 · Richmond, VA 23226 · 804-282-6170

Malcolm P. Friddell · ⑩ · Troutman Sanders · Troutman Sanders Building · 1001 Haxall Point · P.O. Box 1122 · Richmond, VA 23218-1122 · 804-697-1200

J. William Gray, Jr. · ⑩ · Hunton & Williams · Riverfront Plaza, East Tower · 951 East Byrd Street · Richmond, VA 23219-4074 · 804-788-8200

Timothy H. Guare · Timothy H. Guare · 6802 Paragon Place, Suite 100 · Richmond, VA 23230 · 804-288-8480

Helen Lewis Kemp · ⑩ · Virginia Estate Plans · 8401 Patterson Avenue, Suite G-100 · Richmond, VA 23229-6401 · 804-565-2300

Thomas McNally Millhiser · ⑩ · Hunton & Williams · Riverfront Plaza, East Tower · 951 East Byrd Street · Richmond, VA 23219-4074 · 804-788-8200

John B. O'Grady · ⑩ · McGuireWoods · http://www.mcguirewoods.com · One James Center · 901 East Cary Street · Richmond, VA 23219-4030 · 804-775-1000

Amy G. Pesesky · Amy G. Pesesky · 707 East Main Street, Suite 1500 · Richmond, VA 23219-2805 · 804-775-0500

Katherine E. Ramsey · Hunton & Williams · Riverfront Plaza, East Tower · 951 East Byrd Street · Richmond, VA 23219-4074 · 804-788-8200

Nancy Newton Rogers · ⑩ · Troutman Sanders · Troutman Sanders Building · 1001 Haxall Point · P.O. Box 1122 · Richmond, VA 23218-1122 · 804-697-1200

William L. S. Rowe · ⑩ · Hunton & Williams · Riverfront Plaza, East Tower · 951 East Byrd Street · Richmond, VA 23219-4074 · 804-788-8200

Jane L. Schwarzschild · ⑩ · Armstrong, Bristow, Farley & Schwarzschild · 1807 Libbie Avenue, Suite 200 · Richmond, VA 23226 · 804-282-6170

Derek L. Smith · ⑩ · Virginia Estate Plans · 8401 Patterson Avenue, Suite G-100 · Richmond, VA 23229-6401 · 804-565-2300

Julious P. Smith, Jr. · ⑩ · Williams Mullen · http://www.williamsmullen.com · Two James Center · 1021 East Cary Street · P.O. Box 1320 · Richmond, VA 23218-1320 · 804-643-1991

Susan K. Stoneman · Susan K. Stoneman · 700 East Main Street, Suite 1505 · P.O. Box 516 · Richmond, VA 23218 · 804-643-7062

David W. Whitehead · Bowles & Whitehead · 404 West Franklin Street · P.O. Box 12085 · Richmond, VA 23241 · 804-780-0236

Fielding L. Williams, Jr. · ⑩ · Williams Mullen · http://www.williamsmullen.com · Two James Center · 1021 East Cary Street · P.O. Box 1320 · Richmond, VA 23218-1320 · 804-643-1991

Thomas S. Word, Jr. · ㉕ · McGuireWoods · http://www.mcguirewoods.com · One James Center · 901 East Cary Street · Richmond, VA 23219-4030 · 804-775-1000

Roanoke

Robert S. Bersch · Bersch Law Firm · 3800 Electric Road, Suite 306 · Roanoke, VA 24018 · 540-345-7400

Neil V. Birkhoff · Woods Rogers · http://www.woodsrogers.com · Wachovia Tower, Suite 1400 · 10 South Jefferson Street · P.O. Box 14125 · Roanoke, VA 24038-4125 · 540-983-7600

Nan L. Coleman · ⑩ · Coleman & Massey · Coulter Business Center, Suite 310 · 601 South Jefferson Street · P.O. Box 1489 · Roanoke, VA 24007-1489 · 540-343-5100

H. Michael Deneka · Deneka Law Firm · McVitty Executive Center, Suite A · 2758 Electric Road · Roanoke, VA 24018 · 540-725-5800

Talfourd H. Kemper, Sr. · ⑳ · Woods Rogers · http://www.woodsrogers.com · Wachovia Tower, Suite 1400 · 10 South Jefferson Street · P.O. Box 14125 · Roanoke, VA 24038-4125 · 540-983-7600

James B. Massey III · Coleman & Massey · Coulter Business Center, Suite 310 · 601 South Jefferson Street · P.O. Box 1489 · Roanoke, VA 24007-1489 · 540-343-5100

Deborah A. Oehlschlaeger · Plunkett & Oehlschlaeger · Shenandoah Building, Suite 300 · 305 First Street, SW · Roanoke, VA 24011 · 540-345-8837

J. Lee E. Osborne · ⑩ · Carter, Osborne & Miller · 1401 Franklin Road, SW · P.O. Box 13206 · Roanoke, VA 24032-3206 · 540-982-0234

Alexander I. Saunders · Woods Rogers · http://www.woodsrogers.com · Wachovia Tower, Suite 1400 · 10 South Jefferson Street · P.O. Box 14125 · Roanoke, VA 24038-4125 · 540-983-7600

Bruce C. Stockburger · ⑩ · Gentry Locke Rakes & Moore · http://www.gentrylocke.com · 10 Franklin Road, SE · P.O. Box 40013 · Roanoke, VA 24022-0013 · 540-983-9300

Vienna

James L. Boring · ⑩ · Boring & Pilger · 307 Maple Avenue West, Suite D · Vienna, VA 22180 · 703-281-2161

Deborah D. Cochran · Cochran & Owen · 8000 Towers Crescent Drive, Suite 160 · Vienna, VA 22182 · 703-847-4480

Rhonda J. MacDonald · Rhonda J. MacDonald · 2071 Chain Bridge Road · Vienna, VA 22182 · 703-917-8777

Patrick J. Vaughan · ㉕ · Vaughan, Fincher & Sotelo · 8619 Westwood Center Drive, Suite 400 · Vienna, VA 22182 · 703-506-1810

Virginia Beach

Jo Ann Blair-Davis · ⑩ · Pender & Coward · Town Centre, Suite 400 · 222 Central Park Avenue · Virginia Beach, VA 23462 · 757-490-3000

Joseph A. Di Julio · Williams Mullen · http://www.williamsmullen.com · 222 Central Park Avenue, Suite 1700 · Virginia Beach, VA 23462-3035 · 757-499-8800

Thomas R. Frantz · ㉕ · Williams Mullen · http://www.williamsmullen.com · 222 Central Park Avenue, Suite 1700 · Virginia Beach, VA 23462-3035 · 757-499-8800

R. Braxton Hill III · ⑳ · Kaufman & Canoles · 2101 Parks Avenue, Suite 700 · P.O. Box 626 · Virginia Beach, VA 23451 · 757-491-4000

John T. Midgett · Midgett & Preti · 477 Viking Drive, Suite 430 · Virginia Beach, VA 23452 · 757-687-8888

Robert C. Miller · ⑩ · Williams Mullen · http://www.williamsmullen.com · 222 Central Park Avenue, Suite 1700 · Virginia Beach, VA 23462-3035 · 757-499-8800

Kevin B. Rack · The Rack Law Firm · 249 Central Park Avenue, Suite 220 · Virginia Beach, VA 23462 · 757-605-5000

E. Diane Thompson · ⑩ · Pender & Coward · Town Centre, Suite 400 · 222 Central Park Avenue · Virginia Beach, VA 23462 · 757-490-3000

VENTURE CAPITAL LAW

Charlottesville

David L. Dallas, Jr. · Williams Mullen · http://www.williamsmullen.com · 321 East Main Street, Suite 400 Charlottesville, VA 22902-3200 · 434-951-5700

Michael P. Drzal · LeClair Ryan · 123 East Main Street, Suite 800 · Charlottesville, VA 22902 · 434-245-3444

Steven J. Keeler · McGuireWoods · http://www.mcguirewoods.com · Court Square Building, Suite 300 · 310 Fourth Street, NE · P.O. Box 1288 · Charlottesville, VA 22902-1288 · 434-977-2500

McLean

Thomas J. Knox · Morrison & Foerster · http://www.mofo.com · 1650 Tysons Boulevard, Suite 400 · McLean, VA 22102-4840 · 703-760-7700

Reston

Michael Lincoln · Cooley Godward Kronish · One Freedom Square · Reston Town Center · 11951 Freedom Drive · Reston, VA 20190-5656 · 703-456-8000

Richmond

J. Benjamin English · Hirschler Fleischer · http://www.hirschlerfleischer.com · The Edgeworth Building · 2100 East Cary Street · Richmond, VA 23223-7078 · 804-771-9500

S. Brian Farmer · Hirschler Fleischer · http://www.hirschlerfleischer.com · The Edgeworth Building · 2100 East Cary Street · Richmond, VA 23223-7078 · 804-771-9500

Bradley A. Haneberg · Kaufman & Canoles · Three James Center, 12th Floor · 1051 East Cary Street · Richmond, VA 23219 · 804-771-5700

T. Justin Moore III · Hunton & Williams · Riverfront Plaza, East Tower · 951 East Byrd Street · Richmond, VA 23219-4074 · 804-788-8200

Virginia Beach

James J. Wheaton · Troutman Sanders · 222 Central Park Avenue, Suite 2000 · Virginia Beach, VA 23462 · 757-687-7500

WATER LAW

Abingdon

Wade Massie · PennStuart · Virginia House · 208 East Main Street · P.O. Box 2288 · Abingdon, VA 24212-2288 · 276-628-5151

Richmond

David E. Evans · ⑳ · McGuireWoods · http://www.mcguirewoods.com · One James Center · 901 East Cary Street · Richmond, VA 23219-4030 · 804-775-1000

Kevin J. Finto · Hunton & Williams · Riverfront Plaza, East Tower · 951 East Byrd Street · Richmond, VA 23219-4074 · 804-788-8200

Timothy G. Hayes · ⑩ · Hunton & Williams · Riverfront Plaza, East Tower · 951 East Byrd Street · Richmond, VA 23219-4074 · 804-788-8200

John M. Lain · McGuireWoods · http://www.mcguirewoods.com · One James Center · 901 East Cary Street · Richmond, VA 23219-4030 · 804-775-1000

James E. Ryan, Jr. · Troutman Sanders · Troutman Sanders Building · 1001 Haxall Point · P.O. Box 1122 Richmond, VA 23218-1122 · 804-697-1200

Brooks M. Smith · Hunton & Williams · Riverfront Plaza, East Tower · 951 East Byrd Street · Richmond, VA 23219-4074 · 804-788-8200

Roanoke

Paul R. Thomson, Jr. · Woods Rogers · http://www.woodsrogers.com · Wachovia Tower, Suite 1400 · 10 South Jefferson Street · P.O. Box 14125 · Roanoke, VA 24038-4125 · 540-983-7600

Alexandria

James C. Clark · ⑩ · Land, Clark, Carroll, Mendelson & Blair · 524 King Street · P.O. Box 19888 · Alexandria, VA 22320-0888 · 703-836-1000

William B. Cummings · Law Offices of William B. Cummings · P.O. Box 1177 · Alexandria, VA 22313 · 703-836-7997

Marvin D. Miller · ⑩ · Law Offices of Marvin D. Miller · 1203 Duke Street · Alexandria, VA 22314 · 703-548-5000

J. Frederick Sinclair · ⑳ · J. Frederick Sinclair · 100 North Pitt Street, Suite 200 · Alexandria, VA 22314-3134 · 703-299-0600

John Kenneth Zwerling · ⑩ · Zwerling, Leibig & Moseley · 108 North Alfred Street · Alexandria, VA 22314 · 703-684-8000

Charlottesville

Edward B. Lowry · ⑳ · Michie Hamlett Lowry Rasmussen & Tweel · 500 Court Square, Suite 300 · P.O. Box 298 · Charlottesville, VA 22902-0298 · 434-951-7200

Chesterfield

Michael HuYoung · Barnes & Diehl · http://www.thebarneslawfirm.com · Centre Court, Suite A · 9401 Courthouse Road · Chesterfield, VA 23832-6666 · 804-796-1000

Fairfax

Peter D. Greenspun · ⑩ · Greenspun, Davis & Leary · 3955 Chain Bridge Road, Second Floor · Fairfax, VA 22030 · 703-352-0100

Rodney G. Leffler · Leffler & Hyland · http://www.lefflerhyland.com · 4163 Chain Bridge Road · Fairfax, VA 22030-4102 · 703-293-9300

Jonathan Shapiro · ⑩ · Greenspun, Davis & Leary · 3955 Chain Bridge Road, Second Floor · Fairfax, VA 22030 · 703-352-0100

McLean

David G. Barger · Williams Mullen · http://www.williamsmullen.com · 8270 Greensboro Drive, Suite 700 McLean, VA 22102 · 703-760-5200

Norfolk

Alan D. Albert · ⑩ · LeClair Ryan · 999 Waterside Drive, Suite 2525 · Norfolk, VA 23510 · 757-624-1454

Andrew M. Sacks · ⑩ · Sacks & Sacks · Town Point Center, Suite 501 · 150 Boush Street · Norfolk, VA 23510-1615 · 757-623-2753

Stanley E. Sacks · ㉕ · Sacks & Sacks · Town Point Center, Suite 501 · 150 Boush Street · Norfolk, VA 23510-1615 · 757-623-2753

Hunter W. Sims, Jr. · ⑩ · Kaufman & Canoles · 150 West Main Street, Suite 2100 · P.O. Box 3037 · Norfolk, VA 23514-3037 · 757-624-3000

Franklin A. Swartz · ⑩ · Rabinowitz, Swartz, Taliaferro, Swartz & Goodove · Town Point Center, Suite 800 · 150 Boush Street · P.O. Box 3332 · Norfolk, VA 23514-3332 · 757-622-3931

Reston

Sheldon Krantz · DLA Piper · 1775 Wiehle Avenue, Suite 400 · Reston, VA 20190-5159 · 703-773-4000

Richmond

William D. Bayliss · Williams Mullen · http://www.williamsmullen.com · Two James Center · 1021 East Cary Street · P.O. Box 1320 · Richmond, VA 23218-1320 · 804-643-1991

Craig S. Cooley · Craig S. Cooley · 3000 Idlewood Avenue · Richmond, VA 23221 · 804-358-2328

Richard Cullen · McGuireWoods · http://www.mcguirewoods.com · One James Center · 901 East Cary Street · Richmond, VA 23219-4030 · 804-775-1000

Murray J. Janus · ㉕ · Bremner, Janus & Stone · 701 East Franklin Street, Suite 1500 · P.O. Box 826 · Richmond, VA 23219 · 804-643-1400

James C. Roberts · ㉕ · Troutman Sanders · Troutman Sanders Building · 1001 Haxall Point · P.O. Box 1122 · Richmond, VA 23218-1122 · 804-697-1200

Anthony F. Troy · ⑩ · Troutman Sanders · Troutman Sanders Building · 1001 Haxall Point · P.O. Box 1122 · Richmond, VA 23218-1122 · 804-697-1200

Howard C. Vick, Jr. · McGuireWoods · http://www.mcguirewoods.com · One James Center · 901 East Cary Street · Richmond, VA 23219-4030 · 804-775-1000

Anne Marie Whittemore · ⑳ · McGuireWoods · http://www.mcguirewoods.com · One James Center · 901 East Cary Street · Richmond, VA 23219-4030 · 804-775-1000

Roanoke

Anthony F. Anderson · Anderson & Friedman · http://www.afacrimlaw.com · 1102 Second Street, SW · P.O. Box 1525 · Roanoke, VA 24007 · 540-982-1525

William H. Cleaveland · William H. Cleaveland · 40 British Woods Drive, Suite 101 · Roanoke, VA 24019 · 540-591-5959

David J. Damico · David J. Damico · 313 Campbell Avenue, SW · P.O. Box 1578 · Roanoke, VA 24007 · 540-343-0888

Raphael E. Ferris · Ferris, Eakin & Thomas · 22 Luck Avenue · P.O. Box 1791 · Roanoke, VA 24008-1791 · 540-344-3233

John P. Fishwick, Jr. · Lichtenstein Fishwick & Johnson · Liberty Trust Building, Suite 400 · 101 South Jefferson Street · P.O. Box 601 · Roanoke, VA 24004-0601 · 540-343-9711

John E. Lichtenstein · Lichtenstein Fishwick & Johnson · Liberty Trust Building, Suite 400 · 101 South Jefferson Street · P.O. Box 601 · Roanoke, VA 24004-0601 · 540-343-9711

Gary L. Lumsden · ⑩ · Gary L. Lumsden · 1220 Franklin Road · Roanoke, VA 24016 · 540-982-0566

Robert F. Rider · ⑳ · Robert F. Rider · 24 East Church Avenue, Suite 204 · P.O. Box 773 · Roanoke, VA 24004 · 540-767-1717

Paul R. Thomson, Jr. · Woods Rogers · http://www.woodsrogers.com · Wachovia Tower, Suite 1400 · 10 South Jefferson Street · P.O. Box 14125 · Roanoke, VA 24038-4125 · 540-983-7600

Vienna

William D. Dolan III · Venable · http://www.venable.com · 8010 Towers Crescent Drive, Suite 300 · Vienna, VA 22182 · 703-760-1600

Michael Fayad · Akerman Senterfitt · http://www.akerman.com · 8100 Boone Boulevard, Suite 700 · Vienna, VA 22182-2683 · 703-790-8750

Virginia Beach

Robert G. Morecock · ⑩ · Shuttleworth, Ruloff, Swain, Haddad & Morecock · http://www.srgslaw.com · Southport Centre, Suite 300 · 4525 South Boulevard · Virginia Beach, VA 23452-1137 · 757-671-6000

Thomas B. Shuttleworth II · ⑩ · Shuttleworth, Ruloff, Swain, Haddad & Morecock · http://www.srgslaw.com · Southport Centre, Suite 300 · 4525 South Boulevard · Virginia Beach, VA 23452-1137 · 757-671-6000

Stephen C. Swain · ⑩ · Shuttleworth, Ruloff, Swain, Haddad & Morecock · http://www.srgslaw.com · Southport Centre, Suite 300 · 4525 South Boulevard · Virginia Beach, VA 23452-1137 · 757-671-6000

Lawrence H. Woodward, Jr. · Shuttleworth, Ruloff, Swain, Haddad & Morecock · http://www.srgslaw.com · Southport Centre, Suite 300 · 4525 South Boulevard · Virginia Beach, VA 23452-1137 · 757-671-6000

Warrenton

Blair D. Howard · ⑩ · Howard, Morrison, Howard & Whelan · 31 Garrett Street · Warrenton, VA 20186 · 540-349-1155

WORKERS' COMPENSATION LAW

Abingdon

Ramesh Murthy · PennStuart · Virginia House · 208 East Main Street · P.O. Box 2288 · Abingdon, VA 24212-2288 · 276-628-5151

Alexandria

Craig A. Brown · Ashcraft & Gerel · 4900 Seminary Road, Suite 650 · Alexandria, VA 22311 · 703-931-5500

Lawrence J. Pascal · ⑩ · Ashcraft & Gerel · 4900 Seminary Road, Suite 650 · Alexandria, VA 22311 · 703-931-5500

Centreville

James Swiger · Swiger & Cay · 5900 Centreville Road, Suite 101 · Centreville, VA 20121 · 703-222-3800

Danville

James A. L. Daniel · ⑩ · Daniel, Medley & Kirby · 110 North Union Street · P.O. Box 720 · Danville, VA 24543 · 434-792-3911

Fairfax

John Duncan · Duncan & Hopkins · 11130 Main Street, Suite 310 · Fairfax, VA 22030-5009 · 703-359-6555

Susan A. Evans · Siciliano, Ellis, Dyer & Boccarosse · 10521 Judicial Drive, Suite 300 · Fairfax, VA 22030 · 703-385-6692

William S. Sands, Jr. · Duncan & Hopkins · 11130 Main Street, Suite 310 · Fairfax, VA 22030-5009 · 703-359-6555

Benjamin J. Trichilo · (10) · Trichilo, Bancroft, McGavin, Horvath & Judkins · 3920 University Drive · Fairfax, VA 22030 · 703-385-1000

Glen Allen

Ralph L. Whitt, Jr. · (10) · Whitt & Del Bueno · 4461 Cox Road, Suite 100 · Glen Allen, VA 23060 · 804-864-9660

Harrisonburg

A. Thomas Lane, Jr. · A. Thomas Lane, Jr. · http://www.atomlane.com · 35 South Gate Court, Suites 101-102 · Harrisonburg, VA 22801 · 540-434-7666

Cathleen P. Welsh · Lenhart Obenshain · http://www.lenhartobenshain.com · 90 North Main Street, Suite 201 · P.O. Box 1287 · Harrisonburg, VA 22803 · 540-437-3100

Herndon

Douglas K. W. Landau · Abrams Landau · 797 Center Street · Herndon, VA 20170 · 703-796-9555

Hopewell

B. Mayes Marks, Jr. · (10) · Marks & Associates · 901 West Broadway · P.O. Box 1627 · Hopewell, VA 23860 · 804-458-1800

Norfolk

F. Nash Bilisoly · (10) · Vandeventer Black · 500 World Trade Center, Suite 500 · 101 West Main Street · Norfolk, VA 23510 · 757-446-8600

Richmond

Arthur T. Aylward · Midkiff, Muncie & Ross · 9030 Stony Point Parkway, Suite 160 · Richmond, VA 23235 · 804-560-9600

Mary Louise Kramer · (10) · Sands, Anderson, Marks & Miller · http://www.sandsanderson.com · 801 East Main Street, Suite 1800 · P.O. Box 1998 · Richmond, VA 23218-1998 · 804-648-1636

Charles F. Midkiff · (10) · Midkiff, Muncie & Ross · 9030 Stony Point Parkway, Suite 160 · Richmond, VA 23235 · 804-560-9600

James G. Muncie, Jr. · Midkiff, Muncie & Ross · 9030 Stony Point Parkway, Suite 160 · Richmond, VA 23235 · 804-560-9600

Malcolm Parks III · (10) · Maloney, Parks & Clarke · 311 South Boulevard · P.O. Box 5578 · Richmond, VA 23220 · 804-342-1400

Roanoke

Linda D. Frith · (10) · Frith, Anderson & Peake · http://www.faplawfirm.com · 29 Franklin Road, SW · P.O. Box 1240 · Roanoke, VA 24006-1240 · 540-772-4600

Christopher M. Kite · Lucas & Kite · 2965 Colonnade Drive, Suite 118 · Roanoke, VA 24018 · 540-767-2468

Richard D. Lucas · ⑩ · Lucas & Kite · 2965 Colonnade Drive, Suite 118 · Roanoke, VA 24018 · 540-767-2468

Gary L. Lumsden · ⑩ · Gary L. Lumsden · 1220 Franklin Road · Roanoke, VA 24016 · 540-982-0566

Linda D. Slough · The Law Office of Linda D. Slough · 22 Luck Avenue · P.O. Box 206 · Roanoke, VA 24002-0206 · 540-344-3233

Jonnie L. Speight · Johnson, Ayers & Matthews · First Campbell Square, Suite 300 · 210 First Street, SW P.O. Box 2200 · Roanoke, VA 24009-2200 · 540-767-2000

Richard M. Thomas · ⑩ · Ferris, Eakin & Thomas · 22 Luck Avenue · P.O. Box 1791 · Roanoke, VA 24008-1791 · 540-344-3233

Staunton

Thomas G. Bell, Jr. · ⑩ · Timberlake, Smith, Thomas & Moses · The Virginia Building · 25 North Central Avenue · P.O. Box 108 · Staunton, VA 24402-0108 · 540-885-1517

Winchester

Nikolas E. Parthemos · Parthemos & Bryant · 206 South Cameron Street · P.O. Box 408 · Winchester, VA 22604-0408 · 540-662-4222

WASHINGTON

ADMINISTRATIVE LAW

Spokane

Gair B. Petrie · ⑩ · Randall & Danskin · Bank of America Financial Center, Suite 1500 · 601 West Riverside Avenue · Spokane, WA 99201 · 509-747-2052

ALTERNATIVE DISPUTE RESOLUTION

Seattle

Robert H. Alsdorf · Alsdorf Dispute Resolution · Seattle University School of Law, Sullivan Hall · 901 Twelveth Avenue · P.O. Box 222000 · Seattle, WA 98122-1090 · 206-228-8575

Richard M. Clinton · ⑩ · Dorsey & Whitney · U.S. Bank Centre, Suite 3400 · 1420 Fifth Avenue · Seattle, WA 98101-4010 · 206-903-8800

Frederick T. Rasmussen · ⑩ · Stokes Lawrence · 800 Fifth Avenue, Suite 4000 · Seattle, WA 98104-3179 206-626-6000

Spokane

Eugene I. Annis · ⑳ · Lukins & Annis · Washington Trust Financial Center, Suite 1600 · 717 West Sprague Avenue · Spokane, WA 99201-0466 · 509-455-9555

Tacoma

Thomas V. Harris · ⑩ · Washington Arbitration and Mediation · 3600 Port of Tacoma Road, Suite 304 · Tacoma, WA 98424 · 253-922-4140

ANTITRUST LAW

Seattle

Hugh F. Bangasser · K&L Gates · 925 Fourth Avenue, Suite 2900 · Seattle, WA 98104-1158 · 206-623-7580

Thomas L. Boeder · Perkins Coie · http://www.perkinscoie.com · 1201 Third Avenue, Suite 4800 · Seattle, WA 98101-3099 · 206-359-8000

David J. Burman · ⑩ · Perkins Coie · http://www.perkinscoie.com · 1201 Third Avenue, Suite 4800 · Seattle, WA 98101-3099 · 206-359-8000

Michael E. Kipling · Kipling Law Group · 3601 Fremont Avenue North, Suite 414 · Seattle, WA 98103 · 206-545-0345

Jerry R. McNaul · McNaul, Ebel, Nawrot & Helgren · One Union Square, Suite 2700 · 600 University Street · Seattle, WA 98101-3143 · 206-467-1816

Spokane

William D. Symmes · ⑳ · Witherspoon, Kelley, Davenport & Toole · U.S. Bank Building, Suite 1100 · 422 West Riverside Avenue · Spokane, WA 99201-0302 · 509-624-5265

APPELLATE LAW

Bainbridge Island

Charles K. Wiggins · Wiggins & Masters · 241 Madison Avenue North · Bainbridge Island, WA 98110 · 206-780-5033

Seattle

David Allen · ⑩ · Allen, Hansen & Maybrown · One Union Square, Suite 3020 · 600 University Street · Seattle, WA 98101 · 206-447-9681

Robert H. Alsdorf · Alsdorf Dispute Resolution · Seattle University School of Law, Sullivan Hall · 901 Twelveth Avenue · P.O. Box 222000 · Seattle, WA 98122-1090 · 206-228-8575

David J. Burman · ⑩ · Perkins Coie · http://www.perkinscoie.com · 1201 Third Avenue, Suite 4800 · Seattle, WA 98101-3099 · 206-359-8000

Jeffrey L. Fisher · Davis Wright Tremaine · 1201 Third Avenue, Suite 2200 · Seattle, WA 98101-3045 · 206-622-3150

Timothy K. Ford · ⑩ · MacDonald, Hoague & Bayless · Hoge Building, Suite 1500 · 705 Second Avenue · Seattle, WA 98104-1745 · 206-622-1604

Howard M. Goodfriend · Edwards, Sieh, Smith & Goodfriend · 500 Watermark Tower · 1109 First Avenue · Seattle, WA 98101 · 206-624-0974

Richard A. Hansen · ⑳ · Allen, Hansen & Maybrown · One Union Square, Suite 3020 · 600 University Street · Seattle, WA 98101 · 206-447-9681

William R. Hickman · Reed McClure · Two Union Square, Suite 1500 · 601 Union Street · Seattle, WA 98101-1363 · 206-292-4900

Michael B. King · Carney Badley Spellman · 701 Fifth Avenue, Suite 3600 · Seattle, WA 98104 · 206-622-8020

Paul J. Lawrence · K&L Gates · 925 Fourth Avenue, Suite 2900 · Seattle, WA 98104-1158 · 206-623-7580

Catherine Wright Smith · Edwards, Sieh, Smith & Goodfriend · 500 Watermark Tower · 1109 First Avenue · Seattle, WA 98101 · 206-624-0974

Mary H. Spillane · Williams Kastner · Two Union Square, Suite 4100 · 601 Union Street · P.O. Box 21926 Seattle, WA 98111-3926 · 206-628-6600

Tukwila

Philip A. Talmadge · Talmadge Law Group · 18010 Southcenter Parkway · Tukwila, WA 98188 · 206-574-6661

BANKING LAW

Colbert

David B. Goldstein · ⑩ · David B. Goldstein · 3514 West Woolard Road · Colbert, WA 99005-9002 · 509-262-0432

Seattle

Barry J. Briggs · Perkins Coie · http://www.perkinscoie.com · 1201 Third Avenue, Suite 4800 · Seattle, WA 98101-3099 · 206-359-8000

Ward Buringrud · Davis Wright Tremaine · 1201 Third Avenue, Suite 2200 · Seattle, WA 98101-3045 · 206-622-3150

Richard L. Goldfarb · Stoel Rives · http://www.stoel.com · One Union Square, Suite 3600 · 600 University Street · Seattle, WA 98101-3197 · 206-624-0900

James D. Gradel · Perkins Coie · http://www.perkinscoie.com · 1201 Third Avenue, Suite 4800 · Seattle, WA 98101-3099 · 206-359-8000

Brian D. Hulse · Heller Ehrman · 701 Fifth Avenue, Suite 6100 · Seattle, WA 98104-7098 · 206-447-0900

Richard E. Keefe · ㉕ · Foster Pepper · http://www.foster.com · 1111 Third Avenue, Suite 3400 · Seattle, WA 98101-3299 · 206-447-4400

Stephen M. Klein · ⑩ · Graham & Dunn · Pier 70, Suite 300 · 2801 Alaskan Way · Seattle, WA 98121-1128 · 206-624-8300

Bruce W. Leaverton · Lane Powell · http://www.lanepowell.com · U.S. Bank Centre, Suite 4100 · 1420 Fifth Avenue · Seattle, WA 98101-2338 · 206-223-7000

Craig Miller · Davis Wright Tremaine · 1201 Third Avenue, Suite 2200 · Seattle, WA 98101-3045 · 206-622-3150

Peter J. Mucklestone · Davis Wright Tremaine · 1201 Third Avenue, Suite 2200 · Seattle, WA 98101-3045 · 206-622-3150

Norman B. Page · Davis Wright Tremaine · 1201 Third Avenue, Suite 2200 · Seattle, WA 98101-3045 · 206-622-3150

Douglas R. Prince · Foster Pepper · http://www.foster.com · 1111 Third Avenue, Suite 3400 · Seattle, WA 98101-3299 · 206-447-4400

Joan E. Robinson · Lane Powell · http://www.lanepowell.com · U.S. Bank Centre, Suite 4100 · 1420 Fifth Avenue · Seattle, WA 98101-2338 · 206-223-7000

Bernard L. Russell · ⑩ · Davis Wright Tremaine · 1201 Third Avenue, Suite 2200 · Seattle, WA 98101-3045 · 206-622-3150

Holly K. Towle · ⑩ · K&L Gates · 925 Fourth Avenue, Suite 2900 · Seattle, WA 98104-1158 · 206-623-7580

W. Scott Wert · Stoel Rives · http://www.stoel.com · One Union Square, Suite 3600 · 600 University Street · Seattle, WA 98101-3197 · 206-624-0900

Spokane

Ned M. Barnes · ㉕ · Witherspoon, Kelley, Davenport & Toole · U.S. Bank Building, Suite 1100 · 422 West Riverside Avenue · Spokane, WA 99201-0302 · 509-624-5265

Jody K. Hamilton · K&L Gates · 618 West Riverside Avenue, Suite 300 · Spokane, WA 99201-0602 · 509-624-2100

Scott B. Lukins · ㉕ · Lukins & Annis · Washington Trust Financial Center, Suite 1600 · 717 West Sprague Avenue · Spokane, WA 99201-0466 · 509-455-9555

Lawrence R. Small · a · Paine, Hamblen · Washington Trust Financial Center, Suite 1200 · 717 West Sprague Avenue · Spokane, WA 99201-3505 · 509-455-6000

Charles F. Van Marter · a · Lukins & Annis · Washington Trust Financial Center, Suite 1600 · 717 West Sprague Avenue · Spokane, WA 99201-0466 · 509-455-9555

BANKRUPTCY AND CREDITOR-DEBTOR RIGHTS LAW

Seattle

C. Keith Allred · a · Davis Wright Tremaine · 1201 Third Avenue, Suite 2200 · Seattle, WA 98101-3045 206-622-3150

Christopher M. Alston · Foster Pepper · http://www.foster.com · 1111 Third Avenue, Suite 3400 · Seattle, WA 98101-3299 · 206-447-4400

Marc L. Barreca · K&L Gates · 925 Fourth Avenue, Suite 2900 · Seattle, WA 98104-1158 · 206-623-7580

Gayle E. Bush · 2) · Bush, Strout & Kornfeld · Two Union Square, Suite 5000 · 601 Union Street · Seattle, WA 98101-2373 · 206-292-2110

Jack J. Cullen · 2) · Foster Pepper · http://www.foster.com · 1111 Third Avenue, Suite 3400 · Seattle, WA 98101-3299 · 206-447-4400

Charles R. Ekberg · 2) · Lane Powell · http://www.lanepowell.com · U.S. Bank Centre, Suite 4100 · 1420 Fifth Avenue · Seattle, WA 98101-2338 · 206-223-7000

Geoffrey Groshong · Miller Nash · 4400 Two Union Square · 601 Union Street · Seattle, WA 98101-2352 206-622-8484

Dillon E. Jackson · 2% · Foster Pepper · http://www.foster.com · 1111 Third Avenue, Suite 3400 · Seattle, WA 98101-3299 · 206-447-4400

Armand J. Kornfeld · Bush, Strout & Kornfeld · Two Union Square, Suite 5000 · 601 Union Street · Seattle, WA 98101-2373 · 206-292-2110

Bruce W. Leaverton · Lane Powell · http://www.lanepowell.com · U.S. Bank Centre, Suite 4100 · 1420 Fifth Avenue · Seattle, WA 98101-2338 · 206-223-7000

David B. Levant · Stoel Rives · http://www.stoel.com · One Union Square, Suite 3600 · 600 University Street · Seattle, WA 98101-3197 · 206-624-0900

Craig Miller · Davis Wright Tremaine · 1201 Third Avenue, Suite 2200 · Seattle, WA 98101-3045 · 206-622-3150

Kimberly W. Osenbaugh · a · K&L Gates · 925 Fourth Avenue, Suite 2900 · Seattle, WA 98104-1158 · 206-623-7580

Ragan L. Powers · Davis Wright Tremaine · 1201 Third Avenue, Suite 2200 · Seattle, WA 98101-3045 · 206-622-3150

Lawrence Ream · Bullivant Houser Bailey · 1601 Fifth Avenue, Suite 2300 · Seattle, WA 98101-1618 · 206-292-8390

Joseph E. Shickich, Jr. · Riddell Williams · 1001 Fourth Avenue Plaza, Suite 4500 · Seattle, WA 98154-1192 · 206-624-3600

Spokane

Thomas T. Bassett · ⑳ · K&L Gates · 618 West Riverside Avenue, Suite 300 · Spokane, WA 99201-0602 509-624-2100

Daniel P. O'Rourke · ⑳ · Southwell & O'Rourke · Paulsen Center, Suite 960 · 421 West Riverside Avenue · Spokane, WA 99201-0405 · 509-624-0159

Peter A. Witherspoon · Workland & Witherspoon · Washington Mutual Financial Center, Suite 714 · 601 West Main Avenue · Spokane, WA 99201-0677 · 509-455-9077

BET-THE-COMPANY LITIGATION

Seattle

David J. Burman · ⑩ · Perkins Coie · http://www.perkinscoie.com · 1201 Third Avenue, Suite 4800 · Seattle, WA 98101-3099 · 206-359-8000

Kelly P. Corr · ⑩ · Corr Cronin Michelson Baumgardner & Preece · http://www.corrcronin.com · 1001 Fourth Avenue, Suite 3900 · Seattle, WA 98154 · 206-625-8600

BIOTECHNOLOGY LAW

Seattle

Kevin F. Kelly · Cooley Godward Kronish · 719 Second Avenue, Suite 900 · Seattle, WA 98104-7097

James R. Lisbakken · Perkins Coie · http://www.perkinscoie.com · 1201 Third Avenue, Suite 4800 · Seattle, WA 98101-3099 · 206-359-8000

Richard G. Sharkey · Seed Intellectual Property Law Group · http://www.seedip.com · 701 Fifth Avenue, Suite 5400 · Seattle, WA 98104-7092 · 206-622-4900

COMMERCIAL LITIGATION

Seattle

David A. Bateman · K&L Gates · 925 Fourth Avenue, Suite 2900 · Seattle, WA 98104-1158 · 206-623-7580

Kevin C. Baumgardner · Corr Cronin Michelson Baumgardner & Preece · http://www.corrcronin.com · 1001 Fourth Avenue, Suite 3900 · Seattle, WA 98154 · 206-625-8600

Ronald L. Berenstain · Perkins Coie · http://www.perkinscoie.com · 1201 Third Avenue, Suite 4800 · Seattle, WA 98101-3099 · 206-359-8000

Thomas L. Boeder · Perkins Coie · http://www.perkinscoie.com · 1201 Third Avenue, Suite 4800 · Seattle, WA 98101-3099 · 206-359-8000

Christopher I. Brain · ⑩ · Tousley Brain Stephens · 1700 Seventh Avenue, Suite 2200 · Seattle, WA 98101 · 206-682-5600

David J. Burman · ⑩ · Perkins Coie · http://www.perkinscoie.com · 1201 Third Avenue, Suite 4800 · Seattle, WA 98101-3099 · 206-359-8000

Kelly P. Corr · a · Corr Cronin Michelson Baumgardner & Preece · http://www.corrcronin.com · 1001 Fourth Avenue, Suite 3900 · Seattle, WA 98154 · 206-625-8600

William F. Cronin · Corr Cronin Michelson Baumgardner & Preece · http://www.corrcronin.com · 1001 Fourth Avenue, Suite 3900 · Seattle, WA 98154 · 206-625-8600

Peter Ehrlichman · Dorsey & Whitney · U.S. Bank Centre, Suite 3400 · 1420 Fifth Avenue · Seattle, WA 98101-4010 · 206-903-8800

Parker C. Folse III · Susman Godfrey · 1201 Third Avenue, Suite 3800 · Seattle, WA 98101-3000 · 206-516-3880

Keith Gerrard · a · Perkins Coie · http://www.perkinscoie.com · 1201 Third Avenue, Suite 4800 · Seattle, WA 98101-3099 · 206-359-8000

Charles C. Gordon · a · Gordon Tilden Thomas & Cordell · 1001 Fourth Avenue, Suite 4000 · Seattle, WA 98154-1007 · 206-467-6477

Marvin L. Gray, Jr. · a · Davis Wright Tremaine · 1201 Third Avenue, Suite 2200 · Seattle, WA 98101-3045 · 206-622-3150

Thomas J. Greenan · 2) · Gordon, Thomas, Honeywell, Malanca, Peterson & Daheim · One Union Square, Suite 2100 · 600 University Street · Seattle, WA 98101 · 206-676-7500

Camden M. Hall · Camden Hall · 1001 Fourth Avenue, Suite 4301 · Seattle, WA 98154-1119 · 206-749-0200

Arthur W. Harrigan, Jr. · a · Danielson, Harrigan, Leyh & Tollefson · 999 Third Avenue, Suite 4400 · Seattle, WA 98104 · 206-623-1700

David D. Hoff · Tousley Brain Stephens · 1700 Seventh Avenue, Suite 2200 · Seattle, WA 98101 · 206-682-5600

Barry M. Kaplan · Wilson Sonsini Goodrich & Rosati · 701 Fifth Avenue, Suite 5100 · Seattle, WA 98104-7036 · 206-883-2500

Stellman Keehnel · DLA Piper · 701 Fifth Avenue, Suite 7000 · Seattle, WA 98104-7044 · 206-839-4800

Bradley S. Keller · Byrnes & Keller · 1000 Second Avenue, 38th Floor · Seattle, WA 98104 · 206-622-2000

Steve Y. Koh · Perkins Coie · http://www.perkinscoie.com · 1201 Third Avenue, Suite 4800 · Seattle, WA 98101-3099 · 206-359-8000

Ladd B. Leavens · Davis Wright Tremaine · 1201 Third Avenue, Suite 2200 · Seattle, WA 98101-3045 · 206-622-3150

James L. Magee · a · Graham & Dunn · Pier 70, Suite 300 · 2801 Alaskan Way · Seattle, WA 98121-1128 206-624-8300

Jerry R. McNaul · McNaul, Ebel, Nawrot & Helgren · One Union Square, Suite 2700 · 600 University Street · Seattle, WA 98101-3143 · 206-467-1816

Kathleen M. O'Sullivan · Perkins Coie · http://www.perkinscoie.com · 1201 Third Avenue, Suite 4800 · Seattle, WA 98101-3099 · 206-359-8000

Louis D. Peterson · a · Hillis Clark Martin & Peterson · http://www.hcmp.com · 1221 Second Avenue, Suite 500 · Seattle, WA 98101-2925 · 206-623-1745

Joshua J. Preece · Corr Cronin Michelson Baumgardner & Preece · http://www.corrcronin.com · 1001 Fourth Avenue, Suite 3900 · Seattle, WA 98154 · 206-625-8600

Stephen M. Rummage · Davis Wright Tremaine · 1201 Third Avenue, Suite 2200 · Seattle, WA 98101-3045 · 206-622-3150

Harry H. Schneider, Jr. · Perkins Coie · http://www.perkinscoie.com · 1201 Third Avenue, Suite 4800 · Seattle, WA 98101-3099 · 206-359-8000

Mark W. Schneider · Perkins Coie · http://www.perkinscoie.com · 1201 Third Avenue, Suite 4800 · Seattle, WA 98101-3099 · 206-359-8000

William R. Squires III · Corr Cronin Michelson Baumgardner & Preece · http://www.corrcronin.com · 1001 Fourth Avenue, Suite 3900 · Seattle, WA 98154 · 206-625-8600

Kim D. Stephens · Tousley Brain Stephens · 1700 Seventh Avenue, Suite 2200 · Seattle, WA 98101 · 206-682-5600

Robert M. Sulkin · McNaul, Ebel, Nawrot & Helgren · One Union Square, Suite 2700 · 600 University Street · Seattle, WA 98101-3143 · 206-467-1816

Fredric C. Tausend · 2) · K&L Gates · 925 Fourth Avenue, Suite 2900 · Seattle, WA 98104-1158 · 206-623-7580

Jeffrey I. Tilden · Gordon Tilden Thomas & Cordell · 1001 Fourth Avenue, Suite 4000 · Seattle, WA 98154-1007 · 206-467-6477

John D. Wilson, Jr. · Wilson Smith Cochran Dickerson · The Financial Center, Suite 1700 · 1215 Fourth Avenue · Seattle, WA 98161-1007 · 206-623-4100

Richard C. Yarmuth · a · Yarmuth Wilsdon Calfo · The IDX Tower, Suite 2500 · 925 Fourth Avenue · Seattle, WA 98104 · 206-516-3800

Spokane

Eugene I. Annis · 2) · Lukins & Annis · Washington Trust Financial Center, Suite 1600 · 717 West Sprague Avenue · Spokane, WA 99201-0466 · 509-455-9555

Joseph P. Delay · 2) · Delay, Curran, Thompson, Pontarolo & Walker · 601 West Main Avenue, Suite 1212 · Spokane, WA 99201-0684 · 509-455-9500

Robert A. Dunn · Dunn & Black · Peyton Building, Suite 200 · 10 North Post · Spokane, WA 99201 · 509-455-8711

John P. Giesa · a · Reed & Giesa · 222 North Wall Street, Suite 410 · Spokane, WA 99201-0873 · 509-838-8341

John G. Layman · a · Layman, Layman & Robinson · 601 South Division Street · Spokane, WA 99202 · 509-455-8883

William D. Symmes · 2) · Witherspoon, Kelley, Davenport & Toole · U.S. Bank Building, Suite 1100 · 422 West Riverside Avenue · Spokane, WA 99201-0302 · 509-624-5265

Tacoma

Dennis S. Harlowe · Harlowe & Falk · One Tacoma Avenue North, Suite 300 · Tacoma, WA 98403 · 253-284-4410

William J. Rush · 2% · Rush, Hannula, Harkins & Kyler · 4701 South 19th Street, Suite 300 · Tacoma, WA 98405 · 253-383-5388

Yakima

David A. Thorner · Thorner, Kennedy & Gano · The Chestnut Legal Building · 101 South 12th Avenue · P.O. Box 1410 · Yakima, WA 98907-1410 · 509-575-1400

William L. Weigand, Jr. · Lyon, Weigand & Gustafson · 222 North Third Street · P.O. Box 1689 · Yakima, WA 98901 · 509-248-7220

COMMUNICATIONS LAW

Seattle

Richard J. Busch · Graham & Dunn · Pier 70, Suite 300 · 2801 Alaskan Way · Seattle, WA 98121-1128 · 206-624-8300

Arthur A. Butler · Ater Wynne · http://www.aterwynne.com · Two Union Square, Suite 1501 · 601 Union Street · Seattle, WA 98101-2341 · 206-623-4711

Michael Diehl · a · Susman Godfrey · 1201 Third Avenue, Suite 3800 · Seattle, WA 98101-3000 · 206-516-3880

Judith A. Endejan · Graham & Dunn · Pier 70, Suite 300 · 2801 Alaskan Way · Seattle, WA 98121-1128 · 206-624-8300

Gregory J. Kopta · Davis Wright Tremaine · 1201 Third Avenue, Suite 2200 · Seattle, WA 98101-3045 · 206-622-3150

Timothy J. O'Connell · Stoel Rives · http://www.stoel.com · One Union Square, Suite 3600 · 600 University Street · Seattle, WA 98101-3197 · 206-624-0900

Eric M. Stahl · Davis Wright Tremaine · 1201 Third Avenue, Suite 2200 · Seattle, WA 98101-3045 · 206-622-3150

Daniel M. Waggoner · a · Davis Wright Tremaine · 1201 Third Avenue, Suite 2200 · Seattle, WA 98101-3045 · 206-622-3150

Julie Weston · Davis Wright Tremaine · 1201 Third Avenue, Suite 2200 · Seattle, WA 98101-3045 · 206-622-3150

CONSTRUCTION LAW

Seattle

John P. Ahlers · Ahlers & Cressman · 999 Third Avenue, Suite 3100 · Seattle, WA 98104 · 206-287-9900

Stanton Phillip Beck · Lane Powell · http://www.lanepowell.com · U.S. Bank Centre, Suite 4100 · 1420 Fifth Avenue · Seattle, WA 98101-2338 · 206-223-7000

Jesse O. Franklin IV · K&L Gates · 925 Fourth Avenue, Suite 2900 · Seattle, WA 98104-1158 · 206-623-7580

David C. Groff · Groff Murphy Lawyers · 300 East Pine Street · Seattle, WA 98122 · 206-628-9500

Henry C. Jameson · Jameson Babbitt Stites & Lombard · 999 Third Avenue, Suite 1900 · Seattle, WA 98104 · 206-292-1994

Alan R. Merkle · Stoel Rives · http://www.stoel.com · One Union Square, Suite 3600 · 600 University Street · Seattle, WA 98101-3197 · 206-624-0900

Douglas S. Oles · Oles Morrison Rinker & Baker · 701 Pike Street, Suite 1700 · Seattle, WA 98101 · 206-623-3427

Richard O. Prentke · Perkins Coie · http://www.perkinscoie.com · 1201 Third Avenue, Suite 4800 · Seattle, WA 98101-3099 · 206-359-8000

CORPORATE GOVERNANCE AND COMPLIANCE LAW

Seattle

G. Scott Greenburg · K&L Gates · 925 Fourth Avenue, Suite 2900 · Seattle, WA 98104-1158 · 206-623-7580

Mark F. Hoffman · DLA Piper · 701 Fifth Avenue, Suite 7000 · Seattle, WA 98104-7044 · 206-839-4800

CORPORATE LAW

Seattle

Greg F. Adams · ⑩ · Davis Wright Tremaine · 1201 Third Avenue, Suite 2200 · Seattle, WA 98101-3045 · 206-622-3150

Keith G. Baldwin · Davis Wright Tremaine · 1201 Third Avenue, Suite 2200 · Seattle, WA 98101-3045 · 206-622-3150

Christopher Barry · Dorsey & Whitney · U.S. Bank Centre, Suite 3400 · 1420 Fifth Avenue · Seattle, WA 98101-4010 · 206-903-8800

Bruce T. Bjerke · Davis Wright Tremaine · 1201 Third Avenue, Suite 2200 · Seattle, WA 98101-3045 · 206-622-3150

Andrew Bor · Perkins Coie · http://www.perkinscoie.com · 1201 Third Avenue, Suite 4800 · Seattle, WA 98101-3099 · 206-359-8000

Dori E. Brewer · Perkins Coie · http://www.perkinscoie.com · 1201 Third Avenue, Suite 4800 · Seattle, WA 98101-3099 · 206-359-8000

Christopher M. Carletti · K&L Gates · 925 Fourth Avenue, Suite 2900 · Seattle, WA 98104-1158 · 206-623-7580

C. Kent Carlson · ㉕ · K&L Gates · 925 Fourth Avenue, Suite 2900 · Seattle, WA 98104-1158 · 206-623-7580

Stephan H. Coonrod · K&L Gates · 925 Fourth Avenue, Suite 2900 · Seattle, WA 98104-1158 · 206-623-7580

Eric A. Dejong · Perkins Coie · http://www.perkinscoie.com · 1201 Third Avenue, Suite 4800 · Seattle, WA 98101-3099 · 206-359-8000

Robert J. Diercks · ⑳ · Foster Pepper · http://www.foster.com · 1111 Third Avenue, Suite 3400 · Seattle, WA 98101-3299 · 206-447-4400

Richard B. Dodd · K&L Gates · 925 Fourth Avenue, Suite 2900 · Seattle, WA 98104-1158 · 206-623-7580

Michael D. Dwyer · Lane Powell · http://www.lanepowell.com · U.S. Bank Centre, Suite 4100 · 1420 Fifth Avenue · Seattle, WA 98101-2338 · 206-223-7000

Stephen C. Ellis · Davis Wright Tremaine · 1201 Third Avenue, Suite 2200 · Seattle, WA 98101-3045 · 206-622-3150

Michael J. Erickson · Summit Law Group · http://www.summitlaw.com · 315 Fifth Avenue, S, Suite 1000 Seattle, WA 98104-2682 · 206-676-7000

Robert Edward Giles · 2) · Perkins Coie · http://www.perkinscoie.com · 1201 Third Avenue, Suite 4800 · Seattle, WA 98101-3099 · 206-359-8000

D. Wayne Gittinger · 2% · Lane Powell · http://www.lanepowell.com · U.S. Bank Centre, Suite 4100 · 1420 Fifth Avenue · Seattle, WA 98101-2338 · 206-223-7000

Thomas F. Grohman · Lane Powell · http://www.lanepowell.com · U.S. Bank Centre, Suite 4100 · 1420 Fifth Avenue · Seattle, WA 98101-2338 · 206-223-7000

James M. Hilton · 2% · Perkins Coie · http://www.perkinscoie.com · 1201 Third Avenue, Suite 4800 · Seattle, WA 98101-3099 · 206-359-8000

Margaret C. Inouye · K&L Gates · 925 Fourth Avenue, Suite 2900 · Seattle, WA 98104-1158 · 206-623-7580

Allen D. Israel · Foster Pepper · http://www.foster.com · 1111 Third Avenue, Suite 3400 · Seattle, WA 98101-3299 · 206-447-4400

Robert D. Kaplan · 2) · Dorsey & Whitney · U.S. Bank Centre, Suite 3400 · 1420 Fifth Avenue · Seattle, WA 98101-4010 · 206-903-8800

Gary J. Kocher · K&L Gates · 925 Fourth Avenue, Suite 2900 · Seattle, WA 98104-1158 · 206-623-7580

Stewart M. Landefeld · a · Perkins Coie · http://www.perkinscoie.com · 1201 Third Avenue, Suite 4800 · Seattle, WA 98101-3099 · 206-359-8000

Ronald J. Lone · Stoel Rives · http://www.stoel.com · One Union Square, Suite 3600 · 600 University Street · Seattle, WA 98101-3197 · 206-624-0900

Douglas S. MacBain · Perkins Coie · http://www.perkinscoie.com · 1201 Third Avenue, Suite 4800 · Seattle, WA 98101-3099 · 206-359-8000

David F. McShea · Perkins Coie · http://www.perkinscoie.com · 1201 Third Avenue, Suite 4800 · Seattle, WA 98101-3099 · 206-359-8000

Michael E. Morgan · 2) · Lane Powell · http://www.lanepowell.com · U.S. Bank Centre, Suite 4100 · 1420 Fifth Avenue · Seattle, WA 98101-2338 · 206-223-7000

J. Shan Mullin · a · Perkins Coie · http://www.perkinscoie.com · 1201 Third Avenue, Suite 4800 · Seattle, WA 98101-3099 · 206-359-8000

William H. Neukom · K&L Gates · 925 Fourth Avenue, Suite 2900 · Seattle, WA 98104-1158 · 206-623-7580

R. Thomas Olson · a · Miller Nash · 4400 Two Union Square · 601 Union Street · Seattle, WA 98101-2352 · 206-622-8484

William G. Pusch · ⑳ · Davis Wright Tremaine · 1201 Third Avenue, Suite 2200 · Seattle, WA 98101-3045 · 206-622-3150

Douglass A. Raff · ⑩ · Riddell Williams · 1001 Fourth Avenue Plaza, Suite 4500 · Seattle, WA 98154-1192 · 206-624-3600

John A. Reed · ⑩ · Davis Wright Tremaine · 1201 Third Avenue, Suite 2200 · Seattle, WA 98101-3045 · 206-622-3150

John W. Robertson · Cooley Godward Kronish · 719 Second Avenue, Suite 900 · Seattle, WA 98104-7097

Patrick J. Schultheis · Wilson Sonsini Goodrich & Rosati · 701 Fifth Avenue, Suite 5100 · Seattle, WA 98104-7036 · 206-883-2500

Evelyn Cruz Sroufe · Perkins Coie · http://www.perkinscoie.com · 1201 Third Avenue, Suite 4800 · Seattle, WA 98101-3099 · 206-359-8000

Michael E. Stansbury · ⑳ · Perkins Coie · http://www.perkinscoie.com · 1201 Third Avenue, Suite 4800 · Seattle, WA 98101-3099 · 206-359-8000

John M. Steel · ⑩ · DLA Piper · 701 Fifth Avenue, Suite 7000 · Seattle, WA 98104-7044 · 206-839-4800

Jack G. Strother · Graham & Dunn · Pier 70, Suite 300 · 2801 Alaskan Way · Seattle, WA 98121-1128 · 206-624-8300

Irwin L. Treiger · ㉕ · Stoel Rives · http://www.stoel.com · One Union Square, Suite 3600 · 600 University Street · Seattle, WA 98101-3197 · 206-624-0900

William L. Weigand III · ⑳ · Davis Wright Tremaine · 1201 Third Avenue, Suite 2200 · Seattle, WA 98101-3045 · 206-622-3150

Joseph D. Weinstein · Davis Wright Tremaine · 1201 Third Avenue, Suite 2200 · Seattle, WA 98101-3045 · 206-622-3150

Joseph P. Whitford · Davis Wright Tremaine · 1201 Third Avenue, Suite 2200 · Seattle, WA 98101-3045 206-622-3150

Mark F. Worthington · Summit Law Group · http://www.summitlaw.com · 315 Fifth Avenue, S, Suite 1000 · Seattle, WA 98104-2682 · 206-676-7000

Spokane

Ned M. Barnes · ㉕ · Witherspoon, Kelley, Davenport & Toole · U.S. Bank Building, Suite 1100 · 422 West Riverside Avenue · Spokane, WA 99201-0302 · 509-624-5265

Patrick B. Cerutti · ⑳ · Lukins & Annis · Washington Trust Financial Center, Suite 1600 · 717 West Sprague Avenue · Spokane, WA 99201-0466 · 509-455-9555

Paul M. Davis · Lukins & Annis · Washington Trust Financial Center, Suite 1600 · 717 West Sprague Avenue · Spokane, WA 99201-0466 · 509-455-9555

Donald K. Querna · ⑩ · Randall & Danskin · Bank of America Financial Center, Suite 1500 · 601 West Riverside Avenue · Spokane, WA 99201 · 509-747-2052

Lawrence R. Small · ⑩ · Paine, Hamblen · Washington Trust Financial Center, Suite 1200 · 717 West Sprague Avenue · Spokane, WA 99201-3505 · 509-455-6000

Charles F. Van Marter · a · Lukins & Annis · Washington Trust Financial Center, Suite 1600 · 717 West Sprague Avenue · Spokane, WA 99201-0466 · 509-455-9555

Walla Walla

James K. Hayner · a · Minnick-Hayner · 249 West Alder Street · P.O. Box 1757 · Walla Walla, WA 99362-1757 · 509-527-3500

Yakima

Paul M. Larson · 2) · Larson Berg & Perkins · 105 North Third Street · P.O. Box 550 · Yakima, WA 98907 · 509-457-1515

Terry C. Schmalz · a · Velikanje Halverson · 405 East Lincoln Avenue · Yakima, WA 98901 · 509-248-6030

Morris G. Shore · 2) · Stokes Lawrence · 1433 Lakeside Court, Suite 100 · Yakima, WA 98902-7354 · 509-853-3000

EMINENT DOMAIN AND CONDEMNATION LAW

Seattle

Larry J. Smith · Graham & Dunn · Pier 70, Suite 300 · 2801 Alaskan Way · Seattle, WA 98121-1128 · 206-624-8300

Kim D. Stephens · Tousley Brain Stephens · 1700 Seventh Avenue, Suite 2200 · Seattle, WA 98101 · 206-682-5600

EMPLOYEE BENEFITS LAW

Bellevue

Jeff Belfiglio · Davis Wright Tremaine · 777 One-Hundred-Eighth Avenue, NE, Suite 2300 · Bellevue, WA 98004-5149 · 425-646-6100

Edmonds

Thomas P. McCormick · a · BenefitsVoice · 144 Railroad Avenue, Suite 235 · Edmonds, WA 98020 · 425-774-2070

Seattle

Devitt D. Barnett · a · Birmingham, Thorson & Barnett · Two Union Square, Suite 3315 · 601 Union Street · Seattle, WA 98101 · 206-467-1240

Richard J. Birmingham · a · Davis Wright Tremaine · 1201 Third Avenue, Suite 2200 · Seattle, WA 98101-3045 · 206-622-3150

J. Thomas Cristy · Perkins Coie · http://www.perkinscoie.com · 1201 Third Avenue, Suite 4800 · Seattle, WA 98101-3099 · 206-359-8000

Jason T. Froggatt · Davis Wright Tremaine · 1201 Third Avenue, Suite 2200 · Seattle, WA 98101-3045 · 206-622-3150

Nancy L. Gallup · a · Perkins Coie · http://www.perkinscoie.com · 1201 Third Avenue, Suite 4800 · Seattle, WA 98101-3099 · 206-359-8000

Karen E. Glover · a · K&L Gates · 925 Fourth Avenue, Suite 2900 · Seattle, WA 98104-1158 · 206-623-7580

Ralph L. Hawkins, Jr. · a · Davis Wright Tremaine · 1201 Third Avenue, Suite 2200 · Seattle, WA 98101-3045 · 206-622-3150

Richard A. Hopp · 2) · Stoel Rives · http://www.stoel.com · One Union Square, Suite 3600 · 600 University Street · Seattle, WA 98101-3197 · 206-624-0900

Kurt E. Linsenmayer · Perkins Coie · http://www.perkinscoie.com · 1201 Third Avenue, Suite 4800 · Seattle, WA 98101-3099 · 206-359-8000

Douglas M. Love · K&L Gates · 925 Fourth Avenue, Suite 2900 · Seattle, WA 98104-1158 · 206-623-7580

Judd R. Marten · 2) · LeSourd & Patten · One Union Square, Suite 2401 · 600 University Street · Seattle, WA 98101-4121 · 206-624-1040

Paul R. McDonald · a · Birmingham, Thorson & Barnett · Two Union Square, Suite 3315 · 601 Union Street · Seattle, WA 98101 · 206-467-1240

Norman S. Milks · K&L Gates · 925 Fourth Avenue, Suite 2900 · Seattle, WA 98104-1158 · 206-623-7580

Anne L. Northrup · 2) · Davis Wright Tremaine · 1201 Third Avenue, Suite 2200 · Seattle, WA 98101-3045 · 206-622-3150

Marianne O'Bara · Dorsey & Whitney · U.S. Bank Centre, Suite 3400 · 1420 Fifth Avenue · Seattle, WA 98101-4010 · 206-903-8800

Deirdre C. Thomas · K&L Gates · 925 Fourth Avenue, Suite 2900 · Seattle, WA 98104-1158 · 206-623-7580

Lee A. Thorson · 2) · Birmingham, Thorson & Barnett · Two Union Square, Suite 3315 · 601 Union Street · Seattle, WA 98101 · 206-467-1240

Charles H. Thulin · a · Ekman, Bohrer & Thulin · Queen Anne Square, Suite 400 · 220 West Mercer Street · Seattle, WA 98119-3966 · 206-282-8221

Mimi G. Warner · Stoel Rives · http://www.stoel.com · One Union Square, Suite 3600 · 600 University Street · Seattle, WA 98101-3197 · 206-624-0900

Spokane

K. Thomas Connolly · 2) · Witherspoon, Kelley, Davenport & Toole · U.S. Bank Building, Suite 1100 · 422 West Riverside Avenue · Spokane, WA 99201-0302 · 509-624-5265

Gair B. Petrie · a · Randall & Danskin · Bank of America Financial Center, Suite 1500 · 601 West Riverside Avenue · Spokane, WA 99201 · 509-747-2052

Timothy W. Quirk · a · Paine, Hamblen · Washington Trust Financial Center, Suite 1200 · 717 West Sprague Avenue · Spokane, WA 99201-3505 · 509-455-6000

ENERGY LAW

Bellevue

Donald G. Kari · a · Perkins Coie · http://www.perkinscoie.com · The PSE Building, Suite 700 · 10885 Northeast Fourth Street · Bellevue, WA 98004-5579 · 425-635-1400

Markham A. Quehrn · Perkins Coie · http://www.perkinscoie.com · The PSE Building, Suite 700 · 10885 Northeast Fourth Street · Bellevue, WA 98004-5579 · 425-635-1400

Bremerton

William S. Cummings · Friedman, Rubin & White · 1126 Highland Avenue · Bremerton, WA 98337 · 360-782-4300

Mill Creek

Terence L. Mundorf · a · Marsh Mundorf Pratt Sullivan & McKenzie · 16504 Ninth Avenue, SE, Suite 203 · Mill Creek, WA 98012 · 425-742-4545

Seattle

T. Ryan Durkan · a · Hillis Clark Martin & Peterson · http://www.hcmp.com · 1221 Second Avenue, Suite 500 · Seattle, WA 98101-2925 · 206-623-1745

Craig A. Gannett · Davis Wright Tremaine · 1201 Third Avenue, Suite 2200 · Seattle, WA 98101-3045 · 206-622-3150

Jerome L. Hillis · 2% · Hillis Clark Martin & Peterson · http://www.hcmp.com · 1221 Second Avenue, Suite 500 · Seattle, WA 98101-2925 · 206-623-1745

Peter D. Mostow · Wilson Sonsini Goodrich & Rosati · 701 Fifth Avenue, Suite 5100 · Seattle, WA 98104-7036 · 206-883-2500

Eric Redman · Heller Ehrman · 701 Fifth Avenue, Suite 6100 · Seattle, WA 98104-7098 · 206-447-0900

Elizabeth Thomas · K&L Gates · 925 Fourth Avenue, Suite 2900 · Seattle, WA 98104-1158 · 206-623-7580

Richard R. Wilson · a · Hillis Clark Martin & Peterson · http://www.hcmp.com · 1221 Second Avenue, Suite 500 · Seattle, WA 98101-2925 · 206-623-1745

Tacoma

James C. Waldo · a · Gordon, Thomas, Honeywell, Malanca, Peterson & Daheim · Wells Fargo Plaza, Suite 2100 · 1201 Pacific Avenue · Tacoma, WA 98101 · 253-620-6500

ENVIRONMENTAL LAW

Bellevue

Richard W. Elliott · Davis Wright Tremaine · 777 One-Hundred-Eighth Avenue, NE, Suite 2300 · Bellevue, WA 98004-5149 · 425-646-6100

David V. Marshall · Davis Wright Tremaine · 777 One-Hundred-Eighth Avenue, NE, Suite 2300 · Bellevue, WA 98004-5149 · 425-646-6100

J. Richard Aramburu · 2) · Aramburu- Eustis Law Offices · 720 Third Avenue, Suite 2112 · Seattle, WA 98104-1138 · 206-625-9515

Thomas Eli Backer · K&L Gates · 925 Fourth Avenue, Suite 2900 · Seattle, WA 98104-1158 · 206-623-7580

David A. Bricklin · a · Bricklin Newman Dold · http://bnd-law.com · 1001 Fourth Avenue, Suite 3303 · Seattle, WA 98154 · 206-264-8600

Rodney L. Brown, Jr. · a · Cascadia Law Group · 1201 Third Avenue, Suite 320 · Seattle, WA 98101 · 206-292-6300

Peter L. Buck · a · The Buck Law Group · 2030 First Avenue, Suite 201 · Seattle, WA 98121 · 206-448-6229

Brent Carson · GordonDerr · http://www.gordonderr.com · 2025 First Avenue, Suite 500 · Seattle, WA 98121-3140 · 206-382-9540

Jay P. Derr · GordonDerr · http://www.gordonderr.com · 2025 First Avenue, Suite 500 · Seattle, WA 98121-3140 · 206-382-9540

Loren R. Dunn · Riddell Williams · 1001 Fourth Avenue Plaza, Suite 4500 · Seattle, WA 98154-1192 · 206-624-3600

T. Ryan Durkan · a · Hillis Clark Martin & Peterson · http://www.hcmp.com · 1221 Second Avenue, Suite 500 · Seattle, WA 98101-2925 · 206-623-1745

Beth S. Ginsberg · Stoel Rives · http://www.stoel.com · One Union Square, Suite 3600 · 600 University Street · Seattle, WA 98101-3197 · 206-624-0900

Adam W. Gravley · GordonDerr · http://www.gordonderr.com · 2025 First Avenue, Suite 500 · Seattle, WA 98121-3140 · 206-382-9540

David M. Heineck · Summit Law Group · http://www.summitlaw.com · 315 Fifth Avenue, S, Suite 1000 · Seattle, WA 98104-2682 · 206-676-7000

G. Richard Hill · a · McCullough Hill · Columbia Center, Suite 7220 · 701 Fifth Avenue · Seattle, WA 98104 · 206-812-3388

Jerome L. Hillis · 2% · Hillis Clark Martin & Peterson · http://www.hcmp.com · 1221 Second Avenue, Suite 500 · Seattle, WA 98101-2925 · 206-623-1745

L. John Iani · Van Ness Feldman · Millennium Tower, Suite 1150 · 719 Second Avenue · Seattle, WA 98104 · 206-623-9372

Amy L. Kosterlitz · GordonDerr · http://www.gordonderr.com · 2025 First Avenue, Suite 500 · Seattle, WA 98121-3140 · 206-382-9540

Jeffrey W. Leppo · Stoel Rives · http://www.stoel.com · One Union Square, Suite 3600 · 600 University Street · Seattle, WA 98101-3197 · 206-624-0900

Konrad J. Liegel · K&L Gates · 925 Fourth Avenue, Suite 2900 · Seattle, WA 98104-1158 · 206-623-7580

Alexander Mackie · Perkins Coie · http://www.perkinscoie.com · 1201 Third Avenue, Suite 4800 · Seattle, WA 98101-3099 · 206-359-8000

Bradley M. Marten · a · Marten Law Group · 1191 Second Avenue, Suite 2200 · Seattle, WA 98101 · 206-292-2600

John C. McCullough, Jr. · a · McCullough Hill · Columbia Center, Suite 7220 · 701 Fifth Avenue · Seattle, WA 98104 · 206-812-3388

Philip Thomas McDonald · Cascadia Law Group · 1201 Third Avenue, Suite 320 · Seattle, WA 98101 · 206-292-6300

Polly L. McNeill · Summit Law Group · http://www.summitlaw.com · 315 Fifth Avenue, S, Suite 1000 · Seattle, WA 98104-2682 · 206-676-7000

Ralph H. Palumbo · 2) · Summit Law Group · http://www.summitlaw.com · 315 Fifth Avenue, S, Suite 1000 · Seattle, WA 98104-2682 · 206-676-7000

William W. Stelle · K&L Gates · 925 Fourth Avenue, Suite 2900 · Seattle, WA 98104-1158 · 206-623-7580

Daniel D. Syrdal · 2) · Heller Ehrman · 701 Fifth Avenue, Suite 6100 · Seattle, WA 98104-7098 · 206-447-0900

Lori A. Terry · Foster Pepper · http://www.foster.com · 1111 Third Avenue, Suite 3400 · Seattle, WA 98101-3299 · 206-447-4400

Michael R. Thorp · Heller Ehrman · 701 Fifth Avenue, Suite 6100 · Seattle, WA 98104-7098 · 206-447-0900

Craig S. Trueblood · K&L Gates · 925 Fourth Avenue, Suite 2900 · Seattle, WA 98104-1158 · 206-623-7580

J. Taylor Washburn · Foster Pepper · http://www.foster.com · 1111 Third Avenue, Suite 3400 · Seattle, WA 98101-3299 · 206-447-4400

Kenneth S. Weiner · K&L Gates · 925 Fourth Avenue, Suite 2900 · Seattle, WA 98104-1158 · 206-623-7580

Matthew D. Wells · K&L Gates · 925 Fourth Avenue, Suite 2900 · Seattle, WA 98104-1158 · 206-623-7580

Richard R. Wilson · a · Hillis Clark Martin & Peterson · http://www.hcmp.com · 1221 Second Avenue, Suite 500 · Seattle, WA 98101-2925 · 206-623-1745

EQUIPMENT FINANCE LAW

Seattle

Keith Gerrard · a · Perkins Coie · http://www.perkinscoie.com · 1201 Third Avenue, Suite 4800 · Seattle, WA 98101-3099 · 206-359-8000

Kit G. Narodick · Lane Powell · http://www.lanepowell.com · U.S. Bank Centre, Suite 4100 · 1420 Fifth Avenue · Seattle, WA 98101-2338 · 206-223-7000

FAMILY LAW

Bellevue

Thomas G. Hamerlinck · a · Thomas G. Hamerlinck · 10900 Northeast Fourth Street, Suite 2300 · Bellevue, WA 98004-5882 · 425-990-1075

Everett

Elizabeth A. Michelson · a · Elizabeth A. Michelson · 1604 Hewitt Avenue, Suite 516 · Everett, WA 98201-3536 · 425-258-4208

Seattle

Sherri M. Anderson · Sherri M. Anderson · 1411 Fourth Avenue, Suite 1220 · Seattle, WA 98101 · 206-254-1234

Mabry Chambliss DeBuys · a · K&L Gates · 925 Fourth Avenue, Suite 2900 · Seattle, WA 98104-1158 · 206-623-7580

Gordon W. Wilcox · 2) · Gordon W. Wilcox · 1191 Second Avenue, Eighteenth Floor · Seattle, WA 98101-2939 · 206-233-9300

Spokane

Terence R. Whitten · Lukins & Annis · Washington Trust Financial Center, Suite 1600 · 717 West Sprague Avenue · Spokane, WA 99201-0466 · 509-455-9555

Vancouver

Scott J. Horenstein · The Scott Horenstein Law Firm · 900 Washington Street, Suite 1020 · P.O. Box 61507 · Vancouver, WA 98666-1507 · 360-450-5054

FAMILY LAW MEDIATION

Seattle

Lawrence R. Besk · Lawrence R. Besk · 1200 Fifth Avenue, Suite 1820 · Seattle, WA 98101-3128 · 206-903-1820

Terrence A. Carroll · Judicial Dispute Resolution · 1411 Fourth Avenue, Suite 200 · Seattle, WA 98101 · 206-223-1669

Gerard M. Shellan · JAMS · 600 University Street, Suite 1910 · Seattle, WA 98101 · 800-626-5267

Spokane

Terence R. Whitten · Lukins & Annis · Washington Trust Financial Center, Suite 1600 · 717 West Sprague Avenue · Spokane, WA 99201-0466 · 509-455-9555

FIRST AMENDMENT LAW

Seattle

David J. Burman · a · Perkins Coie · http://www.perkinscoie.com · 1201 Third Avenue, Suite 4800 · Seattle, WA 98101-3099 · 206-359-8000

Stephen E. DeForest · Riddell Williams · 1001 Fourth Avenue Plaza, Suite 4500 · Seattle, WA 98154-1192 · 206-624-3600

Michele L. Earl-Hubbard · Allied Law Group · 12354 Thirtieth Avenure, NE · Seattle, WA 98125-5406 · 206-801-7510

Jessica L. Goldman · Summit Law Group · http://www.summitlaw.com · 315 Fifth Avenue, S, Suite 1000 Seattle, WA 98104-2682 · 206-676-7000

Shelley M. Hall · Stokes Lawrence · 800 Fifth Avenue, Suite 4000 · Seattle, WA 98104-3179 · 206-626-6000

Bruce E. H. Johnson · a · Davis Wright Tremaine · 1201 Third Avenue, Suite 2200 · Seattle, WA 98101-3045 · 206-622-3150

Marshall J. Nelson · a · Davis Wright Tremaine · 1201 Third Avenue, Suite 2200 · Seattle, WA 98101-3045 · 206-622-3150

Stephen A. Smith · K&L Gates · 925 Fourth Avenue, Suite 2900 · Seattle, WA 98104-1158 · 206-623-7580

Daniel M. Waggoner · a · Davis Wright Tremaine · 1201 Third Avenue, Suite 2200 · Seattle, WA 98101-3045 · 206-622-3150

Spokane

Duane M. Swinton · a · Witherspoon, Kelley, Davenport & Toole · U.S. Bank Building, Suite 1100 · 422 West Riverside Avenue · Spokane, WA 99201-0302 · 509-624-5265

FRANCHISE LAW

Seattle

Gary R. Duvall · a · Dorsey & Whitney · U.S. Bank Centre, Suite 3400 · 1420 Fifth Avenue · Seattle, WA 98101-4010 · 206-903-8800

GAMING LAW

Tacoma

Frank L. Miller · Miller Malone & Tellefson · 3110 Ruston Way, Suite F · Tacoma, WA 98402-5308 · 253-759-9595

GOVERNMENT RELATIONS LAW

Seattle

Slade Gorton · K&L Gates · 925 Fourth Avenue, Suite 2900 · Seattle, WA 98104-1158 · 206-623-7580

HEALTH CARE LAW

Seattle

Bradley J. Berg · a · Foster Pepper · http://www.foster.com · 1111 Third Avenue, Suite 3400 · Seattle, WA 98101-3299 · 206-447-4400

Carla M. DewBerry · Garvey Schubert Barer · Second & Seneca Building, Suite 1800 · 1191 Second Avenue · Seattle, WA 98101-2939 · 206-464-3939

Susan G. Duffy · a · Davis Wright Tremaine · 1201 Third Avenue, Suite 2200 · Seattle, WA 98101-3045 206-622-3150

Peter N. Grant · a · Davis Wright Tremaine · 1201 Third Avenue, Suite 2200 · Seattle, WA 98101-3045 · 206-622-3150

Robert G. Homchick · Davis Wright Tremaine · 1201 Third Avenue, Suite 2200 · Seattle, WA 98101-3045 · 206-622-3150

David B. Robbins · Bennett, Bigelow & Leedom · 1700 Seventh Avenue, Suite 1900 · Seattle, WA 98101-1397 · 206-622-5511

Douglas C. Ross · Davis Wright Tremaine · 1201 Third Avenue, Suite 2200 · Seattle, WA 98101-3045 · 206-622-3150

Barbara A. Shickich · Riddell Williams · 1001 Fourth Avenue Plaza, Suite 4500 · Seattle, WA 98154-1192 · 206-624-3600

Lee R. Voorhees · a · Foster Pepper · http://www.foster.com · 1111 Third Avenue, Suite 3400 · Seattle, WA 98101-3299 · 206-447-4400

Robert J. Walerius · a · Miller Nash · 4400 Two Union Square · 601 Union Street · Seattle, WA 98101-2352 · 206-622-8484

Rebecca L. Williams · Davis Wright Tremaine · 1201 Third Avenue, Suite 2200 · Seattle, WA 98101-3045 · 206-622-3150

Spokane

Mary R. Giannini · Witherspoon, Kelley, Davenport & Toole · U.S. Bank Building, Suite 1100 · 422 West Riverside Avenue · Spokane, WA 99201-0302 · 509-624-5265

IMMIGRATION LAW

Olympia

Lisa Seifert · Seifert Law Offices · 112 East Fourth Avenue, Suite 200-A · Olympia, WA 98501 · 360-357-7087

Seattle

Janet H. Cheetham · Ryan, Swanson & Cleveland · http://www.ryanlaw.com · 1201 Third Avenue, Suite 3400 · Seattle, WA 98101-3034 · 206-464-4224

Pamela S. Cowan · Cowan, Miller & Lederman · 1000 Second Avenue, Suite 1620 · Seattle, WA 98104 · 206-340-1033

Carol L. Edward · a · Law Offices of Carol L. Edward & Associates · http://www.seattle-immigration.com · 500 Denny Way · Seattle, WA 98109 · 206-956-9556

Robert A. Free · a · MacDonald, Hoague & Bayless · Hoge Building, Suite 1500 · 705 Second Avenue · Seattle, WA 98104-1745 · 206-622-1604

Robert H. Gibbs · Gibbs Houston Pauw · 1000 Second Avenue, Suite 1600 · Seattle, WA 98104 · 206-682-1080

Felicia L. Gittleman · a · MacDonald, Hoague & Bayless · Hoge Building, Suite 1500 · 705 Second Avenue · Seattle, WA 98104-1745 · 206-622-1604

Ester Greenfield · a · MacDonald, Hoague & Bayless · Hoge Building, Suite 1500 · 705 Second Avenue · Seattle, WA 98104-1745 · 206-622-1604

Kevin Lederman · a · Cowan, Miller & Lederman · 1000 Second Avenue, Suite 1620 · Seattle, WA 98104 · 206-340-1033

Steven S. Miller · Cowan, Miller & Lederman · 1000 Second Avenue, Suite 1620 · Seattle, WA 98104 · 206-340-1033

Joel H. Paget · a · Ryan, Swanson & Cleveland · http://www.ryanlaw.com · 1201 Third Avenue, Suite 3400 · Seattle, WA 98101-3034 · 206-464-4224

Richard M. Rawson · Davis Wright Tremaine · 1201 Third Avenue, Suite 2200 · Seattle, WA 98101-3045 206-622-3150

Gregg Rodgers · Garvey Schubert Barer · Second & Seneca Building, Suite 1800 · 1191 Second Avenue · Seattle, WA 98101-2939 · 206-464-3939

Daniel Hoyt Smith · a · MacDonald, Hoague & Bayless · Hoge Building, Suite 1500 · 705 Second Avenue · Seattle, WA 98104-1745 · 206-622-1604

Paul M. Soreff · a · Paul Soreff · Hoge Building, Suite 1601 · 705 Second Avenue · Seattle, WA 98104 · 206-282-1955

INFORMATION TECHNOLOGY LAW

Bellevue

Steven E. Pope · Perkins Coie · http://www.perkinscoie.com · The PSE Building, Suite 700 · 10885 Northeast Fourth Street · Bellevue, WA 98004-5579 · 425-635-1400

Seattle

Robert C. Cumbow · Graham & Dunn · Pier 70, Suite 300 · 2801 Alaskan Way · Seattle, WA 98121-1128 206-624-8300

William O. Ferron, Jr. · a · Seed Intellectual Property Law Group · http://www.seedip.com · 701 Fifth Avenue, Suite 5400 · Seattle, WA 98104-7092 · 206-622-4900

Richard R. Rohde · a · Perkins Coie · http://www.perkinscoie.com · 1201 Third Avenue, Suite 4800 · Seattle, WA 98101-3099 · 206-359-8000

Roger M. Tolbert · a · Fenwick & West · 1191 Second Avenue, Tenth Floor · Seattle, WA 98101 · 206-389-4510

Holly K. Towle · a · K&L Gates · 925 Fourth Avenue, Suite 2900 · Seattle, WA 98104-1158 · 206-623-7580

INSURANCE LAW

Seattle

Thomas F. Ahearne · Foster Pepper · http://www.foster.com · 1111 Third Avenue, Suite 3400 · Seattle, WA 98101-3299 · 206-447-4400

David M. Brenner · Riddell Williams · 1001 Fourth Avenue Plaza, Suite 4500 · Seattle, WA 98154-1192 · 206-624-3600

A. Richard Dykstra · Stafford Frey Cooper · Two Union Square, Suite 3100 · 601 Union Street · Seattle, WA 98101 · 206-623-9900

Charles C. Gordon · a · Gordon Tilden Thomas & Cordell · 1001 Fourth Avenue, Suite 4000 · Seattle, WA 98154-1007 · 206-467-6477

John T. Petrie · Ryan, Swanson & Cleveland · http://www.ryanlaw.com · 1201 Third Avenue, Suite 3400 · Seattle, WA 98101-3034 · 206-464-4224

Jerret E. Sale · Bullivant Houser Bailey · 1601 Fifth Avenue, Suite 2300 · Seattle, WA 98101-1618 · 206-292-8390

Scott M. Stickney · Wilson Smith Cochran Dickerson · The Financial Center, Suite 1700 · 1215 Fourth Avenue · Seattle, WA 98161-1007 · 206-623-4100

Jeffrey I. Tilden · Gordon Tilden Thomas & Cordell · 1001 Fourth Avenue, Suite 4000 · Seattle, WA 98154-1007 · 206-467-6477

Bruce Winchell · Mills Meyers Swartling · 1000 Second Avenue, 30th Floor · Seattle, WA 98104-1064 · 206-382-1000

INTELLECTUAL PROPERTY LAW

Bainbridge Island

Martin F. Smith · Martin F. Smith · 6380 Notheast Mitchell Lane · Bainbridge Island, WA 98110-3659 · 206-842-8597

Mercer Island

Donald S. Chisum · a · Donald S. Chisum · P.O. Box 1678 · Mercer Island, WA 98040-1678 · 206-760-2977

Ramsey M. Al-Salam · ⑩ · Perkins Coie · http://www.perkinscoie.com · 1201 Third Avenue, Suite 4800 · Seattle, WA 98101-3099 · 206-359-8000

Brian G. Bodine · Merchant & Gould · 701 Fifth Avenue, Suite 4100 · Seattle, WA 98104 · 206-342-6200

Stuart R. Dunwoody · Davis Wright Tremaine · 1201 Third Avenue, Suite 2200 · Seattle, WA 98101-3045 · 206-622-3150

William O. Ferron, Jr. · ⑩ · Seed Intellectual Property Law Group · http://www.seedip.com · 701 Fifth Avenue, Suite 5400 · Seattle, WA 98104-7092 · 206-622-4900

Karl R. Hermanns · Seed Intellectual Property Law Group · http://www.seedip.com · 701 Fifth Avenue, Suite 5400 · Seattle, WA 98104-7092 · 206-622-4900

Lee E. Johnson · ⑩ · Christensen, O'Connor, Johnson & Kindness · 1420 Fifth Avenue, Suite 2800 · Seattle, WA 98101-2347 · 206-682-8100

Gary S. Kindness · ⑩ · Christensen, O'Connor, Johnson & Kindness · 1420 Fifth Avenue, Suite 2800 · Seattle, WA 98101-2347 · 206-682-8100

David T. McDonald · K&L Gates · 925 Fourth Avenue, Suite 2900 · Seattle, WA 98104-1158 · 206-623-7580

Jerald E. Nagae · ⑩ · Christensen, O'Connor, Johnson & Kindness · 1420 Fifth Avenue, Suite 2800 · Seattle, WA 98101-2347 · 206-682-8100

Marshall J. Nelson · ⑩ · Davis Wright Tremaine · 1201 Third Avenue, Suite 2200 · Seattle, WA 98101-3045 · 206-622-3150

Paul T. Parker · Perkins Coie · http://www.perkinscoie.com · 1201 Third Avenue, Suite 4800 · Seattle, WA 98101-3099 · 206-359-8000

Maurice J. Pirio · Perkins Coie · http://www.perkinscoie.com · 1201 Third Avenue, Suite 4800 · Seattle, WA 98101-3099 · 206-359-8000

Karl J. Quackenbush · Riddell Williams · 1001 Fourth Avenue Plaza, Suite 4500 · Seattle, WA 98154-1192 · 206-624-3600

Warren J. Rheaume · Davis Wright Tremaine · 1201 Third Avenue, Suite 2200 · Seattle, WA 98101-3045 · 206-622-3150

Jerry A. Riedinger · Perkins Coie · http://www.perkinscoie.com · 1201 Third Avenue, Suite 4800 · Seattle, WA 98101-3099 · 206-359-8000

George C. Rondeau, Jr. · Davis Wright Tremaine · 1201 Third Avenue, Suite 2200 · Seattle, WA 98101-3045 · 206-622-3150

Leslie C. Ruiter · Stokes Lawrence · 800 Fifth Avenue, Suite 4000 · Seattle, WA 98104-3179 · 206-626-6000

Heidi Lynne Sachs · Perkins Coie · http://www.perkinscoie.com · 1201 Third Avenue, Suite 4800 · Seattle, WA 98101-3099 · 206-359-8000

Jeffrey M. Sakoi · Christensen, O'Connor, Johnson & Kindness · 1420 Fifth Avenue, Suite 2800 · Seattle, WA 98101-2347 · 206-682-8100

Richard G. Sharkey · Seed Intellectual Property Law Group · http://www.seedip.com · 701 Fifth Avenue, Suite 5400 · Seattle, WA 98104-7092 · 206-622-4900

Roger M. Tolbert · a · Fenwick & West · 1191 Second Avenue, Tenth Floor · Seattle, WA 98101 · 206-389-4510

James R. Uhlir · a · Christensen, O'Connor, Johnson & Kindness · 1420 Fifth Avenue, Suite 2800 · Seattle, WA 98101-2347 · 206-682-8100

Steve B. Winters · Lane Powell · http://www.lanepowell.com · U.S. Bank Centre, Suite 4100 · 1420 Fifth Avenue · Seattle, WA 98101-2338 · 206-223-7000

INTERNATIONAL TRADE AND FINANCE LAW

Seattle

J. Shan Mullin · a · Perkins Coie · http://www.perkinscoie.com · 1201 Third Avenue, Suite 4800 · Seattle, WA 98101-3099 · 206-359-8000

Gary P. Tober · Lane Powell · http://www.lanepowell.com · U.S. Bank Centre, Suite 4100 · 1420 Fifth Avenue · Seattle, WA 98101-2338 · 206-223-7000

LABOR AND EMPLOYMENT LAW

Bellevue

Jillian Barron · Sebris Busto James · 14205 Southeast 36th Street, Suite 325 · Bellevue, WA 98006 · 425-454-4233

Mark W. Berry · Davis Wright Tremaine · 777 One-Hundred-Eighth Avenue, NE, Suite 2300 · Bellevue, WA 98004-5149 · 425-646-6100

Mark R. Busto · a · Sebris Busto James · 14205 Southeast 36th Street, Suite 325 · Bellevue, WA 98006 · 425-454-4233

Charles N. Eberhardt · Perkins Coie · http://www.perkinscoie.com · The PSE Building, Suite 700 · 10885 Northeast Fourth Street · Bellevue, WA 98004-5579 · 425-635-1400

Henry E. Farber · Davis Wright Tremaine · 777 One-Hundred-Eighth Avenue, NE, Suite 2300 · Bellevue, WA 98004-5149 · 425-646-6100

Lawrence B. Hannah · Perkins Coie · http://www.perkinscoie.com · The PSE Building, Suite 700 · 10885 Northeast Fourth Street · Bellevue, WA 98004-5579 · 425-635-1400

Jeffrey A. James · Sebris Busto James · 14205 Southeast 36th Street, Suite 325 · Bellevue, WA 98006 · 425-454-4233

Robert Sebris, Jr. · a · Sebris Busto James · 14205 Southeast 36th Street, Suite 325 · Bellevue, WA 98006 · 425-454-4233

M. Edward Taylor · Sebris Busto James · 14205 Southeast 36th Street, Suite 325 · Bellevue, WA 98006 · 425-454-4233

Seattle

John F. Aslin · 2% · Perkins Coie · http://www.perkinscoie.com · 1201 Third Avenue, Suite 4800 · Seattle, WA 98101-3099 · 206-359-8000

Margaret L. Barbier · Stoel Rives · http://www.stoel.com · One Union Square, Suite 3600 · 600 University Street · Seattle, WA 98101-3197 · 206-624-0900

Clemens H. Barnes · 2% · Graham & Dunn · Pier 70, Suite 300 · 2801 Alaskan Way · Seattle, WA 98121-1128 · 206-624-8300

Robert A. Blackstone · a · Davis Wright Tremaine · 1201 Third Avenue, Suite 2200 · Seattle, WA 98101-3045 · 206-622-3150

Carolyn Cairns · 2) · Stokes Lawrence · 800 Fifth Avenue, Suite 4000 · Seattle, WA 98104-3179 · 206-626-6000

Bruce Michael Cross · 2% · Perkins Coie · http://www.perkinscoie.com · 1201 Third Avenue, Suite 4800 · Seattle, WA 98101-3099 · 206-359-8000

James R. Dickens · Miller Nash · 4400 Two Union Square · 601 Union Street · Seattle, WA 98101-2352 · 206-622-8484

Mary Elizabeth Drobka · Davis Wright Tremaine · 1201 Third Avenue, Suite 2200 · Seattle, WA 98101-3045 · 206-622-3150

Michael Droke · Dorsey & Whitney · U.S. Bank Centre, Suite 3400 · 1420 Fifth Avenue · Seattle, WA 98101-4010 · 206-903-8800

Clifton L. Elliott · 2% · Davis Wright Tremaine · 1201 Third Avenue, Suite 2200 · Seattle, WA 98101-3045 · 206-622-3150

Kelby D. Fletcher · 2) · Peterson, Young & Putra · 1501 Fourth Avenue, Suite 2800 · Seattle, WA 98101 · 206-624-6800

Katrin E. Frank · a · MacDonald, Hoague & Bayless · Hoge Building, Suite 1500 · 705 Second Avenue · Seattle, WA 98104-1745 · 206-622-1604

Steven B. Frank · a · Frank Freed Subit & Thomas · Hoge Building, Suite 1200 · 705 Second Avenue · Seattle, WA 98104-1729 · 206-682-6711

Clifford Freed · Frank Freed Subit & Thomas · Hoge Building, Suite 1200 · 705 Second Avenue · Seattle, WA 98104-1729 · 206-682-6711

Kevin J. Hamilton · Perkins Coie · http://www.perkinscoie.com · 1201 Third Avenue, Suite 4800 · Seattle, WA 98101-3099 · 206-359-8000

Jeffrey A. Hollingsworth · Perkins Coie · http://www.perkinscoie.com · 1201 Third Avenue, Suite 4800 · Seattle, WA 98101-3099 · 206-359-8000

Robert M. Howie · Riddell Williams · 1001 Fourth Avenue Plaza, Suite 4500 · Seattle, WA 98154-1192 · 206-624-3600

Valerie L. Hughes · Perkins Coie · http://www.perkinscoie.com · 1201 Third Avenue, Suite 4800 · Seattle, WA 98101-3099 · 206-359-8000

Lawton Humphrey · Davis Wright Tremaine · 1201 Third Avenue, Suite 2200 · Seattle, WA 98101-3045 206-622-3150

Mark A. Hutcheson · 2% · Davis Wright Tremaine · 1201 Third Avenue, Suite 2200 · Seattle, WA 98101-3045 · 206-622-3150

Karen F. Jones · a · Riddell Williams · 1001 Fourth Avenue Plaza, Suite 4500 · Seattle, WA 98154-1192 · 206-624-3600

Michael J. Killeen · Davis Wright Tremaine · 1201 Third Avenue, Suite 2200 · Seattle, WA 98101-3045 · 206-622-3150

M. Colleen Kinerk · a · Cable, Langenbach, Kinerk & Bauer · 1000 Second Avenue, Suite 3500 · Seattle, WA 98104-1048 · 206-292-8800

Otto G. Klein III · a · Summit Law Group · http://www.summitlaw.com · 315 Fifth Avenue, S, Suite 1000 · Seattle, WA 98104-2682 · 206-676-7000

Ronald J. Knox · Garvey Schubert Barer · Second & Seneca Building, Suite 1800 · 1191 Second Avenue · Seattle, WA 98101-2939 · 206-464-3939

Thomas A. Lemly · 2) · Davis Wright Tremaine · 1201 Third Avenue, Suite 2200 · Seattle, WA 98101-3045 · 206-622-3150

Judith A. Lonnquist · 2) · Law Offices of Judith A. Lonnquist · Seattle Tower, Suite 1500 · 1218 Third Avenue · Seattle, WA 98101-3021 · 206-622-2086

Patrick M. Madden · K&L Gates · 925 Fourth Avenue, Suite 2900 · Seattle, WA 98104-1158 · 206-623-7580

Marco J. Magnano, Jr. · Foster Pepper · http://www.foster.com · 1111 Third Avenue, Suite 3400 · Seattle, WA 98101-3299 · 206-447-4400

James Markham Marshall · a · Lane Powell · http://www.lanepowell.com · U.S. Bank Centre, Suite 4100 · 1420 Fifth Avenue · Seattle, WA 98101-2338 · 206-223-7000

Timothy J. O'Connell · Stoel Rives · http://www.stoel.com · One Union Square, Suite 3600 · 600 University Street · Seattle, WA 98101-3197 · 206-624-0900

Richard J. Omata · a · Karr Tuttle Campbell · http://www.karrtuttle.com · 1201 Third Avenue, Suite 2900 · Seattle, WA 98101-3028 · 206-223-1313

Kenneth J. Pedersen · Reid, Pedersen, McCarthy & Ballew · 101 Elliott Avenue West, Suite 550 · Seattle, WA 98119 · 206-285-3610

Russell L. Perisho · a · Perkins Coie · http://www.perkinscoie.com · 1201 Third Avenue, Suite 4800 · Seattle, WA 98101-3099 · 206-359-8000

Thomas E. Platt · Perkins Coie · http://www.perkinscoie.com · 1201 Third Avenue, Suite 4800 · Seattle, WA 98101-3099 · 206-359-8000

Anne Preston · Garvey Schubert Barer · Second & Seneca Building, Suite 1800 · 1191 Second Avenue · Seattle, WA 98101-2939 · 206-464-3939

Michael Reiss · a · Davis Wright Tremaine · 1201 Third Avenue, Suite 2200 · Seattle, WA 98101-3045 · 206-622-3150

Michael T. Reynvaan · Perkins Coie · http://www.perkinscoie.com · 1201 Third Avenue, Suite 4800 · Seattle, WA 98101-3099 · 206-359-8000

Richard H. Robblee · a · Rinehart & Robblee · 2101 Fourth Avenue, Suite 200 · Seattle, WA 98121 · 206-467-6700

Jon Howard Rosen · 2) · Rosen Law Firm · Hoge Building, Suite 1200 · 705 Second Avenue · Seattle, WA 98104-1798 · 206-652-1464

Jerome L. Rubin · 2) · Stoel Rives · http://www.stoel.com · One Union Square, Suite 3600 · 600 University Street · Seattle, WA 98101-3197 · 206-624-0900

Bruce L. Schroeder · Summit Law Group · http://www.summitlaw.com · 315 Fifth Avenue, S, Suite 1000 Seattle, WA 98104-2682 · 206-676-7000

Lawrence R. Schwerin · 2) · Schwerin Campbell Barnard & Iglitzin · 18 West Mercer Street, Suite 400 · Seattle, WA 98119 · 206-285-2828

Sidney J. Strong · 2) · Law Offices of Sidney J. Strong · 600 University Street, Suite 2100 · Seattle, WA 98101 · 206-623-5221

Michael Craig Subit · Frank Freed Subit & Thomas · Hoge Building, Suite 1200 · 705 Second Avenue · Seattle, WA 98104-1729 · 206-682-6711

Suzanne J. Thomas · K&L Gates · 925 Fourth Avenue, Suite 2900 · Seattle, WA 98104-1158 · 206-623-7580

Sheryl J. Willert · a · Williams Kastner · Two Union Square, Suite 4100 · 601 Union Street · P.O. Box 21926 · Seattle, WA 98111-3926 · 206-628-6600

Nancy Williams · a · Perkins Coie · http://www.perkinscoie.com · 1201 Third Avenue, Suite 4800 · Seattle, WA 98101-3099 · 206-359-8000

Jesse Wing · MacDonald, Hoague & Bayless · Hoge Building, Suite 1500 · 705 Second Avenue · Seattle, WA 98104-1745 · 206-622-1604

Steven H. Winterbauer · Winterbauer & Diamond · 1200 Fifth Avenue, Suite 1910 · Seattle, WA 98101 · 206-676-8440

Spokane

Thomas W. McLane · Allen & McLane · The Paulsen Center, Suite 421 · 421 West Riverside Avenue · Spokane, WA 99201 · 509-777-2211

Michael F. Nienstedt · Witherspoon, Kelley, Davenport & Toole · U.S. Bank Building, Suite 1100 · 422 West Riverside Avenue · Spokane, WA 99201-0302 · 509-624-5265

Kevin W. Roberts · Dunn & Black · Peyton Building, Suite 200 · 10 North Post · Spokane, WA 99201 · 509-455-8711

LAND USE & ZONING LAW

Seattle

Glenn J. Amster · Lane Powell · http://www.lanepowell.com · U.S. Bank Centre, Suite 4100 · 1420 Fifth Avenue · Seattle, WA 98101-2338 · 206-223-7000

Peter L. Buck · a · The Buck Law Group · 2030 First Avenue, Suite 201 · Seattle, WA 98121 · 206-448-6229

Brent Carson · GordonDerr · http://www.gordonderr.com · 2025 First Avenue, Suite 500 · Seattle, WA 98121-3140 · 206-382-9540

Jay P. Derr · GordonDerr · http://www.gordonderr.com · 2025 First Avenue, Suite 500 · Seattle, WA 98121-3140 · 206-382-9540

T. Ryan Durkan · a · Hillis Clark Martin & Peterson · http://www.hcmp.com · 1221 Second Avenue, Suite 500 · Seattle, WA 98101-2925 · 206-623-1745

Thomas A. Goeltz · a · Davis Wright Tremaine · 1201 Third Avenue, Suite 2200 · Seattle, WA 98101-3045 · 206-622-3150

G. Richard Hill · a · McCullough Hill · Columbia Center, Suite 7220 · 701 Fifth Avenue · Seattle, WA 98104 · 206-812-3388

Jerome L. Hillis · 2% · Hillis Clark Martin & Peterson · http://www.hcmp.com · 1221 Second Avenue, Suite 500 · Seattle, WA 98101-2925 · 206-623-1745

John E. Keegan · Davis Wright Tremaine · 1201 Third Avenue, Suite 2200 · Seattle, WA 98101-3045 · 206-622-3150

Amy L. Kosterlitz · GordonDerr · http://www.gordonderr.com · 2025 First Avenue, Suite 500 · Seattle, WA 98121-3140 · 206-382-9540

Eric S. Laschever · Stoel Rives · http://www.stoel.com · One Union Square, Suite 3600 · 600 University Street · Seattle, WA 98101-3197 · 206-624-0900

John C. McCullough, Jr. · a · McCullough Hill · Columbia Center, Suite 7220 · 701 Fifth Avenue · Seattle, WA 98104 · 206-812-3388

J. Taylor Washburn · Foster Pepper · http://www.foster.com · 1111 Third Avenue, Suite 3400 · Seattle, WA 98101-3299 · 206-447-4400

Richard R. Wilson · a · Hillis Clark Martin & Peterson · http://www.hcmp.com · 1221 Second Avenue, Suite 500 · Seattle, WA 98101-2925 · 206-623-1745

Spokane

Stanley M. Schwartz · Witherspoon, Kelley, Davenport & Toole · U.S. Bank Building, Suite 1100 · 422 West Riverside Avenue · Spokane, WA 99201-0302 · 509-624-5265

Tacoma

William T. Lynn · a · Gordon, Thomas, Honeywell, Malanca, Peterson & Daheim · Wells Fargo Plaza, Suite 2100 · 1201 Pacific Avenue · Tacoma, WA 98101 · 253-620-6500

LEGAL MALPRACTICE LAW

Bellevue

Richard B. Kilpatrick · a · Richard B. Kilpatrick · Nine Lake Bellevue Drive, Suite 210 · Bellevue, WA 98005-2454 · 425-453-8161

Seattle

Roger K. Anderson · a · Roger K. Anderson · 2101 Fourth Avenue, Suite 2100 · Seattle, WA 98121-2359 206-448-2100

Tyna Ek · Soha and Lang · 701 Fifth Avenue, Suite 2400 · Seattle, WA 98104 · 206-624-1800

Samuel B. Franklin · a · Lee, Smart · 1800 One Convention Place · 701 Pike Street · Seattle, WA 98101-3929 · 206-624-7990

Robert B. Gould · a · The Law Offices of Robert B. Gould · Pacific Pointe Building, Suite 100 · 2110 North Pacific Street · Seattle, WA 98103-9181 · 206-633-4442

Mark A. Johnson · a · Johnson Flora · 2505 Second Avenue, Suite 500 · Seattle, WA 98121 · 206-386-5566

Bradley S. Keller · Byrnes & Keller · 1000 Second Avenue, 38th Floor · Seattle, WA 98104 · 206-622-2000

Christopher C. Pence · a · Law Office of Christopher Pence · 1111 Third Avenue, Suite 3400 · Seattle, WA 98101 · 206-254-5630

Paul R. Taylor · Byrnes & Keller · 1000 Second Avenue, 38th Floor · Seattle, WA 98104 · 206-622-2000

Joel E. Wright · Lee, Smart · 1800 One Convention Place · 701 Pike Street · Seattle, WA 98101-3929 · 206-624-7990

MARITIME LAW

Seattle

Michael A. Barcott · a · Holmes Weddle & Barcott · 999 Third Avenue, Suite 2600 · Seattle, WA 98104 206-292-8008

David Danielson · 2) · Danielson, Harrigan, Leyh & Tollefson · 999 Third Avenue, Suite 4400 · Seattle, WA 98104 · 206-623-1700

C. Steven Fury · a · Fury Bailey · 710 Tenth Avenue East · P.O. Box 20397 · Seattle, WA 98102 · 206-726-6600

Barbara L. Holland · Garvey Schubert Barer · Second & Seneca Building, Suite 1800 · 1191 Second Avenue · Seattle, WA 98101-2939 · 206-464-3939

Bruce A. King · Garvey Schubert Barer · Second & Seneca Building, Suite 1800 · 1191 Second Avenue · Seattle, WA 98101-2939 · 206-464-3939

Allan L. MacDougall · a · Montgomery Scarp MacDougall · 1218 Third Avenue, Suite 2700 · Seattle, WA 98101 · 206-625-1801

Thomas F. Paul · LeGros, Buchanan & Paul · 701 Fifth Avenue, Suite 2500 · Seattle, WA 98104-7051 · 206-623-4990

Harold F. Vhugen · a · Kraft Palmer Davies · 720 Third Avenue, Suite 1510 · Seattle, WA 98104-1825 · 206-624-8844

Spokane

Michael F. Nienstedt · Witherspoon, Kelley, Davenport & Toole · U.S. Bank Building, Suite 1100 · 422 West Riverside Avenue · Spokane, WA 99201-0302 · 509-624-5265

MASS TORT LITIGATION

Seattle

V. L. Woolston · Perkins Coie · http://www.perkinscoie.com · 1201 Third Avenue, Suite 4800 · Seattle, WA 98101-3099 · 206-359-8000

MEDICAL MALPRACTICE LAW

Seattle

Ralph J. Brindley · a · Luvera Law Firm · 701 Fifth Avenue, Suite 6700 · Seattle, WA 98104 · 206-467-6090

Joel D. Cunningham · 2) · Luvera Law Firm · 701 Fifth Avenue, Suite 6700 · Seattle, WA 98104 · 206-467-6090

Lembhard G. Howell · 2% · Law Offices of Lembhard G. Howell · Pacific Building, Suite 2105 · 720 Third Avenue · Seattle, WA 98104 · 206-623-5296

Elizabeth Leedom · Bennett, Bigelow & Leedom · 1700 Seventh Avenue, Suite 1900 · Seattle, WA 98101-1397 · 206-622-5511

Eugene M. Moen · a · Chemnick, Moen & Greenstreet · 115 NE 100th Street, Suite 225 · Seattle, WA 98125 · 206-443-8600

Ron Perey · a · Perey Law Group · 1606 Eighth Avenue · Seattle, WA 98109 · 206-443-7600

Rebecca S. Ringer · Floyd, Pflueger & Ringer · 300 Trianon Building · 2505 Third Avenue · Seattle, WA 98121-1445 · 206-441-4455

Spokane

William F. Etter · Etter, McMahon, Lamberson, Clary, Tropmann & Oreskovich · Bank Of Whitman Building, Suite 210 · 618 West Riverside Avenue · Spokane, WA 99201-0602 · 509-747-9100

Daniel E. Huntington · Richter-Wimberley · 422 West Riverside Avenue, Suite 1300 · Spokane, WA 99201-0305 · 509-455-4201

Mark D. Kamitomo · The Markam Group · 421 West Riverside Avenue, Suite 1060 · Spokane, WA 99201-0406 · 509-747-0902

Dan W. Keefe · 2) · Keefe, Bowman, Bruya · Washington Mutual Financial Center, Suite 1102 · 601 West Main Avenue · Spokane, WA 99201 · 509-624-8988

James B. King · Evans, Craven & Lackie · 818 West Riverside Avenue, Suite 250 · Spokane, WA 99201-0910 · 509-455-5200

William D. Symmes · 2) · Witherspoon, Kelley, Davenport & Toole · U.S. Bank Building, Suite 1100 · 422 West Riverside Avenue · Spokane, WA 99201-0302 · 509-624-5265

Tacoma

Thomas V. Harris · a · Washington Arbitration and Mediation · 3600 Port of Tacoma Road, Suite 304 · Tacoma, WA 98424 · 253-922-4140

Yakima

Dennis L. Fluegge · ⑳ · Meyer, Fluegge & Tenney · 230 South Second Street · P.O. Box 22680 · Yakima, WA 98907-2680 · 509-575-8500

MERGERS & ACQUISITIONS LAW

Seattle

Christopher Barry · Dorsey & Whitney · U.S. Bank Centre, Suite 3400 · 1420 Fifth Avenue · Seattle, WA 98101-4010 · 206-903-8800

Bruce T. Bjerke · Davis Wright Tremaine · 1201 Third Avenue, Suite 2200 · Seattle, WA 98101-3045 · 206-622-3150

C. Kent Carlson · ㉕ · K&L Gates · 925 Fourth Avenue, Suite 2900 · Seattle, WA 98104-1158 · 206-623-7580

David C. Clarke · Perkins Coie · http://www.perkinscoie.com · 1201 Third Avenue, Suite 4800 · Seattle, WA 98101-3099 · 206-359-8000

Stephan H. Coonrod · K&L Gates · 925 Fourth Avenue, Suite 2900 · Seattle, WA 98104-1158 · 206-623-7580

Richard B. Dodd · K&L Gates · 925 Fourth Avenue, Suite 2900 · Seattle, WA 98104-1158 · 206-623-7580

Mark F. Hoffman · DLA Piper · 701 Fifth Avenue, Suite 7000 · Seattle, WA 98104-7044 · 206-839-4800

Allen D. Israel · Foster Pepper · http://www.foster.com · 1111 Third Avenue, Suite 3400 · Seattle, WA 98101-3299 · 206-447-4400

Robert S. Jaffe · K&L Gates · 925 Fourth Avenue, Suite 2900 · Seattle, WA 98104-1158 · 206-623-7580

David F. McShea · Perkins Coie · http://www.perkinscoie.com · 1201 Third Avenue, Suite 4800 · Seattle, WA 98101-3099 · 206-359-8000

Michael E. Morgan · ⑳ · Lane Powell · http://www.lanepowell.com · U.S. Bank Centre, Suite 4100 · 1420 Fifth Avenue · Seattle, WA 98101-2338 · 206-223-7000

Patrick J. Schultheis · Wilson Sonsini Goodrich & Rosati 701 Fifth Avenue, Suite 5100 · Seattle, WA 98104-7036 · 206-883-2500

Joseph D. Weinstein · Davis Wright Tremaine · 1201 Third Avenue, Suite 2200 · Seattle, WA 98101-3045 · 206-622-3150

Joseph P. Whitford · Davis Wright Tremaine · 1201 Third Avenue, Suite 2200 · Seattle, WA 98101-3045 206-622-3150

Spokane

Joseph H. Wessman · Witherspoon, Kelley, Davenport & Toole · U.S. Bank Building, Suite 1100 · 422 West Riverside Avenue · Spokane, WA 99201-0302 · 509-624-5265

MUNICIPAL LAW

Seattle

B. Gerald Johnson · K&L Gates · 925 Fourth Avenue, Suite 2900 · Seattle, WA 98104-1158 · 206-623-7580

Spokane

Stanley M. Schwartz · Witherspoon, Kelley, Davenport & Toole · U.S. Bank Building, Suite 1100 · 422 West Riverside Avenue · Spokane, WA 99201-0302 · 509-624-5265

NATIVE AMERICAN LAW

Seattle

Eric D. Eberhard · Dorsey & Whitney · U.S. Bank Centre, Suite 3400 · 1420 Fifth Avenue · Seattle, WA 98101-4010 · 206-903-8800

Gabriel S. Galanda · Williams Kastner · Two Union Square, Suite 4100 · 601 Union Street · P.O. Box 21926 · Seattle, WA 98111-3926 · 206-628-6600

Michael P. O'Connell · Stoel Rives · http://www.stoel.com · One Union Square, Suite 3600 · 600 University Street · Seattle, WA 98101-3197 · 206-624-0900

LynDee Wells · Dorsey & Whitney · U.S. Bank Centre, Suite 3400 · 1420 Fifth Avenue · Seattle, WA 98101-4010 · 206-903-8800

NATURAL RESOURCES LAW

Bellevue

Markham A. Quehrn · Perkins Coie · http://www.perkinscoie.com · The PSE Building, Suite 700 · 10885 Northeast Fourth Street · Bellevue, WA 98004-5579 · 425-635-1400

Seattle

T. Ryan Durkan · a · Hillis Clark Martin & Peterson · http://www.hcmp.com · 1221 Second Avenue, Suite 500 · Seattle, WA 98101-2925 · 206-623-1745

Jerome L. Hillis · 2% · Hillis Clark Martin & Peterson · http://www.hcmp.com · 1221 Second Avenue, Suite 500 · Seattle, WA 98101-2925 · 206-623-1745

Douglas C. MacCourt · Ater Wynne · http://www.aterwynne.com · Two Union Square, Suite 1501 · 601 Union Street · Seattle, WA 98101-2341 · 206-623-4711

Richard R. Wilson · a · Hillis Clark Martin & Peterson · http://www.hcmp.com · 1221 Second Avenue, Suite 500 · Seattle, WA 98101-2925 · 206-623-1745

Tacoma

James C. Waldo · a · Gordon, Thomas, Honeywell, Malanca, Peterson & Daheim · Wells Fargo Plaza, Suite 2100 · 1201 Pacific Avenue · Tacoma, WA 98101 · 253-620-6500

NON-PROFIT/CHARITIES LAW

Seattle

Judith L. Andrews · Gottlieb, Fisher · 520 Pike Street, Suite 2510 · Seattle, WA 98101-4006 · 206-654-1999

Lorri A. Dunsmore · Perkins Coie · http://www.perkinscoie.com · 1201 Third Avenue, Suite 4800 · Seattle, WA 98101-3099 · 206-359-8000

Nell Elizabeth McCaw · Stokes Lawrence · 800 Fifth Avenue, Suite 4000 · Seattle, WA 98104-3179 · 206-626-6000

LaVerne Woods · Davis Wright Tremaine · 1201 Third Avenue, Suite 2200 · Seattle, WA 98101-3045 · 206-622-3150

NON-WHITE-COLLAR CRIMINAL DEFENSE

Seattle

David Allen · a · Allen, Hansen & Maybrown · One Union Square, Suite 3020 · 600 University Street · Seattle, WA 98101 · 206-447-9681

Peter A. Camiel · Mair & Camiel · 710 Cherry Street · Seattle, WA 98104-1925 · 206-624-1551

Timothy K. Ford · a · MacDonald, Hoague & Bayless · Hoge Building, Suite 1500 · 705 Second Avenue · Seattle, WA 98104-1745 · 206-622-1604

Richard A. Hansen · 2) · Allen, Hansen & Maybrown · One Union Square, Suite 3020 · 600 University Street · Seattle, WA 98101 · 206-447-9681

Amanda E. Lee · Schroeter Goldmark & Bender · 810 Third Avenue, Suite 500 · Seattle, WA 98104 · 206-622-8000

Peter K. Mair · 2% · Mair & Camiel · 710 Cherry Street · Seattle, WA 98104-1925 · 206-624-1551

Jeffery Robinson · a · Schroeter, Goldmark & Bender · 810 Third Avenue, Suite 500 · Seattle, WA 98104 · 206-622-8000

Anthony Savage · a · Law Office of Anthony Savage · 615 Second Avenue, Suite 340 · Seattle, WA 98104-2200 · 206-682-1882

Jon Zulauf · a · Zulauf & Chambliss · Tower Building, Suite 1301 · 1809 Seventh Avenue · Seattle, WA 98101 · 206-682-1114

Spokane

Carl J. Oreskovich · Etter, McMahon, Lamberson, Clary, Tropmann & Oreskovich · Bank Of Whitman Building, Suite 210 · 618 West Riverside Avenue · Spokane, WA 99201-0602 · 509-747-9100

Mary Elizabeth Schultz · Mary Schultz Law · Davenport Tower Penthouse 2250 · 111 South Post · Spokane, WA 99201 · 509-458-2750

Mark E. Vovos · 2) · Mark Edmund Vovos · Delphi Building, Suite 100 · 1309 West Dean Avenue · Spokane, WA 99201 · 509-326-5220

Leslie R. Weatherhead · Witherspoon, Kelley, Davenport & Toole · U.S. Bank Building, Suite 1100 · 422 West Riverside Avenue · Spokane, WA 99201-0302 · 509-624-5265

Tacoma

Monte E. Hester · a · Law Office of Monte Hester · 1008 South Yakima Avenue, Suite 302 · Tacoma, WA 98405 · 253-272-2157

Yakima

J. Adam Moore, Jr. · a · The Adam Moore Law Firm · 217 North Second Street · Yakima, WA 98901-2332 · 509-575-0372

PERSONAL INJURY LITIGATION

Bainbridge Island

Judy I. Massong · Otorowski Johnston Diamond & Golden · 298 Winslow Way West · Bainbridge Island, WA 98110 · 206-842-1000

Bremerton

Richard H. Friedman · Friedman, Rubin & White · 1126 Highland Avenue · Bremerton, WA 98337 · 360-782-4300

Donna J. McCready · Friedman, Rubin & White · 1126 Highland Avenue · Bremerton, WA 98337 · 360-782-4300

Hoquiam

Keith L. Kessler · a · Stritmatter Kessler Whelan Coluccio · 413 Eighth Street · Hoquiam, WA 98550-3692 · 360-540-7364

Paul L. Stritmatter · 2) · Stritmatter Kessler Whelan Coluccio · 413 Eighth Street · Hoquiam, WA 98550-3692 · 360-540-7364

Renton

Todd W. Gardner · Swanson & Gardner · 4512 Talbot Road South · Renton, WA 98055-6216 · 425-226-7920

Arthur D. Swanson · a · Swanson & Gardner · 4512 Talbot Road South · Renton, WA 98055-6216 · 425-226-7920

Seattle

C. William Bailey · Mills Meyers Swartling · 1000 Second Avenue, 30th Floor · Seattle, WA 98104-1064 · 206-382-1000

William S. Bailey · Fury Bailey · 710 Tenth Avenue East · P.O. Box 20397 · Seattle, WA 98102 · 206-726-6600

James M. Beecher · Hackett, Beecher & Hart · Westlake Tower, Suite 2200 · 1601 Fifth Avenue · Seattle, WA 98101-1651 · 206-624-2200

David M. Beninger · Luvera Law Firm · 701 Fifth Avenue, Suite 6700 · Seattle, WA 98104 · 206-467-6090

Ralph J. Brindley · a · Luvera Law Firm · 701 Fifth Avenue, Suite 6700 · Seattle, WA 98104 · 206-467-6090

Kathy A. Cochran · a · Wilson Smith Cochran Dickerson · The Financial Center, Suite 1700 · 1215 Fourth Avenue · Seattle, WA 98161-1007 · 206-623-4100

Kelly P. Corr · a · Corr Cronin Michelson Baumgardner & Preece · http://www.corrcronin.com · 1001 Fourth Avenue, Suite 3900 · Seattle, WA 98154 · 206-625-8600

Joel D. Cunningham · 2) · Luvera Law Firm · 701 Fifth Avenue, Suite 6700 · Seattle, WA 98104 · 206-467-6090

Robert K. Dawson · DawsonBrown · 1000 Second Avenue, Suite 1420 · Seattle, WA 98104-1033 · 206-262-1444

Douglas A. Hofmann · Williams Kastner · Two Union Square, Suite 4100 · 601 Union Street · P.O. Box 21926 · Seattle, WA 98111-3926 · 206-628-6600

Lembhard G. Howell · 2% · Law Offices of Lembhard G. Howell · Pacific Building, Suite 2105 · 720 Third Avenue · Seattle, WA 98104 · 206-623-5296

Mark R. Johnsen · Karr Tuttle Campbell · http://www.karrtuttle.com · 1201 Third Avenue, Suite 2900 · Seattle, WA 98101-3028 · 206-223-1313

George Kargianis · a · The Law Offices of George Kargianis · Columbia Center, Suite 4760 · 701 Fifth Avenue · Seattle, WA 98104 · 206-624-5370

Karen K. Koehler · Stritmatter Kessler Whelan Coluccio · 200 Second Avenue West · Seattle, WA 98119-4204 · 206-448-1777

William J. Leedom · Bennett, Bigelow & Leedom · 1700 Seventh Avenue, Suite 1900 · Seattle, WA 98101-1397 · 206-622-5511

Paul N. Luvera, Jr. · 2% · Luvera Law Firm · 701 Fifth Avenue, Suite 6700 · Seattle, WA 98104 · 206-467-6090

David L. Martin · 2) · Lee, Smart · 1800 One Convention Place · 701 Pike Street · Seattle, WA 98101-3929 · 206-624-7990

Thomas R. Merrick · Merrick, Hofstedt & Lindsey · http://www.mhlseattle.com · 3101 Western Avenue, Suite 200 · Seattle, WA 98121 · 206-682-0610

Eugene M. Moen · a · Chemnick, Moen & Greenstreet · 115 NE 100th Street, Suite 225 · Seattle, WA 98125 · 206-443-8600

Ron Perey · a · Perey Law Group · 1606 Eighth Avenue · Seattle, WA 98109 · 206-443-7600

Jan Eric Peterson · 2) · Peterson, Young & Putra · 1501 Fourth Avenue, Suite 2800 · Seattle, WA 98101 · 206-624-6800

Janet L. Rice · Schroeter, Goldmark & Bender · 810 Third Avenue, Suite 500 · Seattle, WA 98104 · 206-622-8000

James S. Rogers · The Law Offices of James S. Rogers · http://www.rogersfleck.com · 1500 Fourth Avenue, Suite 500 · Seattle, WA 98101 · 206-621-8525

Reed P. Schifferman · a · Law Offices of Reed Schifferman · http://www.schifferman.com · 12360 Lake City Way, NE, Suite 420 · Seattle, WA 98125 · 206-365-3650

William C. Smart · Keller Rohrback · 1201 Third Avenue, Suite 3200 · Seattle, WA 98101-3052 · 206-623-1900

Scott M. Stickney · Wilson Smith Cochran Dickerson · The Financial Center, Suite 1700 · 1215 Fourth Avenue · Seattle, WA 98161-1007 · 206-623-4100

Robert M. Sulkin · McNaul, Ebel, Nawrot & Helgren · One Union Square, Suite 2700 · 600 University Street · Seattle, WA 98101-3143 · 206-467-1816

Jeffrey I. Tilden · Gordon Tilden Thomas & Cordell · 1001 Fourth Avenue, Suite 4000 · Seattle, WA 98154-1007 · 206-467-6477

Victoria L. Vreeland · Gordon, Thomas, Honeywell, Malanca, Peterson & Daheim · One Union Square, Suite 2100 · 600 University Street · Seattle, WA 98101 · 206-676-7500

Paul W. Whelan · a · Stritmatter Kessler Whelan Coluccio · 200 Second Avenue West · Seattle, WA 98119-4204 · 206-448-1777

Michael E. Withey · a · Michael E. Withey · Two Union Square, Suite 4200 · 601 Union Street · Seattle, WA 98101 · 206-405-1800

Spokane

Eugene I. Annis · 2) · Lukins & Annis · Washington Trust Financial Center, Suite 1600 · 717 West Sprague Avenue · Spokane, WA 99201-0466 · 509-455-9555

Timothy P. Cronin · a · Mullin, Cronin, Casey & Blair · 115 North Washington Street, Third Floor · Spokane, WA 99201 · 509-455-7999

J. Donald Curran · a · Delay, Curran, Thompson, Pontarolo & Walker · 601 West Main Avenue, Suite 1212 · Spokane, WA 99201-0684 · 509-455-9500

William F. Etter · Etter, McMahon, Lamberson, Clary, Tropmann & Oreskovich · Bank Of Whitman Building, Suite 210 · 618 West Riverside Avenue · Spokane, WA 99201-0602 · 509-747-9100

Richard C. Eymann · Eymann Allison Hunter Jones · 2208 West Second Avenue · Spokane, WA 99201 · 509-747-0101

Daniel E. Huntington · Richter-Wimberley · 422 West Riverside Avenue, Suite 1300 · Spokane, WA 99201-0305 · 509-455-4201

Dan W. Keefe · 2) · Keefe, Bowman, Bruya · Washington Mutual Financial Center, Suite 1102 · 601 West Main Avenue · Spokane, WA 99201 · 509-624-8988

Richard C. Robinson · Layman, Layman & Robinson · 601 South Division Street · Spokane, WA 99202 · 509-455-8883

William D. Symmes · 2) · Witherspoon, Kelley, Davenport & Toole · U.S. Bank Building, Suite 1100 · 422 West Riverside Avenue · Spokane, WA 99201-0302 · 509-624-5265

Tacoma

Stephen L. Bulzomi · Messina Bulzomi Christensen · 5316 Orchard Street West · Tacoma, WA 98467 · 253-472-6000

John R. Connelly, Jr. · Connelly Law Offices · http://www.connelly-law.com · 2301 North 30th Street, Suite 220 · Tacoma, WA 98403 · 253-593-5100

Daniel L. Hannula · a · Rush, Hannula, Harkins & Kyler · 4701 South 19th Street, Suite 300 · Tacoma, WA 98405 · 253-383-5388

Vernon W. Harkins · Rush, Hannula, Harkins & Kyler · 4701 South 19th Street, Suite 300 · Tacoma, WA 98405 · 253-383-5388

Thomas V. Harris · a · Washington Arbitration and Mediation · 3600 Port of Tacoma Road, Suite 304 · Tacoma, WA 98424 · 253-922-4140

James L. Holman · a · James L. Holman Attourney At Law · The Holman Building, Suite 101 · 4041 Ruston Way · P.O. Box 1338 · Tacoma, WA 98401-1338 · 253-627-1866

John L. Messina · 2) · Messina Bulzomi Christensen · 5316 Orchard Street West · Tacoma, WA 98467 · 253-472-6000

William J. Rush · 2% · Rush, Hannula, Harkins & Kyler · 4701 South 19th Street, Suite 300 · Tacoma, WA 98405 · 253-383-5388

Yakima

Terry P. Abeyta · Abeyta Nelson · http://www.abeytanelson.com · 1102 West Yakima Avenue · Yakima, WA 98902-3029 · 509-575-1588

Dennis L. Fluegge · 2) · Meyer, Fluegge & Tenney · 230 South Second Street · P.O. Box 22680 · Yakima, WA 98907-2680 · 509-575-8500

PRODUCT LIABILITY LITIGATION

Seattle

Joel D. Cunningham · 2) · Luvera Law Firm · 701 Fifth Avenue, Suite 6700 · Seattle, WA 98104 · 206-467-6090

Keith Gerrard · a · Perkins Coie · http://www.perkinscoie.com · 1201 Third Avenue, Suite 4800 · Seattle, WA 98101-3099 · 206-359-8000

Lembhard G. Howell · 2% · Law Offices of Lembhard G. Howell · Pacific Building, Suite 2105 · 720 Third Avenue · Seattle, WA 98104 · 206-623-5296

Paul W. Whelan · a · Stritmatter Kessler Whelan Coluccio · 200 Second Avenue West · Seattle, WA 98119-4204 · 206-448-1777

V. L. Woolston · Perkins Coie · http://www.perkinscoie.com · 1201 Third Avenue, Suite 4800 · Seattle, WA 98101-3099 · 206-359-8000

Tacoma

John L. Messina · 2) · Messina Bulzomi Christensen · 5316 Orchard Street West · Tacoma, WA 98467 · 253-472-6000

PROFESSIONAL MALPRACTICE LAW

Seattle

Joel D. Cunningham · 2) · Luvera Law Firm · 701 Fifth Avenue, Suite 6700 · Seattle, WA 98104 · 206-467-6090

Bruce Winchell · Mills Meyers Swartling · 1000 Second Avenue, 30th Floor · Seattle, WA 98104-1064 · 206-382-1000

PUBLIC FINANCE LAW

Seattle

Hugh Spitzer · Foster Pepper · http://www.foster.com · 1111 Third Avenue, Suite 3400 · Seattle, WA 98101-3299 · 206-447-4400

Cynthia M. Weed · K&L Gates · 925 Fourth Avenue, Suite 2900 · Seattle, WA 98104-1158 · 206-623-7580

Spokane

Michael C. Ormsby · K&L Gates · 618 West Riverside Avenue, Suite 300 · Spokane, WA 99201-0602 · 509-624-2100

REAL ESTATE LAW

Bellevue

Craig S. Gilbert · Perkins Coie · http://www.perkinscoie.com · The PSE Building, Suite 700 · 10885 Northeast Fourth Street · Bellevue, WA 98004-5579 · 425-635-1400

Warren E. Koons · Davis Wright Tremaine · 777 One-Hundred-Eighth Avenue, NE, Suite 2300 · Bellevue, WA 98004-5149 · 425-646-6100

Craig H. Shrontz · Perkins Coie · http://www.perkinscoie.com · The PSE Building, Suite 700 · 10885 Northeast Fourth Street · Bellevue, WA 98004-5579 · 425-635-1400

Seattle

Glenn J. Amster · Lane Powell · http://www.lanepowell.com · U.S. Bank Centre, Suite 4100 · 1420 Fifth Avenue · Seattle, WA 98101-2338 · 206-223-7000

Michael A. Barrett · Perkins Coie · http://www.perkinscoie.com · 1201 Third Avenue, Suite 4800 · Seattle, WA 98101-3099 · 206-359-8000

Andrew B. Bassetti · Alston, Courtnage & Bassetti · 1000 Second Avenue, Suite 3900 · Seattle, WA 98104-1045 · 206-623-7600

Christopher I. Brain · a · Tousley Brain Stephens · 1700 Seventh Avenue, Suite 2200 · Seattle, WA 98101 · 206-682-5600

Peter L. Buck · a · The Buck Law Group · 2030 First Avenue, Suite 201 · Seattle, WA 98121 · 206-448-6229

Brent Carson · GordonDerr · http://www.gordonderr.com · 2025 First Avenue, Suite 500 · Seattle, WA 98121-3140 · 206-382-9540

Jennifer Dunn Cobb · Jameson Babbitt Stites & Lombard · 999 Third Avenue, Suite 1900 · Seattle, WA 98104 · 206-292-1994

Michael S. Courtnage · Alston, Courtnage & Bassetti · 1000 Second Avenue, Suite 3900 · Seattle, WA 98104-1045 · 206-623-7600

Joseph E. Delaney · Foster Pepper · http://www.foster.com · 1111 Third Avenue, Suite 3400 · Seattle, WA 98101-3299 · 206-447-4400

Jay P. Derr · GordonDerr · http://www.gordonderr.com · 2025 First Avenue, Suite 500 · Seattle, WA 98121-3140 · 206-382-9540

Ellen Conedera Dial · Perkins Coie · http://www.perkinscoie.com · 1201 Third Avenue, Suite 4800 · Seattle, WA 98101-3099 · 206-359-8000

Thomas E. Dixon · a · Fikso Kretschmer Smith Dixon · Market Place Tower, Suite 1130 · 2025 First Avenue · Seattle, WA 98121-2100 · 206-448-1818

T. Ryan Durkan · a · Hillis Clark Martin & Peterson · http://www.hcmp.com · 1221 Second Avenue, Suite 500 · Seattle, WA 98101-2925 · 206-623-1745

Bob Fikso · Fikso Kretschmer Smith Dixon · Market Place Tower, Suite 1130 · 2025 First Avenue · Seattle, WA 98121-2100 · 206-448-1818

Gary E. Fluhrer · a · Foster Pepper · http://www.foster.com · 1111 Third Avenue, Suite 3400 · Seattle, WA 98101-3299 · 206-447-4400

Thomas A. Goeltz · a · Davis Wright Tremaine · 1201 Third Avenue, Suite 2200 · Seattle, WA 98101-3045 · 206-622-3150

Joel M. Gordon · GordonDerr · http://www.gordonderr.com · 2025 First Avenue, Suite 500 · Seattle, WA 98121-3140 · 206-382-9540

William L. Green · Perkins Coie · http://www.perkinscoie.com · 1201 Third Avenue, Suite 4800 · Seattle, WA 98101-3099 · 206-359-8000

Jim Greenfield · Davis Wright Tremaine · 1201 Third Avenue, Suite 2200 · Seattle, WA 98101-3045 · 206-622-3150

G. Richard Hill · a · McCullough Hill · Columbia Center, Suite 7220 · 701 Fifth Avenue · Seattle, WA 98104 · 206-812-3388

Jerome L. Hillis · 2% · Hillis Clark Martin & Peterson · http://www.hcmp.com · 1221 Second Avenue, Suite 500 · Seattle, WA 98101-2925 · 206-623-1745

B. Gerald Johnson · K&L Gates · 925 Fourth Avenue, Suite 2900 · Seattle, WA 98104-1158 · 206-623-7580

Richard E. Keefe · 2% · Foster Pepper · http://www.foster.com · 1111 Third Avenue, Suite 3400 · Seattle, WA 98101-3299 · 206-447-4400

John E. Keegan · Davis Wright Tremaine · 1201 Third Avenue, Suite 2200 · Seattle, WA 98101-3045 · 206-622-3150

Marc T. Kretschmer · Fikso Kretschmer Smith Dixon · Market Place Tower, Suite 1130 · 2025 First Avenue · Seattle, WA 98121-2100 · 206-448-1818

Michael D. Kuntz · a · Foster Pepper · http://www.foster.com · 1111 Third Avenue, Suite 3400 · Seattle, WA 98101-3299 · 206-447-4400

David N. Lombard · Jameson Babbitt Stites & Lombard · 999 Third Avenue, Suite 1900 · Seattle, WA 98104 · 206-292-1994

J. Parker Mason · Alston, Courtnage & Bassetti · 1000 Second Avenue, Suite 3900 · Seattle, WA 98104-1045 · 206-623-7600

Richard E. McCann · 2) · Perkins Coie · http://www.perkinscoie.com · 1201 Third Avenue, Suite 4800 · Seattle, WA 98101-3099 · 206-359-8000

John C. McCullough, Jr. · a · McCullough Hill · Columbia Center, Suite 7220 · 701 Fifth Avenue · Seattle, WA 98104 · 206-812-3388

Dennis E. McLean · 2) · Davis Wright Tremaine · 1201 Third Avenue, Suite 2200 · Seattle, WA 98101-3045 · 206-622-3150

Robert D. Neugebauer · a · K&L Gates · 925 Fourth Avenue, Suite 2900 · Seattle, WA 98104-1158 · 206-623-7580

Christopher R. Osborn · Foster Pepper · http://www.foster.com · 1111 Third Avenue, Suite 3400 · Seattle, WA 98101-3299 · 206-447-4400

Scott B. Osborne · 2) · K&L Gates · 925 Fourth Avenue, Suite 2900 · Seattle, WA 98104-1158 · 206-623-7580

Daniel P. Pepple · Pepple Johnson Cantu & Schmidt · 1501 Western Avenue, Suite 600 · Seattle, WA 98101-3051 · 206-625-1711

Thomas W. Read · Alston, Courtnage & Bassetti · 1000 Second Avenue, Suite 3900 · Seattle, WA 98104-1045 · 206-623-7600

David H. Rockwell · a · Stoel Rives · http://www.stoel.com · One Union Square, Suite 3600 · 600 University Street · Seattle, WA 98101-3197 · 206-624-0900

Judith M. Runstad · 2% · Foster Pepper · http://www.foster.com · 1111 Third Avenue, Suite 3400 · Seattle, WA 98101-3299 · 206-447-4400

Shannon J. Skinner · K&L Gates · 925 Fourth Avenue, Suite 2900 · Seattle, WA 98104-1158 · 206-623-7580

Gordon W. Tanner · Stoel Rives · http://www.stoel.com · One Union Square, Suite 3600 · 600 University Street · Seattle, WA 98101-3197 · 206-624-0900

Cynthia Thomas · Real Property Law Group · 1326 Fifth Avenue, Suite 654 · Seattle, WA 98101 · 206-625-1717

David W. Thorne · a · Davis Wright Tremaine · 1201 Third Avenue, Suite 2200 · Seattle, WA 98101-3045 · 206-622-3150

Russell F. Tousley · 2% · Tousley Brain Stephens · 1700 Seventh Avenue, Suite 2200 · Seattle, WA 98101 206-682-5600

Richard R. Wilson · a · Hillis Clark Martin & Peterson · http://www.hcmp.com · 1221 Second Avenue, Suite 500 · Seattle, WA 98101-2925 · 206-623-1745

Spokane

Ned M. Barnes · ㉕ · Witherspoon, Kelley, Davenport & Toole · U.S. Bank Building, Suite 1100 · 422 West Riverside Avenue · Spokane, WA 99201-0302 · 509-624-5265

James S. Black, Jr. · ⑩ · Lukins & Annis · Washington Trust Financial Center, Suite 1600 · 717 West Sprague Avenue · Spokane, WA 99201-0466 · 509-455-9555

Frederick J. Dullanty, Jr. · Witherspoon, Kelley, Davenport & Toole · U.S. Bank Building, Suite 1100 · 422 West Riverside Avenue · Spokane, WA 99201-0302 · 509-624-5265

John M. Riley III · ⑩ · Witherspoon, Kelley, Davenport & Toole · U.S. Bank Building, Suite 1100 · 422 West Riverside Avenue · Spokane, WA 99201-0302 · 509-624-5265

Stanley M. Schwartz · Witherspoon, Kelley, Davenport & Toole · U.S. Bank Building, Suite 1100 · 422 West Riverside Avenue · Spokane, WA 99201-0302 · 509-624-5265

Martin G. Weber · ⑩ · Lukins & Annis · Washington Trust Financial Center, Suite 1600 · 717 West Sprague Avenue · Spokane, WA 99201-0466 · 509-455-9555

Tacoma

Dale L. Carlisle · ⑳ · Gordon, Thomas, Honeywell, Malanca, Peterson & Daheim · Wells Fargo Plaza, Suite 2100 · 1201 Pacific Avenue · Tacoma, WA 98101 · 253-620-6500

William T. Lynn · ⑩ · Gordon, Thomas, Honeywell, Malanca, Peterson & Daheim · Wells Fargo Plaza, Suite 2100 · 1201 Pacific Avenue · Tacoma, WA 98101 · 253-620-6500

SECURITIES LAW

Bellevue

Allen R. Sakai · Jeppesen Gray Sakai · 10655 NE Fourth Street, Suite 801 · Bellevue, WA 98004 · 425-454-2344

Seattle

Richard B. Dodd · K&L Gates · 925 Fourth Avenue, Suite 2900 · Seattle, WA 98104-1158 · 206-623-7580

George E. Greer · Orrick, Herrington & Sutcliffe · 719 Second Avenue, Suite 1000 · Seattle, WA 98104-7097 · 206-839-4300

Mark F. Hoffman · DLA Piper · 701 Fifth Avenue, Suite 7000 · Seattle, WA 98104-7044 · 206-839-4800

Barry M. Kaplan · Wilson Sonsini Goodrich & Rosati · 701 Fifth Avenue, Suite 5100 · Seattle, WA 98104-7036 · 206-883-2500

David F. McShea · Perkins Coie · http://www.perkinscoie.com · 1201 Third Avenue, Suite 4800 · Seattle, WA 98101-3099 · 206-359-8000

Patrick J. Schultheis · Wilson Sonsini Goodrich & Rosati · 701 Fifth Avenue, Suite 5100 · Seattle, WA 98104-7036 · 206-883-2500

Evelyn Cruz Sroufe · Perkins Coie · http://www.perkinscoie.com · 1201 Third Avenue, Suite 4800 · Seattle, WA 98101-3099 · 206-359-8000

Spokane

Andrew J. Schultheis · Witherspoon, Kelley, Davenport & Toole · U.S. Bank Building, Suite 1100 · 422 West Riverside Avenue · Spokane, WA 99201-0302 · 509-624-5265

TAX LAW

Bellevue

Richard G. Wood · (10) · Richard G. Wood · 777 One-Hundred-Eighth Avenue, NE, Suite 2240 · Bellevue, WA 98004 · 425-868-1167

Seattle

Gregg D. Barton · Perkins Coie · http://www.perkinscoie.com · 1201 Third Avenue, Suite 4800 · Seattle, WA 98101-3099 · 206-359-8000

Lance W. Behnke · K&L Gates · 925 Fourth Avenue, Suite 2900 · Seattle, WA 98104-1158 · 206-623-7580

Norman J. Bruns · Garvey Schubert Barer · Second & Seneca Building, Suite 1800 · 1191 Second Avenue Seattle, WA 98101-2939 · 206-464-3939

William H. Burkhart · (20) · K&L Gates · 925 Fourth Avenue, Suite 2900 · Seattle, WA 98104-1158 · 206-623-7580

Pamela M. Charles · Davis Wright Tremaine · 1201 Third Avenue, Suite 2200 · Seattle, WA 98101-3045 206-622-3150

Carl T. Crow · Perkins Coie · http://www.perkinscoie.com · 1201 Third Avenue, Suite 4800 · Seattle, WA 98101-3099 · 206-359-8000

Scott L. David · K&L Gates · 925 Fourth Avenue, Suite 2900 · Seattle, WA 98104-1158 · 206-623-7580

Darrell D. Hallett · (20) · Chicoine & Hallett · The Millenium Tower, Suite 425 · 719 Second Avenue · Seattle, WA 98104 · 206-223-0800

James M. Hilton · (25) · Perkins Coie · http://www.perkinscoie.com · 1201 Third Avenue, Suite 4800 · Seattle, WA 98101-3099 · 206-359-8000

Steven J. Hopp · Carney Badley Spellman · 701 Fifth Avenue, Suite 3600 · Seattle, WA 98104 · 206-622-8020

C. James Judson · (25) · Davis Wright Tremaine · 1201 Third Avenue, Suite 2200 · Seattle, WA 98101-3045 · 206-622-3150

Robert M. Kane, Jr. · (10) · LeSourd & Patten · One Union Square, Suite 2401 · 600 University Street · Seattle, WA 98101-4121 · 206-624-1040

Robert D. Kaplan · (20) · Dorsey & Whitney · U.S. Bank Centre, Suite 3400 · 1420 Fifth Avenue · Seattle, WA 98101-4010 · 206-903-8800

Charles S. Lewis III · Stoel Rives · http://www.stoel.com · One Union Square, Suite 3600 · 600 University Street · Seattle, WA 98101-3197 · 206-624-0900

Judd R. Marten · (20) · LeSourd & Patten · One Union Square, Suite 2401 · 600 University Street · Seattle, WA 98101-4121 · 206-624-1040

George C. Mastrodonato · Dorsey & Whitney · U.S. Bank Centre, Suite 3400 · 1420 Fifth Avenue · Seattle, WA 98101-4010 · 206-903-8800

Robert M. McCallum · LeSourd & Patten · One Union Square, Suite 2401 · 600 University Street · Seattle, WA 98101-4121 · 206-624-1040

Martin R. Morfeld · Davis Wright Tremaine · 1201 Third Avenue, Suite 2200 · Seattle, WA 98101-3045 · 206-622-3150

John J. O'Donnell · a · Ogden Murphy Wallace · Westlake Center Tower, Suite 2100 · 1601 Fifth Avenue · Seattle, WA 98101-1686 · 206-447-7000

Charles H. Purcell · K&L Gates · 925 Fourth Avenue, Suite 2900 · Seattle, WA 98104-1158 · 206-623-7580

Jon M. Schorr · 2% · Carney Badley Spellman · 701 Fifth Avenue, Suite 3600 · Seattle, WA 98104 · 206-622-8020

Susan Thorbrogger · Stokes Lawrence · 800 Fifth Avenue, Suite 4000 · Seattle, WA 98104-3179 · 206-626-6000

Gary P. Tober · Lane Powell · http://www.lanepowell.com · U.S. Bank Centre, Suite 4100 · 1420 Fifth Avenue · Seattle, WA 98101-2338 · 206-223-7000

Brian Todd · Davis Wright Tremaine · 1201 Third Avenue, Suite 2200 · Seattle, WA 98101-3045 · 206-622-3150

Irwin L. Treiger · 2% · Stoel Rives · http://www.stoel.com · One Union Square, Suite 3600 · 600 University Street · Seattle, WA 98101-3197 · 206-624-0900

Rodney J. Waldbaum · 2% · LeSourd & Patten · One Union Square, Suite 2401 · 600 University Street · Seattle, WA 98101-4121 · 206-624-1040

LaVerne Woods · Davis Wright Tremaine · 1201 Third Avenue, Suite 2200 · Seattle, WA 98101-3045 · 206-622-3150

James E. Wreggelsworth · Davis Wright Tremaine · 1201 Third Avenue, Suite 2200 · Seattle, WA 98101-3045 · 206-622-3150

Steven R. Yentzer · DLA Piper · 701 Fifth Avenue, Suite 7000 · Seattle, WA 98104-7044 · 206-839-4800

D. Michael Young · Perkins Coie · http://www.perkinscoie.com · 1201 Third Avenue, Suite 4800 · Seattle, WA 98101-3099 · 206-359-8000

Andrew H. Zuccotti · 2% · K&L Gates · 925 Fourth Avenue, Suite 2900 · Seattle, WA 98104-1158 · 206-623-7580

Spokane

Richard P. Algeo · a · Algeo, Clarke & Erickson · 102 East Baldwin Avenue · Spokane, WA 99207-2240 509-328-6123

James S. Black, Jr. · a · Lukins & Annis · Washington Trust Financial Center, Suite 1600 · 717 West Sprague Avenue · Spokane, WA 99201-0466 · 509-455-9555

Philip J. Carstens · a · K&L Gates · 618 West Riverside Avenue, Suite 300 · Spokane, WA 99201-0602 · 509-624-2100

K. Thomas Connolly · 2) · Witherspoon, Kelley, Davenport & Toole · U.S. Bank Building, Suite 1100 · 422 West Riverside Avenue · Spokane, WA 99201-0302 · 509-624-5265

Scott B. Lukins · 2% · Lukins & Annis · Washington Trust Financial Center, Suite 1600 · 717 West Sprague Avenue · Spokane, WA 99201-0466 · 509-455-9555

Neil McKay · Lukins & Annis · Washington Trust Financial Center, Suite 1600 · 717 West Sprague Avenue · Spokane, WA 99201-0466 · 509-455-9555

Donald K. Querna · a · Randall & Danskin · Bank of America Financial Center, Suite 1500 · 601 West Riverside Avenue · Spokane, WA 99201 · 509-747-2052

Gary C. Randall · a · Workland & Witherspoon · Washington Mutual Financial Center, Suite 714 · 601 West Main Avenue · Spokane, WA 99201-0677 · 509-455-9077

TECHNOLOGY LAW

Seattle

Stephen D. Fisher · Bullivant Houser Bailey · 1601 Fifth Avenue, Suite 2300 · Seattle, WA 98101-1618 · 206-292-8390

TRUSTS AND ESTATES

Bellevue

Richard A. Klobucher · a · Davis Wright Tremaine · 777 One-Hundred-Eighth Avenue, NE, Suite 2300 Bellevue, WA 98004-5149 · 425-646-6100

John F. Sherwood, Sr. · 2% · Peterson Russell Kelly · Skyline Tower, Suite 1850 · 10900 Northeast Fourth Street · Bellevue, WA 98004 · 425-462-4700

Bellingham

J. Bruce Smith · Barron Smith Dauget · 300 North Commercial Street · P.O. Box 5008 · Bellingham, WA 98227-5008 · 360-733-0212

Pullman

Kenneth B. Myklebust · a · Irwin, Myklebust, Savage & Brown · 1230 Southeast Bishop Boulevard · P.O. Box 604 · Pullman, WA 99163-0604 · 509-332-3502

Seattle

Steven W. Andreasen · 2) · Davis Wright Tremaine · 1201 Third Avenue, Suite 2200 · Seattle, WA 98101-3045 · 206-622-3150

Colonel F. Betz · Perkins Coie · http://www.perkinscoie.com · 1201 Third Avenue, Suite 4800 · Seattle, WA 98101-3099 · 206-359-8000

Lora L. Brown · Law Offices of Lora L. Brown · 1000 Second Avenue, Suite 3500 · Seattle, WA 98104-1086 · 206-344-8600

Timothy C. Burkart · Garvey Schubert Barer · Second & Seneca Building, Suite 1800 · 1191 Second Avenue · Seattle, WA 98101-2939 · 206-464-3939

Dean V. Butler · Carney Badley Spellman · 701 Fifth Avenue, Suite 3600 · Seattle, WA 98104 · 206-622-8020

Michael D. Carrico · Riddell Williams · 1001 Fourth Avenue Plaza, Suite 4500 · Seattle, WA 98154-1192 206-624-3600

Janis A. Cunningham · 2) · Perkins Coie · http://www.perkinscoie.com · 1201 Third Avenue, Suite 4800 · Seattle, WA 98101-3099 · 206-359-8000

James A. Flaggert · Davis Wright Tremaine · 1201 Third Avenue, Suite 2200 · Seattle, WA 98101-3045 · 206-622-3150

Bruce P. Flynn · 2) · Perkins Coie · http://www.perkinscoie.com · 1201 Third Avenue, Suite 4800 · Seattle, WA 98101-3099 · 206-359-8000

Stanbery Foster, Jr. · Williams Kastner · Two Union Square, Suite 4100 · 601 Union Street · P.O. Box 21926 · Seattle, WA 98111-3926 · 206-628-6600

Joseph Michael Gaffney · a · Dorsey & Whitney · U.S. Bank Centre, Suite 3400 · 1420 Fifth Avenue · Seattle, WA 98101-4010 · 206-903-8800

Wendy S. Goffe · Graham & Dunn · Pier 70, Suite 300 · 2801 Alaskan Way · Seattle, WA 98121-1128 · 206-624-8300

Thomas C. Gores · 2) · Perkins Coie · http://www.perkinscoie.com · 1201 Third Avenue, Suite 4800 · Seattle, WA 98101-3099 · 206-359-8000

Alan H. Kane · 2) · K&L Gates · 925 Fourth Avenue, Suite 2900 · Seattle, WA 98104-1158 · 206-623-7580

Reginald S. Koehler III · 2) · Perkins Coie · http://www.perkinscoie.com · 1201 Third Avenue, Suite 4800 · Seattle, WA 98101-3099 · 206-359-8000

Douglas C. Lawrence · a · Stokes Lawrence · 800 Fifth Avenue, Suite 4000 · Seattle, WA 98104-3179 · 206-626-6000

Pamela McClaren · Foster Pepper · http://www.foster.com · 1111 Third Avenue, Suite 3400 · Seattle, WA 98101-3299 · 206-447-4400

Malcolm A. Moore · 2% · Davis Wright Tremaine · 1201 Third Avenue, Suite 2200 · Seattle, WA 98101-3045 · 206-622-3150

Robert S. Mucklestone · 2% · Perkins Coie · http://www.perkinscoie.com · 1201 Third Avenue, Suite 4800 Seattle, WA 98101-3099 · 206-359-8000

Sandra L. Perkins · Sandra Lynn Perkins · 1325 Fourth Avenue, Suite 940 · Seattle, WA 98101-2509 · 206-381-8500

John R. Price · 2% · Perkins Coie · http://www.perkinscoie.com · 1201 Third Avenue, Suite 4800 · Seattle, WA 98101-3099 · 206-359-8000

Stephen L. Pruss · Ahrens & DeAngeli · 1001 Fourth Avenue Plaza, Suite 4333 · Seattle, WA 98154 · 206-652-0101

Charles W. Riley, Jr. · Lane Powell · http://www.lanepowell.com · U.S. Bank Centre, Suite 4100 · 1420 Fifth Avenue · Seattle, WA 98101-2338 · 206-223-7000

Mark W. Roberts · a · K&L Gates · 925 Fourth Avenue, Suite 2900 · Seattle, WA 98104-1158 · 206-623-7580

Kenneth L. Schubert, Jr. · 2% · Garvey Schubert Barer · Second & Seneca Building, Suite 1800 · 1191 Second Avenue · Seattle, WA 98101-2939 · 206-464-3939

Barbara C. Sherland · a · Stoel Rives · http://www.stoel.com · One Union Square, Suite 3600 · 600 University Street · Seattle, WA 98101-3197 · 206-624-0900

Carrie C. Simchuk · Perkins Coie · http://www.perkinscoie.com · 1201 Third Avenue, Suite 4800 · Seattle, WA 98101-3099 · 206-359-8000

Kimbrough Street · 2) · Davis Wright Tremaine · 1201 Third Avenue, Suite 2200 · Seattle, WA 98101-3045 · 206-622-3150

James K. Treadwell · Karr Tuttle Campbell · http://www.karrtuttle.com · 1201 Third Avenue, Suite 2900 Seattle, WA 98101-3028 · 206-223-1313

Spokane

Thomas M. Culbertson · Lukins & Annis · Washington Trust Financial Center, Suite 1600 · 717 West Sprague Avenue · Spokane, WA 99201-0466 · 509-455-9555

Frederic G. Emry II · Paine, Hamblen · Washington Trust Financial Center, Suite 1200 · 717 West Sprague Avenue · Spokane, WA 99201-3505 · 509-455-6000

Peter J. Glase · K&L Gates · 618 West Riverside Avenue, Suite 300 · Spokane, WA 99201-0602 · 509-624-2100

Scott B. Lukins · 2% · Lukins & Annis · Washington Trust Financial Center, Suite 1600 · 717 West Sprague Avenue · Spokane, WA 99201-0466 · 509-455-9555

Gair B. Petrie · a · Randall & Danskin · Bank of America Financial Center, Suite 1500 · 601 West Riverside Avenue · Spokane, WA 99201 · 509-747-2052

Donald K. Querna · a · Randall & Danskin · Bank of America Financial Center, Suite 1500 · 601 West Riverside Avenue · Spokane, WA 99201 · 509-747-2052

Gerald A. Rein · Lukins & Annis · Washington Trust Financial Center, Suite 1600 · 717 West Sprague Avenue · Spokane, WA 99201-0466 · 509-455-9555

Tacoma

Alfred M. Falk · Harlowe & Falk · One Tacoma Avenue North, Suite 300 · Tacoma, WA 98403 · 253-284-4410

Vancouver

T. Randall Grove · Landerholm, Memovich, Lansverk & Whitesides · 805 Broadway Street, Suite 1000 · P.O. Box 1086 · Vancouver, WA 98666-1086 · 360-696-3312

Walla Walla

James K. Hayner · a · Minnick-Hayner · 249 West Alder Street · P.O. Box 1757 · Walla Walla, WA 99362-1757 · 509-527-3500

John M. Reese · 2) · Reese, Baffney, Schrag & Frol · 216 South Palouse Street · Walla Walla, WA 99362-3025 · 509-525-8130

Yakima

Stanley S. Pratt · ⑩ · Pratt & Boutillier · 105 North Third Street · P.O. Box 1425 · Yakima, WA 98907-1425 · 509-453-9135

George F. Velikanje · ㉕ · Stokes Lawrence · 1433 Lakeside Court, Suite 100 · Yakima, WA 98902-7354 · 509-853-3000

VENTURE CAPITAL LAW

Seattle

David C. Clarke · Perkins Coie · http://www.perkinscoie.com · 1201 Third Avenue, Suite 4800 · Seattle, WA 98101-3099 · 206-359-8000

Sonya F. Erickson · Cooley Godward Kronish · 719 Second Avenue, Suite 900 · Seattle, WA 98104-7097

Mark F. Hoffman · DLA Piper · 701 Fifth Avenue, Suite 7000 · Seattle, WA 98104-7044 · 206-839-4800

David F. McShea · Perkins Coie · http://www.perkinscoie.com · 1201 Third Avenue, Suite 4800 · Seattle, WA 98101-3099 · 206-359-8000

Craig E. Sherman · Wilson Sonsini Goodrich & Rosati · 701 Fifth Avenue, Suite 5100 · Seattle, WA 98104-7036 · 206-883-2500

Steven R. Yentzer · DLA Piper · 701 Fifth Avenue, Suite 7000 · Seattle, WA 98104-7044 · 206-839-4800

WHITE-COLLAR CRIMINAL DEFENSE

Bellevue

David V. Marshall · Davis Wright Tremaine · 777 One-Hundred-Eighth Avenue, NE, Suite 2300 · Bellevue, WA 98004-5149 · 425-646-6100

Seattle

David B. Bukey · ⑩ · David B. Bukey · 1501 Fourth Avenue, Suite 21500 · Seattle, WA 98101 · 206-382-1787

Angelo Calfo · Yarmuth Wilsdon Calfo · The IDX Tower, Suite 2500 · 925 Fourth Avenue · Seattle, WA 98104 · 206-516-3800

Robert G. Chadwell · McKay Chadwell · One Union Square, Suite 1601 · 600 University Street · Seattle, WA 98101 · 206-233-2800

Jenny A. Durkan · Jenny A. Durkan · 411 University Street, Suite 1200 · Seattle, WA 98101-2519 · 206-447-5345

Laurence B. Finegold · ⑳ · The Finegold Law Firm · Tower Building, Suite 1301 · 1809 Seventh Avenue · Seattle, WA 98101-1394 · 206-682-1116

Darrell D. Hallett · ⑳ · Chicoine & Hallett · The Millenium Tower, Suite 425 · 719 Second Avenue · Seattle, WA 98104 · 206-223-0800

Richard A. Hansen · ⑳ · Allen, Hansen & Maybrown · One Union Square, Suite 3020 · 600 University Street · Seattle, WA 98101 · 206-447-9681

Amanda E. Lee · Schroeter Goldmark & Bender · 810 Third Avenue, Suite 500 · Seattle, WA 98104 · 206-622-8000

Robert S. Mahler · Bullivant Houser Bailey · 1601 Fifth Avenue, Suite 2300 · Seattle, WA 98101-1618 · 206-292-8390

Peter K. Mair · 2% · Mair & Camiel · 710 Cherry Street · Seattle, WA 98104-1925 · 206-624-1551

Michael G. Martin · Siderius Lonergan & Martin · 847 Logan Building · 500 Union Street · Seattle, WA 98101-2394 · 206-624-2800

Jeffery Robinson · a · Schroeter, Goldmark & Bender · 810 Third Avenue, Suite 500 · Seattle, WA 98104 · 206-622-8000

Irwin H. Schwartz · 2) · Irwin H. Schwartz · 710 Cherry Street · Seattle, WA 98104 · 206-623-5084

J. Ronald Sim · Stoel Rives · http://www.stoel.com · One Union Square, Suite 3600 · 600 University Street · Seattle, WA 98101-3197 · 206-624-0900

John W. Wolfe · a · Law Office of John W. Wolfe · Bank of America Tower, Suite 6100 · 701 Fifth Avenue · Seattle, WA 98104-7043 · 206-467-9088

Alan Zarky · Dubitzky & Zarky · Waterfront Place One, Suite 803 · 1011 Western Avenue · Seattle, WA 98104 · 206-467-6709

Spokane

Mark E. Vovos · 2) · Mark Edmund Vovos · Delphi Building, Suite 100 · 1309 West Dean Avenue · Spokane, WA 99201 · 509-326-5220

Leslie R. Weatherhead · Witherspoon, Kelley, Davenport & Toole · U.S. Bank Building, Suite 1100 · 422 West Riverside Avenue · Spokane, WA 99201-0302 · 509-624-5265

Tacoma

Monte E. Hester · a · Law Office of Monte Hester · 1008 South Yakima Avenue, Suite 302 · Tacoma, WA 98405 · 253-272-2157

Yakima

J. Adam Moore, Jr. · a · The Adam Moore Law Firm · 217 North Second Street · Yakima, WA 98901-2332 · 509-575-0372

WORKERS' COMPENSATION LAW

Edmonds

William D. Hochberg · William D. Hochberg · 222 Third Avenue North · Edmonds, WA 98020-3109 · 425-744-1220

Olympia

Wayne Lieb · a · Putnam & Lieb · 907 Legion Way, SE · P.O. Box 337 · Olympia, WA 98507-0337 · 360-754-7707

Kim R. Putnam · a · Putnam & Lieb · 907 Legion Way, SE · P.O. Box 337 · Olympia, WA 98507-0337 · 360-754-7707

Seattle

James C. Causey, Jr. · a · Causey Law Firm · 401 Second Avenue South, Suite 303 · Seattle, WA 98104 206-292-8627

Christopher M. Eagan · a · The Walthew Law Firm · The Walthew Building · 123 Third Avenue South Seattle, WA 98104 · 206-792-7838

Kathleen Keenan Kindred · The Walthew Law Firm · The Walthew Building · 123 Third Avenue South Seattle, WA 98104 · 206-792-7838

Thomas Thompson · The Walthew Law Firm · The Walthew Building · 123 Third Avenue South · Seattle, WA 98104 · 206-792-7838

Spokane

Robert C. Milhem · Solan, Milhem & Hertel · 818 West Riverside Avenue, Suite 520 · P.O. Box 97 · Spokane, WA 99201-0097 · 509-744-8555

Micheal J. Pontarolo · Delay, Curran, Thompson, Pontarolo & Walker · 601 West Main Avenue, Suite 1212 · Spokane, WA 99201-0684 · 509-455-9500

WEST VIRGINIA

ADMINISTRATIVE LAW

Charleston

F. Thomas Graff, Jr. · 20 · Bowles Rice McDavid Graff & Love · http://www.bowlesrice.com · 600 Quarrier Street · P.O. Box 1386 · Charleston, WV 25325-1386 · 304-347-1100

Charleston

Robert B. Allen · ⑩ · Allen Guthrie McHugh & Thomas · 500 Lee Street East, Suite 800 · P.O. Box 3394 Charleston, WV 25333-3394 · 304-345-7250

Arden J. Curry II · ⑩ · Pauley, Curry, Sturgeon & Vanderford · 100 Kanawha Boulevard West · P.O. Box 2786 · Charleston, WV 25330-2786 · 304-342-6000

John R. Hoblitzell · Kay Casto & Chaney · http://www.kaycasto.com · Chase Tower, Suite 1500 · 707 Virginia Street East · P.O. Box 2031 · Charleston, WV 25327-2031 · 304-345-8900

W. Henry Jernigan, Jr. · Dinsmore & Shohl · http://www.dinslaw.com · Huntington Square, Suite 600 · 900 Lee Street · Charleston, WV 25301 · 304-357-0900

A. Andrew MacQueen · A. Andrew MacQueen · 55 Abney Circle · Charleston, WV 25314 · 304-344-2994

J. Rudy Martin · Jackson Kelly · Laidley Tower, Suite 1600 · 500 Lee Street East · P.O. Box 553 · Charleston, WV 25322-0553 · 304-340-1000

Thomas E. McHugh · Allen Guthrie McHugh & Thomas · 500 Lee Street East, Suite 800 · P.O. Box 3394 Charleston, WV 25333-3394 · 304-345-7250

Clarksburg

Robert M. Steptoe, Jr. · ⑳ · Steptoe & Johnson · http://www.steptoe-johnson.com · Chase Tower, Sixth Floor · 229 West Main Street · P.O. Box 2190 · Clarksburg, WV 26302-2190 · 304-624-8000

James M. Wilson · Steptoe & Johnson · http://www.steptoe-johnson.com · Chase Tower, Sixth Floor · 229 West Main Street · P.O. Box 2190 · Clarksburg, WV 26302-2190 · 304-624-8000

Fairmont

Michael John Aloi · Manchin & Aloi · 1543 Fairmont Avenue, Suite 203 · Fairmont, WV 26554-2100 · 304-367-1862

Huntington

John F. Cyrus · Cyrus & Adkins · 636 Fourth Avenue · Huntington, WV 25701 · 304-522-9593

Menis E. Ketchum · ⑳ · Greene, Ketchum, Bailey & Tweel · 419 Eleventh Street · P.O. Box 2389 · Huntington, WV 25701-2389 · 866-471-6482

James D. Lamp · Lamp, O'Dell, Bartram, Levy & Trautwein · River Tower, Suite 700 · 1108 Third Avenue · P.O. Box 2488 · Huntington, WV 25701-2488 · 304-523-5400

Donald B. O'Dell · Lamp, O'Dell, Bartram, Levy & Trautwein · River Tower, Suite 700 · 1108 Third Avenue · P.O. Box 2488 · Huntington, WV 25701-2488 · 304-523-5400

Morgantown

Debra H. Scudiere · Kay Casto & Chaney · http://www.kaycasto.com · 5000 Hampton Center, Suite Three · Morgantown, WV 26505 · 304-225-0970

ANTITRUST LAW

Charleston

David A. Barnette · Jackson Kelly · Laidley Tower, Suite 1600 · 500 Lee Street East · P.O. Box 553 · Charleston, WV 25322-0553 · 304-340-1000

George G. Guthrie · Allen Guthrie McHugh & Thomas · 500 Lee Street East, Suite 800 · P.O. Box 3394 · Charleston, WV 25333-3394 · 304-345-7250

W. Henry Jernigan, Jr. · Dinsmore & Shohl · http://www.dinslaw.com · Huntington Square, Suite 600 · 900 Lee Street · Charleston, WV 25301 · 304-357-0900

Clarksburg

Gordon H. Copland · Steptoe & Johnson · http://www.steptoe-johnson.com · Chase Tower, Sixth Floor · 229 West Main Street · P.O. Box 2190 · Clarksburg, WV 26302-2190 · 304-624-8000

APPELLATE LAW

Charleston

Ancil G. Ramey · Steptoe & Johnson · http://www.steptoe-johnson.com · Chase Tower, Eighth Floor · 707 Virginia Street East · P.O. Box 1588 · Charleston, WV 25326-1588 · 304-353-8000

Joanna I. Tabit · Steptoe & Johnson · http://www.steptoe-johnson.com · Chase Tower, Eighth Floor · 707 Virginia Street East · P.O. Box 1588 · Charleston, WV 25326-1588 · 304-353-8000

Morgantown

Rodney L. Bean · Steptoe & Johnson · http://www.steptoe-johnson.com · United Center, Suite 400 · 1085 Van Voorhis Road · P.O. Box 1616 · Morgantown, WV 26507-1616 · 304-598-8000

BANKING LAW

Charleston

William W. Booker · ⑩ · Kay Casto & Chaney · http://www.kaycasto.com · Chase Tower, Suite 1500 · 707 Virginia Street East · P.O. Box 2031 · Charleston, WV 25327-2031 · 304-345-8900

Charles D. Dunbar · ⑩ · Jackson Kelly · Laidley Tower, Suite 1600 · 500 Lee Street East · P.O. Box 553 · Charleston, WV 25322-0553 · 304-340-1000

Sandra M. Murphy · Bowles Rice McDavid Graff & Love · http://www.bowlesrice.com · 600 Quarrier Street · P.O. Box 1386 · Charleston, WV 25325-1386 · 304-347-1100

Clarksburg

Evans L. King, Jr. · ⑩ · Steptoe & Johnson · http://www.steptoe-johnson.com · Chase Tower, Sixth Floor 229 West Main Street · P.O. Box 2190 · Clarksburg, WV 26302-2190 · 304-624-8000

Huntington

J. Patrick Jones · Campbell Woods · 517 Ninth Street, Suite 1000 · P.O. Box 1835 · Huntington, WV 25719-1835 · 304-529-2391

Thomas J. Murray · ⑩ · Huddleston Bolen · 611 Third Avenue · P.O. Box 2185 · Huntington, WV 25701-2185 · 304-529-6181

Wheeling

James C. Gardill · ⑩ · Phillips, Gardill, Kaiser & Altmeyer · 61 Fourteenth Street · Wheeling, WV 26003 304-232-6810

BANKRUPTCY AND CREDITOR-DEBTOR RIGHTS LAW

Charleston

William W. Booker · ⑩ · Kay Casto & Chaney · http://www.kaycasto.com · Chase Tower, Suite 1500 · 707 Virginia Street East · P.O. Box 2031 · Charleston, WV 25327-2031 · 304-345-8900

Ellen S. Cappellanti · ⑩ · Jackson Kelly · Laidley Tower, Suite 1600 · 500 Lee Street East · P.O. Box 553 Charleston, WV 25322-0553 · 304-340-1000

Julia A. Chincheck · Bowles Rice McDavid Graff & Love · http://www.bowlesrice.com · 600 Quarrier Street · P.O. Box 1386 · Charleston, WV 25325-1386 · 304-347-1100

William F. Dobbs, Jr. · ⑳ · Jackson Kelly · Laidley Tower, Suite 1600 · 500 Lee Street East · P.O. Box 553 · Charleston, WV 25322-0553 · 304-340-1000

Richard M. Francis · Bowles Rice McDavid Graff & Love · http://www.bowlesrice.com · 600 Quarrier Street · P.O. Box 1386 · Charleston, WV 25325-1386 · 304-347-1100

Ralph W. Hoyer · ⑩ · Hoyer, Hoyer & Smith · 22 Capitol Street · Charleston, WV 25301 · 304-344-9821

Andrew S. Nason · ⑩ · Pepper & Nason · Eight Hale Street · Charleston, WV 25312 · 304-346-0361

John J. Nesius · Spilman Thomas & Battle · http://www.spilmanlaw.com · Spilman Center · 300 Kanawha Boulevard East · P.O. Box 273 · Charleston, WV 25301-0273 · 304-340-3800

John A. Rollins · ⑩ · Lewis, Glasser, Casey & Rollins · BB&T Square, Suite 700 · 300 Summers Street · P.O. Box 1746 · Charleston, WV 25326-1746 · 304-345-2000

Christopher Sax Smith · ⑩ · Hoyer, Hoyer & Smith · 22 Capitol Street · Charleston, WV 25301 · 304-344-9821

Arthur M. Standish · Steptoe & Johnson · http://www.steptoe-johnson.com · Chase Tower, Eighth Floor 707 Virginia Street East · P.O. Box 1588 · Charleston, WV 25326-1588 · 304-353-8000

Huntington

Thomas H. Gilpin · Huddleston Bolen · 611 Third Avenue · P.O. Box 2185 · Huntington, WV 25701-2185 · 304-529-6181

Janet Holbrook · Huddleston Bolen · 611 Third Avenue · P.O. Box 2185 · Huntington, WV 25701-2185 · 304-529-6181

Wheeling

Arch W. Riley, Jr. · Spilman Thomas & Battle · http://www.spilmanlaw.com · 1217 Chapline Street · Wheeling, WV 26003-0831 · 304-230-6950

Charleston

Rebecca A. Betts · Allen Guthrie McHugh & Thomas · 500 Lee Street East, Suite 800 · P.O. Box 3394 · Charleston, WV 25333-3394 · 304-345-7250

Michael Bonasso · Flaherty, Sensabaugh & Bonasso · 200 Capitol Street · P.O. Box 3843 · Charleston, WV 25338-3843 · 304-345-0200

James S. Crockett, Jr. · Spilman Thomas & Battle · http://www.spilmanlaw.com · Spilman Center · 300 Kanawha Boulevard East · P.O. Box 273 · Charleston, WV 25301-0273 · 304-340-3800

Arden J. Curry II · ⑩ · Pauley, Curry, Sturgeon & Vanderford · 100 Kanawha Boulevard West · P.O. Box 2786 · Charleston, WV 25330-2786 · 304-342-6000

Alvin L. Emch · Jackson Kelly · Laidley Tower, Suite 1600 · 500 Lee Street East · P.O. Box 553 · Charleston, WV 25322-0553 · 304-340-1000

Stephen B. Farmer · ⑩ · Farmer Cline & Campbell · 746 Myrtle Road · P.O. Box 3842 · Charleston, WV 25338-3842 · 304-346-5990

David K. Hendrickson · Hendrickson & Long · 214 Capitol Street · P.O. Box 11070 · Charleston, WV 25339 · 304-346-5500

W. Henry Jernigan, Jr. · Dinsmore & Shohl · http://www.dinslaw.com · Huntington Square, Suite 600 · 900 Lee Street · Charleston, WV 25301 · 304-357-0900

R. Scott Long · Hendrickson & Long · 214 Capitol Street · P.O. Box 11070 · Charleston, WV 25339 · 304-346-5500

Charles M. Love III · ⑩ · Bowles Rice McDavid Graff & Love · http://www.bowlesrice.com · 600 Quarrier Street · P.O. Box 1386 · Charleston, WV 25325-1386 · 304-347-1100

Neva G. Lusk · Spilman Thomas & Battle · http://www.spilmanlaw.com · Spilman Center · 300 Kanawha Boulevard East · P.O. Box 273 · Charleston, WV 25301-0273 · 304-340-3800

Ancil G. Ramey · Steptoe & Johnson · http://www.steptoe-johnson.com · Chase Tower, Eighth Floor · 707 Virginia Street East · P.O. Box 1588 · Charleston, WV 25326-1588 · 304-353-8000

Dennis C. Sauter · Jackson Kelly · Laidley Tower, Suite 1600 · 500 Lee Street East · P.O. Box 553 · Charleston, WV 25322-0553 · 304-340-1000

Gerard R. Stowers · Bowles Rice McDavid Graff & Love · http://www.bowlesrice.com · 600 Quarrier Street · P.O. Box 1386 · Charleston, WV 25325-1386 · 304-347-1100

David B. Thomas · Allen Guthrie McHugh & Thomas · 500 Lee Street East, Suite 800 · P.O. Box 3394 · Charleston, WV 25333-3394 · 304-345-7250

John H. Tinney, Jr. · ⑩ · The Tinney Law Firm · ChaseTower, 14th Floor · 707 Virginia Street East · P.O. Box 3752 · Charleston, WV 25337-3752 · 304-720-3310

Michael B. Victorson · Jackson Kelly · Laidley Tower, Suite 1600 · 500 Lee Street East · P.O. Box 553 · Charleston, WV 25322-0553 · 304-340-1000

Jeffrey M. Wakefield · Flaherty, Sensabaugh & Bonasso · 200 Capitol Street · P.O. Box 3843 · Charleston, WV 25338-3843 · 304-345-0200

Clarksburg

Robert M. Steptoe, Jr. · ⑳ · Steptoe & Johnson · http://www.steptoe-johnson.com · Chase Tower, Sixth Floor · 229 West Main Street · P.O. Box 2190 · Clarksburg, WV 26302-2190 · 304-624-8000

Huntington

Michael J. Farrell · ⑩ · Farrell, Farrell & Farrell · 914 Fifth Avenue · P.O. Box 6457 · Huntington, WV 25772-6457 · 304-522-9100

John H. Mahaney · Huddleston Bolen · 611 Third Avenue · P.O. Box 2185 · Huntington, WV 25701-2185 · 304-529-6181

Thomas E. Scarr · Jenkins Fenstermaker · Coal Exchange Building, Suite 1100 · 401 Eleventh Street · P.O. Box 2688 · Huntington, WV 25726-2688 · 304-523-2100

Marc E. Williams · Huddleston Bolen · 611 Third Avenue · P.O. Box 2185 · Huntington, WV 25701-2185 304-529-6181

Martinsburg

Charles F. Printz, Jr. · Bowles Rice McDavid Graff & Love · http://www.bowlesrice.com · 101 South Queen Street · P.O. Drawer 1419 · Martinsburg, WV 25401-1419 · 304-263-0836

Morgantown

William C. Brewer · Brewer & Giggenbach · 265 High Street, Fourth Floor · P.O. Box 4206 · Morgantown, WV 26504-4206 · 304-291-5800

William E. Galeota · Steptoe & Johnson · http://www.steptoe-johnson.com · United Center, Suite 400 · 1085 Van Voorhis Road · P.O. Box 1616 · Morgantown, WV 26507-1616 · 304-598-8000

Stephen M. LaCagnin · Jackson Kelly · 150 Clay Street, Suite 500 · P.O. Box 619 · Morgantown, WV 26501-0619 · 304-284-4100

Wheeling

James F. Companion · Schrader Byrd & Companion · The Maxwell Center, Suite 500 · 32 Twentieth Street · Wheeling, WV 26003 · 304-233-3390

William D. Wilmoth · Steptoe & Johnson · http://www.steptoe-johnson.com · 1233 Main Street, Suite 3000 · P.O. Box 751 · Wheeling, WV 26003-0751 · 304-233-0000

COMMUNICATIONS LAW

Charleston

Joseph J. Starsick, Jr. · Goodwin & Goodwin · 300 Summers Street, Suite 1500 · P.O. Box 2107 · Charleston, WV 25301 · 304-346-7000

CONSTRUCTION LAW

Charleston

Norman T. Daniels, Jr. · Daniels Law Firm · http://www.danielslawfirm.com · BB&T Square, Suite 1270 300 Summers Street · P.O. Box 1433 · Charleston, WV 25325-1433 · 304-342-6666

Marc A. Monteleone · Bowles Rice McDavid Graff & Love · http://www.bowlesrice.com · 600 Quarrier Street · P.O. Box 1386 · Charleston, WV 25325-1386 · 304-347-1100

CORPORATE LAW

Charleston

Ellen S. Cappellanti · ⑩ · Jackson Kelly · Laidley Tower, Suite 1600 · 500 Lee Street East · P.O. Box 553 Charleston, WV 25322-0553 · 304-340-1000

Michael T. Chaney · Kay Casto & Chaney · http://www.kaycasto.com · Chase Tower, Suite 1500 · 707 Virginia Street East · P.O. Box 2031 · Charleston, WV 25327-2031 · 304-345-8900

Mark D'Antoni · Bowles Rice McDavid Graff & Love · http://www.bowlesrice.com · 600 Quarrier Street · P.O. Box 1386 · Charleston, WV 25325-1386 · 304-347-1100

K. Paul Davis · Spilman Thomas & Battle · http://www.spilmanlaw.com · Spilman Center · 300 Kanawha Boulevard East · P.O. Box 273 · Charleston, WV 25301-0273 · 304-340-3800

Charles D. Dunbar · ⑩ · Jackson Kelly · Laidley Tower, Suite 1600 · 500 Lee Street East · P.O. Box 553 · Charleston, WV 25322-0553 · 304-340-1000

Mark A. Ferguson · Sprouse & Ferguson · 230 Capitol Street, Suite 300 · Charleston, WV 25301 · 304-342-9100

David P. Ferretti · Spilman Thomas & Battle · http://www.spilmanlaw.com · Spilman Center · 300 Kanawha Boulevard East · P.O. Box 273 · Charleston, WV 25301-0273 · 304-340-3800

Samme L. Gee · Jackson Kelly · Laidley Tower, Suite 1600 · 500 Lee Street East · P.O. Box 553 · Charleston, WV 25322-0553 · 304-340-1000

Martin J. Glasser · Lewis, Glasser, Casey & Rollins · BB&T Square, Suite 700 · 300 Summers Street · P.O. Box 1746 · Charleston, WV 25326-1746 · 304-345-2000

Thomas R. Goodwin · ⑳ · Goodwin & Goodwin · 300 Summers Street, Suite 1500 · P.O. Box 2107 · Charleston, WV 25301 · 304-346-7000

F. Thomas Graff, Jr. · ⑳ · Bowles Rice McDavid Graff & Love · http://www.bowlesrice.com · 600 Quarrier Street · P.O. Box 1386 · Charleston, WV 25325-1386 · 304-347-1100

William M. Herlihy · Spilman Thomas & Battle · http://www.spilmanlaw.com · Spilman Center · 300 Kanawha Boulevard East · P.O. Box 273 · Charleston, WV 25301-0273 · 304-340-3800

Thomas A. Heywood · ⑩ · Bowles Rice McDavid Graff & Love · http://www.bowlesrice.com · 600 Quarrier Street · P.O. Box 1386 · Charleston, WV 25325-1385 · 304-347-1100

David K. Higgins · Robinson & McElwee · Fifth Third Center, Suite 400 · 700 Virginia Street East · P.O. Box 1791 · Charleston, WV 25301-1791 · 304-344-5800

Lee O. Hill · Spilman Thomas & Battle · http://www.spilmanlaw.com · Spilman Center · 300 Kanawha Boulevard East · P.O. Box 273 · Charleston, WV 25301-0273 · 304-340-3800

Roger D. Hunter · Spilman Thomas & Battle · http://www.spilmanlaw.com · Spilman Center · 300 Kanawha Boulevard East · P.O. Box 273 · Charleston, WV 25301-0273 · 304-340-3800

Charles W. Loeb, Jr. · Jackson Kelly · Laidley Tower, Suite 1600 · 500 Lee Street East · P.O. Box 553 · Charleston, WV 25322-0553 · 304-340-1000

Elizabeth O. Lord · ⑩ · Jackson Kelly · Laidley Tower, Suite 1600 · 500 Lee Street East · P.O. Box 553 · Charleston, WV 25322-0553 · 304-340-1000

Steven F. Luby · Lewis, Glasser, Casey & Rollins · BB&T Square, Suite 700 · 300 Summers Street · P.O. Box 1746 · Charleston, WV 25326-1746 · 304-345-2000

Marc A. Monteleone · Bowles Rice McDavid Graff & Love · http://www.bowlesrice.com · 600 Quarrier Street · P.O. Box 1386 · Charleston, WV 25325-1386 · 304-347-1100

David B. Shapiro · Spilman Thomas & Battle · http://www.spilmanlaw.com · Spilman Center · 300 Kanawha Boulevard East · P.O. Box 273 · Charleston, WV 25301-0273 · 304-340-3800

Camden P. Siegrist · Bowles Rice McDavid Graff & Love · http://www.bowlesrice.com · 600 Quarrier Street · P.O. Box 1386 · Charleston, WV 25325-1386 · 304-347-1100

Louis S. Southworth II · ⑩ · Jackson Kelly · Laidley Tower, Suite 1600 · 500 Lee Street East · P.O. Box 553 · Charleston, WV 25322-0553 · 304-340-1000

Robert Tweel · Jackson Kelly · Laidley Tower, Suite 1600 · 500 Lee Street East · P.O. Box 553 · Charleston, WV 25322-0553 · 304-340-1000

L. Frederick Williams, Jr. · Steptoe & Johnson · http://www.steptoe-johnson.com · Chase Tower, Eighth Floor · 707 Virginia Street East · P.O. Box 1588 · Charleston, WV 25326-1588 · 304-353-8000

Clarksburg

Patrick D. Deem · ⑩ · Steptoe & Johnson · http://www.steptoe-johnson.com · Chase Tower, Sixth Floor · 229 West Main Street · P.O. Box 2190 · Clarksburg, WV 26302-2190 · 304-624-8000

Evans L. King, Jr. · ⑩ · Steptoe & Johnson · http://www.steptoe-johnson.com · Chase Tower, Sixth Floor 229 West Main Street · P.O. Box 2190 · Clarksburg, WV 26302-2190 · 304-624-8000

Huntington

Thomas J. Murray · ⑩ · Huddleston Bolen · 611 Third Avenue · P.O. Box 2185 · Huntington, WV 25701-2185 · 304-529-6181

Martinsburg

Michael E. Caryl · Bowles Rice McDavid Graff & Love · http://www.bowlesrice.com · 101 South Queen Street · P.O. Drawer 1419 · Martinsburg, WV 25401-1419 · 304-263-0836

Michael B. Keller · Bowles Rice McDavid Graff & Love · http://www.bowlesrice.com · 101 South Queen Street · P.O. Drawer 1419 · Martinsburg, WV 25401-1419 · 304-263-0836

Morgantown

James A. Russell · Steptoe & Johnson · http://www.steptoe-johnson.com · United Center, Suite 400 · 1085 Van Voorhis Road · P.O. Box 1616 · Morgantown, WV 26507-1616 · 304-598-8000

Wheeling

James C. Gardill · ⑩ · Phillips, Gardill, Kaiser & Altmeyer · 61 Fourteenth Street · Wheeling, WV 26003 304-232-6810

Charles J. Kaiser, Jr. · Phillips, Gardill, Kaiser & Altmeyer · 61 Fourteenth Street · Wheeling, WV 26003 304-232-6810

EDUCATION LAW

Charleston

Howard E. Seufer, Jr. · Bowles Rice McDavid Graff & Love · http://www.bowlesrice.com · 600 Quarrier Street · P.O. Box 1386 · Charleston, WV 25325-1386 · 304-347-1100

Morgantown

Gregory Bailey · Bowles Rice McDavid Graff & Love · http://www.bowlesrice.com · 7000 Hampton Center, Suite K · Morgantown, WV 26505-1720 · 304-285-2500

Harry M. Rubenstein · Dinsmore & Shohl · http://www.dinslaw.com · 215 Don Knotts Boulevard, Suite 310 · Morgantown, WV 26501 · 304-296-1100

ELDER LAW

Clarksburg

Sherri S. Whalen · Steptoe & Johnson · http://www.steptoe-johnson.com · Chase Tower, Sixth Floor · 229 West Main Street · P.O. Box 2190 · Clarksburg, WV 26302-2190 · 304-624-8000

Parkersburg

Paul L. Hicks · Bowles Rice McDavid Graff & Love · http://www.bowlesrice.com · United Square, Fifth Floor · 501 Avery Street · P.O. Box 49 · Parkersburg, WV 26102-0049 · 304-485-8500

EMINENT DOMAIN AND CONDEMNATION LAW

Charleston

J. Nicholas Barth · Barth & Thompson · Kanawha Boulevard, West At Berkley Street · P.O. Box 129 · Charleston, WV 25302-0129 · 304-342-7111

Mark A. Sadd · Lewis, Glasser, Casey & Rollins · BB&T Square, Suite 700 · 300 Summers Street · P.O. Box 1746 · Charleston, WV 25326-1746 · 304-345-2000

EMPLOYEE BENEFITS LAW

Charleston

Michael D. Foster · ⑳ · Jackson Kelly · Laidley Tower, Suite 1600 · 500 Lee Street East · P.O. Box 553 · Charleston, WV 25322-0553 · 304-340-1000

Jason E. Huber · Forman and Huber · 100 Capitol Street, Suite 400 · Charleston, WV 25301 · 304-346-6300

Lesley A. Russo · Bowles Rice McDavid Graff & Love · http://www.bowlesrice.com · 600 Quarrier Street P.O. Box 1386 · Charleston, WV 25325-1386 · 304-347-1100

Clarksburg

Kevin A. Wiggins · Jackson Kelly · Ogden Building · 203 West Main Street · P.O. Box 150 · Clarksburg, WV 26301-0150 · 304-624-6555

Huntington

Charlotte A. Hoffman Norris · Farrell, Farrell & Farrell · 914 Fifth Avenue · P.O. Box 6457 · Huntington, WV 25772-6457 · 304-522-9100

Tamela J. White · Farrell, Farrell & Farrell · 914 Fifth Avenue · P.O. Box 6457 · Huntington, WV 25772-6457 · 304-522-9100

Wheeling

Jamie L. Leary · Steptoe & Johnson · http://www.steptoe-johnson.com · 1233 Main Street, Suite 3000 · P.O. Box 751 · Wheeling, WV 26003-0751 · 304-233-0000

ENERGY LAW

Charleston

Christopher L. Callas · Jackson Kelly · Laidley Tower, Suite 1600 · 500 Lee Street East · P.O. Box 553 · Charleston, WV 25322-0553 · 304-340-1000

Lee F. Feinberg · Spilman Thomas & Battle · http://www.spilmanlaw.com · Spilman Center · 300 Kanawha Boulevard East · P.O. Box 273 · Charleston, WV 25301-0273 · 304-340-3800

Sharon O. Flanery · Steptoe & Johnson · http://www.steptoe-johnson.com · Chase Tower, Eighth Floor · 707 Virginia Street East · P.O. Box 1588 · Charleston, WV 25326-1588 · 304-353-8000

David M. Flannery · ⑳ · Jackson Kelly · Laidley Tower, Suite 1600 · 500 Lee Street East · P.O. Box 553 · Charleston, WV 25322-0553 · 304-340-1000

Robert D. Fluharty · Jackson Kelly · Laidley Tower, Suite 1600 · 500 Lee Street East · P.O. Box 553 · Charleston, WV 25322-0553 · 304-340-1000

F. Thomas Graff, Jr. · ⑳ · Bowles Rice McDavid Graff & Love · http://www.bowlesrice.com · 600 Quarrier Street · P.O. Box 1386 · Charleston, WV 25325-1386 · 304-347-1100

William M. Herlihy · Spilman Thomas & Battle · http://www.spilmanlaw.com · Spilman Center · 300 Kanawha Boulevard East · P.O. Box 273 · Charleston, WV 25301-0273 · 304-340-3800

W. Henry Jernigan, Jr. · Dinsmore & Shohl · http://www.dinslaw.com · Huntington Square, Suite 600 · 900 Lee Street · Charleston, WV 25301 · 304-357-0900

J. Thomas Lane · ⑳ · Bowles Rice McDavid Graff & Love · http://www.bowlesrice.com · 600 Quarrier Street · P.O. Box 1386 · Charleston, WV 25325-1386 · 304-347-1100

E. Dandridge McDonald · ⑩ · Steptoe & Johnson · http://www.steptoe-johnson.com · Chase Tower, Eighth Floor · 707 Virginia Street East · P.O. Box 1588 · Charleston, WV 25326-1588 · 304-353-8000

Steven P. McGowan · Steptoe & Johnson · http://www.steptoe-johnson.com · Chase Tower, Eighth Floor 707 Virginia Street East · P.O. Box 1588 · Charleston, WV 25326-1588 · 304-353-8000

Thomas N. McJunkin · ⑩ · Jackson Kelly · Laidley Tower, Suite 1600 · 500 Lee Street East · P.O. Box 553 · Charleston, WV 25322-0553 · 304-340-1000

Robert G. McLusky · ⑩ · Jackson Kelly · Laidley Tower, Suite 1600 · 500 Lee Street East · P.O. Box 553 Charleston, WV 25322-0553 · 304-340-1000

William C. Porth · ⑩ · Robinson & McElwee · Fifth Third Center, Suite 400 · 700 Virginia Street East · P.O. Box 1791 · Charleston, WV 25301-1791 · 304-344-5800

Christopher B. Power · Dinsmore & Shohl · http://www.dinslaw.com · Huntington Square, Suite 600 · 900 Lee Street · Charleston, WV 25301 · 304-357-0900

Robert R. Rodecker · ⑩ · Robert R. Rodecker · BB&T Square, Suite 1230 · 300 Summers Street · P.O. Box 3713 · Charleston, WV 25337 · 304-343-1654

Clarksburg

Ralph J. Bean, Jr. · Steptoe & Johnson · http://www.steptoe-johnson.com · Chase Tower, Sixth Floor · 229 West Main Street · P.O. Box 2190 · Clarksburg, WV 26302-2190 · 304-624-8000

Patrick D. Deem · ⑩ · Steptoe & Johnson · http://www.steptoe-johnson.com · Chase Tower, Sixth Floor · 229 West Main Street · P.O. Box 2190 · Clarksburg, WV 26302-2190 · 304-624-8000

W. Henry Lawrence · ⑩ · Steptoe & Johnson · http://www.steptoe-johnson.com · Chase Tower, Sixth Floor · 229 West Main Street · P.O. Box 2190 · Clarksburg, WV 26302-2190 · 304-624-8000

ENVIRONMENTAL LAW

Charleston

Joshua I. Barrett · DiTrapano, Barrett & DiPiero · 604 Virginia Street East · Charleston, WV 25301-2184 304-342-0133

Kathy G. Beckett · Jackson Kelly · Laidley Tower, Suite 1600 · 500 Lee Street East · P.O. Box 553 · Charleston, WV 25322-0553 · 304-340-1000

M. Ann Bradley · ⑩ · Spilman Thomas & Battle · http://www.spilmanlaw.com · Spilman Center · 300 Kanawha Boulevard East · P.O. Box 273 · Charleston, WV 25301-0273 · 304-340-3800

T. Randolph Cox · ⑩ · Spilman Thomas & Battle · http://www.spilmanlaw.com · Spilman Center · 300 Kanawha Boulevard East · P.O. Box 273 · Charleston, WV 25301-0273 · 304-340-3800

David M. Flannery · ⑳ · Jackson Kelly · Laidley Tower, Suite 1600 · 500 Lee Street East · P.O. Box 553 · Charleston, WV 25322-0553 · 304-340-1000

Leonard B. Knee · Bowles Rice McDavid Graff & Love · http://www.bowlesrice.com · 600 Quarrier Street · P.O. Box 1386 · Charleston, WV 25325-1386 · 304-347-1100

Robert E. Lannan II · Robinson & McElwee · Fifth Third Center, Suite 400 · 700 Virginia Street East · P.O. Box 1791 · Charleston, WV 25301-1791 · 304-344-5800

Richard L. Lewis · Steptoe & Johnson · http://www.steptoe-johnson.com · Chase Tower, Eighth Floor · 707 Virginia Street East · P.O. Box 1588 · Charleston, WV 25326-1588 · 304-353-8000

Barbara D. Little · ⑩ · Jackson Kelly · Laidley Tower, Suite 1600 · 500 Lee Street East · P.O. Box 553 · Charleston, WV 25322-0553 · 304-340-1000

Robert G. McLusky · ⑩ · Jackson Kelly · Laidley Tower, Suite 1600 · 500 Lee Street East · P.O. Box 553 Charleston, WV 25322-0553 · 304-340-1000

Christopher B. Power · Dinsmore & Shohl · http://www.dinslaw.com · Huntington Square, Suite 600 · 900 Lee Street · Charleston, WV 25301 · 304-357-0900

James R. Snyder · ⑩ · Jackson Kelly · Laidley Tower, Suite 1600 · 500 Lee Street East · P.O. Box 553 · Charleston, WV 25322-0553 · 304-340-1000

Allyn G. Turner · Spilman Thomas & Battle · http://www.spilmanlaw.com · Spilman Center · 300 Kanawha Boulevard East · P.O. Box 273 · Charleston, WV 25301-0273 · 304-340-3800

Clarksburg

W. Henry Lawrence · ⑩ · Steptoe & Johnson · http://www.steptoe-johnson.com · Chase Tower, Sixth Floor · 229 West Main Street · P.O. Box 2190 · Clarksburg, WV 26302-2190 · 304-624-8000

Huntington

Andrew Zettle · Huddleston Bolen · 611 Third Avenue · P.O. Box 2185 · Huntington, WV 25701-2185 · 304-529-6181

Lewisburg

Joseph M. Lovett · Appalachian Center for the Economy and the Environment · 117 East Washington Street · P.O. Box 507 · Lewisburg, WV 24901-0507 · 304-645-9006

FAMILY LAW

Beckley

Clair Elton Byron, Jr. · ⑩ · Abrams & Byron · 108 Main Street · P.O. Box 5038 · Beckley, WV 25801 · 304-253-1500

Charleston

Andrew S. Nason · ⑩ · Pepper & Nason · Eight Hale Street · Charleston, WV 25312 · 304-346-0361

R. Joseph Zak · ⑩ · R. Joseph Zak · 607 Ohio Avenue · Charleston, WV 25302 · 304-345-0745

Clarksburg

Delby B. Pool · ⑩ · Delby B. Pool · 230 Court Street · Clarksburg, WV 26301-2906 · 304-623-9711

Morgantown

Debra A. Bowers · Kay Casto & Chaney · http://www.kaycasto.com · 5000 Hampton Center, Suite Three Morgantown, WV 26505 · 304-225-0970

Sutton

James Wilson Douglas · James W. Douglas · 181-B Main Street · Sutton, WV 26601 · 304-765-2821

Wheeling

Jo Lynne Nugent · Sheehan & Nugent · 41 Fifteenth Street · Wheeling, WV 26003 · 304-232-1064

GAMING LAW

Charleston

Richard E. Boyle, Jr. · Kay Casto & Chaney · http://www.kaycasto.com · Chase Tower, Suite 1500 · 707 Virginia Street East · P.O. Box 2031 · Charleston, WV 25327-2031 · 304-345-8900

Wendel B. Turner · Turner & Johns · 216 Brook Street, Suite 301 · Charleston, WV 25301 · 304-720-2300

GOVERNMENT RELATIONS LAW

Charleston

Michael J. Basile · Spilman Thomas & Battle · http://www.spilmanlaw.com · Spilman Center · 300 Kanawha Boulevard East · P.O. Box 273 · Charleston, WV 25301-0273 · 304-340-3800

Jill Cranston Bentz · Dinsmore & Shohl · http://www.dinslaw.com · Huntington Square, Suite 600 · 900 Lee Street · Charleston, WV 25301 · 304-357-0900

George E. Carenbauer · Steptoe & Johnson · http://www.steptoe-johnson.com · Chase Tower, Eighth Floor · 707 Virginia Street East · P.O. Box 1588 · Charleston, WV 25326-1588 · 304-353-8000

G. Nicholas Casey, Jr. · Lewis, Glasser, Casey & Rollins · BB&T Square, Suite 700 · 300 Summers Street · P.O. Box 1746 · Charleston, WV 25326-1746 · 304-345-2000

T. Randolph Cox · ⑩ · Spilman Thomas & Battle · http://www.spilmanlaw.com · Spilman Center · 300 Kanawha Boulevard East · P.O. Box 273 · Charleston, WV 25301-0273 · 304-340-3800

Richard M. Francis · Bowles Rice McDavid Graff & Love · http://www.bowlesrice.com · 600 Quarrier Street · P.O. Box 1386 · Charleston, WV 25325-1386 · 304-347-1100

HEALTH CARE LAW

Charleston

Robert Coffield · Flaherty, Sensabaugh & Bonasso · 200 Capitol Street · P.O. Box 3843 · Charleston, WV 25338-3843 · 304-345-0200

Thomas A. Heywood · ⑩ · Bowles Rice McDavid Graff & Love · http://www.bowlesrice.com · 600 Quarrier Street · P.O. Box 1386 · Charleston, WV 25325-1386 · 304-347-1100

Thomas J. Hurney, Jr. · Jackson Kelly · Laidley Tower, Suite 1600 · 500 Lee Street East · P.O. Box 553 · Charleston, WV 25322-0553 · 304-340-1000

Patrick D. Kelly · Steptoe & Johnson · http://www.steptoe-johnson.com · Chase Tower, Eighth Floor · 707 Virginia Street East · P.O. Box 1588 · Charleston, WV 25326-1588 · 304-353-8000

Robert J. O'Neil · ⑩ · Dinsmore & Shohl · http://www.dinslaw.com · Huntington Square, Suite 600 · 900 Lee Street · Charleston, WV 25301 · 304-357-0900

Michael I. Spiker · Goodwin & Goodwin · 300 Summers Street, Suite 1500 · P.O. Box 2107 · Charleston, WV 25301 · 304-346-7000

James W. Thomas · Jackson Kelly · Laidley Tower, Suite 1600 · 500 Lee Street East · P.O. Box 553 · Charleston, WV 25322-0553 · 304-340-1000

Clarksburg

Gordon H. Copland · Steptoe & Johnson · http://www.steptoe-johnson.com · Chase Tower, Sixth Floor · 229 West Main Street · P.O. Box 2190 · Clarksburg, WV 26302-2190 · 304-624-8000

Walter L. Williams · Steptoe & Johnson · http://www.steptoe-johnson.com · Chase Tower, Sixth Floor · 229 West Main Street · P.O. Box 2190 · Clarksburg, WV 26302-2190 · 304-624-8000

Martinsburg

Taunja Willis-Miller · ⑩ · Jackson Kelly · 310 West Burke Street · P.O. Box 1068 · Martinsburg, WV 25401-1060 · 304-263-8800

INFORMATION TECHNOLOGY LAW

Charleston

David A. Barnette · Jackson Kelly · Laidley Tower, Suite 1600 · 500 Lee Street East · P.O. Box 553 · Charleston, WV 25322-0553 · 304-340-1000

INSURANCE LAW

Bridgeport

Daniel C. Cooper · Cooper Law Offices · 240 West Main Street · Bridgeport, WV 26330 · 304-842-0505

Charleston

W. Randolph Fife · Steptoe & Johnson · http://www.steptoe-johnson.com · Chase Tower, Eighth Floor · 707 Virginia Street East · P.O. Box 1588 · Charleston, WV 25326-1588 · 304-353-8000

John R. Hoblitzell · Kay Casto & Chaney · http://www.kaycasto.com · Chase Tower, Suite 1500 · 707 Virginia Street East · P.O. Box 2031 · Charleston, WV 25327-2031 · 304-345-8900

Brent K. Kesner · Kesner, Kesner & Bramble · 112 Capitol Street · Charleston, WV 25301 · 304-345-5200

J. Rudy Martin · Jackson Kelly · Laidley Tower, Suite 1600 · 500 Lee Street East · P.O. Box 553 · Charleston, WV 25322-0553 · 304-340-1000

John R. McGhee, Jr. · Kay Casto & Chaney · http://www.kaycasto.com · Chase Tower, Suite 1500 · 707 Virginia Street East · P.O. Box 2031 · Charleston, WV 25327-2031 · 304-345-8900

W. Michael Moore · Moore & Biser · 405 Capitol Street, Suite 603 · Charleston, WV 25301 · 304-414-2300

Don C. A. Parker · Spilman Thomas & Battle · http://www.spilmanlaw.com · Spilman Center · 300 Kanawha Boulevard East · P.O. Box 273 · Charleston, WV 25301-0273 · 304-340-3800

John J. Polak · Atkinson & Polak · 1300 BB&T Square · 300 Summers Street · Charleston, WV 25301 · 304-346-5100

Mary H. Sanders · Huddleston Bolen · 707 Virginia Street East, Suite 1300 · P.O. Box 3786 · Charleston, WV 25337-3786 · 304-344-9869

Cross Lanes

Vincent J. King · Vincent J. King · 99 Presidio Pointe · Cross Lanes, WV 25313 · 304-744-7577

Huntington

R. Carter Elkins · Campbell Woods · 517 Ninth Street, Suite 1000 · P.O. Box 1835 · Huntington, WV 25719-1835 · 304-529-2391

Lee Murray Hall · Jenkins Fenstermaker · Coal Exchange Building, Suite 1100 · 401 Eleventh Street · P.O. Box 2688 · Huntington, WV 25726-2688 · 304-523-2100

James D. Lamp · Lamp, O'Dell, Bartram, Levy & Trautwein · River Tower, Suite 700 · 1108 Third Avenue · P.O. Box 2488 · Huntington, WV 25701-2488 · 304-523-5400

Robert L. Massie · Huddleston Bolen · 611 Third Avenue · P.O. Box 2185 · Huntington, WV 25701-2185 304-529-6181

Donald B. O'Dell · Lamp, O'Dell, Bartram, Levy & Trautwein · River Tower, Suite 700 · 1108 Third Avenue · P.O. Box 2488 · Huntington, WV 25701-2488 · 304-523-5400

Morgantown

Laurie C. Barbe · Steptoe & Johnson · http://www.steptoe-johnson.com · United Center, Suite 400 · 1085 Van Voorhis Road · P.O. Box 1616 · Morgantown, WV 26507-1616 · 304-598-8000

Wheeling

Robert P. Fitzsimmons · Fitzsimmons Law Offices · 1609 Warwood Avenue · Wheeling, WV 26003-7110 304-277-1700

INTELLECTUAL PROPERTY LAW

Charleston

David A. Barnette · Jackson Kelly · Laidley Tower, Suite 1600 · 500 Lee Street East · P.O. Box 553 · Charleston, WV 25322-0553 · 304-340-1000

Monika J. Hussell · Dinsmore & Shohl · http://www.dinslaw.com · Huntington Square, Suite 600 · 900 Lee Street · Charleston, WV 25301 · 304-357-0900

INTERNATIONAL ARBITRATION

Charleston

A. Andrew MacQueen · A. Andrew MacQueen · 55 Abney Circle · Charleston, WV 25314 · 304-344-2994

Edward D. McDevitt · Bowles Rice McDavid Graff & Love · http://www.bowlesrice.com · 600 Quarrier Street · P.O. Box 1386 · Charleston, WV 25325-1386 · 304-347-1100

LABOR AND EMPLOYMENT LAW

Charleston

Ricklin Brown · Bowles Rice McDavid Graff & Love · http://www.bowlesrice.com · 600 Quarrier Street · P.O. Box 1386 · Charleston, WV 25325-1386 · 304-347-1100

Kevin L. Carr · Spilman Thomas & Battle · http://www.spilmanlaw.com · Spilman Center · 300 Kanawha Boulevard East · P.O. Box 273 · Charleston, WV 25301-0273 · 304-340-3800

Mark A. Carter · Dinsmore & Shohl · http://www.dinslaw.com · Huntington Square, Suite 600 · 900 Lee Street · Charleston, WV 25301 · 304-357-0900

Bryan R. Cokeley · Steptoe & Johnson · http://www.steptoe-johnson.com · Chase Tower, Eighth Floor · 707 Virginia Street East · P.O. Box 1588 · Charleston, WV 25326-1588 · 304-353-8000

Anna M. Dailey · Dinsmore & Shohl · http://www.dinslaw.com · Huntington Square, Suite 600 · 900 Lee Street · Charleston, WV 25301 · 304-357-0900

Mark A. Ferguson · Sprouse & Ferguson · 230 Capitol Street, Suite 300 · Charleston, WV 25301 · 304-342-9100

Cheryl H. Ledbetter · Jackson Kelly · Laidley Tower, Suite 1600 · 500 Lee Street East · P.O. Box 553 · Charleston, WV 25322-0553 · 304-340-1000

Erin E. Magee · Jackson Kelly · Laidley Tower, Suite 1600 · 500 Lee Street East · P.O. Box 553 · Charleston, WV 25322-0553 · 304-340-1000

Kevin A. Nelson · Huddleston Bolen · 707 Virginia Street East, Suite 1300 · P.O. Box 3786 · Charleston, WV 25337-3786 · 304-344-9869

Joseph M. Price · Robinson & McElwee · Fifth Third Center, Suite 400 · 700 Virginia Street East · P.O. Box 1791 · Charleston, WV 25301-1791 · 304-344-5800

Forrest H. Roles · 20 · Dinsmore & Shohl · http://www.dinslaw.com · Huntington Square, Suite 600 · 900 Lee Street · Charleston, WV 25301 · 304-357-0900

Albert F. Sebok · Jackson Kelly · Laidley Tower, Suite 1600 · 500 Lee Street East · P.O. Box 553 · Charleston, WV 25322-0553 · 304-340-1000

Lonnie C. Simmons · DiTrapano, Barrett & DiPiero · 604 Virginia Street East · Charleston, WV 25301-2184 · 304-342-0133

Elizabeth D. Walker · Bowles Rice McDavid Graff & Love · http://www.bowlesrice.com · 600 Quarrier Street · P.O. Box 1386 · Charleston, WV 25325-1386 · 304-347-1100

Stephen A. Weber · Kay Casto & Chaney · http://www.kaycasto.com · Chase Tower, Suite 1500 · 707 Virginia Street East · P.O. Box 2031 · Charleston, WV 25327-2031 · 304-345-8900

Roger A. Wolfe · 10 · Jackson Kelly · Laidley Tower, Suite 1600 · 500 Lee Street East · P.O. Box 553 · Charleston, WV 25322-0553 · 304-340-1000

Charles L. Woody · Spilman Thomas & Battle · http://www.spilmanlaw.com · Spilman Center · 300 Kanawha Boulevard East · P.O. Box 273 · Charleston, WV 25301-0273 · 304-340-3800

Clarksburg

Michael J. Florio · Florio Law Offices · 333 East Main Street · Clarksburg, WV 26301 · 304-626-3000

John R. Merinar, Jr. · Steptoe & Johnson · http://www.steptoe-johnson.com · Chase Tower, Sixth Floor · 229 West Main Street · P.O. Box 2190 · Clarksburg, WV 26302-2190 · 304-624-8000

C. David Morrison · Steptoe & Johnson · http://www.steptoe-johnson.com · Chase Tower, Sixth Floor · 229 West Main Street · P.O. Box 2190 · Clarksburg, WV 26302-2190 · 304-624-8000

Larry J. Rector · Steptoe & Johnson · http://www.steptoe-johnson.com · Chase Tower, Sixth Floor · 229 West Main Street · P.O. Box 2190 · Clarksburg, WV 26302-2190 · 304-624-8000

Robert M. Steptoe, Jr. · 20 · Steptoe & Johnson · http://www.steptoe-johnson.com · Chase Tower, Sixth Floor · 229 West Main Street · P.O. Box 2190 · Clarksburg, WV 26302-2190 · 304-624-8000

Richard M. Yurko, Jr. · Steptoe & Johnson · http://www.steptoe-johnson.com · Chase Tower, Sixth Floor · 229 West Main Street · P.O. Box 2190 · Clarksburg, WV 26302-2190 · 304-624-8000

Huntington

Thomas E. Scarr · Jenkins Fenstermaker · Coal Exchange Building, Suite 1100 · 401 Eleventh Street · P.O. Box 2688 · Huntington, WV 25726-2688 · 304-523-2100

Christopher L. Slaughter · Steptoe & Johnson · http://www.steptoe-johnson.com · Chase Center, Suite 250 · 1000 Fifth Avenue · P.O. Box 2195 · Huntington, WV 25722-2195 · 304-522-8290

Logan

Bradley J. Pyles · ⑩ · Pyles, Turner & Mick · 408 Main Street · P.O. Box 596 · Logan, WV 25601 · 304-752-6000

Martinsburg

David M. Hammer · Hammer, Feretti & Schiavoni · 408 West King Street · Martinsburg, WV 25401 · 304-264-8505

Robert J. Schiavoni · Hammer, Feretti & Schiavoni · 408 West King Street · Martinsburg, WV 25401 · 304-264-8505

Morgantown

David E. Dick · Steptoe & Johnson · http://www.steptoe-johnson.com · United Center, Suite 400 · 1085 Van Voorhis Road · P.O. Box 1616 · Morgantown, WV 26507-1616 · 304-598-8000

Allan N. Karlin · ⑩ · Allan N. Karlin & Associates · http://www.wvjustice.com · 174 Chancery Row · Morgantown, WV 26505 · 304-296-8266

Stephen M. LaCagnin · Jackson Kelly · 150 Clay Street, Suite 500 · P.O. Box 619 · Morgantown, WV 26501-0619 · 304-284-4100

Jane E. Peak · Allan N. Karlin & Associates · http://www.wvjustice.com · 174 Chancery Row · Morgantown, WV 26505 · 304-296-8266

Parkersburg

Walt L. Auvil · Rusend & Auvil · 1208 Market Street · Parkersburg, WV 26101-4323 · 304-485-3058

Princeton

Kathryn Reed Bayless · Bayless Law Firm · 1607 West Main Street · Princeton, WV 24740 · 304-487-8707

Wheeling

Larry W. Blalock · Jackson Kelly · 1144 Market Street · P.O. Box 871 · Wheeling, WV 26003-0871 · 304-233-4000

Patrick S. Cassidy · Cassidy, Myers, Cogan & Voegelin · The First State Capitol · 1413 Eoff Street · Wheeling, WV 26003-3582 · 304-232-8100

LEGAL MALPRACTICE LAW

Charleston

Stephen R. Crislip · Jackson Kelly · Laidley Tower, Suite 1600 · 500 Lee Street East · P.O. Box 553 · Charleston, WV 25322-0553 · 304-340-1000

David D. Johnson III · Winter Johnson & Hill · http://www.wjh-law.com · United Center, Suite 500 · 500 Virginia Street East · P.O. Box 2187 · Charleston, WV 25328-2187 · 304-345-7800

Gerard R. Stowers · Bowles Rice McDavid Graff & Love · http://www.bowlesrice.com · 600 Quarrier Street · P.O. Box 1386 · Charleston, WV 25325-1386 · 304-347-1100

Larry A. Winter · Winter Johnson & Hill · http://www.wjh-law.com · United Center, Suite 500 · 500 Virginia Street East · P.O. Box 2187 · Charleston, WV 25328-2187 · 304-345-7800

Clarksburg

James A. Varner, Sr. · McNeer, Highland, McMunn and Varner · BB&T Bank Building · Main and Fourth Streets · P.O. Drawer 2040 · Clarksburg, WV 26302-2040 · 304-626-1100

Huntington

Marc E. Williams · Huddleston Bolen · 611 Third Avenue · P.O. Box 2185 · Huntington, WV 25701-2185 304-529-6181

Martinsburg

Bridget M. Cohee · Steptoe & Johnson · http://www.steptoe-johnson.com · Edwin Miller Professional Centre, Suite 300 · 1250 Edwin Miller Boulevard · P.O. Box 2629 · Martinsburg, WV 25402-2629 · 304-263-6991

Morgantown

Susan S. Brewer · Steptoe & Johnson · http://www.steptoe-johnson.com · United Center, Suite 400 · 1085 Van Voorhis Road · P.O. Box 1616 · Morgantown, WV 26507-1616 · 304-598-8000

Wheeling

William D. Wilmoth · Steptoe & Johnson · http://www.steptoe-johnson.com · 1233 Main Street, Suite 3000 · P.O. Box 751 · Wheeling, WV 26003-0751 · 304-233-0000

MASS TORT LITIGATION

Charleston

Michael B. Victorson · Jackson Kelly · Laidley Tower, Suite 1600 · 500 Lee Street East · P.O. Box 553 · Charleston, WV 25322-0553 · 304-340-1000

Huntington

Fred Adkins · Huddleston Bolen · 611 Third Avenue · P.O. Box 2185 · Huntington, WV 25701-2185 · 304-529-6181

Richard L. Lancianese · Baker Law Offices · River Tower, Suite 300 · 1108 Third Avenue · Huntington, WV 25701-1578 · 304-522-6906

John H. Mahaney · Huddleston Bolen · 611 Third Avenue · P.O. Box 2185 · Huntington, WV 25701-2185 · 304-529-6181

Robert H. Sweeney, Jr. · Jenkins Fenstermaker · Coal Exchange Building, Suite 1100 · 401 Eleventh Street · P.O. Box 2688 · Huntington, WV 25726-2688 · 304-523-2100

Marc E. Williams · Huddleston Bolen · 611 Third Avenue · P.O. Box 2185 · Huntington, WV 25701-2185 304-529-6181

MEDICAL MALPRACTICE LAW

Charleston

Thomas J. Hurney, Jr. · Jackson Kelly · Laidley Tower, Suite 1600 · 500 Lee Street East · P.O. Box 553 · Charleston, WV 25322-0553 · 304-340-1000

Edward C. Martin · Flaherty, Sensabaugh & Bonasso · 200 Capitol Street · P.O. Box 3843 · Charleston, WV 25338-3843 · 304-345-0200

Don R. Sensabaugh, Jr. · Flaherty, Sensabaugh & Bonasso · 200 Capitol Street · P.O. Box 3843 · Charleston, WV 25338-3843 · 304-345-0200

Clarksburg

Charles F. Johns · Steptoe & Johnson · http://www.steptoe-johnson.com · Chase Tower, Sixth Floor · 229 West Main Street · P.O. Box 2190 · Clarksburg, WV 26302-2190 · 304-624-8000

Huntington

Menis E. Ketchum · ⑳ · Greene, Ketchum, Bailey & Tweel · 419 Eleventh Street · P.O. Box 2389 · Huntington, WV 25701-2389 · 866-471-6482

D. C. Offutt, Jr. · Offutt Nord · 949 Third Avenue, Suite 300 · P.O. Box 2868 · Huntington, WV 25728-2868 · 304-529-2868

Barry M. Taylor · Jenkins Fenstermaker · Coal Exchange Building, Suite 1100 · 401 Eleventh Street · P.O. Box 2688 · Huntington, WV 25726-2688 · 304-523-2100

Morgantown

Susan S. Brewer · Steptoe & Johnson · http://www.steptoe-johnson.com · United Center, Suite 400 · 1085 Van Voorhis Road · P.O. Box 1616 · Morgantown, WV 26507-1616 · 304-598-8000

Stephen Brooks · Flaherty, Sensabaugh & Bonasso · 965 Hartman Run Road, Suite 1105 · Morgantown, WV 26505 · 304-598-0788

William E. Galeota · Steptoe & Johnson · http://www.steptoe-johnson.com · United Center, Suite 400 · 1085 Van Voorhis Road · P.O. Box 1616 · Morgantown, WV 26507-1616 · 304-598-8000

Wheeling

Patrick S. Casey · Burns, White & Hickton · http://www.bwhllc.com · The Maxwell Center · 32 Twentieth Street · Wheeling, WV 26003 · 304-233-9500

MERGERS & ACQUISITIONS LAW

Charleston

Michael J. Basile · Spilman Thomas & Battle · http://www.spilmanlaw.com · Spilman Center · 300 Kanawha Boulevard East · P.O. Box 273 · Charleston, WV 25301-0273 · 304-340-3800

Ellen S. Cappellanti · ⑩ · Jackson Kelly · Laidley Tower, Suite 1600 · 500 Lee Street East · P.O. Box 553 Charleston, WV 25322-0553 · 304-340-1000

Mark A. Ferguson · Sprouse & Ferguson · 230 Capitol Street, Suite 300 · Charleston, WV 25301 · 304-342-9100

David P. Ferretti · Spilman Thomas & Battle · http://www.spilmanlaw.com · Spilman Center · 300 Kanawha Boulevard East · P.O. Box 273 · Charleston, WV 25301-0273 · 304-340-3800

F. Thomas Graff, Jr. · ⑳ · Bowles Rice McDavid Graff & Love · http://www.bowlesrice.com · 600 Quarrier Street · P.O. Box 1386 · Charleston, WV 25325-1386 · 304-347-1100

David K. Higgins · Robinson & McElwee · Fifth Third Center, Suite 400 · 700 Virginia Street East · P.O. Box 1791 · Charleston, WV 25301-1791 · 304-344-5800

Louis S. Southworth II · ⑩ · Jackson Kelly · Laidley Tower, Suite 1600 · 500 Lee Street East · P.O. Box 553 · Charleston, WV 25322-0553 · 304-340-1000

Robert Tweel · Jackson Kelly · Laidley Tower, Suite 1600 · 500 Lee Street East · P.O. Box 553 · Charleston, WV 25322-0553 · 304-340-1000

Martinsburg

Michael E. Caryl · Bowles Rice McDavid Graff & Love · http://www.bowlesrice.com · 101 South Queen Street · P.O. Drawer 1419 · Martinsburg, WV 25401-1419 · 304-263-0836

MINING LAW

Charleston

Michael T. Cimino · Jackson Kelly · Laidley Tower, Suite 1600 · 500 Lee Street East · P.O. Box 553 · Charleston, WV 25322-0553 · 304-340-1000

Anna M. Dailey · Dinsmore & Shohl · http://www.dinslaw.com · Huntington Square, Suite 600 · 900 Lee Street · Charleston, WV 25301 · 304-357-0900

Sharon O. Flanery · Steptoe & Johnson · http://www.steptoe-johnson.com · Chase Tower, Eighth Floor · 707 Virginia Street East · P.O. Box 1588 · Charleston, WV 25326-1588 · 304-353-8000

Robert D. Fluharty · Jackson Kelly · Laidley Tower, Suite 1600 · 500 Lee Street East · P.O. Box 553 · Charleston, WV 25322-0553 · 304-340-1000

Blair M. Gardner · Jackson Kelly · Laidley Tower, Suite 1600 · 500 Lee Street East · P.O. Box 553 · Charleston, WV 25322-0553 · 304-340-1000

W. Henry Jernigan, Jr. · Dinsmore & Shohl · http://www.dinslaw.com · Huntington Square, Suite 600 · 900 Lee Street · Charleston, WV 25301 · 304-357-0900

E. Forrest Jones · Jones & Associates · 13 Kanawha Boulevard West · P.O. Box 1989 · Charleston, WV 25327-1989 · 304-343-9466

Donna C. Kelly · Dinsmore & Shohl · http://www.dinslaw.com · Huntington Square, Suite 600 · 900 Lee Street · Charleston, WV 25301 · 304-357-0900

Robert G. McLusky · ⑩ · Jackson Kelly · Laidley Tower, Suite 1600 · 500 Lee Street East · P.O. Box 553 Charleston, WV 25322-0553 · 304-340-1000

Robert D. Pollitt · Steptoe & Johnson · http://www.steptoe-johnson.com · Chase Tower, Eighth Floor · 707 Virginia Street East · P.O. Box 1588 · Charleston, WV 25326-1588 · 304-353-8000

Christopher B. Power · Dinsmore & Shohl · http://www.dinslaw.com · Huntington Square, Suite 600 · 900 Lee Street · Charleston, WV 25301 · 304-357-0900

Forrest H. Roles · ⑳ · Dinsmore & Shohl · http://www.dinslaw.com · Huntington Square, Suite 600 · 900 Lee Street · Charleston, WV 25301 · 304-357-0900

Daniel L. Stickler · Jackson Kelly · Laidley Tower, Suite 1600 · 500 Lee Street East · P.O. Box 553 · Charleston, WV 25322-0553 · 304-340-1000

Clarksburg

C. David Morrison · Steptoe & Johnson · http://www.steptoe-johnson.com · Chase Tower, Sixth Floor · 229 West Main Street · P.O. Box 2190 · Clarksburg, WV 26302-2190 · 304-624-8000

NATURAL RESOURCES LAW

Charleston

T. Randolph Cox · ⑩ · Spilman Thomas & Battle · http://www.spilmanlaw.com · Spilman Center · 300 Kanawha Boulevard East · P.O. Box 273 · Charleston, WV 25301-0273 · 304-340-3800

Anna M. Dailey · Dinsmore & Shohl · http://www.dinslaw.com · Huntington Square, Suite 600 · 900 Lee Street · Charleston, WV 25301 · 304-357-0900

Sharon O. Flanery · Steptoe & Johnson · http://www.steptoe-johnson.com · Chase Tower, Eighth Floor · 707 Virginia Street East · P.O. Box 1588 · Charleston, WV 25326-1588 · 304-353-8000

David M. Flannery · ⑳ · Jackson Kelly · Laidley Tower, Suite 1600 · 500 Lee Street East · P.O. Box 553 · Charleston, WV 25322-0553 · 304-340-1000

Robert D. Fluharty · Jackson Kelly · Laidley Tower, Suite 1600 · 500 Lee Street East · P.O. Box 553 · Charleston, WV 25322-0553 · 304-340-1000

Blair M. Gardner · Jackson Kelly · Laidley Tower, Suite 1600 · 500 Lee Street East · P.O. Box 553 · Charleston, WV 25322-0553 · 304-340-1000

F. Thomas Graff, Jr. · ⑳ · Bowles Rice McDavid Graff & Love · http://www.bowlesrice.com · 600 Quarrier Street · P.O. Box 1386 · Charleston, WV 25325-1386 · 304-347-1100

William M. Herlihy · Spilman Thomas & Battle · http://www.spilmanlaw.com · Spilman Center · 300 Kanawha Boulevard East · P.O. Box 273 · Charleston, WV 25301-0273 · 304-340-3800

W. Henry Jernigan, Jr. · Dinsmore & Shohl · http://www.dinslaw.com · Huntington Square, Suite 600 · 900 Lee Street · Charleston, WV 25301 · 304-357-0900

E. Forrest Jones · Jones & Associates · 13 Kanawha Boulevard West · P.O. Box 1989 · Charleston, WV 25327-1989 · 304-343-9466

J. Thomas Lane · ⑳ · Bowles Rice McDavid Graff & Love · http://www.bowlesrice.com · 600 Quarrier Street · P.O. Box 1386 · Charleston, WV 25325-1386 · 304-347-1100

Thomas N. McJunkin · ⑩ · Jackson Kelly · Laidley Tower, Suite 1600 · 500 Lee Street East · P.O. Box 553 · Charleston, WV 25322-0553 · 304-340-1000

Robert G. McLusky · ⑩ · Jackson Kelly · Laidley Tower, Suite 1600 · 500 Lee Street East · P.O. Box 553 Charleston, WV 25322-0553 · 304-340-1000

Christopher B. Power · Dinsmore & Shohl · http://www.dinslaw.com · Huntington Square, Suite 600 · 900 Lee Street · Charleston, WV 25301 · 304-357-0900

Forrest H. Roles · ⑳ · Dinsmore & Shohl · http://www.dinslaw.com · Huntington Square, Suite 600 · 900 Lee Street · Charleston, WV 25301 · 304-357-0900

Clarksburg

Patrick D. Deem · ⑩ · Steptoe & Johnson · http://www.steptoe-johnson.com · Chase Tower, Sixth Floor · 229 West Main Street · P.O. Box 2190 · Clarksburg, WV 26302-2190 · 304-624-8000

Huntington

Richard J. Bolen · Huddleston Bolen · 611 Third Avenue · P.O. Box 2185 · Huntington, WV 25701-2185 304-529-6181

Morgantown

Robert W. Dinsmore · Bowles Rice McDavid Graff & Love · http://www.bowlesrice.com · 7000 Hampton Center, Suite K · Morgantown, WV 26505-1720 · 304-285-2500

F. Thomas Rubenstein · Dinsmore & Shohl · http://www.dinslaw.com · 215 Don Knotts Boulevard, Suite 310 · Morgantown, WV 26501 · 304-296-1100

Stephen Shuman · Reeder & Shuman · 256 High Street · P.O. Box 842 · Morgantown, WV 26507-0842 · 304-292-8488

Williamson

Howard M. Persinger, Jr. · Howard M. Persinger, Jr. · 101 Dickinson Street · P.O. Box 1258 · Williamson, WV 25661-3511 · 304-235-2000

NON-PROFIT/CHARITIES LAW

Charleston

Lesley A. Russo · Bowles Rice McDavid Graff & Love · http://www.bowlesrice.com · 600 Quarrier Street P.O. Box 1386 · Charleston, WV 25325-1386 · 304-347-1100

NON-WHITE-COLLAR CRIMINAL DEFENSE

Charleston

Gregory J. Campbell · Law Offices of Gregory J. Campbell · 602 Virginia Street East, Suite 300 · Charleston, WV 25301 · 304-342-4815

J. Timothy DiPiero · DiTrapano, Barrett & DiPiero · 604 Virginia Street East · Charleston, WV 25301-2184 · 304-342-0133

Rudolph L. DiTrapano · ⑳ · DiTrapano, Barrett & DiPiero · 604 Virginia Street East · Charleston, WV 25301-2184 · 304-342-0133

Martinsburg

Byron Craig Manford · Craig Manford Law Offices · 151 North Queen Street · P.O. Box 5021 · Martinsburg, WV 25402-5021 · 304-263-5698

Kevin D. Mills · Mills & Wagner · 1800 West King Street · Martinsburg, WV 25401 · 304-262-9300

OIL & GAS LAW

Charleston

Sharon O. Flanery · Steptoe & Johnson · http://www.steptoe-johnson.com · Chase Tower, Eighth Floor · 707 Virginia Street East · P.O. Box 1588 · Charleston, WV 25326-1588 · 304-353-8000

Robert D. Fluharty · Jackson Kelly · Laidley Tower, Suite 1600 · 500 Lee Street East · P.O. Box 553 · Charleston, WV 25322-0553 · 304-340-1000

Richard L. Gottlieb · Lewis, Glasser, Casey & Rollins · BB&T Square, Suite 700 · 300 Summers Street · P.O. Box 1746 · Charleston, WV 25326-1746 · 304-345-2000

F. Thomas Graff, Jr. · ⓴ · Bowles Rice McDavid Graff & Love · http://www.bowlesrice.com · 600 Quarrier Street · P.O. Box 1386 · Charleston, WV 25325-1386 · 304-347-1100

John H. Johnston · Steptoe & Johnson · http://www.steptoe-johnson.com · Chase Tower, Eighth Floor · 707 Virginia Street East · P.O. Box 1588 · Charleston, WV 25326-1588 · 304-353-8000

J. Thomas Lane · ⓴ · Bowles Rice McDavid Graff & Love · http://www.bowlesrice.com · 600 Quarrier Street · P.O. Box 1386 · Charleston, WV 25325-1386 · 304-347-1100

Thomas N. McJunkin · ❿ · Jackson Kelly · Laidley Tower, Suite 1600 · 500 Lee Street East · P.O. Box 553 · Charleston, WV 25322-0553 · 304-340-1000

Timothy M. Miller · Robinson & McElwee · Fifth Third Center, Suite 400 · 700 Virginia Street East · P.O. Box 1791 · Charleston, WV 25301-1791 · 304-344-5800

Tammy J. Owen · Goodwin & Goodwin · 300 Summers Street, Suite 1500 · P.O. Box 2107 · Charleston, WV 25301 · 304-346-7000

George A. Patterson III · Bowles Rice McDavid Graff & Love · http://www.bowlesrice.com · 600 Quarrier Street · P.O. Box 1386 · Charleston, WV 25325-1386 · 304-347-1100

Kenneth E. Tawney · Jackson Kelly · Laidley Tower, Suite 1600 · 500 Lee Street East · P.O. Box 553 · Charleston, WV 25322-0553 · 304-340-1000

Clarksburg

Patrick D. Deem · ❿ · Steptoe & Johnson · http://www.steptoe-johnson.com · Chase Tower, Sixth Floor · 229 West Main Street · P.O. Box 2190 · Clarksburg, WV 26302-2190 · 304-624-8000

Huntington

Patricia Proctor · Steptoe & Johnson · http://www.steptoe-johnson.com · Chase Center, Suite 250 · 1000 Fifth Avenue · P.O. Box 2195 · Huntington, WV 25722-2195 · 304-522-8290

PERSONAL INJURY LITIGATION

Charleston

Robert B. Allen · ⑩ · Allen Guthrie McHugh & Thomas · 500 Lee Street East, Suite 800 · P.O. Box 3394 Charleston, WV 25333-3394 · 304-345-7250

Joshua I. Barrett · DiTrapano, Barrett & DiPiero · 604 Virginia Street East · Charleston, WV 25301-2184 304-342-0133

Joseph S. Beeson · Robinson & McElwee · Fifth Third Center, Suite 400 · 700 Virginia Street East · P.O. Box 1791 · Charleston, WV 25301-1791 · 304-344-5800

Robert V. Berthold, Jr. · Berthold, Tiano & O'Dell · 208 Capitol Street · P.O. Box 3508 · Charleston, WV 25335-3508 · 304-345-5700

G. David Brumfield · Brumfield & Watson · 405 Capitol Street, Suite 613 · Charleston, WV 25301 · 304-346-9333

Stephen R. Crislip · Jackson Kelly · Laidley Tower, Suite 1600 · 500 Lee Street East · P.O. Box 553 · Charleston, WV 25322-0553 · 304-340-1000

Rudolph L. DiTrapano · ⑳ · DiTrapano, Barrett & DiPiero · 604 Virginia Street East · Charleston, WV 25301-2184 · 304-342-0133

Alvin L. Emch · Jackson Kelly · Laidley Tower, Suite 1600 · 500 Lee Street East · P.O. Box 553 · Charleston, WV 25322-0553 · 304-340-1000

Stephen B. Farmer · ⑩ · Farmer Cline & Campbell · 746 Myrtle Road · P.O. Box 3842 · Charleston, WV 25338-3842 · 304-346-5990

Thomas V. Flaherty · ⑩ · Flaherty, Sensabaugh & Bonasso · 200 Capitol Street · P.O. Box 3843 · Charleston, WV 25338-3843 · 304-345-0200

Gary W. Hart · Jackson Kelly · Laidley Tower, Suite 1600 · 500 Lee Street East · P.O. Box 553 · Charleston, WV 25322-0553 · 304-340-1000

John R. Hoblitzell · Kay Casto & Chaney · http://www.kaycasto.com · Chase Tower, Suite 1500 · 707 Virginia Street East · P.O. Box 2031 · Charleston, WV 25327-2031 · 304-345-8900

Thomas J. Hurney, Jr. · Jackson Kelly · Laidley Tower, Suite 1600 · 500 Lee Street East · P.O. Box 553 · Charleston, WV 25322-0553 · 304-340-1000

James B. Lees, Jr. · Hunt & Lees · 2306 Kanawha Boulevard East · P.O. Box 2506 · Charleston, WV 25311-2506 · 304-344-9651

Marvin W. Masters · ⑩ · The Masters Law Firm · 181 Summers Street · Charleston, WV 25301 · 304-342-3106

Jeffrey K. Phillips · Steptoe & Johnson · http://www.steptoe-johnson.com · Chase Tower, Eighth Floor · 707 Virginia Street East · P.O. Box 1588 · Charleston, WV 25326-1588 · 304-353-8000

Scott S. Segal · The Segal Law Firm · 810 Kanawha Boulevard East · Charleston, WV 25301 · 304-344-9100

Don R. Sensabaugh, Jr. · Flaherty, Sensabaugh & Bonasso · 200 Capitol Street · P.O. Box 3843 · Charleston, WV 25338-3843 · 304-345-0200

Gerard R. Stowers · Bowles Rice McDavid Graff & Love · http://www.bowlesrice.com · 600 Quarrier Street · P.O. Box 1386 · Charleston, WV 25325-1386 · 304-347-1100

Michael B. Victorson · Jackson Kelly · Laidley Tower, Suite 1600 · 500 Lee Street East · P.O. Box 553 · Charleston, WV 25322-0553 · 304-340-1000

Jeffrey M. Wakefield · Flaherty, Sensabaugh & Bonasso · 200 Capitol Street · P.O. Box 3843 · Charleston, WV 25338-3843 · 304-345-0200

Clarksburg

David J. Romano · David J. Romano · 363 Washington Avenue · Clarksburg, WV 26301 · 304-624-5600

James A. Varner, Sr. · McNeer, Highland, McMunn and Varner · BB&T Bank Building · Main and Fourth Streets · P.O. Drawer 2040 · Clarksburg, WV 26302-2040 · 304-626-1100

James M. Wilson · Steptoe & Johnson · http://www.steptoe-johnson.com · Chase Tower, Sixth Floor · 229 West Main Street · P.O. Box 2190 · Clarksburg, WV 26302-2190 · 304-624-8000

Elkins

John E. Busch · Busch, Zurbuch & Thompson · High & Court Streets · P. O. Box 1819 · Elkins, WV 26241-1819 · 304-636-3560

Huntington

Fred Adkins · Huddleston Bolen · 611 Third Avenue · P.O. Box 2185 · Huntington, WV 25701-2185 · 304-529-6181

Michael J. Farrell · 10 · Farrell, Farrell & Farrell · 914 Fifth Avenue · P.O. Box 6457 · Huntington, WV 25772-6457 · 304-522-9100

Menis E. Ketchum · 20 · Greene, Ketchum, Bailey & Tweel · 419 Eleventh Street · P.O. Box 2389 · Huntington, WV 25701-2389 · 866-471-6482

Robert L. Massie · Huddleston Bolen · 611 Third Avenue · P.O. Box 2185 · Huntington, WV 25701-2185 304-529-6181

D. C. Offutt, Jr. · Offutt Nord · 949 Third Avenue, Suite 300 · P.O. Box 2868 · Huntington, WV 25728-2868 · 304-529-2868

Marc E. Williams · Huddleston Bolen · 611 Third Avenue · P.O. Box 2185 · Huntington, WV 25701-2185 304-529-6181

Martinsburg

Lucien G. Lewin · Steptoe & Johnson · http://www.steptoe-johnson.com · Edwin Miller Professional Centre, Suite 300 · 1250 Edwin Miller Boulevard · P.O. Box 2629 · Martinsburg, WV 25402-2629 · 304-263-6991

Morgantown

Susan S. Brewer · Steptoe & Johnson · http://www.steptoe-johnson.com · United Center, Suite 400 · 1085 Van Voorhis Road · P.O. Box 1616 · Morgantown, WV 26507-1616 · 304-598-8000

Stephen Brooks · Flaherty, Sensabaugh & Bonasso · 965 Hartman Run Road, Suite 1105 · Morgantown, WV 26505 · 304-598-0788

William E. Galeota · Steptoe & Johnson · http://www.steptoe-johnson.com · United Center, Suite 400 · 1085 Van Voorhis Road · P.O. Box 1616 · Morgantown, WV 26507-1616 · 304-598-8000

Stephen M. LaCagnin · Jackson Kelly · 150 Clay Street, Suite 500 · P.O. Box 619 · Morgantown, WV 26501-0619 · 304-284-4100

Parsons

John W. Cooper · Cooper & Preston · 333 Second Street · P.O. Box 365 · Parsons, WV 26287 · 304-478-4600

Wheeling

James F. Companion · Schrader Byrd & Companion · The Maxwell Center, Suite 500 · 32 Twentieth Street · Wheeling, WV 26003 · 304-233-3390

Robert P. Fitzsimmons · Fitzsimmons Law Offices · 1609 Warwood Avenue · Wheeling, WV 26003-7110 304-277-1700

Paul T. Tucker · Bachmann, Hess, Bachmann & Garden · 1226 Chapline Street · P.O. Box 351 · Wheeling, WV 26003-0351 · 304-233-3511

PRODUCT LIABILITY LITIGATION

Charleston

W. Henry Jernigan, Jr. · Dinsmore & Shohl · http://www.dinslaw.com · Huntington Square, Suite 600 · 900 Lee Street · Charleston, WV 25301 · 304-357-0900

Mary H. Sanders · Huddleston Bolen · 707 Virginia Street East, Suite 1300 · P.O. Box 3786 · Charleston, WV 25337-3786 · 304-344-9869

Huntington

Menis E. Ketchum · ⑳ · Greene, Ketchum, Bailey & Tweel · 419 Eleventh Street · P.O. Box 2389 · Huntington, WV 25701-2389 · 866-471-6482

Robert L. Massie · Huddleston Bolen · 611 Third Avenue · P.O. Box 2185 · Huntington, WV 25701-2185 304-529-6181

Marc E. Williams · Huddleston Bolen · 611 Third Avenue · P.O. Box 2185 · Huntington, WV 25701-2185 304-529-6181

PROFESSIONAL MALPRACTICE LAW

Wheeling

Patrick S. Casey · Burns, White & Hickton · http://www.bwhllc.com · The Maxwell Center · 32 Twentieth Street · Wheeling, WV 26003 · 304-233-9500

PROJECT FINANCE LAW

Charleston

John C. Stump · Steptoe & Johnson · http://www.steptoe-johnson.com · Chase Tower, Eighth Floor · 707 Virginia Street East · P.O. Box 1588 · Charleston, WV 25326-1588 · 304-353-8000

L. Frederick Williams, Jr. · Steptoe & Johnson · http://www.steptoe-johnson.com · Chase Tower, Eighth Floor · 707 Virginia Street East · P.O. Box 1588 · Charleston, WV 25326-1588 · 304-353-8000

PUBLIC FINANCE LAW

Charleston

Christopher L. Callas · Jackson Kelly · Laidley Tower, Suite 1600 · 500 Lee Street East · P.O. Box 553 · Charleston, WV 25322-0553 · 304-340-1000

Samme L. Gee · Jackson Kelly · Laidley Tower, Suite 1600 · 500 Lee Street East · P.O. Box 553 · Charleston, WV 25322-0553 · 304-340-1000

Lee O. Hill · Spilman Thomas & Battle · http://www.spilmanlaw.com · Spilman Center · 300 Kanawha Boulevard East · P.O. Box 273 · Charleston, WV 25301-0273 · 304-340-3800

John C. Stump · Steptoe & Johnson · http://www.steptoe-johnson.com · Chase Tower, Eighth Floor · 707 Virginia Street East · P.O. Box 1588 · Charleston, WV 25326-1588 · 304-353-8000

L. Frederick Williams, Jr. · Steptoe & Johnson · http://www.steptoe-johnson.com · Chase Tower, Eighth Floor · 707 Virginia Street East · P.O. Box 1588 · Charleston, WV 25326-1588 · 304-353-8000

Martinsburg

Taunja Willis-Miller · ⑩ · Jackson Kelly · 310 West Burke Street · P.O. Box 1068 · Martinsburg, WV 25401-1060 · 304-263-8800

Morgantown

Vincent A. Collins · Steptoe & Johnson · http://www.steptoe-johnson.com · United Center, Suite 400 · 1085 Van Voorhis Road · P.O. Box 1616 · Morgantown, WV 26507-1616 · 304-598-8000

RAILROAD LAW

Huntington

Fred Adkins · Huddleston Bolen · 611 Third Avenue · P.O. Box 2185 · Huntington, WV 25701-2185 · 304-529-6181

Angela Wynn Konrad · Huddleston Bolen · 611 Third Avenue · P.O. Box 2185 · Huntington, WV 25701-2185 · 304-529-6181

Luke A. Lafferre · Huddleston Bolen · 611 Third Avenue · P.O. Box 2185 · Huntington, WV 25701-2185 304-529-6181

James W. Turner · Huddleston Bolen · 611 Third Avenue · P.O. Box 2185 · Huntington, WV 25701-2185 304-529-6181

Charleston

Carl D. Andrews · Bowles Rice McDavid Graff & Love · http://www.bowlesrice.com · 600 Quarrier Street P.O. Box 1386 · Charleston, WV 25325-1386 · 304-347-1100

Dennis N. Broglio · Turner & Johns · 216 Brook Street, Suite 301 · Charleston, WV 25301 · 304-720-2300

Ellen S. Cappellanti · ⑩ · Jackson Kelly · Laidley Tower, Suite 1600 · 500 Lee Street East · P.O. Box 553 Charleston, WV 25322-0553 · 304-340-1000

Mark D'Antoni · Bowles Rice McDavid Graff & Love · http://www.bowlesrice.com · 600 Quarrier Street · P.O. Box 1386 · Charleston, WV 25325-1386 · 304-347-1100

Robert D. Fluharty · Jackson Kelly · Laidley Tower, Suite 1600 · 500 Lee Street East · P.O. Box 553 · Charleston, WV 25322-0553 · 304-340-1000

J. Thomas Lane · ⑳ · Bowles Rice McDavid Graff & Love · http://www.bowlesrice.com · 600 Quarrier Street · P.O. Box 1386 · Charleston, WV 25325-1386 · 304-347-1100

Jonathan Nicol · Kay Casto & Chaney · http://www.kaycasto.com · Chase Tower, Suite 1500 · 707 Virginia Street East · P.O. Box 2031 · Charleston, WV 25327-2031 · 304-345-8900

Joyce F. Ofsa · Spilman Thomas & Battle · http://www.spilmanlaw.com · Spilman Center · 300 Kanawha Boulevard East · P.O. Box 273 · Charleston, WV 25301-0273 · 304-340-3800

Arthur M. Standish · Steptoe & Johnson · http://www.steptoe-johnson.com · Chase Tower, Eighth Floor 707 Virginia Street East · P.O. Box 1588 · Charleston, WV 25326-1588 · 304-353-8000

Clarksburg

Patrick D. Deem · ⑩ · Steptoe & Johnson · http://www.steptoe-johnson.com · Chase Tower, Sixth Floor · 229 West Main Street · P.O. Box 2190 · Clarksburg, WV 26302-2190 · 304-624-8000

Louis E. Enderle, Jr. · Steptoe & Johnson · http://www.steptoe-johnson.com · Chase Tower, Sixth Floor 229 West Main Street · P.O. Box 2190 · Clarksburg, WV 26302-2190 · 304-624-8000

Randall C. Light · Steptoe & Johnson · http://www.steptoe-johnson.com · Chase Tower, Sixth Floor · 229 West Main Street · P.O. Box 2190 · Clarksburg, WV 26302-2190 · 304-624-8000

Huntington

Stephen J. Golder · Jenkins Fenstermaker · Coal Exchange Building, Suite 1100 · 401 Eleventh Street · P.O. Box 2688 · Huntington, WV 25726-2688 · 304-523-2100

J. Patrick Jones · Campbell Woods · 517 Ninth Street, Suite 1000 · P.O. Box 1835 · Huntington, WV 25719-1835 · 304-529-2391

Christopher J. Plybon · Huddleston Bolen · 611 Third Avenue · P.O. Box 2185 · Huntington, WV 25701-2185 · 304-529-6181

Martinsburg

Kenneth J. Barton, Jr. · Steptoe & Johnson · http://www.steptoe-johnson.com · Edwin Miller Professional Centre, Suite 300 · 1250 Edwin Miller Boulevard · P.O. Box 2629 · Martinsburg, WV 25402-2629 · 304-263-6991

Richard A. Pill · Pill & Pill · 85 Aikens Center · Martinsburg, WV 25404 · 304-263-4971

Morgantown

Robert W. Dinsmore · Bowles Rice McDavid Graff & Love · http://www.bowlesrice.com · 7000 Hampton Center, Suite K · Morgantown, WV 26505-1720 · 304-285-2500

Brian D. Gallagher · Steptoe & Johnson · http://www.steptoe-johnson.com · United Center, Suite 400 · 1085 Van Voorhis Road · P.O. Box 1616 · Morgantown, WV 26507-1616 · 304-598-8000

William T. Holmes · Spilman Thomas & Battle · http://www.spilmanlaw.com · 150 Clay Street, Second Floor · P.O. Box 615 · Morgantown, WV 26507-0615 · 304-291-7920

James A. Russell · Steptoe & Johnson · http://www.steptoe-johnson.com · United Center, Suite 400 · 1085 Van Voorhis Road · P.O. Box 1616 · Morgantown, WV 26507-1616 · 304-598-8000

Robert L. Shuman · Reeder & Shuman · 256 High Street · P.O. Box 842 · Morgantown, WV 26507-0842 · 304-292-8488

Stephen Shuman · Reeder & Shuman · 256 High Street · P.O. Box 842 · Morgantown, WV 26507-0842 · 304-292-8488

Princeton

Thomas S. Lilly · Smith Lilly & Ball · 1421 Princeton Avenue · Princeton, WV 24740 · 304-425-2196

SECURITIES LAW

Charleston

Elizabeth O. Lord · ⑩ · Jackson Kelly · Laidley Tower, Suite 1600 · 500 Lee Street East · P.O. Box 553 · Charleston, WV 25322-0553 · 304-340-1000

Edward D. McDevitt · Bowles Rice McDavid Graff & Love · http://www.bowlesrice.com · 600 Quarrier Street · P.O. Box 1386 · Charleston, WV 25325-1386 · 304-347-1100

Huntington

Thomas J. Murray · ⑩ · Huddleston Bolen · 611 Third Avenue · P.O. Box 2185 · Huntington, WV 25701-2185 · 304-529-6181

STRUCTURED FINANCE LAW

Charleston

L. Frederick Williams, Jr. · Steptoe & Johnson · http://www.steptoe-johnson.com · Chase Tower, Eighth Floor · 707 Virginia Street East · P.O. Box 1588 · Charleston, WV 25326-1588 · 304-353-8000

TAX LAW

Charleston

G. Thomas Battle · Spilman Thomas & Battle · http://www.spilmanlaw.com · Spilman Center · 300 Kanawha Boulevard East · P.O. Box 273 · Charleston, WV 25301-0273 · 304-340-3800

Richard E. Boyle, Jr. · Kay Casto & Chaney · http://www.kaycasto.com · Chase Tower, Suite 1500 · 707 Virginia Street East · P.O. Box 2031 · Charleston, WV 25327-2031 · 304-345-8900

Mark A. Ferguson · Sprouse & Ferguson · 230 Capitol Street, Suite 300 · Charleston, WV 25301 · 304-342-9100

Craig M. Kay · ⑩ · Kay Casto & Chaney · http://www.kaycasto.com · Chase Tower, Suite 1500 · 707 Virginia Street East · P.O. Box 2031 · Charleston, WV 25327-2031 · 304-345-8900

Robert S. Kiss · Bowles Rice McDavid Graff & Love · http://www.bowlesrice.com · 600 Quarrier Street · P.O. Box 1386 · Charleston, WV 25325-1386 · 304-347-1100

Gordon C. Lane · ⑩ · Lane Law Firm · 1538 Kanawha Boulevard East · Charleston, WV 25311 · 304-345-6000

Charles O. Lorensen · ⑩ · George & Lorensen · 1526 Kanawha Boulevard East · Charleston, WV 25311-2413 · 304-343-5555

John A. Mairs · Jackson Kelly · Laidley Tower, Suite 1600 · 500 Lee Street East · P.O. Box 553 · Charleston, WV 25322-0553 · 304-340-1000

Marc A. Monteleone · Bowles Rice McDavid Graff & Love · http://www.bowlesrice.com · 600 Quarrier Street · P.O. Box 1386 · Charleston, WV 25325-1386 · 304-347-1100

Herschel H. Rose III · Rose Law Office · 300 Summer Street, Suite 1440 · P. O.Box 3502 · Charleston, WV 25335 · 304-342-5050

Louis S. Southworth II · ⑩ · Jackson Kelly · Laidley Tower, Suite 1600 · 500 Lee Street East · P.O. Box 553 · Charleston, WV 25322-0553 · 304-340-1000

L. Frederick Williams, Jr. · Steptoe & Johnson · http://www.steptoe-johnson.com · Chase Tower, Eighth Floor · 707 Virginia Street East · P.O. Box 1588 · Charleston, WV 25326-1588 · 304-353-8000

Clarksburg

Marcia A. Broughton · Jackson Kelly · Ogden Building · 203 West Main Street · P.O. Box 150 · Clarksburg, WV 26301-0150 · 304-624-6555

Martinsburg

Michael E. Caryl · Bowles Rice McDavid Graff & Love · http://www.bowlesrice.com · 101 South Queen Street · P.O. Drawer 1419 · Martinsburg, WV 25401-1419 · 304-263-0836

Morgantown

Michael W. Barill · Steptoe & Johnson · http://www.steptoe-johnson.com · United Center, Suite 400 · 1085 Van Voorhis Road · P.O. Box 1616 · Morgantown, WV 26507-1616 · 304-598-8000

Thomas A. Vorbach · Steptoe & Johnson · http://www.steptoe-johnson.com · United Center, Suite 400 · 1085 Van Voorhis Road · P.O. Box 1616 · Morgantown, WV 26507-1616 · 304-598-8000

TRUSTS AND ESTATES

Charleston

John F. Allevato · Spilman Thomas & Battle · http://www.spilmanlaw.com · Spilman Center · 300 Kanawha Boulevard East · P.O. Box 273 · Charleston, WV 25301-0273 · 304-340-3800

Milton T. Herndon · ⑳ · Campbell Woods · 300 Summers Street, Suite 810 · P.O. Box 2393 · Charleston, WV 25328-2393 · 304-346-2391

John F. Hussell IV · Dinsmore & Shohl · http://www.dinslaw.com · Huntington Square, Suite 600 · 900 Lee Street · Charleston, WV 25301 · 304-357-0900

Craig M. Kay · ⑩ · Kay Casto & Chaney · http://www.kaycasto.com · Chase Tower, Suite 1500 · 707 Virginia Street East · P.O. Box 2031 · Charleston, WV 25327-2031 · 304-345-8900

Robert S. Kiss · Bowles Rice McDavid Graff & Love · http://www.bowlesrice.com · 600 Quarrier Street · P.O. Box 1386 · Charleston, WV 25325-1386 · 304-347-1100

L. Frederick Williams, Jr. · Steptoe & Johnson · http://www.steptoe-johnson.com · Chase Tower, Eighth Floor · 707 Virginia Street East · P.O. Box 1588 · Charleston, WV 25326-1588 · 304-353-8000

Clarksburg

Marcia A. Broughton · Jackson Kelly · Ogden Building · 203 West Main Street · P.O. Box 150 · Clarksburg, WV 26301-0150 · 304-624-6555

Huntington

Howard R. Crews, Jr. · Campbell Woods · 517 Ninth Street, Suite 1000 · P.O. Box 1835 · Huntington, WV 25719-1835 · 304-529-2391

Bruce L. Stout · ⑩ · Huddleston Bolen · 611 Third Avenue · P.O. Box 2185 · Huntington, WV 25701-2185 · 304-529-6181

Martinsburg

Michael E. Caryl · Bowles Rice McDavid Graff & Love · http://www.bowlesrice.com · 101 South Queen Street · P.O. Drawer 1419 · Martinsburg, WV 25401-1419 · 304-263-0836

David A. DeJarnett · Bowles Rice McDavid Graff & Love · http://www.bowlesrice.com · 101 South Queen Street · P.O. Drawer 1419 · Martinsburg, WV 25401-1419 · 304-263-0836

Wheeling

Thomas G. Byrum · Thomas G. Byrum · Woodsdale Center, Suite 600 · 1021 National Road · Wheeling, WV 26003-5779 · 304-242-1936

WATER LAW

Charleston

Armando F. Benincasa · Steptoe & Johnson · http://www.steptoe-johnson.com · Chase Tower, Eighth Floor · 707 Virginia Street East · P.O. Box 1588 · Charleston, WV 25326-1588 · 304-353-8000

David M. Flannery · ⑳ · Jackson Kelly · Laidley Tower, Suite 1600 · 500 Lee Street East · P.O. Box 553 · Charleston, WV 25322-0553 · 304-340-1000

WHITE-COLLAR CRIMINAL DEFENSE

Charleston

Robert B. Allen · ⑩ · Allen Guthrie McHugh & Thomas · 500 Lee Street East, Suite 800 · P.O. Box 3394 Charleston, WV 25333-3394 · 304-345-7250

Benjamin L. Bailey · Bailey & Glasser · 227 Capitol Street · Charleston, WV 25301 · 304-345-6555

Gregory J. Campbell · Law Offices of Gregory J. Campbell · 602 Virginia Street East, Suite 300 · Charleston, WV 25301 · 304-342-4815

Michael W. Carey · Carey, Scott & Douglas · 901 Chase Tower · 707 Virginia Street East · P.O. Box 913 · Charleston, WV 25323-0913 · 304-345-1234

J. Timothy DiPiero · DiTrapano, Barrett & DiPiero · 604 Virginia Street East · Charleston, WV 25301-2184 · 304-342-0133

Rudolph L. DiTrapano · ⑳ · DiTrapano, Barrett & DiPiero · 604 Virginia Street East · Charleston, WV 25301-2184 · 304-342-0133

Stephen B. Farmer · ⑩ · Farmer Cline & Campbell · 746 Myrtle Road · P.O. Box 3842 · Charleston, WV 25338-3842 · 304-346-5990

Martinsburg

E. Leslie Hoffman · Jackson Kelly · 310 West Burke Street · P.O. Box 1068 · Martinsburg, WV 25401-1060 · 304-263-8800

William J. Powell · Jackson Kelly · 310 West Burke Street · P.O. Box 1068 · Martinsburg, WV 25401-1060 · 304-263-8800

Wheeling

William D. Wilmoth · Steptoe & Johnson · http://www.steptoe-johnson.com · 1233 Main Street, Suite 3000 · P.O. Box 751 · Wheeling, WV 26003-0751 · 304-233-0000

WORKERS' COMPENSATION LAW

Beckley

Reginald D. Henry · Stacy Law · 600 Neville Street, Suite 200 · Beckley, WV 25801-5352 · 304-255-6566

Charleston

H. Dill Battle III · Spilman Thomas & Battle · http://www.spilmanlaw.com · Spilman Center · 300 Kanawha Boulevard East · P.O. Box 273 · Charleston, WV 25301-0273 · 304-340-3800

Henry C. Bowen · Steptoe & Johnson · http://www.steptoe-johnson.com · Chase Tower, Eighth Floor · 707 Virginia Street East · P.O. Box 1588 · Charleston, WV 25326-1588 · 304-353-8000

Jeffrey B. Brannon · Pullin, Fowler & Flanagan · http://www.pffwv.com · James Mark Building · 901 Quarrier Street · Charleston, WV 25301 · 304-344-0100

Robert J. Busse · Jackson Kelly · Laidley Tower, Suite 1600 · 500 Lee Street East · P.O. Box 553 · Charleston, WV 25322-0553 · 304-340-1000

Barney W. Frazier, Jr. · Kay Casto & Chaney · http://www.kaycasto.com · Chase Tower, Suite 1500 · 707 Virginia Street East · P.O. Box 2031 · Charleston, WV 25327-2031 · 304-345-8900

Timothy E. Huffman · ⑩ · Jackson Kelly · Laidley Tower, Suite 1600 · 500 Lee Street East · P.O. Box 553 · Charleston, WV 25322-0553 · 304-340-1000

Phyllis M. Potterfield · ⑩ · Bowles Rice McDavid Graff & Love · http://www.bowlesrice.com · 600 Quarrier Street · P.O. Box 1386 · Charleston, WV 25325-1386 · 304-347-1100

Ann B. Rembrandt · Jackson Kelly · Laidley Tower, Suite 1600 · 500 Lee Street East · P.O. Box 553 · Charleston, WV 25322-0553 · 304-340-1000

Sarah E. Smith · Bowles Rice McDavid Graff & Love · http://www.bowlesrice.com · 600 Quarrier Street · P.O. Box 1386 · Charleston, WV 25325-1386 · 304-347-1100

Douglas A. Smoot · Jackson Kelly · Laidley Tower, Suite 1600 · 500 Lee Street East · P.O. Box 553 · Charleston, WV 25322-0553 · 304-340-1000

Tracy L. Webb · Bowles Rice McDavid Graff & Love · http://www.bowlesrice.com · 600 Quarrier Street · P.O. Box 1386 · Charleston, WV 25325-1386 · 304-347-1100

Clarksburg

Douglas G. Lee · Steptoe & Johnson · http://www.steptoe-johnson.com · Chase Tower, Sixth Floor · 229 West Main Street · P.O. Box 2190 · Clarksburg, WV 26302-2190 · 304-624-8000

Gary W. Nickerson · Steptoe & Johnson · http://www.steptoe-johnson.com · Chase Tower, Sixth Floor · 229 West Main Street · P.O. Box 2190 · Clarksburg, WV 26302-2190 · 304-624-8000

Morgantown

William S. Mattingly · Jackson Kelly · 150 Clay Street, Suite 500 · P.O. Box 619 · Morgantown, WV 26501-0619 · 304-284-4100

George E. Roeder III · ⑩ · Jackson Kelly · 150 Clay Street, Suite 500 · P.O. Box 619 · Morgantown, WV 26501-0619 · 304-284-4100

Kathy L. Snyder · Jackson Kelly · 150 Clay Street, Suite 500 · P.O. Box 619 · Morgantown, WV 26501-0619 · 304-284-4100

Weston

J. Thomas Greene, Jr. · Bailey, Stultz, Oldaker & Greene · 122 Court Avenue · P.O. Box 1310 · Weston, WV 26452-1310 · 304-269-1311

Robert L. Stultz · Bailey, Stultz, Oldaker & Greene · 122 Court Avenue · P.O. Box 1310 · Weston, WV 26452-1310 · 304-269-1311

Wheeling

M. Jane Glauser · Schrader Byrd & Companion · The Maxwell Center, Suite 500 · 32 Twentieth Street · Wheeling, WV 26003 · 304-233-3390

Sue A. Howard · Howard Law Office · 2235 Chapline Street · Wheeling, WV 26003 · 304-233-8860

WISCONSIN

ALTERNATIVE DISPUTE RESOLUTION

Brookfield

James S. Smith · Smith Gunderson & Rowen · 15460 West Capitol Drive, Suite 100 · Brookfield, WI 53005-2621 · 262-783-6633

Madison

Linda S. Balisle · ⑩ · Balisle & Roberson · 131 West Wilson Street, Suite 802 · P.O. Box 870 · Madison, WI 53701-0870 · 608-259-8702

Jeffrey B. Bartell · ⑩ · Quarles & Brady · http://www.quarles.com · 33 East Main Street, Suite 900 · P.O. Box 2113 · Madison, WI 53701-2113 · 608-251-5000

Howard S. Bellman · Howard S. Bellman Mediation & Arbitration · 82 Oak Creek Trail · Madison, WI 53717-1510 · 608-826-4020

Brian E. Butler · ⑩ · Stafford Rosenbaum · http://www.staffordlaw.com · 222 West Washington Avenue, Suite 900 · P.O. Box 1784 · Madison, WI 53701-1784 · 608-256-0226

James R. Cole · Quarles & Brady · http://www.quarles.com · 33 East Main Street, Suite 900 · P.O. Box 2113 · Madison, WI 53701-2113 · 608-251-5000

William F. Eich · William F. Eich · 840 Farwell Drive · Madison, WI 53704 · 608-244-1004

Henry A. Field, Jr. · ⑳ · Boardman Law Firm · http://www.boardmanlawfirm.com · One South Pinckney Street, Fourth Floor · P.O. Box 927 · Madison, WI 53701-0927 · 608-257-9521

Kim Grimmer · Solheim, Billing & Grimmer · US Bank Plaza, Suite 301 · One South Pinckney Street · P.O. Box 1644 · Madison, WI 53701-1644 · 608-282-1200

Allan R. Koritzinsky · ㉕ · Foley & Lardner · 150 East Gilman Street · P.O. Box 1497 · Madison, WI 53701-1497 · 608-257-5035

David E. McFarlane · Bell, Gierhart & Moore · 44 East Mifflin Street, 10th Floor · P.O. Box 1807 · Madison, WI 53701-1807 · 608-257-3764

John C. Mitby · ⑩ · Axley Brynelson · http://www.axley.com · Two East Mifflin Street, Suite 200 · P.O. Box 1767 · Madison, WI 53701-1767 · 608-257-5661

Terry F. Peppard · Law Office of Terry Peppard · 4814 Marathon Drive · P.O. Box 5101 · Madison, WI 53705-0101 · 608-233-7799

Michael Riley · Axley Brynelson · http://www.axley.com · Two East Mifflin Street, Suite 200 · P.O. Box 1767 · Madison, WI 53701-1767 · 608-257-5661

Marie A. Stanton · Hurley, Burish & Stanton · 33 East Main Street, Suite 400 · Madison, WI 53703 · 608-257-0945

Daphne Webb · ⑩ · Stafford Rosenbaum · http://www.staffordlaw.com · 222 West Washington Avenue, Suite 900 · P.O. Box 1784 · Madison, WI 53701-1784 · 608-256-0226

Middleton

Mark A. Frankel · Frankel ADR · 1409 Club Circle · Middleton, WI 53562-3821 · 608-824-6409

Milwaukee

Robert L. Binder · Foley & Lardner · 777 East Wisconsin Avenue, Suite 3800 · Milwaukee, WI 53202-5306 · 414-271-2400

John R. Dawson · ⑩ · Foley & Lardner · 777 East Wisconsin Avenue, Suite 3800 · Milwaukee, WI 53202-5306 · 414-271-2400

Natalie Fleury · Marquette University Law School · 1103 West Wisconsin Avenue · P.O. Box 1881 · Milwaukee, WI 53201-1881 · 414-288-8038

Gary A. Gerlach · Gunta & Reak · 219 North Milwaukee Street, Fifth Floor · Milwaukee, WI 53202-5818 · 414-291-7979

Janine P. Geske · Marquette University Law School · 1103 West Wisconsin Avenue · P.O. Box 1881 · Milwaukee, WI 53201-1881 · 414-288-8038

William A. Jennaro · Cook & Franke · 660 East Mason Street · Milwaukee, WI 53202 · 414-271-5900

William H. Levit, Jr. · ⑩ · Godfrey & Kahn · 780 North Water Street · Milwaukee, WI 53202-3590 · 414-273-3500

Kevin J. Lyons · Davis & Kuelthau · 111 East Kilbourne Avenue, Suite 1400 · Milwaukee, WI 53202 · 414-276-0200

Joseph D. McDevitt · McDevitt Mediation Service · 2600 North Mayfair Road, Suite 1100 · Milwaukee, WI 53226-1308 · 414-476-8888

W. Stuart Parsons · ㉕ · Quarles & Brady · http://www.quarles.com · 411 East Wisconsin Avenue, Suite 2040 · Milwaukee, WI 53202-4497 · 414-277-5000

Gerald G. Schmidt, Jr. · Schmidt, Darling & Erwin · 2300 North Mayfair Road, Suite 1175 · Milwaukee, WI 53226-1553 · 414-258-4300

Thomas W. Scrivner · ⑳ · Michael Best & Friedrich · 100 East Wisconsin Avenue, Suite 3300 · Milwaukee, WI 53202-4108 · 414-271-6560

Michael J. Skwierawski · Michael J. Skwierawski · 2962 South Superior Street · Milwaukee, WI 53207-2544 · 414-481-0125

Waukesha

Charles F. Stierman · ⑩ · Stierman, Steffens & Kuphall · N14 W23777 Stone Ridge Drive, Suite 280 · Waukesha, WI 53188-1158 · 262-523-8484

ANTITRUST LAW

Madison

Charles Barnhill, Jr. · ⑳ · Miner, Barnhill & Galland · 44 East Mifflin Street, Suite 803 · Madison, WI 53703 · 608-255-5200

Brian E. Butler · ⑩ · Stafford Rosenbaum · http://www.staffordlaw.com · 222 West Washington Avenue, Suite 900 · P.O. Box 1784 · Madison, WI 53701-1784 · 608-256-0226

Edwin J. Hughes · Stafford Rosenbaum · http://www.staffordlaw.com · 222 West Washington Avenue, Suite 900 · P.O. Box 1784 · Madison, WI 53701-1784 · 608-256-0226

Kevin J. O'Connor · Godfrey & Kahn · One East Main Street, Suite 500 · P.O. Box 2719 · Madison, WI 53701-2719 · 608-257-3911

Milwaukee

Darryl S. Bell · Quarles & Brady · http://www.quarles.com · 411 East Wisconsin Avenue, Suite 2040 · Milwaukee, WI 53202-4497 · 414-277-5000

John C. Cooper III · ⑩ · Foley & Lardner · 777 East Wisconsin Avenue, Suite 3800 · Milwaukee, WI 53202-5306 · 414-271-2400

David R. Cross · Quarles & Brady · http://www.quarles.com · 411 East Wisconsin Avenue, Suite 2040 · Milwaukee, WI 53202-4497 · 414-277-5000

Michael D. Fischer · Kravit, Hovel, Krawczyk & Leverson · 825 North Jefferson Street, Fifth Floor · Milwaukee, WI 53202-3737 · 414-271-7100

James T. McKeown · Foley & Lardner · 777 East Wisconsin Avenue, Suite 3800 · Milwaukee, WI 53202-5306 · 414-271-2400

APPELLATE LAW

Madison

Charles G. Curtis, Jr. · Heller Ehrman · One East Main Street, Suite 201 · Madison, WI 53703-5118 · 608-663-7460

Naikang Tsao · Foley & Lardner · 150 East Gilman Street · P.O. Box 1497 · Madison, WI 53701-1497 · 608-257-5035

Michael B. Van Sicklen · ⑩ · Foley & Lardner · 150 East Gilman Street · P.O. Box 1497 · Madison, WI 53701-1497 · 608-257-5035

Milwaukee

Robert H. Friebert · Friebert, Finerty & St. John · Two Plaza East, Suite 1250 · 330 East Kilbourn Avenue · Milwaukee, WI 53202 · 414-271-0130

Appleton

Randall A. Haak · McCarty Curry Wydeven Peeters & Haak · 2401 East Enterprise Avenue · Appleton, WI 54130 · 920-882-4070

Madison

John E. Knight · 10 · Boardman Law Firm · http://www.boardmanlawfirm.com · One South Pinckney Street, Fourth Floor · P.O. Box 927 · Madison, WI 53701-0927 · 608-257-9521

Daniel W. Stolper · Stafford Rosenbaum · http://www.staffordlaw.com · 222 West Washington Avenue, Suite 900 · P.O. Box 1784 · Madison, WI 53701-1784 · 608-256-0226

Thomas D. Zilavy · 10 · DeWitt Ross & Stevens · Two East Mifflin Street, Suite 600 · Madison, WI 53703 · 608-255-8891

Milwaukee

Andrew M. Barnes · 20 · Quarles & Brady · http://www.quarles.com · 411 East Wisconsin Avenue, Suite 2040 · Milwaukee, WI 53202-4497 · 414-277-5000

David I. Cisar · von Briesen & Roper · http://www.vonbriesen.com · 411 East Wisconsin Avenue, Suite 700 · P.O. Box 3262 · Milwaukee, WI 53201-3262 · 414-276-1122

Daryl L. Diesing · Whyte Hirschboeck Dudek · 555 East Wells Street, Suite 1900 · Milwaukee, WI 53202-3819 · 414-273-2100

Rodney H. Dow · Foley & Lardner · 777 East Wisconsin Avenue, Suite 3800 · Milwaukee, WI 53202-5306 · 414-271-2400

William F. Flynn · Reinhart Boerner Van Deuren · http://www.reinhartlaw.com · 1000 North Water Street P.O. Box 2965 · Milwaukee, WI 53201-2965 · 414-298-1000

James D. Friedman · 10 · Quarles & Brady · http://www.quarles.com · 411 East Wisconsin Avenue, Suite 2040 · Milwaukee, WI 53202-4497 · 414-277-5000

Conrad G. Goodkind · 10 · Quarles & Brady · http://www.quarles.com · 411 East Wisconsin Avenue, Suite 2040 · Milwaukee, WI 53202-4497 · 414-277-5000

Kenneth V. Hallett · 10 · Quarles & Brady · http://www.quarles.com · 411 East Wisconsin Avenue, Suite 2040 · Milwaukee, WI 53202-4497 · 414-277-5000

Edward J. Hammond · Foley & Lardner · 777 East Wisconsin Avenue, Suite 3800 · Milwaukee, WI 53202-5306 · 414-271-2400

William R. Hotz · Godfrey & Kahn · 780 North Water Street · Milwaukee, WI 53202-3590 · 414-273-3500

Emory Ireland · Foley & Lardner · 777 East Wisconsin Avenue, Suite 3800 · Milwaukee, WI 53202-5306 414-271-2400

W. Charles Jackson · Michael Best & Friedrich · 100 East Wisconsin Avenue, Suite 3300 · Milwaukee, WI 53202-4108 · 414-271-6560

James A. Sheriff · Godfrey & Kahn · 780 North Water Street · Milwaukee, WI 53202-3590 · 414-273-3500

Hoyt R. Stastney · Quarles & Brady · http://www.quarles.com · 411 East Wisconsin Avenue, Suite 2040 · Milwaukee, WI 53202-4497 · 414-277-5000

William E. Taibl · von Briesen & Roper · http://www.vonbriesen.com · 411 East Wisconsin Avenue, Suite 700 · P.O. Box 3262 · Milwaukee, WI 53201-3262 · 414-276-1122

Kim Marie Wynn · Whyte Hirschboeck Dudek · 555 East Wells Street, Suite 1900 · Milwaukee, WI 53202-3819 · 414-273-2100

Wausau

Arnold J. Kiburz III · Ruder Ware · 500 Third Street, Suite 8000 · P.O. Box 8050 · Wausau, WI 54402-8050 · 715-845-4336

BANKRUPTCY AND CREDITOR-DEBTOR RIGHTS LAW

Green Bay

Timothy F. Nixon · Godfrey & Kahn · 333 Main Street, Suite 600 · P.O. Box 13067 · Green Bay, WI 54307-3067 · 920-432-9300

Madison

Valerie L. Bailey-Rihn · Quarles & Brady · http://www.quarles.com · 33 East Main Street, Suite 900 · P.O. Box 2113 · Madison, WI 53701-2113 · 608-251-5000

Denis P. Bartell · ⑳ · DeWitt Ross & Stevens · Two East Mifflin Street, Suite 600 · Madison, WI 53703 · 608-255-8891

Catherine J. Furay · Murphy Desmond · http://www.murphydesmond.com · 33 East Main Street, Suite 500 · P.O. Box 2038 · Madison, WI 53703-2038 · 608-807-0262

Patricia M. Gibeault · ⑳ · Axley Brynelson · http://www.axley.com · Two East Mifflin Street, Suite 200 · P.O. Box 1767 · Madison, WI 53701-1767 · 608-257-5661

Michael E. Kepler · Kepler & Peyton · 634 West Main Street, Suite 202 · Madison, WI 53703-2697 · 608-257-5424

J. David Krekeler · Krekeler Strother · 15 North Pinckney Street, Suite 200 · Madison, WI 53703 · 608-258-8555

Roy L. Prange, Jr. · ⑳ · Quarles & Brady · http://www.quarles.com · 33 East Main Street, Suite 900 · P.O. Box 2113 · Madison, WI 53701-2113 · 608-251-5000

William J. Rameker · ⑳ · Murphy Desmond · http://www.murphydesmond.com · 33 East Main Street, Suite 500 · P.O. Box 2038 · Madison, WI 53703-2038 · 608-807-0262

Ann Ustad Smith · Michael Best & Friedrich · One South Pinckney Street, Suite 700 · P.O. Box 1806 · Madison, WI 53701-1806 · 608-257-3501

Daniel W. Stolper · Stafford Rosenbaum · http://www.staffordlaw.com · 222 West Washington Avenue, Suite 900 · P.O. Box 1784 · Madison, WI 53701-1784 · 608-256-0226

James D. Sweet · ⑳ · Murphy Desmond · http://www.murphydesmond.com · 33 East Main Street, Suite 500 · P.O. Box 2038 · Madison, WI 53703-2038 · 608-807-0262

Michael B. Van Sicklen · ⑩ · Foley & Lardner · 150 East Gilman Street · P.O. Box 1497 · Madison, WI 53701-1497 · 608-257-5035

David G. Walsh · ⑩ · Foley & Lardner · 150 East Gilman Street · P.O. Box 1497 · Madison, WI 53701-1497 · 608-257-5035

Brady C. Williamson · ⑩ · Godfrey & Kahn · One East Main Street, Suite 500 · P.O. Box 2719 · Madison, WI 53701-2719 · 608-257-3911

Jane Zimmerman · Murphy Desmond · http://www.murphydesmond.com · 33 East Main Street, Suite 500 · P.O. Box 2038 · Madison, WI 53703-2038 · 608-807-0262

Milwaukee

Bruce Arnold · Whyte Hirschboeck Dudek · 555 East Wells Street, Suite 1900 · Milwaukee, WI 53202-3819 · 414-273-2100

Andrew M. Barnes · ⑳ · Quarles & Brady · http://www.quarles.com · 411 East Wisconsin Avenue, Suite 2040 · Milwaukee, WI 53202-4497 · 414-277-5000

Peter C. Blain · ⑳ · Reinhart Boerner Van Deuren · http://www.reinhartlaw.com · 1000 North Water Street · P.O. Box 2965 · Milwaukee, WI 53201-2965 · 414-298-1000

Richard H. Casper · ⑳ · Foley & Lardner · 777 East Wisconsin Avenue, Suite 3800 · Milwaukee, WI 53202-5306 · 414-271-2400

David I. Cisar · von Briesen & Roper · http://www.vonbriesen.com · 411 East Wisconsin Avenue, Suite 700 · P.O. Box 3262 · Milwaukee, WI 53201-3262 · 414-276-1122

Randall D. Crocker · ⑩ · von Briesen & Roper · http://www.vonbriesen.com · 411 East Wisconsin Avenue, Suite 700 · P.O. Box 3262 · Milwaukee, WI 53201-3262 · 414-276-1122

Daryl L. Diesing · Whyte Hirschboeck Dudek · 555 East Wells Street, Suite 1900 · Milwaukee, WI 53202-3819 · 414-273-2100

Todd C. Esser · Todd C. Esser & Associates · 11805 West Hampton Avenue · Milwaukee, WI 53226-3612 · 414-777-7676

Mark F. Foley · ⑩ · Foley & Lardner · 777 East Wisconsin Avenue, Suite 3800 · Milwaukee, WI 53202-5306 · 414-271-2400

Edward J. Heiser, Jr. · ⑩ · Whyte Hirschboeck Dudek · 555 East Wells Street, Suite 1900 · Milwaukee, WI 53202-3819 · 414-273-2100

Patrick B. Howell · Whyte Hirschboeck Dudek · 555 East Wells Street, Suite 1900 · Milwaukee, WI 53202-3819 · 414-273-2100

Michael D. Jankowski · Reinhart Boerner Van Deuren · http://www.reinhartlaw.com · 1000 North Water Street · P.O. Box 2965 · Milwaukee, WI 53201-2965 · 414-298-1000

Bruce A. Lanser · Lanser Law Office · 205 East Wisconsin Avenue, Suite 140 · Milwaukee, WI 53202-4207 · 414-272-5700

Leonard G. Leverson · Leverson & Metz · 225 East Mason Street, Suite 100 · Milwaukee, WI 53202 · 414-271-8500

Paul A. Lucey · Michael Best & Friedrich · 100 East Wisconsin Avenue, Suite 3300 · Milwaukee, WI 53202-4108 · 414-271-6560

Paul S. Medved · 20 · Mallery & Zimmerman · 731 North Jackson Street, Suite 900 · Milwaukee, WI 53202-4697 · 414-271-2424

Mark L. Metz · Leverson & Metz · 225 East Mason Street, Suite 100 · Milwaukee, WI 53202 · 414-271-8500

Ann M. Murphy · Quarles & Brady · http://www.quarles.com · 411 East Wisconsin Avenue, Suite 2040 · Milwaukee, WI 53202-4497 · 414-277-5000

Michael S. Polsky · Beck, Chaet, Bamberger & Polsky · http://www.bcblaw.net · Two Plaza East, Suite 1085 · 330 East Kilbourn Avenue · Milwaukee, WI 53202 · 414-273-4200

Thomas L. Shriner, Jr. · 10 · Foley & Lardner · 777 East Wisconsin Avenue, Suite 3800 · Milwaukee, WI 53202-5306 · 414-271-2400

Robert K. Steuer · Robert K. Steuer Law Office · 320 East Buffalo Street, Suite 611 · Milwaukee, WI 53202-5866 · 414-220-4280

Robert M. Waud · Schober & Radtke · 15525 West National Avenue · P.O. Box 510155 · Milwaukee, WI 53151-0155 · 262-782-7820

Oshkosh

Paul G. Swanson · Steinhilber, Swanson, Mares, Marone & McDermott · 107 Church Avenue · P.O. Box 617 · Oshkosh, WI 54903-0617 · 920-235-6690

Whitewater

Mark Bromley · 10 · F. Mark Bromley · W5838 Greening Road · Whitewater, WI 53190-4026 · 262-495-8530

BET-THE-COMPANY LITIGATION

Madison

Ward I. Richter · 10 · Bell, Gierhart & Moore · 44 East Mifflin Street, 10th Floor · P.O. Box 1807 · Madison, WI 53701-1807 · 608-257-3764

Michael B. Van Sicklen · 10 · Foley & Lardner · 150 East Gilman Street · P.O. Box 1497 · Madison, WI 53701-1497 · 608-257-5035

David G. Walsh · 10 · Foley & Lardner · 150 East Gilman Street · P.O. Box 1497 · Madison, WI 53701-1497 · 608-257-5035

Milwaukee

Jon P. Christiansen · 10 · Foley & Lardner · 777 East Wisconsin Avenue, Suite 3800 · Milwaukee, WI 53202-5306 · 414-271-2400

James R. Clark · 20 · Foley & Lardner · 777 East Wisconsin Avenue, Suite 3800 · Milwaukee, WI 53202-5306 · 414-271-2400

W. Stuart Parsons · 25 · Quarles & Brady · http://www.quarles.com · 411 East Wisconsin Avenue, Suite 2040 · Milwaukee, WI 53202-4497 · 414-277-5000

Thomas L. Shriner, Jr. · ⑩ · Foley & Lardner · 777 East Wisconsin Avenue, Suite 3800 · Milwaukee, WI 53202-5306 · 414-271-2400

BIOTECHNOLOGY LAW

Madison

Mark A. Kassel · Foley & Lardner · 150 East Gilman Street · P.O. Box 1497 · Madison, WI 53701-1497 · 608-257-5035

CIVIL RIGHTS LAW

Milwaukee

Raymond M. Dall'Osto · Gimbel, Reilly, Guerin & Brown · Two Plaza East, Suite 1170 · 330 East Kilbourn Avenue · Milwaukee, WI 53202 · 414-271-1440

COLLABORATIVE LAW: FAMILY LAW

Madison

Steven A. Bach · ⑳ · Cullen, Weston, Pines & Bach · http://www.cwpb.com · 122 West Washington Avenue, Suite 900 · Madison, WI 53703 · 608-251-0101

COMMERCIAL LITIGATION

Appleton

Daniel T. Flaherty · Godfrey & Kahn · 100 West Lawrence · P.O. Box 2728 · Appleton, WI 54912-2728 · 920-830-2800

Brookfield

David V. Meany · DeWitt Ross & Stevens · 13935 Bishop's Drive, Suite 300 · Brookfield, WI 53005-6605 262-754-2840

Eau Claire

Webster A. Hart · ⑩ · Herrick & Hart · 116 West Grand Avenue · P.O. Box 167 · Eau Claire, WI 54702 · 715-832-3491

Green Bay

Gregory B. Conway · Liebmann, Conway, Olejniczak & Jerry · 231 South Adams Street · P.O. Box 23200 Green Bay, WI 54305-3200 · 920-437-0476

Madison

Allen A. Arntsen · Foley & Lardner · 150 East Gilman Street · P.O. Box 1497 · Madison, WI 53701-1497 608-257-5035

Jon P. Axelrod · ⑩ · DeWitt Ross & Stevens · Two East Mifflin Street, Suite 600 · Madison, WI 53703 · 608-255-8891

Denis P. Bartell · (20) · DeWitt Ross & Stevens · Two East Mifflin Street, Suite 600 · Madison, WI 53703 · 608-255-8891

James E. Bartzen · Boardman Law Firm · http://www.boardmanlawfirm.com · One South Pinckney Street, Fourth Floor · P.O. Box 927 · Madison, WI 53701-0927 · 608-257-9521

Brian E. Butler · (10) · Stafford Rosenbaum · http://www.staffordlaw.com · 222 West Washington Avenue, Suite 900 · P.O. Box 1784 · Madison, WI 53701-1784 · 608-256-0226

William M. Conley · Foley & Lardner · 150 East Gilman Street · P.O. Box 1497 · Madison, WI 53701-1497 · 608-257-5035

Charles G. Curtis, Jr. · Heller Ehrman · One East Main Street, Suite 201 · Madison, WI 53703-5118 · 608-663-7460

Michael R. Davis · DeWitt Ross & Stevens · Two East Mifflin Street, Suite 600 · Madison, WI 53703 · 608-255-8891

Stephen A. DiTullio · DeWitt Ross & Stevens · Two East Mifflin Street, Suite 600 · Madison, WI 53703 608-255-8891

James A. Friedman · Godfrey & Kahn · One East Main Street, Suite 500 · P.O. Box 2719 · Madison, WI 53701-2719 · 608-257-3911

David J. Harth · Perkins Coie · One East Main Street, Suite 201 · Madison, WI 53703-5118 · 608-663-7460

Donald L. Heaney · (10) · Lathrop & Clark · 740 Regent Street, Suite 400 · P.O. Box 1507 · Madison, WI 53701-1507 · 608-257-7766

John C. Mitby · (10) · Axley Brynelson · http://www.axley.com · Two East Mifflin Street, Suite 200 · P.O. Box 1767 · Madison, WI 53701-1767 · 608-257-5661

Michael J. Modl · Axley Brynelson · http://www.axley.com · Two East Mifflin Street, Suite 200 · P.O. Box 1767 · Madison, WI 53701-1767 · 608-257-5661

Earl H. Munson · (10) · Boardman Law Firm · http://www.boardmanlawfirm.com · One South Pinckney Street, Fourth Floor · P.O. Box 927 · Madison, WI 53701-0927 · 608-257-9521

Barbara A. Neider · Stafford Rosenbaum · http://www.staffordlaw.com · 222 West Washington Avenue, Suite 900 · P.O. Box 1784 · Madison, WI 53701-1784 · 608-256-0226

Paul R. Norman · Boardman Law Firm · http://www.boardmanlawfirm.com · One South Pinckney Street, Fourth Floor · P.O. Box 927 · Madison, WI 53701-0927 · 608-257-9521

H. Dale Peterson · Stroud, Willink & Howard · 25 West Main Street, Suite 300 · P.O. Box 2236 · Madison, WI 53701-2236 · 608-257-2281

Ward I. Richter · (10) · Bell, Gierhart & Moore · 44 East Mifflin Street, 10th Floor · P.O. Box 1807 · Madison, WI 53701-1807 · 608-257-3764

Donald K. Schott · Quarles & Brady · http://www.quarles.com · 33 East Main Street, Suite 900 · P.O. Box 2113 · Madison, WI 53701-2113 · 608-251-5000

John S. Skilton · (20) · Perkins Coie · One East Main Street, Suite 201 · Madison, WI 53703-5118 · 608-663-7460

Ann Ustad Smith · Michael Best & Friedrich · One South Pinckney Street, Suite 700 · P.O. Box 1806 · Madison, WI 53701-1806 · 608-257-3501

Wrede H. Smith, Jr. · DeWitt Ross & Stevens · 8000 Excelsior Drive, Suite 401 · Madison, WI 53717-1914 · 608-831-2100

James R. Troupis · Michael Best & Friedrich · One South Pinckney Street, Suite 700 · P.O. Box 1806 · Madison, WI 53701-1806 · 608-257-3501

Michael B. Van Sicklen · (10) · Foley & Lardner · 150 East Gilman Street · P.O. Box 1497 · Madison, WI 53701-1497 · 608-257-5035

David G. Walsh · (10) · Foley & Lardner · 150 East Gilman Street · P.O. Box 1497 · Madison, WI 53701-1497 · 608-257-5035

Milwaukee

Robert L. Binder · Foley & Lardner · 777 East Wisconsin Avenue, Suite 3800 · Milwaukee, WI 53202-5306 · 414-271-2400

Michael A. Bowen · (10) · Foley & Lardner · 777 East Wisconsin Avenue, Suite 3800 · Milwaukee, WI 53202-5306 · 414-271-2400

John A. Busch · (10) · Michael Best & Friedrich · 100 East Wisconsin Avenue, Suite 3300 · Milwaukee, WI 53202-4108 · 414-271-6560

Jon P. Christiansen · (10) · Foley & Lardner · 777 East Wisconsin Avenue, Suite 3800 · Milwaukee, WI 53202-5306 · 414-271-2400

James R. Clark · (20) · Foley & Lardner · 777 East Wisconsin Avenue, Suite 3800 · Milwaukee, WI 53202-5306 · 414-271-2400

Daniel E. Conley · Quarles & Brady · http://www.quarles.com · 411 East Wisconsin Avenue, Suite 2040 · Milwaukee, WI 53202-4497 · 414-277-5000

Francis R. Croak · (25) · Cook & Franke · 660 East Mason Street · Milwaukee, WI 53202 · 414-271-5900

Robert H. Friebert · Friebert, Finerty & St. John · Two Plaza East, Suite 1250 · 330 East Kilbourn Avenue · Milwaukee, WI 53202 · 414-271-0130

Scott W. Hansen · Reinhart Boerner Van Deuren · http://www.reinhartlaw.com · 1000 North Water Street P.O. Box 2965 · Milwaukee, WI 53201-2965 · 414-298-1000

Peter C. Karegeannes · Quarles & Brady · http://www.quarles.com · 411 East Wisconsin Avenue, Suite 2040 · Milwaukee, WI 53202-4497 · 414-277-5000

Beth J. Kushner · von Briesen & Roper · http://www.vonbriesen.com · 411 East Wisconsin Avenue, Suite 700 · P.O. Box 3262 · Milwaukee, WI 53201-3262 · 414-276-1122

William H. Levit, Jr. · (10) · Godfrey & Kahn · 780 North Water Street · Milwaukee, WI 53202-3590 · 414-273-3500

Brian W. McGrath · Foley & Lardner · 777 East Wisconsin Avenue, Suite 3800 · Milwaukee, WI 53202-5306 · 414-271-2400

William J. Mulligan · (10) · Davis & Kuelthau · 111 East Kilbourne Avenue, Suite 1400 · Milwaukee, WI 53202 · 414-276-0200

James T. Murray, Jr. · (25) · Peterson, Johnson & Murray · 733 North Van Buren Street, Sixth Floor · Milwaukee, WI 53202 · 414-278-8800

W. Stuart Parsons · (25) · Quarles & Brady · http://www.quarles.com · 411 East Wisconsin Avenue, Suite 2040 · Milwaukee, WI 53202-4497 · 414-277-5000

Howard A. Pollack · Godfrey & Kahn · 780 North Water Street · Milwaukee, WI 53202-3590 · 414-273-3500

John A. Rothstein · Quarles & Brady · http://www.quarles.com · 411 East Wisconsin Avenue, Suite 2040 · Milwaukee, WI 53202-4497 · 414-277-5000

Nancy J. Sennett · Foley & Lardner · 777 East Wisconsin Avenue, Suite 3800 · Milwaukee, WI 53202-5306 · 414-271-2400

Thomas L. Shriner, Jr. · ⑩ · Foley & Lardner · 777 East Wisconsin Avenue, Suite 3800 · Milwaukee, WI 53202-5306 · 414-271-2400

Peter J. Stone · Foley & Lardner · 777 East Wisconsin Avenue, Suite 3800 · Milwaukee, WI 53202-5306 414-271-2400

Eric J. Van Vugt · Quarles & Brady · http://www.quarles.com · 411 East Wisconsin Avenue, Suite 2040 · Milwaukee, WI 53202-4497 · 414-277-5000

Ralph A. Weber · Gass Weber Mullins · 309 North Water Street · Milwaukee, WI 53202 · 414-223-3300

Wausau

G. Lane Ware · ⑩ · Ruder Ware · 500 Third Street, Suite 8000 · P.O. Box 8050 · Wausau, WI 54402-8050 715-845-4336

Russell W. Wilson · ⑩ · Ruder Ware · 500 Third Street, Suite 8000 · P.O. Box 8050 · Wausau, WI 54402-8050 · 715-845-4336

COMMUNICATIONS LAW

Madison

Dennis P. Birke · DeWitt Ross & Stevens · Two East Mifflin Street, Suite 600 · Madison, WI 53703 · 608-255-8891

Lee Cullen · ⑳ · Cullen, Weston, Pines & Bach · http://www.cwpb.com · 122 West Washington Avenue, Suite 900 · Madison, WI 53703 · 608-251-0101

Peter L. Gardon · Reinhart Boerner Van Deuren · http://www.reinhartlaw.com · 22 East Mifflin Street, Suite 600 · P.O. Box 2018 · Madison, WI 53701-2018 · 608-229-2200

Daniel T. Hardy · Axley Brynelson · http://www.axley.com · Two East Mifflin Street, Suite 200 · P.O. Box 1767 · Madison, WI 53701-1767 · 608-257-5661

Jordan J. Hemaidan · Michael Best & Friedrich · One South Pinckney Street, Suite 700 · P.O. Box 1806 · Madison, WI 53701-1806 · 608-257-3501

Edwin J. Hughes · Stafford Rosenbaum · http://www.staffordlaw.com · 222 West Washington Avenue, Suite 900 · P.O. Box 1784 · Madison, WI 53701-1784 · 608-256-0226

Bradley D. Jackson · ⑩ · Foley & Lardner · 150 East Gilman Street · P.O. Box 1497 · Madison, WI 53701-1497 · 608-257-5035

David G. Walsh · ⑩ · Foley & Lardner · 150 East Gilman Street · P.O. Box 1497 · Madison, WI 53701-1497 · 608-257-5035

CONSTRUCTION LAW

Brookfield

Ken E. Voss · DeWitt Ross & Stevens · 13935 Bishop's Drive, Suite 300 · Brookfield, WI 53005-6605 · 262-754-2840

Madison

Hugh N. Anderson · Akerman Senterfitt · http://www.akerman.com · 222 West Washington Avenue, Suite 380 · Madison, WI 53703 · 608-257-5335

Philip J. Bradbury · Jack D Walker Law Office · 1006 Willow Lane · Madison, WI 53705-1137 · 608-225-0385

Kent I. Carnell · Lawton & Cates · 10 East Doty Street · P.O. Box 2965 · Madison, WI 53703 · 608-282-6200

William E. McCardell · DeWitt Ross & Stevens · Two East Mifflin Street, Suite 600 · Madison, WI 53703 · 608-255-8891

Brian W. Mullins · Axley Brynelson · http://www.axley.com · Two East Mifflin Street, Suite 200 · P.O. Box 1767 · Madison, WI 53701-1767 · 608-257-5661

Robert J. Smith · Akerman Senterfitt · http://www.akerman.com · 222 West Washington Avenue, Suite 380 · Madison, WI 53703 · 608-257-5335

Charles V. Sweeney · Axley Brynelson · http://www.axley.com · Two East Mifflin Street, Suite 200 · P.O. Box 1767 · Madison, WI 53701-1767 · 608-257-5661

Ronald W. Todd · Stroud, Willink & Howard · 25 West Main Street, Suite 300 · P.O. Box 2236 · Madison, WI 53701-2236 · 608-257-2281

Milwaukee

John G. Gehringer · O'Neil, Cannon, Hollman, Dejong · 111 East Wisconsin Avenue, Suite 1400 · Milwaukee, WI 53202 · 414-276-5000

Kevin J. Lyons · Davis & Kuelthau · 111 East Kilbourne Avenue, Suite 1400 · Milwaukee, WI 53202 · 414-276-0200

W. Wayne Siesennop · Siesennop & Sullivan · 200 North Jefferson Street, Suite 200 · Milwaukee, WI 53202-5900 · 414-223-7900

Ronald L. Wallenfang · Quarles & Brady · http://www.quarles.com · 411 East Wisconsin Avenue, Suite 2040 · Milwaukee, WI 53202-4497 · 414-277-5000

Waukesha

David A. Krutz · Michael Best & Friedrich · Two Riverwood Place, Suite 200 · N19 W24133 Riverwood Drive · Waukesha, WI 53188-1174 · 262-956-6560

CORPORATE GOVERNANCE AND COMPLIANCE LAW

Madison

Richard A. Latta · Michael Best & Friedrich · One South Pinckney Street, Suite 700 · P.O. Box 1806 · Madison, WI 53701-1806 · 608-257-3501

Milwaukee

Kathleen S. Donius · Reinhart Boerner Van Deuren · http://www.reinhartlaw.com · 1000 North Water Street · P.O. Box 2965 · Milwaukee, WI 53201-2965 · 414-298-1000

Geoffrey R. Morgan · Michael Best & Friedrich · 100 East Wisconsin Avenue, Suite 3300 · Milwaukee, WI 53202-4108 · 414-271-6560

CORPORATE LAW

Janesville

Robert H. Consigny · ⑳ · Consigny, Andrews, Hemming & Grant · 303 East Court Street · P.O. Box 1449 Janesville, WI 53547 · 608-755-5050

James R. Cripe · ⑩ · Nowlan & Mouat · 100 South Main Street · P.O. Box 8100 · Janesville, WI 53547-8100 · 608-755-8100

George K. Steil, Sr. · ⑩ · Brennan, Steil & Basting · One East Milwaukee Street · P.O. Box 1148 · Janesville, WI 53547-1148 · 608-756-4141

Madison

Jeffrey B. Bartell · ⑩ · Quarles & Brady · http://www.quarles.com · 33 East Main Street, Suite 900 · P.O. Box 2113 · Madison, WI 53701-2113 · 608-251-5000

Robert E. Chritton · Godfrey & Kahn · One East Main Street, Suite 500 · P.O. Box 2719 · Madison, WI 53701-2719 · 608-257-3911

Paul A. Croake · DeWitt Ross & Stevens · Two East Mifflin Street, Suite 600 · Madison, WI 53703 · 608-255-8891

Peter R. Dohr · DeWitt Ross & Stevens · Two East Mifflin Street, Suite 600 · Madison, WI 53703 · 608-255-8891

Mark T. Ehrmann · Quarles & Brady · http://www.quarles.com · 33 East Main Street, Suite 900 · P.O. Box 2113 · Madison, WI 53701-2113 · 608-251-5000

John E. Knight · ⑩ · Boardman Law Firm · http://www.boardmanlawfirm.com · One South Pinckney Street, Fourth Floor · P.O. Box 927 · Madison, WI 53701-0927 · 608-257-9521

Richard A. Latta · Michael Best & Friedrich · One South Pinckney Street, Suite 700 · P.O. Box 1806 · Madison, WI 53701-1806 · 608-257-3501

Tod B. Linstroth · ⑳ · Michael Best & Friedrich · One South Pinckney Street, Suite 700 · P.O. Box 1806 Madison, WI 53701-1806 · 608-257-3501

Gregory J. Lynch · Michael Best & Friedrich · One South Pinckney Street, Suite 700 · P.O. Box 1806 · Madison, WI 53701-1806 · 608-257-3501

Charles E. Neider · Neider & Boucher · 440 Science Drive, Suite 300 · P.O. Box 5510 · Madison, WI 53705-0510 · 608-661-4500

Richard W. Pitzner · ㉕ · Murphy Desmond · http://www.murphydesmond.com · 33 East Main Street, Suite 500 · P.O. Box 2038 · Madison, WI 53703-2038 · 608-807-0262

Blaine R. Renfert · Foley & Lardner · 150 East Gilman Street · P.O. Box 1497 · Madison, WI 53701-1497 608-257-5035

John S. Robison · ⑩ · Quarles & Brady · http://www.quarles.com · 33 East Main Street, Suite 900 · P.O. Box 2113 · Madison, WI 53701-2113 · 608-251-5000

Michael E. Skindrud · Godfrey & Kahn · One East Main Street, Suite 500 · P.O. Box 2719 · Madison, WI 53701-2719 · 608-257-3911

Wrede H. Smith, Jr. · DeWitt Ross & Stevens · 8000 Excelsior Drive, Suite 401 · Madison, WI 53717-1914 · 608-831-2100

Robert R. Stroud · Stroud, Willink & Howard · 25 West Main Street, Suite 300 · P.O. Box 2236 · Madison, WI 53701-2236 · 608-257-2281

David G. Walsh · ⑩ · Foley & Lardner · 150 East Gilman Street · P.O. Box 1497 · Madison, WI 53701-1497 · 608-257-5035

Paul T. Wrycha · Foley & Lardner · 150 East Gilman Street · P.O. Box 1497 · Madison, WI 53701-1497 · 608-257-5035

Thomas D. Zilavy · ⑩ · DeWitt Ross & Stevens · Two East Mifflin Street, Suite 600 · Madison, WI 53703 · 608-255-8891

Milwaukee

William J. Abraham, Jr. · ⑳ · Foley & Lardner · 777 East Wisconsin Avenue, Suite 3800 · Milwaukee, WI 53202-5306 · 414-271-2400

Anthony W. Asmuth III · ㉕ · Quarles & Brady · http://www.quarles.com · 411 East Wisconsin Avenue, Suite 2040 · Milwaukee, WI 53202-4497 · 414-277-5000

James M. Bedore · Reinhart Boerner Van Deuren · http://www.reinhartlaw.com · 1000 North Water Street · P.O. Box 2965 · Milwaukee, WI 53201-2965 · 414-298-1000

Robert E. Bellin · Reinhart Boerner Van Deuren · http://www.reinhartlaw.com · 1000 North Water Street P.O. Box 2965 · Milwaukee, WI 53201-2965 · 414-298-1000

Richard J. Bliss · ⑩ · Godfrey & Kahn · 780 North Water Street · Milwaukee, WI 53202-3590 · 414-273-3500

Ralf-Reinhard Boer · Foley & Lardner · 777 East Wisconsin Avenue, Suite 3800 · Milwaukee, WI 53202-5306 · 414-271-2400

Kathryn M. Buono · Quarles & Brady · http://www.quarles.com · 411 East Wisconsin Avenue, Suite 2040 Milwaukee, WI 53202-4497 · 414-277-5000

Gerald E. Connolly · ⑳ · Quarles & Brady · http://www.quarles.com · 411 East Wisconsin Avenue, Suite 2040 · Milwaukee, WI 53202-4497 · 414-277-5000

Bruce C. Davidson · Quarles & Brady · http://www.quarles.com · 411 East Wisconsin Avenue, Suite 2040 Milwaukee, WI 53202-4497 · 414-277-5000

John A. Dickens · Godfrey & Kahn · 780 North Water Street · Milwaukee, WI 53202-3590 · 414-273-3500

Benjamin F. Garmer III · ⑳ · Foley & Lardner · 777 East Wisconsin Avenue, Suite 3800 · Milwaukee, WI 53202-5306 · 414-271-2400

Carol A. Gehl · Godfrey & Kahn · 780 North Water Street · Milwaukee, WI 53202-3590 · 414-273-3500

Patrick J. Goebel · Quarles & Brady · http://www.quarles.com · 411 East Wisconsin Avenue, Suite 2040 · Milwaukee, WI 53202-4497 · 414-277-5000

Conrad G. Goodkind · ❿ · Quarles & Brady · http://www.quarles.com · 411 East Wisconsin Avenue, Suite 2040 · Milwaukee, WI 53202-4497 · 414-277-5000

Michael M. Grebe · Quarles & Brady · http://www.quarles.com · 411 East Wisconsin Avenue, Suite 2040 · Milwaukee, WI 53202-4497 · 414-277-5000

Kevin J. Howley · Reinhart Boerner Van Deuren · http://www.reinhartlaw.com · 1000 North Water Street P.O. Box 2965 · Milwaukee, WI 53201-2965 · 414-298-1000

Jerome H. Kringel · ❿ · Michael Best & Friedrich · 100 East Wisconsin Avenue, Suite 3300 · Milwaukee, WI 53202-4108 · 414-271-6560

Michael H. Lappin · Quarles & Brady · http://www.quarles.com · 411 East Wisconsin Avenue, Suite 2040 Milwaukee, WI 53202-4497 · 414-277-5000

Fredrick G. Lautz · Quarles & Brady · http://www.quarles.com · 411 East Wisconsin Avenue, Suite 2040 · Milwaukee, WI 53202-4497 · 414-277-5000

K. Thor Lundgren · Michael Best & Friedrich · 100 East Wisconsin Avenue, Suite 3300 · Milwaukee, WI 53202-4108 · 414-271-6560

Quinn W. Martin · Quarles & Brady · http://www.quarles.com · 411 East Wisconsin Avenue, Suite 2040 · Milwaukee, WI 53202-4497 · 414-277-5000

Geoffrey R. Morgan · Michael Best & Friedrich · 100 East Wisconsin Avenue, Suite 3300 · Milwaukee, WI 53202-4108 · 414-271-6560

Christopher B. Noyes · Godfrey & Kahn · 780 North Water Street · Milwaukee, WI 53202-3590 · 414-273-3500

Elizabeth A. Orelup · Quarles & Brady · http://www.quarles.com · 411 East Wisconsin Avenue, Suite 2040 · Milwaukee, WI 53202-4497 · 414-277-5000

Michael T. Pepke · Reinhart Boerner Van Deuren · http://www.reinhartlaw.com · 1000 North Water Street · P.O. Box 2965 · Milwaukee, WI 53201-2965 · 414-298-1000

Patrick G. Quick · Foley & Lardner · 777 East Wisconsin Avenue, Suite 3800 · Milwaukee, WI 53202-5306 · 414-271-2400

Jay O. Rothman · Foley & Lardner · 777 East Wisconsin Avenue, Suite 3800 · Milwaukee, WI 53202-5306 · 414-271-2400

Thomas A. Simonis · Quarles & Brady · http://www.quarles.com · 411 East Wisconsin Avenue, Suite 2040 Milwaukee, WI 53202-4497 · 414-277-5000

Luke E. Sims · Foley & Lardner · 777 East Wisconsin Avenue, Suite 3800 · Milwaukee, WI 53202-5306 · 414-271-2400

Walter J. Skipper · Quarles & Brady · http://www.quarles.com · 411 East Wisconsin Avenue, Suite 2040 · Milwaukee, WI 53202-4497 · 414-277-5000

Peter M. Sommerhauser · ❿ · Godfrey & Kahn · 780 North Water Street · Milwaukee, WI 53202-3590 · 414-273-3500

Richard A. Van Deuren · ㉕ · Reinhart Boerner Van Deuren · http://www.reinhartlaw.com · 1000 North Water Street · P.O. Box 2965 · Milwaukee, WI 53201-2965 · 414-298-1000

Charles G. Vogel · Godfrey & Kahn · 780 North Water Street · Milwaukee, WI 53202-3590 · 414-273-3500

Nicholas P. Wahl · Godfrey & Kahn · 780 North Water Street · Milwaukee, WI 53202-3590 · 414-273-3500

Mark Witt · Godfrey & Kahn · 780 North Water Street · Milwaukee, WI 53202-3590 · 414-273-3500

Wausau

Lon E. Roberts · Ruder Ware · 500 Third Street, Suite 8000 · P.O. Box 8050 · Wausau, WI 54402-8050 · 715-845-4336

G. Lane Ware · ⑩ · Ruder Ware · 500 Third Street, Suite 8000 · P.O. Box 8050 · Wausau, WI 54402-8050 715-845-4336

EDUCATION LAW

Eau Claire

Kathryn J. Prenn · ⑩ · Weld, Riley, Prenn & Ricci · 3624 Oakwood Hills Parkway · P.O. Box 1030 · Eau Claire, WI 54702-1030 · 715-839-7786

Madison

Jon E. Anderson · Godfrey & Kahn · One East Main Street, Suite 500 · P.O. Box 2719 · Madison, WI 53701-2719 · 608-257-3911

David R. Friedman · Friedman Law Firm · 30 West Mifflin Street, Suite 1001 · Madison, WI 53703 · 608-256-0155

JoAnn M. Hart · Stafford Rosenbaum · http://www.staffordlaw.com · 222 West Washington Avenue, Suite 900 · P.O. Box 1784 · Madison, WI 53701-1784 · 608-256-0226

Michael J. Julka · Lathrop & Clark · 740 Regent Street, Suite 400 · P.O. Box 1507 · Madison, WI 53701-1507 · 608-257-7766

Jayne K. Kuehn · DeWitt Ross & Stevens · Two East Mifflin Street, Suite 600 · Madison, WI 53703 · 608-255-8891

James K. Ruhly · ⑳ · Jack D Walker Law Office · 1006 Willow Lane · Madison, WI 53705-1137 · 608-225-0385

Thomas N. Shorter · Godfrey & Kahn · One East Main Street, Suite 500 · P.O. Box 2719 · Madison, WI 53701-2719 · 608-257-3911

Milwaukee

Gary M. Ruesch · Quarles & Brady · http://www.quarles.com · 411 East Wisconsin Avenue, Suite 2040 · Milwaukee, WI 53202-4497 · 414-277-5000

ELDER LAW

De Pere

Daniel J. Walsh · Walsh & Walsh · 1000 North Broadway · De Pere, WI 54115-2610 · 920-337-0272

Eau Claire

Peter E. Grosskopf · Grosskopf & Black · 1324 West Clairemont Avenue, Suite 10 · Eau Claire, WI 54701 · 715-835-6196

Jane E. Lokken · Ruder Ware · 402 Graham Avenue · P.O. Box 187 · Eau Claire, WI 54702-0187 · 715-834-3425

Hurley

Paul A. Sturgul · Paul A. Sturgul Law Office · 312 Silver Street · Hurley, WI 54534-1254 · 715-561-4600

Iron River

James Bowen Noble · James B. Noble · 8025 U.S. Highway Two · P.O. Box 335 · Iron River, WI 54847-4669 · 608-784-1544

Madison

Roy W. Froemming · Froemming Law Office · 354 West Main Street · Madison, WI 53703 · 608-663-2747

Barbara S. Hughes · Hill, Glowacki, Jaeger & Hughes · 2010 Eastwood Drive, Suite 301 · Madison, WI 53704-5459 · 608-244-1354

James A. Jaeger · Hill, Glowacki, Jaeger & Hughes · 2010 Eastwood Drive, Suite 301 · Madison, WI 53704-5459 · 608-244-1354

Milwaukee

Angela E. Canellos · Angela E. Canellos · 631 North Mayfair Road · Milwaukee, WI 53226 · 414-257-9200

Margaret W. Hickey · ⑩ · Becker & Hickey · 312 East Wisconsin Avenue, Suite 306 · Milwaukee, WI 53202-4305 · 414-273-1414

Bruce A. Tammi · Tammi & Cavey · 405 East Lincoln Avenue · Milwaukee, WI 53207-1759 · 414-744-8120

Neenah

Benjamin M. Adams · Adams & Woodrow · 301 Nicolet Boulevard · Neenah, WI 54956 · 920-725-8401

Louis E. Archambault · Adams & Woodrow · 301 Nicolet Boulevard · Neenah, WI 54956 · 920-725-8401

Wausau

Jeffery J. Drach · Drach Law Firm · First American Center, Suite 202 · 500 Third Street · Wausau, WI 54403 · 715-842-0606

Wauwatosa

Andrew P. Brusky · Brusky & Sjostrom · 2300 North Mayfair Road, Suite 530 · Wauwatosa, WI 53226 · 414-259-0010

Patricia J. Nelson · Nelson, Irvings & Waeffler · 3077 North Mayfair Road, Suite 203 · Wauwatosa, WI 53222-4305 · 414-777-0220

EMINENT DOMAIN AND CONDEMNATION LAW

Elkhorn

Lowell E. Sweet · (25) · Sweet & Maier · Inns Of Court Building · 114 North Church Street · P.O. Box 318 · Elkhorn, WI 53121-0318 · 262-723-5480

Madison

Allen A. Arntsen · Foley & Lardner · 150 East Gilman Street · P.O. Box 1497 · Madison, WI 53701-1497 608-257-5035

Mark J. Steichen · Boardman Law Firm · http://www.boardmanlawfirm.com · One South Pinckney Street, Fourth Floor · P.O. Box 927 · Madison, WI 53701-0927 · 608-257-9521

Milwaukee

Alan H. Marcuvitz · Michael Best & Friedrich · 100 East Wisconsin Avenue, Suite 3300 · Milwaukee, WI 53202-4108 · 414-271-6560

Richland Center

Benjamin Southwick · Benjamin Southwick Law Office · 130 West Court Street · Richland Center, WI 53581-2343 · 608-647-4111

Waukesha

Charles P. Graupner · Michael Best & Friedrich · Two Riverwood Place, Suite 200 · N19 W24133 Riverwood Drive · Waukesha, WI 53188-1174 · 262-956-6560

Dean B. Richards · Reinhart Boerner Van Deuren · http://www.reinhartlaw.com · N16 W23250 Stoneridge Drive · P.O. Box 2265 · Waukesha, WI 53187-2265 · 262-951-4500

Wausau

W. Thomas Terwilliger · Terwilliger Law Firm · 327 North Seventeenth Avenue, Suite 201 · Wausau, WI 54402-8063 · 715-845-2121

EMPLOYEE BENEFITS LAW

Madison

Brian L. Anderson · DeWitt Ross & Stevens · Two East Mifflin Street, Suite 600 · Madison, WI 53703 · 608-255-8891

Christopher S. Berry · (10) · Foley & Lardner · 150 East Gilman Street · P.O. Box 1497 · Madison, WI 53701-1497 · 608-257-5035

John Rashke · (20) · DeWitt Ross & Stevens · 8000 Excelsior Drive, Suite 401 · Madison, WI 53717-1914 · 608-831-2100

Milwaukee

Kristin M. Bergstrom · (10) · Reinhart Boerner Van Deuren · http://www.reinhartlaw.com · 1000 North Water Street · P.O. Box 2965 · Milwaukee, WI 53201-2965 · 414-298-1000

Bennett E. Choice · Reinhart Boerner Van Deuren · http://www.reinhartlaw.com · 1000 North Water Street · P.O. Box 2965 · Milwaukee, WI 53201-2965 · 414-298-1000

Donald J. Christl · ⑩ · Reinhart Boerner Van Deuren · http://www.reinhartlaw.com · 1000 North Water Street · P.O. Box 2965 · Milwaukee, WI 53201-2965 · 414-298-1000

Catherine Conway · von Briesen & Roper · http://www.vonbriesen.com · 411 East Wisconsin Avenue, Suite 700 · P.O. Box 3262 · Milwaukee, WI 53201-3262 · 414-276-1122

Lloyd J. Dickinson · ⑳ · Foley & Lardner · 777 East Wisconsin Avenue, Suite 3800 · Milwaukee, WI 53202-5306 · 414-271-2400

John E. Donahue · ⑩ · Godfrey & Kahn · 780 North Water Street · Milwaukee, WI 53202-3590 · 414-273-3500

Gregg H. Dooge · ⑩ · Foley & Lardner · 777 East Wisconsin Avenue, Suite 3800 · Milwaukee, WI 53202-5306 · 414-271-2400

Scott H. Engroff · ⑩ · Scott H. Engroff · Coventry Office Building, Suite 111 · 250 West Coventry Court · Milwaukee, WI 53217-3963 · 414-228-5815

Jeffrey R. Fuller · Reinhart Boerner Van Deuren · http://www.reinhartlaw.com · 1000 North Water Street P.O. Box 2965 · Milwaukee, WI 53201-2965 · 414-298-1000

Thomas E. Funk · Reinhart Boerner Van Deuren · http://www.reinhartlaw.com · 1000 North Water Street P.O. Box 2965 · Milwaukee, WI 53201-2965 · 414-298-1000

Steven D. Huff · Reinhart Boerner Van Deuren · http://www.reinhartlaw.com · 1000 North Water Street · P.O. Box 2965 · Milwaukee, WI 53201-2965 · 414-298-1000

Harvey Kurtz · Foley & Lardner · 777 East Wisconsin Avenue, Suite 3800 · Milwaukee, WI 53202-5306 · 414-271-2400

Timothy C. McDonald · von Briesen & Roper · http://www.vonbriesen.com · 411 East Wisconsin Avenue, Suite 700 · P.O. Box 3262 · Milwaukee, WI 53201-3262 · 414-276-1122

David P. Olson · Quarles & Brady · http://www.quarles.com · 411 East Wisconsin Avenue, Suite 2040 · Milwaukee, WI 53202-4497 · 414-277-5000

Greg W. Renz · ⑳ · Foley & Lardner · 777 East Wisconsin Avenue, Suite 3800 · Milwaukee, WI 53202-5306 · 414-271-2400

Leigh C. Riley · Foley & Lardner · 777 East Wisconsin Avenue, Suite 3800 · Milwaukee, WI 53202-5306 414-271-2400

Robert D. Rothacker · Quarles & Brady · http://www.quarles.com · 411 East Wisconsin Avenue, Suite 2040 · Milwaukee, WI 53202-4497 · 414-277-5000

Charles P. Stevens · Michael Best & Friedrich · 100 East Wisconsin Avenue, Suite 3300 · Milwaukee, WI 53202-4108 · 414-271-6560

ENERGY LAW

Madison

Niles Berman · ⑩ · Wheeler, Van Sickle & Anderson · 25 West Main Street, Suite 801 · Madison, WI 53703-3398 · 608-255-7277

Lee Cullen · ⑳ · Cullen, Weston, Pines & Bach · http://www.cwpb.com · 122 West Washington Avenue, Suite 900 · Madison, WI 53703 · 608-251-0101

Peter L. Gardon · Reinhart Boerner Van Deuren · http://www.reinhartlaw.com · 22 East Mifflin Street, Suite 600 · P.O. Box 2018 · Madison, WI 53701-2018 · 608-229-2200

David J. Hanson · ⑩ · Michael Best & Friedrich · One South Pinckney Street, Suite 700 · P.O. Box 1806 · Madison, WI 53701-1806 · 608-257-3501

Daniel T. Hardy · Axley Brynelson · http://www.axley.com · Two East Mifflin Street, Suite 200 · P.O. Box 1767 · Madison, WI 53701-1767 · 608-257-5661

Bradley D. Jackson · ⑩ · Foley & Lardner · 150 East Gilman Street · P.O. Box 1497 · Madison, WI 53701-1497 · 608-257-5035

Jeffrey Landsman · Wheeler, Van Sickle & Anderson · 25 West Main Street, Suite 801 · Madison, WI 53703-3398 · 608-255-7277

Richard K. Nordeng · Stafford Rosenbaum · http://www.staffordlaw.com · 222 West Washington Avenue, Suite 900 · P.O. Box 1784 · Madison, WI 53701-1784 · 608-256-0226

John D. Wilson · Michael Best & Friedrich · One South Pinckney Street, Suite 700 · P.O. Box 1806 · Madison, WI 53701-1806 · 608-257-3501

Milwaukee

Larry J. Martin · ⑩ · Quarles & Brady · http://www.quarles.com · 411 East Wisconsin Avenue, Suite 2040 Milwaukee, WI 53202-4497 · 414-277-5000

Bartholomew F. Reuter · Foley & Lardner · 777 East Wisconsin Avenue, Suite 3800 · Milwaukee, WI 53202-5306 · 414-271-2400

Trevor J. Will · Foley & Lardner · 777 East Wisconsin Avenue, Suite 3800 · Milwaukee, WI 53202-5306 · 414-271-2400

Allen W. Williams, Jr. · ⑳ · Foley & Lardner · 777 East Wisconsin Avenue, Suite 3800 · Milwaukee, WI 53202-5306 · 414-271-2400

Brian D. Winters · Quarles & Brady · http://www.quarles.com · 411 East Wisconsin Avenue, Suite 2040 · Milwaukee, WI 53202-4497 · 414-277-5000

ENVIRONMENTAL LAW

Madison

Dennis P. Birke · DeWitt Ross & Stevens · Two East Mifflin Street, Suite 600 · Madison, WI 53703 · 608-255-8891

Linda H. Bochert · ⑩ · Michael Best & Friedrich · One South Pinckney Street, Suite 700 · P.O. Box 1806 Madison, WI 53701-1806 · 608-257-3501

Douglas B. Clark · Foley & Lardner · 150 East Gilman Street · P.O. Box 1497 · Madison, WI 53701-1497 608-257-5035

David A. Crass · ⑩ · Michael Best & Friedrich · One South Pinckney Street, Suite 700 · P.O. Box 1806 · Madison, WI 53701-1806 · 608-257-3501

Henry J. Handzel, Jr. · ⓴ · DeWitt Ross & Stevens · Two East Mifflin Street, Suite 600 · Madison, WI 53703 · 608-255-8891

Paul G. Kent · ⑩ · Anderson & Kent · One North Pinckney Street, Suite 200 · Madison, WI 53703-5809 · 608-246-8500

Todd E. Palmer · DeWitt Ross & Stevens · Two East Mifflin Street, Suite 600 · Madison, WI 53703 · 608-255-8891

Peter A. Peshek · ⑩ · DeWitt Ross & Stevens · Two East Mifflin Street, Suite 600 · Madison, WI 53703 · 608-255-8891

Ronald R. Ragatz · DeWitt Ross & Stevens · Two East Mifflin Street, Suite 600 · Madison, WI 53703 · 608-255-8891

Carl A. Sinderbrand · Axley Brynelson · http://www.axley.com · Two East Mifflin Street, Suite 200 · P.O. Box 1767 · Madison, WI 53701-1767 · 608-257-5661

Timm P. Speerschneider · DeWitt Ross & Stevens · Two East Mifflin Street, Suite 600 · Madison, WI 53703 · 608-255-8891

Milwaukee

Linda E. Benfield · ⑩ · Foley & Lardner · 777 East Wisconsin Avenue, Suite 3800 · Milwaukee, WI 53202-5306 · 414-271-2400

Michael P. Carlton · von Briesen & Roper · http://www.vonbriesen.com · 411 East Wisconsin Avenue, Suite 700 · P.O. Box 3262 · Milwaukee, WI 53201-3262 · 414-276-1122

Michael D. Flanagan · Foley & Lardner · 777 East Wisconsin Avenue, Suite 3800 · Milwaukee, WI 53202-5306 · 414-271-2400

Dennis M. Grzezinski · Dennis Grzezinski Law Office · 312 East Wisconsin Avenue, Suite 210 · Milwaukee, WI 53202 · 414-289-9200

William H. Harbeck · Quarles & Brady · http://www.quarles.com · 411 East Wisconsin Avenue, Suite 2040 · Milwaukee, WI 53202-4497 · 414-277-5000

Arthur J. Harrington · ⓴ · Godfrey & Kahn · 780 North Water Street · Milwaukee, WI 53202-3590 · 414-273-3500

Bruce A. Keyes · Foley & Lardner · 777 East Wisconsin Avenue, Suite 3800 · Milwaukee, WI 53202-5306 · 414-271-2400

Raymond R. Krueger · ⓴ · Michael Best & Friedrich · 100 East Wisconsin Avenue, Suite 3300 · Milwaukee, WI 53202-4108 · 414-271-6560

Richard J. Lewandowski · Whyte Hirschboeck Dudek · 555 East Wells Street, Suite 1900 · Milwaukee, WI 53202-3819 · 414-273-2100

Kevin J. Lyons · Davis & Kuelthau · 111 East Kilbourne Avenue, Suite 1400 · Milwaukee, WI 53202 · 414-276-0200

Diane M. Marchik · Godfrey & Kahn · 780 North Water Street · Milwaukee, WI 53202-3590 · 414-273-3500

George J. Marek · Quarles & Brady · http://www.quarles.com · 411 East Wisconsin Avenue, Suite 2040 · Milwaukee, WI 53202-4497 · 414-277-5000

Michael S. McCauley · ⑩ · Quarles & Brady · http://www.quarles.com · 411 East Wisconsin Avenue, Suite 2040 · Milwaukee, WI 53202-4497 · 414-277-5000

Thomas P. McElligott · ⑩ · Quarles & Brady · http://www.quarles.com · 411 East Wisconsin Avenue, Suite 2040 · Milwaukee, WI 53202-4497 · 414-277-5000

Nancy K. Peterson · ⑩ · Quarles & Brady · http://www.quarles.com · 411 East Wisconsin Avenue, Suite 2040 · Milwaukee, WI 53202-4497 · 414-277-5000

Rachel A. Schneider · Quarles & Brady · http://www.quarles.com · 411 East Wisconsin Avenue, Suite 2040 · Milwaukee, WI 53202-4497 · 414-277-5000

Michael H. Simpson · Reinhart Boerner Van Deuren · http://www.reinhartlaw.com · 1000 North Water Street · P.O. Box 2965 · Milwaukee, WI 53201-2965 · 414-298-1000

Cynthia E. Smith · Michael Best & Friedrich · 100 East Wisconsin Avenue, Suite 3300 · Milwaukee, WI 53202-4108 · 414-271-6560

Mark A. Thimke · ⑳ · Foley & Lardner · 777 East Wisconsin Avenue, Suite 3800 · Milwaukee, WI 53202-5306 · 414-271-2400

John M. Van Lieshout · ⑩ · Reinhart Boerner Van Deuren · http://www.reinhartlaw.com · 1000 North Water Street · P.O. Box 2965 · Milwaukee, WI 53201-2965 · 414-298-1000

Arthur A. Vogel, Jr. · ⑩ · Quarles & Brady · http://www.quarles.com · 411 East Wisconsin Avenue, Suite 2040 · Milwaukee, WI 53202-4497 · 414-277-5000

Allen W. Williams, Jr. · ⑳ · Foley & Lardner · 777 East Wisconsin Avenue, Suite 3800 · Milwaukee, WI 53202-5306 · 414-271-2400

Edward B. Witte · Gonzalez Saggio & Harlan · http://www.gshllp.com · 225 East Michigan Street, Fourth Floor · Milwaukee, WI 53202 · 414-277-8500

FAMILY LAW

Baraboo

Kenneth H. Conway, Jr. · ㉕ · Conway & Seefeld · 121 Fifth Street · P.O. Box 66 · Baraboo, WI 53913 · 608-356-9441

Cedarburg

Donald A. Levy · ㉕ · Levy & Levy · http://levyandlevy.com · N61 W6058 Columbia Road · P.O. Box 127 Cedarburg, WI 53012-0127 · 262-377-5555

La Crosse

Sabina Bosshard · Bosshard Parke · 505 King Street, Suite 334 · La Crosse, WI 54601 · 608-782-1469

G. Jeffrey George · Moen, Sheehan, Meyer · 201 Main Street, Suite 700 · P.O. Box 786 · La Crosse, WI 54602-0786 · 608-784-8310

Patricia M. Heim · ⑩ · O'Flaherty Heim & Egan · U.S. Bank Place, 10th Floor · 201 Main Street · La Crosse, WI 54601 · 608-784-1605

Thomas S. Sleik · ⑩ · Hale, Skemp, Hanson, Skemp & Sleik · 505 King Street, Suite 300 · P.O. Box 1927 La Crosse, WI 54602-1927 · 608-784-3540

Madison

Steven A. Bach · ⑳ · Cullen, Weston, Pines & Bach · http://www.cwpb.com · 122 West Washington Avenue, Suite 900 · Madison, WI 53703 · 608-251-0101

Linda S. Balisle · ⑩ · Balisle & Roberson · 131 West Wilson Street, Suite 802 · P.O. Box 870 · Madison, WI 53701-0870 · 608-259-8702

Stephen C. Beilke · Murphy Desmond · http://www.murphydesmond.com · 33 East Main Street, Suite 500 · P.O. Box 2038 · Madison, WI 53703-2038 · 608-807-0262

Janice Bensky · Stafford Rosenbaum · http://www.staffordlaw.com · 222 West Washington Avenue, Suite 900 · P.O. Box 1784 · Madison, WI 53701-1784 · 608-256-0226

Michael S. Heffernan · Foley & Lardner · 150 East Gilman Street · P.O. Box 1497 · Madison, WI 53701-1497 · 608-257-5035

David E. Joanis · Balisle & Roberson · 131 West Wilson Street, Suite 802 · P.O. Box 870 · Madison, WI 53701-0870 · 608-259-8702

Allan R. Koritzinsky · ㉕ · Foley & Lardner · 150 East Gilman Street · P.O. Box 1497 · Madison, WI 53701-1497 · 608-257-5035

Marta Meyers · Boardman Law Firm · http://www.boardmanlawfirm.com · One South Pinckney Street, Fourth Floor · P.O. Box 927 · Madison, WI 53701-0927 · 608-257-9521

Linda Roberson · ⑩ · Balisle & Roberson · 131 West Wilson Street, Suite 802 · P.O. Box 870 · Madison, WI 53701-0870 · 608-259-8702

Anne T. Wadsack · DeWitt Ross & Stevens · Two East Mifflin Street, Suite 600 · Madison, WI 53703 · 608-255-8891

Daphne Webb · ⑩ · Stafford Rosenbaum · http://www.staffordlaw.com · 222 West Washington Avenue, Suite 900 · P.O. Box 1784 · Madison, WI 53701-1784 · 608-256-0226

Milwaukee

Thomas A. Bailey · ⑩ · Bailey Law Offices · 130 West Silver Spring Drive · Milwaukee, WI 53217-4707 · 414-962-8200

Patricia K. Ballman · Quarles & Brady · http://www.quarles.com · 411 East Wisconsin Avenue, Suite 2040 Milwaukee, WI 53202-4497 · 414-277-5000

Barbara L. Burbach · ⑩ · Burbach & Stansbury · 10850 West Park Place, Suite 530 · Milwaukee, WI 53224 · 414-359-9100

Martin P. Gagne · Gagne & O'Halloran · 735 North Water Street, Suite 731 · Milwaukee, WI 53202 · 414-273-5551

Gregg Herman · ⑩ · Loeb & Herman · Chase Tower, Suite 1725 · 111 East Wisconsin Avenue · Milwaukee, WI 53202-4868 · 414-272-5632

Margaret W. Hickey · ⑩ · Becker & Hickey · 312 East Wisconsin Avenue, Suite 306 · Milwaukee, WI 53202-4305 · 414-273-1414

David B. Karp · Karp, Karp & Zirbgibel · 933 North Mayfair Road, Suite 300 · Milwaukee, WI 53226 · 414-453-0800

Thomas D. Klein · Peckerman & Klein · 920 East Mason Street · Milwaukee, WI 53202-4015 · 414-271-9300

Marvin A. Margolis · ㉕ · Marvin A. Margolis · 6110 North Lake Drive Court · Milwaukee, WI 53217-4649 · 414-962-4567

Thomas A. Merkle · O'Neil, Cannon, Hollman, Dejong · 111 East Wisconsin Avenue, Suite 1400 · Milwaukee, WI 53202 · 414-276-5000

Bruce M. Peckerman · ⑳ · Peckerman & Klein · 920 East Mason Street · Milwaukee, WI 53202-4015 · 414-271-9300

Peggy L. Podell · Peggy L. Podell · http://www.podell-law.com · Coventry Office Building, Suite 111 · 250 West Coventry Court · Milwaukee, WI 53217 · 414-228-5800

Thomas W. St. John · Friebert, Finerty & St. John · Two Plaza East, Suite 1250 · 330 East Kilbourn Avenue · Milwaukee, WI 53202 · 414-271-0130

Carlton D. Stansbury · Burbach & Stansbury · 10850 West Park Place, Suite 530 · Milwaukee, WI 53224 414-359-9100

New Richmond

Gary L. Bakke · ㉕ · Bakke Norman · 1200 Heritage Drive · P.O. Box 308 · New Richmond, WI 54017 · 715-246-3800

Racine

Gerald M. Crawford · ⑳ · Crawford, Crawford & Stutt · Lake Forum Building, Suite 200 · 840 Lake Avenue · Racine, WI 53403 · 262-634-6659

Sheboygan

Herbert C. Humke, Sr. · ⑳ · O'Neil, Cannon, Hollman, Dejong · 607 North Eighth Street, Suite 400 · Sheboygan, WI 53081 · 920-457-8400

Waukesha

Charles I. Phillips · ⑳ · Phillips & Gemignani · 358 West Main Street · Waukesha, WI 53186-4611 · 262-544-9998

Wausau

Kenneth J. Andraski · Lonsdorf & Andraski · 610 Jackson Street · P.O. Box 1585 · Wausau, WI 54402-1585 · 715-842-1647

Barbara A. Hermanson · ⑩ · Hermanson Law Office · 350 Grand Avenue · Wausau, WI 54403-6221 · 715-845-5923

Jeffrey A. Hertz · Mallery & Zimmerman · 500 Third Street, Suite 800 · P.O. Box 479 · Wausau, WI 54402-0479 · 715-845-8234

FAMILY LAW MEDIATION

Madison

Steven A. Bach · ⑳ · Cullen, Weston, Pines & Bach · http://www.cwpb.com · 122 West Washington Avenue, Suite 900 · Madison, WI 53703 · 608-251-0101

Linda S. Balisle · ⑩ · Balisle & Roberson · 131 West Wilson Street, Suite 802 · P.O. Box 870 · Madison, WI 53701-0870 · 608-259-8702

Allan R. Koritzinsky · ㉕ · Foley & Lardner · 150 East Gilman Street · P.O. Box 1497 · Madison, WI 53701-1497 · 608-257-5035

Daphne Webb · ⑩ · Stafford Rosenbaum · http://www.staffordlaw.com · 222 West Washington Avenue, Suite 900 · P.O. Box 1784 · Madison, WI 53701-1784 · 608-256-0226

Milwaukee

Sharon Drew · Law Office of Sharon A. Drew · 6450 West Forest Home Avenue, Suite 202 · Milwaukee, WI 53220-2402 · 414-546-8822

Susan A. Hansen · Hansen & Hildebrand · 126 North Jefferson Street, Suite 401 · Milwaukee, WI 53202 414-273-2422

FIRST AMENDMENT LAW

Madison

Linda M. Clifford · ⑩ · Linda Clifford Law Office · 44 East Mifflin Street, Suite 800 · Madison, WI 53703-2800 · 608-255-1115

Brady C. Williamson · ⑩ · Godfrey & Kahn · One East Main Street, Suite 500 · P.O. Box 2719 · Madison, WI 53701-2719 · 608-257-3911

FRANCHISE LAW

Madison

Brian E. Butler · ⑩ · Stafford Rosenbaum · http://www.staffordlaw.com · 222 West Washington Avenue, Suite 900 · P.O. Box 1784 · Madison, WI 53701-1784 · 608-256-0226

Milwaukee

Jon P. Christiansen · ⑩ · Foley & Lardner · 777 East Wisconsin Avenue, Suite 3800 · Milwaukee, WI 53202-5306 · 414-271-2400

Scott W. Hansen · Reinhart Boerner Van Deuren · http://www.reinhartlaw.com · 1000 North Water Street P.O. Box 2965 · Milwaukee, WI 53201-2965 · 414-298-1000

Brian W. McGrath · Foley & Lardner · 777 East Wisconsin Avenue, Suite 3800 · Milwaukee, WI 53202-5306 · 414-271-2400

Peter J. Stone · Foley & Lardner · 777 East Wisconsin Avenue, Suite 3800 · Milwaukee, WI 53202-5306 414-271-2400

GAMING LAW

Madison

Waltraud A. Arts · Quarles & Brady · http://www.quarles.com · 33 East Main Street, Suite 900 · P.O. Box 2113 · Madison, WI 53701-2113 · 608-251-5000

GOVERNMENT RELATIONS LAW

Madison

Ron W. Kuehn · DeWitt Ross & Stevens · Two East Mifflin Street, Suite 600 · Madison, WI 53703 · 608-255-8891

Jordan K. Lamb · DeWitt Ross & Stevens · Two East Mifflin Street, Suite 600 · Madison, WI 53703 · 608-255-8891

Curt Pawlisch · Cullen, Weston, Pines & Bach · http://www.cwpb.com · 122 West Washington Avenue, Suite 900 · Madison, WI 53703 · 608-251-0101

Michael R. Vaughan · Murphy Desmond · http://www.murphydesmond.com · 33 East Main Street, Suite 500 · P.O. Box 2038 · Madison, WI 53703-2038 · 608-807-0262

HEALTH CARE LAW

Madison

Sarah E. Coyne · Quarles & Brady · http://www.quarles.com · 33 East Main Street, Suite 900 · P.O. Box 2113 · Madison, WI 53701-2113 · 608-251-5000

David J. Hanson · ⑩ · Michael Best & Friedrich · One South Pinckney Street, Suite 700 · P.O. Box 1806 · Madison, WI 53701-1806 · 608-257-3501

Mary H. Michal · Reinhart Boerner Van Deuren · http://www.reinhartlaw.com · 22 East Mifflin Street, Suite 600 · P.O. Box 2018 · Madison, WI 53701-2018 · 608-229-2200

Noreen J. Parrett · Parrett & O'Connell · 10 East Doty Street, Suite 621 · Madison, WI 53703-3376 · 608-251-1542

Michael E. Skindrud · Godfrey & Kahn · One East Main Street, Suite 500 · P.O. Box 2719 · Madison, WI 53701-2719 · 608-257-3911

Michael S. Weiden · ⑩ · Quarles & Brady · http://www.quarles.com · 33 East Main Street, Suite 900 · P.O. Box 2113 · Madison, WI 53701-2113 · 608-251-5000

Milwaukee

Bruce Arnold · Whyte Hirschboeck Dudek · 555 East Wells Street, Suite 1900 · Milwaukee, WI 53202-3819 · 414-273-2100

Michael M. Biehl · ⑩ · Foley & Lardner · 777 East Wisconsin Avenue, Suite 3800 · Milwaukee, WI 53202-5306 · 414-271-2400

Larri J. Broomfield · Reinhart Boerner Van Deuren · http://www.reinhartlaw.com · 1000 North Water Street · P.O. Box 2965 · Milwaukee, WI 53201-2965 · 414-298-1000

James P. Connelly · ⑩ · Foley & Lardner · 777 East Wisconsin Avenue, Suite 3800 · Milwaukee, WI 53202-5306 · 414-271-2400

Lawrence K. Coon · Hall, Render, Killian, Heath & Lyman · 111 East Wisconsin Avenue, Suite 1300 · Milwaukee, WI 53202 · 414-721-0442

Laura J. Gage · Foley & Lardner · 777 East Wisconsin Avenue, Suite 3800 · Milwaukee, WI 53202-5306 · 414-271-2400

Lisa M. Gingerich · von Briesen & Roper · http://www.vonbriesen.com · 411 East Wisconsin Avenue, Suite 700 · P.O. Box 3262 · Milwaukee, WI 53201-3262 · 414-276-1122

Maria E. Gonzalez Knavel · Foley & Lardner · 777 East Wisconsin Avenue, Suite 3800 · Milwaukee, WI 53202-5306 · 414-271-2400

Rachelle R. Hart · Foley & Lardner · 777 East Wisconsin Avenue, Suite 3800 · Milwaukee, WI 53202-5306 · 414-271-2400

Robert J. Heath · Reinhart Boerner Van Deuren · http://www.reinhartlaw.com · 1000 North Water Street P.O. Box 2965 · Milwaukee, WI 53201-2965 · 414-298-1000

Alyce C. Katayama · ⑩ · Quarles & Brady · http://www.quarles.com · 411 East Wisconsin Avenue, Suite 2040 · Milwaukee, WI 53202-4497 · 414-277-5000

Michael A. Levey · Quarles & Brady · http://www.quarles.com · 411 East Wisconsin Avenue, Suite 2040 · Milwaukee, WI 53202-4497 · 414-277-5000

Linda S. Moroney · Drinker Biddle & Reath · 777 East Wisconsin Avenue, Suite 2000 · Milwaukee, WI 53202-5319 · 414-221-6040

Robyn S. Shapiro · ⑩ · Drinker Biddle & Reath · 777 East Wisconsin Avenue, Suite 2000 · Milwaukee, WI 53202-5319 · 414-221-6040

IMMIGRATION LAW

Madison

Glorily A. Lopez · Lopez Law Group · 6417 Odana Road · Madison, WI 53719-1128 · 608-270-5550

Anita M. Sorensen · Foley & Lardner · 150 East Gilman Street · P.O. Box 1497 · Madison, WI 53701-1497 · 608-257-5035

Grant Sovern · Quarles & Brady · http://www.quarles.com · 33 East Main Street, Suite 900 · P.O. Box 2113 · Madison, WI 53701-2113 · 608-251-5000

Milwaukee

Jerome G. Grzeca · Grzeca Law Group · http://www.grzecalaw.com · 1434 West State Street · Milwaukee, WI 53233 · 414-342-3000

Thomas C. Hochstatter · ⑩ · Hochstatter, McCarthy, Rivas & Runde · 5555 North Port Washington Road, Suite 300 · Milwaukee, WI 53217-4928 · 414-962-7440

Benjamin T. Kurten · Quarles & Brady · http://www.quarles.com · 411 East Wisconsin Avenue, Suite 2040 · Milwaukee, WI 53202-4497 · 414-277-5000

Gail K. McCarthy · ⑩ · Hochstatter, McCarthy, Rivas & Runde · 5555 North Port Washington Road, Suite 300 · Milwaukee, WI 53217-4928 · 414-962-7440

José A. Olivieri · Michael Best & Friedrich · 100 East Wisconsin Avenue, Suite 3300 · Milwaukee, WI 53202-4108 · 414-271-6560

Joseph M. Rivas · ⑩ · Hochstatter, McCarthy, Rivas & Runde · 5555 North Port Washington Road, Suite 300 · Milwaukee, WI 53217-4928 · 414-962-7440

Michael C. Runde · Hochstatter, McCarthy, Rivas & Runde · 5555 North Port Washington Road, Suite 300 · Milwaukee, WI 53217-4928 · 414-962-7440

Mary Corbett Stevenson · ⑩ · The Stevenson Group · 333 North Broadway · Milwaukee, WI 53202 · 414-271-5272

Erich C. Straub · Erich C. Straub · 260 East Highland Avenue, Suite 400 · Milwaukee, WI 53202 · 414-224-8472

Dennis M. Sullivan · ⑩ · Sullivan Law Firm · 759 North Milwaukee Street · Milwaukee, WI 53202-3795 414-270-0400

INFORMATION TECHNOLOGY LAW

Brookfield

David V. Meany · DeWitt Ross & Stevens · 13935 Bishop's Drive, Suite 300 · Brookfield, WI 53005-6605 262-754-2840

Milwaukee

Mark F. Foley · ⑩ · Foley & Lardner · 777 East Wisconsin Avenue, Suite 3800 · Milwaukee, WI 53202-5306 · 414-271-2400

INSURANCE LAW

Madison

Timothy W. Burns · Perkins Coie · One East Main Street, Suite 201 · Madison, WI 53703-5118 · 608-663-7460

Michael P. Crooks · Peterson, Johnson & Murray · Three South Pinckney Street, Ninth Floor · Madison, WI 53703 · 608-256-5220

Connie L. O'Connell · Parrett & O'Connell · 10 East Doty Street, Suite 621 · Madison, WI 53703-3376 · 608-251-1542

Noreen J. Parrett · Parrett & O'Connell · 10 East Doty Street, Suite 621 · Madison, WI 53703-3376 · 608-251-1542

Anne E. Ross · Foley & Lardner · 150 East Gilman Street · P.O. Box 1497 · Madison, WI 53701-1497 · 608-257-5035

William J. Toman · Quarles & Brady · http://www.quarles.com · 33 East Main Street, Suite 900 · P.O. Box 2113 · Madison, WI 53701-2113 · 608-251-5000

Ted Waskowski · Stafford Rosenbaum · http://www.staffordlaw.com · 222 West Washington Avenue, Suite 900 · P.O. Box 1784 · Madison, WI 53701-1784 · 608-256-0226

Milwaukee

Kevin G. Fitzgerald · Foley & Lardner · 777 East Wisconsin Avenue, Suite 3800 · Milwaukee, WI 53202-5306 · 414-271-2400

Thomas K. Mullins · Gass Weber Mullins · 309 North Water Street · Milwaukee, WI 53202 · 414-223-3300

Ronald G. Pezze, Jr. · Peterson, Johnson & Murray · 733 North Van Buren Street, Sixth Floor · Milwaukee, WI 53202 · 414-278-8800

INTELLECTUAL PROPERTY LAW

Brookfield

John M. Manion · Ryan Kromholz & Manion · 3360 Gateway Road · P.O. Box 26618 · Brookfield, WI 53226-0618 · 262-783-1300

Daniel D. Ryan · ⑩ · Ryan Kromholz & Manion · 3360 Gateway Road · P.O. Box 26618 · Brookfield, WI 53226-0618 · 262-783-1300

Madison

Bennett J. Berson · Quarles & Brady · http://www.quarles.com · 33 East Main Street, Suite 900 · P.O. Box 2113 · Madison, WI 53701-2113 · 608-251-5000

J. Donald Best · Michael Best & Friedrich · One South Pinckney Street, Suite 700 · P.O. Box 1806 · Madison, WI 53701-1806 · 608-257-3501

David J. Harth · Perkins Coie · One East Main Street, Suite 201 · Madison, WI 53703-5118 · 608-663-7460

Mark A. Kassel · Foley & Lardner · 150 East Gilman Street · P.O. Box 1497 · Madison, WI 53701-1497 · 608-257-5035

Joseph T. Leone · DeWitt Ross & Stevens · 8000 Excelsior Drive, Suite 401 · Madison, WI 53717-1914 · 608-831-2100

Naikang Tsao · Foley & Lardner · 150 East Gilman Street · P.O. Box 1497 · Madison, WI 53701-1497 · 608-257-5035

Teresa J. Welch · Michael Best & Friedrich · One South Pinckney Street, Suite 700 · P.O. Box 1806 · Madison, WI 53701-1806 · 608-257-3501

Milwaukee

Jean C. Baker · Quarles & Brady · http://www.quarles.com · 411 East Wisconsin Avenue, Suite 2040 · Milwaukee, WI 53202-4497 · 414-277-5000

Keith M. Baxter · Boyle Fredrickson · 840 North Plankinton Avenue · Milwaukee, WI 53203 · 414-225-9755

John C. Cooper III · ⑩ · Foley & Lardner · 777 East Wisconsin Avenue, Suite 3800 · Milwaukee, WI 53202-5306 · 414-271-2400

David R. Cross · Quarles & Brady · http://www.quarles.com · 411 East Wisconsin Avenue, Suite 2040 · Milwaukee, WI 53202-4497 · 414-277-5000

Gary A. Essmann · ⑩ · Andrus, Sceales, Starke & Sawall · 100 East Wisconsin Avenue, Suite 1100 · Milwaukee, WI 53202 · 414-271-7590

Daniel D. Fetterley · ⑩ · Andrus, Sceales, Starke & Sawall · 100 East Wisconsin Avenue, Suite 1100 · Milwaukee, WI 53202 · 414-271-7590

Richard S. Florsheim · Foley & Lardner · 777 East Wisconsin Avenue, Suite 3800 · Milwaukee, WI 53202-5306 · 414-271-2400

John D. Franzini · ⑩ · Quarles & Brady · http://www.quarles.com · 411 East Wisconsin Avenue, Suite 2040 · Milwaukee, WI 53202-4497 · 414-277-5000

George Haas · Quarles & Brady · http://www.quarles.com · 411 East Wisconsin Avenue, Suite 2040 · Milwaukee, WI 53202-4497 · 414-277-5000

Michael A. Jaskolski · Quarles & Brady · http://www.quarles.com · 411 East Wisconsin Avenue, Suite 2040 · Milwaukee, WI 53202-4497 · 414-277-5000

James G. Morrow · Foley & Lardner · 777 East Wisconsin Avenue, Suite 3800 · Milwaukee, WI 53202-5306 · 414-271-2400

David R. Price · ⑩ · Michael Best & Friedrich · 100 East Wisconsin Avenue, Suite 3300 · Milwaukee, WI 53202-4108 · 414-271-6560

Barry E. Sammons · ⑩ · Quarles & Brady · http://www.quarles.com · 411 East Wisconsin Avenue, Suite 2040 · Milwaukee, WI 53202-4497 · 414-277-5000

Carl R. Schwartz · ⑩ · Quarles & Brady · http://www.quarles.com · 411 East Wisconsin Avenue, Suite 2040 · Milwaukee, WI 53202-4497 · 414-277-5000

David B. Smith · ⑩ · Michael Best & Friedrich · 100 East Wisconsin Avenue, Suite 3300 · Milwaukee, WI 53202-4108 · 414-271-6560

INTERNATIONAL ARBITRATION

Madison

Kim Grimmer · Solheim, Billing & Grimmer · US Bank Plaza, Suite 301 · One South Pinckney Street · P.O. Box 1644 · Madison, WI 53701-1644 · 608-282-1200

Milwaukee

William H. Levit, Jr. · ⑩ · Godfrey & Kahn · 780 North Water Street · Milwaukee, WI 53202-3590 · 414-273-3500

INTERNATIONAL TRADE AND FINANCE LAW

Brookfield

David V. Meany · DeWitt Ross & Stevens · 13935 Bishop's Drive, Suite 300 · Brookfield, WI 53005-6605 262-754-2840

Milwaukee

Anthony W. Asmuth III · ㉕ · Quarles & Brady · http://www.quarles.com · 411 East Wisconsin Avenue, Suite 2040 · Milwaukee, WI 53202-4497 · 414-277-5000

Ralf-Reinhard Boer · Foley & Lardner · 777 East Wisconsin Avenue, Suite 3800 · Milwaukee, WI 53202-5306 · 414-271-2400

Jerome H. Kringel · ⑩ · Michael Best & Friedrich · 100 East Wisconsin Avenue, Suite 3300 · Milwaukee, WI 53202-4108 · 414-271-6560

LABOR AND EMPLOYMENT LAW

Brookfield

Robert H. Buikema · Davis & Kuelthau · 300 North Corporate Drive, Suite 150 · Brookfield, WI 53045 · 262-792-2400

Eau Claire

Kathryn J. Prenn · ⑩ · Weld, Riley, Prenn & Ricci · 3624 Oakwood Hills Parkway · P.O. Box 1030 · Eau Claire, WI 54702-1030 · 715-839-7786

Stephen L. Weld · ⑩ · Weld, Riley, Prenn & Ricci · 3624 Oakwood Hills Parkway · P.O. Box 1030 · Eau Claire, WI 54702-1030 · 715-839-7786

Madison

Jon E. Anderson · Godfrey & Kahn · One East Main Street, Suite 500 · P.O. Box 2719 · Madison, WI 53701-2719 · 608-257-3911

Charles Barnhill, Jr. · ⑳ · Miner, Barnhill & Galland · 44 East Mifflin Street, Suite 803 · Madison, WI 53703 · 608-255-5200

Thomas R. Crone · Jack D Walker Law Office · 1006 Willow Lane · Madison, WI 53705-1137 · 608-225-0385

Lee Cullen · ⑳ · Cullen, Weston, Pines & Bach · http://www.cwpb.com · 122 West Washington Avenue, Suite 900 · Madison, WI 53703 · 608-251-0101

Bruce M. Davey · ⑳ · Lawton & Cates · 10 East Doty Street · P.O. Box 2965 · Madison, WI 53703 · 608-282-6200

Stephen A. DiTullio · DeWitt Ross & Stevens · Two East Mifflin Street, Suite 600 · Madison, WI 53703 608-255-8891

Fred Gants · Quarles & Brady · http://www.quarles.com · 33 East Main Street, Suite 900 · P.O. Box 2113 · Madison, WI 53701-2113 · 608-251-5000

Robert J. Gingras · ⑳ · Gingras, Cates & Luebke · 8150 Excelsior Drive · Madison, WI 53717 · 608-833-2632

Aaron N. Halstead · Hawks, Quindel, Ehlke & Perry · 222 West Washington Avenue, Suite 705 · P.O. Box 2155 · Madison, WI 53701-2155 · 608-257-0040

JoAnn M. Hart · Stafford Rosenbaum · http://www.staffordlaw.com · 222 West Washington Avenue, Suite 900 · P.O. Box 1784 · Madison, WI 53701-1784 · 608-256-0226

Michael J. Julka · Lathrop & Clark · 740 Regent Street, Suite 400 · P.O. Box 1507 · Madison, WI 53701-1507 · 608-257-7766

Daniel A. Kaplan · Foley & Lardner · 150 East Gilman Street · P.O. Box 1497 · Madison, WI 53701-1497 608-257-5035

William E. McCardell · DeWitt Ross & Stevens · Two East Mifflin Street, Suite 600 · Madison, WI 53703 · 608-255-8891

Jeff Scott Olson · ⑳ · The Jeff Scott Olson Law Firm · 131 West Wilson Street, Suite 1200 · Madison, WI 53703 · 608-283-6001

James K. Pease, Jr. · ⑳ · Jack D Walker Law Office · 1006 Willow Lane · Madison, WI 53705-1137 · 608-225-0385

Lester A. Pines · Cullen, Weston, Pines & Bach · http://www.cwpb.com · 122 West Washington Avenue, Suite 900 · Madison, WI 53703 · 608-251-0101

James K. Ruhly · ⑳ · Jack D Walker Law Office · 1006 Willow Lane · Madison, WI 53705-1137 · 608-225-0385

Lynn M. Stathas · Reinhart Boerner Van Deuren · http://www.reinhartlaw.com · 22 East Mifflin Street, Suite 600 · P.O. Box 2018 · Madison, WI 53701-2018 · 608-229-2200

Jack D. Walker · ⑳ · Jack D Walker Law Office · 1006 Willow Lane · Madison, WI 53705-1137 · 608-225-0385

Milwaukee

Michael Aldana · Quarles & Brady · http://www.quarles.com · 411 East Wisconsin Avenue, Suite 2040 · Milwaukee, WI 53202-4497 · 414-277-5000

Bradden C. Backer · Friebert, Finerty & St. John · Two Plaza East, Suite 1250 · 330 East Kilbourn Avenue · Milwaukee, WI 53202 · 414-271-0130

Scott C. Beightol · Michael Best & Friedrich · 100 East Wisconsin Avenue, Suite 3300 · Milwaukee, WI 53202-4108 · 414-271-6560

Bernard J. Bobber · Foley & Lardner · 777 East Wisconsin Avenue, Suite 3800 · Milwaukee, WI 53202-5306 · 414-271-2400

Clifford B. Buelow · Davis & Kuelthau · 111 East Kilbourne Avenue, Suite 1400 · Milwaukee, WI 53202 414-276-0200

Katherine L. Charlton · Hawks, Quindel, Ehlke & Perry · 700 West Michigan Street, Suite 500 · P.O. Box 442 · Milwaukee, WI 53201-0442 · 414-271-8650

David W. Croysdale · ⑩ · Michael Best & Friedrich · 100 East Wisconsin Avenue, Suite 3300 · Milwaukee, WI 53202-4108 · 414-271-6560

George D. Cunningham · ⑩ · Foley & Lardner · 777 East Wisconsin Avenue, Suite 3800 · Milwaukee, WI 53202-5306 · 414-271-2400

Robert H. Duffy · ⑩ · Quarles & Brady · http://www.quarles.com · 411 East Wisconsin Avenue, Suite 2040 · Milwaukee, WI 53202-4497 · 414-277-5000

Thomas P. Godar · Whyte Hirschboeck Dudek · 555 East Wells Street, Suite 1900 · Milwaukee, WI 53202-3819 · 414-273-2100

George F. Graf · ⑳ · Gillick, Wicht, Gillick & Graf · 6300 West Bluemound Road · Milwaukee, WI 53213 · 414-257-2667

Timothy E. Hawks · ⑳ · Hawks, Quindel, Ehlke & Perry · 700 West Michigan Street, Suite 500 · P.O. Box 442 · Milwaukee, WI 53201-0442 · 414-271-8650

Eric E. Hobbs · Michael Best & Friedrich · 100 East Wisconsin Avenue, Suite 3300 · Milwaukee, WI 53202-4108 · 414-271-6560

Stanley S. Jaspan · ⑩ · Foley & Lardner · 777 East Wisconsin Avenue, Suite 3800 · Milwaukee, WI 53202-5306 · 414-271-2400

Walter F. Kelly · ⑳ · Walter F. Kelly · 700 West Michigan Avenue, Suite 400 · Milwaukee, WI 53233 · 414-271-6989

David B. Kern · ⑩ · Quarles & Brady · http://www.quarles.com · 411 East Wisconsin Avenue, Suite 2040 · Milwaukee, WI 53202-4497 · 414-277-5000

Ely A. Leichtling · ⑩ · Quarles & Brady · http://www.quarles.com · 411 East Wisconsin Avenue, Suite 2040 · Milwaukee, WI 53202-4497 · 414-277-5000

Jonathan O. Levine · Michael Best & Friedrich · 100 East Wisconsin Avenue, Suite 3300 · Milwaukee, WI 53202-4108 · 414-271-6560

Lawrence T. Lynch · Foley & Lardner · 777 East Wisconsin Avenue, Suite 3800 · Milwaukee, WI 53202-5306 · 414-271-2400

Gary A. Marsack · ⑩ · Lindner & Marsack · 411 East Wisconsin Avenue, Suite 1800 · Milwaukee, WI 53202 · 414-273-3910

Gerry M. Miller · ㉕ · Previant, Goldberg, Uelmen, Gratz, Miller & Brueggeman · 1555 North RiverCenter Drive, Suite 202 · P.O. Box 12993 · Milwaukee, WI 53212 · 414-271-4500

Mary Pat Ninneman · Quarles & Brady · http://www.quarles.com · 411 East Wisconsin Avenue, Suite 2040 · Milwaukee, WI 53202-4497 · 414-277-5000

Lynn M. Novotnak · Hawks, Quindel, Ehlke & Perry · 700 West Michigan Street, Suite 500 · P.O. Box 442 · Milwaukee, WI 53201-0442 · 414-271-8650

Thomas E. Obenberger · ⑳ · Michael Best & Friedrich · 100 East Wisconsin Avenue, Suite 3300 · Milwaukee, WI 53202-4108 · 414-271-6560

Thomas C. Pence · Foley & Lardner · 777 East Wisconsin Avenue, Suite 3800 · Milwaukee, WI 53202-5306 · 414-271-2400

Frederick Perillo · ⑩ · Previant, Goldberg, Uelmen, Gratz, Miller & Brueggeman · 1555 North RiverCenter Drive, Suite 202 · P.O. Box 12993 · Milwaukee, WI 53212 · 414-271-4500

Barbara Zack Quindel · ⑳ · Hawks, Quindel, Ehlke & Perry · 700 West Michigan Street, Suite 500 · P.O. Box 442 · Milwaukee, WI 53201-0442 · 414-271-8650

Matthew R. Robbins · ⑩ · Previant, Goldberg, Uelmen, Gratz, Miller & Brueggeman · 1555 North RiverCenter Drive, Suite 202 · P.O. Box 12993 · Milwaukee, WI 53212 · 414-271-4500

Gary M. Ruesch · Quarles & Brady · http://www.quarles.com · 411 East Wisconsin Avenue, Suite 2040 · Milwaukee, WI 53202-4497 · 414-277-5000

John R. Sapp · 20 · Michael Best & Friedrich · 100 East Wisconsin Avenue, Suite 3300 · Milwaukee, WI 53202-4108 · 414-271-6560

Thomas W. Scrivner · 20 · Michael Best & Friedrich · 100 East Wisconsin Avenue, Suite 3300 · Milwaukee, WI 53202-4108 · 414-271-6560

Daniel L. Shneidman · 20 · Hawks, Quindel, Ehlke & Perry · 700 West Michigan Street, Suite 500 · P.O. Box 442 · Milwaukee, WI 53201-0442 · 414-271-8650

Robert K. Sholl · Reinhart Boerner Van Deuren · http://www.reinhartlaw.com · 1000 North Water Street · P.O. Box 2965 · Milwaukee, WI 53201-2965 · 414-298-1000

Scott D. Soldon · 10 · Previant, Goldberg, Uelmen, Gratz, Miller & Brueggeman · 1555 North RiverCenter Drive, Suite 202 · P.O. Box 12993 · Milwaukee, WI 53212 · 414-271-4500

Jeffrey P. Sweetland · Hawks, Quindel, Ehlke & Perry · 700 West Michigan Street, Suite 500 · P.O. Box 442 · Milwaukee, WI 53201-0442 · 414-271-8650

Mark F. Vetter · 10 · Davis & Kuelthau · 111 East Kilbourne Avenue, Suite 1400 · Milwaukee, WI 53202 414-276-0200

Daniel G. Vliet · Davis & Kuelthau · 111 East Kilbourne Avenue, Suite 1400 · Milwaukee, WI 53202 · 414-276-0200

Monona

Michael R. Fox · 20 · Fox & Fox · Fox Building · 124 West Broadway · Monona, WI 53716 · 608-258-9588

Mary E. Kennelly · Fox & Fox · Fox Building · 124 West Broadway · Monona, WI 53716 · 608-258-9588

Oshkosh

James R. Macy · Davis & Kuelthau · 219 Washington Avenue · P.O. Box 1278 · Oshkosh, WI 54903 · 920-233-6050

Edward J. Williams · Davis & Kuelthau · 219 Washington Avenue · P.O. Box 1278 · Oshkosh, WI 54903 · 920-233-6050

Wausau

Dean R. Dietrich · Ruder Ware · 500 Third Street, Suite 8000 · P.O. Box 8050 · Wausau, WI 54402-8050 · 715-845-4336

Ronald J. Rutlin · 10 · Ruder Ware · 500 Third Street, Suite 8000 · P.O. Box 8050 · Wausau, WI 54402-8050 · 715-845-4336

LAND USE & ZONING LAW

Cedarburg

Donald A. Levy · 25 · Levy & Levy · http://levyandlevy.com · N61 W6058 Columbia Road · P.O. Box 127 Cedarburg, WI 53012-0127 · 262-377-5555

Elkhorn

Lowell E. Sweet · ㉕ · Sweet & Maier · Inns Of Court Building · 114 North Church Street · P.O. Box 318 · Elkhorn, WI 53121-0318 · 262-723-5480

Madison

Constance L. Anderson · Anderson & Kent · One North Pinckney Street, Suite 200 · Madison, WI 53703-5809 · 608-246-8500

Matthew P. Dregne · Stafford Rosenbaum · http://www.staffordlaw.com · 222 West Washington Avenue, Suite 900 · P.O. Box 1784 · Madison, WI 53701-1784 · 608-256-0226

Paul G. Kent · ⑩ · Anderson & Kent · One North Pinckney Street, Suite 200 · Madison, WI 53703-5809 · 608-246-8500

Richard A. Lehmann · Boardman Law Firm · http://www.boardmanlawfirm.com · One South Pinckney Street, Fourth Floor · P.O. Box 927 · Madison, WI 53701-0927 · 608-257-9521

Mark R. Sewell · DeWitt Ross & Stevens · Two East Mifflin Street, Suite 600 · Madison, WI 53703 · 608-255-8891

Timm P. Speerschneider · DeWitt Ross & Stevens · Two East Mifflin Street, Suite 600 · Madison, WI 53703 · 608-255-8891

William F. White · ⑩ · Michael Best & Friedrich · One South Pinckney Street, Suite 700 · P.O. Box 1806 Madison, WI 53701-1806 · 608-257-3501

Richard C. Yde · Stafford Rosenbaum · http://www.staffordlaw.com · 222 West Washington Avenue, Suite 900 · P.O. Box 1784 · Madison, WI 53701-1784 · 608-256-0226

Milwaukee

Bruce T. Block · ⑩ · Reinhart Boerner Van Deuren · http://www.reinhartlaw.com · 1000 North Water Street · P.O. Box 2965 · Milwaukee, WI 53201-2965 · 414-298-1000

John D. Finerty, Sr. · Friebert, Finerty & St. John · Two Plaza East, Suite 1250 · 330 East Kilbourn Avenue · Milwaukee, WI 53202 · 414-271-0130

Alan H. Marcuvitz · Michael Best & Friedrich · 100 East Wisconsin Avenue, Suite 3300 · Milwaukee, WI 53202-4108 · 414-271-6560

Susan M. Sager · Michael Best & Friedrich · 100 East Wisconsin Avenue, Suite 3300 · Milwaukee, WI 53202-4108 · 414-271-6560

LEGAL MALPRACTICE LAW

Madison

Claude J. Covelli · ⑩ · Boardman Law Firm · http://www.boardmanlawfirm.com · One South Pinckney Street, Fourth Floor · P.O. Box 927 · Madison, WI 53701-0927 · 608-257-9521

LEVERAGED BUYOUTS AND PRIVATE EQUITY LAW

Milwaukee

William J. Abraham, Jr. · ⑳ · Foley & Lardner · 777 East Wisconsin Avenue, Suite 3800 · Milwaukee, WI 53202-5306 · 414-271-2400

Kathryn M. Buono · Quarles & Brady · http://www.quarles.com · 411 East Wisconsin Avenue, Suite 2040 Milwaukee, WI 53202-4497 · 414-277-5000

John A. Dickens · Godfrey & Kahn · 780 North Water Street · Milwaukee, WI 53202-3590 · 414-273-3500

Benjamin F. Garmer III · ⑳ · Foley & Lardner · 777 East Wisconsin Avenue, Suite 3800 · Milwaukee, WI 53202-5306 · 414-271-2400

Patrick J. Goebel · Quarles & Brady · http://www.quarles.com · 411 East Wisconsin Avenue, Suite 2040 · Milwaukee, WI 53202-4497 · 414-277-5000

Michael H. Lappin · Quarles & Brady · http://www.quarles.com · 411 East Wisconsin Avenue, Suite 2040 Milwaukee, WI 53202-4497 · 414-277-5000

Luke E. Sims · Foley & Lardner · 777 East Wisconsin Avenue, Suite 3800 · Milwaukee, WI 53202-5306 · 414-271-2400

Peter M. Sommerhauser · ⑩ · Godfrey & Kahn · 780 North Water Street · Milwaukee, WI 53202-3590 · 414-273-3500

MASS TORT LITIGATION

Milwaukee

David B. Bartel · Quarles & Brady · http://www.quarles.com · 411 East Wisconsin Avenue, Suite 2040 · Milwaukee, WI 53202-4497 · 414-277-5000

Frank J. Daily · ⑩ · Quarles & Brady · http://www.quarles.com · 411 East Wisconsin Avenue, Suite 2040 · Milwaukee, WI 53202-4497 · 414-277-5000

Francis H. LoCoco · Whyte Hirschboeck Dudek · 555 East Wells Street, Suite 1900 · Milwaukee, WI 53202-3819 · 414-273-2100

Trevor J. Will · Foley & Lardner · 777 East Wisconsin Avenue, Suite 3800 · Milwaukee, WI 53202-5306 · 414-271-2400

MEDICAL MALPRACTICE LAW

Madison

John L. Cates · Gingras, Cates & Luebke · 8150 Excelsior Drive · Madison, WI 53717 · 608-833-2632

Barrett J. Corneille · Corneille Law Group · 7618 Westward Way, Suite 100 · Madison, WI 53717 · 608-662-1180

Eric A. Farnsworth · DeWitt Ross & Stevens · Two East Mifflin Street, Suite 600 · Madison, WI 53703 · 608-255-8891

Stephen O. Murray · Otjen, Van Ert & Weir · University Research Park, Suite 110 · 450 Science Drive · Madison, WI 53711-1169 · 608-238-9500

Daniel A. Rottier · ⑩ · Habush Habush & Rottier · http://www.habush.com · 150 East Gilman Street, Suite 2000 · Madison, WI 53703 · 608-255-6663

Curtis S. Swanson · Corneille Law Group · 7618 Westward Way, Suite 100 · Madison, WI 53717 · 608-662-1180

Manitowoc

Paul H. Grimstad · ⑩ · Nash, Spindler, Grimstad & McCracken · 201 East Waldo Boulevard · Manitowoc, WI 54220-2908 · 920-684-3321

William R. Wick · Nash, Spindler, Grimstad & McCracken · 201 East Waldo Boulevard · Manitowoc, WI 54220-2908 · 920-684-3321

Milwaukee

Timothy J. Aiken · ⑩ · Aiken & Scoptur · 2600 North Mayfair Road, Suite 1030 · Milwaukee, WI 53202 · 414-225-0260

James M. Fergal · ⑩ · Habush Habush & Rottier · http://www.habush.com · U.S. Bank Center, Suite 2300 · 777 East Wisconsin Avenue · Milwaukee, WI 53202-5381 · 414-271-0900

Lori Gendelman · Otjen, Van Ert & Weir · First Financial Centre, Suite 800 · 700 North Water Street · Milwaukee, WI 53202-4206 · 414-271-7271

James R. Gutglass · Gutglass, Erickson, Bonville & Larson · 735 North Water Street, Suite 1400 · Milwaukee, WI 53202-4267 · 414-273-1144

Robert L. Habush · ㉕ · Habush Habush & Rottier · http://www.habush.com · U.S. Bank Center, Suite 2300 · 777 East Wisconsin Avenue · Milwaukee, WI 53202-5381 · 414-271-0900

Michael P. Malone · Hinshaw & Culbertson · http://www.hinshawlaw.com · 100 East Wisconsin Avenue, Suite 2600 · Milwaukee, WI 53202-4115 · 414-276-6464

Donald R. Peterson · ㉕ · Peterson, Johnson & Murray · 733 North Van Buren Street, Sixth Floor · Milwaukee, WI 53202 · 414-278-8800

Mary Lee Ratzel · Peterson, Johnson & Murray · 733 North Van Buren Street, Sixth Floor · Milwaukee, WI 53202 · 414-278-8800

Todd M. Weir · Otjen, Van Ert & Weir · First Financial Centre, Suite 800 · 700 North Water Street · Milwaukee, WI 53202-4206 · 414-271-7271

Rhinelander

D. James Weis · ⑩ · Habush Habush & Rottier · http://www.habush.com · 126 East Davenport Street · Rhinelander, WI 54501 · 715-365-1900

MERGERS & ACQUISITIONS LAW

Madison

Blaine R. Renfert · Foley & Lardner · 150 East Gilman Street · P.O. Box 1497 · Madison, WI 53701-1497 608-257-5035

Michael E. Skindrud · Godfrey & Kahn · One East Main Street, Suite 500 · P.O. Box 2719 · Madison, WI 53701-2719 · 608-257-3911

Milwaukee

William J. Abraham, Jr. · ⑳ · Foley & Lardner · 777 East Wisconsin Avenue, Suite 3800 · Milwaukee, WI 53202-5306 · 414-271-2400

Steve R. Barth · Foley & Lardner · 777 East Wisconsin Avenue, Suite 3800 · Milwaukee, WI 53202-5306 414-271-2400

James M. Bedore · Reinhart Boerner Van Deuren · http://www.reinhartlaw.com · 1000 North Water Street · P.O. Box 2965 · Milwaukee, WI 53201-2965 · 414-298-1000

Ralf-Reinhard Boer · Foley & Lardner · 777 East Wisconsin Avenue, Suite 3800 · Milwaukee, WI 53202-5306 · 414-271-2400

Kathryn M. Buono · Quarles & Brady · http://www.quarles.com · 411 East Wisconsin Avenue, Suite 2040 Milwaukee, WI 53202-4497 · 414-277-5000

John A. Dickens · Godfrey & Kahn · 780 North Water Street · Milwaukee, WI 53202-3590 · 414-273-3500

Benjamin F. Garmer III · ⑳ · Foley & Lardner · 777 East Wisconsin Avenue, Suite 3800 · Milwaukee, WI 53202-5306 · 414-271-2400

Patrick J. Goebel · Quarles & Brady · http://www.quarles.com · 411 East Wisconsin Avenue, Suite 2040 · Milwaukee, WI 53202-4497 · 414-277-5000

W. Charles Jackson · Michael Best & Friedrich · 100 East Wisconsin Avenue, Suite 3300 · Milwaukee, WI 53202-4108 · 414-271-6560

Fredrick G. Lautz · Quarles & Brady · http://www.quarles.com · 411 East Wisconsin Avenue, Suite 2040 · Milwaukee, WI 53202-4497 · 414-277-5000

K. Thor Lundgren · Michael Best & Friedrich · 100 East Wisconsin Avenue, Suite 3300 · Milwaukee, WI 53202-4108 · 414-271-6560

Christopher B. Noyes · Godfrey & Kahn · 780 North Water Street · Milwaukee, WI 53202-3590 · 414-273-3500

Patrick G. Quick · Foley & Lardner · 777 East Wisconsin Avenue, Suite 3800 · Milwaukee, WI 53202-5306 · 414-271-2400

Thomas A. Simonis · Quarles & Brady · http://www.quarles.com · 411 East Wisconsin Avenue, Suite 2040 Milwaukee, WI 53202-4497 · 414-277-5000

Luke E. Sims · Foley & Lardner · 777 East Wisconsin Avenue, Suite 3800 · Milwaukee, WI 53202-5306 · 414-271-2400

Peter M. Sommerhauser · ⑩ · Godfrey & Kahn · 780 North Water Street · Milwaukee, WI 53202-3590 · 414-273-3500

MUNICIPAL LAW

Madison

Lawrence E. Bechler · Murphy Desmond · http://www.murphydesmond.com · 33 East Main Street, Suite 500 · P.O. Box 2038 · Madison, WI 53703-2038 · 608-807-0262

Matthew P. Dregne · Stafford Rosenbaum · http://www.staffordlaw.com · 222 West Washington Avenue, Suite 900 · P.O. Box 1784 · Madison, WI 53701-1784 · 608-256-0226

Christopher B. Hughes · Stafford Rosenbaum · http://www.staffordlaw.com · 222 West Washington Avenue, Suite 900 · P.O. Box 1784 · Madison, WI 53701-1784 · 608-256-0226

Richard K. Nordeng · Stafford Rosenbaum · http://www.staffordlaw.com · 222 West Washington Avenue, Suite 900 · P.O. Box 1784 · Madison, WI 53701-1784 · 608-256-0226

Jane Zimmerman · Murphy Desmond · http://www.murphydesmond.com · 33 East Main Street, Suite 500 · P.O. Box 2038 · Madison, WI 53703-2038 · 608-807-0262

Milwaukee

Raymond J. Pollen · Crivello, Carlson & Mentkowski · The Empire Building, Suite 500 · 710 North Plankinton Avenue · Milwaukee, WI 53203 · 414-271-7722

Daniel G. Vliet · Davis & Kuelthau · 111 East Kilbourne Avenue, Suite 1400 · Milwaukee, WI 53202 · 414-276-0200

Waukesha

John P. Macy · Arenz Molter Macy & Riffle · 720 North East Avenue · P.O. Box 1348 · Waukesha, WI 53187-1348 · 262-548-1340

MUTUAL FUNDS LAW

Milwaukee

Carol A. Gehl · Godfrey & Kahn · 780 North Water Street · Milwaukee, WI 53202-3590 · 414-273-3500

Helge K. Lee · Godfrey & Kahn · 780 North Water Street · Milwaukee, WI 53202-3590 · 414-273-3500

NON-PROFIT/CHARITIES LAW

Milwaukee

Richard S. Gallagher · 25 · Foley & Lardner · 777 East Wisconsin Avenue, Suite 3800 · Milwaukee, WI 53202-5306 · 414-271-2400

David L. Kinnamon · 20 · Quarles & Brady · http://www.quarles.com · 411 East Wisconsin Avenue, Suite 2040 · Milwaukee, WI 53202-4497 · 414-277-5000

Andrew R. Lauritzen · Godfrey & Kahn · 780 North Water Street · Milwaukee, WI 53202-3590 · 414-273-3500

Michael A. Levey · Quarles & Brady · http://www.quarles.com · 411 East Wisconsin Avenue, Suite 2040 · Milwaukee, WI 53202-4497 · 414-277-5000

Lynette M. Zigman · Foley & Lardner · 777 East Wisconsin Avenue, Suite 3800 · Milwaukee, WI 53202-5306 · 414-271-2400

NON-WHITE-COLLAR CRIMINAL DEFENSE

Madison

Charles W. Giesen · ⑳ · Giesen Law Offices · 14 South Broom Street · P.O. Box 909 · Madison, WI 53701 · 608-255-8200

Stephen P. Hurley · ⑩ · Hurley, Burish & Stanton · 33 East Main Street, Suite 400 · Madison, WI 53703 608-257-0945

Stephen J. Meyer · ⑩ · Meyer Law Office · 10 East Doty Street, Suite 507 · Madison, WI 53703-3397 · 608-255-0911

Lester A. Pines · Cullen, Weston, Pines & Bach · http://www.cwpb.com · 122 West Washington Avenue, Suite 900 · Madison, WI 53703 · 608-251-0101

Bruce J. Rosen · ⑳ · Pellino, Rosen, Mowris & Kirkhuff · James Wilson Plaza, Suite 1201 · 131 West Wilson Street · Madison, WI 53703 · 608-255-4501

Dean A. Strang · Hurley, Burish & Stanton · 33 East Main Street, Suite 400 · Madison, WI 53703 · 608-257-0945

Milwaukee

Craig W. Albee · Glynn, Fitzgerald & Albee · 526 East Wisconsin Avenue · Milwaukee, WI 53202-4503 · 414-221-9600

Dennis P. Coffey · ㉕ · Mawicke & Goisman · 1509 North Prospect Avenue · Milwaukee, WI 53202 · 414-224-0600

Rodney L. Cubbie · Law Offices of Rodney Cubbie · 3333 North Mayfair Road, Suite 312 · Milwaukee, WI 53222 · 414-291-9741

Michael J. Fitzgerald · Glynn, Fitzgerald & Albee · 526 East Wisconsin Avenue · Milwaukee, WI 53202-4503 · 414-221-9600

Stephen M. Glynn · ㉕ · Glynn, Fitzgerald & Albee · 526 East Wisconsin Avenue · Milwaukee, WI 53202-4503 · 414-221-9600

James M. Shellow · ㉕ · Shellow & Shellow · 324 West Vine Street · Milwaukee, WI 53212-3606 · 414-271-8535

Michael J. Steinle · Terschan, Steinle & Ness · 309 North Water Street, Suite 215 · Milwaukee, WI 53202 · 414-258-1010

PERSONAL INJURY LITIGATION

Brookfield

William M. Cannon · ⑩ · Cannon & Dunphy · 595 North Barker Road · P.O. Box 1750 · Brookfield, WI 53008-1750 · 262-782-2700

Patrick O. Dunphy · ⑩ · Cannon & Dunphy · 595 North Barker Road · P.O. Box 1750 · Brookfield, WI 53008-1750 · 262-782-2700

Mark L. Thomsen · Cannon & Dunphy · 595 North Barker Road · P.O. Box 1750 · Brookfield, WI 53008-1750 · 262-782-2700

Dousman

Robert A. Slattery · ⑩ · Slattery & Duffey · N3075 Hardscrabble Road · Dousman, WI 53118 · 262-495-2098

Eau Claire

Webster A. Hart · ⑩ · Herrick & Hart · 116 West Grand Avenue · P.O. Box 167 · Eau Claire, WI 54702 · 715-832-3491

J. Drew Ryberg · ⑩ · Ryberg & Happe · 200 Riverfront Terrace, Suite 100 · Eau Claire, WI 54702-1999 · 715-833-9699

La Crosse

James G. Curtis · Hale, Skemp, Hanson, Skemp & Sleik · 505 King Street, Suite 300 · P.O. Box 1927 · La Crosse, WI 54602-1927 · 608-784-3540

Madison

Bradley D. Armstrong · ⑩ · Axley Brynelson · http://www.axley.com · Two East Mifflin Street, Suite 200 P.O. Box 1767 · Madison, WI 53701-1767 · 608-257-5661

Kent I. Carnell · Lawton & Cates · 10 East Doty Street · P.O. Box 2965 · Madison, WI 53703 · 608-282-6200

Claude J. Covelli · ⑩ · Boardman Law Firm · http://www.boardmanlawfirm.com · One South Pinckney Street, Fourth Floor · P.O. Box 927 · Madison, WI 53701-0927 · 608-257-9521

Michael P. Crooks · Peterson, Johnson & Murray · Three South Pinckney Street, Ninth Floor · Madison, WI 53703 · 608-256-5220

Michael R. Davis · DeWitt Ross & Stevens · Two East Mifflin Street, Suite 600 · Madison, WI 53703 · 608-255-8891

Eric A. Farnsworth · DeWitt Ross & Stevens · Two East Mifflin Street, Suite 600 · Madison, WI 53703 · 608-255-8891

Henry A. Field, Jr. · ⑳ · Boardman Law Firm · http://www.boardmanlawfirm.com · One South Pinckney Street, Fourth Floor · P.O. Box 927 · Madison, WI 53701-0927 · 608-257-9521

James W. Gardner · Lawton & Cates · 10 East Doty Street · P.O. Box 2965 · Madison, WI 53703 · 608-282-6200

Bruce D. Huibregtse · Stafford Rosenbaum · http://www.staffordlaw.com · 222 West Washington Avenue, Suite 900 · P.O. Box 1784 · Madison, WI 53701-1784 · 608-256-0226

James R. Jansen · ⑩ · Habush Habush & Rottier · http://www.habush.com · 150 East Gilman Street, Suite 2000 · Madison, WI 53703 · 608-255-6663

Bradway Liddle, Jr. · ⑩ · Boardman Law Firm · http://www.boardmanlawfirm.com · One South Pinckney Street, Fourth Floor · P.O. Box 927 · Madison, WI 53701-0927 · 608-257-9521

David E. McFarlane · Bell, Gierhart & Moore · 44 East Mifflin Street, 10th Floor · P.O. Box 1807 · Madison, WI 53701-1807 · 608-257-3764

John M. Moore · ⑳ · Bell, Gierhart & Moore · 44 East Mifflin Street, 10th Floor · P.O. Box 1807 · Madison, WI 53701-1807 · 608-257-3764

James A. Olson · Lawton & Cates · 10 East Doty Street · P.O. Box 2965 · Madison, WI 53703 · 608-282-6200

Ward I. Richter · ⑩ · Bell, Gierhart & Moore · 44 East Mifflin Street, 10th Floor · P.O. Box 1807 · Madison, WI 53701-1807 · 608-257-3764

Michael Riley · Axley Brynelson · http://www.axley.com · Two East Mifflin Street, Suite 200 · P.O. Box 1767 · Madison, WI 53701-1767 · 608-257-5661

Catherine M. Rottier · Boardman Law Firm · http://www.boardmanlawfirm.com · One South Pinckney Street, Fourth Floor · P.O. Box 927 · Madison, WI 53701-0927 · 608-257-9521

Daniel A. Rottier · ⑩ · Habush Habush & Rottier · http://www.habush.com · 150 East Gilman Street, Suite 2000 · Madison, WI 53703 · 608-255-6663

Bruce A. Schultz · Coyne, Schultz, Becker & Bauer · 150 East Gilman Street, Suite 1000 · Madison, WI 53703 · 608-255-1388

Marie A. Stanton · Hurley, Burish & Stanton · 33 East Main Street, Suite 400 · Madison, WI 53703 · 608-257-0945

Susan Ross Steingass · ⑩ · Habush Habush & Rottier · http://www.habush.com · 150 East Gilman Street, Suite 2000 · Madison, WI 53703 · 608-255-6663

John Walsh · ⑩ · Axley Brynelson · http://www.axley.com · Two East Mifflin Street, Suite 200 · P.O. Box 1767 · Madison, WI 53701-1767 · 608-257-5661

Manitowoc

Paul H. Grimstad · ⑩ · Nash, Spindler, Grimstad & McCracken · 201 East Waldo Boulevard · Manitowoc, WI 54220-2908 · 920-684-3321

Robert L. McCracken · Nash, Spindler, Grimstad & McCracken · 201 East Waldo Boulevard · Manitowoc, WI 54220-2908 · 920-684-3321

Mequon

John C. Cabaniss · Cabaniss Law · 10200 North Washington Road · Mequon, WI 53092 · 262-240-0635

Middleton

Alexander S. Kammer · Atterbury & Kammer · 8500 Greenway Boulevard, Suite 103 · P.O. Box 620437 · Middleton, WI 53562 · 608-821-4600

Milwaukee

Timothy J. Aiken · ⑩ · Aiken & Scoptur · 2600 North Mayfair Road, Suite 1030 · Milwaukee, WI 53202 · 414-225-0260

David B. Bartel · Quarles & Brady · http://www.quarles.com · 411 East Wisconsin Avenue, Suite 2040 · Milwaukee, WI 53202-4497 · 414-277-5000

Gerald J. Bloch · ⑳ · Warshafsky, Rotter, Tarnoff, Reinhardt & Bloch · 839 North Jefferson Street, Suite 300 · Milwaukee, WI 53202 · 414-276-4970

Larry Brueggeman · Previant, Goldberg, Uelmen, Gratz, Miller & Brueggeman · 1555 North RiverCenter Drive, Suite 202 · P.O. Box 12993 · Milwaukee, WI 53212 · 414-271-4500

Frank J. Daily · ⑩ · Quarles & Brady · http://www.quarles.com · 411 East Wisconsin Avenue, Suite 2040 · Milwaukee, WI 53202-4497 · 414-277-5000

Merrick R. Domnitz · ⑩ · Domnitz & Skemp · 825 North Jefferson Street, Fifth Floor · Milwaukee, WI 53202 · 414-289-0909

Robert L. Elliott · Robert L. Elliott Attorney at Law · 633 West Wisconsin Avenue, Suite 1001 · Milwaukee, WI 53203-1918 · 414-225-9000

James M. Fergal · ⑩ · Habush Habush & Rottier · http://www.habush.com · U.S. Bank Center, Suite 2300 · 777 East Wisconsin Avenue · Milwaukee, WI 53202-5381 · 414-271-0900

J. Ric Gass · ⑩ · Gass Weber Mullins · 309 North Water Street · Milwaukee, WI 53202 · 414-223-3300

Michael J. Gonring · Quarles & Brady · http://www.quarles.com · 411 East Wisconsin Avenue, Suite 2040 Milwaukee, WI 53202-4497 · 414-277-5000

D. Michael Guerin · Gimbel, Reilly, Guerin & Brown · Two Plaza East, Suite 1170 · 330 East Kilbourn Avenue · Milwaukee, WI 53202 · 414-271-1440

Robert L. Habush · ㉕ · Habush Habush & Rottier · http://www.habush.com · U.S. Bank Center, Suite 2300 · 777 East Wisconsin Avenue · Milwaukee, WI 53202-5381 · 414-271-0900

Robert L. Jaskulski · Habush Habush & Rottier · http://www.habush.com · U.S. Bank Center, Suite 2300 777 East Wisconsin Avenue · Milwaukee, WI 53202-5381 · 414-271-0900

Terry E. Johnson · ⑩ · Peterson, Johnson & Murray · 733 North Van Buren Street, Sixth Floor · Milwaukee, WI 53202 · 414-278-8800

Mark A. Kircher · Quarles & Brady · http://www.quarles.com · 411 East Wisconsin Avenue, Suite 2040 · Milwaukee, WI 53202-4497 · 414-277-5000

Lynn R. Laufenberg · ⑩ · Laufenberg & Hoefle · 115 South 84th Street, Suite 330 · Milwaukee, WI 53214 · 414-778-0700

Francis H. LoCoco · Whyte Hirschboeck Dudek · 555 East Wells Street, Suite 1900 · Milwaukee, WI 53202-3819 · 414-273-2100

James T. Murray, Jr. · ㉕ · Peterson, Johnson & Murray · 733 North Van Buren Street, Sixth Floor · Milwaukee, WI 53202 · 414-278-8800

Donald R. Peterson · ㉕ · Peterson, Johnson & Murray · 733 North Van Buren Street, Sixth Floor · Milwaukee, WI 53202 · 414-278-8800

Don C. Prachthauser · ⑩ · Murphy & Prachthauser · One Plaza East Building, Suite 1200 · 330 East Kilbourn Avenue · Milwaukee, WI 53202 · 414-271-1011

Paul J. Scoptur · Aiken & Scoptur · 2600 North Mayfair Road, Suite 1030 · Milwaukee, WI 53202 · 414-225-0260

Michael I. Tarnoff · ⑩ · Warshafsky, Rotter, Tarnoff, Reinhardt & Bloch · 839 North Jefferson Street, Suite 300 · Milwaukee, WI 53202 · 414-276-4970

Jay Urban · Urban & Taylor · http://www.wisconsininjury.com · The Urban Taylor Law Building · 4701 North Port Washington Road · Milwaukee, WI 53212 · 414-906-1700

Eric J. Van Vugt · Quarles & Brady · http://www.quarles.com · 411 East Wisconsin Avenue, Suite 2040 · Milwaukee, WI 53202-4497 · 414-277-5000

Ted M. Warshafsky · ㉕ · Warshafsky, Rotter, Tarnoff, Reinhardt & Bloch · 839 North Jefferson Street, Suite 300 · Milwaukee, WI 53202 · 414-276-4970

Todd M. Weir · Otjen, Van Ert & Weir · First Financial Centre, Suite 800 · 700 North Water Street · Milwaukee, WI 53202-4206 · 414-271-7271

Mark S. Young · Habush Habush & Rottier · http://www.habush.com · U.S. Bank Center, Suite 2300 · 777 East Wisconsin Avenue · Milwaukee, WI 53202-5381 · 414-271-0900

New Richmond

James A. Drill · ⑩ · Doar Drill · 103 North Knowles Avenue · New Richmond, WI 54017 · 715-246-2211

Rhinelander

Michael L. Eckert · ⑩ · Eckert Kost & Vocke · 729 Lincoln Street · P.O. Box 1247 · Rhinelander, WI 54501 · 715-369-1624

James A. Johnson · ⑩ · Johnson & Houlihan · 28 North Stevens Street · Rhinelander, WI 54501-3156 · 715-365-5060

D. James Weis · ⑩ · Habush Habush & Rottier · http://www.habush.com · 126 East Davenport Street · Rhinelander, WI 54501 · 715-365-1900

Rice Lake

Joseph Thrasher · ⑩ · Thrasher, Doyle, Pelish & Franti · 13 East Eau Claire Street · P.O. Box 31 · Rice Lake, WI 54868-1747 · 715-234-8106

River Falls

Ardell W. Skow · ⑩ · Bye, Goff, Rohde & Skow · 258 Riverside Drive · P.O. Box 167 · River Falls, WI 54022 · 715-425-8161

Waukesha

Charles F. Stierman · ⑩ · Stierman, Steffens & Kuphall · N14 W23777 Stone Ridge Drive, Suite 280 · Waukesha, WI 53188-1158 · 262-523-8484

Wausau

Terrance E. Davczyk · ⑩ · Davczyk & Varline · 2100 Stewart Avenue, Suite 230 · P.O. Box 1192 · Wausau, WI 54402-1192 · 715-848-9250

Douglas J. Klingberg · ⑩ · Ruder Ware · 500 Third Street, Suite 8000 · P.O. Box 8050 · Wausau, WI 54402-8050 · 715-845-4336

Richard J. Weber · Pietz, Vander Waal, Stacker & Rottier · 530 Jackson Street · Wausau, WI 54403-5589 715-845-9211

PRODUCT LIABILITY LITIGATION

Madison

Claude J. Covelli · ⑩ · Boardman Law Firm · http://www.boardmanlawfirm.com · One South Pinckney Street, Fourth Floor · P.O. Box 927 · Madison, WI 53701-0927 · 608-257-9521

Henry A. Field, Jr. · ⑳ · Boardman Law Firm · http://www.boardmanlawfirm.com · One South Pinckney Street, Fourth Floor · P.O. Box 927 · Madison, WI 53701-0927 · 608-257-9521

John M. Moore · ⑳ · Bell, Gierhart & Moore · 44 East Mifflin Street, 10th Floor · P.O. Box 1807 · Madison, WI 53701-1807 · 608-257-3764

Ted Waskowski · Stafford Rosenbaum · http://www.staffordlaw.com · 222 West Washington Avenue, Suite 900 · P.O. Box 1784 · Madison, WI 53701-1784 · 608-256-0226

Michael L. Zaleski · Quarles & Brady · http://www.quarles.com · 33 East Main Street, Suite 900 · P.O. Box 2113 · Madison, WI 53701-2113 · 608-251-5000

Milwaukee

David B. Bartel · Quarles & Brady · http://www.quarles.com · 411 East Wisconsin Avenue, Suite 2040 · Milwaukee, WI 53202-4497 · 414-277-5000

Paul E. Benson · Michael Best & Friedrich · 100 East Wisconsin Avenue, Suite 3300 · Milwaukee, WI 53202-4108 · 414-271-6560

Frank J. Daily · ⑩ · Quarles & Brady · http://www.quarles.com · 411 East Wisconsin Avenue, Suite 2040 · Milwaukee, WI 53202-4497 · 414-277-5000

Michael J. Gonring · Quarles & Brady · http://www.quarles.com · 411 East Wisconsin Avenue, Suite 2040 Milwaukee, WI 53202-4497 · 414-277-5000

Robert L. Habush · ㉕ · Habush Habush & Rottier · http://www.habush.com · U.S. Bank Center, Suite 2300 · 777 East Wisconsin Avenue · Milwaukee, WI 53202-5381 · 414-271-0900

Dean Laing · O'Neil, Cannon, Hollman, Dejong · 111 East Wisconsin Avenue, Suite 1400 · Milwaukee, WI 53202 · 414-276-5000

Lynn R. Laufenberg · ⑩ · Laufenberg & Hoefle · 115 South 84th Street, Suite 330 · Milwaukee, WI 53214 · 414-778-0700

Donald R. Peterson · ㉕ · Peterson, Johnson & Murray · 733 North Van Buren Street, Sixth Floor · Milwaukee, WI 53202 · 414-278-8800

Patrick W. Schmidt · Quarles & Brady · http://www.quarles.com · 411 East Wisconsin Avenue, Suite 2040 · Milwaukee, WI 53202-4497 · 414-277-5000

Thomas R. Schrimpf · Hinshaw & Culbertson · http://www.hinshawlaw.com · 100 East Wisconsin Avenue, Suite 2600 · Milwaukee, WI 53202-4115 · 414-276-6464

Ted M. Warshafsky · ㉕ · Warshafsky, Rotter, Tarnoff, Reinhardt & Bloch · 839 North Jefferson Street, Suite 300 · Milwaukee, WI 53202 · 414-276-4970

Trevor J. Will · Foley & Lardner · 777 East Wisconsin Avenue, Suite 3800 · Milwaukee, WI 53202-5306 · 414-271-2400

PROFESSIONAL MALPRACTICE LAW

Madison

Claude J. Covelli · ⑩ · Boardman Law Firm · http://www.boardmanlawfirm.com · One South Pinckney Street, Fourth Floor · P.O. Box 927 · Madison, WI 53701-0927 · 608-257-9521

John C. Mitby · ⑩ · Axley Brynelson · http://www.axley.com · Two East Mifflin Street, Suite 200 · P.O. Box 1767 · Madison, WI 53701-1767 · 608-257-5661

John M. Moore · ⑳ · Bell, Gierhart & Moore · 44 East Mifflin Street, 10th Floor · P.O. Box 1807 · Madison, WI 53701-1807 · 608-257-3764

Milwaukee

Donald R. Peterson · ㉕ · Peterson, Johnson & Murray · 733 North Van Buren Street, Sixth Floor · Milwaukee, WI 53202 · 414-278-8800

PROJECT FINANCE LAW

Milwaukee

Julianna Ebert · Quarles & Brady · http://www.quarles.com · 411 East Wisconsin Avenue, Suite 2040 · Milwaukee, WI 53202-4497 · 414-277-5000

Edward J. Hammond · Foley & Lardner · 777 East Wisconsin Avenue, Suite 3800 · Milwaukee, WI 53202-5306 · 414-271-2400

Brian G. Lanser · Quarles & Brady · http://www.quarles.com · 411 East Wisconsin Avenue, Suite 2040 · Milwaukee, WI 53202-4497 · 414-277-5000

Michael L. Roshar · Quarles & Brady · http://www.quarles.com · 411 East Wisconsin Avenue, Suite 2040 · Milwaukee, WI 53202-4497 · 414-277-5000

James T. Tynion III · Foley & Lardner · 777 East Wisconsin Avenue, Suite 3800 · Milwaukee, WI 53202-5306 · 414-271-2400

Patrick D. Walsh · Quarles & Brady · http://www.quarles.com · 411 East Wisconsin Avenue, Suite 2040 · Milwaukee, WI 53202-4497 · 414-277-5000

PUBLIC FINANCE LAW

Milwaukee

Elizabeth S. Blutstein · Foley & Lardner · 777 East Wisconsin Avenue, Suite 3800 · Milwaukee, WI 53202-5306 · 414-271-2400

Julianna Ebert · Quarles & Brady · http://www.quarles.com · 411 East Wisconsin Avenue, Suite 2040 · Milwaukee, WI 53202-4497 · 414-277-5000

Reed Groethe · Foley & Lardner · 777 East Wisconsin Avenue, Suite 3800 · Milwaukee, WI 53202-5306 · 414-271-2400

Brian G. Lanser · Quarles & Brady · http://www.quarles.com · 411 East Wisconsin Avenue, Suite 2040 · Milwaukee, WI 53202-4497 · 414-277-5000

Jennifer V. Powers · Quarles & Brady · http://www.quarles.com · 411 East Wisconsin Avenue, Suite 2040 Milwaukee, WI 53202-4497 · 414-277-5000

Rebecca A. Speckhard · Quarles & Brady · http://www.quarles.com · 411 East Wisconsin Avenue, Suite 2040 · Milwaukee, WI 53202-4497 · 414-277-5000

RAILROAD LAW

Milwaukee

Brian D. Baird · ⑩ · Borgelt, Powell, Peterson & Frauen · 735 North Water Street, Suite 1500 · Milwaukee, WI 53202-4188 · 414-276-3600

REAL ESTATE LAW

Brookfield

Charles H. McMullen · DeWitt Ross & Stevens · 13935 Bishop's Drive, Suite 300 · Brookfield, WI 53005-6605 · 262-754-2840

Eau Claire

David G. Anderson · ⑩ · Ruder Ware · 402 Graham Avenue · P.O. Box 187 · Eau Claire, WI 54702-0187 · 715-834-3425

Stephen R. Schrage · ⑩ · Schrage & Kaiser · 204 East Grand Avenue · P.O. Box 358 · Eau Claire, WI 54702-0358 · 715-832-3494

John F. Wilcox · ⑩ · John F. Wilcox Law Office · 2215 East Clairemont Avenue, Suite Five · Eau Claire, WI 54701-4635 · 715-832-6645

Elkhorn

Robert C. Leibsle · ⑩ · Godfrey, Leibsle, Blackbourn & Howarth · http://www.godfreylaw.com · 354 Seymour Court · Elkhorn, WI 53121 · 262-723-3220

Lowell E. Sweet · ㉕ · Sweet & Maier · Inns Of Court Building · 114 North Church Street · P.O. Box 318 · Elkhorn, WI 53121-0318 · 262-723-5480

Fort Atkinson

James J. Vance · ㉕ · Vance, Wilcox & Short · 79 North Main Street · P.O. Box 338 · Fort Atkinson, WI 53538-0338 · 920-563-9523

Madison

Denis P. Bartell · ⑳ · DeWitt Ross & Stevens · Two East Mifflin Street, Suite 600 · Madison, WI 53703 · 608-255-8891

Joseph P. Bartol · Stroud, Willink & Howard · 25 West Main Street, Suite 300 · P.O. Box 2236 · Madison, WI 53701-2236 · 608-257-2281

Michelle A. Behnke · Michelle A. Behnke · 222 North Midvale Boulevard, Suite 17 · Madison, WI 53705-5004 · 608-233-9024

Frederic J. Brouner · DeWitt Ross & Stevens · Two East Mifflin Street, Suite 600 · Madison, WI 53703 608-255-8891

Robert E. Chritton · Godfrey & Kahn · One East Main Street, Suite 500 · P.O. Box 2719 · Madison, WI 53701-2719 · 608-257-3911

Kevin A. Delorey · ⑩ · Quarles & Brady · http://www.quarles.com · 33 East Main Street, Suite 900 · P.O. Box 2113 · Madison, WI 53701-2113 · 608-251-5000

Paul J. Dombrowski · ⑩ · Godfrey & Kahn · One East Main Street, Suite 500 · P.O. Box 2719 · Madison, WI 53701-2719 · 608-257-3911

Bruce L. Harms · Axley Brynelson · http://www.axley.com · Two East Mifflin Street, Suite 200 · P.O. Box 1767 · Madison, WI 53701-1767 · 608-257-5661

W. Pharis Horton · ㉕ · Horton Law Office · 222 North Midvale Boulevard, Suite Seven · Madison, WI 53705 · 608-231-3220

Christopher B. Hughes · Stafford Rosenbaum · http://www.staffordlaw.com · 222 West Washington Avenue, Suite 900 · P.O. Box 1784 · Madison, WI 53701-1784 · 608-256-0226

Jesse S. Ishikawa · ⑩ · Reinhart Boerner Van Deuren · http://www.reinhartlaw.com · 22 East Mifflin Street, Suite 600 · P.O. Box 2018 · Madison, WI 53701-2018 · 608-229-2200

Larry K. Libman · Axley Brynelson · http://www.axley.com · Two East Mifflin Street, Suite 200 · P.O. Box 1767 · Madison, WI 53701-1767 · 608-257-5661

Daniel Lipman · Murphy Desmond · http://www.murphydesmond.com · 33 East Main Street, Suite 500 · P.O. Box 2038 · Madison, WI 53703-2038 · 608-807-0262

Richard E. Petershack · Axley Brynelson · http://www.axley.com · Two East Mifflin Street, Suite 200 · P.O. Box 1767 · Madison, WI 53701-1767 · 608-257-5661

Blaine R. Renfert · Foley & Lardner · 150 East Gilman Street · P.O. Box 1497 · Madison, WI 53701-1497 608-257-5035

Wrede H. Smith, Jr. · DeWitt Ross & Stevens · 8000 Excelsior Drive, Suite 401 · Madison, WI 53717-1914 · 608-831-2100

Harvey L. Temkin · ⑩ · Reinhart Boerner Van Deuren · http://www.reinhartlaw.com · 22 East Mifflin Street, Suite 600 · P.O. Box 2018 · Madison, WI 53701-2018 · 608-229-2200

John W. Van Note · Mohs, MacDonald, Widder & Paradise · 20 North Carroll Street · Madison, WI 53703-2707 · 608-256-1978

William F. White · ⑩ · Michael Best & Friedrich · One South Pinckney Street, Suite 700 · P.O. Box 1806 Madison, WI 53701-1806 · 608-257-3501

Theodore C. Widder III · ⑩ · Mohs, MacDonald, Widder & Paradise · 20 North Carroll Street · Madison, WI 53703-2707 · 608-256-1978

Thomas D. Zilavy · ⑩ · DeWitt Ross & Stevens · Two East Mifflin Street, Suite 600 · Madison, WI 53703 · 608-255-8891

Milwaukee

Benjamin J. Abrohams · ㉕ · Foley & Lardner · 777 East Wisconsin Avenue, Suite 3800 · Milwaukee, WI 53202-5306 · 414-271-2400

Bruce T. Block · ⑩ · Reinhart Boerner Van Deuren · http://www.reinhartlaw.com · 1000 North Water Street · P.O. Box 2965 · Milwaukee, WI 53201-2965 · 414-298-1000

Stephen L. Chernof · Godfrey & Kahn · 780 North Water Street · Milwaukee, WI 53202-3590 · 414-273-3500

Gerald E. Connolly · ⑳ · Quarles & Brady · http://www.quarles.com · 411 East Wisconsin Avenue, Suite 2040 · Milwaukee, WI 53202-4497 · 414-277-5000

Bradley I. Dallet · Whyte Hirschboeck Dudek · 555 East Wells Street, Suite 1900 · Milwaukee, WI 53202-3819 · 414-273-2100

Larry R. Dalton · Whyte Hirschboeck Dudek · 555 East Wells Street, Suite 1900 · Milwaukee, WI 53202-3819 · 414-273-2100

John W. Daniels, Jr. · ⑩ · Quarles & Brady · http://www.quarles.com · 411 East Wisconsin Avenue, Suite 2040 · Milwaukee, WI 53202-4497 · 414-277-5000

Michael J. Dwyer · Godfrey & Kahn · 780 North Water Street · Milwaukee, WI 53202-3590 · 414-273-3500

John A. Erich · Reinhart Boerner Van Deuren · http://www.reinhartlaw.com · 1000 North Water Street · P.O. Box 2965 · Milwaukee, WI 53201-2965 · 414-298-1000

Mary Neese Fertl · Quarles & Brady · http://www.quarles.com · 411 East Wisconsin Avenue, Suite 2040 · Milwaukee, WI 53202-4497 · 414-277-5000

John D. Finerty, Jr. · Michael Best & Friedrich · 100 East Wisconsin Avenue, Suite 3300 · Milwaukee, WI 53202-4108 · 414-271-6560

Michael W. Hatch · ⑳ · Foley & Lardner · 777 East Wisconsin Avenue, Suite 3800 · Milwaukee, WI 53202-5306 · 414-271-2400

Ronald S. Jacobs · Galanis, Pollack, Jacobs & Johnson · Two Plaza East, Suite 560 · 330 East Kilbourn Avenue · Milwaukee, WI 53202 · 414-271-5400

Jerome M. Janzer · Reinhart Boerner Van Deuren · http://www.reinhartlaw.com · 1000 North Water Street · P.O. Box 2965 · Milwaukee, WI 53201-2965 · 414-298-1000

Sarah O. Jelencic · Foley & Lardner · 777 East Wisconsin Avenue, Suite 3800 · Milwaukee, WI 53202-5306 · 414-271-2400

Lawrence J. Jost · ⑳ · Quarles & Brady · http://www.quarles.com · 411 East Wisconsin Avenue, Suite 2040 · Milwaukee, WI 53202-4497 · 414-277-5000

Hal Karas · Whyte Hirschboeck Dudek · 555 East Wells Street, Suite 1900 · Milwaukee, WI 53202-3819 · 414-273-2100

Scott L. Langlois · Quarles & Brady · http://www.quarles.com · 411 East Wisconsin Avenue, Suite 2040 · Milwaukee, WI 53202-4497 · 414-277-5000

Benjamin D. Levin · Foley & Lardner · 777 East Wisconsin Avenue, Suite 3800 · Milwaukee, WI 53202-5306 · 414-271-2400

James S. Levin · Michael Best & Friedrich · 100 East Wisconsin Avenue, Suite 3300 · Milwaukee, WI 53202-4108 · 414-271-6560

Michael Ostermeyer · Quarles & Brady · http://www.quarles.com · 411 East Wisconsin Avenue, Suite 2040 · Milwaukee, WI 53202-4497 · 414-277-5000

Joseph E. Puchner · Quarles & Brady · http://www.quarles.com · 411 East Wisconsin Avenue, Suite 2040 Milwaukee, WI 53202-4497 · 414-277-5000

George F. Roth · Whyte Hirschboeck Dudek · 555 East Wells Street, Suite 1900 · Milwaukee, WI 53202-3819 · 414-273-2100

Deborah C. Tomczyk · Reinhart Boerner Van Deuren · http://www.reinhartlaw.com · 1000 North Water Street · P.O. Box 2965 · Milwaukee, WI 53201-2965 · 414-298-1000

Racine

Robert R. Henzl · ㉕ · Hostak, Henzl & Bichler · 840 Lake Avenue · Racine, WI 53403 · 262-632-7541

Waukesha

J. Bushnell Nielsen · Reinhart Boerner Van Deuren · http://www.reinhartlaw.com · N16 W23250 Stoneridge Drive · P.O. Box 2265 · Waukesha, WI 53187-2265 · 262-951-4500

Wausau

Colin D. Pietz · ⑩ · Pietz, Vander Waal, Stacker & Rottier · 530 Jackson Street · Wausau, WI 54403-5589 715-845-9211

SECURITIES LAW

Madison

Jeffrey B. Bartell · ⑩ · Quarles & Brady · http://www.quarles.com · 33 East Main Street, Suite 900 · P.O. Box 2113 · Madison, WI 53701-2113 · 608-251-5000

Stephen L. Morgan · Murphy Desmond · http://www.murphydesmond.com · 33 East Main Street, Suite 500 · P.O. Box 2038 · Madison, WI 53703-2038 · 608-807-0262

Milwaukee

William J. Abraham, Jr. · ⑳ · Foley & Lardner · 777 East Wisconsin Avenue, Suite 3800 · Milwaukee, WI 53202-5306 · 414-271-2400

Steve R. Barth · Foley & Lardner · 777 East Wisconsin Avenue, Suite 3800 · Milwaukee, WI 53202-5306 414-271-2400

Benjamin F. Garmer III · ⑳ · Foley & Lardner · 777 East Wisconsin Avenue, Suite 3800 · Milwaukee, WI 53202-5306 · 414-271-2400

Conrad G. Goodkind · ⑩ · Quarles & Brady · http://www.quarles.com · 411 East Wisconsin Avenue, Suite 2040 · Milwaukee, WI 53202-4497 · 414-277-5000

Christopher B. Noyes · Godfrey & Kahn · 780 North Water Street · Milwaukee, WI 53202-3590 · 414-273-3500

Patrick G. Quick · Foley & Lardner · 777 East Wisconsin Avenue, Suite 3800 · Milwaukee, WI 53202-5306 · 414-271-2400

Jay O. Rothman · Foley & Lardner · 777 East Wisconsin Avenue, Suite 3800 · Milwaukee, WI 53202-5306 · 414-271-2400

Luke E. Sims · Foley & Lardner · 777 East Wisconsin Avenue, Suite 3800 · Milwaukee, WI 53202-5306 · 414-271-2400

Hoyt R. Stastney · Quarles & Brady · http://www.quarles.com · 411 East Wisconsin Avenue, Suite 2040 · Milwaukee, WI 53202-4497 · 414-277-5000

SPORTS LAW

Milwaukee

Mary K. Braza · Foley & Lardner · 777 East Wisconsin Avenue, Suite 3800 · Milwaukee, WI 53202-5306 414-271-2400

Martin J. Greenberg · Greenberg & Hoeschen · 3127 West Wisconsin Avenue · Milwaukee, WI 53208 · 414-271-4849

James T. McKeown · Foley & Lardner · 777 East Wisconsin Avenue, Suite 3800 · Milwaukee, WI 53202-5306 · 414-271-2400

TAX LAW

Brookfield

Douglas H. Frazer · DeWitt Ross & Stevens · 13935 Bishop's Drive, Suite 300 · Brookfield, WI 53005-6605 · 262-754-2840

Eau Claire

Sebastian J. Geraci · ⑩ · Ruder Ware · 402 Graham Avenue · P.O. Box 187 · Eau Claire, WI 54702-0187 · 715-834-3425

Green Bay

Brian Mudd · ⑩ · Nelson & Schmeling · 130 East Walnut Street, Eighth Floor · P.O. Box 22130 · Green Bay, WI 54305-2130 · 920-432-1400

Madison

Brian L. Anderson · DeWitt Ross & Stevens · Two East Mifflin Street, Suite 600 · Madison, WI 53703 · 608-255-8891

Frederic J. Brouner · DeWitt Ross & Stevens · Two East Mifflin Street, Suite 600 · Madison, WI 53703 608-255-8891

Robert Horowitz · Stafford Rosenbaum · http://www.staffordlaw.com · 222 West Washington Avenue, Suite 900 · P.O. Box 1784 · Madison, WI 53701-1784 · 608-256-0226

Richard Z. Kabaker · ㉕ · Michael Best & Friedrich · One South Pinckney Street, Suite 700 · P.O. Box 1806 · Madison, WI 53701-1806 · 608-257-3501

Richard W. Pitzner · ㉕ · Murphy Desmond · http://www.murphydesmond.com · 33 East Main Street, Suite 500 · P.O. Box 2038 · Madison, WI 53703-2038 · 608-807-0262

John T. Barry · Quarles & Brady · http://www.quarles.com · 411 East Wisconsin Avenue, Suite 2040 · Milwaukee, WI 53202-4497 · 414-277-5000

Daniel P. Cooper · Reinhart Boerner Van Deuren · http://www.reinhartlaw.com · 1000 North Water Street · P.O. Box 2965 · Milwaukee, WI 53201-2965 · 414-298-1000

Robert E. Dallman · ⑩ · Reinhart Boerner Van Deuren · http://www.reinhartlaw.com · 1000 North Water Street · P.O. Box 2965 · Milwaukee, WI 53201-2965 · 414-298-1000

Margaret M. Derus · Reinhart Boerner Van Deuren · http://www.reinhartlaw.com · 1000 North Water Street · P.O. Box 2965 · Milwaukee, WI 53201-2965 · 414-298-1000

Steven R. Duback · Quarles & Brady · http://www.quarles.com · 411 East Wisconsin Avenue, Suite 2040 · Milwaukee, WI 53202-4497 · 414-277-5000

John F. Emanuel · ⑩ · Whyte Hirschboeck Dudek · 555 East Wells Street, Suite 1900 · Milwaukee, WI 53202-3819 · 414-273-2100

Carl D. Fortner · Foley & Lardner · 777 East Wisconsin Avenue, Suite 3800 · Milwaukee, WI 53202-5306 · 414-271-2400

Richard S. Gallagher · ㉕ · Foley & Lardner · 777 East Wisconsin Avenue, Suite 3800 · Milwaukee, WI 53202-5306 · 414-271-2400

Michael G. Goller · Reinhart Boerner Van Deuren · http://www.reinhartlaw.com · 1000 North Water Street · P.O. Box 2965 · Milwaukee, WI 53201-2965 · 414-298-1000

Robert L. Gordon · Michael Best & Friedrich · 100 East Wisconsin Avenue, Suite 3300 · Milwaukee, WI 53202-4108 · 414-271-6560

Thomas P. Guszkowski · von Briesen & Roper · http://www.vonbriesen.com · 411 East Wisconsin Avenue, Suite 700 · P.O. Box 3262 · Milwaukee, WI 53201-3262 · 414-276-1122

John A. Herbers · Reinhart Boerner Van Deuren · http://www.reinhartlaw.com · 1000 North Water Street P.O. Box 2965 · Milwaukee, WI 53201-2965 · 414-298-1000

Patricia A. Hintz · Quarles & Brady · http://www.quarles.com · 411 East Wisconsin Avenue, Suite 2040 · Milwaukee, WI 53202-4497 · 414-277-5000

Gary A. Hollman · ⑩ · Reinhart Boerner Van Deuren · http://www.reinhartlaw.com · 1000 North Water Street · P.O. Box 2965 · Milwaukee, WI 53201-2965 · 414-298-1000

Myron L. Joseph · ⑩ · Whyte Hirschboeck Dudek · 555 East Wells Street, Suite 1900 · Milwaukee, WI 53202-3819 · 414-273-2100

Debra S. Koenig · ⑩ · Godfrey & Kahn · 780 North Water Street · Milwaukee, WI 53202-3590 · 414-273-3500

James R. Lowe · Whyte Hirschboeck Dudek · 555 East Wells Street, Suite 1900 · Milwaukee, WI 53202-3819 · 414-273-2100

Robert E. Meldman · ㉕ · Reinhart Boerner Van Deuren · http://www.reinhartlaw.com · 1000 North Water Street · P.O. Box 2965 · Milwaukee, WI 53201-2965 · 414-298-1000

Robert J. Misey, Jr. · Reinhart Boerner Van Deuren · http://www.reinhartlaw.com · 1000 North Water Street · P.O. Box 2965 · Milwaukee, WI 53201-2965 · 414-298-1000

Linda S. Moroney · Drinker Biddle & Reath · 777 East Wisconsin Avenue, Suite 2000 · Milwaukee, WI 53202-5319 · 414-221-6040

Thomas J. Nichols · Meissner Tierney Fisher & Nichols · http://www.mtfn.com · The Milwaukee Center, 19th Floor · 111 East Kilbourne Avenue · Milwaukee, WI 53202 · 414-273-1300

Elizabeth G. Nowakowski · Quarles & Brady · http://www.quarles.com · 411 East Wisconsin Avenue, Suite 2040 · Milwaukee, WI 53202-4497 · 414-277-5000

Jamshed J. Patel · Foley & Lardner · 777 East Wisconsin Avenue, Suite 3800 · Milwaukee, WI 53202-5306 · 414-271-2400

James N. Phillips · ⑩ · Godfrey & Kahn · 780 North Water Street · Milwaukee, WI 53202-3590 · 414-273-3500

Thomas J. Phillips · Quarles & Brady · http://www.quarles.com · 411 East Wisconsin Avenue, Suite 2040 Milwaukee, WI 53202-4497 · 414-277-5000

Bret A. Roge · ⑩ · Michael Best & Friedrich · 100 East Wisconsin Avenue, Suite 3300 · Milwaukee, WI 53202-4108 · 414-271-6560

Timothy G. Schally · ⑩ · Michael Best & Friedrich · 100 East Wisconsin Avenue, Suite 3300 · Milwaukee, WI 53202-4108 · 414-271-6560

Robert A. Schnur · ㉕ · Michael Best & Friedrich · 100 East Wisconsin Avenue, Suite 3300 · Milwaukee, WI 53202-4108 · 414-271-6560

John A. Sikora · Weiss Berzowski Brady · 700 North Water Street, Suite 1500 · Milwaukee, WI 53202-4273 · 414-276-5800

Thomas A. Simonis · Quarles & Brady · http://www.quarles.com · 411 East Wisconsin Avenue, Suite 2040 Milwaukee, WI 53202-4497 · 414-277-5000

Joseph E. Tierney III · ⑩ · Meissner Tierney Fisher & Nichols · http://www.mtfn.com · The Milwaukee Center, 19th Floor · 111 East Kilbourne Avenue · Milwaukee, WI 53202 · 414-273-1300

David D. Wilmoth · ⑩ · Quarles & Brady · http://www.quarles.com · 411 East Wisconsin Avenue, Suite 2040 · Milwaukee, WI 53202-4497 · 414-277-5000

Craig H. Zetley · Zetley & Cohn · 324 East Wisconsin Avenue, Suite 1400 · Milwaukee, WI 53202 · 414-272-1424

Lynette M. Zigman · Foley & Lardner · 777 East Wisconsin Avenue, Suite 3800 · Milwaukee, WI 53202-5306 · 414-271-2400

Racine

Gregory A. Ruidl · DeMark, Kolbe & Brodek · 6216 Washington Avenue · P.O. Box 085009 · Racine, WI 53408 · 262-886-9720

Waukesha

John R. Austin · Reinhart Boerner Van Deuren · http://www.reinhartlaw.com · N16 W23250 Stoneridge Drive · P.O. Box 2265 · Waukesha, WI 53187-2265 · 262-951-4500

Steven R. Battenberg · Michael Best & Friedrich · Two Riverwood Place, Suite 200 · N19 W24133 Riverwood Drive · Waukesha, WI 53188-1174 · 262-956-6560

Timothy A. Nettesheim · ⑩ · Reinhart Boerner Van Deuren · http://www.reinhartlaw.com · N16 W23250 Stoneridge Drive · P.O. Box 2265 · Waukesha, WI 53187-2265 · 262-951-4500

TECHNOLOGY LAW

Madison

Mark A. Kassel · Foley & Lardner · 150 East Gilman Street · P.O. Box 1497 · Madison, WI 53701-1497 · 608-257-5035

TRUSTS AND ESTATES

Appleton

Jeffrey D. Riester · Godfrey & Kahn · 100 West Lawrence · P.O. Box 2728 · Appleton, WI 54912-2728 · 920-830-2800

Eau Claire

Sebastian J. Geraci · ⑩ · Ruder Ware · 402 Graham Avenue · P.O. Box 187 · Eau Claire, WI 54702-0187 · 715-834-3425

Stephen R. Schrage · ⑩ · Schrage & Kaiser · 204 East Grand Avenue · P.O. Box 358 · Eau Claire, WI 54702-0358 · 715-832-3494

John F. Wilcox · ⑩ · John F. Wilcox Law Office · 2215 East Clairemont Avenue, Suite Five · Eau Claire, WI 54701-4635 · 715-832-6645

Fox Point

Diane K. O'Connor · O'Connor & Sachs · 1461 East Goodrich Lane · Fox Point, WI 53217-2950 · 414-352-4179

Janesville

Robert H. Consigny · ⑳ · Consigny, Andrews, Hemming & Grant · 303 East Court Street · P.O. Box 1449 Janesville, WI 53547 · 608-755-5050

James R. Cripe · ⑩ · Nowlan & Mouat · 100 South Main Street · P.O. Box 8100 · Janesville, WI 53547-8100 · 608-755-8100

George K. Steil, Sr. · ⑩ · Brennan, Steil & Basting · One East Milwaukee Street · P.O. Box 1148 · Janesville, WI 53547-1148 · 608-756-4141

Jefferson

Henry B. Miller · Miller Law Office · 121 South Main Street · P.O. Box 417 · Jefferson, WI 53549-0417 · 920-674-3345

Madison

Brian L. Anderson · DeWitt Ross & Stevens · Two East Mifflin Street, Suite 600 · Madison, WI 53703 · 608-255-8891

Janice Bensky · Stafford Rosenbaum · http://www.staffordlaw.com · 222 West Washington Avenue, Suite 900 · P.O. Box 1784 · Madison, WI 53701-1784 · 608-256-0226

Ronald C. Berman · Neider & Boucher · 440 Science Drive, Suite 300 · P.O. Box 5510 · Madison, WI 53705-0510 · 608-661-4500

John C. Frank · ⑩ · Lathrop & Clark · 740 Regent Street, Suite 400 · P.O. Box 1507 · Madison, WI 53701-1507 · 608-257-7766

Thomas A. Hoffner · ⑩ · Godfrey & Kahn · One East Main Street, Suite 500 · P.O. Box 2719 · Madison, WI 53701-2719 · 608-257-3911

Barbara S. Hughes · Hill, Glowacki, Jaeger & Hughes · 2010 Eastwood Drive, Suite 301 · Madison, WI 53704-5459 · 608-244-1354

James A. Jaeger · Hill, Glowacki, Jaeger & Hughes · 2010 Eastwood Drive, Suite 301 · Madison, WI 53704-5459 · 608-244-1354

Richard Z. Kabaker · ㉕ · Michael Best & Friedrich · One South Pinckney Street, Suite 700 · P.O. Box 1806 · Madison, WI 53701-1806 · 608-257-3501

Richard J. Langer · ⑩ · Michael Best & Friedrich · One South Pinckney Street, Suite 700 · P.O. Box 1806 · Madison, WI 53701-1806 · 608-257-3501

Gregory F. Monday · Foley & Lardner · 150 East Gilman Street · P.O. Box 1497 · Madison, WI 53701-1497 · 608-257-5035

William F. Mundt · ⑩ · Murphy Desmond · http://www.murphydesmond.com · 33 East Main Street, Suite 500 · P.O. Box 2038 · Madison, WI 53703-2038 · 608-807-0262

Carl J. Rasmussen · ⑩ · Boardman Law Firm · http://www.boardmanlawfirm.com · One South Pinckney Street, Fourth Floor · P.O. Box 927 · Madison, WI 53701-0927 · 608-257-9521

David W. Reinecke · ⑩ · Foley & Lardner · 150 East Gilman Street · P.O. Box 1497 · Madison, WI 53701-1497 · 608-257-5035

Paul Schmidt · Boardman Law Firm · http://www.boardmanlawfirm.com · One South Pinckney Street, Fourth Floor · P.O. Box 927 · Madison, WI 53701-0927 · 608-257-9521

Wrede H. Smith, Jr. · DeWitt Ross & Stevens · 8000 Excelsior Drive, Suite 401 · Madison, WI 53717-1914 · 608-831-2100

Sheila Boothby Stevens · Michael Best & Friedrich · One South Pinckney Street, Suite 700 · P.O. Box 1806 · Madison, WI 53701-1806 · 608-257-3501

Howard A. Sweet · Hurley, Burish & Stanton · 33 East Main Street, Suite 400 · Madison, WI 53703 · 608-257-0945

Michael W. Wilcox · ㉕ · DeWitt Ross & Stevens · 8000 Excelsior Drive, Suite 401 · Madison, WI 53717-1914 · 608-831-2100

Thomas D. Zilavy · ⑩ · DeWitt Ross & Stevens · Two East Mifflin Street, Suite 600 · Madison, WI 53703 · 608-255-8891

Milwaukee

Steven R. Allen · Whyte Hirschboeck Dudek · 555 East Wells Street, Suite 1900 · Milwaukee, WI 53202-3819 · 414-273-2100

John T. Bannen · ⑩ · Quarles & Brady · http://www.quarles.com · 411 East Wisconsin Avenue, Suite 2040 · Milwaukee, WI 53202-4497 · 414-277-5000

Kenneth Barczak · Schober & Radtke · 15525 West National Avenue · P.O. Box 510155 · Milwaukee, WI 53151-0155 · 262-782-7820

John F. Callan · Foley & Lardner · 777 East Wisconsin Avenue, Suite 3800 · Milwaukee, WI 53202-5306 414-271-2400

Keith A. Christiansen · ⑳ · Foley & Lardner · 777 East Wisconsin Avenue, Suite 3800 · Milwaukee, WI 53202-5306 · 414-271-2400

Jennifer R. D'Amato · Reinhart Boerner Van Deuren · http://www.reinhartlaw.com · 1000 North Water Street · P.O. Box 2965 · Milwaukee, WI 53201-2965 · 414-298-1000

James F. Daly · Quarles & Brady · http://www.quarles.com · 411 East Wisconsin Avenue, Suite 2040 · Milwaukee, WI 53202-4497 · 414-277-5000

George A. Dionisopoulos · ⑩ · Foley & Lardner · 777 East Wisconsin Avenue, Suite 3800 · Milwaukee, WI 53202-5306 · 414-271-2400

Thomas J. Drought · ⑳ · Cook & Franke · 660 East Mason Street · Milwaukee, WI 53202 · 414-271-5900

Dwight H. Ellis III · ⑩ · Dwight H. Ellis Law Office · 241 North Broadway Street, Suite 501 · Milwaukee, WI 53202 · 414-347-0260

George A. Evans, Jr. · von Briesen & Roper · http://www.vonbriesen.com · 411 East Wisconsin Avenue, Suite 700 · P.O. Box 3262 · Milwaukee, WI 53201-3262 · 414-276-1122

Stephen M. Fisher · ⑩ · Stephen M. Fisher & Associates · 11414 West Park Place, Suite 107 · Milwaukee, WI 53224-3500 · 414-359-9067

Frederic G. Friedman · ⑩ · Reinhart Boerner Van Deuren · http://www.reinhartlaw.com · 1000 North Water Street · P.O. Box 2965 · Milwaukee, WI 53201-2965 · 414-298-1000

Henry E. Fuldner · ⑳ · Godfrey & Kahn · 780 North Water Street · Milwaukee, WI 53202-3590 · 414-273-3500

Richard S. Gallagher · ㉕ · Foley & Lardner · 777 East Wisconsin Avenue, Suite 3800 · Milwaukee, WI 53202-5306 · 414-271-2400

Christopher K. Gawart · Quarles & Brady · http://www.quarles.com · 411 East Wisconsin Avenue, Suite 2040 · Milwaukee, WI 53202-4497 · 414-277-5000

Julie Gorens- Winston · Michael Best & Friedrich · 100 East Wisconsin Avenue, Suite 3300 · Milwaukee, WI 53202-4108 · 414-271-6560

Gardner Govan · Godfrey & Kahn · 780 North Water Street · Milwaukee, WI 53202-3590 · 414-273-3500

Kathleen A. Gray · Quarles & Brady · http://www.quarles.com · 411 East Wisconsin Avenue, Suite 2040 · Milwaukee, WI 53202-4497 · 414-277-5000

F. William Haberman · ⑳ · Michael Best & Friedrich · 100 East Wisconsin Avenue, Suite 3300 · Milwaukee, WI 53202-4108 · 414-271-6560

Philip J. Halley · ⑩ · Whyte Hirschboeck Dudek · 555 East Wells Street, Suite 1900 · Milwaukee, WI 53202-3819 · 414-273-2100

John B. Haydon · ⑳ · Whyte Hirschboeck Dudek · 555 East Wells Street, Suite 1900 · Milwaukee, WI 53202-3819 · 414-273-2100

John A. Herbers · Reinhart Boerner Van Deuren · http://www.reinhartlaw.com · 1000 North Water Street P.O. Box 2965 · Milwaukee, WI 53201-2965 · 414-298-1000

David L. Kinnamon · ⑳ · Quarles & Brady · http://www.quarles.com · 411 East Wisconsin Avenue, Suite 2040 · Milwaukee, WI 53202-4497 · 414-277-5000

Joan D. Klimpel · Godfrey & Kahn · 780 North Water Street · Milwaukee, WI 53202-3590 · 414-273-3500

Katherine W. Lambert · Whyte Hirschboeck Dudek · 555 East Wells Street, Suite 1900 · Milwaukee, WI 53202-3819 · 414-273-2100

Kristi E. Leswing · Godfrey & Kahn · 780 North Water Street · Milwaukee, WI 53202-3590 · 414-273-3500

John H. Lhost · Quarles & Brady · http://www.quarles.com · 411 East Wisconsin Avenue, Suite 2040 · Milwaukee, WI 53202-4497 · 414-277-5000

Henry J. Loos · ⑩ · Quarles & Brady · http://www.quarles.com · 411 East Wisconsin Avenue, Suite 2040 · Milwaukee, WI 53202-4497 · 414-277-5000

Robert J. Loots · ㉕ · von Briesen & Roper · http://www.vonbriesen.com · 411 East Wisconsin Avenue, Suite 700 · P.O. Box 3262 · Milwaukee, WI 53201-3262 · 414-276-1122

Wayne R. Lueders · ⑩ · Foley & Lardner · 777 East Wisconsin Avenue, Suite 3800 · Milwaukee, WI 53202-5306 · 414-271-2400

Sally C. Merrell · ⑩ · Quarles & Brady · http://www.quarles.com · 411 East Wisconsin Avenue, Suite 2040 Milwaukee, WI 53202-4497 · 414-277-5000

Philip J. Miller · Weiss Berzowski Brady · 700 North Water Street, Suite 1500 · Milwaukee, WI 53202-4273 · 414-276-5800

Randy S. Nelson · ⑩ · Weiss Berzowski Brady · 700 North Water Street, Suite 1500 · Milwaukee, WI 53202-4273 · 414-276-5800

J. Lewis Perlson · ⑩ · Michael Best & Friedrich · 100 East Wisconsin Avenue, Suite 3300 · Milwaukee, WI 53202-4108 · 414-271-6560

Catherine M. Priebe-Hertzberg · Davis & Kuelthau · 111 East Kilbourne Avenue, Suite 1400 · Milwaukee, WI 53202 · 414-276-0200

Mark A. Shiller · Godfrey & Kahn · 780 North Water Street · Milwaukee, WI 53202-3590 · 414-273-3500

Paul J. Tilleman · ⑩ · Quarles & Brady · http://www.quarles.com · 411 East Wisconsin Avenue, Suite 2040 · Milwaukee, WI 53202-4497 · 414-277-5000

Adam J. Wiensch · Foley & Lardner · 777 East Wisconsin Avenue, Suite 3800 · Milwaukee, WI 53202-5306 · 414-271-2400

Oshkosh

Timothy M. Dempsey · ⑳ · Dempsey, Williamson, Young, Kelly & Hertel · U.S. Bank Building, Suite 302 · One Pearl Avenue · P.O. Box 886 · Oshkosh, WI 54903-0886 · 920-235-7300

Waukesha

Arthur F. Lubke, Jr. · ㉕ · Reinhart Boerner Van Deuren · http://www.reinhartlaw.com · N16 W23250 Stoneridge Drive · P.O. Box 2265 · Waukesha, WI 53187-2265 · 262-951-4500

Mark S. Poker · Michael Best & Friedrich · Two Riverwood Place, Suite 200 · N19 W24133 Riverwood Drive · Waukesha, WI 53188-1174 · 262-956-6560

Wausau

Mark J. Bradley · ⑳ · Ruder Ware · 500 Third Street, Suite 8000 · P.O. Box 8050 · Wausau, WI 54402-8050 · 715-845-4336

Wauwatosa

Ruth J. Irvings · Nelson, Irvings & Waeffler · 3077 North Mayfair Road, Suite 203 · Wauwatosa, WI 53222-4305 · 414-777-0220

Patricia J. Nelson · Nelson, Irvings & Waeffler · 3077 North Mayfair Road, Suite 203 · Wauwatosa, WI 53222-4305 · 414-777-0220

West Bend

Elaine A. Shanebrook · ⑩ · Shanebrook & Falkowski · 120 North Main Street, Suite 310 · West Bend, WI 53095-3353 · 262-338-1750

VENTURE CAPITAL LAW

Madison

Mark T. Ehrmann · Quarles & Brady · http://www.quarles.com · 33 East Main Street, Suite 900 · P.O. Box 2113 · Madison, WI 53701-2113 · 608-251-5000

Tod B. Linstroth · ⑳ · Michael Best & Friedrich · One South Pinckney Street, Suite 700 · P.O. Box 1806 Madison, WI 53701-1806 · 608-257-3501

WATER LAW

Madison

Waltraud A. Arts · Quarles & Brady · http://www.quarles.com · 33 East Main Street, Suite 900 · P.O. Box 2113 · Madison, WI 53701-2113 · 608-251-5000

Donald Leo Bach · DeWitt Ross & Stevens · Two East Mifflin Street, Suite 600 · Madison, WI 53703 · 608-255-8891

Paul G. Kent · ⑩ · Anderson & Kent · One North Pinckney Street, Suite 200 · Madison, WI 53703-5809 · 608-246-8500

WHITE-COLLAR CRIMINAL DEFENSE

Madison

Charles W. Giesen · ⑳ · Giesen Law Offices · 14 South Broom Street · P.O. Box 909 · Madison, WI 53701 · 608-255-8200

Stephen P. Hurley · ⑩ · Hurley, Burish & Stanton · 33 East Main Street, Suite 400 · Madison, WI 53703 608-257-0945

Stephen J. Meyer · ⑩ · Meyer Law Office · 10 East Doty Street, Suite 507 · Madison, WI 53703-3397 · 608-255-0911

Lester A. Pines · Cullen, Weston, Pines & Bach · http://www.cwpb.com · 122 West Washington Avenue, Suite 900 · Madison, WI 53703 · 608-251-0101

Bruce J. Rosen · ⑳ · Pellino, Rosen, Mowris & Kirkhuff · James Wilson Plaza, Suite 1201 · 131 West Wilson Street · Madison, WI 53703 · 608-255-4501

Dean A. Strang · Hurley, Burish & Stanton · 33 East Main Street, Suite 400 · Madison, WI 53703 · 608-257-0945

Milwaukee

Craig W. Albee · Glynn, Fitzgerald & Albee · 526 East Wisconsin Avenue · Milwaukee, WI 53202-4503 · 414-221-9600

Thomas E. Brown · ⑳ · Gimbel, Reilly, Guerin & Brown · Two Plaza East, Suite 1170 · 330 East Kilbourn Avenue · Milwaukee, WI 53202 · 414-271-1440

David J. Cannon · ⑳ · Michael Best & Friedrich · 100 East Wisconsin Avenue, Suite 3300 · Milwaukee, WI 53202-4108 · 414-271-6560

Dennis P. Coffey · ㉕ · Mawicke & Goisman · 1509 North Prospect Avenue · Milwaukee, WI 53202 · 414-224-0600

Francis R. Croak · ㉕ · Cook & Franke · 660 East Mason Street · Milwaukee, WI 53202 · 414-271-5900

Rodney L. Cubbie · Law Offices of Rodney Cubbie · 3333 North Mayfair Road, Suite 312 · Milwaukee, WI 53222 · 414-291-9741

Michael J. Fitzgerald · Glynn, Fitzgerald & Albee · 526 East Wisconsin Avenue · Milwaukee, WI 53202-4503 · 414-221-9600

Franklyn M. Gimbel · ㉕ · Gimbel, Reilly, Guerin & Brown · Two Plaza East, Suite 1170 · 330 East Kilbourn Avenue · Milwaukee, WI 53202 · 414-271-1440

Stephen M. Glynn · ㉕ · Glynn, Fitzgerald & Albee · 526 East Wisconsin Avenue · Milwaukee, WI 53202-4503 · 414-221-9600

Stephen E. Kravit · ⑩ · Kravit, Hovel, Krawczyk & Leverson · 825 North Jefferson Street, Fifth Floor · Milwaukee, WI 53202-3737 · 414-271-7100

James M. Shellow · ㉕ · Shellow & Shellow · 324 West Vine Street · Milwaukee, WI 53212-3606 · 414-271-8535

Michael J. Steinle · Terschan, Steinle & Ness · 309 North Water Street, Suite 215 · Milwaukee, WI 53202 · 414-258-1010

Appleton

Anthony W. Welhouse · ⑩ · Welhouse Law Office · 100 West Lawrence Street, Fourth Floor · Appleton, WI 54911 · 920-730-0200

Brookfield

Michael D. Stotler · Mark H. Miller Law Office · Bishop's Woods Pinnacle III, Suite 110 · 13845 Bishop Drive · Brookfield, WI 53005-6618 · 262-821-4622

Robert Zilske · ⑩ · Zilske Law Firm · Eastbrook Office Park · 12630 West North Avenue · Brookfield, WI 53005 · 262-796-2400

Deerfield

Ronald S. Aplin · ⑩ · Aplin & Ringsmuth · 51 North Main Street · P. O. Box 348 · Deerfield, WI 53531-0348 · 608-764-2907

Mark Ringsmuth · Aplin & Ringsmuth · 51 North Main Street · P. O. Box 348 · Deerfield, WI 53531-0348 · 608-764-2907

Eau Claire

Steve M. Jackson · ⑩ · Siedow & Jackson · 3430 Oakwood Mall Drive, Suite 100 · Eau Claire, WI 54701-3021 · 715-834-7771

Richard J. Kelly · ⑩ · Kelly Law Offices · 2215 East Clairemont Avenue, Suite One · Eau Claire, WI 54702 · 715-835-5345

Thomas A. Siedow · ⑩ · Siedow & Jackson · 3430 Oakwood Mall Drive, Suite 100 · Eau Claire, WI 54701-3021 · 715-834-7771

Green Bay

Mary Beth Callan · ⑩ · Denissen, Kranzush, Mahoney & Ewald · 3000 Riverside Drive, Suite 200 · Green Bay, WI 54301 · 920-435-4391

Janesville

James A. Meier · ⑩ · Meier, Wickham, Lyons & Schulz · 25 North Atwood Avenue · Janesville, WI 53545 · 608-752-8787

Madison

John D. Neal · ⑩ · Stafford & Neal · 900 John Nolen Drive, Suite 120 · Madison, WI 53713-1476 · 608-251-6045

Andrew J. Quartaro · Peterson, Johnson & Murray · Three South Pinckney Street, Ninth Floor · Madison, WI 53703 · 608-256-5220

John H. Schmid, Jr. · ⑩ · Axley Brynelson · http://www.axley.com · Two East Mifflin Street, Suite 200 · P.O. Box 1767 · Madison, WI 53701-1767 · 608-257-5661

Margaret Stafford · ⑩ · Stafford & Neal · 900 John Nolen Drive, Suite 120 · Madison, WI 53713-1476 · 608-251-6045

Timothy J. Yanacheck · ⑩ · Bell, Gierhart & Moore · 44 East Mifflin Street, 10th Floor · P.O. Box 1807 · Madison, WI 53701-1807 · 608-257-3764

Milwaukee

Joseph P. Danas, Jr. · ⑩ · Borgelt, Powell, Peterson & Frauen · 735 North Water Street, Suite 1500 · Milwaukee, WI 53202-4188 · 414-276-3600

Thomas M. Domer · ⑩ · Domer Law · 3970 North Oakland Avenue, Suite 701 · Milwaukee, WI 53211 · 414-967-5656

Douglas M. Feldman · Lindner & Marsack · 411 East Wisconsin Avenue, Suite 1800 · Milwaukee, WI 53202 · 414-273-3910

Thomas J. Flanagan · Previant, Goldberg, Uelmen, Gratz, Miller & Brueggeman · 1555 North RiverCenter Drive, Suite 202 · P.O. Box 12993 · Milwaukee, WI 53212 · 414-271-4500

Michael H. Gillick · ⑩ · Gillick, Wicht, Gillick & Graf · 6300 West Bluemound Road · Milwaukee, WI 53213 · 414-257-2667

Patrick J. Gillick · ⑩ · Gillick, Wicht, Gillick & Graf · 6300 West Bluemound Road · Milwaukee, WI 53213 · 414-257-2667

Maryeve Heath · Whyte Hirschboeck Dudek · 555 East Wells Street, Suite 1900 · Milwaukee, WI 53202-3819 · 414-273-2100

Richard T. Mueller · ⑩ · Mueller, Goss & Possi · Commerce Center, Suite 600 · 744 North Fourth Street Milwaukee, WI 53203-2108 · 414-278-0303

William R. Sachse, Jr. · ⑩ · Peterson, Johnson & Murray · 733 North Van Buren Street, Sixth Floor · Milwaukee, WI 53202 · 414-278-8800

Jan M. Schroeder · Peterson, Johnson & Murray · 733 North Van Buren Street, Sixth Floor · Milwaukee, WI 53202 · 414-278-8800

Dennis H. Wicht · ⑩ · Gillick, Wicht, Gillick & Graf · 6300 West Bluemound Road · Milwaukee, WI 53213 · 414-257-2667

Racine

Richard A. Fortune · ⑩ · Fortune & McGillis · 1300 South Green Bay Road, Suite 302 · Racine, WI 53406 · 262-632-2300

Daniel J. Kelley · Schoone, Leuck, Kelly, Pitts & Knurr · 6800 Washington Avenue · P.O. Box 086500 · Racine, WI 53408-5600 · 262-886-8240

Waukesha

Robert T. Ward · Ward Law Firm · N14 W23755 Stone Ridge Drive, Suite 280 · Waukesha, WI 53188-1147 · 262-523-1610

Wausau

James L. Bartells · ⑩ · James L. Bartells · 613 Forest Street · Wausau, WI 54403-5524 · 715-848-1801

Kathleen E. Grant · ⑩ · Schneider Grant · 210 McClellan Street, Suite 400 · P.O. Box 1586 · Wausau, WI 54403-1586 · 715-848-2111

David A. Piehler · ⑩ · Piehler & Strande · 401 Fifth Street, Suite 350 · P.O. Box 1287 · Wausau, WI 54402-1287 · 715-849-1000

Russell W. Wilson · ⑩ · Ruder Ware · 500 Third Street, Suite 8000 · P.O. Box 8050 · Wausau, WI 54402-8050 · 715-845-4336

WYOMING

ADMINISTRATIVE LAW

Cheyenne

Dale W. Cottam · Hirst & Applegate · 1720 Carey Avenue, Suite 200 · P.O. Box 1083 · Cheyenne, WY 82003-1083 · 307-632-0541

Walter F. Eggers III · Holland & Hart · 2515 Warren Avenue, Suite 450 · P.O. Box 1347 · Cheyenne, WY 82003-1347 · 307-778-4200

Nancy D. Freudenthal · Davis & Cannon · 422 West 26th Street · P.O. Box 43 · Cheyenne, WY 82003 · 307-634-3210

Paul J. Hickey · Hickey & Evans · 1800 Carey Avenue, Suite 700 · P.O. Box 467 · Cheyenne, WY 82003-0467 · 307-634-1525

Lawrence J. Wolfe · Holland & Hart · 2515 Warren Avenue, Suite 450 · P.O. Box 1347 · Cheyenne, WY 82003-1347 · 307-778-4200

ALTERNATIVE DISPUTE RESOLUTION

Casper

Mark W. Gifford · ⑩ · Gifford & Brinkerhoff · 243 South Park Street · P.O. Box 2508 · Casper, WY 82602-2508 · 307-265-3265

Michael J. Sullivan · Rothgerber Johnson & Lyons · 123 West First Street, Suite 200 · Casper, WY 82601-2480 · 307-232-0222

Cheyenne

William M. McKellar · McKellar, Tiedeken & Scoggin · 702 Randall Avenue · P.O. Box 748 · Cheyenne, WY 82003-0748 · 307-637-5575

Laramie

Amy B. Jenkins · Mediation Specialists · 1063 Duna Drive · P.O. Box 504 · Laramie, WY 82073-0504 · 307-745-5065

APPELLATE LAW

Cheyenne

Gregory C. Dyekman · ⑩ · Dray, Thomson & Dyekman · 204 East 22nd Street · Cheyenne, WY 82001 · 307-634-8891

Sharon A. Fitzgerald · The Fitzgerald Law Firm · The Fitzgerald Building · 2108 Warren Avenue · Cheyenne, WY 82001-3740 · 307-634-4000

Worland

John W. Davis · Davis & Harrington · 921 Coburn Avenue · P.O. Box 953 · Worland, WY 82401 · 307-347-6645

BANKING LAW

Jackson

Glenn M. Ford · Moore Myers & Garland · 235 East Broadway · P.O. Box 8498 · Jackson, WY 83002 · 307-733-8668

BANKRUPTCY AND CREDITOR-DEBTOR RIGHTS LAW

Cheyenne

James R. Belcher · Schultz & Belcher · 7000 Yellowtail Road, Suite 220 · Cheyenne, WY 82009 · 307-426-4100

Gregory C. Dyekman · ⑩ · Dray, Thomson & Dyekman · 204 East 22nd Street · Cheyenne, WY 82001 · 307-634-8891

COMMERCIAL LITIGATION

Casper

Richard E. Day · ⑩ · Williams, Porter, Day & Neville · 159 North Wolcott Street, Suite 400 · P.O. Box 10700 · Casper, WY 82602 · 307-265-0700

Mark W. Gifford · ⑩ · Gifford & Brinkerhoff · 243 South Park Street · P.O. Box 2508 · Casper, WY 82602-2508 · 307-265-3265

J. Nicholas Murdock · ⑩ · Murdock Law Firm · 123 West First Street, Suite 675 · Casper, WY 82601 · 307-235-0480

Patrick J. Murphy · ⑩ · Williams, Porter, Day & Neville · 159 North Wolcott Street, Suite 400 · P.O. Box 10700 · Casper, WY 82602 · 307-265-0700

William T. Schwartz · ㉕ · Schwartz, Bon, Walker & Studer · Conroy Building, Suite 500 · 141 South Center Street · Casper, WY 82601 · 307-235-6681

Cheyenne

Patrick R. Day · Holland & Hart · 2515 Warren Avenue, Suite 450 · P.O. Box 1347 · Cheyenne, WY 82003-1347 · 307-778-4200

W. Perry Dray · ⑩ · Dray, Thomson & Dyekman · 204 East 22nd Street · Cheyenne, WY 82001 · 307-634-8891

Gregory C. Dyekman · ⑩ · Dray, Thomson & Dyekman · 204 East 22nd Street · Cheyenne, WY 82001 · 307-634-8891

James E. Fitzgerald · ⑳ · The Fitzgerald Law Firm · The Fitzgerald Building · 2108 Warren Avenue · Cheyenne, WY 82001-3740 · 307-634-4000

Terry W. Mackey · ⑩ · Moriarity, Badaruddin & Booke · 314 East 21st Street · Cheyenne, WY 82001 · 307-635-7517

Michael B. Rosenthal · Hathaway & Kunz · 2515 Warren Avenue, Suite 500 · P.O. Box 1208 · Cheyenne, WY 82003 · 307-634-7723

Rhonda S. Woodard · ⑩ · Woodard & White · Boyd Building, Suite 600 · 1720 Carey Avenue · P.O. Box 329 · Cheyenne, WY 82003 · 307-634-2731

Jackson

Larry L. Jorgenson · ⑩ · Jorgenson Law Office · 215 South Willow Street · P.O. Box 4978 · Jackson, WY 83001 · 307-733-6021

Joseph F. Moore, Jr. · ⑩ · Moore Myers & Garland · 235 East Broadway · P.O. Box 8498 · Jackson, WY 83002 · 307-733-8668

Robert P. Schuster · Robert P. Schuster · 250 Veronica Lane, Suite 204 · P.O. Box 13160 · Jackson, WY 83002 · 307-732-7800

Gerald L. Spence · ㉕ · The Spence Law Firm · 15 South Jackson Street · P.O. Box 548 · Jackson, WY 83001-0548 · 307-733-7290

Wheatland

Raymond B. Hunkins · ⑩ · Jones, Jones, Vines & Hunkins · 709 Ninth Street · P.O. Drawer 189 · Wheatland, WY 82201-0189 · 307-322-2896

COMMUNICATIONS LAW

Cheyenne

Paul J. Hickey · Hickey & Evans · 1800 Carey Avenue, Suite 700 · P.O. Box 467 · Cheyenne, WY 82003-0467 · 307-634-1525

CORPORATE LAW

Casper

J. Kenneth Barbe · Brown, Drew & Massey · http://www.browndrew.com · 159 North Wolcott Street, Suite 200 · Ohio Office Building · Casper, WY 82601-7009 · 307-234-1000

Richard E. Day · ⑩ · Williams, Porter, Day & Neville · 159 North Wolcott Street, Suite 400 · P.O. Box 10700 · Casper, WY 82602 · 307-265-0700

Morris R. Massey · ⑳ · Brown, Drew & Massey · http://www.browndrew.com · 159 North Wolcott Street, Suite 200 · Ohio Office Building · Casper, WY 82601-7009 · 307-234-1000

William T. Schwartz · ㉕ · Schwartz, Bon, Walker & Studer · Conroy Building, Suite 500 · 141 South Center Street · Casper, WY 82601 · 307-235-6681

Cheyenne

Teresa Burkett Buffington · Holland & Hart · 2515 Warren Avenue, Suite 450 · P.O. Box 1347 · Cheyenne, WY 82003-1347 · 307-778-4200

Dale W. Cottam · Hirst & Applegate · 1720 Carey Avenue, Suite 200 · P.O. Box 1083 · Cheyenne, WY 82003-1083 · 307-632-0541

W. Perry Dray · ⑩ · Dray, Thomson & Dyekman · 204 East 22nd Street · Cheyenne, WY 82001 · 307-634-8891

Thomas N. Long · ⑩ · Long Reimer Winegar · 2120 Carey Avenue, Suite 300 · P.O. Box 87 · Cheyenne, WY 82003-0087 · 307-635-0710

John J. Metzke · Hirst & Applegate · 1720 Carey Avenue, Suite 200 · P.O. Box 1083 · Cheyenne, WY 82003-1083 · 307-632-0541

Randall B. Reed · Dray, Thomson & Dyekman · 204 East 22nd Street · Cheyenne, WY 82001 · 307-634-8891

Sheridan

Richard M. Davis, Jr. · ㉕ · Davis & Cannon · 40 South Main Street · P.O. Box 728 · Sheridan, WY 82801 307-672-7491

EDUCATION LAW

Riverton

Joel M. Vincent · Vincent & Vincent · 606 East Washington Street · P.O. Box 1758 · Riverton, WY 82501 307-856-1902

Rock Springs

Ford T. Bussart · Bussart, West & Tyler · 409 Broadway, Suite A · P.O. Box 1020 · Rock Springs, WY 82902-1020 · 307-362-3300

ENERGY LAW

Buffalo

Timothy J. Kirven · Kirven & Kirven · 104 Fort Street · P.O. Box 640 · Buffalo, WY 82834 · 307-684-2248

Casper

Morris R. Massey · ⑳ · Brown, Drew & Massey · http://www.browndrew.com · 159 North Wolcott Street, Suite 200 · Ohio Office Building · Casper, WY 82601-7009 · 307-234-1000

Craig Newman · ⑩ · The Law Office Of Craig Newman · 123 West First Street, Suite 675 · P.O. Box 2310 Casper, WY 82602-2310 · 307-237-9588

William T. Schwartz · ㉕ · Schwartz, Bon, Walker & Studer · Conroy Building, Suite 500 · 141 South Center Street · Casper, WY 82601 · 307-235-6681

Cheyenne

Paul J. Hickey · Hickey & Evans · 1800 Carey Avenue, Suite 700 · P.O. Box 467 · Cheyenne, WY 82003-0467 · 307-634-1525

Jack D. Palma · Holland & Hart · 2515 Warren Avenue, Suite 450 · P.O. Box 1347 · Cheyenne, WY 82003-1347 · 307-778-4200

Lawrence J. Wolfe · Holland & Hart · 2515 Warren Avenue, Suite 450 · P.O. Box 1347 · Cheyenne, WY 82003-1347 · 307-778-4200

Sheridan

Richard M. Davis, Jr. · ㉕ · Davis & Cannon · 40 South Main Street · P.O. Box 728 · Sheridan, WY 82801 307-672-7491

Thomas C. Toner · ⑩ · Yonkee & Toner · 319 West Dow Street · P.O. Box 6288 · Sheridan, WY 82801 · 307-674-7451

ENVIRONMENTAL LAW

Casper

J. Nicholas Murdock · ⑩ · Murdock Law Firm · 123 West First Street, Suite 675 · Casper, WY 82601 · 307-235-0480

Cheyenne

Patrick R. Day · Holland & Hart · 2515 Warren Avenue, Suite 450 · P.O. Box 1347 · Cheyenne, WY 82003-1347 · 307-778-4200

Jack D. Palma · Holland & Hart · 2515 Warren Avenue, Suite 450 · P.O. Box 1347 · Cheyenne, WY 82003-1347 · 307-778-4200

Thomas L. Sansonetti · Holland & Hart · 2515 Warren Avenue, Suite 450 · P.O. Box 1347 · Cheyenne, WY 82003-1347 · 307-778-4200

Lawrence J. Wolfe · Holland & Hart · 2515 Warren Avenue, Suite 450 · P.O. Box 1347 · Cheyenne, WY 82003-1347 · 307-778-4200

Jackson

Michael J. Brennan · Holland & Hart · 25 South Willow Street, Suite 200 · P.O. Box 68 · Jackson, WY 83001 · 307-739-9741

Sheridan

Richard M. Davis, Jr. · ㉕ · Davis & Cannon · 40 South Main Street · P.O. Box 728 · Sheridan, WY 82801 307-672-7491

FAMILY LAW

Casper

Larry R. Clapp · Clapp and Associates · 323 South David Street · Casper, WY 82601 · 307-234-3239

Cheyenne

Anthony F. Ross · Ross, Ross and Santini · 307 East 18th Street · Cheyenne, WY 82001 · 307-632-8957

Julie Nye Tiedeken · McKellar, Tiedeken & Scoggin · 702 Randall Avenue · P.O. Box 748 · Cheyenne, WY 82003-0748 · 307-637-5575

Cody

Colin M. Simpson · Burg Simpson Eldredge Hersh & Jardine · 1135 Fourteenth Street · P.O. Box 490 · Cody, WY 82414-0490 · 307-527-7891

Rawlins

Catherine MacPherson · MacPherson, Kelly & Thompson · 616 West Buffalo Street · P.O. Box 999 · Rawlins, WY 82301-0999 · 307-324-2713

GOVERNMENT RELATIONS LAW

Cheyenne

Thomas L. Sansonetti · Holland & Hart · 2515 Warren Avenue, Suite 450 · P.O. Box 1347 · Cheyenne, WY 82003-1347 · 307-778-4200

Lawrence J. Wolfe · Holland & Hart · 2515 Warren Avenue, Suite 450 · P.O. Box 1347 · Cheyenne, WY 82003-1347 · 307-778-4200

HEALTH CARE LAW

Casper

W. Henry Combs III · ⑩ · Murane & Bostwick · 201 North Wolcott Street · Casper, WY 82601 · 307-234-9345

Robert M. Shively · ⑩ · Rochelle Law Offices · 152 North Durbin Street, Suite 120 · Casper, WY 82601-1912 · 307-266-5000

Joseph E. Vlastos · ⑩ · Vlastos, Henley & Drell · 300 South Wolcott Street, Suite 320 · P.O. Box 10 · Casper, WY 82602 · 307-235-6613

Cheyenne

W. Perry Dray · ⑩ · Dray, Thomson & Dyekman · 204 East 22nd Street · Cheyenne, WY 82001 · 307-634-8891

Sheridan

Thomas C. Toner · ⑩ · Yonkee & Toner · 319 West Dow Street · P.O. Box 6288 · Sheridan, WY 82801 · 307-674-7451

INTERNATIONAL ARBITRATION

Casper

Michael J. Sullivan · Rothgerber Johnson & Lyons · 123 West First Street, Suite 200 · Casper, WY 82601-2480 · 307-232-0222

LABOR AND EMPLOYMENT LAW

Casper

Patrick Dixon · Chapin & Dixon · First Interstate Bank Building, Suite 600 · 104 South Wolcott Street · Casper, WY 82601 · 307-234-7321

Scott E. Ortiz · Williams, Porter, Day & Neville · 159 North Wolcott Street, Suite 400 · P.O. Box 10700 · Casper, WY 82602 · 307-265-0700

Cheyenne

Bradley T. Cave · Holland & Hart · 2515 Warren Avenue, Suite 450 · P.O. Box 1347 · Cheyenne, WY 82003-1347 · 307-778-4200

Stephen H. Kline · Kline Law Office · 19th & Pioneer, Suite 306 · P.O. Box 1938 · Cheyenne, WY 82003 307-778-7056

LEGAL MALPRACTICE LAW

Jackson

P. Richard Meyer · ⑩ · Meyer and Williams · 350 East Broadway · P.O. Box 2608 · Jackson, WY 83001-2608 · 307-733-8300

MEDICAL MALPRACTICE LAW

Casper

Jeffrey C. Brinkerhoff · ⑩ · Gifford & Brinkerhoff · 243 South Park Street · P.O. Box 2508 · Casper, WY 82602-2508 · 307-265-3265

Scott E. Ortiz · Williams, Porter, Day & Neville · 159 North Wolcott Street, Suite 400 · P.O. Box 10700 · Casper, WY 82602 · 307-265-0700

Cheyenne

J. Kent Rutledge · ⑩ · Lathrop & Rutledge · City Center Building, Suite 500 · 1920 Thomes Avenue · P.O. Box 4068 · Cheyenne, WY 82003-4068 · 307-632-0554

MERGERS & ACQUISITIONS LAW

Casper

J. Kenneth Barbe · Brown, Drew & Massey · http://www.browndrew.com · 159 North Wolcott Street, Suite 200 · Ohio Office Building · Casper, WY 82601-7009 · 307-234-1000

Cheyenne

Teresa Burkett Buffington · Holland & Hart · 2515 Warren Avenue, Suite 450 · P.O. Box 1347 · Cheyenne, WY 82003-1347 · 307-778-4200

Dale W. Cottam · Hirst & Applegate · 1720 Carey Avenue, Suite 200 · P.O. Box 1083 · Cheyenne, WY 82003-1083 · 307-632-0541

W. Perry Dray · ⑩ · Dray, Thomson & Dyekman · 204 East 22nd Street · Cheyenne, WY 82001 · 307-634-8891

Thomas N. Long · ⑩ · Long Reimer Winegar · 2120 Carey Avenue, Suite 300 · P.O. Box 87 · Cheyenne, WY 82003-0087 · 307-635-0710

John J. Metzke · Hirst & Applegate · 1720 Carey Avenue, Suite 200 · P.O. Box 1083 · Cheyenne, WY 82003-1083 · 307-632-0541

Randall B. Reed · Dray, Thomson & Dyekman · 204 East 22nd Street · Cheyenne, WY 82001 · 307-634-8891

MINING LAW

Casper

William T. Schwartz · ㉕ · Schwartz, Bon, Walker & Studer · Conroy Building, Suite 500 · 141 South Center Street · Casper, WY 82601 · 307-235-6681

NATURAL RESOURCES LAW

Buffalo

Timothy J. Kirven · Kirven & Kirven · 104 Fort Street · P.O. Box 640 · Buffalo, WY 82834 · 307-684-2248

Casper

Morris R. Massey · ⑳ · Brown, Drew & Massey · http://www.browndrew.com · 159 North Wolcott Street, Suite 200 · Ohio Office Building · Casper, WY 82601-7009 · 307-234-1000

Craig Newman · ⑩ · The Law Office Of Craig Newman · 123 West First Street, Suite 675 · P.O. Box 2310 Casper, WY 82602-2310 · 307-237-9588

William T. Schwartz · ㉕ · Schwartz, Bon, Walker & Studer · Conroy Building, Suite 500 · 141 South Center Street · Casper, WY 82601 · 307-235-6681

Cheyenne

Jack D. Palma · Holland & Hart · 2515 Warren Avenue, Suite 450 · P.O. Box 1347 · Cheyenne, WY 82003-1347 · 307-778-4200

Lawrence J. Wolfe · Holland & Hart · 2515 Warren Avenue, Suite 450 · P.O. Box 1347 · Cheyenne, WY 82003-1347 · 307-778-4200

Cody

Charles G. Kepler · ⑩ · Burg Simpson Eldredge Hersh & Jardine · 1135 Fourteenth Street · P.O. Box 490 Cody, WY 82414-0490 · 307-527-7891

Jackson

Michael J. Brennan · Holland & Hart · 25 South Willow Street, Suite 200 · P.O. Box 68 · Jackson, WY 83001 · 307-739-9741

Sheridan

Richard M. Davis, Jr. · ㉕ · Davis & Cannon · 40 South Main Street · P.O. Box 728 · Sheridan, WY 82801 307-672-7491

Thomas C. Toner · ⑩ · Yonkee & Toner · 319 West Dow Street · P.O. Box 6288 · Sheridan, WY 82801 · 307-674-7451

NON-PROFIT/CHARITIES LAW

Cody

Charles G. Kepler · ⑩ · Burg Simpson Eldredge Hersh & Jardine · 1135 Fourteenth Street · P.O. Box 490 Cody, WY 82414-0490 · 307-527-7891

NON-WHITE-COLLAR CRIMINAL DEFENSE

Casper

Michael J. Krampner · Krampner, Fuller & Hambrick · 242 South Grant · Casper, WY 82601 · 307-265-3455

Dallas J. Laird · ⑩ · Dallas J. Laird · The Ormsby Mansion · 536 South Center Street · Casper, WY 82601-3195 · 307-265-6352

Cheyenne

Terry W. Mackey · ⑩ · Moriarity, Badaruddin & Booke · 314 East 21st Street · Cheyenne, WY 82001 · 307-635-7517

Robert W. Tiedeken · ⑩ · Wolf & Tiedeken · First Interstate Bank Building, Suite 300 · 401 West 19th Street · P.O. Box 491 · Cheyenne, WY 82003 · 307-635-2876

Richard C. Wolf · ⑳ · Wolf & Tiedeken · First Interstate Bank Building, Suite 300 · 401 West 19th Street P.O. Box 491 · Cheyenne, WY 82003 · 307-635-2876

Jackson

Gerald L. Spence · ㉕ · The Spence Law Firm · 15 South Jackson Street · P.O. Box 548 · Jackson, WY 83001-0548 · 307-733-7290

Rock Springs

Richard H. Honaker · ⑩ · Honaker Law Offices · 214 Winston Drive · P.O. Box 366 · Rock Springs, WY 82902-0366 · 307-362-5800

OIL & GAS LAW

Casper

Morris R. Massey · ⑳ · Brown, Drew & Massey · http://www.browndrew.com · 159 North Wolcott Street, Suite 200 · Ohio Office Building · Casper, WY 82601-7009 · 307-234-1000

J. Nicholas Murdock · ⑩ · Murdock Law Firm · 123 West First Street, Suite 675 · Casper, WY 82601 · 307-235-0480

Craig Newman · ⑩ · The Law Office Of Craig Newman · 123 West First Street, Suite 675 · P.O. Box 2310 Casper, WY 82602-2310 · 307-237-9588

Sheridan

Thomas C. Toner · ⑩ · Yonkee & Toner · 319 West Dow Street · P.O. Box 6288 · Sheridan, WY 82801 · 307-674-7451

PERSONAL INJURY LITIGATION

Casper

Jeffrey C. Brinkerhoff · ⑩ · Gifford & Brinkerhoff · 243 South Park Street · P.O. Box 2508 · Casper, WY 82602-2508 · 307-265-3265

Patrick Dixon · Chapin & Dixon · First Interstate Bank Building, Suite 600 · 104 South Wolcott Street · Casper, WY 82601 · 307-234-7321

Dallas J. Laird · ⑩ · Dallas J. Laird · The Ormsby Mansion · 536 South Center Street · Casper, WY 82601-3195 · 307-265-6352

J. Nicholas Murdock · ⑩ · Murdock Law Firm · 123 West First Street, Suite 675 · Casper, WY 82601 · 307-235-0480

Frank D. Neville · ⑩ · Williams, Porter, Day & Neville · 159 North Wolcott Street, Suite 400 · P.O. Box 10700 · Casper, WY 82602 · 307-265-0700

Scott E. Ortiz · Williams, Porter, Day & Neville · 159 North Wolcott Street, Suite 400 · P.O. Box 10700 · Casper, WY 82602 · 307-265-0700

Weston W. Reeves · ⑩ · Park Street Law Office · 242 South Park Street · Casper, WY 82601 · 307-265-3843

Ann M. Rochelle · Rochelle Law Offices · 152 North Durbin Street, Suite 120 · Casper, WY 82601-1912 · 307-266-5000

Joseph E. Vlastos · ⑩ · Vlastos, Henley & Drell · 300 South Wolcott Street, Suite 320 · P.O. Box 10 · Casper, WY 82602 · 307-235-6613

John D. Whitaker · John D. Whitaker · 536 South Center Street · Casper, WY 82601-3195 · 307-265-6204

Cheyenne

James E. Fitzgerald · ⑳ · The Fitzgerald Law Firm · The Fitzgerald Building · 2108 Warren Avenue · Cheyenne, WY 82001-3740 · 307-634-4000

Kate M. Fox · Davis & Cannon · 422 West 26th Street · P.O. Box 43 · Cheyenne, WY 82003 · 307-634-3210

G. G. Greenlee · ⑩ · Murane & Bostwick · 508 West 27th Street · Cheyenne, WY 82001 · 307-634-7500

Paul Kapp · Sundahl, Powers, Kapp & Martin · 1725 Carey Avenue · P.O. Box 328 · Cheyenne, WY 82003 · 307-632-6421

Terry W. Mackey · ⑩ · Moriarity, Badaruddin & Booke · 314 East 21st Street · Cheyenne, WY 82001 · 307-635-7517

Raymond W. Martin · Sundahl, Powers, Kapp & Martin · 1725 Carey Avenue · P.O. Box 328 · Cheyenne, WY 82003 · 307-632-6421

Thomas A. Nicholas III · ⑩ · Hirst & Applegate · 1720 Carey Avenue, Suite 200 · P.O. Box 1083 · Cheyenne, WY 82003-1083 · 307-632-0541

George E. Powers, Jr. · Sundahl, Powers, Kapp & Martin · 1725 Carey Avenue · P.O. Box 328 · Cheyenne, WY 82003 · 307-632-6421

Michael B. Rosenthal · Hathaway & Kunz · 2515 Warren Avenue, Suite 500 · P.O. Box 1208 · Cheyenne, WY 82003 · 307-634-7723

J. Kent Rutledge · ⑩ · Lathrop & Rutledge · City Center Building, Suite 500 · 1920 Thomes Avenue · P.O. Box 4068 · Cheyenne, WY 82003-4068 · 307-632-0554

George Santini · ⑩ · Ross, Ross and Santini · 307 East 18th Street · Cheyenne, WY 82001 · 307-632-8957

John B. Speight · ⑩ · Speight, McCue & Associates · 2515 Warren Avenue, Suite 505 · P.O. Box 1709 · Cheyenne, WY 82003-1709 · 307-634-2994

John A. Sundahl · ⑩ · Sundahl, Powers, Kapp & Martin · 1725 Carey Avenue · P.O. Box 328 · Cheyenne, WY 82003 · 307-632-6421

Julie Nye Tiedeken · McKellar, Tiedeken & Scoggin · 702 Randall Avenue · P.O. Box 748 · Cheyenne, WY 82003-0748 · 307-637-5575

Robert W. Tiedeken · ⑩ · Wolf & Tiedeken · First Interstate Bank Building, Suite 300 · 401 West 19th Street · P.O. Box 491 · Cheyenne, WY 82003 · 307-635-2876

Rhonda S. Woodard · ⑩ · Woodard & White · Boyd Building, Suite 600 · 1720 Carey Avenue · P.O. Box 329 · Cheyenne, WY 82003 · 307-634-2731

Cody

Stephen L. Simonton · Stephen L. Simonton · 1222 Eleventh Street · Cody, WY 82414 · 307-587-7010

Jackson

P. Richard Meyer · ⑩ · Meyer and Williams · 350 East Broadway · P.O. Box 2608 · Jackson, WY 83001-2608 · 307-733-8300

Robert P. Schuster · Robert P. Schuster · 250 Veronica Lane, Suite 204 · P.O. Box 13160 · Jackson, WY 83002 · 307-732-7800

Gary L. Shockey · ⑩ · Gary L. Shockey · P.O. Box 10773 · 480 South Cache · Jackson, WY 83002 · 307-733-5974

Gerald L. Spence · ㉕ · The Spence Law Firm · 15 South Jackson Street · P.O. Box 548 · Jackson, WY 83001-0548 · 307-733-7290

Joe Teig · Holland & Hart · 25 South Willow Street, Suite 200 · P.O. Box 68 · Jackson, WY 83001 · 307-739-9741

Robert N. Williams · ⑩ · Meyer and Williams · 350 East Broadway · P.O. Box 2608 · Jackson, WY 83001-2608 · 307-733-8300

Laramie

Rebecca A. Lewis · Pence and MacMillan · 501 East Garfield Street · P.O. Box 1285 · Laramie, WY 82073-1285 · 307-745-3626

Riverton

John R. Hursh · ⑳ · Central Wyoming Law Associates · 105 South Sixth Street East · P.O. Box 1783 · Riverton, WY 82501 · 307-856-4157

John R. Vincent · ⑩ · Vincent Law Office · 301 East Adams Avenue · P.O. Box 433 · Riverton, WY 82501 · 307-857-6005

Rock Springs

Ford T. Bussart · Bussart, West & Tyler · 409 Broadway, Suite A · P.O. Box 1020 · Rock Springs, WY 82902-1020 · 307-362-3300

Richard H. Honaker · ⑩ · Honaker Law Offices · 214 Winston Drive · P.O. Box 366 · Rock Springs, WY 82902-0366 · 307-362-5800

Sheridan

Kim D. Cannon · ⑩ · Davis & Cannon · 40 South Main Street · P.O. Box 728 · Sheridan, WY 82801 · 307-672-7491

Jeffrey J. Gonda · Lonabaugh and Riggs · 50 East Loucks Street, Suite 110 · P.O. Drawer 5059 · Sheridan, WY 82801-5059 · 307-672-7444

Wheatland

Raymond B. Hunkins · ⑩ · Jones, Jones, Vines & Hunkins · 709 Ninth Street · P.O. Drawer 189 · Wheatland, WY 82201-0189 · 307-322-2896

PRODUCT LIABILITY LITIGATION

Cheyenne

James E. Fitzgerald · ⑳ · The Fitzgerald Law Firm · The Fitzgerald Building · 2108 Warren Avenue · Cheyenne, WY 82001-3740 · 307-634-4000

Kate M. Fox · Davis & Cannon · 422 West 26th Street · P.O. Box 43 · Cheyenne, WY 82003 · 307-634-3210

Riverton

John R. Hursh · ⑳ · Central Wyoming Law Associates · 105 South Sixth Street East · P.O. Box 1783 · Riverton, WY 82501 · 307-856-4157

REAL ESTATE LAW

Buffalo

Dennis M. Kirven · ⑩ · Kirven & Kirven · 104 Fort Street · P.O. Box 640 · Buffalo, WY 82834 · 307-684-2248

Casper

Morris R. Massey · ⑳ · Brown, Drew & Massey · http://www.browndrew.com · 159 North Wolcott Street, Suite 200 · Ohio Office Building · Casper, WY 82601-7009 · 307-234-1000

William T. Schwartz · ㉕ · Schwartz, Bon, Walker & Studer · Conroy Building, Suite 500 · 141 South Center Street · Casper, WY 82601 · 307-235-6681

Cheyenne

Dale W. Cottam · Hirst & Applegate · 1720 Carey Avenue, Suite 200 · P.O. Box 1083 · Cheyenne, WY 82003-1083 · 307-632-0541

Gregory C. Dyekman · ⑩ · Dray, Thomson & Dyekman · 204 East 22nd Street · Cheyenne, WY 82001 · 307-634-8891

Cody

Charles G. Kepler · ⑩ · Burg Simpson Eldredge Hersh & Jardine · 1135 Fourteenth Street · P.O. Box 490 Cody, WY 82414-0490 · 307-527-7891

Jackson

Glenn M. Ford · Moore Myers & Garland · 235 East Broadway · P.O. Box 8498 · Jackson, WY 83002 · 307-733-8668

Larry L. Jorgenson · ⑩ · Jorgenson Law Office · 215 South Willow Street · P.O. Box 4978 · Jackson, WY 83001 · 307-733-6021

David K. Larson · ⑩ · Mullikin, Larson & Swift · 155 East Pearl Street, Suite 200 · P.O. Box 4099 · Jackson, WY 83001-4099 · 307-733-3923

Joseph F. Moore, Jr. · ⑩ · Moore Myers & Garland · 235 East Broadway · P.O. Box 8498 · Jackson, WY 83002 · 307-733-8668

Paul O. Vaughn · ⑩ · Moore Myers and Garland · 235 East Broadway · P.O. Box 4128 · Jackson, WY 83001 · 307-733-7792

Sheridan

Richard M. Davis, Jr. · ㉕ · Davis & Cannon · 40 South Main Street · P.O. Box 728 · Sheridan, WY 82801 307-672-7491

TAX LAW

Cheyenne

W. Perry Dray · ⑩ · Dray, Thomson & Dyekman · 204 East 22nd Street · Cheyenne, WY 82001 · 307-634-8891

Thomas N. Long · ⑩ · Long Reimer Winegar · 2120 Carey Avenue, Suite 300 · P.O. Box 87 · Cheyenne, WY 82003-0087 · 307-635-0710

Lawrence J. Wolfe · Holland & Hart · 2515 Warren Avenue, Suite 450 · P.O. Box 1347 · Cheyenne, WY 82003-1347 · 307-778-4200

TRUSTS AND ESTATES

Casper

William T. Schwartz · ㉕ · Schwartz, Bon, Walker & Studer · Conroy Building, Suite 500 · 141 South Center Street · Casper, WY 82601 · 307-235-6681

Cheyenne

Thomas N. Long · ⑩ · Long Reimer Winegar · 2120 Carey Avenue, Suite 300 · P.O. Box 87 · Cheyenne, WY 82003-0087 · 307-635-0710

John J. Metzke · Hirst & Applegate · 1720 Carey Avenue, Suite 200 · P.O. Box 1083 · Cheyenne, WY 82003-1083 · 307-632-0541

Cody

Charles G. Kepler · ⑩ · Burg Simpson Eldredge Hersh & Jardine · 1135 Fourteenth Street · P.O. Box 490 Cody, WY 82414-0490 · 307-527-7891

WATER LAW

Cheyenne

Lawrence J. Wolfe · Holland & Hart · 2515 Warren Avenue, Suite 450 · P.O. Box 1347 · Cheyenne, WY 82003-1347 · 307-778-4200

WHITE-COLLAR CRIMINAL DEFENSE

Casper

Michael J. Krampner · Krampner, Fuller & Hambrick · 242 South Grant · Casper, WY 82601 · 307-265-3455

Dallas J. Laird · ⑩ · Dallas J. Laird · The Ormsby Mansion · 536 South Center Street · Casper, WY 82601-3195 · 307-265-6352

Cheyenne

Terry W. Mackey · ⑩ · Moriarity, Badaruddin & Booke · 314 East 21st Street · Cheyenne, WY 82001 · 307-635-7517

Robert W. Tiedeken · ⑩ · Wolf & Tiedeken · First Interstate Bank Building, Suite 300 · 401 West 19th Street · P.O. Box 491 · Cheyenne, WY 82003 · 307-635-2876

Richard C. Wolf · ⑳ · Wolf & Tiedeken · First Interstate Bank Building, Suite 300 · 401 West 19th Street P.O. Box 491 · Cheyenne, WY 82003 · 307-635-2876

Gillette

Nicholas Carter · The Nick Carter Law Firm · 310 South Gillette Avenue, Suite B · P.O. Box 909 · Gillette, WY 82717-0909 · 307-682-9349

Jackson

Gerald L. Spence · ㉕ · The Spence Law Firm · 15 South Jackson Street · P.O. Box 548 · Jackson, WY 83001-0548 · 307-733-7290

Rock Springs

Richard H. Honaker · ⑩ · Honaker Law Offices · 214 Winston Drive · P.O. Box 366 · Rock Springs, WY 82902-0366 · 307-362-5800

WORKERS' COMPENSATION LAW

Casper

David A. Drell · Vlastos, Henley & Drell · 300 South Wolcott Street, Suite 320 · P.O. Box 10 · Casper, WY 82602 · 307-235-6613

Cheyenne

George Santini · ⑩ · Ross, Ross and Santini · 307 East 18th Street · Cheyenne, WY 82001 · 307-632-8957

Rock Springs

Michael D. Newman · ⑩ · Hampton & Newman · 118 Third Street · P.O. Box 1000 · Rock Springs, WY 82902-1000 · 307-382-6443

INDEX

A

B

C

D

E

F

G

H

I

J

K

L

M

N

O

P

Q

R

S

T

U

V

W

Y

Z